D1544958

Addison-Wesley Secondary Math

An Integrated Approach

Focus on **Geometry**

Teacher's Edition

Alan R. Hoffer
Roberta Koss
Jerry D. Beckmann • Phillip E. Duren • Julia L. Hernandez
Beth M. Schlesinger • Catherine Wiehe

PROGRAM CONCEPTUALIZERS

Barbara Alcala
Randall I. Charles
John A. Dossey
Betty M. Foxx
Alan R. Hoffer
Roberta Koss
Sid Rachlin
Freddie L. Renfro
Cathy L. Seeley
Charles B. Vonder Embse

Addison-Wesley Publishing Company

Menlo Park, California • Reading, Massachusetts • New York
Don Mills, Ontario • Wokingham, England • Amsterdam • Bonn
Paris • Milan • Madrid • Sydney • Singapore • Tokyo
Seoul • Taipei • Mexico City • San Juan

PROJECT TEAM ACKNOWLEDGMENTS

Editorial
Lila Nissen
Mary Fraser
Joe Todaro
Rob Cooper
John Kerwin
Casey FitzSimons
Judy Breen
Sharon Harrison

Design
Debbie Costello
Kathy Cunningham
Emily Hamilton
Nina Lisowski

Market Research
Shirley Black

Photo Edit
Dede Lee

Production Editorial
Ellen Williams
Pam Suwinsky
Chris Hofer
Cate Lowe

Production
Jenny Blackburn
Bill Hollowell
Steve Rogers
Don Shelonko
Ben Schroeter
Keiko Tsuyuki
Trevin Lowrey
Cathleen Veraldi
Dan Robbins
Therese DeRogatis
Laura Rosendahl
Qin Zhong Yu
Steve Desmond

Manufacturing
Stan Robinson
Lisa Bandini
Janet Carney
Shelley Thesing

Marketing Services
Carol Wolfe
Marjorie Fox

Permissions
Marty Granahan

Electronic Media
Jack Hankin
Rob Cooper
Barclay Holmes

All Teacher's Edition photographic icons by Geoffrey Nilsen Photography* except the computer screen by Cesar Rubio*.
*Photographed expressly for Addison-Wesley Publishing Company, Inc.

Printed in the United States of America.

ISBN 0-201-86781-8

1 2 3 4 5 6 7 8 9 10–VH–98 97 96 95 94

DEAR EDUCATOR,

We are pleased to present to you *Addison-Wesley Secondary Math (AWSM)*, a four-book program designed to meet the demands of mathematics education as we move into the technological world of the twenty-first century.

We used the *Curriculum and Evaluation Standards* and the *Professional Standards for Teaching Mathematics* (developed by the National Council of Teachers of Mathematics) as a starting point in developing the scope and sequence and the lesson design. Through further refinements and reviews, *AWSM* was created to meet the following assumptions.

Students should be actively involved in their own learning.
Getting students actively involved in their own learning is one of the primary goals of *AWSM.* Students are encouraged to participate in explorations, make conjectures, clarify or explain their thinking, discuss their ideas, and look back on their findings.

Communication should be encouraged throughout the program.
What makes an answer right is often more important than what the right answer actually is. As students learn to talk about, write about, develop models, and reflect on their understanding of mathematics, they will learn to communicate mathematically.

Problem solving should be integral to every lesson.
Creating a systematic approach to solving problems is a fundamental goal of many industries today and is an important goal of *AWSM.* Problem solving is integral to every lesson in *AWSM.* Students learn to use and apply problem-solving approaches, recognize, formulate, solve, and describe their work, as well as think creatively in the real world.

Technology should be assumed as an integral part of mathematics instruction.
The primary purpose of technology in *AWSM* is to support and advance the mathematical content and instructional process.

Learning should be organized around a few big ideas.
In order to solve interesting, realistic problems, the content of *AWSM* is organized by key mathematical concepts, referred to as *Big Ideas.* Formulas, generalizations, and procedures are intended to be the result of the instruction, rather than the focus.

Connections should be made to other disciplines, to the world we live in, and to a variety of mathematical approaches.
Superlessons present themes, which are used to introduce new mathematical ideas. These themes were carefully chosen to motivate mathematics in our world and to show the relevance of mathematics to the lives of a diverse population of students.

Assessment should be ongoing.
Ongoing assessment is part of the *AWSM* plan, with opportunities for all types of assessment provided throughout each book.

THE AUTHORS

ADDISON-WESLEY SECONDARY MATHEMATICS PROGRAM AUTHORS AND CONCEPTUALIZERS

Barbara Alcala
Conceptualizer
Associate lead author
Whittier, California

Jerry D. Beckmann
Project author
Lincoln, Nebraska

Penelope P. Booth
Project author
Towson, Maryland

Randall I. Charles
Conceptualizer
Lead author
San Jose, California

James R. Choike
Project author
Stillwater, Oklahoma

David S. Daniels
Project author
Longmeadow, Massachusetts

John A. Dossey
Conceptualizer
Lead author
Normal, Illinois

Phillip E. Duren
Project author
Hayward, California

Betty M. Foxx
Conceptualizer
Chicago, Illinois

Trudi Hammel Garland
Project author
Oakland, California

Pamela Patton Giles
Project author
Sandy, Utah

Virginia Gray
Project author
Medford, Oregon

Julia L. Hernandez
Project author
Rosemead, California

Alan R. Hoffer
Conceptualizer
Lead author
Irvine, California

Howard C. Johnson
Project author
Syracuse, New York

Roberta Koss
Conceptualizer
Associate lead author
Larkspur, California

Stephen E. Moresh
Project author
New York, New York

J. Irene Murphy
Project author
Barrow, Alaska

Sid Rachlin
Conceptualizer
Greenville, North Carolina

Andy Reeves
Project author
Tallahassee, Florida

Freddie L. Renfro
Conceptualizer
Baytown, Texas

Kathy A. Ross
Project author
Harvey, Louisiana

Beth M. Schlesinger
Project author
San Diego, California

Cathy L. Seeley
Conceptualizer
Lead author
Austin, Texas

Alba González Thompson
Associate lead author
San Diego, California

Charles B. Vonder Embse
Conceptualizer
Associate lead author
Mt. Pleasant, Michigan

Catherine Wiehe
Project author
San Jose, California

Sheryl M. Yamada
Project author
Beverly Hills, California

PILOT TEACHERS

Don Castle
Rialto High School
Rialto, California

Ronald D. Coleman
Kelvyn Park High School
Chicago, Illinois

Thomas A. Edwards
Gateway Institute of Technology
St. Louis, Missouri

Stuart H. Grove
North Haven High School
North Haven, Connecticut

Peggy Hardegree
Southeast High School
Macon, Georgia

John Harmon
Wayland High School
Wayland, Massachusetts

Larry G. Hirigoyen
Arroyo High School
El Monte, California

Bob Kolar
Kennedy High School
Cedar Rapids, Iowa

Norine Lescoe
O. H. Platt High School
Meriden, Connecticut

Tim Nurrenbern
Boonville High School
Boonville, Indiana

Mary LeBlanc Ohlsen
West Vigo High School
West Terre Haute, Indiana

James William Pendarvis
Stratford High School
Goose Creek, South Carolina

Michael Riley
Near North Career
Metropolitan High School
Chicago, Illinois

Terri L. Saunders
Glynn Academy High School
Brunswick, Georgia

Reuben A. Schadler
Palo Alto High School
Palo Alto, California

Joan Adams Sloan
Brookwood High School
Snellville, Georgia

Maureen Sneed
Berkmar High School
Lilburn, Georgia

Jerry Staniszewski
Hinsdale Central High School
Hinsdale, Illinois

Amy R. Timms
T. L. Hanna High School
Anderson, South Carolina

James Tremper
Boonville High School
Boonville, Indiana

Linda P. Wyatt
Brookwood High School
Snellville, Georgia

Ethel Ruth M. Young
James A. Garfield High School
Los Angeles, California

Stephen Zenk
Parkway North High School
St. Louis, Missouri

CONTENT REVIEWERS

Bridget Arvold
University of Georgia
Athens, Georgia

Paul G. Dillenberger
Franklin Middle School
Minneapolis, Minnesota

Catherine Y. Figuracion
San Pedro High School
San Pedro, California

Donald Hastings
Stratford Public Schools
Stratford, Connecticut

Melanie Hildreth
Walnut High School
Walnut, California

Jim Velo
West High School
Columbus, Ohio

Joanne Wainscott
Mission Bay High School
San Diego, California

Denise Walston
Maury High School
Norfolk, Virginia

Dr. Art W. Wilson
Abraham Lincoln High School
Denver, Colorado

MULTICULTURAL REVIEWERS

LaVerne Bitsie
Oklahoma State University
Stillwater, Oklahoma

Claudette Bradley
University of Alaska
Fairbanks, Alaska

Yolanda De La Cruz
Arizona State University West
Phoenix, Arizona

Genevieve Lau
Skyline College
San Bruno, California

William Tate
University of Wisconsin
Madison, Wisconsin

INDUSTRY CONSULTANTS

Joseph M. Cahalen
Xerox Corporation
Stamford, Connecticut

Clare DeYonker
AMATECH
Bingham Farms, Michigan

Harry Garland
Canon Research Center America, Inc.
Palo Alto, California

Timothy M. Schwalm, Sr.
Eastman Kodak Company
Rochester, New York

Diane Sotos
Maxim Integrated Products
Sunnyvale, California

Earl R. Westerlund
Kodak Corporation
Rochester, New York

John Zils
Skidmore, Owings & Merrill
Chicago, Illinois

Addison-Wesley Secondary Math

AWSM FOUNDATIONS OF ALGEBRA AND GEOMETRY

AWSM Foundations of Algebra and Geometry is a one-year fully-integrated mathematics course designed to prepare and motivate students for success in future mathematics courses. There is a strong intuitive development of many of the topics that are covered in an algebra or geometry course. Students will learn important mathematical ideas that serve as a solid foundation for these courses.

AWSM allows students to experiment with many different approaches to a task, to approach a difficult problem in their own way, and to learn from their mistakes and try over again. There are many opportunities for visualization, exploration, and connections of mathematics to familiar models.

The use of technology is encouraged throughout the course. The availability of a calculator is assumed, and while not required, the use of graphing technology enhances students' learning experience.

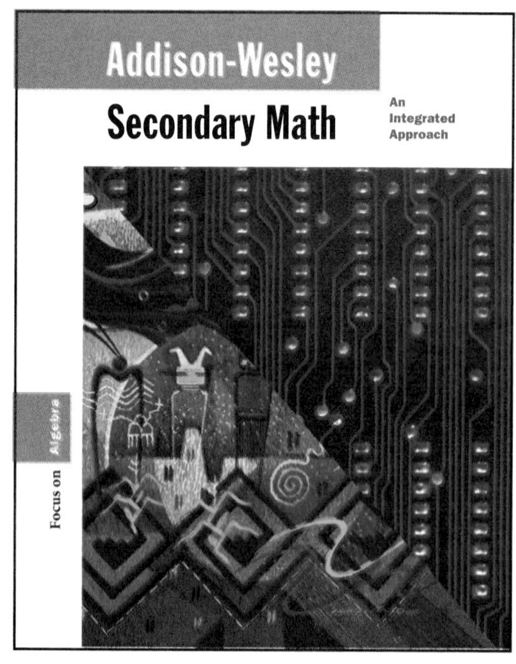

Addison-Wesley
Secondary Math
An Integrated Approach
Foundations of Algebra and Geometry

A pacing guide is provided for a one semester or summer school course, as well as for a one year complete course.

AWSM FOCUS ON ALGEBRA

AWSM Focus on Algebra is the study of functional relationships, the connections among ways of representing these relationships, and the use of representations of functions to solve problems. The book begins with data and ways of organizing data. Numerical patterns are explored, which leads to determining relationships formed by patterns. Functional relationships provide the basis for looking at equations and solving them graphically, prior to solving equations symbolically.

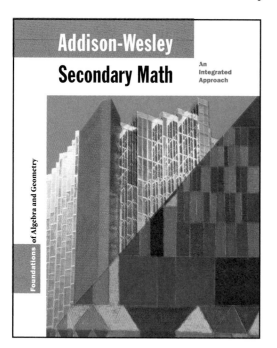

Students learn to work with quantities that vary, and they learn to express relationships between quantities verbally, tabularly, pictorially, graphically, and symbolically. A strong conceptual basis for understanding a solution to an equation is developed before introducing traditional methods for finding solutions.

In *AWSM Focus on Algebra*, the emphasis is on connections, including connections to the real world, as well as connections to the various mathematical strands. Geometric models are used as a context for connecting the visual and the symbolic. Probability and discrete mathematics are interwoven in the text.

AWSM FOCUS ON GEOMETRY

AWSM Focus on Geometry begins with a strong development of visualization and drawing skills. Both algebraic and geometric models are introduced and are further developed throughout the course, as students use geometry to model a variety of real-world situations.

Proof is developed slowly in the first half of the book, leading to a five-step sequence in Chapter 3 and to formal proofs in Chapter 6. Various proof formats, including paragraph, flow-chart, and two-column proofs, are presented, compared, and used whenever appropriate.

AWSM Focus on Geometry promotes the use of synthetic, coordinate, transformation, and vector approaches, alone and in combination, to help students understand and communicate the big ideas of mathematics. Coordinate and transformation techniques are introduced early and used when appropriate.

Students are expected to be actively involved in their own learning, and *AWSM Focus on Geometry* integrates the use of manipulatives, computer software, and constructions.

AWSM FOCUS ON ADVANCED ALGEBRA

AWSM Focus on Advanced Algebra carefully builds on the sequential approaches to content and learning begun in the preceding texts in the *AWSM* series. The sequence from variable to equation to function is extended into using functions as models for a number of applied settings. Geometric and algebraic concepts are extended and connected to topics in probability and statistics, trigonometry, and discrete mathematics.

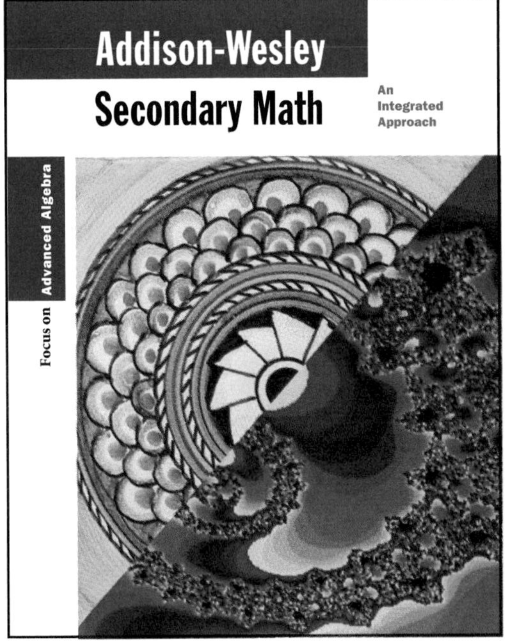

There is a focus on the development of students' abilities to reason both numerically and spatially; to communicate via reading, writing, speaking, modeling, and listening to others; to solve problems employing a wide variety of heuristical approaches; and to connect these abilities with others within mathematics and other disciplines.

Students will actively experience the empowering view of their world and associated problem-solving and modeling skills. This is made possible in *AWSM Focus on Advanced Algebra* with a carefully articulated development of functions through tabular and graphical approaches aided by technology. Special emphasis is given to seeing the nature of change as it is embodied in linear, polynomial, exponential, logarithmic, and trigonometric functions.

CONTENT SPECIALISTS

Algebra	Sid Rachlin
Assessment	Frank K. Lester, Jr.; Diana V. Lambdin
Communication	Cathy L. Seeley
Connections	Freddie L. Renfro
Critical Thinking	Phares G. O'Daffer
Discrete Mathematics	John A. Dossey
Functions and Underpinnings of Calculus	Roberta Koss
Geometry	Alan R. Hoffer
Mathematical Reasoning	Phares G. O'Daffer
Mathematical Structure	John A. Dossey
Multiculturalism	Betty M. Foxx
Problem Solving	Randall I. Charles
Statistics and Probability	Barbara Alcala
Technology	Charles B. Vonder Embse
Visualization	Alan R. Hoffer
Special Consultant	Dale Seymour

Table of Contents

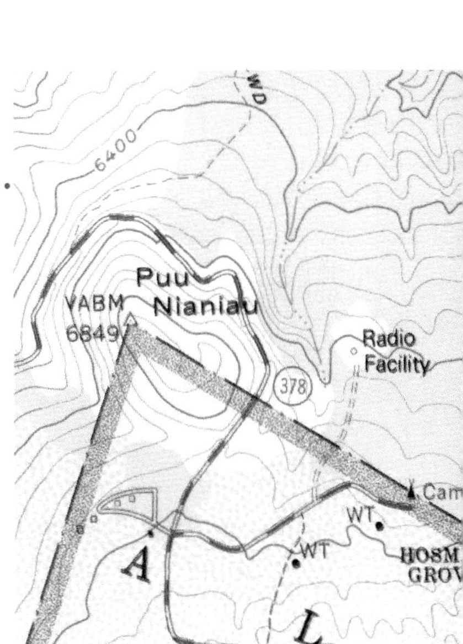

6400
Puu
Nianiau
VABM
6849
Radio
Facility
378
WT
A
L

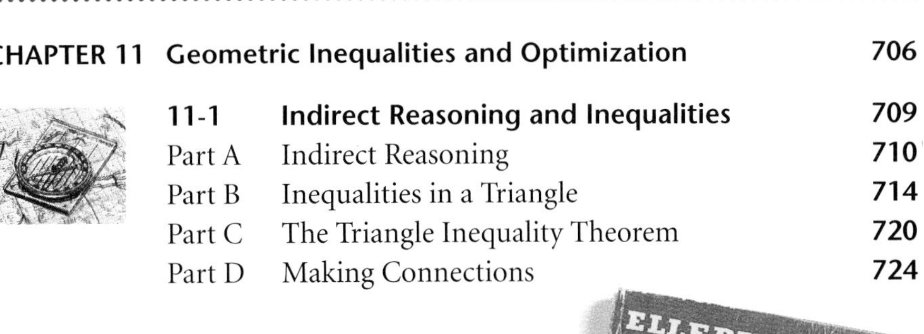

ELLERY QUEEN
THE SPANISH
CAPE MYSTERY

REFERENCE CENTER

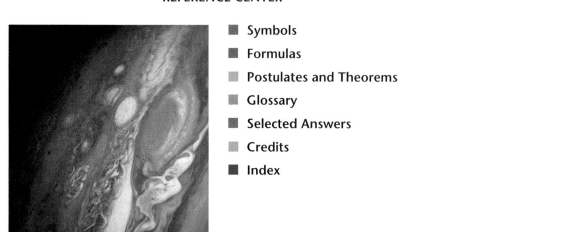

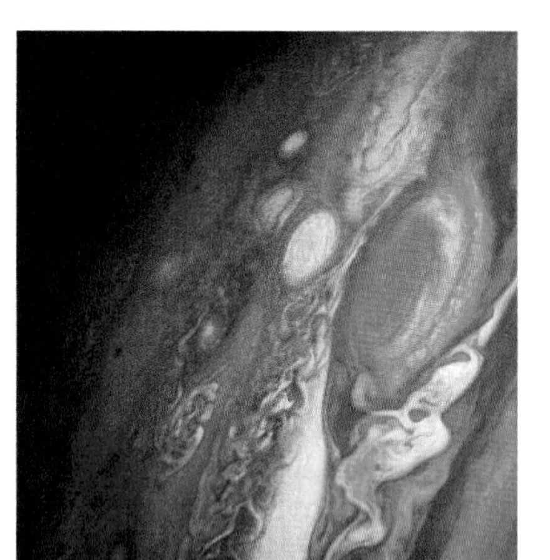

Teacher's Edition Contents

In *AWSM*, chapters are organized into *Superlessons.*

Superlessons help students connect the big ideas of math.

Our unique *Superlesson* structure reflects the latest research in how students best learn mathematics. By first providing a real-world connection to the content to follow, *Superlessons* help students develop deeper understandings of the big ideas of mathematics.

Each *Superlesson* is introduced with a thematically motivating situation. Each contains several *Parts* — starting with the *Superlesson* opener, followed by *Parts* that provide in-depth exploration of key concepts and skills. The last *Part*, *Making Connections*, gives students a chance to stop, reflect, revisit the theme, and connect what they've learned.

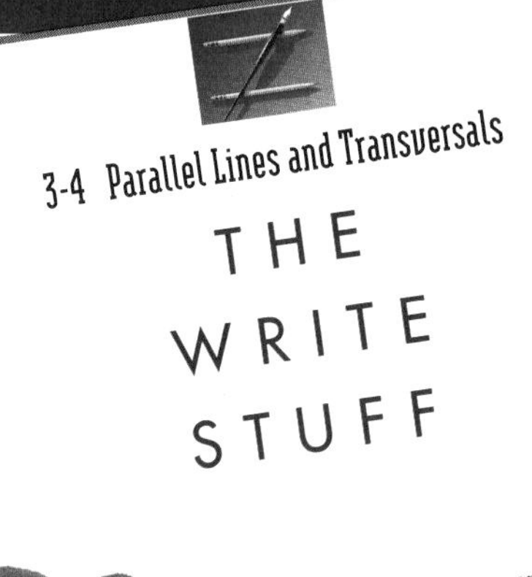

Calligraphy (kal-lig´-ra-fee), from the Greek *kalos* meaning beautiful and *grapho*, to write, is an art form with ancient roots. The developmental stages of writing took thousands of years. Calligraphy was stimulated, cultivated, and shaped from ancient times until the fifteenth century. At that time, calligraphy was used primarily in book production. Scribes, skillful in the art of calligraphy (but having no access to a copy machine), copied the works of Cicero and other statesmen and orators by hand. There was also a great demand for multiple copies of the Bible. But with the invention of the printing press by Johann Gutenberg in about 1440, the demand for skilled calligraphers decreased.

The elegance of calligraphy has endured through time, from the days of scratching on the surface of a wax tablet with hollow reeds to today's use of precision pens and highly refined papers. Though it is no longer critical for communication, calligraphy is still

Superlesson Opener

Each opener is derived from a real-world situation.

Parts

Every *Superlesson* is divided into *Parts*. *Parts* are organized to offer teachers a range of instructional approaches.

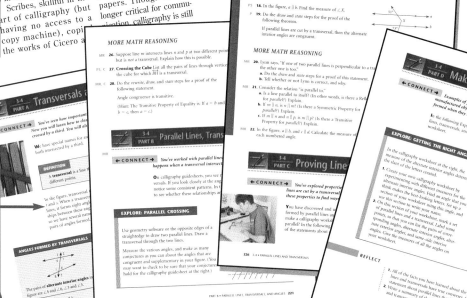

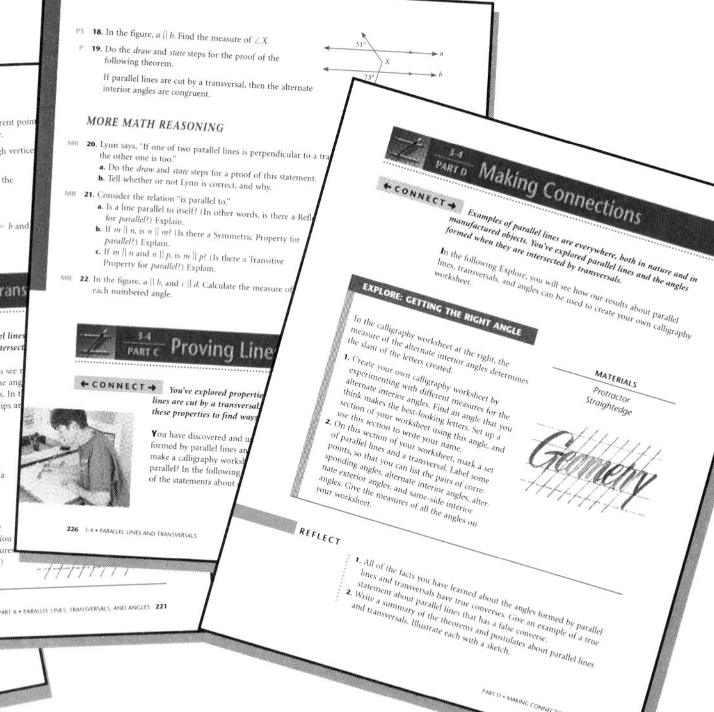

An *AWSM Superlesson* Sampler

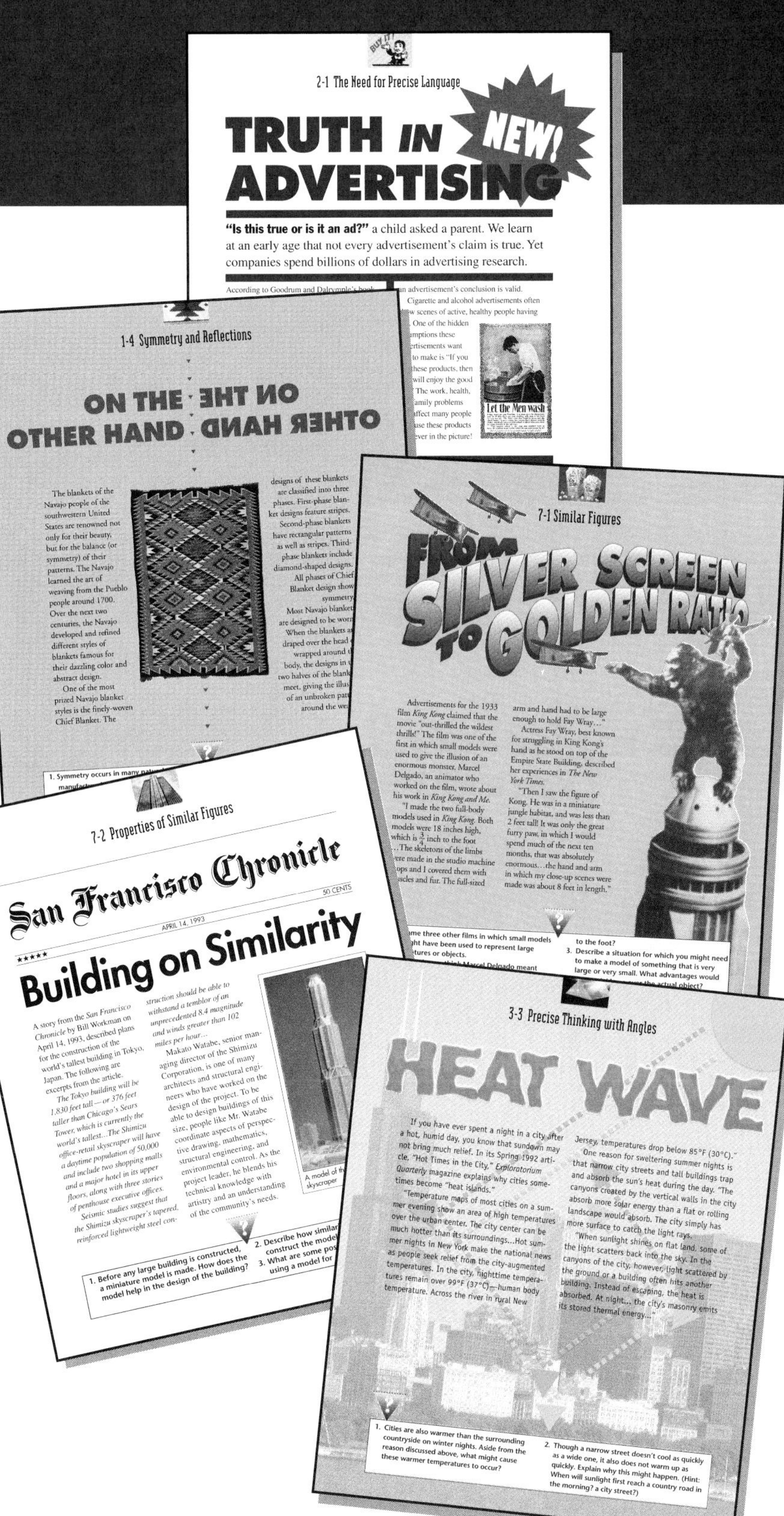

The engaging, colorful, real-world situation in each *Superlesson* opener gets students attention and draws them into the math that follows. Different facets of the situation are presented in *Parts* throughout the *Superlesson*. Here's just a sampling of the *Superlesson* openers.

- *As the World Turns*
  (Using Familiar Models)
- *It's All Babylonian To Me*
  (The Pythagorean Theorem)
- *Why Don't Elephants Have Skinny Legs?*
  (Similar Solids: Surface Area and Volume)
- *Techno Proofs*
  (Deductive Proof with Quadrilaterals)
- *Pushing Paper*
  (Putting Transformations Together)
- *Decorative Detectives*
  (Classifying Patterns)
- *A Little Better All the Time*
  (Optimization)
- *From Stars to City Planning*
  (Trigonometry)
- *Gearing Up? Or Is It Down?*
  (Rotations)
- *Hurry, Hurry, Step Right UP!*
  (Understanding and Applying Area)
- *I Say What I Mean*
  (Reasoning and Logic)

Superlesson Parts include a range of student-friendly features.

AWSM program features are designed to encourage mathematical exploration, discovery, practice, application, reflection, and self-assessment. Learning is constructed so that formulas, generalizations, and algorithms are the results of instruction, enabling students to internalize processes and develop math power.

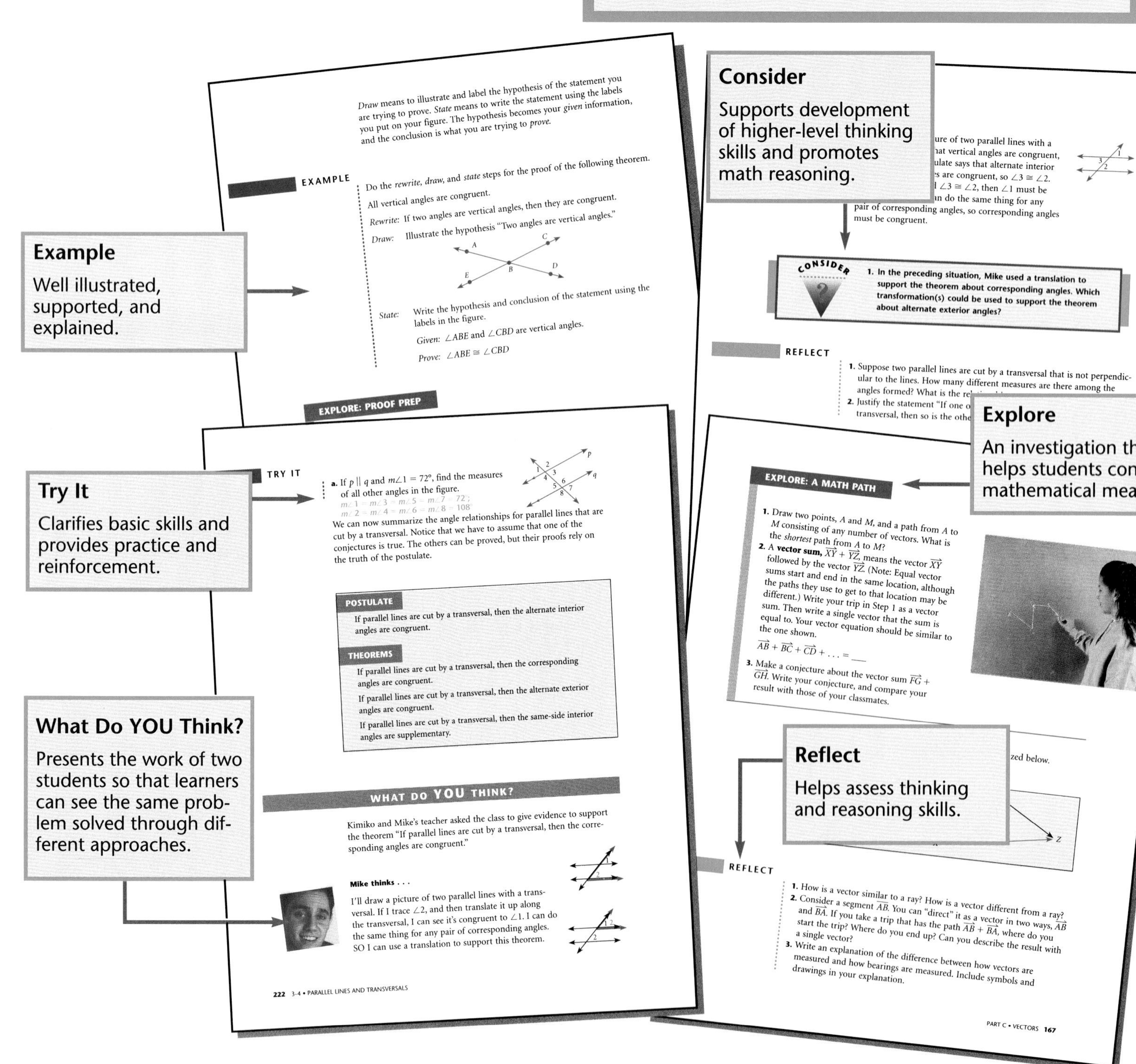

Example
Well illustrated, supported, and explained.
Try It
Clarifies basic skills and provides practice and reinforcement.
What Do YOU Think?
Presents the work of two students so that learners can see the same problem solved through different approaches.
Consider
Supports development of higher-level thinking skills and promotes math reasoning.
Explore
Reflect
Helps assess thinking and reasoning skills.

Exercises integrate skills and concepts and check content understanding.

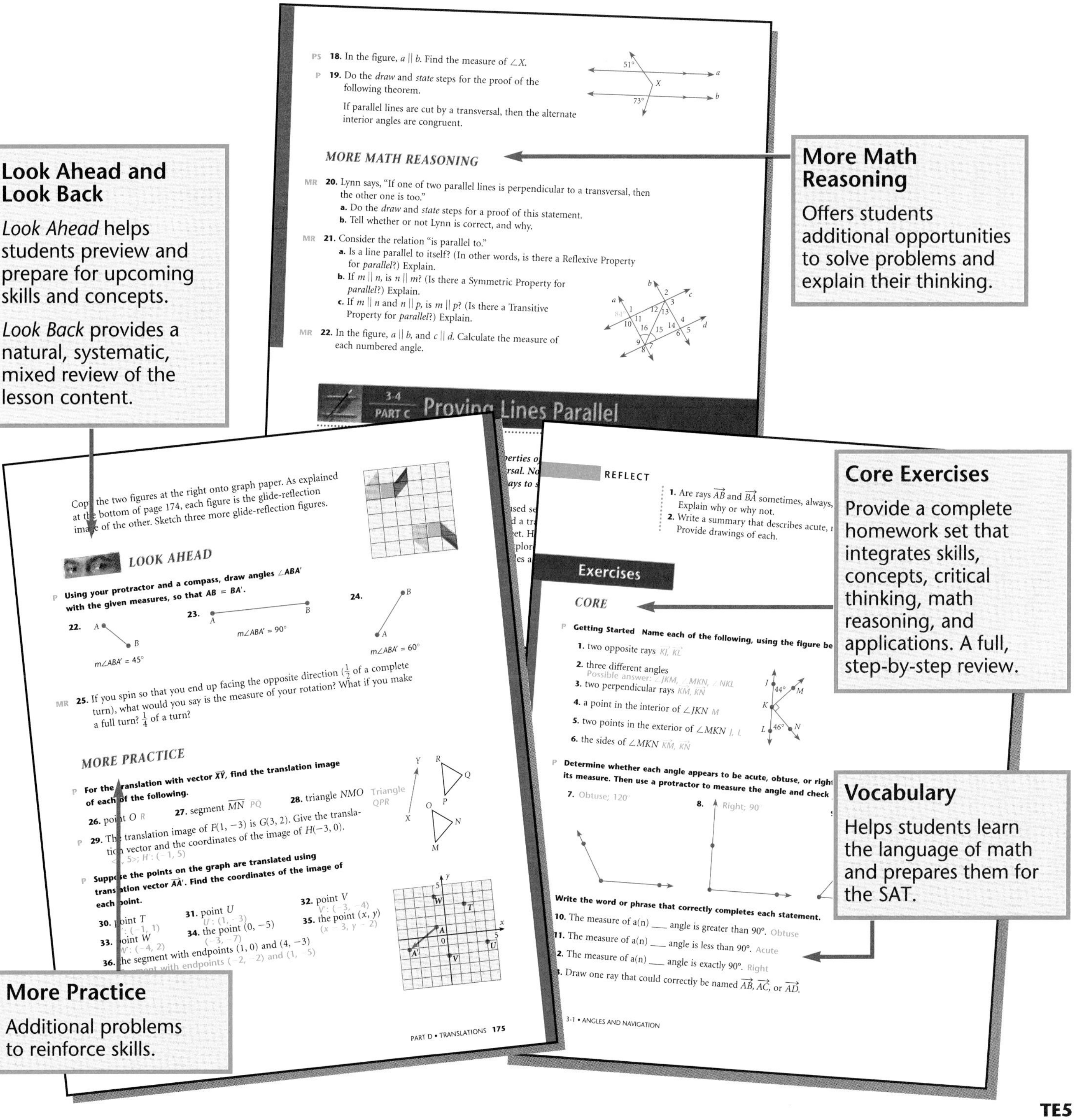

Look Ahead and Look Back

Look Ahead helps students preview and prepare for upcoming skills and concepts.

Look Back provides a natural, systematic, mixed review of the lesson content.

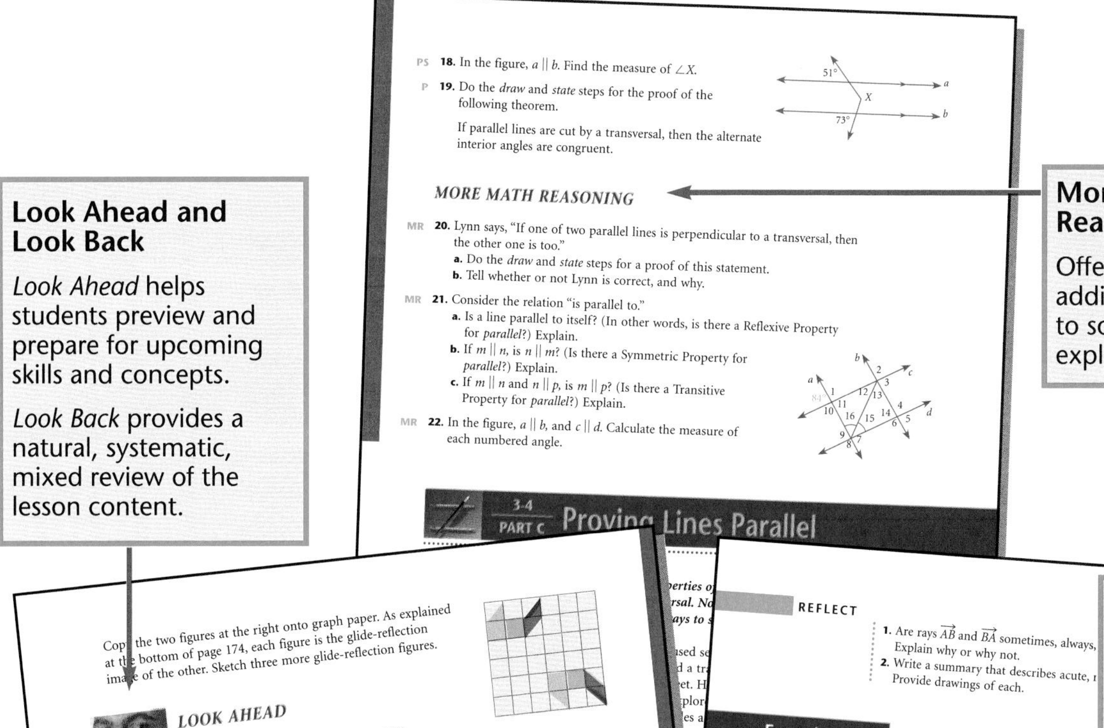

PS 18. In the figure, $a \parallel b$. Find the measure of $\angle X$.

P 19. Do the *draw* and *state* steps for the proof of the following theorem.

If parallel lines are cut by a transversal, then the alternate interior angles are congruent.

MORE MATH REASONING

MR 20. Lynn says, "If one of two parallel lines is perpendicular to a transversal, then the other one is too."

a. Do the *draw* and *state* steps for a proof of this statement.

b. Tell whether or not Lynn is correct, and why.

MR 21. Consider the relation "is parallel to."

a. Is a line parallel to itself? (In other words, is there a Reflexive Property for *parallel*?) Explain.

b. If $m \parallel n$, is $n \parallel m$? (Is there a Symmetric Property for *parallel*?) Explain.

c. If $m \parallel n$ and $n \parallel p$, is $m \parallel p$? (Is there a Transitive Property for *parallel*?) Explain.

MR 22. In the figure, $a \parallel b$, and $c \parallel d$. Calculate the measure of each numbered angle.

3-4 PART C Proving Lines Parallel

More Math Reasoning

Offers students additional opportunities to solve problems and explain their thinking.

Copy the two figures at the right onto graph paper. As explained at the bottom of page 174, each figure is the glide-reflection image of the other. Sketch three more glide-reflection figures.

LOOK AHEAD

P Using your protractor and a compass, draw angles $\angle ABA'$ with the given measures, so that $AB = BA'$.

22. $m\angle ABA' = 45°$ 23. $m\angle ABA' = 90°$ 24. $m\angle ABA' = 60°$

MR 25. If you spin so that you end up facing the opposite direction ($\frac{1}{2}$ of a complete turn), what would you say is the measure of your rotation? What if you make a full turn? $\frac{1}{4}$ of a turn?

MORE PRACTICE

P For the translation with vector $\overrightarrow{XY}$, find the translation image of each of the following.

26. point O *R* 27. segment $\overline{MN}$ *PQ* 28. triangle NMO *Triangle QPR*

P 29. The translation image of $F(1, -3)$ is $G(3, 2)$. Give the translation vector and the coordinates of the image of $H(-3, 0)$.

P Suppose the points on the graph are translated using translation vector $\overrightarrow{AA'}$. Find the coordinates of the image of each point.

30. point T 31. point U 32. point V 33. point W 34. the point $(0, -5)$ 35. the point (x, y)

36. the segment with endpoints $(1, 0)$ and $(4, -3)$

More Practice

Additional problems to reinforce skills.

REFLECT

1. Are rays $\overrightarrow{AB}$ and $\overrightarrow{BA}$ sometimes, always, … Explain why or why not.
2. Write a summary that describes acute, … Provide drawings of each.

Exercises

CORE

P Getting Started Name each of the following, using the figure be…

1. two opposite rays *KJ, KL*
2. three different angles *Possible answer: ∠JKM, ∠MKN, ∠NKL*
3. two perpendicular rays *KM, KN*
4. a point in the interior of $\angle JKN$ *M*
5. two points in the exterior of $\angle MKN$ *J, L*
6. the sides of $\angle MKN$ *KM, KN*

P Determine whether each angle appears to be acute, obtuse, or right… its measure. Then use a protractor to measure the angle and check…

7. *Obtuse; 120°* 8. *Right; 90°*

Write the word or phrase that correctly completes each statement.

10. The measure of a(n) ___ angle is greater than 90°. *Obtuse*
11. The measure of a(n) ___ angle is less than 90°. *Acute*
12. The measure of a(n) ___ angle is exactly 90°. *Right*
13. Draw one ray that could correctly be named $\overrightarrow{AB}$, $\overrightarrow{AC}$, or $\overrightarrow{AD}$.

Core Exercises

Provide a complete homework set that integrates skills, concepts, critical thinking, math reasoning, and applications. A full, step-by-step review.

Vocabulary

Helps students learn the language of math and prepares them for the SAT.

Every Superlesson concludes with *Making Connections.*

Once students complete a *Superlesson,* they have a firm grasp of key skills and concepts and how they fit into a larger context. In *Making Connections,* students integrate, apply, and extend what they've learned; demonstrate their math reasoning; and begin to use their mastery and link it to real life.

Making Connections

The last *Part* of each *Superlesson* wraps up the *Superlesson* theme and encourages students to connect and apply new concepts.

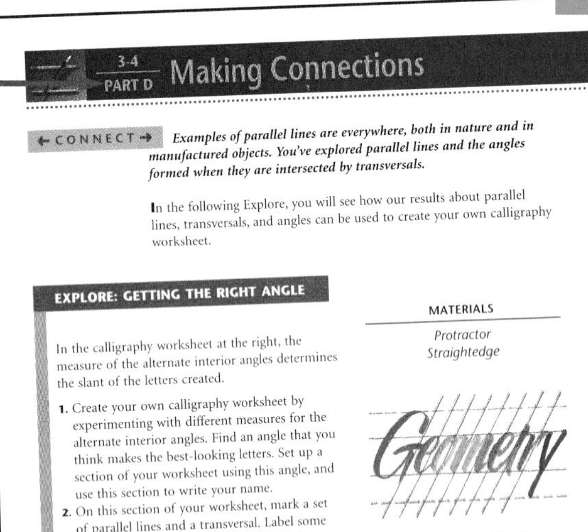

3-4 PART D **Making Connections**

← CONNECT → *Examples of parallel lines are everywhere, both in nature and in manufactured objects. You've explored parallel lines and the angles formed when they are intersected by transversals.*

In the following Explore, you will see how our results about parallel lines, transversals, and angles can be used to create your own calligraphy worksheet.

EXPLORE: GETTING THE RIGHT ANGLE

MATERIALS
Protractor
Straightedge

In the calligraphy worksheet at the right, the measure of the alternate interior angles determines the slant of the letters created.

1. Create your own calligraphy worksheet by experimenting with different measures for the alternate interior angles. Find an angle that you think makes the best-looking letters. Set up a section of your worksheet using this angle, and use this section to write your name.
2. On this section of your worksheet, mark a set of parallel lines and a transversal. Label some points, so that you can list the pairs of corre-

Connect

Statements tap prior knowledge and link the previous concept or skill with those to follow.

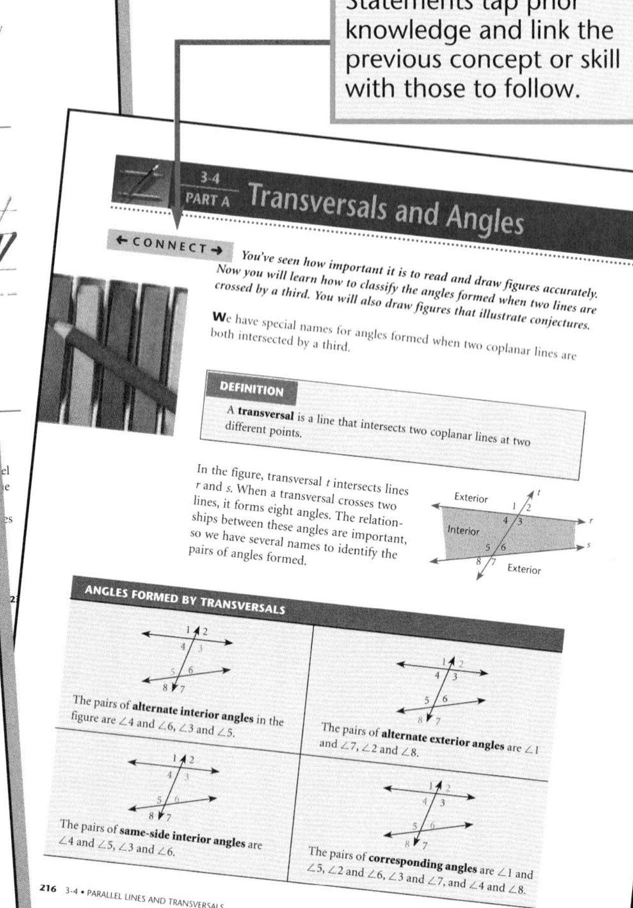

3-4 PART A **Transversals and Angles**

← CONNECT → *You've seen how important it is to read and draw figures accurately. Now you will learn how to classify the angles formed when two lines are crossed by a third. You will also draw figures that illustrate conjectures.*

We have special names for angles formed when two coplanar lines are both intersected by a third.

DEFINITION

A **transversal** is a line that intersects two coplanar lines at two different points.

In the figure, transversal t intersects lines r and s. When a transversal crosses two lines, it forms eight angles. The relationships between these angles are important, so we have several names to identify the pairs of angles formed.

ANGLES FORMED BY TRANSVERSALS

The pairs of **alternate interior angles** in the figure are ∠4 and ∠6, ∠3 and ∠5.

The pairs of **alternate exterior angles** are ∠1 and ∠7, ∠2 and ∠8.

The pairs of **same-side interior angles** are ∠4 and ∠5, ∠3 and ∠6.

The pairs of **corresponding angles** are ∠1 and ∠5, ∠2 and ∠6, ∠3 and ∠7, and ∠4 and ∠8.

216 3-4 • PARALLEL LINES AND TRANSVERSALS

Self-Assessment

Complete each statement with *always, sometimes,* or *never.* Explain your answers.

1. An angle is ___ formed by two rays.
2. Opposite rays ___ form a straight line.
3. An acute angle ___ measures 90°.
4. An angle with measure less than 100° is ___ acute.
5. The length of a vector is ___ a negative number.
6. A translation ___ preserves angle measures.
7. What range of values is possible for each of the following?
   a. an angle's measure
   b. a bearing
8. The measure of ∠A is twice the measure of ∠B. If ∠B is an acute angle, which of the following must be true of ∠A?
   (a) It is obtuse. (b) It is acute. (c) It is a right angle. (d) Not here

Determine whether each statement is true or false. If it is true, state a postulate or postulates that justify the statement. If false, state or sketch a counterexample. [2-2]

9. If points X and Y are in plane $\mathcal{P}$, then $\overleftrightarrow{XY}$ is also in plane $\mathcal{P}$.
10. The intersection of planes $\mathcal{Q}$ and $\mathcal{R}$ is a line.
11. Any three points can be contained in one line.
12. List the critical attributes of acute angles. Then write a definition of acute angles using "if and only if." [2-2]
13. Suppose you are given the pre-image and image for a transformation shown at the right. Explain how you can determine whether the transformation was a reflection or a translation.

Pre-image Image

14. The graphs of two equations are shown at the right. (Recall from algebra that graphs like these are called *parabolas.*) Find the translation vector for the translation that maps the parabola on the left onto the parabola on the right.

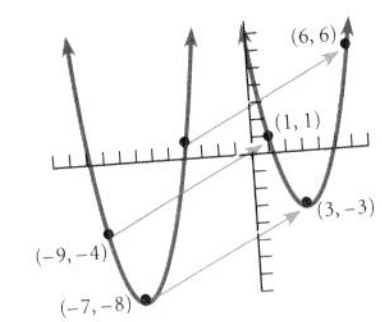

PS, C 15. **Sketch Artist** Sketch a tower, airplane, and helicopter so that the following are true. The bearing of the airplane from the tower is 045. The bearing of the helicopter from the tower is 270. The helicopter is closer to the tower than the airplane is.

178 3-1 • ANGLES AND NAVIGATION

Self-Assessment

A *Self-Assessment* in every *Making Connections* part provides a review of skills and concepts every few days.

Anatomy of a Chapter

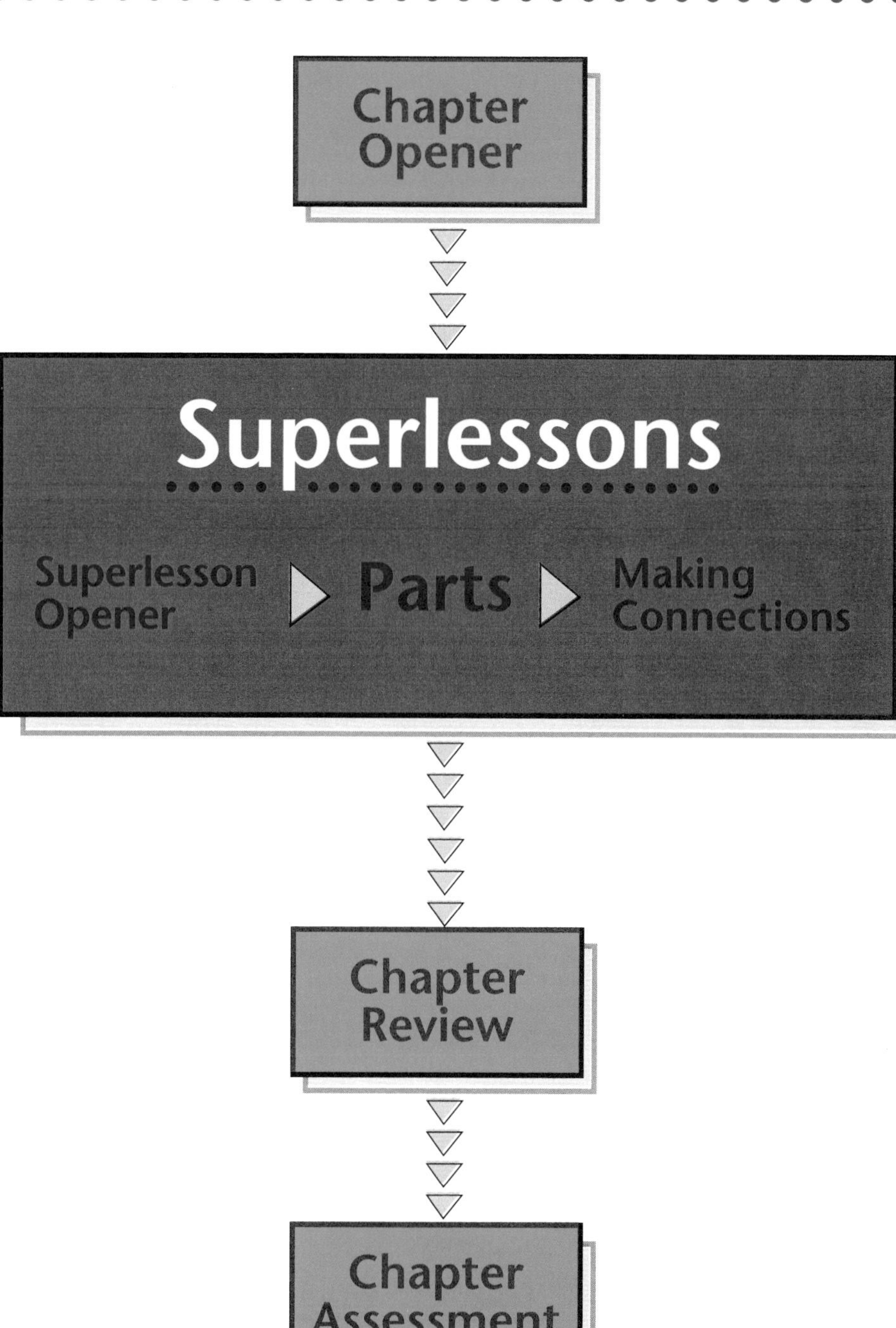

Each *AWSM* chapter begins with a motivational opener highlighting a real person and his or her career, and includes *Projects* that relate to the mathematics in the chapter.

Each *Superlesson* is divided into *Parts. Making Connections* is always the last *Part,* enabling students to revisit the theme and connect and apply new learning.

Chapters include a *Chapter Review,* which offers a review of vocabulary, concepts, connections, and a self-assessment.

Chapters close with a *Chapter Assessment,* which provides an end-of-chapter test and a performance assessment.

The Teacher's Edition offers a host of management and teaching options.

The *AWSM* Teacher's Edition provides instructional approaches to address a range of learning styles while supporting a variety of teaching styles. A pacing guide, at-a-glance overviews, and correlations to NCTM Standards make lesson planning efficient and effective.

Margin notes on each page include class openers, suggestions for cooperative grouping, alternative examples, and much more. A spectrum of topics across the top shows you key points for integrating related mathematics, industry connections, and other disciplines. Professional notes along the bottom highlight current research, diversity issues, connections to other disciplines, and technology options.

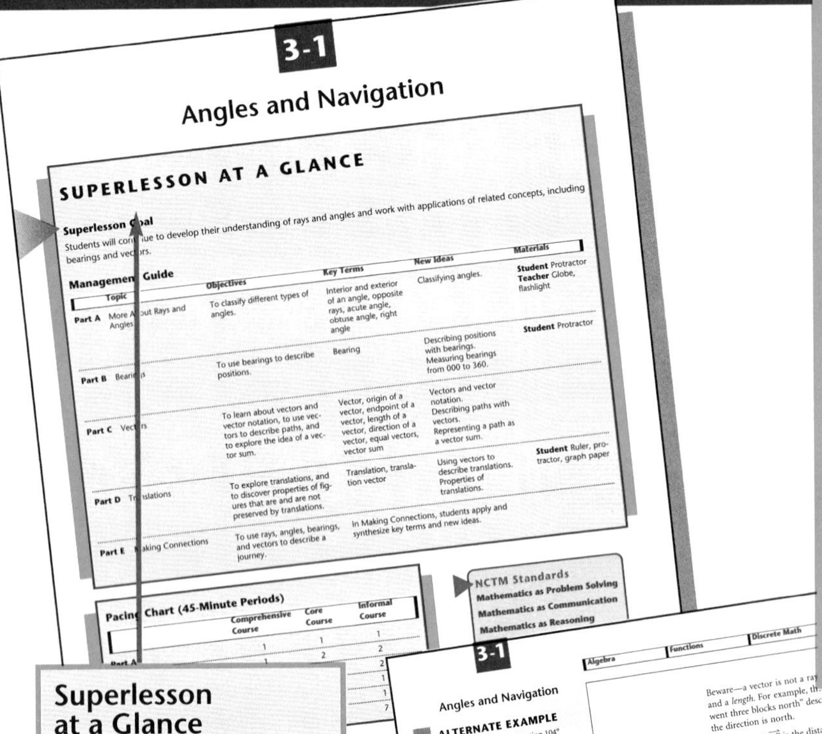

3-1

Angles and Navigation

SUPERLESSON AT A GLANCE

Superlesson Goal
Students will continue to develop their understanding of rays and angles and work with applications of related concepts, including bearings and vectors.

Management Guide

	Topic	Objectives	Key Terms	New Ideas	Materials
Part A	More About Rays and Angles	To classify different types of angles.	Interior and exterior of an angle, opposite rays, acute angle, obtuse angle, right angle	Classifying angles.	**Student** Protractor **Teacher** Globe, flashlight
Part B	Bearings	To use bearings to describe positions.	Bearing	Describing positions with bearings. Measuring bearings from 000 to 360.	**Student** Protractor
Part C	Vectors	To learn about vectors and vector notation, to use vectors to describe paths, and to explore the idea of a vector sum.	Vector, origin of a vector, endpoint of a vector, length of a vector, direction of a vector, equal vectors, vector sum	Vectors and vector notation. Describing paths with vectors. Representing a path as a vector sum.	
Part D	Translations	To explore translations, and to discover properties of figures that are and are not preserved by translations.	Translation, translation vector	Using vectors to describe translations. Properties of translations.	**Student** Ruler, protractor, graph paper
Part E	Making Connections	To use rays, angles, bearings, and vectors to describe a journey.	In Making Connections, students apply and synthesize key terms and new ideas.		

Pacing Chart (45-Minute Periods)

	Comprehensive Course	Core Course	Informal Course
	1	1	1
Part A	1	2	2
			2
			1
			1
			7

NCTM Standards
Mathematics as Problem Solving
Mathematics as Communication
Mathematics as Reasoning

Superlesson at a Glance

One quick look at this handy management tool and you will know how to align *AWSM* to your curriculum objectives and achieve them.

3-1

Algebra | Functions | Discrete Math

Angles and Navigation

ALTERNATE EXAMPLE

Draw vector $\overrightarrow{JK}$ with direction 104° and length 36 mm. Then draw a second vector, $\overrightarrow{RS}$, that is equal to $\overrightarrow{JK}$.

CONSIDER

Introduces students to the idea that equal vectors must be parallel.

Possible Answer
1. They appear to be parallel.

Beware—a vector is not a ray ... and a *length*. For example, "I went three blocks north" describes a vector. ... the direction is north.

The **length** of $\overrightarrow{AB}$ is the distance between *A* and *B*. The **direction** of a vector is measured counterclockwise from the horizontal (the positive *x*-axis). Two different vectors are **equal vectors** if they have the same direction and the same length.

EXAMPLE

Draw vector $\overrightarrow{YZ}$ with direction 45° and length 27 mm. Then draw a second vector, $\overrightarrow{EF}$, that is equal to $\overrightarrow{YZ}$.

Draw a horizontal line. Then use a ruler and protractor to draw $\overrightarrow{YZ}$ with the correct length and direction. Repeat the process to draw $\overrightarrow{EF}$.

CONSIDER

1. In the example above, vectors $\overrightarrow{YZ}$ and $\overrightarrow{EF}$ are equal. What else appears to be true about $\overrightarrow{YZ}$ and $\overrightarrow{EF}$?

TRY IT

a. Use your protractor and ruler to find the length and direction of $\overrightarrow{VW}$. Then draw vector $\overrightarrow{PQ}$, which is equal to $\overrightarrow{VW}$.
Length: 2.7 cm, Direction: 138°

A path or trip that consists of several segments can be modeled by a sequence of vectors. The endpoint of one vector is the origin of the next vector in the chain. The figure surrounding this paragraph shows a ship's path from point *M* to point *N* that consists of five vectors.

166 3-1 • ANGLES AND NAVIGATION

Science Connection

Vectors are often used in physics to model forces and velocities. One of the most respected U.S. physicists is Dr. Luis Walter Alvarez. Born in 1911 in San Francisco, he earned a Ph.D. from the University of Chicago in 1936. A Nobel Prize winner in physics (1968), Dr. Alvarez has done work in particle physics, astrophysics, geophysics, optics, and air navigation.

166

Alternate Examples

Provide additional examples for classroom presentation. All are available on overhead transparencies.

Professional Notes

AWSM authors, educational specialists, and teachers from across the nation provide *Research Notes, Diversity Issues, Connections* to other disciplines, and *Technology Notes.*

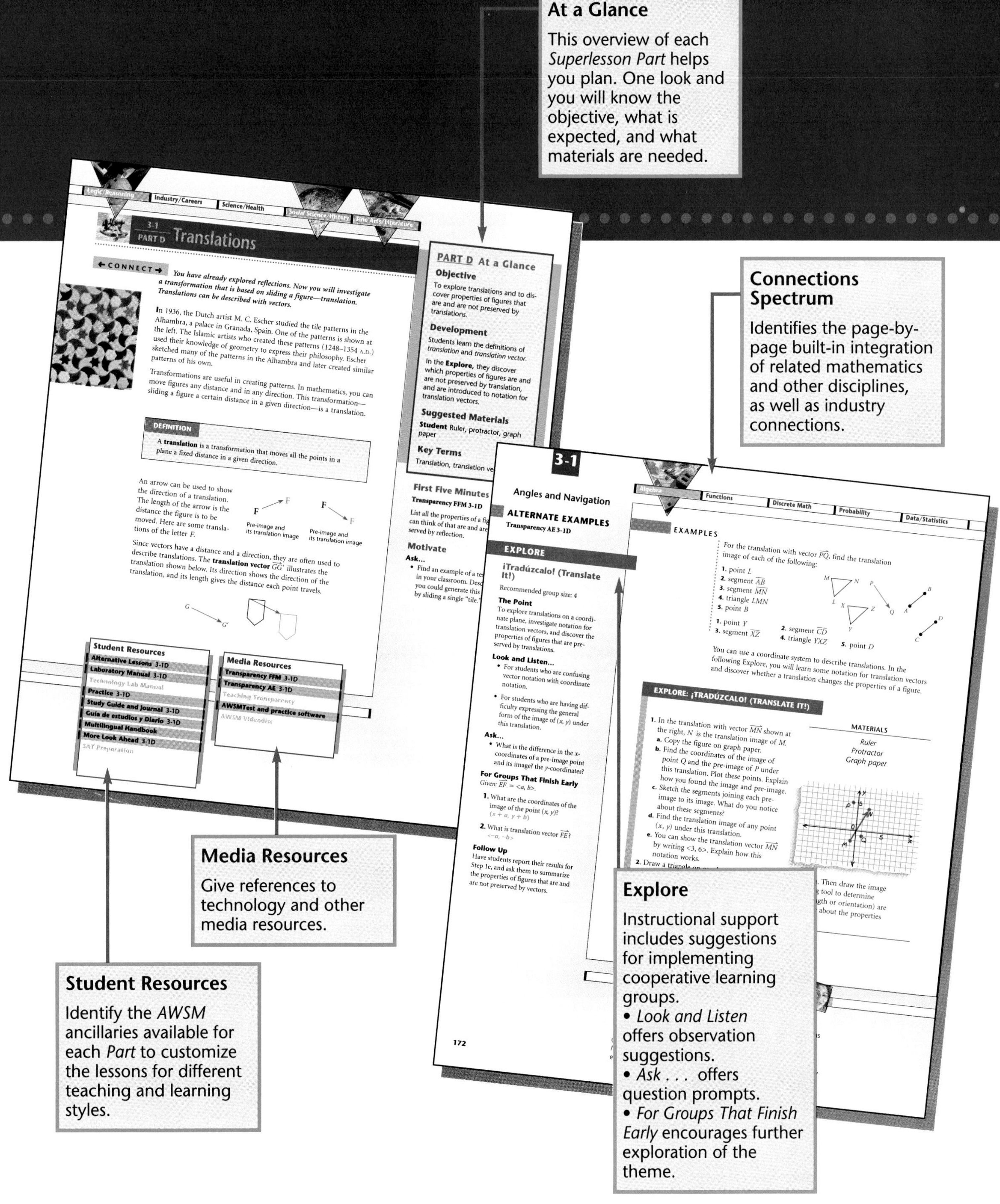

At a Glance

This overview of each *Superlesson Part* helps you plan. One look and you will know the objective, what is expected, and what materials are needed.

Connections Spectrum

Identifies the page-by-page built-in integration of related mathematics and other disciplines, as well as industry connections.

Media Resources

Give references to technology and other media resources.

Explore

Instructional support includes suggestions for implementing cooperative learning groups.

- *Look and Listen* offers observation suggestions.
- *Ask . . .* offers question prompts.
- *For Groups That Finish Early* encourages further exploration of the theme.

Student Resources

Identify the *AWSM* ancillaries available for each *Part* to customize the lessons for different teaching and learning styles.

AWSM ancillaries give you additional tools to reach and assess every student.

AWSM ancillaries provide plenty of the right kind of practice for students and flexible teaching options for you.

Teacher's Resource Package

Projects connect mathematics to social studies, science, business, and the arts. Students apply math through data collection, research, and oral and written communication.

Study Guide and Journal helps students develop a deeper understanding of math through writing and thinking. (Also available in Spanish.)

Assessment includes *Superlesson* quizzes; end-of-chapter, mid-year, and end-of-year tests; and performance assessments; plus scoring rubrics for assessing portfolios and journals.

Laboratory Manual expands on the *Explore* feature in the Student Edition and provides student recording sheets.

Technology Laboratory Manual helps students use technology with the Student Edition *Explores.*

Practice provides plenty of additional exercises for students who still need to master key skills and concepts covered in *Superlesson Parts.*

Alternative Lessons support students who have missed class. Perfect for substitute teachers.

More Look Ahead and Look Back provides practice of skills needed for upcoming lessons *(Look Ahead)* and additional mixed review of concepts covered *(Look Back).*

SAT Preparation gets students ready for the new SAT with test-taking strategies and sample problems for practice.

Multilingual Handbook provides vocabulary help and theorems and postulates in Spanish, Cantonese, Cambodian, Vietnamese, and Hmong.

Teacher's Tools provide a collection of transparencies, forms, and other teacher support to assist with classroom management.

Also Available

Guía de estudios y diario is a Spanish version of the *Study Guide and Journal.*

Overhead Transparency Package offers *First Five Minutes* warm-ups, color visuals to encourage discussion, and every *Alternate Example* for easy presentation.

Solutions Manual provides step-by-step solutions for all exercises in the Student Edition.

AWSMTest and Practice software provides options for quizzes, tests, andpractice worksheets, as well as for performance assessment.

AWSM Videodisc introduces each chapter with an intriguing video to stimulate interest. It also includes hundreds of animated and still images for analysis or discussion.

Industry Connections

"What used to be relevant to the engineer is now relevant to everyone."

— Lester C. Thurow
Economist

One of the most dynamic aspects of the current curriculum reform movement is the partnership of educators and businesspeople dedicated to connecting what is learned in the classroom with the demands of the workplace. In no discipline is this partnership more alive and visible than in mathematics. "Every worker needs mathematics to solve problems, guide decision making, and build models to predict outcomes everyday in their jobs," reports John Dossey, *AWSM* author and Distinguished University Professor of Mathematics, Illinois State University.

"Every worker needs math to solve problems, guide decision making, and build models to predict outcomes everyday in their jobs."

TODAY'S JOBS REQUIRE MORE KNOWLEDGE OF MATH.

"We can no longer implement curriculum as if mathematics were a specialist's skill, rather than a generalist's. What used to be relevant to the engineer is now relevant to everyone," says Lester C. Thurow, economist and Dean, School of Management, Massachusetts Institute of Technology.

In a 1994 report, *Quality Education: School Reform for the New American Economy,* published by the Department of Education Office of Educational Research and Improvement, it is predicted that between 1992 and 2000, 89 percent of new jobs will require post-secondary math skills. The report's authors also predict that if present trends continue, only half of the newcomers to the workforce will have those skills.

CLASSROOM AND WORKPLACE: SOME COMMON VALUES

Many values and needs of the business community are congruent with those of schools, and vice versa. In school and in the workforce, we value:

Working in teams In many companies, the days when one individual was assigned to one project are a thing of the past. Often people work in teams, and individuals on the team work together to successfully achieve a common goal. In schools, faculties work as a team to improve teaching and learning. And in the classroom, greater emphasis is placed on cooperative learning, shared problem-solving activities, and on group reports and projects.

Communicating with power and precision In industry, being a good communicator is a critical skill for all employees; as a result, companies provide their employees with a great deal of training to ensure it. Communication is also increasingly valued in the mathematics classroom. Instruction is designed to get students to verbalize their problem-solving ideas, insights, and attempts.

Approaching and solving problems in a variety of ways
Successful companies strive to be innovative, discarding products and methods that prove ineffective. These companies seek employees who are always thinking about improving a process, getting a job

"In industry, being a good communicator is a critically important skill for all employees."

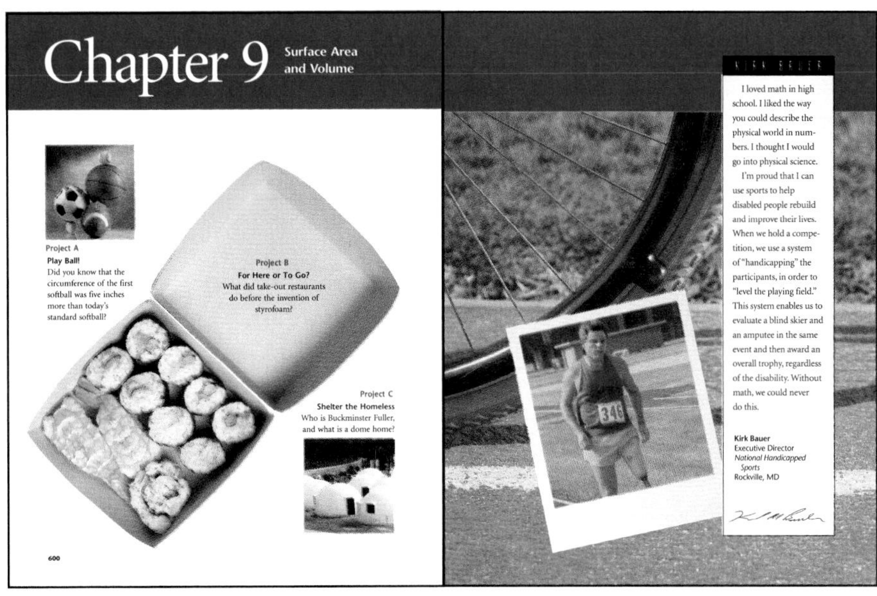

Chapter 9 Surface Area and Volume

Project A
Play Ball!
Did you know that the circumference of the first softball was five inches more than today's standard softball?

Project B
For Here or To Go?
What did take-out restaurants do before the invention of styrofoam?

Project C
Shelter the Homeless
Who is Buckminster Fuller, and what is a dome home?

600

KIRK BAUER

I loved math in high school. I liked the way you could describe the physical world in numbers. I thought I would go into physical science.

I'm proud that I can use sports to help disabled people rebuild and improve their lives. When we hold a competition, we use a system of "handicapping" the participants, in order to "level the playing field." This system enables us to evaluate a blind skier and an amputee in the same event and then award an overall trophy, regardless of the disability. Without math, we could never do this.

Kirk Bauer
Executive Director
National Handicapped Sports
Rockville, MD

Today's mathematics educators encourage students to work with open-ended problems using a multi-step process. Students use logic and mathematical evidence to verify their results, instead of looking to the teacher as the sole authority for right answers.

SCHOOL/BUSINESS PARTNERSHIPS ARE A TWO-WAY STREET.

Local business and industries are forming relationships with schools in greater numbers each year. Both schools and industry are discovering that each can benefit from such partnerships.

done more quickly, and saving time or money in accomplishing a task.

Mathematics educators encourage students to use a range of techniques to approach a problem, rather than focusing on getting one "right answer." Educators value open discussion among students and prompt it with "what if" questions to generate new ideas and new ways to think about a situation.

Knowing how to formulate problems Because problems are often not well formulated in the workplace, employees must learn to define them. Imagine for a moment what goes through the mind of a newly hired stockroom clerk or office assistant who has been given this assignment: "Don't ever let the office run out of copy paper. Save money by ordering it in large quantities, but don't order too much because there's not a lot of storage room."

TIPS FOR SCHOOL/INDUSTRY COOPERATION

- Find the right partner for your school. If you want to be referred to potentially receptive businesses in your area, contact the National Association of Partners in Education (NAPE), 209 Madison Street, Suite 401, Alexandria, VA 22314. NAPE will send you an information packet about partnerships and a business contact near you.

- Determine the scope of your proposed relationship and define what you want to get out of it. It can range from using local professionals as mentors and resources to exchanges in which teacher and students work in businesses after school hours or during the summer. Relationships can be structured where businesspeople teach courses, tutor, make equipment donations, sponsor field trips, and offer scholarships.

- Plan ahead. Industry tutors, for example, may need to be reminded how strictly schools run by the clock. Even an engineer who uses math daily may need to be refreshed on math curriculum so that tutoring efforts can be focused on student needs.

- Be aware that company participation with schools may require various departmental approvals. What may appear to be reluctance on a prospective company's part may in fact be the normal time it takes to secure approval at higher levels. Be persistent.

- Build in mechanisms for evaluation and feedback. Use what you've discovered to expand your program and make it even better the next year.

- Honor the industry connection with a year-end awards program or publicize the relationship. An article in the local newspaper or school newsletter will encourage a long-term relationship.

Problem Solving

Mathematical problem solving, in its broadest sense, is nearly synonymous with doing mathematics. — *NCTM Standards*

In high school mathematics, students traditionally worked with applications only *after* they had learned the skills. A complete mathematics program for the '90s embeds problem solving in day-to-day instruction. Problem solving is the vehicle through which important mathematical ideas are developed.

Problem-solving experiences require higher-order thinking skills and include open-ended problems. Investigating, questioning, and representing situations in a variety of ways (verbally, numerically, graphically, and, symbolically) are all part of problem solving.

The ability to problem solve is something employers look for in the employees they hire. Many businesses devote time and resources to developing problem-solving skills among employees, and creating a systematic approach to problem solving is a fundamental goal.

GETTING STARTED

"A good way to integrate problem solving is to spend some time building positive attitudes and dispositions about problem solving," says Randy Charles, *AWSM* author and Professor of Mathematics and Computer Science at San Jose State University, San Jose, California. "Get students to communicate their thinking about problem solving and to work on different approaches, rather than focusing on getting the right answers."

Techniques such as using problem-solving guidelines, looking at a variety of strategies, and having students work in cooperative groups can help students become successful problem solvers.

> "A good way to integrate problem solving is to spend some time building positive attitudes and dispositions about problem solving."
> – *Randy Charles*

GUIDELINES

One way to systematically approach problem solving is to use a step-by-step process, sometimes referred to as Problem-Solving Guidelines. Both businesspeople and educators have developed such guidelines. Notice the similarities between the two sets of guidelines. The first set was developed for use by businesses. The second set comprises the *AWSM* guidelines for use with this book.

Problem-Solving Guidelines from Total Quality Management Training

- Describe the problem.
- Determine the cause or causes.
- Choose a solution.
- Plan action steps and follow-up.

STRATEGIES

Introduce students to a variety of strategies that can be used to solve a problem. Here are some strategies with which they may already be familiar.

- Draw a diagram.
- Guess and check.
- Look for a pattern.
- Make an organized list.
- Make a table.
- Make a physical model.
- Simplify the problem.
- Use logical reasoning.
- Work backward.
- Write an equation.

Brainstorm other strategies that students can use when solving problems. Students may want to keep a list in their journals of the strategies that they have used or post the strategies on a bulletin board.

TIPS FOR PROBLEM-SOLVERS WHO ARE STUCK

Guide and encourage students who can't seem to get started to use one or more of the following prompts.

- Try restating the problem in your own words.
- Identify key information that might be needed in solving the problem, including the quantity or quantities in the situation.
- Think about strategies that might be used.
- Identify the unknown quantity you are trying to find.
- Think about problems, theorems, and definitions you have worked with that might be used.
- Make a model or a drawing to help illustrate the situation.
- Use special notation to help simplify your work.
- Put the problem aside and come back to it later.

After solving a problem, ask students to think about what they learned that might be used in future problems.

PROJECTS

Open-ended projects are useful for stimulating creativity while encouraging problem solving.

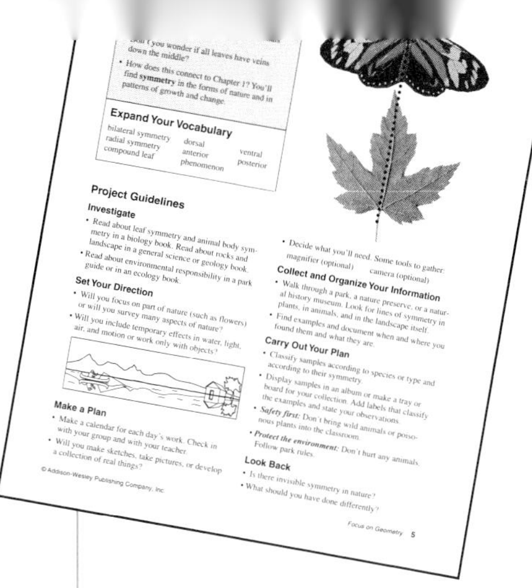

Don't you wonder if all leaves have veins down the middle?

- How does this connect to Chapter 1? You'll find **symmetry** in the forms of nature and in patterns of growth and change.

Expand Your Vocabulary

bilateral symmetry, radial symmetry, compound leaf, dorsal, anterior, phenomenon, ventral, posterior

Project Guidelines

Investigate

- Read about leaf symmetry and animal body symmetry in a biology book. Read about rocks and landscape in a general science or geology book.
- Read about environmental responsibility in a park guide or in an ecology book.

Set Your Direction

- Will you focus on part of nature (such as flowers) or will you survey many aspects of nature?
- Will you include temporary effects in water, light, air, and motion or work only with objects?

Make a Plan

- Make a calendar for each day's work. Check in with your group and with your teacher.
- Will you make sketches, take pictures, or develop a collection of real things?

- Decide what you'll need. Some tools to gather: magnifier (optional) camera (optional)

Collect and Organize Your Information

- Walk through a park, a nature preserve, or a natural history museum. Look for lines of symmetry in plants, in animals, and in the landscape itself.
- Find examples and document when and where you found them and what they are.

Carry Out Your Plan

- Classify samples according to species or type and according to their symmetry.
- Display samples in an album or make a tray or board for your collection. Add labels that classify the examples and state your observations.
- ***Safety first:*** Don't bring wild animals or poisonous plants into the classroom.
- ***Protect the environment:*** Don't hurt any animals. Follow park rules.

Look Back

- Is there invisible symmetry in nature?
- What should you have done differently?

Focus on Geometry 5

Projects should simulate activities that students might encounter in the real world.

TEACHER'S ROLE

It is important for the teacher to be a facilitator who supports students, rather than being the single source of answers. Questions should be posed to stimulate thought, rather than to get an answer.

Making students responsible for their own learning is the goal of the teacher. Organize the classroom so that students feel comfortable sharing their ideas. Students understand a mathematical explanation best when they have personally questioned the ideas and have grappled with the answers and the explanations for the answers.

Whole-class learning, including teacher-guided discussions, is still an important role for the teacher, as is conducting lectures that promote active student participation.

ASSESSMENT

Evaluation of each student's proficiency with problem solving should be ongoing, using informal observation and questioning.

A *Problem-Solving Observation Form* is provided in the teacher's ancillary materials, as well as rubrics for scoring performance assessment. (See also *Assessment*, page TE28.)

AWSM PROBLEM-SOLVING

PROBLEM-SOLVING GUIDELINES

Understand the Problem	**Develop a Plan**
What is the situation all about? What are you trying to find out? What are the key data/conditions? What are the assumptions?	Have you ever worked a similar problem before? Will you estimate or calculate? What strategies can you use?
Implement the Plan	**Look Back**
What is the solution? Did you interpret correctly? Did you calculate correctly? Did you answer the question?	Could you work the problem another way? Is there another solution? Is the answer reasonable?

AWSM TEACHER'S NOTES

Teacher's notes for each *AWSM* **Explore** includes **Look and Listen** (what to listen for as students work on the **Explore**), and **Ask** (questions for students who are stuck).

EXPLORE

Climbing to New Heights

Recommended group size: 4

The Point

To use trigonometry to find the range of safe heights for a ladder.

Look and Listen...

- For students who do not see which angle they are changing.
- For students who do not see which trigonometric ratio to apply.

Ask...

- Have you drawn a sketch of the situation?
- Which angle measures between 50° and 75°?
- Which side length do you know? Which side length do you need? For the angle you're working with, are these sides the opposite and adjacent, opposite and hypotenuse, or adjacent and hypotenuse?

Communication

In listening to students, we understand why.

In 1991, a writer was asked by a national think tank to visit high school math classrooms where teachers were beginning to implement the NCTM Teaching Standards. The writer's task was to observe and describe what she saw from the perspective of a layperson.

In presenting her report, the writer noted that one thing that impressed her most was that students were no longer sitting at desks, heads bowed, pencils in hand, quietly poring over books and worksheets, the way she remembered math class. They were, in her words, "doing a whole lot of talking, writing, listening, arguing — thinking about math!"

Teachers who emphasize communication in mathematics instruction say it infuses their classes with a new dynamism and makes mathematics learning more accessible to more students. Everyone — teacher and student alike — begins to think of math as a language that can be used to reason and explore.

FACILITATING MATHEMATICS COMMUNICATION

What's the best way to get students to communicate about math? Listen and ask, respond educators. They stress that often it's more important to hear *why* a student presents a wrong answer than to compliment a student on a quick correct response.

Teachers who are listeners are roving monitors of small group discussions. They're aware of the dynamics of each group and encourage the full participation of each member. These teachers shape the discussion when necessary. They know when to supply information, when to let students struggle, and when to ask a question that provides a new avenue or insight. They know when to bring the discussion to closure in a way that permits everyone to share in the accomplishment. These teachers monitor how well students have internalized concepts and help relate these concepts to different content strands.

THE ROLE OF REFLECTION IN MATHEMATICS COMMUNICATION

In addition to speaking, listening, reading, and writing in class, there should be opportunities for reflection about mathematical ideas. Reflection allows students to express generalizations, extend ideas, describe difficulties, and share triumphs on their road to mathematical competence. Math journals are good tools for students to use to capture those reflections, and note follow-up and "what-if" questions.

WHY COMMUNICATE ABOUT MATHEMATICS?

We communicate about mathematics:

- to build mathematical meaning.
- to know that we know.
- to generalize from experiences and patterns.
- to develop mathematical language.
- to understand different perspectives.
- to expand mathematical understanding.
- to show what we know rather than what we don't know.

When students communicate about math, they begin to use the precise language of mathematics, which they eventually incorporate into their own vocabularies. They have an opportunity to discuss and debate the mathematical implications of a range of issues (whether cultural, political, or economic) that shape our society. They then begin to see the math inherent in our everyday lives.

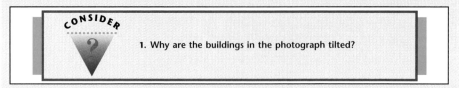

COMMUNICATION IN *AWSM*

Opportunities for communication in *AWSM* can be found in **Explore, Reflect, Consider,** and **Journal,** as well as in **Exercises.**

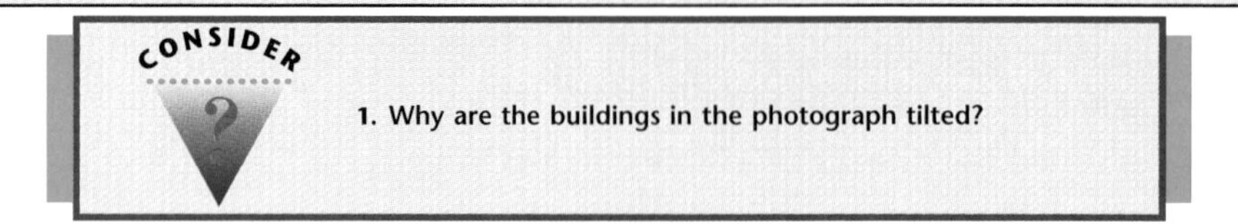

CONSIDER
1. Why are the buildings in the photograph tilted?

Reasoning

To give more students access to mathematics as a powerful way of making sense of the world, it is essential that an emphasis on reasoning pervade all mathematical activity.

— *NCTM Standards*

"A fundamental characteristic of the individual who chooses to stay in mathematics is the ability to engage in productive mathematical reasoning, rather than simply follow demonstrations and use formulas," writes Leslie P. Steffe in the 1990 NCTM Yearbook. In order to increase the number of students who take higher level mathematics, we must increase the number of students who learn to reason mathematically.

Both inductive and deductive reasoning are necessary skills, and neither should be limited to a geometry course. Students can learn to use reasoning skills to understand ideas, discover relationships among those ideas, draw conclusions about the ideas, and solve problems involving these ideas.

DEVELOPING REASONING SKILLS

Developing the ability to reason mathematically involves communication skills and an understanding of how each process is connected.

MATHEMATICAL MODELING

One can begin with mathematical modeling: for example, representing a line as a model of the path that light travels, a sphere as a model of the surface of the earth, an ellipse as a model of the path of a planet around a star, or an icosahedron as a model of a virus.

INDUCTIVE REASONING

After recognizing the mathematical objects that are used in the modeling process, we raise the question of how to discover information by studying the models. This leads to the development of inductive reasoning skills to explore shapes and search for patterns and explanations of our observations.

DEDUCTIVE REASONING

The next step is to raise the question: how do we know if the observations we make, and conclusions we reach in the inductive step, are actually correct? How can we justify our conjectures? This leads to the development of deductive reasoning.

Discovering patterns and making conjectures based on observation come naturally to young children. We must work to retain this natural curiosity as today's children grow into adulthood.

AWSM REASONING

In *AWSM Focus on Geometry*, students will begin by looking at mathematical models as found in art, nature, science, and society. (First van Hiele level)

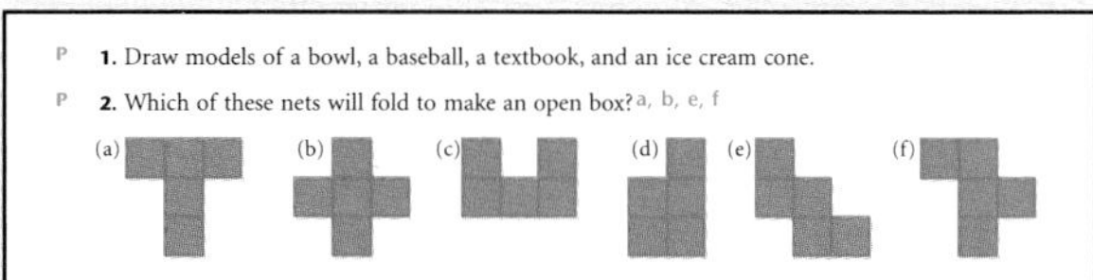

P **1.** Draw models of a bowl, a baseball, a textbook, and an ice cream cone.

P **2.** Which of these nets will fold to make an open box? a, b, e, f

(a) (b) (c) (d) (e) (f)

Students then use visual thinking, along with inductive reasoning, to explore objects and search for relationships in order to understand their properties, as well as draw conceptions on paper or on a computer screen. (Second van Hiele level)

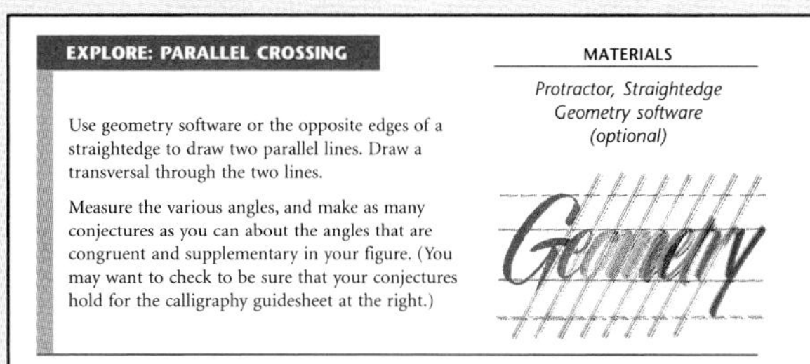

EXPLORE: PARALLEL CROSSING

Use geometry software or the opposite edges of a straightedge to draw two parallel lines. Draw a transversal through the two lines.

Measure the various angles, and make as many conjectures as you can about the angles that are congruent and supplementary in your figure. (You may want to check to be sure that your conjectures hold for the calligraphy guidesheet at the right.)

MATERIALS

Protractor, Straightedge
Geometry software (optional)

This is followed by deductive reasoning skills, where students learn to organize their thinking as logical arguments and to verify the conjectures using all types of proofs. (Third van Hiele level)

Connections

If you want to understand nature, you must be conversant with the language in which nature speaks to us. — *Richard Feynman*

For too many students, mathematics has been an isolated, compartmentalized part of their school experience, disconnected from the real world, from other subjects, and even from itself. To answer the question, "Why do we have to learn this," mathematics educators are now paying increasing attention to the notion of "connections." Connections are generally classified into three types:

- connections to real life,
- connections to other disciplines, and
- connections within mathematics.

CONNECTIONS TO REAL LIFE

More than ever, facility with mathematics is a requirement for success in the world that students will encounter when they leave school. And as technology takes over the role of low-level computation that most students think is synonymous with mathematics, industry will be looking for contributors who are proficient in more sophisticated reasoning and communicating.

Bringing the real world into the classroom does more than prepare students for the workplace. When students can see that mathematics is a part of almost everything they do, their motivation to learn increases.

> "Specific knowledge quickly becomes outdated in our fast-paced society. Ways of learning, developing general concepts, finding relationships — these are what must be important to our students and, consequently, in our classrooms."

Bringing the outside world into the classroom isn't easy. Today's students are distracted by a flood of bids competing for their attention. Mathematics educators will be most successful by choosing activities and instructional materials that succeed in connecting students to the world they know and will encounter:

- Instruction in new ideas can often begin with open-ended issues from real-world situations. Students should have the opportunity to wrestle with conflicting information and problems that others have to resolve.
- When possible, students should work in groups to solve problems, just as they will in real life.
- Problem sets, as well as examples, should come from a broad cross section of life. Sports and building construction have long been staples of mathematics materials; it's time to draw on art, television, current events, and other issues.
- Materials must present a diverse world. Seeing a variety of people and their cultures, previously disinterested students may realize

AWSM CONNECTIONS

EXPLORE: A STRONG CONSTITUTION

Develop a one-page written constitution for a new club for your school. Discuss the following questions with classmates to help formulate your constitution.

1. What assumptions (postulates) will you take as true without proof?
2. What key words will you leave undefined? (for instance, *participation*, *freedom*, etc.)
3. What words will you choose to define carefully? Give an example of one such word and provide your definition for it.
4. How will you provide for new laws (theorems) or amendments (postulates) to be added to your club's constitution?
5. Present a description of your club and its constitution to your class.

that people similar to themselves consider mathematics important.

CONNECTIONS TO OTHER DISCIPLINES

Researchers conclude that making connections to other subjects in school enhances the understanding of mathematics, as well as the other subjects.

Mathematics applications and by-products are numerous in the sciences and in engineering, but they embrace other fields as well. Scale diagrams are used in art, architecture, and medical models. Graphing techniques are important to social scientists. Businesspeople use sophisticated techniques as they seek and analyze economic trends. Manufacturing managers work to define the fine line between excess inventory and unfilled orders. Measurement skills are crucial in nursing, pharmacology, agriculture, landscaping, and art.

Stressing the connections between mathematics and both the real world and other disciplines creates a synergistic learning environment in which everyone benefits — the student, the teacher, and the community.

CONNECTIONS WITHIN MATHEMATICS

Educators know that the daily study of mathematics connects to a larger, more eclectic body of understanding of how the world works. Students must be encouraged to think about mathematics in this connected way or they will have difficulty with the necessary shifts in thinking that allow problem solving and communication with others. The best way to show the interconnectedness of mathematics is by stressing the Big Ideas.

"Stressing the connections between mathematics and both the real world and other disciplines creates a synergistic learning environment in which everyone benefits — the student, the teacher, and the community."

WHAT ARE "BIG IDEAS"?

Big ideas refer to those concepts, principles, or learning techniques that recur and cut across specific content lines. An example of a big idea with great unifying power comes from the area of functional patterns and relationships. Consider the relationship between a function $y = f(x)$ and the related function $y = f(ax)$. The influence of the constant a is the same whether the function is linear, quadratic, exponential, or trigonometric. Learning the effect of the constant a on the function and its related graph becomes more important — more educational — than specific formulas, generalizations, or algorithms that may apply to a single relationship.

AWSM'S BIG IDEAS

The authors of *Addison-Wesley Secondary Math* have identified the Big Ideas that underlie all instruction in the series:

- Proportional thinking
- Functional patterns and relationships
- Quantifying and representing data
- Mathematical representations
- Spatial patterns and relationships
- Mathematical decision making

FOCUSING ON BIG IDEAS HELPS STUDENTS LEARN.

If asked, "What is one of the big ideas of algebra," many students would be hard pressed to find an answer. Helping students to make these connections requires us to step back occasionally and look at the bigger picture.

Big ideas affect the teacher's role by putting the curriculum into a broader perspective. It is these big ideas that will come up again and again in future problems and will appear in more advanced concepts. The well prepared student will meet them as time-honored friends that smooth the way to greater understanding. This concept is in keeping with the realization that specific knowledge quickly becomes outdated in our fast-paced society. Ways of learning, developing general concepts, finding relationships — these concepts are vital to our students and, consequently, important in our classrooms.

NCTM Content Strands

	Foundations of Algebra and Geometry	Focus on Algebra
Algebra	■ Variables and expressions ■ Proportions and proportionality ■ Linear relationships ■ Exponential and power relationships ■ Modeling expressions and equations ■ Solving linear equations	■ Variables and expressions ■ Quantities and relationships ■ Solving equations and inequalities ■ Linear and quadratic equations and their graphs ■ Linear inequalities and their graphs ■ Solving systems of equations and inequalities ■ Exponents and polynomials ■ Solving rational and radical equations
Functions	■ Development of functions from number patterns ■ Linear relationships ■ Exponential and power relationships	■ Linear, quadratic, and polynomial functions ■ Absolute value and square root functions ■ Exponential and logarithmic functions ■ Multiple representations of functions: patterns, tables, equations, and graphs
Geometry from a Synthetic Perspective	■ Geometric patterns ■ Scale ■ Congruence and similarity ■ Transformations ■ Two- and three-dimensional drawings	■ Geometric methods for solving equations ■ Scale and similarity ■ Triangle Inequality ■ Symmetry and reflections
Geometry from an Algebraic Perspective	■ Measurement ■ Perimeter, area, and volume ■ Coordinate graphs ■ Pythagorean Theorem	■ Parallel and perpendicular lines ■ Distance formula ■ Pythagorean Theorem ■ Reasoning with coordinates
Trigonometry	■ Introduction to similar triangles ■ Basics of right triangle trigonometry	■ Right triangle trigonometry
Statistics	■ Data representation on maps, graphs, and spreadsheets ■ Interpretation of maps, graphs, and spreadsheets ■ Scatter plots ■ Measures of central tendency	■ Interpret data displayed in graphs ■ Measures of central tendency ■ Scatter plots ■ Trend lines ■ Using a spreadsheet
Probability	■ Games and probability ■ Fairness ■ Experimental probability ■ Geometric probability ■ Theoretical probability	■ Theoretical probability ■ Experimental probability ■ Geometric probability
Discrete Math	■ Basic counting techniques ■ Sequences ■ Venn diagrams	■ Matrix algebra ■ Counting principle ■ Solving systems of equations with matrices
Conceptual Underpinnings of Calculus	■ Exploring maximums and minimums in problem situations	■ Rate of change ■ Maximum and minimum values of functions ■ Families of functions ■ Rational and radical functions
Mathematical Structure	■ Justifying solutions ■ Making generalizations ■ Using approximations	■ Properties of real numbers ■ Real number system ■ The structure and properties of algebra

"The real impact of the NCTM Standards on school mathematics is the joining of process outcomes (problem-solving, communication, reasoning, and connecting) across the long-held content strands."
– John Dossey, President, NCTM, 1986–1988

Focus on Geometry	Focus on Advanced Algebra
■ Using variable quantities in expressions ■ Solving linear equations and inequalities ■ Solving quadratic equations ■ Slope, coordinate distance ■ Equations for parallel and perpendicular lines ■ Modeling binomial multiplication	■ Solving equations and inequalities ■ Solving systems of equations and inequalities ■ Matrix applications to systems of equation ■ Exponents and logarithms ■ Polynomials
■ Composition of transformations ■ Maxima and minima of quadratic functions ■ Transformations of graphs	■ Polynomial functions ■ Rational and radical functions ■ Exponential and logarithmic functions ■ Trigonometric functions
■ Properties of figures ■ Measurement ■ Similarity and congruence ■ Transformations ■ The structure of geometry	■ Similarity and congruence ■ Conic sections ■ Graphs and networks
■ Applications of vectors, transformations, and coordinates ■ Vectors and bearings ■ Transformations on a coordinate plane ■ Proof by vector, transformation, and coordinate methods	■ Coordinate geometry ■ Transformations on a coordinate plane ■ Vectors
■ Right triangle trigonometry ■ Applications of trigonometry to vectors, indirect measurement, etc.	■ The unit circle ■ Right triangle trigonometry ■ Law of Sines, Cosines ■ Graphs of trigonometric functions
■ Scatter plots ■ Circle graphs ■ Data collection for geometric figures ■ Designing experiments	■ Scatter plots and lines of best fit ■ Curve fitting ■ Sampling methods ■ Normal distribution
■ Geometric probability ■ Theoretical probability	■ Theoretical probability ■ Geometric probability ■ Simulations ■ Experimental probability ■ Compound and conditional probability
■ Counting procedures in geometry ■ Optimization; shortest paths ■ Fractals and recursion ■ Euler's formula ■ Venn diagrams	■ Matrix algebra ■ Linear programming ■ Graphs and networks ■ Difference equations ■ Combinations and permutations ■ Recursive relations and fractals
■ Area under curves ■ Maximum and minimum values ■ Limits	■ Rate of change ■ Families of functions ■ Maximum and minimum values and end behavior of functions ■ Concept of a limit ■ Sequences and series ■ Inverse relations
■ Inductive and deductive reasoning ■ Laws of logic ■ Axiomatic systems ■ Non-Euclidean geometry	■ Real number system ■ Complex number system ■ Field properties

Cooperative Learning

When you use cooperative learning, students do some of the teaching.

Working in cooperative groups helps students solve problems together and work as a team. It's noisier than a lecture class, but there's a lot of learning going on.

WHAT IS COOPERATIVE LEARNING? HOW DOES IT WORK?

To understand what cooperative learning is, it is important to understand what it isn't. It's not a rap session in the classroom, or a chance for students to work together to get their homework done. While it has a decidedly social dynamic, the purpose of cooperative learning is clearly academic. Although it is a noncompetitive technique, students are evaluated and graded on their work as a team, as well as individually.

SUCCESS DEPENDS ON FOUR FACTORS...

While learning to work effectively in teams prepares students for the workforce, it is not the primary benefit of cooperative learning. Many educators like it because they can see in their classrooms what two decades of research has shown — cooperative learning can increase student achievement. Ensuring that achievement depends upon four key factors:

- The teacher must structure and monitor student roles, being a very active "guide on the side."
- Students must believe that they are responsible for their own learning and for the learning of others in the group. Researchers today refer to this as positive interdependence.
- Each student must demonstrate mastery of the assigned work.
- Students must learn to accept and support each other and to resolve conflicts constructively.

WHAT A VISITOR SEES...

A visitor sees a full-class introduction by the mathematics teacher — perhaps the teacher poses a situation that leads to a generalization that needs to be brought into focus. Students then move their chairs into predetermined groups of three or four, and a babble ensues that could put off anyone who judges the success of a classroom by its quiet level. The teacher moves about the room, observing and prompting with "what if . . ." questions, and eventually pulls the lesson together with input from each group.

WHAT A TEACHER EXPECTS...

As they work together, students get ideas that they would not have developed working alone. Working together toward a common goal generates a spirit that enlivens the group and makes math a vital activity. And because of their training, students who need in-depth explanations are not afraid to ask their classmates who have already mastered a topic, thereby reinforcing the understanding and confidence of all students involved in the exchange.

Throughout the period, the teacher circulates around the room, prompting groups with open-ended questions, ensuring that groups are working within the parameters of

AWSM EXPLORES

The **Explores** in *AWSM* are particularly suitable for cooperative learning. In the Teacher's Edition, suggestions are given **For Groups That Finish Early,** and **Follow Up** questions are provided.

EXPLORE: ARCHITECTURE MADE EASY

MATERIALS
Cubes
Isometric dot paper

1. Make a building out of 10 cubes. To make the building interesting, have at least 3 stacks of cubes with different heights.
2. Sketch the orthographic top view of your building, giving the number of cubes in each stack.
3. Use isometric dot paper to sketch views of your building from two different corners.
4. Exchange your isometric sketches with those of another student. See if you can build his or her building correctly.

cooperation, and generally managing the classroom without being the focus of attention.

HOW STUDENTS BENEFIT

Students greatly expand their thinking, problem-solving, and communication skills. Discussion of problems means that math vocabulary becomes more familiar, alternative approaches to a solution are presented and resolved, and insights are verbalized and defended that may convince (or dissuade) others in the group. Once students become comfortable with the process, they freely propose hypotheses and solution techniques that they might hesitate to volunteer in front of the whole class. Students ultimately benefit from cooperative learning by becoming "active learners."

HOW TEACHERS BENEFIT

Classes are more interesting and students often learn more — and have the test scores to prove it! Some teachers say the best benefit is that they are freed from being the constant leader and evaluator. Instead they can attend to the needs of the groups and the individuals within those groups who benefit greatly from the one-on-one instruction.

"It's very exciting for a teacher to see students who are not stars, particularly those that haven't had successful experiences in math, begin to succeed as part of a group. You see a whole change in their attitude about mathematics. I've had students who lacked confidence in math class really bloom because of cooperative learning. They see that they really can think mathematically; they have strong thought processes. They begin to lead discussions and do work they never dreamed they'd do. When that happens," says Barbara Alcala, *AWSM* author and teacher at Whittier High School, Whittier, California, "encourage it, reinforce it, and enjoy it!"

> "It's very exciting for a teacher to see students who are not stars, particularly those that haven't had successful experiences in math, begin to succeed as part of a group. You see a whole change in their attitude about mathematics...encourage it, reinforce it, and enjoy it!"
>
> – Barbara Alcala

TIPS TO REMEMBER...

ASWM authors share these tips:

- Begin slowly. Some teachers start with groups of two or three for part of a class period, once a week. By easing into it, you can adjust the classroom environment session by session.
- When students are working in groups of two or three, it often helps to assign each student a specific role. Some of the typical roles are:
  - Facilitator
  - Timer
  - Recorder
  - Questioner
  - Material Gatherer
  - Spokesperson
- Choose challenging topics for cooperative groups. Simple questions can be explored by having students work in pairs.
- Start with heterogeneous groups of your own selection. Alter membership as group dynamics require.
- Keep the groupings long enough so that members develop the confidence they need to operate in what may be to them a radically different classroom setting.
- Ask students to evaluate how well they work together in their groups to keep them aware of the goals of cooperative learning and provide motivation for greater cooperation.
- Because competition among students has been a powerful force in schools, it will take students some time to adjust to working in groups.
- Take pleasure in the new interest you will see in math! When students who are not stars, particularly those that haven't had successful experiences in math, begin to succeed as part of a group, you will see a positive change in their attitude about mathematics.

You can find practical information about cooperative learning in *Professional Standards for Teaching Mathematics,* National Council of Teachers of Mathematics, Reston, VA, 1991; *The New Circles of Learning,* Association for Supervision and Curriculum Development, Alexandria, VA, 1994; and *Cooperative Learning in Mathematics,* Addison-Wesley, 1990.

Student Diversity

Building a community of learners in the mathematics classroom

In years past, as students moved through high school, mathematics classes served as a filter, not a pump. But to be able to succeed in tomorrow's workforce, even the most challenged students must develop math power today.

As a nation, we weren't particularly concerned about math proficiency until the 1983 release of the government report, "A Nation at Risk." It confirmed what business and policy leaders were beginning to suspect: on average, American students were falling behind students in other countries in mathematical achievement. The report warned that if the trend continued, the United States would loose its ability to compete in worldwide markets, and our citizens would suffer economic consequences as a result.

The report launched a national curriculum reform movement; the NCTM Standards are one result of this movement. The explosion of technology and a shift from an industrial society to an information society require that all our workers, not just a few, be able to use the problem-solving tools mathematics provides.

OUR GOAL TODAY: EVERY STUDENT SUCCEEDS IN MATH

Students enter high school with diverse backgrounds, different levels of English proficiency, and varied learning experiences. To compound the situation, research has shown that individuals, even those from similar backgrounds, do not all learn in the same way.

Research on students' learning styles, begun in the early 1970s and catapulted to prominence with the publication of Howard Gardner's work on multiple intelligences, has much to offer teachers who seek to develop these strategies to pull in every learner.

> "Because so many students have been sent the message that math is hard or that they can't expect to be good in it, we need to praise small positive steps in developing mathematical understanding, for they'll lead to larger ones."
>
> – Freddie Renfro

SUPPORTING A CLASSROOM COMMUNITY OF LEARNERS

While it is challenging to ensure that every student achieves success in high school mathematics, we shouldn't think of this task as impossible. In every classroom, teachers can build a community of mathematics learners. Within this environment, rich opportunities to foster communication, creativity, and critical thinking can be structured to support every student on the road to mathematical literacy.

TEACHING STRATEGIES TO MEET DIVERSE NEEDS

Opportunities, provided through a range of teaching strategies, enable a teacher who listens and observes to work with each student until he or she finds success. Some students are visual learners: once you draw a diagram of the oral or written representation, they get the concept immediately. Other students are kinesthetic learners: they may need to make a model of the diagram in order to achieve understanding.

STRATEGIES EVOLVE NATURALLY AS TEACHERS CHANGE ROLES

As teachers shift their roles from "tellers" to listeners and facilitators, strategies often evolve naturally. When acting as facilitators, teachers become more proficient at determining individual student needs. In observing cooperative groups, a teacher might observe that a student would work better independently for a while. The student would then reenter a group at the teacher's discretion.

SELF-CONFIDENCE IS THE KEY

"Promoting self-confidence is the key," stresses Freddie Renfro, *AWSM* author and Director of Mathematics for Goose Creek ISD, Baytown, Texas. "Because so many students have been sent the message that math is hard or that they can't expect to be good in it, we need to praise small positive steps, for they'll lead to larger ones. The goal of these strategies is to help students have some small successes on which to build larger ones. Success is the very best motivator for students. When we can help each one find success, we can help each one develop their mathematical abilities."

LEARNING STYLES

Research has found that we all have different learning styles. The accompanying table describes some learning-style characteristics and relates them informally to the ways in which students learn. The last column, Math Response, offers insights into strategies that may be effective in engaging learners with these varied styles.

LEARNING STYLES	LIKES TO	IS GOOD AT ...	LEARNS BY ...	MATH RESPONSE
Linguistic	Read Write Talk	Remembering Explaining Interacting	Expressing verbally Hearing and seeing words	Needs to see written explanations, hear and give verbal explanations
Logical/ Mathematical	Experiment Figure things out Work with numbers Ask questions Explore patterns and relationships	Math reasoning Logic Problem solving	Categorizing Classifying Working with abstract patterns and relationships	Prefers to explain, reason, and solve problems by reasoning logically
Visual/ Spatial	Draw Build Design/Create	Imagining Puzzles Sensing changes	Visualizing Working with pictures and diagrams	Can visualize relationships, develop patterns
Kinesthetic	Touch objects Move Use body language	Physical activities Sports	Touching Moving Interacting with space	Prefers to classify, build, measure, model
Musical	Sing Play an instrument Respond to rhythm	Noticing pitches Identifying rhythms	Logical approaches Concentrated practice	Responds to logic, structure, patterns, rhythm
Interpersonal	Talk Work in groups	Organizing ideas and people Communicating Mediating	Sharing Cooperating	Excels by explaining, comparing, solving problems
Individual	Work alone Pursue own interests	Understanding self Following instincts Being original	Working alone on individual projects Self-paced instruction	Successful with individual work, own projects, problem solving, critical thinking

The Technology-Rich Classroom

"Effective use of technology requires objectives for mathematics education that are aligned with the mathematical needs of the information age. — *Reshaping School Mathematics, MSEB*

Today's world is one where information is controlled, interpreted, and organized by technology; this trend will probably be more prevalent in tomorrow's world. To prepare students for both, we need to help them discover the power of technology tools to investigate and solve real mathematics problems.

THE ROLE OF TECHNOLOGY IN MATH CLASSES

In any discussion of technology use in instruction, the question arises: when should students use calculators? The NCTM Standards assume that in grades 9 through 12, "*Scientific calculators with graphing capabilities will be available to all students at all times.*" In deciding appropriate roles for technology, it is important to understand that those who proposed the standards based their recommendation on three assumptions:

- First, they assumed that high school students have a command of basic operations. Proficiency in basic computational skills is critical, especially for mental mathematics and estimation. It is not appropriate for a high school student to use a calculator to add $5 + 9$ or find half of 42. It is appropriate for a student to use a calculator to find three numbers whose product is 2520, sin 63.43°, or $\sqrt{34.56}$. Using a calculator can help students tackle real-world problems that are otherwise inaccessible to them using paper and pencil (making better use of precious classroom time).
- The second assumption is that teachers will help students decide when it is appropriate to use technology and when it would be more beneficial to use other methods, such as mental math or paper and pencil.
- The third assumption concerns the change we're undergoing in mathematics curriculum. The mathematical problems we want students to experience today are not the simple, skills-based problems of computation-based programs of the past (using technology with those curricula would be pointless). Today's math curriculum supports a wide variety of technology applications for many types of activities, not just computation, but table building, graphing, and programming.

> "*AWSM* supports the vision of the classroom as a mathematics laboratory, where students investigate and experience real mathematics relevant to their lives; where mathematics learning is a cooperative venture; and where technology is a powerful tool to support problem solving."

THE ROLE OF COMPUTERS IN THE MATH CLASSROOM

Computers are a part of almost every aspect of our daily lives — from the computer chip that controls fuel flow to your car's engine, to the mainframe in which our travel reservations are stored, to the bar code reader on a cash register that ensures we get the sale price advertised in the newspaper. Today's mathematics curriculum must take advantage of computers for problem investigation, data organization and analysis, and communication of mathematical ideas. To do otherwise would shortchange our students.

Technology supports, not supplants, the development of basic skills. It is a powerful tool to help *all* students reach high levels of mathematical understanding.

"Calculators and computers with appropriate software transform the mathematics classroom into a laboratory much like the environment in many science classes, where students use technology to investigate, conjecture, and verify their findings. In this setting, ... (there emerges) a new classroom dynamic in which teachers and students become natural partners in developing mathematical ideas and solving mathematical problems."

— NCTM Curriculum and Evaluation Standards for School Mathematics

TECHNOLOGY IN *AWSM*

AWSM's technology starts where you are and supports what you have.

AWSM was developed to support the new vision of the mathematics classroom as a mathematics laboratory, where students investigate and experience real mathematics that is relevant to their lives; where mathematics learning is a cooperative venture between and among students and teachers; and where technology is a powerful tool used to support mathematical concepts and problem-solving activities. This is the spirit that integrates technology into the mathematics classrooms of the 1990s and beyond.

The problems and activities in *AWSM* are rich and flexible enough to support a range of teaching styles and technological experience. If you're beginning to integrate technology, start with the problems and activities accessible with scientific calculators. If you're already experimenting with technology, you will find plenty of support in integrating graphics calculators and computers. If you are an experienced technology user, you will be able to extend *AWSM* problems and activities to take full advantage of the technology available in your classrooms.

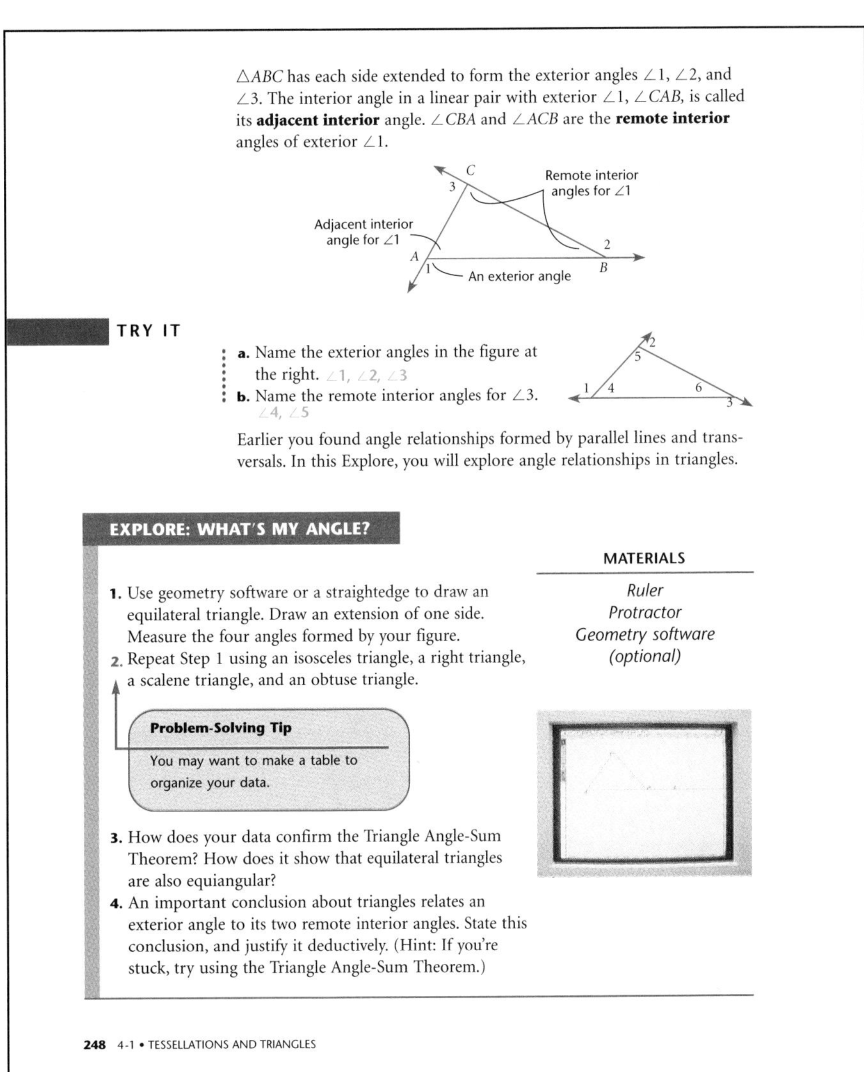

$\triangle ABC$ has each side extended to form the exterior angles $\angle 1$, $\angle 2$, and $\angle 3$. The interior angle in a linear pair with exterior $\angle 1$, $\angle CAB$, is called its **adjacent interior** angle. $\angle CBA$ and $\angle ACB$ are the **remote interior** angles of exterior $\angle 1$.

TRY IT

a. Name the exterior angles in the figure at the right. ∠1, ∠2, ∠3

b. Name the remote interior angles for ∠3. ∠4, ∠5

Earlier you found angle relationships formed by parallel lines and transversals. In this Explore, you will explore angle relationships in triangles.

EXPLORE: WHAT'S MY ANGLE?

MATERIALS

Ruler
Protractor
Geometry software (optional)

1. Use geometry software or a straightedge to draw an equilateral triangle. Draw an extension of one side. Measure the four angles formed by your figure.
2. Repeat Step 1 using an isosceles triangle, a right triangle, a scalene triangle, and an obtuse triangle.

Problem-Solving Tip

You may want to make a table to organize your data.

3. How does your data confirm the Triangle Angle-Sum Theorem? How does it show that equilateral triangles are also equiangular?
4. An important conclusion about triangles relates an exterior angle to its two remote interior angles. State this conclusion, and justify it deductively. (Hint: If you're stuck, try using the Triangle Angle-Sum Theorem.)

248 4-1 • TESSELLATIONS AND TRIANGLES

Assessment

In order to develop mathematical power in all students, assessment needs to support the continued mathematics learning of each student. — *NCTM Assessment Standards*

Because styles of mathematics teaching are becoming more diverse (with more emphasis being placed on reasoning and communication), the styles of assessment must change as well. No longer will short-answer and multiple-choice tests provide sufficient information on students' progress. "We must ensure that tests measure what is of value, not just what is easy to test," reports the National Research Council in *Everybody Counts,* Mathematical Sciences Education Board, 1989.

WHAT IS ASSESSMENT?

Assessment is a process used to determine what students know and what they are capable of doing. Testing is only one means of assessment, yet it has been the primary means of assessment for the last half century. More recently, educators are beginning to argue that tests promote rote learning, and that alternative forms of assessment are necessary in order to change the focus of what students learn.

STANDARDIZED TESTS

The *standardized test,* developed in the early 1900s, was the result of the search for consistent and objective forms of assessment. "The idea that schools could be run as efficient learning factories appealed to Americans in the 1950s. The trick to making the factory-like school work was to break down learning into small skills and bits of knowledge that could be taught and learned sequentially as students moved along the education assembly line. Standardized tests complemented this model of teaching," reports Diane Hart in *Authentic Assessment,* Addison-Wesley Publishing Company, 1994.

Most traditional tests used in mathematics classrooms mimic these standardized tests. And while short-answer and multiple-choice tests can provide valuable information about certain aspects of students' mathematical knowledge, these tests should be only one of many pieces of a complete assessment plan.

ALTERNATIVE ASSESSMENT

The search for alternatives to standardized tests has lead to a variety of new ways of assessing.

Embedded Assessment

Assessment that occurs as students are actively involved in learning is called *embedded assessment.* This can include reading a student's conclusion to an exploration or listening to a student working through a process. Teacher observations are an important embedded assessment technique. Although embedded assessment is by its nature a more informal type of assessment, it should become a systematic part of the assessment program.

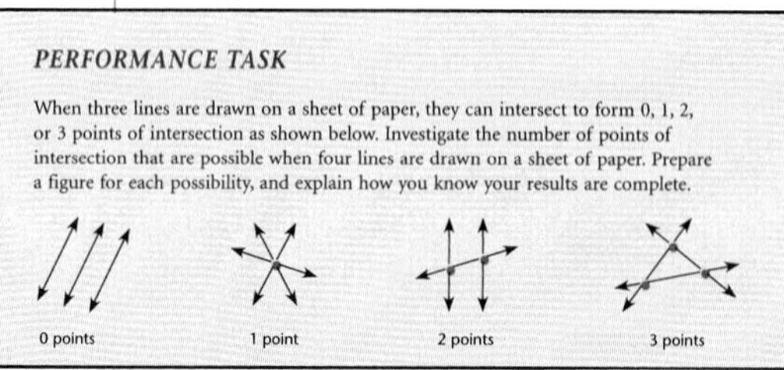

PERFORMANCE TASK
When three lines are drawn on a sheet of paper, they can intersect to form 0, 1, 2, or 3 points of intersection as shown below. Investigate the number of points of intersection that are possible when four lines are drawn on a sheet of paper. Prepare a figure for each possibility, and explain how you know your results are complete.
0 points
1 point
2 points
3 points

Performance Assessment

Musicians, artists, and athletic coaches have used performance assessment for centuries. All of these coaches assess the craft that is being performed. Mathematics performance assessment involves the presentation of a performance task — a task that simulates real-world challenges. A good performance task seldom has one right way to approach the problem or one correct answer.

Portfolio Assessment

A portfolio is a student's personal collection of work that illustrates their accomplishments and ideas and demonstrates growth. A well-prepared portfolio documents learning over a period of time and can reveal how well a student is progressing.

As students learn to determine what to include in their portfolio and why, they become partners with the teacher in the assessment process. The portfolio then becomes a tremendous self-evaluation tool.

Self-Assessment

As students learn to take more responsibility for their own learning, they will also learn to take more responsibility for their own assessment. Rather than being surprised by a low test score, students can learn to apply evaluation standards to their own efforts.

ADDISON-WESLEY SECONDARY MATH ASSESSMENT OPPORTUNITIES

The assessment program for Addison-Wesley Secondary Math is based on the philosophy that assessment should be an integral and ongoing part of the students' learning experience. Opportunities are provided for both traditional and alternative assessment.

	ASSESSMENT	STUDENT EDITION	TEACHER'S EDITION	ANCILLARIES
TRADITIONAL ASSESSMENT	Tests	■ Try It ■ Practice exercises ■ Chapter Test		■ Superlesson quiz ■ AWSMTest software ■ Chapter Assessment ■ End-of-Year and Mid-Year Assessment
	Standardized Tests	■ Vocabulary exercises ■ Multiple-choice exercises	■ Exercise notes indicate type of test.	■ SAT Preparation
ALTERNATIVE ASSESSMENT	Embedded Assessment	■ Reflect ■ Consider ■ Math Reasoning exercises	■ First Five Minutes ■ Embedded Assessment suggestions ■ Look & Listen... Ask... ■ Follow Up	■ Observation Form ■ Laboratory Manual ■ Technology Laboratory Manual ■ Study Guide and Journal
	Performance Assessment	■ Explore ■ Chapter Performance Task	■ Suggested journal entries ■ Rubric for scoring Performance Task	■ Chapter Alternative Assessment ■ Projects
	Portfolio Assessment	■ Explore ■ Reflect ■ Math Reasoning exercises	■ Suggestions for Portfolios ■ Suggested Projects	■ Laboratory Manual ■ Technology Laboratory Manual ■ Projects
	Self-Assessment	■ Superlesson Self-Assessment ■ Chapter Self-Evaluation		■ Study Guide and Journal

Planning and Pacing Guide

COMPREHENSIVE COURSE

Chapter	Getting Started	1	2	3	4	5	6
Days for instruction	4	15	12	17	13	14	12
Days for review, testing, or projects	0	2	2	2	2	2	3
TOTAL DAYS	4	17	14	19	15	16	15
Superlessons	All	All	All	All	All	All	All

CORE COURSE

Chapter	Getting Started	1	2	3	4	5	6
Days for instruction	4	15	13	19	17	16	14
Days for review, testing, or projects	0	2	2	2	2	3	2
TOTAL DAYS	4	17	15	21	19	19	16
Superlessons	All	All	All	All	All	All	All

INFORMAL COURSE

Chapter	Getting Started	1	2	3	4	5	6
Days for instruction	4	16	13	22	14	15	13
Days for review, testing, or projects	0	2	2	2	2	2	2
TOTAL DAYS	4	18	15	24	16	17	15
Superlessons	All	All	All	All	Omit 4-2C, 4-2D	Omit 5-2C	Omit 6-2E

COMPREHENSIVE COURSE

Chapter	7	8	9	10	11	12	Total
Days for instruction	14	12	12	7	7	7	146
Days for review, testing, or projects	2	2	2	1	1	3	24
TOTAL DAYS	16	14	14	8	8	12	170
Superlessons	All	All	All	All	All	All	

CORE COURSE

Chapter	7	8	9	10*	11*	12*	Total
Days for instruction	15	15	13	7			148
Days for review, testing, or projects	2	2	2	3			22
TOTAL DAYS	17	17	15	10			170
Superlessons	All	All	All	All	All	None	

*Choose two superlessons from Chapters 10–12.

INFORMAL COURSE

Chapter	7	8	9	10	11	12	Total
Days for instruction	18	14	15	0	5	0	149
Days for review, testing, or projects	2	2	2	0	3	0	21
TOTAL DAYS	20	16	17	0	8	0	170
Superlessons	Omit 7-2D, 7-3C	Omit 8-3	All	None	Omit 11-2	None	

ADDISON-WESLEY SECONDARY MATH

An Integrated Approach

Focus on **Geometry**

Alan R. Hoffer
Roberta Koss
Jerry D. Beckmann • Phillip E. Duren • Julia L. Hernandez • Beth M. Schlesinger • Catherine Wiehe

PROGRAM CONCEPTUALIZERS

Barbara Alcala
Randall I. Charles
John A. Dossey
Betty M. Foxx
Alan R. Hoffer
Roberta Koss
Sid Rachlin
Freddie L. Renfro
Cathy L. Seeley
Charles B. Vonder Embse

Addison-Wesley Publishing Company

Menlo Park, California • Reading, Massachusetts • New York • Don Mills, Ontario
Wokingham, England • Amsterdam • Bonn • Paris • Milan • Madrid • Sydney
Singapore • Tokyo • Seoul • Taipei • Mexico City • San Juan

Printed in the United States of America.

ISBN 0-201-86780-X

1 2 3 4 5 6 7 8 9 10-VH-98 97 96 95 94

PROGRAM CONCEPTUALIZERS

Barbara Alcala
Whittier High School
Whittier, California

Randall I. Charles
San Jose State University
San Jose, California

John A. Dossey
Illinois State University
Normal, Illinois

Betty M. Foxx
Collins High School
Chicago, Illinois

Alan R. Hoffer
University of California
Irvine, California

Roberta Koss
Redwood High School
Larkspur, California

Sid Rachlin
East Carolina University
Greenville, North Carolina

Freddie L. Renfro
Goose Creek Independent
School District
Baytown, Texas

Cathy L. Seeley
(Formerly) Texas
Education Agency
Austin, Texas

Charles B. Vonder Embse
Central Michigan University
Mt. Pleasant, Michigan

FOCUS ON GEOMETRY AUTHORS

Alan R. Hoffer
Lead author
University of California
Irvine, California

Roberta Koss
Associate lead author
Redwood High School
Larkspur, California

Jerry D. Beckmann
East High School
Lincoln, Nebraska

Phillip E. Duren
California State University
Hayward, California

Julia L. Hernandez
Rosemead High School
Rosemead, California

Beth M. Schlesinger
San Diego High School
San Diego, California

Catherine Wiehe
San Jose High Academy
San Jose, California

OTHER SERIES AUTHORS

Barbara Alcala
Whittier High School
Whittier, California

Penelope P. Booth
Baltimore County Public Schools
Towson, Maryland

Randall I. Charles
San Jose State University
San Jose, California

James R. Choike
Oklahoma State University
Stillwater, Oklahoma

David S. Daniels
Longmeadow High School
Longmeadow, Massachusetts

John A. Dossey
Illinois State University
Normal, Illinois

Trudi Hammel Garland
The Head-Royce School
Oakland, California

Pamela Patton Giles
Jordan School District
Sandy, Utah

Virginia Gray
South Medford High School
Medford, Oregon

Howard C. Johnson
Syracuse University
Syracuse, New York

Stephen E. Moresh
City College of New York
(Formerly) Seward Park
High School
New York, New York

J. Irene Murphy
North Slope Borough
School District
Barrow, Alaska

Andy Reeves
Florida Department of Education
Tallahassee, Florida

Kathy A. Ross
(Formerly) Jefferson Parish
Public School System
Harvey, Louisiana

Cathy L. Seeley
(Formerly) Texas
Education Agency
Austin, Texas

Alba González Thompson
San Diego State University
San Diego, California

Charles B. Vonder Embse
Central Michigan University
Mt. Pleasant, Michigan

Sheryl M. Yamada
Beverly Hills High School
Beverly Hills, California

CONSULTANTS AND REVIEWERS

CONTENT REVIEWERS

Bridget Arvold
University of Georgia
Athens, Georgia

Paul G. Dillenberger
Franklin Middle School
Minneapolis, Minnesota

Catherine Y. Figuracion
San Pedro High School
San Pedro, California

Donald Hastings
Stratford Public Schools
Stratford, Connecticut

Melanie Hildreth
Walnut High School
Walnut, California

Jim Velo
West High School
Columbus, Ohio

Joanne Wainscott
Mission Bay High School
San Diego, California

Denise Walston
Maury High School
Norfolk, Virginia

Dr. Art W. Wilson
Abraham Lincoln High School
Denver, Colorado

MULTICULTURAL REVIEWERS

LaVerne Bitsie
Oklahoma State University
Stillwater, Oklahoma

Claudette Bradley
University of Alaska
Fairbanks, Alaska

Yolanda De La Cruz
Arizona State University West
Phoenix, Arizona

Genevieve Lau
Skyline College
San Bruno, California

William Tate
University of Wisconsin
Madison, Wisconsin

INDUSTRY CONSULTANTS

Joseph M. Cahalen
Xerox Corporation
Stamford, Connecticut

Clare DeYonker
AMATECH
Bingham Farms, Michigan

Harry Garland
Cannon Research Center
America, Inc.
Palo Alto, California

Timothy M. Schwalm, Sr.
Eastman Kodak Company
Rochester, New York

Diane Sotos
Maxim Integrated Products
Sunnyvale, California

Earl R. Westerlund
Eastman Kodak Company
Rochester, New York

John Zils
Skidmore, Owings & Merrill
Chicago, Illinois

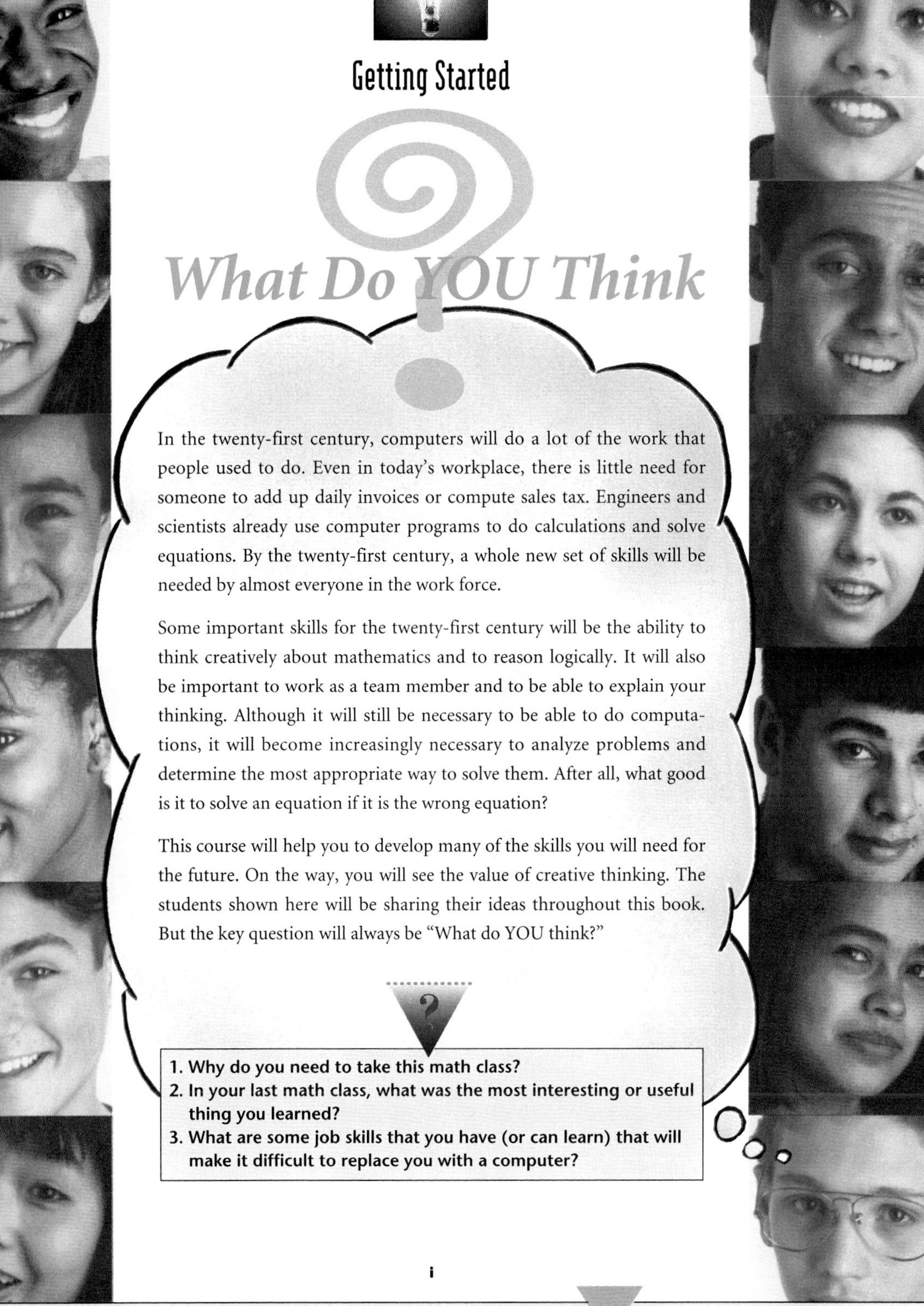

Getting Started

What Do YOU Think

In the twenty-first century, computers will do a lot of the work that people used to do. Even in today's workplace, there is little need for someone to add up daily invoices or compute sales tax. Engineers and scientists already use computer programs to do calculations and solve equations. By the twenty-first century, a whole new set of skills will be needed by almost everyone in the work force.

Some important skills for the twenty-first century will be the ability to think creatively about mathematics and to reason logically. It will also be important to work as a team member and to be able to explain your thinking. Although it will still be necessary to be able to do computations, it will become increasingly necessary to analyze problems and determine the most appropriate way to solve them. After all, what good is it to solve an equation if it is the wrong equation?

This course will help you to develop many of the skills you will need for the future. On the way, you will see the value of creative thinking. The students shown here will be sharing their ideas throughout this book. But the key question will always be "What do YOU think?"

1. Why do you need to take this math class?
2. In your last math class, what was the most interesting or useful thing you learned?
3. What are some job skills that you have (or can learn) that will make it difficult to replace you with a computer?

i

Where Are We Now?

Students generally come to this course with diverse backgrounds and varying degrees of experience with geometry concepts. Most should at least be familiar with basic geometric shapes.

Where Are We Going?

Students will see how cooperative learning and problem-solving strategies can help make learning mathematics more effective and enjoyable. Students will also begin to work with geometric figures, which are an important aspect of any mathematics course.

Possible Answers

1. Answers may include a variety of career options. Also, mathematics courses are frequently prerequisites for other areas of study.

3. Answers may include creative or artistic abilities, communication skills, etc.

More About the Twenty-First Century

In 1984, 25% of the workers in the workplace used computers in their jobs. By 1989, that percentage was up to 37%. This rapid increase in computer use in the workplace will doubtless continue well into the twenty-first century.

Getting Started

PART A At a Glance

Objective

To see that working cooperatively in teams can make learning mathematics more effective and enjoyable.

Development

Students begin to think about effective teamwork in the **Consider.**

In the **Explore,** students work together on an estimation problem.

First Five Minutes

Read the top of page *ii* and answer **Consider** 1–3.

Motivate

Ask...

- Have you worked in a group before? What roles did the participants play in these groups?

Gets students to think about effective teamwork.

Possible Answers

1. To exchange ideas clearly and effectively.
2. Students can be assigned specific roles.
3. Only if all students in a group have the same question.

PART A Working Together

← CONNECT → ***There are many times when working together can be more productive than working alone. If you have had experience working in groups, you are aware that working together effectively takes skill and planning. We will look at some of the ways to make working together more effective.***

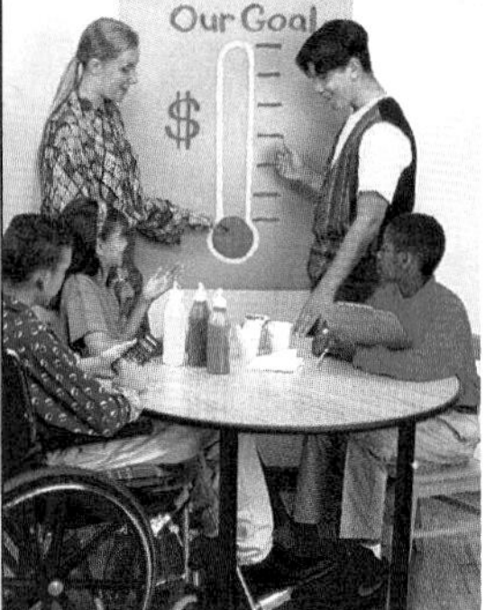

Working as a team member is an important skill in today's workplace. Many industries assign teams of employees to work on projects. Each employee brings a different skill to the team. Teamwork is also important in other situations. For example, in organizing a school fund-raiser, each person on the committee may have a specific role.

Working in a group can also make learning more productive and enjoyable. In order to work together, you must be able to communicate clearly with your group members.

1. **What does it mean to communicate?**
2. **How can everyone in a group be encouraged to participate?**
3. **When you're working in a group, when should you ask the teacher for help?**

In the following Explore, you will have a chance to work with your classmates. Be sure to pay attention to how well your group is working as a team!

EXPLORE: FIGURE IT OUT!

Figures such as the ones shown here are an important part of a geometry textbook.

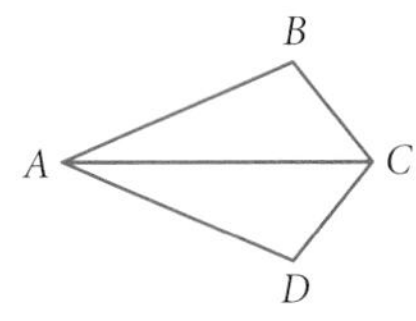

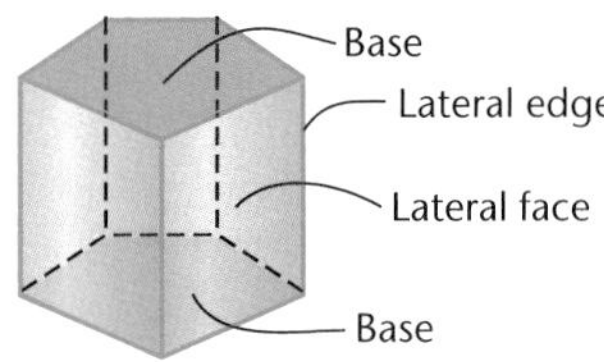

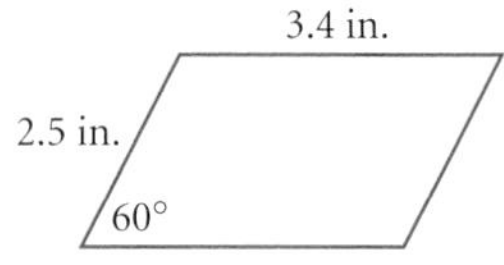

Diversity Issues

Some students enjoy working with others and can do so effectively. Others are uncomfortable working in groups. It may be helpful to assign these students various roles to help them become more comfortable with a group dynamic.

1. Work in a group to estimate how many such figures are contained in this book.
2. Does everyone in your group agree with the final estimate? Why or why not?
3. Compare your group's estimate with those of other groups. Were your estimates very different? Do you want to revise your estimate?

Working in a group can be an exciting way to learn mathematics. Throughout this course, you will have many opportunities to team up with your classmates.

REFLECT

1. Develop a list of at least five rules for successful cooperative groups. These rules should address any problems you may have had working in a group in the preceding Explore.
2. Describe some ways in which working in a group may be helpful to you throughout this course.

Exercises

1. Describe a situation in which you were part of a team (for example, a club or a sports team). What were the advantages and disadvantages of being part of this group? Were you able to do things with the group that you couldn't have done individually?

The following figures all occur elsewhere in this textbook. Using what you already know about geometry, describe each figure as best you can. (You will learn more about each figure later.)

2.

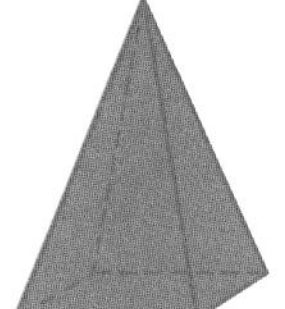

3.

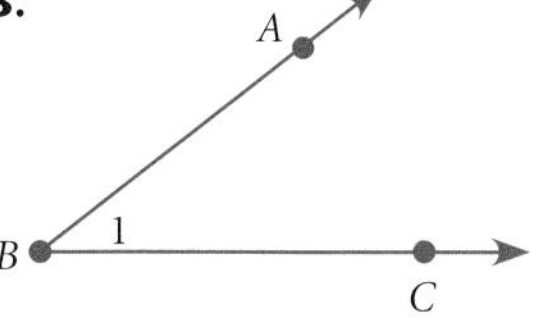

4.

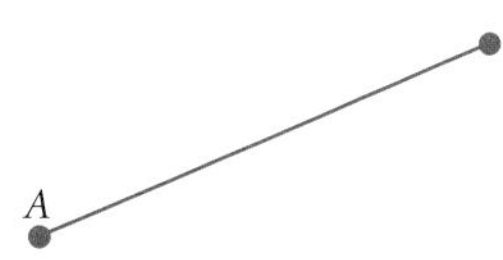

5.

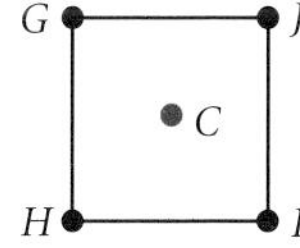

6.

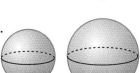

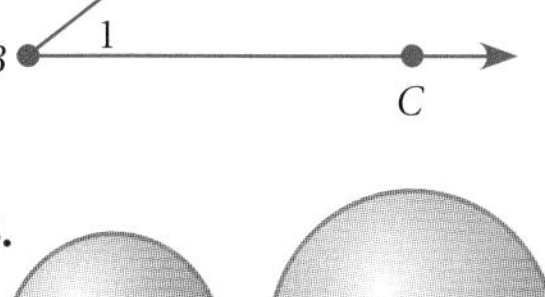

7.

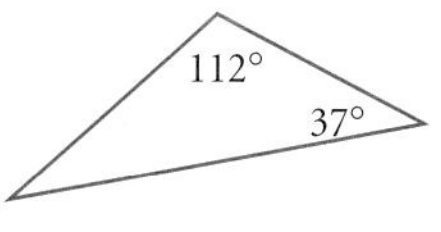

Vocabulary
Practice/Skills
Review
Math Reasoning
Problem Solving
Challenge

EXPLORE

Figure It Out!

Recommended group size: 4

The Point
To work in a group to estimate the number of figures in this textbook.

Look and Listen...
- For students who are uncomfortable working with other students.
- For students who don't give others a chance to be heard.

Ask...
- How can you divide up the task of estimation to make it more efficient?

For Groups That Finish Early
Ask students to estimate the number of periods in the textbook.

Follow Up
Discuss plans for organizing cooperative groups. See page TE22–23.

Possible Answers
1. An estimate of around 3000 is reasonable.

Journal

Reflect 1 and 2 are suitable for journal entries.

REFLECT

Possible Answers
1. Answers may suggest ways to ensure participation, so that all students can be heard. See pages TE22–23 for more cooperative learning.
2. Students may mention the benefits of brainstorming problem-solving strategies.

Part A Exercises

Exercise Answers

2. Pyramid
3. Angle
4. Line segment
5. Square with center C
6. Two spheres
7. Triangle with 112° and 37° angles

PART B At a Glance

Objective

To think about problem-solving strategies and guidelines that can be used throughout this course.

Development

Students reflect on their previous experiences with problem solving in the **Consider.**

In the **Explore,** students apply problem-solving guidelines to help solve a problem.

First Five Minutes

Read the top of page *iv* and answer **Consider** 1 and 2.

Motivate

Ask...

- Have you ever been stuck on a problem, changed your approach, and found the solution?

Encourages students to reflect on strategies they have used in the past.

Possible Answers

1. Make a table, work backwards, etc.

2. Restate the problem, list data, etc.

PART B Solving Problems

← CONNECT → ***You have solved many mathematical problems before taking this class, and you have probably already used some type of problem-solving guidelines and strategies. All of these strategies and techniques can be used in this class.***

Problem solving does not mean just finding the answer to a problem in a math book! All through our lives we are presented with new and challenging problems. Learning to think critically and creatively gives us the ability (mathematical and otherwise) to solve the problems we encounter.

1. What are some different strategies you have used to solve problems?

2. If you do not immediately understand a problem, what are some things you can do to help get started?

Whenever the solution to a problem is not immediately apparent, it may be helpful to follow some guidelines and questions for problem solving, such as the ones listed below.

PROBLEM-SOLVING GUIDELINES

Understand the Problem	**Develop a Plan**
What is the situation all about? What are you trying to find out? What are the key data/conditions? What are the assumptions?	Have you ever worked a similar problem before? Will you estimate or calculate? What strategies can you use?
Implement the Plan	**Look Back**
What is the solution? Did you interpret correctly? Did you calculate correctly? Did you answer the question?	Could you work the problem another way? Is there another solution? Is the answer reasonable?

EXPLORE: GETTING SQUARED AWAY

1. How many squares are contained in the figure at the right? (Be sure to consider squares of various sizes.)

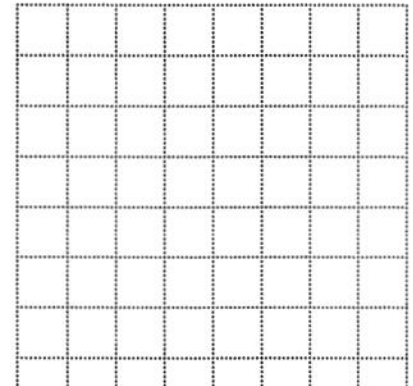

Problem-Solving Tip

Make a table.

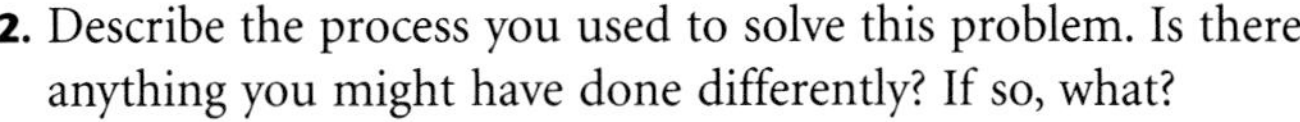

2. Describe the process you used to solve this problem. Is there anything you might have done differently? If so, what?

Have you ever had the feeling of a light bulb going on when you made a new discovery or solved a challenging problem? This book is dedicated to that rewarding "aha!" feeling. We hope many light bulbs will go on as you use this textbook.

REFLECT

1. You may have used the strategy of making a table in the preceding Explore. List some other common strategies for solving problems.
2. Can you think of anything to add to the Problem-Solving Guidelines on the preceding page? If so, describe a situation in which your suggestion might be useful.

Exercises

1. **a.** Farmer McDonald raises cows and ducks. He is standing in his field and sees 9 heads and 26 feet. How many ducks and how many cows does Farmer McDonald have?
   b. Describe the process you used to solve this problem.
2. The figure at the right shows the water level of a bathtub over time. Write a short paragraph to describe what might have occurred.

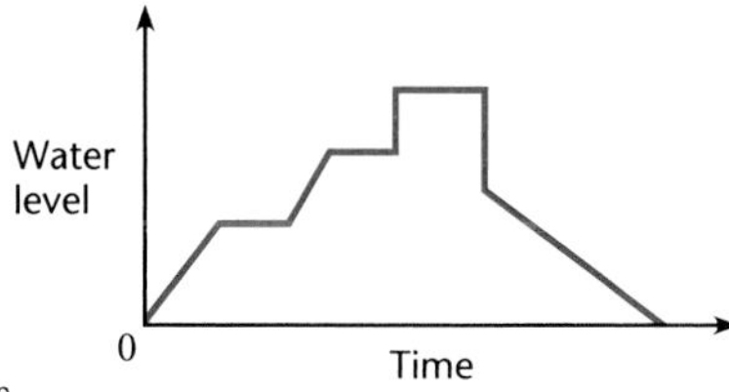

3. What is the maximum number of pieces into which a circular pizza can be cut with 4 straight cuts? (The pieces cannot be moved or stacked after cuts are made.)

Vocabulary
Practice/Skills
Review
Math Reasoning
Problem Solving
Challenge

EXPLORE

Getting Squared Away

Recommended group size: 4

The Point
To use the Problem-Solving Guidelines to help solve a counting problem.

Look and Listen...
- For students who do not see how to begin organizing a table.

Ask...
- What are the dimensions of the different squares in the figure?

For Groups That Finish Early
Ask students how many squares are contained in a 9-by-9 grid. **285**

Follow Up
Discuss how students organized their thinking and chose appropriate strategies.

Possible Answers
1. 204

Journal

Reflect 1 and 2 are suitable for journal entries.

REFLECT

Possible Answers
1. Guess and check, work backwards, simplify the problem, etc.

Part B Exercises

Exercise Answers

1. a. 4 cows, 5 ducks

2. The tub was filled, then the water was turned off for a while. The water was turned back on and then switched off again. A bucket of water was added to the tub all at once. A while later, a larger bucket of water was taken out of the tub. Finally, the tub was drained.

3. 11

PART C At a Glance

Objective

To investigate the connections between areas within mathematics and other disciplines.

Development

In **What Do You Think?** students investigate a connection between algebra and geometry. They discuss this further in the **Consider.**

First Five Minutes

Describe some ways in which mathematics and another discipline (such as science, art, or music) are connected.

Motivate

Ask...

- Is there always one best way to solve a problem?

WHAT DO YOU THINK?

Shows one connection between algebra and geometry. Also encourages students to see different ways of describing this connection.

PART C Making Connections

← CONNECT → ***You have seen how to use problem-solving guidelines to help you solve problems, and you have practiced working in a group. Now you will use these skills as we look at other important techniques.***

As you use this book, you will have many opportunities to work in groups (in Explore activities) and many opportunities to practice what you have learned (in Try It activities). You will also look at how the topics you learn are connected to each other, and you will see how mathematics is connected to other things.

Another important component of this book is a feature called What Do YOU Think? There is often more than one correct way to approach a problem. The students you have been introduced to on page *i* will be sharing their thinking throughout this book. You may find that you agree with their thinking, or you may have your own ideas.

WHAT DO YOU THINK?

Describe the connection between the equation on the left and the figure on the right.

$y = 3x + 2$

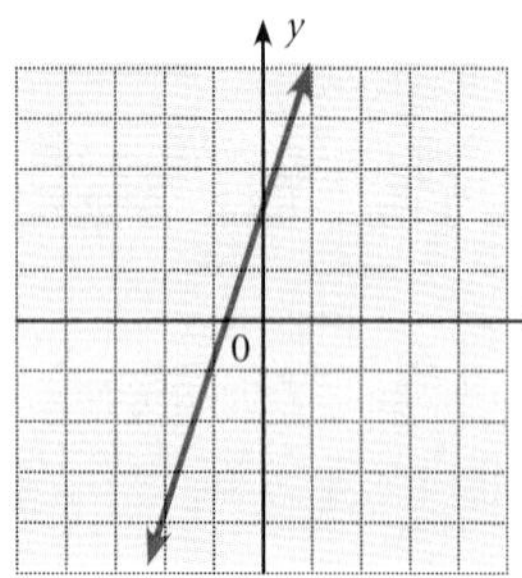

Henry Thinks . . .

I can make a table of values for the equation $y = 3x + 2$. If I plot these points, they will lie on a straight line. The line is the one shown in the graph.

x	y
−1	−1
0	2
1	5

Heather Thinks . . .

The equation is in the form $y = mx + b$. The value of m is 3, and this the slope of the graph of the equation. The value of b is 2, and this is means that the y-intercept of the graph is 2. If I put those two things together, I get the line in the figure.

1. Do you agree with Heather and Henry's thinking? Can you think of another way to describe the connection between the equation and the graph on the preceding page?

You will often be asked to explain your thinking. As you study geometry, you may find that *how* you communicate your thoughts is as important as getting the "right answer."

REFLECT

1. Describe two different methods for solving a problem that you studied in a previous course. Discuss the advantages or disadvantages of each method.
2. Why do you think it is important to understand the connections between mathematics and other disciplines?
3. Why do you think it is important to understand the connections between different subjects within mathematics?

Exercises

1. Describe the connection between the figure below left and the figure on the right.

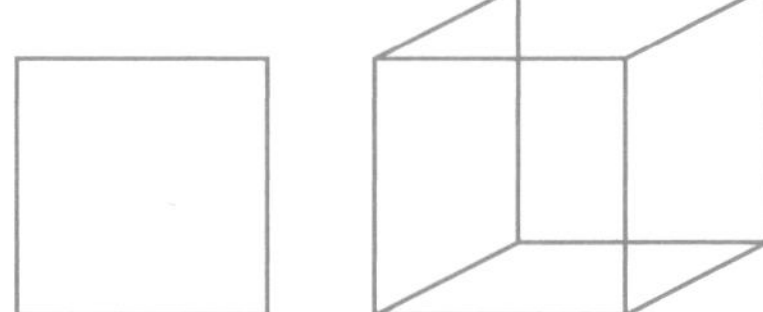

2. Write a short paragraph describing the optical illusion shown at the right.

3. There is an important connection between geometry and language. Make a chart that illustrates basic geometric figures. For each figure, include a sketch as well as a brief written description of the figure. If you know the names of the figures, be sure to include them.

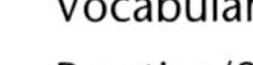

Vocabulary
Practice/Skills
Review
Math Reasoning
Problem Solving
Challenge

Portfolio

Have students select items from their work that demonstrate their understanding of the material in this superlesson. You may want to suggest that their selections include a problem solved using some of the Problem-Solving Guidelines.

REFLECT

Possible Answers

1. Students may mention different methods for solving a quadratic equation (graphing, factoring, the quadratic equation, etc.).
2. This helps us apply mathematical ideas to situations in other fields.
3. Techniques from one area of mathematics may be useful in a different area.

Part C Exercises

Exercise Answers

1. The figure on the left is a square. The figure on the right is a cube, whose faces are 6 squares.
2. It shows both a young woman and an older woman.
3. Check students' work. You may want to pay particular attention to their knowledge of geometry vocabulary.

1

Chapter 1 Visual Thinking and Mathematical Models

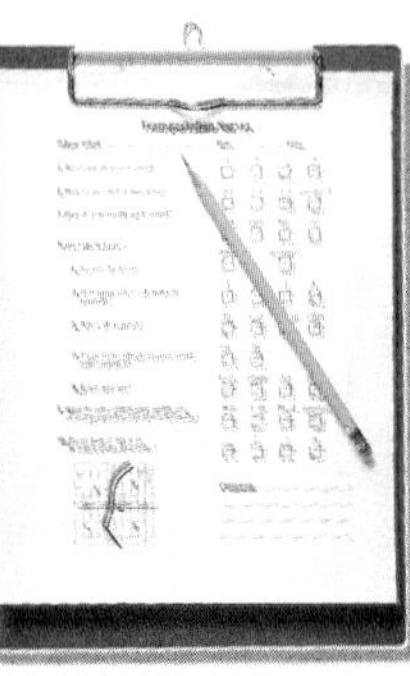

Project A
May I Have a Moment of Your Time?

Did you ever take part in a survey? Who decides what questions will be asked?

Project B
How Do You Get There From Here?

How are city maps made? How are they different from other maps?

Project C
Let Nature Unfold

How does nature mirror itself? Why don't you have two left feet?

2

Chapter 1 Project A **May I Have a Moment of Your Time?**

Conduct a Survey

Decide what questions to ask and when and where you should ask them.

- Did you know that the first Gallup poll predicted that Franklin D. Roosevelt would become president?
- Don't you wonder if surveys are reliable?
- How does this connect to Chapter 1? Drawing correct conclusions from survey data depends on **logic**. Many survey results are shown as **visual displays**.

Expand Your Vocabulary

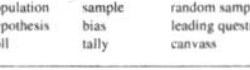

population	sample	random sample
hypothesis	bias	leading question
poll	tally	canvass

Project Guidelines

Investigate
- Read about surveys in a consumer magazine or high school economics book. Read about opinion polls in a civics book.
- Find reports of surveys and polls in newspapers and consumer magazines. Find out how the people responding to the polls were chosen.

Set Your Direction
- Decide a topic for your survey. How can you make sure the questions in your survey are fair?
- Will you poll a sample of the people whose opinions you want or survey all the people in that group?

Make a Plan
- Make a calendar for each day's work. Check in with your group and with your teacher.
- Form a hypothesis that the survey will prove or disprove.

Collect and Organize Your Information
- Make a list of questions you want to ask.
- Decide how to collect your information.

Carry Out Your Plan
- Write the questions for your survey.
- Interview people or mail your survey to them.
- Tally the information that you get.
- Make a visual display that shows the conclusions you reached.
- Which measure of central tendency best describes your results numerically?

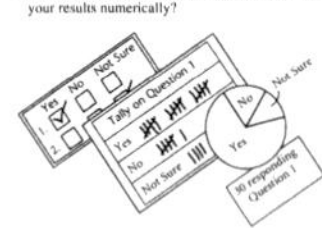

Look Back
- Who could use the information you collected?
- Is your display in any way misleading?

© Addison-Wesley Publishing Company, Inc. *Focus on Geometry* 1

Chapter 1 Project B **How Do You Get There From Here?**

Map Your Neighborhood

Draw a large-scale map to meet a particular need.

- Did you know that most city maps have a scale of 1:24,000?
- Don't you wonder why are there so many kinds of maps?
- How does this connect to Chapter 1? A town map is a **visual model** that can serve many purposes.

A hill is a geographic feature. A one-way street is an example of a cultural feature. If you were driving, which one would be more important? If you were riding, which one would you notice?

Expand Your Vocabulary

cartography	topography	compass rose
thematic map	cultural feature	legend
field survey	geographical feature	

Project Guidelines

Investigate
- Read about thematic mapmaking in a geography book or in an atlas.
- Study a map of your city or town. Notice the kinds of information it provides.

Set Your Direction
- What special need will your map serve? Will you designate a scenic walk, a shopping tour? Will you show statistical information?
- Will map users be visitors or local people? children or adults?

Make a Plan
- Make a calendar for each day's work. Check in with your group and with your teacher.
- Decide whether to take measurements or to adapt an existing map. Estimate the map area and scale.
- Decide what you'll need. Some tools to gather:

ruler	calculator (optional)
graph paper	large drawing paper

Collect and Organize Your Information
- Take all the measurements you need. Record them on a preliminary sketch using graph paper.
- List the cultural and geographical features you want to show on the map.

Carry Out Your Plan
- Decide the exact area and scale of your map.
- Transfer features from your sketch to the map.
- Label the features with names and symbols. Add a legend, a scale, and a compass rose.
- Let a real user field-test your map.

Look Back
- Did your field test show that the map was helpful?
- What should you have done differently?

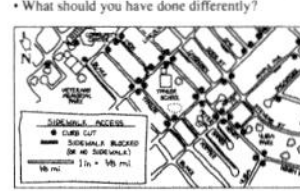

© Addison-Wesley Publishing Company, Inc. *Focus on Geometry* 3

ANN GREENWAY

I was not good at math in high school, so I got very frustrated. I thought I would need math only for personal things, like paying bills.

Now I conduct surveys on drug use in schools. I organize the results using technology. I use the displays in teacher training programs. Our world demands increasing communication and technology. Math is critical in both of these areas.

Ann Greenway
Drug Free Schools and Communities Administrator
Louisiana State Department of Education
Baton Rouge, Louisiana

Chapter 1 Project C

Let Nature Unfold

Make a Nature Scrapbook

Show samples of symmetry in nature in an album or as a collection.

- Did you know that symmetry helps animals move efficiently?
- Don't you wonder if all leaves have veins down the middle?
- How does this connect to Chapter 1? You'll find **symmetry** in the forms of nature and in patterns of growth and change.

Expand Your Vocabulary

bilateral symmetry, dorsal, ventral, radial symmetry, anterior, posterior, compound leaf, phenomenon

Project Guidelines

Investigate

- Read about leaf symmetry and animal body symmetry in a biology book. Read about rocks and landscape in a general science or geology book.
- Read about environmental responsibility in a park guide or in an ecology book.

Set Your Direction

- Will you focus on part of nature (such as flowers) or will you survey many aspects of nature?
- Will you include temporary effects in water, light, air, and motion or work only with objects?

Make a Plan

- Make a calendar for each day's work. Check in with your group and with your teacher.
- Will you make sketches, take pictures, or develop a collection of real things?
- Decide what you'll need. Some tools to gather: magnifier (optional) camera (optional)

Collect and Organize Your Information

- Walk through a park, a nature preserve, or a natural history museum. Look for lines of symmetry in plants, in animals, and in the landscape itself.
- Find examples and document when and where you found them and what they are.

Carry Out Your Plan

- Classify samples according to species or type and according to their symmetry.
- Display samples in an album or make a tray or board for your collection. Add labels that classify the examples and state your observations.
- *Safety first:* Don't bring wild animals or poisonous plants into the classroom.
- ***Protect the environment:*** Don't hurt any animals. Follow park rules.

Look Back

- Is there invisible symmetry in nature?
- What should you have done differently?

 Focus on Geometry 5

Biographical Note

Ann Greenway graduated from Glynn Academy in Brunswick, Georgia. She took Algebra I and Algebra II.

Chapter 1

Overview

Visual Thinking and Mathematical Models

1-1 Using Familiar Models

Models help people understand things that are too large, too small, or too complicated to study directly. You will learn how to recognize, visualize, and create algebraic and geometric models.

1-2 Reasoning and Logic

You need strong reasoning skills to be able to draw sound conclusions from known information. You will explore two important types of thinking—inductive and deductive reasoning.

1-3 Measuring Figures

Many careers require measurement skills. Architects, carpenters, and football players all rely on accurate measurement to do their jobs correctly. You will learn how to use the tools of geometric measurement—the ruler, compass, and protractor.

1-4 Symmetry and Reflections

Reflections and symmetry are important in nature, art, and architecture. You will discover symmetry in a variety of situations, and learn how reflections and symmetry are related. You will also investigate the properties of reflected figures.

CHAPTERS

Chapter 1 Planning Guide

The following ancillaries are recommended for each course level. The additional resources, *Technology Lab Manual, Study Guide and Journal, Multilingual Handbook,* and *Assessment,* are recommended for all levels.

	Comprehensive Course	Core Course	Informal Course
1-1 Part A	▲	▲	▲
Alternative Lessons			▲
Laboratory Manuals	▲	▲	▲
Practice			▲
More Look Ahead		▲	▲
1-1 Part B	▲	▲	▲
Alternative Lessons			▲
Laboratory Manuals	▲	▲	▲
Practice			▲
More Look Back		▲	▲
1-1 Part C	▲	▲	▲
More Look Back		▲	▲
Quiz 1-1	▲	▲	▲
1-2 Part A	▲	▲	▲
Alternative Lessons			▲
Laboratory Manuals	▲	▲	▲
Practice			▲
More Look Ahead		▲	▲
1-2 Part B	▲	▲	▲
Alternative Lessons			▲
Laboratory Manuals	▲	▲	▲
Practice			▲
More Look Back		▲	▲
1-2 Part C	▲	▲	▲
Alternative Lessons			▲
Laboratory Manuals	▲	▲	▲
Practice			▲
More Look Ahead		▲	▲
1-2 Part D	▲	▲	▲
More Look Back		▲	▲
Quiz 1-2	▲	▲	▲
1-3 Part A	▲	▲	▲
Alternative Lessons			▲
Laboratory Manuals	▲	▲	▲
Practice			▲
More Look Back		▲	▲
1-3 Part B	▲	▲	▲
Alternative Lessons			▲
Laboratory Manuals	▲	▲	▲
Practice			▲
More Look Ahead		▲	▲
1-3 Part C	▲	▲	▲
Alternative Lessons			▲
Laboratory Manuals	▲	▲	▲
Practice			▲
More Look Back		▲	▲
1-3 Part D	▲	▲	▲
More Look Back		▲	▲
Quiz 1-3	▲	▲	▲
1-4 Part A	▲	▲	▲
Alternative Lessons			▲
Laboratory Manuals	▲	▲	▲
Practice			▲
More Look Ahead		▲	▲
1-4 Part B	▲	▲	▲
Alternative Lessons			▲
Laboratory Manuals	▲	▲	▲
Practice			▲
More Look Back		▲	▲
1-4 Part C	▲	▲	▲
Alternative Lessons			▲
Laboratory Manuals	▲	▲	▲
Practice			▲
More Look Ahead		▲	▲
1-4 Part D	▲	▲	▲
More Look Back		▲	▲
Quiz 1-4	▲	▲	▲

BIBLIOGRAPHY

Teacher Resources

Problem-Solving Experiences in Geometry, Randall I. Charles, Deborah A. Seldomridge, Gary A. Seldomridge, Robert P. Mason. Addison-Wesley, 1991 (25183).

Mira Math Activities for High School, Mira Math Co., 1973.

Geometry Problems: One Step Beyond, Reuben Schadler. Dale Seymour Publications, 1984 (NS01430).

Posters

Ascending and Descending, M.C. Escher. Available through Dale Seymour Publications (NS18841).

Waterfall, M.C. Escher. Available through Dale Seymour Publications (NS22259).

Relativity, M. C. Escher. Available through Dale Seymour Publications (NS18838).

1-1

Using Familiar Models

SUPERLESSON AT A GLANCE

Superlesson Goal

Students will develop skills in making and using geometric and algebraic models.

Management Guide

	Topic	Objectives	Key Terms	New Ideas	Materials
Part A	Geometric Models	To develop skills in working with geometric models.	Geometry, mathematical model, net	Modeling 3-dimensional figures.	**Student** Ruler, paper, scissors, tape **Teacher** Optical illusions
Part B	Algebraic Models	To review the coordinate plane and use scatter plots to model and analyze data.	Scatter plot	Scatter plots as mathematical models.	**Student** Graph paper, watch or clock
Part C	Making Connections	To summarize modeling concepts.	In Making Connections, students apply and synthesize key terms and new ideas.		**Student** Graph paper, ruler

Pacing Chart (45-Minute Periods)

	Comprehensive Course	Core Course	Informal Course
Part A	1	1	1
Part B	1	1	1
Part C	1	1	1
TOTAL periods for Superlesson	3	3	3

NCTM Standards

Mathematics as Problem Solving

Mathematics as Communication

Mathematics as Reasoning

Mathematical Connections

Statistics

Social Science/History

1-1 Using Familiar Models

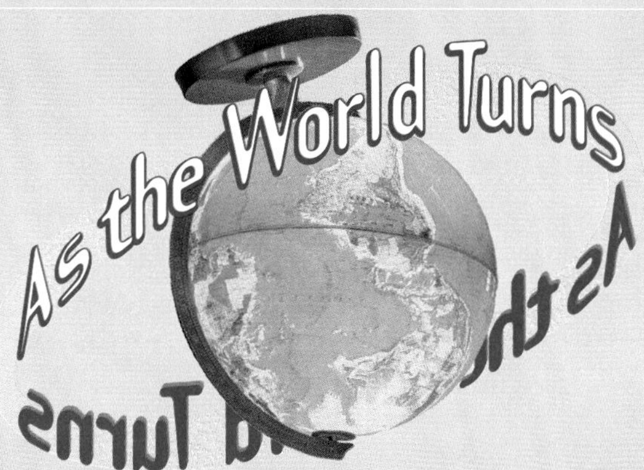

Do you recognize the globe above? It looks familiar, but we are used to seeing it in a different position. Maps and globes are usually shown with north at the top. When the position (or orientation) changes, it is difficult to recognize what region the map represents. You may need to orient yourself by finding familiar landmarks.

Maps and globes are models of the earth. One commonly used model is the Mercator projection. Mercator drew the earth as if it were a cylinder, not a sphere. The Mercator projection is useful for navigation, but it has problems with size distortion. The farther you move from the equator, the more distorted the map becomes! Canada is not twice the size of the United States, although it looks that way on Mercator's map.

In 1923, a "better" map was drawn by J. P. Goode at the University of Chicago. This earth model is not nearly as distorted as the Mercator projection. Goode's projection is like flattening an orange peel. Although Goode's projection shows accurate shapes, areas, and distances, people like their world without gaps. This "orange peel" projection has never been popular.

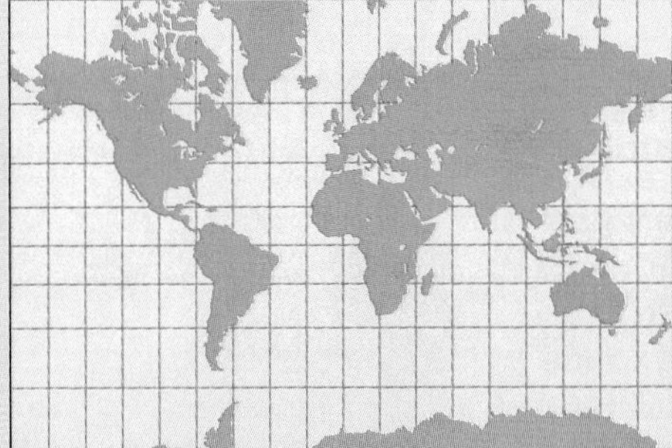

Mercator projection

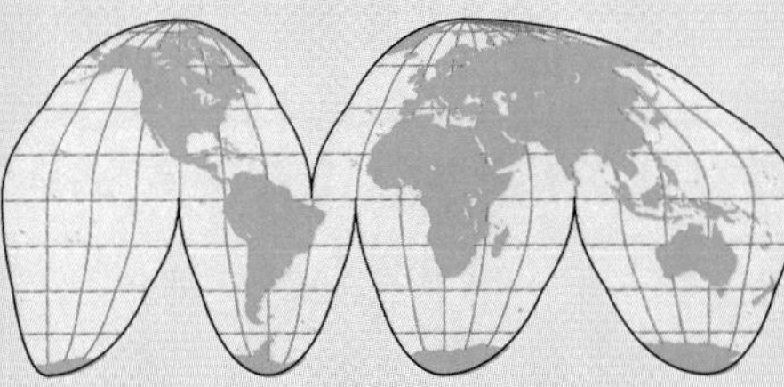

Goode's projection

1. **Why do you think it is difficult to represent the earth's surface on a flat map? How might this problem explain the distortions in Mercator's map?**
2. **A map and a globe are models of the earth. How do these models differ from the earth itself?**
3. **Which representation of the earth seems best—a map or a globe? Why?**

More About Mapmaking

Many of the maps made by early European explorers of the Americas had south at the top of the map. Students may be surprised to realize that placing north at the top of a map is an arbitrary decision.

Where Are We Now?

Students entering a geometry course may have different levels of experience and skill in visual thinking and mathematical modeling.

Where Are We Going?

In 1-1, students will develop their understanding of and skills in mathematical modeling. They will make geometric models (nets), algebraic models (scatter plots), and models that use both algebraic and geometric ideas (maps).

Possible Answers

1. It is difficult to represent the earth's surface on a flat map because the earth is a sphere—its surface is actually curved.

Mercator's map is distorted because, in order to make a "flat earth," he stretched out regions near the poles more than those near the equator.

2. Maps and globes are smaller than the earth and are made of different materials. A map is flat, but the earth is a sphere.

3. A globe is a more accurate representation, since it shows the earth as a sphere.

AWSM Videodisc

Focus on Geometry

▶ **1-1** Using Familiar Models

Search:

Play: Step:

Using Familiar Models

PART A At a Glance

Objective

To develop skills in working with geometric models.

Development

In **Consider** questions, students see misleading visual information. This helps to show the need for mathematical models.

In the **Explore,** students make a model (a net) for a cube and find all of the different nets for a cube.

Suggested Materials

Student Ruler, paper, scissors, tape

Teacher Optical illusions

Key Terms

Geometry, mathematical model, net

First Five Minutes

Transparency FFM 1-1A

Read the opening paragraphs on page 6, and answer **Consider** 1.

Motivate

Ask...

- Can we always trust our eyes?
- Is a photograph a model?

Possible Answer

1. The buildings in the photo are actually vertical. The photo is oriented so that they look tilted.

1-1 PART A Geometric Models

← CONNECT → *In algebra, you used equations and formulas to model real-world situations. As you will see, you can also use geometry to create models. You will build some geometric models of your own and see why you have to be careful not to assume too much from visual information.*

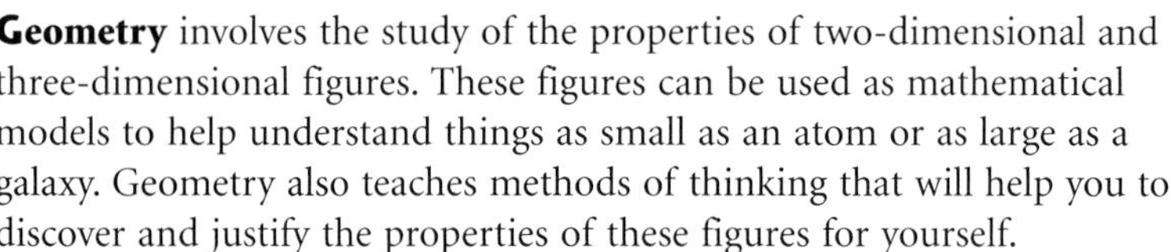

Geometry involves the study of the properties of two-dimensional and three-dimensional figures. These figures can be used as mathematical models to help understand things as small as an atom or as large as a galaxy. Geometry also teaches methods of thinking that will help you to discover and justify the properties of these figures for yourself.

Geometry helps us to sort out visual information. In geometry, you must be careful not to assume too much from a picture or figure. Look at the photograph at the left. This San Francisco street has an unfamiliar orientation. The buildings look dangerously tilted. If one of them toppled, the domino effect could be devastating.

1. Why are the buildings in the photograph tilted?

When you see an optical illusion, your eyes seem to play tricks on your mind. Even your lifetime of experience doesn't help; in fact, it may sometimes confuse you. Optical illusions are fun, but they are also important reminders that we can't always trust our eyes.

M. C. Escher was an artist and mathematician who enjoyed creating optical illusions. In this lithograph titled *Ascending and Descending,* Escher created a building topped by a very interesting staircase.

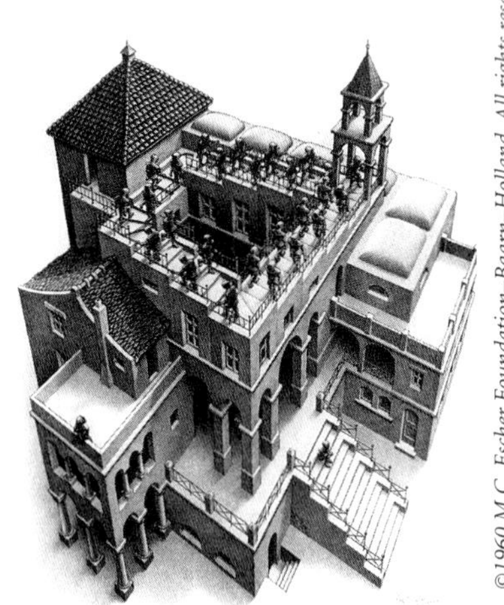

Diversity Issues

Many students are not primarily visual learners. You may wish to have your class use books to try to model Escher's staircase. This will help kinesthetically oriented students understand why such a staircase could not exist.

2. What is unusual about the staircase?
3. Is it possible to build a three-dimensional model of Escher's staircase? Explain your answer.

Models can give people a clearer understanding of a real-world object, idea, or phenomenon. A **mathematical model** uses geometry, algebra, or other mathematical tools to represent an idea or concept in the real world. These representations include figures, equations, graphs, and computer programs.

Some people spike volleyballs over nets. Mathematicians use nets to build and model geometric figures. A **net** is a pattern that can be cut out and folded into a three-dimensional figure (sometimes called a *solid*). In the following Explore, you'll investigate different nets for a familiar solid.

EXPLORE: SHAPE UP!

MATERIALS

Ruler, Paper, Scissors, Tape

1. The T-shaped net at the right can be folded to create a solid. Carefully draw an enlarged version of the net.
   - Use a ruler to make sure that all sides are straight and the same length.
   - Use the corner of a rectangular sheet of paper to draw the corners.
   - Label squares A, B, and C.
   - Cut out your net. Fold up squares A and B. Fold up square C and tape it to A and B. Then fold up and tape the other squares. What figure do you get?
2. The T-shaped net is not the only one that folds into this figure. Which of the nets illustrated at the right can be used to create the same figure? Try to visualize the nets folded into this solid.
3. How many different nets are there for this solid? Sketch as many as you can. Discuss your results with your classmates.

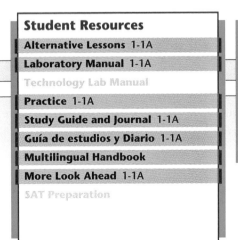

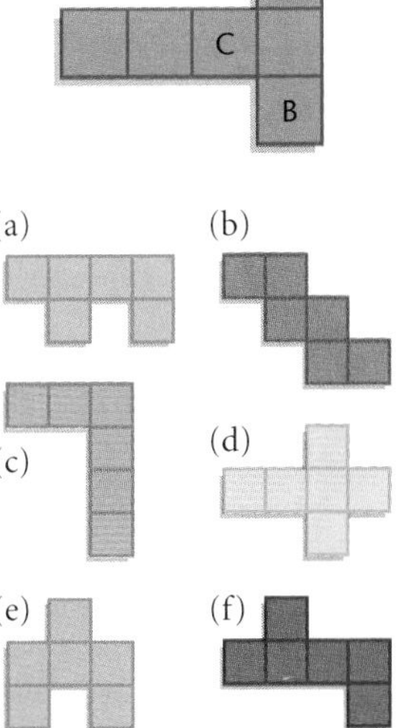

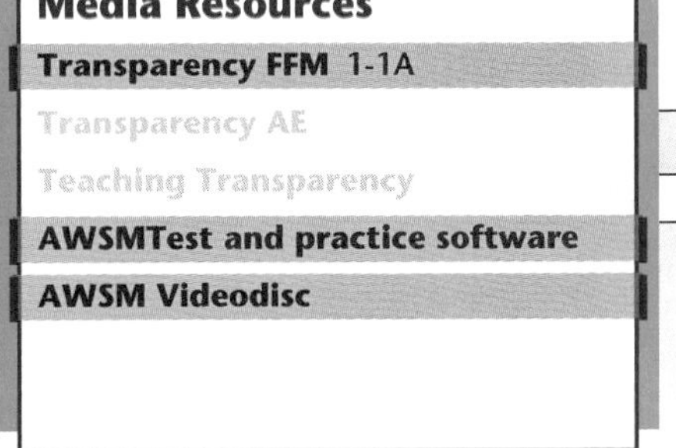

Student Resources
Alternative Lessons 1-1A
Laboratory Manual 1-1A
Technology Lab Manual
Practice 1-1A
Study Guide and Journal 1-1A
Guía de estudios y Diario 1-1A
Multilingual Handbook
More Look Ahead 1-1A
SAT Preparation
Media Resources
Transparency FFM 1-1A
Transparency AE
Teaching Transparency
AWSMTest and practice software
AWSM Videodisc

Provides a connection between misleading visual information and mathematical modeling.

Possible Answers

2. It appears that you can go up or down the staircase forever.
3. It is impossible to build a model of this staircase. Suppose you started climbing at a corner of the staircase. After a loop, you'd return to the same location, so you couldn't have been going upstairs the whole time.

EXPLORE

Shape Up!

Recommended group size: 4

The Point

To identify the nets for a cube.

Look and Listen...

- For students who are not searching for new nets in an organized way.

Ask...

- Is a reflected version of a net a "different" net?

For Groups That Finish Early

Devise a way to classify the nets for a cube.

Follow Up

Ask how many different nets there are for a cube.

Possible Answers

1. A cube.
2. (b), (d), (f)
3. 11; one is seen in Step 1; three more are nets (b), (d), and (f). The other seven are below.

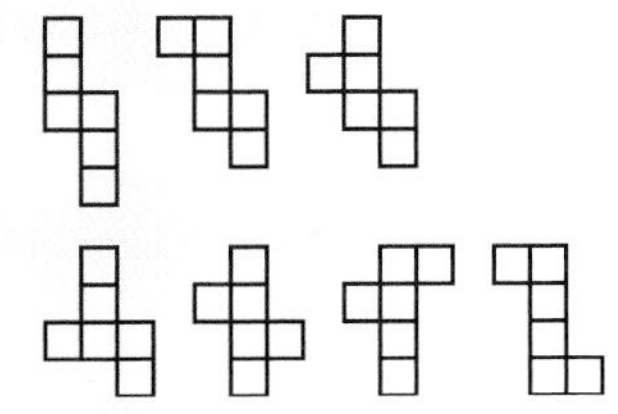

1-1

Using Familiar Models

Journal 

Reflect 1 and 2 are suitable for journal entries.

REFLECT

Possible Answers

1. 6; there should be 6 squares in the net, because a cube has 6 faces.
2. A mathematical model uses algebra, geometry, or other mathematical ideas to represent something in the real world.
3. A can may be modeled by a cylinder. If we know how to calculate the surface area and volume of a cylinder, we can find the values of those quantities for the can.

Part A Exercises

Exercise Notes

Core

1. The **Getting Started** exercise gives students step-by-step practice in constructing a net.
4. This is similar to multiple-choice analogy items on standardized tests.
11. When reviewing this exercise, you might ask, "If you had wood strips and glue, could you build the crate? Why or why not?"
13. This is important for getting students to think about the limitations of a model.

Mathematical models come in many shapes and sizes. They can be flat (two-dimensional) or solid (three-dimensional). The common three-dimensional geometric figures below can be useful models. For example, the earth can be modeled by a sphere, a shoe box by a rectangular prism, and a juice can by a cylinder.

Cylinder

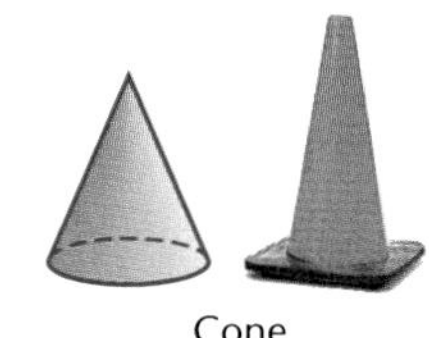
Cone

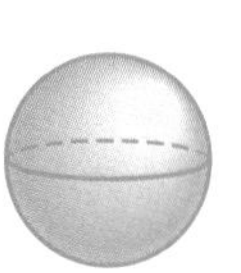

Sphere

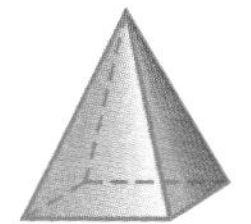

Square pyramid

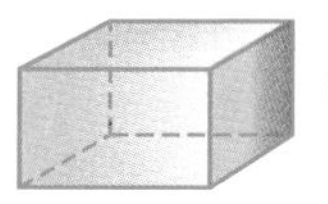

Rectangular prism

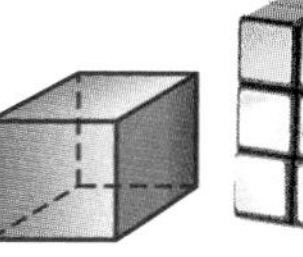
Cube

REFLECT

1. How many squares are needed in a net for a cube? How do you know?
2. Define *mathematical model* in your own words.
3. Geometry involves the study of figures like triangles, circles, pyramids, and cylinders. Describe something that could be modeled by one of those figures. Explain how understanding the figure might help you understand the real-world object.

Exercises

CORE

P **1. Getting Started** Draw a net for a square pyramid as follows.
  a. Name all of the two-dimensional figures that are part of the net. How many of each are there? 4 triangles, 1 square
  b. Sketch one of the figures as the "base" of your net. Square
  c. Identify the other figures that touch the base. Include these in your net, sketching them adjacent to the sides of the base.
  d. Check to see whether you are missing any of the figures listed in **1a**. (Sometimes the base of a three-dimensional figure will not touch all of the sides.) If any are missing, add them to the net.

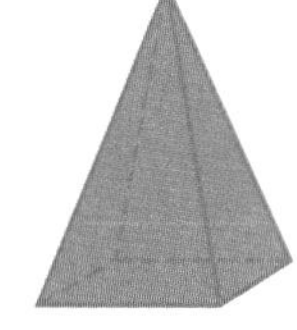

P **2.** Draw a net for the rectangular solid at the right.

Key

- V Vocabulary
- P Practice/Skills
- R Review
- MR Math Reasoning
- PS Problem Solving
- C Challenge

Research Note

By talking with, and listening to, each other, students can solidify or change their thinking, together coming to a new synthesis that will be more robust than the thinking of any one of them alone. (Ellen Davidson and Jim Hammerman, "Homogenized Is Only Better for Milk," *Reaching All Students with Mathematics,* Gilbert Cuevas and Mark Driscoll, eds., p. 202. © 1993 NCTM.)

P 3. How many vertices, edges, and faces does a cube have? 8 vertices, 12 edges, 6 faces

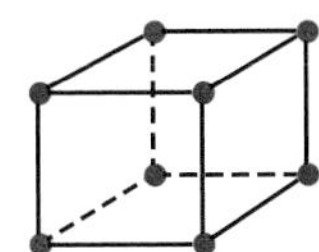
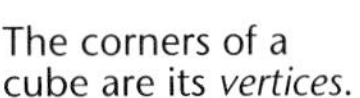

The corners of a cube are its *vertices*.

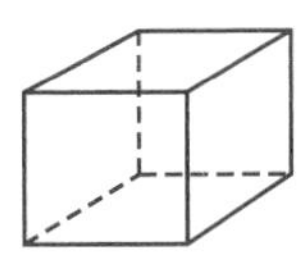

These are the *edges* of the cube.

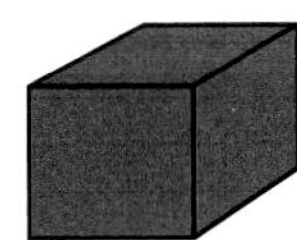

The sides of the cube are its *faces*.

V 4. Write the letter of the second pair that best matches the first pair. (b)

Net: solid as (a) oak: tree, (b) wrapping: box, (c) cube: square, (d) coordinate: axis

P 5. **Dot's Right** Three different views of the same die are shown.

a. How many dots are opposite the one-dot side? the two-dot side? the three-dot side? 6, 5, 4

b. What is the sum of the dots on opposite sides of a die? 7

c. Sketch at least four differently shaped nets for a die. Include the dots. Be sure that the rule you found in **5b** applies when your nets are folded up.

d. What is the probability that a single roll of this die will give you a six? Explain.

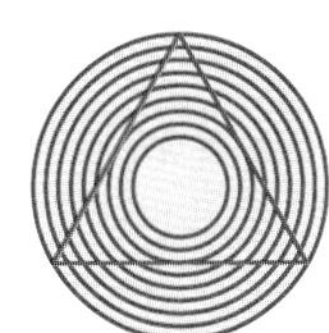

R 6. Are the sides of the triangle straight or bent? What do you think causes this illusion? The sides are straight. The circles make the lines look bent.

P **Sketch a model for each of the following three-dimensional objects using geometric figures. Do your best to make your sketches look three-dimensional. If you know the name of the geometric figure, use it to label the sketch.**

7. a soup can 8. a refrigerator 9. a football

R 10. The perspective drawing at the right gives the illusion of depth and distance. Are the three penguins in the picture all the same size? Which one appears to be the tallest? Use a ruler to check. Why do you think this illusion consistently fools people?

R 11. **Freemish Shipping and Handling** Figures that are impossible to make in three dimensions can be drawn in two dimensions. In 1966, an artist produced the "freemish crate." (Perhaps this crate is used for shipping optical illusions!) Describe what is impossible about the crate.

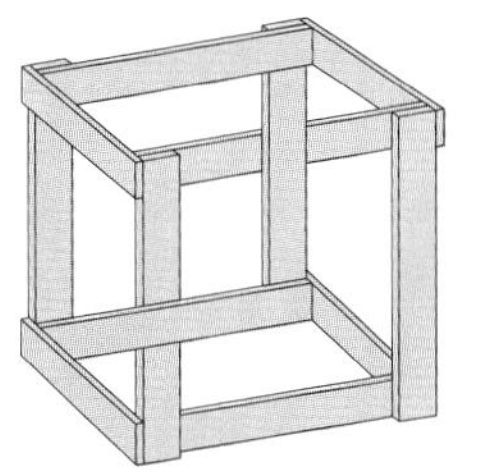

Ongoing Assessment

Self-Assessment Exercises 1–9 odd, 12

Embedded Assessment Reflect 2; Exercises 2, 8, 10, 13

Look Ahead

These exercises review graphing skills needed in 1-1 Part B.

More Math Reasoning

24. and 25. These exercises help students develop visualization skills.

Extension to **25**: What would happen if you painted a large cube blue and then cut it into 1000 small cubes? Look for patterns to help you find the numbers of cubes with 0, 1, 2, . . . , 6 blue faces. **0 blue = 512; 1 blue = 384; 2 blue = 96; 3 blue = 8.**

Repeat the question for a general cube cut into n^3 small ones. **0 blue = $(n-2)^3$; 1 blue = $6(n-2)^2$; 2 blue = $12(n-2)$; 3 blue = 8.**

Exercise Answers

Core

1. c. Triangles

2. Possible answer:

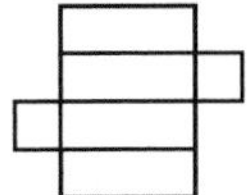

5. c. Possible answer:

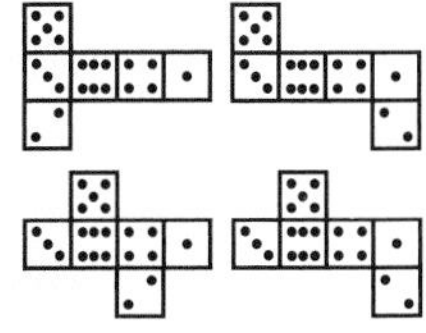

d. $\frac{1}{6}$; There are six sides and one has a six, so the probability is one in six.

7. Cylinder

8. Rectangular prism

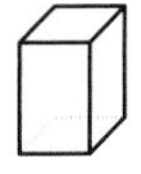

9.

10. The three penguins are all the same size, but the one at the right appears tallest because the lines in the picture make the third penguin look farther away.

Using Familiar Models

11. The boards on the crate cannot physically be attached in this way.

13. Possible answer: The curvature of the earth in a neighborhood is negligible. The curvature only causes distortion on maps that cover a large area.

Look Ahead

14. a.

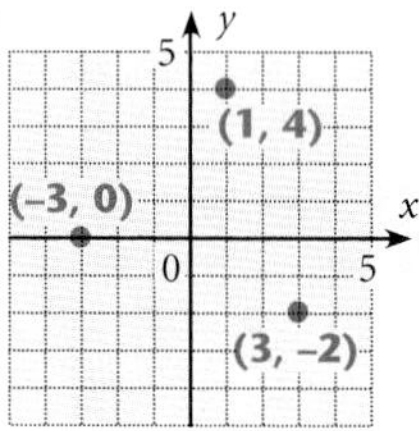

b. Possible answer: (0, 2)

c. Possible answer: $(-1, -3)$; III

15.

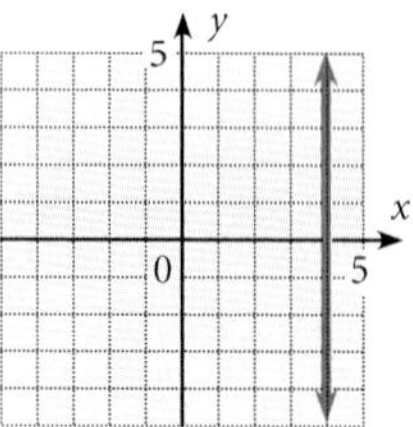

The line is parallel to the y-axis and each point on the line has x-coordinate equal to 4.

16.

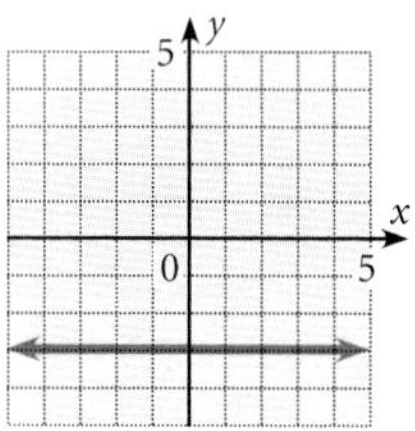

The line is parallel to the x-axis and each point on the line has y-coordinate equal to -3.

17.

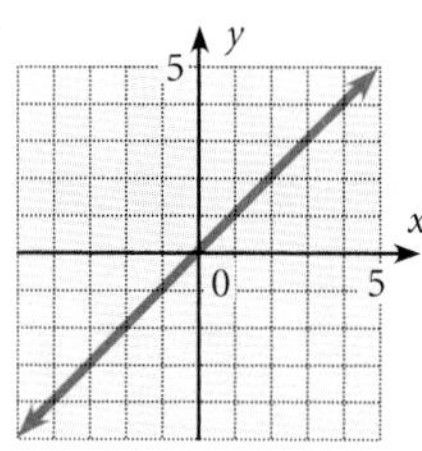

The line splits the angle between the x-axis and y-axis.

18–23. See Additional Answers p. T18.

PS **12.** The pictures below are small sections of larger photographs. What do you think is shown in each photograph? Explain how you were able to predict the larger photographs from the small sections shown.

a.

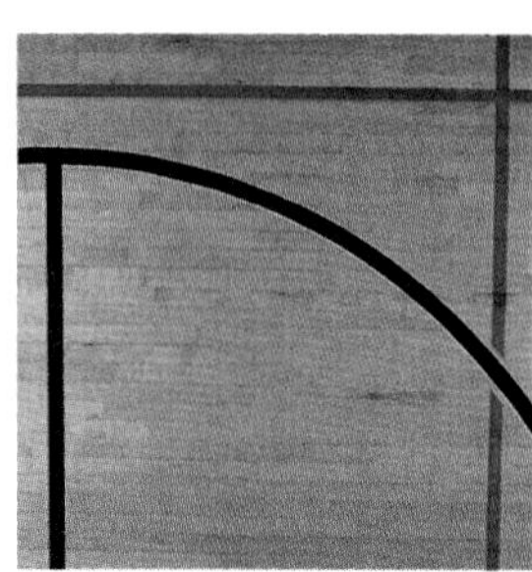

Basketball court

b.

Tomato

MR **13.** Like a map of the world, a map of your neighborhood is also a flat model of a curved area. Why aren't there problems with size distortion in these neighborhood maps as there are in the Mercator projection? Or are there? Explain.

Social Science

LOOK AHEAD

R **14.** Plot each of the following on the same coordinate plane.

a. Plot the points $(1, 4)$, $(3, -2)$, and $(-3, 0)$.

b. Plot a point on the y-axis. What is its ordered pair?

c. Plot a point with negative x- and y-coordinates. Which quadrant is it in?

R **15.** Graph the line $x = 4$ on a coordinate plane. Describe the line.

R **16.** Graph the line $y = -3$ on a coordinate plane. Describe the line.

R **17.** Graph the line $y = x$ on a coordinate plane. Describe the line.

MORE PRACTICE

P **18.** A tetrahedron is a pyramid with four triangular faces. Create a net for a tetrahedron. How many vertices, edges, and faces does a tetrahedron have?

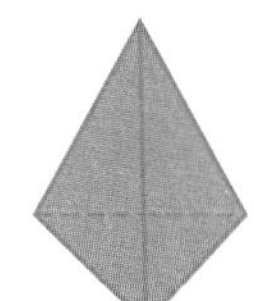

P **19.** Create a net for a cylinder.

P **Sketch a model for each of the following three-dimensional objects using geometric figures.**

20. a brick **21.** a television set **22.** a drinking glass **23.** a hamburger

Key

V Vocabulary
P Practice/Skills
R Review
MR Math Reasoning
PS Problem Solving
C Challenge

MORE MATH REASONING

MR **24. Merging the 'Mids** A tetrahedron is a pyramid with four triangular faces. A square pyramid is a pyramid with a square base and four triangular faces. The two pyramids shown at the right are special because all of the edges in both figures are the same length.

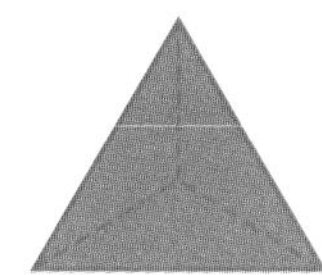
Regular tetrahedron

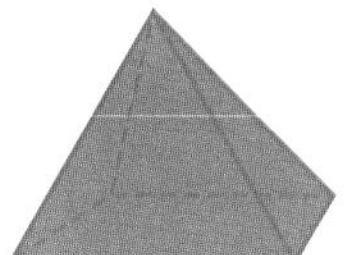
Square pyramid

(Due to perspective, lengths of some edges may appear unequal.)

If the tetrahedron and the square pyramid are joined together by joining two triangular faces so that they coincide (match exactly), how many faces will the resulting solid have? 7 After you have made your best guess, create nets for the two pyramids similar to the nets shown. Build the pyramids. Join them together and count the number of faces. Was your prediction correct?

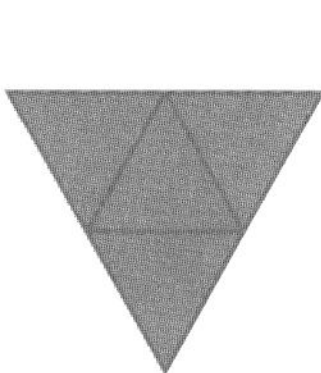

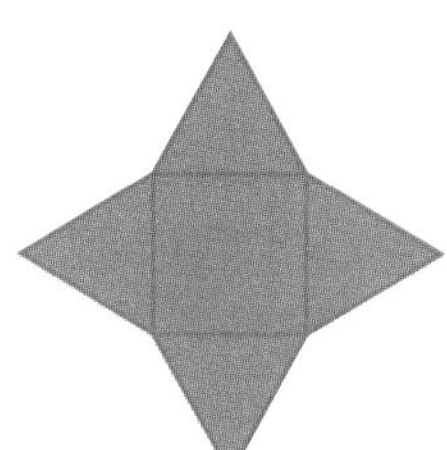

C **25. The Painted Cube** The 6 outside surfaces of a cube are painted blue. The cube is then cut up into 27 small cubes ($3 \times 3 \times 3$). How many of the small cubes have no blue faces? 1 blue face? 2 blue faces? 3 blue faces? 4 blue faces? 5 blue faces? 6 blue faces? 1; 6; 12; 8; 0; 0; 0

1-1 PART B Algebraic Models

← CONNECT → ***You've used coordinate planes in algebra. The coordinate plane is one of the most frequently used models. Now you will see how coordinate planes are used to display data and in map making.***

The figure points out some familiar features of the coordinate plane. It should help you refresh your memory about the four quadrants, the x- and y-axes, the origin, and ordered pairs.

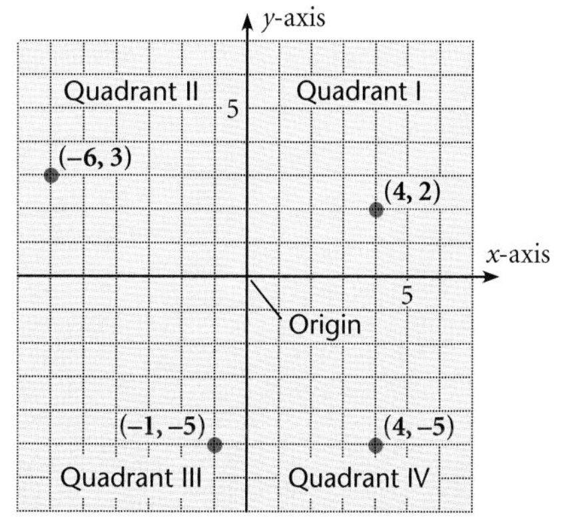

Student Resources

- **Alternative Lessons 1-1B**
- **Laboratory Manual 1-1B**
- Technology Lab Manual
- **Practice 1-1B**
- **Study Guide and Journal 1-1B**
- **Guía de estudios y Diario 1-1B**
- **Multilingual Handbook**
- **More Look Back 1-1B**
- SAT Preparation

Media Resources

- **Transparency FFM 1-1B**
- Transparency AE
- Teaching Transparency
- **AWSMTest and practice software**
- AWSM Videodisc

PART B At a Glance

Objective

To review the coordinate plane and use scatter plots to model and analyze data.

Development

Students review graphing skills and concepts.

In the **Explore,** students collect data and make a scatter plot to model the distribution of left- and right-handedness in the class.

Suggested Materials

Student Graph paper, watch or clock

Key Terms

Scatter plot

First Five Minutes

Transparency FFM 1-1B

Read the introductory paragraph on page 11, and do **Try It a–d** on page 12.

Motivate

Ask...

- Do you know what a scatter plot is?
- How are coordinate grids used on local maps?

Using Familiar Models

Possible Answer

1. Approximately (−14, 13). (Allow for a range of answers.)

EXPLORE

Handy-Dandy Survey

Recommended group size: 6.

The Point

To plot and interpret data on a scatter plot.

Look and Listen...

- For students who do not remember which is the horizontal coordinate.
- For students who need help adding the line $y = x$ in Step 4.

Ask...

- What does it mean if a point on your graph is near the x-axis? the y-axis?

For Groups That Finish Early

Predict the number of left-handed and right-handed *X*s for an "average" student.

Follow Up

Ask students in what sense this scatter plot is a mathematical model.

Possible Answers

4. a. Students are left-handed if their point lies above $y = x$.

5. Students may look for an "average" y-value when $x = 75$.

The data should be fairly scattered, so students should not be confident of their predictions.

TRY IT

Plot each point on a coordinate plane.

a. (3, 1) **b.** (2, −1) **c.** (0, −9) **d.** (−3, −4)

The map of the continental United States is shown on a coordinate plane.

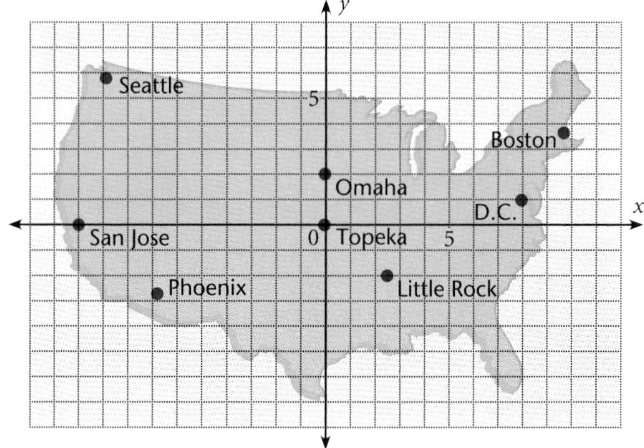

e. Which city is located at the origin? Topeka

f. Name a city or state in each quadrant. I:Boston, MA; II: Seattle, WA; III: Phoenix, AZ; IV: Little Rock, AK

g. Name a city on the x-axis and a city on the y-axis. x-axis: San Jose; y-axis: Omaha

h. Give the ordered pair for each of the following.

(1) Seattle, Washington (−9, 6)

(2) Washington, D.C. (8, 1)

(3) Little Rock, Arkansas $\left(\frac{5}{2}, -2\right)$

1. Using the preceding map, estimate the ordered pair for Anchorage, Alaska.

A coordinate plane can be used as a model to locate points on a map. Coordinate planes are also used as models in statistics. A graph showing a set of points based on paired data is a **scatter plot**. In the following Explore, you'll collect data and analyze it with the help of a scatter plot.

Tips from Teachers

The *Consider* provides an opportunity to discuss the distortions created by flat maps. You may want to ask whether the coordinate system shown becomes less useful when it is extended to larger areas or ask whether the western part of the U.S./Canadian border is actually a curve.

Technology Note

Students use lines of best fit (regression lines) informally in **Exercises** in this Part. You may wish to show students how to use a graphing utility to find the equation of a line of best fit.

EXPLORE: HANDY-DANDY SURVEY

MATERIALS

Graph paper
Watch or clock

Are you right-handed or left-handed? Are you ambidextrous: that is, can you use both hands equally well? The following is a "handedness survey" that will help you find out how ambidextrous you are.

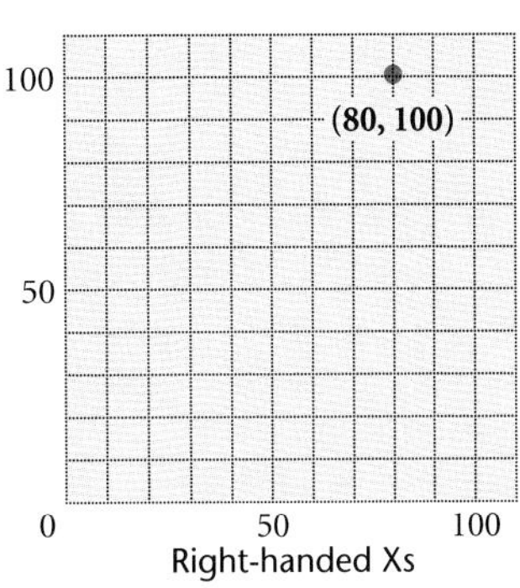

If you make 80 Xs with your right hand and 100 Xs with your left, plot the ordered pair (80, 100).

1. Which hand do you use most often and most easily? This is your dominant hand. Do you think your dominant hand is extremely, moderately, or only slightly dominant over the other hand?
2. Have one person be a timer. For 60 seconds, draw small Xs with your right hand in the squares on a sheet of graph paper as quickly as possible. Count the Xs. Repeat using your left hand.
3. Plot the data you collected on graph paper. Let the right-hand count be the x-coordinate and the left-hand count be the y-coordinate. (See the example at the right.) Gather data from other students and plot their ordered pairs on your graph.
4. **a.** From the graph you made in **3,** determine which students are left-handed. Explain how you can tell. (It may help to draw the line $y = x$ on your graph. If you do this, explain how you might use this line.) What percentage of the class is left-handed?
   b. Are any students ambidextrous? close to being ambidextrous? Explain your answer in terms of your scatter plot.
5. Suppose that a classmate makes 75 Xs with her right hand in one minute. Use the data you've gathered to predict how many Xs she could make with her left hand. Explain your method. How confident are you that your prediction is accurate?

REFLECT

1. What are some ways of displaying data besides using a scatter plot? If you have a lot of data to show, which method is the most practical? Why?
2. Name a way to use coordinates besides in maps and scatter plots. Explain why coordinates are helpful in this situation.
3. Write a brief definition of each of the following in your own words.
   a. the x- and y-axes **b.** an ordered pair
   c. the origin **d.** the four quadrants

Statistics Connection

Approximately 10% of all people are left-handed.

Journal

Reflect 1 and 3 are suitable for journal entries.

REFLECT

Possible Answers

1. A list or table can be used to display data. A scatter plot shows a large amount of data more clearly, because all of the data can be seen at once in a small space.
2. Points on a radar grid. Coordinates can be used to pinpoint locations of ships, airplanes, or other objects.
3. **a.** x-axis: horizontal axis, y-axis: vertical axis.
   b. Ordered pair: the coordinates for a point.
   c. (0, 0)
   d. Regions of the plane determined by the axes. I is upper right, II is upper left, III is lower left, and IV is lower right.

TRY IT

Answers a–d.

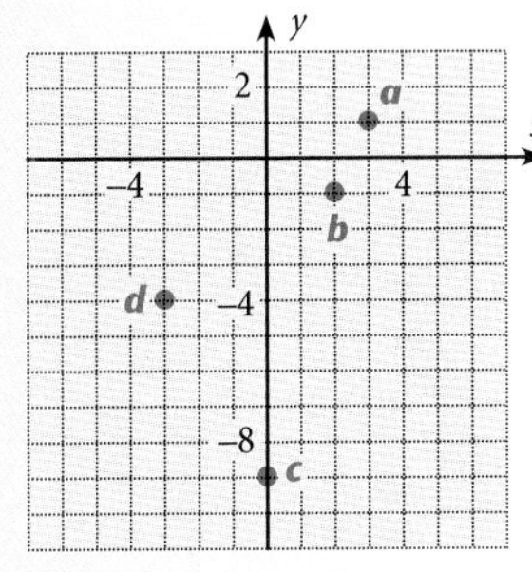

Part B Exercises

Exercise Notes

Core

1–7. The **Getting Started** exercises review basic graphing skills.

16. Some students may need to be reminded what an *integer* is.

18. Students use a scatter plot to model scientific data and to make predictions.

Look Back

These exercises review algebra skills.

More Math Reasoning

44. Asks students to think visually.

Exercise Answers

Core

1–7.

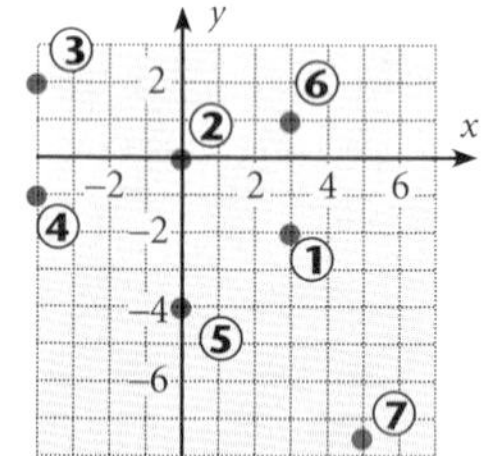

13.

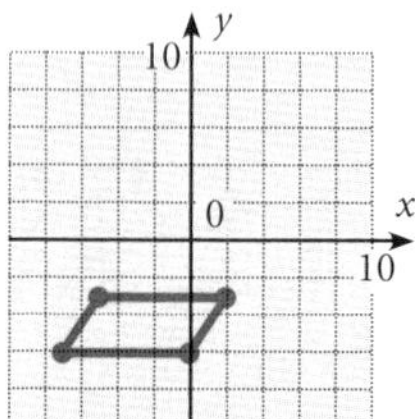

14.

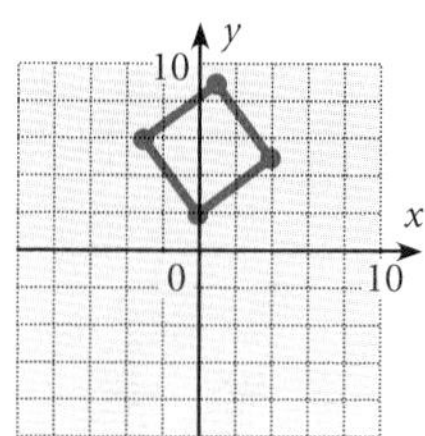

17. a. (1, 6), (1, 9), (2, 7), (3, 5), (4, 2), (5, 5), (6, 4), (7, 2), (7, 3), (9, 1)

b. Hours reading = Hours of TV

c. Hours reading > Hours of TV

d. Most students will have coordinates either above or below the line $x = y$. Very few will be on it.

Exercises

CORE

P **Getting Started** **Plot the following points on a coordinate plane.**

1. (3, −2) **2.** (0, 0) **3.** (−4, 2) **4.** (−4, −1)

5. (0, −4) **6.** (3, 1) **7.** (5, −7.5)

P **Give the coordinates for each point.**

8. M (−1, 3) **9.** N (2, 3) **10.** P (2, −3)

11. Q (−4, −2) **12.** R (−2, 0)

P **Draw four-sided figures (quadrilaterals) with the given vertices on a coordinate plane.**

13. (2, −3), (−5, −3), (−7, −6), (0, −6)

14. (0, 2), (4, 5), (1, 9), (−3, 6)

V **15.** Write the word or phrase that correctly completes the statement.

A ___ is a graph showing a set of points based on paired data. Scatter plot

PS, MR **16.** Draw a rectangle on a coordinate plane so that each corner (vertex) has integer coordinates.

a. What are the coordinates of the vertices you chose? Possible answer: (0, 0), (2, 0), (2, 1), (0

b. Is it possible to draw a rectangle whose vertices have integer coordinates so that no side is parallel to either the x-axis or the y-axis? If so, sketch such a rectangle on a coordinate plane. Yes, see Exercise 14.

PS **17. Flipping Pages, Flipping Channels** The hypothetical scatter plot below represents how many hours 10 people watch television and how many hours they read each week. The line $y = x$ is also shown on the graph.

a. What are the ordered pairs for each of the points on the scatter plot?

b. One point lies on the line $y = x$. What does this mean?

c. What can you conclude about the points above the line $y = x$?

d. Estimate the number of hours per week you spend watching TV. Estimate the number of hours per week you spend reading. Where does your point lie on the scatter plot? Explain.

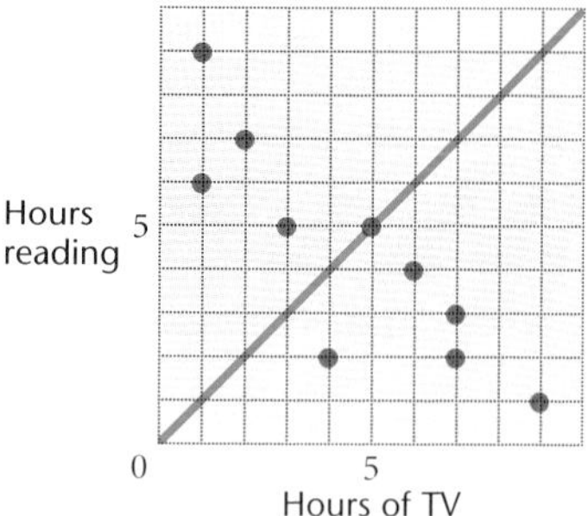

Key

V Vocabulary
P Practice/Skills
R Review
MR Math Reasoning
PS Problem Solving
C Challenge

18. a. Plot the data below on a scatter plot, and then draw a line that seems to fit the data best. (The *gestation period* is the length of time from conception to birth.)

Animal	Cat	Fox	Hamster	Rabbit	Rat	Squirrel
Average Life Span (years)	12	7	2	5	3	10
Average Gestation Period (days)	63	52	16	31	21	44

b. The average life span of a chipmunk is 6 years. Use your scatter plot to predict the gestation period of a chipmunk.

LOOK BACK

R **Simplify each expression. [Previous course]**

19. $2y + 7y - 6y$ $3y$ **20.** $6(3 - 2x)$ $18 - 12x$ **21.** $-2r + 3r(r - 4)$ $3r^2 - 14r$

R **Evaluate each expression for $x = 2$ and $y = -3$. [Previous course]**

22. $5(x + 2)$ 20 **23.** $5x^2 - 2y$ 26 **24.** $2y^3$ -54 **25.** $(2y)^3$ -216

MORE PRACTICE

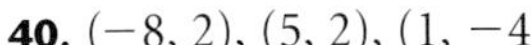

P **Plot the following points on a coordinate plane.**

26. $(5, -2)$ **27.** $(0, -3)$ **28.** $(2, 0)$

29. $(-3, 1)$ **30.** $(-2, -4)$ **31.** $(1.5, 1)$

32. $(-2.5, 4)$ **33.** $\left(-1\frac{1}{2}, 2\frac{3}{4}\right)$

P **Give the coordinates for each point.**

34. C (2, 4) **35.** D (−2, −1) **36.** E (3, −3)

37. F (2, 0) **38.** G (−4, 4) **39.** H (0, −3)

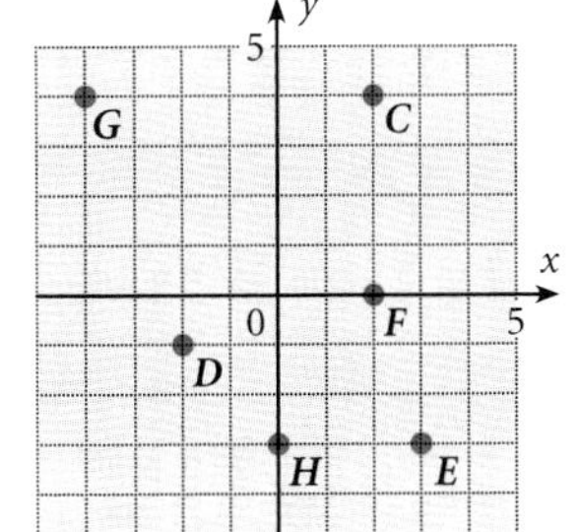

P **Draw triangles with the given vertices on a coordinate plane.**

40. $(-8, 2), (5, 2), (1, -4)$

41. $(0, 0), (-4, 2), (-3, -3)$

Ongoing Assessment

Self-Assessment Exercises 1–7 all, 9–15 odd

Embedded Assessment Reflect 1, 3; Exercises 14, 17, 18

18. a.

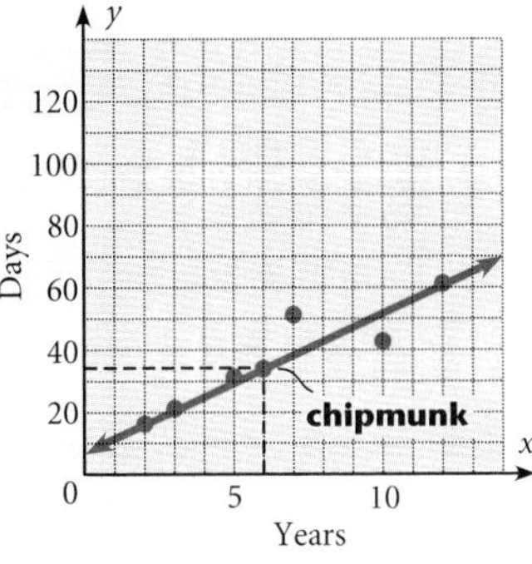

b. Answers will be near 36 days.

More Practice
26–33.

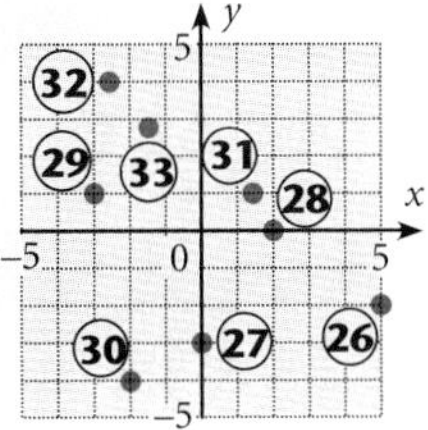

40–41.

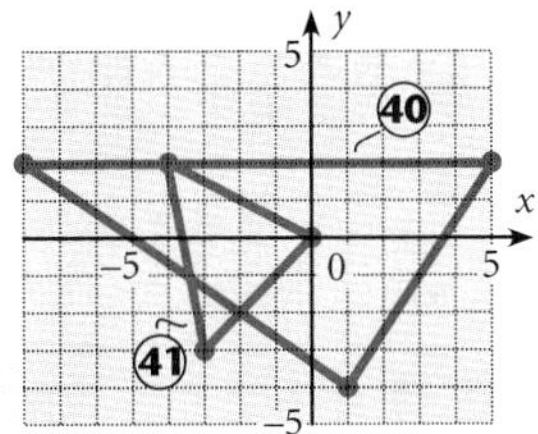

More Math Reasoning

43. c. Most answers will be about 450 miles. (Using the actual regression line, the answer is about 415 miles.) This answer can be derived by drawing a straight line from the origin through the middle of the data and using this line to predict the point.

Using Familiar Models

PART C At a Glance

Objective

To summarize modeling concepts.

Development

In the **Explore,** students make a map of their school and superimpose a coordinate system. Then they describe locations and routes on the map.

Suggested Materials

Student Graph paper, ruler

First Five Minutes

Transparency FFM 1-1C

Write your own definition of *mathematical model,* and give an example of a model you worked with in 1-1.

EXPLORE

Map Maker, Map Maker, Make Me a Map

Recommended group size: 4

The Point

To make a map of the school and add a coordinate system.

Look and Listen...

- For students who are overly concerned about exact sizes and locations of objects on the map.

Ask...

- How can you choose a convenient location for the origin of your coordinate system?

P **42.** The scatter plot at the right shows miles traveled and gallons of gas consumed for 15 automobiles.
  a. Which car traveled the most miles? N
  b. Which car consumed the most gallons of gas? P

MORE MATH REASONING

MR **43.** This exercise uses the same data as Exercise 42.
  a. Which car had the best mileage (miles per gallon)? C
  b. Which car had the poorest mileage (miles per gallon)? P
  c. Use the scatter plot from Exercise 42 to predict the number of miles traveled by a car that consumed 25 gallons of gas. Explain how you made this prediction.

PS, C **44.** **Cube Cutter** What is the smallest number of cuts needed to cut the block of wood at the left into 9 small cubes? What is the smallest number needed to cut the block at the right into 27 small cubes?
Left: 4; Right: 6

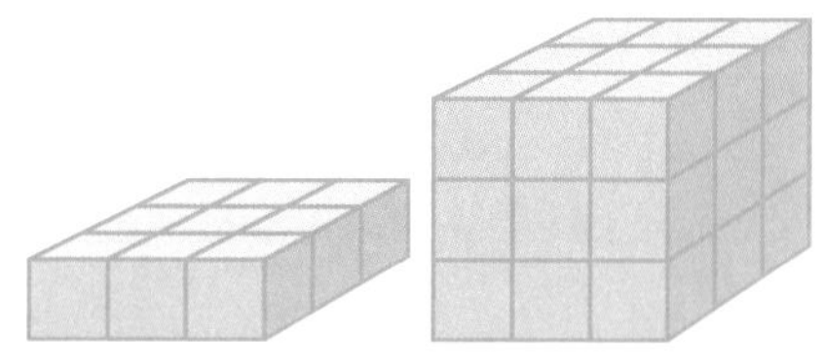

1-1 PART C Making Connections

← CONNECT → ***Models help people understand things that are too large, too small, or too complicated to study directly. Algebra showed you some ways to use mathematics to model real-world situations. Now you've learned how to recognize, visualize, and create models.***

Maps, geometric figures, coordinate planes, and scatter plots are different types of mathematical models. You are now more familiar with some of the uses of mathematical models and more aware of the dangers of assuming too much from limited or misleading information.

Vertical and horizontal lines form grids across most local maps. Many maps have letters spaced evenly along the horizontal axis and numbers placed along the vertical axis. One letter and one number can describe the approximate location of any landmark on a typical map.

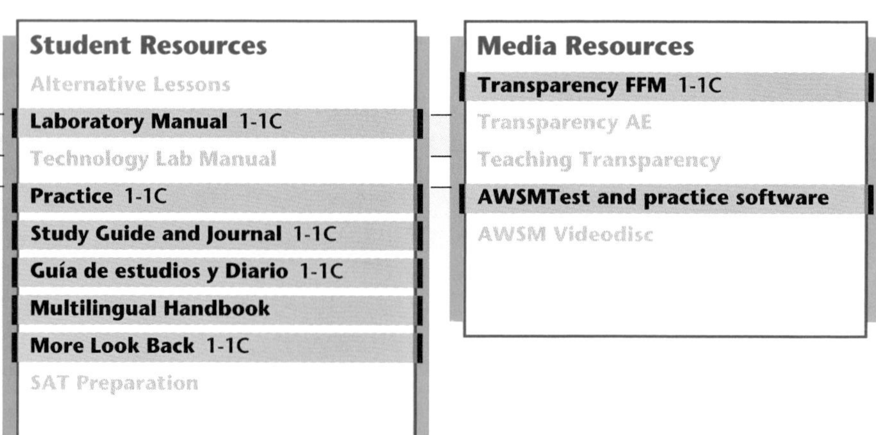

Student Resources

Alternative Lessons
Laboratory Manual 1-1C
Technology Lab Manual
Practice 1-1C
Study Guide and Journal 1-1C
Guía de estudios y Diario 1-1C
Multilingual Handbook
More Look Back 1-1C
SAT Preparation

Media Resources

Transparency FFM 1-1C
Transparency AE
Teaching Transparency
AWSMTest and practice software
AWSM Videodisc

EXPLORE: MAP MAKER, MAP MAKER, MAKE ME A MAP

MATERIALS

Graph paper
Ruler

As shown at the right, modern map makers use computers in their work; however, maps were once drawn by hand. You can make a hand-drawn map of your school on graph paper. Begin by setting up a coordinate system, selecting a convenient point for the origin, and drawing the coordinate axes. Label points of interest such as the main office, the cafeteria, and the library.

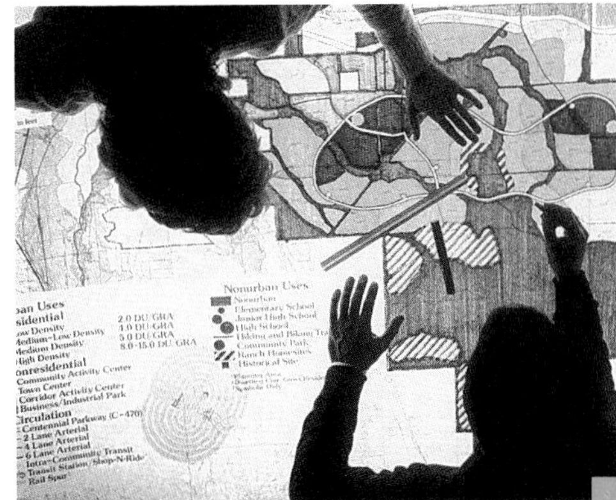

1. Describe the coordinate system you chose for your school map. Why did you choose this particular coordinate system?
2. Write a paragraph describing your daily route from class to class. Use the coordinate system you've devised to help describe locations.

REFLECT

1. Write a paragraph explaining how mathematical models can be helpful. Give some examples of useful mathematical models besides a map.
2. Describe some of the possible weaknesses of mathematical models.
3. Mathematical modeling has become much more powerful since the invention of computers. Explain why computers might improve mathematical models and make them easier to use.

Self-Assessment

P 1. Draw models of a bowl, a baseball, a textbook, and an ice cream cone.

P 2. Which of these nets will fold to make an open box? a, b, e, f

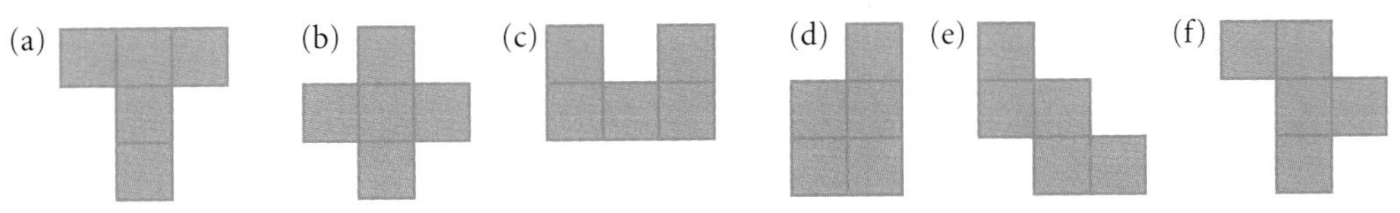

Key

V Vocabulary
P Practice/Skills
R Review
MR Math Reasoning
PS Problem Solving
C Challenge

For Groups That Finish Early
Estimate the scale for the map.

Follow Up
Ask students to explain how they chose their origin and set up their axes.

Portfolio

Have students select items from their work that demonstrate their understanding of the material in this Superlesson.

You may wish to have students include their best sketch of a 2-dimensional model, the scatter plot **Exercise** that they found most interesting, and the **Exercise** that they found most challenging.

REFLECT

Possible Answers

1. Mathematical models are simpler than the things they model. They can focus on important characteristics and ignore details, and are often smaller than the real object. Example: Computer modeling of car frames.
2. Models may be too simple to capture important features.
3. Because computers can handle large amounts of information, computer models can be more complete and accurate.

Self-Assessment

Exercise Notes

10. This exercise looks ahead to the Golden Ratio in 7-1.
11. Asks students to think about how models are used in industry.
12. Students see that they must be careful when using data to make predictions.
13. Students see that correlation does not imply causality—you cannot assume that a clear pattern in data explains *why* something happens.

1-1

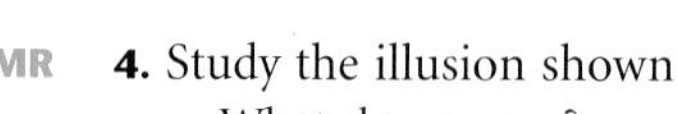

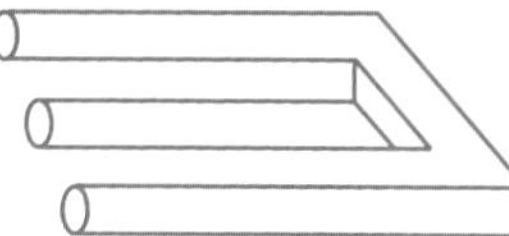

Algebra | Data/Statistics | Logic/Reasoning | Industry/Careers | Science/Health

Using Familiar Models

Self-Assessment Answers

1. Check students' art

3. ☆

4. a. An object similar to a tuning fork

b. The left side shows 3 prongs, the right side 2.

c. Check students' art.

10. Many students will detect a "typical" ratio close to the golden ratio, which is approximately 1.6.

11. Possible answer: Models can be tested under controlled conditions, modeling does not place astronauts at risk, and it is easier to change a model than to modify a spacecraft.

12–13. See Additional Answers p. T18.

P **3.** Sketch a net for the pyramid shown at the right.

MR **4.** Study the illusion shown.

a. What do you see?

b. Why are the left and right sides of the drawing inconsistent?

c. Sketch an optical illusion of your own in which the top half and the bottom half are inconsistent.

R **Simplify each expression. [Previous course]**

5. $9x + 5x - 3x$ $11x$ **6.** $4(5 - 8z) + 11z$ $20 - 21z$

R **Evaluate each expression for $x = 3$ and $y = -1$. [Previous course]**

7. $4(y - 7) + 3x$ -23 **8.** $5x^2 - 4y$ 49

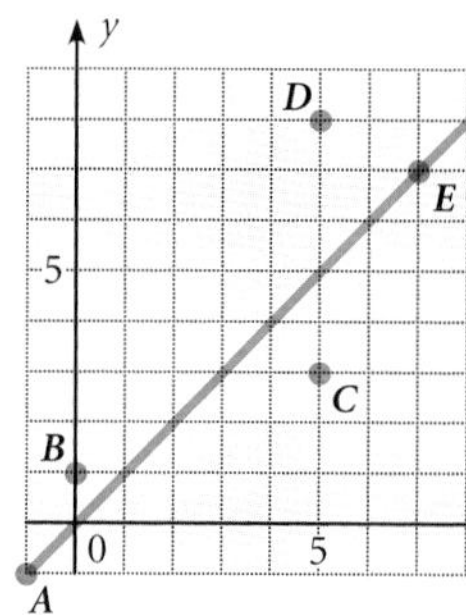

P **9.** The line $x = y$ is drawn in the graph at the right. If $r > s$, which of the points shown could have coordinates (r, s)? (c)

(a) A (b) B (c) C (d) D (e) E

P **10.** Find 10 different rectangular objects in your room. Measure the length and width of each, and plot the results on a scatter plot. Does the ratio of length to width of these objects vary widely, or can you identify a "typical" ratio? Explain.

MR Careers **11. Testing, Testing** Engineers at NASA build models of spacecraft for simulations. Give at least three reasons for building models before an actual space flight.

MR, PS Science **12.** The following pairs give the age and height, in inches, of 10 female elementary school students: (7, 49), (7, 46), (8, 50), (8, 52), (9, 51), (9, 55), (10, 57), (10, 56), (11, 57), (11, 59).

a. Make a scatter plot of this data. Use your scatter plot to predict the height of a 6-year-old girl and a 13-year-old girl. How did you made these predictions?

b. Use your scatter plot to predict the height of a 20-year-old woman. Does your result make sense? If not, explain.

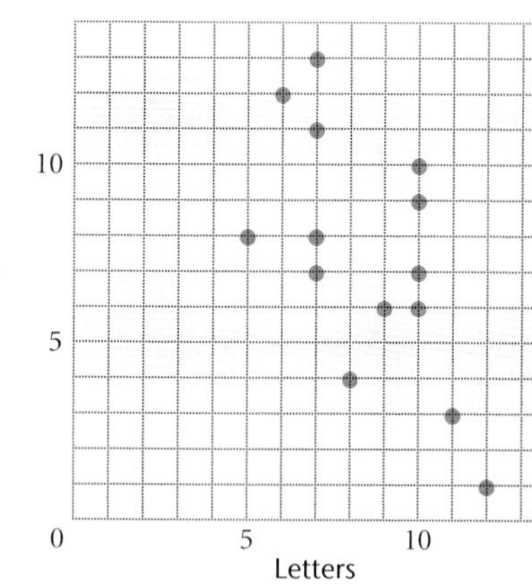

MR, C **13.** For each team in the NFL's American Football Conference, the scatter plot at the right plots the length of the name of the home city versus the number of games it won during the 1991 season. What does the scatter plot tell you about the relationship between the length of the city's name and the number of wins? Do you think the number of letters in a city's name actually affects a team's performance?

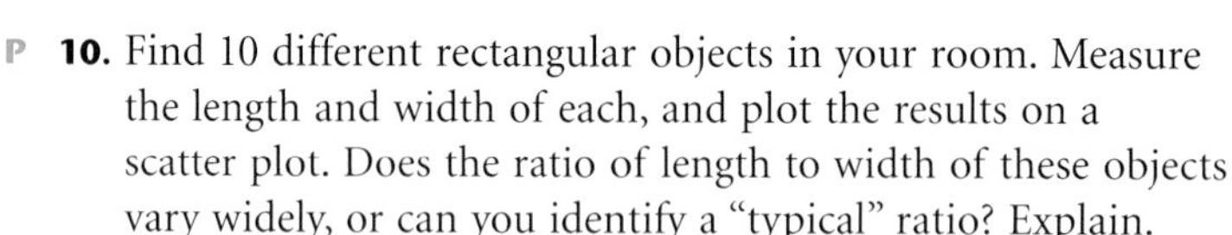

Assessment Resources

Quiz 1-1

Chapter Assessment Form A

Chapter Assessment Form B

Chapter Alternative Assessment

Mid-Year Assessment

End-of-Year Assessment

AWSMTest and practice software

Ongoing Assessment

Self-Assessment Self-Assessment Exercises

Embedded Assessment Explore Steps 1, 2; Reflec 1, 2

ADDITIONAL ANSWERS

1-1 Part A Exercises

More Practice

18. Possible answer: 4 vertices, 6 edges, 4 faces

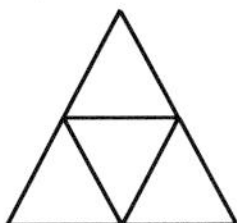

19. Possible answer:

20.

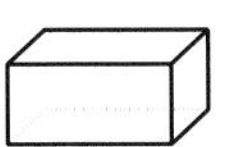

21.

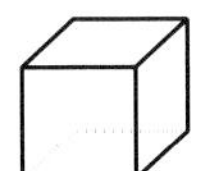

22.

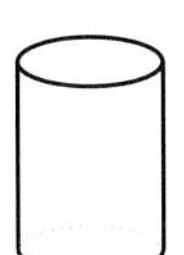

23.

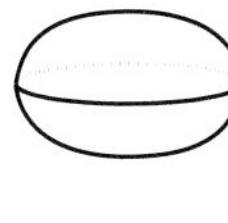

1-1 Part C Self-Assessment

12. a. Approximately 45 inches and 64 inches, respectively. Predictions are made by fitting a line through the data and then finding the y-coordinate on the line for the given x.

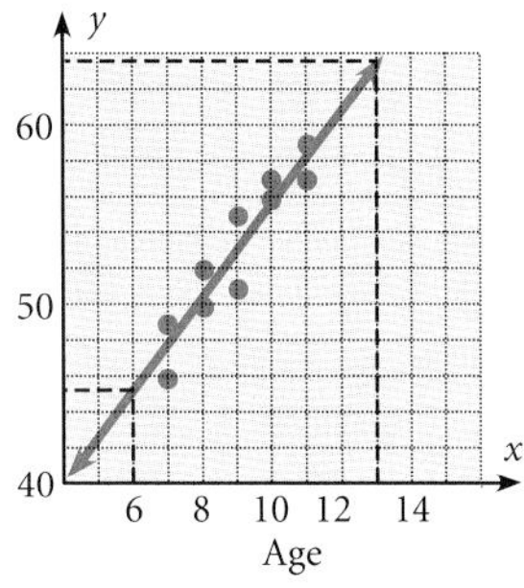

b. About 82 inches (nearly 7 feet tall). Generally girls do not grow at the same rate after their middle teens.

13. It appears that length and wins are negatively related (longer named cities have fewer wins). This result is probably just an interesting coincidence.

1-2

Reasoning and Logic

SUPERLESSON AT A GLANCE

Superlesson Goal

Students will develop inductive and deductive reasoning skills and be introduced to the language of logic.

Management Guide

	Topic	Objectives	Key Terms	New Ideas	Materials
Part A	Inductive Reasoning	To explore basic geometric figures and to develop skills in inductive reasoning.	Point, line, line segment, endpoints, intersect, point of intersection, collinear, inductive reasoning, conjecture	Forming conjectures by searching for patterns.	
Part B	The Language of Logic	To use the words *all, some,* and *none* to make conjectures and look for counterexamples.	Counterexample, *all, some, none, and, or,* Venn diagram	Disproving conjectures by identifying counterexamples. Using Venn diagrams to illustrate logical statements.	
Part C	Deductive Reasoning	To develop skills in deductive reasoning and to explore the differences between inductive and deductive reasoning.	Deductive reasoning, defined term, undefined term, postulate, theorem	Solving problems and verifying conjectures through reasoning.	**Teacher** Colored cards
Part D	Making Connections	To combine inductive and deductive reasoning to help interpret data.	In Making Connections, students apply and synthesize key terms and new ideas.		

Pacing Chart (45-Minute Periods)

	Comprehensive Course	Core Course	Informal Course
Part A	1	1	1
Part B	1	1	1
Part C	1	1	1
Part D	1	1	1
TOTAL periods for Superlesson	4	4	4

NCTM Standards

Mathematics as Problem Solving
Mathematics as Communication
Mathematics as Reasoning
Mathematical Connections
Discrete Mathematics
Mathematical Structure

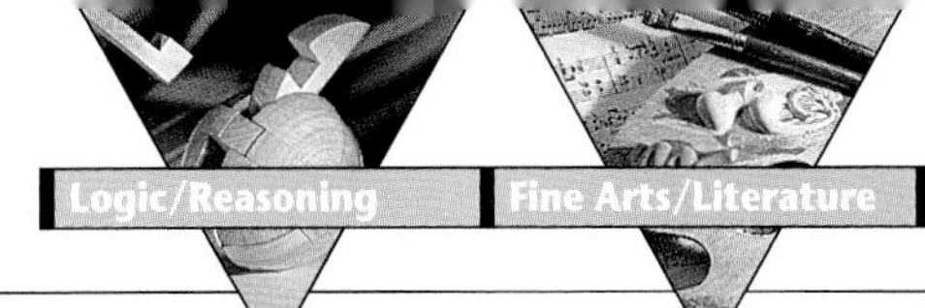

1-2 Reasoning and Logic

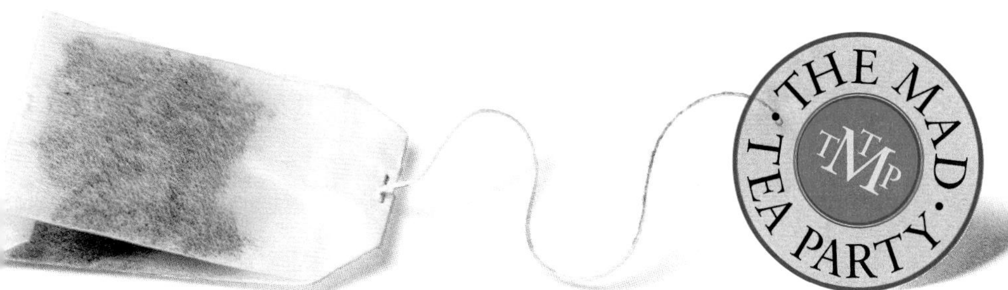

In the following excerpt from *Alice in Wonderland* by Lewis Carroll, Alice and several of the Wonderland characters attend a "Mad Tea Party."

The Hatter opened his eyes very wide... but all he said *was, "Why is a raven like a writing-desk?"*

"Come, we shall have some fun now!" thought Alice. "I'm glad they've begun asking riddles—I believe I can guess that," she added aloud.

"Do you mean that you think you can find out the answer to it?" said the March Hare.

"Exactly so," said Alice.

"Then you should say what you mean," the March Hare went on.

"I do," Alice hastily replied; "at least—at least I mean what I say—that's the same thing, you know."

"Not the same thing a bit!" said the Hatter. "Why, you might just as well say that 'I see what I eat' is the same thing as 'I eat what I see'!"

"You might just as well say," added the March Hare, "that 'I like what I get' is the same thing as 'I get what I like'!"

"You might just as well say," added the Dormouse, which seemed to be talking in its sleep, "that 'I breathe when I sleep' is the same thing as 'I sleep when I breathe'!"

"It is the same thing with you," said the Hatter, and here the conversation dropped, and the party sat silent for a minute, while Alice thought over all she could remember about ravens and writing-desks, which wasn't much.

1. Why do *you* think a raven is like a writing desk?
2. Why do you think using precise language is important in mathematics?
3. Give some examples of every-day situations where saying exactly what you mean is very important. Explain why precise language is necessary in each situation.

More About Lewis Carroll

Lewis Carroll was actually the pen name for English writer Charles Dodgson (1832–1898). His most famous works, *Alice in Wonderland* and *Through the Looking-Glass,* show his interest in mathematical logic.

"'Contrariwise,' continued Tweedledee, 'if it was so, it might be; and if it were so, it would be: but as it isn't, it ain't. That's logic.'" *Through the Looking-Glass.*

Where Are We Now?

Students have used simple geometric and algebraic models.

Where Are We Going?

In 1–2 students will become familiar with some basic geometric figures as they explore inductive and deductive reasoning. Throughout the course, they will use inductive reasoning to make conjectures about observations and deductive reasoning to see whether those conjectures are always true.

Possible Answers

1. Famous answers:

"Because Poe wrote on both."
—Sam Loyd

"Because bills and tales are amongst their characteristics."
—Frances Huxley

Frances Huxley, *The Raven and the Writing-Desk.* © 1976 Harper and Row.

2. When giving directions.

3. Precise language is important for clear communication between mathematicians.

In mathematics, we must know exactly what a figure is before we can make accurate conjectures about it.

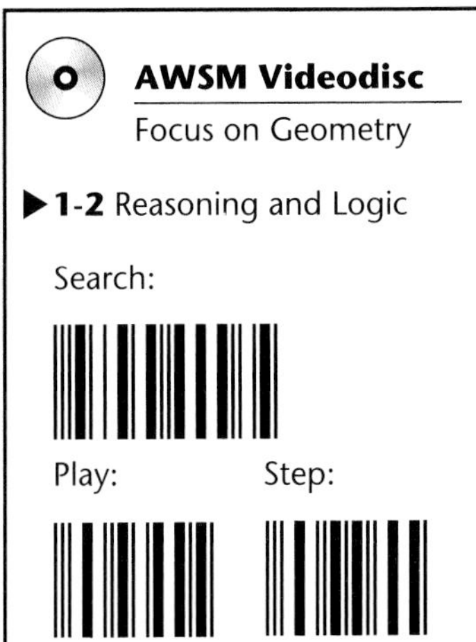

PART A At a Glance

Objective

To explore basic geometric figures and to develop skills in inductive reasoning.

Development

Students are introduced to *points, lines,* and *segments.*

In the **Explore,** students use inductive reasoning with these ideas to write a formula for the number of segments determined by *n* points on a line.

Key Terms

Point, line, line segment, endpoints, intersect, point of intersection, collinear, inductive reasoning, conjecture

First Five Minutes

Transparency FFM 1-2A

Write a brief description of several everyday objects that model a *point* and a *line*.

Motivate

Ask...

- What is a pattern?
- How might you use familiar patterns to make predictions?

1-2 PART A Inductive Reasoning

← CONNECT → *You've already been using reasoning skills to choose appropriate mathematical models. Now you will learn more about one particular type of reasoning.*

You will soon be investigating basic geometric figures. So that everyone can use the same vocabulary and notation, some of these figures are described below.

A **point** is a specific location. It has no size, but it can be modeled by a dot, such as a dot on a map or a computer screen. To illustrate a point, we use a dot labeled with a capital letter. Points *A*, *B*, and *C* are shown.

A •　　• C　　B •

A **line** is a set of points. It is straight, and it continues forever in both directions. A line has no thickness, but it has infinite length. A line can be named by a single lowercase letter or by any two points on the line. This is line ℓ, $\overleftrightarrow{DE}$, or $\overleftrightarrow{ED}$.

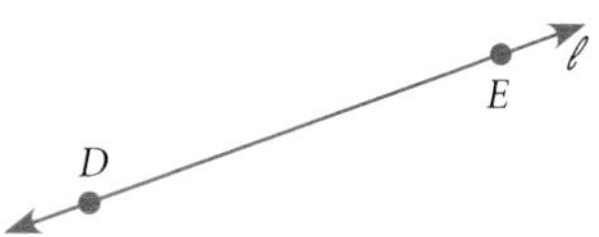

A **line segment** is a part of a line consisting of two **endpoints** and all the points between these points. Segments are named by their endpoints. This is segment $\overline{PQ}$ or $\overline{QP}$.

Note that when we refer to "two points" (lines, segments), we mean two *different* points (lines, segments).

When two geometric figures have points in common, we say that they **intersect**. $\overleftrightarrow{EF}$ intersects $\overleftrightarrow{HI}$ at *J*. (*J* is the **point of intersection** of $\overleftrightarrow{EF}$ and $\overleftrightarrow{HI}$.)

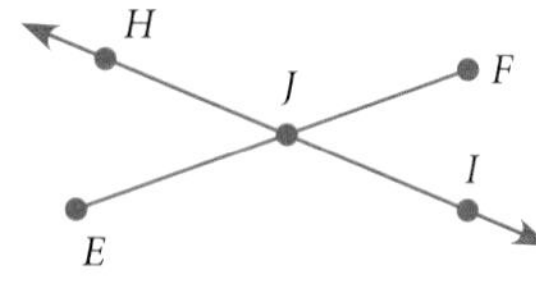

Alert

Students may refer to the descriptions of *point* and *line* as *definitions*. Encourage them to resist this tendency. In Chapter 2, they will learn the difference between defined and undefined terms.

Discrete Math Connection

The number of segments on a line determined by *n* points is the $(n - 1)$st triangular number. You may want to describe triangular numbers (shown by the patterns in Exercise 37 on page 332) and ask why they have the same pattern shown in the **Explore.** They do because both are generated by adding the counting numbers from 1 to $(n - 1)$.

TRY IT

a. Draw a line $\overleftrightarrow{XY}$.
b. Add points M and N to your drawing so that M is on $\overleftrightarrow{XY}$ and N is not on $\overleftrightarrow{XY}$.
c. Name all of the segments that are determined by the labeled points on $\overleftrightarrow{XY}$. $\overline{XM}$, $\overline{MY}$, $\overline{XY}$

In the following Explore, you'll be placing several points on the same line. Points on the same line are **collinear.**

EXPLORE: GET THE POINT

1. Draw a line. Draw points A and B on the line. How many different segments are determined by points A and B? Name the segment(s).
2. Draw another line. Draw points A, B, and C on the line. How many segments are determined by points A, B, and C? Name them.
3. Continue to draw lines, adding one point each time. Make a table showing the number of points and the number of segments they determine.

Problem-Solving Tip

Look for patterns in your data.

Continue the process until you are confident that you've found a pattern for the relationship between the number of points and the number of segments they determine.

4. If you draw 10 points on a line, how many segments do they determine?
5. If you draw n points on a line, how many segments do they determine? Can you find a formula? Compare your formula to those of your classmates. Discuss how you found these formulas.

In solving the problem in the Explore, you looked for a pattern in the data so you could make an educated guess about the formula. In mathematical terms, you used **inductive reasoning** to make a **conjecture.**

Student Resources

- Alternative Lessons 1-2A
- Laboratory Manual 1-2A
- Technology Lab Manual
- Practice 1-2A
- Study Guide and Journal 1-2A
- Guía de estudios y Diario 1-2A
- Multilingual Handbook
- More Look Ahead 1-2A
- SAT Preparation

Media Resources

- Transparency FFM 1-2A
- Transparency AE 1-2A
- Teaching Transparency
- AWSMTest and practice software
- AWSM Videodisc

EXPLORE

Get the Point

Recommended group size: 2

The Point

To write a formula for the number of segments determined by n points on a line.

Look and Listen...

- For students who are having difficulty expressing their results as a mathematical formula.

Ask...

- Should $\overline{AB}$ and $\overline{BA}$ count as two different segments?

For Groups That Finish Early

Find a formula for the number of segments determined by n points on a *circle*, and explain the result. $\frac{n(n-1)}{2}$

Follow Up

Ask for different formulas that seem to work. Have the class discuss advantages and disadvantages of each.

Possible Answers

1. One: $\overline{AB}$.

2. Three: $\overline{AB}$, $\overline{AC}$, and $\overline{BC}$.

3. 4 points, 6 segments; 5 points, 10 segments; 6 points, 15 segments

4. 10 points, 45 segments

5. $\frac{n(n-1)}{2}$

1-2

Reasoning and Logic

ALTERNATE EXAMPLE

Predict the equation that comes next.

$5^2 = 25$

$15^2 = 225$

$25^2 = 625$

$35^2 = 1225$

From 5^2 to 15^2, the product increases by 200; from 15^2 to 25^2, by 400, and from 25^2 to 35^2, by 600.

If the pattern continues, 45^2 should be 800 greater than 35^2.
$45^2 = 1225 + 800 = 2025$

Journal

Reflect 1 and 4 are suitable for journal entries.

REFLECT

Possible Answers

1. Inductive reasoning is used when conjectures are based on patterns seen in specific cases. Once we identify a pattern that seems to fit those cases, we use it to make predictions.
2. The sun rises in the east; geese fly in a V formation; spiders have eight legs.
3. 2, 4, 6, 8, … (even numbers)

   1, 4, 9, … (n^2)

   1, 4, 7, 10, … ($3n - 2$)
4. Conjectures made by inductive reasoning are not necessarily true. Example: "Since 3, 5, and 7 are prime numbers, all odd numbers greater than 3 are prime" is false.

TRY IT

Answers

a–b. Possible answer:

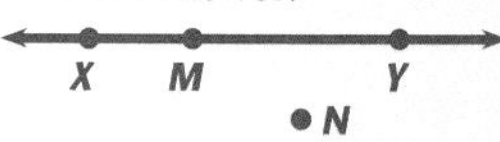

A **conjecture** is a conclusion made from observing evidence. A conjecture may or may not be true.

Inductive reasoning is the process of making a conjecture by looking at several specific examples and recognizing a pattern.

EXAMPLE

If you make c cuts in a rope, how many pieces will you end up with?

The following table shows the relationship between the number of cuts and the number of pieces. By using inductive reasoning, we make the conjecture that if you make c cuts, you end up with $c + 1$ pieces.

Cuts	0	1	2	3	4	...
Pieces	1	2	3	4	5	...

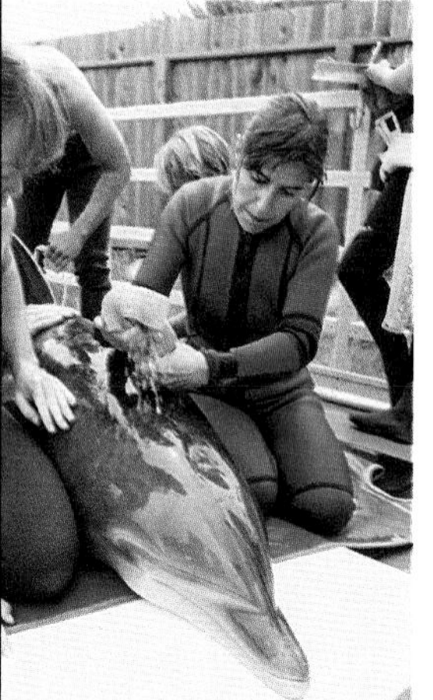

Inductive reasoning is a practical, though not foolproof, way to make conjectures. Inuits observe patterns in the sun, clouds, ocean, wind, and animals to predict the weather far in advance. A biologist uses inductive reasoning when she observes the behavior of one group of dolphins and then assumes that their behavior is typical of most dolphins. Scientists use inductive reasoning to help construct and check their current best guesses (*theories*) about how the world works.

Mathematics also frequently involves a search for patterns. When a mathematician first observes a pattern, she may make a conjecture about what it means. She might make hundreds or even thousands of observations before she believes her guess is true. For a mathematician, a conjecture is "true" only when she is certain that it is *always* true.

REFLECT

1. What is inductive reasoning? How are patterns used in inductive reasoning?
2. Describe three patterns that occur in nature.
3. Write three different number patterns. Explain the rule for each of your patterns.
4. Are conjectures made through inductive reasoning necessarily true? If not, give an example of a pattern that only holds in certain instances.

History Connection

Sophie Germain (1776–1831) was a French mathematician who did important work in mathematics and mathematical physics. Her work on elastic surfaces, submitted anonymously at first, won her a *grand prix* from the French Academy of Sciences.

Exercises

CORE

1. Getting Started All sides of an equilateral triangle have the same length. Following the steps below, use inductive reasoning to find the perimeter (distance around the figure) when 100 equilateral triangles are pushed together as shown.

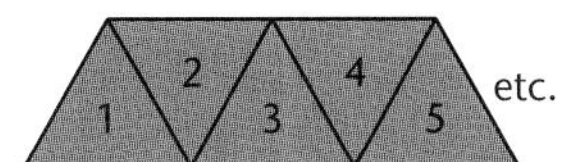

Problem-Solving Tip

Make a table to show your data.

a. One row of your table should show the number of triangles and the other the perimeter of the figure.
b. Sketch an equilateral triangle. Suppose the length of each side of the triangle is 1. Find the perimeter of the triangle, and record your results in the table.
c. Add a second triangle to your sketch. Find the perimeter of this figure and record your data.
d. Repeat **1c** for three and four triangles. Look for a pattern in your results.
e. Find a formula that relates n, the number of triangles, to p, the perimeter.
f. Check to see that your formula works. Then use it to predict the perimeter for 100 triangles pushed together.

Find the next number in each sequence. Explain the pattern.

2. 1, 4, 9, 16, 25, . . . **3.** $0, \frac{1}{2}, \frac{3}{4}, \frac{7}{8}, \frac{15}{16}, \ldots$ **4.** 1, 2, 4, 8, 16, . . .

5. Name all the lines, points, and segments in the figure below.

6. List all sets of three collinear points in the figure.

7. Draw a figure that shows the following:
- ℓ intersects m at G.
- $\overline{DO}$ is on m.
- K is not on ℓ or m.

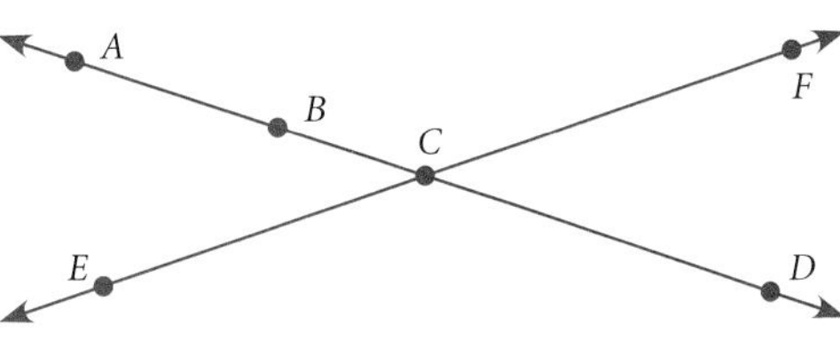

Complete each statement with *point, line,* or *line segment.*

8. A ___ has no thickness, but it has infinite length. Line

9. A ___ has no thickness and has a finite length. Segment

10. A ___ is a specific location. Point

Ongoing Assessment

Vocabulary
Practice/Skills
Review
Math Reasoning
Problem Solving
Challenge

Self-Assessment Exercises 1, 3, 5, 6, 9, 11

Embedded Assessment Explore Step 5; Reflect 1, 3; Exercises 4, 7, 13

Part A Exercises

Exercise Notes

Core

1. Provides a step-by-step procedure for using inductive reasoning to solve a problem. It emphasizes the importance of using a table to organize information.

12. Shows a connection between the algebraic idea of prime numbers and geometric areas.

Look Ahead

These exercises preview the use of *all, some,* and *none* in 1-2 Part B. Students should see that they already have a good intuition for what these logical terms mean.

More Math Reasoning

29. Fibonacci numbers are the basis for the inductive pattern seen here. The connection between Fibonacci numbers and the Golden Ratio is explored in Exercise 11 in 7-1 Part D.

Exercise Answers

Core

1.a–d.

Triangles	1	2	3	4
Perimeter	3	4	5	6

e. $p = n + 2$ **f.** 102

2. 36; n^2 where n = term number

3. $\frac{31}{32}$; Each term is the sum of the numerator and denominator of the previous number, divided by this value plus 1; $\frac{a}{b}, \frac{a+b}{a+b+1}, \ldots$

4. 32; 2^{n-1}

5. Lines: $\overleftrightarrow{AB}$, (or $\overleftrightarrow{AC}$, $\overleftrightarrow{AD}$, $\overleftrightarrow{BC}$, $\overleftrightarrow{BD}$, or $\overleftrightarrow{CD}$), and $\overleftrightarrow{EC}$ (or $\overleftrightarrow{EF}$ or $\overleftrightarrow{CF}$); points: A, B, C, D, E, F; segments: $\overline{AB}, \overline{AC}, \overline{AD}, \overline{BC}, \overline{BD}, \overline{CD}, \overline{EC}, \overline{EF}$, and $\overline{CF}$

6. A, B, C; A, B, D; A, C, D; B, C, D; E, C, F

7. Possible answer:

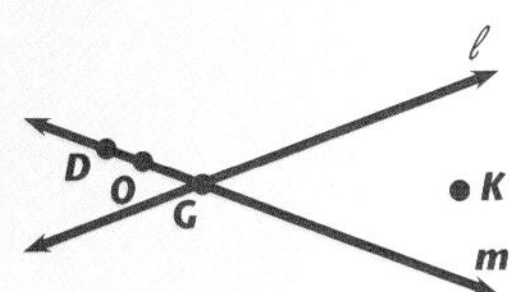

1-2

Reasoning and Logic

11.

Tiers high	Triangles
2	4
3	9
4	16
5	25
10	100
n	n^2

12.

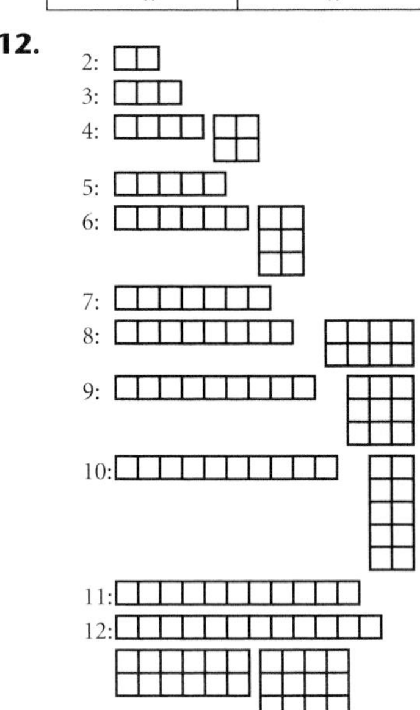

Only one rectangle: 2, 3, 5, 7, 11; the area is a prime number (no whole number factors except itself and 1)

13. The sums are 1, 4, 9, 16, 25, 36, 49, respectively. Pattern: sum = (number of terms)^2; Sum first 10: $10^2 = 100$; Sum first 25: $25^2 = 625$; Sum of first n odd numbers $= n^2$

14. Gauss paired numbers starting with 1, 300: $(1 + 300) + (2 + 299) + (3 + 298) + \ldots = \frac{300}{2}(301) = \frac{n(n+1)}{2} = 45{,}150$

Look Ahead

15. F; Not books which have had their pages cut out

16. T: For example, this book

17. F; A robin is a bird, and this bird is a robin.

18. T; Eagles are both birds and eagles.

19. F; A robin is not a bluejay.

20. T; An oriole is a bird.

21–29. See Additional Answers p. T38.

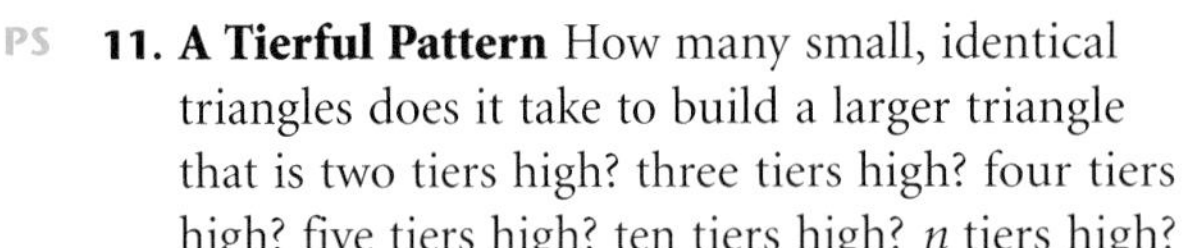

PS **11. A Tierful Pattern** How many small, identical triangles does it take to build a larger triangle that is two tiers high? three tiers high? four tiers high? five tiers high? ten tiers high? n tiers high?

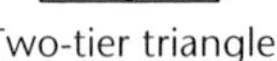

Two-tier triangle

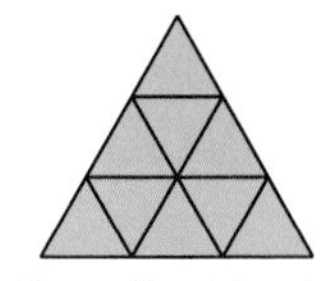

Three-tier triangle

PS **12.** Using graph paper, draw rectangles with integer side lengths that cover areas 2, 3, 4, 5, 6, 7, 8, 9, 10, 11, and 12. When there is more than one possible way to draw a rectangle, draw all possibilities. (A 1×3 rectangle and a 3×1 rectangle do not count as different rectangles.) Identify the areas that have only one rectangle. What is true about these areas? Make a connection to a type of number you studied in algebra.

PS **13.** Look at the number pattern at the right. Find the sums. Find a pattern. What is the sum of the first 10 odd numbers? the first 25 odd numbers? Make a conjecture about the sum of the first n odd numbers.

$1 =$
$1 + 3 =$
$1 + 3 + 5 =$
$1 + 3 + 5 + 7 =$
$1 + 3 + 5 + 7 + 9 =$
$1 + 3 + 5 + 7 + 9 + 11 =$
$1 + 3 + 5 + 7 + 9 + 11 + 13 =$

PS History **14.** When he was in the third grade, the mathematician Karl F. Gauss was told to add all the numbers from 1 through 300. In a few minutes, Gauss gave the teacher the correct answer. How do you think he added these numbers so quickly without a calculator? What was his answer? (Hint: Find pairs of numbers in the line below that have the same sum.)

$1 + 2 + 3 + 4 + 5 + 6 + \ldots + 295 + 296 + 297 + 298 + 299 + 300 = ?$

LOOK AHEAD

MR **Determine whether each statement below is true or false. Explain your reasoning.**

15. All books have pages.
16. Some books have pages.
17. No birds are robins.
18. Some birds are eagles.
19. All birds are blue jays.
20. All orioles are birds.

MORE PRACTICE

P **Find the next number in each sequence. Explain the pattern.**

21. 3, 9, 27, 81, . . .
22. 8, −4, 2, −1, . . .
23. 2, 4, 3, 9, 4, 16, 5, . . .

P **24.** Name all the lines, points, and segments in the figure at the right.

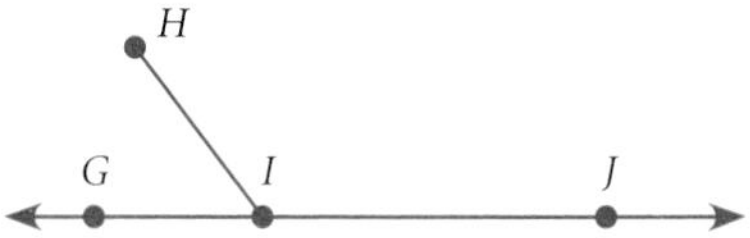

P **25.** Name a set of three collinear points in the figure.

H, G, I, J

P **26.** Draw one figure that shows the following: $\overline{AB}$ intersects $\overline{CD}$ at E; Line n does not intersect $\overline{AB}$ or $\overline{CD}$; F is on n.

Key

V Vocabulary
P Practice/Skills
R Review
MR Math Reasoning
PS Problem Solving
C Challenge

MORE MATH REASONING

27. Athena claimed that any two points are collinear. Do you agree or disagree? Why?

28. Patterns with Squares Each square shown is made of smaller unit squares. Some of the unit squares touch the shaded region on two sides, some on one side, and some do not touch it at all. Suppose an $n \times n$ square is drawn in the shaded region. How many unit squares will touch the shaded region on two sides? one side? zero sides?

29. Habits of Rabbits Rabbits have very consistent breeding habits. Suppose that, starting in the second month of their lives, a pair of adult rabbits produces an average of two offspring a month. Suppose you have a pair of baby bunnies, one male and one female. Assuming that each pair of babies consists of one male and one female and that no rabbits die, find the number of pairs of rabbits you would have each month for 12 months. Explain the pattern that these numbers follow.

Month	1st	2nd	3rd	4th	5th	. . .	12th
Pairs of Rabbits	bb	BB	BB bb	BB BB bb	BB BB BB bb bb	. . .	??

Note: bb denotes a pair of baby bunnies; BB denotes a pair of adult rabbits.

The problem about rabbits was first described in a math book by Leonardo Fibonacci of Pisa, Italy. The number pattern you've found is commonly known as the Fibonacci sequence.

1-2 PART B The Language of Logic

← CONNECT → ***You've seen that inductive reasoning is a practical form of reasoning. As you learn the language of logic, you will keep making conjectures and begin looking for counterexamples.***

When Alice in Wonderland claimed that "I mean what I say" is the same as "I say what I mean," the Mad Hatter, the March Hare, and the Dormouse each gave a counterexample of Alice's imperfect logic. A **counterexample** is an example that shows a statement to be false.

Student Resources

- Alternative Lessons 1-2B
- Laboratory Manual 1-2B
- Technology Lab Manual
- Practice 1-2B
- Study Guide and Journal 1-2B
- Guía de estudios y Diario 1-2B
- Multilingual Handbook
- More Look Back 1-2B
- SAT Preparation

Media Resources

- Transparency FFM 1-2B
- Transparency AE 1-2B
- Teaching Transparency
- AWSMTest and practice software
- AWSM Videodisc

PART B At a Glance

Objective

To use the words *all, some,* and *none* to make conjectures and look for counterexamples.

Development

In **Consider** questions, students use an excerpt from *Alice in Wonderland* to investigate logical statements and counterexamples.

The logical meanings of *all, some,* and *none* are presented and illustrated with Venn diagrams.

In the **Explore,** students apply *all, some,* and *none* to triangles.

And and *or* are introduced, and **Examples** illustrate their use.

Key Terms

Counterexample, *all, some, none, and, or,* Venn diagram

First Five Minutes

Transparency FFM 1-2B

Read the paragraph at the bottom of page 25, and answer **Consider** questions 1–4 at the top of page 26.

Motivate

Ask...

- Can you define *counterexample* in your own words?
- Do *all* cars have four doors? Do *some* cars have four doors?
- Do *all* homes have doorways? Do *some* homes have doorways?

Algebra	Functions	Discrete Math	Probability	Data/Statistics

Reasoning and Logic

Possible Answers

1. That "I mean what I say" and "I say what I mean" are equivalent statements.
2. Mad Hatter: I see what I eat = I eat what I see.

   March Hare: I like what I get = I get what I like.

   Dormouse: I breathe when I sleep = I sleep when I breathe.
3. "I mean what I say" means that I believe in my statements. "I say what I mean" means that my statements say exactly what I intended them to—whether or not I believe they are true.
4. I whistle while I work = I work when I whistle.

Note: Because a statement like "Some collies are dogs" is logically true, not all Venn diagrams representing a true statement with *some* involve intersecting circles.

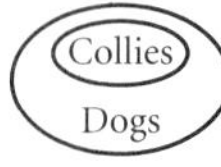

Refer back to *The Mad Tea Party* on page 19 to answer the following questions.

1. What was Alice's false statement?
2. What counterexamples to Alice's logic were given by the Mad Hatter, the March Hare, and the Dormouse?
3. What is the difference between "I mean what I say" and "I say what I mean"?
4. If you had attended the tea party, what counterexample to Alice's logic could you have added to the conversation?

TRY IT

Give a counterexample that disproves each conjecture below.

a. All birds can fly. Ostrich

b. All four-sided figures (quadrilaterals) are rectangles. Parallelogram

Notice that *one* counterexample proves that a conjecture is false!

When making a conjecture, you must be careful to say exactly what you mean. You need to use common terms like **all, some,** and **none** very carefully when making *logical statements.*

Here are some examples of how *all (every, each), some (at least one, one or more),* and *none (no, not any)* are used in mathematical and nonmathematical sentences.

All dogs in town need a license.	*All* squares are rectangles.
Some dogs have fleas.	*Some* quadrilaterals are squares.
No dogs say "meow."	*No* square is a circle.

Another way to represent these statements is by using **Venn diagrams.** Venn diagrams can help illustrate the relationships described by *all, some,* and *none.*

All whales are mammals.

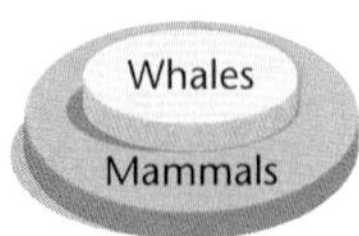

Some mammals can swim.

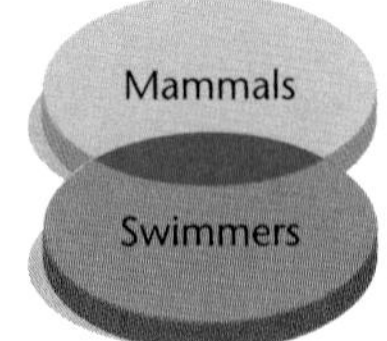

No whales can fly.

Alert

Students may need frequent reminders that just one counterexample disproves a mathematical conjecture.

Tips from Teachers

Students may have trouble understanding that *A or B* is true when both *A* and *B* are true. You may want to explain that a second form of logical *or*—the *exclusive or*—does mean that exactly one of the things listed is true. However, the meaning of *or* that we will use (the *inclusive or*) actually makes it easier to verify conjectures.

EXPLORE: SOME TRIANGLES ARE . . .

Consider the triangles at the right as you answer the following.

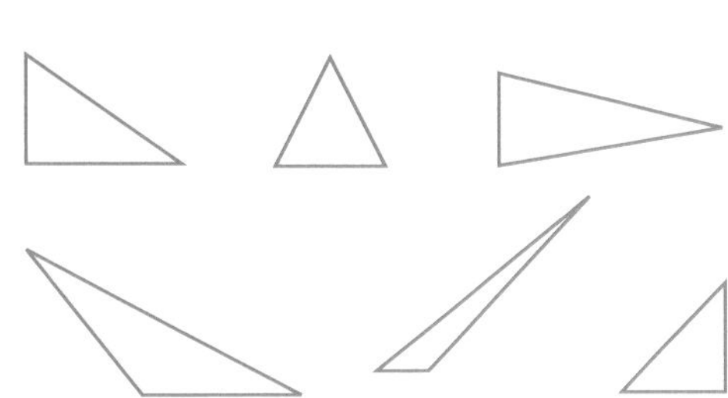

1. Write three statements beginning with the words *All triangles.*
2. Write three statements beginning with the words *Some triangles.*
3. Write three statements beginning with the words *No triangle.*
4. Does the statement *"Some triangles have three sides"* present an acceptable use of the word *some*? Discuss this with your classmates.

There are times when it is helpful to link two or more logical statements. The familiar words *and* and *or* give us an easy way to do this. Mathematicians are very particular about the meanings of these words. If you link two statements with *and,* both parts must be true for the combined statement to be true.

The word *or* is a little trickier. In daily life, a statement that uses *or* usually means that you are making a choice: you will do only one of two things. But in mathematics, a true statement with *or* can have one part true or both parts true.

EXAMPLES

Describe the conditions that make the following logical statements true and the conditions that make them false.

1. Seema will compete in the long jump, *and* she will run the 100 meters.

   This is true only if Seema does both.

   It is false under the following conditions:
   - She competes in the long jump but doesn't run the 100 meters.
   - She runs the 100 meters but doesn't compete in the long jump.
   - She does not compete in either event.

Logic Connection

Many teachers find that *Truth Tables* are helpful for teaching logic.

A	*B*	*A* and *B*	*A* or *B*
T	T	T	T
T	F	F	T
F	T	F	T
F	F	F	F

EXPLORE

Some Triangles Are...

Recommended group size: 4

The Point
Students use *all, some,* and *none* to make precise statements about a geometric figure.

Look and Listen...
- For students who use terms like *isosceles* that may be unfamiliar to other students.
- For students who make incorrect statements. Work with them to see if they misunderstand *all, some,* and *none* or have misconceptions about triangles.

Ask...
- Do *some* of the students in this room take geometry?

For Groups That Finish Early
Write true statements about circles, using *all, some,* and *none.*

Follow Up
Ask whether the meaning of *some* in logical statements is consistent with the way it is used in everyday conversation.

Possible Answers

1. All triangles have three sides; all have three corners (vertices); all have straight sides.
2. Some triangles have two sides with equal lengths; some have three sides with equal lengths; some have a right angle.
3. No triangle has a break in its sides; no triangle has four sides; no triangle has curved sides.
4. Yes

ALTERNATE EXAMPLES

Transparency AE 1-2B

Reasoning and Logic

Journal

Reflect 1 and 3 are suitable for journal entries.

REFLECT

Possible Answers

1. For a statement to be considered logically true, it must *always* be true.
2. None of the students in this class are sophomores. Counterexample: ________ is a sophomore.
3. If they are using *or* in the logical sense, this statement is true if you clean your room—whether or not you get to see your friends.

Part B Exercises

Exercise Notes

Core

1. This exercise is a warm-up to the ideas of this exercise set. It may also provide an opportunity for discussion. At first, many students will feel that the statement is true, because they interpret it as "Birds lay eggs" or "All species of birds lay eggs." Since we must interpret the statement exactly as it is, however, it is *false*—male birds do not lay eggs.

3, 4, 13. Exercises 3 and 4 remind students of common algebraic misconceptions. Exercises 4 and 13 involve important inequalities that are frequently seen in comparison items on standardized tests.

14. Reviews inductive reasoning.

Look Back

15–19. Provide review of algebra skills.

More Math Reasoning

31. Students use a Venn diagram to solve a problem. This exercise also reviews probability concepts.

2. Juan is going to the store *or* he is going swimming.

This is true if either of the following is true:

- Juan goes to the store (whether he goes swimming or not).
- Juan goes swimming (whether he goes to the store or not).

It is false only if Juan neither goes to the store nor goes swimming.

REFLECT

1. Explain why just one counterexample to a conjecture proves that the conjecture is false.
2. Make a false statement about your school, using *all* or *none*. Give a counterexample that shows why the statement is false.
3. Suppose someone tells you, "You will clean your room, or you can't see your friends this weekend." Explain why you hope that they didn't learn about logic.

Exercises

CORE

P **1. Getting Started** Give a counterexample that disproves the conjecture "All birds lay eggs." Possible answer: Roosters are birds, but being male, they don't lay eggs.

P **Give a counterexample that disproves each conjecture below.**

2. No triangles can have three equal sides. Equilateral triangle

3. For any real numbers a and b, $(a + b)^2 = a^2 + b^2$. Possible answer: Let $a = b = 1$

4. For any real number x, $x^2 \geq 1$. Possible answer: Let $x = 0$

P **Describe the conditions that make each of the following logical statements true and the conditions that make them false.**

5. Steven will buy a newspaper, and he will eat lunch.

6. Tonya will visit her aunt or she will see a movie.

P **Draw a Venn diagram to illustrate each of the following statements.**

7. All carrots are vegetables. **8.** Some apples are green. **9.** No apples are vegetables.

Key

- V Vocabulary
- P Practice/Skills
- R Review
- MR Math Reasoning
- PS Problem Solving
- C Challenge

Determine whether each statement is true or false. If the statement is false, change the underlined word to make it true.

10. A conjecture disproves a rule.

11. A line has two endpoints.

12. Write three true statements about the United States using the terms *all, some,* and *none.* For example:

All states have governors.

Some states border Canada.

No states are larger than Alaska.

13. The following conjecture is false; it has only one counterexample.
For any real number x, $x^2 > 0$.
- **a.** Find the counterexample for this conjecture.
- **b.** Give another conjecture that has only one counterexample.

14. a. Make a conjecture about the number of pieces of string into which the folded string is divided by n cuts.

b. Make a conjecture about the number of pieces of string into which the loop of string is divided by n cuts.

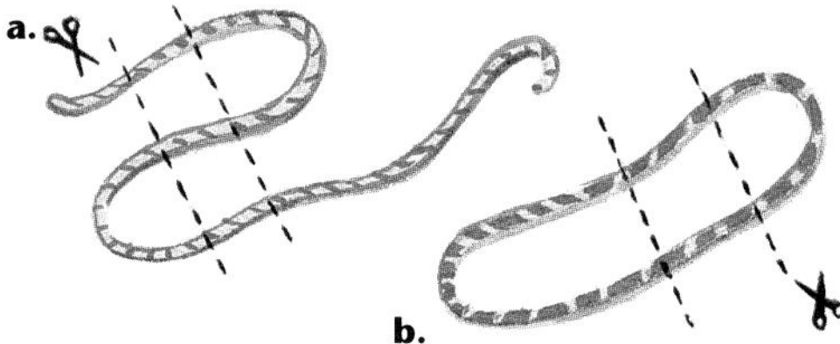

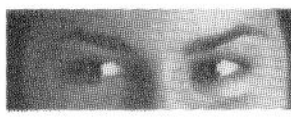

LOOK BACK

Solve each equation. [Previous course]

15. $18 = 4x + 2$ $x = 4$ **16.** $5(x + 2) = 17 - 3x$ $x = \frac{7}{8}$

Graph each equation on a coordinate plane. [Previous course]

17. $y = 3x - 5$ **18.** $y = -2x + 3$ **19.** $y = x^2 - 2$

20. Sketch a net for the pyramid at the right. [1-1]

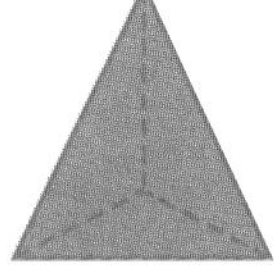

MORE PRACTICE

Give a counterexample that disproves each conjecture below.

21. No triangles have two sides of the same length.

22. All figures with four sides of equal length are squares.

23. No women have been elected U.S. senators.

24. Everyone who lives in Texas lives in Houston.

Ongoing Assessment

Self-Assessment Exercises 1–11 odd

Embedded Assessment Explore Step 4; Reflect 1; Exercises 2, 6, 12, 14

Exercise Answers

Core

5. True if he buys a newspaper and eats lunch; False if he doesn't buy a newspaper, or doesn't eat lunch, or both

6. True if she visits her aunt, sees a movie, or both; False if she neither sees her aunt nor sees a movie

7. Vegetables (Carrots)

8.

9.

10. F; Counterexample

11. F; Line segment

12. Possible answers: All states have two senators. Some states have more than one representative. No state is on both the Atlantic Coast and the Pacific Coast.

13. a. $x = 0$

b. Possible answer: All prime numbers are odd.

14. a. Possible answer: $3(n + 1) - 2$

b. Possible answer: $2n$

Look Back

17–19.

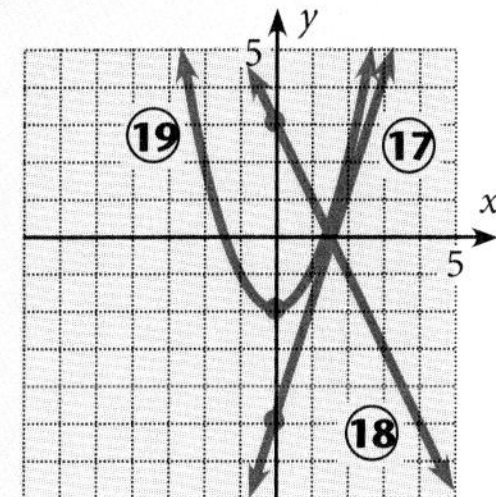

20. Possible answer:

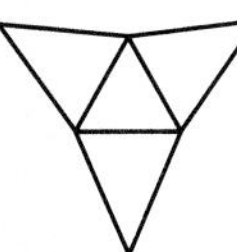

More Practice

21. Equilateral triangle

22. Parallelogram with no 90° angles but all sides of same length

23–31.
See Additional Answers p. T38.

Reasoning and Logic

PART C At a Glance

Objective

To develop skills in deductive reasoning and to explore the differences between inductive and deductive reasoning.

Development

In the **Explore,** students use deductive reasoning to draw conclusions.

What Do You Think? and the **Consider** that follows it illustrate the difference between inductive and deductive reasoning.

Suggested Materials

Teacher Colored cards

Key Terms

Deductive reasoning, defined term, undefined term, postulate, theorem

First Five Minutes

Transparency FFM 1-2C

Solve the following logic puzzle.

At a school assembly, students sit, by class, in the gym bleachers.

The sophomores sit next to the juniors.

The juniors sit to the right of the freshmen.

The seniors sit at the far right end of the bleachers.

Which class sits at the far left end of the bleachers? **The freshmen.**

Motivate

Ask...

- What fictional detectives have you read about or seen on television? How do they use reasoning to solve their cases?

P **Describe the conditions that make each of the following logical statements true and the conditions that make them false.**

25. I did my homework, and I cleaned my bedroom.

26. I'll borrow Janet's calculator, or I'll buy a calculator.

P **Write statements using *all, some,* and *none* to explain each Venn diagram.**

27. Joggers / Swimmers

28. Dogs / Cats

29. Quadrilaterals / Squares

MORE MATH REASONING

MR **30.** Write three true statements about your school using the terms *all, some,* and *none.*

PS, C **31.** At Rosemead High School, 94 students take biology, 86 take ethnic studies, and 95 take geometry. Thirty-seven students take both biology and geometry, 43 take geometry and ethnic studies, and 42 take ethnic studies and biology. Twenty-eight students take all three subjects.

a. Draw a Venn diagram to illustrate this problem. How many students take geometry but not ethnic studies or biology?

b. What is the probability that a student chosen at random will be taking all three of the courses?

1-2 PART C Deductive Reasoning

← CONNECT → ***You've used inductive reasoning to make conjectures based on patterns and evidence. Now you will look at a different way to make conjectures—deductive reasoning.***

Raymond Smullyan, a professor of mathematical logic, based his book of brainteasers, *Alice in Puzzleland,* on the characters in the original *Alice in Wonderland.* The following Explore is based on one of the sets of puzzles in his book.

Key

V Vocabulary
P Practice/Skills
R Review
MR Math Reasoning
PS Problem Solving
C Challenge

Diversity Issues

Students who are kinesthetic learners may find the **Explore** easier if they use colored cards to act out the possibilities.

EXPLORE: DUM DEEDUCING

Tweedledum and Tweedledee are identical twins who usually have their names embroidered on their collars so people can tell them apart. Today, however, they have decided to entertain themselves by confusing Alice.

One of the brothers—of course, we don't know which—says, "In these puzzles, each of us will pick one of two cards, either an orange one or a blue one. The one with the orange card will always tell the truth. The one with the blue card will always lie."

1. The two brothers hide behind a wall, draw cards, and return with the cards hidden behind their backs.
   The one on the left says, "I have the blue card, and I am Tweedledee."
   The one on the right says, "You are not! *I* am Tweedledee!"
   "This is fun!" Alice says, and picks out Tweedledee immediately! Which one is it, and how did she (or you) figure it out?
2. "Not bad," one of the brothers says, and they walk behind the wall again, looking very determined. They return, having picked cards again.
   The one on the left says, "Tweedledum is now carrying a blue card."
   The one on the right just smiles!
   Alice looked confused for a moment, then thought as logically as she could and solved the puzzle. Who is Tweedledum? How can you tell? Explain your reasoning.
3. You are *not* using inductive reasoning as you solve these puzzles—there's no pattern! Explain how the type of reasoning you are using is different from inductive reasoning.

In this Explore, you used **deductive reasoning.**

Deductive reasoning is the process of drawing conclusions from given information by using rules of logic. In deductive reasoning, we must be able to justify any statement that we make.

EXPLORE

Dum Deeducing

Recommended group size: 4

The Point
To use deductive reasoning to solve logic puzzles.

Look and Listen...
- For students who are having difficulty interpreting the rules of the game.

Ask...
- Could you make a list or table to help you solve this problem?

For Groups That Finish Early
Make up a Tweedledum and Tweedledee logic puzzle.

Follow Up
Ask whether inductive reasoning could have been used to solve these puzzles.

Possible Answers
1. The one on the right is Tweedledee.
2. The one on the left is Tweedledee.
3. To solve these problems, students reasoned from known facts and used rules of logic. In inductive reasoning, conclusions are drawn by looking for patterns in data.

Student Resources

- **Alternative Lessons** 1-2C
- **Laboratory Manual** 1-2C
- Technology Lab Manual
- **Practice** 1-2C
- **Study Guide and Journal** 1-2C
- **Guía de estudios y Diario** 1-2C
- **Multilingual Handbook**
- **More Look Ahead** 1-2C
- SAT Preparation

Media Resources

- **Transparency FFM** 1-2C
- Transparency AE
- Teaching Transparency
- **AWSMTest and practice software**
- AWSM Videodisc

Reasoning and Logic

WHAT DO YOU THINK?

In **What Do You Think?** features, students see different valid ways of thinking about a problem.

Maria uses deductive reasoning to decide whether or not she passed a quiz, and Kevin uses inductive reasoning. In this situation, deductive reasoning seems more convincing.

Possible Answers

1. Kevin is using inductive reasoning; Maria is using deductive reasoning.
2. Deductive reasoning.

Note: In a mathematics course, students may begin to believe that deductive reasoning is "better" than inductive reasoning. It is important for them to recognize that both methods are important and valid.

When you solve algebraic equations step by step, you are using deductive reasoning. You can justify every step (for instance, adding 3 to each side) with one or more properties (the Addition Property of Equality).

WHAT DO YOU THINK?

Kevin and Maria are both trying to figure out how they did on yesterday's history quiz.

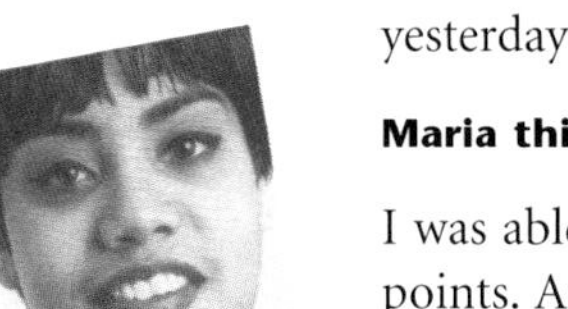

Maria thinks . . .

I was able to answer all four questions, so I have a chance to get all 20 points. After class, I checked three answers in the book, and all of them were right. So I should get at least 15 out of 20. Since 12 is a passing score, I'm sure that I passed the quiz.

Kevin thinks . . .

We've had five history quizzes this quarter, and I've passed all of them. Also, Leah and I almost always get similar scores, and she got a perfect score on hers. So, I'm sure that I passed the quiz.

1. In the preceding situation, who is using inductive reasoning, Kevin or Maria? Who is using deductive reasoning?

2. In this case, which type of reasoning seems more convincing? Why?

Deductive reasoning can be a powerful tool. Lawyers use it to prove things true beyond a reasonable doubt. Mathematicians have an even stronger use for deductive reasoning. They use it to prove that their conjectures *must* be true given certain assumptions. Euclid, a Greek mathematician, based his famous geometry book, *The Elements,* on a system of deductive reasoning.

TRY IT

Suppose that the statements at the top of page 33 are true. For each set of statements, use deductive reasoning to give another statement that must also be true.

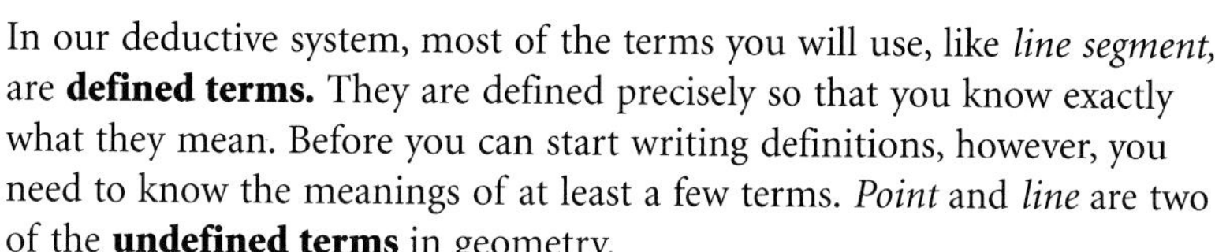

a. All reptiles have scales. An iguana is a reptile. Iguanas have scales.
b. No fish have toes. I have toes. I am not a fish.

In our deductive system, most of the terms you will use, like *line segment,* are **defined terms.** They are defined precisely so that you know exactly what they mean. Before you can start writing definitions, however, you need to know the meanings of at least a few terms. *Point* and *line* are two of the **undefined terms** in geometry.

Geometric conjectures also fall into two categories. Many of them, called **theorems,** are possible to prove deductively. However, you cannot prove anything unless you start with a few basic assumptions, called **postulates.** Postulates are assumed to be true without proof.

You'll investigate these parts of a deductive system in Chapter 2. As you develop your thinking skills and geometric knowledge, you'll be able to write good definitions and prove theorems yourself.

REFLECT

1. Explain, in your own words, how deductive reasoning works.
2. How is deductive reasoning different from inductive reasoning? Is one more reliable than the other? Why?
3. Is it possible for a valid deductive argument to lead to a false conclusion? How?

Exercises

CORE

1. **Getting Started** Suppose that the statements "All cats have fur" and "Fluffy is a cat" are true. Use deductive reasoning to give another statement that must also be true. Fluffy has fur.

Suppose that each statement below is true. Use deductive reasoning to give another statement that must also be true.

2. No one living in Wyoming has a house on the beach. Chao-Yee has a beachfront house. Chao-Yee does not live in Wyoming.
3. The figure Kai drew is a parallelogram. All parallelograms have four sides. Kai drew a four-sided figure.
4. No elementary school student is old enough to vote. Kendrick is old enough to vote. Kendrick is not an elementary school student.

Journal

Reflect 1, 2, and 3 are suitable for journal entries.

REFLECT

Possible Answers

1. In deductive reasoning, you use given information to draw conclusions, using step-by-step, logical thinking.
2. In inductive reasoning, you draw conclusions from looking at evidence. In deductive reasoning, (as used in mathematics) evidence is not enough—you must use logic to draw conclusions that you know are always true. Because of this, deductive reasoning can lead to more reliable results.
3. A valid deductive argument in mathematics can lead to a false conclusion only if the given information (assumed to be true) is actually false.

Part C Exercises

Exercise Notes

Core

1–4. These exercises ask students to use deductive reasoning on statements with *all, some,* and *none.*

7. Students use deductive reasoning with algebra to show how a number trick works.

11. Students review scatter plots and inductive reasoning.

Key

V Vocabulary
P Practice/Skills
R Review
MR Math Reasoning
PS Problem Solving
C Challenge

Ongoing Assessment

Self-Assessment Exercises 1, 2, 3, 6, 8, 9

Embedded Assessment Explore Step 3; Consider 1; Reflect 1; Exercises 4, 7, 11

Reasoning and Logic

Look Ahead

These exercises preview skills needed for 1-3 Part A, where students find distances between points on a number line and a coordinate plane.

More Math Reasoning

23. Involves logic puzzles written by Lewis Carroll.

Exercise Answers

Core

5. If the lion is telling the truth, then it is Thursday. If the lion is lying, it is Monday. If the unicorn is telling the truth, then it is Sunday; if he is lying, it is Thursday. Hence it is either Thursday or Monday *and* it is either Sunday or Thursday. This can be true only if it is Thursday.

6. Fill in row 2, column 3, then cell (3, 3), then (1, 1), then the rest in any order to get

5	0	1
7	3	9
8	6	4

7. 12, since $\frac{2n + 10}{2} + 7 - n$ $= n + 5 + 7 - n = 12$

8. The statement is true; some snakes are reptiles. However, it is also true that *all* snakes are reptiles.

9. $3x - 2(25 - 3x) = 40$
$3x - 50 + 6x = 40$, Distributive Property; $9x = 90$, added 50 to both sides and combined like terms; $x = 10$, divided both sides by 9. Deductive

10. Deductive: $2n + 2m = 2(n + m)$ which is even. Inductive reasoning relies on recognizing a pattern; deductive reasoning relies on logic.

PS, MR **5. Days Daze** In Lewis Carroll's *Through the Looking-Glass,* Alice met a lion and a unicorn. Suppose that the lion lies on Monday, Tuesday, and Wednesday, and the unicorn lies on Thursday, Friday, and Saturday. At all other times both animals tell the truth. Alice has forgotten the day of the week during her travels through the Forest of Forgetfulness.

"Yesterday was one of my lying days," said the lion.

"Yesterday was one of my lying days, too," said the unicorn. Alice, who was very smart, was able to deduce the day.

What day of the week is it? Explain.

PS **6.** What are the missing numbers in the square at the right? Explain your answers. (The numbers outside the square show the sums of the numbers in the rows, columns, and diagonal.)

		1	6
7	3		19
			18
20	9	14	12

PS **7.** Make a conjecture about the following number trick.

a. Choose a number. **b.** Double it. **c.** Add 10.
d. Divide by 2. **e.** Add 7. **f.** Subtract the original number.

Conjecture: The result is always ____.

Now, use algebra to verify your conjecture.

Problem-Solving Tip

Use your skills in translating words into algebraic terms to write an expression to represent each step. (Hint: First, let n equal the number. Simplify each expression.)

P **8.** Is the following statement true or false? Explain. *Some snakes are reptiles.*

MR **9.** Solve the following equation for x. Show each step, and explain why each step is valid.
$3x - 2(25 - 3x) = 40$

Did you use inductive or deductive reasoning to solve this equation?

MR **10.** One way to try to convince you that the sum of two even numbers is always even is to show you that this conjecture is true for several examples. This is an inductive argument. Describe another method that would convince you that this statement is true. Explain how it differs from inductive reasoning.

R, MR **11. Population Explosion!** The growth of the world's population in the 20th century is shown in the table below.

Social Science

Year	1900	1950	1980	1991
Population (billions)	1.6	2.6	4.5	5.4

a. Make a scatter plot of the population data.
b. Though you have limited data, use your scatter plot to predict the world's population in the year 2010. Did you use inductive or deductive reasoning? Explain.

Key

- V Vocabulary
- P Practice/Skills
- R Review
- MR Math Reasoning
- PS Problem Solving
- C Challenge

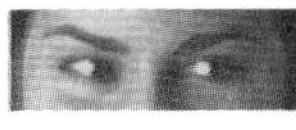

LOOK AHEAD

Simplify each expression.

12. $3 - (-4)$ 7 **13.** $-5 - 8$ −13 **14.** $-7 - (-2)$ −5 **15.** $6 - 11$ −5

16. Plot points with coordinates -2, 3, $\frac{1}{3}$, and -4.5 on a number line.

17. Plot points with coordinates $(-1, 4)$, $(2, 5)$, and $(0, -3.5)$ on a coordinate plane.

MORE PRACTICE

Suppose that each statement below is true. Use deductive reasoning to give another statement that must also be true.

18. Every child needs attention. William is a child. William needs attention.

19. No one who lives in San Diego lives in Illinois. Tamika lives in Illinois. Tamika does not live in San Diego.

20. No mathematicians are boring. Kenji is a mathematician. Kenji is not boring.

21. Every square is also a rectangle. Every rectangle is also a parallelogram. Every square is a parallelogram.

MORE MATH REASONING

22. Finding Your Marbles Three containers each contain two marbles. One container has two blue marbles, another has two white marbles, and the third has a blue and a white marble. The containers are labeled BB, WW, and BW, but, unfortunately, all of the labels are wrong! What is the least number of draws that you must make to determine the contents of the containers? Explain.

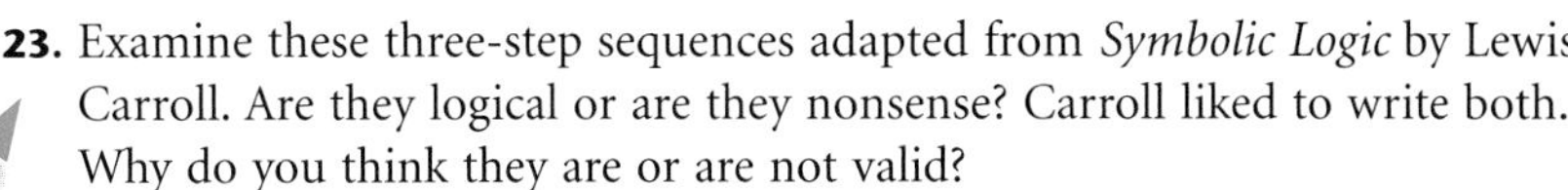

23. Examine these three-step sequences adapted from *Symbolic Logic* by Lewis Carroll. Are they logical or are they nonsense? Carroll liked to write both. Why do you think they are or are not valid?

a. All well-fed canaries sing loudly.
No canary is sad if it sings loudly.
Therefore, all well-fed canaries are not sad.

b. Every eagle can fly.
Some pigs cannot fly.
Therefore, some pigs are not eagles.

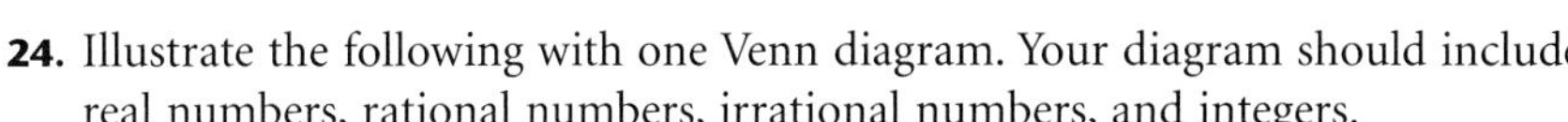

24. Illustrate the following with one Venn diagram. Your diagram should include real numbers, rational numbers, irrational numbers, and integers.
- All real numbers are either rational numbers or irrational numbers.
- No rational numbers are irrational numbers.
- All integers are rational numbers.
- All rational numbers and irrational numbers are real numbers.

11. a.

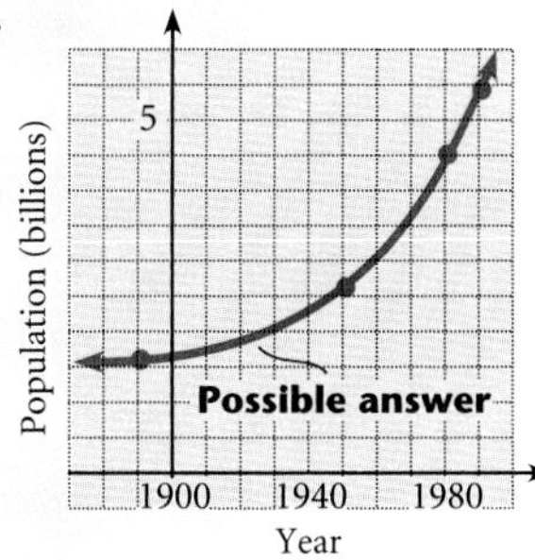

b. 6.6 billion; Inductive; Assumes the pattern seen will be true 20 years from now.

Look Ahead

16.

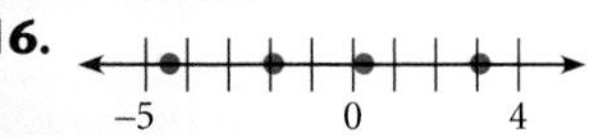

17.

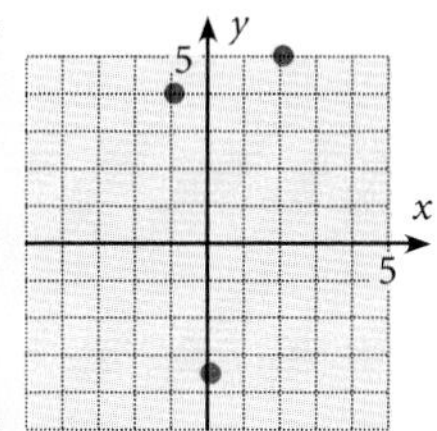

More Math Reasoning

22. One. Draw from the BW container. If a B is drawn, it's the BB. Now the WW is neither WW or BB, so it's BW and the BB is really WW. If the marble drawn from the BW is W, it's really WW, BB is BW, and WW is BB.

23. a. Valid; In set notation: $W \subset L$, $L \cap S = \varnothing$, so $W \cap S = \varnothing$.

b. Valid; In set notation: $E \subset F$, $P \not\subset F$, so $P \not\subset E$.

24. Real numbers

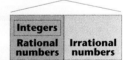

Integers Rational numbers	Irrational numbers

1-2

Reasoning and Logic

PART D At a Glance

Objective

To combine inductive and deductive reasoning to help interpret data.

Development

In the **Explore,** students use data and their own ideas to develop an argument that uses both inductive and deductive reasoning.

First Five Minutes

Transparency FFM 1-2D

In your own words, write descriptions of inductive and deductive reasoning.

EXPLORE

Density and Dollars

Recommended group size: 4

The Point

To use both inductive and deductive reasoning to create a convincing argument.

Look and Listen...

- For students who have trouble distinguishing types of reasoning.

Ask...

- Why might states with a high population density tend to have a higher average income?

For Groups That Finish Early

Find states that don't fit the pattern, and explain why they are atypical.

Follow Up

Ask whether strong arguments tend to use one or both types of reasoning.

Possible Answers

1. States with a greater density tend to have higher per-capita incomes. Supporting argument: states with (relatively) more rural workers tend to have a lower density.

1-2 PART D Making Connections

← CONNECT → ***Reasoning involves many skills, including the ability to recognize patterns and to justify conclusions by using accepted facts. You need these skills to be able to draw sound conclusions from known information. You've looked at some ways of reasoning. The two types of thinking you've explored are inductive and deductive reasoning.***

You've seen inductive and deductive reasoning used in Wonderland and in the real world. People—even fictional characters like the Mad Hatter—use both types of reasoning in mathematics, science, and everyday conversation. In the following Explore, you will use your reasoning skills to help make a convincing argument.

EXPLORE: DENSITY AND DOLLARS

The following tables show 1990 population densities and per-capita income for the eight most densely populated and least densely populated states. The data comes from *The 1993 Information Please Almanac.*

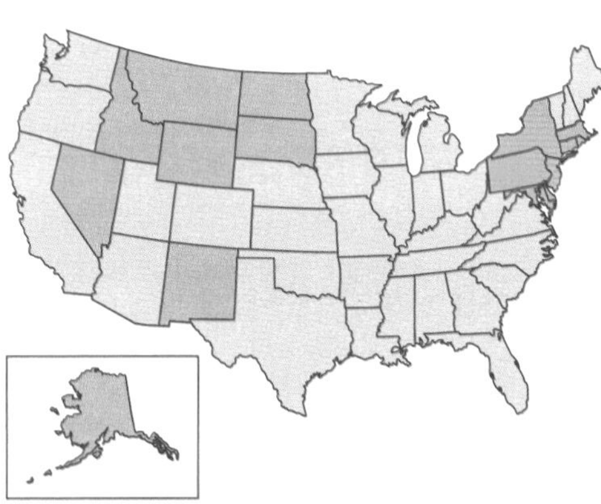

State	Population Density (people per square mile)	Per-capita Income (dollars per person)
New Jersey	1035.1	24,881
Rhode Island	951.1	18,809
Massachusetts	768.9	22,555
Connecticut	674.7	25,395
Maryland	486.0	21,857
New York	379.7	22,129
Delaware	344.8	20,095
Pennsylvania	264.7	18,679

Technology Note

While working on this **Explore,** students could do inductive work by entering the data on a graphing utility and finding the equation for the line of best fit.

State	Population Density (people per square mile)	Per-capita Income (dollars per person)
New Mexico	12.5	14,254
Idaho	12.2	15,250
Nevada	10.9	19,049
South Dakota	9.1	15,890
North Dakota	9.0	15,355
Montana	5.5	15,304
Wyoming	4.7	16,283
Alaska	1.0	21,646

1. In your group, create the *strongest argument that you can* to convince someone that states with a greater population density tend to have a higher per-capita income. You need not rely on the table alone; you may also use your own thinking to strengthen your argument.
2. Analyze how your argument uses inductive reasoning.
3. Analyze how your argument uses deductive reasoning.
4. Do the most convincing arguments rely on inductive reasoning, deductive reasoning, or both? Explain.

REFLECT

1. Is a scientist more likely to use inductive or deductive reasoning? Why?
2. Is a mathematician more likely to use inductive or deductive reasoning to show that a conjecture is true? Why?
3. When showing *that* something is true, do people tend to rely more on inductive or deductive reasoning? How about when they are showing *why* it is true? Explain your answer.

Self-Assessment

P **Indicate whether each of the following statements is more illustrative of inductive or deductive reasoning.**

1. One counterexample proves that a conjecture is false. Deductive
2. Gathering many examples helps to verify the conjecture. Inductive
3. You give evidence that your conjecture is true. Inductive
4. You show why your conjecture makes sense. Deductive

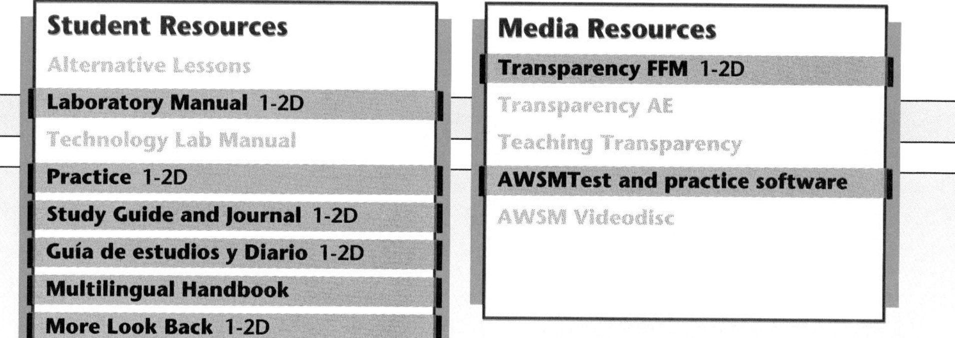

Student Resources
Alternative Lessons
Laboratory Manual 1-2D
Technology Lab Manual
Practice 1-2D
Study Guide and Journal 1-2D
Guía de estudios y Diario 1-2D
Multilingual Handbook
More Look Back 1-2D
SAT Preparation
Media Resources
Transparency FFM 1-2D
Transparency AE
Teaching Transparency
AWSMTest and practice software
AWSM Videodisc

2. Points that make use of patterns in the data rely on inductive reasoning.
3. Points that tell why patterns make sense use deductive reasoning.
4. Convincing arguments usually feature both types of reasoning. (In real life, there is often a scarcity of "known" facts and shared assumptions. In these cases, deductive reasoning may support an argument, but it can rarely *prove* a point.)

Portfolio

Have students select items from their work that demonstrate their understanding of the material in this Superlesson.

Students might include their best solution to one inductive and one deductive reasoning **Exercise,** an example of a problem where drawing a diagram helped them, and a reasoning **Exercise** that they found difficult.

REFLECT

Possible Answers

1. A scientist is more likely to use inductive reasoning. He must have evidence for his ideas.
2. A mathematician is more likely to rely on deductive reasoning. She needs to show that her idea is always true, and only deductive reasoning can do this.
3. When showing *why* something is true, people tend to use deductive reasoning in a step-by-step argument. When showing *that* it is true, they give evidence, using inductive reasoning.

Self-Assessment

Exercise Notes

13. This exercise is similar to multiple-choice items found on standardized tests.

Reasoning and Logic

14. Shows that conclusions drawn from inductive reasoning may not be true.

16. Students may notice that the pattern that emerges in this exercise is exactly like the one in the **Explore** on page 21. You may want to have students explain why this is the case. (The problems are mathematically identical; each handshake is analogous to a segment.)

Extension: Show how the formula for the sum of the integers from 1 to n from Exercise 14 on page 24 $\left(\frac{n(n+1)}{2}\right)$ is related to this exercise. **To find the number of handshakes, add the integers from 1 to $n-1$. Substituting $n-1$ for n into the formula above gives $\frac{(n-1)n}{2}$.**

Self-Assessment Answers

5. 26; $5n+1$

6. 35; To find the second number, 3 was added to the first. Subsequent numbers are found by adding 5, 7, 9,...

7. 125; n^3

10–11.

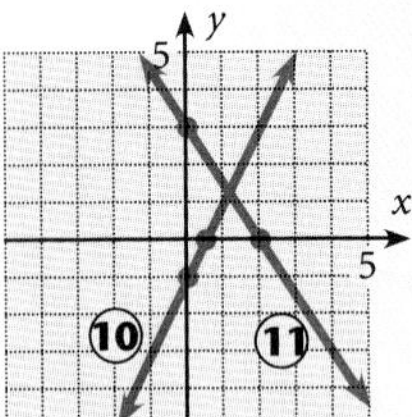

12. Possible answer: 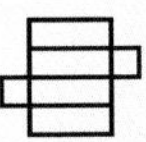

14. a. 2^{n-1}

b. Conjecture: $2^{6-1} = 2^5 = 32$; not valid; works for $n \leq 5$ but not $n = 6$ because for $n = 6$, number of regions = 30 or 31.

 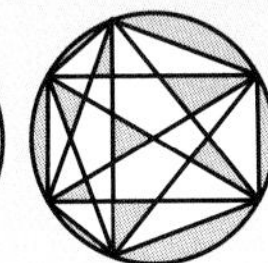

15–16. See Additional Answers p. T38.

Algebra | Discrete Math | Probability | Logic/Reasoning

P **Find the next number in each sequence. Explain the pattern.**

5. 6, 11, 16, 21, . . .
6. 0, 3, 8, 15, 24, . . .
7. 1, 8, 27, 64, . . .

R **Solve each equation. [Previous course]**

8. $12 = 5x - 3$ $x = 3$
9. $7y + 2(y - 5) = 3y$ $y = \frac{5}{3}$

R **Graph each equation on a coordinate plane. [Previous course]**

R **10.** $y = 2x - 1$
11. $y = -\frac{3}{2}x + 3$

12. Sketch a net for the rectangular solid at the right. [1-1]

P **13.** If a dart is thrown randomly at the figure shown, what is the probability that it will land in a green region? (Assume all small squares have the same size.) (d)

(a) $\frac{3}{8}$ (b) $\frac{1}{2}$ (c) $\frac{9}{16}$ (d) $\frac{7}{16}$ (e) $\frac{1}{3}$

PS, C **14.** How many regions are formed in a circle by segments connecting points on the circle? The sequence is begun at the right.

a. Make a conjecture about the number of regions formed by connecting n points on a circle.

b. Test your conjecture by drawing 6 points on a circle and drawing segments to connect the points in all possible ways. Count the regions formed. Is your conjecture valid? Explain.

1 point
1 region

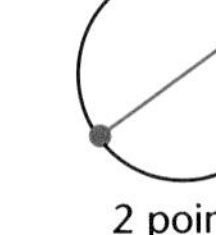
2 points
2 regions

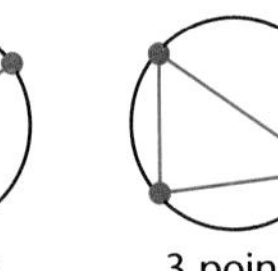
3 points
4 regions

4 points
? regions

MR **15. Step-by-Step Reasoning** Find an expression for the number of small squares in a "staircase" that is n units high. Explain how you found your answer and whether you used inductive reasoning, deductive reasoning, or both.

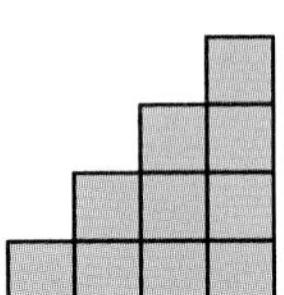

PS Literature **16. Glad to Meet You!** During her adventures in Wonderland, Alice made many unusual acquaintances. Imagine that Alice held a tea party for 10 of her new acquaintances. As each guest arrived, he or she shook hands exactly once with every other person, including Alice. How many handshakes were there all together? Write a brief explanation of how you found your answer.

Problem-Solving Tip

It may help to draw a diagram to represent the problem.

Assessment Resources

Quiz 1-2
Chapter Assessment Form A
Chapter Assessment Form B
Chapter Alternative Assessment
Mid-Year Assessment
End-of-Year Assessment
AWSMTest and practice software

Ongoing Assessment

Self-Assessment Self-Assessment Exercises

Embedded Assessment Explore Steps 2, 3, 4; Reflect 1, 2

ADDITIONAL ANSWERS

1-2 Part A Exercises

More Practice

21. 243; 3^n where n = term number

22. $\left(-\frac{1}{2}\right)(-1) = \frac{1}{2}$; If one term is a, the next is $\left(-\frac{1}{2}\right)a$.

23. 25; Sequence is a, a^2, $(a + 1)$, $(a + 1)^2$, etc.

24. Lines: $\overleftrightarrow{GJ}$ (or $\overleftrightarrow{GI}$ or $\overleftrightarrow{IJ}$); Points: G, H, I, J; Segments: $\overline{GI}$, $\overline{GJ}$, $\overline{IJ}$, $\overline{HI}$

25. G, I, J

26. Possible answer:

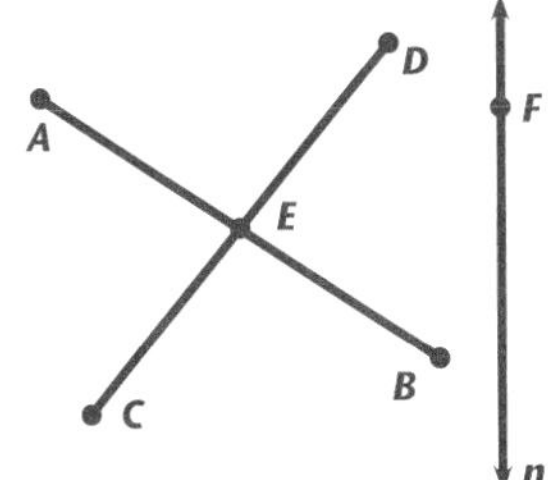

More Math Reasoning

27. Yes; two points determine a line.

28. Square size: $n \times n$ $(n \geq 2)$;
Touch 2 sides: 4;
Touch 1 side: $4(n - 2)$;
Touch 0 sides: $n^2 - 4n + 4$

29.

Month	Total pairs
1	1
2	1
3	2
4	3
5	5
6	8
7	13
8	21
9	34
10	55
11	89
12	144

The total number of pairs for each month past the second is the sum of the numbers of pairs for the previous two months.

1-2 Part B Exercises

23. Possible answer: Kay Bailey Hutchison (R–TX)

24. Possible answer: Someone who lives in Dallas

25. True if homework done and bedroom cleaned; False if homework not done, or bedroom not cleaned, or both.

26. True if calculator bought or Janet's calculator borrowed or both; False if calculator not bought and Janet's not borrowed.

27. Some joggers swim (or some swimmers jog).

28. No dogs are cats (or no cats are dogs).

29. All squares are quadrilaterals.

More Math Reasoning

30. Possible answer: All students are under 50 years old. Some teachers are women. None of the students has a college diploma.

31. a.

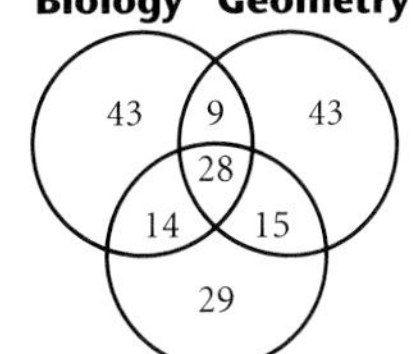

43 will take geometry only.

b. $\frac{28}{181}$

1-2 Part D Self-Assessment

15. $\frac{n(n + 1)}{2}$

Inductive, by observing that the nth step added n small squares. Other reasoning is possible.

16. The nth arrival shakes hands with n people—Alice and the $(n - 1)$ people who arrived earlier. Therefore, the answer is:
$\frac{n(n + 1)}{2} = \frac{10(11)}{2} = 55.$

1-3

Measuring Figures

SUPERLESSON AT A GLANCE

Superlesson Goal

Students will review and extend measurement techniques for segments and angles and will be introduced to the idea of congruence.

Management Guide

	Topic	Objectives	Key Terms	New Ideas	Materials
Part A	Measuring Segments	To find the lengths of segments on a number line and a coordinate plane.	Length of a segment, distance (between two points)	Length of a segment. Distance between two points.	
Part B	Measuring Angles	To become familiar with angles and angle measurement, and to explore right angles and perpendicular lines.	Ray, endpoint of a ray, angle, sides, vertex of an angle, angle measure, degree measure, right angle, perpendicular lines	Angle measurement. Shortest segment from a point to a line.	**Student** Ruler, protractor, geometry software
Part C	Congruence	To investigate congruent figures and learn construction techniques.	Congruent, construction, compass, straightedge	Congruence. Constructions of congruent figures.	**Student** Compass, straightedge
Part D	Making Connections	To use construction and measurement skills in a single context.	In Making Connections, students apply and synthesize key terms and new ideas.		**Student** Scissors, tape, large sheets of paper, compass, ruler, protractor

Pacing Chart (45-Minute Periods)

	Comprehensive Course	Core Course	Informal Course
Part A	1	1	1
Part B	1	1	1
Part C	1	1	2
Part D	1	1	1
TOTAL periods for Superlesson	4	4	5

NCTM Standards

Mathematics as Problem Solving

Mathematics as Communication

Mathematics as Reasoning

Mathematical Connections

Geometry from an Algebraic Perspective

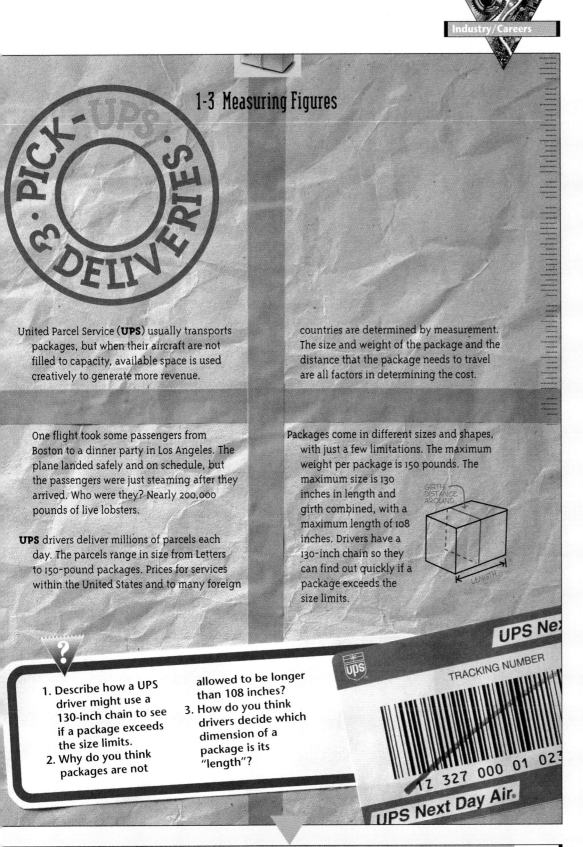

1-3 Measuring Figures

PICK-UPS & DELIVERIES

United Parcel Service (**UPS**) usually transports packages, but when their aircraft are not filled to capacity, available space is used creatively to generate more revenue.

One flight took some passengers from Boston to a dinner party in Los Angeles. The plane landed safely and on schedule, but the passengers were just steaming after they arrived. Who were they? Nearly 200,000 pounds of live lobsters.

UPS drivers deliver millions of parcels each day. The parcels range in size from Letters to 150-pound packages. Prices for services within the United States and to many foreign countries are determined by measurement. The size and weight of the package and the distance that the package needs to travel are all factors in determining the cost.

Packages come in different sizes and shapes, with just a few limitations. The maximum weight per package is 150 pounds. The maximum size is 130 inches in length and girth combined, with a maximum length of 108 inches. Drivers have a 130-inch chain so they can find out quickly if a package exceeds the size limits.

GIRTH: DISTANCE AROUND

LENGTH

1. Describe how a UPS driver might use a 130-inch chain to see if a package exceeds the size limits.
2. Why do you think packages are not allowed to be longer than 108 inches?
3. How do you think drivers decide which dimension of a package is its "length"?

UPS Next Day Air

TRACKING NUMBER

1Z 327 000 01 02

More About the Package-Delivery Industry

Over the past 25 years, the express package-delivery industry has boomed. In 1970, U.S. air carriers shipped 3,274 million mile-tons of domestic freight. (A mile-ton is one ton transported one mile.) In 1990, 10,410 mile-tons of domestic freight were shipped by air—an increase of 218%. Over the same period, rail freight increased 39% and truck freight increased 35%.

You may want to have students discuss possible reasons for these different rates of increase and the recent boom in on-time delivery services.

Where Are We Now?

Students have probably measured segments with a ruler. They may also have measured angles with a protractor and used algebra to find distances between points on a coordinate plane.

Where Are We Going?

In 1-3, students will become familiar with ways to measure geometric figures and with the concept of congruence. The topic of measurement recurs when students find and optimize areas, perimeters, and volumes in Chapters 5, 9, and 11. Congruence is a key concept throughout the text, particularly in Chapter 4 on congruent triangles, but also in describing the properties of transformations in Chapters 1, 3, 7, and 10.

Possible Answers

1. Measure the length of the longest side first, to see if it is shorter than 108 in. Then wrap the remaining chain around the package. If the chain reaches all the way around, the package is under the size limit.
2. May be too long to fit in the truck easily.
3. They choose the longest side.

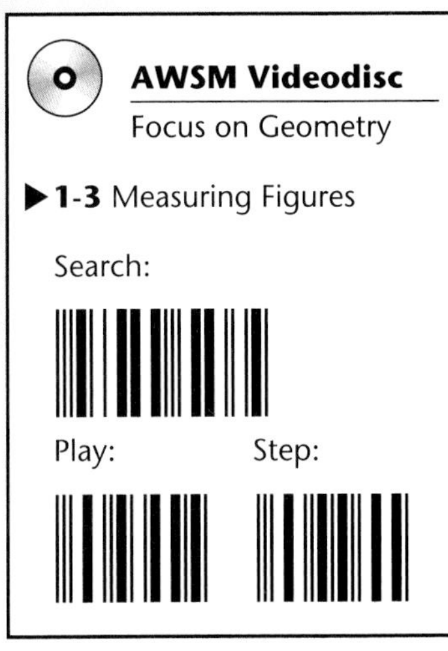

1-3

Measuring Figures

PART A At a Glance

Objective

To find the lengths of segments on a number line and a coordinate plane.

Development

Students learn the meaning of and the notation for the length of a segment. In an **Example,** students see how distances are measured on a number line.

In the **Explore,** students learn methods for finding the lengths of horizontal and vertical segments on a coordinate plane. Then they use the distance formula to find the perimeter of a triangle.

Key Terms

Length of a segment, distance (between two points)

First Five Minutes

Transparency FFM 1-3A

Evaluate the following expressions.

$4 - 6$ **−2**

$-4.1 - 6.4$ **−10.5**

$(5 - 3)^2$ **4**

$(-5 - 3)^2$ **64**

$\sqrt{(4 - (-2))^2 + (-3 - 5)^2}$ **10**

Motivate

Ask...

- Ask students to define *length* and *distance* in their own words and to find similarities and differences in the two ideas.

ALTERNATE EXAMPLE

Find the lengths of segments $\overline{DE}$, $\overline{EF}$, and $\overline{DF}$ on the number line.

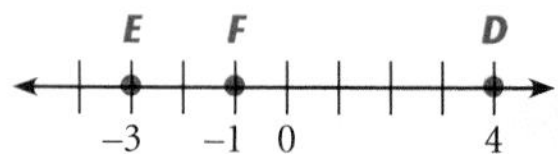

$DE = |4 - (-3)| = 7$

$EF = |-3 - (-1)| = 2$

$DF = |4 - (-1)| = 5$

Alert

When measuring segments on a number line, some students count the number of integers between the endpoints instead of the unit distances. If students are consistently getting answers that are one unit too small, this may be the problem.

Algebra | Functions | Discrete Math | Probability | Data/Statistics

1-3 PART A Measuring Segments

← CONNECT → *You've measured lengths with a ruler. Lengths can also be measured mathematically by counting units or by using formulas. You will now review some of these methods.*

How long is an inch? If you had to show someone how long an inch is, you could probably cut a string to about the right length. Or you could bend your thumb. The distance from the tip of your thumb to the knuckle is about one inch.

Although people are not all the same size, some countries once based standard units on their kings or queens—on the person's height or the length of an arm, for example. When a new "ruler" came to power, the sizes of the units of measure changed. This was obviously inconvenient! It is said that the English yard was permanently established in the 1100s as the distance from the nose to the thumb of King Henry I. A line segment has a length, but the length of a segment is not the same thing as the segment itself. Some simple notation helps us know which we are talking about.

The **length** of segment $\overline{RS}$ is written RS (with no segment symbol above the letters). If the length of $\overline{RS}$ is 4 units, we write $RS = 4$. When we refer to RS, you know we mean a number, not a geometric figure.

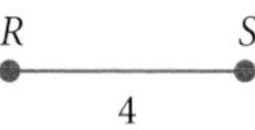

To find the length of a segment on a number line, find the distance between the coordinates of its endpoints.

EXAMPLE

Find the lengths of segments $\overline{AB}$, $\overline{AC}$, and $\overline{BC}$ on the number line below. (In other words, find AB, AC, and BC.)

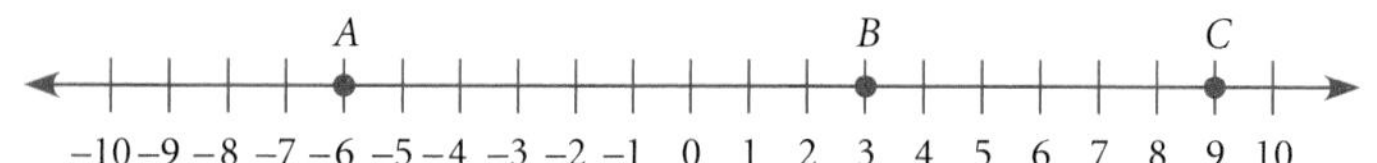

To find the length of a segment, first find the difference of the coordinates of its endpoints. Then, since distance is always positive, take the absolute value of the result, as shown on page 41.

$AB = |-6 - 3| = |-9| = 9$ or $AB = |3 - (-6)| = |9| = 9$

$BC = |3 - 9| = |-6| = 6$ or $BC = |9 - 3| = |6| = 6$

$AC = |-6 - 9| = |-15| = 15$ or $AC = |9 - (-6)| = |15| = 15$

In the Explore, you'll look at lengths and distances on a coordinate plane.

EXPLORE: FAR FROM IT

1. Look at the vertical segment $\overline{AB}$ on the coordinate plane. What is the ordered pair for point *A*? point *B*? What is *AB*?
2. What do you notice about the *x*-coordinates for the endpoints of $\overline{AB}$? their *y*-coordinates?
3. Explain how the method for finding the length of a segment on a number line can be applied to a vertical segment on a coordinate plane.
4. Now find the length of the horizontal segment $\overline{EF}$. Give a written explanation of how you found this length.

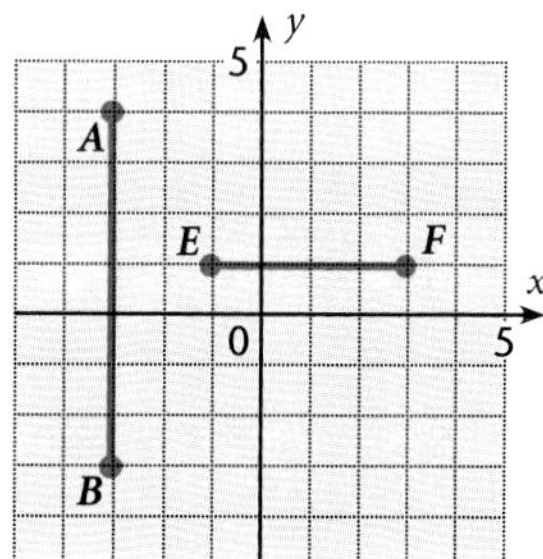

In algebra, you used the *distance formula* to find the distance between any two points, $A(x_1, y_1)$ and $B(x_2, y_2)$, on a coordinate plane.

$$D = \sqrt{(x_1 - x_2)^2 + (y_1 - y_2)^2}$$

(Later on, you will discover *why* this formula works.)

5. Record the length of each side of the triangle to the nearest tenth. Then find the perimeter of triangle *ABC*. (The perimeter of a figure is the sum of the lengths of its sides.)

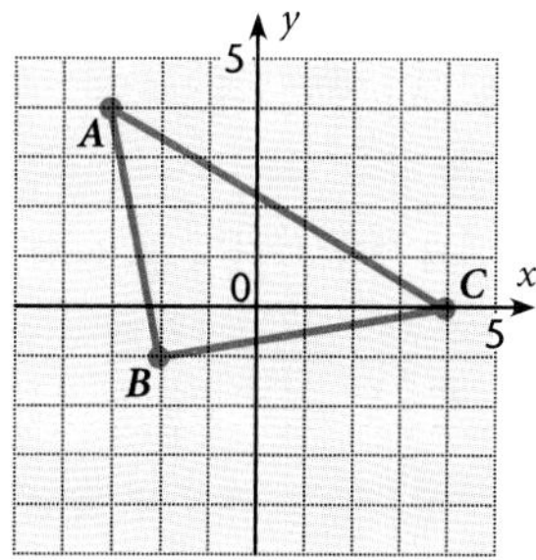

The *distance between two points on a number line* with coordinates *a* and *b* is the absolute value of the difference of their coordinates.

$D = |a - b|$

The *distance between two points on a coordinate plane* whose coordinates are (x_1, y_1) and (x_2, y_2) is:

$D = \sqrt{(x_1 - x_2)^2 + (y_1 - y_2)^2}$

EXPLORE

Far from It

Recommended group size: 4

The Point

To find distances between points on a coordinate plane.

Look and Listen...

- For students who are having difficulty using the algebraic formula or using radicals.

Ask...

- Why can't we just count spaces to find the length of a diagonal segment?

For Groups That Finish Early

Find all possible integer coordinates for points less than 4 units away from (0, 0).

Follow Up

Ask students how to find the length of a segment on a coordinate plane if it is (a) horizontal; (b) vertical; (c) slanted.

Possible Answers

1. $A(-3, 4)$, $B(-3, -3)$, $AB = 7$
2. The *x*-coordinates are equal; the *y*-coordinates are unequal.
3. Length of a vertical segment is the absolute value of the difference of the *y*-coordinates of its endpoints.
4. $EF = 4$; took the absolute value of the difference in the *x*-coordinates of the endpoints.
5. $AB = 5.1$, $BC = 6.1$, $AC = 8.1$, perimeter $= 19.3$

Student Resources

- Alternative Lessons 1-3A
- Laboratory Manual 1-3A
- Technology Lab Manual
- Practice 1-3A
- Study Guide and Journal 1-3A
- Guía de estudios y Diario 1-3A
- Multilingual Handbook
- More Look Back 1-3A
- SAT Preparation

Media Resources

- Transparency FFM 1-3A
- Transparency AE 1-3A
- Teaching Transparency
- AWSMTest and practice software
- AWSM Videodisc

Measuring Figures

Journal

Reflect 1 and 2 are suitable for journal entries.

REFLECT

Possible Answers

1. A formula can give an exact answer. There is no ruler precise enough to give an exact answer.
2. If the endpoints have equal *x*-coordinates or *y*-coordinates, you can find the length by taking the absolute value of the difference of the other coordinates. Otherwise, use the distance formula.

Part A Exercises

Exercise Notes

Core

1. Walks students through an exercise that uses the distance formula.

10. Reminds students that numbers have both a positive and a negative square root. In this context, we can disregard the negative possibility, but students should know why we may do this.

12. The idea of appropriate units could provide a basis for a class discussion.

13. Students must make an approximation.

More Math Reasoning

31. Involves geometric probability. Students can simplify the problem by solving it for only one quadrant, but must be careful to include only one of the axes and consider the origin.

Exercise Answers

Core

10. Last step: distance is always positive, so take only the positive square root, namely 10.

11. $LM = 6.3$; $MN = 6.3$; $NL = 5.7$; Perimeter $= 18.3$

TRY IT

a. Find the lengths of $\overline{XY}$, $\overline{XZ}$, and $\overline{YZ}$ on a number line if the coordinate of X is -1.3, the coordinate of Y is -4, and the coordinate of Z is 2.7. $XY = 2.7$; $XZ = 4$; $YZ = 6.7$

b. Find the lengths of $\overline{RS}$, $\overline{ST}$, and $\overline{TR}$ to the nearest tenth in the figure at the right. $RS = 5.1$; $ST = 7.1$; $TR = 6$

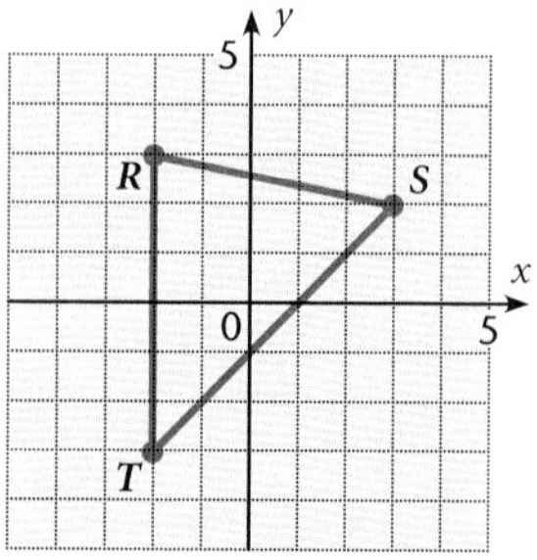

REFLECT

1. Segments on a coordinate plane can be measured by using a ruler or a formula. Which method gives you an exact answer? Explain.
2. How can you tell whether you'll have to use the distance formula to find the distance between two points on a coordinate plane or if you can use a simpler method?

Exercises

CORE

Where necessary, round your answers to the nearest tenth.

P **1. Getting Started** Follow these steps to find the distance from $(-3, 4)$ to $(6, -4)$.

a. Label one of the points (x_1, y_1) and the other (x_2, y_2). $(x_1, y_1) = (-3, 4)$; $(x_2, y_2) = (6, -4)$

b. Calculate $(x_1 - x_2)$ and square the result. -9; 81

c. Calculate $(y_1 - y_2)$ and square the result. 8; 64

d. Add the squared values from **1b** and **1c**. 145

e. Take the square root of the result in Part **1d.** $\sqrt{145} \approx 12.0$

P **Find the length of segment $\overline{AB}$ for each set of coordinates.**

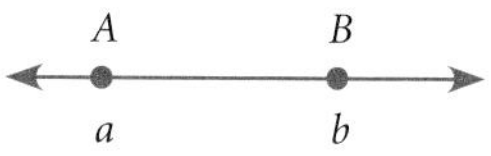

2. $a = 3$, $b = 6$ 3

3. $a = -3$, $b = 6$ 9

4. $a = 0.45$, $b = 2.23$ 1.78

5. $a = -10$, $b = -4$ 6

P **R and S are points on a coordinate plane. Find RS using the given coordinates.**

6. $R(2, 4)$, $S(5, 4)$ 3

7. $R(2, 4)$, $S(2, -3)$ 7

8. $R(-1, -3)$, $S(-4, 4)$ 7.6

9. $R(1.3, 2.8)$, $S(5.1, 4.3)$ 4.1

Key

V Vocabulary
P Practice/Skills
R Review
MR Math Reasoning
PS Problem Solving
C Challenge

History Connection

Many measurements were originally based on the human body. The inch was the width of a thumb, and the foot the length of a foot. After the French Revolution, the new French government was influenced by the European Age of Reason to set up a "logical" metric measurement system. The meter was $\frac{1}{10{,}000{,}000}$ of the known distance from the equator to the North Pole.

10. Explain the error in the following calculation of the distance from (2, −5) to (−6, 1).

$D = \sqrt{(-6 - 2)^2 + (1 - (-5))^2}$

$D = \sqrt{(-8)^2 + 6^2}$

$D = \sqrt{64 + 36}$

$D = \sqrt{100}$

$D = 10$ or -10

11. Find *LM*, *MN*, and *NL* in the figure at the right. Then find the perimeter of triangle *LMN*.

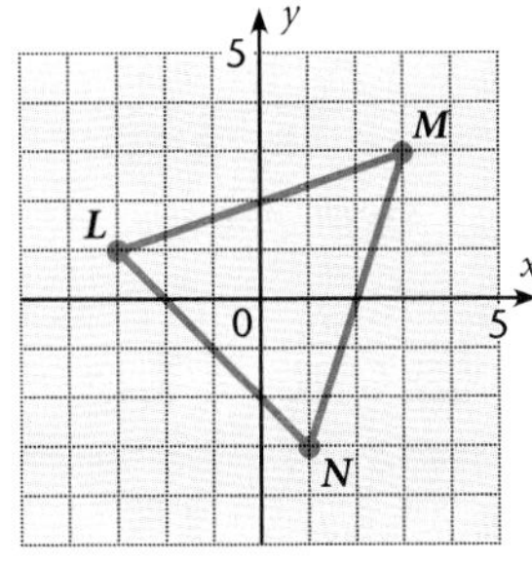

12. It may seem that the finer (more exact) a measurement is, the better it is. This is not always so. There are different units of measurement for different purposes. Choose the most appropriate unit of measure for each of the following. Explain your choice.

a. How far is it from your house to school?

b. How much milk is left in the refrigerator?

c. How far did the quarterback throw that pass?

13. Paper Folding I How thick is a piece of paper? How thick will the paper be after 1 fold? after 2 folds? after 3 folds? How thick will the paper be after 50 folds? Give estimates, and explain your answers.

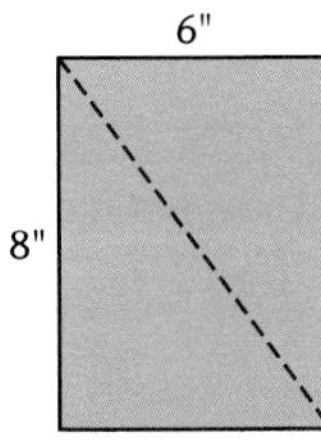

14. Paper Folding II A 6″ × 8″ paper rectangle is folded to create a diagonal. Find the length of the fold.

15. Printing on Paper A *pica* is a standard unit of measure in printing. (According to legend, movable type was invented by a Chinese woodcarver named Pi, and the term *pica* comes from his name.) A pica is approximately $\frac{1}{6}$ of an inch, and a point is $\frac{1}{12}$ of a pica.

a. How many points are in one inch?

b. This is 18-point type.
How many picas are equal to 18 points?

16. Taking Aim This student is shooting a basketball. Describe several of the measurements that he is instinctively making.

12. a. Possible answer: Blocks, as walked

b. Possible answer: Gallons, as stored

c. Possible answer: Yards, standard unit

13. Students will select their own estimated thickness for the thickness of paper. Once folded, the paper should be twice as thick; after 2 folds, 4 times as thick; and after 3 folds, 8 times as thick. After 50 folds, the paper will be 2^{50} times as thick as the initial thickness.

14. 10 in.

15. a. 72 points **b.** 1.5 picas

16. Possible answer: The height of the basket, the distance to the basket

Ongoing Assessment

Self-Assessment Exercises 1, 3, 5, 7, 9, 14, 15

Embedded Assessment Explore Step 5; Reflect 2; Exercises 8, 11, 12, 14

1-3

Measuring Figures

Look Back

17. Points: R, S, T, U, V
Lines: ℓ
Segments: $\overline{TS}, \overline{TR}, \overline{SR}, \overline{SU}, \overline{SV}, \overline{UV}$

18. T, S, R, and S, U, V

19. $\overleftrightarrow{TS}, \overleftrightarrow{TR}, \overleftrightarrow{SR}, \ell$

Algebra | Functions | Discrete Math | Probability | Data/Statistics

LOOK BACK

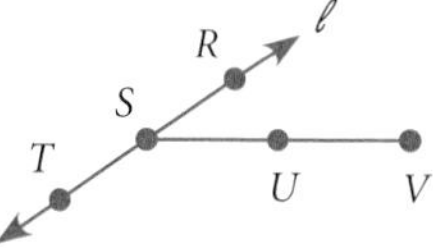

R **17.** Name all the points, lines, and segments in the figure. [1-1]

R **18.** Name all the sets of three collinear points in the figure. [1-1]

R **19.** List all the different names for line ℓ in the figure. [1-1]

R **Find the next number in each sequence. Explain the pattern. [1-2]**

20. 4.5, 6, 7.5, 9, . . . 10.5; $3 + 1.5n$

21. $1, -\frac{1}{2}, \frac{1}{4}, -\frac{1}{8}, \ldots$ $\frac{1}{16}$; $\left(-\frac{1}{2}\right)^n, n \geq 0$

R, MR **22. Gym Dandy** Buff's Gym is open Monday through Saturday. Volleyball classes meet daily except Wednesdays. Tennis instruction is daily except Tuesdays and Saturdays. Swimming classes are held every other day starting on Mondays. Gymnastics instruction is available every day starting on Tuesdays. Which day has the most activities? Explain your reasoning. [1-2] Friday, by enumeration

MORE PRACTICE

P **Find the length of segment $\overline{AB}$ for each set of coordinates.**

23. $a = 4, b = 19$ 15

24. $a = -4, b = 9$ 13

25. $a = 0.21, b = 5.13$ 4.92

26. $a = -41, b = -18$ 23

P ***R* and *S* are points on a coordinate plane. Find *RS* using the given coordinates.**

27. $R(0, 4), S(3, 8)$ 5

28. $R(-1, -4), S(-2, 4)$ 8.1

29. $R(1.5, 3.8), S(3.4, 2.8)$ 2.1

MORE MATH REASONING

PS **30. The Lost City of Lead** On an old map, Gold City is at (0, 0), and Silver Town is at (5, 2). The distance from Gold City to Lead Junction is 10, and the distance from Silver Town to Lead Junction is 5. The x-coordinate of Lead Junction is 8, but the y-coordinate has been lost. Where is Lead Junction? Lead Junction is at (8, 6)

PS, C **31.** Consider the 10×10 coordinate system at the right. Find the probability that a randomly selected point with integer coordinates will be more than 3 units away from the origin. 0.76

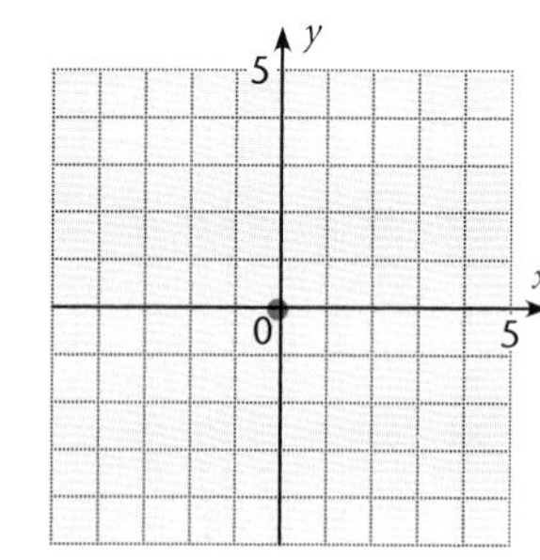

Problem-Solving Tip

Simplify the problem.

Key

V Vocabulary
P Practice/Skills
R Review
MR Math Reasoning
PS Problem Solving
C Challenge

1-3 PART B Measuring Angles

← CONNECT → ***You've learned how to name and measure segments. Now you will see how to name and measure angles. You will also investigate the shortest distance from a point to a line.***

Before you name and measure angles, we need to introduce some vocabulary. You are probably familiar with many of these terms.

DEFINITION

A **ray** is a part of a line. It has one **endpoint** and extends infinitely in one direction.

A ray is named with its endpoint first, followed by another point on the ray. The ray shown above can be named $\overrightarrow{DB}$ or $\overrightarrow{DC}$.

TRY IT

a. Name the ray below in as many ways as you can. $\overrightarrow{MN}$, $\overrightarrow{MO}$, $\overrightarrow{MP}$

An angle is made up of two rays.

DEFINITION

An **angle** is formed by two rays (that are not collinear) with a common endpoint, or **vertex.** The two rays are the **sides** of the angle.

The vertex of the angle shown is S, and its sides are $\overrightarrow{SR}$ and $\overrightarrow{ST}$.

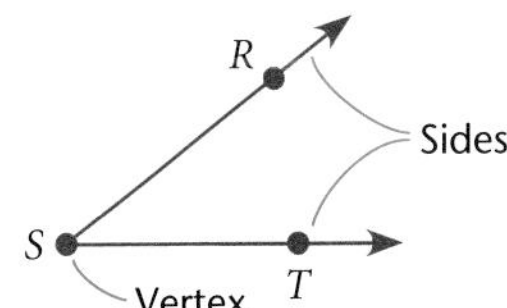

Student Resources

- Alternative Lessons 1-3B
- Laboratory Manual 1-3B
- Technology Lab Manual
- Practice 1-3B
- Study Guide and Journal 1-3B
- Guía de estudios y Diario 1-3B
- Multilingual Handbook
- More Look Ahead 1-3B
- SAT Preparation

Media Resources

- Transparency FFM 1-3B
- Transparency AE 1-3B
- Teaching Transparency
- AWSMTest and practice software
- AWSM Videodisc

PART B At a Glance

Objective

To become familiar with angles and angle measurement, and to explore right angles and perpendicular lines.

Development

Rays and angles are defined, and students learn about angle measures and protractor use.

A right angle and perpendicular lines are defined.

In the **Explore,** students find that the shortest segment from a point to a line is the perpendicular segment.

Suggested Materials

Student Ruler, protractor, geometry software

Key Terms

Ray, endpoint of a ray, angle, sides of an angle, vertex of an angle, measure of an angle, degree measure, right angle, perpendicular lines

First Five Minutes

Transparency FFM 1-3B

Read the top of page 45, do **Try It a,** and then read the bottom of page 45.

Motivate

Ask...

- What is the difference between a line and a line segment? Can you draw a figure that has some characteristics of each?
- Are any two lines coplanar? If two lines intersect, must they be coplanar?

Measuring Figures

Note: In this text, an angle is made up of two *noncollinear* rays. "Straight angles" are not used.

Because there are no straight angles, angles in this context cannot measure 180°. However, when students measure rotations, degree measures can equal or exceed 180°.

ALTERNATE EXAMPLE

Give four ways of naming the angle shown.

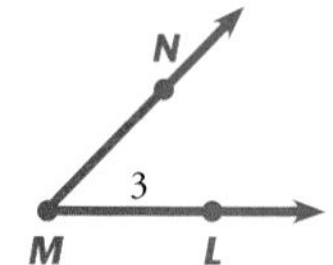

$\angle M$, $\angle LMN$, $\angle NML$, or $\angle 3$

Note: You may wish to show students that although figures like triangles have segments for sides, we say that there are angles at each vertex.

Angles can be named by using three different letters. The vertex is always written in the middle. The angle on page 45 can be called $\angle RST$ or $\angle TSR$. When no other angles share the same vertex point, an angle can be named by using just the vertex letter or a number.

EXAMPLE

Give four ways of naming the angle shown at the right.

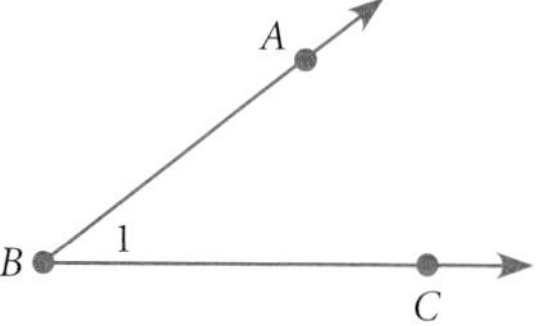

This is $\angle ABC$ or $\angle CBA$. Since there is no chance of confusion, it can also be named $\angle B$ or $\angle 1$.

Like segments, angles have different sizes. Angles are usually measured in **degrees.** The symbol for degree is °. A 1-degree angle looks like this:

Angles measure between 0° and 180°. (They cannot measure 0° or 180°.) As with segments, the size of an angle is not the same thing as the angle itself. The **measure** of angle $\angle XYZ$ is written $m\angle XYZ$. If $\angle XYZ$ is an 80° angle, we write $m\angle XYZ = 80°$.

We use a protractor to measure angles. The arc of a protractor measures 180°. The figure below shows protractors being used to measure $\angle ABC$ and $\angle CBD$.

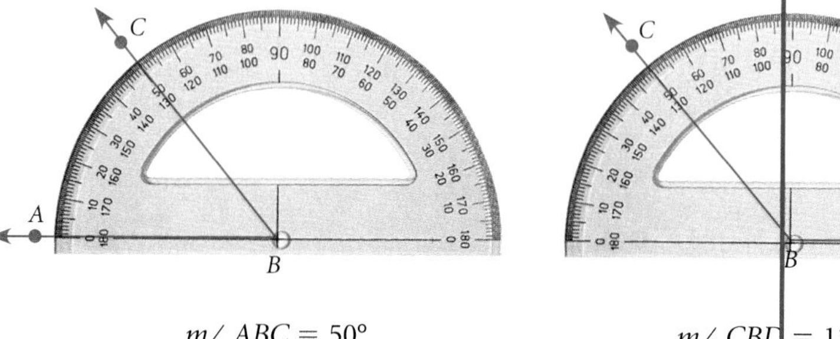

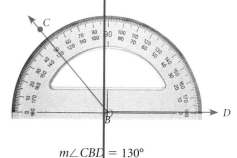

$m\angle ABC = 50°$ $m\angle CBD = 130°$

Notice that the small hole in the protractor is placed over the vertex of the angle.

History Connection

According to Jeanne Bendick, the sexagesimal (base 60) system used by the Babylonians may be the foundation of the degree-measurement system. Because they observed that a year was approximately 360 days long, they divided circles into 360 parts. (Jeanne Bendick, *How Much and How Many*, pp. 86–88. © 1989 Franklin Watts.)

Alert

To emphasize that angle measure has units, we include the degree symbol when giving the measure of an angle (e.g., $m\angle A = 73°$, not $m\angle A = 73$).

TRY IT

Use your protractor to find the measure of each angle below.

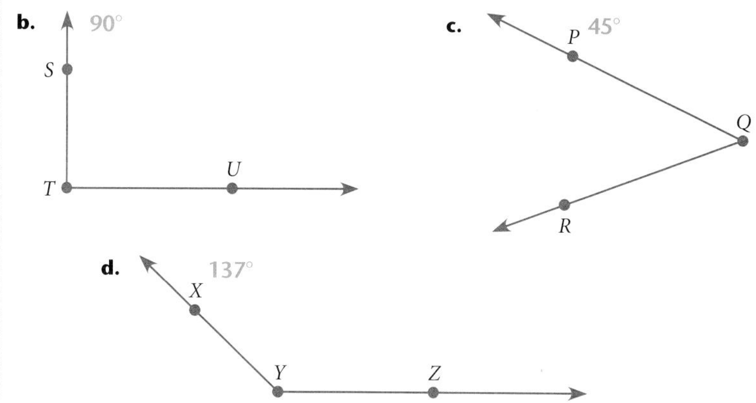

CONSIDER

1. **Describe how you know whether to use the outer number or the inner number on a protractor when measuring an angle.**

Angles that measure 90° are particularly important in geometry. You see these angles everywhere: in buildings, on maps, and on basketball, volleyball, and tennis courts.

DEFINITIONS

A **right angle** is an angle that measures 90°.

Two lines that intersect at right angles are called **perpendicular lines.**

Right angles are sometimes marked with a small box at the vertex of the angle. The symbol for perpendicular is $\perp$. In the figure, $m \perp n$. Segments and rays that intersect lines or intersect each other at right angles are also considered perpendicular.

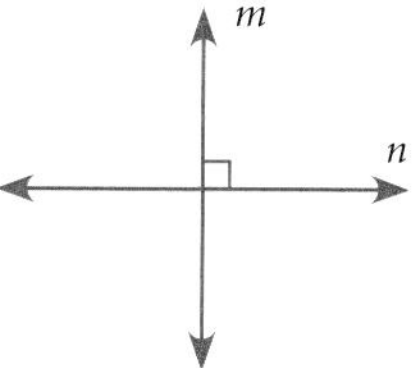

Possible Answer

1. If the angle is measured clockwise, use the bottom number; if counterclockwise, use the top number.

Note: The definitions of *right angle* and *perpendicular lines* are especially important ones.

To avoid introducing too much terminology at one time, we do not introduce *acute* and *obtuse* angles at this point. These are defined in Chapter 3.

This text stresses both inductive discovery and deductive justification. To avoid the confusion of having a conjecture turn into a theorem later, we will state all provable conjectures as theorems.

Diversity Issues

Recommendations for encouraging women to study mathematics, by respondents to an Association for Women in Mathematics survey.

1. Increase the emphasis on mathematics education; advise girls to take four years of high school mathematics. **2.** Encourage women; don't discourage them. **3.** Strive for more equal treatment of women and men.

(Edith H. Luchins and Abraham S. Luchins, "Female Mathematicians: A Contemporary Appraisal," *Women and the Mathematical Mystique*, Lynn H. Fox, Linda Brody, and Dianne Tobin, eds., p. 16. © 1980 The Johns Hopkins University Press.)

1-3

Algebra	Functions	Discrete Math	Probability	Data/Statistics

Measuring Figures

EXPLORE

Short Cuts

Recommended group size: 4

The Point
Students discover that the shortest segment from a point to a line is the perpendicular segment.

Look and Listen...

- For students who have trouble measuring the angles and segments precisely.
- For students who are drawing more than one segment that is very close to perpendicular.

Ask...

- Are you trying to make measurements that are too precise for your ruler?

For Groups That Finish Early
Draw pairs of segments of *equal* length from a point to a line, measure the angles the paired segments make with the line, and make a conjecture. **The angles are congruent.**

Follow Up
Ask what is true about the shortest segment from a point to a line.

Possible Answers

3. 90°

4. The shortest segment from a point to a line is the perpendicular segment.

Journal 

Reflect 2 and 3 are suitable for journal entries.

REFLECT

Possible Answers

1. Because 180° is divisible by many whole numbers, including 2, 3, 4, 5, 6, 10, 12, 15, 20, and 30.

In the following Explore, you will use measuring tools to find the shortest segment from a point to a line.

EXPLORE: SHORT CUTS

MATERIALS

Ruler
Protractor
Geometry software (optional)

1. Sketch a line and a point not on the line. (It's best if the point is several inches away from the line.) Draw several segments from the point to the line, including the segment you think is the shortest one possible.

2. Using a ruler to measure the segments, identify the shortest segment from the point to the line.

3. Use a protractor to measure the angle formed by the line and the shortest segment.

4. Repeat **1, 2,** and **3** until you feel confident enough to make a conjecture about the shortest segment from a point to a line. Compare your conjecture with those of your classmates.

It is possible to prove the conjecture you made about the shortest segment from a point to a line, so we state it as a theorem (our first!).

THEOREM

The shortest segment from a point not on a line to the line is the perpendicular segment.

REFLECT

1. Why is 0° to 180° a convenient range of measurement for angles?

2. Suppose you're in a field next to a road. Describe the shortest path to the road from where you are. If you had a protractor, would it help you find the shortest path? Explain.

3. Name two things that can be modeled by a ray and two that can be modeled by an angle. Discuss the strengths and weaknesses of using a ray or angle as a model for each.

48 1-3 • MEASURING FIGURES

Technology Note 

If you use geometry software in this **Explore,** you may want to precede it with a brief orientation session. It may be most efficient to show students a few features (e.g., drawing a point and a line, measuring the length of a segment), and allow them to learn others by working with the software under your observation.

Exercises

CORE

P **1. Getting Started** Give four ways of naming the angle shown at the right. ∠*BCD*, ∠*DCB*, ∠*C*, ∠1

P **2.** Name all of the rays in the lower figure at the right. $\overrightarrow{BD}$, $\overrightarrow{BA}$, $\overrightarrow{BC}$;

P **3.** Name all of the angles in the figure. How many angles are there? ∠*DBA*, ∠*DBC*, ∠*ABC*, 3 unique angles

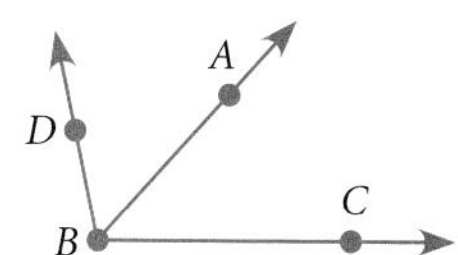

P **Estimate the measure of each angle below. Then use your protractor to find its measure.**

4. 29°

5. 148°

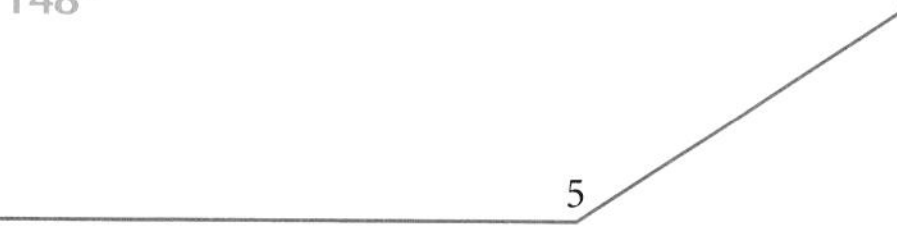

P **Use your protractor to draw angles with the given measures. Include points so that the names of the angles are correct.**

6. $m\angle ABC = 70°$ **7.** $m\angle FGH = 157°$ **8.** $m\angle LMN = 12°$

P **Make freehand sketches of angles that have approximately the following measures.**

9. 45° **10.** 90° **11.** 150°

V **12.** Write the letter of the second pair that best matches the first pair. (d)

Segment: length as (a) distance: road, (b) travel: distance, (c) number: figure, (d) angle: angle measure.

R **13.** Explain why you can use *AB* to refer to the length of segment $\overline{AB}$ without confusion. How do you know it doesn't refer to the length of $\overrightarrow{AB}$ or $\overleftrightarrow{AB}$?

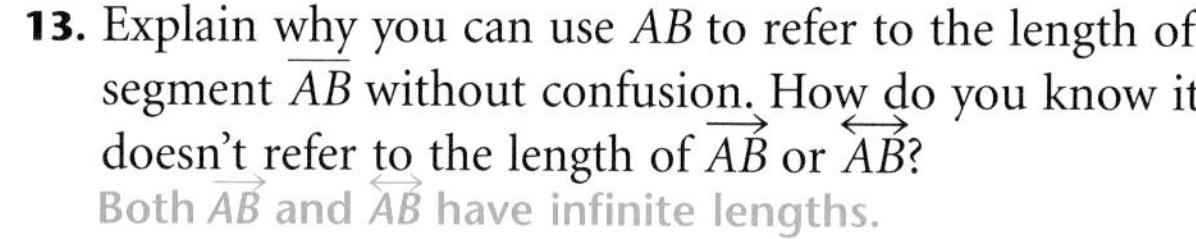

Both $\overrightarrow{AB}$ and $\overleftrightarrow{AB}$ have infinite lengths.

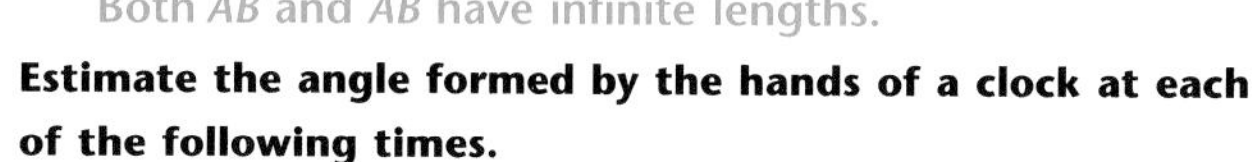

P **Estimate the angle formed by the hands of a clock at each of the following times.**

14. 3:00 90° **15.** 11:00 30°

16. 5:00 150° **17.** 8:20 130°

R **18.** An angle is a model for the hands of a clock. Describe several other objects that can be modeled by angles. Possible answers: Spinners in a children's game; slices of a pie or cake

2. The shortest path is the perpendicular path. A protractor would not help you identify this path from the middle of the field.

3. Ray, light ray. Both start at one point and go on forever, but a ray does not model brightness.

Ray, path of an arrow. Reasonable model for short distances, but the path of the arrow actually curves.

Angle, corner of a window. Good model to represent the size of a corner. However, the corner does not go on forever.

Angle, an arm bent at the elbow. The elbow is like a vertex, and the upper and lower arm are like sides. The arm doesn't go on forever.

Part B Exercises

Exercise Notes

Core

4–5, 9–11. Help students develop visual estimation skills.

14–18. Reinforce mathematical modeling concepts.

22. Students use inductive reasoning to find a formula.

Look Ahead

These exercises preview the concept of congruent segments.

Exercise Answers

Core

6. Possible answer:

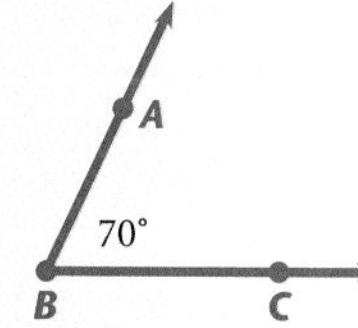

7. Possible answer:

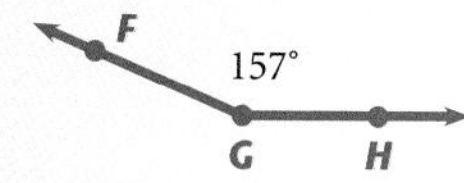

8. Possible answer:

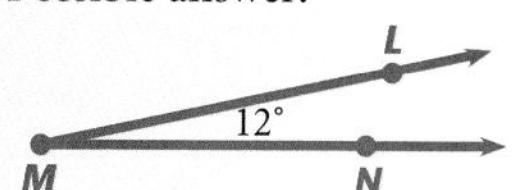

Key

V Vocabulary
P Practice/Skills
Review
R Math Reasoning
S Problem Solving
Challenge

Ongoing Assessment

Self-Assessment Exercises 1–11 odd, 15, 17, 19, 21

Embedded Assessment Explore Step 4; Reflect 3; Exercises 4, 16, 22, 23

Measuring Figures

9. Possible answer:

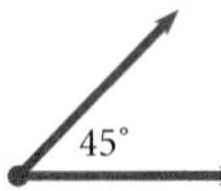

10. Possible answer:

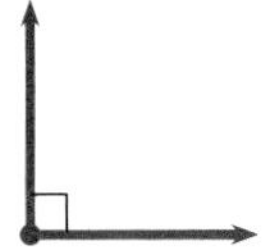

11. Possible answer:

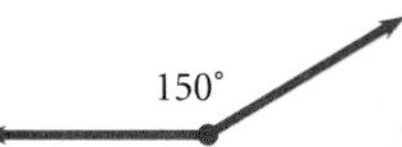

More Practice

27. $\overrightarrow{UR}$, $\overrightarrow{US}$, $\overrightarrow{UT}$, $\overrightarrow{UV}$, $\overrightarrow{VU}$ (or $\overrightarrow{VS}$), and $\overrightarrow{SU}$ (or $\overrightarrow{SV}$)

28. $\angle RUS$, $\angle SUT$, $\angle TUV$, $\angle RUT$, $\angle VUR$

31. Possible answer:

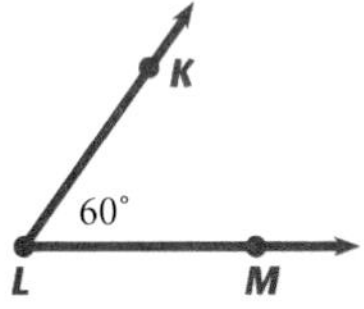

32. Possible answer:

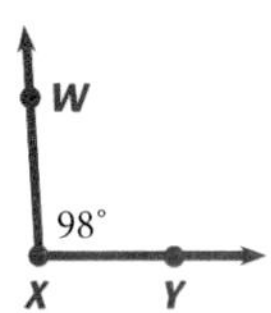

33. Possible answer:

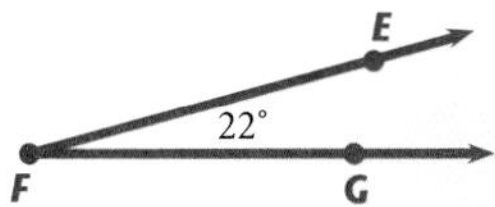

More Math Reasoning

34. a. Possible answer: They are located on five different continental plates; they are at the same latitude.

b. Possible answer: Continental drift causes changes in observatory-star-observatory angles.

35. $RT < RS$ because the shortest segment from R to $\overleftrightarrow{TS}$ is the perpendicular segment. Similarly, $ST < RS$ because the shortest segment from S to $\overleftrightarrow{TR}$ is the perpendicular segment.

Algebra | Functions | Discrete Math | Probability | Data/Statistics

P **Find the measures of the following angles on a baseball diamond.**

19. from home plate to first base to second base 90°

20. from first base to home plate to second base 45°

21. from the shortstop to home plate to first base (give an estimate) Possible Answer: 63°

Second
Shortstop
Third
First
Home plate

PS **22.** When 1 ray is drawn inside an angle as shown at the right, 3 angles are formed. When 2 rays are drawn, 6 angles are formed. How many different angles are formed when 10 rays are drawn? 66

Problem-Solving Tip

Make a table and look for a pattern to help you make your prediction.

PS, MR **23.** In the figure at the right, which segment is shorter, $\overline{LM}$ or $\overline{LN}$? Write a brief justification of your answer. $\overline{LM}$, because it is the perpendicular segment

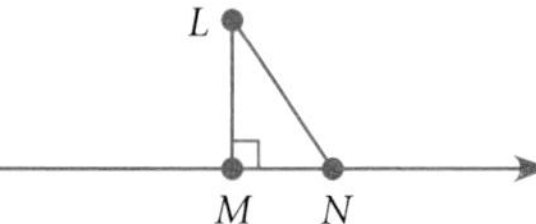

LOOK AHEAD

P **Points *A* and *B* have coordinates *a* and *b* on a number line. Find the coordinate of *C* so that *AB* = *BC*.**

24. $a = 2$, $b = 4$ 6

25. $a = -5$, $b = 3$ 11

26. $a = -9$, $b = -12$ −15

MORE PRACTICE

P **27.** Name all of the rays in the figure.

P **28.** Name all of the angles in the figure.

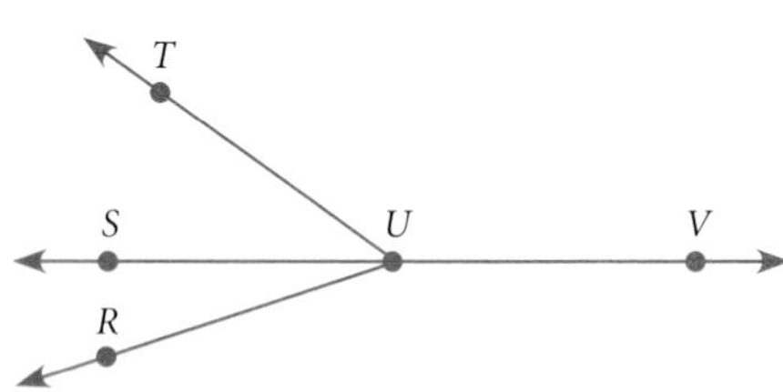

Key

V Vocabulary
P Practice/Skills
R Review
MR Math Reasoning
PS Problem Solving
C Challenge

Estimate the measure of each angle below. Then use your protractor to find its measure.

29. 139°

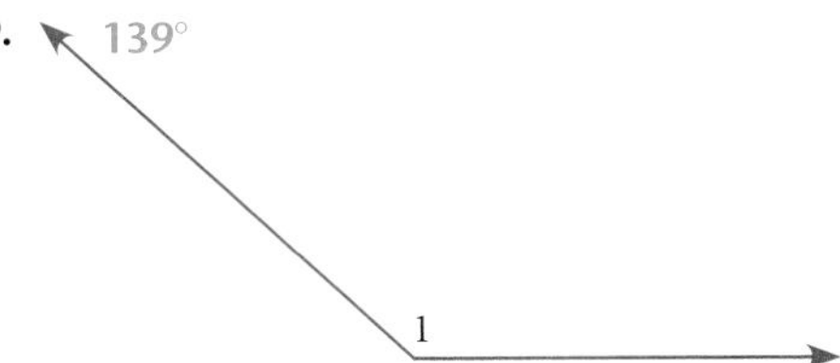

30. 11°

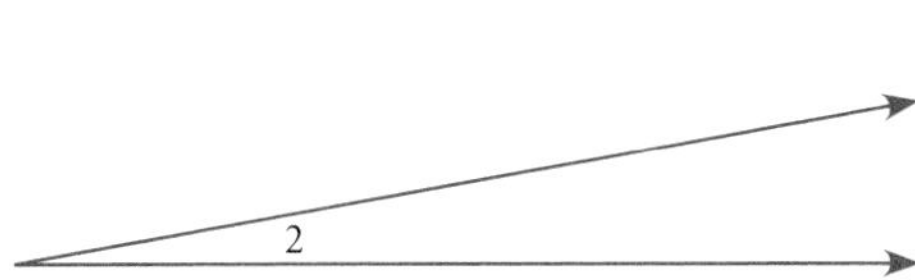

Use your protractor to draw angles with the given measures. Include points so that the names of the angles are correct.

31. $m\angle KLM = 60°$

32. $m\angle WXY = 98°$

33. $m\angle EFG = 22°$

MORE MATH REASONING

34. Continental Drift As part of an international project that began in 1900, five observatories were set up to study changes in latitude caused by continental drift. The American observatories are located in Gaithersburg, Maryland, and Ukiah, California. Other observatories are on Sardinia, an island off the southwest coast of Italy, in Turkmenistan (the former Soviet Turkistan) in central Asia, and north of Tokyo on Honshu, the largest of the Japanese islands.

a. Why do you think these five locations were chosen for the project?

b. Each of the observatories makes nightly observations of 18 pairs of stars. How do you think scientists use these data to look for continental drift?

35. Explain why $\overline{RS}$ must be longer than either $\overline{ST}$ or $\overline{RT}$ in the triangle shown. (Hint: First show that $\overline{RT}$ is shorter than $\overline{RS}$.)

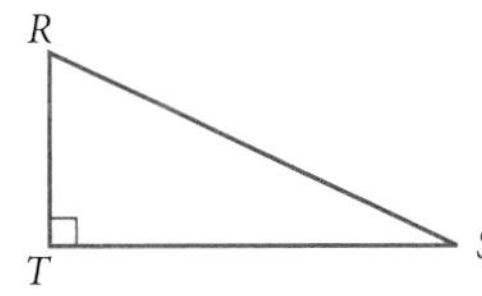

Algebra	Functions	Discrete Math	Probability	Data/Statistics

PART C At a Glance

Objective

To investigate congruent figures and learn construction techniques.

Development

Congruent figures are defined, and markings for congruent segments and angles are introduced.

The tools and rules of geometric constructions are presented. **Constructions** of congruent segments and congruent angles are demonstrated. Each is followed by a **Consider** that asks about the roles played by the compass and the straightedge.

Suggested Materials

Student Compass, straightedge

Teacher Chalkboard/overhead compass

Key Terms

Congruent, construction, compass, straightedge

First Five Minutes

Transparency FFM 1-3C

Read the introductory paragraphs and the **Example** on page 52, then do **Try It a.**

Motivate

Ask...

- What does it mean for two segments to have the same size? for two angles to have the same size?
- Give some examples of real-world situations in which it is important to make things that are exactly the same size.

ALTERNATE EXAMPLE

Is $\overline{WX} \cong \overline{XY}$?

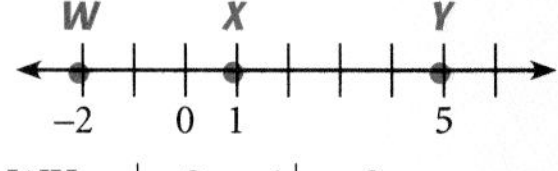

$WX = |-2 - 1| = 3$

$XY = |1 - 5| = 4$

Therefore, $\overline{WX}$ is not congruent to $\overline{XY}$.

1-3 PART C Congruence

← CONNECT → ***You've learned how to measure angles and segments. Now you will investigate angles and segments that have equal measures. You will also begin to use a compass and straightedge to do geometric constructions.***

In geometry, we often work with figures that are exactly the same size and shape. There is a special term for this relationship.

DEFINITION

Congruent figures have the same shape and size.

When two segments have the same length or two angles have the same measure, they are congruent. The symbol for congruence is ≅.

EXAMPLE

Is $\overline{PR} \cong \overline{RQ}$?

$PR = |1 - (-3)| = |4| = 4$

$RQ = |5 - 1| = 4$

Since $PR = RQ$, $\overline{PR} \cong \overline{RQ}$.

We show congruent segments by marking them with the same number of "tick marks." In the figure, $\overline{WX} \cong \overline{XY}$.

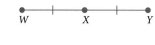

We show congruent angles by marking them with the same number of arcs near their vertices. In the figure, $\angle EIF \cong \angle FIG$.

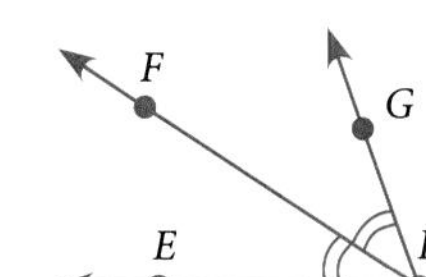

TRY IT

a. Draw and mark one figure that shows all of the following relationships. On line $\overleftrightarrow{AB}$, $\overline{AB} \cong \overline{BC}$. Also, $\angle ABD \cong \angle ABE$.

Tips from Teachers

Students learn constructions more easily if they understand the functions of the straightedge and compass. If they know that a compass is used to measure lengths, they are less likely to change its setting arbitrarily.

A geometric **construction** is a technique for drawing precise figures using only a straightedge and compass. The ancient Greeks used these tools in their geometric constructions. The straightedge (a ruler with no markings) lets you draw straight line segments; the compass, when kept in one position, can be used to measure a consistent distance. When doing a construction, you are not allowed to do numerical measurement.

CONSTRUCTION: CONGRUENT SEGMENTS

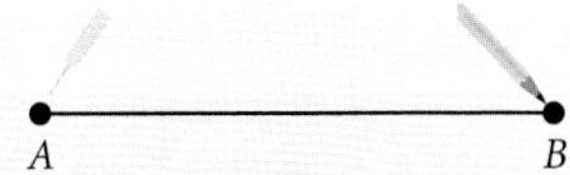

1. Begin by drawing a segment $\overline{AB}$ on your paper. This is the segment that you will copy in your construction.

2. Draw a point *C*. Then use a straightedge to draw a line segment starting at *C* that is obviously longer than $\overline{AB}$. Point *C* corresponds to point *A* on the original segment.

3. Place the metal tip of your compass at *A*, and open up your compass to the size of $\overline{AB}$ by moving the tip of the pencil to point *B*.

4. Without altering the compass opening, move the point of the compass to *C* and swing the pencil so that you make a mark on the line at distance *AB*. Place a point at this location, and label it *D*. $\overline{AB}$ and $\overline{CD}$ have the same length. We can write $\overline{AB} \cong \overline{CD}$.

1. **What job did the straightedge do in this construction? What was the compass used for?**

You can also use a straightedge and compass to construct congruent angles.

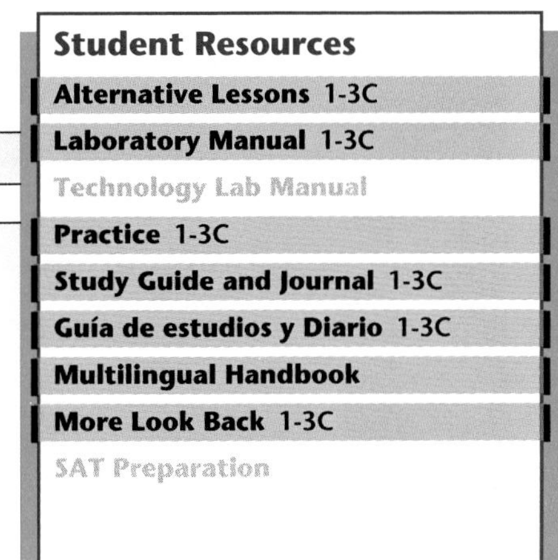

Student Resources
Alternative Lessons 1-3C
Laboratory Manual 1-3C
Technology Lab Manual
Practice 1-3C
Study Guide and Journal 1-3C
Guía de estudios y Diario 1-3C
Multilingual Handbook
More Look Back 1-3C
SAT Preparation

Media Resources

Transparency FFM 1-3C

Transparency AE 1-3C

Teaching Transparency

AWSMTest and practice software

AWSM Videodisc

Construction: Congruent Segments

The Point

To construct a segment congruent to a given segment.

Presenting the Construction

Since this is the first construction of the year, you may wish to model this construction technique for the students yourself and then have them do one or two of their own.

Asks students to think about the functions of a compass and a straightedge.

Possible Answer

1. The straightedge insured that the segments drawn were straight. The compass was used to measure the segment's length.

Measuring Figures

Construction: Congruent Angles

The Point

To construct an angle congruent to a given angle.

Presenting the Construction

You may want to have students follow the steps in the text to do the **Construction,** and circulate to help students who are having difficulty.

If time permits, you can follow up by having students work in pairs. You could ask each student to draw an angle and pass it to a partner to copy.

Asks students to think about why the construction technique for congruent angles works.

Possible Answers

2. Since the same compass setting is used in each case to find the second endpoint, the segments must have equal lengths.

3. Because of the way we used compass settings, $\overline{MQ} \cong \overline{TU}$, $\overline{MP} \cong \overline{TV}$, and $\overline{PQ} \cong \overline{VU}$. This should mean that the angles are exactly the same size. (Note that this previews the idea of SSS triangle congruence.)

CONSTRUCTION: CONGRUENT ANGLES

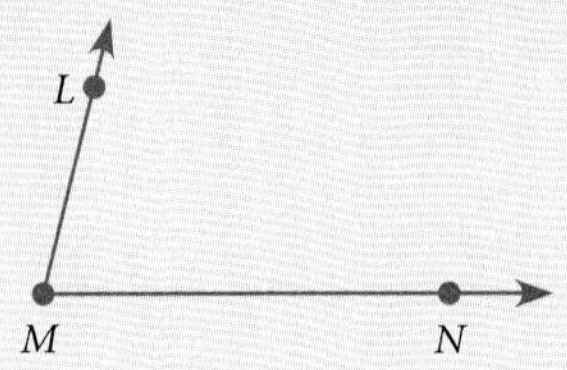

1. Begin by drawing angle $\angle LMN$ on your paper. This will be the angle that you copy in your construction.

2. Use your straightedge to draw a ray. This will be one side of the copy. Label its endpoint T.

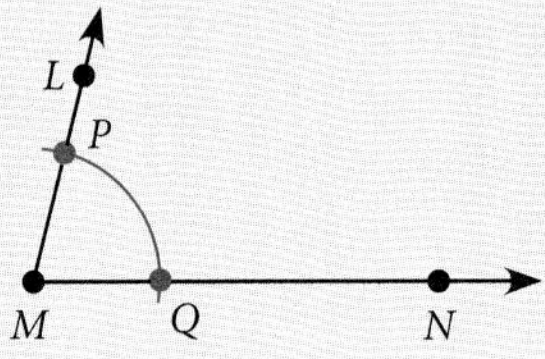

3. Place the compass tip on the vertex of $\angle LMN$. Draw an arc that intersects both rays of $\angle LMN$ as shown. Label the points of intersection of the angle and the arc P and Q.

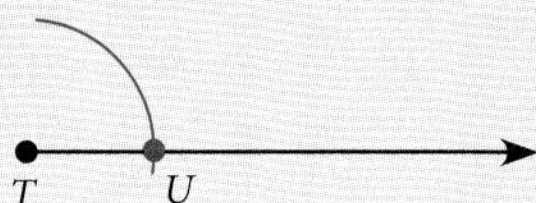

4. Without changing the compass opening, place the tip on the endpoint of the ray, T. Draw an arc about the same length as the arc on $\angle LMN$. Label the intersection of the arc and the ray point U, as shown.

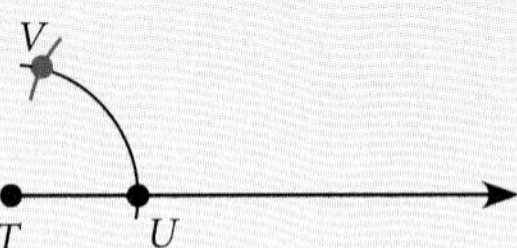

5. Use the compass to measure from point P to point Q. Without changing the compass opening, place the tip of the compass on point U. Make a small arc across the existing arc through U. Call the intersection point V.

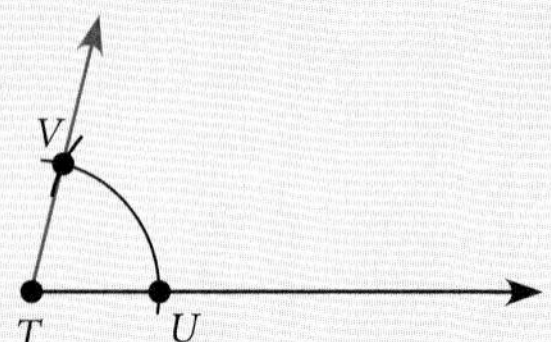

6. Draw the second ray of the new angle through point V. $\angle VTU \cong \angle LMN$.

2. Explain how this construction technique guarantees that $\overline{MQ} \cong \overline{TU}$ and $\overline{UV} \cong \overline{PQ}$.

3. Why do you think this construction works? (We will be looking at this more closely in Chapter 8.)

Alert

Students often make construction marks that are small, light, and difficult to see. You may need to emphasize the importance of these marks, which show that a student has actually done a compass-and-straightedge construction.

Tips from Teachers

It is helpful to have a piece of paper or cardboard under the sheet on which a construction is done to anchor the top paper and keep the compass from tearing through the paper.

REFLECT

1. Explain how the statements below are related but different.
   - $EF = GH$
   - $\overline{EF} \cong \overline{GH}$
2. Many of the constructions you will do in this book were first developed in ancient Greece. Why do you think that making numerical measurements was not allowed in these techniques? Do some of the same concerns apply today?

Exercises

CORE

1. **Getting Started** Identify the pairs of figures that appear to be congruent from the six shown.

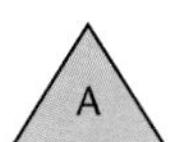

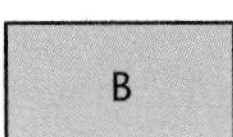

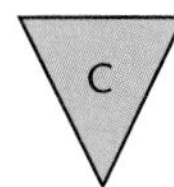

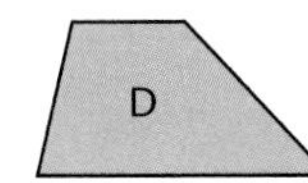

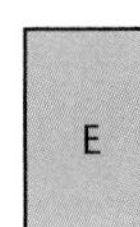

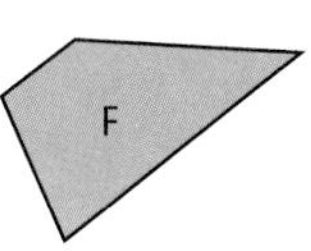

2. Is $\overline{XY} \cong \overline{YZ}$? Explain.

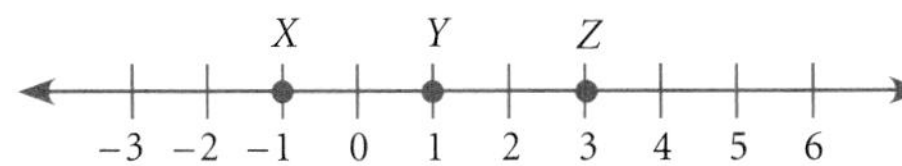

Copy the segments below. Then use a compass and straightedge to construct segments congruent to them.

3. 

4. 

Copy the angles below. Then use a compass and straightedge to construct angles congruent to them.

5. 

6. 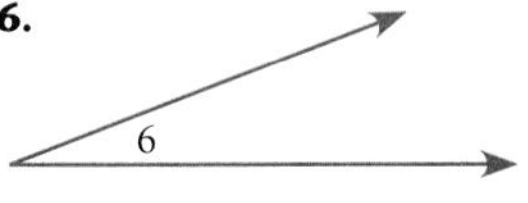

7. Construct a copy of the figure at the right. Make sure that the segments are the correct lengths.

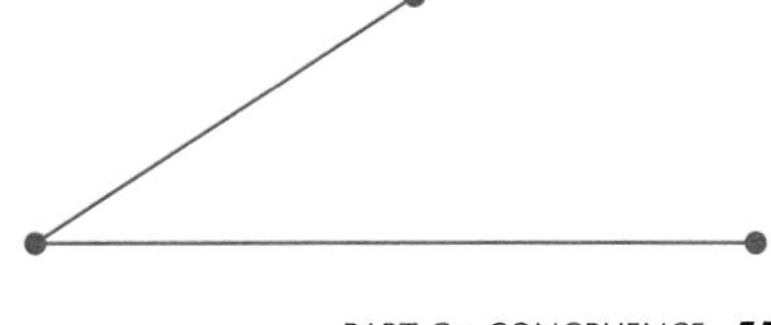

Ongoing Assessment

Vocabulary
Practice/Skills
Review
Math Reasoning
Problem Solving
Challenge

Self-Assessment Exercises 1, 2, 9, 10, 11, 13

Embedded Assessment Consider 2; Reflect 1; Exercises 7, 8, 12, 17

Journal

Consider 2 and **Reflect** 1 are suitable for journal entries.

REFLECT

Possible Answers

1. The first statement is an equation. It shows that two numbers (lengths) are equal. The congruence statement expresses a relationship between geometric figures.
2. Numerical measurements are always inaccurate to some degree. Constructions use geometric properties to make figures, so they can (theoretically) be exact. Measurements are more accurate today, but constructions are still useful for showing how geometric properties can be used to create "exact" figures.

TRY IT

Answer

a. Possible answer:

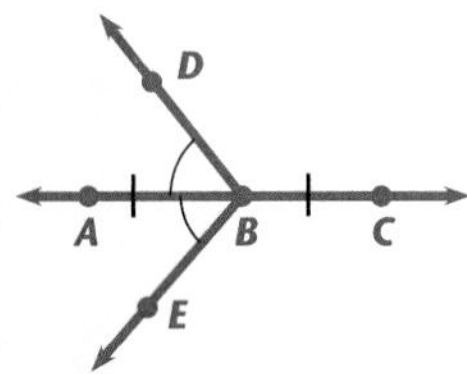

Part C Exercises

Exercise Notes

Core

15. Previews the definition of congruent triangles.
17. Illustrates an important optical relationship. This relationship will be used in several contexts in the text.

More Math Reasoning

31. Helps students realize that inexpensive construction and measurement tools (and inexperienced people using them) will usually introduce inaccuracies. Students need to think about what degree of error might be expected in solving a problem or using a technique.

Exercise Answers

Core

1. B and E, A and C, D and F

1-3

Measuring Figures

2. Yes, since both have length 2.

3. 

4. 

5.  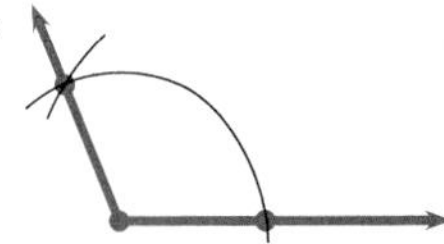

6. 

7. 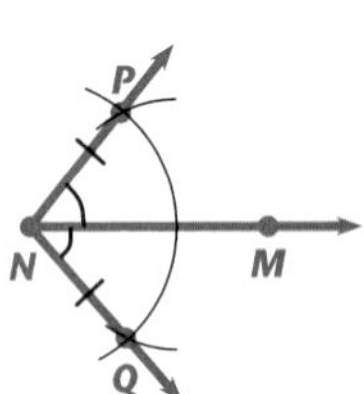

8. 

15. 

The triangles are congruent because the sides of the second are, by construction, congruent to those of the first.

16. Along a straight line, construct four adjacent segments of the given length.

Look Back
18–20.

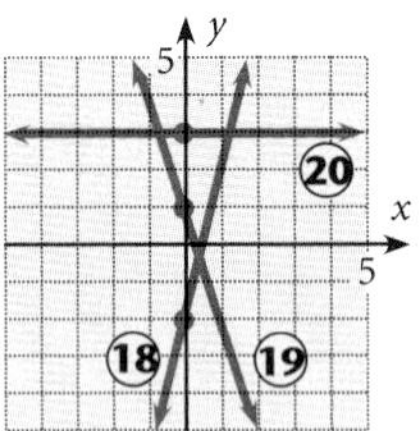

More Practice
24. 

25.

Algebra | Functions | Discrete Math | Probability | Data/Statistics

P **8.** Draw and mark one figure that shows all of the following relationships.
$\angle MNP \cong \angle MNQ$. Also, $\overline{NP} \cong \overline{NQ}$.

P **9.** Suppose $\overline{GH} \cong \overline{HK}$. If all three points lie on a number line, and H has coordinate -4, and K has coordinate -12, find the coordinate of G. 4

P **10.** Sketch $\angle ABC$ and $\angle ABD$ so that $\angle ABC \cong \angle ABD$. What is $m\angle ABC$ in terms of $m\angle CBD$? (Assume $m\angle ABC < 90°$.) $m\angle ABC = \frac{1}{2}m\angle CBD$

P **Suppose $\overline{RS} \cong \overline{MN}$. For each set of lengths, solve for x, and find the length of each segment.**

11. $RS = 3x + 17$, $MN = 7x - 15$
$x = 8$; $RS = 41$; $MN = 41$

12. $RS = \frac{x}{3} + 10$, $MN = \frac{2x}{3} + 4$
$x = 18$; $RS = 16$; $MN = 16$

V **Write the letter of the second pair that best matches the first pair.**

13. Congruent: equal as (a) similar: same, (b) length: distance, (c) segment: length, (d) construction: sketch. (c)

14. Construction: sketch as (a) congruent: equal, (b) draft: book, (c) dog: puppy, (d) exact: approximate. (d)

PS **15.** Use a straightedge to draw a triangle. Then use construction techniques to help you draw a second triangle that is congruent to the first. Explain how you made sure that the second triangle is congruent to the first. What do you think it means to say that two triangles are congruent?

PS **16.** Develop a method for constructing a segment four times as long as the one below. Show your construction and explain your method.

17. Light Exercise When a beam of light reflects off a mirror, the *angle of incidence* is congruent to the *angle of reflection*. If $m\angle ABC = 48°$, find $m\angle ABD$. 96°

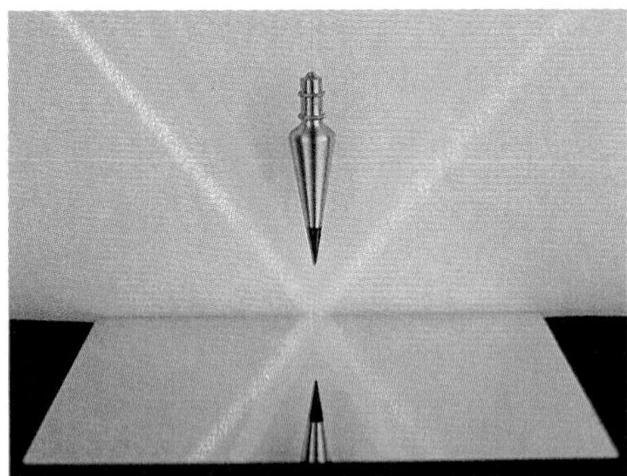

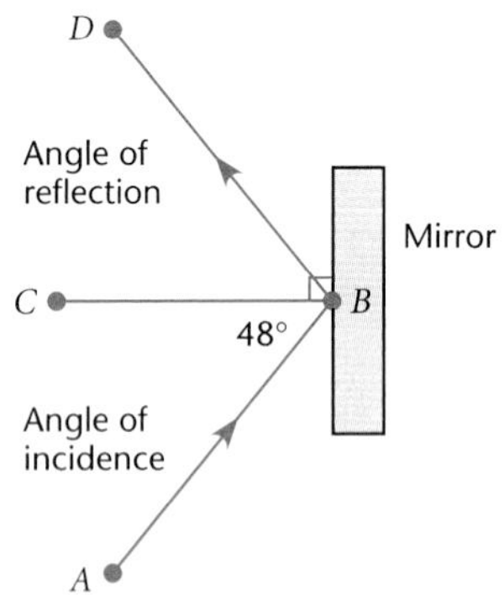

Key

V Vocabulary
P Practice/Skills
R Review
MR Math Reasoning
PS Problem Solving
C Challenge

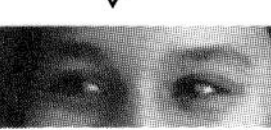

LOOK BACK

Graph each linear equation below. Give the slope and y-intercept of each line. [Previous course]

18. $y = 4x - 2$
Slope = 4, intercept = −2

19. $y = -3x + 1$
Slope = −3, intercept = 1

20. $y = 3$
Slope = 0, intercept = 3

Find the slope of $\overleftrightarrow{AB}$ if A and B have the following coordinates. [Previous course]

21. $A(3, 4)$, $B(5, 8)$
2

22. $A(-2, 7)$, $B(5, -2)$
$-\frac{9}{7}$

23. $A(-4.2, 2.7)$, $B(-4.2, -3.8)$
Undefined (vertical line)

MORE PRACTICE

Construct segments congruent to the ones below.

24.

25.

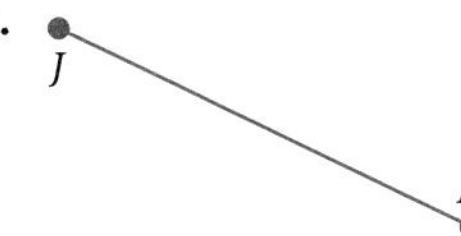

Construct angles congruent to the ones below.

26.

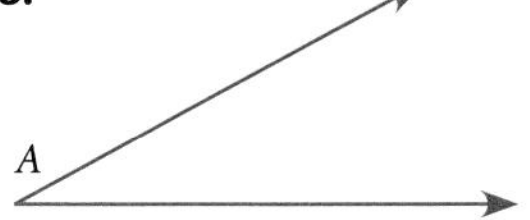

27.

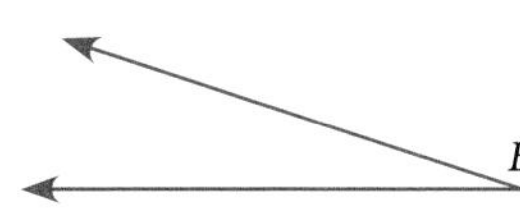

$\angle DEF \cong \angle RST$. For each set of angle measures, solve for x, and find the measure of each angle.

28. $m\angle DEF = (x + 20)°$, $m\angle RST = (3x - 42)°$

29. $m\angle DEF = (5x + 18)°$, $m\angle RST = (6x - 5)°$

MORE MATH REASONING

30. Square Counts How many congruent squares of various sizes are there on a 4-by-4 grid?

31. Suppose you use the congruent-angle construction to construct $\angle MNO \cong \angle PQR$. Then you use your protractor to measure each and find that $m\angle MNO = 76°$ and $m\angle PQR = 79°$. Give an explanation for what might have happened.

26.

27.

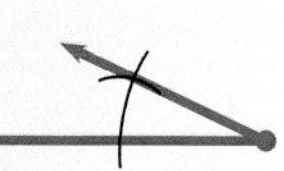

28. $x = 31$; $m\angle DEF = 51°$; $m\angle RST = 51°$

29. $x = 23$; $m\angle DEF = 133°$; $m\angle RST = 133°$

More Math Reasoning

30. 16 of size 1×1, 9 of 2×2, 4 of 3×3

31. Possible answer: Compass may have opened wider while constructing $\angle PQR$, your measurements of $\angle MNO$ and $\angle PQR$ may not be precise, etc.

Measuring Figures

PART D At a Glance

Objective

To use construction and measurement skills in a single context.

Development

In the **Explore,** students design a net for a package that must meet certain requirements. They will need to use both measurement and construction tools.

Suggested Materials

Student Scissors, tape, large sheets of paper, compass, ruler, protractor

First Five Minutes

Transparency FFM 1-3D

Write a brief summary of the new terms and concepts you learned in 1-3.

EXPLORE

Net-working

Recommended group size: 2

The Point

Students will revisit nets. They will use congruent segments and angles and their construction techniques to design a net for a package.

Look and Listen...

- For students who are having difficulty understanding the combined length and girth restriction.
- For students who are attempting to make an overly complicated net.

Ask...

- What type of angles do most packages have? Why?

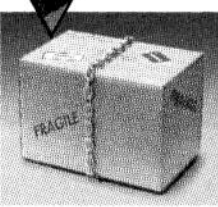

1-3 PART D Making Connections

← CONNECT → *Measurement is used in many careers in many different ways. You've learned how to use the tools of geometric measurement—the ruler, compass, and protractor.*

You've seen that measurement is important in the shipping industry. It is also crucial in designing packages that the shipping industry can actually ship! The photo at the right shows shipping containers at the port of Los Angeles.

EXPLORE: NET-WORKING

MATERIALS

Scissors, Tape
Large sheets of paper
Compass, Ruler
Protractor

Design a net to make a small shipping package for UPS. It must meet the following standards.

- It must have a combined length and girth of no more than 36 in.
- To draw a side that is the same length as another side, you must use the congruent-segment construction. Show the construction marks on your paper.
- To make an angle that is the same measure as another angle, you must use the congruent-angle construction. Show the construction marks.
- All side and angle measures should be labeled on your net.
- When folded up, the package must have no open sides, gaps, or extra material.

Draw a net that you feel will meet these standards on one sheet of paper. Then make a copy of your net on a second piece of paper and check that it folds up properly. (You do not need to copy the construction marks.) Compare your design with those of your classmates.

Student Resources

Alternative Lessons
Laboratory Manual 1-3D
Technology Lab Manual
Practice 1-3D
Study Guide and Journal 1-3D
Guía de estudios y Diario 1-3D
Multilingual Handbook
More Look Back 1-3D
SAT Preparation

Media Resources

Transparency FFM 1-3D
Transparency AE
Teaching Transparency
AWSMTest and practice software
AWSM Videodisc

REFLECT

1. Why are congruent sides and angles important in making a net that folds up into a good package?
2. How might measurement be used by an architect? an automobile mechanic? a baker? a softball player?
3. In your own words, explain how to find the length of a segment on the number line and how to find the length of a slanted segment on a coordinate plane.

Self-Assessment

For the coordinates listed, determine whether $\overline{AB} \cong \overline{BC}$.

Coordinates of *A*	Coordinates of *B*	Coordinates of *C*	
1. (0, 3)	(0, 7)	(−4, 3)	No
2. (4, −2)	(−1, 1)	(−2, −3)	No
3. (3, 7)	(8, −5)	(−4, 0)	Yes

4. Does the order in which the letters are written matter when naming a segment? a ray? a line? an angle? Explain.

Explain what is wrong with each statement in Exercises 5–8.

5. $RS \cong YZ$ 6. $\angle PQR = 55°$ 7. $m\angle TRS = 216°$
8. For two angles to be congruent, their sides must be congruent.

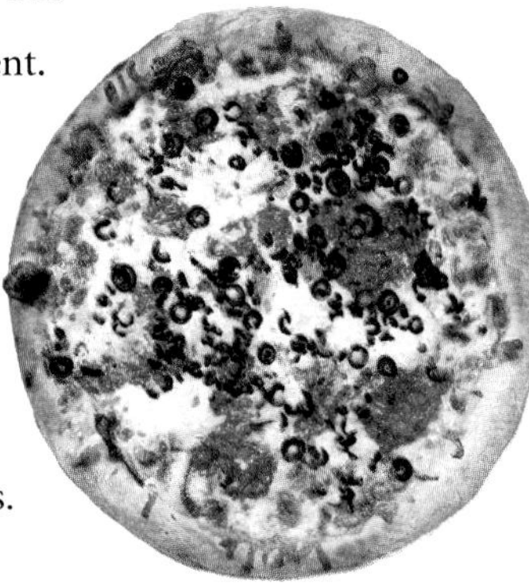

9. **A Slice of the Pie** What is the angle measure of a pizza slice if the whole pizza is cut in the following ways?
   a. five equal slices 72° b. six equal slices 60°
   51.4° c. seven equal slices d. eight equal slices 45°
   e. nine equal slices 40° f. ten equal slices 36°
   g. Suppose you are very hungry. Will you get more to eat if you have two slices of a five-slice pizza or four slices of a twelve-slice pizza? Compare the angle measures. 2 of the 5-slice; 144° vs. 120°
10. Use a compass and straightedge to construct a segment congruent to the one shown at the right.
11. Draw angle $\angle JKL$ using a straightedge. Then construct an angle congruent to $\angle JKL$.

y

Vocabulary
Practice/Skills
Review
R Math Reasoning
Problem Solving
Challenge

For Groups That Finish Early
Explain how the net for the package would change if the box had to be open on top.

Follow Up
Ask students to share their packages with the rest of the class and explain what item they might mail in their package.

Possible Answer
Check students' nets.

Portfolio

Have students select items from their work that demonstrate their understanding of the material in this Superlesson.

You may want to have students include two constructions that they feel are especially clear, their best answer to a **Reflect,** and a measurement or congruence **Exercise** that gave them difficulty.

REFLECT

Possible Answers

1. If sides and angles are not congruent, there may be overlaps or gaps in the package.
2. Architect: dimensions of a building. Automobile mechanic: to see whether a part is the right size. Baker: in measuring ingredients. Softball player: estimating distances to bases.
3. On a number line: take the absolute value of the difference of the coordinates of the endpoints. On a coordinate plane: label points (x_1, y_1) and (x_2, y_2), then use distance formula, $\sqrt{(x_1 - x_2)^2 + (y_1 - y_2)^2}$.

Self-Assessment

Exercise Notes

9. This exercise previews the idea of a central angle developed in Chapter 8. If students need a hint, ask how many right angles "fill" the center of a circle.

1-3

Algebra | Discrete Math | Logic/Reasoning | Industry/Careers

Measuring Figures

16. Provides an application of slope. Students may need to be reminded of the meanings of *rise* and *run.*

17. Open-ended exercise that asks students to devise a measurement system of their own.

Self-Assessment Answers

4. No, the segment is the same whether it is called $\overline{AB}$ or $\overline{BA}$; Yes, the first letter is the endpoint of the ray; No, the points are any two locations on the line; Yes, the center letter denotes the vertex.

5. Segments are congruent, lengths are equal.

6. The notation $\angle PQR$ names the angle, not its size.

7. $0° < \text{angle size} < 180°$.

8. "Congruent angles" requires the angles' measures, not the lengths of their sides, to be the same.

10. 

11. 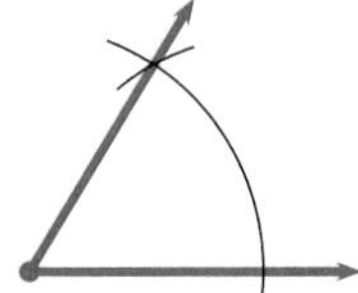

12. $m\angle 1 = m\angle 4 = m\angle 5 = m\angle 8 = 60°$, and $m\angle 2 = m\angle 3 = m\angle 6 = m\angle 7 = 120°$

13. (e)

14. 16; $a_n = (n-1)^2$

15. 63; To get the second number, add 2 to the first. Subsequent numbers are found by adding 4, 8, 16,...(doubling each time).

16–18. See Additional Answers p. T60.

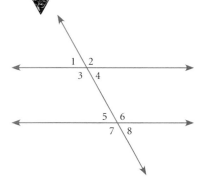

P **12.** Use a protractor to find the measures of these angles. Which angles appear to be congruent? (You may need to copy the figure and extend the lines to make measurement easier.)

1 2 3 4 5 6 7 8

P **13.** Suppose two points, Y and Z, are placed on m to the right of point X so that $XY = 2YZ$. What is $\frac{XZ}{YZ}$?

(a) 1 (b) $\frac{1}{2}$

(c) $\frac{3}{2}$ (d) 2

(e) Cannot be determined.

R **Find the next number in each sequence. Explain the pattern. [1-2]**

14. 0, 1, 4, 9, . . .

15. 1, 3, 7, 15, 31 . . .

PS, MR Careers **16. Here's the Pitch** When an architect designs a home, the roof *pitch* (slope) must be carefully planned. According to Chiao Clerkin Architects, the climate, wind speed, and potential snow load are some of the factors used to determine the best roof pitch for any particular location.

a. Estimate the measure of the angle that the left side of each roof makes with a horizontal line.

b. Measure the rise and the run of a small section of the left side of each roof. Use these measurements to find their slopes. [Previous course]

c. Compare slope with angle measurement. As the slope gets larger, what happens to the angle measure?

d. Which roof pitch is appropriate for a very windy city? a town that experiences major blizzards? a dry desert climate? Explain your choices.

e. Which roof pitch do you find the most visually pleasing? Why?

C **17.** Develop and describe a method for measuring angles that is different from the one you've used in this chapter.

PS **18.** Develop a way to construct an angle whose measure is twice the measure of the angle shown. Show your construction, and explain why it works.

Assessment Resources

- **Quiz 1-3**
- Chapter Assessment Form A
- Chapter Assessment Form B
- Chapter Alternative Assessment
- Mid-Year Assessment
- End-of-Year Assessment
- **AWSMTest and practice software**

Ongoing Assessment

Self-Assessment Self-Assessment Exercises

Embedded Assessment Net from Explore; Reflec 1, 2, 3

ADDITIONAL ANSWERS

1-3 Part D Self-Assessment

16. a. Approximately 20°, 35°, 55°

b. Approximately 0.36, 0.70, and 1.43

c. As slope increases, so does angle measure

d. Possible answers: Lower pitch means lower profile, less wind resistance; Higher pitch reduces snow buildup; Lower pitch means less attic space to store hot air

e. Check students' answers.

17. Check students' answers.

18. Possible answer: Construct a congruent angle, then, using one of the sides of the angle as a base, construct a second congruent angle. Observe that the common side bisects the large angle.

1-4

Symmetry and Reflections

SUPERLESSON AT A GLANCE

Superlesson Goal

Students will be introduced to the concept of line symmetry and investigate the properties of reflections.

Management Guide

	Topic	Objectives	Key Terms	New Ideas	Materials
Part A	Symmetry	To explore line symmetry and to be able to identify figures that do and do not have line symmetry.	Symmetry, line symmetry, line (axis) of symmetry	Symmetry and line symmetry.	**Student** Straightedge, tracing paper, protractor **Teacher** Mirror or Miras, photos or artwork with line symmetry
Part B	Reflections	To learn transformation terminology and investigate reflections.	Reflection, transformation, line of reflection, pre-image, image, reflection image, equidistant, bisect, perpendicular bisector, distance (from a point to a line)	Transformations, reflections of figures. Distance from a point to a line. Bisect, perpendicular bisector.	**Student** Paper, ruler, compass, protractor
Part C	Properties of Reflections	To discover properties of figures that are and are not preserved by reflection.	Orientation	Properties of transformations, orientation.	**Student** Compass, ruler, protractor
Part D	Making Connections	To bring together the ideas of line symmetry and reflection.	In Making Connections, students apply and synthesize key terms and new ideas.		**Student** Construction paper, straightedge, compass

Pacing Chart (45-Minute Periods)

	Comprehensive Course	Core Course	Informal Course
Part A	1	1	1
Part B	1	1	1
Part C	1	1	1
Part D	1	1	1
TOTAL periods for Superlesson	4	4	4

NCTM Standards

Mathematics as Problem Solving

Mathematics as Communication

Mathematics as Reasoning

Mathematical Connections

Conceptual Underpinnings of Calculus

Mathematical Structure

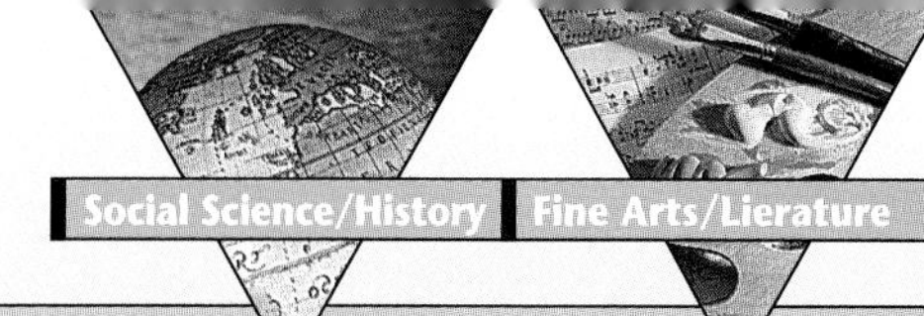

1-4 Symmetry and Reflections

ON THE OTHER HAND

ON THE OTHER HAND

The blankets of the Navajo people of the southwestern United States are renowned not only for their beauty, but for the balance (or symmetry) of their patterns. The Navajo learned the art of weaving from the Pueblo people around 1700. Over the next two centuries, the Navajo developed and refined different styles of blankets famous for their dazzling color and abstract design.

One of the most prized Navajo blanket styles is the finely-woven Chief Blanket. The designs of these blankets are classified into three phases. First-phase blanket designs feature stripes. Second-phase blankets have rectangular patterns as well as stripes. Third-phase blankets include diamond-shaped designs. All phases of Chief Blanket design show symmetry.

Most Navajo blankets are designed to be worn. When the blankets are draped over the head or wrapped around the body, the designs in the two halves of the blankets meet, giving the illusion of an unbroken pattern around the wearer.

1. Symmetry occurs in many natural and manufactured objects in our environment: Navajo blankets, spiders, and spider webs are some examples. What are some other examples of symmetry in the world around us?

2. Is the human face symmetrical or *asymmetrical* (not symmetrical)? Explain your answer.

61

Where Are We Now?

Students know how to measure segments and angles, are familiar with perpendicular lines and right angles, and have explored congruent angles and segments.

Where Are We Going?

In 1-4, the students will investigate line symmetry. They will also explore their first transformation—the reflection. Transformations will be threaded throughout the text. New transformations are introduced in 3-1 (translations), 3-2 (rotations), and 7-2 (dilations), and students investigate compositions of these transformations in Chapter 10.

Possible Answers

1. Birds and other animals tend to be symmetric; cars are symmetric.
2. The human face is approximately symmetric, although there are always some differences between the left and right sides.

More About Symmetry

According to Matt Ridley, in selecting mates, female swallows look for males with symmetrical tails and female scorpion flies prefer males with symmetrical bodies. Disease or genetic defects can cause asymmetrical development, so symmetrical males may have "better" genes. (Matt Ridley, "Swallows and Scorpion Flies Find Symmetry Is Beautiful," *Science,* pp. 327–328. July, 1992.)

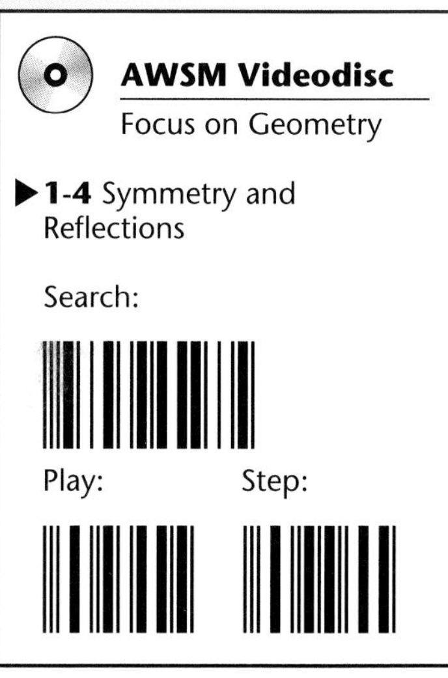

Algebra	Functions	Discrete Math	Probability	Data/Statistics

Symmetry and Reflections

PART A At a Glance

Objective

To explore line symmetry and to be able to identify figures that do and do not have line symmetry.

Development

Students are introduced to the idea of line symmetry.

In the **Explore,** students draw figures with different numbers of lines of symmetry.

Suggested Materials

Student Straightedge, tracing paper, protractor

Teacher Mirror or Miras, photos or artwork with line symmetry

Key Terms

Symmetry, line symmetry, line (axis) of symmetry

First Five Minutes

Transparency FFM 1-4A

Read the first two paragraphs on page 62. Then sketch an object that has a line of symmetry.

Motivate

Ask...

- What geometric figures do you know that can be folded onto themselves?

ALTERNATE EXAMPLES

Transparency AE 1-4A

1-4 PART A Symmetry

← CONNECT → *You've already explored some patterns in geometry. Now you will explore the patterns and the balance of symmetrical figures.*

The word **symmetry** comes from Greek. The prefix *sym-* means "together," and *metry* means "measure." So *symmetry* means "measuring together."

If you fold a picture in half and both halves match each other perfectly, then the figure has **line symmetry** (*symmetry* for short). The fold is the **line of symmetry,** or **axis of symmetry.** A line of symmetry divides a figure into two mirror-image halves. All the Native American masks shown above have line symmetry.

EXAMPLES

Consider the alphabet shown below.

A B C D E F G H I J K L M N O P
Q R S T U V W X Y Z

1. Which letters have a vertical axis of symmetry?
   A H I M O T U V W X Y
   The vertical lines of symmetry for A and H are shown.

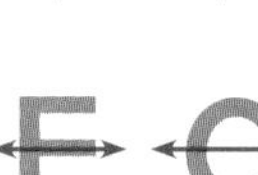

2. Which letters have a horizontal axis of symmetry?
   C D E H I K O X
   The horizontal lines of symmetry for E and C are shown.

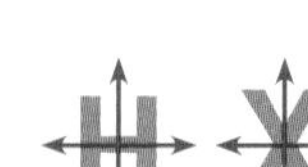

3. Which letters have two or more axes of symmetry?
   H I O X
   Both lines of symmetry are shown for H and X.

62 1-4 • SYMMETRY AND REFLECTIONS

Tips from Teachers

You may want to pass around a mirror or Miras and pictures or photographs with line symmetry, and have students use the mirror to see lines of symmetry.

TRY IT

Copy the figures below and sketch all lines of symmetry for each.

a.

b.

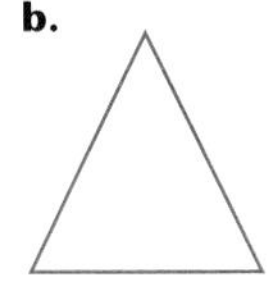

c.

In the following Explore, you will investigate figures with different numbers of lines of symmetry.

EXPLORE: KEEPING IT SYMMETRIC

MATERIALS

Straightedge
Tracing paper
Protractor

1. Use a straightedge to draw a line on tracing paper. Then draw a curve from one point on the line to another point on the line, as shown at the right.
2. Fold the paper on the line so that you can copy the curve, and draw the other half of the pattern. Check to see if your finished design has symmetry.
3. Now draw two perpendicular lines of symmetry. (Use a protractor if necessary.) Draw a quarter of your figure from one of the lines to the next, as shown in the middle figure at the right.
4. Fold the tracing paper, and complete a symmetric design. How many times did you need to fold the paper?
5. Try four lines of symmetry, as shown in the drawing. (The angles between the lines measure 45°.) Again, report on how many folds you needed to make before your design was complete.
6. Make any conjectures you can relating lines of symmetry, folds, and the characteristics of your final figure.

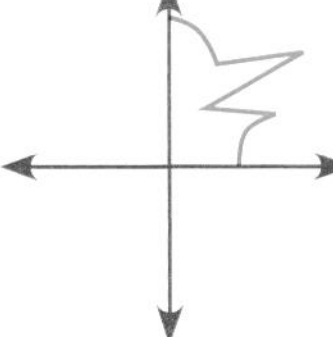

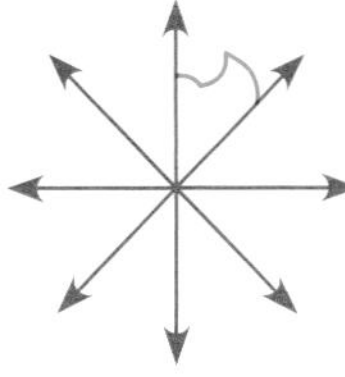

REFLECT

1. Explain how a mirror can help to illustrate line symmetry.
2. Define *symmetry* and *axis of symmetry* in your own words.
3. Can you draw triangles with the following characteristics?
   a. no lines of symmetry
   b. exactly one line of symmetry
   c. exactly two lines of symmetry
   d. exactly three lines of symmetry

Student Resources

- **Alternative Lessons** 1-4A
- **Laboratory Manual** 1-4A
- Technology Lab Manual
- **Practice** 1-4A
- **Study Guide and Journal** 1-4A
- **Guía de estudios y Diario** 1-4A
- **Multilingual Handbook**
- **More Look Ahead** 1-4A
- SAT Preparation

Media Resources

- **Transparency FFM** 1-4A
- **Transparency AE** 1-4A
- Teaching Transparency
- **AWSMTest and practice software**
- **AWSM Videodisc**

EXPLORE

Keeping It Symmetric

Recommended group size: 2

The Point

To draw figures with different numbers of lines of symmetry.

Look and Listen...

- For students who are having difficulty understanding how best to trace their design.

Ask...

- Do you know that you can draw on both sides of the paper?

For Groups That Finish Early

Draw a figure with exactly three lines of symmetry. Make a conjecture about the angles between the lines. **They measure 60°.**

Follow Up

Ask what the connection is between the number of lines of symmetry and the number of folds needed.

Possible Answers

4. Twice
5. Four folds are needed.
6. Number of folds = number of lines of symmetry. In general, the more lines of symmetry, the "rounder" the figure.

Journal

Reflect 1 and 2 are suitable for journal entries.

REFLECT

Possible Answers

1. Place a rectangular mirror against an object. The mirror's edge is an axis of symmetry between the object and its reflection.
2. A symmetric object has an evenness, or balance. An axis of symmetry divides an object into two mirror-image halves.
3. **a.** Yes
   b. Yes
   c. No
   d. Yes

TRY IT

Answers

a. 

b. 

c. 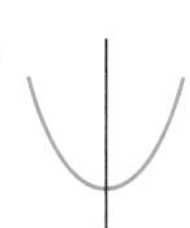

Part A Exercises

Exercise Notes

Core

16. Students see that a circle has an infinite number of lines of symmetry.

19. Students may be surprised to see mathematical terms in literature.

Literature Note: William Blake was an artist and poet in the 1700s during the European Age of Reason. The growing importance of science and mathematics influenced many philosophers, writers, and artists at this time.

22. Students may disagree as to which alphabet is the more appealing. You may want to discuss other factors that contribute to the visual appeal of an object.

Look Ahead

These exercises preview reflections, which students will explore in 1-4 Part B.

More Math Reasoning

34–36. These exercises explore symmetry in the graphs of algebraic equations.

Exercise Answers

Core

1. One line

2. Two lines

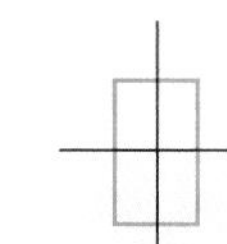

3. No lines

4. Six lines

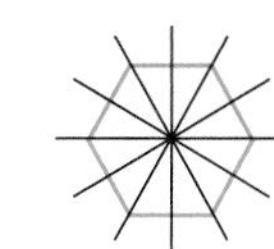

Exercises

CORE

P **Getting Started Copy the figures below, and sketch all lines of symmetry for each. If there are no such lines, say so.**

1. 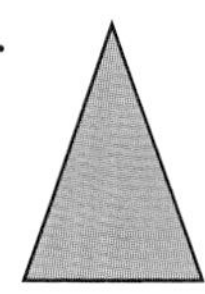

2. 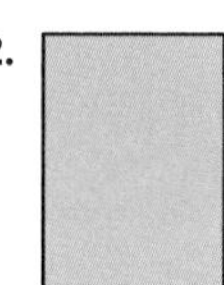

3. 

4. 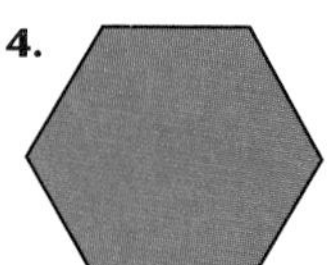

P **Is the red line in each figure a line of symmetry? Are there other lines of symmetry for any of the figures? If so, copy those figures, and draw the other lines of symmetry.**

5.

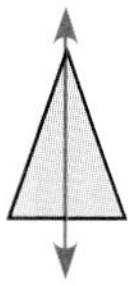

6. 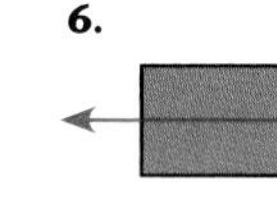

7. 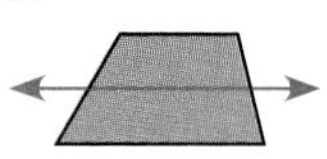

P **Copy each figure. Then draw the other half of each figure so that the red line is a line of symmetry.**

8. 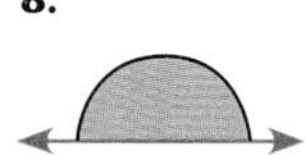

9.

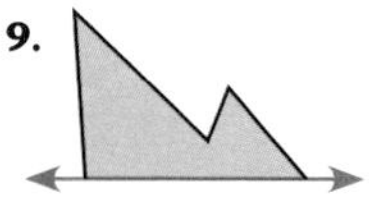

10. 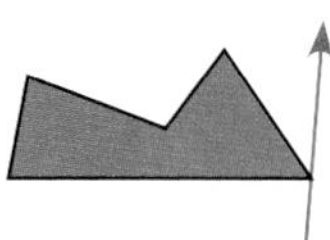

P **Give the number of lines of symmetry for each traffic sign. Then copy the signs, and draw the lines of symmetry.**

11. 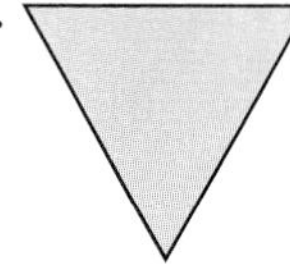

12. 

13. 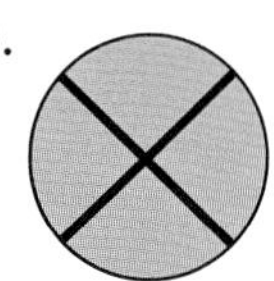

14. 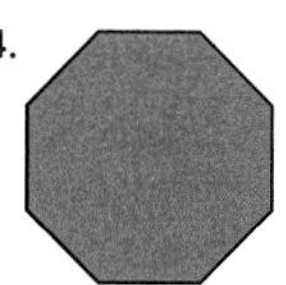

V **15.** Write the word or phrase that correctly completes the statement.

If a line divides a figure into two mirror-image halves, it is a ____ for the figure.

MR **16.** A rectangle has two lines of symmetry.

a. How many lines of symmetry does a square have?

b. How many lines of symmetry does a circle have?

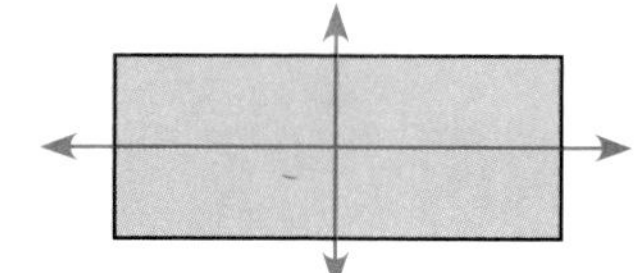

Key

V Vocabulary

P Practice/Skills

R Review

MR Math Reasoning

PS Problem Solving

C Challenge

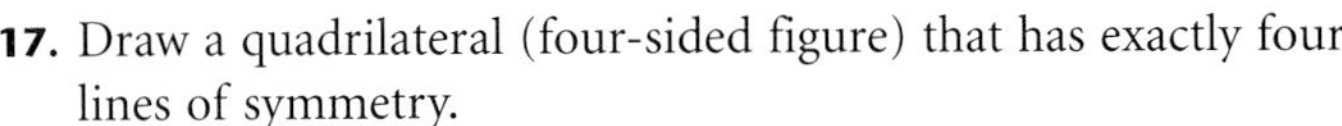

17. Draw a quadrilateral (four-sided figure) that has exactly four lines of symmetry.

18. Make a design that has two lines of symmetry. Show both lines of symmetry in your sketch.

19. Symmetry in Poetry The following passage is an excerpt from a poem written by William Blake (1757–1827).

Tiger! Tiger! burning bright
In the forests of the night,
What immortal hand or eye
Could frame thy fearful symmetry?

Describe or illustrate a line of symmetry for a tiger.

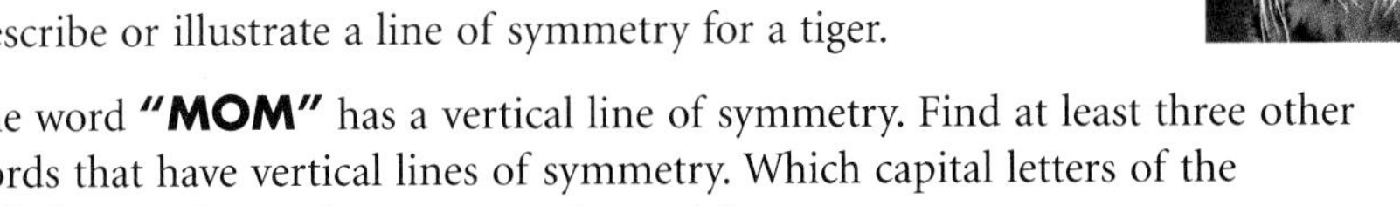

20. The word **"MOM"** has a vertical line of symmetry. Find at least three other words that have vertical lines of symmetry. Which capital letters of the alphabet can be used to create such words?

21. The word **"BOB"** has a horizontal line of symmetry. (Disregard the slight difference between the upper and lower halves of the letter "B".) Find at least three other words that have horizontal lines of symmetry. Which capital letters of the alphabet can be used to create such words?

22. The Best "Bet"? Which of the two alphabets below has more symmetrical letters? Do you feel that the more symmetrical alphabet is more appealing to look at? Explain.

A B C D E F G H I J K L M N O P Q R S T U V W X Y Z

A B C D E F G H I J K L M N O P Q R S T U V W X Y Z

23. A triangle with two vertices at G and H is to be completed by selecting one of the other points shown, A–F. What is the probability that the triangle will have line symmetry?

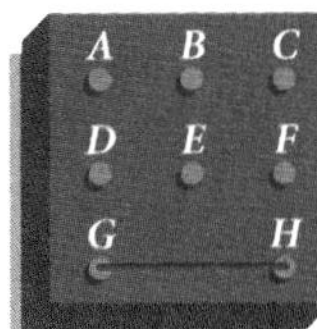

LOOK AHEAD

24. Finish the figure at the right so that it has line symmetry. Explain the method you used to complete the figure. Is there more than one way to complete the figure?

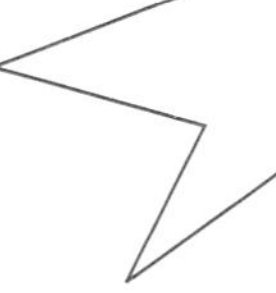

25. Explain how the reflected image of an object in a mirror is different from the object itself.

Ongoing Assessment

Self-Assessment Exercises 1–17 odd, 20, 21, 23

Embedded Assessment Try It a; Explore Step 6; Reflect 1; Exercises 4, 10, 18

5. Yes; No

6. Yes; Yes

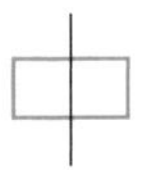

7. No; No

8.

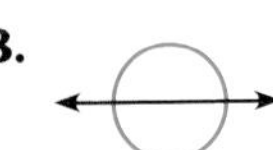

9.

10.

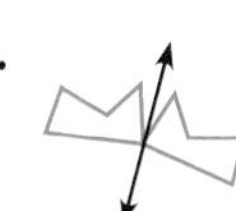

11. 3

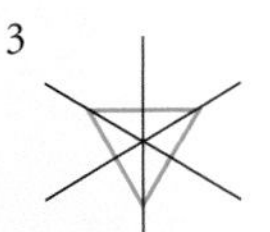

12. 2

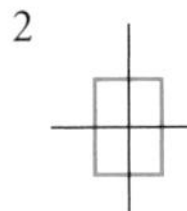

13. 4

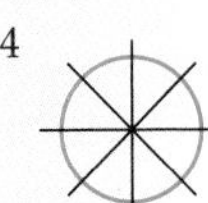

14. 8

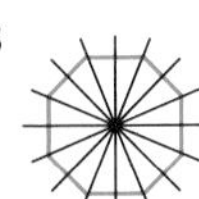

15. Line of symmetry (or an axis of symmetry)

16. a. 4

b. An infinite number (every possible diameter line)

17. Square

18. Possible answer: Rectangle

19. Possible answer: Line down middle of a face separating it into left and right sides

20. Possible answers: WOW, TUT, AVA (name); AHIMOTUVWXY

21. Possible answers: BOX, BED, HEX; BCDEHIKOX

22. Possible answer: Second; No, the variation in the widths of the lines of the letters is easier on the eyes

23. $\frac{4}{6} = \frac{2}{3}$

Look Ahead

24. Reflect figure over line joining open endpoints; Yes, add an arbitrary segment and then use the previous method

25. Possible answer: The left and right sides of the object are reversed.

Symmetry and Reflections

More Practice

26. None

27. 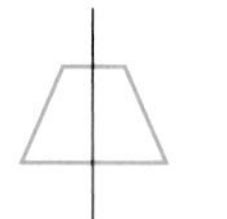

28. 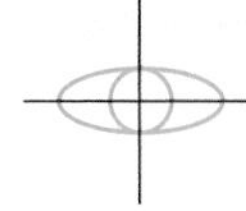

29. 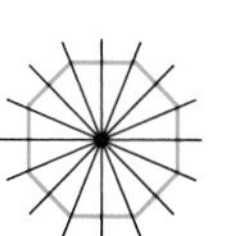

30. 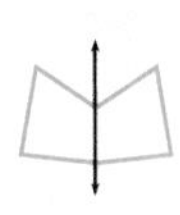

31. **32.**

More Math Reasoning

33. a. 6

b. Check students' answers.

34–36.

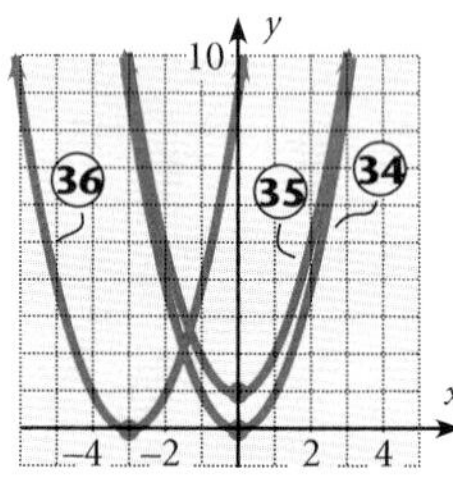

For $y = x^2$ and $y = x^2 + 1$, the line of symmetry is $x = 0$, and for $y = (x + 3)^2$, it is $x = -3$.

37. If a polygon is divided by a symmetric axis, each side consists of line segments that have congruent segments on the other side.

MORE PRACTICE

P **Copy the figures below and sketch all lines of symmetry for each. If there are no such lines, say so.**

26. 

27. 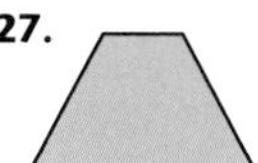

28. 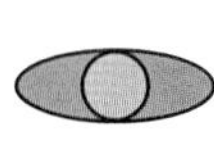

29. 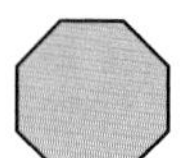

P **Copy each figure. Then draw the other half of each figure so that the red line is a line of symmetry.**

30. 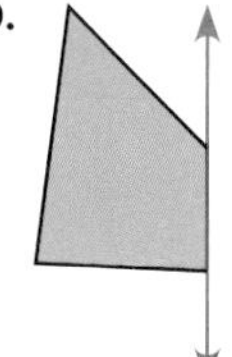

31. 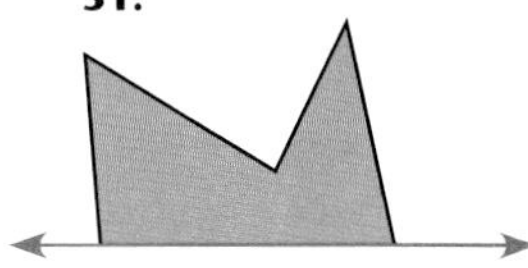

32. 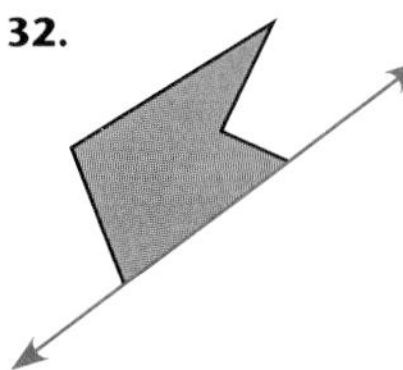

MORE MATH REASONING

MR, PS Science **33. Snowflake Problem** Snowflakes are examples of symmetry in nature.

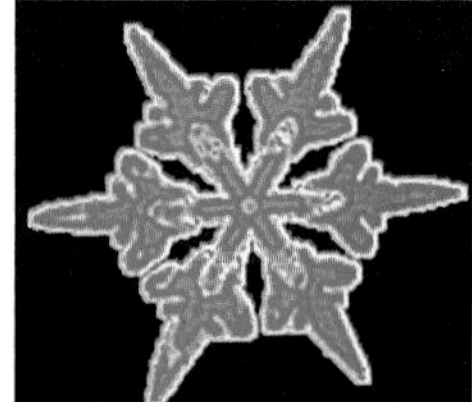

a. How many lines of symmetry do these snowflakes have?

b. You can make a model of a snowflake by folding a round piece of paper and cutting out shapes along the fold lines. Explain how you can fold a piece of paper to get a model of the lines of symmetry for a snowflake.

Graph the following equations. Show the line of symmetry for each graph. Then write the equation of the line of symmetry.

MR **34.** $y = x^2$ **35.** $y = x^2 + 1$ **36.** $y = (x + 3)^2$

MR, C **37.** How is congruence related to symmetry? Write a brief paragraph explaining the connection.

Key

V Vocabulary
P Practice/Skills
R Review
MR Math Reasoning
PS Problem Solving
C Challenge

1-4 PART B Reflections

← CONNECT → ***You've explored figures that have lines of symmetry. Now you will reflect geometric figures over lines. Your measuring skills will help you understand the relationship between a figure and its reflection.***

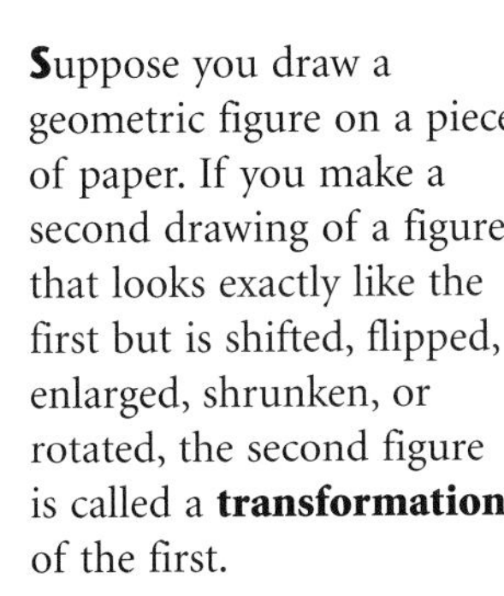

Suppose you draw a geometric figure on a piece of paper. If you make a second drawing of a figure that looks exactly like the first but is shifted, flipped, enlarged, shrunken, or rotated, the second figure is called a **transformation** of the first.

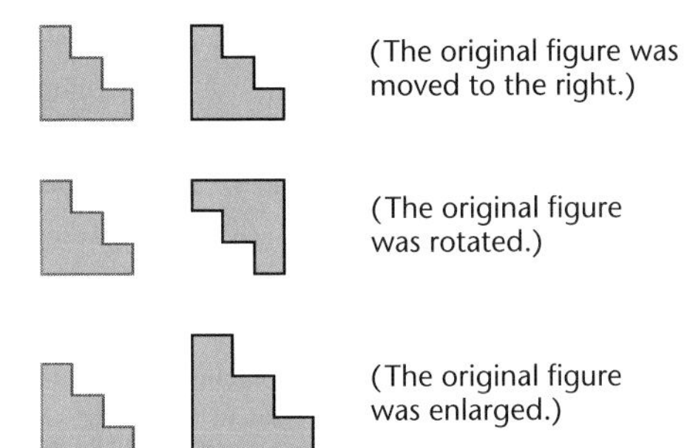

(The original figure was moved to the right.)

(The original figure was rotated.)

(The original figure was enlarged.)

A reflection is a special type of transformation. A **reflection** is a flipping of a figure over a line. This line is the **line of reflection.** Line ℓ below is a line of reflection. The original figure, called the **pre-image,** is shown in black. The **image,** after the transformation, is in blue.

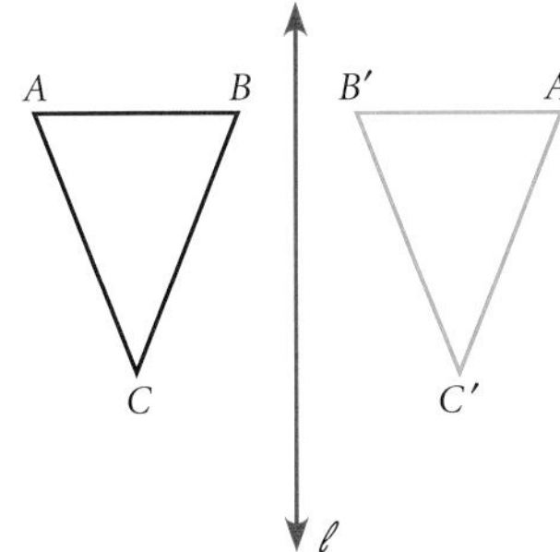

When a point on the pre-image is labeled, like A, B, or C in the figure, the matching (or corresponding) point on the image is often labeled with the same letter followed by a prime sign. So C' (C-prime) is the image of point C. The image of triangle ABC is triangle $A'B'C'$. (When naming images of figures, we list corresponding points in the same order.)

In the following Explore, you will investigate the relationship between measurement and reflection.

PART B At a Glance

Objective

To learn transformation terminology and investigate reflections.

Development

Students see the idea of a transformation for the first time and learn important terminology.

In the **Explore,** students discover relationships between a reflection point and its pre-image.

Terminology important for describing reflections is introduced, including *perpendicular bisector* and the *distance from a point to a line.*

Suggested Materials

Student Paper, ruler, compass, protractor

Key Terms

Reflection, transformation, line of reflection, pre-image, image, reflection image, equidistant, bisect, perpendicular bisector

First Five Minutes

Transparency FFM 1-4B

Sketch a segment and an angle. Then use a compass and straightedge to construct a segment and an angle congruent to them.

Motivate

Ask...

- What does *transformation* mean?
- What transformations in nature do you know about?

Student Resources

- Alternative Lessons 1-4B
- Laboratory Manual 1-4B
- Technology Lab Manual
- Practice 1-4B
- Study Guide and Journal 1-4B
- Guía de estudios y Diario 1-4B
- Multilingual Handbook
- More Look Back 1-4B
- SAT Preparation

Media Resources

- Transparency FFM 1-4B
- Transparency AE
- Teaching Transparency
- AWSMTest and practice software
- AWSM Videodisc

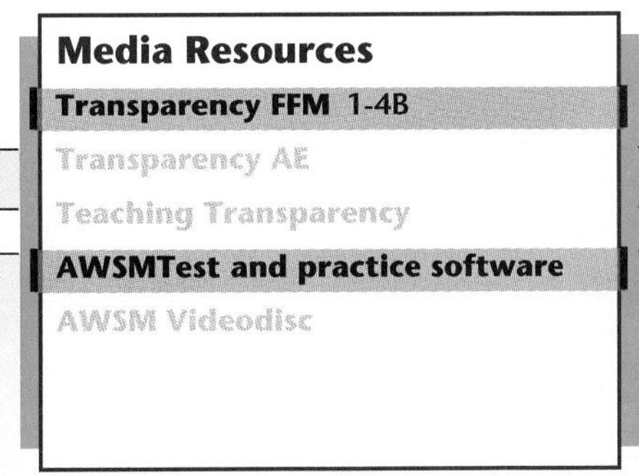

1-4

Symmetry and Reflections

Note: In Step 3 of the **Explore,** students are asked to find the distance from a point to the fold prior to seeing the formal definition of the distance from a point to a line. This shows them that the definition is consistent with their intuition.

EXPLORE

Reflective Detective

Recommended group size: 4

The Point

To find the relationship between a point, a line of reflection, and its image under the reflection.

Look and Listen...

- For students who are having difficulty matching pre-image points with their images.
- For students who do not realize that they can write on both sides of the tracing paper.

Ask...

- How do you find the distance from a point to the fold?

For Groups That Finish Early

Compare other aspects of the triangle formed by the pre-image points and the triangle formed by the image points.

Follow Up

Ask students to read the definitions at the bottom of page 68. Then have them summarize their answers to Step 4 using this vocabulary.

Possible Answer

4. The distances are equal, and the angles are right angles. (Equivalent answers: The line of reflection is the perpendicular bisector of the segment joining a point to its image; a point and its image are equidistant from the line of reflection.)

Algebra	Functions	Discrete Math	Probability	Data/Statistics

EXPLORE: REFLECTIVE DETECTIVE

MATERIALS

Paper, Ruler
Protractor

1. Fold a rectangular sheet of paper in half. Poke the tip of a pencil through the folded paper at three points that are not collinear.

2. Open the paper and draw segments connecting the holes on each side of the fold. (You should have two triangles, with the fold as the line of reflection.) Label the vertices of the pre-image, and use prime notation to label the points of the image.

3. Draw segments connecting the points of the image with the corresponding points of the pre-image. Measure some of the segments that cross the fold. Then measure the distances from the points to the fold. Finally, measure the angles these segments make with the fold.

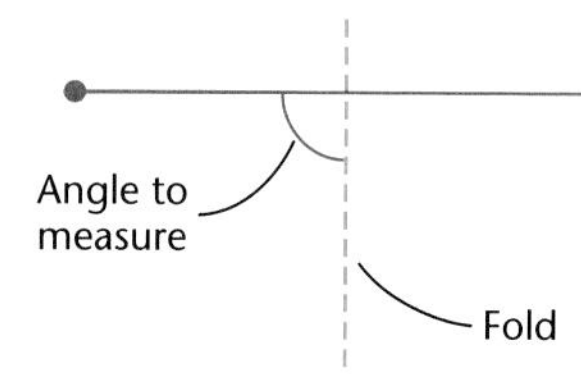

4. What do you notice about the distances? the angles? Make any conjectures you can about the angle and distance measurements involving a point and its reflection image. Discuss your conjectures with your classmates.

The following terms are useful in describing reflections.

The **distance from a point to a line** is the length of the perpendicular segment from the point to the line.

If two points are the same distance from another point (or segment, line, or other element), they are **equidistant** from it.

A figure is **bisected** by another figure when it is cut into two congruent halves. So a **perpendicular bisector** of a segment is a line (or segment) that divides the segment into two congruent segments and is perpendicular to it.

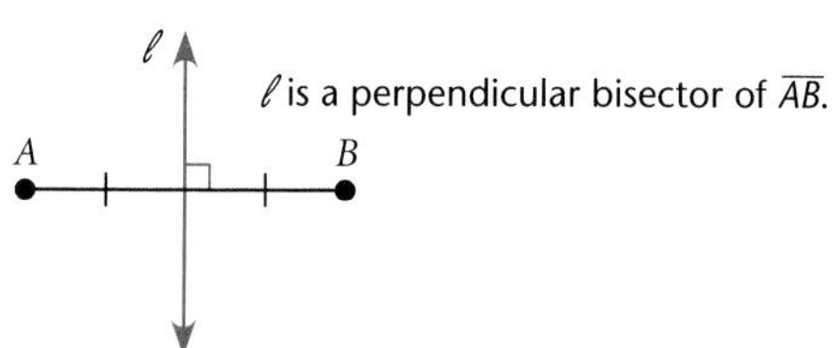

Using a compass and straightedge, you can construct a perpendicular to a line from a given point, as shown on page 69.

Alert

Students may find prime notation difficult. You may wish to emphasize that *A* and *A′* are *different* points.

CONSTRUCTION: PERPENDICULAR TO A LINE

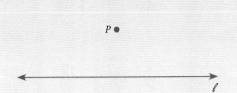

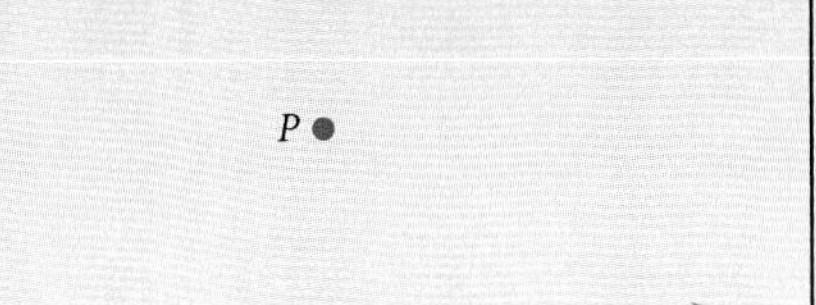

1. Begin by sketching line ℓ and point P, not on ℓ. You will construct the line that goes through P and is perpendicular to ℓ.

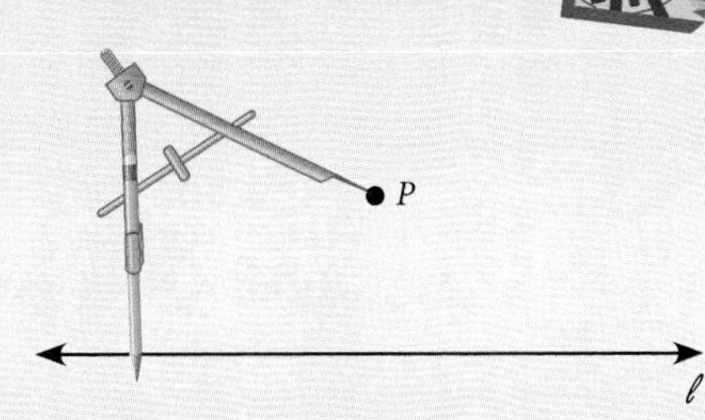

2. Open your compass to a measure greater than the distance from P to line ℓ. Place the point of the compass on P.

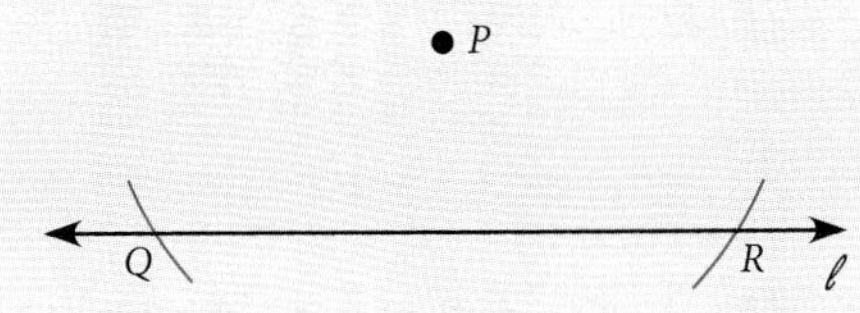

3. Keeping the setting of the compass consistent, make two arcs that intersect line ℓ. Label the intersection points of the arcs and the line Q and R.

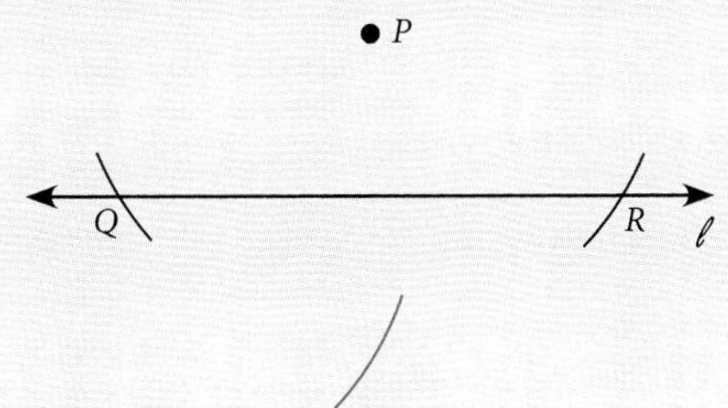

4. Now place the tip of the compass on point Q. Make an arc on the opposite side of the line from point P.

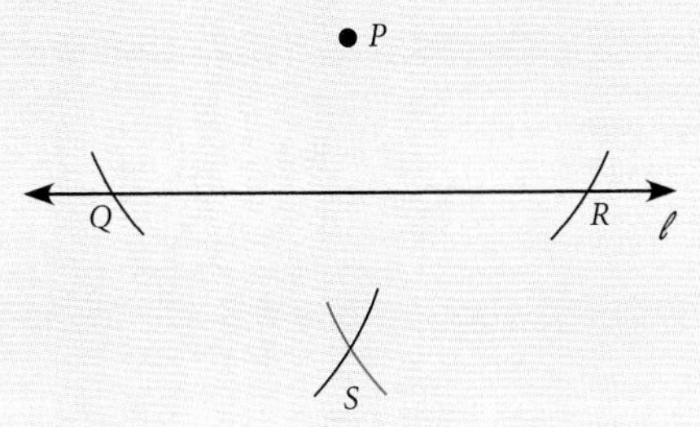

5. Leaving the compass opening the same size, move the tip of the compass to point R. Make an arc that intersects the arc you made in Step 4. Label the point where the arcs intersect S.

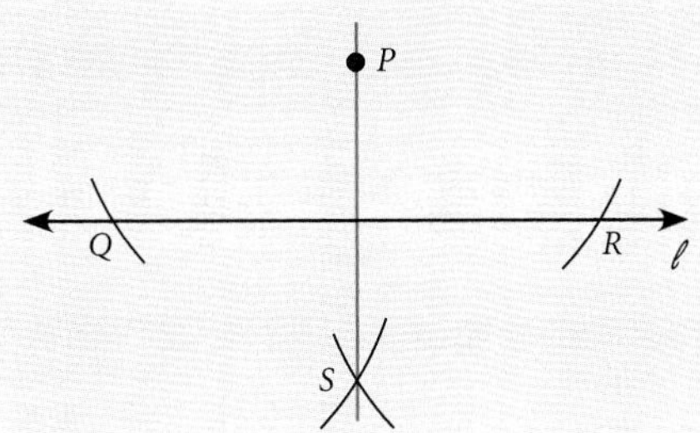

6. Draw the line through P and S. $\overleftrightarrow{PS}$ is perpendicular to line ℓ.

Construction: Perpendicular to a Line

The Point

To construct a perpendicular to a given line through a point not on the line.

Presenting the Construction

You may want to have students follow the instructions given for Steps 1–3 and then model these steps of the construction for the class, so they can check their work. Then you might have the students proceed through Steps 4–6. After they have finished, complete the construction on the board or overhead projector.

Extension: You may want to have students mark their finished constructions to show perpendicular lines and congruent segments.

Alert

Students may have difficulty understanding the difference between a line of symmetry and a line of reflection. You may want to explain that a figure with a line of symmetry isn't necessarily the product of a reflection.

Symmetry and Reflections

Shows students the connection between the construction of a perpendicular and the construction of a reflection point. This will be an important skill for constructing reflection images.

Possible Answer

1. Use a compass to measure the distance from P to ℓ. Using this compass setting, place the tip of the compass at the point of intersection of $\overleftrightarrow{PS}$ and ℓ, and swing an arc onto the "S side" of $\overleftrightarrow{PS}$. The point where the arc intersects $\overleftrightarrow{PS}$ is the reflection image of P over ℓ.

Journal

Consider 1 and **Reflect** 1 are suitable for journal entries.

REFLECT

Possible Answers

1. A figure and its reflection image, taken together, always have line symmetry. The line of reflection is an axis of symmetry. However, a figure with line symmetry may not be the product of a reflection.
2. Line ℓ is the perpendicular bisector of $\overline{PP'}$.
3. A and its image are the same point.

Part B Exercises

Exercise Notes

Core

1. Provides step-by-step guidance for constructing reflection images.

CONSIDER

1. **How could you use the preceding construction to help you find the image of P after a reflection over line ℓ?**

We can now give a more formal definition of *reflection.*

DEFINITION

Point A' is the **reflection image over line ℓ** of point A if ℓ is the perpendicular bisector of $\overline{AA'}$.

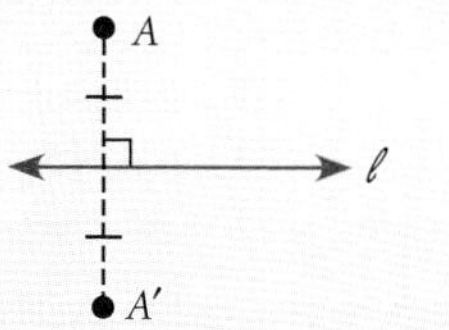

REFLECT

1. Describe how reflection is related to symmetry.
2. Suppose P' is the image of P after a reflection over line ℓ. Using the term *perpendicular bisector,* describe the relationship of ℓ to P and P'.
3. Suppose point A lies on line m. If point A is reflected over line m, what can you say about point A and its image?

Exercises

CORE

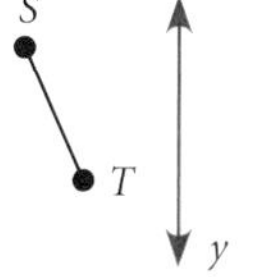

P 1. **Getting Started** Follow the steps below and at the top of page 71 to construct the reflection image of segment $\overline{ST}$ over line y.

a. Sketch a figure with $\overline{ST}$ and line y similar to the one at the top right.

b. Use your compass and straightedge to construct a line through S perpendicular to y. (The construction marks are not shown in the figure.)

c. Use your compass to measure the perpendicular segment from S to y. Construct another segment congruent to it on the same line, but on the other side of y. You have located the reflection image of S. Label it S'.

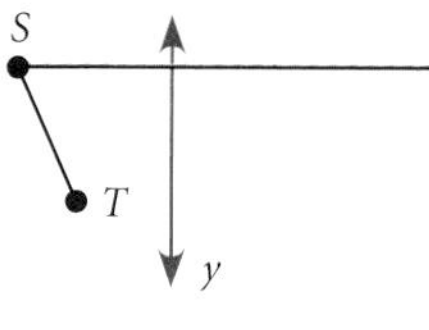

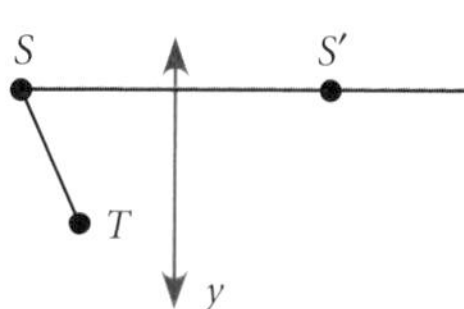

Key

V Vocabulary
P Practice/Skills
R Review
MR Math Reasoning
PS Problem Solving
C Challenge

Diversity Issues

When evaluating student explanations, you may wish to separate the thinking process that you are evaluating from the words that express it, especially when working with students of limited English proficiency. Sophisticated ideas are not always expressed in complex sentences.

d. Repeat **1b** and **1c** to find the reflection image of *T*. Label it *T'*.
e. Use your straightedge to connect *S'* and *T'*. $\overline{S'T'}$ is the reflection image of $\overline{ST}$ over line *y*.

2. Draw a triangle with vertices *F*, *G*, and *H*. Add a line of reflection, ℓ. Then use a compass and straightedge to construct the reflection of the triangle over line ℓ.

Line ℓ is a line of reflection in the figure.

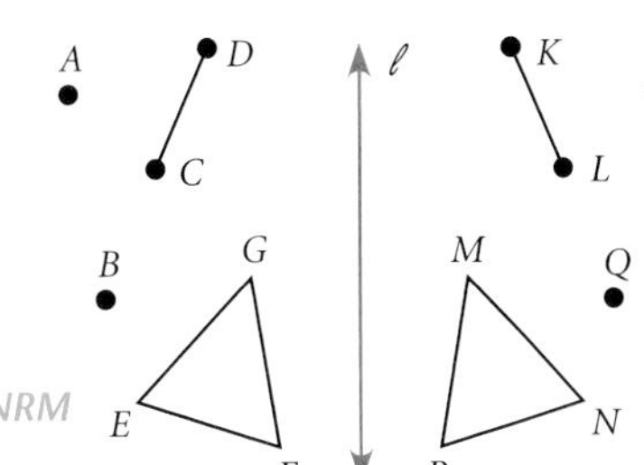

3. What is the reflection image of *A*? P
4. What is the reflection image of *B*? Q
5. What is the reflection image of $\overline{CD}$? LK
6. What is the reflection image of triangle *EFG*? Triangle *NRM*

In the figure, *X'* is the reflection image of *X*.

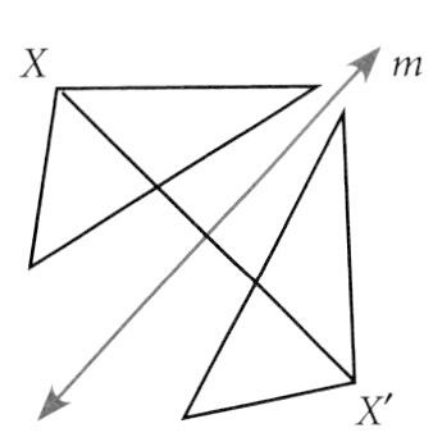

7. What is the measure of the angle formed by the line of reflection and the segment connecting points *X* and *X'*? Explain. F; Reflection
8. How is the distance from *X* to the line of reflection related to the distance from *X* to *X'*? How do you know?

Determine whether each statement is true or false. If the statement is false, change the underlined word to make it true.

9. Symmetry is a transformation. F; Reflection
10. A line of symmetry divides a figure into two halves that are mirror images. T
11. The coordinate system is useful in analyzing reflections.
    a. Point *C* has coordinates (2, 3). Find the coordinates of the image of point *C* after a reflection over the *x*-axis. (2, −3)
    b. Find the coordinates of the image of point *C* after a reflection over the *y*-axis. (−2, 3)
    c. What is the reflection image of (*a*, *b*) over the *x*-axis? (*a*, −*b*)

Problem-Solving Tip

Look for a pattern.

    d. What is the reflection image of (*a*, *b*) over the *y*-axis? (−*a*, *b*)

12. **Blanket Symmetry** Describe the lines of symmetry in this Navajo blanket. How are these related to reflections?

Ongoing Assessment

Self-Assessment Exercises 1, 3, 4, 5, 7, 9, 12

Embedded Assessment Explore Step 4; Reflect 1; Exercises 2, 6, 11, 13

11. Provides a connection between reflections and the coordinate system.

More Math Reasoning

26. Students see that the reflection image of (*a*, *b*) over $y = x$ is (*b*, *a*). This discovery connects inverses of functions to reflections. You may want to point out this connection formally.

27. Students use perpendicular bisectors to make conjectures about quadrilaterals. These conjectures preview explorations of quadrilaterals in Chapter 6.

Exercise Answers

Core

1.

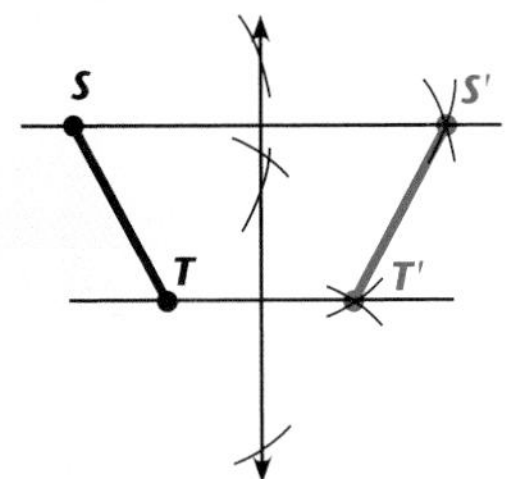

2. Possible answer:

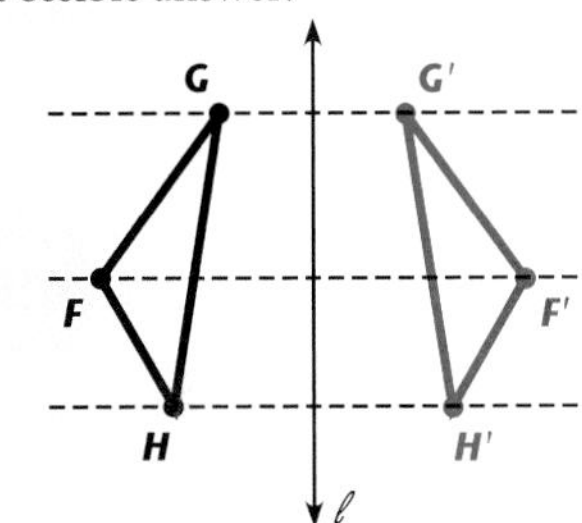

7. 90°; In order for *m* to be the line of reflection, it must be a perpendicular bisector of $\overline{XX'}$.

8. *X* to $m = \frac{1}{2}(XX')$ because *m* bisects $\overline{XX'}$.

12. One is vertical, one horizontal; The top and bottom halves are reflections of each other, as are the left and right halves.

13. a. 3, *GH* or *HG*
    b. $GI = 5 > GH = 3$
    c. The shortest distance from a point to a line is the length of the perpendicular line segment from the point to the line.

Look Back

14.

15.

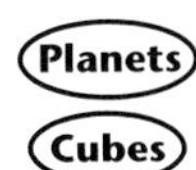

Symmetry and Reflections

16.

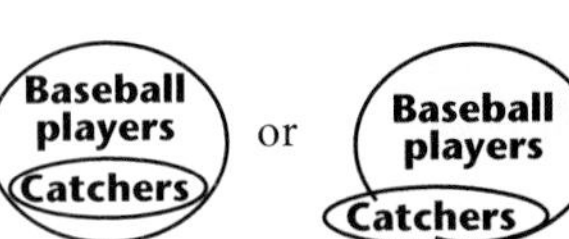

17.

More Practice

21. Possible answer:

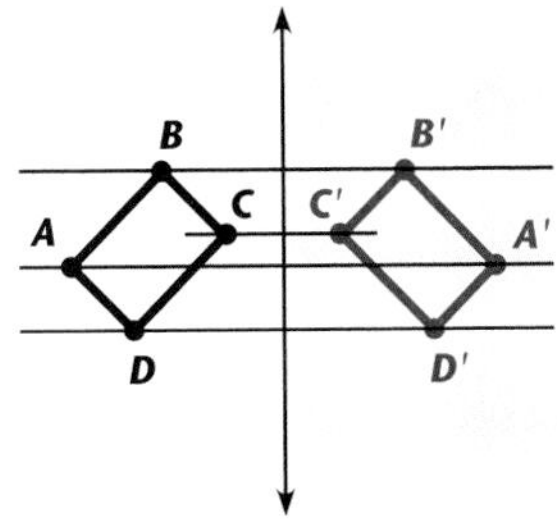

More Math Reasoning

26. a. $A(0, 2)$ and $C(2, 0)$, and $B(1, 4)$ and $D(4, 1)$

b.

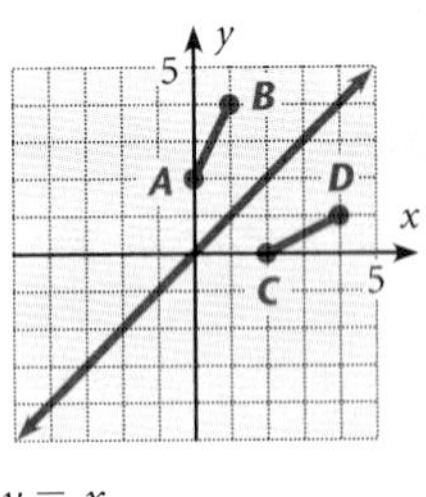

$y = x$

c. (a, b)'s reflection is (b, a)

27. a.

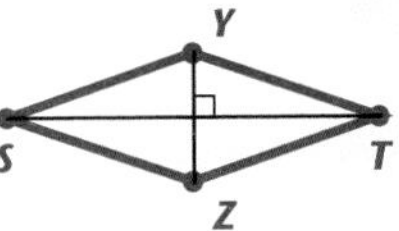

The four segments are congruent.

b.

The four segments are congruent

c. Possible answer: Connecting the endpoints of the bisectors forms an equilateral parallelogram (rhombus). If the bisectors are congruent, the parallelogram is a square.

MR **13. a.** Find the distance from point G to line $\overleftrightarrow{HI}$ in the figure at the right. What is another name for the distance you found?

b. Find GI. How does this compare to the distance from G to $\overleftrightarrow{HI}$?

c. What property of segments from a point to a line does your work in **13a** and **13b** illustrate?

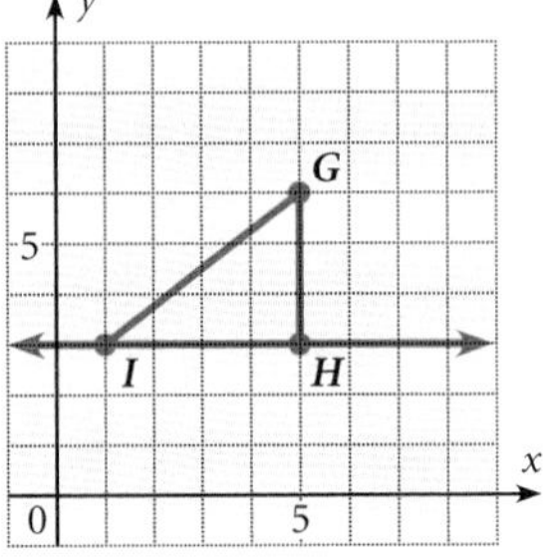

LOOK BACK

R **Draw a Venn diagram to illustrate each of the following. [1-2]**

14. All horses are mammals.

15. No planets are cubes.

16. Some baseball players are catchers.

17. Every turtle is a reptile.

R **Find *AB* for each set of coordinates. Where necessary, round answers to the nearest tenth. [1-3]**

18. $A(2, 5)$, $B(5, 1)$ 5

19. $A(-3, -11)$, $B(2, -23)$ 13

20. $A(2.2, 1.3)$, $B(6.4, -2.7)$ 5.8

MORE PRACTICE

P **21.** Draw a rectangle and a line of reflection that is not parallel to any of the sides of the rectangle. Then construct the reflection of the rectangle.

P **Line ℓ is a line of reflection in the figure.**

22. What is the reflection image of A? Y

23. What is the reflection image of B? Z

24. What is the reflection image of $\overline{CD}$? $\overline{JH}$

25. What is the reflection image of triangle EFG? Triangle RTS

Y, Z, T, R, S, J, H, ℓ, E, F, G, A, B, D, C

MORE MATH REASONING

PS, C **26.** A segment and its reflection image are shown.

a. Name two pairs of corresponding points and their coordinates.

b. Copy the figure, and sketch the line of reflection. Write the equation for the line of reflection.

c. Make and justify a conjecture about the reflection of any point (a, b) over the line $y = x$.

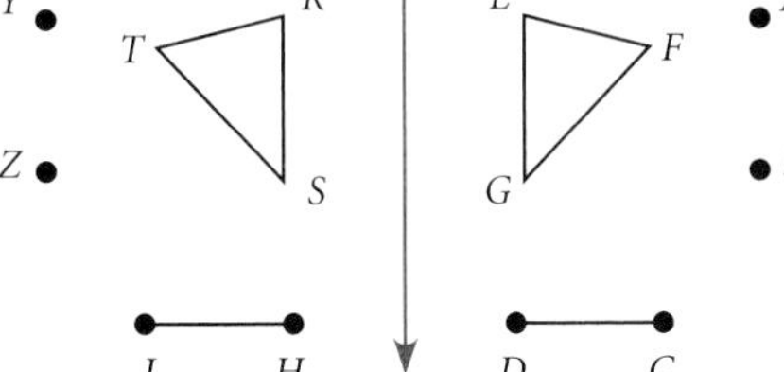

Key

V Vocabulary
P Practice/Skills
R Review
MR Math Reasoning
PS Problem Solving
C Challenge

Technology Note

If you use geometry software in the **Explore** on page 73, you may need to show students how to measure angles in triangles. This is generally done by selecting the three vertices of the triangle (with the vertex of the angle you wish to measure selected second) and then using the measurement tool.

27. Use a ruler and protractor for the following.
   a. Draw two segments, $\overline{ST}$ and $\overline{YZ}$, that are perpendicular bisectors of each other but are not congruent. Draw the segments $\overline{SY}$, $\overline{YT}$, $\overline{TZ}$, and $\overline{ZS}$. What do you notice?
   b. Repeat **27a**, but this time make $\overline{ST}$ congruent to $\overline{YZ}$. What do you notice?
   c. Make as many conjectures as you can about your results in **27a** and **27b.** (If you need to, make additional drawings to convince yourself of your conjectures.)

1-4 PART C Properties of Reflections

← CONNECT → ***You know how to reflect a geometric figure over a line. Now you will discover some of the properties of reflections.***

In our informal definition of transformations, we said that an image "looks exactly like" its pre-image. But the image *is* usually different from the pre-image in some ways. Exactly which characteristics of the pre-image are changed and which stay the same depends on the transformation. You will now investigate this for reflections.

EXPLORE: TO PRESERVE OR NOT TO PRESERVE

MATERIALS

Compass, Ruler
Protractor

1. Draw a line, m, to divide your paper in half. On one side of the line, draw a scalene triangle. (Scalene triangles have no two sides the same length.) Label the vertices of the triangle ABC.
2. Use a compass and straightedge to construct the reflection of the triangle over line m. Label the reflection image $A'B'C'$.
3. Investigate the triangles using any methods and measuring tools you think are appropriate. Identify the characteristics of the image that are preserved (kept the same) by reflection and the characteristics that are not preserved. (For example, how does AB compare to $A'B'$?) Summarize your conclusions.

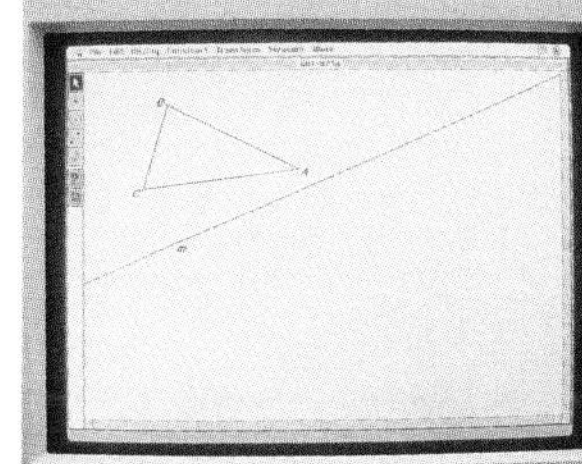

Student Resources
- **Alternative Lessons 1-4C**
- **Laboratory Manual 1-4C**
- Technology Lab Manual
- **Practice 1-4C**
- **Study Guide and Journal 1-4C**
- **Guía de estudios y Diario 1-4C**
- **Multilingual Handbook**
- **More Look Ahead 1-4C**
- SAT Preparation

Media Resources
- **Transparency FFM 1-4C**
- Transparency AE
- Teaching Transparency
- **AWSMTest and practice software**
- AWSM Videodisc

PART C At a Glance

Objective
To discover properties of figures that are and are not preserved by reflection.

Development
In the **Explore,** students draw a triangle, construct its reflection image, and then discover which properties of a figure are preserved by reflection.

Orientation is defined. In a **Consider,** students see that reflection reverses orientation.

Suggested Materials
Student Compass, ruler, protractor

Key Terms
Orientation

First Five Minutes
Transparency FFM 1-4C

Sketch a point and a line of reflection. Then construct the image of the point, using a compass and straightedge.

Motivate
Ask...
- What are some differences between a reflection of a figure and the original figure?

EXPLORE

To Preserve or Not to Preserve
Recommended group size: 4

The Point
To discover the properties of figures that are and are not preserved by reflections.

Look and Listen...
- For students who do not understand the meaning of *preserved* in this context.

Ask...
- How does your own reflection image in a mirror differ from the real you?

Symmetry and Reflections

For Groups That Finish Early
Investigate whether reflections preserve collinearity. To do this, sketch segment $\overline{AB}$ and C on $\overline{AB}$. Then draw a line of reflection, and construct their reflection images.

Follow Up
Ask students to summarize the properties of figures that are and are not preserved by reflection.

Possible Answer

3. Lengths of segments and measures of angles stay the same, and the triangles have the same area and perimeter. However, the image triangle is "flipped over."

Uses the term *orientation* to help students formalize the discovery that reflections flip figures.

Possible Answer

1. Reflections reverse orientation. When moving around the triangle from A' to B' to C', your direction is the opposite of your direction when moving from A to B to C.

Journal 

Reflect 1 and 3 are suitable for journal entries.

REFLECT

Possible Answers

1. A figure is always congruent to its reflection image, because reflections preserve size.

2. Sliding a figure (translation) preserves its orientation.

3. You cannot tell which figure is a pre-image or an image just by looking. If a point B is the reflection image of A over ℓ, A could also be considered the reflection image of B over ℓ.

The **orientation** of a figure can be clockwise or counterclockwise, depending on how you look at it! Tracing this triangle from J to L to K shows a clockwise orientation. But tracing from J to K to L shows a counterclockwise orientation.

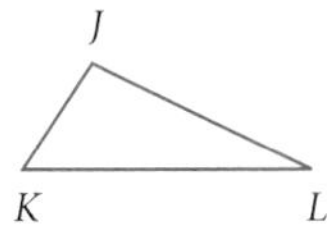

1. In the figure at the right, triangle $A'B'C'$ is the reflection image of triangle ABC over line m. Does reflection preserve the orientation of a figure? Explain.

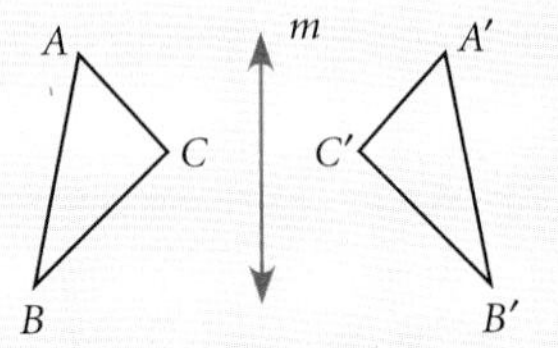

TRY IT

Suppose triangle $M'N'P'$ is the reflection image of triangle MNP. State any conclusions you can make if you know each of the following.

a. $MP = 8$ $M'P' = 8$ also

b. $m\angle P'M'N' = 75°$ $m\angle PMN = 75°$ also

c. As you move from M to P, you are going clockwise. As you move from M' to P', you are going counterclockwi

d. The perimeter of triangle $M'N'P'$ is 20. Perimeter of triangle MNP is 20.

e. The area of triangle MNP is 24. Area of triangle $M'N'P'$ is 24.

The properties of reflections you've discovered are summarized below.

> Reflections preserve any property of a figure having to do with size. This includes lengths of sides, measures of angles, area, and perimeter. Reflections reverse the orientation of a figure.

REFLECT

1. Is a figure always congruent to its reflection image? Why or why not?

2. Describe at least one transformation that preserves the orientation of a figure.

3. Suppose you have the reflection pre-image and image of a figure. Can you tell which is which just by looking? Explain why or why not.

Research Note

[When tutored by peers] students being tutored not only learned more than they did without tutoring, they also developed a more positive attitude.... Their tutors also learned more than students who did not tutor. (U.S. Department of Education, *What Works: Research About Teaching and Learning,* p. 36. 1986.)

Exercises

CORE

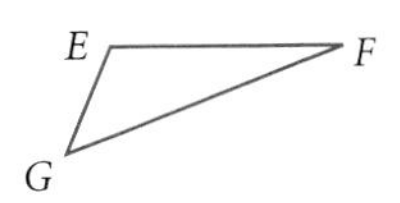

1. **Getting Started** Sketch triangle *JKL* congruent to triangle *EFG* so that *JKL* and *EFG* do not have the same orientation.

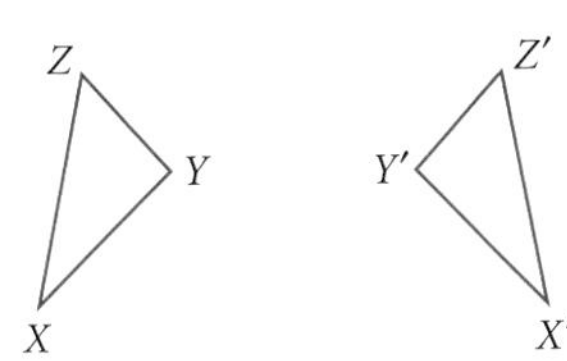

2. Mika knows that $m\angle X = 53°$, $YZ = 5$, and $X'Z' = 6$. She also knows that triangle $X'Y'Z'$ is a reflection of triangle *XYZ*. What else can Mika conclude about the two triangles?

Triangle $A'B'C'$ is the reflection of triangle *ABC* over line *m*.

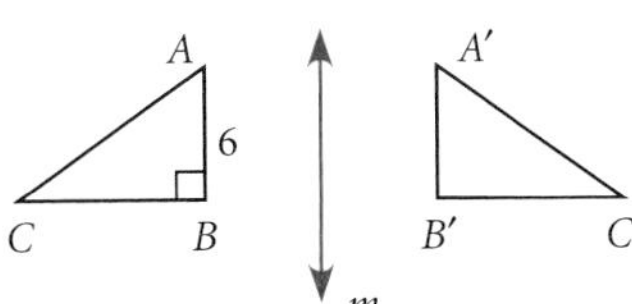

3. Find $m\angle A'B'C'$. 90°
4. Find the length of $\overline{A'B'}$. 6
5. $\overline{D'E'}$ is the reflection image of $\overline{DE}$. The coordinates of *D* and *E* are $(-5, 4)$ and $(4, -8)$. Find $D'E'$. 15

Use each of the following words in a sentence that describes a property of reflection. (Write one sentence using each word.)

6. *equidistant* or *equal distance*
7. *perpendicular*
8. *orientation*
9. *preserves*

10. **Twelve Models to Choose From!** An architect designed six floor plans for an apartment complex. Because of the layout of the land and the desire for greater variety, she created an additional six floor plans by using mirror images of the original designs. The blueprint at the right shows the floor plan for apartment 207 with the bedrooms on the right.
    a. Draw the reflection of apartment 207 so that the bedrooms are on the left. (This is apartment 208.)
    b. If the distance from the kitchen door to one bedroom in apartment 207 is 8 ft, how far is it to the same bedroom in apartment 208? 8 feet
    c. If the entry door is on the east side of apartment 208, where is it in apartment 207? East

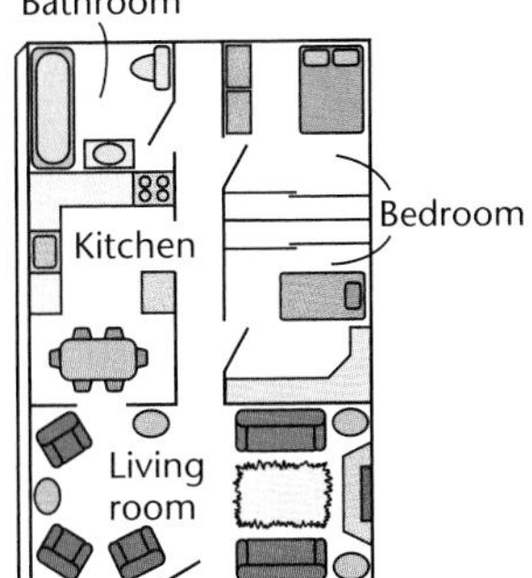

11. **A Pointed Question** Rglph is a glove maker on planet Pmrgk, where everyone has pointed fingers. One of her customers, Vwzxr, has lost his right glove. Using the left glove shown here, draw a pattern for the right glove. Explain why your process works.

Part C Exercises

Exercise Notes

Core

10. Shows an application of reflections.

12. Provides a connection to chemistry. No prior knowledge is necessary for this exercise (nor any other **Exercise** in this text that is related to chemistry). Students often gain confidence when they see that they can understand aspects of a subject before they take a formal course.

Look Ahead

These exercises preview conditional statements seen in Chapter 2.

More Math Reasoning

24. Provides a preview for translations (Chapter 3) and composition of reflections (Chapter 10).

Exercise Answers

Core

1. Possible answer:

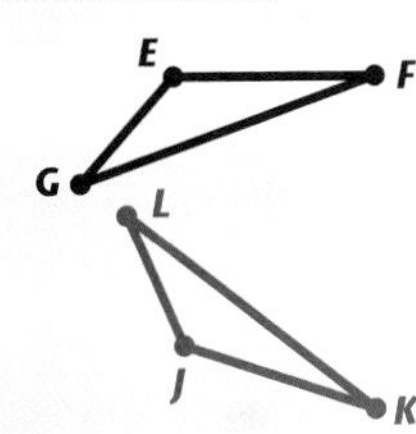

2. $m\angle X' = 53°$, $Y'Z' = 5$, and $XZ = 6$. Also, corresponding sides and angles are congruent.

6. Possible answer: A point and its reflection image are equidistant from the line of reflection.

7. Possible answer: A segment from a point to its reflection image is perpendicular to the line of reflection.

8. Possible answer: Reflection reverses the orientation of a figure.

9. Possible answer: Reflection preserves the size of a figure.

10. a.

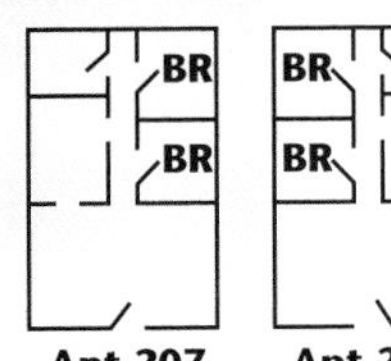

ey
Vocabulary
Practice/Skills
Review
R Math Reasoning
S Problem Solving
Challenge

Ongoing Assessment

Self-Assessment Exercises 1, 3, 4, 7, 9, 12

Embedded Assessment Explore Step 3; Reflect 1; Exercises 2, 5, 10, 11

Symmetry and Reflections

11. Mirror image of the one shown; Reflecting the left glove gives the size, shape and orientation of the right glove.

12.

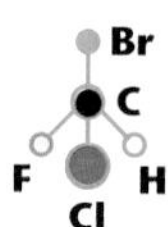

Look Ahead

13. If a person lives in San Francisco, then he or she lives in California.

14. If a creature is a bird, then it has wings.

15. If Kendrick is 16, then he can get a driver's license.

More Practice

16. $m\angle P' = 65°$, $m\angle Q = 70°$, and $R'Q' = 7$. Also, corresponding sides and angles are congruent.

More Math Reasoning

20. Always; Possible answer: The line of reflection is the perpendicular bisector of the segment connecting the points.

21. Always; Possible answer: Reflection preserves size.

22. Always; Possible answer: All pairs of pre-image and image points are equidistant from the line of reflection.

23. Never; Reflection always reverses the orientation.

24. a.

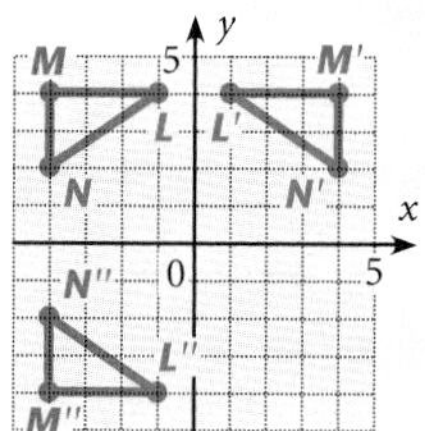

Original triangle LMN: counterclockwise; Triangle $L'M'N'$: clockwise; Triangle $L''M''N''$: clockwise

b. The orientation of both is the same so one can't be the reflection of the other.

c. Possible answer: Rotate about origin 180°

P **12.** Stereoisomers are molecules made of the same materials that are mirror images of each other. Even though they are made of the same materials, stereoisomers can have different chemical properties.

One of the possible arrangements of a molecule is shown at the right. Draw its stereoisomer using the given line of reflection.

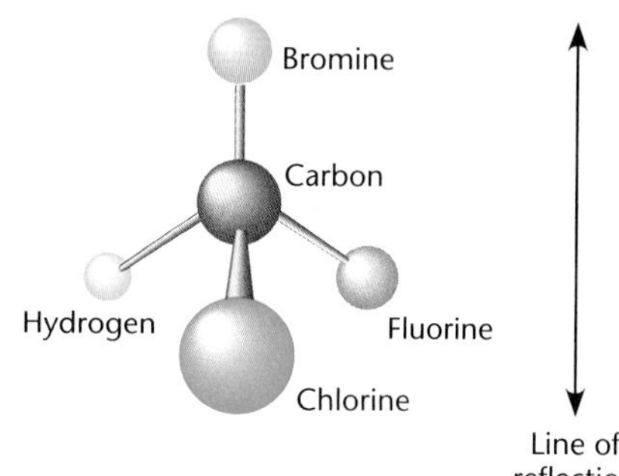

(Note: The fluorine, chlorine, bromine, and hydrogen atoms are arranged like the corners of a pyramid.)

LOOK AHEAD

MR **The statement "Every student in the 10th grade is a sophomore" can be rewritten as: "If a student is in the 10th grade, then he or she is a sophomore." Rewrite each of the following statements in the form, "If . . . , then . . ."**

13. Everyone who lives in San Francisco lives in California.

14. All birds have wings.

15. Kendrick can get a driver's license if he is 16.

MORE PRACTICE

P **16.** Sabine knows that triangle $P'Q'R'$ is the reflection of triangle PQR. She also knows that $m\angle P = 65°$, $m\angle Q' = 70°$, and $RQ = 7$. What else can Sabine conclude about the two triangles?

P **17.** $\overline{M'N'}$ is the reflection image of $\overline{MN}$. The coordinates of M and N are $(-3, 2)$ and $(-6, -5)$. Find $M'N'$. 7.6

P **Triangle $A'B'C'$ is the reflection of triangle ABC over line m.**

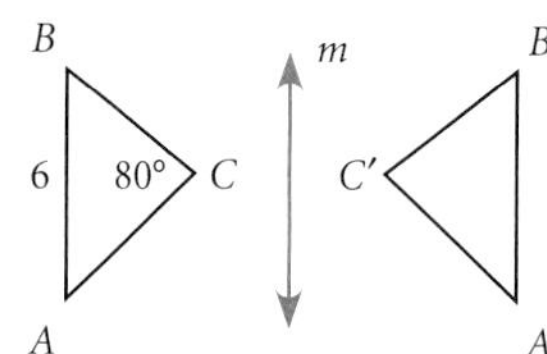

18. Find $m\angle A'C'B'$. 80°

19. Find the length of $A'B'$. 6

Key

V Vocabulary
P Practice/Skills
R Review
MR Math Reasoning
PS Problem Solving
C Challenge

MORE MATH REASONING

Complete each statement with *always, sometimes,* or *never.* Explain your answer.

20. A line of reflection is ___ the perpendicular bisector of the segment from the pre-image of a point to its reflection image.

21. A segment and its reflection image are ___ congruent.

22. A point and its reflection image are ___ equidistant from the line of reflection.

23. Reflections ___ preserve orientation.

24. On a coordinate plane, copy the triangle, and draw its reflection over the y-axis. Then draw its reflection over the x-axis.

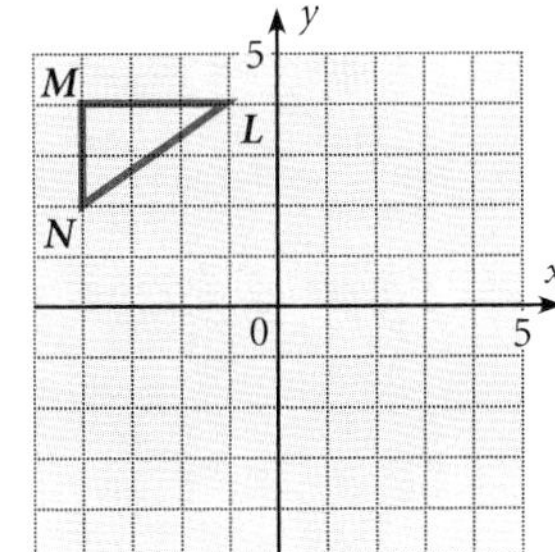

a. Describe the orientation of each of the triangles.

b. Suppose you think of the y-axis reflection as a pre-image and the x-axis reflection as its image. How can you tell that this image is *not* a reflection of this pre-image?

c. Describe a transformation that gives you this image (the x-axis reflection) from this pre-image (the y-axis reflection). Do not use *reflection* in describing this new transformation.

PART D At a Glance

Objective

To bring together the ideas of line symmetry and reflection.

Development

In the **Explore,** students create a blanket design, using both symmetry and reflections.

Suggested Materials

Student Construction paper, straightedge, compass

First Five Minutes

Transparency FFM 1-4D

Write a brief summary of everything you know about symmetry and reflections that another student could use as a study guide.

1-4 PART D Making Connections

← CONNECT → ***Reflections and symmetry are important in nature, architecture, and art. You've discovered symmetry in a variety of settings and learned how reflections and symmetry are related.***

You've seen examples of symmetry in math, art, architecture, and language. Part of the beauty of Navajo blankets is due to their symmetry. Blankets of other cultures, such as the *kilims* of the Middle East, also contain beautifully symmetrical patterns. The photo at the left shows symmetry in a plate by Maria Martinez of San Ildefonso Pueblo, New Mexico.

In the following Explore, you will use symmetry and reflections to create your own blanket design.

Student Resources

Alternative Lessons
Laboratory Manual 1-4D
Technology Lab Manual
Practice 1-4D
Study Guide and Journal 1-4D
Guía de estudios y Diario 1-4D
Multilingual Handbook
More Look Back 1-4D
SAT Preparation

Media Resources

Transparency FFM 1-4D
Transparency AE
Teaching Transparency
AWSMTest and practice software
AWSM Videodisc

1-4

Symmetry and Reflections

EXPLORE

Do-It-Yourself Symmetry

Recommended group size: 2

The Point
To use reflections and symmetry to make a blanket design.

Look and Listen...

- For students who are having trouble remembering construction techniques.

For Groups That Finish Early
Make a second design with two perpendicular lines of symmetry.

Follow Up
Have the groups display their blanket designs.

Possible Answers
Check students' art.

Portfolio

Have students select items from their work that demonstrate their understanding of the material in this Superlesson.

You may want to have students submit an example of symmetry in nature, an **Exercise** that involved constructing a reflection image, and their blanket design.

REFLECT

Possible Answers

1. Construct the perpendicular from the point to the line of reflection. The image point is on the perpendicular line and is the same distance from the line of reflection as the pre-image.
2. Reflections preserve segment length, angle measure, and other properties of a figure involving size. Reflections do not preserve orientation.
3. Circle

Self-Assessment

Exercise Notes

12. Provides a good summary of the properties of a reflection.

EXPLORE: DO-IT-YOURSELF SYMMETRY

MATERIALS

Construction paper
Straightedge
Compass

Create a design for a blanket that uses reflection and symmetry. Follow the guidelines below.

1. Fold your paper in half. Create a design on one half of the paper. Be sure to use at least three different geometric figures that have line symmetry.
2. Draw the lines of symmetry in these figures.
3. Now use construction techniques and measurement to reflect the design over the fold. (You do not have to reflect the lines of symmetry.)

REFLECT

1. Explain how the construction of a perpendicular from a point not on a line can be used to find the reflection of a point over a line.
2. Write a list of properties of reflections. Draw a picture to illustrate each property.
3. Describe a figure with infinitely many lines of symmetry. Sketch the figure. Can you think of another?

Self-Assessment

P **Line ℓ is a line of reflection in the figure shown. Name the image or pre-image of each figure.**

1. the image of A P
2. the pre-image of $\overleftrightarrow{QR}$ $\overleftrightarrow{BC}$
3. the image of $\overline{AB}$ $\overline{PQ}$
4. the pre-image of Q B
5. If $AC = 12$, find PR. 12

MR 6. Does every angle have a line of symmetry? If so, describe it, and provide a figure.

R **Draw a Venn diagram to illustrate each of the following. [1-2]**

7. Some pilots are women.
8. No Democrats are Republicans.
9. All segments have two endpoints.

Key

V Vocabulary
P Practice/Skills
R Review
MR Math Reasoning
PS Problem Solving
C Challenge

Fine Arts Connection

Symmetry is seen in many artistic forms across almost all cultures. For example, instances of line symmetry are seen in Ibo (Nigeria) costumes, Cheyenne beadwork, and Portuguese embroidery.

Find *AB* for each set of coordinates below. Where necessary, round answers to the nearest tenth. [1-3]

10. $A(-2, 4)$, $B(4, 12)$ 10

11. $A(1.5, 2.6)$, $B(-2, 5.8)$ 4.7

12. Write a list of properties of reflections. Then draw a triangle, a line of reflection, and the reflection image of the triangle. Explain how your pre-image and image demonstrate each of the properties you listed.

13. a. Is the figure at the right a net for a cube? Yes

b. Sketch a reflection of the net. Is the reflection still a net for a cube?

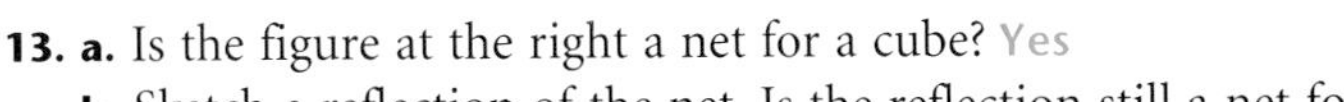

14. If one illustration is selected randomly from those shown below, what is the probability that it will *not* have line symmetry? (e)

(a) $\frac{1}{2}$ (b) 1 (c) $\frac{3}{4}$ (d) 0 (e) $\frac{1}{4}$

Butterfly

Star

Leaf

Yin-yang symbol

15. This alphabet, created by Scott Kim, is symmetrical. Or is it? Describe three different places inside the dotted rectangle where part of the design does not exactly match its reflection image.

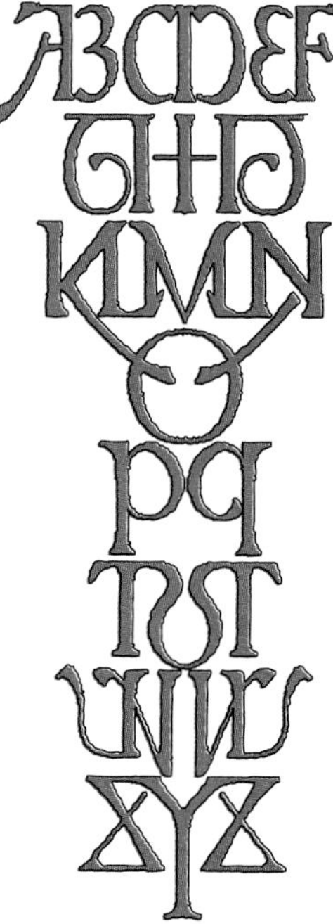

16. A symmetrical relation is always reversible. For example, the relation "is married to" is symmetrical. If Ramon is married to Julia, then Julia is married to Ramon. Equality is a symmetrical relation. Other examples of symmetrical relations are "is perpendicular to" and "is a cousin of." Many relations are not symmetrical. For example, "is taller than" is not symmetrical.

a. Give two other examples of symmetrical relations.

b. Give two other examples of asymmetrical relations.

Two vertices of a rectangle and a line of symmetry for the rectangle are given. Find the other vertices of the rectangle.

17. (4, 1) and (4, 5); $x = 3$ (2, 1), (2, 5)

18. (4, 1) and (9, 1); $y = 3$ (4, 5), (9, 5)

ssessment Resources

uiz 1-4

hapter Assessment Form A

hapter Assessment Form B

hapter Alternative Assessment

lid-Year Assessment

nd-of-Year Assessment

WSMTest and practice software

Ongoing Assessment

Self-Assessment Self-Assessment Exercises

Embedded Assessment Explore Step 3; Reflect 1, 2, 3

16. Demonstrates the idea of symmetry in logical relationships.

17–18. Illustrate symmetry on a coordinate plane.

Self-Assessment Answers

6. Yes, the line bisecting the angle

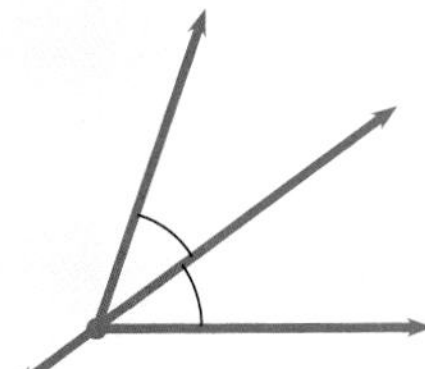

7. Pilots / Women

8.

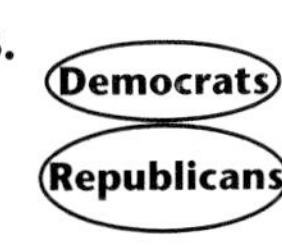

9. Things with 2 endpoints / Segments

12. Reflection preserves congruence but reverses orientation. Possible answer:

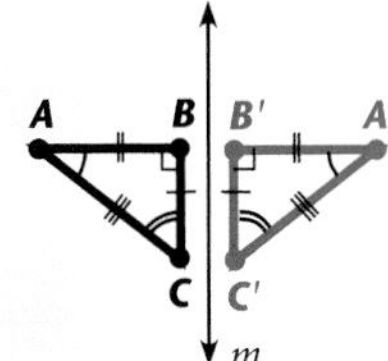

The sides, angles, perimeter, and area of both triangles have the same measures as their counterparts; the orientations are reversed.

13. b. Yes

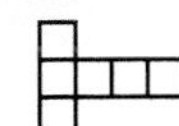

15. Crossbar of F; Loop of Q; Crossbar of N

16. a. Possible answer: "is not equal to," "is in the same class as"

b. Possible answer: "is greater than," "is less than"

Chapter 1 Review

Journal

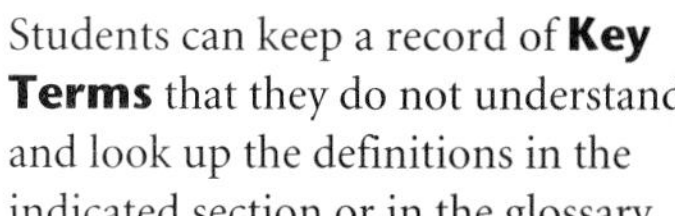

Students can keep a record of **Key Terms** that they do not understand and look up the definitions in the indicated section or in the glossary.

Vocabulary exercises and the **Self-Evaluation** are useful journal entries.

Review Answers

5.

6. $A(1, 40)$, $B(1, 70)$, $C(2, 60)$, $D(2, 90)$, $E(4, 80)$, $F(4, 97)$, $G(5, 100)$, $H(6, 80)$

8. About 76 points; Best guess would be the y-coordinate of the point where the line $x = 3$ intersects the line fitted through the data.

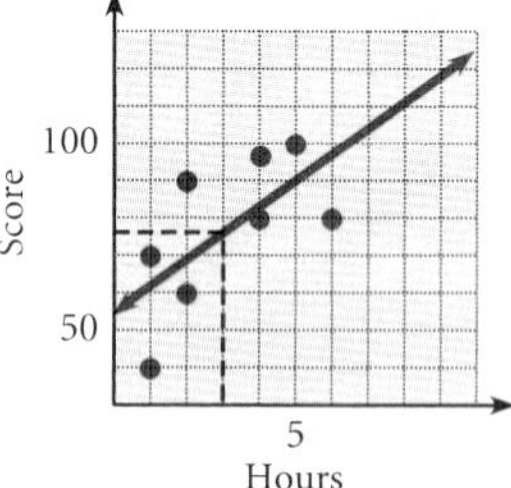

11. Possible answer: Deductive reasoning proceeds from the premises to the conclusion by logical steps; Solving an algebra problem, reasoning from "all triangles have 3 sides" and "John drew a triangle" to "John's figure has 3 sides."

17.

18. Possible answer:

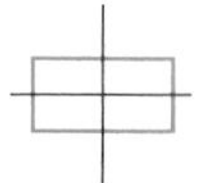

Concepts and Connections

22. Check students' art.

Chapter 1 Review

In Chapter 1, you investigated mathematical models. You explored algebraic models (for example, scatter plots) and geometric models (for example, nets). Developing inductive and deductive reasoning skills and learning some basic geometric terms helped you to make better geometric models. These ideas are all useful in studying symmetry and reflections, our first transformation.

KEY TERMS

- angle [1-3]
- bisect [1-4]
- collinear [1-2]
- congruent [1-3]
- conjecture [1-2]
- construction [1-3]
- counterexample [1-2]
- deductive reasoning [1-2]
- degree [1-3]
- endpoint of a ray [1-3]
- endpoints of a segment [1-2]
- equidistant [1-4]
- image [1-4]
- inductive reasoning [1-2]
- intersect [1-2]
- length [1-3]
- line of reflection [1-4]
- line of symmetry [1-4]
- line segment [1-2]
- line [1-2]
- mathematical model [1-1]
- measure of an angle [1-3]
- net [1-1]
- orientation [1-4]
- perpendicular bisector [1-4]
- perpendicular lines [1-3]
- point [1-2]
- pre-image [1-4]
- ray [1-3]
- reflection image [1-4]
- reflection [1-4]
- right angle [1-3]
- scatter plot [1-1]
- sides of an angle [1-3]
- symmetry [1-4]
- transformation [1-4]
- Venn diagram [1-2]
- vertex [1-3]

V **Write the word or phrase that correctly completes each statement.**

1. The process of making a conjecture by looking at specific examples and recognizing a pattern is ___ reasoning. Inductive
2. The two rays that form an angle have a common endpoint, called the ___ of the angle. Vertex
3. The figure that results after a transformation of a figure is the ___ of the original figure. Image
4. Two lines that intersect at ___ are perpendicular lines. Right angles (90°)

CONCEPTS AND APPLICATIONS

P 5. Draw a net for the solid at the right. [1-1]

Key

V Vocabulary
P Practice/Skills
R Review
MR Math Reasoning
PS Problem Solving
C Challenge

The scatter plot shown represents how many hours eight students studied and the scores they received on a history test. Use this scatter plot for items 6–8. [1-2]

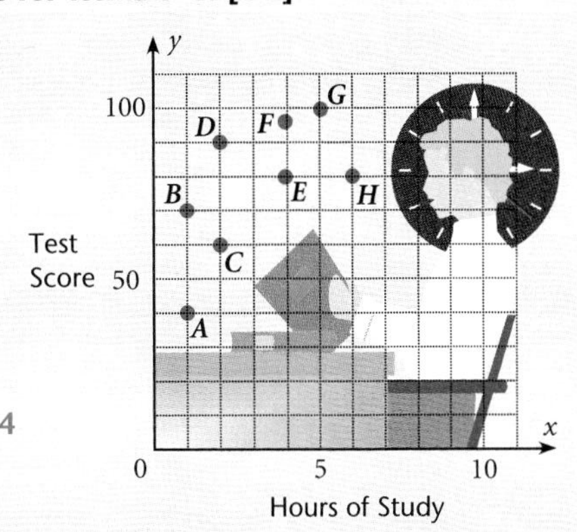

6. Give the ordered pairs for each point on the scatter plot.

7. Which student studied the longest? Did that student get the highest score? *H*; No

8. Suppose a student not shown on the scatter plot told you he studied three hours for the test. What score would you predict he received? Why?

9. Solve $5x + 9 = 3(x - 1) + 4$. [Previous course] $x = -4$

10. A sequence of figures is made from small squares, as shown. [1-2]

a. How many small squares would it take to make the figure at Step 7? 25

b. How many small squares would it take to make the figure at Step *n*? $4n - 3$

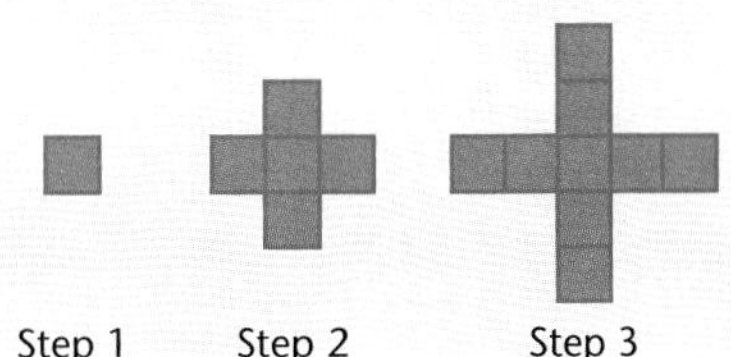

11. Write a brief paragraph describing what deductive reasoning is. Give specific examples of its use. [1-2]

Suppose that each statement below is true. Use deductive reasoning to give another statement that must also be true. [1-2]

12. Every freshman has attended orientation. Luis has never been to orientation. Luis is not a freshman.

13. No triangle has four sides. Marie drew a four-sided figure. Marie did not draw a triangle.

Find the length of $\overline{FG}$ using the given coordinates. [1-3]

14. $F(-2, 0)$, $G(3, 8)$ 9.4

15. $F(5, -5)$, $G(-3, -6)$ 8.1

16. Name the angle at the right in as many ways as possible. [1-3] $\angle RTS$, $\angle STR$, $\angle T$, $\angle 2$

R
2
T
S

17. Use a compass and straightedge to construct an angle congruent to the angle at the right. [1-3]

18. Draw a figure with exactly two lines of symmetry. [1-4]

Line *m* is a line of reflection in the figure at the right. [1-4]

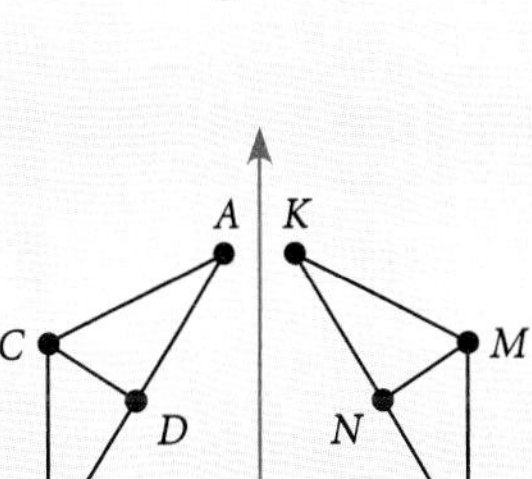

19. What is the reflection image of point *A*? *K*

20. What is the reflection image of $\overline{CD}$? $\overline{MN}$

21. What is the pre-image of triangle *KLM*? Triangle *ABC*

Student Resources

Alternative Lessons
Laboratory Manual
Technology Lab Manual
Practice
Study Guide and Journal Ch 1
Guía de estudios y Diario Ch 1
Multilingual Handbook
More Look Ahead
SAT Preparation

Media Resources

Transparency FFM
Transparency AE
Teaching Transparency
AWSMTest and practice software
AWSM Videodisc

Chapter 1 Assessment

Portfolio

Students may select items that represent their mathematical understanding of the ideas in Chapter 1 and that illustrate the effort they put forth on this chapter.

Assessment Answers

1. Possible answer:

6. a. 136

b. $\frac{n(n+1)}{2}$

c. Inductive; Possible answer: Conjectures are based on observed patterns.

11. Possible answer: As per-capita income increases, so does the literacy rate; J has a low literacy rate but a high per-capita income.

12. About \$3600

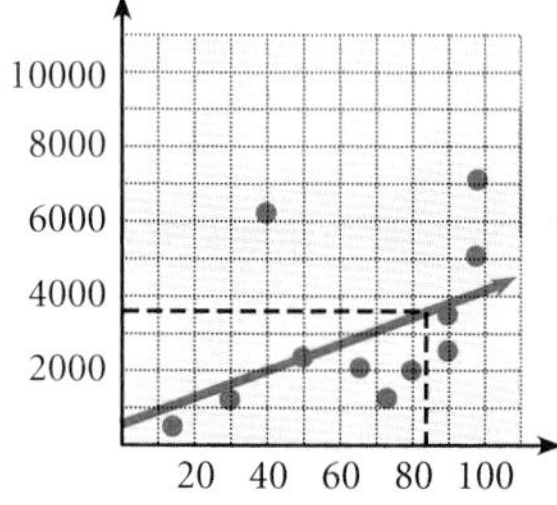

13.

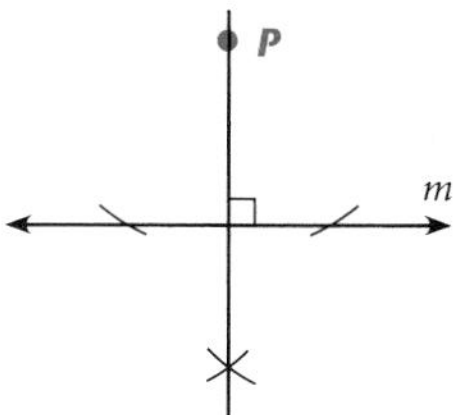

17. Reflection preserves congruence; it reverses orientation; Possible answer:

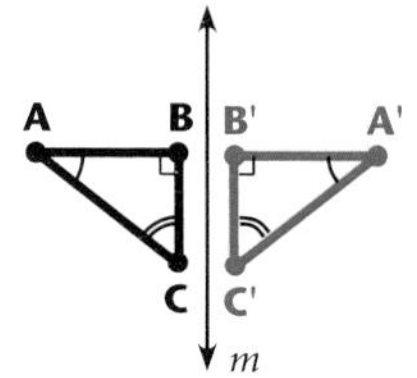

CONCEPTS AND CONNECTIONS

PS Careers **22. Architecture** As an architect, you've been asked to prepare a floor plan for a two-bedroom apartment. Your clients want you to make the apartment as symmetrical as possible. They would also like the apartment to contain at least one angle that is not a right angle. Draw a simple floor plan for such an apartment, marking congruent lengths, congruent angles, and right angles as appropriate.

SELF-EVALUATION

Write a paragraph describing how geometry can be used to model the world around you. Include in your paragraph the new ideas you learned in Chapter 1, and give specific examples of how you can use these ideas in modeling real-world situations. Be sure to include any topics that you found difficult, and describe your plans for studying those topics.

Chapter 1 Assessment

TEST

P **1.** Draw a net for the solid at the right.

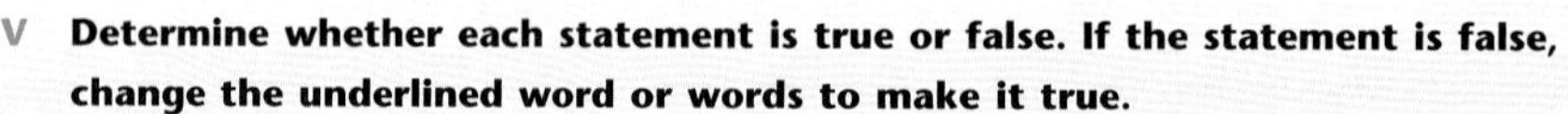

V **Determine whether each statement is true or false. If the statement is false, change the underlined word or words to make it true.**

2. Two lines that intersect at right angles are <u>equidistant</u> lines. F; Perpendicular

3. <u>Deductive reasoning</u> is a process in which conclusions are drawn from given information by rules of logic. T

P **Give a counterexample for each of the following conjectures.**

4. All triangles have three sides of equal length. Possible answer: Right triangle

5. No positive numbers are less than 1. Possible answer: $\frac{1}{2}$

MR **6.** Consider the sequence of figures shown at the right.

a. How many dots will be in the figure at Step 16?

b. How many dots will be in the figure at Step n?

c. What type of reasoning did you use to solve this problem? Write a brief description of how this type of reasoning works.

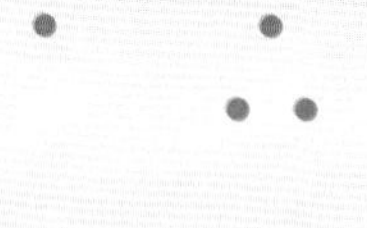

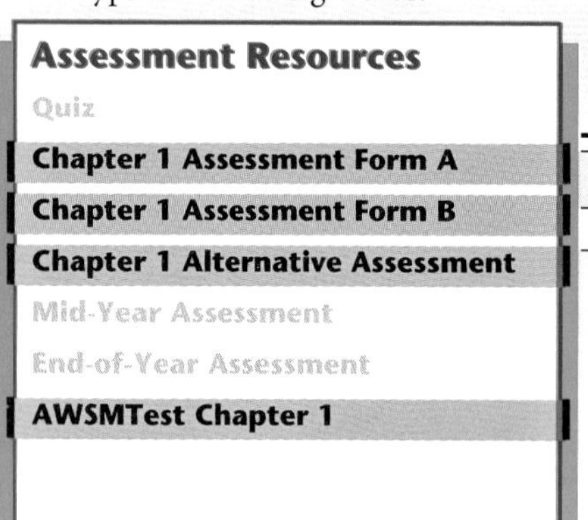

Assessment Resources

Quiz

Chapter 1 Assessment Form A

Chapter 1 Assessment Form B

Chapter 1 Alternative Assessment

Mid-Year Assessment

End-of-Year Assessment

AWSMTest Chapter 1

Ongoing Assessment

Self-Assessment Chapter 1 Review and Self-Evaluation

Embedded Assessment Chapter 1 Performance Task

Test Chapter 1 Test

Find the length of $\overline{AB}$ using the given coordinates.

7. $A(4, -6)$, $B(6, -4)$ 2.8

8. $A(-3, -2)$, $B(-1, 7)$ 9.2

9. Find the slope of $\overleftrightarrow{RS}$ if R and S have coordinates $R(3, -9)$ and $S(-4, -2)$. −1

The scatter plot shows the literacy rate and the yearly per-capita income for 11 nations.

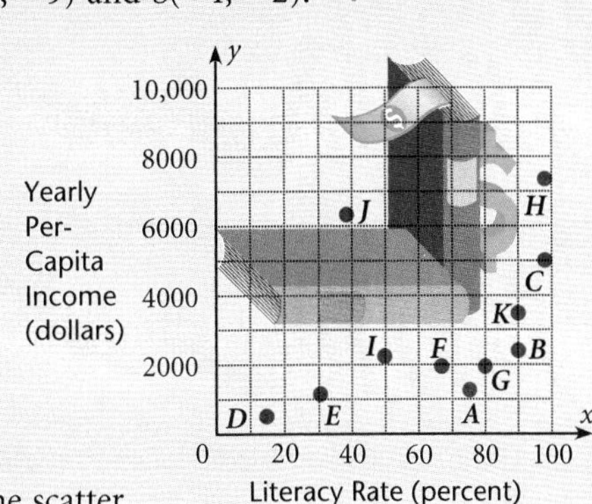

10. Which nation has the highest literacy rate? the lowest? Highest: *C* or *H*; Lowest: *D*

11. What conclusion can you draw from the scatter plot about the relationship between the literacy rate and per-capita income? Is there a nation that doesn't seem to fit this conclusion? Explain.

12. Suppose Country L has a literacy rate of 83%. Use the scatter plot to make a prediction of its yearly per-capita income.

13. Copy the figure at the right. Then use a compass and straightedge to construct a perpendicular from point P to line m.

• *P*

⟷ *m*

Line *n* is a line of reflection in the figure at the right.

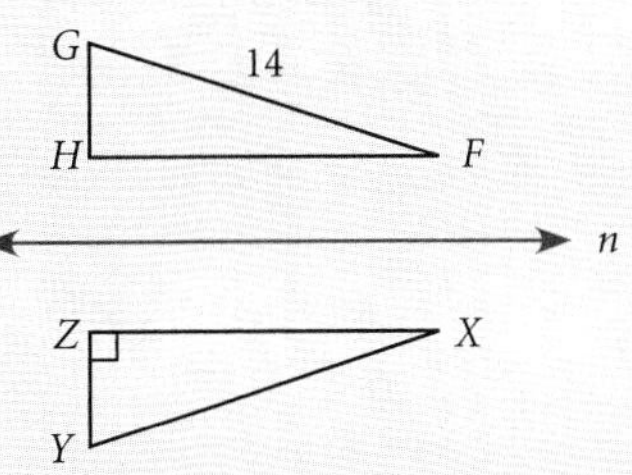

14. Name the pre-image of $\overline{XY}$. $\overline{FG}$

15. Find $m\angle H$. 90°

16. Find XY. 14

17. Write a list of as many properties as you can that are preserved by reflections. Then give at least one property that is not preserved by reflections. Include an illustration.

PERFORMANCE TASK

When three lines are drawn on a sheet of paper, they can intersect to form 0, 1, 2, or 3 points of intersection as shown below. Investigate the number of points of intersection that are possible when four lines are drawn on a sheet of paper. Prepare a figure for each possibility, and explain how you know your results are complete.

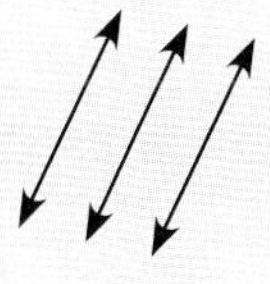
0 points

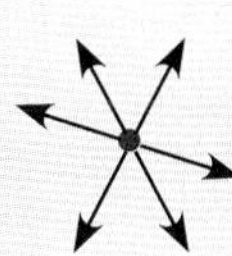
1 point

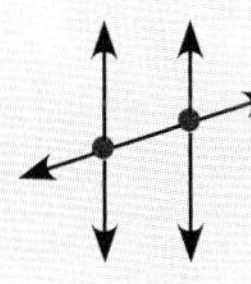
2 points

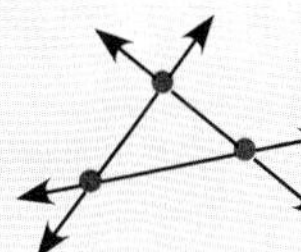
3 points

Performance Task

Answer

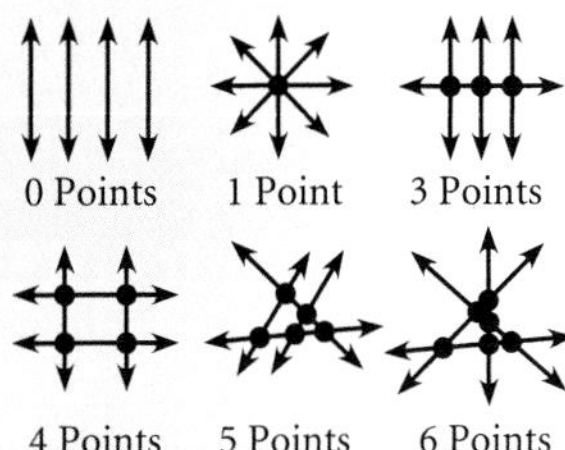

Suggested Scoring Rubric

Level 4 Full Accomplishment

- Shows full understanding of the concepts of lines and intersection points. Answer is complete and sketches accurate.
- Recorded work communicates thinking clearly and explains why there cannot be 2, or more than 6, points of intersection.

Level 3 Substantial Accomplishment

- Shows essential grasp of the concepts of lines and intersection points. Answer is complete and sketches accurate.
- Recorded work communicates thinking, but pieces may be missing. May not show why there cannot be more than 6 points of intersection.

Level 2 Partial Accomplishment

- Shows partial grasp of the concepts of lines and intersection points. Answer may be incomplete and sketches inaccurate in some details.
- Recorded work may be incomplete or not clearly presented.

Level 1 Little Accomplishment

- Shows little or no grasp of the concepts of lines and intersection points. Answer is incomplete and sketches, if included, are mathematically inaccurate.
- Reasoning in recorded work is extremely difficult to follow.

2

Chapter 2 The Foundations of Geometry

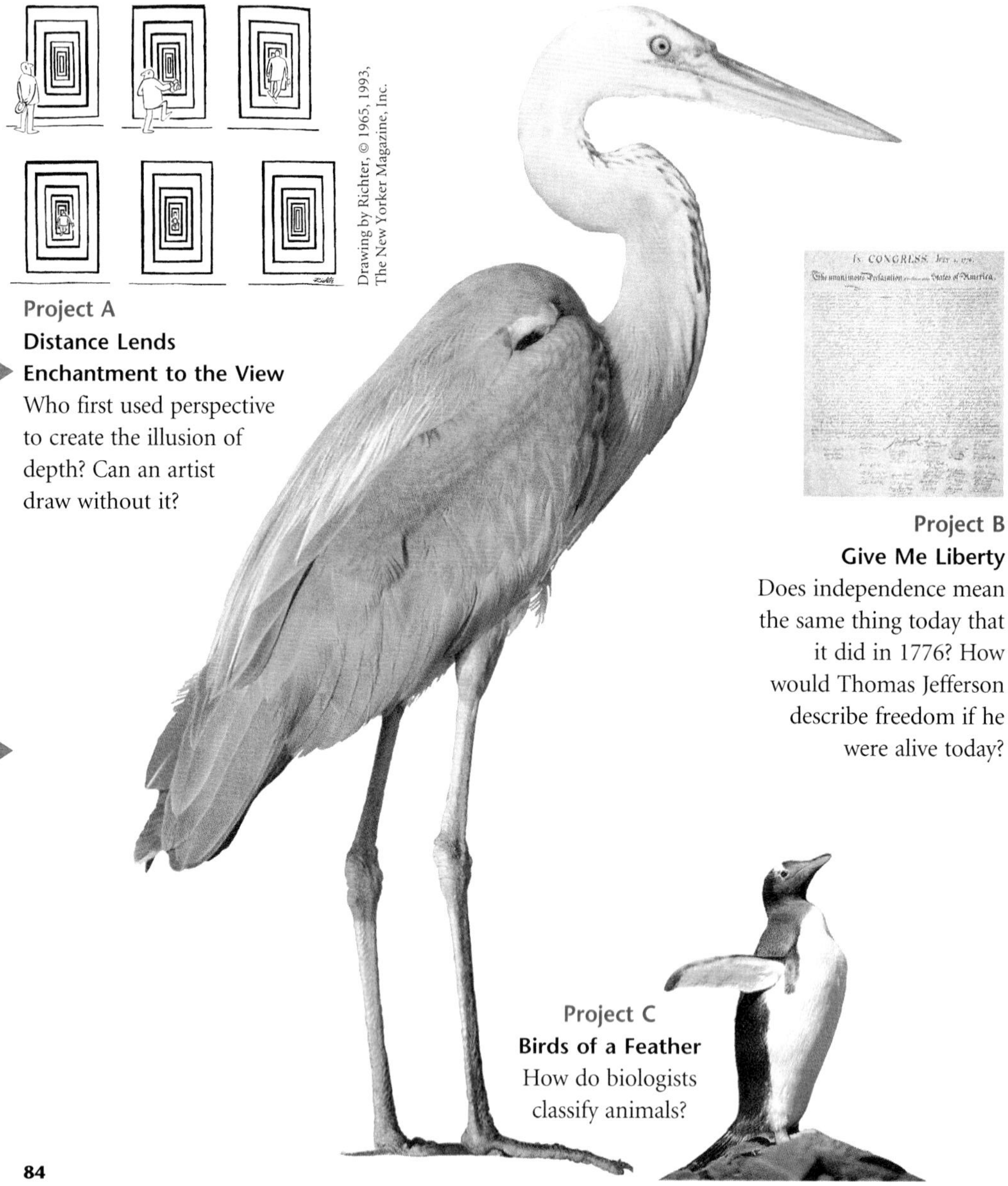

Chapter 2 Project A **Distance Lends Enchantment**

Create an Art Scrapbook

Learn to recognize different artistic methods for creating an illusion of depth.

- Did you know that the first book on perspective was written in 1505?
- Don't you wonder if there is another way to show deep space on a flat canvas?
- How does this connect to Chapter 2? Artists achieve an illusion of depth using **perspective** as well as other devices.

Expand Your Vocabulary

abstraction, representation, collage, aerial perspective, picture plane, illusion, line of sight, vertical perspective

Project Guidelines

Investigate
- Read about perspective in a how-to-draw book.
- Find examples in galleries or in art history books.
- Visit a gallery or talk to an artist about perspective.

Set Your Direction
- Will you concentrate on the art of a certain period or culture or do a general survey?
- Will you sketch or photocopy reproductions of art or create your own originals?

Make a Plan
- Make a calendar for each day's work. Check in with your group and with your teacher.
- You might need art materials.

Collect and Organize Your Information
- Make copies or sketches of various artworks.
- Write a sentence for each telling how the work conveys a sense of deep space.
- Classify the artworks according to the type of perspective in each.
- ***Respect books*** Don't mark on art reproductions.

Carry Out Your Plan
- Arrange your pictures in an album according to the time period, culture, or type of perspective.
- Label pictures with the name of the artist, title, date of the work, and the museum where it is kept.
- Write a paragraph and draw a diagram for each section that tells how the pictures illustrate the heading you put them under.

Look Back
- Can an artist make a picture that has no illusion of depth at all?
- What could you have done differently?

© Addison-Wesley Publishing Company, Inc. Focus on Geometry 7

Drawing by Richter, © 1965, 1993, The New Yorker Magazine, Inc.

A

Project A

Distance Lends Enchantment to the View

Who first used perspective to create the illusion of depth? Can an artist draw without it?

Project B

Give Me Liberty

Does independence mean the same thing today that it did in 1776? How would Thomas Jefferson describe freedom if he were alive today?

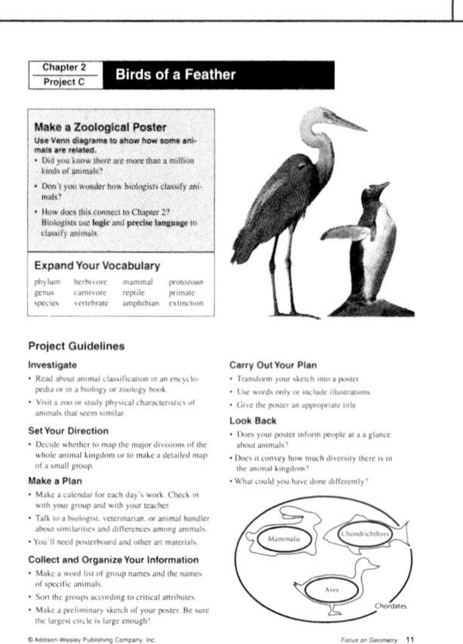

Chapter 2 Project C **Birds of a Feather**

Make a Zoological Poster

Use Venn diagrams to show how some animals are related.

- Did you know there are more than a million kinds of animals?
- Don't you wonder how biologists classify animals?
- How does this connect to Chapter 2? Biologists use **logic** and **precise language** to classify animals.

Expand Your Vocabulary

phylum, herbivore, mammal, protozoan, genus, carnivore, reptile, primate, species, vertebrate, amphibian, extinction

Project Guidelines

Investigate
- Read about animal classification in an encyclopedia or in a biology or zoology book.
- Visit a zoo or study physical characteristics of animals that seem similar.

Set Your Direction
- Decide whether to map the major divisions of the whole animal kingdom or to make a detailed map of a small group.

Make a Plan
- Make a calendar for each day's work. Check in with your group and with your teacher.
- Talk to a biologist, veterinarian, or animal handler about similarities and differences among animals.
- You'll need posterboard and other art materials.

Collect and Organize Your Information
- Make a word list of group names and the names of specific animals.
- Sort the groups according to critical attributes.
- Make a preliminary sketch of your poster. Be sure the largest circle is large enough!

Carry Out Your Plan
- Transform your sketch into a poster.
- Use words only or include illustrations.
- Give the poster an appropriate title.

Look Back
- Does your poster inform people at a a glance about animals?
- Does it convey how much diversity there is in the animal kingdom?
- What could you have done differently?

© Addison-Wesley Publishing Company, Inc. Focus on Geometry 11

C

Project C

Birds of a Feather

How do biologists classify animals?

84

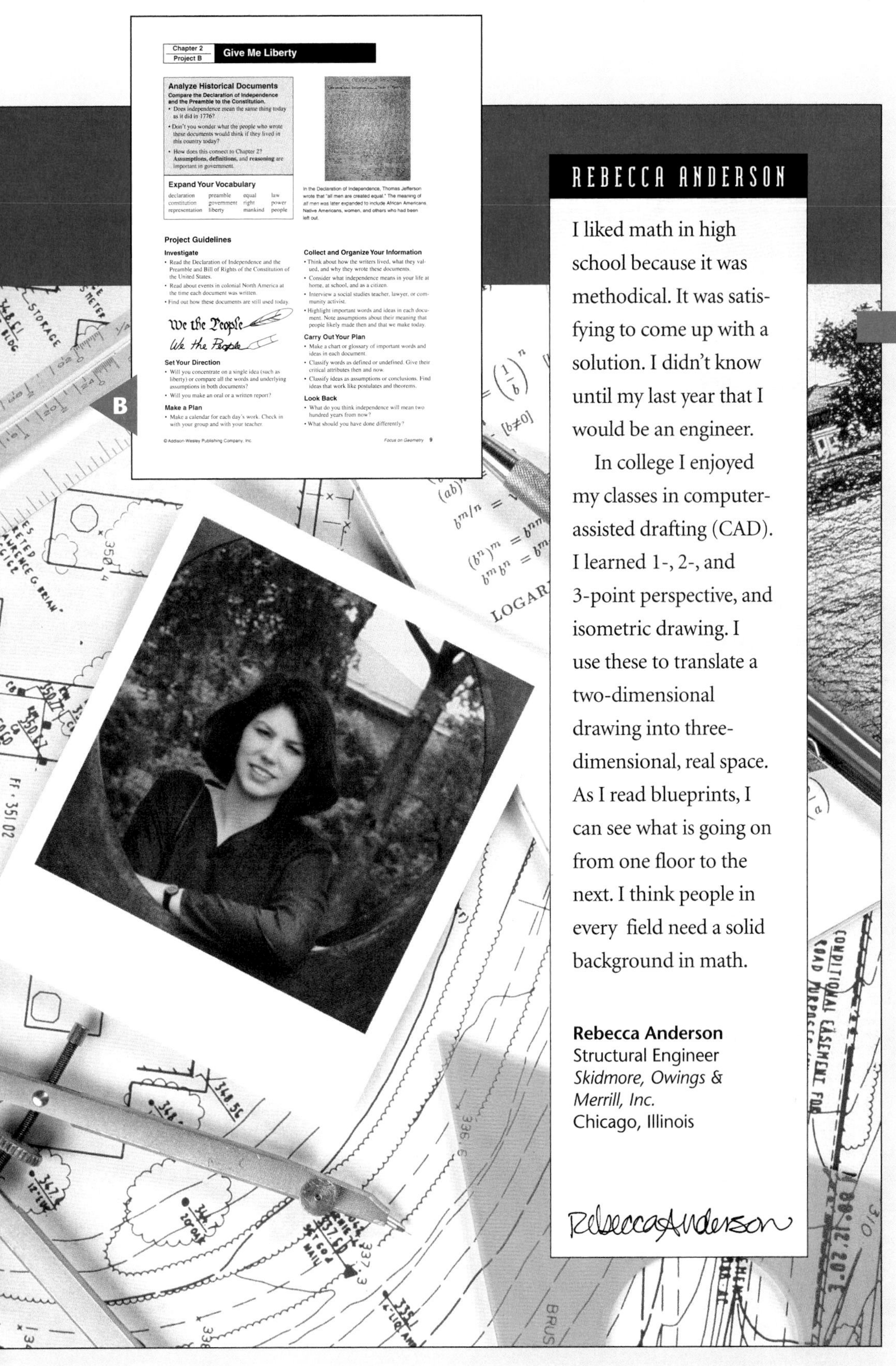

Chapter 2
Project B

Give Me Liberty

Analyze Historical Documents

Compare the Declaration of Independence and the Preamble to the Constitution.

- Does independence mean the same thing today as it did in 1776?
- Don't you wonder what the people who wrote these documents would think if they lived in this country today?
- How does this connect to Chapter 2? **Assumptions, definitions,** and **reasoning** are important in government.

Expand Your Vocabulary

declaration	preamble	equal	law
constitution	government	right	power
representation	liberty	mankind	people

In the Declaration of Independence, Thomas Jefferson wrote that "all men are created equal." The meaning of *all men* was later expanded to include African Americans, Native Americans, women, and others who had been left out.

Project Guidelines

Investigate

- Read the Declaration of Independence and the Preamble and Bill of Rights of the Constitution of the United States.
- Read about events in colonial North America at the time each document was written.
- Find out how these documents are still used today.

We the People

We the People

Set Your Direction

- Will you concentrate on a single idea (such as liberty) or compare all the words and underlying assumptions in both documents?
- Will you make an oral or a written report?

Make a Plan

- Make a calendar for each day's work. Check in with your group and with your teacher.

Collect and Organize Your Information

- Think about how the writers lived, what they valued, and why they wrote these documents.
- Consider what independence means in your life at home, at school, and as a citizen.
- Interview a social studies teacher, lawyer, or community activist.
- Highlight important words and ideas in each document. Note assumptions about their meaning that people likely made then and that we make today.

Carry Out Your Plan

- Make a chart or glossary of important words and ideas in each document.
- Classify words as defined or undefined. Give their critical attributes then and now.
- Classify ideas as assumptions or conclusions. Find ideas that work like postulates and theorems.

Look Back

- What do you think independence will mean two hundred years from now?
- What should you have done differently?

© Addison-Wesley Publishing Company, Inc.　　*Focus on Geometry* 9

REBECCA ANDERSON

I liked math in high school because it was methodical. It was satisfying to come up with a solution. I didn't know until my last year that I would be an engineer.

In college I enjoyed my classes in computer-assisted drafting (CAD). I learned 1-, 2-, and 3-point perspective, and isometric drawing. I use these to translate a two-dimensional drawing into three-dimensional, real space. As I read blueprints, I can see what is going on from one floor to the next. I think people in every field need a solid background in math.

Rebecca Anderson
Structural Engineer
Skidmore, Owings & Merrill, Inc.
Chicago, Illinois

Rebecca Anderson

Biographical Note

Rebecca Anderson graduated from Windward High School in Los Angeles, CA. She took Algebra, Algebra II, Advanced Algebra, Geometry, and Calculus.

Chapter 2

Overview

The Foundations of Geometry

2-1 The Need for Precise Language

To make accurate mathematical statements, you must use words precisely and apply deductive reasoning correctly. You will learn how to form and use the most common type of logical statement in geometry—the conditional statement.

2-2 Stating Our Assumptions

Postulates, undefined terms, defined terms, and theorems are the components of our system of geometry. You will see why some terms are undefined, and why postulates are assumed to be true. You will also learn how to develop definitions and theorems.

2-3 Drawing Techniques and Parallel Lines

The ability to represent a three-dimensional figure on two-dimensional paper is important in industry and in geometry. You will investigate different ways to sketch three-dimensional figures. You will also see how parallel lines are shown in perspective drawing, and learn definitions and postulates about parallel lines.

CHAPTERS

86

Chapter 2 Planning Guide

The following ancillaries are recommended for each course level. The additional resources, *Technology Lab Manual, Study Guide and Journal, Multilingual Handbook,* and *Assessment,* are recommended for all levels.

	Comprehensive Course	Core Course	Informal Course
2-1 Part A	▲	▲	▲
Alternative Lessons			▲
Laboratory Manuals	▲	▲	▲
Practice			▲
More Look Back		▲	▲
2-1 Part B	▲	▲	▲
Alternative Lessons			▲
Laboratory Manuals	▲	▲	▲
Practice			▲
More Look Ahead		▲	▲
2-1 Part C	▲	▲	▲
Alternative Lessons			▲
Laboratory Manuals	▲	▲	▲
Practice			▲
More Look Back		▲	▲
2-1 Part D	▲	▲	▲
More Look Back		▲	▲
Quiz 2-1	▲	▲	▲
2-2 Part A	▲	▲	▲
Alternative Lessons			▲
Laboratory Manuals	▲	▲	▲
Practice			▲
More Look Ahead		▲	▲
2-2 Part B	▲	▲	▲
Alternative Lessons			▲
Laboratory Manuals	▲	▲	▲
Practice			▲
More Look Back		▲	▲
2-2 Part C	▲	▲	▲
Alternative Lessons			▲
Laboratory Manuals	▲	▲	▲
Practice			▲
More Look Ahead		▲	▲
2-2 Part D	▲	▲	▲
More Look Back		▲	▲
Quiz 2-2	▲	▲	▲
2-3 Part A	▲	▲	▲
Alternative Lessons			▲
Laboratory Manuals	▲	▲	▲
Practice			▲
More Look Back		▲	▲
2-3 Part B	▲	▲	▲
Alternative Lessons			▲
Laboratory Manuals	▲	▲	▲
Practice			▲
More Look Ahead		▲	▲
2-3 Part C	▲	▲	▲
Alternative Lessons			▲
Laboratory Manuals	▲	▲	▲
Practice			▲
More Look Back		▲	▲
2-3 Part D	▲	▲	▲
More Look Back		▲	▲
Quiz 2-3	▲	▲	▲

BIBLIOGRAPHY

Reading for Students

Flatland, Edwin Abbott. Penguin Books, 1987.

Math Equals, Teri Perl. Addison-Wesley, 1978 (05709).

Teacher Resources

Middle Grades Mathematics Project: Spatial Visualization, Mary Jean Winter, Glenda Lappan, Elizabeth Phillips, William Fitzgerald. Addison-Wesley, 1986 (21477).

Dot Paper Geometry: With Or Without a Geoboard, Charles Lund. Cuisinaire Company of America, Inc., 1980.

Critical Thinking Activities in Patterns, Imagery, Logic, Dale Seymour and Ed Beardslee. Dale Seymour Publications, 1990 (NS01908).

2-1

The Need for Precise Language

SUPERLESSON AT A GLANCE

Superlesson Goal

Students will learn about conditional statements and statements related to a conditional statement and will use some fundamental rules of logic.

Management Guide

	Topic	Objectives	Key Terms	New Ideas	Materials
Part A	Conditional Statements	To identify the characteristics of true and false conditional statements.	Conditional statement, hypothesis, conclusion, *if-then*	Identifying true and false conditional statements. Rewriting statements in *if-then* form.	
Part B	Related Conditional Statements	To write the inverse, converse, and contrapositive of a conditional statement, and to understand the relationships among the truth values of these statements.	Inverse, converse, contrapositive	Seeing relationships among truth values of a statement and its related statements.	
Part C	The Rules of Logic	To use given information and rules of logic to reach valid conclusions.	Law of Detachment, Chain Rule	Linking logical statements.	
Part D	Making Connections	To use conditional statements and rules of logic to make a persuasive argument.	In Making Connections, students apply and synthesize key terms and new ideas.		**Student** Construction paper, marking pens

Pacing Chart (45-Minute Periods)

	Comprehensive Course	Core Course	Informal Course
Part A	1	1	1
Part B	1	1	1
Part C	1	1	1
Part D	1	1	1
TOTAL periods for Superlesson	4	4	4

NCTM Standards

Mathematics as Problem Solving

Mathematics as Communication

Mathematics as Reasoning

Mathematical Connections

2-1 The Need for Precise Language

TRUTH *IN* ADVERTISING

NEW!

"Is this true or is it an ad?" a child asked a parent. We learn at an early age that not every advertisement's claim is true. Yet companies spend billions of dollars in advertising research.

According to Goodrum and Dalrymple's book *Advertising in America*, one of the classic sayings in advertising is "We are certain that half the money we spend on advertising is wasted. The trouble is, we don't know which half."

Advertisers often use subtle "hidden assumptions" to call your attention to their product. They want to persuade you that their hidden assumption—the condition that the advertisement is based on—is true. In the 1903 advertisement shown, one of the hidden assumptions is that women want men to help with the wash. It is important for consumers to be able to determine whether an advertisement's conclusion is valid.

Cigarette and alcohol advertisements often show scenes of active, healthy people having fun. One of the hidden assumptions these advertisements want you to make is "If you use these products, then you will enjoy the good life." The work, health, and family problems that affect many people who use these products are never in the picture!

1. **Identify a hidden assumption in an advertisement you have recently seen.**
2. **Suppose that, for this particular advertisement only, the hidden assumption is true. Should you necessarily conclude that you ought to buy the product?**
3. **How might knowing the assumptions behind advertisements help you from being fooled by them?**

More About Advertising

According to Charles Goodrum and Helen Dalrymple, although there are frequent complaints about the number of advertisements in newspapers today, the ratio of news to advertising is higher now than in the early days of newspaper publishing in America. The first daily newspaper in the United States had 16 columns, and 10 of these were devoted to advertising. This ratio was typical into the 1800s. (Charles Goodrum and Helen Dalrymple, *Advertising in America: The First 200 Years*. © 1990 Harry N. Abrams.)

Where Are We Now?

Students have become familiar with inductive and deductive reasoning and with the uses of *all, some,* and *none* in logic.

Where Are We Going?

In 2-1, students will investigate conditional statements and rules of logic. This continues an ongoing development of reasoning skills. In Chapter 3, students will draw figures for proofs, and will identify both given information and what they need to prove. In Chapter 4, they will complete proofs, and in Chapter 5 they will write plans for proofs. Beginning with Chapter 6, students will deductively justify conjectures on their own.

Possible Answers

1. Example: If you drink a particular sports drink, you will become a better athlete.
2. No, the conclusion may still be inaccurate. (Example: Hidden assumption: You want to be able to jump higher. Ad: If you want to jump higher, wear Big Hop shoes. You may want to be able to jump higher, but this does not mean that you should buy Big Hop shoes.)
3. If you know the assumption behind an advertisement, it is easier to decide if the ad is truthful. It also helps you keep from being distracted by famous spokespeople, graphics, or music.

Extension: The ad on page 87 provides an opportunity to discuss changing gender roles.

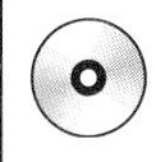

AWSM Videodisc

Focus on Geometry

▶**2-1** The Need for Precise Language

Search:

Play: Step:

The Need for Precise Language

PART A At a Glance

Objective

To identify the characteristics of true and false conditional statements.

Development

Students learn how to identify the hypothesis and conclusion of a conditional statement.

In the **Explore,** students identify the characteristics of true and false conditional statements.

Key Terms

Conditional statement, hypothesis, conclusion, *if-then*

First Five Minutes

Transparency FFM 2-1A

Read page 86 through the **Example.** Then do **Try It a** at the bottom of the page.

Motivate

Ask...

- Give an example of a familiar advertising slogan. What is the assumption behind the slogan?

ALTERNATE EXAMPLE 1

Identify the hypothesis and conclusion of the statement "If you use Squeek shampoo, then your hair will be squeaky clean!"

Hypothesis: You use Squeek shampoo.

Conclusion: Your hair will be squeaky clean.

2-1 PART A Conditional Statements

← CONNECT → *You've already learned some of the language of logic. Now you will investigate a type of logical statement that is especially important: the conditional statement.*

Businesses hope that consumers will believe their advertising claims. These claims are often made indirectly, perhaps through pictures. Sometimes the claim *is* directly stated. In the advertisement from the late 1800s shown at the right, the claim is "If you use Carter's Little Liver Pills, then you will have no more sick headache."

In mathematics, statements in if-then form are called **conditional statements.** The *if* part is the **hypothesis,** and the *then* part is the **conclusion.** The hypothesis and conclusion of a conditional statement are illustrated below.

If <u>you use Mighty Mousse</u>, then <u>your hair will stay in place in a hurricane</u>.

↑ Hypothesis ↑ Conclusion

EXAMPLE

1. Identify the hypothesis and the conclusion of the statement "If you use Carter's Little Liver Pills, then you will have no more sick headache."

   Hypothesis: You use Carter's Little Liver Pills.

   Conclusion: You will have no more sick headache.

   Notice that the words *if* and *then* are not part of the hypothesis or the conclusion.

TRY IT

Write a conditional statement from the given information.

a. Hypothesis: You talk on the telephone more than one hour per night.

Conclusion: Your grade will drop one letter. If you talk on the telephon more than one hour per night, then your grade will drop one letter.

Tips from Teachers

You may want to emphasize the convenience of the *if-then* form for identifying the hypothesis and conclusion of conditional statements. This helps students understand the need to rewrite statements in this form when doing deductive proofs.

Conditional statements aren't always in if-then form. However, any conditional statement can be rewritten in that form. When you put a statement in if-then form, it is much easier to identify its hypothesis and conclusion.

The 1902 advertisement at the right claims that eating Quaker Oats will keep you young. You could rewrite this claim as a conditional statement: "If you eat Quaker Oats, then you will put off old age."

It Puts Off Old Age

by nourishing the entire system. Quaker Oats makes your blood tingle; nerves strong and steady; brain clear and active; muscles powerful. It makes flesh rather than fat, but enough fat for reserve force. It builds children up symmetrically into brainy and robust men and women. You can work on Quaker Oats. It stays by you. At all grocers' in 2 lb. packages only.

EXPLORE

Check the Conditionals

Recommended group size: 2

The Point

To identify the characteristics of true and false conditional statements.

Look and Listen...

- For students who write "false" conditionals by joining a false hypothesis to a false conclusion.

Ask...

- Can a statement be false even if part of it is true?
- What happens when the hypothesis of a true conditional is true? What happens when the hypothesis of a true conditional is false?
- Can you use the photos to help write a conditional statement?

For Groups That Finish Early

Create a table to summarize your results. The column headings should be Hypothesis, Conclusion, Conditional Statement; the table entries should be T or F.

Follow Up

Ask students to list the characteristics of true and false conditional statements.

Possible Answer

2. A conditional statement is false when it is possible for its conclusion to be false when the hypothesis is true. It is true when the conclusion is true whenever the hypothesis is true, or when the hypothesis is false (whether or not the conclusion is true).

TRY IT

Rewrite each conditional statement in if-then form.

b. Help save our forests by using recycled paper. If you use recycled paper, then you will help save our forests.

c. A whole number with three or more factors is not a prime number. If a whole number has three or more factors, then it is not a prime number.

Both consumers and mathematicians must be able to determine when a statement is true. In the following Explore, you will discover when a conditional statement is true and when it is false.

EXPLORE: CHECK THE CONDITIONALS

1. Write a list of several conditional statements in if-then form that you believe are true. Then make a list of several that you feel are false.
2. Use your lists to decide how you can determine whether a conditional statement is true or false by experimenting with the "truth values" of the hypotheses and the conclusions of your statements. Write a short summary describing how you can tell whether a conditional is true or false. Compare your ideas with those of your classmates.

Student Resources

- Alternative Lessons 2-1A
- Laboratory Manual 2-1A
- Technology Lab Manual
- Practice 2-1A
- Study Guide and Journal 2-1A
- Guía de estudios y Diario 2-1A
- Multilingual Handbook
- More Look Back 2-1A
- SAT Preparation

Media Resources

- Transparency FFM 2-1A
- Transparency AE 2-1A
- Teaching Transparency
- AWSMTest and practice software
- AWSM Videodisc

2-1

The Need for Precise Language

ALTERNATE EXAMPLE 2

Determine whether the conditional below is true or false. Explain how you know.

If a number is prime, then it is odd.

False. The number 2 is prime. Since its conclusion can be false when its hypothesis is true, the conditional is false.

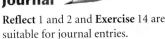

Note: Students are often confused by the idea that a conditional with a false hypothesis is considered true. To ease their minds, you may want to tell them that we'll rarely investigate a conditional when its hypothesis is false. The rules for conditional statements with true hypotheses are more important to understand.

Journal

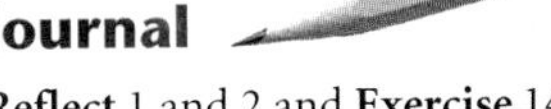

Reflect 1 and 2 and **Exercise** 14 are suitable for journal entries.

REFLECT

Possible Answers

1. When a statement is in *if-then* form, its hypothesis and conclusion are easy to identify. This makes it easier to see whether the statement itself is true or false.
2. No. A conditional statement is considered true only if the conclusion is true whenever the hypothesis is true.

EXAMPLE

2. Determine whether the conditional statement below is true or false. Explain how you know.

   If two numbers are both odd, then their sum is odd.

   Suppose that two numbers are odd, for example, 3 and 5. Their sum, 8, is not odd. This counterexample shows that the conditional is false, because its conclusion is false even though its hypothesis is true.

The properties of true and false conditional statements are summarized below.

> For a conditional statement to be true, the conclusion must be true whenever the hypothesis is true. A conditional is false only if there is a case in which the hypothesis is true and the conclusion is false.

In formal logic, a conditional statement is considered true if the hypothesis is false. (In everyday situations, a conditional is usually considered *irrelevant* when the hypothesis is false.)

You can use a Venn diagram to illustrate conditional statements. The Venn diagram below illustrates the statement "If an animal is a collie, then it is a dog." Since all collies are dogs, this is a true conditional statement. Notice that in this true conditional, no part of the "if circle" lies outside the "then circle."

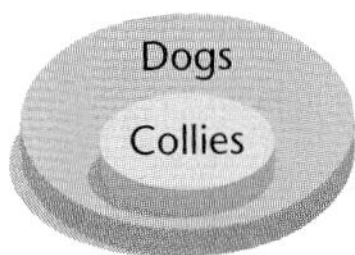

REFLECT

1. Why might companies choose not to put their advertisements in if-then form?
2. Should a conditional statement be considered true if the conclusion is *sometimes* true when the hypothesis is true? For instance, is "If it is cloudy, then it will rain" a true statement?

Alert

Students often include the words *if* and *then* as part of the hypothesis and conclusion. You might need to remind them that they should not do so. You might also point out that in some sentences *when* really means the same thing as *if*.

Exercises

CORE

Getting Started Identify the hypothesis and the conclusion of each conditional.

1. If you want to stay healthy, then you should eat fruits, grains, and vegetables.

2. If $a > b$, then $a + c > b + c$.

For each hypothesis and conclusion, write a conditional statement from the given information.

3. Hypothesis: It rains.

Conclusion: I won't go swimming.

4. Hypothesis: You eat too much spicy food.

Conclusion: You will want a glass of milk.

Rewrite each conditional statement in if-then form.

5. Cherry flavoring will make children love to take their medicine.

6. A burst of mint flavor brightens your mouth when you eat Sparkos!

7. Integers divisible by 4 are also divisible by 2.

8. Write the letter of the second pair that best matches the first pair.

Hypothesis: conclusion as (a) some: all, (b) fact: belief, (c) if: then, (d) rectangle: square

Refer to the Venn diagram at the right.

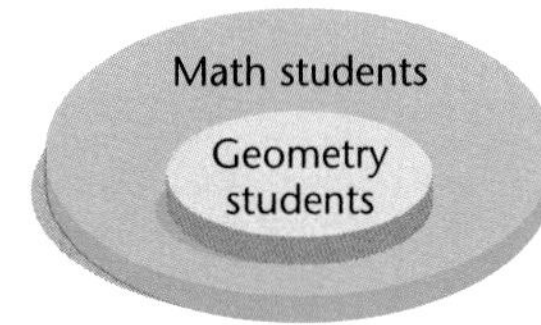

9. Use the Venn diagram to write a conditional that is true.

10. Use the Venn diagram to write a conditional that is false.

Determine whether each conditional is true or false. Explain how you know.

11. If you smoke cigarettes, then you increase your risk of heart disease or lung cancer.

12. If a figure is a rectangle, then it is a square.

13. If $3x - 4 = 17$, then $x = 7$.

14. Write a brief summary explaining how you decide whether a conditional statement is true or false.

y

Vocabulary
Practice/Skills
Review
Math Reasoning
Problem Solving
Challenge

Ongoing Assessment

Self-Assessment Exercises 1–13 odd

Embedded Assessment Explore Step 2; Reflect 2; Exercises 4, 6, 12, 16

Part A Exercises

Exercise Notes

Core

8. Similar to multiple-choice analogy items on standardized tests.

16. Students see that statements beginning with *all* are easily rewritten in *if-then* form.

Look Back

These exercises review scientific notation. These skills will be important in later chapters, especially Chapters 8 and 12.

More Math Reasoning

34. Shows a common advertising strategy. Students should see that a statement may imply more than it actually says.

Exercise Answers

Core

1. Hypothesis: you want to stay healthy; Conclusion: you should eat fruits, grains, and vegetables

2. Hypothesis: $a > b$; Conclusion: $a + c < b + c$

3. If it rains, then I won't go swimming.

4. If you eat too much spicy food, then you will want a glass of milk.

5. If medicine is cherry-flavored, then children will love to take it.

6. If you eat Sparkos, then a burst of mint flavor brightens your mouth.

7. If an integer is divisible by 4, then it is also divisible by 2.

8. (c)

9. If a student is a geometry student, then he or she is a math student.

10. Possible answer: If a student is a math student, then he or she is a geometry student.

11. T; The only way this could be false would be if you smoked and didn't increase your risk.

12. F; There are numerous counterexamples.

13. T; The conclusion is true when the hypothesis is true, by algebra.

2-1

The Need for Precise Language

14. Possible answer: A conditional statement is true unless the hypothesis can be true when the conclusion is false.

15. Possible answer: If you use Giant Sam's Pest Control, then you will not have pests on your property.

16. a.

b. If a dog eats Muscle Pup, then it will be healthy and strong.

c. Yes. "All p's are q's" can be rewritten as, "If something is a p, then it is a q."

Look Back

23.

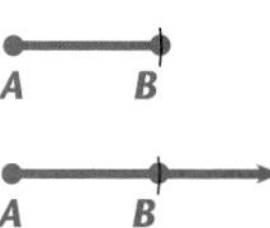

24.

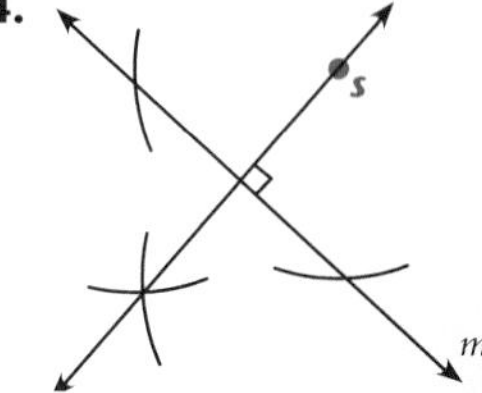

More Practice

25. Hypothesis: A student enrolls in Algebra II; Conclusion: He will learn about logarithms

26. Hypothesis: $|3x - 2| = 10$; Conclusion: $x = 4$ or $x = -\frac{8}{3}$

27. If a mosquito bites you, then you will get a bump on your arm.

28. If a person doesn't stop at a stop sign, then she may get a ticket.

29. If the power is off, then the computer won't run.

30. If a quantity is the product of two negative numbers, then the quantity is positive.

MR **15. A Future in Advertising** Invent a conditional advertisement in if-then form for one of your favorite products.

MR **16. Condition-All a.** Sketch a Venn diagram to illustrate the statement "All dogs who eat Muscle Pup are healthy and strong!"

b. Write a conditional statement in if-then form that has the same meaning.

c. Can you always convert a statement that begins with *all* *(each, every)* into a conditional in if-then form? If so, explain how.

LOOK BACK

Write each number using scientific notation. [Previous course]

R

17. 1875 1.875×10^3 **18.** 0.234 2.34×10^{-1} **19.** 602,300,000,000,000,000,000,000 6.023×10^{23}

Write each number without using scientific notation. [Previous course]

R

20. 7×10^3 7,000 **21.** 1.4×10^{-6} 0.0000014 **22.** 7.02×10^8 702,000,000

R **23.** Copy segment $\overline{AB}$. Then use a compass and straightedge to construct a segment congruent to $\overline{AB}$. [1-3]

A B

R **24.** Sketch line m and point S not on m. Then use a compass and straightedge to construct the line through S that is perpendicular to m. [1-4]

MORE PRACTICE

Identify the hypothesis and the conclusion of each conditional.

P

25. If a student enrolls in Algebra II, then he will learn about logarithms.

26. If $|3x - 2| = 10$, then $x = 4$ or $x = -\frac{8}{3}$.

P **For each hypothesis and conclusion, write a conditional statement from the given information.**

27. Hypothesis: A mosquito bites you.

Conclusion: You will get a bump on your arm.

28. Hypothesis: A person doesn't stop at a stop sign.

Conclusion: She may get a ticket.

Key

V Vocabulary
P Practice/Skills
R Review
MR Math Reasoning
PS Problem Solving
C Challenge

Rewrite each conditional statement in if-then form.

29. The computer won't run if the power is off.

30. The product of two negative numbers is positive.

Determine whether each conditional is true or false.

31. If it is raining, then there are clouds in the sky. T

32. If there are clouds in the sky, then it is raining. F

33. If $x^2 = 4$, then $x = 2$. F

MORE MATH REASONING

34. Mail Order Randy received the letter shown at the right from the Buy-It-Today Corporation. Randy thought, "If I don't buy today, then I won't get the lowest price!" Is his thinking valid? If so, explain why. If not, explain why not, and give a possible reason why the company made this statement.

35. Computer Conditionals A computer program includes these statements:

100 Let $x = n + 1$

200 If $x < 3$, then go to 500

300 Print "I am the greatest."

400 Jump to 600

500 Print "Your wish is my command."

600 End

Predict the output of the program (the things that are printed) for the following values of n.

a. $n = 0$ Your wish is my command.
b. $n = 3$ I am the greatest.
c. $n = 2$ I am the greatest.
d. Suppose you use an if-then statement in a computer program. Under what circumstances does the computer execute the *then* part? Only when the "if" part is true

More Math Reasoning

34. Possible answer: Not valid; Logically, if he doesn't buy today there is no conclusion regarding the price. The company writes this for precisely this reason—to get people to think like Randy and then rush to order the item.

PART B At a Glance

Objective

To write the inverse, converse, and contrapositive of a conditional statement, and to understand the relationships among the truth values of these statements.

Development

Students see the relationship between a conditional statement and its inverse, converse, and contrapositive.

In the **Explore,** students discover how the truth value of a conditional statement is related to the truth values of its inverse, converse, and contrapositive statements.

Key Terms

Inverse, converse, contrapositive

First Five Minutes

Transparency FFM 2-1B

Read the opening paragraphs and the table on page 94. Then do **Try It a** at the bottom of the page.

Motivate

Ask...

- Give an example of a statement and its converse. Do these two statements mean the same thing?

Note: Students often confuse *inverse* and *converse.* You may want to use a mnemonic device to help them. One possibility: You might *con* someone by switching things around. The *con*verse and the *con*trapositive switch the hypothesis and the conclusion.

2-1 PART B Related Conditional Statements

← CONNECT → *You've explored conditional statements, and you know how to determine whether they are true or false. Now you will look at several ways to rearrange conditionals and see whether these rearrangements affect the truth of the conditionals.*

Every conditional has three related statements. These statements are the converse, inverse, and contrapositive of the conditional. Consider the map at the left as you read the following examples.

CONVERSE	
The **converse** of a conditional is formed by interchanging the hypothesis and the conclusion.	*Conditional:* (If p, then q.) If you live in Miami, then you live in Florida. *Converse:* (If q, then p.) If you live in Florida, then you live in Miami.
INVERSE	
The **inverse** of a conditional is formed by taking the *negations* of the hypothesis and the conclusion. (Negations state the opposite of the original phrase.)	*Conditional:* (If p, then q.) If you live in Miami, then you live in Florida. *Inverse:* (If not p, then not q.) If you do *not* live in Miami, then you do *not* live in Florida.
CONTRAPOSITIVE	
The **contrapositive** of a conditional is formed by taking the negation of the hypothesis and conclusion, then interchanging them.	*Conditional:* (If p, then q.) If you live in Miami, then you live in Florida. *Contrapositive:* (If not q, then not p.) If you do *not* live in Florida, then you do *not* live in Miami.

TRY IT

a. Write the inverse, the converse, and the contrapositive of the statement "If you are fifteen, then you are a teenager."

Inverse: If you are not fifteen, then you are not a teenager; Converse: If you are a teenager, then you are fifteen; Contrapositive: If you are not a teenager, then you are not fifteen.

In the following Explore, you will investigate a conditional and its converse, inverse, and contrapositive.

Research Note

The inference patterns, from easiest to most difficult for students to use or in which to detect a fallacy are, *modus ponens* [Law of Detachment], *contrapositive, inverse,* and *converse.* (Phares G. O'Daffer and Bruce A. Thornquist, "Critical Thinking, Mathematical Reasoning, and Proof," *Research Ideas for the Classroom: High School Mathematics,* NCTM Research Interpretation Project, Patricia S. Wilson, ed., p. 45. © 1993 NCTM.)

EXPLORE: WHAT'S THE RELATIONSHIP?

1. Write a list of several true conditional statements. Use your list to investigate the following questions.
   a. If a conditional statement is true, is its converse always true?
   b. If a conditional statement is true, is its inverse always true?
   c. If a conditional statement is true, is its contrapositive always true?
2. What conclusion can you draw from your investigation in Step 1? Are there any pairs of statements that always have the same truth value for a given hypothesis and conclusion? Discuss your conclusion with your classmates.

Problem-Solving Tip

Make a generalization.

A Venn diagram can help you see the relationship between a statement and its inverse, converse, and contrapositive. Suppose you need to investigate the statement "If you are a surgeon, then you wear a mask." Using the Venn diagram below, we see that Person A is a surgeon, and he is also a mask-wearer. The statement is *true*.

Now, suppose you need to investigate the inverse of the statement: "If you are not a surgeon, then you do not wear a mask." According to the diagram, this could be Person B (perhaps a deep-sea diver?) or Person C. But Person B does wear a mask, so the inverse of the original statement is false.

Student Resources

- Alternative Lessons 2-1B
- Laboratory Manual 2-1B
- Technology Lab Manual
- Practice 2-1B
- Study Guide and Journal 2-1B
- Guía de estudios y Diario 2-1B
- Multilingual Handbook
- More Look Ahead 2-1B
- SAT Preparation

Media Resources

- Transparency FFM 2-1B
- Transparency AE
- Teaching Transparency
- AWSMTest and practice software
- AWSM Videodisc

EXPLORE

What's the Relationship?

Recommended group size: 4

The Point

To discover how the truth value of a conditional statement is related to the truth values of its inverse, converse, and contrapositive statements.

Look and Listen...

- For students who are confusing the inverse and the converse.
- For students who are starting with conditionals that are actually false.

Ask...

- When is a conditional statement true? When is it false?
- Can you write a conditional statement based on the pair of photographs shown?

For Groups That Finish Early

Are there some true conditionals that have a true inverse? If so, do they have any special characteristics? **Such statements can usually serve as definitions.**

Follow Up

Ask students to summarize the relationships among the truth values of the statements.

Possible Answers

1. a. No

b. No

c. Yes

2. A conditional statement and its contrapositive always have the same truth value. The statement may or may not have the same truth value as its inverse and converse, but the inverse and the converse have the same truth value.

The Need for Precise Language

Journal

Explore Step 2 and **Reflect** 1 and 2 are suitable for journal entries.

REFLECT

Possible Answers

1. The inverse and the converse always have the same truth values. The inverse of a statement is the contrapositive of its converse, so they have the same truth values.
2. She is correct. Taking the inverse negates the hypothesis and conclusion, and taking the converse then interchanges them. This forms the contrapositive.
3. It is usually beneficial to have both the statement and its converse appear true. This makes a stronger claim for the product.

Part B Exercises

Exercise Notes

Core

14–15. These exercises show common fallacies in logical thinking. Exercise 14 shows the fallacy of assuming that the converse of a statement is true. Exercise 15 shows the fallacy of assuming that the inverse is true.

Look Ahead

16–17. These exercises introduce students to the biconditional statement. Biconditional statements are developed in 2-2 Part A, where students look at formal definitions.

18–21. These exercises look ahead to supplementary angles, first defined formally in 3-3.

More Math Reasoning

28. Shows a practical application of the idea that a statement and its contrapositive are logically equivalent.

The relationships between the truth values of a conditional and its inverse, converse, and contrapositive are summarized below.

- If a conditional statement is true, its contrapositive is true; if a conditional statement is false, its contrapositive is false.
- The truth value of a conditional statement does not tell you whether its converse or its inverse is true or false. You must analyze those statements separately.

REFLECT

1. Are the truth values of the inverse and converse of a statement related? If so, describe how and explain why.
2. Consuela says, "If I take the converse of the inverse of a conditional statement, I get the statement's contrapositive." Show whether she is right or wrong.
3. Write an advertisement with a conditional statement for a fictitious product. Would it benefit your company if people assumed that the inverse of your statement was also true? Explain.

Exercises

CORE

P 1. **Getting Started** The photo at the lower right shows the Katsura Imperial Villa in Kyoto. Write the inverse, converse, and contrapositive of the statement "If you live in Kyoto, then you live in Japan."

P **Write the inverse, converse, and contrapositive of each conditional. Then determine which statements are true and which are false.**

2. If $x^2 = 4$, then $x = 2$.
3. If two angles are right angles, then they are congruent.
4. If you finish a triathlon, then you are in good shape.
5. If you are an elephant, then you do not know how to fly.
6. If you have a cold, then you are sick.

Key

V Vocabulary
P Practice/Skills
R Review
MR Math Reasoning
PS Problem Solving
C Challenge

In Exercises 7 and 8, determine whether each statement is true or false. If the statement is false, change the underlined word to make it true.

7. To form the converse of a conditional statement, switch the hypothesis and the conclusion. T

8. If a conditional statement is true, its contrapositive must be false. F; True

9. Write a false conditional statement. Then write its inverse, converse, and contrapositive, and determine whether each statement is true or false. Possible answer: Same as Exercise 2

Write a conditional statement with each of the following sets of characteristics.

10. The conditional is true, and its converse is false.

11. The conditional is false, and its inverse is true.

12. The conditional is true, and its inverse and converse are false.

13. The conditional and all of its related statements are true.

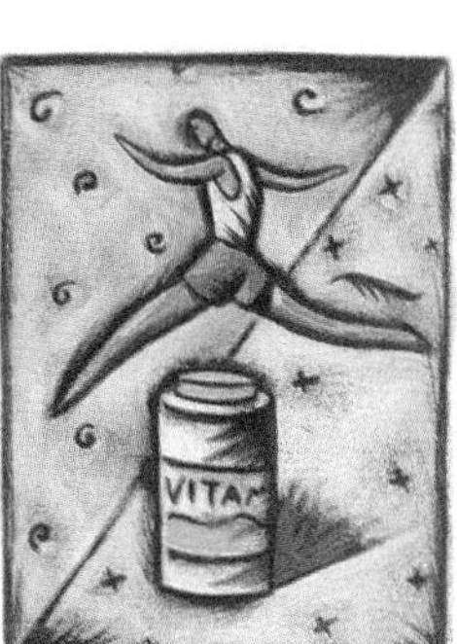

14. Take Your Vitamins! Mr. Perkins heard an advertisement that said, "If you take a multivitamin tablet each day, then you'll stay healthy." Mr. Perkins began to feel uneasy, thinking, "If I don't take a multivitamin tablet each day, then I won't stay healthy." Is his thinking valid? If so, explain why. If not, explain the error he is making.

15. On Cloud Nine Judy's mother received an advertisement that said, "If you are fashionable, then you wear Cloud Nine shoes." She said to Judy, "I wear Cloud Nine shoes; therefore, I must be fashionable."

a. If you use "if p, then q" to abbreviate the statement in the advertisement, how would you abbreviate the assumption that Judy's mother made? If q then p

b. Was her mother's reasoning logically correct? Explain why or why not. No; When the original is true, the converse is not necessarily true.

LOOK AHEAD

When a conditional and its converse are both true, you can combine the two statements into one statement, called a *biconditional,* by using the phrase "if and only if." For example, the two statements "if tomorrow is Saturday, then today is Friday" and "if today is Friday, then tomorrow is Saturday" become "tomorrow is Saturday if and only if today is Friday." Use this information to help you with Exercises 16 and 17 on page 98.

Exercise Answers

Core

1. Inverse: If you don't live in Kyoto, then you don't live in Japan; Converse: If you live in Japan, then you live in Kyoto; Contrapositive: If you don't live in Japan, then you don't live in Kyoto.

2. Original: F
Inverse: If $x^2 \neq 4$, then $x \neq 2$. T
Converse: If $x = 2$, then $x^2 = 4$. T
Contrapositive: If $x \neq 2$, then $x^2 \neq 4$. F

3. Original: T
Inverse: If two angles are not right angles, then they are not congruent. F
Converse: If two angles are congruent, then they are right angles. F
Contrapositive: If two angles are not congruent, then they are not (both) right angles. T

4. Original: T
Inverse: If you don't finish a triathlon, then you are not in good shape. F
Converse: If you are in good shape, then you will finish a triathlon. F
Contrapositive: If you are not in good shape, then you won't finish a triathlon. T

5. Original: T
Inverse: If you are not an elephant, then you know how to fly. F
Converse: If you don't know how to fly, then you are an elephant. F
Contrapositive: If you know how to fly, then you are not an elephant. T

6. Original: T
Inverse: If you don't have a cold, then you are not sick. F
Converse: If you are sick then you have a cold. F
Contrapositive: If you are not sick, then you don't have a cold. T

Ongoing Assessment

Self-Assessment Exercises 1, 2, 3, 5, 7, 11, 13

Embedded Assessment Explore Step 2; Reflect 2; Exercises 4, 9, 14

2-1

The Need for Precise Language

10. If $x > 7$, then $x > 3$.

11. If $x > 3$, then $x > 7$.

12. If $x = 0$, then $xy = 0$.

13. If x is negative, then $-x$ is positive.

14. Possible answer: No; For example, he could eat lots of vitamin-rich vegetables and still stay healthy. He is (erroneously) assuming that if the original statement is true, so is its inverse.

Look Ahead

16. Original: T
Converse: If an angle measures 90°, then it is a right angle; T
An angle is a right angle if and only if it measures 90°.

17. Original: T
Converse: If two angles have the same measure, then they are congruent; T
Two angles are congruent if and only if they have the same measure.

More Practice

22. Original: T
Inverse: If it is not raining, then the sidewalk is not wet. F
Converse: If the sidewalk is wet, then it is raining. F
Contrapositive: If the sidewalk is not wet, then it is not raining. T

23. Original: F
Inverse: If $t^2 \leq 0$, then $t \leq 0$. T
Converse: If $t > 0$, then $t^2 > 0$. T
Contrapositive: If $t \leq 0$, then $t^2 \leq 0$. F

24. Original: T
Inverse: If a whole number does not have exactly two whole-number factors, then it is not a prime. T
Converse: If a whole number is a prime, then it has exactly two whole-number factors. T
Contrapositive: If a whole number is not a prime, then it does not have exactly two whole-number factors. T

25–28. See Additional Answers p. T106.

Algebra | Functions | Discrete Math | Probability | Data/Statistics

P **Write the converse of each conditional. If both the original statement and its converse are true, then rewrite them as a single biconditional statement.**

16. If an angle is a right angle, then it measures 90°.

17. If two angles are congruent, then they have the same measure.

P **Suppose $m\angle A + m\angle B = 180°$. Find $m\angle A$ for each $m\angle B$ below.**

18. $m\angle B = 120°$ 60° **19.** $m\angle B = 45°$ 135° **20.** $m\angle B = 90°$ 90°

P **21.** Write an expression for $m\angle A$ in terms of $m\angle B$. $m\angle A = 180° - m\angle B$

MORE PRACTICE

P **For Excercises 22–25, write the inverse, converse, and contrapositive of each conditional. Then determine which statements are true and which are false.**

22. If it is raining, then the sidewalk is wet.

23. If $t^2 > 0$, then $t > 0$.

24. If a whole number has exactly two whole-number factors, then it is a prime.

25. If you are not over four feet tall, then you are not riding the RocketCoaster.

P **26. a.** Assume the following statement is true, and illustrate it with a Venn diagram.

If you want to become a businessperson, then you will need to take math.

b. Write the converse of the statement. Is the converse true or false?
c. Write the inverse of the statement. Is the inverse true or false?
d. Write the contrapositive of the statement. Is the contrapositive true or false?

MORE MATH REASONING

C, MR **27.** Write a conditional statement in if-then form. Then write the inverse of the converse of its contrapositive. Explain why your statement turns out the way it does.

MR, PS **28. Vase Case** Latasha is a lawyer. She wants to prove that her client, Chip, did not break an expensive vase in a gift shop. Obviously, if her client broke the vase, then he was in the gift shop. How can Latasha prove that Chip is innocent without ever saying that he did not break the vase? Why will this strategy work?

Key

V Vocabulary
P Practice/Skills
R Review
MR Math Reasoning
PS Problem Solving
C Challenge

2-1 PART C The Rules of Logic

← CONNECT → ***You know the conditions that make a single conditional statement true. Now you will investigate rules of logic that allow you to link logical statements together to make a valid deductive argument.***

Advertisements often try to persuade you to buy a product by getting you to believe a conditional statement is true. Once the conditional statement is accepted, the advertisement tries to persuade you to buy the product (hypothesis) and benefit from the promise (conclusion).

There are some rules of logic that people frequently use without realizing it. In the following Explore, you will identify some of your intuitive rules of logic.

EXPLORE: LOGICAL LINKS

Assume that the statements below are true. Some of them fit together. Use them to write other statements that must be true. Then summarize any general rules of logic that you seemed to use consistently.

If I get a better English grade, then I can go to college and become a famous scientist.

If I learn more about my culture, then I can share it better with other people.

If a self-portrait is by Frida Kahlo, then it was painted before 1955.

I'm proud of my heritage.

If my vision is blurry, then I will get glasses.

The self-portrait at the right is by Frida Kahlo.

Frida Kahlo, *Self-Portrait with Monkey,* 1945. Fundacion Dolores Olmedo, Mexico City, Mexico.

If I see better, then I can read faster.

If I can read faster, then I'll get a better English grade.

If I'm proud of my heritage, then I will learn more about my culture.

If I get glasses, then I'll see better.

Student Resources

- Alternative Lessons 2-1C
- Laboratory Manual 2-1C
- Technology Lab Manual
- Practice 2-1C
- Study Guide and Journal 2-1C
- Guía de estudios y Diario 2-1C
- Multilingual Handbook
- More Look Back 2-1C
- SAT Preparation

Media Resources

- Transparency FFM 2-1C
- Transparency AE
- Teaching Transparency
- AWSMTest and practice software
- AWSM Videodisc

PART C At a Glance

Objective

To use given information and rules of logic to reach valid conclusions.

Development

In the **Explore,** students use their intuitive ideas about logical thinking to discover the Law of Detachment and the Chain Rule. These intuitive ideas are then stated formally.

Key Terms

Law of Detachment, Chain Rule

First Five Minutes

Transparency FFM 2-1C

Are the following statements true or false?

If an animal is a trout, then it is a fish. **True**

If an animal is a fish, then it is a trout. **False**

If $x + 2 = 4$, then $x = 3$. **False**

If $x = 2$ and $y = -3$, then $x^2y = -12$. **True**

Motivate

Ask...

- Suppose you know a conditional statement is true. Do you know that the conclusion of the statement is true? Why or why not?

EXPLORE

Logical Links

Recommended group size: 4

The Point

To discover the Law of Detachment and the Chain Rule.

2-1

The Need for Precise Language

Look and Listen...

- For students who are not separating the statements into different scenarios.

Ask...

- Which groups of statements seem to go together?

For Groups That Finish Early

Make up a fairly long logic chain of the type in the **Explore,** scramble it, and give it to another group of early finishers to untangle.

Follow Up

Ask students to summarize their logical rules.

Possible Answers

Logical rules that students may discover are:

1. p and $(p \rightarrow q) = q$
2. $(p \rightarrow q)$ and $(q \rightarrow r) = (p \rightarrow r)$

Note: The Law of Detachment is sometimes referred to by its Latin name, *modus ponens.* Reasoning that uses the contrapositive is called *modus tolens.*

TRY IT

Assume that the following statements are true. Write another true statement if possible. If it is not possible, explain why.

a. If I clean my room, then I'll find my shoes. If I find my shoes, then I'll be able to go to the store. If I clean my room, then I'll be able to go to the store.

b. If Fran gets an A in Spanish, then she will make the Honor Roll. Fran gets an A in Spanish. Fran will make the honor roll.

One pattern you may have discovered is the **Law of Detachment.** If you are given a true conditional statement and you know the hypothesis is true, then the conclusion must also be true. The pattern is called the Law of Detachment because it detaches the conclusion from a conditional. The following summary of the Law of Detachment includes an example on the right.

LAW OF DETACHMENT	
Assumption: If p is true, then q is true.	If Chanelle is in 12th grade, then she is a senior.
Assumption: p is true.	Chanelle is in 12th grade.
Conclusion: q is true.	Chanelle is a senior.

Another rule of logic that you might have found is the **Chain Rule** (see the summary and example that follow). The Chain Rule links two true conditional statements. It can only be used if the hypothesis of one statement is the conclusion of the other.

CHAIN RULE	
Assumption: If p is true, then q is true.	If Chanelle is in 12th grade, then she is a senior.
Assumption: If q is true, then r is true.	If she is a senior, then she is in government class.
Conclusion: If p is true, then r is true.	If Chanelle is in 12th grade, then she is in government class.

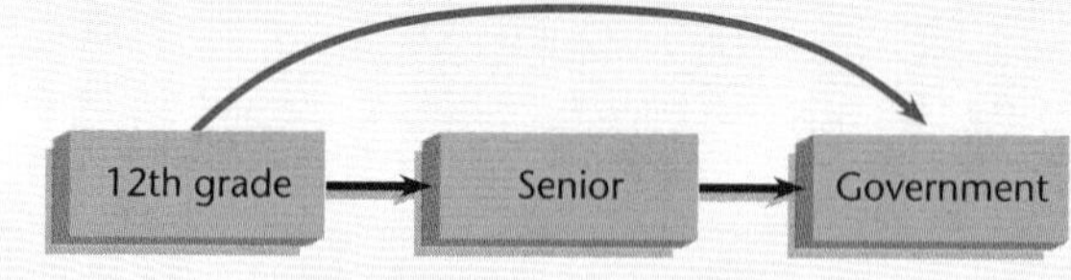

Diversity Issues

Illustrating the Chain Rule with a Venn diagram may be helpful for visual learners. The fact that "If *A,* then *B*" and "If *B,* then *C*" imply "If *A,* then *C*" can be shown by an "A circle" inside a "B circle" inside a "C circle."

Fine Arts Connection

The painting on page 99 was done by Frida Kahlo (1907–1954). Kahlo was born in Coyoacán, Mexico, and was named a professor of painting at La Esmeralda, Mexico City, in 1940. She had several exhibitions in the United States in the 1930s and 1940s. Her work was intensely personal and includes a number of self-portraits.

These laws of logic may seem obvious, but we need to agree on them so that we understand and believe each other's deductive arguments. These laws also help you to think about what you are doing when you work with mathematical statements instead of ordinary sentences.

REFLECT

1. In your own words, explain when you can make a valid deduction by the following rules of logic.

   a. the Law of Detachment
   b. the Chain Rule

2. Give your own examples of logical reasoning that illustrate the Law of Detachment and the Chain Rule.

Exercises

CORE

1. **Getting Started** Assume that the following statements are true. Use the Law of Detachment to write another true statement.

   If figure *EFGH* is a square, then $\overline{EG} \cong \overline{HF}$. Figure *EFGH* is a square. $\overline{EG} \cong \overline{HF}$

Assume that the following statements are true. Use the Law of Detachment to write another true statement if possible. If it is not possible, explain why.

2. If two lines are perpendicular, then they intersect. Lines $\overleftrightarrow{AB}$ and $\overleftrightarrow{CD}$ intersect.
3. If a state has 9 members of the House of Representatives, then it has 11 electoral votes. In 1992, the state of Washington had 9 representatives.

Assume that the following statements are true. Use the Chain Rule to write another true statement if possible. If it is not possible, explain why.

4. If it is raining, the sky is cloudy. If the sky is cloudy, then you can't see the sun.
5. If the legal minimum wage is too high, then employers will hire fewer people. If the legal minimum wage is too low, then there will be a shortage of workers.

Key
- Vocabulary
- Practice/Skills
- Review
- MR Math Reasoning
- PS Problem Solving
- Challenge

Ongoing Assessment

Self-Assessment Exercises 1–13 odd

Embedded Assessment Reflect 1; Exercises 2, 8, 12, 14

Journal

Reflect 1 and 2 are suitable for journal entries.

REFLECT

Possible Answers

1. a. When you have a true conditional statement, and you know that its hypothesis is true.

   b. When you have two conditional statements, and the hypothesis of one is the conclusion of the other.

2. Law of Detachment: If a person is 18 or older, then that person can vote. Aileen is 18. Therefore, she can vote.

   Chain Rule: If the statements "If you drive over the speed limit, then you will get a ticket" and "If you get a ticket, then you will have to pay a fine" are true, then the statement "If you drive over the speed limit, then you will have to pay a fine" is also true.

Part C Exercises

Exercise Notes

Core

9. Shows that valid logical reasoning with imprecise statements can lead to incorrect conclusions.

10–11. In these exercises, students "reason backwards" to decide which logical rule was used to reach a given conclusion.

14. Applies the laws of logic in a real-world situation.

More Math Reasoning

25. This logic puzzle explores the difference between a logical chain and a logical circle.

Exercise Answers

Core

2. Not possible; Detachment starts with a conditional statement and the truth of the hypothesis, not a conditional statement and the truth of the conclusion.
3. Washington state had 11 electoral votes in 1992.
4. If it is raining, then you can't see the sun.

Algebra | Functions | Discrete Math | Probability | Data/Statistics

2-1

The Need for Precise Language

5. Not possible: The Chain Rule requires the conclusion of one statement to be the hypothesis of the other.

6. If someone is the Secretary of Transportation, then he or she is a member of the Cabinet; In 1993 Federico Peña became a member of the Cabinet.

7. If someone is a baseball player, then he or she wears spikes on natural-grass fields. Ken Griffey, Jr., wears spikes on natural-grass fields.

8. If a creature is a stag beetle, then it is an insect. If a creature is an insect, then it has 6 legs. Stag beetles have 6 legs.

9. If a number can be written as a fraction, then it is a rational number. If a number is pi, then it can be written as the fraction $\frac{\pi}{1}$. Pi is a rational number.

14. Possible answer: Apply Law of Detachment to "If his knee is swollen..." and "His knee is badly swollen" to conclude there may be ligament damage. She will probably recommend an MRI scan at this point. If ligament damage is detected, she may then (using the Law of Detachment) decide to recommend surgery.

More Practice

20. A seal is warm-blooded.

21. A rectangle is a quadrilateral.

22. If it rains, then we get popcorn.

23. If you reflect a segment across a line, then the segment and its reflected image are congruent.

More Math Reasoning

24. Possible answer: If you vote for me, then I will vote for lower taxes. If I vote for lower taxes, then the bill to lower taxes will pass. If the bill to lower taxes passes, then your taxes will be lower.

P **Rewrite the first statement in if-then form. Then make a deduction using the Law of Detachment.**

6. The Secretary of Transportation is a member of the Cabinet. In 1993, Federico Peña became the Secretary of Transportation.

7. Baseball players wear spikes on natural-grass fields. Ken Griffey, Jr., is a baseball player.

P **Rewrite both statements in each pair in if-then form. Then make a deduction using the Chain Rule if possible.**

8. Stag beetles are insects. All insects have six legs.

9. A rational number can be written as a fraction. Pi can be written as the fraction $\frac{\pi}{1}$.

P **Identify the law of logic used to reach each of the following conclusions.**

10. If $\overrightarrow{BD}$ is perpendicular to $\overleftrightarrow{AC}$, then $\angle ABD$ and $\angle DBC$ are right angles. If $\angle ABD$ and $\angle DBC$ are right angles, then $\angle ABD$ and $\angle DBC$ measure 90°. Conclusion: If $\overrightarrow{BD}$ is perpendicular to $\overleftrightarrow{AC}$, then $\angle ABD$ and $\angle DBC$ measure 90°. Chain rule

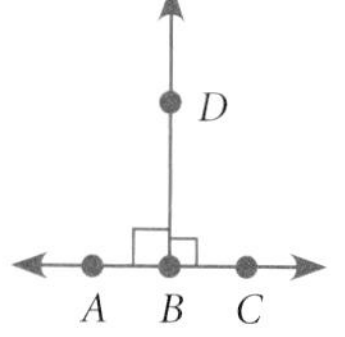

11. If I can't find my keys, then I'll have to stay home. I can't find my keys. Conclusion: I'll have to stay home. Law of Detachment

P **Arrange some or all of the following conditionals into an order that allows you to make the given conclusions.**

If *A*, then *B*. If *X*, then *R*. If *M*, then *Y*. If *R*, then *M*. If *Y*, then *A*.

12. If *X*, then *Y*. If *X*, then *R*. If *R*, then *M*. If *M*, then *Y*.

13. If *X*, then *B*. If *X*, then *R*. If *R*, then *M*. If *M*, then *Y*. If *Y* then *A*. If *A* then *B*.

MR **14. Do I Kneed Surgery?** A patient comes to a doctor with an injured knee. The doctor knows that if the patient has torn a ligament, he may need to have arthroscopic surgery. She also knows that if his knee is swollen, there may be ligament damage. An MRI (magnetic resonance imaging) scan can detect ligament damage. Her patient's knee is badly swollen, painful, and difficult to move. Given only this information, what do you think the doctor will recommend? Explain how you reached this conclusion, and describe how you used the Chain Rule and the Law of Detachment in your reasoning.

Science

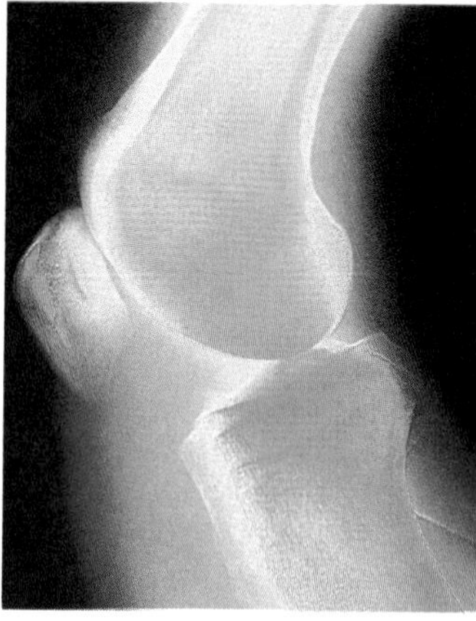

Key

- V Vocabulary
- P Practice/Skills
- R Review
- MR Math Reasoning
- PS Problem Solving
- C Challenge

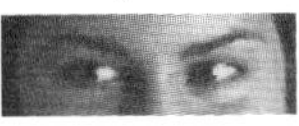

LOOK BACK

Factor each expression. [Previous course]

15. $x^2 - 6x + 9$ $(x - 3)^2$

16. $y^2 + 11y + 28$ $(y + 4)(y + 7)$

17. $3c^2 - 4c - 15$ $(c - 3)(3c + 5)$

Answer each of the following. Then state the type of reasoning you used to solve the problem. [1-2]

18. The first four numbers in a sequence are 1, 3, 6, and 10. Find the fifth and sixth numbers. 5th term: 15; 6th term: 21

19. Harvey never tells the truth. Alex always tells the truth. Roger sometimes tells the truth. Who is the person in the middle? Harvey

MORE PRACTICE

Assume that the following statements are true. Use the Law of Detachment to write another true statement if possible. If it is not possible, explain why.

20. If an animal is a mammal, then it is warm-blooded. A seal is a mammal.

21. If a figure has four sides, then it is a quadrilateral. A rectangle has four sides.

Assume that the following statements are true. Use the Chain Rule to write another true statement if possible. If it is not possible, explain why.

22. If it rains, then we go to the movies. If we go to the movies, then we get popcorn.

23. If you reflect a segment across a line, the image has the same length as the pre-image. If two segments have the same length, then they are congruent.

MORE MATH REASONING

24. Write a chain of three conditional statements in if-then form that will allow you to conclude, "If you vote for me, then your taxes will be lower."

2-1

The Need for Precise Language

PART D At a Glance

Objective

To use conditional statements and rules of logic to make a persuasive argument.

Development

In the **Explore,** students design an advertisement using conditional statements, the Law of Detachment, and the Chain Rule.

Suggested Materials

Student Construction paper, marking pens

First Five Minutes

Transparency FFM 2-1D

Give brief definitions of each of the following in your own words.

Hypothesis, conclusion, inverse, converse, contrapositive, Law of Detachment, Chain Rule

EXPLORE

I'll Buy That!

Recommended group size: 4

The Point

To use conditional statements and laws of logic to design a persuasive advertisement.

Look and Listen...

- For students who are having difficulty remembering the details of the two logic rules.

Ask...

- How will your commercial convince a person to buy your product?

For Groups That Finish Early

Add art or music to make your advertisement more entertaining.

Algebra	Functions	Discrete Math	Probability	Data/Statistics

PS, C **25. Grade Gossip** Arthur, Beth, Carlos, and Diane were discussing their geometry grades. All of their statements were true.

Arthur said, "If I get an A, then Beth will get an A."
Beth said, "If I get an A, then Carlos will get an A."
Carlos said, "If I get an A, then Diane will get an A."

a. Only two of the students received an A. Which two? Carlos and Diane

b. How would the answer to **25a** change if Diane had said, "If I get an A, then Arthur will get an A"? Problem has no answer in this case; either all of the students get A's or none do.

2-1 PART D Making Connections

← CONNECT → ***You've learned how to form and to use the most common type of logical statement in geometry—the conditional statement.***

The Law of Detachment and the Chain Rule are ways to build logical arguments from conditional statements. You will now use conditional statements and rules of logic to create your own advertisement.

EXPLORE: I'LL BUY THAT!

MATERIALS

Construction paper (optional)
Marking pens (optional)

1. Design your own 30-second TV advertisement for a product of your choice. You may use dialogue, visuals, or music, but your advertisement must have the following characteristics:
   - the use of several conditional statements (they do not have to be in if-then form);
   - the use of both rules of logic;
   - the use of persuasion to convince your audience to buy your product.

   What do you want the customer to believe after seeing your advertisement? Show the rules of logic, and explain the thought process you hope customers go through when they see your ad.
2. Present your advertisement to the class.

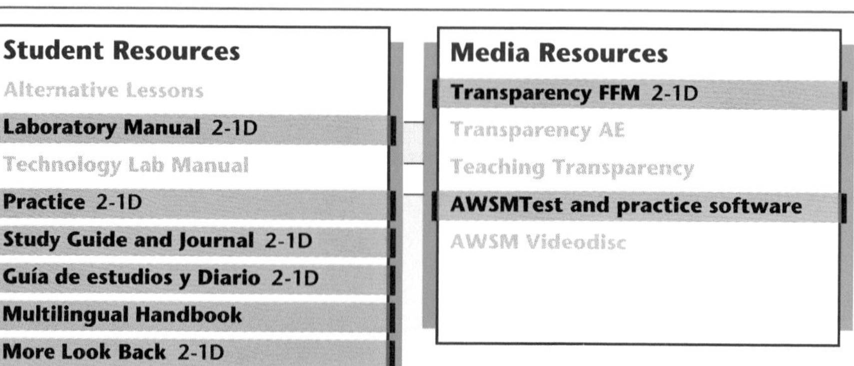

Student Resources

Alternative Lessons
Laboratory Manual 2-1D
Technology Lab Manual
Practice 2-1D
Study Guide and Journal 2-1D
Guía de estudios y Diario 2-1D
Multilingual Handbook
More Look Back 2-1D
SAT Preparation

Media Resources

Transparency FFM 2-1D
Transparency AE
Teaching Transparency
AWSMTest and practice software
AWSM Videodisc

REFLECT

1. Describe some ways that advertisements use logical statements and rules of logic.
2. Explain how you can determine whether a conditional statement is true or false.
3. Write a letter to a friend who has not studied geometry explaining how you can use the Law of Detachment or the Chain Rule to prove a point. Use a real-life example from history, current events, or your own experience to help illustrate the rule.

Self-Assessment

In Exercises 1–3, rewrite each conditional statement in if-then form. Then identify its hypothesis and conclusion.

1. All squares are quadrilaterals.
2. You should buy Frumworts because they make you happy!
3. You waste gasoline when you drive too fast.

R 4. A student says, "If I don't have a lot of homework, then my book bag will not be heavy."
   a. Write the converse, inverse, and contrapositive of this conditional.
   b. Determine whether each of the four statements is true or false. Give a counterexample to justify a false value.

P 5. Draw a Venn diagram to show that the following argument is valid.

   If a family lives in Chicago, then they live in Illinois.

   The Dias family lives in Chicago.

   Therefore, the Dias family lives in Illinois.

R 6. **Broken Promise?** Jon told his younger brother, "If you don't clean up your mess in my room, then I won't take you to the game tonight." Jon's brother did clean up his mess in Jon's room, but Jon decided not to take his brother to the game. Jon's brother claims he broke his promise. Explain to Jon's brother why Jon didn't really break his promise.

R **Write each number using scientific notation. [Previous course]**

7. 327 3.27×10^2 8. 0.003042 3.042×10^{-3}

9. 186,282 (This is the number of miles light travels in 1 sec.) 1.86282×10^5

ey

Vocabulary
Practice/Skills
Review
R Math Reasoning
S Problem Solving
Challenge

Follow Up

Have students present their advertisements to the class as suggested in Step 2. You might have them vote for the most clever or persuasive ad.

Possible Answer

Check students' work.

Portfolio

Have students select items from their work that demonstrate their understanding of the material in 2-1.

Students might submit their best use of a Venn diagram, an **Exercise** that used inverses, converses, or contrapositives, an **Exercise** that they found difficult that used a rule of logic, and the text of their advertisement from the **Explore** in Part D.

REFLECT

Possible Answers

1. Many advertisements have conditional statements, although they may not be in *if-then* form. Advertisements use the Chain Rule to link claims.
2. A conditional statement is false if an example can be found where the hypothesis is true and the conclusion is false. Otherwise, it is true.
3. Example of reasoning that might be used: "If I ride the bus to school, then I can get up 15 minutes later. I decided to ride the bus to school today. Therefore, I was able to get up 15 minutes later."

Self-Assessment

Exercise Notes

Core

10. A logic puzzle that has students use the deductive reasoning they first worked with in 1-2.
11. This logic puzzle requires use of the Chain Rule and the Law of Detachment. It is similar to reasoning problems found on some standardized tests.

2-1

The Need for Precise Language

Self-Assessment Answers

1. If a figure is a square, then it is a quadrilateral. Hypothesis: The figure is a square; Conclusion: The figure is a quadrilateral.

2. If you buy Frumworts, then you will be happy. Hypothesis: You buy Frumworts. Conclusion: You will be happy.

3. If you drive too fast, then you waste gasoline. Hypothesis: You drive too fast; Conclusion: You waste gasoline.

4. a. Converse: If my book bag is not heavy, then I don't have a lot of homework. Inverse: If I have a lot of homework, then my book bag will be heavy. Contrapositive: If my book bag is heavy, then I have a lot of homework.

b. Converse and inverse: F; The student might be carrying only a math book but have 500 problems to do. Contrapositive and original: F; The student might be carrying something besides homework materials in the bag.

5.

6. A true conditional (the promise) does not necessarily mean a true inverse, and so Detachment using the inverse won't work.

Logic/Reasoning

PS **10. The Pizza Puzzle** Carol decided to make a mystery game for her birthday party. Can you deduce how the game ended? Which friend found the real pizza, what topping was on the pizza, and where was it hidden? [1-2] Fumiko found the real, sausage pizza under the sink.

- There were four pizzas, but only one was real. Four friends were looking for the real pizza. Each pizza had a different topping: pepperoni, sausage, ham, or extra cheese.
- Sara found the ham pizza behind the wall picture in the living room.
- The friend who found the pepperoni pizza did not find it under the kitchen sink.
- The real pizza was not found under the couch or in the freezer; two false pizzas were found there.
- Fumiko found a pizza under the kitchen sink.
- Michelle found the pizza with extra cheese, but it was a fake.
- Zuri did not find her pizza in the freezer.
- Sara did not find the real pizza.

MR **11.** Assume that each of the following statements is true.

If you are a dreet, then you are a drook.
If you are not a dran, then you are not a drook.
If you are a dran, then you are not a drilp.
You are a drook.

Which of the following statements must also be true? (b), (d), (e)

(a) You are a drilp. (b) You are a dran.
(c) You are a dreet. (d) You are not a drilp.
(e) both (b) and (d) (f) both (a) and (c)

MR, C **12. The Contrapositive Argument** Use what you have learned about the contrapositive to investigate the following situation. Julio thinks he has discovered a new rule of logic for making a valid argument. He uses the following example as an illustration.

If a whale is a killer whale, then it has a dorsal fin.
This whale does not have a dorsal fin.
Therefore, this whale is not a killer whale.

a. Is Julio's conclusion logical? Yes

b. In your own words, describe the rule he is using. Given: A conditional statement and the negation of its conclusion. Infer: The negation of the hypothesis.

c. Investigate other conditionals using Julio's rule. Does this rule always work? Check students' answers; Yes.

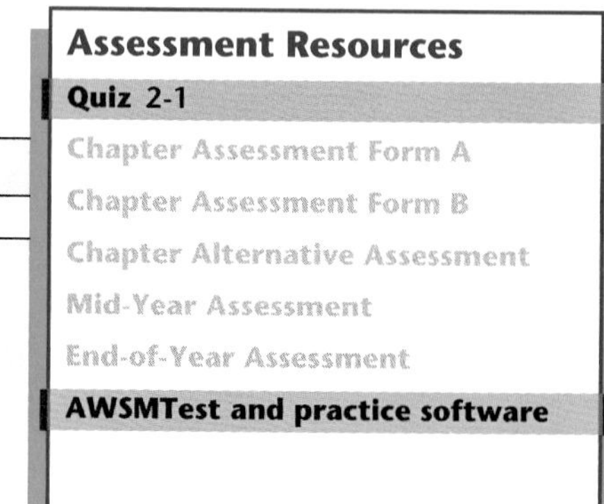

Assessment Resources

Quiz 2-1
Chapter Assessment Form A
Chapter Assessment Form B
Chapter Alternative Assessment
Mid-Year Assessment
End-of-Year Assessment
AWSMTest and practice software

Ongoing Assessment

Self-Assessment Self-Assessment Exercises

Embedded Assessment Explore Step 1; Reflect 1–3

ADDITIONAL ANSWERS

2-1 Part B Exercises

25. Original: (presumed) T
Inverse: If you are over four feet tall, then you are riding the RocketCoaster. F
Converse: If you are not riding the RocketCoaster, then you are not over four feet tall. F
Contrapositive: If you are riding the RocketCoaster, then you are over four feet tall. T

26. a.

b. If you need to take math, then you want to become a businessperson. F

c. If you don't want to become a businessperson, then you don't need to take math. F

d. If you don't need to take math, then you don't want to become a businessperson. T

More Math Reasoning

27. Possible answer: Same as original conditional statement; if you interchange the hypothesis and conclusion twice and reverse their truth values twice, you come back to the original statement.

28. Possible answer: Use the contrapositive. If she can show that her client was not in the gift shop, the jury must conclude that he didn't break the vase. The strategy relies on the fact that a statement and its contrapositive have the same truth value.

2-2

Stating Our Assumptions

SUPERLESSON AT A GLANCE

Superlesson Goal

Students will see the importance of undefined terms, begin writing definitions, and learn the first postulates about the properties of geometric figures.

Management Guide

	Topic	Objectives	Key Terms	New Ideas	Materials
Part A	Undefined Terms and Definitions	To learn which geometric terms are undefined, and to begin writing definitions.	Plane, coplanar, noncoplanar, biconditional, midpoint	Identifying critical attributes. Writing definitions in biconditional form.	
Part B	Postulates	To discover and use basic postulates about geometric figures.	Space	The importance of unproved assumptions. Working with basic properties of geometric figures.	**Student** Everyday objects to represent points, lines, and planes
Part C	Working in a Deductive System	To see the relationships among collinearity, betweenness, and midpoint as students explore betweenness.	Between	Seeing how postulates and definitions fit together to form theorems. Finding coordinates of midpoints.	**Student** Ruler, compass **Teacher** Chalkboard/overhead compass, straightedge
Part D	Making Connections	To use the ideas of undefined terms, definitions, postulates, and theorems in a nonmathematical context.	In Making Connections, students apply and synthesize key terms and new ideas.		

Pacing Chart (45-Minute Periods)

	Comprehensive Course	Core Course	Informal Course
Part A	1	1	1
Part B	1	1	1
Part C	1	1	1
Part D	1	1	1
TOTAL periods for Superlesson	4	4	4

NCTM Standards

Mathematics as Problem Solving

Mathematics as Communication

Mathematics as Reasoning

Mathematical Connections

Geometry from a Synthetic Perspective

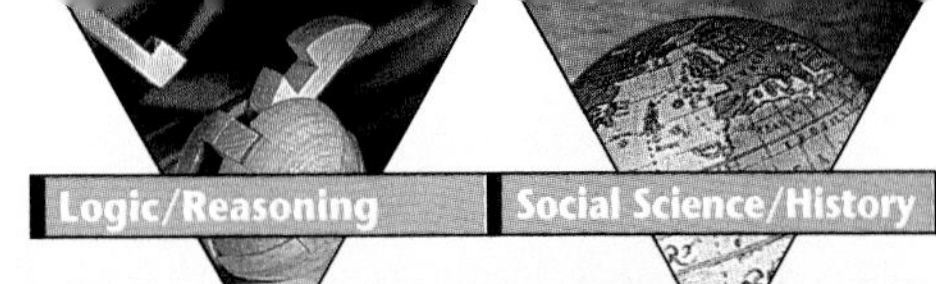

2-2 Stating Our Assumptions

Building a Foundation

On July 4, 1776, 56 representatives of the 13 colonies unanimously passed and signed the Declaration of Independence marking the beginning of the United States of America. The heart of the document is highlighted here. The colonists formed a new nation based on the assumptions stated in the Declaration. Any system of government has some basic assumptions that are taken to be true without proof. In the Declaration of Independence, assumptions are either words that are not defined or ideas that are taken for granted with no justification given.

We hold these truths to be *self-evident*, that all men are created equal, that they are endowed by their Creator with certain unalienable Rights, that among these are Life, Liberty and the pursuit of Happiness.—That to secure these *rights*, Governments are instituted among Men, deriving their just powers from the *consent* of the governed,—That whenever any Form of Government becomes destructive of these ends, it is the Right of the People to alter or to abolish it, and to institute new Government, laying its *foundation* on such principles and organizing its powers in such form, as to them shall seem most likely to effect their Safety and Happiness.

1. In this excerpt from the Declaration of Independence, which statements are assumptions made without any proof? Explain your choices.
2. Why do you think some assumptions in government and mathematics have to be made without proof?

More About the Declaration of Independence

As later defined in the Constitution, the statement "All men are created equal" referred to Caucasian male property owners. You may want to explain this to your class and discuss how and when our government expanded this definition. Another possible discussion could focus on nonsexist language.

Where Are We Now?

Students have become familiar with conditional statements and fundamental rules of logic.

Where Are We Going?

In 2-2, students will become familiar with the components of a deductive system: undefined terms, defined terms, postulates, and theorems. They will begin to see how undefined terms are used in definitions and how theorems are built, continuing the logic and proof strand of the course.

Possible Answers

1. All men are created equal; they have rights; the governments that are set up to secure these rights must have the consent of their citizens; the people may set up a new government if the old one no longer defends their rights.
2. Nothing can be proven true without prior knowledge. Unless some common terminology and fundamental beliefs are shared, other ideas cannot be proven true.

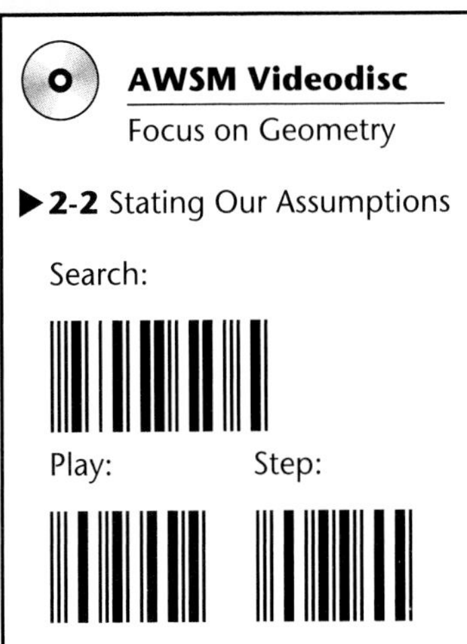

Stating Our Assumptions

PART A At a Glance

Objective

To learn which geometric terms are undefined, and to begin writing definitions.

Development

Students first learn why undefined terms are necessary. They review points and lines and are introduced to planes.

Students see the characteristics of good definitions.

In the **Explore,** students apply these characteristics to write a definition of *midpoint.* Then they see how to write this definition in biconditional form.

Key Terms

Plane, coplanar, noncoplanar, biconditional, midpoint

First Five Minutes

Transparency FFM 2-2A

Read the first two paragraphs on page 108. Then answer the **Consider** question.

Motivate

Ask...

- What are some characteristics of a good definition?

Possible Answer

1. *Point* and *line* are the basic terms studied so far. Segments, rays, and angles all involve points and parts of lines.

2-2 PART A Undefined Terms and Definitions

← CONNECT → ***You are familiar with some of the important logical statements and rules of logic in our deductive system. Now you'll see why undefined terms are needed, and you'll begin to write accurate definitions of other terms.***

Over the years, we have needed to interpret key words and phrases from the Declaration of Independence. For example, did *liberty* mean freedom to vote, freedom of speech, or more? We must define key words precisely in a system of government and in a deductive system like geometry, so that everyone can use these words in the same way.

Dictionaries seem to define almost every word in a language, but you can't use a dictionary if you don't already know some of the words in it! Before you can begin to define words in geometry, you must know terms that are fundamental to the whole system.

1. Which of the geometry terms that you've learned do you think are the most basic? Explain why you selected these terms.

In geometry, we need some undefined terms—words that we simply "understand." You have already seen explanations (not definitions!) of two of these.

A **point** is a specific location that has no size.

A **line** is an infinite, straight set of points that continues forever in both directions. A line has no width or thickness, but it has infinite length.

A third undefined term in geometry is *plane.* A **plane** is a flat surface that extends infinitely. A plane has infinite length and width, but no thickness. A plane is named by a single capital letter.

This is plane $\mathcal{P}$.

Tips from Teachers

To help students see the necessity of undefined terms, you may want to have them look up a term in a dictionary (choose a suitable term beforehand) and then trace the definitions until they become circular. For example, *king* may be defined as a male monarch, and *monarch* may be defined as a king or queen. (An elementary dictionary with short definitions may facilitate this activity.)

We use these undefined terms to build definitions such as the following.

DEFINITION

Coplanar points are points that lie in the same plane.

A, *B*, *C*, and *D* are coplanar—they all lie in plane $\mathcal{P}$. But *A*, *B*, *C*, *D*, and *E* are **noncoplanar**—there is no flat surface that contains all of them.

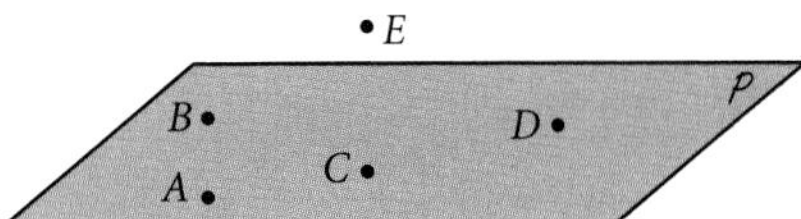

In mathematics, there are two important steps to making a good definition. The first step involves identifying the *critical attributes* of a concept. These are characteristics that are always true of the concept.

EXAMPLE

List the critical attributes of right angles.

These are right angles. These are not.

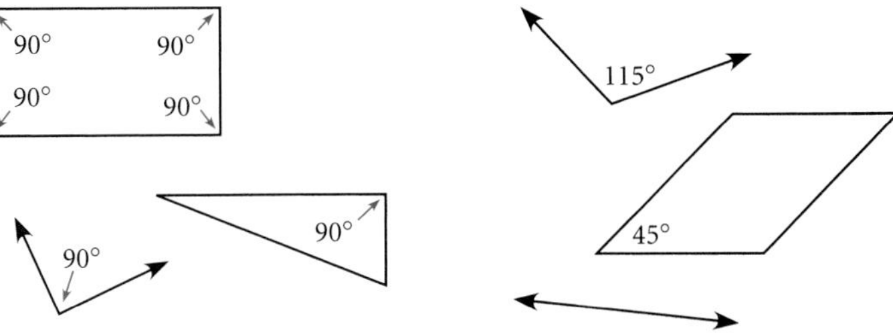

The critical attributes of a right angle are the characteristics that all right angles share.

Critical Attributes
It must be an angle.
It must measure 90°.

Other characteristics of an angle, like its color or the type of figure it's in, don't determine whether or not it's a right angle. Such characteristics are not critical attributes of right angles.

ALTERNATE EXAMPLE

List the critical attributes of rays.

These are rays.

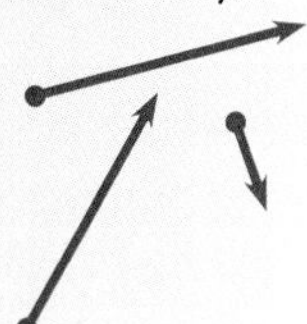

These are not.

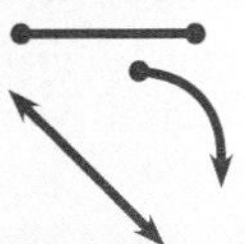

Critical Attributes:

They must be straight.

They must extend forever in one direction.

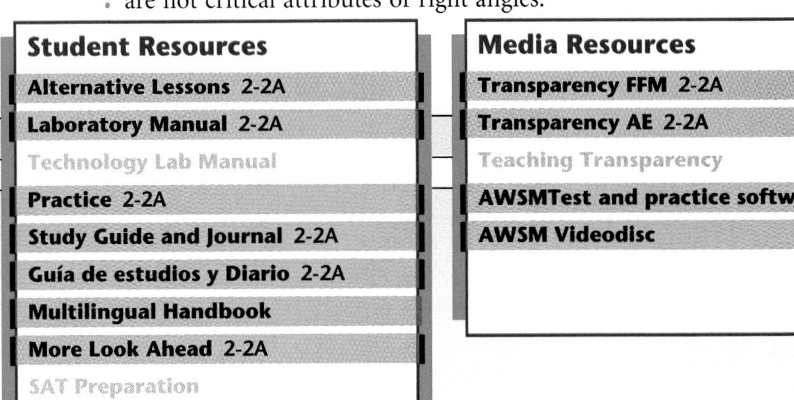

Student Resources
- Alternative Lessons 2-2A
- Laboratory Manual 2-2A
- Technology Lab Manual
- Practice 2-2A
- Study Guide and Journal 2-2A
- Guía de estudios y Diario 2-2A
- Multilingual Handbook
- More Look Ahead 2-2A
- SAT Preparation

Media Resources
- Transparency FFM 2-2A
- Transparency AE 2-2A
- Teaching Transparency
- AWSMTest and practice software
- AWSM Videodisc

Algebra	Functions	Discrete Math	Probability	Data/Statistics

Stating Our Assumptions

EXPLORE

What Makes a Midpoint?

Recommended group size: 4

The Point
To have students write their own definition of a midpoint.

Look and Listen...
- For students who do not see that a midpoint must be defined with respect to a line segment.

Ask...
- Can a line have a midpoint?

For Groups That Finish Early
Can a segment have more than one midpoint? Why or why not?

Follow Up
Ask students to share their definitions. If definitions seem different, have the class decide whether or not they actually mean the same thing.

Possible Answers

1. The midpoint is a point; it is on a line segment; it divides a line segment into two segments of equal length.
2. A midpoint is a point that divides a segment into two congruent segments (or two segments that have equal lengths).

Note: If your students did Look Ahead **Exercises** 16 and 17 in 2-1 Part B, they have already been introduced to biconditional statements. You may want to remind them of these exercises.

The second step in making a good definition is to put the critical attributes into a statement that defines the term precisely in as few words as possible. Keep these goals in mind as you write your own definition of *midpoint* in the following Explore.

EXPLORE: WHAT MAKES A MIDPOINT?

1. Examine the examples and nonexamples of midpoints. Identify the critical attributes of a midpoint.

These red points are *midpoints of a segment* whose endpoints are shown in black.

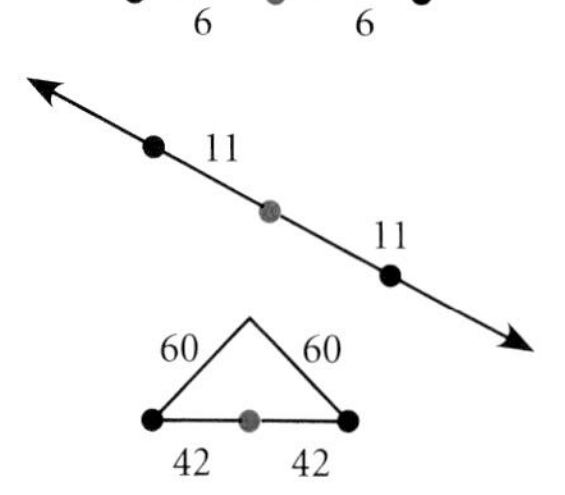

These red points are not.

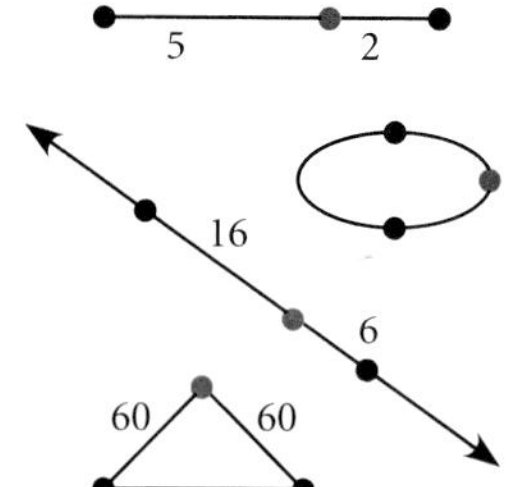

2. Using the critical attributes you found, write a definition of the midpoint of a segment.

When both a conditional and its converse are true, you can combine the two into one **biconditional** statement using the connector phrase "if and only if." Our formal definition of the midpoint of a segment, in biconditional form, is shown below.

DEFINITION

Point M is the **midpoint** of $\overline{AB}$ if and only if it divides $\overline{AB}$ into two congruent segments, $\overline{AM}$ and $\overline{MB}$.

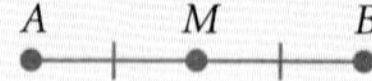

Compare this definition to the one you developed in the Explore.

Alert

There are many "correct" definitions of midpoint. You may want to tell students that the text's definition is not the only possible one (though it is the one they will need to work with). You may also want to point out that imprecise definitions, such as "The midpoint cuts it into equal pieces," are good intuitive definitions but need to be refined before they can be mathematically useful.

Our definition of *midpoint* means that *both* of the following statements are true.

- If M is the midpoint of $\overline{AB}$, then it divides $\overline{AB}$ into two congruent segments.
- If a point M divides $\overline{AB}$ into two congruent segments, then it is the midpoint of $\overline{AB}$.

REFLECT

1. Suppose we propose the following definitions of *right angle* and *perpendicular*.
   - *Perpendicular* lines are lines that form right angles.
   - *Right angles* are the angles formed by perpendicular lines.

   Are these good definitions? Explain why or why not.
2. Obviously, all terms in a definition have to be understood before you can use the definition. Identify the geometric terms used in the formal definition of *midpoint*. Are all of them either undefined terms or previously defined terms? Explain.
3. What are the characteristics of a good definition?

Exercises

CORE

1. **Getting Started** Use the steps below to write a definition of *collinear* as a biconditional statement.
   a. Take the definition "Collinear points are points that lie on the same line," and write it in if-then form, starting with "If a set of points is collinear . . ."
   b. Write the converse of the conditional statement you wrote in **1a.** Check to see that both statements are true.
   c. If both the statement and its converse are true, write the biconditional by linking the hypothesis of either of the statements to its conclusion with the words "if and only if."

Write each definition as a biconditional statement.

2. Two lines that meet to form a right angle are **perpendicular.**
3. The **converse** of a conditional statement is formed by interchanging the hypothesis and conclusion.

y

Vocabulary
Practice/Skills
Review
R Math Reasoning
Problem Solving
Challenge

Ongoing Assessment

Self-Assessment Exercises 1, 3, 4, 5, 7, 9, 11

Embedded Assessment Explore Step 2; Reflect 3; Exercises 2, 8, 10

Journal

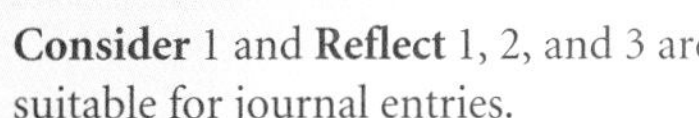

Consider 1 and **Reflect** 1, 2, and 3 are suitable for journal entries.

REFLECT

Possible Answers

1. These are not good definitions—they are circular.
2. Point (undefined), congruent (defined), segment (defined).
3. It includes all of the critical attributes of the concept or figure. It is precise and concise (uses as few words as possible).

Part A Exercises

Exercise Notes

Core

6. Applies a biconditional statement to a government policy. (The actual policy has another restriction that was omitted to save space: The candidate, when elected by a state, must be a resident of that state.)

13. Uses Venn diagrams to illustrate a biconditional statement. Since the *then* set must be a subset of the *if* set, the only way that a conditional and its converse can both be true is if the sets are identical (i.e., the circles coincide).

Look Ahead

These exercises look ahead to the fundamental postulates explored in 2-2 Part B.

More Math Reasoning

22. Reviews the algebraic Principle of Zero Products. Students will use this property to solve equations in 5-1.

Stating Our Assumptions

Exercise Answers

Core

1. a. If a set of points is collinear, then the points lie on the same line.

   b. If a set of points lie on the same line, then the points are collinear.

   c. A set of points is collinear if and only if the points lie on the same line.

2. Two lines are perpendicular if and only if they meet to form a right angle.

3. The converse of a conditional statement is formed if and only if the hypothesis and the conclusion of the conditional statement are interchanged.

4. If an angle is a right angle, then it measures 90°; If an angle measures 90°, then it is a right angle.

5. If M is the midpoint of $\overline{AB}$, then it divides $\overline{AB}$ into two congruent segments, $\overline{AM}$ and $\overline{MB}$; If a point M divides $\overline{AB}$ into two congruent segments $\overline{AM}$ and $\overline{MB}$, then it is the midpoint of $\overline{AB}$.

6. If you are at least 30 years old and have been a citizen of the U.S. for at least nine years, then you may run for the Senate. If you run for the Senate, then you must be at least 30 years old and have been a a citizen for at least nine years.

7. Is a segment, ray or line, intersects the other segment perpendicularly, and bisects the other segment; A segment, ray or line is a perpendicular bisector if and only if it intersects a segment at right angles and bisects the segment.

8. Point lying in the same plane; A set of points is coplanar if and only if all of the points lie in the same plane.

P **Write each statement as two conditional statements in if-then form.**

4. An angle is a right angle if and only if it measures 90°.

5. M is the midpoint of $\overline{AB}$ if and only if it divides $\overline{AB}$ into two congruent segments, $\overline{AM}$ and $\overline{MB}$.

6. You may run for the United States Senate if and only if you are at least 30 years old and have been a citizen of the United States for at least 9 years.

P **List the critical attributes of the following terms. Then write a definition for each word, using "if and only if."**

7. These are **perpendicular bisectors.** These are not.

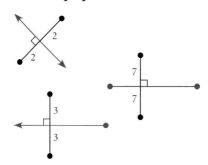

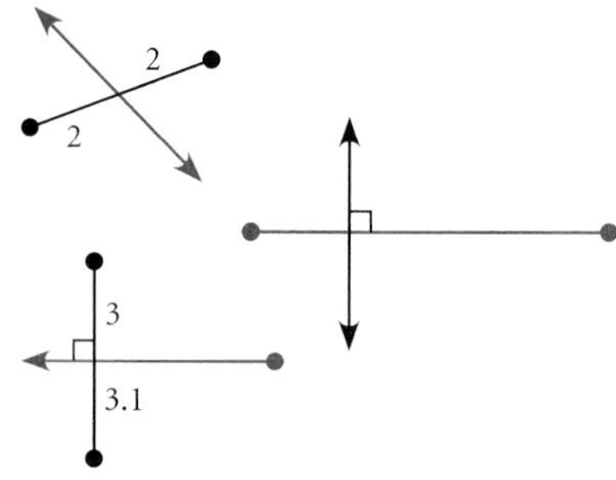

8. These are **coplanar points.** These are not.

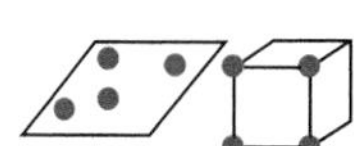

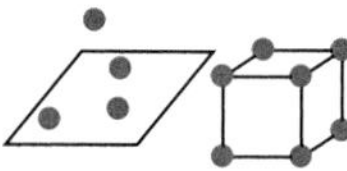

P ***M* is the midpoint of $\overline{JK}$. Find each missing length.**

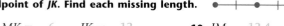

9. $JM = 6$, $MK =$ <u>6</u>, $JK =$ <u>12</u>.

10. $JM =$ <u>12.4</u>, $MK = 12.4$, $JK =$ <u>24.8</u>.

11. $JM =$ <u>2.5</u>, $MK =$ <u>2.5</u>, $JK = 5$.

12. $JM =$ <u>$4\frac{1}{3}$</u>, $MK =$ <u>$4\frac{1}{3}$</u>, $JK = 8\frac{2}{3}$.

MR **13. Venn Is a Statement Biconditional?** Remember that you can illustrate a true conditional statement with a Venn diagram.

a. Sketch a Venn diagram to illustrate the biconditional statement "An integer is even if and only if it is divisible by two." (Hint: It may be helpful to break it down into two conditional statements, one of which is the converse of the other.)

b. What does your diagram look like? Do you think a diagram that shows a true biconditional statement will always look like this? Explain why or why not.

c. Explain how this diagram demonstrates the idea that we should be able to express good definitions as biconditionals.

Key

- V Vocabulary
- P Practice/Skills
- R Review
- MR Math Reasoning
- PS Problem Solving
- C Challenge

LOOK AHEAD

State whether you believe each of the following is true or false. Explain.

14. Two points may be contained in two different lines.

15. Whenever two planes intersect, their intersection is a single point.

16. Any three points can be contained by a single line.

MORE PRACTICE

List the critical attributes of the following terms. Then write a definition for each word, using "if and only if."

17. These are **line segments.** These are not.

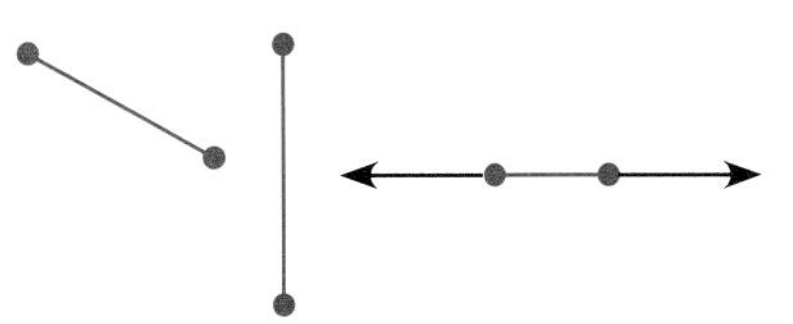

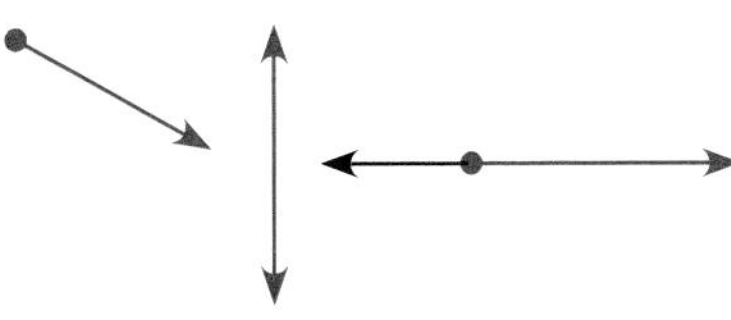

18. These are **collinear points.** These are not.

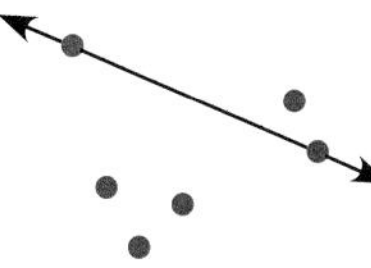

***M* is the midpoint of $\overline{FG}$. Find each missing length.**

19. $FM = 15$, $MG =$ 15, $FG =$ 30.

20. $FM =$ 11.7, $MG = 11.7$, $FG =$ 23.4.

21. $FM = \frac{9}{10}$, $MG = \frac{9}{10}$, $FG = 1\frac{4}{5}$.

MORE MATH REASONING

Determine whether each biconditional statement is true or false. If the statement is false, give a counterexample.

22. $x \times y = 0$ if and only if $x = 0$ or $y = 0$. T

23. The contrapositive of a statement is true if and only if the statement is true. T

24. Three points are coplanar if and only if they are collinear. F; Consider (1, 1), (2, 2) and (2, 1).

25. K is the midpoint of $\overline{LM}$. The coordinates of L and M are $(-3, -5)$ and $(4, -5)$, respectively. $\overline{KN} \perp \overline{LM}$ and $\overline{KN} \cong \overline{KL}$. Find all possible coordinates for N.

13. a. Even integers, Integers divisible by two

b. The region for even integers exactly coincides with the region for integers divisible by two; Yes, if there were points in one region and not the other, then one of the two conditional statements would be false.

c. Both statements should describe exactly the same set of things.

Look Ahead

14. F; Two points determine a line, so these two points cannot also lie on a second line.

15. F; The intersection of two planes is a line.

16. F; Only some sets of three points are collinear.

More Practice

17. Two endpoints, part of line, ray, or segment; Part of a line (ray or another segment) is a line segment if and only if it consists of two endpoints and all the points between them.

18. Points lying on the same line; A collection of points is collinear if and only if all the points lie on the same line.

More Math Reasoning

25. N can be either $(0.5, -1.5)$ or $(0.5, -8.5)$

Algebra | Functions | Discrete Math | Probability | Data/Statistics

Stating Our Assumptions

PART B At a Glance

Objective

To discover and use basic postulates about geometric figures.

Development

Students see properties of real numbers that will be used to justify algebraic steps.

In the **Consider,** students identify unproved assumptions that affect their daily lives.

Following this motivation, students use everyday objects to discover basic postulates in the **Explore.** Some of the postulates they may discover are then formalized.

Suggested Materials

Student Everyday objects to represent points, lines, and planes

Key Terms

Space

First Five Minutes

Transparency FFM 2-2B

Read the first two paragraphs and the algebraic properties listed on page 114. Then answer **Try It a** and **b.**

Motivate

Ask...

- Can you give examples of some things that people believe are true without proof?

2-2 PART B Postulates

← CONNECT → *You've seen the need to accept some terms without definitions. Now you will investigate some facts that are accepted without proof.*

The Continental Congress used the assumptions stated in the Declaration of Independence in writing the original United States Constitution in 1787. Over time, 26 amendments have been added to give us our current Constitution. For example, in 1920 the nineteenth amendment gave women the right to vote.

Mathematical systems are also built on assumptions. You have seen some properties of numbers in algebra. These properties are assumptions about how numbers behave. Segment lengths and angle measures are numbers, so these assumptions are also important in geometry.

For all real numbers a, b, c, and d, the following are true.

PROPERTIES OF EQUALITY	
Reflexive Property	$a = a$
Symmetric Property	If $a = b$, then $b = a$.
Transitive Property	If $a = b$ and $b = c$, then $a = c$.
Addition Property	If $a = b$, then $a + c = b + c$.
Multiplication Property	If $a = b$, then $ac = bc$.
PROPERTIES OF ADDITION AND MULTIPLICATION	
Associative Properties	$a + (b + c) = (a + b) + c$; $a(bc) = (ab)c$
Commutative Properties	$a + b = b + a$; $ab = ba$
Distributive Property	$a(b + c) = ab + ac$

TRY IT

State the property of real numbers that justifies each statement.

a. $AB + CD = CD + AB$ Commutative Property of Addition

b. If $x - 20 = 44$, then $x - 20 + 20 = 44 + 20$ Addition Property of Equa

We all make decisions based on unproved assumptions. The organizations that affect your life also operate on certain assumptions.

Science Connection

Laws of science are similar to algebraic properties and geometric postulates. They are assumptions that cannot be proved. Some of the most famous follow:

For every action, there is an equal and opposite reaction.

An object moving in a straight line continues along that path unless acted on by an outside force.

$E = mc^2$ (the relationship between matter and energy).

Each of the situations or organizations listed below has a set of rules. These rules are based on assumptions about how things "should" be done. See if you can identify some of the underlying assumptions behind the rules.

1. your school's graduation requirements
2. driving a car or riding a bicycle

The ancient Egyptians and Babylonians had many practical uses for mathematics. The Greeks expanded on their knowledge. Euclid, a Greek mathematician, wrote *The Elements* around the year 300 B.C. This work organized much of the geometry and other mathematics known at that time into a deductive system. Euclid called the basic assumptions of his system *self-evident truths.*

For most of this course, you will be investigating a geometry system based on Euclid's work. In the following Explore, you will discover some of the self-evident truths, or *postulates,* of our geometric system.

EXPLORE: POSSIBLE POSTULATES

Use everyday objects to help investigate each of the following. For each question, make a conjecture based on your observations. If possible, write your conjecture as a conditional statement in if-then form. After you finish, compare your conjectures with those of your classmates.

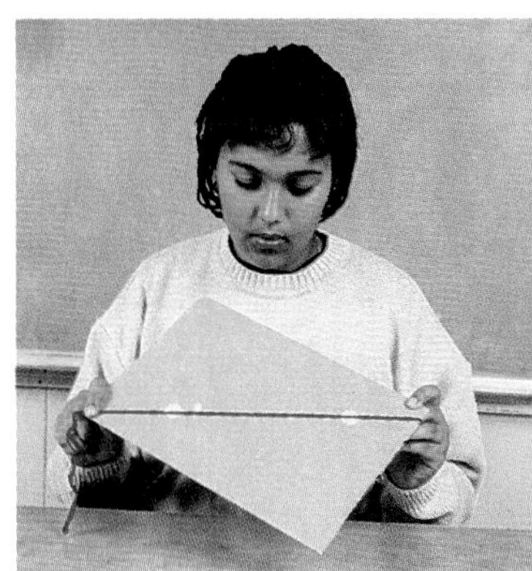

1. What is the smallest number of points through which only one line can be drawn?
2. Three points, *A, B,* and *C,* are not all on the same line. How many planes contain all three of the points?
3. What does the intersection of two planes look like?
4. If a plane contains two points of a line, must it contain the whole line?
5. What is the smallest number of points that cannot be contained in just one plane?

Student Resources

- Alternative Lessons 2-2B
- Laboratory Manual 2-2B
- Technology Lab Manual
- Practice 2-2B
- Study Guide and Journal 2-2B
- Guía de estudios y Diario 2-2B
- Multilingual Handbook
- More Look Back 2-2B
- SAT Preparation

Media Resources

- Transparency FFM 2-2B
- Transparency AE
- Teaching Transparency
- AWSMTest and practice software
- AWSM Videodisc

Possible Answers

1. It is good to take courses in many different subjects; it is important to learn English, science, and other subjects.
2. Safety is important; a written test is a good way to evaluate potential drivers; people under 16 are too young to be responsible drivers.

EXPLORE

Possible Postulates

Recommended group size: 4

The Point

To discover basic postulates about points, lines, and planes.

Look and Listen...

- For students who have difficulty finding a model for a plane.
- For students who do not remember that lines and planes extend indefinitely.

Ask...

- Can you see examples of intersecting planes in this room?

For Groups That Finish Early

Look in the classroom for real-world models of the postulates you discovered. Write descriptions of these.

Follow Up

Ask students to list the postulates they discovered.

Possible Answers

1. Two
2. One
3. A line.
4. Yes
5. Four

Algebra | Functions | Discrete Math | Probability | Data/Statistics

Stating Our Assumptions

Compare the postulates you discovered to those stated below. Note how the first postulates involve undefined terms.

DEFINITION

Space is the set of all points.

POINTS-EXISTENCE POSTULATE

Space contains at least four noncoplanar points. Every plane contains at least three noncollinear points. Every line contains at least two points.

STRAIGHT-LINE POSTULATE

Two points are contained in one and only one line. (Two points determine a line.)

PLANE POSTULATE

Three noncollinear points are contained in one and only one plane. (Three noncollinear points determine a plane.)

FLAT-PLANE POSTULATE

If two points are in a plane, then the line containing the points is in the same plane.

PLANE-INTERSECTION POSTULATE

If two planes intersect, then their intersection is a line.

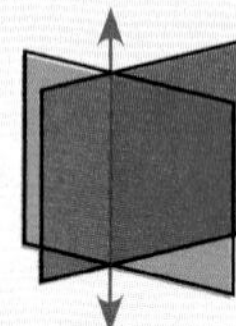

Diversity Issues

For students with limited English proficiency, the formal language in definitions, postulates, and theorems may be intimidating. You may want to ask students who find the reading level difficult to write these definitions in their own words while the concepts are fresh in their minds.

TRY IT

State the postulate or postulates that justify each statement.

c. If ℓ contains A and B, then there is no other line that contains these points. Straight-Line Postulate

d. If points H and K lie in plane $\mathcal{R}$, then $\overleftrightarrow{HK}$ lies in plane $\mathcal{R}$. Flat-Plane Postulate

e. A plane contains at least one line.
Points-Existence Postulate, Flat-Plane Postulate

REFLECT

1. Name some everyday situations that suggest each of the five postulates listed above.

2. Explain why it is necessary for a deductive system to start with some unproved assumptions.

Exercises

CORE

Getting Started Draw a figure to represent each situation described below, and name the postulate it illustrates.

1. Points R and S are in plane $\mathcal{A}$. $\overleftrightarrow{RS}$ is also in plane $\mathcal{A}$.

2. There is some point F that is not in the plane containing B, C, and D.

Determine whether each statement is true or false. If true, state the postulate or postulates that justify it. If false, state or sketch a counterexample.

3. P lies in plane $\mathcal{B}$. The line containing P and Q must lie in plane $\mathcal{B}$.

4. Planes $\mathcal{A}$ and $\mathcal{B}$ intersect. Their intersection is a line.

5. Points E and F determine a line.

6. $\overleftrightarrow{FE}$ and $\overleftrightarrow{NF}$ determine a plane.

Determine whether each conjecture is true or false. If true, state the postulate(s) that justify it. If false, state or sketch a counterexample.

7. If three points lie in a plane, then they are collinear.

8. If two lines do not intersect, then they are not in the same plane.

Ongoing Assessment

Vocabulary
Practice/Skills
Review
Math Reasoning
Problem Solving
Challenge

Self-Assessment Exercises 1–15 odd

Embedded Assessment Exercises 2, 4, 8, 10, 16

Journal 

Reflect 1 and 2 are suitable for journal entries.

REFLECT

Possible Answers

1. Points existence: Identify four distinct, noncoplanar locations in a room, three noncollinear ones on a wall, and two on the edge of a bookshelf.

Straight line: There is only one straight line from one corner of the room to another.

Plane: The floor is the only plane that contains the corners of three different tiles.

Flat plane: Two points on the edge of a bookshelf are also on the shelf.

Plane intersection: The intersection of a wall and the ceiling is a line (segment).

2. Nothing can be proven true without some prior knowledge. In beginning a system, we must share at least one belief as a foundation for other discoveries.

Part B Exercises

Exercise Notes

Core

9–13. These exercises involve the properties of real numbers in geometric contexts. Some students find these properties difficult to identify in these new contexts. You may want to provide simple arithmetic parallels to each exercise to help them make a connection.

15–17. These exercises show how the basic postulates apply to everyday situations.

More Math Reasoning

28. Explores non-Euclidean geometry, which is investigated in detail in 12-2.

Algebra	Functions	Discrete Math	Probability	Data/Statistics

Stating Our Assumptions

Exercise Answers

Core

1. Flat-Plane Postulate

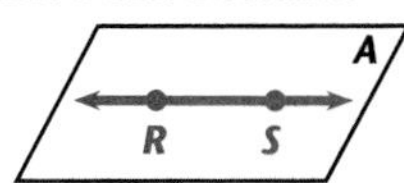

2. Points-Existence Postulate

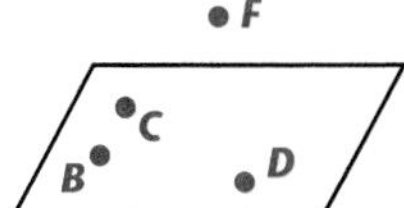

3. F;

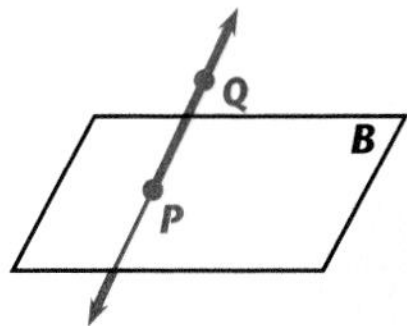

4. T; Plane-Intersection Postulate

5. T; Straight Line Postulate

6. F; Let *E, F,* and *N* be collinear

7. F; Possible answer:

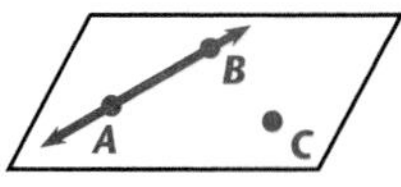

8. F; Let the lines be parallel.

9. Symmetric Property of Equality

10. Associative Property of Addition

11. Distributive Property

12. Multiplication Property of Equality

13. Addition Property of Equality

14. a. Infinitely many

b. Infinitely many

c. One

15. Plane Postulate

16. Straight-Line Postulate

17. Plane-Intersection Postulate

Look Back

18.

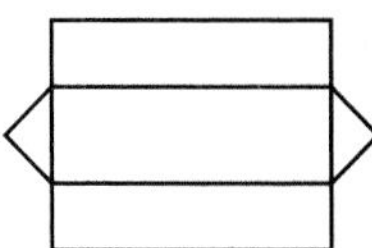

19–28. See Additional Answers p. T128.

P **State the property of real numbers that justifies each statement.**

9. $m\angle RST = m\angle UVW$. Therefore, $m\angle UVW = m\angle RST$.

10. $m\angle ABC + (m\angle DEF + m\angle GHI) = (m\angle ABC + m\angle DEF) + m\angle GHI$

11. $5(TM + JF) = 5TM + 5JF$

12. If $m\angle XYZ = m\angle TUV$, then $\frac{1}{2}m\angle XYZ = \frac{1}{2}m\angle TUV$.

13. If $JK = KL$, then $JK + 6 = KL + 6$.

P **14.** How many planes contain the following numbers of points?
a. one point
b. two points
c. three noncollinear points

MR Careers 

Use postulates to explain each situation.

15. Rocking Chair A carpenter knows that a four-legged chair will sometimes rock on a level floor, but a three-legged stool is always steady.

16. A surveyor (shown at the right) can always find a straight line from the point where he is to any other point that he can see.

17. When constructing a building, a contractor knows that the corner formed by two flat walls is a straight line.

LOOK BACK

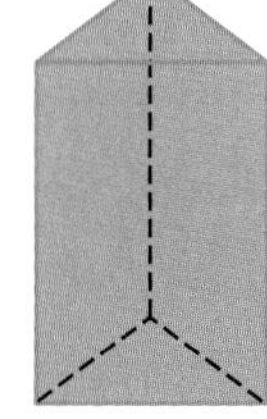

R **18.** Draw a net for the figure at the right. [1-1]

R **19.** Write the converse, inverse, and contrapositive of the following statement. Then determine whether each statement is true or false. [2-1]

If a number is evenly divisible by 3, then it is evenly divisible by 9.

MORE PRACTICE

P **Sketch figures for the situations described below, and name the postulate that each illustrates.**

20. The noncollinear points *T, S,* and *R* are all contained in plane $\mathcal{M}$.

21. In plane $\mathcal{M}$, there is some point, *W*, that is not on the line containing *P* and *Q*.

Key

V Vocabulary
P Practice/Skills
R Review
MR Math Reasoning
PS Problem Solving
C Challenge

Determine whether each statement is true or false. If true, state the postulate(s) that justify it. If false, state or sketch a counterexample.

22. Points *A*, *B*, and *C* determine a plane.

23. The line containing points *F* and *G* lies in exactly one plane.

Determine whether each conjecture is true or false. If true, state the postulate(s) that justify it. If false, state or sketch a counterexample.

24. Three points cannot be contained in two different planes.

25. If three lines intersect in the same point, then they are coplanar.

26. Three planes cannot intersect in just one point.

MORE MATH REASONING

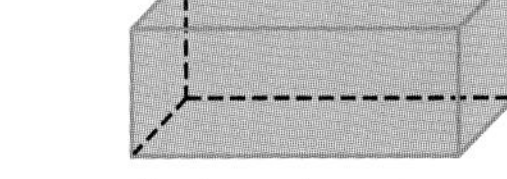

Cube

Rectangular prism

27. How many planes are determined by the vertices of a cube? Does this change if the cube is stretched in one direction to form a rectangular prism (box)?

28. Airplane pilots take routes that are curved lines because the earth is nearly spherical. To create a geometry system that makes sense for global travel, assume that "lines" are *great circles*—that is, circles whose centers are at the center of the earth. Does the Straight-Line Postulate still hold? If not, propose a different version of the postulate that is true for this type of geometry.

2-2 PART C Working in a Deductive System

← CONNECT → ***You have worked with undefined terms, definitions, and postulates. Now you will begin to see how they fit together to form a system of geometry.***

In beginning to build a system of geometry, you have identified three undefined terms and five postulates. You have seen some defined terms, whose definitions use undefined terms and previously defined terms. And you've seen your first theorem, a statement whose truth can be proved using postulates, definitions, and previously proved theorems.

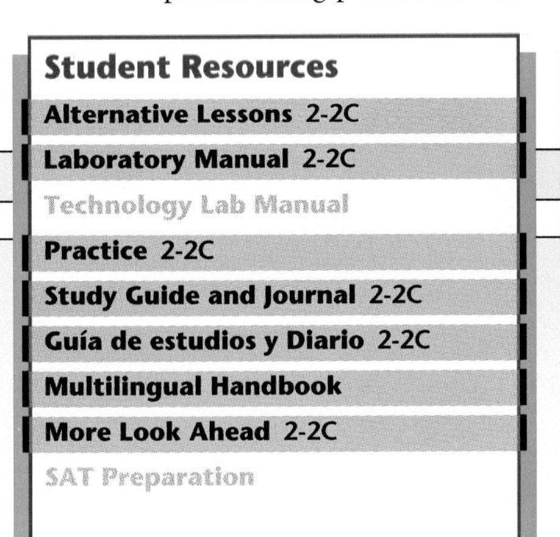

Student Resources
- **Alternative Lessons 2-2C**
- **Laboratory Manual 2-2C**
- Technology Lab Manual
- **Practice 2-2C**
- **Study Guide and Journal 2-2C**
- **Guía de estudios y Diario 2-2C**
- **Multilingual Handbook**
- **More Look Ahead 2-2C**
- SAT Preparation

Media Resources
- **Transparency FFM 2-2C**
- Transparency AE
- Teaching Transparency
- **AWSMTest and practice software**
- AWSM Videodisc

PART C At a Glance

Objective

To use the concepts of betweenness, collinearity, and midpoint, and to see the relationships among undefined terms, defined terms, postulates, and theorems.

Development

Students see the relationships among undefined terms, definitions, postulates, and theorems.

In the **Explore,** students discover how the distance relationship of three collinear points is related to betweenness. This leads to the Segment-Addition Postulate.

Finally, to illustrate how deductive systems are built, a theorem about the midpoint of a segment is presented. Students see that this theorem depends on definitions, postulates, and algebraic properties.

Suggested Materials

Student Ruler, compass

Teacher Chalkboard/overhead compass, straightedge

Key Terms

Between

First Five Minutes

Transparency FFM 2-2C

List three examples of undefined terms, defined terms, and postulates. **Undefined Terms: Point, line, plane Defined Terms: Segment, ray, angle, and so on. Postulates: Two points are contained in one and only one line; three noncollinear points are contained in one and only one plane; if two planes intersect, then their intersection is a line; and so on.**

Motivate

Ask...

- Why do we need undefined terms? Why do we need postulates?

Stating Our Assumptions

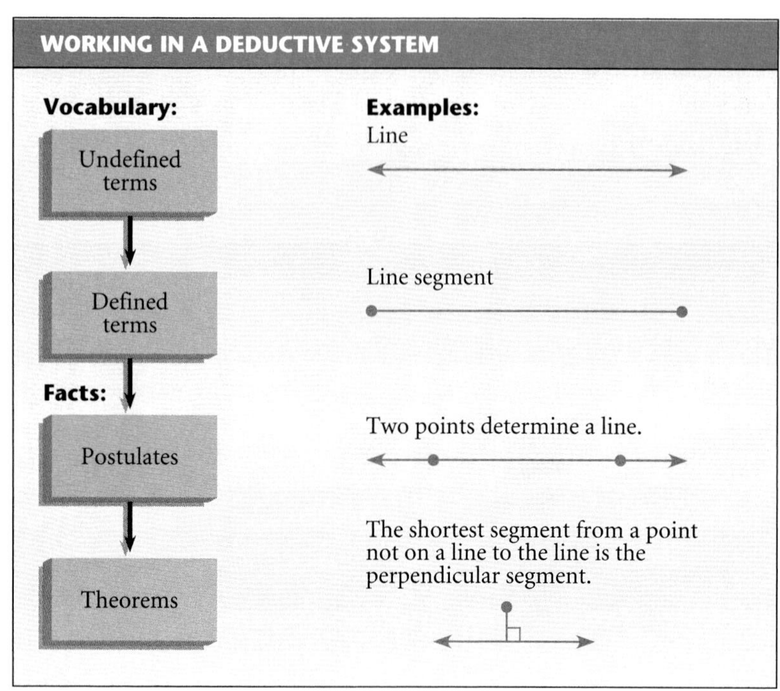

WORKING IN A DEDUCTIVE SYSTEM
Vocabulary:
Undefined terms
Defined terms
Facts:
Postulates
Theorems
Examples:
Line
Line segment
Two points determine a line.
The shortest segment from a point not on a line to the line is the perpendicular segment.

Because you are working in a deductive system, you must be able to justify everything you do, even measuring with a ruler! For example, the Ruler Postulate says that our method for finding distances between points on a number line is valid.

RULER POSTULATE

The points on a line can be paired with the real numbers so that the following statements are true.

- One of the points has coordinate 0, and another has coordinate 1.
- For any choice for coordinates 0 and 1 and for each real number x, there is exactly one point on the line with coordinate x.
- The distance between any two points with coordinates x and y is the absolute value of the difference of their coordinates, $|x - y|$.

In the following Explore, you will discover some properties of distances related to collinear points.

Tips from Teachers

Note: The Ruler Postulate may be difficult for students because it involves formal language. However, the concepts involved are straightforward and match student intuition. You may want to model the postulate by drawing a line, labeling points with coordinates 0 and 1, and then asking different students to choose an *x*-value and show you the point with that coordinate.

EXPLORE: IT ADDS UP

MATERIALS

Ruler

1. Identify the critical attributes of *betweenness.*

These red points are **between** the black points.

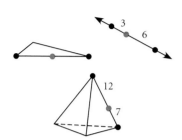

These red points are **not between** the black points.

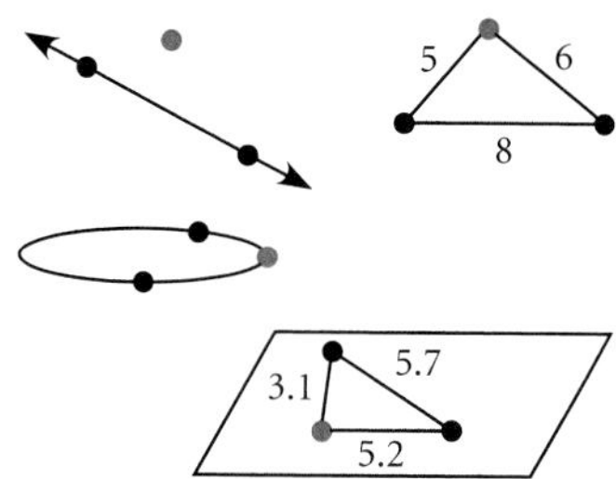

2. Mark three points, A, B, and C, on a line. Measure the distance between each pair of points (AB, BC, and AC). What is their relationship?

3. Reposition the three points on the line, keeping the same point between the other two. Measure AB, BC, and AC again. What changed and what stayed the same? Give a short written summary.

Problem-Solving Tip

Look for a pattern.

4. Suppose you know that R, S, and T are collinear points, with $RT = 8$, $ST = 6$, and $RS = 14$. Which point is between the other two? How do you know?

5. Write a generalization about the relationship of three collinear points, betweenness, and distance.

In geometry, you will need to be able to add the lengths of adjacent segments to find the length of longer segments.

SEGMENT-ADDITION POSTULATE

Point B is between points A and C if and only if A, B, and C are collinear and $AB + BC = AC$.

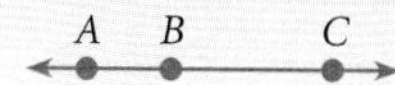

EXPLORE

It Adds Up

Recommended group size: 4

The Point

To discover the Segment-Addition Postulate and its relationship to betweenness.

Look and Listen...

- For students who are having trouble summarizing their discoveries in Step 5.

Ask...

- If your hypothesis is "If B is between A and C," what would your conclusion be?

For Groups That Finish Early

Do Step 2 using three noncollinear points. What conclusions can you draw?

Follow Up

Ask students to summarize their conclusions from Step 5. Then have them summarize their conclusions in a single biconditional statement.

Possible Answers

1. The points are collinear; the sum of the lengths of the smaller segments is equal to the length of the whole segment.

2. If B is the point between the others, then $AB + BC = AC$.

3. The specific distances will change, but the equation will still be true.

4. T is between R and S because $RT + ST = RS$.

5. Point B is between points A and C if and only if A, B, and C are collinear and $AB + BC = AC$.

Note: Students may see that the biconditional form for the Segment-Addition Postulate makes it look like a definition. In fact, this postulate does serve as our definition of *between,* and we could have chosen either title. In Chapter 3, we make a similar choice—we have an Angle-Addition Postulate, rather than a definition for betweenness of rays.

History Connection

The first two African-American women to be awarded the Ph.D. in mathematics were Marjorie Lee Brown (University of Michigan, 1949), and Evelyn Boyd Granville (Yale, 1949). Dr. Granville specialized in numerical analysis. She researched space trajectories and orbits while working on the Vanguard and Mercury space projects.

Algebra | Functions | Discrete Math | Probability | Data/Statistics

Stating Our Assumptions

Note: You may want to ask students what definition this theorem depends on.

CONSTRUCTION

Midpoint of a Segment (Perpendicular Bisector)

The Point
To construct the midpoint of a segment (by constructing its perpendicular bisector).

Presenting the Construction
Students should be able to do this construction on their own by following the steps in the text. After they have completed it, you may want to have a student model the construction on the chalkboard or overhead.

The **Consider** is a brief, but important, follow-up question for this construction.

The midpoint of a segment is a special type of point that lies between two other points. We have already defined *midpoint* geometrically as the point that divides a segment into two congruent segments. Combining these ideas with some algebra gives us the following theorem.

THEOREM

If M is the midpoint of $\overline{AB}$, then $AM = \frac{1}{2}AB$.

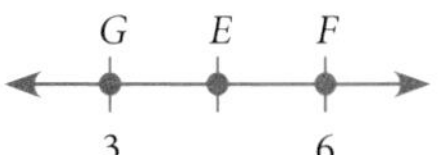

In particular, the coordinate of the midpoint of $\overline{AB}$ is $\frac{a+b}{2}$, where a and b are the coordinates of A and B. The preceding statement is a theorem because we can prove it. (You will investigate this proof in Exercise 9.)

TRY IT

a. E is the midpoint of $\overline{FG}$. Find FE and the coordinate of E. 4.5

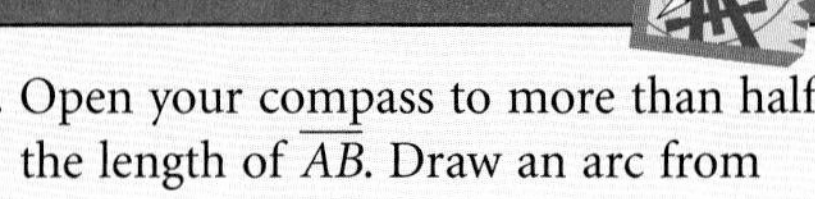

CONSTRUCTION: MIDPOINT OF A SEGMENT

1. Begin by drawing segment $\overline{AB}$. This will be the segment you bisect in your construction.

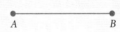

2. Open your compass to more than half the length of $\overline{AB}$. Draw an arc from point A.

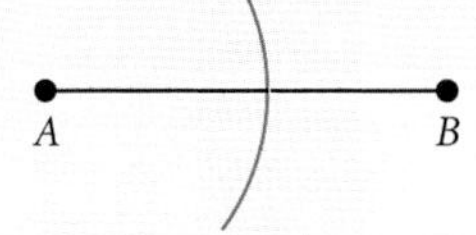

3. Using the same compass setting, draw an arc from point B that intersects the previous arc at points C and D.

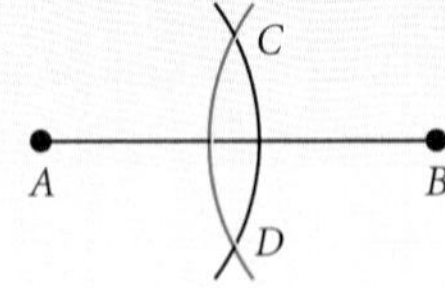

4. Draw the line connecting points C and D to intersect $\overline{AB}$ at E. E is the midpoint of $\overline{AB}$.

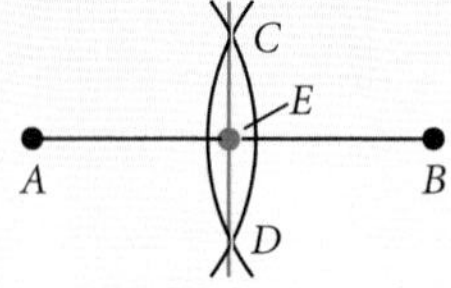

Tips from Teachers

It may be helpful to point out that the coordinate form of the midpoint equation says that the coordinate of the midpoint of a segment on a number line is the *average* of the coordinates of the endpoints. (This may give students a head start on *Exercise* 8 as well.)

1. The preceding construction finds the midpoint of a segment. What other geometric figure do you construct when you find the midpoint?

You've now seen the components of a deductive system in action. Notice how combining a postulate (the Segment-Addition Postulate) with some algebra and a definition (the definition of midpoint) led to a theorem (if M is the midpoint of $\overline{AB}$, then $AM = \frac{1}{2}AB$).

REFLECT

1. What are the components of our deductive system? Which parts of the system form our geometry vocabulary? Which are our geometry "facts"?
2. Name two ideas from this lesson that are important to both algebra and geometry. How does this connection help you to understand the ideas?

Exercises

CORE

Getting Started Find the coordinate of the midpoint of $\overline{XY}$ if X and Y have coordinates x and y, respectively.

1. $x = 1, y = 7$ 4 **2.** $x = -1, y = 7$ 3 **3.** $x = -3\frac{1}{2}, y = 5\frac{3}{4}$ $1\frac{1}{8}$

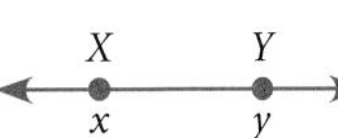

4. Use the figure to find the length of each segment.

a. $\overline{AF}$ 9.4 **b.** $\overline{AE}$ 5.6 **c.** $\overline{BF}$ 7.4

d. What postulate or theorem justifies your answers to **4a, 4b,** and **4c**? Segment Addition Postulate

2 3.6 3.8
A B E F

5. R, S, and T are three points on a line. The coordinates of R and S are -14.5 and 2.7, respectively. If S is the midpoint of $\overline{RT}$, what is the coordinate of T? Make a sketch that illustrates R, S, and T.

6. Draw a line segment, and label it $\overline{EF}$. Use a compass and straightedge to construct the midpoint of $\overline{EF}$, and label it G.

Possible Answer

1. The perpendicular bisector of the segment.

Journal

Explore Step 5 and **Reflect** 1 and 2 are suitable for journal entries.

REFLECT

Possible Answers

1. Undefined terms, defined terms, postulates, and theorems. The undefined and defined terms are the vocabulary; the postulates and theorems are the facts.

2. The Ruler Postulate shows that subtracting coordinates (algebra) gives the length of a segment (geometry). The theorem shows that we can use the midpoint of a segment (geometry) to write an equation (algebra).

Part C Exercises

Exercise Notes

Core

7. Similar to multiple-choice analogy items on standardized tests.

8. A derivation of the midpoint formula.

9. An early encounter with a flow proof.

Look Ahead

These exercises preview perspective drawing in 2-3 Parts A and B.

More Math Reasoning

24. Introduces students to a simple non-Euclidean geometry.

Exercise Answers

Core

5. 19.9;

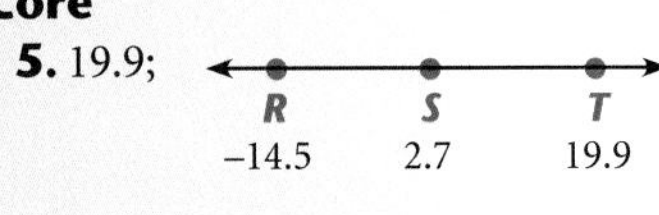

6.

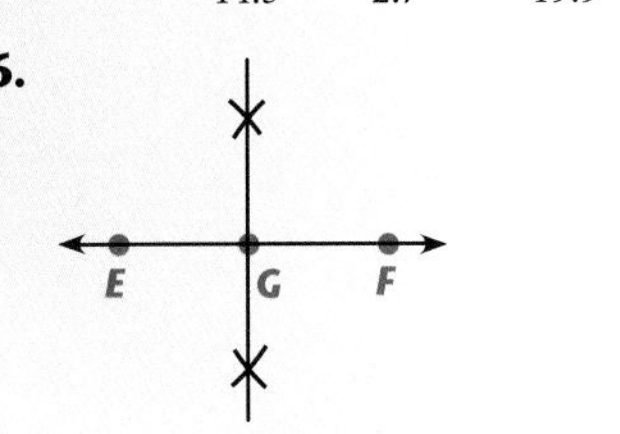

y

Vocabulary
Practice/Skills
Review
R Math Reasoning
Problem Solving
Challenge

Ongoing Assessment

Self-Assessment Exercises 1–9 odd

Embedded Assessment Explore Step 5; Reflect 1; Exercises 2, 4, 10

Stating Our Assumptions

8. a. Midpoint of $\overline{OL}$: (2, 0);
Midpoint of $\overline{OM}$: $\left(0, -\frac{3}{2}\right)$;
Midpoint of $\overline{MN}$: (2, −3);
For (x_1, y) and (x_2, y): $\left(\frac{x_1 + x_2}{2}, y\right)$;
For (x, y_1) and (x, y_2): $\left(x, \frac{y_1 + y_2}{2}\right)$

b. Midpoint of $\overline{PQ}$ = (4, 5);
Midpoint of $\overline{PR}$ = (0, 2);
For (x_1, y_1) and (x_2, y_2): $\left(\frac{x_1 + x_2}{2}, \frac{y_1 + y_2}{2}\right)$

c.

1st point	2nd point	midpoint	segment
(0, 0)	(4, 0)	(2, 0)	$\overline{OL}$
(0, 0)	(0, −3)	$\left(0, -\frac{3}{2}\right)$	$\overline{OM}$
(0, −3)	(4, −3)	(2, −3)	$\overline{MN}$
(2, 3)	(6, 7)	(4, 5)	$\overline{PQ}$
(2, 3)	(−2, 1)	(0, 2)	$\overline{PR}$

d. $(x_m, y_m) = \left(\frac{x_1 + x_2}{2}, \frac{y_1 + y_2}{2}\right)$

10. (a), (c), and (d) are true;

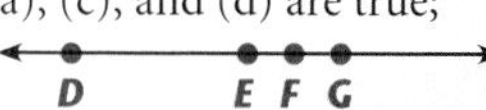

More Practice

19. Yes; Possible answer:

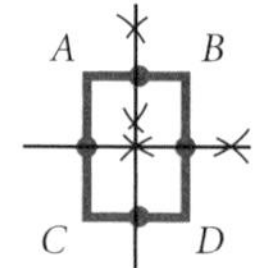

V **7.** Write the letter of the second pair that best matches the first pair.

Postulate: theorem as (a) belief: fact, (b) hypothesis: conclusion, (c) proof: conjecture, (d) deductive: inductive (a)

MR **8.** Follow the steps below to discover a formula for the coordinates of the midpoint of a segment on a coordinate plane.

a. Find the coordinates of the midpoints of segments $\overline{OL}$, $\overline{OM}$, and $\overline{MN}$. Explain how you found the coordinates of these midpoints.

b. Find the coordinates of the midpoints of $\overline{PQ}$ and $\overline{PR}$. Explain your method.

c. Make a table that contains the coordinates of the two endpoints of each segment in **8a** and **8b** and the coordinates of the midpoint you found for each segment.

d. Use your results to write a formula for the midpoint of the segment with endpoints (x_1, y_1) and (x_2, y_2). (Hint: It may be easier to do this by writing formulas for the *x*- and *y*-coordinates separately.)

MR, C **9. I Want Proof!** The following is part of a flow proof of the theorem "If *M* is the midpoint of $\overline{AB}$, then $AM = \frac{1}{2}AB$." Tell *why* each statement must be true. As justification, use a postulate or definition from the list below the diagram.

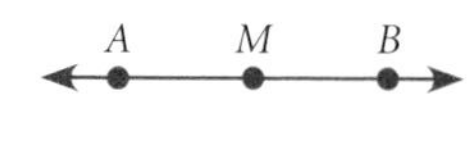

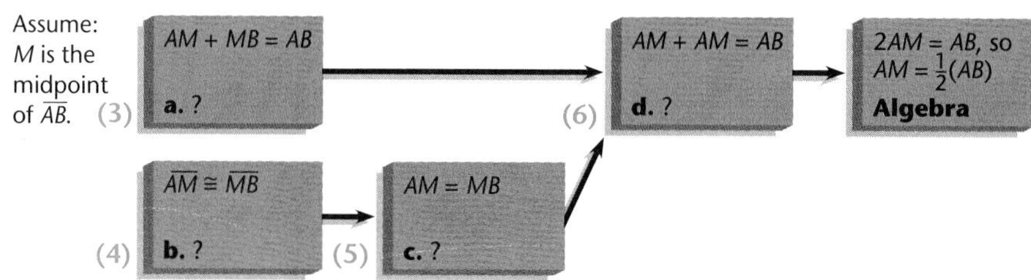

1. Straight-Line Postulate
2. Plane Postulate
3. Segment-Addition Postulate
4. Definition of Midpoint
5. Definition of Congruent
6. Substitution

PS **10. D Tour** Points *D*, *E*, *F*, and *G* represent four towns on a map. If you draw a line from *D* to *F*, it passes through *E*. If you draw a line from *E* to *G*, it passes through *F*. List all of the following statements that must be true. Provide a sketch to support your choice(s).

(a) *E* is between *D* and *F*.
(b) $\overline{DF}$ and $\overline{EG}$ are congruent.
(c) *D*, *E*, *F*, and *G* are collinear.
(d) *E* and *F* are between *D* and *G*.

Key

V Vocabulary
P Practice/Skills
R Review
MR Math Reasoning
PS Problem Solving
C Challenge

LOOK AHEAD

Find the total number of cubes in each building. Assume that the visible cubes are resting on others, and that there are no hidden stacks of cubes.

11. 11 **12.** 8 **13.** 11 **14.** 16

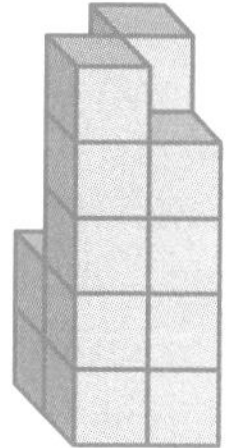

MORE PRACTICE

Find the coordinate of the midpoint of $\overline{XY}$ if X and Y have coordinates x and y, respectively.

15. $x = 4, y = 14$ 9

16. $x = -3, y = -2.2$ −2.6

17. $x = 1.6, y = 1.7$ 1.65

18. Use the figure to find the length of each segment.

a. $\overline{PS}$ 15.4 **b.** $\overline{QS}$ 12.9 **c.** $\overline{QT}$ 15.4

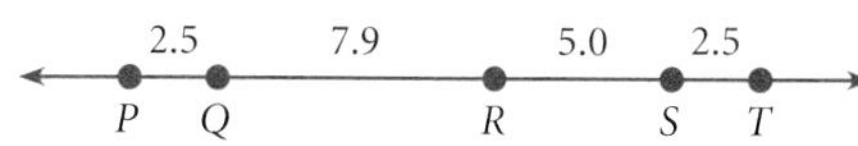

19. Draw a rectangle, and label its vertices. Construct the midpoint of each side. Can you find all four midpoints with only two constructions?

Find the coordinates of the midpoint of each segment.

20. $\overline{AO}$ (−1.5, 1) **21.** $\overline{BF}$ (2, 3)

22. $\overline{AD}$ (−4, 1) **23.** $\overline{BC}$ $\left(\frac{1}{2}, -\frac{3}{2}\right)$

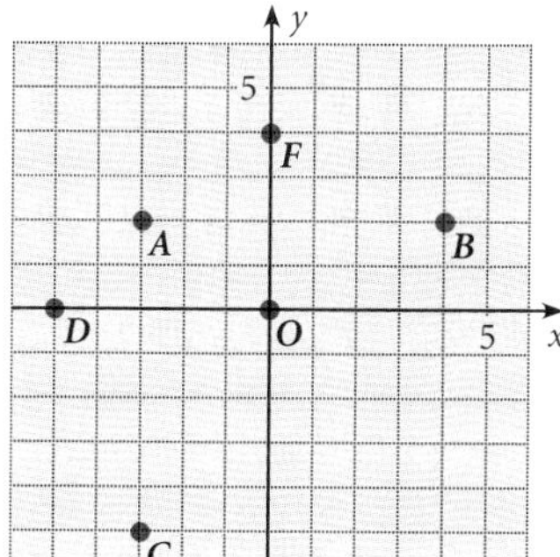

More Math Reasoning

24. a. $A(-4, -3), B(2, 1)$

b. 4

c.

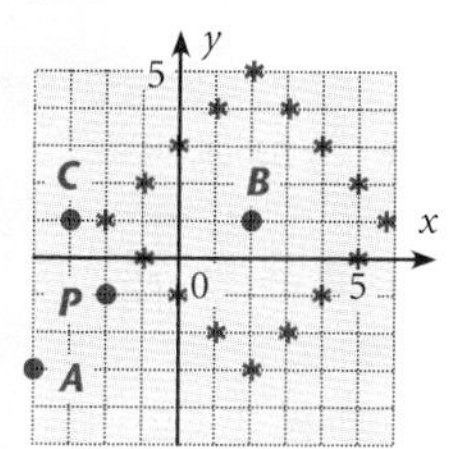

d. Shortest taxi distance from A to $B = 10$; There is more than one such path.

e. 10

f.

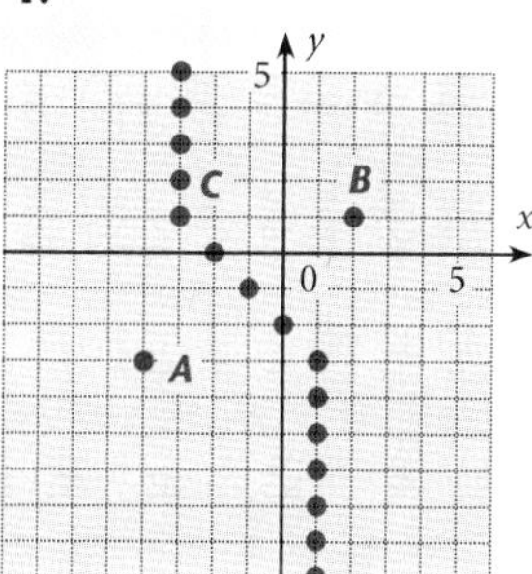

Stating Our Assumptions

PART D At a Glance

Objective

To use the ideas of undefined terms, definitions, postulates, and theorems in a nonmathematical context.

Development

In the **Explore,** students use the parts of a deductive system to draw up a constitution for a student organization.

First Five Minutes

Transparency FFM 2-2D

Make a list of all of the facts you can think of relating to points, lines, line segments, and midpoints. Illustrate as many of these as you can.

EXPLORE

A Strong Constitution

Recommended group size: 4

The Point

To write a constitution for a club involving undefined terms, defined terms, postulates (basic assumptions and amendments), and theorems (laws).

Look and Listen...

- For students who are unfamiliar with constitutions.

Ask...

- Will you make *member* a defined or undefined term?
- What must people do who are in the club? Do you want to assume that they will do these things, or do you need to write some of them down as laws?

MORE MATH REASONING

PS, C **24. Taxicab Geometry** "It's eight blocks to the subway station from my office." "The Jacksons' house is four blocks from ours." These are the actual distances a person has to walk to get from one place to another. *Taxicab geometry* is based on these distances instead of the straight-line distance that is sometimes called "as the crow flies." In taxicab geometry, any point can be reached by traveling along vertical or horizontal lines.

The grid at the right represents a map of a city. The center of town is at the origin. Think of the lines of the grid as streets.

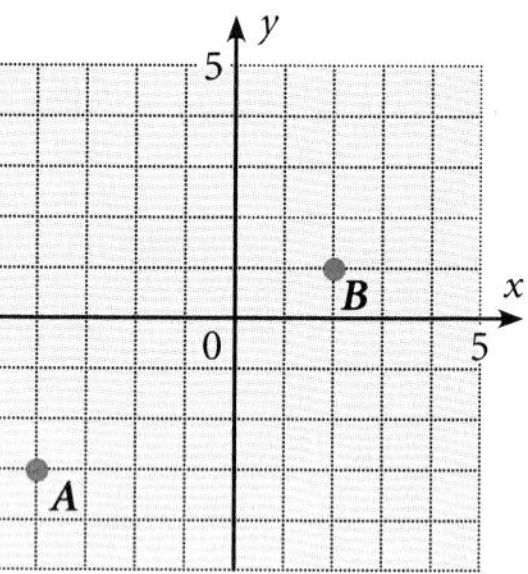

a. What are the coordinates of A and B?

b. Plot P at $(-2, -1)$. What is the taxi distance from A to P?

c. Plot all the points you can find at a taxi distance of 4 from B. Connect these points. This figure is a *taxi circle.*

d. What is the shortest taxi distance from A to B? Is there only one shortest taxi path between them?

e. Plot C at $(-3, 1)$. What is the sum of the taxi distance from C to A plus the taxi distance from C to B?

f. Plot all the points that are an equal taxi distance from A and B.

2-2 PART D Making Connections

← CONNECT → ***Postulates, undefined terms, defined terms, and theorems are the components of our system of geometry. You've seen why some terms are undefined, and why postulates are assumed to be true. You've also learned how to develop definitions and theorems.***

THE EUCLIDEAN CLUB
Rule #1: Two points determine a line.

The initial postulates, undefined terms, defined terms, and theorems that you have investigated form a modern version of a geometry system developed by Euclid over 2000 years ago. In the following Explore, you will use these ideas to develop a constitution for a club at your school.

Student Resources

- Alternative Lessons
- **Laboratory Manual 2-2D**
- Technology Lab Manual
- **Practice 2-2D**
- **Study Guide and Journal 2-2D**
- **Guía de estudios y Diario 2-2D**
- **Multilingual Handbook**
- **More Look Back 2-2D**
- SAT Preparation

Media Resources

- **Transparency FFM 2-2D**
- Transparency AE
- Teaching Transparency
- **AWSMTest and practice software**
- AWSM Videodisc

ic/Reasoning | Industry/Careers | Science/Health | Social Science/History | Fine Arts/Literature

EXPLORE: A STRONG CONSTITUTION

Develop a one-page written constitution for a new club for your school. Discuss the following questions with classmates to help formulate your constitution.

1. What assumptions (postulates) will you take as true without proof?
2. What key words will you leave undefined? (for instance, *participation, freedom,* etc.)
3. What words will you choose to define carefully? Give an example of one such word and provide your definition for it.
4. How will you provide for new laws (theorems) or amendments (postulates) to be added to your club's constitution?
5. Present a description of your club and its constitution to your class.

THE EUCLIDIAN CLUB

I. Space contains at least four noncoplanier points. Every plane contains at least three contains at least two points. noncollinier points. Every line

2. Two points are contained in one and only one line.

3. If two points are in a plane, then the line containing the points is in the same plane.

REFLECT

1. Why do you think Euclid chose the undefined terms that he did?
2. Write the five postulates on Page 116 in your own words. Draw figures where needed.
3. Why is it important to justify any new theorems by using postulates, previously defined terms, and previously proved theorems?

Self-Assessment

Determine whether each statement is true or false. Draw sketches to justify your answers. If the statement is true, state the postulate that it illustrates. If the statement is false, correct it so that it is true.

1. Three points determine three distinct lines.
2. Two lines ℓ and m intersect in points E and F.
3. Two lines determine a plane.
4. Planes $\mathcal{N}$ and $\mathcal{P}$ intersect. Their intersection is a line.

y

Vocabulary
Practice/Skills
Review
R Math Reasoning
Problem Solving
Challenge

For Groups That Finish Early

Make a budget for your club. Decide how much money you will need, what you will spend it on, and how you will raise the money.

Follow Up

Have groups present their constitutions. Ask students which club they'd most like to join. Is this decision related to the postulates and theorems in its constitution?

Possible Answers

Check students' work.

Portfolio

Have students select items from their work that demonstrate their understanding of the material in 2-2.

You may wish to have students include their favorite definition written in their own words, their best sketch illustrating a postulate, and an **Exercise** that they found interesting or challenging.

REFLECT

Possible Answers

1. Point: because all other figures are made of points. Line: because it is an infinite, one-dimensional object (so it can be broken down into rays, segments, or other parts). Plane: because it is an infinite, two-dimensional object.
2. Check students' work.
3. So that we can be certain that they are always true. (They depend only on known facts.)

Self-Assessment

Exercise Notes

Core

10. Similar to multiple-choice items on standardized tests.

Algebra | Logic/Reasoning | Fine Arts/Literature

Stating Our Assumptions

13. Students make a conjecture based on a construction.

14. An application involving distances. This is an example of an exercise that is much simpler to solve visually (using a ruler) than algebraically. The map and advertisements shown are from Chicago.

15. Evaluating this statement might lead to an interesting discussion. You may want to ask students whether it is possible to prove *anything* without making assumptions.

Self-Assessment Answers

1. F; Three *noncollinear* points determine three lines;

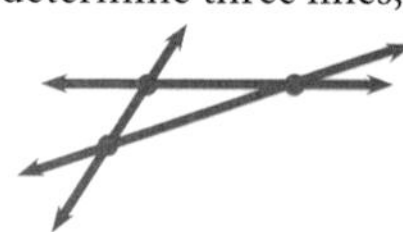

2. F; Two lines ℓ and m intersect at point E.

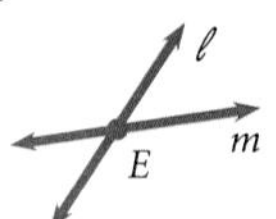

3. F; The lines must be coplanar.

4. T; Plane-Intersection Postulate

5. Flat-Plane Postulate

6. Flat-Plane and Plane-Intersection Postulates together

7. $LK + KM = LM$; Segment-Addition Postulate

8. $\mathcal{P}$ and $\mathcal{Q}$ intersect in a line; Plane-Intersection Postulate

9. S is the midpoint of $\overline{RT}$; Definition of Midpoint

10. (d)

11. Possible answer: If you are fifteen, then you are a teenager.

12. Possible answer: If $a > b$, then $b > a$.

13–15. See Additional Answers p. T128.

P **In each of the following, the first statement is true. State the postulate that allows you to conclude that the second statement is true.**

5. Points E and F are in plane $\mathcal{P}$. Therefore, every point of $\overleftrightarrow{EF}$ is in plane $\mathcal{P}$.

6. Points C and D are both contained in planes $\mathcal{R}$ and $\mathcal{S}$. Therefore, $\overleftrightarrow{CD}$ is the intersection of $\mathcal{R}$ and $\mathcal{S}$.

P **Draw a conclusion from each of the following if possible. State postulates or definitions to justify your conclusion.**

7. Point K is between L and M.

8. Planes $\mathcal{P}$ and $\mathcal{Q}$ have at least one point in common.

9. Points R, S, and T are collinear, and $\overline{RS} \cong \overline{ST}$.

R **10.** Choose the best answer to complete the sentence below. [1-1]

A mathematical model ____ .

(a) is an attempt to simulate something real
(b) can be an equation
(c) is not exactly like the thing it models
(d) has characteristics (a), (b), and (c)
(e) has characteristics (a) and (b) only

R **In Exercises 11–12, write a conditional statement with each of the following sets of characteristics. [2-1]**

11. The conditional is true, and its inverse is false.

12. The conditional and all of its related statements are false.

MR **13.** Carefully draw a square. Use a compass and straightedge to construct the midpoint of each side. Then connect the consecutive midpoints and make a conjecture about what you see.

PS **14. Apartment Hunting** Amanda and Ricardo are looking for an apartment. Amanda manages a store at $(-3, 2)$. Ricardo works in an office at $(2, -5)$. They would like their apartment to be located the same distance from each of their jobs. They also want the sum of the distances that they must commute to work to be as small as possible. Prepare a graph to show where their apartment should be located. Give the coordinates of this location. Explain how you found your answer.

MR, C **15.** In *The Physiology of Common Life*, the English author George Henry Lewes (1817–1878) wrote, "We must never assume that which is incapable of proof." Is this statement true for geometry? Explain.

Literature

Assessment Resources

Quiz 2-2
Chapter Assessment Form A
Chapter Assessment Form B
Chapter Alternative Assessment
Mid-Year Assessment
End-of-Year Assessment
AWSMTest and practice software

Ongoing Assessment

Self-Assessment Self-Assessment Exercises

Embedded Assessment Reflect 1, 2, and 3

ADDITIONAL ANSWERS

2-2 Part B Exercises

19. Original: F
Converse: If a number is evenly divisible by nine, it is evenly divisible by three. T
Inverse: If a number is not evenly divisible by three, then it is not evenly divisible by nine. T
Contrapositive: If a number is not evenly divisible by nine, then it is not evenly divisible by three. F

More Practice

20. Plane Postulate

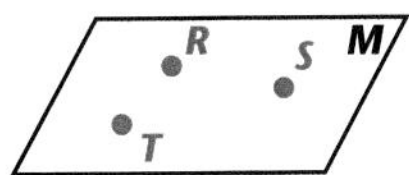

21. Plane Postulate

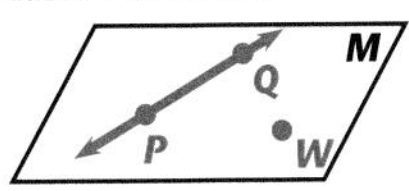

22. F; Let A, B, and C be collinear

23. F; Let F and G be in the line of intersection of 2 planes.

24. F; Three points may be collinear

25. F;

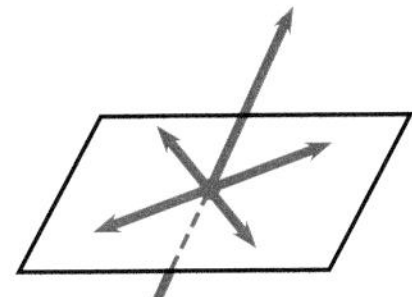

26. F;

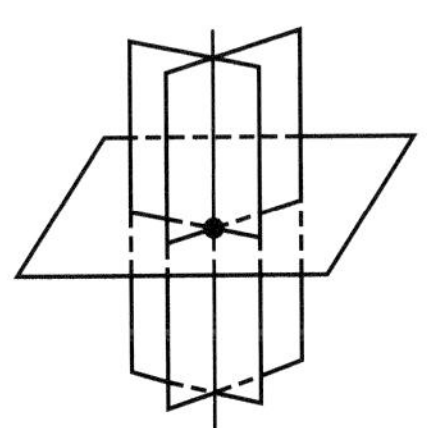

More Math Reasoning

27. 20; No

28. No; Possible answer: If two points are not contained in infinitely many "lines" (great circles), then they are contained in one and only one "line."

2-2 Part D Self-Assessment

13.

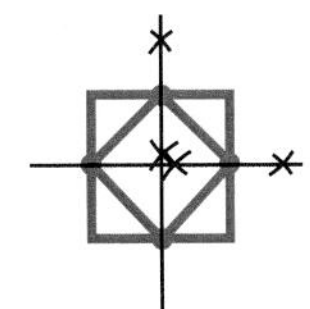

The result is a square.

14.

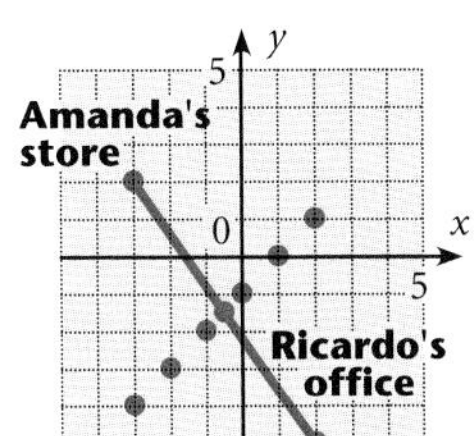

Midpoint between jobs is

$\left(\frac{-3+2}{2}, \frac{2-5}{2}\right) = \left(-\frac{1}{2}, -\frac{3}{2}\right)$.

The midpoint of the line segment between their jobs would be ideal since the home-to-job distance is the same for both, and since the shortest distance between two points is a straight line, this would give the minimum commuting distance, too. If Amanda and Ricardo can live only at integer coordinates and travel only horizontally and vertically, then they may choose from several locations (shown).

15. No; Postulates cannot be proven.

2-3 Part C Exercises

More Practice

26. $\overleftrightarrow{US}, \overleftrightarrow{VT}, \overleftrightarrow{VZ}, \overleftrightarrow{UW}$

27. Plane with W, X, Y, Z

28. $\overleftrightarrow{UV}, \overleftrightarrow{ST}, \overleftrightarrow{XY}$

29. Not possible; If $p \parallel n$ and $n \parallel m$, then p must be parallel to m

30.

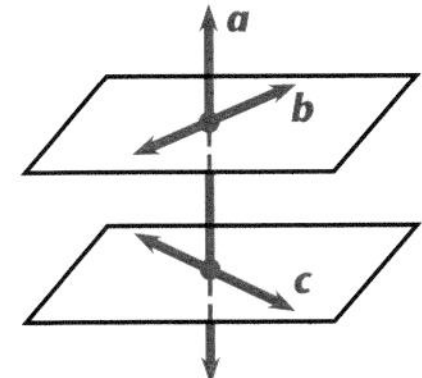

31. Possible answer: $y = \frac{3}{7}x$

32. Possible answer: $y = -\frac{7}{3}x$

More Math Reasoning

33. a. B: (2, 5, 0), C: (2, 5, 3), D: (2, 0, 3), F: (0, 5, 3), H: (0, 0, 0)

b. Possible answer: $\overline{AH} \parallel \overline{BE}$, $\overline{HE} \parallel \overline{AB}$, $\overline{AD} \parallel \overline{BC}$

34. ℓ intersects q;

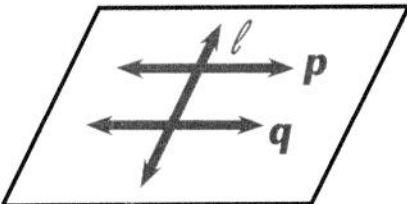

35. $t \perp s$;

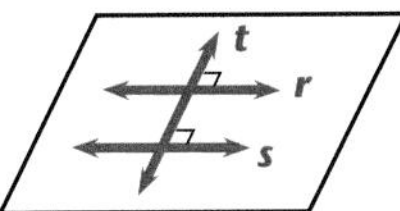

36. Plane $\mathcal{N}$ intersects plane $\mathcal{Q}$;

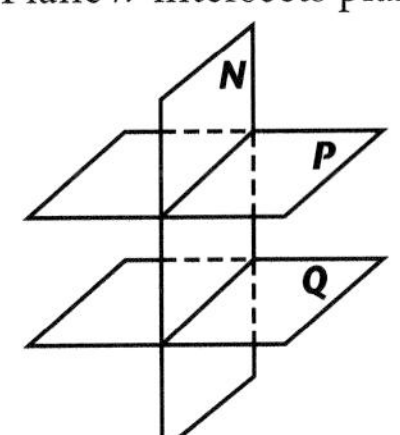

2-3

Drawing Techniques and Parallel Lines

SUPERLESSON AT A GLANCE

Superlesson Goal

Students will develop drawing skills and explore basic facts and terms about parallel lines.

Management Guide

	Topic	Objectives	Key Terms	New Ideas	Materials
Part A	Perspective Drawing	To explore ways to make realistic perspective sketches.	Horizon line, vanishing point, one-point and two-point perspective	Drawing objects using perspective techniques.	**Student** 5″ × 8″ card or notebook paper
Part B	Orthographic and Isometric Drawing	To use drawing techniques to show different views of three-dimensional objects.	Orthographic (orthogonal), isometric	Drawing objects using orthographic and isometric views. Reading orthographic and isometric drawings.	**Student** Cubes, isometric dot paper
Part C	Parallel Lines and Planes	To learn terms related to parallel lines, to review graphs of linear equations, and to explore the Parallel Postulate.	Parallel, skew	Identifying equations for parallel lines. Finding that there is only one line parallel to a given line through a point not on the line.	**Student** Graph paper or graphing utility
Part D	Making Connections	To use drawing skills to sketch a design for a commuter station.	In Making Connections, students apply and synthesize key terms and new ideas.		**Student** Drawing materials

Pacing Chart (45-Minute Periods)

	Comprehensive Course	Core Course	Informal Course
Part A	1	1	1
Part B	1	2	2
Part C	1	1	1
Part D	1	1	1
TOTAL periods for Superlesson	4	5	5

NCTM Standards

Mathematics as Problem Solving
Mathematics as Communication
Mathematics as Reasoning
Mathematical Connections
Algebra
Functions
Geometry from an Algebraic Perspective
Geometry from a Synthetic Perspective

Fine Arts/Literature

2-3 Drawing Techniques and Parallel Lines

PUTTING IT IN Perspective

Have you ever stood on a railroad track or a straight road and looked far down the track or road to the horizon? If you did, you probably noticed how the parallel sides appear to get closer together as they get farther from you. You also know that objects appear larger when they are near you and smaller when they are farther from you.

Perspective is a method of showing three-dimensional objects on a flat surface so that they appear real. People of all cultures have struggled with the problem of how to capture the reality of the three-dimensional world in a two-dimensional drawing or painting. For example, Japanese artists skillfully used landscapes to try to give an illusion of depth and space.

At the beginning of the Renaissance period (the early 1400s A.D.), Brunelleschi, an Italian architect, discovered a mathematical way to create perspective by using a *horizon line* and *vanishing points*.

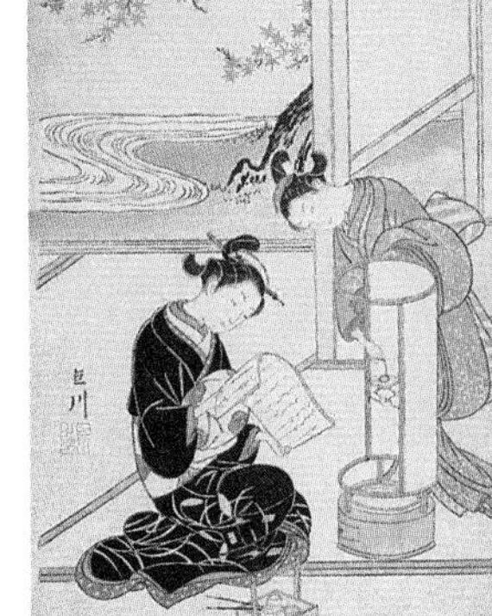

Left: *Canaletto (Giovanni Antonio Canal),* Piazza San Marco, *The Metropolitan Museum of Art, Purchase, Mrs. Charles Wrightman Gift, 1988 (1988.162)*

Right: *Suzuki Harunobu,* The Evening Glow of the Ando *from the series* Eight Parlor Views. *© The Art Institute of Chicago, All Rights Reserved*

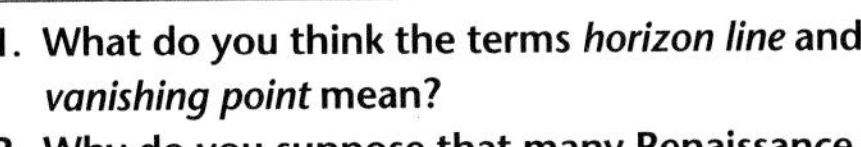

1. **What do you think the terms *horizon line* and *vanishing point* mean?**
2. **Why do you suppose that many Renaissance artists like Raphael, Leonardo Da Vinci, and Michelangelo were engineers and architects who knew a great deal about mathematics?**

129

More About Perspective in Art

Ancient cultures had various approaches to showing depth in art. Cretan and Egyptian art showed the head and legs of a person in profile, but the eyes and torso were shown as if viewed from the front. Indian, Islamic, and pre-Renaissance European art showed people as if seen from ground level, while the plane on which they stood was shown as if viewed from above. This gave the effect of a highly compressed surface.

Where Are We Now?

Students have learned about basic geometric figures and some of their properties.

Where Are We Going?

In 2-3, students will develop skills in reading and making drawings. This helps them to develop visualization skills and to draw figures to illustrate conjectures (which they will begin to do in 3-3).

Students will also learn basic terminology related to parallel lines, explore equations of parallel lines, and discover the Parallel Postulate. (An alternative Parallel Postulate is given in Chapter 12.)

Possible Answers

1. Horizon line: A horizontal line at the eye level of the artist that represents the horizon.

   Vanishing point: A point where parallel lines seem to meet.

2. Their knowledge of the behavior of lines and other figures helped them paint objects realistically.

AWSM Videodisc

Focus on Geometry

▶ **2-3** Drawing Techniques and Parallel Lines

Search:

Play: Step:

Drawing Techniques and Parallel Lines

PART A At a Glance

Objective

To explore ways to make realistic perspective sketches.

Development

Students begin by seeing **Examples** of perspective drawing.

In the **Explore,** students develop rules of thumb for drawing geometric figures. Then they see how to apply these rules to three-dimensional objects.

Suggested Materials

Student 5″× 8″ card or notebook paper

Key Terms

Horizon line, vanishing point, one-point and two-point perspective

First Five Minutes

Transparency FFM 2-3A

Read the first paragraph on page 130, and answer the **Consider** question.

Motivate

Ask...

- How do you judge how far away an object is from you?
- Why does the bottom line in the sketch appear shorter?

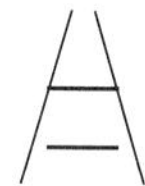

Possible Answer

1. The horizon line is where the highway and mountains seem to meet. The vanishing point is on the horizon line at middle left.

2-3 PART A Perspective Drawing

← CONNECT → ***You have already sketched two- and three-dimensional figures informally. Now you will explore some ways to make your sketches more realistic.***

In attempting to sketch a solid object or scene on a flat piece of paper, we must deal with the fact that parallel lines seem to get closer together as they get farther away. One way to take this into account is to use a horizon line and one or more vanishing points. The **horizon line** is a horizontal line at the eye level of the artist. A **vanishing point** is a point on the horizon line where parallel lines appear to meet. In the photo at the left, the horizon line is shown in red and the vanishing point is shown in green.

1. Describe the locations of the vanishing point and the horizon line drawn in the picture above.

If converging parallel lines in a picture appear to come together at one vanishing point, the drawing is in **one-point perspective.** If there are two vanishing points, the drawing is in **two-point perspective.**

EXAMPLES

1. Draw a cube in one-point perspective.

Step 1 Start with a square. Choose a horizon line and a vanishing point.

Step 2 Draw lines from the vertices to the vanishing point.

Step 3 Complete the figure by drawing lines parallel to the edges of the original figure.

Step 4 Erase the lines to the vanishing point; make hidden lines in the figure dashed.

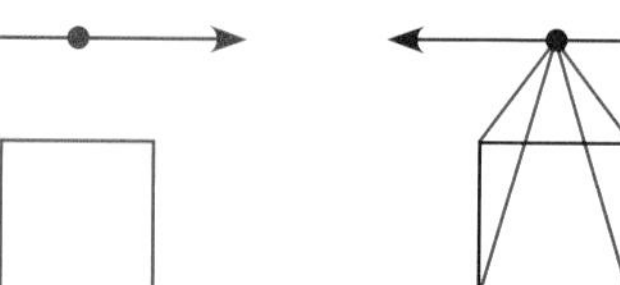

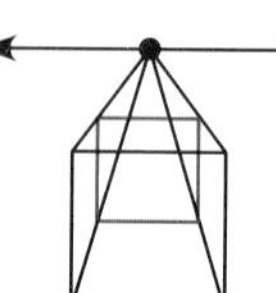

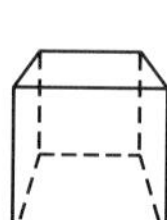

2. Draw a cube in two-point perspective.

Step 1
Start with a vertical segment. Choose a horizon line and vanishing points.

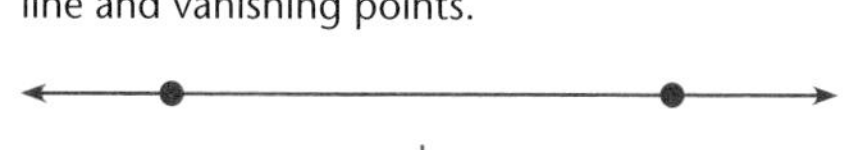

Step 2
Draw lines from the endpoints to the vanishing points. Add lines to complete the two front faces of the cube.

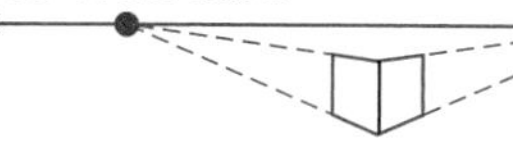

Step 3
Draw lines from the vertices of the front faces to the vanishing points. Use these lines to complete the cube.

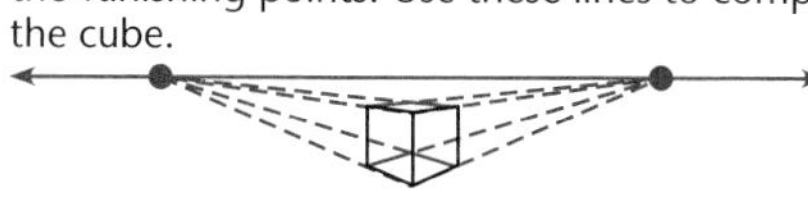

Step 4
Erase the lines to the vanishing points; make hidden lines in the figure dashed.

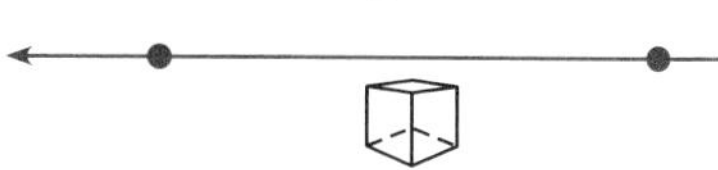

TRY IT

a. Draw a long rectangular box (prism) in one-point perspective.

Sometimes you need to draw figures to help you solve problems, but you may not want to take the time to use one- or two-point perspective. The following Explore will help you develop some rules of thumb for drawing figures.

EXPLORE: GETTING A NEW PERSPECTIVE

MATERIALS

5″× 8″ card or notebook paper

1. Draw a square, a circle, and a vertical line segment on the card or paper. Make them large enough to fill the card.
2. Hold the card about 1 ft in front of you. Slowly tilt the card away from you, and watch what happens to the three figures. Repeat by tilting to the right and left. Use your observations to answer the following questions.
   - **a.** Describe what appears to happen to the square as it tilts directly away from you. What type of figure is it? What type of figure does the square appear to be when you tilt it to the right or left?
   - **b.** Describe what the circle looks like when you tilt the card.
   - **c.** Describe what seems to happen to the segment.
3. Explain how you would sketch a circle, a square, and a segment on a plane that tilts away from you.

Student Resources
- Alternative Lessons 2-3A
- Laboratory Manual 2-3A
- Technology Lab Manual
- Practice 2-3A
- Study Guide and Journal 2-3A
- Guía de estudios y Diario 2-3A
- Multilingual Handbook
- More Look Back 2-3A
- SAT Preparation

Media Resources
- Transparency FFM 2-3A
- Transparency AE 2-3A
- Teaching Transparency
- AWSMTest and practice software
- AWSM Videodisc

ALTERNATE EXAMPLES

Transparency AE 2-3A

EXPLORE

Getting a New Perspective

Recommended group size: 2

The Point
To develop rules of thumb for sketching simple geometric figures.

Look and Listen...
- For students who do not realize that they are to draw the object as it appears in perspective.

Ask...
- Are you drawing what you see, rather than what you know the object is?

For Groups That Finish Early
Use your rules to help sketch a picture of the Olympic flag (five interlocking circles, three on top, two on the bottom) extending away from you.

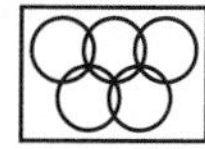
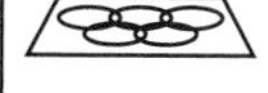

Follow Up
Ask students for a summary of their results from Step 3.

Possible Answers

2. a. A trapezoid; a parallelogram.

b. An oval (ellipse).

c. It slants and may seem to shorten.

3. The circle would be an oval; the square a trapezoid. The segment would slant away from you.

Drawing Techniques and Parallel Lines

ALTERNATE EXAMPLES

3. Sketch an empty ice-cream cone.

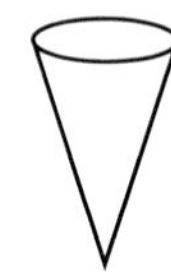

4. Sketch a phone booth with a square top and bottom.

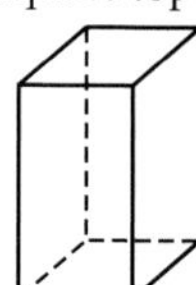

If you need to draw a three-dimensional object, you can use what you have learned about sketching simpler figures.

EXAMPLES

Sketch each figure.

3. a triangular prism (slice of pie or cake)

Step 1

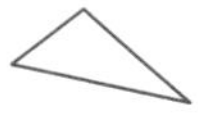

Step 2

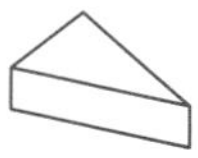

Step 3

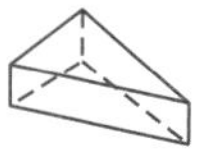

4. a cylinder on its side (can of soup)

Step 1

Step 2

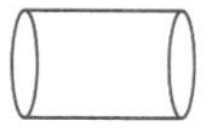

Step 3

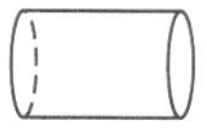

Visible edges are solid lines, and edges that are hidden are dashed. The following chart summarizes the key rules of thumb for making a quick three-dimensional sketch.

RULES OF THUMB FOR THREE-DIMENSIONAL DRAWING

Represent a plane by a rectangle or parallelogram, depending on where it is with respect to your line of sight.

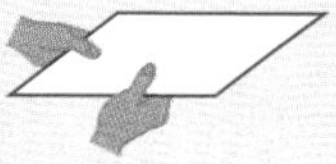

Represent a line by an oblique (slanted) segment if it extends away from you. Represent a circle by an oval if it extends away from you.

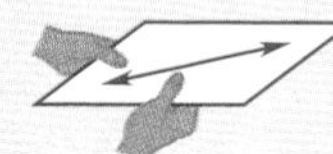

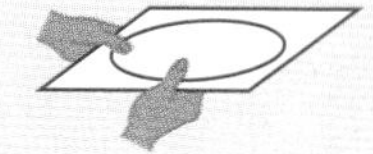

To draw a cube, show the front and back faces as squares. Then connect the corresponding vertices. Represent the hidden edges with dashed segments.

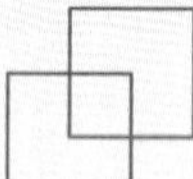

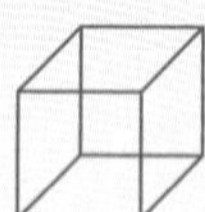

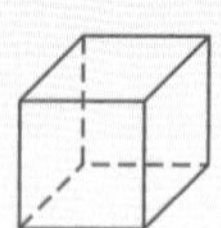

To draw other three-dimensional figures, draw lines, circles, and planes as already shown.

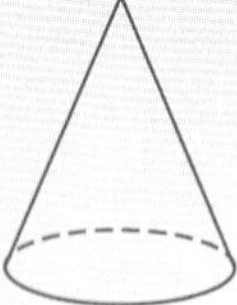

REFLECT

1. When you sketch a cube using the method in the rules of thumb, are you using one-point perspective, two-point perspective, or a different method? How does this sketch show perspective? In what ways does it fail to show perspective?
2. How can you use the position of the horizon line to help determine where an artist was when he made a perspective drawing?

Exercises

CORE

Getting Started How many vanishing points are there in each photograph or painting? Describe where the artist or photographer was in relation to the subject.

1. 

2. 

Gustave Caillebotte, *Paris Street; Rainy Day*. Photograph © The Art Institute of Chicago, All Rights Reserved.

Write the word or phrase that correctly completes each statement.

3. In a perspective drawing, the ____ is a horizontal line at the artist's eye level. Horizon line
4. In a perspective drawing, a ____ is a point where parallel lines appear to meet. Vanishing point

Sketch each of the following.

5. a line in a plane that appears to be tilted away from you
6. a pyramid with a square bottom
7. a basketball court (shown at the right) viewed from one corner of the court

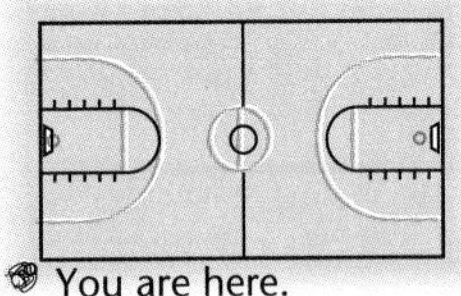

8. Use graph paper or dot paper and a straightedge to draw a two-point perspective sketch of a building. Assume you are standing opposite a corner of the building.

Journal

Explore Step 3 and **Reflect** 1 and 2 are suitable for journal entries.

REFLECT

Possible Answers

1. You are using a different method. The sketch shows perspective, because angle measures are modified (to indicate a point of view), and hidden segments are dashed. It does not show perspective, because parallel sides, when extended, would never meet at a vanishing point.
2. The horizon line is at the eye level of the viewer.

TRY IT

Answers

a. 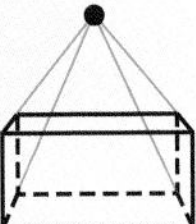

Part A Exercises

Exercise Notes

Core

5–7. In these exercises, students make sketches using rules of thumb.

8. Students sketch a building in two-point perspective.

9. Shows an application of perspective drawing in interior design.

More Math Reasoning

23. Helps students see that the placement of vanishing points affects the realism of a perspective sketch.

Exercise Answers

Core

1. One; Directly in line with the reflecting pool
2. Two; Directly in line with the building to the left of center.

5.  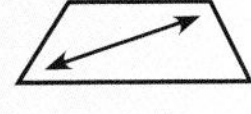

6.  or 

ey | Ongoing Assessment

Vocabulary
Practice/Skills
Review
MR Math Reasoning
PS Problem Solving
Challenge

Self-Assessment Exercises 1–7 odd

Embedded Assessment Reflect 1; Exercises 2, 6, 8, 9

Drawing Techniques and Parallel Lines

7.

8.

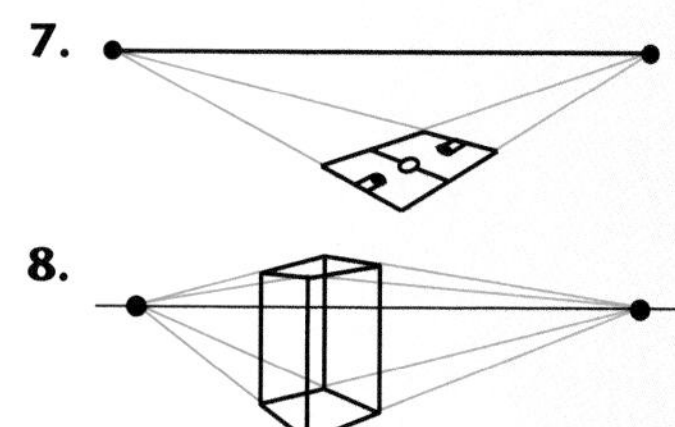

9. Possible answer: One-point is easier, and so more appropriate for a sketch.

More Practice

18. 19.

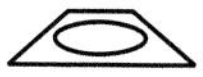

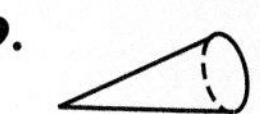

20. 21.

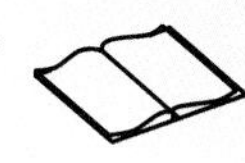

More Math Reasoning

22. Possible answer:

23. a.

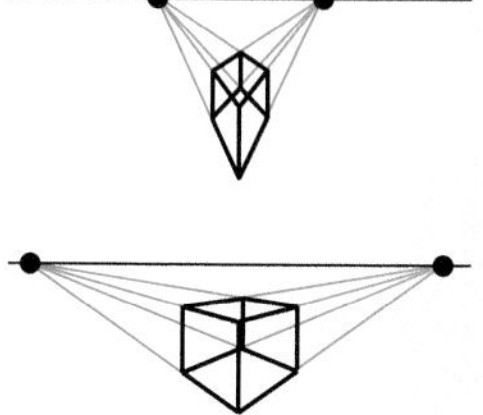

b. The second sketch looks more realistic.

c. In the first drawing, the artist is located very close to the cube. The closer the artist is to an object, the more distorted the artist's perspective.

MR Careers **9. A Question of Perspective** Designers often use one-point perspective when making a sketch of the interior of a room. Write a short paragraph explaining why they might choose to use one-point perspective instead of two-point perspective.

LOOK BACK

R **The figure at the right shows the reflection of triangle *XYZ* over line *v*. [1-4]**

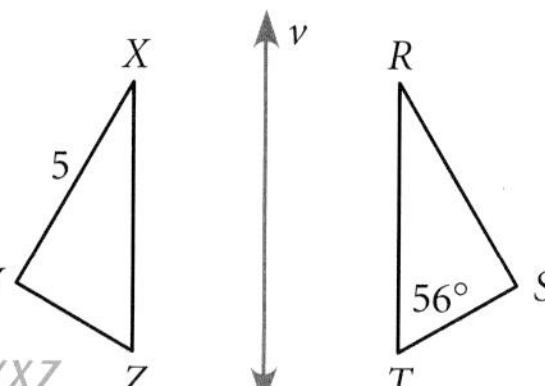

10. Name the image of Z. T

11. Name the pre-image of $\overline{RS}$. $\overline{XY}$

12. Give the length of $\overline{RS}$. 5

13. Find $m\angle YZX$. 56°

14. Find the pre-image of triangle SRT. Triangle YXZ

R **Determine whether each statement is true or false. If it is true, state the postulate or postulates that justify it. If false, explain why. [2-2]**

15. Points S and T lie in plane $\mathcal{R}$. $\overleftrightarrow{ST}$ lies in $\mathcal{R}$. T; Flat-Plane Postulate

16. Lines m and n intersect. Their intersection is $\overline{AB}$. F; The intersection of two lines is a point.

17. Plane $\mathcal{K}$ is the only plane that contains noncollinear points L, M, and N. T; Plane Postulate

MORE PRACTICE

P **Draw each of the following.**

18. a circle in a plane tilted away from you

19. a cone lying on its side

20. a flashlight resting at a slight angle away from you on a table

21. your geometry book lying on a desk top as you stand to the left of the desk

MORE MATH REASONING

C **22. The Road Ahead** Imagine a straight road ahead of you for as far as you can see to the horizon (the place where the sky and level ground appear to meet). Draw the road in one-point perspective. Add a fence along one side of the road and a railroad track on the other side. Add other details in perspective.

Key

V Vocabulary
P Practice/Skills
R Review
MR Math Reasoning
PS Problem Solving
C Challenge

R **23. Which Cube Looks More Cubic?**

a. Make two different sketches of cubes using two-point perspective. Keep the position of the horizon line and the length of the front edge of the cube the same in each drawing, but have the vanishing points close together in the first and far apart in the second.

b. Which sketch looks more realistic?

c. Describe where the artist is located for each drawing. Explain how the distance of the artist from the cube affects the appearance of the cube.

2-3 PART B Orthographic and Isometric Drawing

← CONNECT → ***You have polished your perspective-drawing skills. Now you will explore another way to show a three-dimensional object—by showing two or more views of the object. This is especially important to architects, designers, and engineers who produce detailed plans for making new products.***

Drawings are important tools in many careers. Manufacturing companies employ engineers, designers, and draftspeople to prepare technical drawings of products. **Orthographic** (or **orthogonal**) views show an object's exact shape and dimensions. You see orthographic views when you look directly at an object's top, front, back, left side, or right side.

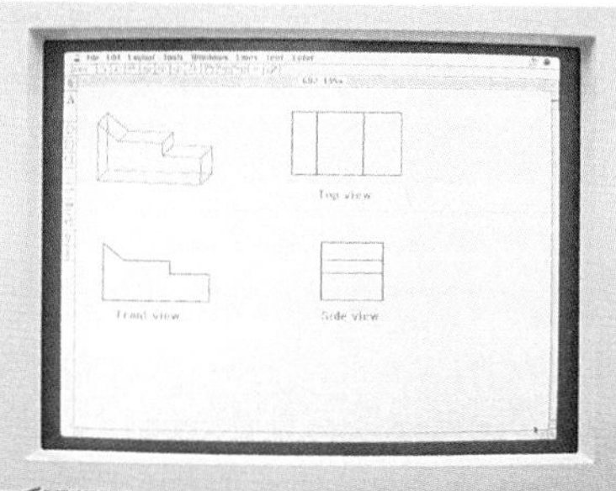

Alan Hoffer and Richard Koch, 3D Images, William K. Bradford Publishing Co.

The top orthographic view shows what the foundation (base) of an object or building looks like. If you build a building by stacking cubes, you can describe the heights of the stacks by writing the number of cubes on the columns shown in the top view.

In the figure at the right, a square with the number 3 means that the "building" is 3 cubes high at that point. When looking at a stack of cubes in this book, you may assume that all cubes are stacked on other cubes.

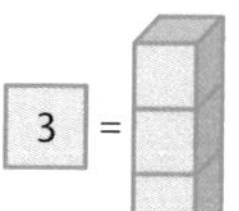

Student Resources

- Alternative Lessons 2-3B
- Laboratory Manual 2-3B
- Technology Lab Manual
- Practice 2-3B
- Study Guide and Journal 2-3B
- Guía de estudios y Diario 2-3B
- Multilingual Handbook
- More Look Ahead 2-3B
- SAT Preparation

Media Resources

- Transparency FFM 2-3B
- Transparency AE 2-3B
- Teaching Transparency
- AWSMTest and practice software
- AWSM Videodisc

PART B At a Glance

Objective

To use drawing techniques to show different views of three-dimensional objects.

Development

Students learn what orthographic and isometric views are. They see **Examples,** and they practice orthographic drawing in a **Try It.**

In the **Explore,** students apply these skills to make "buildings" from cubes and then draw orthographic and isometric views.

Key Terms

Orthographic (orthogonal), isometric

First Five Minutes

Transparency FFM 2-3B

Sketch a cube, using one-point perspective and the rules of thumb.

Motivate

Ask...

- What does a cube look like when you look at it from directly in front?
- Does the building you live in have the same shape when you look at it from different sides?

Drawing Techniques and Parallel Lines

ALTERNATE EXAMPLES

Transparency AE 2-3B

Provides a connection between reflections and perspective drawing.

Possible Answer

1. The front and back views of the cube buildings are reflections of each other. This is always true of these simple cube drawings; moving from the front to the back only reverses the orientation of the cubes.

EXAMPLES

1. Draw the top view of the building shown at the left below. Assume that there are no unseen stacks of cubes, and that you are looking at the building from the left front corner.

The building has a 2-by-2 square foundation. The top view is shown at the right below.

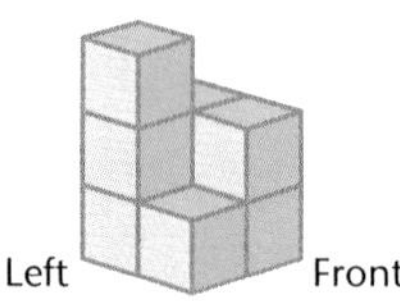

	Back		
Left	3	2	Right
	1	2	
	Front		

2. The top view of a building made of cubes is shown. Draw the orthographic views from the front, back, left, and right sides.

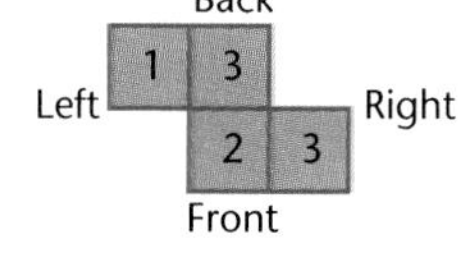

Remember that you are looking straight down at the building. Decide how many columns of cubes wide each view should be, and look for the largest number of cubes in each row to determine how high each stack should be. You could also visualize the building as shown in the first figure at the right, and then sketch the orthographic views.

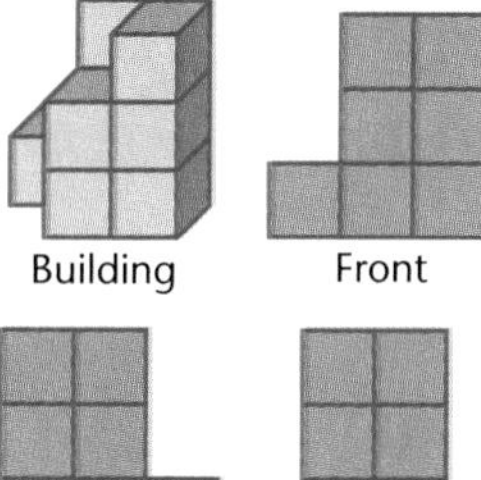

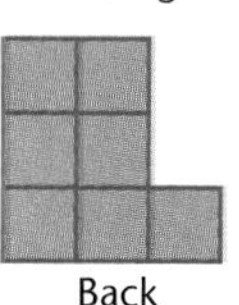
Back

Left/Right

CONSIDER

1. **You may notice a familiar relationship between the front and back views of the building shown in Example 2. How are the views related? Do you think this is always true? Explain.**

TRY IT

Front and Back

Left and Right

a. The top view of a building is shown at the right. Draw the front, back, and left orthographic views.

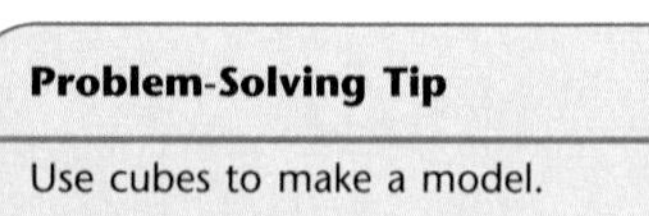

Problem-Solving Tip
Use cubes to make a model.

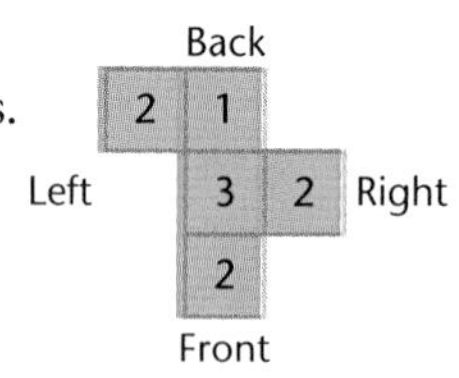

Diversity Issues

Students with weak visualization skills may have difficulty with this subject matter. You may want to suggest that they use cubes to help them with their homework assignments. You may wish to pair students who need help with a drawing tutor—a student strong in this area who can explain how he does perspective and isometric drawing.

Tips from Teachers

You might point out to students that in one-point perspective we look at the face of an object, whereas in two-point perspective we look at the edge of an object.

A special type of drawing, called **isometric drawing,** helps to show the connection between perspective and orthographic views. It is often faster to draw an isometric view rather than a two-point perspective sketch because the isometric drawing is done on isometric dot paper. You do not need to use a horizon line and vanishing points.

This is how you can use isometric paper to show a stack of two cubes. In the drawing, we have shaded the top and left sides of the cubes to give an illusion of depth.

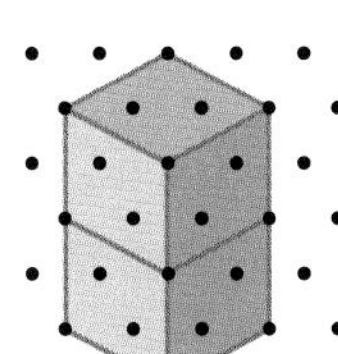

Isometric drawing is different from one-point or two-point perspective because parallel edges are actually parallel in the drawing. If you extend the edges of the cubes shown, they do not meet at a vanishing point.

In the following Explore, you will look at cube buildings from both orthographic and isometric views.

EXPLORE: ARCHITECTURE MADE EASY

MATERIALS

Cubes
Isometric dot paper

1. Make a building out of 10 cubes. To make the building interesting, have at least 3 stacks of cubes with different heights.
2. Sketch the orthographic top view of your building, giving the number of cubes in each stack.
3. Use isometric dot paper to sketch views of your building from two different corners.
4. Exchange your isometric sketches with those of another student. See if you can build his or her building correctly.

REFLECT

1. What characteristics of an object are better seen from an orthographic rather than an isometric view?
2. In isometric drawings of an object, two views, from opposite corners, are often shown. What is the purpose of showing these two views?

EXPLORE

Architecture Made Easy

Recommended group size: 2

The Point
To practice isometric and orthographic drawing; to draw isometric views of the same object from different perspectives.

Look and Listen...
- For students who are or are not having difficulty, so that you may be able to identify those who are especially strong or weak in spatial skills.
- For students who have problems sketching partially hidden cubes.
- For students who are having difficulty using isometric dot paper.

Ask...
- Can you use the picture at the top of page 137 to help guide you?

For Groups That Finish Early
Sketch the isometric views of your buildings from the other two corners.

Follow Up
Ask students whether two isometric views were enough to reconstruct the building.

Possible Answers
Check students' work.

Journal

Reflect 1 and 2 are suitable for journal entries.

REFLECT

Possible Answers
1. Dimensions (height, width) are better seen from an orthographic view because segments are not drawn in perspective.
2. Parts of the object that are hidden in one view will be revealed by the other.

Tips from Teachers

If students have not had practice with isometric drawing, consider having them do one or two simple drawings first. They should start with the front blocks and work their way back. Also, shading the visible tops of the blocks gives the drawing more depth.

Drawing Techniques and Parallel Lines

Part B Exercises

Exercise Notes

Core

6. Reviews the connection between reflections and orthographic views, and then applies basic probability concepts.

10. An open-ended question asking students to compare strengths and weaknesses of the two types of drawing.

Look Ahead

These exercises look ahead to parallel and skew lines in 2-3 Part C.

More Math Reasoning

18. Provides a good opportunity to discuss problem-solving strategies. Students who use an organized search method will find this exercise easier than those who do not. You may want to have students share methods for listing all of the possibilities, so that the whole class sees the benefits of an organized search.

Exercise Answers

Core

6. a. Front

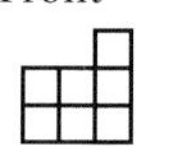

Left

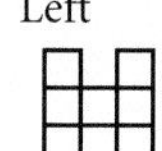

Front and back are mirror images, as are left and right (here left and right are the same due to symmetry)

b. $\frac{5}{14}$

10. Possible answer: Orthographic: see object's exact shape and dimensions but some features may be obscured from a given viewpoint; Isometric: three-dimensional perspective, but distorts side lengths and angle measures.

Exercises

CORE

P Science **1. Getting Started** Is the sketch of the space shuttle at the right an isometric or orthographic view? Why? Orthographic; Shows only one side of the shuttle.

P **Draw the top view of each building. (Assume that no stacks of blocks are hidden.) Label the heights of the columns.**

2.

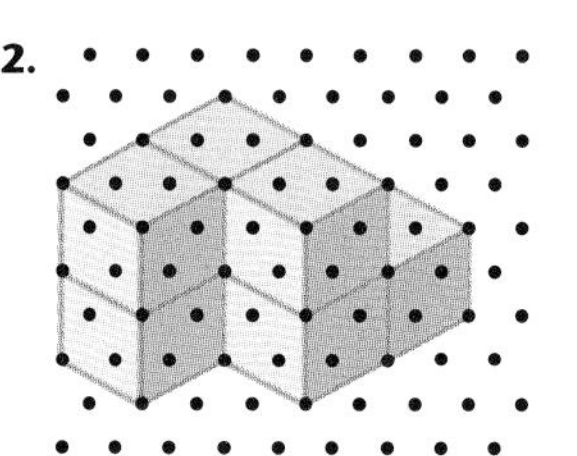

3.

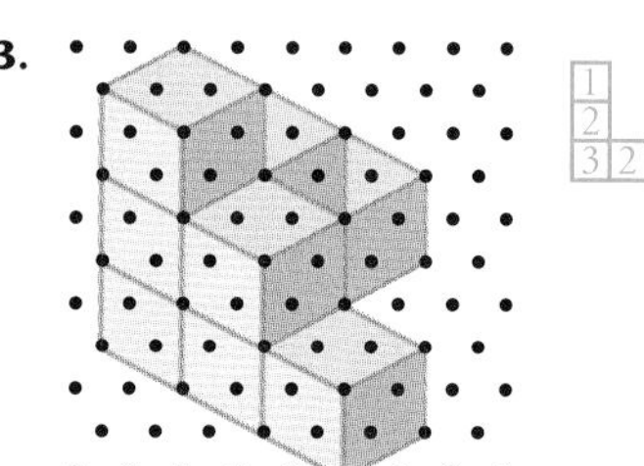

P **4.** Match the letter of each corner view with the corresponding isometric drawing.

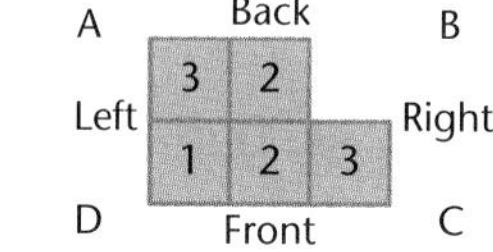

(a) (a) (b) (c) (c) (b) (d) (d)

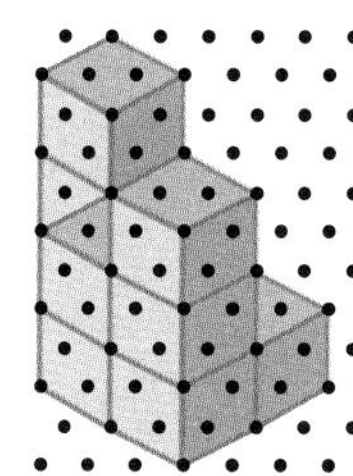

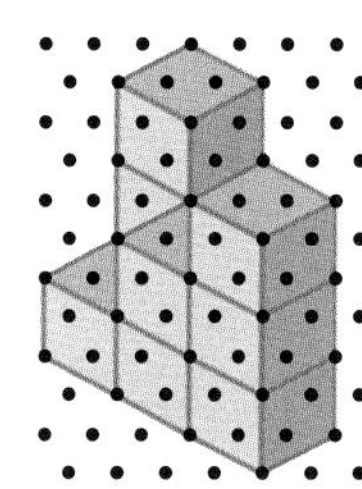

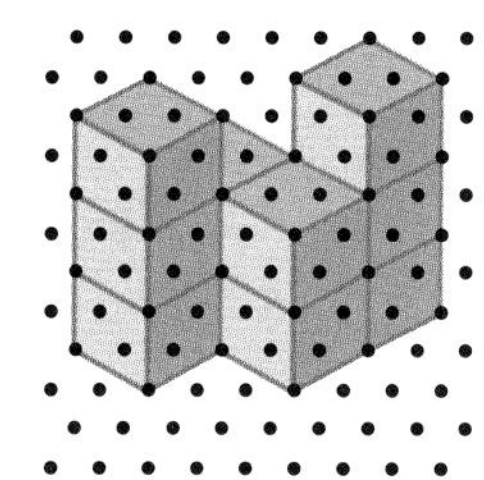

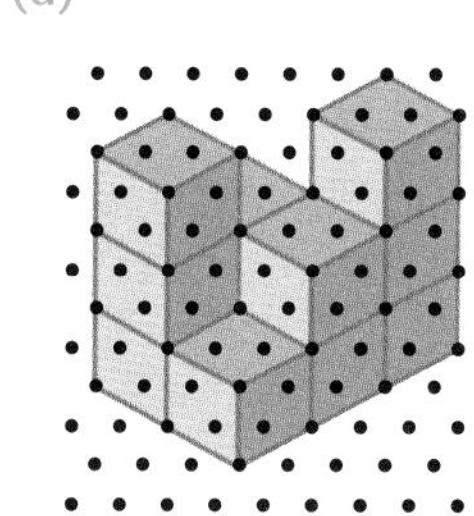

V **5.** Write the word or phrase that correctly completes the statement below.

A view that shows only the front of a building is an ____ view. Orthographic

P **6.** The top view of a building is shown at the right.

a. Draw the front and left orthographic views. How are these related to the back and right views?

b. Suppose that an electrician is rewiring the offices in one of the cubes. What is the probability that she is working on the second floor of the building?

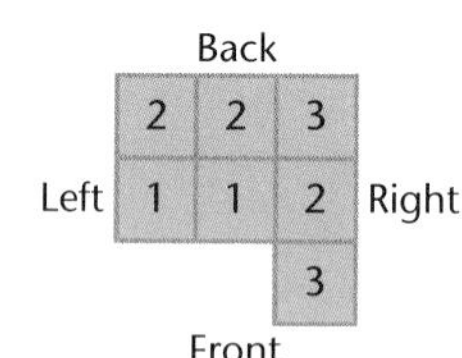

Key

V Vocabulary
P Practice/Skills
R Review
MR Math Reasoning
PS Problem Solving
C Challenge

Match each isometric view with the correct orthographic views. In each case, the figure on top is a possible top view; the other views are front and right views.

7. (a)

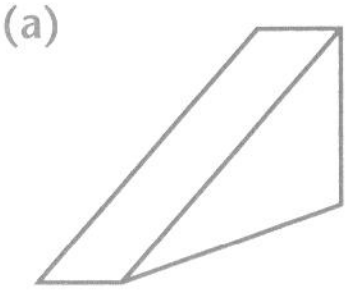

(a)

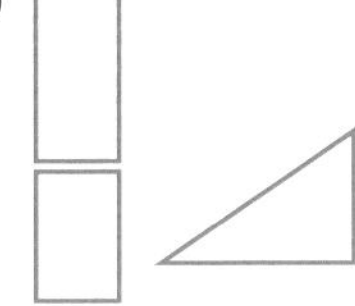

(b)

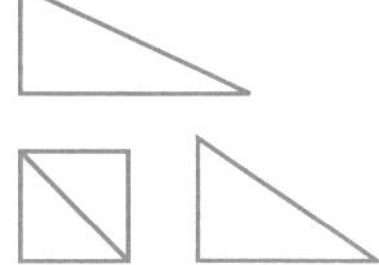

(c)

8. (c)

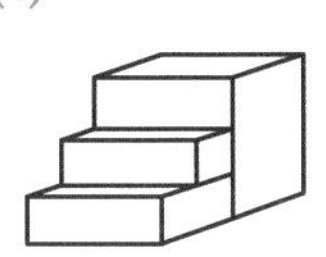

(a)

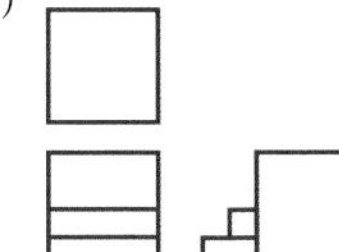

(b)

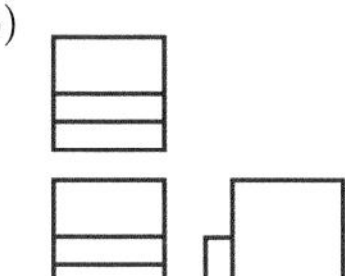

(c)

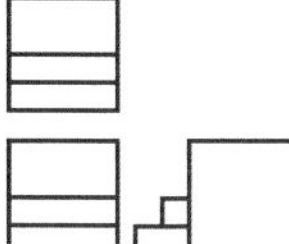

9. (c)

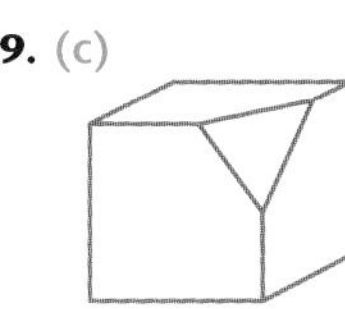

(a)

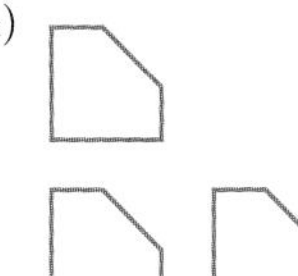

(b)

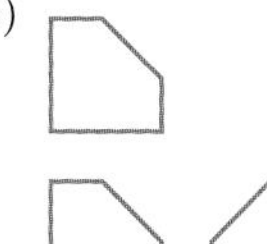

(c)

10. Summarize the advantages and disadvantages of orthographic and isometric views.

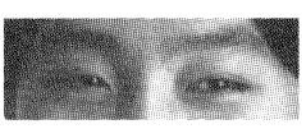

LOOK AHEAD

11. Use the cube at the right to give examples of Possible answers:

a. two coplanar lines that intersect $\overleftrightarrow{GL}$ and $\overleftrightarrow{LK}$

b. two coplanar lines that do not intersect $\overleftrightarrow{GL}$ and $\overleftrightarrow{NK}$

c. two noncoplanar lines $\overleftrightarrow{JN}$ and $\overleftrightarrow{LM}$

d. In which of the above would you say you found two *parallel* lines? (b)

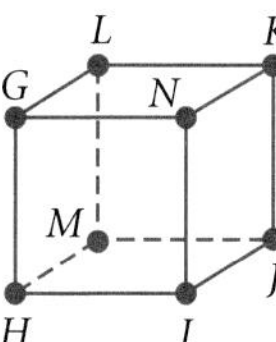

MORE PRACTICE

Draw the top view of each building. (Assume that no stacks of blocks are hidden.) Label the heights of the columns.

12.

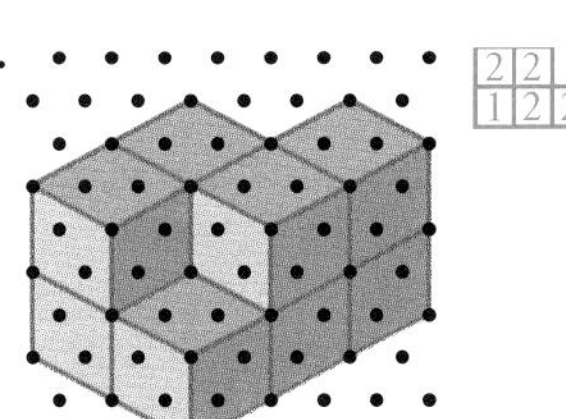

2	2	
1	2	2

13.

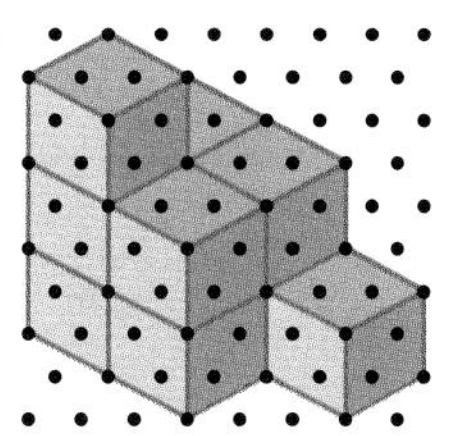

2	2	1
3	2	

Ongoing Assessment

Self-Assessment Exercises 1–9

Embedded Assessment Reflect 2; Exercises 2, 4, 6, 10

Drawing Techniques and Parallel Lines

P **Match each isometric view with the correct orthographic views. In each case, the figure on top is a possible top view; the other views are front and right views.**

14. (b) (a) (b) (c)

15. (c) (a) (b) (c)

16. (c) (a) (b) (c)

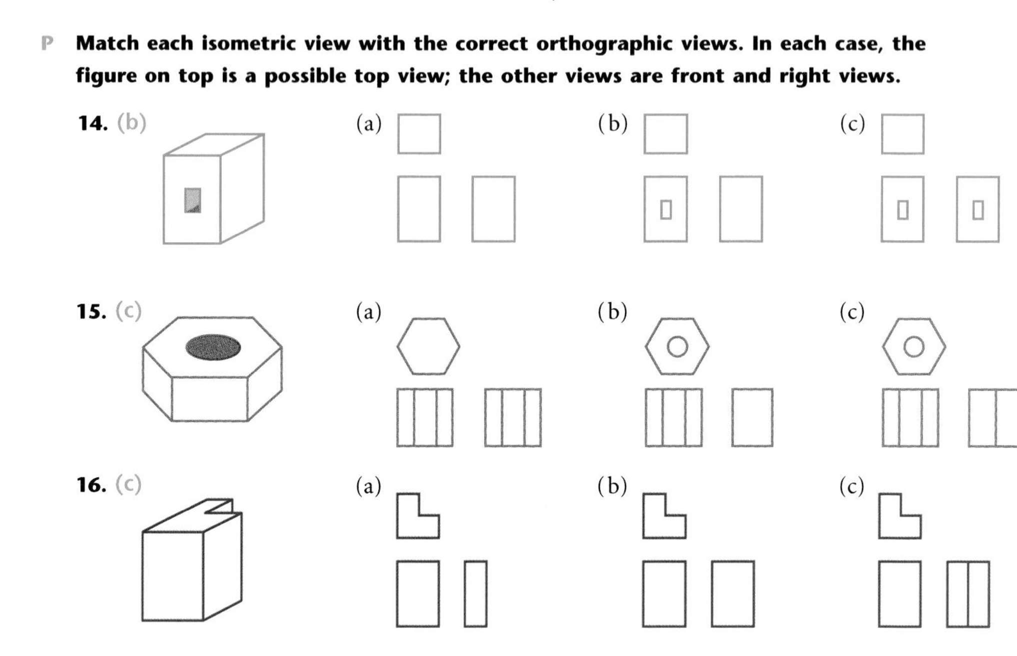

MORE MATH REASONING

PS, C **17. Polycube Search** Polycubes are formed by arranging cubes so that each cube has at least one face exactly matching a face of another cube.

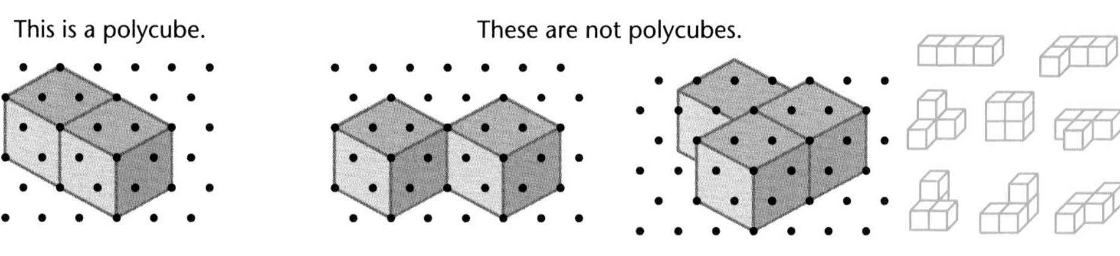
This is a polycube.
These are not polycubes.

Find as many different shapes of four-cube polycubes (*quadracubes*) as you can. Draw each one on isometric dot paper.

PS **18. Can You Top This?** The front and right views of a building are shown. Draw three possible top views showing the number of cubes in each column. (Assume that the building is made of stacked cubes.)

Possible answers:

3		3
4	2	4

3	1	3
4	2	4

3	2	3
4	2	4

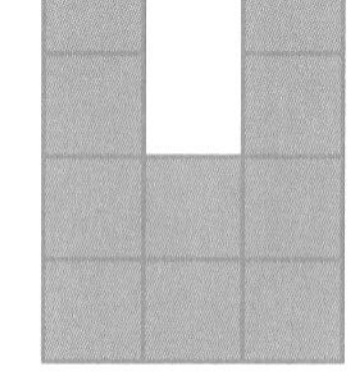

Front view

Right view

Key

- V Vocabulary
- P Practice/Skills
- R Review
- MR Math Reasoning
- PS Problem Solving
- C Challenge

2-3 PART C Parallel Lines and Planes

← CONNECT → *Parallel lines play an important role in the drawings you've been making. Now you will take a closer look at parallel lines. You will see a precise definition of parallel lines, make an important assumption about them, and investigate the relationship between parallel lines and slope.*

From your experience with parallel lines in algebra, you probably developed the idea that parallel lines do not meet. To write formal definitions, we need to refine our notion of parallel lines and planes.

DEFINITION

Parallel lines are coplanar lines that do not intersect.

Lines p and q in plane $\mathcal{S}$ are parallel. To show this, we use the symbol $||$, and write $p \parallel q$.

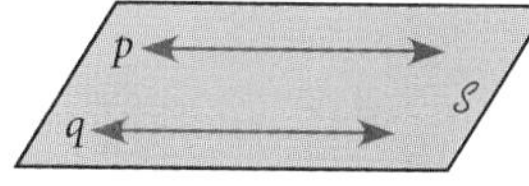

To show that two lines in a figure are parallel, we can use arrows, as shown below.

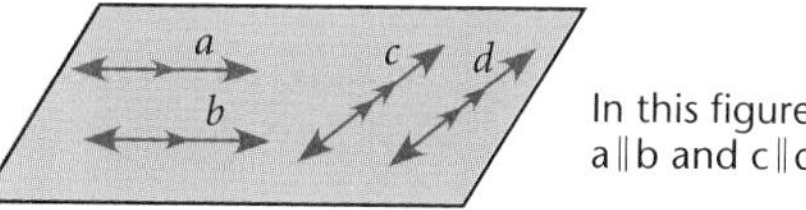

In this figure a ‖ b and c ‖ d.

A line may be parallel to a plane, and planes may be parallel to each other.

DEFINITION

A line and a plane, or two planes, are **parallel** if and only if they do not intersect.

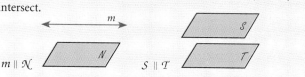

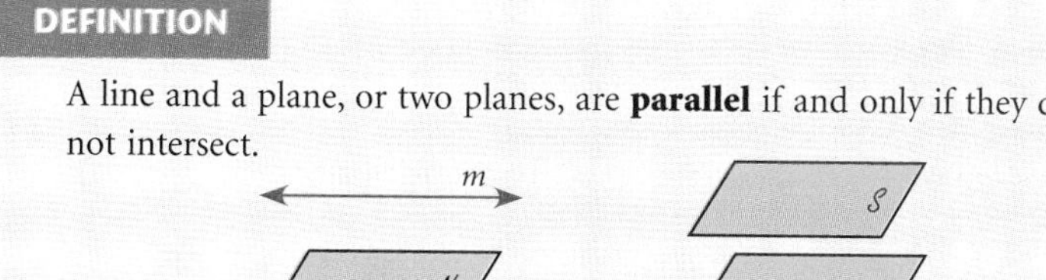

PART C At a Glance

Objective

To learn terminology related to parallel lines, review graphs of linear equations, and explore the Parallel Postulate.

Development

Students begin by looking at definitions of parallel lines and skew lines.

In the **Explore,** students review graphs of linear equations in slope-intercept form, which motivates the Parallel Postulate. The postulate is then presented formally, and some of its history is discussed.

Suggested Materials

Student Graph paper, graphing utility

Key Terms

Parallel, skew

First Five Minutes

Transparency FFM 2-3C

Read the paragraphs on pages 141 and 142 up to the **Try It** on page 142. Then do **Try It a** and **b.**

Motivate

Ask...

- Can you find examples of parallel lines in nature? Do parallel lines seem as common in nature as in things designed or planned by humans? Why might this be true?

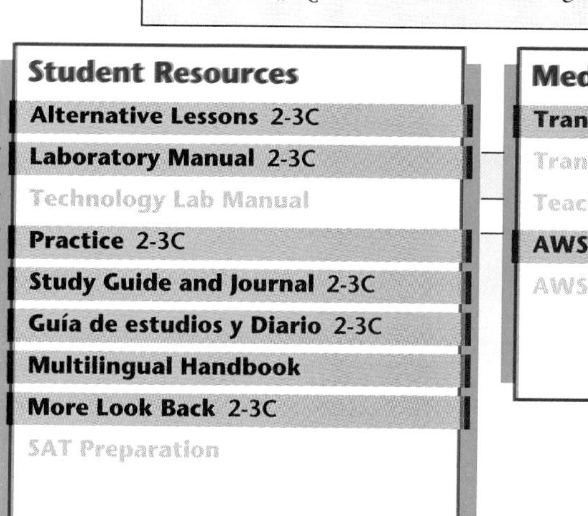

Student Resources

- Alternative Lessons 2-3C
- Laboratory Manual 2-3C
- Technology Lab Manual
- Practice 2-3C
- Study Guide and Journal 2-3C
- Guía de estudios y Diario 2-3C
- Multilingual Handbook
- More Look Back 2-3C
- SAT Preparation

Media Resources

- Transparency FFM 2-3C
- Transparency AE
- Teaching Transparency
- AWSMTest and practice software
- AWSM Videodisc

2-3

Drawing Techniques and Parallel Lines

EXPLORE

Connections to Algebra

Recommended group size: 2

The Point

To discover a relationship between equations of parallel lines, and to preview the Parallel Postulate.

Look and Listen...

- For students who do not remember the meanings of *slope* and *y-intercept.*

Ask...

- How can you use the slope and y-intercept to sketch the graph of a linear equation quickly?

For Groups That Finish Early

Find the equations of lines that are parallel to $y = -2$ and $x = 4$. What are the slopes of each of these sets of lines?

Follow Up

Ask students how they can determine whether or not two linear equations in slope-intercept form represent parallel lines.

Possible Answers

2. a. $y = 3x + 1$

b. An infinite number. There are an infinite number of possible y-intercepts for these lines.

c. $y = 3x + 5$

d. None; $y = 3x + 5$ is the only line with a y-intercept of 5 that has a slope of 3.

3. Equations in $y = mx + b$ form represent parallel lines if the m-values are equal.

4. The parallel line has the equation $y = mx + b$, where m is the slope of line ℓ, and b is the y-value of P.

Noncoplanar lines cannot intersect. There is a special name for these lines, as defined below.

DEFINITION

Skew lines are noncoplanar lines.

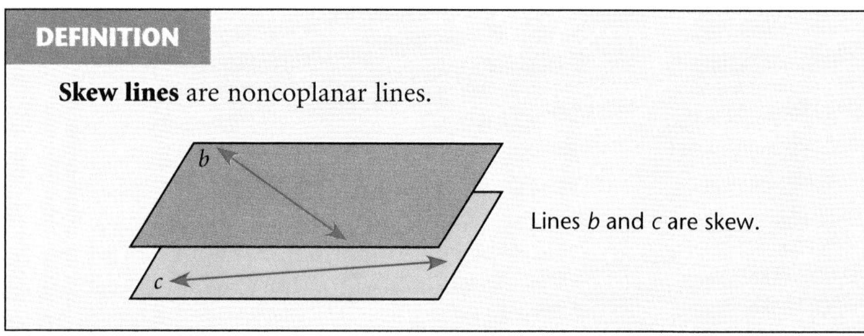

TRY IT

a. Name all the lines parallel to $\overleftrightarrow{AB}$ that contain edges of the cube at the right. $\overleftrightarrow{FG}$, $\overleftrightarrow{HC}$, $\overleftrightarrow{ED}$

b. Name all of the lines that are skew to $\overleftrightarrow{EF}$ that contain edges of the cube. $\overleftrightarrow{BC}$, $\overleftrightarrow{AB}$, $\overleftrightarrow{HC}$, $\overleftrightarrow{BG}$, $\overleftrightarrow{CD}$

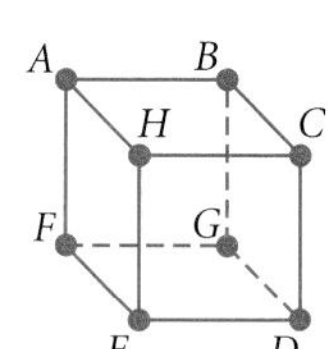

How many lines can be drawn parallel to a given line through a point not on that line? The following Explore will give you a chance to think about this question.

EXPLORE: CONNECTIONS TO ALGEBRA

MATERIALS

Graph paper
Graphing utility (optional)

In algebra, you learned about the $y = mx + b$ form for the equation of a line. Recall that m is the slope of the line, and b is the y-intercept.

1. Graph $y = 3x - 2$.
2. Graph other linear equations, using other values of m and b in the equation $y = mx + b$. Use your results to help answer the following questions.

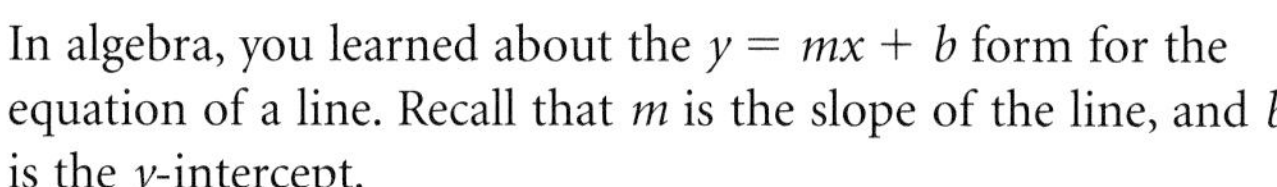

Problem-Solving Tip

Look for patterns.

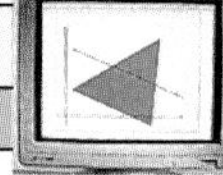

Technology Note

When using a graphing utility in the **Explore,** first have students enter and graph $y = 3x - 2$. If possible, they should keep this equation active while they do Step 2, so that they can compare it to the new equations they are experimenting with.

The standard range for the graphing utility should be suitable for this **Explore.**

Alert

Students may not have a good recall of the meaning of *slope* or of linear equations in slope-intercept form. You may want to take a few minutes to review these topics before beginning the *Explore*.

a. Find an equation of a line whose graph is parallel to $y = 3x - 2$.
b. How many other equations of lines parallel to $y = 3x - 2$ can you find? Explain why this is the case.
c. Write an equation of a line parallel to $y = 3x - 2$ that has a y-intercept of 5.
d. How many other equations of lines parallel to $y = 3x - 2$ with a y-intercept of 5 are there? Explain.

3. How can you tell whether or not two linear equations represent parallel lines? Give your conclusion in writing.
4. If you are given the equation of line ℓ and the coordinates of point P on the y-axis that is not on the line, describe how you can find an equation of a line that goes through P and is parallel to ℓ.

Your conclusions in the preceding Explore should make the following postulate seem reasonable.

PARALLEL POSTULATE

Through a given point, P, not on a line, ℓ, exactly one line may be drawn parallel to line ℓ.

This postulate was first stated by Euclid. For over 2000 years after Euclid, mathematicians doubted that this assumption was necessary. Many tried to prove the Parallel Postulate, but all failed. Instead, mathematicians found that by making different assumptions about parallel lines, they could create other, non-Euclidean systems of geometry. Nevertheless, we will use Euclid's Parallel Postulate. It most closely fits our ideas about geometric figures and their relationships in the world around us. We will look at non-Euclidean systems of geometry in Chapter 12.

REFLECT

1. Two noncoplanar lines cannot intersect. Why?
2. Can two planes ever be skew? Why or why not?
3. If a line is parallel to a plane, is it parallel to every line in the plane? Justify your answer with a sketch.

Journal

Explore Step 3 and **Reflect** 1 and 3 are suitable for journal entries.

REFLECT

Possible Answers

1. Two noncoplanar lines cannot intersect, because three points (the point of intersection and one other point on each line) would determine the two lines. Those points would determine a plane, and both lines, having two points in the plane, would be contained in it.
2. No. By the definition, nonintersecting planes are parallel. If two planes are not parallel, they must intersect.
3. No.

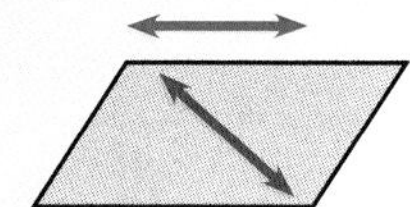

Algebra | Functions | Discrete Math | Probability | Data/Statistics

Drawing Techniques and Parallel Lines

Part C Exercises

Exercise Notes

Core

5–8. These exercises apply the ideas of parallel lines to a map of Washington, D.C.

9. Similar to multiple-choice analogy items on standardized tests.

14. Reviews the algebraic idea that perpendicular lines have negative reciprocal slopes.

More Math Reasoning

33. Introduces students to the three-dimensional coordinate system. Working with this system encourages visual thinking. There are also some interesting extensions of two-dimensional ideas to three dimensions that can be exploited later. For instance, in 9-2 Part D, on page 643, Exercise 23 shows the relationship between the equation of a circle and the equation of a sphere.

Exercise Answers

Core

1. $\overleftrightarrow{BF}, \overleftrightarrow{DH}, \overleftrightarrow{AG}$

2. Possible answer: $\overleftrightarrow{AG}$

3. Plane with E, F, G, H

10. Check students' answers

11.

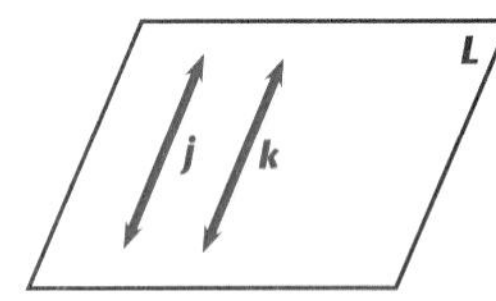

12.

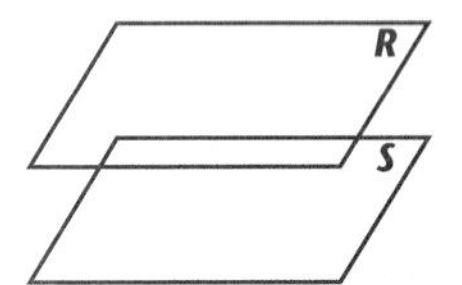

Exercises

CORE

P **Getting Started** **Refer to the cube at the right for Exercises 1–4.**

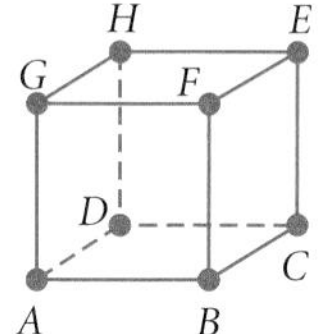

1. Name all of the lines parallel to $\overleftrightarrow{CE}$ that contain edges of the cube.

2. Name a line parallel to the plane containing points F, B, and H.

3. Identify a plane parallel to the plane containing A, B, and C.

4. Name a line through F that contains an edge of the cube and is skew to $\overleftrightarrow{AG}$. $\overleftrightarrow{EF}$

P 

Using the map of Washington, D.C., tell whether the streets given in Exercises 5–8 suggest parallel lines, intersecting lines, some of both, or neither.

5. streets passing through Dupont Circle Intersecting

6. 15th St., 16th St., 17th St., and so on Parallel

7. O, P, and Q Streets Parallel

8. streets whose names are neither letters nor numbers Both

CityFlash Map ©1994 by Rand McNally R.L. 94-S-140

V **9.** Write the letter of the second pair that best matches the first pair. (d)

Skew: coplanar as (a) flat: plane, (b) points: collinear, (c) plane: line, (d) parallel: intersecting

MR **10.** Identify objects in your classroom that suggest parallel and skew lines.

P **Draw each figure if possible. If it is not possible, explain why.**

11. Line $j \parallel k$; j and k lie on plane $\mathcal{L}$.

12. Planes $\mathcal{R}$ and $\mathcal{S}$ are parallel.

13. Line $p \parallel q$, lines p and r are skew, and lines q and r are skew.

MR **14. Slopes of Perpendicular Lines** By following the steps below, you will discover a relationship between the slopes of perpendicular lines.

a. Use graph paper to graph the lines represented by the following equations.

i. $y = 3x + 2$ **ii.** $y = -3x - 3$ **iii.** $y = -\frac{1}{3}x - 2$ **iv.** $y = \frac{1}{3}x + 3$

b. Which of the lines in **14a** appear to be perpendicular?

c. Make a conjecture about the slopes of perpendicular lines.

Key

V Vocabulary
P Practice/Skills
R Review
MR Math Reasoning
PS Problem Solving
C Challenge

Write an equation of a line that meets the given requirements.

15. parallel to $y = -3x + 4$

16. through (0, 4) and parallel to $y = \frac{3}{5}x - \frac{1}{5}$

17. perpendicular to $y = \frac{3}{4}x + 2$

18. through (0, 0) and parallel to $y = -6$

19. In the figure at the right, a line is to be drawn that passes through two points chosen randomly from those labeled *A–F*.

a. What is the probability that the line will be parallel to *m*?

b. What is the probability that the line will be perpendicular to *m*?

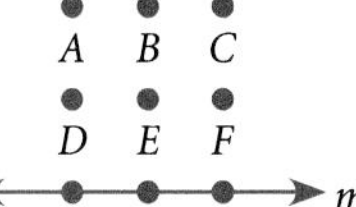

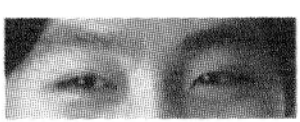

LOOK BACK

Use a protractor to draw angles with each of the following measures. [1-3]

20. 10° **21.** 45° **22.** 150°

Write each biconditional statement as two separate conditional statements in if-then form. [2-2]

23. Two lines are noncoplanar if and only if they are skew lines.

24. Two lines are parallel if and only if they are coplanar and do not intersect.

25. Point *B* is between points *A* and *C* if and only if $AB + BC = AC$.

MORE PRACTICE

Refer to the cube at the right for Exercises 26–28.

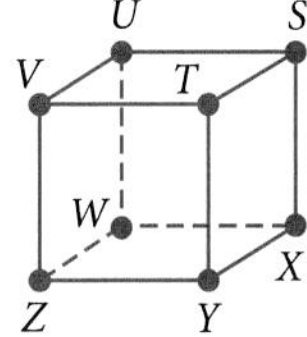

26. Name all of the lines skew to $\overleftrightarrow{XY}$ that contain an edge of the cube.

27. Identify a plane parallel to the plane containing *U, V,* and *S.*

28. Name three lines parallel to $\overleftrightarrow{WZ}$ that contain an edge of the cube.

Sketch each figure if possible. If it is not possible, explain why.

29. Line *p* intersects line *m*, line $p \parallel$ line *n*, and line $m \parallel$ line *n*.

30. Line *a* intersects line *b*, line *a* intersects line *c*, and line *b* is skew to line *c*.

Write an equation of a line that meets the given requirements.

31. parallel to $y = \frac{3}{7}x + 1$

32. perpendicular to $y = \frac{3}{7}x + 1$

Ongoing Assessment

Self-Assessment Exercises 1–19 odd

Embedded Assessment Try It a; Exercises 4, 10, 14, 16

13.

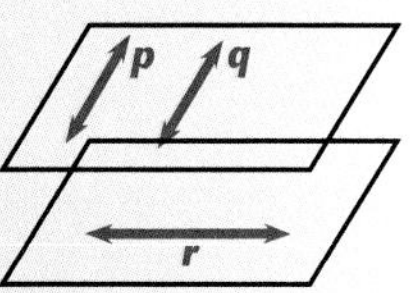

14. a.

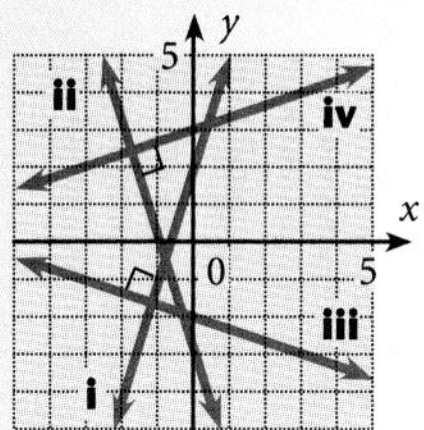

b. ii and iv, and i and iii

c. Line $q \perp r$ when $m_q = -\frac{1}{m_r}$

15. Possible answer: $y = -3x$

16. $y = \frac{3}{5}x + 4$

17. Possible answer: $y = -\frac{4}{3}x$

18. $y = 0$

19. a. 40% **b.** 20%

Look Back

20.

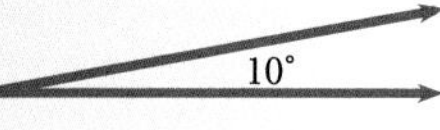

21.

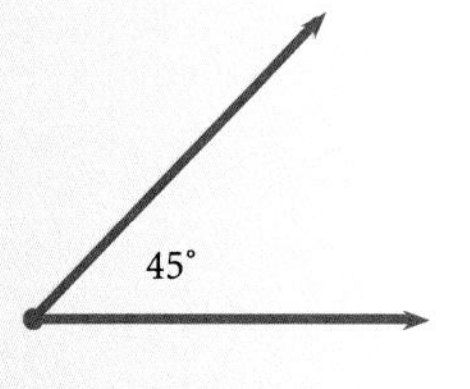

22. 150°

23. If two lines are noncoplanar, then they are skew. If two lines are skew, then they are noncoplanar.

24. If two lines are parallel, then they are coplanar and do not intersect. If two lines are coplanar and do not intersect, then they are parallel.

25. If point *B* is between points *A* and *C*, then $AB + BC = AC$. If $AB + BC = AC$, then point *B* is between *A* and *C*.

26–36. See Additional Answers p. T128.

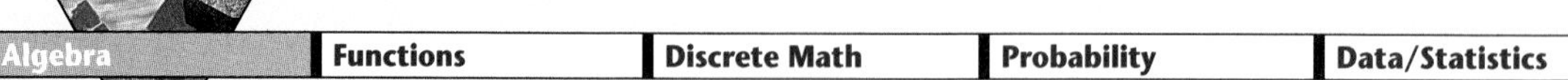

Drawing Techniques and Parallel Lines

PART D At a Glance

Objective

To use drawing skills to sketch a design for a commuter station.

Development

In the **Explore,** students design one aspect of a new commuter station. Their design must include parallel lines and planes. To sketch the design, students choose from perspective, isometric, or orthographic drawing.

Suggested Materials

Student Drawing materials

First Five Minutes

Transparency FFM 2-3D

Make a sketch of each of the following:

- a pair of parallel lines
- a pair of skew lines
- a line that is parallel to a plane
- a pair of parallel planes

MORE MATH REASONING

C **33. 3-D Coordinates** By now you know how to set up an x-y coordinate system on a plane. To locate a point in three-dimensional space, we need to add a third axis. Any point in an x-y-z coordinate system can be named by three coordinates (x first, y second, z third). In the figure, the x-y-z coordinates of three vertices of a box (rectangular prism) are given.

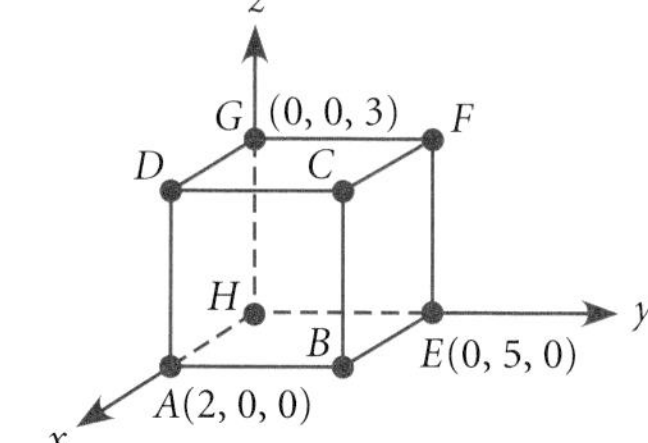

a. Give the coordinates for each of the other vertices of the box.

b. Name three sets of parallel line segments.

MR **Assume the following statements are true. Make a conjecture using each set of statements. Make a sketch to illustrate each conjecture.**

34. Lines ℓ, p, and q are coplanar. Line $p \parallel q$, and ℓ intersects p.

35. Lines r, s, and t are coplanar. Line $r \parallel s$, and $t \perp r$.

36. Plane $\mathcal{P} \parallel \mathcal{Q}$. Plane $\mathcal{N}$ intersects $\mathcal{P}$.

2-3 PART D Making Connections

← CONNECT → *The ability to represent a three-dimensional figure on a two-dimensional sheet of paper is important in industry and in geometry. You've investigated different ways to sketch three-dimensional figures, including isometric and orthogonal drawings. You've also seen how parallel lines are shown in perspective drawing and learned some definitions and postulates about parallel lines.*

Different cultures and professions have looked at and used parallel lines in many different ways. The photo at the left shows a racetrack with lane markings that are indicated by parallel lines.

You have learned how to use parallel lines and planes to make more realistic-looking drawings of three-dimensional objects. In the following Explore, you will use these new skills to design a transit station.

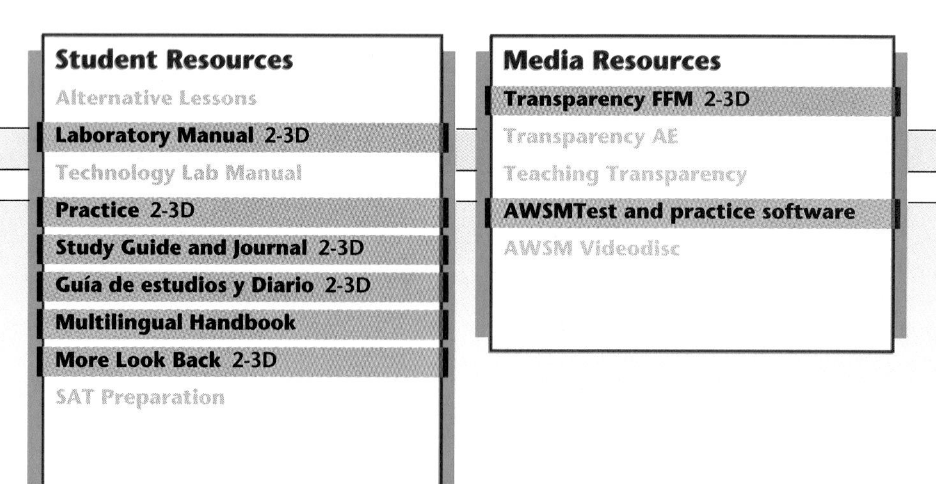

Student Resources

Alternative Lessons
Laboratory Manual 2-3D
Technology Lab Manual
Practice 2-3D
Study Guide and Journal 2-3D
Guía de estudios y Diario 2-3D
Multilingual Handbook
More Look Back 2-3D
SAT Preparation

Media Resources

Transparency FFM 2-3D
Transparency AE
Teaching Transparency
AWSMTest and practice software
AWSM Videodisc

EXPLORE: STATION DESIGNER

MATERIALS

Drawing materials

The photo at the right shows a commuter station in Washington, D.C. Your class has been asked to design a new commuter station for your home town. Since it is too big a task to do alone, you are to design one of the following aspects of the station.

- the front layout of the site
- the passenger building
- the docking terminal
- the parking area

Choose the type of drawing (one-point or two-point perspective, orthographic, or isometric) that will convey your idea best. Your drawing must include parallel lines and planes. When you have finished, your work should be suitable for a presentation to your class or the community.

REFLECT

1. What are the advantages and disadvantages of using perspective drawings instead of orthographic drawings to represent three-dimensional objects?
2. There are only three different relationships possible for two lines. Describe and illustrate all three relationships.

Self-Assessment

Determine whether each statement is true or false. Explain your answers.

1. Two lines that do not intersect are parallel. F; They could be skew.
2. A line and a plane that do not intersect are parallel. T; Definition of parallel
3. In an isometric drawing of a cube, parallel edges will appear to meet at one point. F; Parallel edges remain parallel.
4. The right and left orthographic views of a building made of cubes are always reflections of one another. T; They are the same profile seen from opposite sides.

Vocabulary
Practice/Skills
Review
Math Reasoning
Problem Solving
Challenge

EXPLORE

Station Designer

Recommended group size: 4

The Point
To use drawing techniques to design a commuter station.

Look and Listen...
- For students who are having difficulty remembering the different drawing techniques.

Ask...
- Have you decided where the artist is positioned?

For Groups That Finish Early
Design another aspect of the commuter station.

Follow Up
Have students present their designs to the class.

Possible Answers
Check students' work.

Portfolio

Have students select items that demonstrate their understanding of the material in 2-3.

You may want to have students include their best perspective and isometric drawings, an **Exercise** involving equations of parallel or perpendicular lines, and an **Exercise** they found difficult.

REFLECT

Possible Answers

1. Perspective drawings give depth to the picture, so that it looks more realistic. However, segment lengths and angle measures are distorted.
2. The lines can intersect, be parallel, or be skew.

Self-Assessment

Exercise Notes

Core

5. This architectural drawing uses the techniques learned in 2-3.

Drawing Techniques and Parallel Lines

18. An open-ended question that uses drawing skills.

Self-Assessment Answers

5. Orthographic; It shows only one side of the building at a time.

6. Possible answers: $y = \frac{3}{2}x$, $y = \frac{3}{2}x + 1$, $y = \frac{3}{2}x + 2$

7. $y = -\frac{2}{3}x + 5$

9.

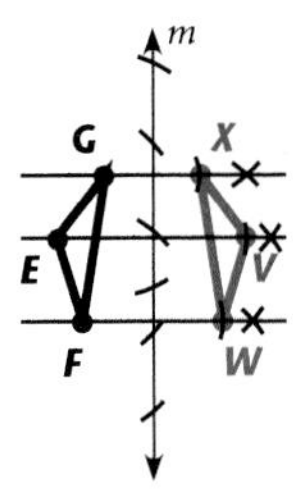

a. 120°

b. 120° (reflection preserves angle measure)

10. T; Straight Line Postulate

11. F; Planes intersect in line

12. T; Plane Postulate; Flat-Plane Postulate

13. Front Right

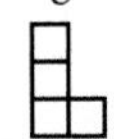

18. Check students' answers

MR Fine Arts **5.** The architectural drawing at the right is by Julia Morgan. Is it an isometric view, an orthographic view, in one-point perspective, or in two-point perspective? Explain how you decided.

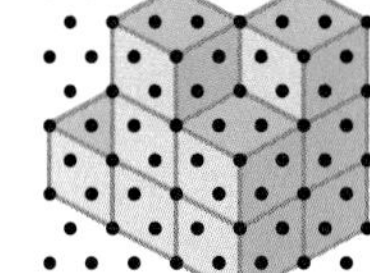

P **6.** Give the equations of three lines parallel to $y = \frac{3}{2}x - 3$.

P **7.** Give an equation for a line through (0, 5) perpendicular to $y = \frac{3}{2}x - 3$.

P **8.** The top view and an isometric view of a block building are shown. From which corner of the building was the isometric view drawn? (a)

(a) right front (b) left front

(c) right rear (d) left rear

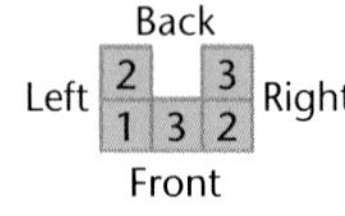

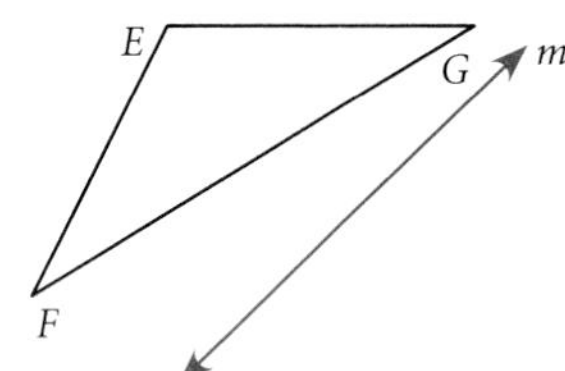

R **9.** Copy the figure at the right. Sketch the reflection of the triangle EFG across line m. Label its image triangle VWX. Then do the following: [1-3, 1-4]

a. Use your protractor to find the measure of $\angle E$.

b. Without measuring, find the measure of $\angle V$. Explain your reasoning.

E G m F

R **Determine whether each statement is true or false. If true, state the postulate or postulates that justify it. If false, explain why. [2-2]**

10. Line $\overleftrightarrow{JK}$ is the only line containing J and K.

11. The intersection of planes $\mathcal{F}$ and $\mathcal{G}$ is point H.

12. The intersecting lines $\overleftrightarrow{AB}$ and $\overleftrightarrow{BC}$ must be coplanar.

P **13.** The top view of a block building is shown at the right. Draw an orthogonal view from the front side and the right side of the building.

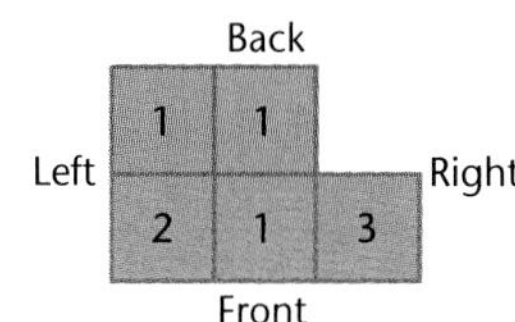

P **Determine whether each statement is true or false. For each false statement, give a counterexample.**

14. If two lines have the same slope, then they are parallel. T

15. Two lines with the same y-intercept are perpendicular. F; For example, $y = 2x + 3$ and $y = 6x + 3$

16. If the product of the slopes of two lines is -1, then they are perpendicular. T

17. If two lines are perpendicular, then the product of their slopes is -1. F; horizontal and vertical lines.

C **18. You Be the Architect!** Sketch a building of your own design, using one of the techniques you have learned in this chapter. Identify the technique you are using.

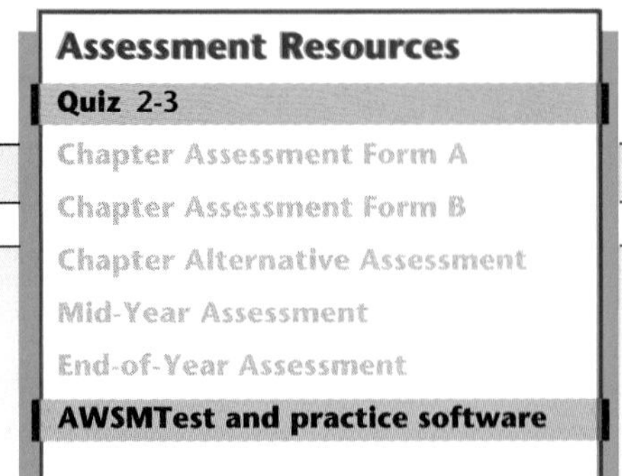

Assessment Resources

Quiz 2-3

Chapter Assessment Form A

Chapter Assessment Form B

Chapter Alternative Assessment

Mid-Year Assessment

End-of-Year Assessment

AWSMTest and practice software

Ongoing Assessment

Self-Assessment Self-Assessment Exercises

Embedded Assessment Drawing from the Explore; Reflect 1 and 2

Chapter 2 Review

In Chapter 2, you investigated the rules and language of logic, including conditionals and their related statements. You learned how to write definitions of geometric terms, and how undefined terms, definitions, postulates, and theorems fit together to form our system of geometry. You also explored two-dimensional representations of three-dimensional objects and investigated parallel lines.

KEY TERMS

biconditional statement [2-2]	hypothesis [2-1]	orthographic view [2-3]
Chain Rule [2-1]	inverse [2-1]	parallel [2-3]
conclusion [2-1]	isometric drawing [2-3]	parallel lines [2-3]
conditional statement [2-1]	Law of Detachment [2-1]	plane [2-2]
contrapositive [2-1]	midpoint [2-2]	skew lines [2-3]
converse [2-1]	noncoplanar [2-2]	space [2-2]
coplanar points [2-2]	one-point perspective [2-3]	two-point perspective [2-3]
horizon line [2-3]	orthogonal view [2-3]	vanishing point [2-3]

Write the word or phrase that correctly completes each statement.

1. A statement containing a hypothesis and a conclusion is called a ____ statement. Conditional
2. A conjecture that is accepted without proof is called a ____ . Postulate
3. Coplanar lines that do not intersect are called ____ lines. Parallel

CONCEPTS AND APPLICATIONS

4. Write a false conditional statement that has a true inverse. [2-1]
5. Determine whether the following conditional statement is true. "If a number is divisible by 4, then it is divisible by 16." Write the inverse, converse, and contrapositive of the conditional, and determine whether each is true or false. [2-1]

Determine whether each statement is true or false. If true, state the postulate that it illustrates. If false, correct it so that it is true. [2-2]

6. Two planes intersect only in the point P. F; Two planes intersect in a line
7. If points A and B lie in a plane, then the midpoint of $\overline{AB}$ also lies in that plane. T: Flat-Plane Postulate

Vocabulary
Practice/Skills
Review
Math Reasoning
Problem Solving
Challenge

Chapter 2 Review

Journal

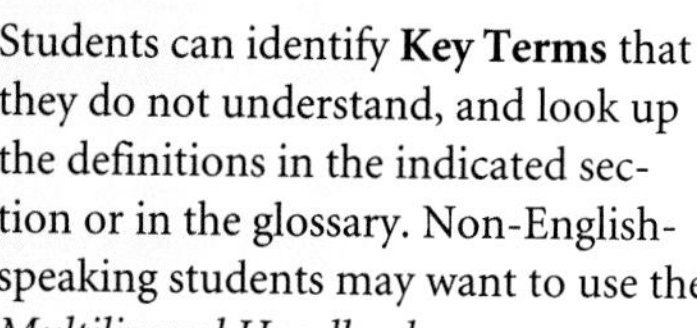

Students can identify **Key Terms** that they do not understand, and look up the definitions in the indicated section or in the glossary. Non-English-speaking students may want to use the *Multilingual Handbook.*

Vocabulary exercises and the **Self-Evaluation** are useful journal entries.

Review Answers

4. Possible answer: If you are a teenager, then you are fifteen.

5. Original: F
Inverse: If a number is not divisible by 4, then it is not divisible by 16. T
Converse: If a number is divisible by 16, then it is divisible by 4. T
Contrapositive: If a number is not divisible by 16, then it is not divisible by 4. F

Chapter 2 Assessment

Portfolio

Students may select items that represent their mathematical understanding of the ideas in Chapter 2 and that illustrate the effort they put forth on this chapter.

A rubric for assessing portfolios is included in the introduction to the Teacher's Edition.

Assessment Answers

2. F; Possible answer: Conditional (F): If you live in Oklahoma City, then you live in Japan. Inverse (F): If you don't live in Oklahoma City, then you don't live in Japan.

3. Possible answer: Law of Detachment: from "If there is fire, there is smoke" and "There is fire" to "There is smoke." Chain Rule: from "If I get rich, I will go to Hawaii" and "If I go to Hawaii, I will go surfing" to "If I get rich, I will go surfing."

4. Conditional: T; Converse: If the square of a number is odd, the number itself is odd. T; Biconditional: A number is odd if and only if its square is odd.

10.

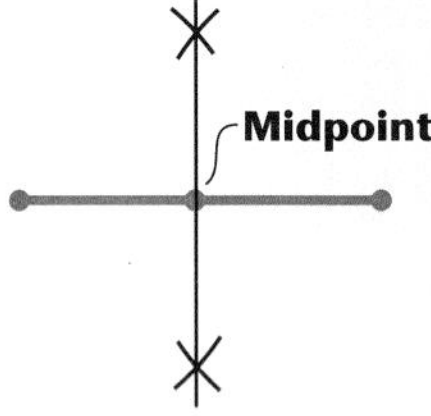

11. In general, it is not possible to construct a system without some words that are accepted without definition.

14.

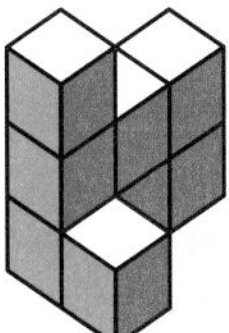

15.

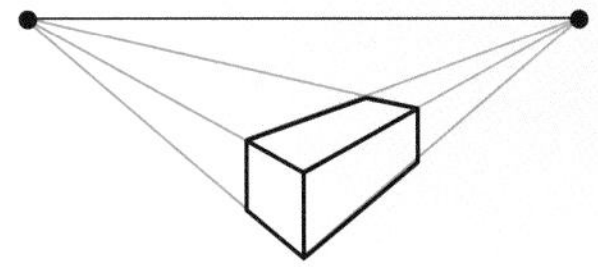

R **8.** Factor the expression $x^2 + 4x - 12$. [Previous course] $(x + 6)(x - 2)$

P **9.** Find the coordinates of the midpoint of the segment with endpoints $(3, -8)$ and $(-1, 6)$. [2-2] $(1, -1)$

P **10.** Give the equation of the line that is parallel to the line $y = 5x - 7$ that passes through $(0, 6)$. [2-3] $y = 5x + 6$

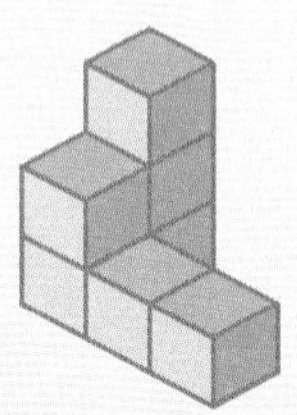

P **11.** Draw the top view of the building shown. Label the heights of the columns. Assume that there are no unseen stacks of cubes. [2-3] 3 / 2 1 1

CONCEPTS AND CONNECTIONS

PS **12. Computer Games** You are designing pieces for a "three-dimensional" computer game in which players put together buildings made of small cubes. Design a set of three pieces that can be put together to form a $3 \times 3 \times 3$ cube. Draw your pieces using a different method of representation for each. Include one isometric drawing, one set of orthographic views, and one perspective drawing.

SELF-EVALUATION

Write a summary of what you have learned in this chapter. Include examples of how the new ideas you learned in Chapter 2 can be used to model real-world situations. Include topics that you found difficult, and describe your plans for reviewing them.

Chapter 2 Assessment

TEST

P **In items 1 and 2, determine whether each statement is true or false. If a statement is false, provide a counterexample to illustrate this.**

1. If a conditional statement is true, then its contrapositive must be true. T

2. If a conditional statement is false, then its inverse must be true.

MR **3.** Assume that the statements below are true. Some of them fit together. Use them to write at least two other statements that must be true. For each new statement, name the rule that you used.

If there is fire, there is smoke. If I win the lottery, I will be rich. If I go to Hawaii, I will go surfing. If I get rich, I will go to Hawaii. There is fire.

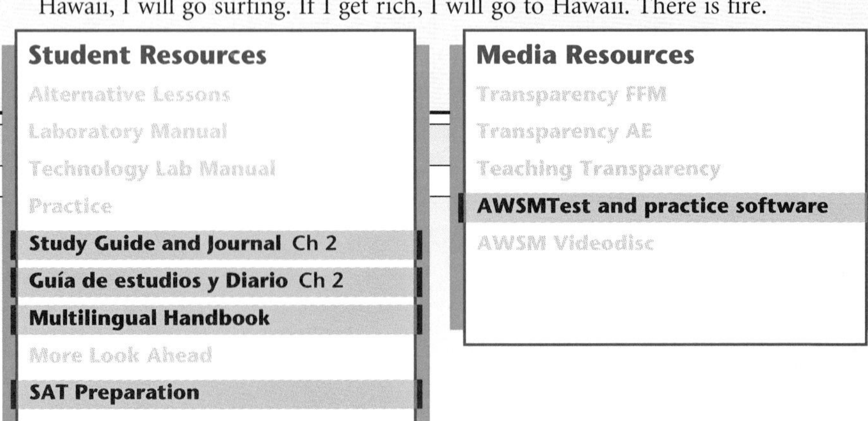

Student Resources
- Alternative Lessons
- Laboratory Manual
- Technology Lab Manual
- Practice
- **Study Guide and Journal** Ch 2
- **Guía de estudios y Diario** Ch 2
- **Multilingual Handbook**
- More Look Ahead
- **SAT Preparation**

Media Resources
- Transparency FFM
- Transparency AE
- Teaching Transparency
- **AWSMTest and practice software**
- AWSM Videodisc

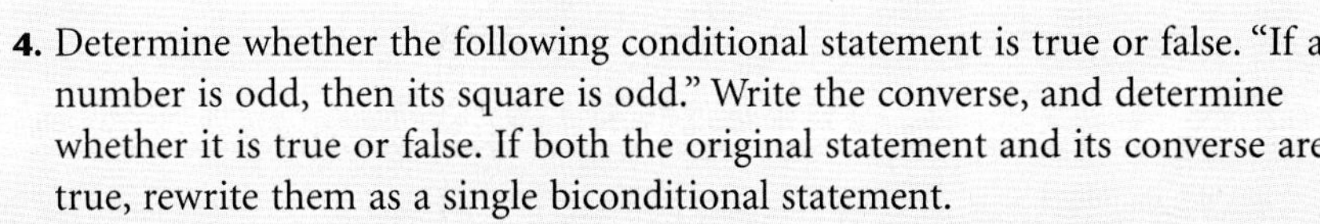

4. Determine whether the following conditional statement is true or false. "If a number is odd, then its square is odd." Write the converse, and determine whether it is true or false. If both the original statement and its converse are true, rewrite them as a single biconditional statement.

Write each number using scientific notation.

5. 0.000206 2.06×10^{-4} 6. 1800 1.8×10^3 7. 306,000,000 3.06×10^8

Points *R* and *S* are points on a coordinate plane. Find the midpoint of $\overline{RS}$ using the given coordinates.

8. $R(-2, 3), S(1, 8)$ $\left(-\frac{1}{2}, \frac{11}{2}\right)$ 9. $R(4, -3), S(10, -5)$ $(7, -4)$

10. Use a straightedge to draw a line segment about 3 in. long. Then use your compass and straightedge to construct its midpoint.

11. Do you think it is possible to construct a system of geometry that does not include any undefined terms? Write a paragraph explaining why or why not.

12. Points *A*, *B*, *C*, and *D* are coplanar points. A line segment drawn from *A* to *B* passes through *C*. A line segment drawn from *C* to *B* passes through *D*. Determine which of the following must be true. (c)
(a) $AC + CD = AB$ (b) $AD + CD = AC$
(c) Points *A*, *B*, *C*, and *D* are collinear. (d) Point *C* is the midpoint of $\overline{AB}$.

13. Give the equation of the line parallel to $y = 6x - 2$ that passes through $(0, 1)$. $y = 6x + 1$

14. The top view of a building is shown. Sketch an isometric view of the building from the left front corner.

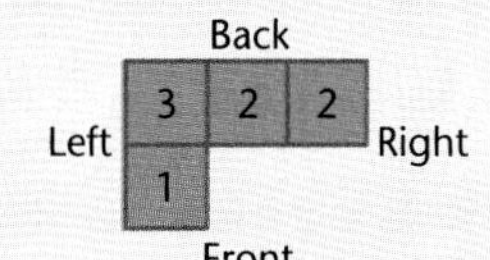

15. Draw a wide rectangular box (prism) in two-point perspective.

PERFORMANCE TASK

Given a conditional statement, how many possibilities are there for the truth values of the statement, its converse, its inverse, and its contrapositive? For example, one possibility is that the statement, its converse, its inverse, and its contrapositive are all true. What are the other possibilities? Show the other possibilities in a table like the one begun for you below. For each row in the table, give an example of a conditional statement with the specified truth values.

Conditional	Converse	Inverse	Contrapositive
True	True	True	True

Performance Task

Answer

Cond.	Conv.	Inv.	Cont.
T	F	F	T
F	T	T	F
F	F	F	F

Suggested Scoring Rubric

Level 4 Full Accomplishment

- Shows full understanding of the relationships between the statements. Table is complete and accurate.
- All example statements and their inverses, converses, and contrapositives have appropriate truth values.

Level 3 Substantial Accomplishment

- Shows essential understanding of the relationships between the statements. Table is complete and accurate.
- All example statements have appropriate truth values to match the conditional entry in the table, but some may be incorrect for other entries. (Example: Student gives a true conditional with a true converse as an example of a true conditional with a false converse.)

Level 2 Partial Accomplishment

- Shows partial understanding of the relationships between the statements. Table may be incomplete and inaccurate in some details.
- Some examples may have incorrect truth values.

Level 1 Little Accomplishment

- Shows little or no understanding of conditional statements or the relationships between the statements. Table is incomplete and many entries incorrect.
- Examples show that the student cannot distinguish true and false conditional statements.

ssessment Resources

uiz
apter 2 Assessment Form A
apter 2 Assessment Form B
apter 2 Alternative Assessment
id-Year Assessment
d-of-Year Assessment
WSMTest Chapter 2

Ongoing Assessment

Self-Assessment Chapter 2 Review and Self-Evaluation

Embedded Assessment Chapter 2 Performance Task

Test Chapter 2 Test

3

Chapter 3 Angles and Parallel Lines

Project A
Can You Read My Writing?
How were books duplicated before the days of movable type?

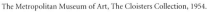

The Metropolitan Museum of Art, The Cloisters Collection, 1954.

Project B
Steer by the Stars
How did the early Polynesians find their way among the islands of the Pacific Ocean? Why was Columbus indebted to China?

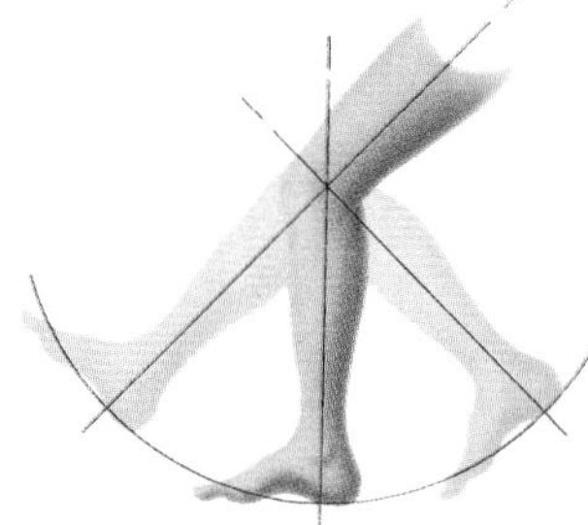

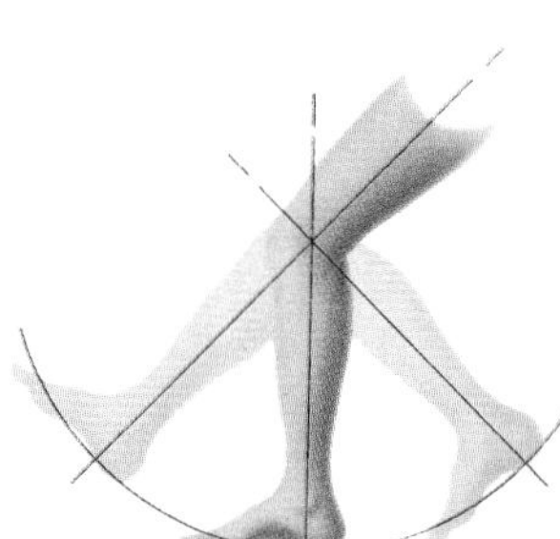

Project C
The Squeaky Hinge Gets the Oil
Why is arthritis painful? What is the normal range of motion for a knee or an elbow?

A

Chapter 3 Project A	Can You Read My Writing?

Create a Hand-Lettered Design
Learn the Gothic style and use it to make a greeting card or a certificate.
- Did you know that modern typography is based on early styles of handwriting?
- Don't you wonder whether you can master an ancient "hand"?
- How does this connect to Chapter 3? Gothic calligraphy is an application of **parallel lines.**

Expand Your Vocabulary

Gothic	Fraktur	descender	script
Textura	uncial	ascender	nib
parchment	illumination	hairline	serif

Project Guidelines

Investigate
- Look at reproductions of old writing in an art history book.
- Look at announcements, greeting cards, and advertisements for modern calligraphy examples.
- Borrow a calligraphy book from the library.

Set Your Direction
- Notice the variation in Gothic styles, especially of capital letters. Select the alphabet you want to learn.
- Will you make a greeting card or a certificate?

Make a Plan
- Set aside time for short practice sessions.
- Gather tools. You'll need:
  2.0 mm or 3.5 mm calligraphy pen
  straightedge protractor
  parchment or writing paper

Collect and Organize Your Information
- Study the size and angles of basic strokes. Learn how to draw your own guidelines.
- Practice until you can write sentences clearly, with parallel strokes, even spacing, and appropriate capital letter forms.

Carry Out Your Plan
- Decide on the text and layout for your design.
- Sketch the text onto guidelines on a practice sheet.
- Do a "rehearsal" in actual size.
- Execute your design and present it to a friend.

Look Back
- Why did different styles of writing develop?
- Does the content of a message influence the choice of a calligraphic style or vice versa?
- How much practice would it take to become a professional calligrapher?

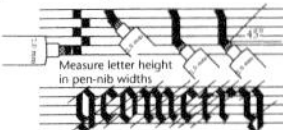

Focus on Geometry 13

C

Chapter 3 Project C	The Squeaky Hinge Gets the Oil

Measure the Range of a Human Joint
Devise an experiment to discover the mean range of motion of a joint.
- Did you know that early Chinese and Roman cultures used physical therapy to reduce pain in joints?
- Don't you wonder what range of motion is normal for a shoulder?
- How does this connect to Chapter 3? Range of motion in a joint is an **angle** measure

Expand Your Vocabulary

hinge joint	ball & socket joint	arthritis
pivot joint	range of motion	traction
saddle joint	physical therapy	protocol

The vertex of the angle made by a moving joint is *inside the joint*, not on the skin surface. You'll need to experiment to find the best way to measure the range of motion.

Project Guidelines

Investigate
- Visit a physical therapy or sports medicine clinic. Find out what joint measurements are often made.
- Read about joints in a biology or anatomy book.
- Consult a coach or a P.E. teacher about safe physical activities.

Set Your Direction
- Will you measure the range of your own joints or collect data about the average range of motion for a single joint in different people?

Make a Plan
- Make a calendar for each day's work. Check in with your group and with your teacher.
- Gather materials. You'll need:
  protractor ruler cardboard

Collect and Organize Your Information
- Classify the joints you study as hinge, pivot, saddle, or ball-and-socket.
- Make a large protractor from cardboard whose outer arch has about a 3-ft radius.
- Write a protocol for data collection
- Conduct your experiment and keep good records.
- ***Safety first:*** Never force a motion that causes discomfort. Let test subjects set their own limits.

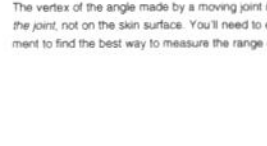

Carry Out Your Plan
- Display your data visually.
- Find the mean of your data set.
- Write a report that describes your experiment and gives your results.
- Tell how a limited range of motion affects daily activities and general health.

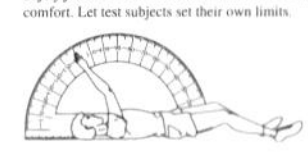

Look Back
- What factors can affect range-of-motion measurements? How can you correct for these factors?
- How is the *mean* range of motion that you found different from the *normal* range of motion?

Focus on Geometry 17

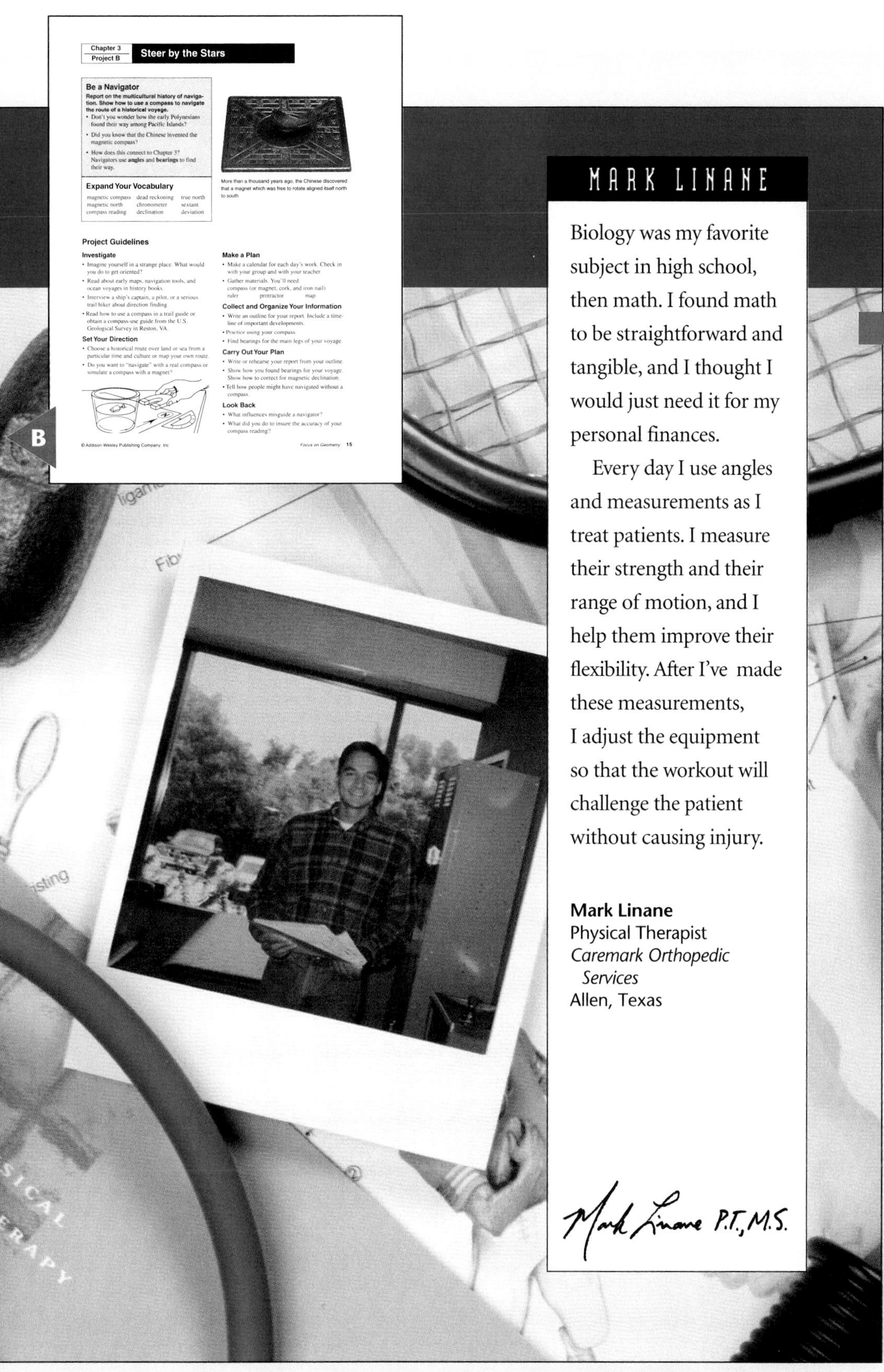

Chapter 3
Project B

Steer by the Stars

Be a Navigator

Report on the multicultural history of navigation. Show how to use a compass to navigate the route of a historical voyage.

- Don't you wonder how the early Polynesians found their way among Pacific Islands?
- Did you know that the Chinese invented the magnetic compass?
- How does this connect to Chapter 3? Navigators use **angles** and **bearings** to find their way.

More than a thousand years ago, the Chinese discovered that a magnet which was free to rotate aligned itself north to south.

Expand Your Vocabulary

magnetic compass	dead reckoning	true north
magnetic north	chronometer	sextant
compass reading	declination	deviation

Project Guidelines

Investigate

- Imagine yourself in a strange place. What would you do to get oriented?
- Read about early maps, navigation tools, and ocean voyages in history books.
- Interview a ship's captain, a pilot, or a serious trail hiker about direction finding.
- Read how to use a compass in a trail guide or obtain a compass-use guide from the U.S. Geological Survey in Reston, VA.

Set Your Direction

- Choose a historical route over land or sea from a particular time and culture or map your own route.
- Do you want to "navigate" with a real compass or simulate a compass with a magnet?

Make a Plan

- Make a calendar for each day's work. Check in with your group and with your teacher.
- Gather materials. You'll need:
  compass (or magnet, cork, and iron nail)
  ruler protractor map

Collect and Organize Your Information

- Write an outline for your report. Include a timeline of important developments.
- Practice using your compass.
- Find bearings for the main legs of your voyage.

Carry Out Your Plan

- Write or rehearse your report from your outline.
- Show how you found bearings for your voyage. Show how to correct for magnetic declination.
- Tell how people might have navigated without a compass.

Look Back

- What influences misguide a navigator?
- What did you do to insure the accuracy of your compass reading?

MARK LINANE

Biology was my favorite subject in high school, then math. I found math to be straightforward and tangible, and I thought I would just need it for my personal finances.

Every day I use angles and measurements as I treat patients. I measure their strength and their range of motion, and I help them improve their flexibility. After I've made these measurements, I adjust the equipment so that the workout will challenge the patient without causing injury.

Mark Linane
Physical Therapist
Caremark Orthopedic Services
Allen, Texas

Mark Linane P.T., M.S.

Biographical Note

Mark Linane graduated from Texas City High School, Texas City, TX. He took Algebra, Algebra II, Trigonometry, Calculus, and Computer Algebra.

Chapter 3

Overview

Angles and Parallel Lines

3-1 Angles and Navigation

Angles, bearings, and vectors are important for anyone who needs to describe positions. You will learn how to describe and measure angles, bearings, and vectors.

3-2 Rotations

Rotating objects are an important part of many mechanical devices. Gears and wheels are critical parts in machines, from salad spinners to cars. You will learn some basic facts about rotations, and examine figures for rotational symmetry.

3-3 Precise Thinking with Angles

In geometry and in everyday life, you must be careful to avoid making assumptions that are not based on evidence. Now you will learn what you may and may not assume from a figure. You will investigate different angle pairs and relationships.

3-4 Parallel Lines and Transversals

Examples of parallel lines are all around you, both in nature and in manufactured objects. You will explore parallel lines and the angles formed when the parallel lines are intersected by another line.

CHAPTERS

154

Chapter 3 Planning Guide

The following ancillaries are recommended for each course level. The additional resources, *Technology Lab Manual, Study Guide and Journal, Multilingual Handbook,* and *Assessment,* are recommended for all levels.

	Comprehensive Course	Core Course	Informal Course
3-1 Part A	▲	▲	▲
Alternative Lessons			▲
Laboratory Manuals	▲	▲	▲
Practice			▲
More Look Back		▲	▲
3-1 Part B	▲	▲	▲
Alternative Lessons			▲
Laboratory Manuals	▲	▲	▲
Practice			▲
More Look Ahead		▲	▲
3-1 Part C	▲	▲	▲
Alternative Lessons			▲
Laboratory Manuals	▲	▲	▲
Practice			▲
More Look Back		▲	▲
3-1 Part D	▲	▲	▲
Alternative Lessons			▲
Laboratory Manuals	▲	▲	▲
Practice			▲
More Look Ahead		▲	▲
3-1 Part E	▲	▲	▲
More Look Back		▲	▲
Quiz 3-1	▲	▲	▲
3-2 Part A	▲	▲	▲
Alternative Lessons			▲
Laboratory Manuals	▲	▲	▲
Practice			▲
More Look Back		▲	▲
3-2 Part B	▲	▲	▲
Alternative Lessons			▲
Laboratory Manuals	▲	▲	▲
Practice			▲
More Look Ahead		▲	▲
3-2 Part C	▲	▲	▲
More Look Back		▲	▲
Quiz 3-2	▲	▲	▲
3-3 Part A	▲	▲	▲
Alternative Lessons			▲
Laboratory Manuals	▲	▲	▲

	Comprehensive Course	Core Course	Informal Course
Practice			▲
More Look Back		▲	▲
3-3 Part B	▲	▲	▲
Alternative Lessons			▲
Laboratory Manuals	▲	▲	▲
Practice			▲
More Look Ahead		▲	▲
3-3 Part C	▲	▲	▲
Alternative Lessons			▲
Laboratory Manuals	▲	▲	▲
Practice			▲
More Look Back		▲	▲
3-3 Part D	▲	▲	▲
Alternative Lessons			▲
Laboratory Manuals	▲	▲	▲
Practice			▲
More Look Ahead		▲	▲
3-3 Part E	▲	▲	▲
More Look Back		▲	▲
Quiz 3-3	▲	▲	▲
3-4 Part A	▲	▲	▲
Alternative Lessons			▲
Laboratory Manuals	▲	▲	▲
Practice			▲
More Look Back		▲	▲
3-4 Part B	▲	▲	▲
Alternative Lessons			▲
Laboratory Manuals	▲	▲	▲
Practice			▲
More Look Ahead		▲	▲
3-4 Part C	▲	▲	▲
Alternative Lessons			▲
Laboratory Manuals	▲	▲	▲
Practice			▲
More Look Back		▲	▲
3-4 Part D	▲	▲	▲
More Look Back		▲	▲
Quiz 3-4	▲	▲	▲

BIBLIOGRAPHY

Reading for Teachers

Curriculum and Evaluation Standards for School Mathematics, Addenda Series: Geometry from Multiple Perspectives, Arthur F. Coxford, Jr. NCTM, 1991.

Teacher Resources

Paper Capers, Jack Botermans. ©1986 by Plenary Publications International (Europe) bv, De Meern, The Netherlands and ADM International bv, Amsterdam, The Netherlands. Published in the United States by Henry Holt & Company, Inc.

3-1

Angles and Navigation

SUPERLESSON AT A GLANCE

Superlesson Goal

Students will continue to develop their understanding of rays and angles and work with applications of related concepts, including bearings and vectors.

Management Guide

	Topic	Objectives	Key Terms	New Ideas	Materials
Part A	More About Rays and Angles	To classify different types of angles.	Interior and exterior of an angle, opposite rays, acute angle, obtuse angle, right angle	Classifying angles.	**Student** Protractor **Teacher** Globe, flashlight
Part B	Bearings	To use bearings to describe positions.	Bearing	Describing positions with bearings. Measuring bearings from 000 to 360.	**Student** Protractor
Part C	Vectors	To learn about vectors and vector notation, to use vectors to describe paths, and to explore the idea of a vector sum.	Vector, origin of a vector, endpoint of a vector, length of a vector, direction of a vector, equal vectors, vector sum	Vectors and vector notation. Describing paths with vectors. Representing a path as a vector sum.	
Part D	Translations	To explore translations, and to discover properties of figures that are and are not preserved by translations.	Translation, translation vector	Using vectors to describe translations. Properties of translations.	**Student** Ruler, protractor, graph paper
Part E	Making Connections	To use rays, angles, bearings, and vectors to describe a journey.	In Making Connections, students apply and synthesize key terms and new ideas.		

Pacing Chart (45-Minute Periods)

	Comprehensive Course	Core Course	Informal Course
Part A	1	1	1
Part B	1	2	2
Part C	1	2	2
Part D	1	1	1
Part E	1	1	1
TOTAL periods for Superlesson	5	7	7

NCTM Standards

Mathematics as Problem Solving

Mathematics as Communication

Mathematics as Reasoning

Mathematical Connections

Geometry from a Synthetic Perspective

Geometry from an Algebraic Perspective

Conceptual Underpinnings of Calculus

3-1 Angles and Navigation

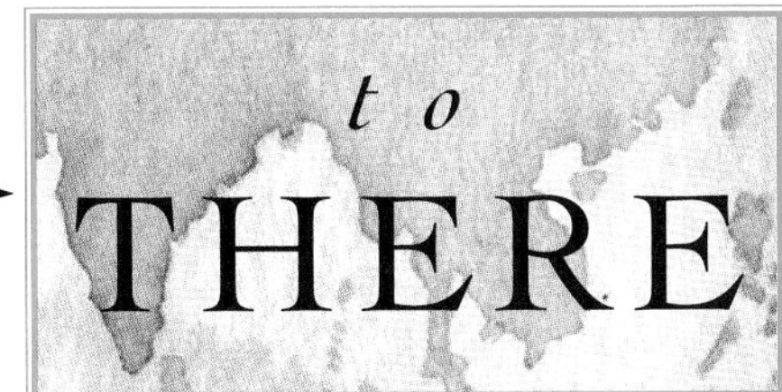

The Portuguese explorer Ferdinand Magellan began the first voyage around the world in 1519. Navigating by the stars with simple tools, Magellan and his crew sailed through one of the roughest stretches of the sea: just south of the tip of South America, where the Atlantic and Pacific oceans meet. Although Magellan died during the voyage, one of his five ships eventually circled the globe.

The following excerpt from *Magellan*, by Alan Villiers, appeared in *National Geographic*, June 1976.

As beautiful day followed beautiful day, and the Pacific trade winds wafted the small ships along, the same monotonous, empty horizon encircled what appeared to be the last three ships on earth. The crews, by then gaunt, wild-eyed men, fiercely hunted over their craft for something, anything to sustain life. As [a crew member] recorded, they not only pursued rats to make into stew, but they also cut down the leather chafing mats for food. This hard sunbaked stuff they soaked for days, then beat it as soft as possible with belaying pins, and boiled and boiled it. The soup tasted like old hides and provided little nourishment.

By chance of the route he took, [Magellan] sighted only two lonely islands of all the great South Pacific groups, and could not land on those. He saw none of the many isles where he might have found glorious fruits and fat fish. But had he sailed among them, he might have struck a hidden reef and been lost in mid-Pacific.

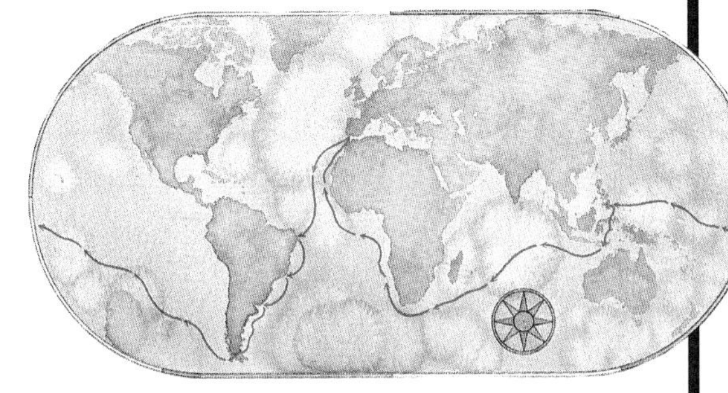

?

1. The line on the map shows Magellan's route. Describe this path in your own words.
2. Suppose you want to give directions to friends telling them how to travel from your school to your home. How would you describe a path for them to follow?
3. What are some ways that angles are used to describe directions?

Where Are We Now?

Students have been introduced to rays, angles, and angle measures.

Where Are We Going?

In 3-1, students will learn to classify angles. They will also use rays and angles as a basis for exploring bearings and vectors, and use different methods to describe directions and paths. The idea of vectors leads to an exploration of translations and translation vectors.

Angles and rays are important throughout the course. Translation is the second of four transformations that students will work with. Vectors provide a basis for a trigonometric analysis of forces and velocities in 7-3 Part C.

Possible Answers

1. Magellan's ships left Spain, sailed southwest across the Atlantic, went around the southern tip of South America, went northwest across the Pacific to the Philippines, west to India, southwest to the southern tip of Africa, and north back to Spain.
2. Answers will probably involve street names and turn directions.
3. Angles are sometimes used to describe a turn; for example, "Turn 180°."

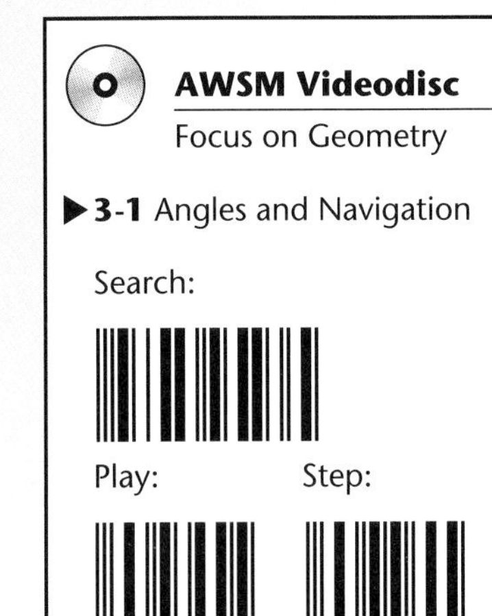

More About Magellan's Voyage

Ferdinand Magellan, a Portuguese explorer sailing under the Spanish flag, was the first European to find a route around the southern tip of the Americas. This narrow passage, between the South American continent and the islands of Tierra del Fuego, was named the Strait of Magellan. The voyage took over three years. Of the 280 sailors who began the voyage, only 18 returned to Spain.

Algebra	Functions	Discrete Math	Probability	Data/Statistics

Angles and Navigation

PART A At a Glance

Objective

To classify different types of angles.

Development

First, students see vocabulary associated with angles and learn to classify angles as obtuse, right, or acute.

In the **Explore,** students measure and classify angles superimposed on a globe. Then they see these angles' connection to time zones.

Suggested Materials

Student Protractor

Teacher Globe, flashlight

Key Terms

Interior and exterior of an angle, opposite rays, acute angle, obtuse angle, right angle

First Five Minutes

Transparency FFM 3-1A

Read page 156 and the definition of opposite rays at the top of page 157. Then do the **Try It** on page 157.

Motivate

Ask...

- Can you name three things in the classroom that can be modeled by angles. Are the angles obtuse, right, or acute?
- Is a pair of opposite rays an angle? Why or why not?

3-1 PART A More About Rays and Angles

← CONNECT → ***You've learned about angles before. Now you will see how to identify different types of angles.***

An accurate description of a route for a ship or an airplane is essential for these crafts to get to the right place at the right time. Navigators depend on rays and angles to plan a course and ensure that they stay on it.

The figure below shows some vocabulary associated with angles.

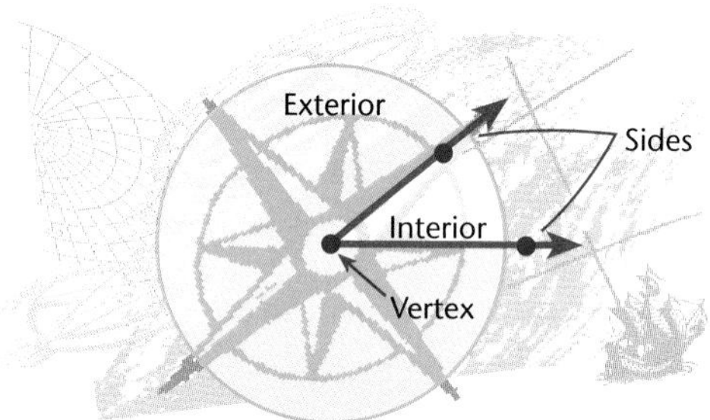

Angle measurement is important in describing directions. It is sometimes useful to talk about an angle's size in a more general way. We have already defined one of the terms below; you are probably familiar with all of them.

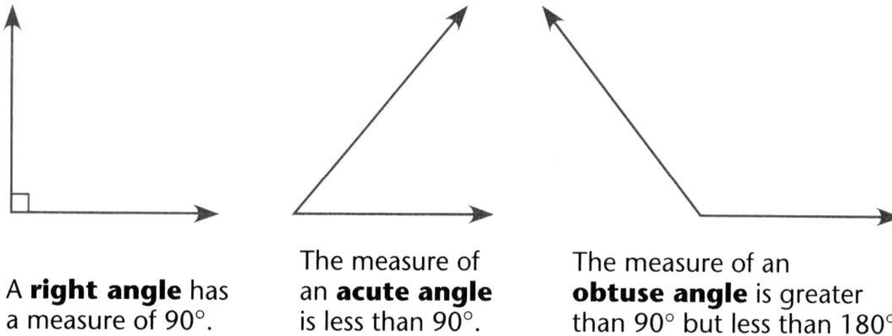

A **right angle** has a measure of 90°.

The measure of an **acute angle** is less than 90°.

The measure of an **obtuse angle** is greater than 90° but less than 180°.

These angle classifications are critical in the design and use of navigational tools. The navigational tool shown at the left is called a *sextant.*

As you know, angles are two noncollinear rays that have the same endpoint. There is also a special name for two collinear rays with the same endpoint that point in opposite directions.

Tips from Teachers

You may want to have a globe and flashlight available to model the *Explore.* By shining the light so that New York is on the light/shadow border (shadow to the west), you can simulate dawn. By turning the globe counterclockwise, you can show students why the sun rises later in San Francisco. Time zones make "noon" similar in both places.

DEFINITION

If point M is between X and Y on line $\overleftrightarrow{XY}$, the rays $\overrightarrow{MX}$ and $\overrightarrow{MY}$ are **opposite rays.**

TRY IT

a. Name a pair of opposite rays in the figure at the right. $\overrightarrow{EA}$ and $\overrightarrow{ED}$

b. Name all the acute angles, right angles, and obtuse angles in the figure.

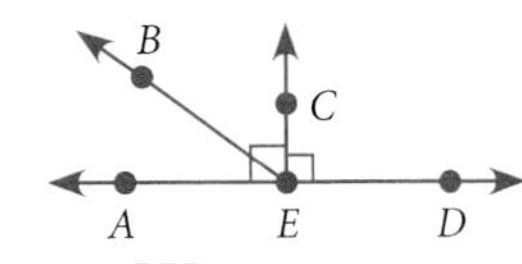

Acute: ∠AEB, ∠BEC; Right: ∠AEC, ∠CED; Obtuse: ∠BED

EXPLORE: AS THE EARTH TURNS

MATERIALS

Protractor

Reading and using maps are crucial skills in navigation. This map shows the earth viewed from the North Pole (P). The map also shows Tokyo (T), Rome (R), Lisbon (L), New York (N), and San Francisco (S).

1. Name all of the rays shown on the map.
2. Name a city that lies in the interior of $\angle SPN$. Name a city that lies in the exterior of $\angle SPN$.
3. Name all of the angles in the diagram. Classify each as acute, right, or obtuse. If necessary, use your protractor to measure the angles.
4. Use your protractor to find the measure of the angle through which the earth rotates from
   a. San Francisco to New York
   b. Lisbon to Rome
   c. Rome to Tokyo
   d. Lisbon to Tokyo
5. When viewed from above, as in the map, the earth rotates counterclockwise. It takes the earth approximately 24 hr to make one complete rotation (360°). Use a proportion and your angle measurements to find out how long it should take for the earth to rotate from San Francisco to New York. Compare your result with those of your classmates.
6. Does your result in **5** above fit what you know about time zones? Explain.

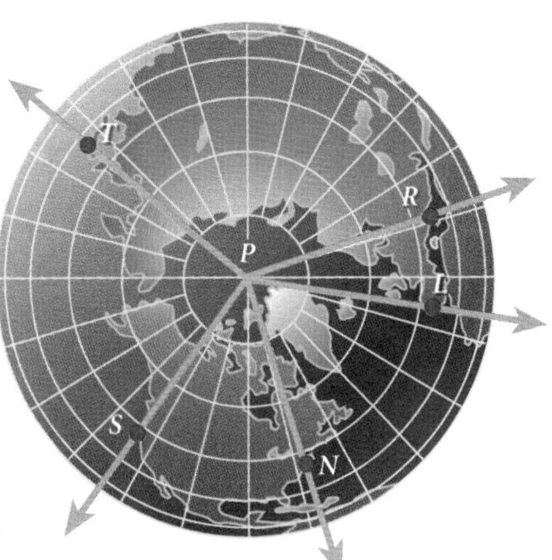

Student Resources

- Alternative Lessons 3-1A
- Laboratory Manual 3-1A
- Technology Lab Manual
- Practice 3-1A
- Study Guide and Journal 3-1A
- Guía de estudios y Diario 3-1A
- Multilingual Handbook
- More Look Back 3-1A
- SAT Preparation

Media Resources

- Transparency FFM 3-1A
- Transparency AE
- Teaching Transparency
- AWSMTest and practice software
- AWSM Videodisc

EXPLORE

As the Earth Turns

Recommended group size: 2

The Point

To classify angles on a globe and to see the connections of these angles to time zones.

Look and Listen...

- For students who are unfamiliar with time zones.
- For students who do not see larger angles formed by the smaller adjacent angles.

Ask...

- Are there only five angles in the figure?

For Groups That Finish Early

Locate your city on the map. When it is midnight in your city, where is it noon? If your city is C, noon is on the opposite ray to $\overrightarrow{PC}$.

Follow Up

Ask students to share their answers to Steps 3, 5, and 6.

Possible Answers

1. $\overrightarrow{PN}$, $\overrightarrow{PS}$, $\overrightarrow{PT}$, $\overrightarrow{PR}$, $\overrightarrow{PL}$
2. Interior: Chicago; exterior: Hong Kong.
3. $\angle SPN$ (acute), $\angle SPL$ (obtuse), $\angle SPR$ (obtuse), $\angle NPL$ (acute), $\angle NPR$ (obtuse), $\angle LPR$ (acute), $\angle LPT$ (obtuse), $\angle RPT$ (obtuse) $\angle TPS$ (obtuse), $\angle TPN$ (obtuse).
4. **a.** Approximately 49°.
   b. Approximately 22°.
   c. Approximately 127°.
   d. Approximately 149°.
5. About 3.3 hours. The earth rotates $\frac{360}{24} = 15°$ in an hour. $\angle SPN \approx 49°$; $\frac{49}{15} \approx 3.3$.
6. The result makes sense. There is a three-hour time difference between the cities.

3-1

Angles and Navigation

Journal

Explore Step 6 and **Reflect** 1 and 2 are suitable for journal entries.

REFLECT

Possible Answers

1. They are never opposite rays because they do not have the same endpoint.
2. Acute: measures less than 90°.

   Right: measures exactly 90°.

   Obtuse: measures more than 90°.

Part A Exercises

Exercise Notes

Core

14. Connects rays with graphs of linear inequalities on a number line.

17. Shows properties of angles of reflection.

More Math Reasoning

31. Involves the use of inductive reasoning.

32. An application of angles in air-traffic control.

Exercise Answers

Core

13. Possible answer:

A B C D

14. $x \geq 4$

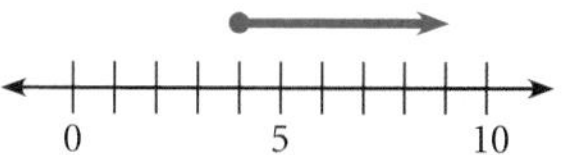

a. Yes; It has an endpoint and extends an infinite distance in one direction.

b. The point $x = 4$

15. a. 2; $\angle BJD$ and $\angle DJL$

b. Number of possible angles: 10
Probability: $\frac{2}{10} = 0.2$

16. 8;

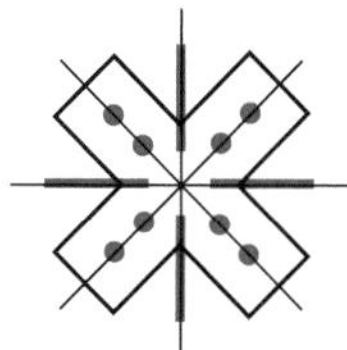

17. $m\angle DBC = 35°$

REFLECT

1. Are rays $\overrightarrow{AB}$ and $\overrightarrow{BA}$ sometimes, always, or never opposite rays? Explain why or why not.
2. Write a summary that describes acute, right, and obtuse angles. Provide drawings of each.

Exercises

CORE

P **Getting Started** **Name each of the following, using the figure below.**

1. two opposite rays $\overrightarrow{KJ}$, $\overrightarrow{KL}$
2. three different angles
   Possible answer: $\angle JKM$, $\angle MKN$, $\angle NKL$
3. two perpendicular rays $\overrightarrow{KM}$, $\overrightarrow{KN}$
4. a point in the interior of $\angle JKN$ M
5. two points in the exterior of $\angle MKN$ J, L
6. the sides of $\angle MKN$ $\overrightarrow{KM}$, $\overrightarrow{KN}$

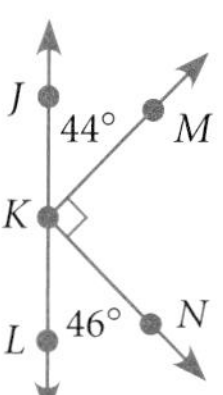

P **Determine whether each angle appears to be acute, obtuse, or right, and estimate its measure. Then use a protractor to measure the angle and check your estimate.**

7. Obtuse; 120°

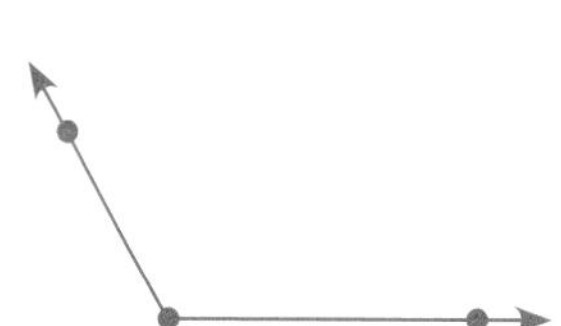

8. Right; 90°

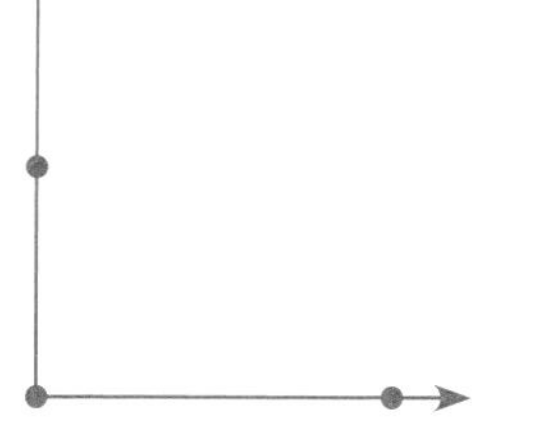

9. Acute; 50°

V **Write the word or phrase that correctly completes each statement.**

10. The measure of a(n) ___ angle is greater than 90°. Obtuse
11. The measure of a(n) ___ angle is less than 90°. Acute
12. The measure of a(n) ___ angle is exactly 90°. Right

P **13.** Draw one ray that could correctly be named $\overrightarrow{AB}$, $\overrightarrow{AC}$, or $\overrightarrow{AD}$.

Key

V Vocabulary
P Practice/Skills
R Review
MR Math Reasoning
PS Problem Solving
C Challenge

Tips from Teachers

Some students' protractors may be too large to measure angles in the text. So that they do not extend the sides of the angles by drawing in the text, you may want to suggest that they use folded pieces of notebook paper for this purpose.

14. Solve the inequality $3x + 7 \geq 19$, and graph the solution on a number line.
  a. Is the graph a ray? Why or why not?
  b. If the graph is a ray, what is the endpoint?

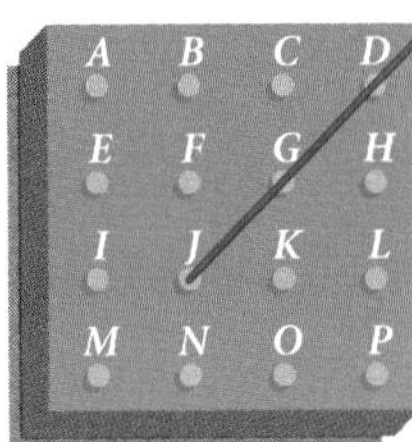

15. Use the points on the grid for each of the following.
  a. How many different angles can be drawn with vertex J, side $\overrightarrow{JD}$, another side containing a grid point, and exactly one grid point in the interior? Name the angles.
  b. What is the probability that a randomly drawn angle with vertex J, side $\overrightarrow{JD}$, and another side containing at least one grid point will have exactly one grid point in the interior?

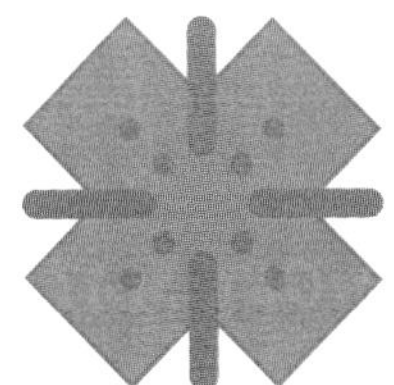

16. Copy the figure at the right. Then draw all lines of symmetry. How many right angles are formed by the lines of symmetry?

17. A Good Reflection When a beam of light reflects off a mirror, the angle of incidence is congruent to the angle of reflection. What can you say about $\angle DBC$ in the figure below?

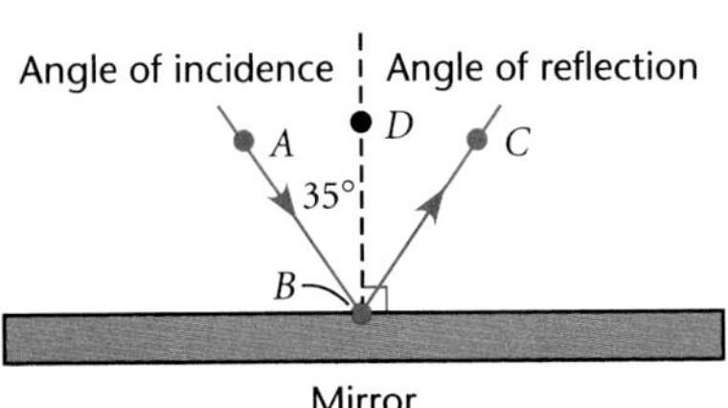

LOOK BACK

Give a counterexample for each conjecture. [1-2]

18. If two angles are acute, then they are congruent. Possible answer: $m\angle A = 35°$, $m\angle B = 25°$

19. No mammals live in the ocean. Possible answer: Whales

Determine whether each statement is true or false. If true, state one or more postulates that justify the statement. If false, state or sketch a counterexample. [2-2]

20. The line containing points G and H lies in exactly one plane.

21. Any four noncollinear points can be contained in one plane.

22. There is at least one point that is not on plane $\mathcal{P}$.

Look Back

20. F; Let G and H lie on the intersection of two planes.

21. F; Let three of the points determine a plane and let the fourth be on another plane.

22. T; Points Existence Postulate

More Practice

23. Possible answer: $\overrightarrow{YT}, \overrightarrow{YW}$

24. Possible answer: $\angle TYU$, $\angle UYV$, $\angle VYW$

25. Possible answer: $\overrightarrow{YT}, \overrightarrow{YV}$

26. $\overrightarrow{YT}, \overrightarrow{YX}$ **27.** U

28. W, X

29. Acute: $\angle TYU$, $\angle UYV$, $\angle WYX$;
Right: $\angle VYW$, $\angle TYV$;
Obtuse: $\angle XYT$, $\angle UYW$, $\angle VYX$

30. $-4 \leq y$; Endpoint is -4

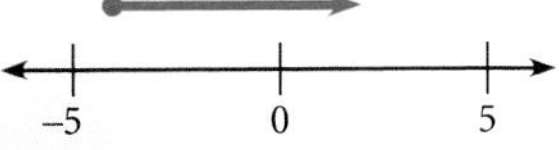

More Math Reasoning

31.

rays	angles
1	$3 = 1 + 2$
2	$6 = 1 + 2 + 3$
3	$10 = 1 + 2 + 3 + 4$
4	$15 = 1 + 2 + 3 + 4 + 5$
10	$66 = 1 + 2 + 3 + ... + 10 + 11$

32. a. Possible answer: 145°

b. About 4 seconds

Ongoing Assessment

Self-Assessment Exercises 1–17 odd

Embedded Assessment Explore Step 3; Reflect 1, 2; Exercises 14, 16

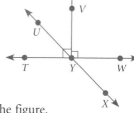

MORE PRACTICE

P **Name each of the following, using the figure at the right.**

23. two opposite rays

24. three different angles

25. two perpendicular rays

26. the sides of $\angle TYX$

27. a point in the interior of $\angle VYT$

28. two points in the exterior of $\angle VYT$

P **29.** Name all of the acute angles, right angles, and obtuse angles in the figure.

P **30.** Solve the inequality $4y \leq 7y + 12$, and graph the solution on a number line. Name the endpoint of the ray you have drawn.

MORE MATH REASONING

PS, MR **31.** How many different angles are formed when 10 distinct rays are drawn in the interior of an angle as shown at the right?

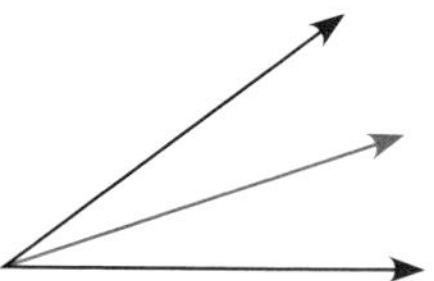

When one ray is drawn, three angles are formed.

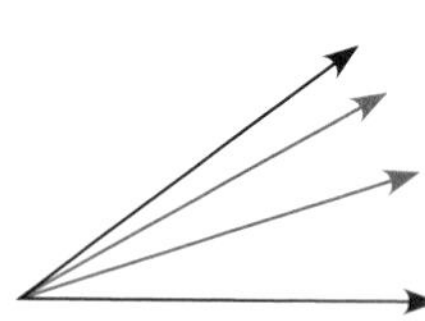

When two rays are drawn, six angles are formed.

Problem-Solving Tip

Make a table and look for a pattern to help predict the number of angles formed when 10 rays are drawn.

PS Careers **32. The Plane Truth** Modern navigation relies heavily on radar. For example, air traffic controllers depend on radar to track and guide airplanes. Radar screens show the position of every plane within 50 mi of the airport. Use the screen shown to answer the following.

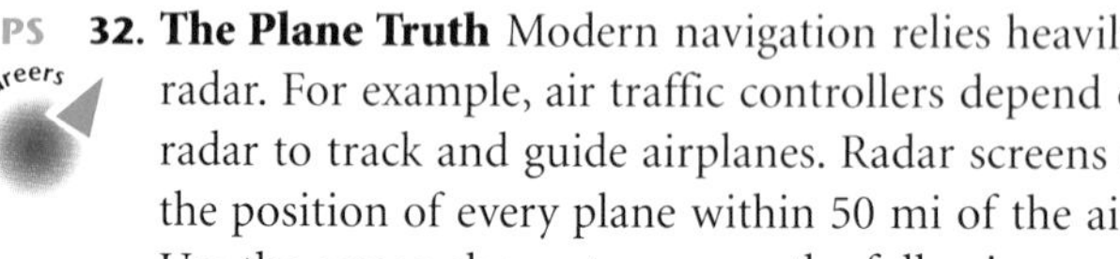

a. Estimate the number of degrees through which the radar must sweep to "see" the planes at points *A, B, C, D,* and *E.* (Assume that the radar sweep moves clockwise.)

b. Suppose it takes the radar 10 sec to make one full sweep of the screen. Approximately how long should it take to sweep past the 5 planes?

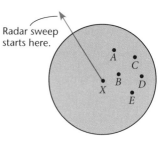

Radar sweep starts here.

Key

V Vocabulary
P Practice/Skills
R Review
MR Math Reasoning
PS Problem Solving
C Challenge

3-1 PART B Bearings

← CONNECT → *You know how to measure and classify angles. Bearings, which are related to angles, are used in navigation to describe positions. Now you will discover how to use bearings.*

Bearings help describe positions. To find the bearing of an object, first locate north (N), which is toward the top of most maps. Then turn clockwise from north to point in the direction of the object, and measure the angle of the turn. Since there are 360° in a full turn, three digits are usually used to describe bearing. For example, a bearing of 075 means a 75°-clockwise turn is needed to point in the direction of the object.

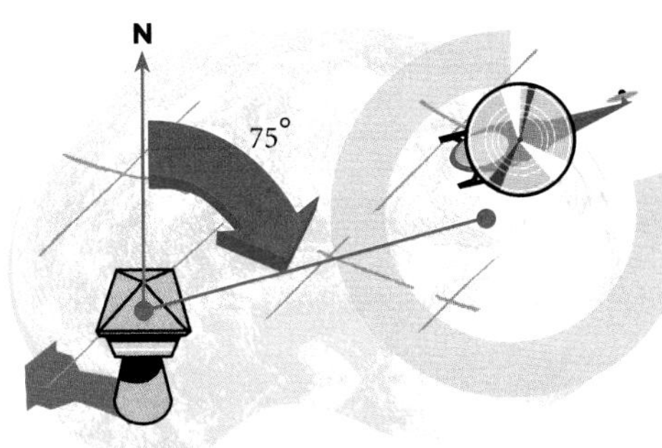

In the figure above, the bearing of the helicopter from the control tower is 075. In the following Explore, you will investigate bearings greater than 180.

EXPLORE: BEARING WITH IT

MATERIALS

Protractor

How should you measure the bearing of the airplane from the tower in the figure at the right? Describe a method for measuring bearings equal to or greater than 180. Compare your method with the ones your classmates develop. Then use a protractor to find the bearing of the airplane.

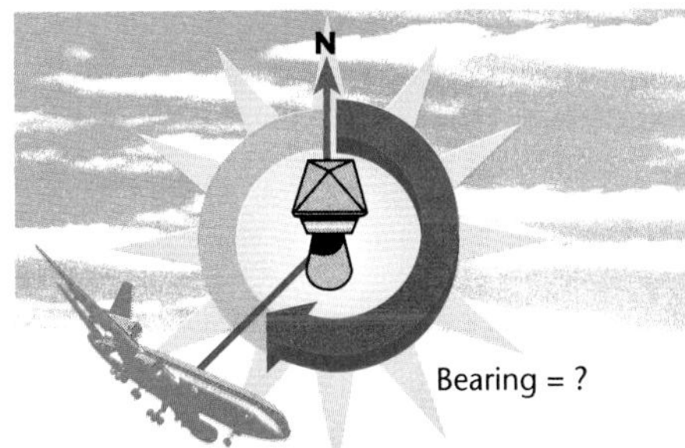

Student Resources

- Alternative Lessons 3-1B
- Laboratory Manual 3-1B
- Technology Lab Manual
- Practice 3-1B
- Study Guide and Journal 3-1B
- Guía de estudios y Diario 3-1B
- Multilingual Handbook
- More Look Ahead 3-1B
- SAT Preparation

Media Resources

- Transparency FFM 3-1B
- Transparency AE
- Teaching Transparency
- AWSMTest and practice software
- AWSM Videodisc

PART B At a Glance

Objective

To use bearings to describe positions.

Development

Students learn the definition of *bearing* and see how bearings are measured.

In the **Explore,** students devise a way to measure bearings greater than 180.

Suggested Materials

Student Protractor

Key Terms

Bearing

First Five Minutes

Transparency FFM 3-1B

Read the first two paragraphs on page 161. Then give the measure of each bearing below.

From due north:

A 27° clockwise turn is needed to point toward an object. 027

A right-angle clockwise turn is needed. 090

A half-turn is needed. 180

Motivate

Ask...

- Why do we need to know that bearings are measured from due north?

EXPLORE

Bearing with It

Recommended group size: 4

The Point

To devise a method for measuring bearings greater than 180.

Angles and Navigation

Look and Listen...

- For students who are measuring the bearing counterclockwise instead of clockwise.

Ask...

- Which direction should you turn?
- What is the measure of a whole turn?

For Groups That Finish Early

Find the bearings for the compass points N, NE, E, SE, S, SW, W, and NW.

Follow Up

Have students summarize their methods. They should agree on the "subtract from 360" method before proceeding.

Possible Answers

To measure bearings greater than 180, find the measure of the angle from object to observer to due north, and subtract from 360. The bearing of the plane is approximately 220.

Possible Answer

1. It must be between 090 and 270 (not including 090, 180, and 270).

Journal

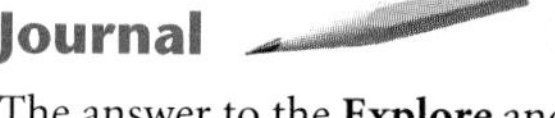

The answer to the **Explore** and **Reflect** 1 and 2 are suitable for journal entries.

REFLECT

Possible Answers

1. As he left Spain, Magellan's bearing was approximately 240°.
2. 360 represents a full-circle turn; 000 to 180 could be used if clockwise/counterclockwise directions were specified.

TRY IT

a. Use a protractor to measure each bearing in the figure below.
  - **i.** the bearing of the fire from the observation tower 000
  - **ii.** the bearing of the cabin from the observation tower 055
  - **iii.** the bearing of the boat from the cabin 120

b. Estimate the bearing of the observation tower from the cabin in the figure below. ≈ 235

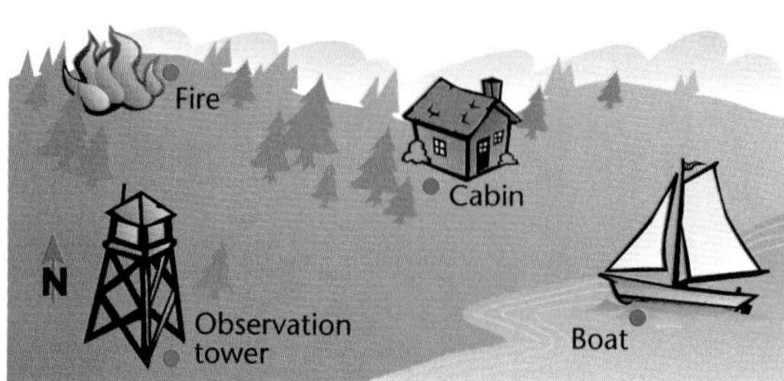

1. In the figure above, suppose you know that the angle formed by the fire, the observation tower (at the vertex), and a campsite is obtuse. What can you say about the campsite's bearing from the observation tower?

It is important to understand the differences and similarities between bearings and angles. For instance, angle measures are between 0° and 180°. However, since bearings measure rotations, we need a range of 000 to 360 to measure bearings. Although an angle cannot measure 200°, you can have a bearing of 200.

REFLECT

1. Look at the map of Magellan's route on page 155. How could you use bearings to describe his initial path as he left the coast of Spain? Give an estimate of Magellan's bearing at this stage of his journey.
2. Why do you think bearing measures are between 000 and 360 instead of between 000 and 180? Describe an alternate method for measuring bearings that only involves measures between 000 and 180.

Alert

Students may think that the direction of the plane in the *Explore* affects its bearing. You can remind them that the *position,* not the *direction,* of an object determines its current bearing from you. (The direction of an object, measured clockwise from north, is its *heading*.)

Exercises

CORE

1. **Getting Started** Follow the steps below to find the bearing of the helicopter from the landing pad.
   a. Copy the figure at the right. Sketch ray $\overrightarrow{LH}$ and a ray $\overrightarrow{LT}$ pointing due north.
   b. Use your protractor to measure the angle formed by the rays you drew in **1a.**
   c. If you placed your protractor on the right side of $\overrightarrow{LT}$ to measure the angle, the angle measure you found in **1b** is the bearing. If you placed the protractor on the left side of $\overrightarrow{LT}$, subtract the measure from 360° to find the bearing. Write your answer as a three-digit number, and remember that bearings are not expressed in degrees.

Use a protractor to measure each bearing.

2. the treasure from the ship ≈ 180
3. the giant squid from the treasure ≈ 055
4. the ship from the whirlpool ≈ 260
5. the whirlpool from the giant squid ≈ 025

A forest ranger spots plumes of smoke having each of the following bearings. Give the compass direction to the fire.

6. 090 East
7. 180 South
8. 270 West
9. 225 Southwest

10. Name all points on the grid with a bearing of 045 from point M. J, G, D
11. Name all points on the grid whose bearing from point C is greater than 180. A, B, E, F, I, J, M, N
12. **Where There's Smoke . . .** A forest fire has a bearing of 135 from point E (on the grid at the right) and 270 from point P. Where is the forest fire? O

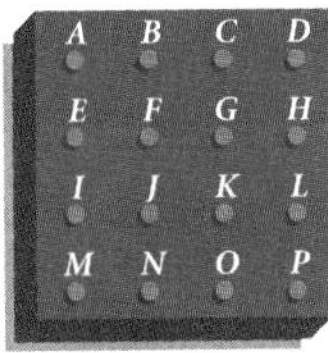

Complete each conditional statement.

13. If an object is at a bearing of 090 from you, then it is directly ___ of you. East
14. If an object is directly south of you, then its bearing from you is ___. 180
15. If an object is at a bearing of 180 from you, then it is directly ___ of you. South

Part B Exercises

Exercise Notes

Look Ahead

17. Looks ahead to vector sums in 3-1 Part C.

18. Looks ahead to linear pairs in 3-3 Part C.

More Math Reasoning

26. After discussing this exercise, you might want to present the following puzzle.

A person walked 1 mi south, 1 mi east, and 1 mi north. She found that she had returned to her starting point. She then spotted a bear. What color was the bear? **White (she is at the North Pole).**

Exercise Answers

Core

1. a.

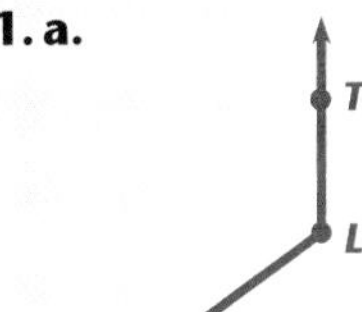

b. 125° **c.** 235

Look Ahead

17.

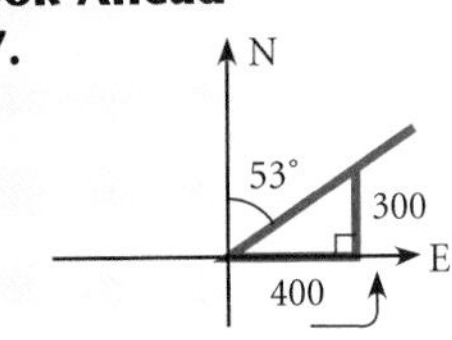

Fly 500 miles at bearing 053.

18. If N, Q, and R are collinear, then $m\angle PQR = 180° - 30° = 150°$.

More Math Reasoning

25. No; A one-point bearing gives only the ray the object is located on. You need to know how far the object is from you, or you need a second bearing. The object is at the intersection of the rays determined by the two bearings.

ey

Vocabulary
Practice/Skills
Review
MR Math Reasoning
PS Problem Solving
Challenge

Ongoing Assessment

Self-Assessment Exercises 1–15 odd

Embedded Assessment Reflect 2; Exercises 8, 10, 12, 16

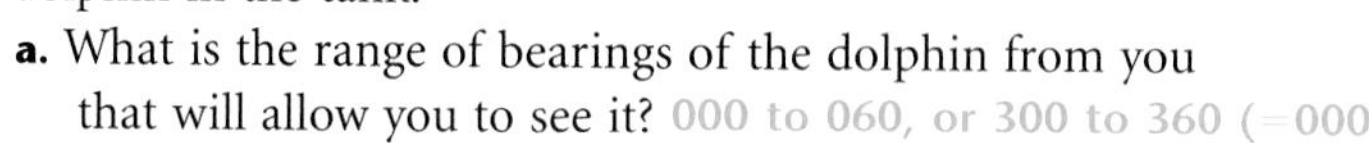

PS **16. Water, Water, Everywhere** A city aquarium has a tank that surrounds a circular viewing platform. If you face due north, you can see the part of the tank up to 60° left or right of due north. You especially want to see the baby dolphin in the tank.

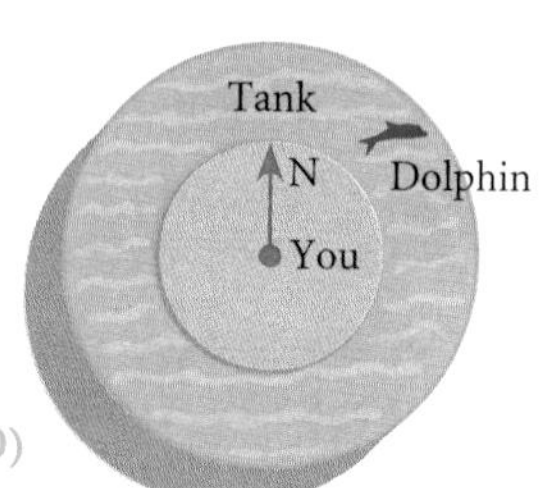

a. What is the range of bearings of the dolphin from you that will allow you to see it? 000 to 060, or 300 to 360 (= 000)

b. If the dolphin swims randomly around the tank, what is the probability that you will be able to see it at any particular time? $\frac{1}{3}$

LOOK AHEAD

P **17.** Suppose you take a trip in which you fly 400 mi due east and then 300 mi due north. Sketch this trip on graph paper. Then describe, as accurately as you can, how you could get to the same destination in one (straight) flight. Use any tools that you find helpful.

P **18.** What do you think is the measure of $\angle PQR$? Explain your reasoning.

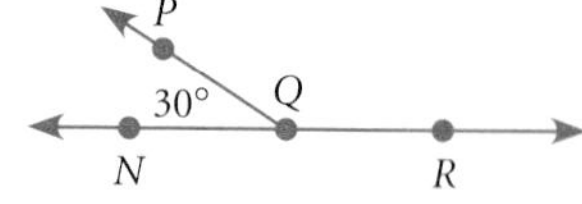

MORE PRACTICE

P **Use a protractor to find the bearing from the watchtower to each of the following.**

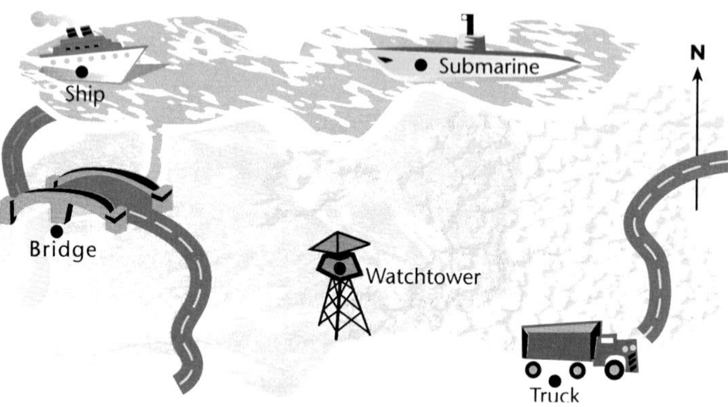

19. the ship ≈ 315 **20.** the submarine ≈ 025 **21.** the truck ≈ 115 **22.** the bridge ≈ 280

23. Measure the bearing from the submarine to the truck. ≈ 165

24. Measure the bearing from the bridge to the truck. ≈ 105

Key

V Vocabulary
P Practice/Skills
R Review
MR Math Reasoning
PS Problem Solving
C Challenge

MORE MATH REASONING

25. Is the bearing from one point enough to determine the exact position of an object? Why or why not? If not, what additional information do you need to determine the position?

26. Bear Mountain Suppose you are flying an airplane near a large mountain. You fly only in a straight-line path.

a. At noon, the bearing of the mountaintop (from you) is 000. Later, the bearing of the mountaintop is 180. In what direction are you flying? North

b. A while later, you find that the bearing of *everything* from you is 180. Where are you? North Pole

3-1 PART C Vectors

← CONNECT → ***You've seen that a ray can be thought of as a figure that begins at a point and travels in one direction forever. Vectors also begin at a point and have a direction, but they do not go on forever. Now you will learn some properties of vectors and discover how vector addition works.***

Vectors are useful in describing paths.

DEFINITION

The **vector** $\overrightarrow{AB}$ is a model of the straight-line path from point A to point B.

A Origin — B Endpoint

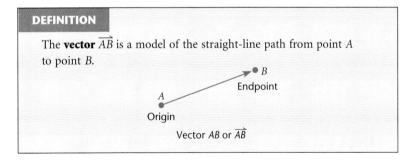

Vector AB or $\overrightarrow{AB}$

In other words, a vector is a "directed" line segment—we begin at point A and move in a straight line to point B. Point A is the *origin* and point B is the *endpoint* of vector $\overrightarrow{AB}$.

PART C At a Glance

Objective

To learn about vectors and vector notation, to use vectors to describe paths, and to explore the idea of a vector sum.

Development

Students are first introduced to vectors and vector notation. The definition of equal vectors follows.

In the **Explore,** students discover that a path of connected vectors is equivalent to a single vector. This idea is used to motivate vector addition.

Key Terms

Vector, origin of a vector, endpoint of a vector, length of a vector, direction of a vector, equal vectors, vector sum

First Five Minutes

Transparency FFM 3-1C

Read the beginning of 3-1 Part C on page 165. Then draw an example of each of the following:

$\overline{MN}$, $\overleftrightarrow{MN}$, $\overrightarrow{MN}$, MN.

Motivate

Ask...

- How can a vector be a mathematical model for a trip? When would it be difficult to use a vector to model a trip?

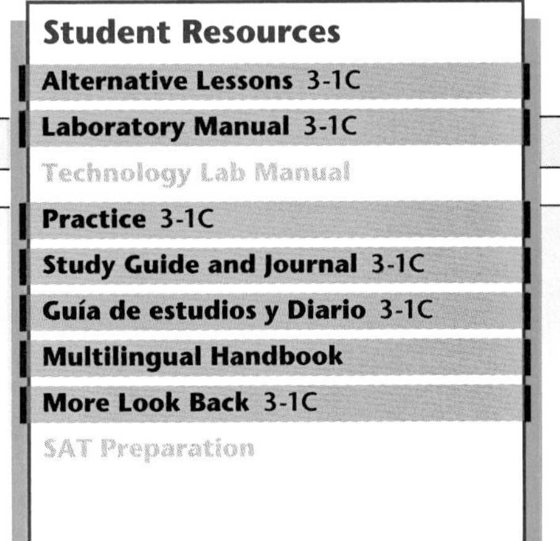

Student Resources

- Alternative Lessons 3-1C
- Laboratory Manual 3-1C
- Technology Lab Manual
- Practice 3-1C
- Study Guide and Journal 3-1C
- Guía de estudios y Diario 3-1C
- Multilingual Handbook
- More Look Back 3-1C
- SAT Preparation

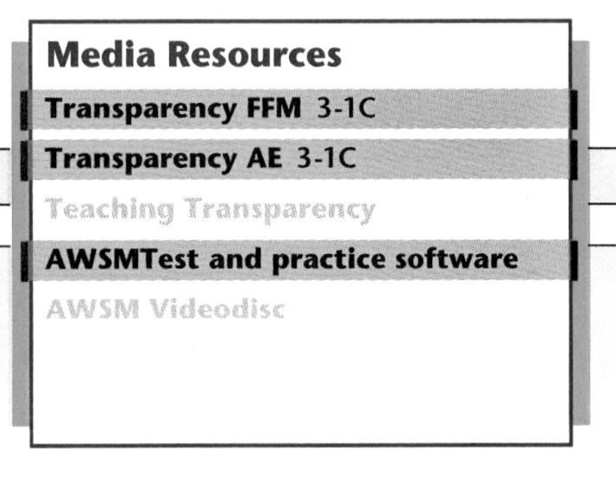

Media Resources

- Transparency FFM 3-1C
- Transparency AE 3-1C
- Teaching Transparency
- AWSMTest and practice software
- AWSM Videodisc

Angles and Navigation

ALTERNATE EXAMPLE

Draw vector $\overrightarrow{JK}$ with direction 104° and length 36 mm. Then draw a second vector, $\overrightarrow{RS}$, that is equal to $\overrightarrow{JK}$.

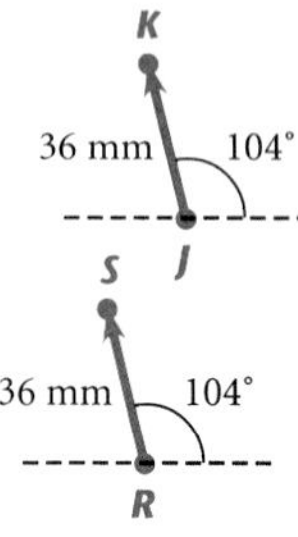

Introduces students to the idea that equal vectors must be parallel.

Possible Answer

1. They appear to be parallel.

Beware—a vector is not a ray! Unlike a ray, a vector has both a *direction* and a *length*. For example, the statement "From the school entrance, I went three blocks north" describes a vector. The distance is three blocks; the direction is north.

The **length** of $\overrightarrow{AB}$ is the distance between A and B. The **direction** of a vector is measured counterclockwise from the horizontal (the positive x-axis). Two different vectors are **equal vectors** if they have the same direction and the same length.

EXAMPLE

Draw vector $\overrightarrow{YZ}$ with direction 45° and length 27 mm. Then draw a second vector, $\overrightarrow{EF}$, that is equal to $\overrightarrow{YZ}$.

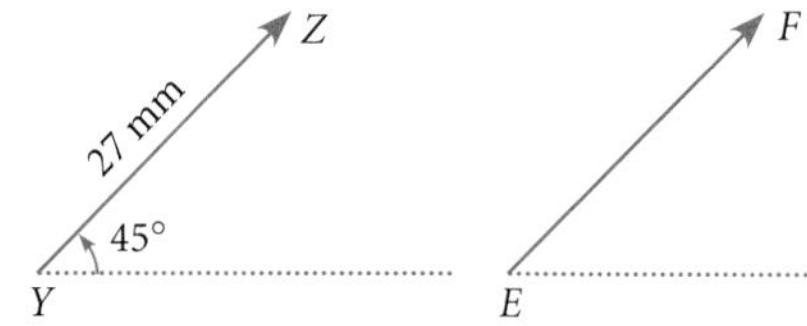

Draw a horizontal line. Then use a ruler and protractor to draw $\overrightarrow{YZ}$ with the correct length and direction. Repeat the process to draw $\overrightarrow{EF}$.

1. In the example above, vectors $\overrightarrow{YZ}$ and $\overrightarrow{EF}$ are equal. What else appears to be true about $\overrightarrow{YZ}$ and $\overrightarrow{EF}$?

TRY IT

a. Use your protractor and ruler to find the length and direction of $\overrightarrow{VW}$. Then draw vector $\overrightarrow{PQ}$, which is equal to $\overrightarrow{VW}$.
Length: 2.7 cm, Direction: 138°

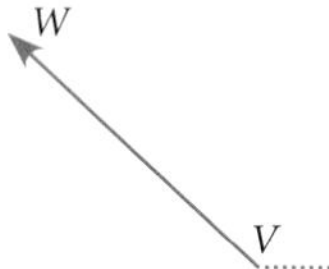

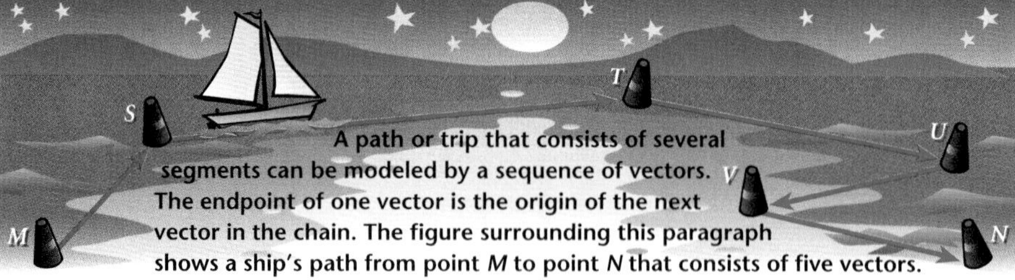

A path or trip that consists of several segments can be modeled by a sequence of vectors. The endpoint of one vector is the origin of the next vector in the chain. The figure surrounding this paragraph shows a ship's path from point M to point N that consists of five vectors.

Science Connection

Vectors are often used in physics to model forces and velocities. One of the most respected U.S. physicists is Dr. Luis Walter Alvarez. Born in 1911 in San Francisco, he earned a Ph.D. from the University of Chicago in 1936. A Nobel Prize winner in physics (1968), Dr. Alvarez has done work in particle physics, astrophysics, geophysics, optics, and air navigation.

EXPLORE: A MATH PATH

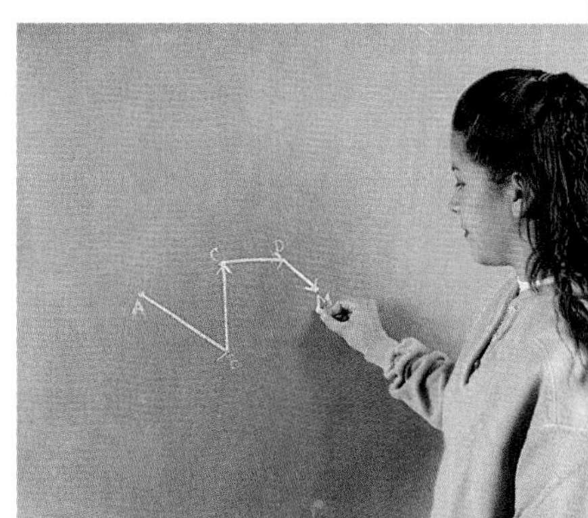

1. Draw two points, A and M, and a path from A to M consisting of any number of vectors. What is the *shortest* path from A to M?
2. A **vector sum,** $\overrightarrow{XY} + \overrightarrow{YZ}$, means the vector $\overrightarrow{XY}$ followed by the vector $\overrightarrow{YZ}$. (Note: Equal vector sums start and end in the same location, although the paths they use to get to that location may be different.) Write your trip in Step 1 as a vector sum. Then write a single vector that the sum is equal to. Your vector equation should be similar to the one shown.

   $\overrightarrow{AB} + \overrightarrow{BC} + \overrightarrow{CD} + \ldots = \_\_\_$
3. Make a conjecture about the vector sum $\overrightarrow{FG} + \overrightarrow{GH}$. Write your conjecture, and compare your result with those of your classmates.

An important property of vector addition is summarized below.

For vector sums, the following is true: $\overrightarrow{XY} + \overrightarrow{YZ} = \overrightarrow{XZ}$.

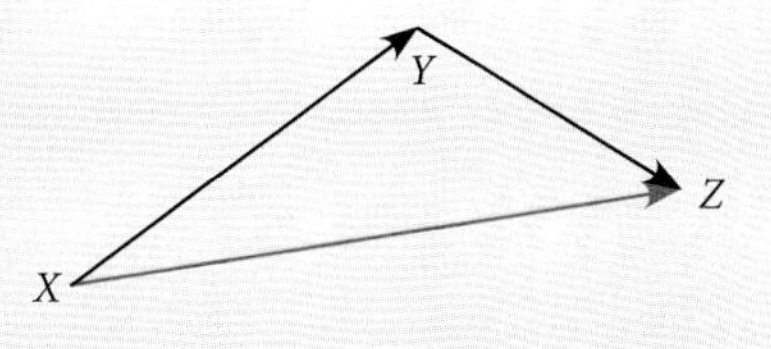

REFLECT

1. How is a vector similar to a ray? How is a vector different from a ray?
2. Consider a segment $\overline{AB}$. You can "direct" it as a vector in two ways, $\overrightarrow{AB}$ and $\overrightarrow{BA}$. If you take a trip that has the path $\overrightarrow{AB} + \overrightarrow{BA}$, where do you start the trip? Where do you end up? Can you describe the result with a single vector?
3. Write an explanation of the difference between how vectors are measured and how bearings are measured. Include symbols and drawings in your explanation.

Research Note

Students benefit academically when their teachers share ideas....[But] in some studies, as many as 45 percent of the teachers report *no* contact with each other during the workday....(U.S. Department of Education, *What Works: Research About Teaching and Learning,* p. 51. 1986.)

EXPLORE

A Math Path

Recommended group size: 4

The Point

To have students explore vector sums.

Look and Listen...

- For students who are not drawing a path so that the endpoint of one vector is the origin of the next.
- For students who do not see how to represent the entire path as one vector.

Ask...

- Where is the origin of the vector sum? Where is the endpoint?

For Groups That Finish Early

Sketch a vector sum, $\overrightarrow{AB} + \overrightarrow{BC} + \overrightarrow{CD} + \overrightarrow{DE}$, so that $\overrightarrow{AE}$ is 4 cm long and has a direction of 45°.

Follow Up

Ask students to make a statement about the sum of any two vectors if the endpoint of the first is the origin of the second.

Possible Answers

1. The shortest path is $\overrightarrow{AM}$.
3. $\overrightarrow{FG} + \overrightarrow{GH} = \overrightarrow{FH}$

Journal

Reflect 1 and 3 and **Exercise** 11 are suitable for journal entries.

REFLECT

Possible Answers

1. Both have a starting point and a direction. A vector has a length; a ray goes on forever.
2. You start and end at A. You can describe the trip as a zero vector.
3. Vectors have a length; bearings do not. The measure of a bearing's direction is taken clockwise from due north; the direction of a vector is measured counterclockwise from the positive x-axis.

TRY IT

Answer

a.

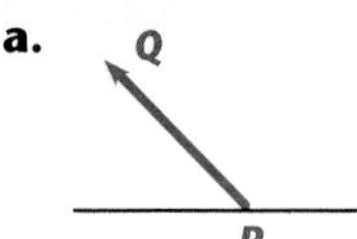

Angles and Navigation

Part C Exercises

Exercise Notes

Core

9. Similar to multiple-choice analogy items on standardized tests.

10. Places vectors on a coordinate plane. Students use the distance formula to find their lengths.

More Math Reasoning

25. Uses vectors to describe the edges of a cube.

Science Note: This method is used in materials science for identifying locations of the vertices of crystalline solids.

Exercise Answers

Core

1. $\overrightarrow{CD}$, 33 mm at 126°

2. $\overrightarrow{QR}$, 28 mm at 72°

3. $\overrightarrow{XY}$, 52 mm at 354°

4. The vectors have the same direction and are of equal length.

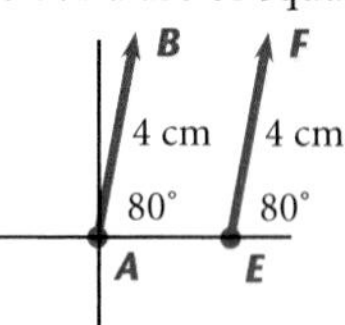

8. Possible answer:

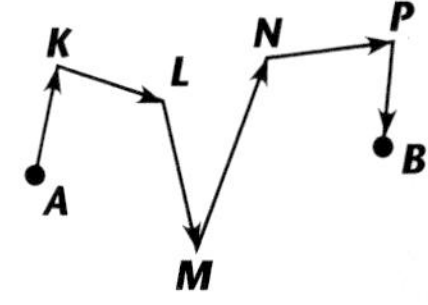

$\overrightarrow{AK} + \overrightarrow{KL} + \overrightarrow{LM} + \overrightarrow{MN} + \overrightarrow{NP} + \overrightarrow{PB} = \overrightarrow{AB}$

10. Lengths: $OH = 2\sqrt{5}$; $OF = 5$; $OI = \sqrt{29}$; $OG = 4$
Directions: $\overrightarrow{OH} \approx 153°$; $\overrightarrow{OF} \approx 53°$; $\overrightarrow{OI} \approx 292°$; $\overrightarrow{OG} = 90°$

11. a. 50 units at 210°

b. They have the same length but their directions differ by 180°. This is because opposite vectors are a 180° rotation of each other.

Exercises

CORE

P **Getting Started Write the name of each vector. Then use a ruler and protractor to find its direction and length.**

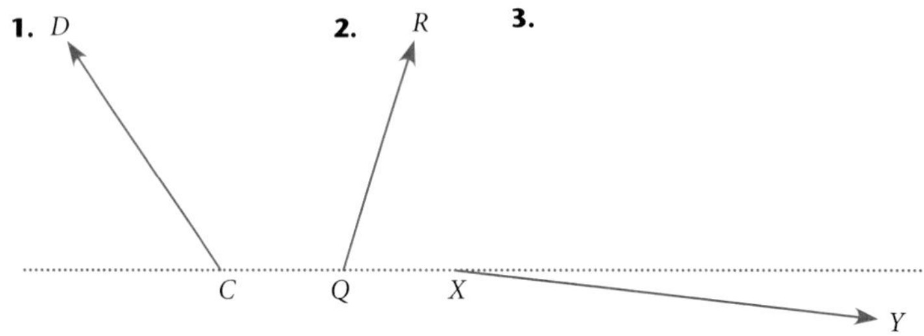

4. Draw vector $\overrightarrow{AB}$ with direction 80° and length 4 cm. Then draw a second vector, $\overrightarrow{EF}$, that is equal to $\overrightarrow{AB}$. Explain why the vectors are equal.

5. Estimate the length and direction of $\overrightarrow{KL}$. 2.7 cm, 247°

6. Use a ruler and protractor to find the length and direction of $\overrightarrow{JK}$. 3.6 cm, 21°

7. Write a vector equation for the sum of vectors $\overrightarrow{JK}$ and $\overrightarrow{KL}$. $\overrightarrow{JK} + \overrightarrow{KL} = \overrightarrow{JL}$

P **8.** Draw two points, *A* and *B*. Draw and label a vector path from *A* to *B* that consists of six vectors. Write a vector equation based on this path.

P **9.** Write the letter of the second pair that best matches the first pair. (b)

Vector: ray as (a) direction: length, (b) segment: line, (c) segment: length, (d) angle: interior

P, R **10.** Use the distance formula to find the length of each vector below. Then use a protractor to find the direction of each vector. Recall that the distance formula is
$D = \sqrt{(x_1 - x_2)^2 + (y_1 - y_2)^2}$.

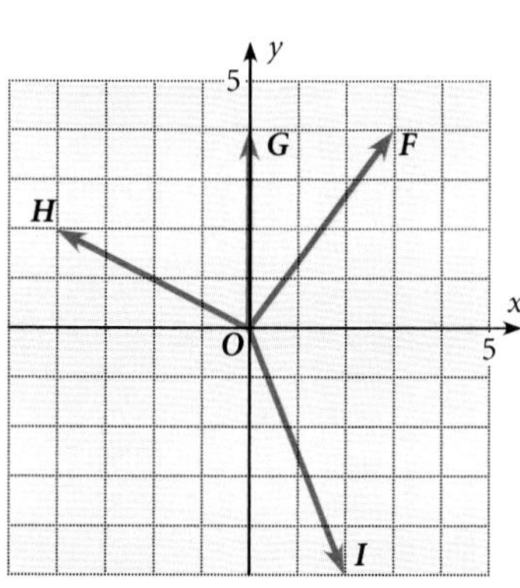

Key

V Vocabulary
P Practice/Skills
R Review
MR Math Reasoning
PS Problem Solving
C Challenge

11. a. In the figure, vector $\overrightarrow{ST}$ has direction 30° and length 50 units. What is the length and direction of the vector $\overrightarrow{TS}$?

b. Vectors like $\overrightarrow{ST}$ and $\overrightarrow{TS}$ are **opposite vectors.** Make a generalization about opposite vectors based on **11a.** Write a short paragraph justifying your idea.

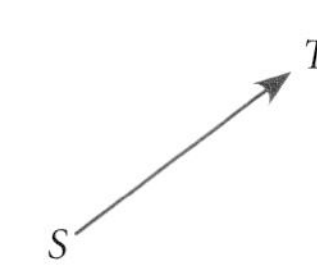

12. You can assign vectors to the sides of geometric figures. For example, in triangle ABC, use the sides $\overline{AB}$ and $\overline{BC}$ to form vectors $\overrightarrow{AB}$ and $\overrightarrow{BC}$. Draw the figure and label the vectors. What is another vector you can use to describe the path formed by the two vectors? (Hint: $\overrightarrow{AB} + \overrightarrow{BC} = ?$)

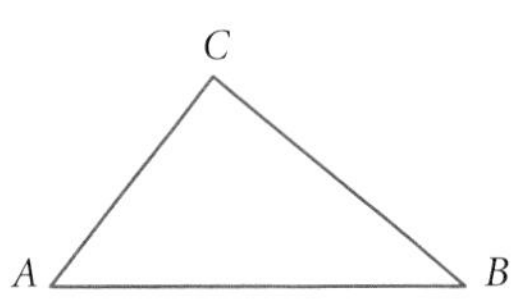

13. Smooth Sailing Use a ruler and protractor to draw a vector model of the following. Use 1 cm to represent 1 km.

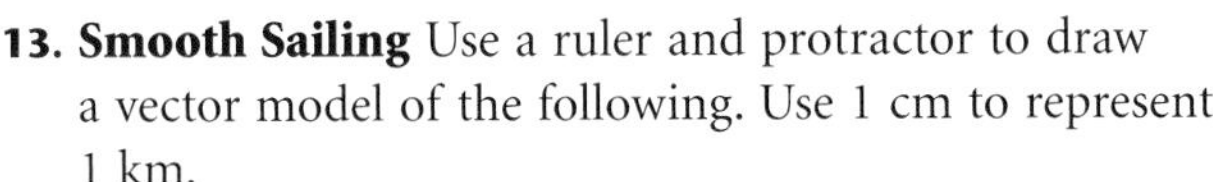

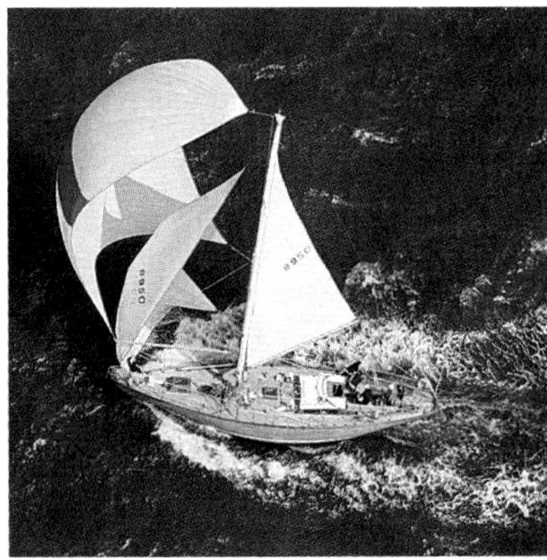

Akeli left the harbor at East Baytown (E) and sailed 3 km east to an island (I). She then sailed 6 km north to Rocky Point (R). She completed her trip by sailing 5 km northwest to Cape Thomas (T).

a. Write Akeli's trip as a sum of vectors.

b. What vector represents a trip in which Akeli sails directly from East Baytown to Cape Thomas?

c. Use your ruler to find the length of this vector. What is its direction?

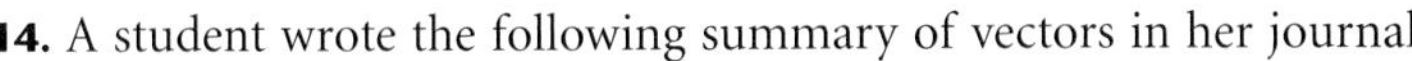

14. A student wrote the following summary of vectors in her journal.

A vector has direction and length. It doesn't matter where you draw it, as long as it has the right length and points in the right direction.

Evaluate the student's summary. Is there anything you would add or change? If so, write your own version of this journal entry.

LOOK BACK

15. Draw a four-sided figure with exactly one line of symmetry. Then draw a four-sided figure with two lines of symmetry. [1-4]

16. List the critical attributes of equal vectors. Then write a definition of equal vectors using "if and only if." [2-2]

12. $\overrightarrow{AC}$

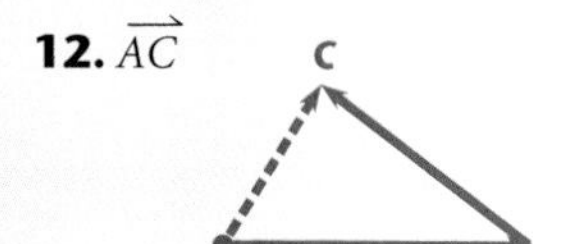

13.

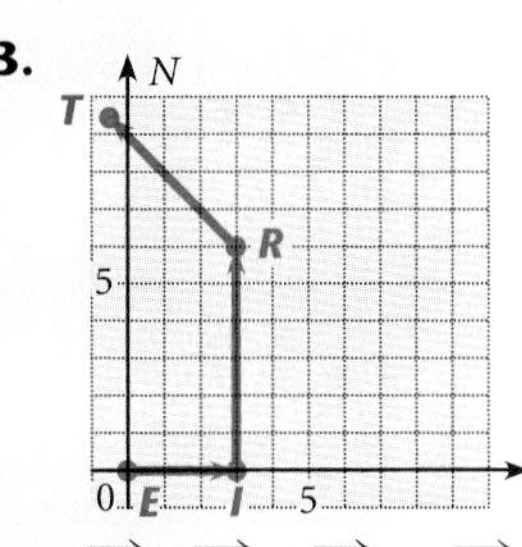

a. $\overrightarrow{EI} + \overrightarrow{IR} + \overrightarrow{RT}$ **b.** $\overrightarrow{ET}$

c. ≈ 9.5 km; ≈ 93°

14. A vector also has a specific origin and a specific endpoint.

Look Back

15. Possible answers:

16. Same length, same direction; Two vectors are equal if and only if they have the same length and the same direction.

More Practice

17. $\overrightarrow{RS}$: 2.3 cm at 82°

18. $\overrightarrow{TU}$: 4 cm at 20°

19. $\overrightarrow{WV}$: 4.2 cm at 198°

More Math Reasoning

23. a. $\overrightarrow{LN}$

b. No;

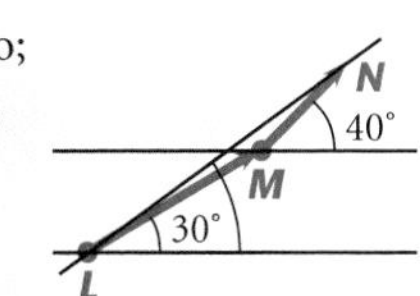

24. a. $\overrightarrow{AD}, \overrightarrow{AE}, \overrightarrow{AB}$

b. Possible answer: $\overrightarrow{DC}, \overrightarrow{DH}, \overrightarrow{CB}, \overrightarrow{CG}, \overrightarrow{BF}, \overrightarrow{EH}, \overrightarrow{EF}, \overrightarrow{HG}, \overrightarrow{FG}$

c. Possible answer: $\overrightarrow{EF}, \overrightarrow{HG}, \overrightarrow{AB}, \overrightarrow{DC}$; These again with the origins and endpoints reversed; and several other sets.

Ongoing Assessment

Self-Assessment Exercises 1, 2, 3, 5, 7, 9, 10, 12

Embedded Assessment Reflect 1 and 3; Exercises 4, 6, 8, 14

Angles and Navigation

25.

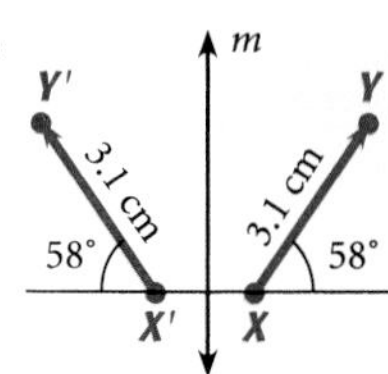

a. Same length

b. $\overrightarrow{XY}$ at 58°, $\overrightarrow{X'Y'}$ at 122°

c. The lengths of the pre-image and image vectors are the same. If the pre-image makes an angle of measurement *a* with the horizontal (*x*-axis) in the counterclockwise direction; then the image makes an angle of measurement *a* with the *x*-axis in the opposite direction.

26. F; The shortest distance between points *X* and *Z* is the length of vector $\overrightarrow{XZ}$, but the sum of the lengths of the vectors along alternate paths is larger than that whenever *X*, *Y*, and *Z* are noncollinear.

Algebra	Functions	Discrete Math	Probability	Data/Statistics

MORE PRACTICE

P **Write the name of each vector. Then use a ruler and protractor to find its direction and length.**

17. **18.** **19.**

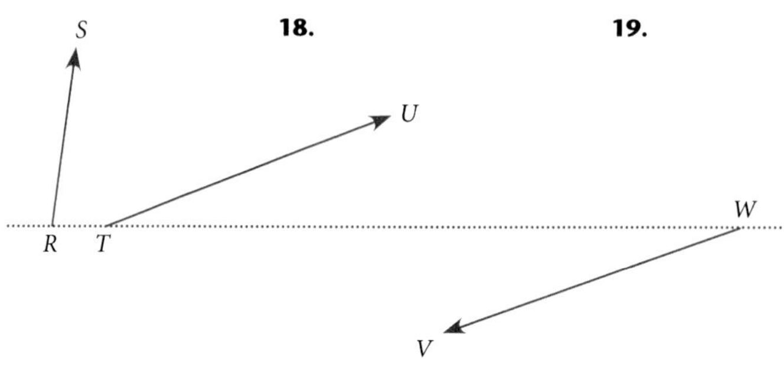

20. Estimate the length and direction of $\overrightarrow{LM}$. 2.2 cm at 198°

21. Use a ruler and protractor to find the length and direction of $\overrightarrow{MN}$. 3 cm at 57°

22. Write a vector equation for the sum of vectors $\overrightarrow{LM}$ and $\overrightarrow{MN}$. $\overrightarrow{LM} + \overrightarrow{MN} = \overrightarrow{LN}$

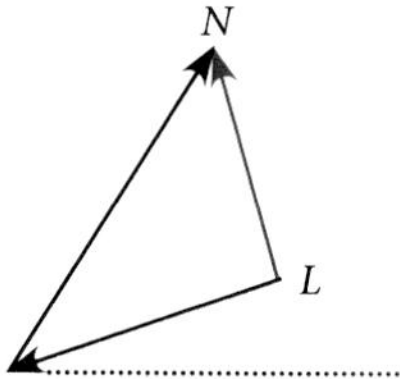

MORE MATH REASONING

MR **23.** Is it true that vector directions add when you add vectors? For example, suppose $\overrightarrow{LM}$ has direction 30° and $\overrightarrow{MN}$ has direction 40°.

a. What vector represents the sum of $\overrightarrow{LM}$ and $\overrightarrow{MN}$?

b. Does this vector have direction 70°? Draw a picture to support your answer.

MR **24. Vectors in Space** In this exercise you will see how to use vectors to describe the edges of a cube.

a. Using point *A* as the origin for your vectors, what three vectors describe the edges that intersect at point *A*?

b. What vectors describe the other edges of the cube?

c. Name a set of four equal vectors. Is there another set?

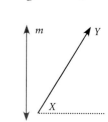

MR **25.** Copy the figure and draw the reflection image of $\overrightarrow{XY}$ across line *m*.

a. Use a ruler to find the length of $\overrightarrow{XY}$. How does the length of the image compare to the length of the pre-image?

b. Use a protractor to find the direction of $\overrightarrow{XY}$. How does the direction of the image compare to the direction of the pre-image?

c. State a generalization about the effect that a reflection across a vertical line has on a vector.

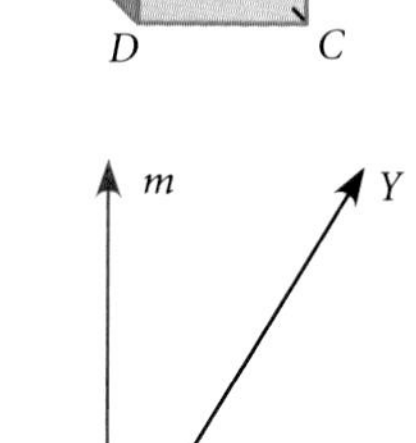

C **26.** Determine whether the statement "If $\overrightarrow{XY} + \overrightarrow{YZ} = \overrightarrow{XZ}$, then $XY + YZ = XZ$" is true or false. If true, explain why. If false, explain why, and sketch a counterexample.

Key

V Vocabulary
P Practice/Skills
R Review
MR Math Reasoning
PS Problem Solving
C Challenge

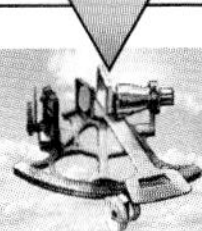

3-1 PART D Translations

← CONNECT → *You have already explored reflections. Now you will investigate a transformation that is based on sliding a figure—translation. Translations can be described with vectors.*

In 1936, the Dutch artist M. C. Escher studied the tile patterns in the Alhambra, a palace in Granada, Spain. One of the patterns is shown at the left. The Islamic artists who created these patterns (1248–1354 A.D.) used their knowledge of geometry to express their philosophy. Escher sketched many of the patterns in the Alhambra and later created similar patterns of his own.

Transformations are useful in creating patterns. In mathematics, you can move figures any distance and in any direction. This transformation—sliding a figure a certain distance in a given direction—is a translation.

DEFINITION

A **translation** is a transformation that moves all the points in a plane a fixed distance in a given direction.

An arrow can be used to show the direction of a translation. The length of the arrow is the distance the figure is to be moved. Here are some translations of the letter *F*.

Pre-image and its translation image

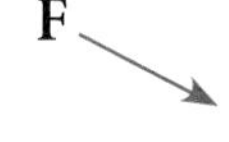

Pre-image and its translation image

Since vectors have a distance and a direction, they are often used to describe translations. The **translation vector** $\overrightarrow{GG'}$ illustrates the translation shown below. Its direction shows the direction of the translation, and its length gives the distance each point travels.

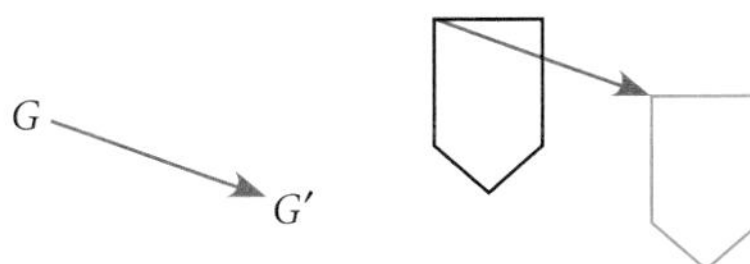

PART D At a Glance

Objective

To explore translations and to discover properties of figures that are and are not preserved by translations.

Development

Students learn the definitions of *translation* and *translation vector.*

In the **Explore,** they discover which properties of figures are and are not preserved by translation, and are introduced to notation for translation vectors.

Suggested Materials

Student Ruler, protractor, graph paper

Key Terms

Translation, translation vector

First Five Minutes

Transparency FFM 3-1D

List all the properties of a figure you can think of that are and are not preserved by reflection.

Motivate

Ask...

- Find an example of a tessellation in your classroom. Describe how you could generate this pattern by sliding a single "tile."

Student Resources

Alternative Lessons 3-1D
Laboratory Manual 3-1D
Technology Lab Manual
Practice 3-1D
Study Guide and Journal 3-1D
Guía de estudios y Diario 3-1D
Multilingual Handbook
More Look Ahead 3-1D
SAT Preparation

Media Resources

Transparency FFM 3-1D
Transparency AE 3-1D
Teaching Transparency
AWSMTest and practice software
AWSM Videodisc

Angles and Navigation

ALTERNATE EXAMPLES

Transparency AE 3-1D

EXPLORE

¡Tradúzcalo! (Translate It!)

Recommended group size: 4

The Point

To explore translations on a coordinate plane, investigate notation for translation vectors, and discover the properties of figures that are preserved by translations.

Look and Listen...

- For students who are confusing vector notation with coordinate notation.
- For students who are having difficulty expressing the general form of the image of (x, y) under this translation.

Ask...

- What is the difference in the x-coordinates of a pre-image point and its image? the y-coordinates?

For Groups That Finish Early

Given: $\overrightarrow{EF} = \langle a, b \rangle$.

1. What are the coordinates of the image of the point (x, y)?
   $(x + a, y + b)$
2. What is translation vector $\overrightarrow{FE}$?
   $\langle -a, -b \rangle$

Follow Up

Have students report their results for Step 1e, and ask them to summarize the properties of figures that are and are not preserved by vectors.

EXAMPLES

For the translation with vector $\overrightarrow{PQ}$, find the translation image of each of the following:

1. point L
2. segment $\overline{AB}$
3. segment $\overline{MN}$
4. triangle LMN
5. point B

M N L X Z Y P Q A B C D

1. point Y 2. segment $\overline{CD}$
3. segment $\overline{XZ}$ 4. triangle YXZ 5. point D

You can use a coordinate system to describe translations. In the following Explore, you will learn some notation for translation vectors and discover whether a translation changes the properties of a figure.

EXPLORE: ¡TRADÚZCALO! (TRANSLATE IT!)

MATERIALS

Ruler
Protractor
Graph paper

1. In the translation with vector $\overrightarrow{MN}$ shown at the right, N is the translation image of M.
   a. Copy the figure on graph paper.
   b. Find the coordinates of the image of point Q and the pre-image of P under this translation. Plot these points. Explain how you found the image and pre-image.
   c. Sketch the segments joining each pre-image to its image. What do you notice about these segments?
   d. Find the translation image of any point (x, y) under this translation.
   e. You can show the translation vector $\overrightarrow{MN}$ by writing $\langle 3, 6 \rangle$. Explain how this notation works.

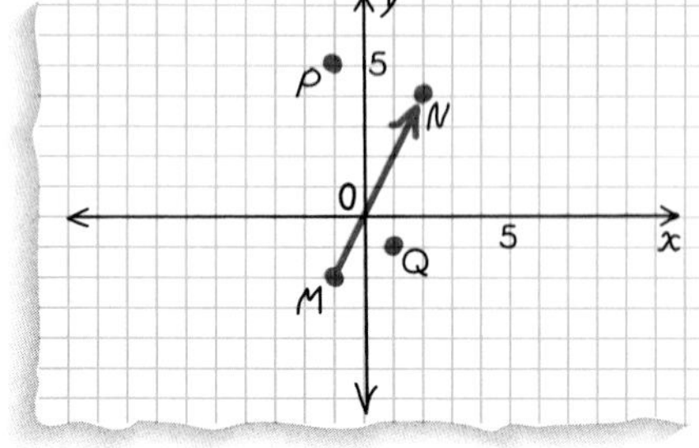

2. Draw a triangle on graph paper, and choose a translation. Then draw the image of the triangle. Use a ruler, protractor, or other measuring tool to determine which characteristics of the triangle (for example, side length or orientation) are or are not preserved by the translation. Make a conjecture about the properties of figures that translations do and do not preserve.

Diversity Issues

[S]ociologist Sanford Dornbusch...found that "female students in every ethnic group in San Francisco were more than three times as likely to give, 'I'm not good in math' as the basis for a poor grade as 'I'm good in math' as the basis for a good grade. This pattern was found in no other subject for females and in no subject for males." (John Ernest, "Is Mathematics a Sexist Discipline?" *Women and the Mathematical Mystique,* Lynn H. Fox, Linda Brody, and Dianne Tobin, eds., p. 62. © 1980 The Johns Hopkins University Press.)

TRY IT

a. The translation image of $A(4, -2)$ is $B(5, 2)$. Give the translation vector and the coordinates of the image of $C(-1, 4)$. $<1, 4>$; $C' = (0, 8)$

The properties of a figure that translations do and do not preserve are summarized below.

> Translations **change** only the location of a figure.
>
> Translations **preserve** any property that has to do with the size of a figure, including
> - the lengths of its sides
> - the measures of its angles
> - the area and perimeter of the figure
>
> Translations also **preserve** the orientation of the figure.

REFLECT

1. Describe how translations and reflections are similar. How are they different?
2. Explain why vectors are useful for describing translations.

Exercises

CORE

Getting Started For each set of figures below, identify the figure on the right that can be obtained from the figure on the left by one translation.

1. (c) 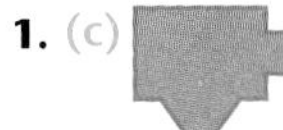 (a) 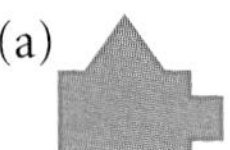  (b) 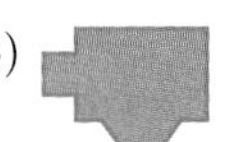 (c) 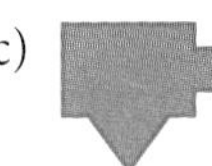 (d) 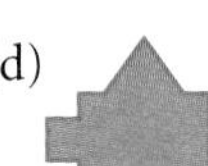

2. (b)  (a) 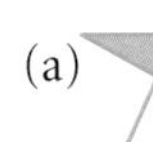 (b) 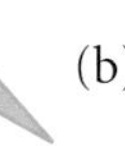  (c) 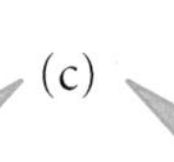 (d) 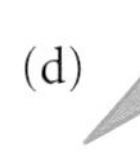

3. (d) 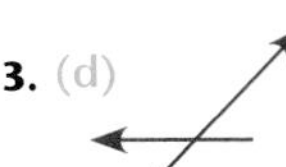 (a) 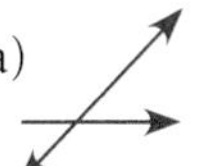 (b) 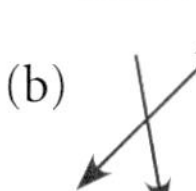 (c) 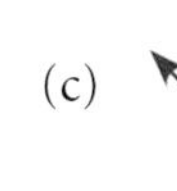 (d) 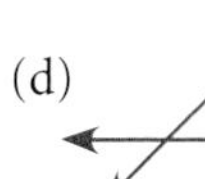

Possible Answers

1.b. Image of $Q(4, 6)$; pre-image of $P(-4, -1)$.

c. They are parallel.

d. $(x + 3, y + 6)$

e. The first number indicates the number of units shifted in the x-direction; the second represents the number in the y-direction.

2. Translations preserve all properties of a figure (except for its position).

Journal 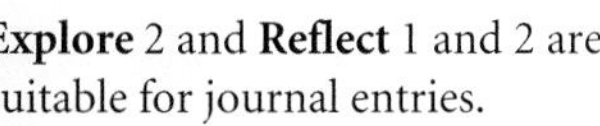

Explore 2 and **Reflect** 1 and 2 are suitable for journal entries.

REFLECT

Possible Answers

1. Both are transformations; both preserve sizes of figures. Reflections reverse orientation; translations preserve it.

2. A translation slides a figure a given distance in a given direction. Since vectors have direction and length, they can describe translations.

Part D Exercises

Exercise Notes

Core

20. Introduces the idea that parallel lines can be thought of as translations of one another. In 10-1 Part C, students will see how to use translations and other transformations to describe how changes in a function's equation affect its graph.

21. Previews glide reflections, an important transformation in Chapter 10.

Ongoing Assessment

Vocabulary
Practice/Skills
Review
Math Reasoning
Problem Solving
Challenge

Self-Assessment Exercises 1–19 odd

Embedded Assessment Try It a; Reflect 2; Exercises 6, 12, 20

3-1

Angles and Navigation

Look Ahead

22–24. These exercises review skills needed in 3-2 Part A to draw rotation images.

25. Prepares students for angles of rotation in 3-2 Part A.

More Math Reasoning

38. Shows a composition of two translations. Composition of transformations is a main theme in Chapter 10.

Exercise Answers

Core

6.

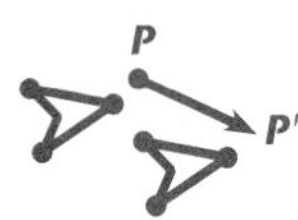

19. The segment with endpoints (0, 6) and (4, 2)

20. $y = \frac{3}{2}x - \frac{17}{2}$

21. Check students' art.

Look Ahead

22. Possible answer:

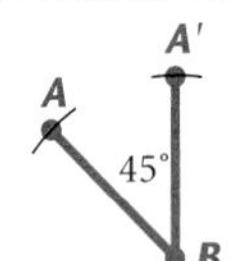

23. Possible answer:

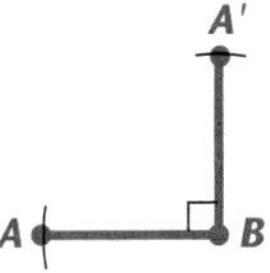

24. Possible answer:

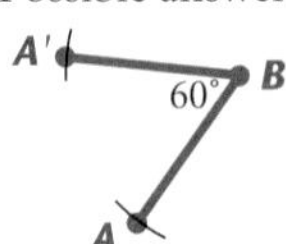

25. 180°, 360°, 90°

More Math Reasoning

37. R': $(c + (t - a), d + (u - b))$

P **State whether each pair of figures below illustrates a reflection or a translation.**

4. Translation

5. Reflection

P **6.** Copy the figure and the translation vector $\overrightarrow{PP'}$ onto your paper. Sketch the translation image of the figure.

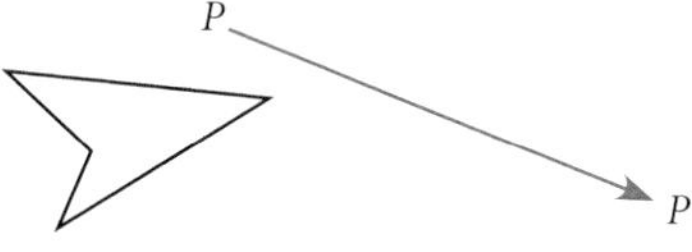

P **For the translation with vector $\overrightarrow{UV}$, find the translation image of each of the following.**

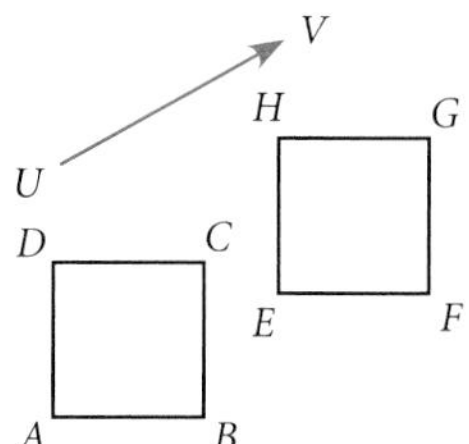

7. point B F

8. segment $\overline{DC}$ HG

9. point C G

10. square $ABCD$ Square EFGH

P **11.** The translation image of $M(-4, 3)$ is $N(-5, -4)$. Give the translation vector and the coordinates of the image of $P(4, 5)$. <−1, −7>; P′: (3, −2)

P **Suppose the points on the graph are translated using translation vector $\overrightarrow{WW'}$. Find the coordinates of the image of each point.**

12. point E E′ = (4, 7)

13. point F F′ = (4, 0)

14. point G G′ = (0, −1)

15. point H H′ = (−2, 6)

16. the point (3, 1) (5, 4)

17. the point (4, −2) (6, 1)

18. the point (x, y) $(x + 2, y + 3)$

19. the segment with endpoints (−2, 3) and (2, −1)

P **20.** Suppose the line $y = \frac{3}{2}x - 3$ undergoes translation <3, −1>. What is the equation of its image?

P **21.** When you create a pattern by doing a translation followed by a reflection, followed by a translation, followed by a reflection, and so on, you have made a **glide-reflection** pattern. Many artists have used glide reflections to create patterns. Footprints are an example of a glide-reflection pattern.

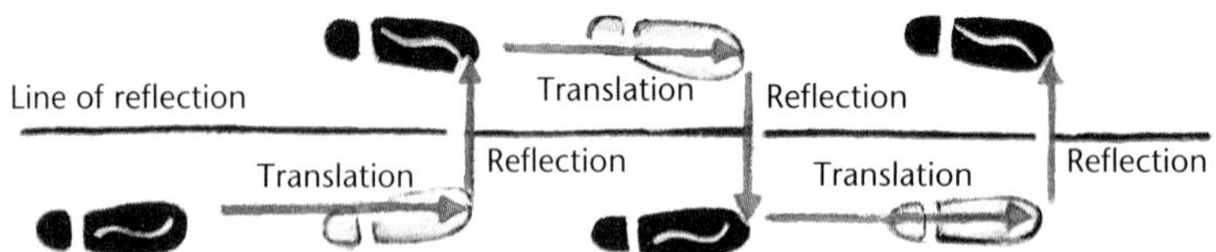

174 3-1 • ANGLES AND NAVIGATION

Key

V Vocabulary
P Practice/Skills
R Review
MR Math Reasoning
PS Problem Solving
C Challenge

Copy the two figures at the right onto graph paper. As explained at the bottom of page 174, each figure is the glide-reflection image of the other. Sketch three more glide-reflection figures.

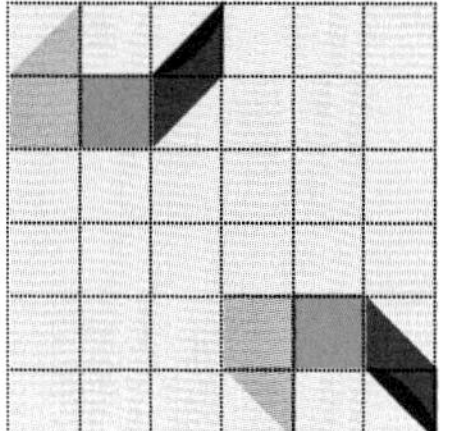

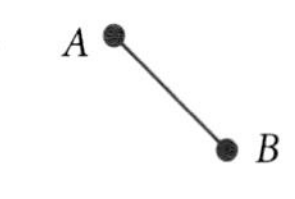

LOOK AHEAD

Using your protractor and a compass, draw angles ∠*ABA*′ with the given measures, so that *AB* = *BA*′.

22.

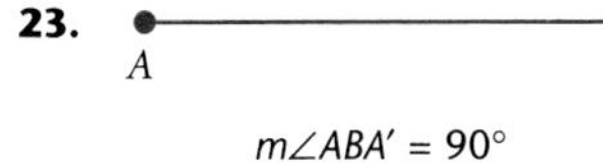

$m\angle ABA' = 45°$

23. $m\angle ABA' = 90°$

24.

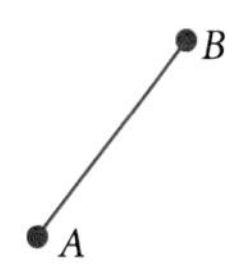

$m\angle ABA' = 60°$

25. If you spin so that you end up facing the opposite direction ($\frac{1}{2}$ of a complete turn), what would you say is the measure of your rotation? What if you make a full turn? $\frac{1}{4}$ of a turn?

MORE PRACTICE

For the translation with vector $\overrightarrow{XY}$, find the translation image of each of the following.

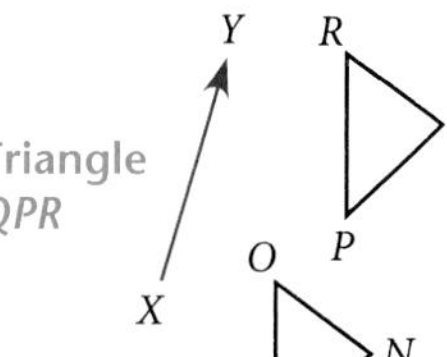

26. point *O* R

27. segment $\overline{MN}$ PQ

28. triangle *NMO* Triangle QPR

29. The translation image of *F*(1, −3) is *G*(3, 2). Give the translation vector and the coordinates of the image of *H*(−3, 0).
<2, 5>; *H*′: (−1, 5)

Suppose the points on the graph are translated using translation vector $\overrightarrow{AA'}$. Find the coordinates of the image of each point.

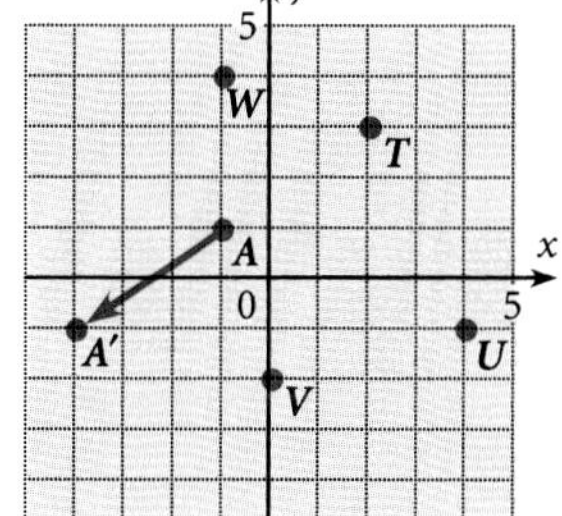

30. point *T*
T′: (−1, 1)

31. point *U*
U′: (1, −3)

32. point *V*
V′: (−3, −4)

33. point *W*
W′: (−4, 2)

34. the point (0, −5)
(−3, −7)

35. the point (*x*, *y*)
(*x* − 3, *y* − 2)

36. the segment with endpoints (1, 0) and (4, −3)

Segment with endpoints (−2, −2) and (1, −5)

38. a. Vertices: (6, 2), (10, −1), (14, 3)

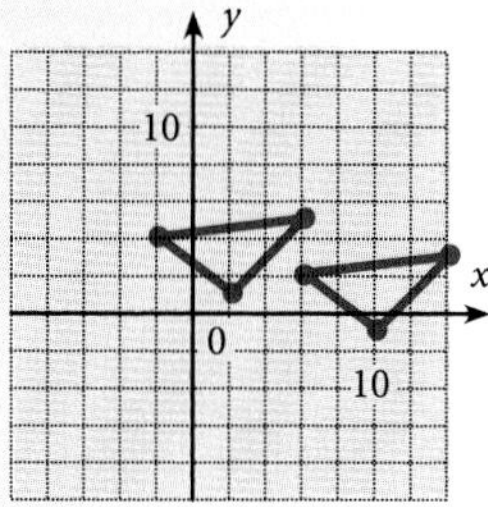

b. <8, −2>

c. A translation with vector $\overrightarrow{AC}$

d. Vector addition; Translating the coordinates of each point is like treating the translation vectors as vectors to be added. Makes sense because translation vectors are vectors.

Research Note

[E]ight studies found that homework involving preparation for new material or practice of old material led to higher scores on tests than homework that dealt solely with the content of the present day's lesson. (Harris Cooper, *Homework,* p. 122. © 1989 Longman.)

Angles and Navigation

PART E At a Glance

Objective

To use rays, angles, bearings, and vectors to describe a journey.

Development

In the **Explore,** students describe Magellan's voyage in different ways: using angles and rays, using bearings, and using vectors and translations.

First Five Minutes

Transparency FFM 3-1E

In your own words, describe how to measure bearings and vectors.

EXPLORE

Travels with Magellan

Recommended group size: 4

The Point

To use angles, rays, bearings, and vectors to describe Magellan's voyage, and to compare their usefulness in this context.

Look and Listen...

- For students who are trying to be too precise in their description of the voyage.

Ask...

- Can you explain *how* you could use (angles and rays, bearings, vectors and translations) to describe the voyage?

For Groups That Finish Early

Describe a different round-the-world voyage of your own design using whichever of the methods seems best.

Follow Up

Ask students to identify the method(s) that seemed most suitable for describing voyages and to defend their choice.

MORE MATH REASONING

MR **37.** On a coordinate plane, $\overrightarrow{PQ}$ is a translation vector, where P is (a, b), and Q is (t, u). What are the coordinates of the translation image of point $R(c, d)$?

MR, C **38. Summing It Up** Copy the figure below on graph paper.

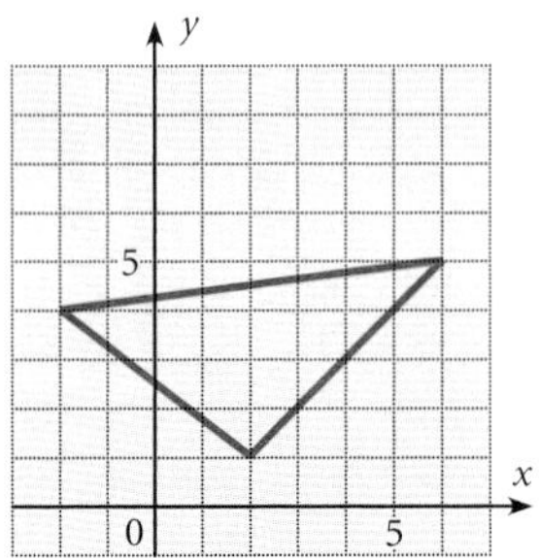

a. Locate the vertices of the image of the triangle after a translation with vector $<-6, -5>$ followed by a translation with vector $<14, 3>$. Create the translated image by connecting the vertices.

b. Give the vector for the single translation that is equivalent to the two translations above.

c. Make a conjecture: A translation with vector $\overrightarrow{AB}$ followed by a translation with vector $\overrightarrow{BC}$ is equivalent to ___.

d. Have you seen a property similar to the one you discovered in **38c**? If so, identify it, and explain why the connection makes sense.

3-1 PART E Making Connections

← CONNECT → ***Angles, bearings, vectors, and translations are important for anyone who needs to describe positions. You have learned how to describe and measure each of these.***

The concepts of angles, bearings, vectors, and translations are useful in navigation because they are well suited to describing positions, directions, and paths. In the following Explore, you will use these concepts to discuss Magellan's route.

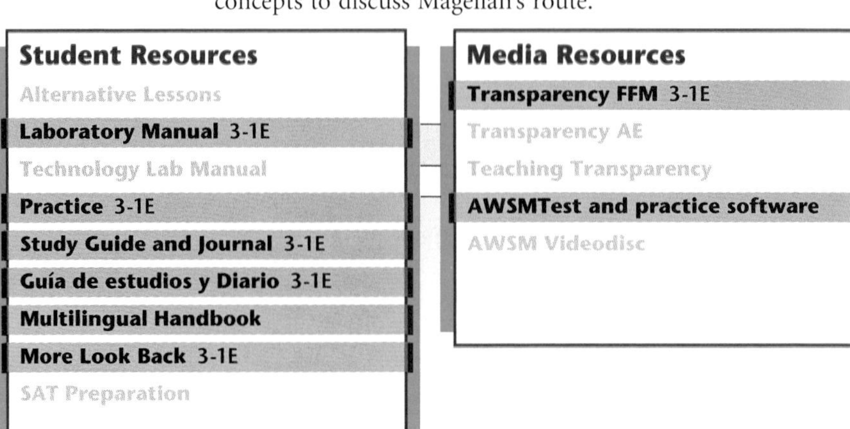

Student Resources

- Alternative Lessons
- **Laboratory Manual** 3-1E
- Technology Lab Manual
- **Practice** 3-1E
- **Study Guide and Journal** 3-1E
- **Guía de estudios y Diario** 3-1E
- **Multilingual Handbook**
- **More Look Back** 3-1E
- SAT Preparation

Media Resources

- **Transparency FFM** 3-1E
- Transparency AE
- Teaching Transparency
- **AWSMTest and practice software**
- AWSM Videodisc

EXPLORE: TRAVELS WITH MAGELLAN

Revisit Magellan's route shown on the map on page 155.

1. Describe Magellan's route using the language of rays and angles.
2. Describe Magellan's route using the language of bearings.
3. Describe Magellan's route using the language of vectors and translations.
4. Which of the above do you think provides the best description of Magellan's route? Would it be helpful to use the vocabulary and ideas of **1–3** above in some combination? If so, how?

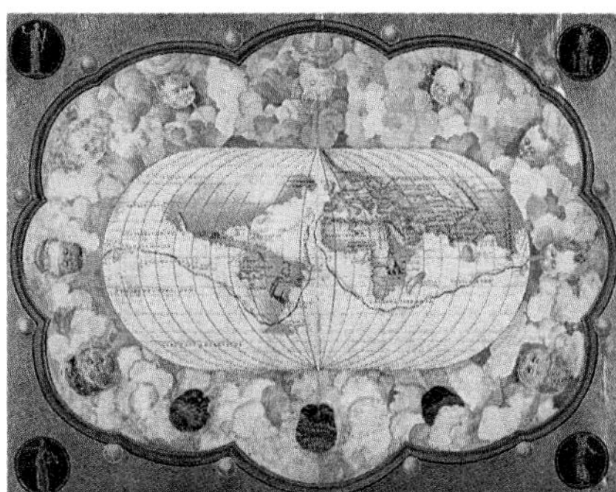

World Map by Battista Agnese. Courtesy of the John Carter Brown Library at Brown University.

Possible Answers

1. Use angles to describe direction from a coast, angle with previous direction, and so on. State distance to the next change in direction. Rays are not very useful in this context.
2. Use bearings to show changes in direction. Include distances from one bearing to the next.
3. Specify a vector or translation vector for each stage of the journey.
4. Angles and rays are probably the least useful. Bearings are convenient for describing direction but not distance. Vectors may be most convenient because they describe both direction and distance.

REFLECT

1. Draw a visual summary of rays, angles, bearings, and vectors. Include any information you need to be able to tell them apart. Also include a verbal description of how they are measured.
2. Use the map of the Mediterranean to plot a ship's course from Athens to Rome. The course should use only straight segments and need not be the shortest one possible. Describe the course as accurately as possible, using rays, angles, bearings, vectors, or any other concepts.

Portfolio

Have students select items from their work that demonstrate their understanding of the material in 3-1.

You may wish to have students include their best use of the chapter concepts in a geographical context, their favorite **Exercise** on bearings, an **Exercise** that applies translation vectors, and a **Reflect** question that they found interesting.

REFLECT

Possible Answers

1. To distinguish rays from vectors, you need to know whether or not they continue indefinitely. To tell bearings from vectors, you need to know how direction is measured.
2. Answers will show a sequence of linked segments or vectors.

sessment Resources

- iz 3-1
- apter Assessment Form A
- apter Assessment Form B
- apter Alternative Assessment
- d-Year Assessment
- l-of-Year Assessment
- SMTest and practice software

Ongoing Assessment

Self-Assessment Self-Assessment Exercises

Embedded Assessment Explore Step 4; Reflect 1, 2

Angles and Navigation

Self-Assessment

Exercise Notes

8. Similar to multiple-choice questions on standardized tests.

14. Shows a relationship between graphs of quadratic functions and translations.

15. Students use bearings to sketch a real-world situation.

Self-Assessment Answers

1. Always; Definition of angle

2. Always; Definition of opposite rays

3. Never; Acute angles are less than 90°

4. Sometimes; When less than 90°

5. Never; Definition of length

6. Always; Angle measure is a size property.

7. a. $0° < \text{measure} < 180°$

b. $000 \leq \text{bearing} < 360$

8. (d)

9. T; Flat-Plane Postulate

10. T; Plane-Intersection Postulate

11. F; Let them be noncollinear points.

12. It is an angle; it measures less than 90°; Angle *A* is an acute angle if and only if $m\angle A < 90°$.

13. Reflections and translations both preserve shape, but reflections change orientation. The figure shown is a reflection because orientation is reversed.

14. <10, 5>

15. Possible answer:

• Plane

Helicopter • • Tower

Algebra | Functions | Logic/Reasoning

Self-Assessment

P **Complete each statement with *always, sometimes,* or *never.* Explain your answers.**

1. An angle is ___ formed by two rays.

2. Opposite rays ___ form a straight line.

3. An acute angle ___ measures 90°.

4. An angle with measure less than 100° is ___ acute.

5. The length of a vector is ___ a negative number.

6. A translation ___ preserves angle measures.

P **7.** What range of values is possible for each of the following?
a. an angle's measure
b. a bearing

P **8.** The measure of $\angle A$ is twice the measure of $\angle B$. If $\angle B$ is an acute angle, which of the following must be true of $\angle A$?
(a) It is obtuse. (b) It is acute. (c) It is a right angle. (d) Not here

R **Determine whether each statement is true or false. If it is true, state a postulate or postulates that justify the statement. If false, state or sketch a counterexample. [2-2]**

9. If points *X* and *Y* are in plane $\mathcal{P}$, then $\overleftrightarrow{XY}$ is also in plane $\mathcal{P}$.

10. The intersection of planes $\mathcal{Q}$ and $\mathcal{R}$ is a line.

11. Any three points can be contained in one line.

R **12.** List the critical attributes of acute angles. Then write a definition of acute angles using "if and only if." [2-2]

MR **13.** Suppose you are given the pre-image and image for a transformation shown at the right. Explain how you can determine whether the transformation was a reflection or a translation.

Pre-image   Image

MR **14.** The graphs of two equations are shown at the right. (Recall from algebra that graphs like these are called *parabolas.*) Find the translation vector for the translation that maps the parabola on the left onto the parabola on the right.

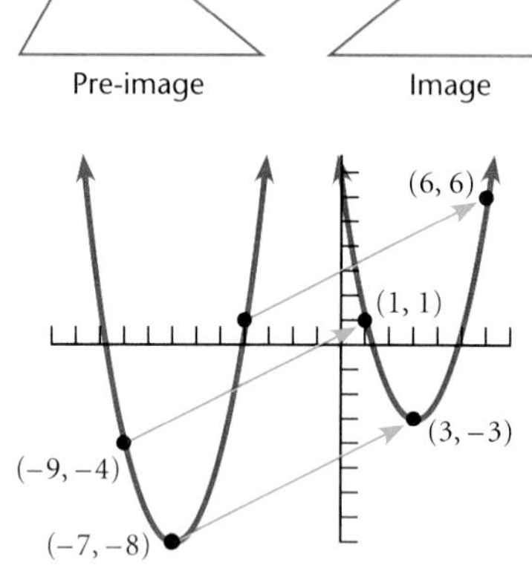

PS, C **15. Sketch Artist** Sketch a tower, airplane, and helicopter so that the following are true. The bearing of the airplane from the tower is 045. The bearing of the helicopter from the tower is 270. The helicopter is closer to the tower than the airplane is.

Key

V Vocabulary
P Practice/Skills
R Review
MR Math Reasoning
PS Problem Solving
C Challenge

6-2 Part B Exercises

17. Possible answer:

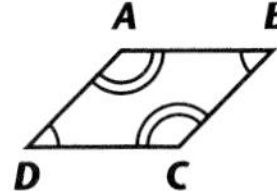

Given: $\angle A \cong \angle C$ and $\angle D \cong \angle B$
Prove: $ABCD$ is a parallelogram.
Proof: $\angle A \cong \angle C$ and $\angle D \cong \angle B$ is given. $m\angle A = m\angle C$ and $m\angle D = m\angle B$ by definition of *congruent.* $m\angle A + m\angle B + m\angle C + m\angle D = 360°$ by the Angle-Sum Theorem for Quadrilaterals. $2(m\angle A) + 2(m\angle B) = 2(m\angle B) + 2(m\angle C) = 360°$ by substituting $m\angle A = m\angle C$ and $m\angle D = m\angle B$. Dividing by two, $m\angle A + m\angle B = m\angle B + m\angle C = 180°$. Therefore the pairs $\angle A$ and $\angle B$ and $\angle B$ and $\angle C$ are supplementary by definition. $\overline{AB} \parallel \overline{CD}$ and $\overline{AD} \parallel \overline{BC}$ since same-side interior angles are supplementary. $ABCD$ is a parallelogram by definition.

More Practice

25. Parallelogram; Both pairs of opposite sides are congruent.

26. Parallelogram; Both pairs of opposite angles are congruent.

27. Parallelogram; The diagonals bisect each other.

28. May not be a parallelogram; It could be an isosceles trapezoid.

6-2 Part B Exercises

More Math Reasoning

29. Possible answer:

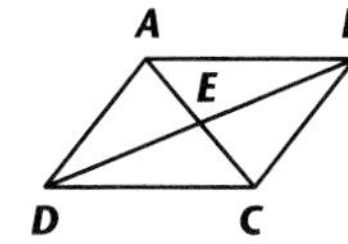

Given: $\overline{AC}$ and $\overline{BD}$ bisect each other.
Prove: $ABCD$ is a parallelogram.
Proof: $\overline{AC}$ and $\overline{DB}$ bisect each other by the given information. Let E be the point of intersection. $\overline{AE} \cong \overline{EC}$ and $\overline{DE} \cong \overline{EB}$ by definition of *bisect.* $\angle AEB \cong \angle CED$ and $\angle AED \cong \angle CEB$ because vertical angles are congruent. $\triangle AEB \cong \triangle CED$ and $\triangle AED \cong \triangle CEB$ by the SAS Postulate. Then $\angle BAE \cong \angle DCE$ and $\angle DAE \cong \angle BCE$ by CPCTC. $\overline{AB} \parallel \overline{DC}$ and $\overline{AD} \parallel \overline{BC}$ because alternate interior angles are congruent. Therefore, $ABCD$ is a parallelogram by definition.

30. Possible answer:

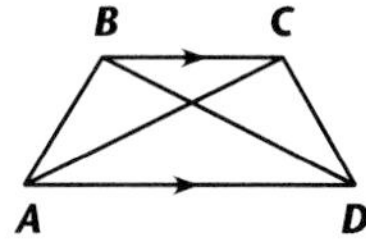

Given: $ABCD$ is an isosceles trapezoid.
Prove: $\overline{AC} \cong \overline{DB}$
Proof: $ABCD$ is an isosceles trapezoid is given. $\overline{AB} \cong \overline{DC}$ by definition of *isosceles trapezoid.* $\overline{AD} \cong \overline{AD}$ by Reflexive Property. $\angle BAD \cong \angle CDA$ by Exercise 19 in Part A. $\triangle BAD \cong \triangle CDA$ by the SAS Postulate. $\overline{AC} \cong \overline{DB}$ by CPCTC.

6-2 Part B Exercises

31. Possible answer:

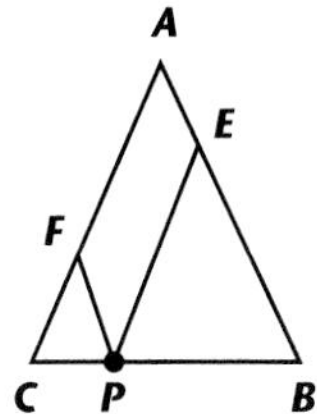

Given: $\triangle ABC$ is an isosceles triangle, $\overline{PE} \parallel \overline{CA}$ and $\overline{PF} \parallel \overline{BA}$.
Prove: $AEPF$ is a parallelogram.
Proof: $\overline{CA} \parallel \overline{PE}$ and $\overline{PF} \parallel \overline{BA}$ is given. $\overline{FA}$ is contained in $\overline{CA}$ and $\overline{EA}$ is contained in $\overline{BA}$ so $\overline{PE} \parallel \overline{FA}$ and $\overline{PF} \parallel \overline{EA}$. $AEPF$ is a parallelogram by definition.

32. Possible answer:

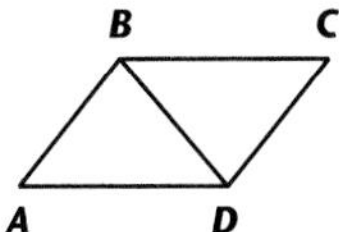

Given: $ABCD$ is a parallelogram.
Prove: $\triangle ABD \cong \triangle CDB$
Proof: $ABCD$ is a parallelogram by the given information. $\overline{AB} \cong \overline{CD}$ and $\overline{BC} \cong \overline{AD}$ because opposite sides of a parallelogram are congruent. $\overline{BD} \cong \overline{BD}$ by the Reflexive Property. $\triangle ABD \cong \triangle CDB$ by SSS.
The converse is not true.

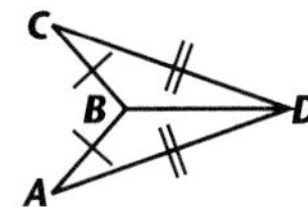

$\triangle ABD \cong \triangle CBD$ but $ABCD$ is not a parallelogram.

3-2

Rotations

SUPERLESSON AT A GLANCE

Superlesson Goal

Students will investigate rotations and rotational symmetry and learn how to measure angles of rotation.

Management Guide

	Topic	Objectives	Key Terms	New Ideas	Materials
Part A	Rotational Symmetry	To identify figures that have rotational symmetry.	Rotation, center of rotation, angle of rotation, rotational symmetry, rosette, point symmetry, half-turn	Rotations, rotational symmetry. Rotations around the center of a figure. Measuring angles of rotation.	**Student** Straightedge, protractor, geometry software
Part B	Rotations	To investigate properties of a figure that are and are not preserved by rotations.		Rotations around other points. Identifying properties of a figure that are and are not preserved by rotations.	**Student** Ruler, protractor, geometry software
Part C	Making Connections	To use rotations in an applications context.	In Making Connections, students apply and synthesize key terms and new ideas.		

Pacing Chart (45-Minute Periods)

	Comprehensive Course	Core Course	Informal Course
Part A	1	1	1
Part B	1	1	2
Part C	1	1	1
TOTAL periods for Superlesson	3	3	4

NCTM Standards

Mathematics as Problem Solving

Mathematics as Communication

Mathematics as Reasoning

Mathematical Connections

Geometry from a Synthetic Perspective

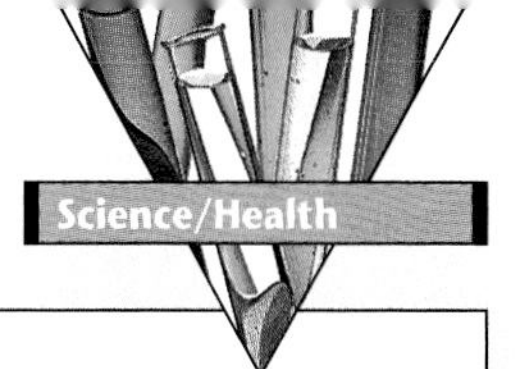

Science/Health

3-2 Rotations

Gearing Up... Or Is It Down?

The following whimsical passage is an excerpt from *The Way Things Work* by David Macaulay.

ON EARLY MAMMOTH POWER

As far as I can ascertain, the first use of mammoths in industry was to provide power for the famous merry-go-round experiment. The equipment consisted of two wheels, one large and one small, placed edge to edge so that when the mammoths turned one wheel, the other would turn automatically. At first seats were hung from the small wheel which was driven by the large wheel. The result was a hair-raising ride. When the wheels were reversed, the ride was far too sedate. Eventually belts connected to drive wheels of different sizes operated two rides simultaneously, one fast and one gentle. Carrot consumption during the experiment was astronomical.

?

1. When the mammoths walked clockwise, in what direction did the children move? Explain your answer.
2. Why do you think the children were thrown from their seats when the mammoths were on the larger wheel?
3. Name some household items that use wheels or gears.

179

More about Machines

It was formerly believed that all machines were combinations of a few "simple machines." These included the lever (multiplies force), the pulley (makes it easier to lift objects), the inclined plane and wedge (an inclined plane "dilutes" the force of gravity), and the screw (an inclined plane turned by a lever). The wheel (or gear) and axle essentially form a 360° lever that is also used to magnify force.

Where Are We Now?

Students have measured bearings and vectors. These measurements, which can exceed 180, prepare students to measure angles of rotation.

Where Are We Going?

In 3-2, students will investigate rotations and rotational symmetry.

Rotation is the third of four transformations that students will work with. They will explore dilations in 7-2, and investigate compositions of the four transformations in Chapter 10.

Possible Answers

1. Counterclockwise; the wheels turn in opposite directions.
2. The distance around the larger wheel is greater. As the wheels rub together, the smaller wheel will turn around more times than the larger, so it spins faster.
3. A blender, a can opener, a garage door opener.

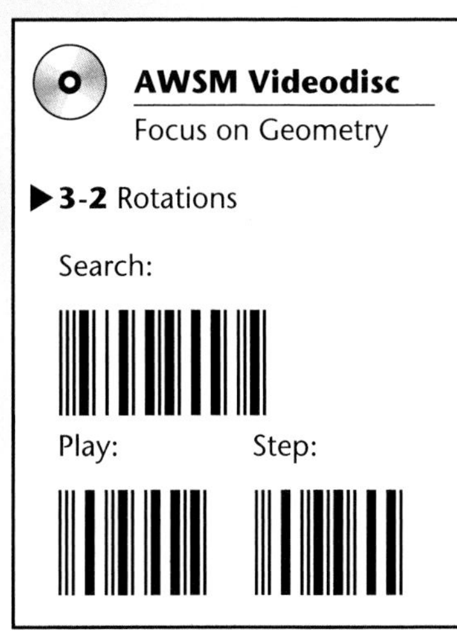

AWSM Videodisc
Focus on Geometry
▶ 3-2 Rotations
Search:
Play:
Step:

Rotations

PART A At a Glance

Objective

To explore rotations and rotational symmetry, and to identify figures that have rotational symmetry.

Development

Students are introduced to rotations and rotation terminology.

In the **Explore,** students investigate rotations of a regular hexagon. This introduces them to rotational symmetry.

Suggested Materials

Student Straightedge, protractor, geometry software

Key Terms

Rotation, center of rotation, angle of rotation, rotational symmetry, rosette, point symmetry, half-turn

First Five Minutes

Transparency FFM 3-2A

Read the paragraph above the definitions on page 180. Then answer the following.

1. How many degrees are in a half-turn? **180°**
2. How many degrees are in a quarter-turn? **90°**
3. How many degrees are in three-quarters of a turn? **270°**
4. If you rotate 210°, what fraction of a complete rotation have you turned? $\frac{7}{12}$

Motivate

Ask...

- On the classroom clock, how many degrees has the hour hand traveled since 12:00? the minute hand?

ALTERNATE EXAMPLE

Transparency AE 3-2A

3-2 PART A Rotational Symmetry

← CONNECT → ***You've already seen figures that show line symmetry. Now you will learn about rotational symmetry.***

When you worked with bearings and vectors, you had to allow for measures greater than 180°. You will also need to do this whenever you are measuring rotations. You probably know that "a 360" is a complete rotation. The basketball player "doing a 360" at the left makes a complete turn in mid-air.

DEFINITIONS

A **rotation** is a transformation that turns a set of points about one point, the **center of rotation.** The pre-image and image of any point are the same distance from the center of rotation.

The **angle of rotation** measures how much a point is turned about the center. For example, if point P is rotated 45° clockwise about center of rotation Q, $m\angle PQP' = 45°$.

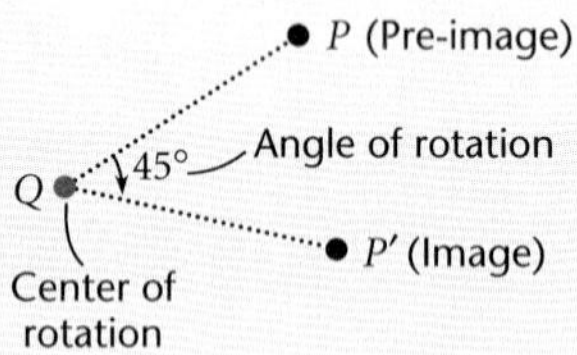

EXAMPLE

Rotate triangle RST 90° clockwise about point C. Label the images of points R, S, and T points X, Y, and Z, respectively.

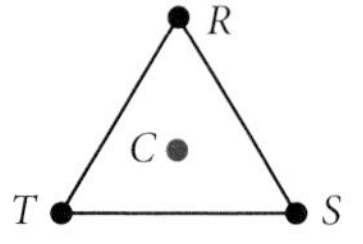

Draw $\overline{CR}$. Then use your protractor to draw a 90° clockwise angle, $\angle RCM$. Measure $\overline{CR}$, and place X on $\overline{CM}$ so that $CR = CX$. Repeat the process for points S and T to find points Y and Z.

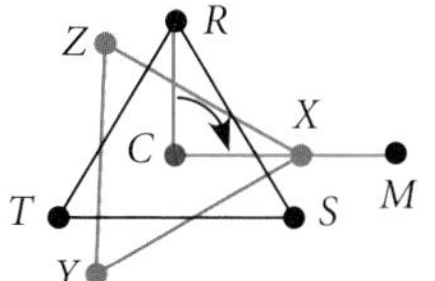

Diversity Issues

Kinesthetic learners may have difficulty visualizing angles of rotation in figures that have rotational symmetry. You might suggest that they sketch the figures on tracing paper and hold the pre-image and image together by a compass point at the center of rotation. They can then put a protractor on top and rotate the tracing paper through the required angle.

EXPLORE: SPIN IT

MATERIALS

Straightedge
Protractor
Geometry software (optional)

Use paper and pencil or geometry software to investigate rotations of the figure at the right.

1. Copy the figure and the center of rotation *C*. Then make a rotation image of the figure for each rotation.

a. 30° clockwise **b.** 60° clockwise
c. 90° clockwise **d.** 120° clockwise

2. Which rotations gave you an image that exactly overlapped the pre-image? Find all clockwise and counterclockwise angles of rotation between 0° and 360° that have this property.

3. If a figure can be rotated onto itself with an angle of rotation between 0° and 360°, the figure has *rotational symmetry.* Sketch one figure that has rotational symmetry and one that does not. Show the center of rotation in your sketch.

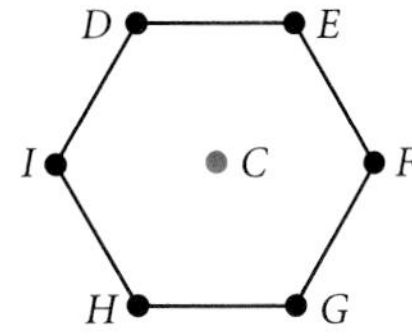

TRY IT

Identify the figure(s) that have rotational symmetry and the clockwise angles of rotation between 0° and 360° that cause the image and pre-image to overlap.

a. 180°

b. No rotational symmetry

c. 90°, 180°, 270°

d. 180°

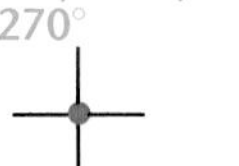

e. 90°, 180°, 270°

The definitions of rotational symmetry and some associated terms are given below.

DEFINITIONS

If a figure can be rotated about some point onto itself through a rotation of between 0° and 360°, then it has **rotational symmetry.**

A design with rotational symmetry is a **rosette.**

A figure that can be rotated onto itself through an angle of 180° has **point symmetry.**

A rotation of 180° is also known as a **half-turn.**

Student Resources

- **Alternative Lessons** 3-2A
- **Laboratory Manual** 3-2A
- Technology Lab Manual
- **Practice** 3-2A
- **Study Guide and Journal** 3-2A
- **Guía de estudios y Diario** 3-2A
- **Multilingual Handbook**
- **More Look Back** 3-2A
- SAT Preparation

Media Resources

- **Transparency FFM** 3-2A
- **Transparency AE** 3-2A
- Teaching Transparency
- **AWSMTest and practice software**
- **AWSM Videodisc**

EXPLORE

Spin It

Recommended group size: 4

The Point

To rotate a regular hexagon using center and angle of rotation, and to discover rotational symmetry.

Look and Listen...

- For students who are having trouble finding image points for vertices.

Ask...

- Do you understand the **Example** on page 180?
- Are you starting by drawing a segment from the center of rotation to a vertex?

For Groups That Finish Early

Are there any angles of rotation *greater than* 360° that map the hexagon onto itself? If so, list as many as you can. If possible, make a general rule. **Angles with measures of 360° + *n* • 60°, where *n* is an integer > 1.**

Follow Up

Ask students to summarize their results for Step 3 and to define *rotational symmetry.*

Possible Answers

2. 60°, 120°, 180°, 240°, 300°

3. A square has rotational symmetry; a parallelogram does not.

Rotations

Journal

Reflect 1 and 2 are suitable for journal entries.

REFLECT

Possible Answers

1. Figures with line symmetry "fold over" onto themselves; those with rotational symmetry rotate onto themselves. Figures with both types of symmetry show "evenness." Also, if a figure has two or more lines of symmetry, it has rotational symmetry around the point of intersection.
2. The rotation images are identical. The only difference is that the 400° rotation is a full-turn greater than the 40° rotation.

Part A Exercises

Exercise Notes

Core

5. Shows rotational symmetry in nature. You may want to have students list other natural objects with rotational symmetry and discuss why this might occur naturally.

More Math Reasoning

29. Previews equivalent angles of rotation (coterminal angles), which students will encounter in trigonometry courses.

31. Shows rotational symmetry in art.

Exercise Answers

Core

10.

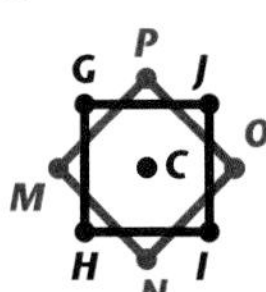

11. a. 90°, 180°, 270°

b. 180°

c. No rotational symmetry

Look Back

16. Possible answer:

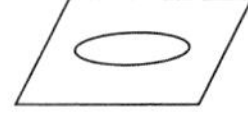

When a rectangle is given a half-turn about its center point, you can see that it has point symmetry.

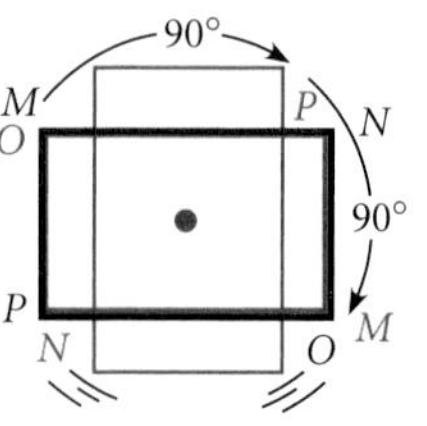

REFLECT

1. Describe the differences between point symmetry and line symmetry. Also describe any connections that you see between these two concepts.
2. Consider two clockwise rotations—one of 40° and one of 400°. How are they different? How are they alike?

Exercises

CORE

P **Getting Started** **When square *EFGH* is rotated 90° counterclockwise about point *P*, it is rotated onto itself. Find each image or pre-image.**

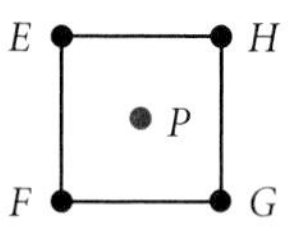

1. the image of point E *F*
2. the pre-image of point E *H*
3. the image of segment $\overline{FG}$ *GH*

P 4. Which capital letters of the alphabet shown below have point symmetry? *H, I, N, S, O, X, Z*

A B C D E F G H I J K L M N O P Q R S T U V W X Y Z

P 5. Pictures of diatoms, single-celled sea plants, are shown below. Which of them exhibit rotational symmetry? For those that do, what clockwise angles of rotation between 0° and 360° make the diatoms rotate onto themselves?

Science

a. *180°*

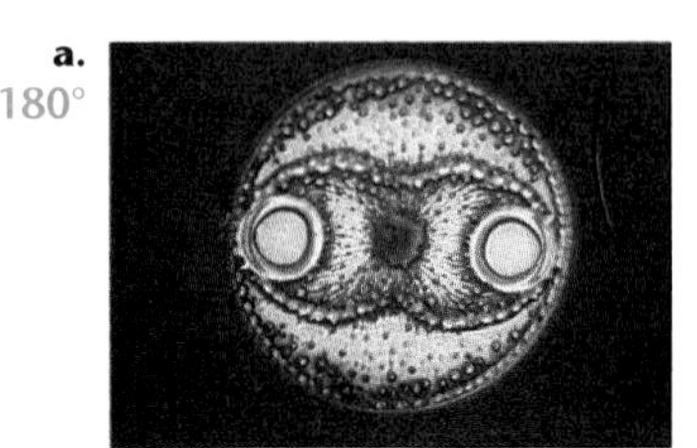

b. *180°*

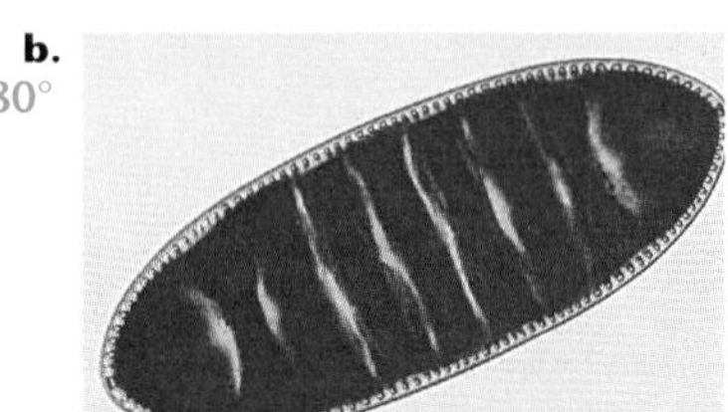

P **Parallelogram *STUV* is rotated 90° clockwise about point *P*. Find each image or pre-image.**

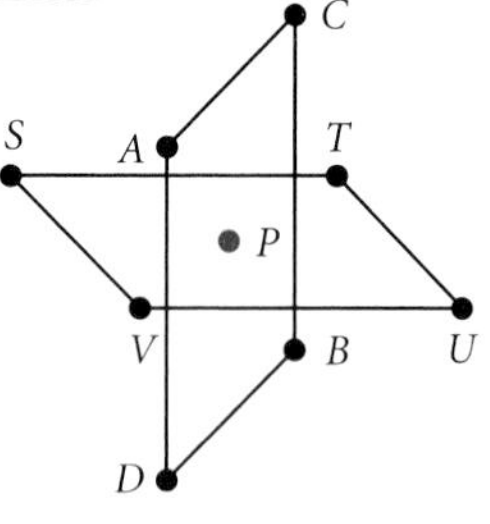

6. the image of point S *C*
7. the pre-image of point A *V*
8. the image of $\overline{TU}$ *$\overline{BD}$*

Key

V Vocabulary
P Practice/Skills
R Review
MR Math Reasoning
PS Problem Solving
C Challenge

9. Determine whether the following statement is true or false. If the statement is false, change the underlined word or phrase to make it true. F; Rotational

All rosettes have point symmetry.

10. Copy square *GHIJ* and point *C*. Rotate square *GHIJ* 45° counterclockwise about *C*. Label the images of points *G*, *H*, *I*, and *J* points *M*, *N*, *O*, and *P*, respectively.

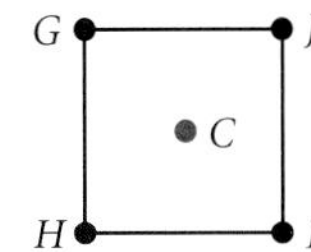

11. Determine if each figure below has rotational symmetry. If it does, give the number of degrees of all clockwise rotations less than 360° that map the figure onto itself.

a. 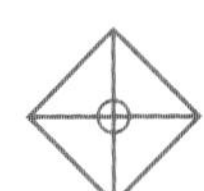

b. 

c. 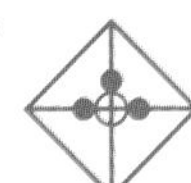

Determine which of these basic geometric figures have rotational symmetry.

12. line Yes

13. segment Yes

14. ray No

15. Four cards from an ordinary deck of playing cards are shown below.
   a. Which have point symmetry, and which do not? Six of diamonds does, others do not
   b. If you choose one of these four cards at random, what is the probability that it will have point symmetry? $\frac{1}{4}$

LOOK BACK

Sketch each of the following. [2-3]

16. a circle in a plane that is tilted away from you

17. a cereal box

Use the translation vector $\overrightarrow{KL}$ to name the image of each of the following. [3-1]

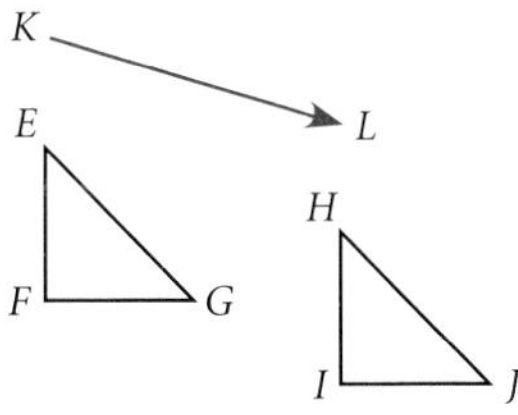

18. point *E* *H*

19. segment $\overline{FG}$ $\overline{IJ}$

20. point *G* *J*

21. triangle *EFG* Triangle *HIJ*

Ongoing Assessment

Self-Assessment Exercises 1, 3, 5, 7, 9, 13, 15

Embedded Assessment Try It a; Reflect 2; Exercises 4, 10, 11

17. Possible answer:

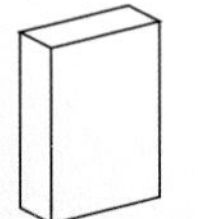

More Practice

25. 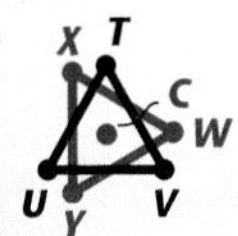

26. Yes; 180° (either way)

27. Yes; Any number of degrees (either way)

28. No rotational symmetry

More Math Reasoning

29. a. Possible answer: 320° clockwise; 400° counterclockwise

   b. Possible answer: 1° counterclockwise; 719° clockwise

   c. Possible answer: 270° counterclockwise; 450° clockwise

   d. Possible answer: If the rotations are in the same direction, then they differ by a multiple of 360°; if in the same direction, their sum is a multiple of 360°. Reason: A 360° rotation returns an object to its original position.

30. Yes; Possible answer: The letter Z; Yes; Possible answer: An isosceles right triangle.

31. a. 90°, 180°, 270°

   b. Check students' art.

Algebra	Functions	Discrete Math	Probability	Data/Statistics

MORE PRACTICE

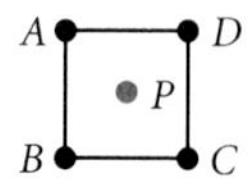

P **When square *ABCD* is rotated 180° clockwise about point *P*, it is rotated onto itself. Find each image or pre-image.**

22. the image of point A C

23. the pre-image of point A C

24. the image of $\overline{BC}$ $\overline{DA}$

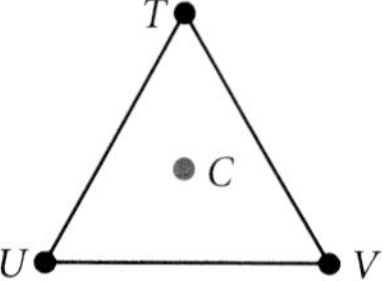

P **25.** Copy triangle TUV and point C. Rotate TUV 90° clockwise about C. Label the images of points T, U, and V points W, X, and Y, respectively.

P **Determine which of these basic geometric figures have rotational symmetry. For those that do, sketch an example, and give the direction and number of degrees of the rotation.**

26. a line **27.** a circle **28.** a 40° angle

MORE MATH REASONING

MR **29.** Describe two rotations that each have the same effect as the ones listed.
- **a.** 40° counterclockwise **b.** 359° clockwise **c.** 90° clockwise
- **d.** Make a conjecture about rotations that have the same effect. Explain your reasoning in making this conjecture.

MR, C **30.** Can a figure have rotational symmetry but not line symmetry? If so, draw an example. Can a figure have line symmetry but not rotational symmetry? If so, draw an example.

PS **31. Tile in Style** Use the tiles at the right for the following.
- **a.** Give the number of degrees of all clockwise rotations of less than 360° that map one tile onto itself.
- **b.** Sketch a design of your own that has the same rotational symmetries as those you found in **31a.** The design should fit in a square tile.

Key

V Vocabulary
P Practice/Skills
R Review
MR Math Reasoning
PS Problem Solving
C Challenge

Technology Note

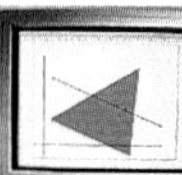

Students may need help learning how to use the rotation capabilities of geometry software. You may want to do a quick tutorial with them before starting the **Explore** on page 185. In some software, you can draw a rectangle and rotate the figure. In other programs, you must draw four segments and then select all of them before you can rotate the rectangle as one figure.

3-2 PART B Rotations

← CONNECT → *You've seen that many two-dimensional figures have rotational symmetry. Now you will work with rotations of figures in a plane. You will investigate the properties of a figure that are and are not preserved by rotations.*

The rotations you've done so far have all had the center of rotation at the center of the rotated figure. It is also possible to rotate a figure about other points.

EXAMPLE

Draw the rotation image of triangle *FGH* about center of rotation *K* with a 120° counterclockwise angle of rotation.

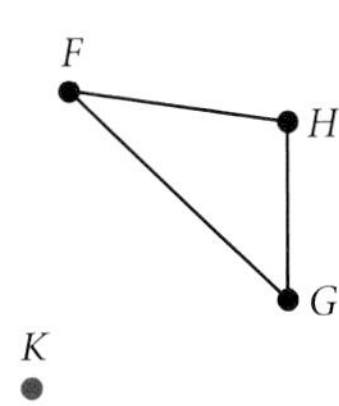

Use a protractor to draw a 120° angle, $\angle GKZ$, in the counterclockwise direction. Then place G' on $\overrightarrow{KZ}$ so that $KG' = KG$. Repeat the process for points *H* and *F*.

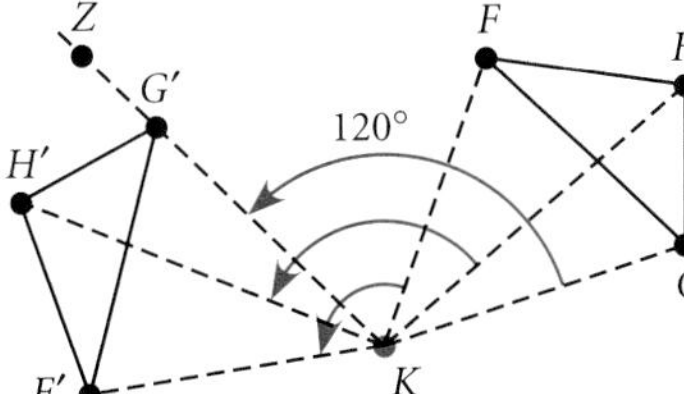

EXPLORE: RECTANGLE ROTATIONS

MATERIALS

Ruler, Protractor
Geometry software (optional)

1. Copy the rectangle *ABCD* and center of rotation *E*. Draw the rotation image of *ABCD* under a 60° counterclockwise rotation about *E*.
2. Use this rotation to help you determine the characteristics of a figure that are and are not preserved by a rotation.

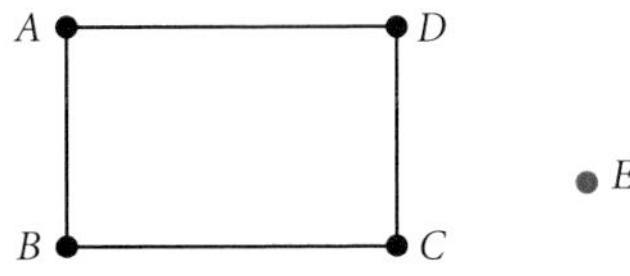

Student Resources

- Alternative Lessons 3-2B
- Laboratory Manual 3-2B
- Technology Lab Manual
- Practice 3-2B
- Study Guide and Journal 3-2B
- Guía de estudios y Diario 3-2B
- Multilingual Handbook
- More Look Ahead 3-2B
- SAT Preparation

Media Resources

- Transparency FFM 3-2B
- Transparency AE 3-2B
- Teaching Transparency
- AWSMTest and practice software
- AWSM Videodisc

PART B At a Glance

Objective

To investigate properties of a figure that are and are not preserved by rotations.

Development

Students first see an **Example** of a rotation whose center is not at the center of the rotated figure.

In the **Explore,** students discover properties of a figure that are and are not preserved by a rotation.

Suggested Materials

Student Ruler, protractor, geometry software

First Five Minutes

Transparency FFM 3-2B

Use a protractor to draw a 70° angle. Then use compass and straightedge to construct an angle congruent to it.

Motivate

Ask...

- What happens if you rotate a square around one of its vertices? Sketch a square and its rotation image for a 180° rotation around one vertex.

ALTERNATE EXAMPLE

Transparency AE 3-2B

EXPLORE

Rectangle Rotations

Recommended group size: 4

The Point

To discover the properties of a figure that are and are not preserved by rotation.

3-2

Rotations

Look and Listen...

- For students who may feel that the orientation has changed because the figure is positioned differently.

Ask...

- Label the images of *A*, *B*, *C*, and *D* with primes. Is the direction around the pre-image from *A* to *B* to *C* to *D* the same as the direction around the image from *A′* to *B′* to *C′* to *D′*?

For Groups That Finish Early

Use your compass to draw a circle. Mark a point outside the circle. Devise a method for rotating the circle 135° clockwise around that point. **Students may select points on the circle, find their images, and then fit a circle through the points with a compass.**

Follow Up

Ask students to summarize the properties that are and are not preserved by rotation.

Possible Answer

2. All properties of a figure (except its position) are preserved by rotation.

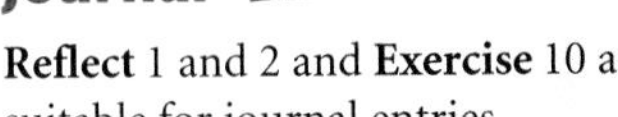

Journal

Reflect 1 and 2 and **Exercise** 10 are suitable for journal entries.

REFLECT

Possible Answers

1. The two rotations are equivalent to a 70° clockwise rotation around that point.
2. 360° counterclockwise; 720° clockwise. Any multiple of 360° will produce complete rotations.

TRY IT

In the figure, $\angle STU$ has been rotated 180° about point *V*. Fill in each blank.

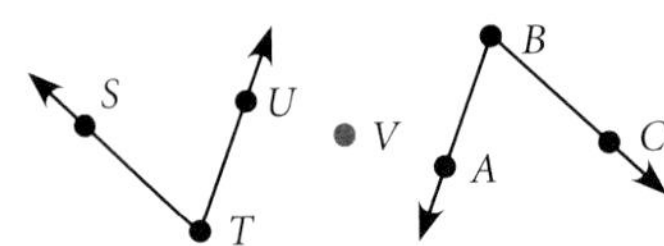

a. The image of $\overline{ST}$ is ____. $\overline{CB}$
b. The pre-image of *C* is ____. *S*
c. $AB =$ ____ *UT*
d. $\angle STU \cong$ ____ $\angle CBA$
e. $CV =$ ____ *SV*

You've now investigated three transformations: reflection, rotation, and translation. Properties of rotations are summarized below.

> Rotations **preserve** any property that has to do with the size of a figure, including
> - the lengths of its sides
> - the measures of its angles
> - the area and perimeter of the figure
>
> Rotations also **preserve** the orientation of the figure.

In Chapter 7, you will explore a fourth transformation—the dilation. In Chapter 10, you will see how all of these transformations can be used together.

REFLECT

1. What can you say about a 30° clockwise rotation followed by a 40° clockwise rotation about the same point?
2. Describe two different rotations that each have the same effect as a 360° clockwise rotation. Are even more answers possible? Explain.

Exercises

CORE

1. **Getting Started** Follow the steps below to draw the rotation image of segment $\overline{AB}$ under a 90° counterclockwise rotation about C.
   a. Use a protractor to draw a 90° angle, $\angle ACZ$, in the counterclockwise direction.
   b. Use a compass or ruler to place A' on $\overrightarrow{CZ}$ so that $CA' = CA$.
   c. Repeat **1a** and **1b** for point B to find B'. Finally, draw $\overline{A'B'}$.

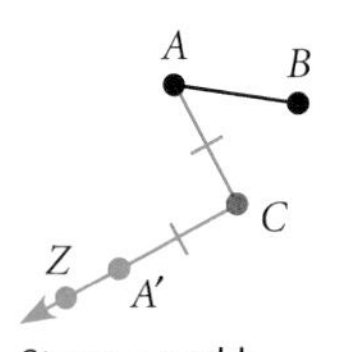
Steps a and b

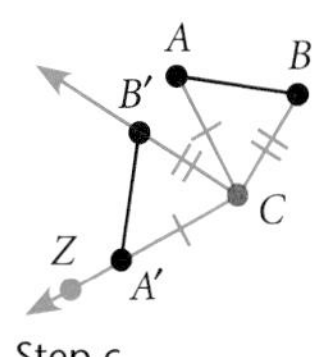
Step c

Rectangle *ZXWY* is the image of rectangle *OPMN* under a 90° counterclockwise rotation about point *C*.

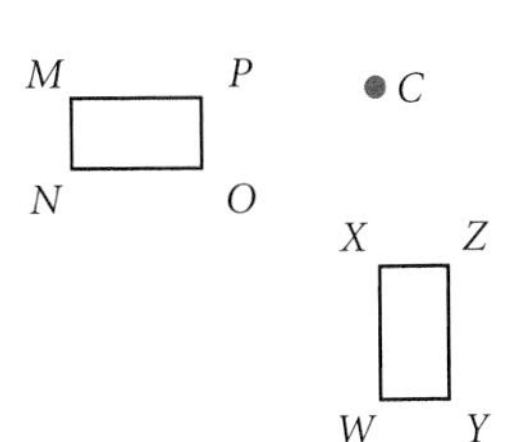

2. Find the image of point M. W
3. Find the pre-image of point Z. O
4. Find the image of $\angle NOP$. $\angle YZX$
5. Find the pre-image of $\angle XWY$. $\angle PMN$
6. Copy triangle QRS and point C. Draw the rotation image of triangle QRS about C with a 120° clockwise angle of rotation. Label the images of points Q, R, and S points T, U, and V, respectively.

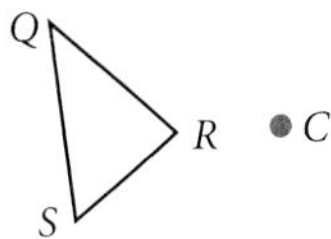

Plot points $C(0, 4)$ and $D(3, 4)$ on a coordinate plane. Then find the coordinates of the rotation images of C and D when they are rotated about the origin with each rotation angle below.

7. 90° clockwise
8. 180° clockwise
9. 270° clockwise
10. Make conjectures about the effects of clockwise rotations of 90°, 180°, and 270° on the coordinates of a point.
11. The minute hand of a clock is shown at the right.
   a. What are the center of rotation and the direction of the rotation of the minute hand?
   b. How long does it take the minute hand to rotate through an angle of
      i. 360°? ii. 90°? iii. 180°? iv. 36°?
   c. Through how many degrees does the minute hand rotate in
      i. 30 minutes? ii. 45 minutes? iii. 1 minute?

Ongoing Assessment

Self-Assessment Exercises 1–11 odd

Embedded Assessment Explore Step 2; Reflect 1; Exercises 6, 10

Vocabulary
Practice/Skills
Review
Math Reasoning
Problem Solving
Challenge

Part B Exercises

Exercise Notes

Core

7–10. These exercises explore rotations on a coordinate plane.

Look Ahead

These exercises review drawing skills. Students explore what can and cannot be assumed from a figure in 3-3 Part B. In 3-4 Part A, they begin drawing figures to illustrate deductive proofs.

More Math Reasoning

22. A real-world application of rotation. The general principle that you turn a bolt, screw, or jar lid counterclockwise to loosen it is unfamiliar to many high school students.

Exercise Answers

Core

1.

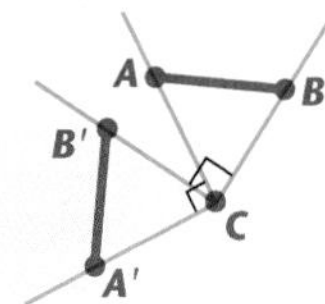

6.

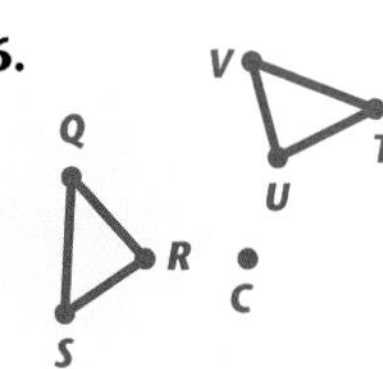

7. $C'(4, 0)$, $D'(4, -3)$

8. $C''(0, -4)$, $D''(-3, -4)$

9. $C'''(-4, 0)$, $D'''(-4, 3)$

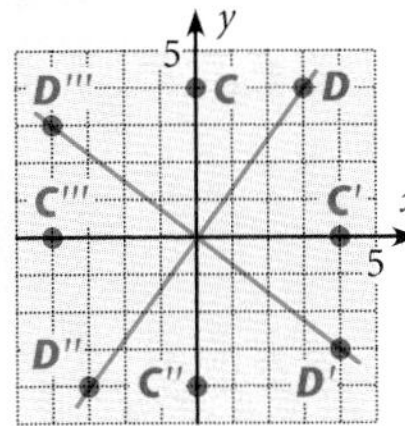

10. Original: (x, y); 90°: $(y, -x)$; 180°: $(-x, -y)$; 270°: $(-y, x)$

11. a. Clockwise from middle of clock face.

b. i. 1 hour = 60 min
ii. 15 min **iii.** 30 min
iv. 6 min

c. i. 180° **ii.** 270° **iii.** 6°

Rotations

Look Ahead

12.

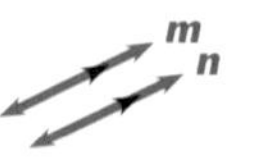

13.

14. Possible answer:

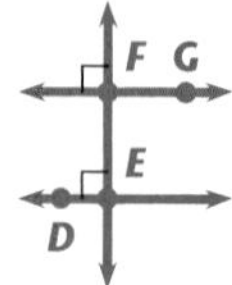

15. Possible answer:

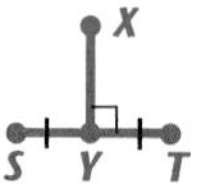

More Math Reasoning

22. Clockwise; Clockwise screws the lid on and counterclockwise removes it. In general, clockwise turns close/tighten; counterclockwise turns open/loosen.

23. A parallelogram with a crossbar; Yes

LOOK AHEAD

P **Draw a figure to illustrate each situation below. Include appropriate marks in your figures.**

12. Lines *m* and *n* are parallel.

13. Lines *s* and *t* are perpendicular.

14. $\overleftrightarrow{DE} \perp \overleftrightarrow{EF}$. $\overleftrightarrow{DE} \parallel \overleftrightarrow{FG}$.

15. $\overline{YX}$ is the perpendicular bisector of $\overline{ST}$.

MORE PRACTICE

P **Square *IJLK* is the image of square *QRST* under a 180° clockwise rotation about point *Z*. Find each image or pre-image.**

16. the image of point *S* L

17. the pre-image of point *I* Q

18. the image of $\overline{RQ}$ $\overline{JI}$

P **Point *T* has coordinates (−3, 1). Find the coordinates of the rotation image of *T* when it is rotated about the origin with each rotation angle below.**

19. 90° clockwise (1, 3)

20. 180° clockwise (3, −1)

21. 270° clockwise (−1, −3)

MORE MATH REASONING

PS **22. Geometry Hardware** To insert a screw with a screwdriver, do you turn the screwdriver clockwise or counterclockwise? Are there any other tools or household items that tighten or open when turned one way and loosen or close when turned the other? Collect data and make a table to show the effects of clockwise and counterclockwise turns on a few of these items. Make any generalizations that you can.

Item	Clockwise	Counterclockwise
Jar lid	?	?

MR **23. Triangle Twists** Suppose a triangle is rotated 180° about the midpoint of one of its sides. What figure is formed by union of the image and pre-image? Does your result hold for any triangle?

Key

V Vocabulary
P Practice/Skills
R Review
MR Math Reasoning
PS Problem Solving
C Challenge

ic/Reasoning | Industry/Careers | Science/Health | Social Science/History | Fine Arts/Literature

3-2 PART C Making Connections

← CONNECT → *Rotating objects, such as gears and wheels, are critical parts in many machines. You have learned some basic facts about rotations and examined figures for rotational symmetry.*

Many of the ideas you've learned about rotations will be useful in understanding the problems with the mammoth merry-go-round from *The Way Things Work* described on page 179.

EXPLORE: A MAMMOTH RIDE

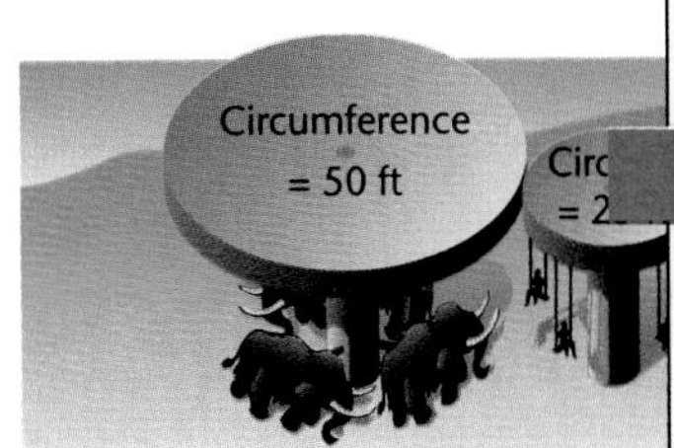

The figure at the right shows the large and small wheels in the mammoth merry-go-round and their circumferences. (The *circumference* is the distance around a circle.)

One wheel turns the other by friction: as one wheel turns, it "drags" the other along with it. When the edge of the drive wheel—the one that is powered by the mammoths—turns one foot, the edge of the other wheel also turns one foot.

1. Suppose that the mammoths are hitched to the larger wheel, and the children's seats are attached to the smaller wheel.
   a. If the larger wheel makes four complete revolutions (turns), how many revolutions will the smaller wheel make? How many revolutions will it make if the larger wheel makes one revolution?
   b. If the mammoths turn the wheel at eight revolutions per minute, at how many revolutions per minute will the children's wheel turn?
   c. If Elly (one of the mammoths) walks 60° counterclockwise, as shown at the right, what will be the direction and degree of rotation of Cathy (one of the children)?
2. If the mammoths are hitched to the smaller wheel, and the children's chairs are on the larger wheel, what are the answers to the preceding questions?
3. Explain why the children were thrown from the wheel when they were on the smaller wheel, but were put to sleep when they rode on the larger one.

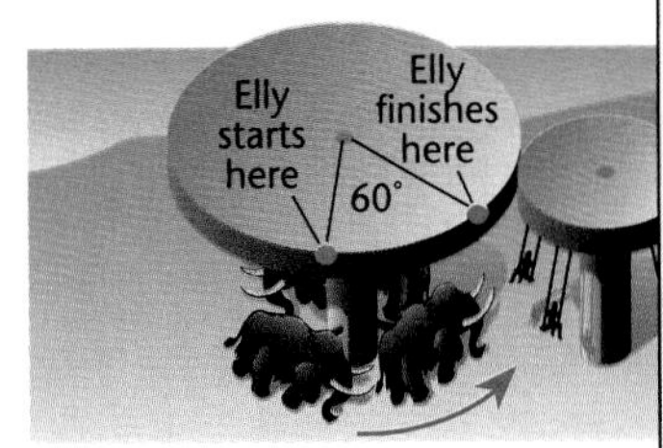

Student Resources
- Alternative Lessons
- **Laboratory Manual 3-2C**
- Technology Lab Manual
- **Practice 3-2C**
- **Study Guide and Journal 3-2C**
- **Guía de estudios y Diario 3-2C**
- **Multilingual Handbook**
- **More Look Back 3-2C**
- SAT Preparation

Media Resources
- **Transparency FFM 3-2C**
- Transparency AE
- Teaching Transparency
- **AWSMTest and practice software**
- AWSM Videodisc

PART C At a Glance

Objective
To use rotations in an applications context.

Development
In the **Explore,** students use their knowledge of rotations to investigate how gears work.

First Five Minutes
Transparency FFM 3-2C

Write a summary of the facts you've learned about rotations and rotational symmetry.

EXPLORE

A Mammoth Ride
Recommended group size: 4

The Point
To use rotations to explore how gears work.

Look and Listen...
- For students who do not see the importance of the ratio of the wheels' circumferences.

Ask...
- If the circumference of the larger wheel is twice that of the smaller, how many times will the smaller turn for one turn of the larger?

For Groups That Finish Early
Design a system of gears so that turning one gear clockwise will make another turn clockwise at the same speed. **The system must have an odd number of gears, and the product of the gear ratios must be 1.**

Follow Up
Ask students to present their answers to Step 3.

Possible Answers

1. **a.** 8; 2
   b. 16
   c. 120° clockwise
2. **a.** 8; 2
   b. 4
   c. 30° clockwise

3. When the mammoths drive the larger wheel, one turn results in two turns of the smaller, and the children spin quickly. When the mammoths drive the smaller wheel, one turn results in a half-turn of the larger.

Portfolio

Have students select items from their work that demonstrate their understanding of the material in 3-2.

You may wish to have students include their favorite example of point symmetry, an **Exercise** that required them to construct a rotation image, and an **Exercise** that they found challenging.

REFLECT

Possible Answers

1. Counterclockwise 330°; clockwise 390°.
2. Rotation is a transformation; symmetry is a property. Point symmetry is a special type of rotational symmetry (180°).
3. All properties having to do with the size of a figure and its parts are preserved.

Self-Assessment

Exercise Notes

14. Features the idea of angular velocity in an applications context.

Self-Assessment Answers

1. Possible answer: All three preserve size-related properties. Reflection reverses the orientation whereas translation and rotation preserve orientation. Translation shifts the location of the figure.

8.  or 

9. 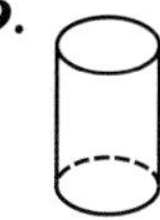

REFLECT

1. Describe some other rotations that have the same effect as a clockwise rotation of 30°.
2. Explain the differences between *rotation, rotational symmetry,* and *point symmetry.*
3. Compare the properties of a figure that are and are not preserved by reflections, rotations, and translations. Which properties are preserved by all three of these transformations?

Self-Assessment

MR 1. In your own words, explain the similarities and differences between rotations, translations, and reflections.

P 2. Which of the following sets of letters form a rosette? (b)

(a) **TOT** (b) **NON** (c) **HAH** (d) **WOW**

P 3. Is it possible to draw a triangle that does not have rotational symmetry? If so, draw such a triangle. Any non-equilateral triangle lacks rotational symmetry.

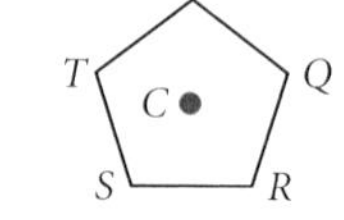

P **Refer to the pentagon (five-sided figure) at the right. A rotation of the pentagon about point *C* maps the pentagon onto itself. Point *P* maps onto *Q*. Find each image or pre-image.**

4. the image of point S T
5. the pre-image of point S R
6. the pre-image of segment $\overline{TP}$ $\overline{ST}$
7. the image of $\angle PQR$ $\angle QRS$

R **Sketch each of the following. [2-3]**

8. a pyramid with a square base
9. a can of soda

R **Use the translation vector <1, −3> to give the coordinates of the image of each of the following. [3-1]**

10. point X $(-2, 0)$
11. point Y $(-1, -4)$
12. point Z $(4, -3)$
13. the origin $(1, -3)$

PS, C 14. **A Missing Tooth** Gear 1 at the right has lost a tooth, as shown. Gear 2 slips each time the missing tooth moves to point A. If Gear 1 rotates 12° each second, how many times will Gear 2 slip in one minute? Twice

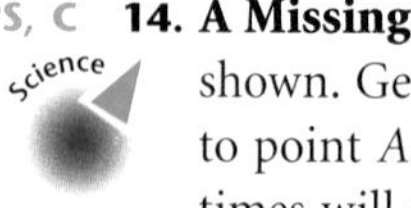

Assessment Resources

- **Quiz 3-2**
- Chapter Assessment Form A
- Chapter Assessment Form B
- Chapter Alternative Assessment
- Mid-Year Assessment
- End-of-Year Assessment
- **AWSMTest and practice software**

Ongoing Assessment

Self-Assessment Self-Assessment Exercises

Embedded Assessment Explore Step 3; Reflect 2, 3

ADDITIONAL ANSWERS

6-2 Part C Exercises

27. Possible answer:

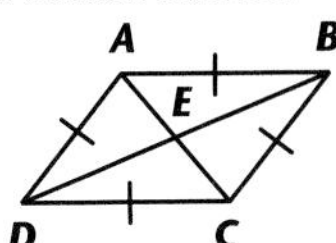

Given: $ABCD$ is a rhombus.
Prove: $\overline{AC} \perp \overline{DB}$
Proof: $ABCD$ is a rhombus by the given information. $\overline{AD} \cong \overline{AB}$ by definition of a *rhombus.* $\overline{AC}$ bisects $\overline{DB}$ because diagonals of a parallelogram bisect each other. $\overline{DE} \cong \overline{EB}$ by definition of *bisect.* $\overline{AE} \cong \overline{AE}$ by the Reflexive Property. $\triangle AEB \cong \triangle AED$ by the SSS Postulate. $\angle AEB \cong \angle AED$ by CPCTC. $m\angle AEB + m\angle AED = 180°$ by the Linear-Pair Postulate. $m\angle AEB = m\angle AED$ by definition of *congruent.* $2(m\angle AEB) = 180°$ by substituting. Divide by 2 to get $m\angle AEB = 90°$. $\angle AEB$ is a right angle by definition of *right angle.* $\overline{AC} \perp \overline{DB}$ by definition of *perpendicular.*

Look Ahead

28. $3\sqrt{2}$

29. 1, 1, -1

30. Yes; They have the same slope.

31. Yes; The slopes are negative reciprocals of each other.

32. Yes; The opposite sides are parallel.

More Practice

33. The diagonals are congruent and bisect each other.

34. The diagonals are perpendicular and bisect each other.

35. The diagonals are congruent, perpendicular, and bisect each other.

36. $2x - 1 = x + 2$ because the diagonals bisect each other. So $x = 3$. $(5)^2 + (5)^2 = y^2$ by the Pythagorean Theorem and because the diagonals are perpendicular. So $y = 5\sqrt{2}$.

37. Diagonals are congruent so $x = 20$ by the SSS Postulate and CPCTC. $x + y = 90$ because all angles are right angles. Solve for y when $x = 20$ to get $y = 70$.

6-2 Part C Exercises

38. $3y + 3y = 90$ because diagonals of squares bisect angles and angles of squares are right angles. Solve for y to get $y = 15$.

More Math Reasoning

39.

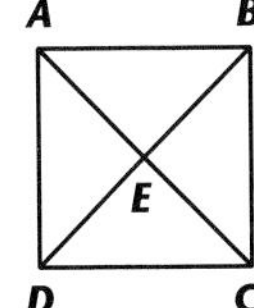

Given: $\overline{AC} \perp \overline{BD}$, $\overline{AC} \cong \overline{BD}$, $ABCD$ is a parallelogram.
Prove: $ABCD$ is a square.
Proof: $\overline{AC} \perp \overline{BD}$ from the given information, so $\angle AEB$ and $\angle CEB$ are right angles, and $\triangle AEB$ and $\triangle CEB$ are right triangles by definition. $\overline{BE} \cong \overline{BE}$ (reflexive), and $\overline{AE} \cong \overline{EC}$ because diagonals of a parallelogram bisect each other. $\triangle AEB \cong \triangle CEB$ by LL, so $\overline{AB} \cong \overline{BC}$ by CPCTC. Repeating the process shows all four sides congruent. Because $\overline{AC} \cong \overline{BD}$ (given), $\overline{AB} \cong \overline{AB}$ (reflexive), and $\overline{AD} \cong \overline{BC}$ (opposite sides of a parallelogram are conguent), $\triangle DAB \cong \triangle CBA$ by SSS. It can be shown that $\angle DAB$ and $\angle CBA$ are congruent and supplementary, and therefore are right angles. Repeating the process shows all four angles are right angles. Because $ABCD$ has all sides congruent and four right angles, it is a square.

40. Possible answer:

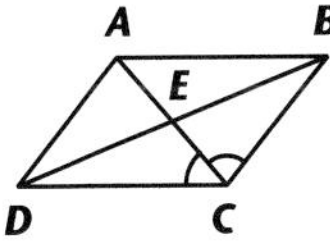

Given: $ABCD$ is a parallelogram. $\overline{AC}$ bisects $\angle DCB$.
Prove: $ABCD$ is a rhombus.
Proof: $ABCD$ is a parallelogram by the given information. $\overline{AB} \parallel \overline{DC}$ and $\overline{AD} \parallel \overline{BC}$ by definition of a *parallelogram.* $\angle DAC \cong \angle BCA$ since alternate interior angles of parallel lines cut by a transversal are congruent. $\overline{AC}$ bisects $\angle DCB$ is given. $\angle BCA \cong \angle ACD$ by definition of *bisect.* $\angle DAC \cong \angle ACD$ by the Transitive Property.

6-2 Part C Exercises

40. (continued)
$\triangle ACD$ is isosceles by the converse of the Isosceles-Triangle Theorem. $\overline{AD} \cong \overline{DC}$ by the definition of *isosceles triangle.* $\overline{AD} \cong \overline{BC}$ and $\overline{DC} \cong \overline{AB}$ because opposite sides of a parallelogram are congruent. $\overline{AD} \cong \overline{BC} \cong \overline{DC} \cong \overline{AB}$ by the Transitive Property. $ABCD$ is a rhombus by definition.

41. Possible answer:

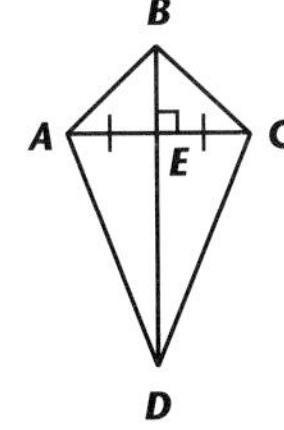

Given: $\overline{AC} \perp \overline{BD}$, $\overline{BD}$ bisects $\overline{AC}$, $\overline{AC}$ does not bisect $\overline{BD}$.
Prove: $ABCD$ is a kite.
Proof: $\overline{AC} \perp \overline{BD}$ is given. $\angle BEC$, $\angle BEA$, $\angle DEA$, and $\angle DEC$ are right angles by definition of *perpendicular.* $\angle BEC \cong \angle BEA$ and $\angle DEA \cong \angle DEC$ because right angles are congruent. $\overline{BD}$ bisects $\overline{AC}$ is given. $\overline{AE} \cong \overline{EC}$ by definition of *bisect.* $\overline{BE} \cong \overline{BE}$ and $\overline{ED} \cong \overline{ED}$ by the Reflexive Property. $\triangle AEB \cong \triangle CEB$ and $\triangle AED \cong \triangle CED$ by the SAS Postulate. $\overline{AB} \cong \overline{BC}$ and $\overline{AD} \cong \overline{CD}$ by CPCTC. By the Pythagorean Theorem, $AB^2 = AE^2 + BE^2$ and $AD^2 = AE^2 + DE^2$. Since $\overline{AC}$ does not bisect $\overline{BD}$, $BE \neq DE$, so $AB \neq AD$. $ABCD$ is a kite by definition.

42. Place two congruent ropes across each other so that they bisect. When the measurements between the rope ends are equal, mark corners for a square foundation.

3-3

Precise Thinking with Angles

SUPERLESSON AT A GLANCE

Superlesson Goal

Students will explore special pairs of angles and learn what can and cannot be assumed from figures.

Management Guide

	Topic	Objectives	Key Terms	New Ideas	Materials
Part A	Postulates About Angles	To discover the Angle-Addition Postulate.		Adding measures of adjacent angles to find the measure of the larger angle they form.	
Part B	Assumptions and Figures	To determine what can and cannot be assumed from figures.		Identifying what information is implied in a figure.	
Part C	Angle Pairs	To develop definitions and theorems about special angle pairs.	Complementary angles, supplementary angles, linear pair	Complementary and supplementary angles. Angles in a linear pair are supplementary.	**Student** Straightedge, protractor
Part D	Vertical Angles and Angle Bisectors	To discover that vertical angles are congruent.	Vertical angles, angle bisector	Vertical angles, angle bisectors. Vertical angles are congruent.	**Student** Compass, straightedge, protractor, geometry software **Teacher** Chalkboard/overhead compass
Part E	Making Connections	To apply relationships of angles to a real-world problem.	In Making Connections, students apply and synthesize key terms and new ideas.		**Student** Straightedge, protractor

Pacing Chart (45-Minute Periods)

	Comprehensive Course	Core Course	Informal Course
Part A	1	1	1
Part B	1	1	1
Part C	1	1	1
Part D	1	1	1
Part E	1	1	1
TOTAL periods for Superlesson	5	5	5

NCTM Standards

Mathematics as Problem Solving

Mathematics as Communication

Mathematics as Reasoning

Mathematical Connections

Geometry from a Synthetic Perspective

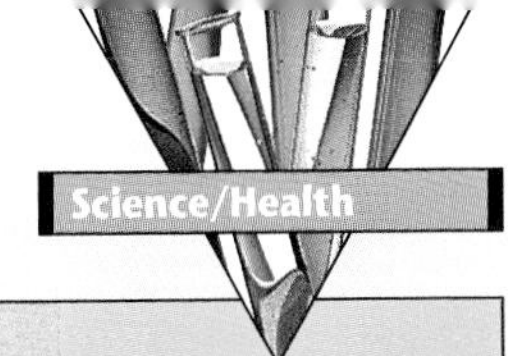

3-3 Precise Thinking with Angles

HEAT WAVE

If you have ever spent a night in a city after a hot, humid day, you know that sundown may not bring much relief. In its Spring 1992 article, "Hot Times in the City," *Exploratorium Quarterly* magazine explains why cities sometimes become "heat islands."

"Temperature maps of most cities on a summer evening show an area of high temperatures over the urban center. The city center can be much hotter than its surroundings...Hot summer nights in New York make the national news as people seek relief from the city-augmented temperatures. In the city, nighttime temperatures remain over 99°F (37°C)—human body temperature. Across the river in rural New Jersey, temperatures drop below 85°F (30°C)."

One reason for sweltering summer nights is that narrow city streets and tall buildings trap and absorb the sun's heat during the day. "The canyons created by the vertical walls in the city absorb more solar energy than a flat or rolling landscape would absorb. The city simply has more surface to catch the light rays.

"When sunlight shines on flat land, some of the light scatters back into the sky. In the canyons of the city, however, light scattered by the ground or a building often hits another building. Instead of escaping, the heat is absorbed. At night... the city's masonry emits its stored thermal energy..."

?

1. Cities are also warmer than the surrounding countryside on winter nights. Aside from the reason discussed above, what might cause these warmer temperatures to occur?
2. Though a narrow street doesn't cool as quickly as a wide one, it also does not warm up as quickly. Explain why this might happen. (Hint: When will sunlight first reach a country road in the morning? a city street?)

More About City Weather

San Francisco and New York City are both coastal cities, and their latitudes are not much different. Yet winter temperatures are colder *and* the summer temperatures hotter in New York. (Average January temperatures: New York 31.8°, San Francisco 48.5°; July: NY 76.4°, SF 62.2°.) Weather patterns in the Northern Hemisphere tend to flow from west to east. San Francisco gets breezes from the Pacific Ocean, which has a fairly constant temperature and a cool current. New York's winds tend to come from the land, which heats and cools more drastically as seasons change.

Where Are We Now?

Students have become familiar with angles and angle measurement in many contexts.

Where Are We Going?

In 3-3, students will learn about properties of special angle pairs. This information will be important throughout the course, and it will have immediate application in 3-4, when students learn properties of angles formed by parallel lines and their transversals.

Students also see what information they can and cannot assume from a figure. This knowledge is especially important in 3-4, where students begin to draw figures for use in deductive proofs.

Possible Answers

1. There is a high concentration of heated buildings, which lose heat to the outside air. Cars also give off heat.
2. The buildings shade the narrow street for a longer period.

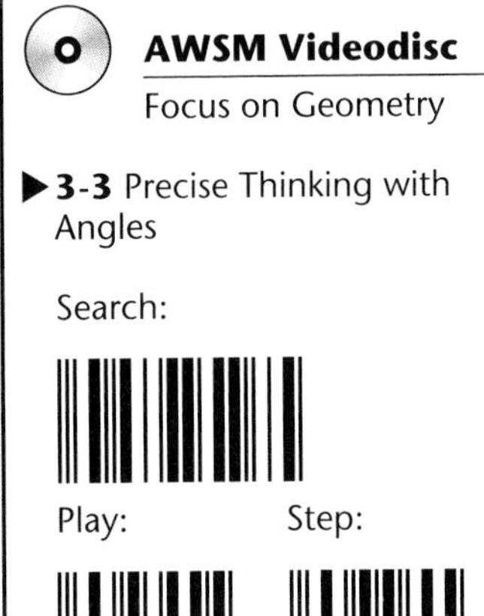

AWSM Videodisc
Focus on Geometry
▶ 3-3 Precise Thinking with Angles
Search:
Play:
Step:

Precise Thinking with Angles

PART A At a Glance

Objective

To discover the Angle-Addition Postulate.

Development

First, students see the Protractor Postulate.

In the **Explore,** they use their mathematical intuition to discover the Angle-Addition Postulate.

First Five Minutes

Transparency FFM 3-3A

Read the first paragraph on page 192 and answer the **Consider** question.

Motivate

Ask...

- Why is it important to agree on one method for measuring angles?

Shows the need for choosing one method of measuring angles.

Possible Answer

1. Although all three students have reasonable methods, we adopt Reggie's because of the agreement that angles must measure between 0° and 180°.

3-3 PART A Postulates About Angles

← CONNECT → *You've learned what an angle is and measured angles with a protractor. Now you will learn and use two postulates about angles.*

Although there are several ways to look at measuring angles, we will need to agree on one method for most purposes.

1. Reggie says $m\angle JFI = 50°$ because $160° - 110° = 50°$. Amy says $m\angle JFI = -50°$ because $110° - 160° = -50°$. Naoki says $m\angle JFI = 310°$ because $360° - 50° = 310°$. Who do you think is right? Why?

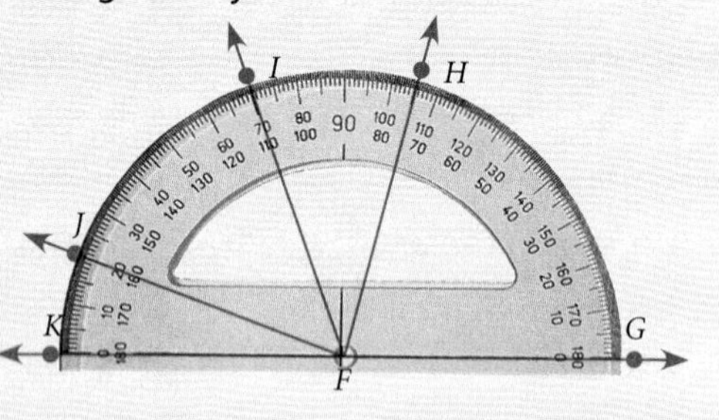

To avoid confusion, we adopt the following postulate.

PROTRACTOR POSTULATE

Given any line $\overleftrightarrow{AB}$ in a plane with point O between A and B; $\overrightarrow{OA}$, $\overrightarrow{OB}$, and all the rays from point O on one side of line $\overleftrightarrow{AB}$ can be matched one-to-one with the real numbers from 0 through 180 so that:

a. ray $\overrightarrow{OA}$ is matched with 0. **b.** ray $\overrightarrow{OB}$ is matched with 180.

c. if ray $\overrightarrow{OR}$ is matched with the number r and $\overrightarrow{OS}$ is matched with the number s, then $m\angle ROS = |r - s| = |s - r|$

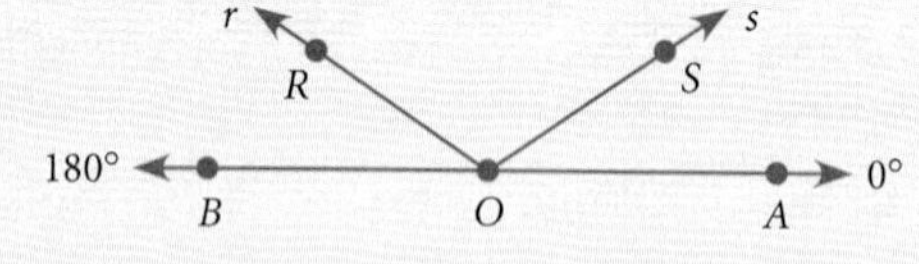

Tips from Teachers

The formal language in the Protractor Postulate may seem difficult to some students. You may want to demonstrate the postulate by drawing the rays described on a chalkboard or overhead and overlaying a protractor, as specified in Parts *a* and *b* of the postulate. You can then ask the students how to find $m\angle ROS$. Their intuitive method should match the postulate.

The Protractor Postulate does for angles what the Ruler Postulate does for segments. It guarantees that any angle has exactly one measure. Notice that the Protractor Postulate also ensures that all angle measures are less than 180°. (We will generally use this restriction; however, remember that measures for bearings, vectors, and rotations can be greater than or equal to 180°!)

TRY IT

a. Find the measure of each angle. What postulate assures you that each angle has a unique measure assigned to it?

i. $\angle SAQ$ 45° **ii.** $\angle PAQ$ 10°

iii. $\angle VAT$ 80° 95° **iv.** $\angle WAT$

Protractor Postulate

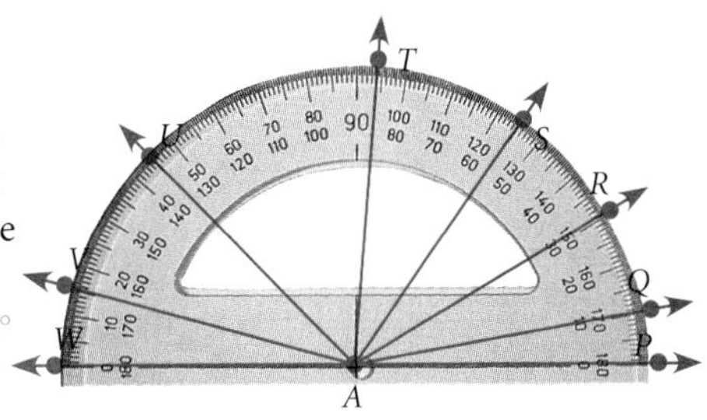

The following Explore will help you to discover another postulate about measuring angles.

EXPLORE: ANGLES, ANGLES, EVERYWHERE

1. Use the figure to find the measures of the angles listed below. (Don't use a protractor—use the measures shown!)

$m\angle AIC =$ ___ $m\angle BID =$ ___
$m\angle DIF =$ ___ $m\angle EIG =$ ___
$m\angle GID =$ ___ $m\angle FIH =$ ___
$m\angle AIG =$ ___

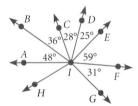

2. Explain how you found the measures of these angles. If there are any that you cannot find, explain why.

TRY IT

b. $m\angle QRP = 45°$, and $m\angle QRN = 132°$. Find $m\angle PRN$. $m\angle PRN = 87°$

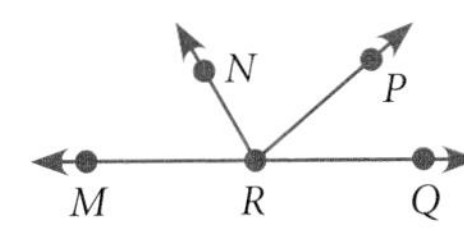

EXPLORE

Angles, Angles Everywhere

Recommended group size: 2

The Point

To discover the Protractor Postulate.

Look and Listen...

- For students who give angle measures greater than 180°.

Ask...

- What is the largest measure that an *angle* can have?

For Groups That Finish Early

How many angles are there in the figure? Find an organized method for listing them all.

Follow Up

Ask students to make a conjecture about the measure of an angle formed by two other angles.

Possible Answers

1. $m\angle AIC = 84°$; $m\angle BID = 64°$; $m\angle DIF = 84°$; $m\angle EIG = 90°$; $m\angle GID = 115°$; $m\angle FIH$ cannot be determined; $m\angle AIG = 133°$.

2. Measures of angles with rays in their interiors are found by adding the measures of the smaller angles. It is impossible to find $m\angle FIH$, since $m\angle GIH$ cannot be determined.

Student Resources

- Alternative Lessons 3-3A
- Laboratory Manual 3-3A
- Technology Lab Manual
- Practice 3-3A
- Study Guide and Journal 3-3A
- Guía de estudios y Diario 3-3A
- Multilingual Handbook
- More Look Back 3-3A
- SAT Preparation

Media Resources

- Transparency FFM 3-3A
- Transparency AE
- Teaching Transparency
- AWSMTest and practice software
- AWSM Videodisc

3-3

Precise Thinking with Angles

Journal

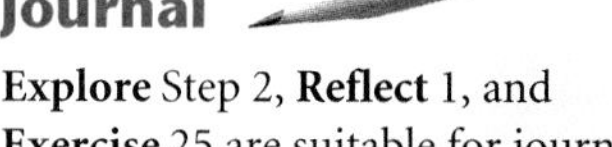

Explore Step 2, **Reflect** 1, and **Exercise** 25 are suitable for journal entries.

REFLECT

Possible Answers

1. The Segment-Addition Postulate. Although it applies to segments rather than angles, both say that the measure of the whole is equal to the sum of the measures of its parts.
2. If *F* is in the exterior of the angle, $m\angle FHG$ should be greater than $m\angle EHG$, so $m\angle EHF + m\angle FHG$ cannot equal $m\angle EHG$. In the Segment-Addition Postulate, we specify that one point is between the other two.

Part A Exercises

Exercise Notes

Core

8. and 9. These exercises (as well as Exercises 38 and 39) involve solving linear equations to find angle measures.

20. Shows how the Angle-Addition Postulate can be used to explain compositions of rotations.

More Math Reasoning

40. Similar to problems found on some standardized tests. Students must use proportional thinking, particularly in 40c.

Exercise Answers

Core

6. $m\angle BCE - m\angle DCE = m\angle BCD$; 19°

7. $m\angle BCE - m\angle BCD = m\angle DCE$; 43°

8. $m\angle BCE - m\angle DCE = m\angle BCD$; $m\angle DCE = 24°$ and $m\angle BCE = 48°$

9. $m\angle BCD + m\angle DCE = m\angle BCE$; $m\angle BCD = 39°$ and $m\angle DCE = 37°$

19. 55°; Angle-Addition Postulate

$m\angle BAD = 77°$; $m\angle DAC = 60°$

c. Suppose $m\angle BAC = 137°$. Find $m\angle BAD$ and $m\angle DAC$.

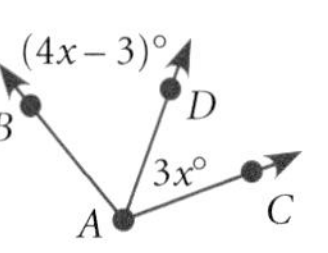

Problem-Solving Tip

Write an equation to represent the situation.

The method you have discovered for adding angle measures is formalized in the Angle-Addition Postulate.

ANGLE-ADDITION POSTULATE

If *F* is in the interior of $\angle EHG$, then $m\angle EHF + m\angle FHG = m\angle EHG$.

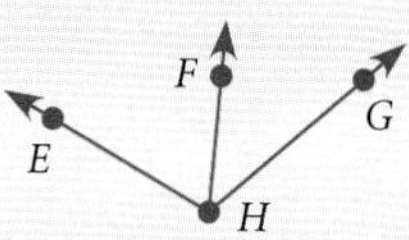

REFLECT

1. What postulate about segments is like the Angle-Addition Postulate? Explain the similarities and differences between the postulates.
2. Explain why the Angle-Addition Postulate begins with "If *F* is in the interior . . ." Use a sketch of $\angle EHG$ with a point, *F*, that is not in its interior to illustrate your answer. What requirement for adding segment lengths is similar to the requirement that *F* be in the interior of the angle?

Exercises

CORE

P **Getting Started** **Find the measure of each angle.**

1. $\angle WXV$ 15° **2.** $\angle VXU$ 30° **3.** $\angle VXS$ 110°

4. $\angle UXT$ 50° **5.** $\angle RXP$ 30°

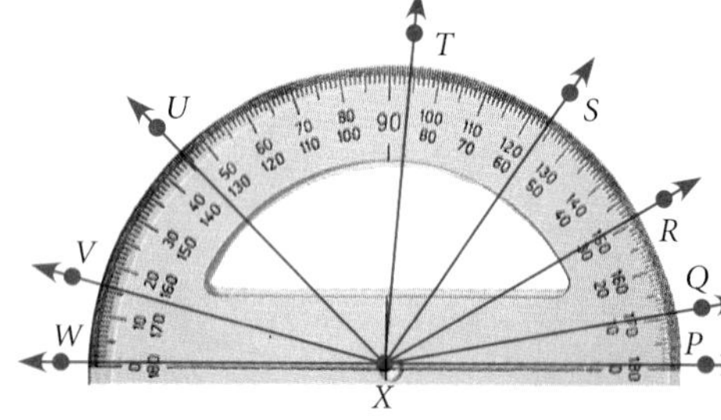

Key

V Vocabulary
P Practice/Skills
R Review
MR Math Reasoning
PS Problem Solving
C Challenge

Alert

The different contexts in which angle-like measurements occur may be confusing. You may need to remind some students of the difference between measures of angles, which must be between 0° and 180°, and those of bearings, vector directions, and angles of rotation, which can have measures outside this range. In general, students should use the 0° to 180° range, unless the measurement involves a turn or rotation.

Write and solve an equation to find the measure of each angle.

6. $m\angle BCE = 45°$ and $m\angle DCE = 26°$. Find $m\angle BCD$.

7. $m\angle BCE = 80°$ and $m\angle BCD = 37°$. Find $m\angle DCE$.

8. $m\angle BCE = 4x°$, $m\angle DCE = 2x°$, and $m\angle BCD = 24°$. Find $m\angle DCE$ and $m\angle BCE$.

9. $m\angle BCD = (2x + 7)°$, $m\angle DCE = (3x - 11)°$, and $m\angle BCE = 76°$. Find $m\angle BCD$ and $m\angle DCE$.

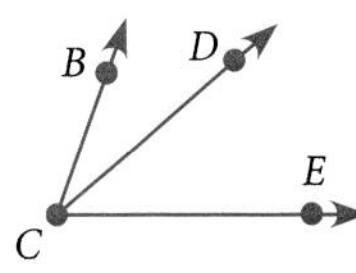

In the figure at the right, $\angle HML$ is a right angle, $m\angle KML = 20°$, $m\angle JMK = m\angle HMJ$, and $m\angle FMG = m\angle KML$. Find the measure of each angle.

10. $\angle JMK$ 35° **11.** $\angle HMK$ 70° **12.** $\angle FMG$ 20°

13. $\angle GMH$ 70° **14.** $\angle GMK$ 140° **15.** $\angle GML$ 160°

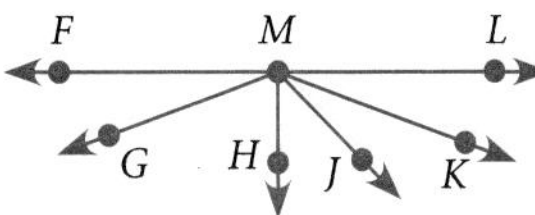

A light ray reflects off a mirror as shown. Find the measure of each angle.

16. $\angle NSQ$ 102° **17.** $\angle MSN$ 39° **18.** $\angle NSR$ 141°

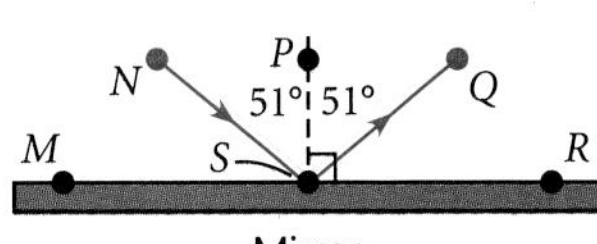

19. Don't Scratch the Paint! A car door is pushed open 35°. An additional push opens the door another 20°. What is the final angle of opening of the door? Which postulate justifies your answer?

20. Copy segment $\overline{AB}$ and point V. Rotate $\overline{AB}$ 90° clockwise around V. Label the rotation image $\overline{CD}$. Then rotate $\overline{CD}$ 45° clockwise around V, and label its image $\overline{EF}$. What is the angle of rotation from $\overline{AB}$ to $\overline{EF}$? Explain your answer.

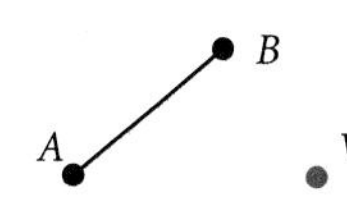

21. Using the figure at the right, justify the conjecture "If $\angle LMN \cong \angle OMP$, then $\angle LMO \cong \angle NMP$."

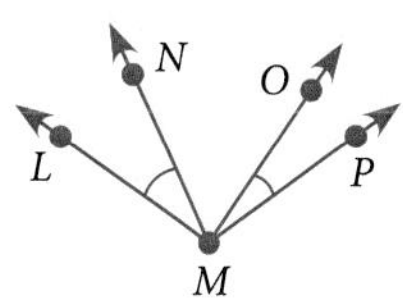

Sketch each figure.

22. two angles with equal measures that each have $\overrightarrow{AB}$ as a side

23. two angles in which the vertex of each is in the interior of the other

24. two angles that intersect in exactly one point

25. Two sides of a picture frame are glued together to form a corner.

a. If each side is cut at a 45° angle, what is the angle measure of the corner of the frame? Which postulate or definition justifies your answer?

b. You need to make a six-sided frame whose corners measure 120°. Explain how you would cut the sides of the frame.

Ongoing Assessment

Self-Assessment Exercises 1–19 odd

Embedded Assessment Try It a; Reflect 1; Exercises 8, 14, 25

20. 135°; Sum of separate rotation angles; Angle-Addition Postulate

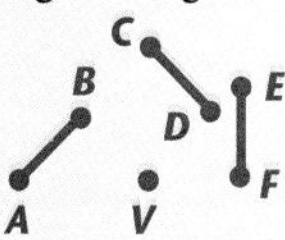

21. $m\angle LMN + m\angle NMO = m\angle LMO$; By substitution, $m\angle OMP + m\angle NMO = m\angle LMO$; By Angle-Addition $m\angle OMP + m\angle NMO = m\angle NMP$, so $\angle LMO \cong \angle NMP$

22. Possible answer: $\angle CAB$ and $\angle BAD$

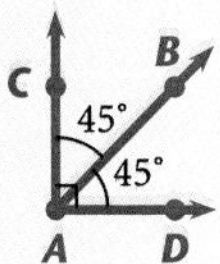

23. Possible answer: $\angle BAC$ and $\angle DFE$

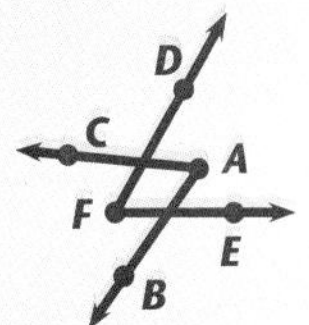

24. Possible answer: $\angle CAB$ and $\angle DAE$

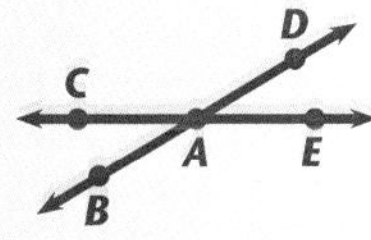

25. a. 90°; Angle-Addition Postulate

b. Each side is cut at a 60° angle.

Look Back

26. If a point is the midpoint of a segment, then it must be between the endpoints of the segment.

27. If a figure is a quadrilateral, then it has four sides.

28. If you love life, then do not squander time.

29. Yes; 90°, 180°, 270°

30. No **31.** Yes; 180°

More Practice

38. $m\angle BCE - m\angle DCE = m\angle BCD$; 83°

39. $m\angle BCD + m\angle DCE = m\angle BCE$; $m\angle BCD = 60°$ and $m\angle DCE = 2°$

Precise Thinking with Angles

More Math Reasoning

41. They are all possible except the last, as shown by the various ways $\overrightarrow{AB}$ can intersect $\angle CDE$:

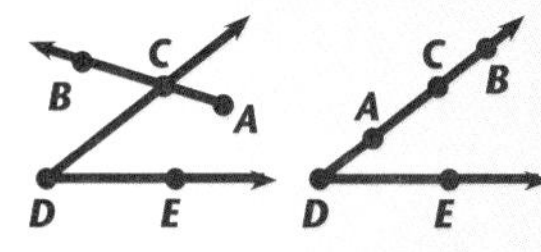

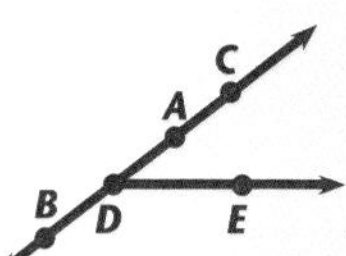

42. Measure the "other" angle instead.

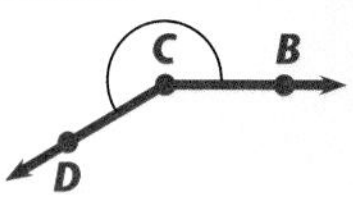

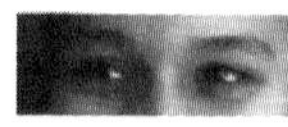

Algebra | Functions | Discrete Math | Probability | Data/Statistics

LOOK BACK

R **Rewrite each statement or set of statements as a single conditional in if-then form. [2-1]**

26. The midpoint of a segment must be between its endpoints.

27. All quadrilaterals have four sides.

Literature **28.** "[Do you] love life? Then do not squander time. . . ." (Benjamin Franklin, *Poor Richard's Almanac*)

R **Determine whether each figure at the right has rotational symmetry. If it does, give the clockwise angles of rotation between 0° and 360° that cause the image and pre-image to coincide. [3-2]**

29. **30.** **31.**

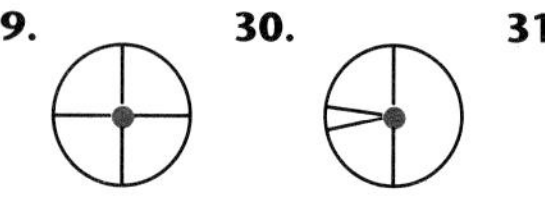

MORE PRACTICE

P **Find the measure of each angle.**

32. $\angle SRT$ 20° **33.** $\angle TRV$ 80°

34. $\angle URW$ 90° **35.** $\angle TRX$ 160°

36. $\angle SRU$ 55° **37.** $\angle VRX$ 80°

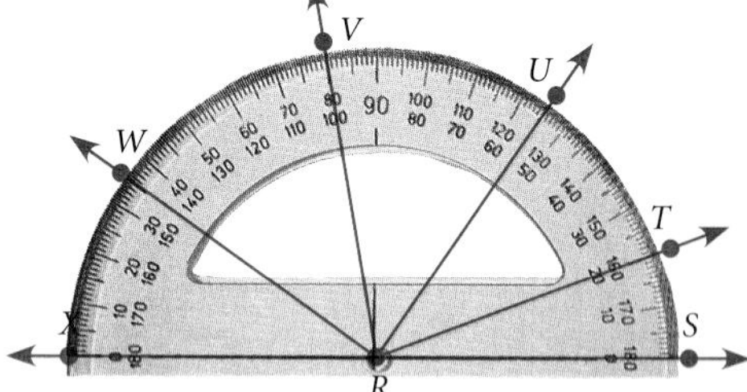

P **Write and solve an equation to find the measure of each angle.**

38. $m\angle BCE = 131°$, and $m\angle DCE = 48°$. Find $m\angle BCD$.

39. $m\angle BCD = (4x + 20)°$, $m\angle DCE = (32 - 3x)°$, and $m\angle BCE = 62°$. Find $m\angle BCD$ and $m\angle DCE$.

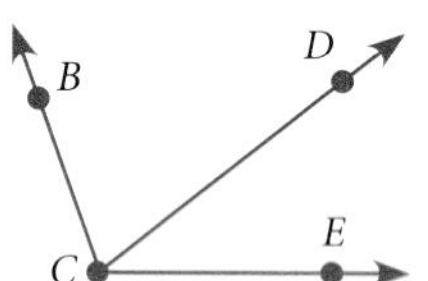

MORE MATH REASONING

MR **40. Angle Time** Find the exact measure of the angle made by the hands of a clock at each of the following times.
a. 8:00 120° **b.** 8:30 75° **c.** 8:25 102.5

MR, C **41.** Tonyetta wondered how many different figures could be formed by the intersection of a ray and an angle. Could they, for example, be drawn to intersect in a point? a segment? a ray? an angle? Try sketching each situation. Determine which are possible and which, if any, are not.

MR **42.** Sketch an "angle" that appears to be greater than 180°. What does the Protractor Postulate say about how to measure it?

Key

V Vocabulary
P Practice/Skills
R Review
MR Math Reasoning
PS Problem Solving
C Challenge

3-3 PART B Assumptions and Figures

← CONNECT → *You've seen how assuming too much from a picture can mislead you. Now you will discover the assumptions that you can and cannot make when you look at a geometric figure.*

The Angle-Addition Postulate makes sense, but you must be sure not to assume too much when you use it. For example, you can't say that $m\angle WXY + m\angle YXZ = m\angle WXZ$ unless you know something about the location of point *Y*.

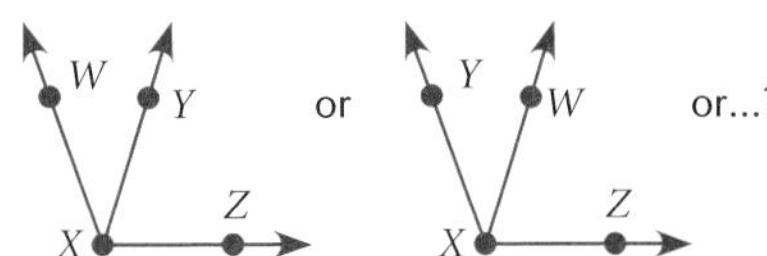

Unjustified assumptions can cause problems in geometry just as they can in everyday life. In a figure, what looks like a right angle might really measure 89.4°. Although this difference may seem unimportant, it is significant when you are placing a communications satellite in space or constructing a skyscraper.

Since you cannot always trust what you see, you must be careful of the assumptions you make when looking at a figure. In the following Explore, you will think about what can and cannot be assumed from a figure.

EXPLORE: TO ASSUME OR NOT TO ASSUME . . .

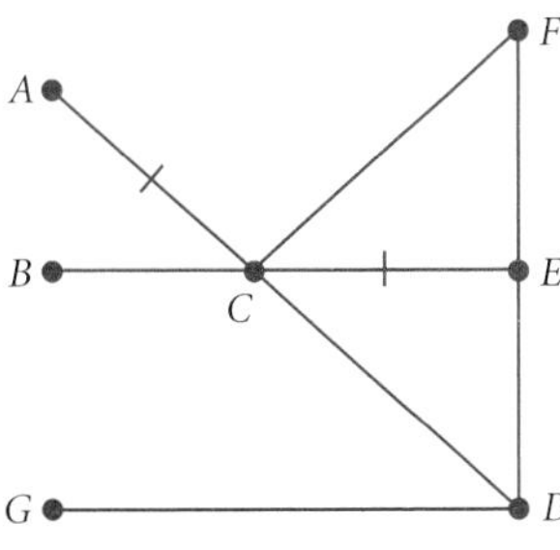

1. In the figure, do you think you would be justified in assuming that *B, C,* and *E* are collinear? that $\angle ACB \cong \angle FCE$? that $\overline{BE} \parallel \overline{GD}$? Make a list of things you think you can and cannot assume from this figure.
2. Make a list of rules about what you think you can and cannot assume. Compare your list with others. Then try to make a general statement about what you can and cannot assume from a figure.

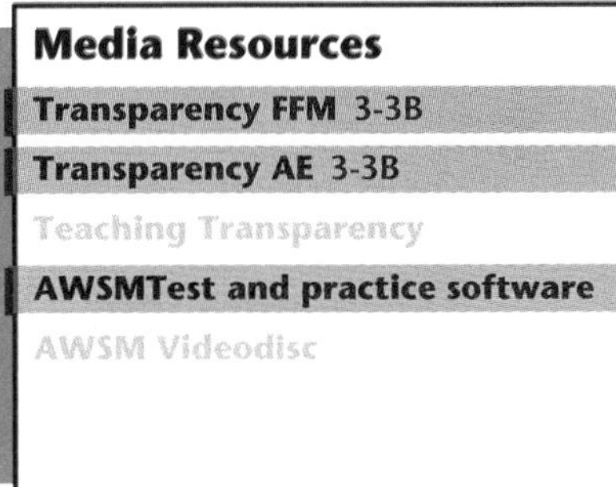

Student Resources
- Alternative Lessons 3-3B
- Laboratory Manual 3-3B
- Technology Lab Manual
- Practice 3-3B
- Study Guide and Journal 3-3B
- Guía de estudios y Diario 3-3B
- Multilingual Handbook
- More Look Ahead 3-3B
- SAT Preparation

Media Resources
- Transparency FFM 3-3B
- Transparency AE 3-3B
- Teaching Transparency
- AWSMTest and practice software
- AWSM Videodisc

PART B At a Glance

Objective

To determine what can and cannot be assumed from figures.

Development

In the **Explore,** students examine a figure to decide what should and should not be assumed visually. Guidelines are given to help them summarize their findings.

Finally, students see an **Example** of these concepts and show their understanding in a **Try It.**

First Five Minutes

Transparency FFM 3-3B

Sketch and mark a figure to show the following:

$\overline{AB} \perp \overline{CD}$ at *C*; $\overline{AC} \cong \overline{CB}$; $\angle ACE \cong \angle CAF$.

Possible Answer

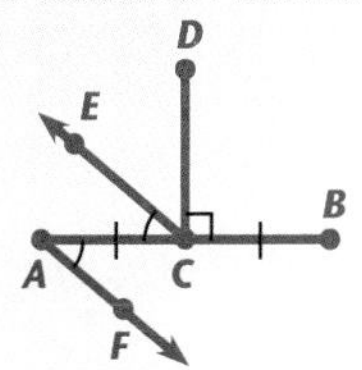

Motivate

Ask...

- Can you give examples of real-world situations where you should not make an assumption based on what you see?

EXPLORE

To Assume or Not to Assume...

Recommended group size: 4

The Point

To decide what can and cannot be assumed from a figure.

3-3

Algebra	Functions	Discrete Math	Probability	Data/Statistics

Precise Thinking with Angles

Look and Listen...

- For students who are using rulers and protractors to measure parts of the figure. Remind them that such measurements are inexact and cannot be used to draw mathematical conclusions.
- For students who are only considering congruence, perpendicularity, and parallelism in their lists.

Ask...

- Can you assume that C is between B and E? that $\overline{AD}$ and $\overline{BE}$ intersect at C?

For Groups That Finish Early

Sketch one figure that involves every type of geometric marking that you can think of.

Follow Up

Use a protractor to draw angles of 84°, 86°, 88°, 90°, 92°, 94°, and 96°. Mix them up and see whether you can identify the one that measures 90° by sight.

Possible Answers

1. Can assume: $\overline{AC} \cong \overline{CE}$; B, C, and E are collinear; E is between F and D, and so on.

   Cannot assume: $\overline{AC} \cong \overline{CF}$; $\overline{BE} \parallel \overline{GD}$; $\overline{FD} \perp \overline{BE}$; C is the midpoint of $\overline{AD}$; $\overline{AD}$ bisects $\overline{BE}$, and so on.
2. You may not assume things that require specific measures (e.g., perpendicularity, congruence, midpoint). You may assume that positional relationships are accurate (e.g., between, collinear, intersecting).

ALTERNATE EXAMPLES

Transparency AE 3-3B

The table below summarizes what can and cannot be assumed from a figure.

You *May* Assume:	You *May Not* Assume (unless marked):
• Things that look straight are straight.	• Exact measurements and relative sizes of figures.
• Points of intersection are shown accurately.	• Parallel or perpendicular lines.
• Points shown on a line are collinear. Unless planes are drawn, all points shown are coplanar.	• Congruence.
• Relative positions of points are accurate.	

EXAMPLES

Determine whether the following specific relationships can be assumed from the figure.

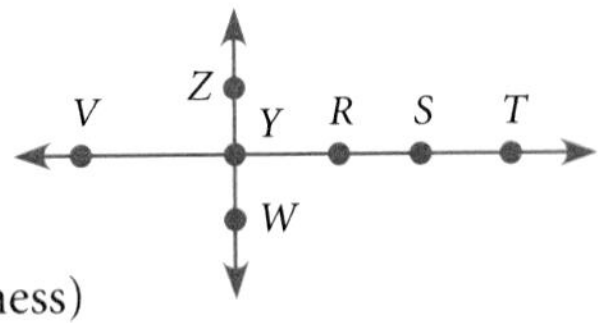

1. Point S is between R and T. (betweenness)
   Yes; relative positions are accurate.
2. Points R, S, and T are collinear. (collinearity)
   Yes; points shown on a line are collinear.
3. $\overline{RS} \cong \overline{ST}$ (congruence)
   No; congruence cannot be assumed unless marked.
4. Point S is the midpoint of $\overline{RT}$. (midpoint)
   No; you cannot assume that point S divides $\overline{RT}$ into two congruent segments.
5. $\overleftrightarrow{VR} \perp \overleftrightarrow{ZW}$ (perpendicularity)
   No; perpendicularity cannot be assumed unless marked.
6. $\angle ZYV$ is a right angle. (angle size)
   No; you cannot assume exact measurements.
7. $VY < TY$ (relative sizes of segments or angles)
   No; you cannot assume that relative sizes of segments or angles are shown accurately.

You will soon draw and mark figures to illustrate deductive arguments. The following Try It will give you an opportunity to put together everything you know about figures.

TRY IT

a. Draw and mark one figure that shows all of the following relationships.

On line m, B is the midpoint of $\overline{AC}$.
Line $n \parallel m$
$\angle ABD \cong \angle ABE$

REFLECT

1. Identify the figures that allow you to conclude that $\overline{ST} \cong \overline{TU}$. Explain your choice(s).

(a) S T U

(b)

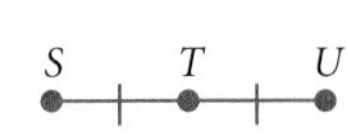

(c)

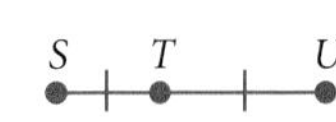

2. Do the guidelines for what you can and cannot assume from a figure make sense? If they do, explain why. If they do not, explain how you would change them and why you think they should be different.

Exercises

CORE

Getting Started In Exercises 1–4, determine whether the following specific relationships can be assumed from the figure at the right.

1. $\overrightarrow{GF}$ and $\overrightarrow{GI}$ are opposite rays. Yes
2. $\angle HGF$ is a right angle. No
3. $\overleftrightarrow{FI}$ is a straight line. Yes
4. $\angle GFH$ and $\angle GHF$ are congruent. No

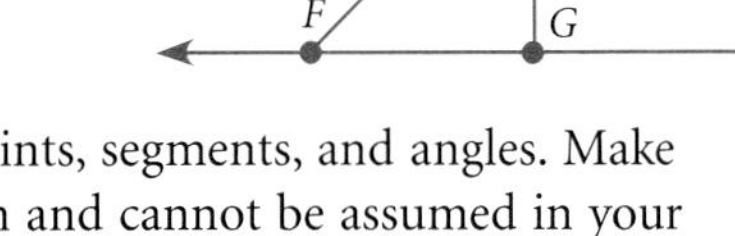

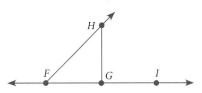

5. Make a sketch of your own that includes points, segments, and angles. Make up three true/false questions about what can and cannot be assumed in your figure, and give the answers for the questions. Check students' answers.

Ongoing Assessment

Vocabulary
Practice/Skills
Review
Math Reasoning
Problem Solving
Challenge

Self-Assessment Exercises 1, 2, 3, 7, 9, 11, 13

Embedded Assessment Explore Step 2; Exercises 5, 8, 10, 12

Journal

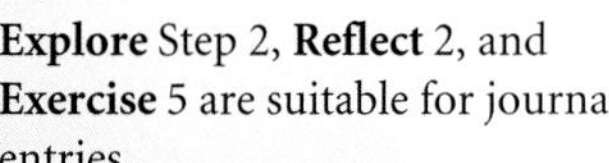

Explore Step 2, **Reflect** 2, and **Exercise** 5 are suitable for journal entries.

REFLECT

Possible Answers

1. Figures (b) and (c), because of congruence markings.
2. The guidelines make sense. Because our eyes and measuring instruments can be inaccurate or imprecise, we should not assume anything that depends on exact measurements, for example, that an angle measures exactly 90°. We have to be able to assume that a figure is not misleading about locations of points, however, or else it would be worthless.

TRY IT

Answer

a. Possible answer:

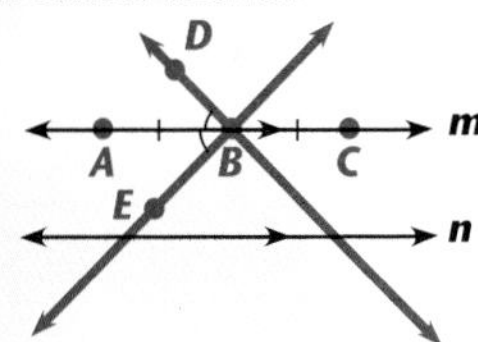

Part B Exercises

Exercise Notes

Core

5. Students make up questions about a sketch of their own. You may want to have students exchange copies of these and answer each other's questions.

Look Ahead

15. and 16. These exercises preview complementary and supplementary angles, which are introduced in 3-3 Part C.

More Math Reasoning

24. Shows students that inaccuracies that might seem small can have significant consequences. This helps show the importance of not making unjustified assumptions from visual information.

Exercise Answers

Core

6. No; Cannot be assumed to be perpendicular

7. Yes; Points shown on a line are collinear

Precise Thinking with Angles

8. No; Congruence cannot be assumed.

9. Yes; Relative positions of points are accurate.

10. Yes; Points of intersection are shown accurately.

11. No; Cannot be assumed to be parallel

12. Possible answer: Assume: A, C, and D are collinear; C is between B and E (relative positions); $\overline{BE}$ and $\overline{AD}$ intersect at C; Cannot assume: $m\angle ACB = 30°$; $\overline{AB} \perp \overline{AC}$; $\overline{AC} \cong \overline{CD}$

13.

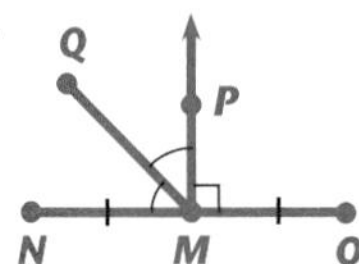

14.

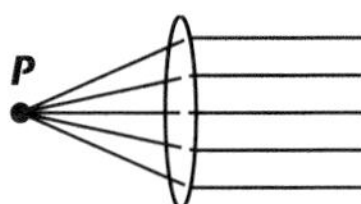

Look Ahead

15. $m\angle FGH = 55°$; $m\angle PQR = 145°$

16. $\angle STU \cong \angle XYZ$

More Practice

21. Possible answer: Assume $\overline{WZ} \cong \overline{ZY}$; Z is midpoint of $\overline{WY}$; W, Z, Y are collinear; Cannot assume: $\overline{WX} \cong \overline{XY}$; $\overline{ZX} \perp \overline{WY}$; $m\angle W = m\angle Y$

22.

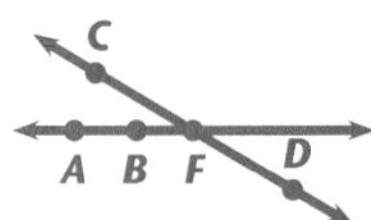

More Math Reasoning

23. 25 possible angle combinations, 5 of which make the angles congruent: $\frac{5}{25} = \frac{1}{5}$.

24. Assuming the wall remains a straight line, it goes farther out of line at the rate of 1 in. every 5 feet for a total of $\frac{1}{5} \times 250 = 50$ in.

P **Determine whether the following specific relationships can be assumed from the figure at the right. Explain.**

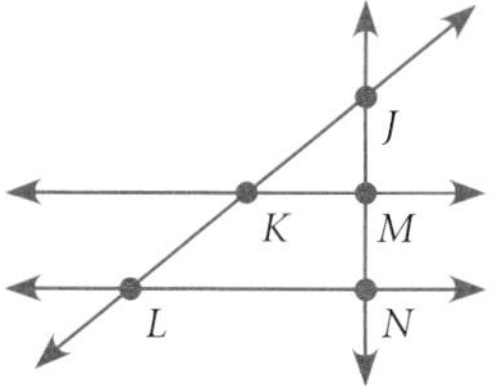

6. $\overline{JN} \perp \overline{LN}$ **7.** Points J, M, and N are collinear.

8. $\overline{JM} \cong \overline{KM}$ **9.** Point M is between J and N.

10. $\overleftrightarrow{JL}$ intersects $\overleftrightarrow{KM}$. **11.** $\overleftrightarrow{KM} \parallel \overleftrightarrow{LN}$

P **12.** List three things you *can* assume and three things you *cannot* assume from the figure at the right.

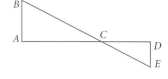

P **13.** Draw and mark one figure that shows all of the following relationships.

Point M is the midpoint of $\overline{NO}$. $\overrightarrow{MP} \perp \overline{NO}$. $\angle NMQ \cong \angle QMP$.

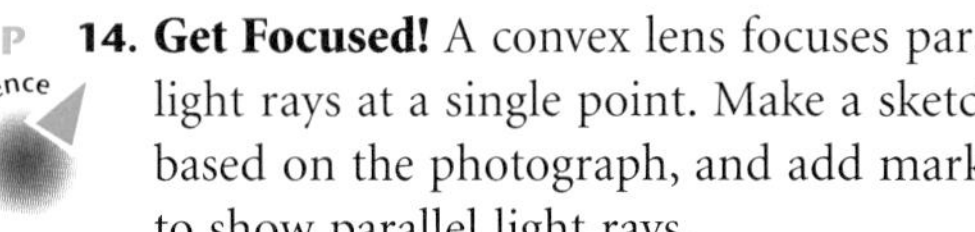

P **14. Get Focused!** A convex lens focuses parallel light rays at a single point. Make a sketch based on the photograph, and add markings to show parallel light rays.

Science

LOOK AHEAD

P **15.** $m\angle ABC = 35°$. Determine the measures of angles $\angle FGH$ and $\angle PQR$ so that $m\angle ABC + m\angle FGH = 90°$, and $m\angle ABC + m\angle PQR = 180°$.

P **16.** Suppose $m\angle JKL + m\angle STU = 90°$, and $m\angle JKL + m\angle XYZ = 90°$. What can you say about $\angle STU$ and $\angle XYZ$?

MORE PRACTICE

P **Determine whether the following specific relationships can be assumed from the figure at the right.**

17. $\angle P$ is a right angle. No **18.** $\angle O$ is a right angle. Yes

19. $\overline{MP} \cong \overline{NO}$ No **20.** $MNOP$ is a rectangle. No

P **21.** List three things you *can* assume and three that you *cannot* assume in the figure at the right.

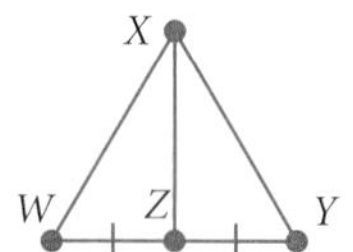

P **22.** Draw and mark one figure that shows all of the following.

Lines $\overleftrightarrow{AB}$ and $\overleftrightarrow{CD}$ intersect at F. Point B is between points A and F. $\angle AFD$ is not congruent to $\angle AFC$.

Key

V Vocabulary
P Practice/Skills
R Review
MR Math Reasoning
PS Problem Solving
C Challenge

MORE MATH REASONING

23. Angles $\angle OPQ$ and $\angle TSR$ are completed by randomly selecting points from the grid, as shown. What is the probability that the angles will be congruent? Explain.

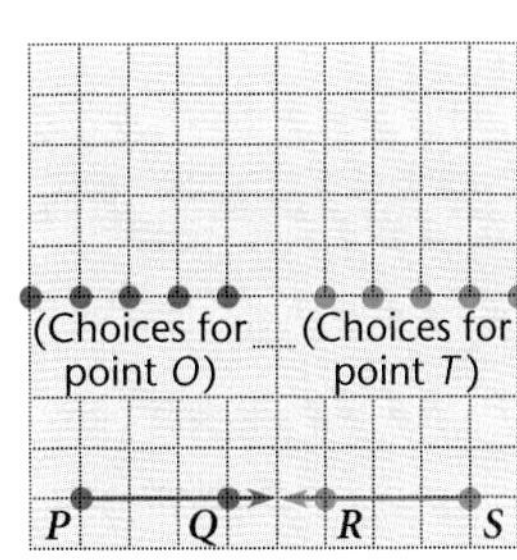

24. A Matter of Degree Suppose that a person working on the construction of an office building assumed that the corner at the right measured exactly 90° when it actually measured 89°. After the wall is extended 5 ft, it is 1 in. out of alignment.

If the office building is 250 ft long, how far out of alignment will the end of the wall be? Explain your reasoning, and state any assumptions that you are making.

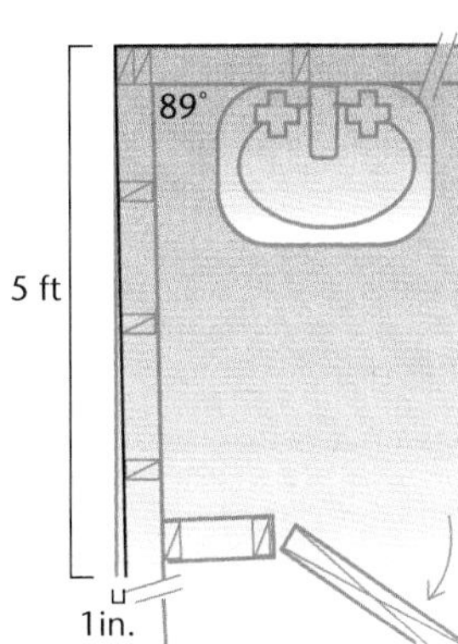

PART C At a Glance

Objective

To develop definitions and theorems about special angle pairs.

Development

Students learn definitions of complementary/supplementary angles and of a linear pair.

In the **Explore,** students discover that angles in a linear pair are supplementary and that complements and supplements of congruent angles (or the same angle) are congruent.

Suggested Materials

Student Straightedge, protractor

Key Terms

Complementary angles, supplementary angles, linear pair

3-3 PART C Angle Pairs

← CONNECT → *You know quite a bit about individual angles. Now you will develop some definitions and theorems about pairs of angles.*

You have seen how the Angle-Addition Postulate allows you to add the measures of angles under certain conditions. Now you will combine that postulate with some new angle classifications to make some new conjectures.

DEFINITIONS

Complementary angles are two angles whose measures add up to 90°.

Supplementary angles are two angles whose measures add up to 180°.

Student Resources

- Alternative Lessons 3-3C
- Laboratory Manual 3-3C
- Technology Lab Manual
- Practice 3-3C
- Study Guide and Journal 3-3C
- Guía de estudios y Diario 3-3C
- Multilingual Handbook
- More Look Back 3-3C
- SAT Preparation

Media Resources

- Transparency FFM 3-3C
- Transparency AE 3-3C
- Teaching Transparency
- AWSMTest and practice software
- AWSM Videodisc

First Five Minutes

Transparency FFM 3-3C

Read the first paragraph on page 201 and the definitions of complementary and supplementary angles. Find measures of angles complementary and supplementary to $\angle A$ in the following cases.

1. $m\angle A = 40°$ 50°, 140°

2. $m\angle A = 85°$ 5°, 95°

3. $m\angle A = 100°$ No complement, 80°.

Motivate

Ask...

- What is special about the degree measures 90° and 180°?

Precise Thinking with Angles

ALTERNATE EXAMPLES

1. Name all linear pairs in the figure below.

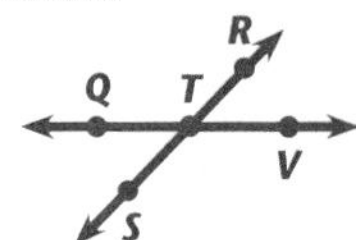

$\angle QTR$ and $\angle RTV$; $\angle RTV$ and $\angle VTS$; $\angle VTS$ and $\angle STQ$; $\angle STQ$ and $\angle QTR$

2. If $m\angle S = 39°$, find the measures of angles complementary and supplementary to $\angle S$.

The measure of the angle complementary to $\angle S$ is 51°, because $90° - 39° = 51°$.

The measure of the angle supplementary to $\angle S$ is 141°, because $180° - 39° = 141°$.

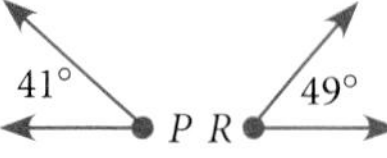

$\angle R$ is complementary to $\angle P$. ($\angle R$ is the *complement* of $\angle P$.)

$\angle S$ is supplementary to $\angle P$. ($\angle S$ is the *supplement* of $\angle P$.)

Angles can be complementary or supplementary regardless of their location. However, some angle pairs are determined by location.

DEFINITION

Two angles, $\angle ABD$ and $\angle DBC$, form a **linear pair** if and only if A, B, and C are collinear and D is not on $\overleftrightarrow{AC}$.

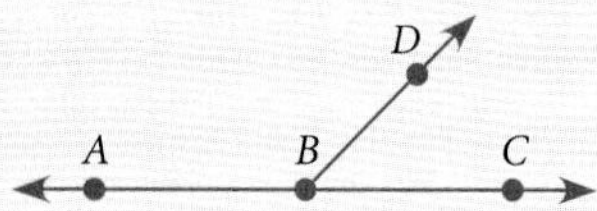

EXAMPLES

1. Name all linear pairs in the figure below.

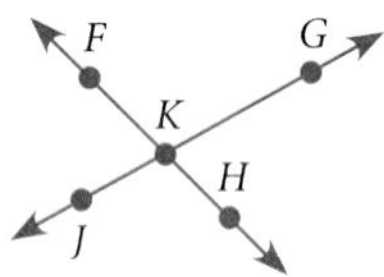

The four linear pairs are $\angle JKF$ and $\angle FKG$, $\angle FKG$ and $\angle GKH$, $\angle GKH$ and $\angle HKJ$, and $\angle HKJ$ and $\angle JKF$.

2. If $m\angle X = 64°$, find the measures of the angles that are complementary and supplementary to $\angle X$.
The measures of two complementary angles must add to 90°, so the measure of the complement of $\angle X$ is $90° - 64° = 26°$.
The measures of two supplementary angles must add to 180°, so the measure of the supplement of $\angle X$ is $180° - 64° = 116°$.

In the following Explore, you will make some conjectures about angles in a linear pair, complementary angles, and supplementary angles.

History Connection

Srinivasa Ramujnan (1887–1920) was one of the greatest mathematical geniuses of this century. Born in South India into a poor family, he was largely self-taught. Ramujnan's chief interest was in number theory. His work has had applications in cancer research, statistical mechanics, and the development of techniques for measuring extreme temperatures.

EXPLORE: ANGLING FOR THEOREMS

MATERIALS

Straightedge
Protractor

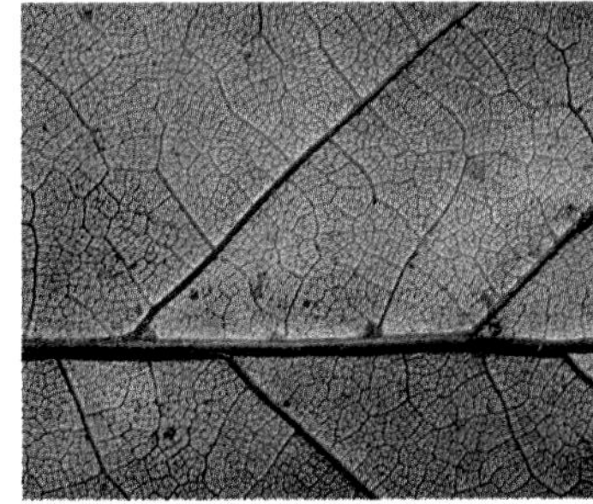

1. The photo shows linear pairs of angles in a leaf. Make as many conjectures about the angles in a linear pair as you can. Drawing one or more linear pairs and taking some measurements may help you.
2. Now you will investigate a relationship between angles and their supplements.
   a. Suppose an angle measures 50°. What is the measure of any angle that is supplementary to it?
   b. Suppose *two* angles each measure 50°. What is the measure of any angle supplementary to both of them?
   c. Make a conjecture about supplements of congruent angles. See if you can make a similar conjecture about any two angles that are supplementary to the same angle.
3. Using your conjectures from Step 2 as a guideline, make similar conjectures about complements of congruent angles and complements of the same angle.

TRY IT

a. List all pairs of congruent angles in the figure. $\angle MTR$ and $\angle MTN$, $\angle RTS$ and $\angle NTP$, $\angle MTS$ and $\angle MTP$

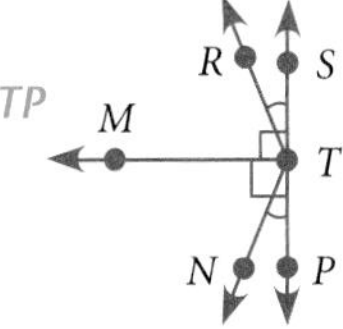

Find the measure of each of the following angles.

b. $\angle WZX$ 69° **c.** $\angle WZY$ 159° **d.** $\angle XZY$ 90°

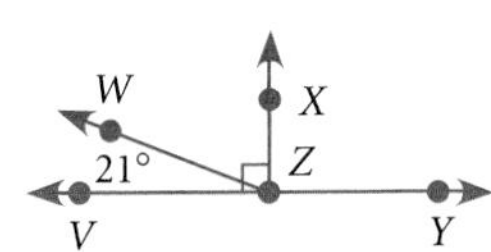

Some properties of angles and angle pairs are summarized below.

LINEAR-PAIR POSTULATE

The angles in a linear pair are supplementary.

EXPLORE

Angling for Theorems

Recommended group size: 4

The Point
To discover the Linear-Pair Postulate and theorems about the congruence of angles that are complementary and supplementary to congruent angles (or the same angle).

Look and Listen...
- For students who do not notice that the two 50° angles in Step 2b. are the congruent angles referred to in Step 2c.

Ask...
- Do you think you would get the same results for an angle that did not measure 50°? Do you want to try another angle measure to make sure?

For Groups That Finish Early
Use algebra to justify as many of your conjectures as you can. Hint: If $m\angle A = x°$, what is the measure of its complement? its supplement?

Follow Up
List all of the conjectures students have made about complementary and supplementary angles.

Possible Answers
1. The angles in a linear pair are supplementary.
2. a. 130°
   b. 130°
   c. Supplements of congruent angles are congruent; supplements of the same angle are congruent.
3. Complements of congruent angles are congruent; complements of the same angle are congruent.

Research Note

At a higher cognitive level, questions...call for a deeper comprehension of the mathematical situation....In a study of 8 ninth-grade algebra classes, Koehler found an average of 64.1 interactions in a 50 minute period. Of these, an average of 50.3 interactions involved low-level mathematics, [and] 1.0 involved high-level mathematics. (Mary Schatz Koehler and Millie Prior, "Classroom Interactions: The Heartbeat of the Teaching/Learning Process," *Research Ideas for the Classroom: Middle Grades Mathematics,* NCTM Research Interpretation Project, Douglas T. Owens, ed., pp. 289–90. © 1993 NCTM.)

3-3

Precise Thinking with Angles

Journal

Reflect 1 and **Exercises** 16 and 19 are suitable for journal entries.

REFLECT

Possible Answers

1. They are right angles. If their measures add to 180° and are equal, each must measure 90°.
2. Complement: $(90 - x)°$; supplement: $(180 - x)°$.

Part C Exercises

Exercise Notes

Core

16. and 17. These exercises apply the ideas of this part in real-world contexts.

19. Presents a theorem that students will use frequently. You may want to mention this to the class.

More Math Reasoning

30. Students justify steps in a flow proof.

Exercise Answers

Core

1. $\angle BEC$ and $\angle CED$
2. $\angle AEB$ and $\angle BED$ or $\angle AEC$ and $\angle CED$
3. $\angle AEB$ and $\angle BED$ or $\angle AEC$ and $\angle CED$
4. Complement: 17°; Supplement: 107°
5. Complement: 78.3°; Supplement: 168.3°
6. Complement: $67\frac{1}{2}°$; Supplement: $157\frac{1}{2}°$
7. $m\angle NRP = 49°$; $m\angle NRO = 139°$
8. 29°
9. $m\angle MRN = 12°$; $m\angle NRP = 78°$

10. 30° **11.** 30°

12. T **13.** F; Right

14. 45° **15.** 142°

THEOREMS

Supplements of congruent angles (or of the same angle) are congruent.

Complements of congruent angles (or of the same angle) are congruent.

REFLECT

1. Suppose that two angles that form a linear pair are congruent. What else can you say about them? Explain.
2. If the measure of an angle is $x°$, what are the measures of its complement and its supplement?

Exercises

CORE

P **Getting Started Use the figure at the right to name each of the following.**

1. a pair of complementary angles
2. a pair of supplementary angles
3. a linear pair

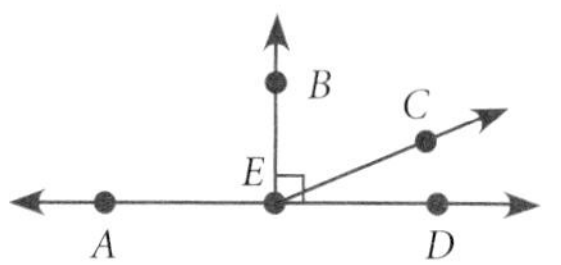

P **For each measure of $\angle 1$, find the measure of its complement and its supplement.**

4. $m\angle 1 = 73°$
5. $m\angle 1 = 11.7°$
6. $m\angle 1 = 22\frac{1}{2}°$

P **Use the given information and the figure at the right to find each angle measure.**

7. $m\angle MRN = 41°$. Find $m\angle NRP$ and $m\angle NRO$.
8. $m\angle NRP = 61°$. Find $m\angle MRN$.
9. $m\angle MRN = (45 - 3x)°$ and $m\angle NRP = (8x - 10)°$. Find $m\angle MRN$ and $m\angle NRP$.

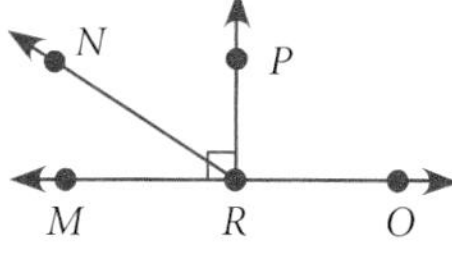

P 10. In the figure at the right, $\overrightarrow{HJ} \perp \overrightarrow{HG}$, and $m\angle JHF = 60°$. Find $m\angle FHG$.

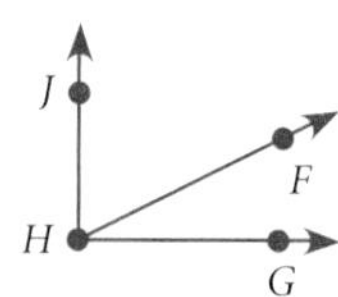

Key

- V Vocabulary
- P Practice/Skills
- R Review
- MR Math Reasoning
- PS Problem Solving
- C Challenge

11. In the figure below, $\angle 2$ is five times as large as $\angle 1$. Find $m\angle 1$.

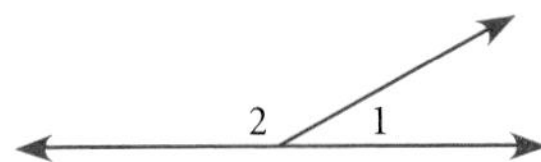

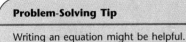

Determine whether each statement is true or false. If the statement is false, change the underlined word or phrase to make it true.

12. The sum of the measures of two <u>supplementary</u> angles is 180°.

13. If two congruent angles form a linear pair, then both of them must be <u>acute</u> angles.

14. Find the measure of an angle whose supplement is three times its complement.

Problem-Solving Tip

Writing an equation might be helpful.

15. One of two supplementary angles is 104° more than the second. Find the measure of the larger angle.

16. Clearly Right When installing a window, a carpenter must be sure the vertical support forms a right angle with the window ledge. If she finds that $\angle 1$ is a right angle, must she also measure $\angle 2$? Write a brief justification of your decision.

17. When a beam of light reflects off a mirror, the angle of incidence is congruent to the angle of reflection. If the angle of incidence is 55°, find $m\angle EBF$.

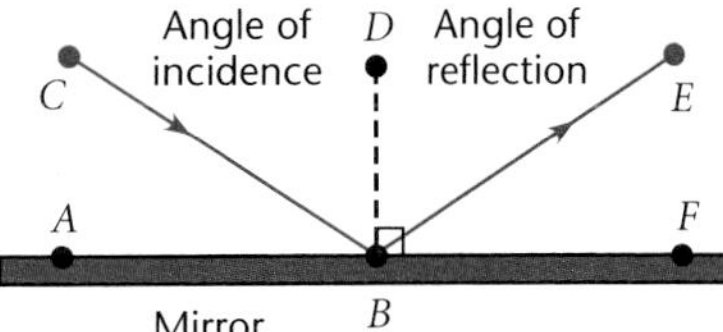

18. Why do you suppose that complementary and supplementary angles are important? In other words, why do we only have special names for angles whose measures add to 90° or 180°?

19. The following theorem is important, but it is not difficult to understand.

THEOREM

All right angles are congruent.

Give a deductive argument to justify this theorem.

Ongoing Assessment

Self-Assessment Exercises 1–17 odd

Embedded Assessment Try It a; Exercises 6, 10, 14, 19

16. Not if the window ledge is flat (straight), in which case $m\angle 1 + m\angle 2 = 90° + m\angle 2 = 180°$ so $m\angle 2 = 90°$.

17. 35°

18. Possible answer: Straight lines and perpendicular lines are basic to geometry.

19. All right angles have the same measure, namely 90°. All angles with the same measure are congruent. Thus all right angles are congruent.

Look Back

20. If a number is a natural number, it is positive. If a number is positive, it is greater than zero. If a number is a natural number, it is greater than zero.

21. If an artist used geometric forms to represent real objects, then he/she was a cubist. If an artist was a cubist, he/she was not a realist. If an artist used geometric forms to represent real objects, then he/she was not a realist.

More Practice

25. Complement: 70°; Supplement: 160°

26. Complement: 41°; Supplement: 131°

27. Complement: 34.5°; Supplement: 124.5°

More Math Reasoning

28. $2x + 2y = 180$, $x + y = 90$, so $\angle GMH$ (measure y) is complementary to all measure x angles, including $\angle JMK$.

29. $m\angle 1 = 15°$, $m\angle 2 = 30°$, $m\angle 3 = 45°$

30. a. Given information

b. Definition of *right angle*

c. Angle-Addition Postulate

d. Substitution

e. Definition of *complementary*

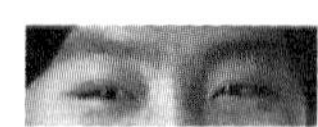

LOOK BACK

R **Rewrite both statements in each pair below in if-then form. Then make a deduction using the Chain Rule, if possible. [2-1]**

20. All natural numbers are positive. Positive numbers are greater than zero.

21. Artists who used geometric forms to represent real objects were called *cubists.* Cubists were not realists.

P **Triangle *XYZ* is the image of triangle *TUV* under a 90° clockwise rotation around point C. Find each image or pre-image. [3-2]**

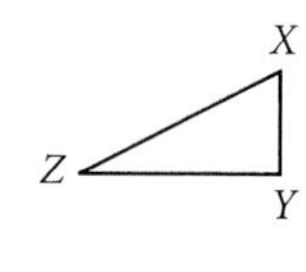

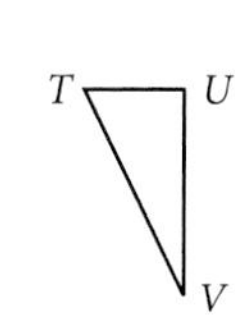

22. the image of point T X **23.** the pre-image of point Y U

24. the image of $\angle VTU$ $\angle ZXY$

MORE PRACTICE

P **For each measure of $\angle 1$, find the measure of its complement and its supplement.**

25. $m\angle 1 = 20°$ **26.** $m\angle 1 = 49°$ **27.** $m\angle 1 = 55.5°$

MORE MATH REASONING

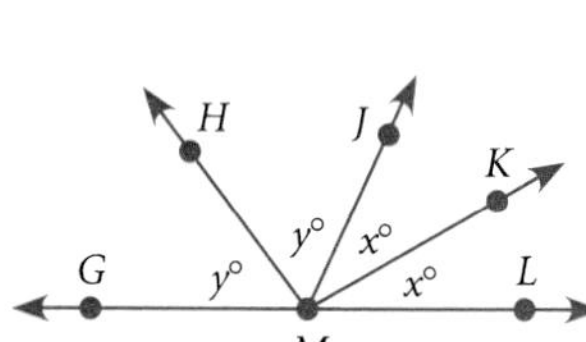

MR **28.** Explain why $\angle GMH$ is complementary to $\angle JMK$.

PS **29.** The measures of angles 1, 2, and 3 are in the ratio of 1:2:3 respectively. Find the measure of each angle.

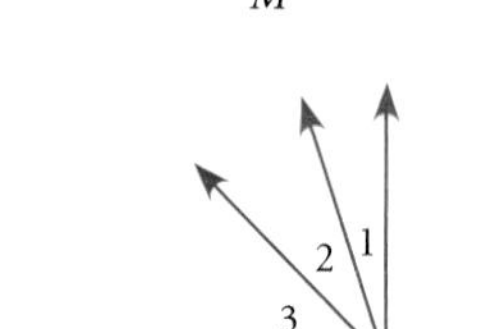

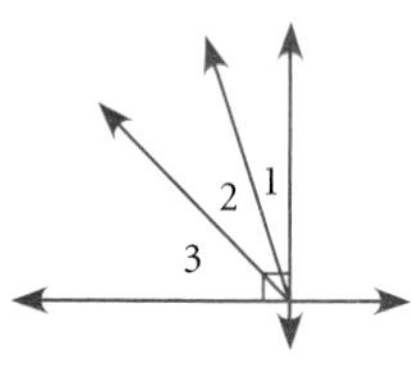

MR, C **30.** The flow proof shown below proves the following theorem.

If $\angle DEF$ is a right angle and point C is in the interior of $\angle DEF$, then $\angle DEC$ is complementary to $\angle CEF$.

Give a postulate, theorem, or definition to justify each step.

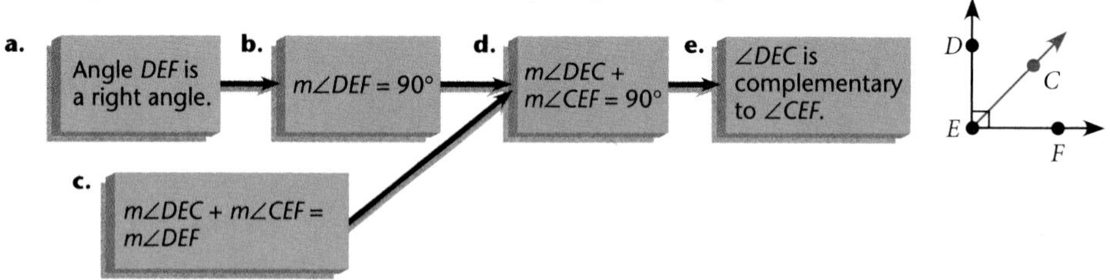

Key

V Vocabulary
P Practice/Skills
R Review
MR Math Reasoning
PS Problem Solving
C Challenge

3-3 PART D Vertical Angles and Angle Bisectors

← CONNECT → *You've explored several angle-pair relationships. Now you will discover and justify a theorem about a new angle pair and learn about angle bisectors.*

When two lines intersect, they form two pairs of *vertical angles.*

DEFINITION

Two angles are **vertical angles** if and only if their sides form two pairs of opposite rays.

In the figure at the right, ∠1 and ∠3 are vertical angles, and ∠2 and ∠4 are vertical angles.

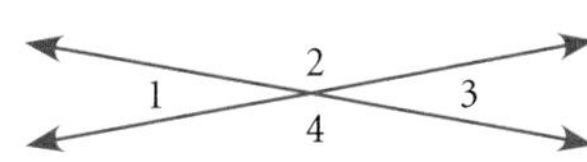

EXPLORE: "X" MARKS THE SPOT

MATERIALS

Straightedge, Protractor
Geometry software (optional)

1. Use a straightedge or geometry software to draw a large X. Measure the four angles formed. Then draw a second X so that the angles are different sizes, and repeat your measurements. Make a conjecture about vertical angles.
2. Provide a deductive argument to support your conjecture. It may help to sketch and label two intersecting lines. However, you cannot assume that any of your angles has a specific measure. (Hint: Think about linear pairs of angles.)

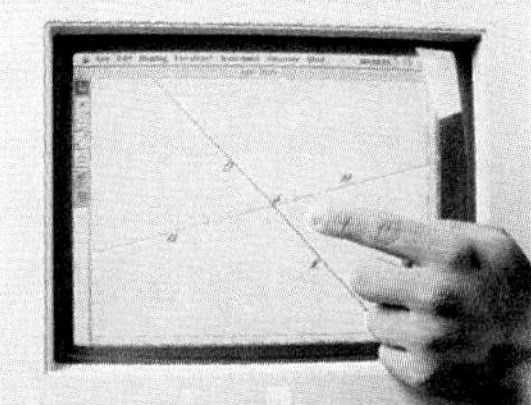

TRY IT

a. Find the measures of ∠1, ∠2, and ∠3. $m\angle 1 = 46°$; $m\angle 2 = 134°$; $m\angle 3 = 46°$

1 2 3 134°

Student Resources
- Alternative Lessons 3-3D
- Laboratory Manual 3-3D
- Technology Lab Manual
- Practice 3-3D
- Study Guide and Journal 3-3D
- Guía de estudios y Diario 3-3D
- Multilingual Handbook
- More Look Ahead 3-3D
- SAT Preparation

Media Resources
- Transparency FFM 3-3D
- Transparency AE
- Teaching Transparency
- AWSMTest and practice software
- AWSM Videodisc

PART D At a Glance

Objective
To discover that vertical angles are congruent.

Development
Students see the definition of vertical angles.

In the **Explore,** students discover that vertical angles are congruent, and support their conjecture with a deductive argument.

Suggested Materials
Student Compass, straightedge, protractor, geometry software

Teacher Chalkboard/overhead compass

Key Terms
Vertical angles, angle bisector

First Five Minutes
Transparency FFM 3-3D

Draw two intersecting lines and label the angles formed. Then list all pairs of supplementary angles in your figure.

Motivate
Ask...
- What happens to the angle formed by the blades of a pair of scissors when you open the "handle angle"? when you make the angle smaller?

EXPLORE

"X" Marks the Spot
Recommended group size: 4

The Point
To discover that vertical angles are congruent, and to justify that discovery deductively.

Look and Listen...
- For students who are not using deductive reasoning to justify their conjectures.

Ask...
- How can you show that your conjecture is *always* true? What is true about angles in a linear pair?

Precise Thinking with Angles

For Groups That Finish Early

List all of the definitions, postulates, and theorems needed for your deductive justification.

Follow Up

Ask students to state their conjecture and outline their justification.

Possible Answers

1. Vertical angles are congruent.
2. Sketch:

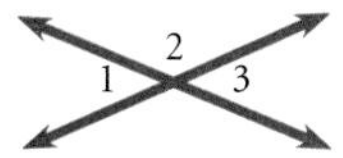

Because $\angle 1$ and $\angle 2$ form a linear pair, as do $\angle 3$ and $\angle 2$, these pairs of angles are supplementary. Therefore, $\angle 1 \cong \angle 3$ because supplements of the same angle are congruent.

CONSTRUCTION:

Angle Bisector

The Point

To construct a ray that bisects a given angle.

Presenting the Construction

This is a fairly straightforward construction, so it may be most time-efficient for you to model the steps for the class.

Possible Answer

1. Construct the bisector of the angle. Then construct the bisector of each of the two new angles.

You've seen the term *bisect* before. You may be able to predict what an angle bisector is before reading the following definition.

DEFINITION

$\overrightarrow{LM}$ is the **angle bisector** of $\angle NLP$ if and only if M is in the interior of $\angle NLP$ and $\angle NLM \cong \angle MLP$.

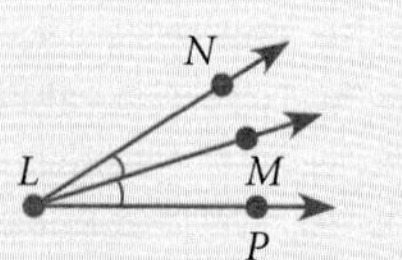

CONSTRUCTION: ANGLE BISECTOR

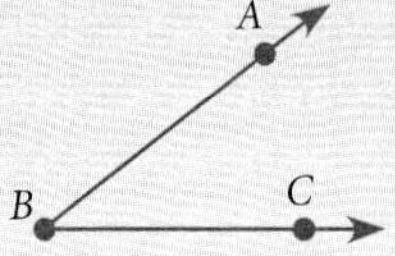

1. Begin by drawing angle $\angle ABC$. This will be the angle you bisect in your construction.

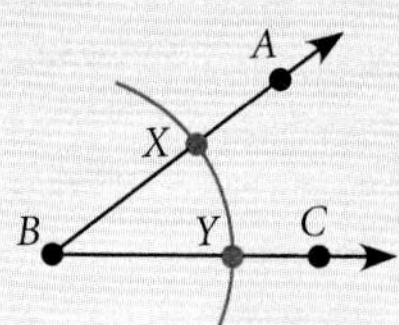

2. Using the vertex of the angle as the center, swing an arc through sides $\overrightarrow{BA}$ and $\overrightarrow{BC}$. Label the points where the arc intersects the sides X and Y.

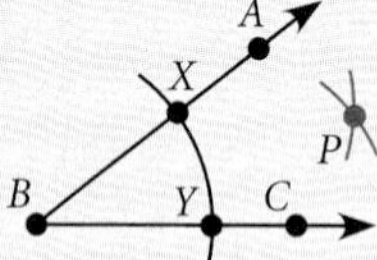

3. With the compass point at X, swing an arc in the interior of the angle. Using the same compass setting, make a similar arc from point Y. Label the intersection of the two arcs P.

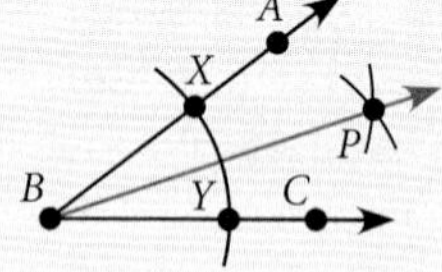

4. Use a straightedge to draw $\overrightarrow{BP}$, the angle bisector of $\angle ABC$.

1. Describe how you can *quadrisect* (divide into fourths) an angle using a straightedge and compass.

Technology Note

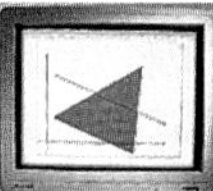

If you used software for the **Explore** on page 207, this might be a good time to have students find out which figures the software allows them to "construct" by selecting the Construct option or icon on the pull-down menu. If time permits, you might ask students to see which items on this list match the compass-and-straightedge constructions that they know at this point.

Now you can begin to see how theorems are built up from undefined terms, definitions, postulates, and other theorems. To justify the vertical-angle conjecture that you made, you need to know definitions (linear pair, congruent), a postulate (the angles in a linear pair are supplementary), and a theorem (supplements of the same angle are congruent). So the first theorem below has quite a family tree!

The second theorem below can be proved by using the first. Exercise 30 gives you the opportunity to complete a plan for its proof.

THEOREMS

Vertical angles are congruent.

Two perpendicular lines form four right angles.

REFLECT

1. Suppose three coplanar lines intersect at one point. How many pairs of vertical angles are formed? Support your answer with a sketch.
2. Describe a method for constructing a 45° angle, using a compass and straightedge.
3. Give a real-world example of vertical angles.

Exercises

CORE

Getting Started Find the measures of ∠2, ∠3, and ∠4 for each value of m∠1.

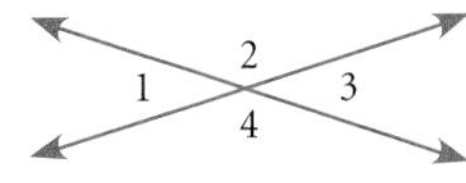

1. $m\angle 1 = 32°$
2. $m\angle 1 = 77°$
3. $m\angle 1 = 125°$
4. $m\angle 1 = 102.7°$
5. In the figure, ∠6 is complementary to ∠7, and $m\angle 5 = 141°$. Find the measure of each numbered angle in the figure.

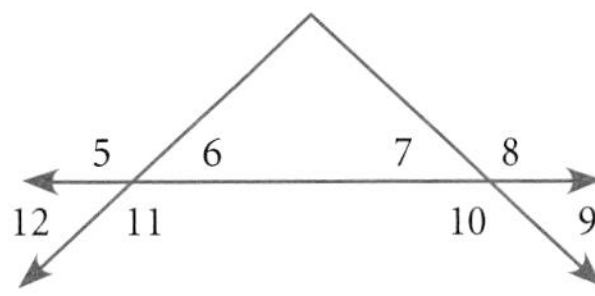

y

Vocabulary
Practice/Skills
Review
Math Reasoning
Problem Solving
Challenge

Ongoing Assessment

Self-Assessment Exercises 1–17 odd, 18, 20

Embedded Assessment Reflect 1; Exercises 6, 12, 19

Journal

Reflect 1 and 3 are suitable for journal entries.

REFLECT

Possible Answers

1. Six pairs are formed. Three of them are formed by adjacent angles.
2. Draw a line and a point not on it. Construct the perpendicular to the line from the point. Then construct the angle bisector of one of the right angles formed.
3. Scissors, tongs, street intersections.

Part D Exercises

Exercise Notes

Core

12. and 13. These exercises (as well as Exercises 28 and 29) ask students to use algebra to solve for angle measures.

Look Ahead

22. Previews parallel lines and transversals, which are seen throughout 3-4.

23. Looks ahead to deductive proof. In 3-4 Part A, students begin to set up formal proofs.

More Math Reasoning

30. Walks students through a plan for a deductive proof. They will begin planning proofs in Chapter 5.

Exercise Answers

Core

1. $m\angle 2 = 148°$; $m\angle 3 = 32°$; $m\angle 4 = 148°$
2. $m\angle 2 = 103°$; $m\angle 3 = 77°$; $m\angle 4 = 103°$
3. $m\angle 2 = 55°$; $m\angle 3 = 125°$; $m\angle 4 = 55°$
4. $m\angle 2 = 77.3°$; $m\angle 3 = 102.7°$; $m\angle 4 = 77.3°$
5. $m\angle 5 = 141° = m\angle 11$; $m\angle 6 = 39° = m\angle 12$; $m\angle 7 = 51° = m\angle 9$; $m\angle 8 = m\angle 10 = 129°$

14. All right angles measure 90° and are thus congruent.

15. Definition of *complementary*

3-3

Precise Thinking with Angles

16. Vertical angles are congruent.

17. Vertex

18. If two angles are vertical angles, then they are congruent.

19. The grip angle and the tong angle always remain congruent because they are vertical angles.

20. 25°

21. Possible answer:

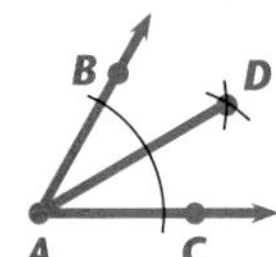

Algebra	Functions	Discrete Math	Probability	Data/Statistics

P **Find each of the following, assuming that $m\angle GXF = 53°$ and $m\angle FXE = 29°$.**

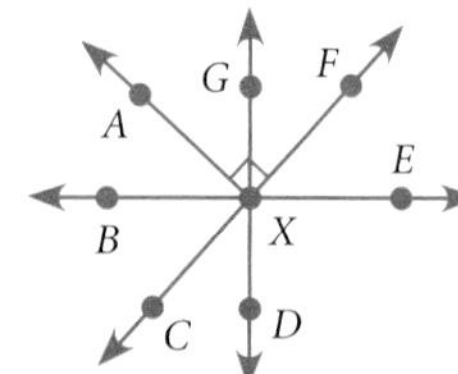

6. $m\angle AXG$ 37° **7.** $m\angle CXB$ 29° **8.** $m\angle CXA$ 90°

9. $m\angle BXF$ 151° **10.** $m\angle AXD$ 143° **11.** $m\angle BXD$ 82°

P **Suppose that angles $\angle JKL$ and $\angle MKN$ are vertical angles. Find their measures if the following conditions apply.**

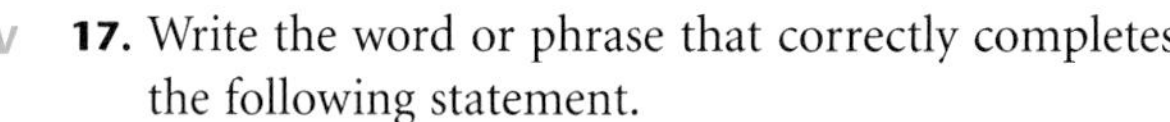

12. $m\angle JKL = (5x - 30)°$, $m\angle MKN = (3x + 30)°$ $m\angle JKL = m\angle MKN = 120°$

13. $m\angle JKL = 4(y + 7)°$, $m\angle MKN = 3(2y - 12)°$ $m\angle JKL = m\angle MKN = 156°$

P **Give a reason (or reasons) to justify each statement.**

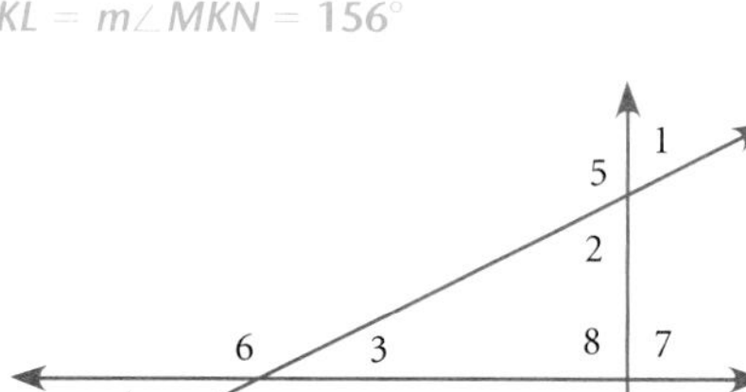

14. If $\angle 7$ and $\angle 8$ are right angles, then $\angle 7 \cong \angle 8$.

15. If $m\angle 2 + m\angle 3 = 90°$, then $\angle 2$ and $\angle 3$ are complementary.

16. $\angle 3 \cong \angle 4$

V **17.** Write the word or phrase that correctly completes the following statement.

The point of intersection of two vertical angles is the ___ of each angle.

R **18.** Rewrite the theorem "Vertical angles are congruent" in if-then form.

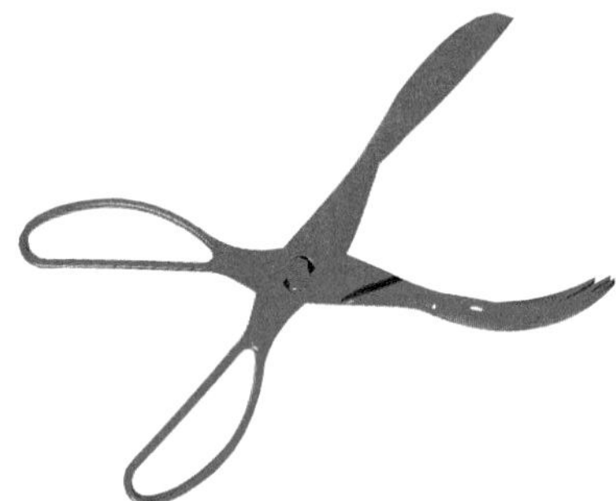

MR **19. Tongs a Lot** A pair of salad tongs is shown at the right. Use geometry to explain why closing the grips together allows you to pick up food.

P **20. Head for the Snow** Olympic ski jumpers know that the angle of the ski jumper's body on take-off is critical for getting the maximum distance on a jump. If $m\angle 1 = 155°$, find $m\angle 2$.

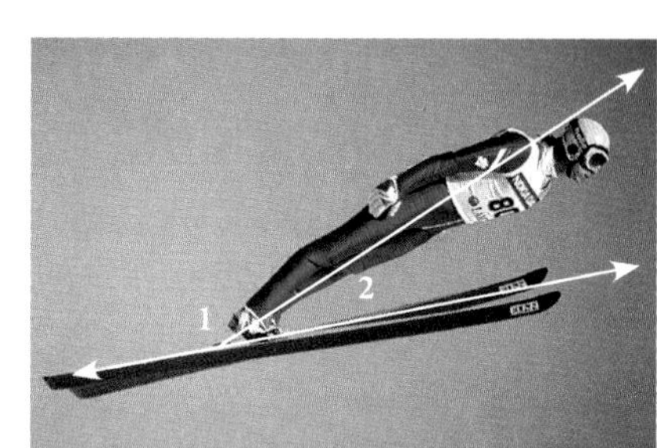

R **21.** Draw an acute angle. Then use a compass and straightedge to construct its bisector.

Key

V Vocabulary
P Practice/Skills
R Review
MR Math Reasoning
PS Problem Solving
C Challenge

LOOK AHEAD

22. Sketch two parallel lines. Then add a third line that intersects the two parallel lines. Label the angles formed, and list the pairs of vertical angles.

23. Draw a figure to illustrate the following statement.

Given: $\angle STU$ and $\angle UTV$ are a linear pair. $\angle STU \cong \angle UTV$.

What do you think you could *prove* about these angles?

MORE PRACTICE

In the figure at the right, $m\angle AEC = 42°$. Find each of the following.

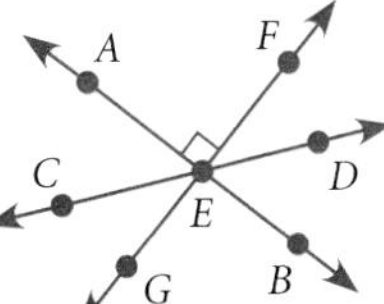

24. $m\angle DEB$ 42° **25.** $m\angle CEG$ 48° **26.** $m\angle FED$ 48° **27.** $m\angle GEB$ 90°

Suppose that angles $\angle JKL$ and $\angle MKN$ are vertical angles. Find their measures under the following conditions.

28. $m\angle JKL = (2x + 40)°$, $m\angle MKN = (8x - 32)°$ $m\angle JKL = m\angle MKN = 64°$

29. $m\angle JKL = 3(y + 11)°$, $m\angle MKN = 2(10 + 2y)°$ $m\angle JKL = m\angle MKN = 72°$

MORE MATH REASONING

30. A Plan for Proof A plan for a deductive proof of the theorem "Two perpendicular lines form four right angles" is shown below. Fill in each blank to complete this plan for a proof.

Assume that $m \perp n$. Then m and n form at least one right angle because of the **a.** ____. This angle, $\angle 1$ in the figure, measures **b.** ____ because of the definition of a right angle. $\angle 3 \cong \angle 1$ because **c.** ____. Thus, $m\angle 3 = m\angle 1 = 90°$. Therefore, $\angle 3$ is a right angle, by the **d.** ____.

$\angle 1$ and $\angle 4$ form a **e.** ____. Therefore, they are supplementary because of the **f.** ____. This means that $m\angle 1 + m\angle 4 =$ **g.** ____. We know that $m\angle 1 = 90°$, so $90° + m\angle 4 = 180°$. Therefore, $m\angle 4$ must be **h.** ____, and $\angle 4$ is a **i.** ____.

The reasoning above can also be used to show that **j.** ____ is a right angle. Therefore, we can show that all four angles formed by two **k.** ____ must be **l.** ____.

31. Construct an angle that measures 135°. Explain your method.

32. Find the values of x and y in the figure at the right.

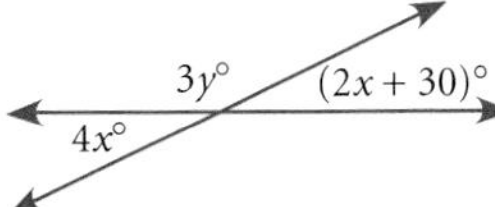

Look Ahead

22. Possible answer:

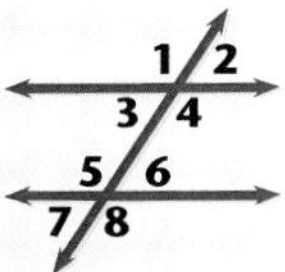

1 and 4, 2 and 3, 5 and 8, 6 and 7

23. Possible answer:

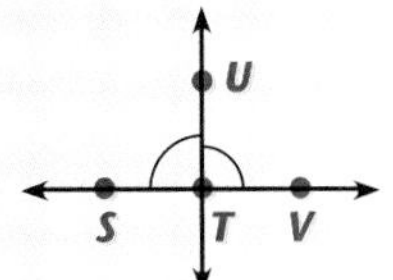

They are both right angles.

More Math Reasoning

30. a. Definition of *perpendicular*

b. 90°

c. They are vertical angles.

d. Definition of *right angle*

e. Linear pair

f. Linear-Pair Postulate

g. 180° **h.** 90°

i. Right angle **j.** $\angle 2$

k. Perpendicular lines

l. Right angles

31. Bisect a right angle in a linear pair:

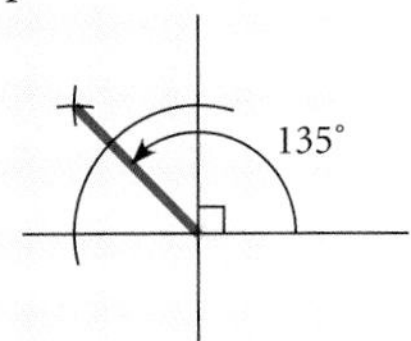

32. $x = 15$; $y = 40$

Precise Thinking with Angles

PART E At a Glance

Objective

To apply relationships of angles to a real-world problem.

Development

In the **Explore,** students identify angle pairs and congruent angles in a figure showing reflections of the sun's rays in a street. They also design a street that traps less heat.

Suggested Materials

Student Straightedge, protractor

First Five Minutes

Transparency FFM 3-3E

List all of the postulates and theorems that can be used to show that angles are congruent.

EXPLORE

City Canyons

Recommended group size: 4

The Point

To identify angle pairs, and to use angles of reflection to design a street that is not a heat trap.

Look and Listen...

- For students who do not understand how to illustrate reflections of the sun's rays.

Ask...

- How can you use a protractor to help you draw the reflections?

For Groups That Finish Early

List several reasons that downtown areas tend to have more tall buildings than suburban ones.

Follow Up

Have students share designs.

Possible Answers

1. a. ∠*JBE*, ∠*FBC*
 b. ∠*FCB*, ∠*HCB*
 c. ∠*KEB*, ∠*BEJ*
 d. ∠*FCB*, ∠*BCI*
 e. $\overline{CH}$

3-3 PART E Making Connections

← CONNECT → ***In geometry and in everyday life, you must be careful not to make assumptions that are not based on evidence. You've learned what you may and may not assume from a figure. You have also investigated different angle pairs and angle relationships.***

You've discovered relationships between several types of angles. In the Explore that follows, you will use these relationships to help analyze how the sun's heat gets trapped in city streets.

EXPLORE: CITY CANYONS

MATERIALS

Straightedge
Protractor

The figure on the left below shows the reflections of a ray of sunlight in a city street. As shown on page 191, the amount of heat absorbed by buildings on a street depends on the number of times the sun's rays are reflected.

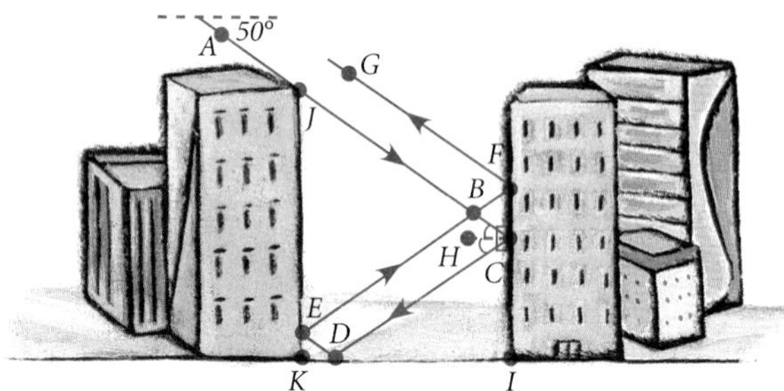

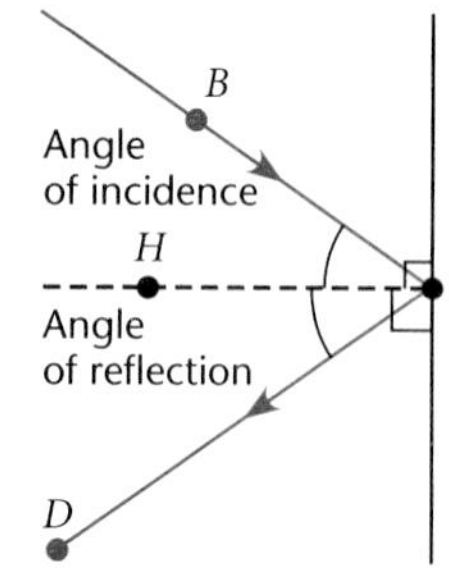

The figure on the right is an enlarged view of the first reflection at point *C*. In the following, it will help if you remember that when light rays are reflected, the *angle of incidence* is congruent to the *angle of reflection.*

1. Use the figure on the left above to find an example of each type of angle or angle pair.
 a. a pair of vertical angles
 b. a pair of complementary angles
 c. a linear pair
 d. a pair of supplementary angles
 e. an angle bisector

Student Resources

Alternative Lessons
Laboratory Manual 3-3E
Technology Lab Manual
Practice 3-3E
Study Guide and Journal 3-3E
Guía de estudios y Diario 3-3E
Multilingual Handbook
More Look Back 3-3E
SAT Preparation

Media Resources

Transparency FFM 3-3E
Transparency AE
Teaching Transparency
AWSMTest and practice software
AWSM Videodisc

ic/Reasoning | Industry/Careers | Science/Health | Social Science/History | Fine Arts/Literature

2. Name a pair of angles in the figure on page 212 that are congruent because of each theorem.
   a. Vertical angles are congruent.
   b. Right angles are congruent.
   c. Complements of congruent angles are congruent.
   d. Supplements of congruent angles are congruent.
3. As a city planner, you might like to design a city street that does not become a heat island at night. Give one or more changes that you could make to the street in the figure that would help the problem. Explain the effect of each of your suggestions. Use a drawing like the preceding one on the left to illustrate your plan. Show what happens to a ray of sunlight that comes in just over the top of a building at the 50° angle shown.

REFLECT

1. Write a description of each term in your own words. Include a sketch with each definition.
   a. vertical angles
   b. linear pair
   c. complementary angles
   d. supplementary angles
   e. perpendicular lines
2. Describe an example of how making an unjustified mathematical assumption about a figure can cause a problem. When do you think an unjustified assumption might create a problem in a nonmathematical setting?

Self-Assessment

For each measure of $\angle A$, find the measure of its complement and its supplement.

1. $m\angle A = 65°$
2. $m\angle A = x$
3. $m\angle A = (20 - x)°$

In the following, assume that $m\angle TVU = 32°$. Find each measure.

4. $m\angle SVT$ 58°
5. $m\angle YVX$ 32°
6. $m\angle UVX$ 148°
7. $m\angle SVX$ 122°

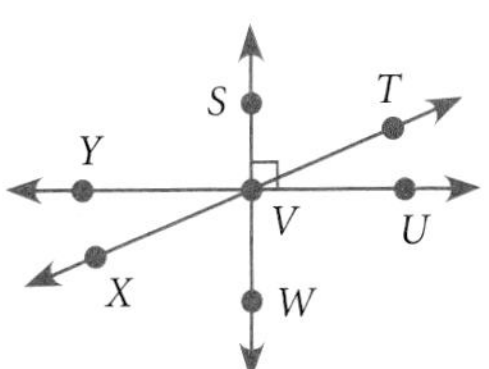

Vocabulary
Practice/Skills
Review
Math Reasoning
Problem Solving
Challenge

2. a. $\angle JBE \cong \angle FBC$
   b. $\angle FCH \cong \angle HCI$
   c. $\angle FCB \cong \angle ICD$
   d. $\angle BCI \cong \angle DCF$
3. Shorter buildings and wider streets allow energy to escape after fewer reflections.

Portfolio

Have students select items from their work that demonstrate their understanding of material in 3-3.

You may have students include their favorite real-world example of one of the angle pairs, an **Exercise** where they identified assumptions that could and could not be made about a figure, and an example of their use of deductive reasoning to justify a conjecture.

REFLECT

Possible Answers

1. a. Opposite angles formed by intersecting lines.
   b. Angles formed by a pair of opposite rays and another ray.
   c. Measures add to 90°.
   d. Measures add to 180°.
   e. Lines that intersect to form a right angle.
2. Mathematics: Incorrectly assuming that two angles in a linear pair are congruent leads to the invalid conclusion that they are right angles. Nonmathematics: Assuming that people will behave in certain ways on the basis of their appearance.

Self-Assessment

Exercise Notes

13. Asks students to summarize assumptions that can and cannot be made from a figure.
16. Asks students to use algebra to verify a conjecture.
17. Illustrates an application of angles in chemistry.

Precise Thinking with Angles

Self-Assessment Answers

1. Complement: 25°; Supplement: 115°

2. Complement: $(90 - x)°$; Supplement: $(180 - x)°$

3. Complement: $(70 + x)°$; Supplement: $(160 + x)°$

12. a.

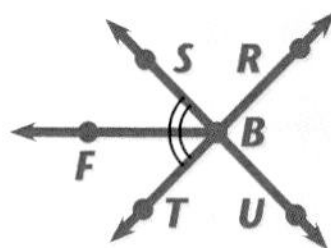

b. $m\angle TBU = 140°$; $m\angle RBS = 140°$; $m\angle SBT = 40°$

13. Can assume: Things that look straight are; Points of intersection are shown accurately; Points shown on a line are collinear; Unless otherwise indicated, all points are coplanar; Relative positions of points are accurate. Cannot assume: Exact measurement and relative sizes of figures; That lines are parallel or perpendicular; That angles (or segments) are congruent. Check students' answers for examples.

14. (e)

15. a. Yes; 120°, 240°

b. No

c. Yes; 90°, 180°, 270°

16. The supplement is 90° larger than the complement; x + complement = 90° so complement = $(90 - x)°$; x + supplement = 180° so supplement = $(180 - x)°$; supplement − complement = $(180 - x)° - (90 - x)° = 90°$

17. 120°

P **A billiard ball bounces off the sides of a billiard table at the same angle at which it arrives. Use the figure at the right to find an example of each type of angle pair.**

8. a pair of complementary angles Possible answer: $\angle LBM$ and $\angle MBC$

9. a linear pair $\angle JMB$ and $\angle BMD$

10. a pair of angles that are congruent because vertical angles are congruent $\angle BMD$ and $\angle IME$

11. a pair of angles that are congruent because complements of congruent angles are congruent $\angle KBL$ and $\angle LBM$

P **12. a.** Make a single sketch of the following situation. Include markings where needed. $\angle TBU$ and $\angle RBS$ are vertical angles. $\angle RBS$ and $\angle SBT$ form a linear pair. $\overrightarrow{BF}$ bisects $\angle SBT$.

b. If the measure of $\angle FBS$ is 20°, find $m\angle TBU$, $m\angle RBS$, and $m\angle SBT$.

P **13.** Explain what can and cannot be assumed from a geometric figure. Give specific examples of things that you may not assume from a figure unless they are marked.

P **14.** In the figure at the right, what is the value of x in terms of y?

(a) $135 + y$ (b) $315 - 2y$ (c) $180 - y$
(d) $45 + 2y$ (e) $135 - y$

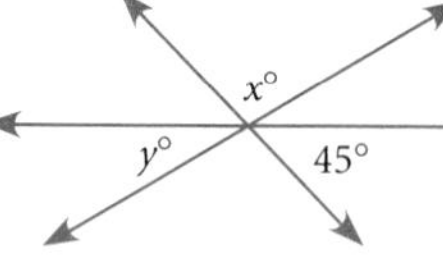

R **15.** Determine whether or not each figure at the right has rotational symmetry. If the figure has rotational symmetry, give the clockwise angles of rotation between 0° and 360° that cause the image and pre-image to overlap. [3-2]

a.  **b.**  **c.**

PS, MR **16.** For any acute angle, what is the difference between its supplement and its complement? Make a generalization and use algebraic expressions to prove that the generalization is true.

> **Problem-Solving Tip**
>
> Try some examples with specific numbers.

PS **17. Chemistry Lesson** In an ethene molecule, two carbon atoms are bonded together, and each carbon atom is bonded to two hydrogen atoms. The centers of the six atoms in an ethene molecule lie in one plane. If all of the angles determined by the bonds shown are congruent, what is the measure of a hydrogen-carbon-hydrogen angle?

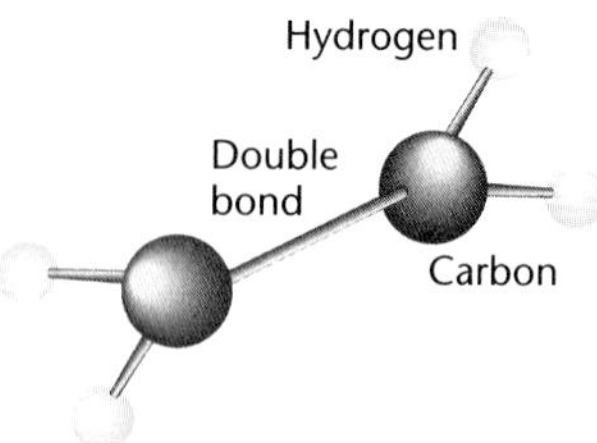

Assessment Resources

- **Quiz 3-3**
- Chapter Assessment Form A
- Chapter Assessment Form B
- Chapter Alternative Assessment
- Mid-Year Assessment
- End-of-Year Assessment
- **AWSMTest and practice software**

Ongoing Assessment

Self-Assessment Self-Assessment Exercises

Embedded Assessment Reflect 1, 2

ADDITIONAL ANSWERS

3-4 Part A Exercises

12.

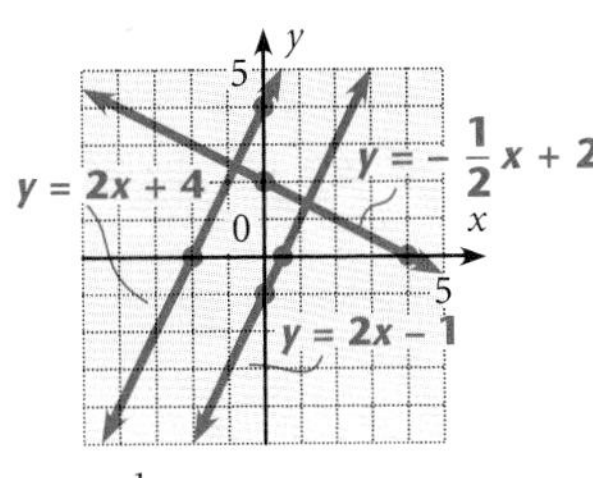

$y = -\frac{1}{2}x + 2$

13. $\angle 2$ and $\angle 3$

Look Back

14. Possible answer: If you live in Miami, then you live in Florida.

15. Possible answer: If you are an elephant, then you know how to fly.

16. Complement: 48°; Supplement: 138°

17. Complement: 2°; Supplement: 92°

18. Complement: 57.6°; Supplement: 147.6°

More Practice

24. *Rewrite:* If two lines are perpendicular, then they form four right angles. *Draw:*

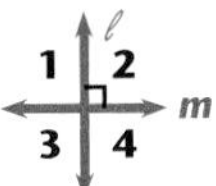

State: Given: $\ell \perp m$; *Prove:* $\angle 1$, $\angle 2$, $\angle 3$, and $\angle 4$ are right angles

25. *Rewrite:* If two angles are supplementary to the same angle, then they are congruent. *Draw:*

State: Given: $\angle 2$ and $\angle 3$ are supplementary to $\angle 1$; *Prove:* $\angle 2 \cong \angle 3$.

More Math Reasoning

26. Let n and p be non-coplanar

27. $\overleftrightarrow{AB}$ and $\overleftrightarrow{HG}$; $\overleftrightarrow{BC}$ and $\overleftrightarrow{EH}$; $\overleftrightarrow{BF}$ and $\overleftrightarrow{DH}$; $\overleftrightarrow{BE}$ and $\overleftrightarrow{CH}$; $\overleftrightarrow{BD}$ and $\overleftrightarrow{FH}$; $\overleftrightarrow{BG}$ and $\overleftrightarrow{AH}$

3-4 Part A Exercises

28. *Rewrite:* If one angle is congruent to a second angle and the second angle is congruent to a third angle, then the first and third angles are congruent. *Draw:*

State: Given: $\angle 1 \cong \angle 2$ and $\angle 2 \cong \angle 3$, *Prove:* $\angle 1 \cong \angle 3$

3-4

Parallel Lines and Transversals

SUPERLESSON AT A GLANCE

Superlesson Goal

Students will see relationships among angles formed by parallel lines and a transversal.

Management Guide

	Topic	Objectives	Key Terms	New Ideas	Materials
Part A	Transversals and Angles	To learn vocabulary and practice the first three steps of a five-step process for deductive proof.	Transversal, alternate interior angles, alternate exterior angles, same-side interior angles, corresponding angles	Transversals and their angles. Drawing an illustration for a deductive proof. Stating the *Given* and *Prove* for a conjecture.	
Part B	Parallel Lines, Transversals, and Angles	To see relationships among angles formed when a transversal intersects two parallel lines.		Corresponding, alternate interior, and alternate exterior angles of parallel lines are congruent. Same-side interior angles are supplementary.	**Student** Protractor, straightedge, geometry software
Part C	Proving Lines Parallel	To find ways to use angles formed by transversals to prove lines parallel.		Using angle relationships to prove lines parallel.	**Student** Compass, straightedge, protractor
Part D	Making Connections	To identify relationships among angles formed by parallel lines and transversals on a calligraphy worksheet.	In Making Connections, students apply and synthesize key terms and new ideas.		**Student** Protractor, straightedge

Pacing Chart (45-Minute Periods)

	Comprehensive Course	Core Course	Informal Course
Part A	1	1	1*
Part B	1	1	2
Part C	1	1	2
Part D	1	1	1
TOTAL periods for Superlesson	4	4	6

*Material on proof in this part may be omitted or downplayed in an Informal Course.

NCTM Standards

Mathematics as Problem Solving

Mathematics as Communication

Mathematics as Reasoning

Mathematical Connections

Geometry from a Synthetic Perspective

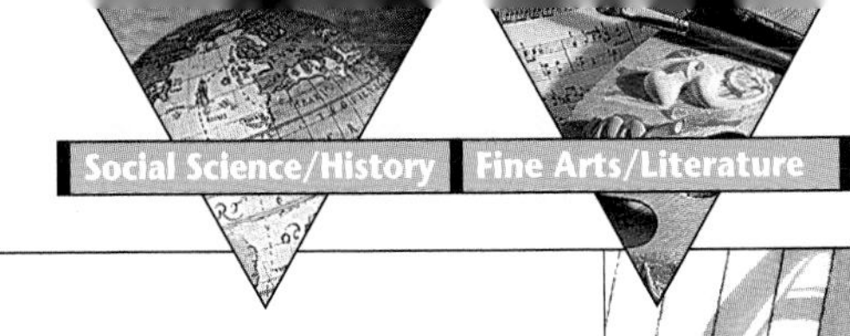

3-4 Parallel Lines and Transversals

THE WRITE STUFF

Calligraphy (kal-lig´-ra-fee), from the Greek *kalos* meaning beautiful and *grapho*, to write, is an art form with ancient roots. The developmental stages of writing took thousands of years. Calligraphy was stimulated, cultivated, and shaped from ancient times until the fifteenth century. At that time, calligraphy was used primarily in book production.

Scribes, skillful in the art of calligraphy (but having no access to a copy machine), copied the works of Cicero and other statesmen and orators by hand. There was also a great demand for multiple copies of the Bible. But with the invention of the printing press by Johann Gutenberg in about 1440, the demand for skilled calligraphers decreased.

The elegance of calligraphy has endured through time, from the days of scratching on the surface of a wax tablet with hollow reeds to today's use of precision pens and highly refined papers. Though it is no longer critical for communication, calligraphy is still important as an art form.

1. What role do parallel lines play in calligraphy?
2. Describe any relationships you see between angles in the calligraphy samples shown.
3. Calligraphy fonts (type styles) are available for personal computers. Why might you still want to learn how to do calligraphy with pen and ink?

215

Where Are We Now?

Students have seen special angle pairs and relationships between the angles in them.

Where Are We Going?

In 3-4, students will see the angles formed by two coplanar lines and a transversal. They will discover relationships among these angles when the lines are parallel and see how to use them to prove that lines are parallel. These relationships are important in many topics throughout the text.

Students also apply the first three steps of our five-step plan for deductive proof—the *rewrite, draw,* and *state* steps. After filling in statements and reasons in proofs in Chapter 4, students *plan* proofs in Chapter 5 and *demonstrate* them on their own in Chapter 6.

Possible Answers

1. They are guidelines for keeping letters the same height and at the same slant.
2. Angles in the figure include vertical angles and angles in a linear pair. (Students may also note that these angles must be congruent and supplementary, respectively.)
3. For personal enjoyment and satisfaction, and for use when a computer is either inconvenient or unavailable. Also, hand-drawn calligraphy allows for different personal styles.

More About Calligraphy

Cultures across the world have used calligraphic writing. In some Asian cultures, calligraphy is regarded as an art form on an equal footing with painting. Chinese calligraphers work with a soft brush on paper.

In ancient Egyptian, Greek, and Islamic calligraphy, scribes used reed pens to write on leather, vellum, or papyrus. Variations in calligraphic styles were the predecessors of the different fonts used by printers.

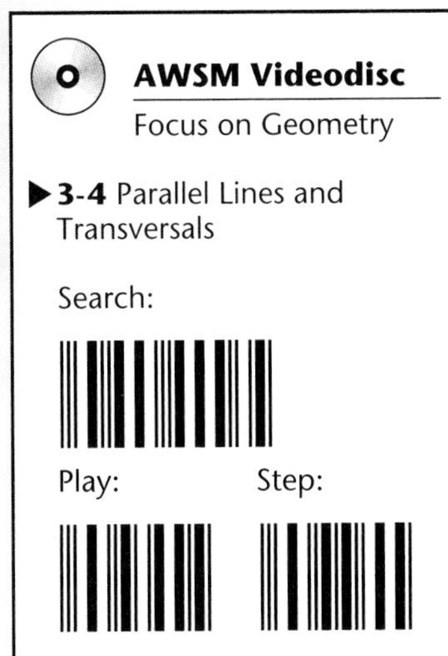

Parallel Lines and Transversals

PART A At a Glance

Objective

To learn vocabulary and practice the first three steps of a five-step process for deductive proof.

Development

First, students see vocabulary for the angles formed by two lines and a transversal.

Then a five-step plan for deductive proof is presented. In the **Explore,** students do the first three steps (*rewrite, draw,* and *state*) for a proof of a theorem that involves lines intersected by a transversal.

Key Terms

Transversal, alternate interior angles, alternate exterior angles, same-side interior angles, corresponding angles

First Five Minutes

Transparency FFM 3-4A

Read page 216 and the first paragraph on page 217. Then do **Try It a–e.**

Motivate

Ask...

As a transition to working with proof, ask...

- Why is the *if-then* form for conditional statements convenient?
- If you are trying to prove a conjecture in *if-then* form, does it make more sense to assume that the hypothesis is true or the conclusion is true? Why? (Students may need a concrete example to help them answer this question; perhaps, "If two angles are right angles, then they are congruent.")

3-4 PART A Transversals and Angles

← CONNECT → *You've seen how important it is to read and draw figures accurately. Now you will learn how to classify the angles formed when two lines are crossed by a third. You will also draw figures that illustrate conjectures.*

We have special names for angles formed when two coplanar lines are both intersected by a third.

DEFINITION

A **transversal** is a line that intersects two coplanar lines at two different points.

In the figure, transversal *t* intersects lines *r* and *s*. When a transversal crosses two lines, it forms eight angles. The relationships between these angles are important, so we have several names to identify the pairs of angles formed.

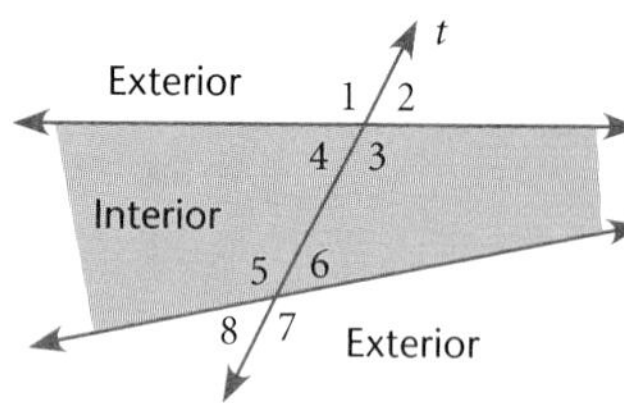

ANGLES FORMED BY TRANSVERSALS

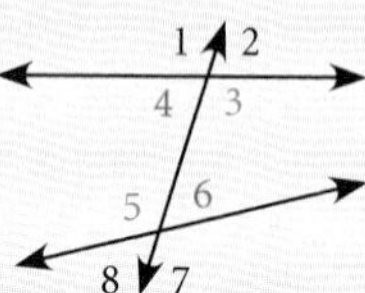

The pairs of **alternate interior angles** in the figure are ∠4 and ∠6, ∠3 and ∠5.

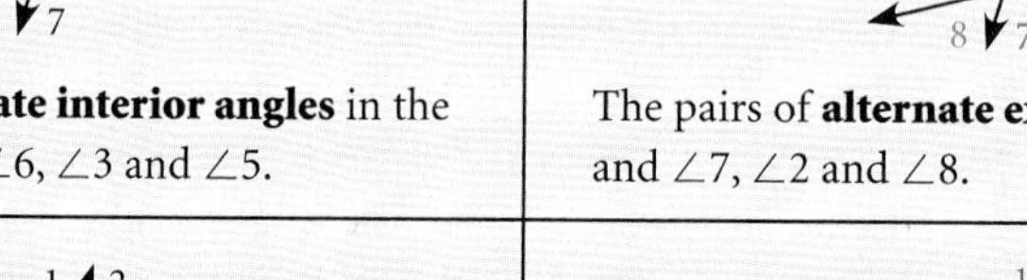

The pairs of **alternate exterior angles** are ∠1 and ∠7, ∠2 and ∠8.

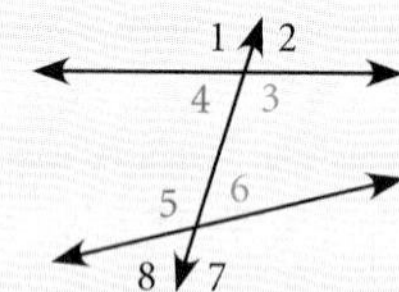

The pairs of **same-side interior angles** are ∠4 and ∠5, ∠3 and ∠6.

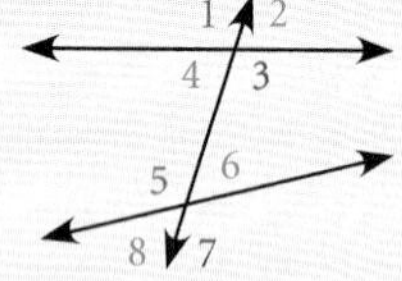

The pairs of **corresponding angles** are ∠1 and ∠5, ∠2 and ∠6, ∠3 and ∠7, and ∠4 and ∠8.

Tips from Teachers

You might want to remind students that they have already rewritten statements in *if-then* form and drawn and labeled figures to illustrate statements. This may help some students who feel intimidated by proof.

Although this seems like a lot to remember, it all makes sense. If you know the difference between *interior* and *exterior,* the difference between *same-side* and *alternate,* and what *corresponding* means, you can identify all of these pairs of angles easily.

Note: Inductive conjecture and deductive proof are both important aspects of mathematical thinking. You may want to precede the introduction of the five-step process with a brief discussion of the importance and uses of both inductive and deductive reasoning.

TRY IT

Name each of the following in the figure at the right.

a. the transversal
b. two pairs of same-side interior angles
c. two pairs of alternate exterior angles
d. four pairs of corresponding angles
e. two pairs of alternate interior angles

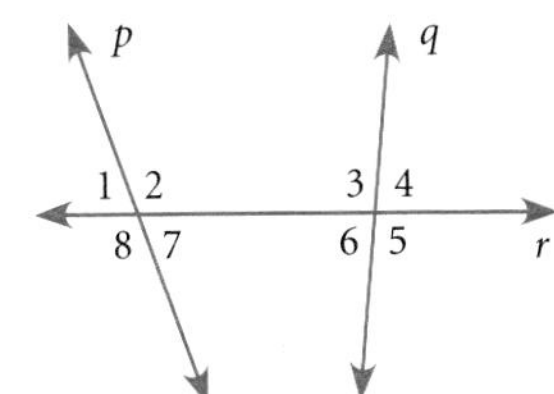

a. r
b. $\angle 2$ and $\angle 3$; $\angle 6$ and $\angle 7$
c. $\angle 4$ and $\angle 8$; $\angle 5$ and $\angle 1$
d. $\angle 4$ and $\angle 2$; $\angle 5$ and $\angle 7$; $\angle 3$ and $\angle 1$; $\angle 6$ and $\angle 8$
e. $\angle 3$ and $\angle 7$; $\angle 2$ and $\angle 6$

You will soon make and prove some conjectures about the relationships between these angles when the lines that are cut by the transversal are parallel.

As you continue to develop your thinking skills, you will start to prove conjectures by deductive reasoning. The five-step process, outlined for you below, is one way to help you organize your thinking when proving a conjecture.

FIVE-STEP PROCESS FOR DEDUCTIVE PROOF

1. **Rewrite** the conjecture to be proved in if-then form.
2. **Draw** and label a figure to represent the given information.
3. **State** the statement to be proved in terms of the figure.
4. **Plan** the proof. (Find a logical sequence of steps that shows why the conjecture must be true. We'll look at this more closely in Chapter 5.)
5. **Demonstrate** the argument by translating your plan into writing. Every statement you make must be justified with a reason. (We'll look at this more closely in Chapter 6.)

Earlier, you learned how to *rewrite* a conjecture by writing it in if-then form. Now you will practice this step and the next two steps—the *draw* and *state* steps.

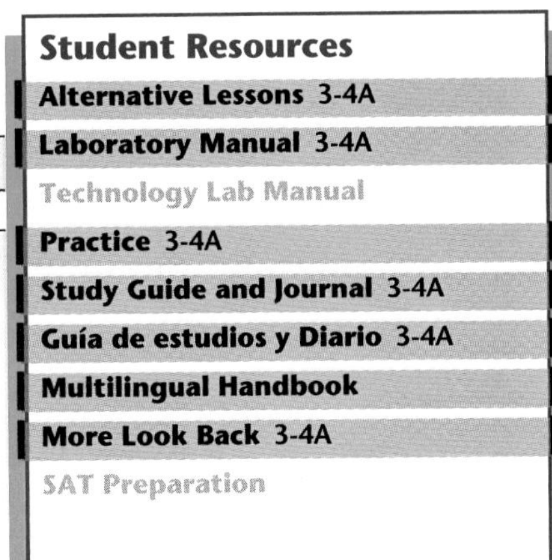

Student Resources
Alternative Lessons 3-4A
Laboratory Manual 3-4A
Technology Lab Manual
Practice 3-4A
Study Guide and Journal 3-4A
Guía de estudios y Diario 3-4A
Multilingual Handbook
More Look Back 3-4A
SAT Preparation

Media Resources
- **Transparency FFM** 3-4A
- **Transparency AE** 3-4A
- Teaching Transparency
- **AWSMTest and practice software**
- **AWSM Videodisc**

Parallel Lines and Transversals

ALTERNATE EXAMPLE

Do the *rewrite, draw,* and *state* steps for a proof of the following.

In a linear pair where one angle measures 45°, the other measures 135°.

Rewrite: If one angle in a linear pair measures 45°, then the other measures 135°.

Draw:

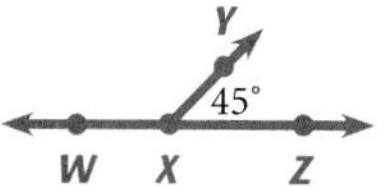

State: Given: $\angle WXY$ and $\angle YXZ$ form a linear pair; $m\angle YXZ = 45°$

Prove: $m\angle WXY = 135°$

Note: You may want to point out that in the Example in the text, $\angle ABC$ and $\angle EBD$ could have been used as the vertical angles.

Draw means to illustrate and label the hypothesis of the statement you are trying to prove. *State* means to write the statement using the labels you put on your figure. The hypothesis becomes your *given* information, and the conclusion is what you are trying to *prove.*

EXAMPLE

Do the *rewrite, draw,* and *state* steps for the proof of the following theorem.

All vertical angles are congruent.

Rewrite: If two angles are vertical angles, then they are congruent.

Draw: Illustrate the hypothesis "Two angles are vertical angles."

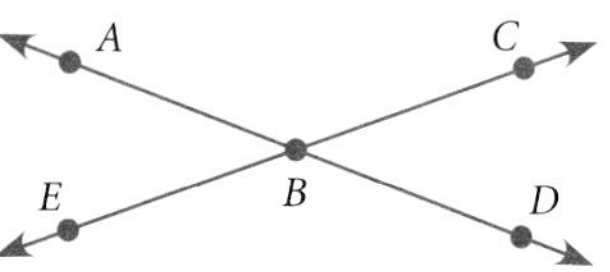

State: Write the hypothesis and conclusion of the statement using the labels in the figure.

Given: $\angle ABE$ and $\angle CBD$ are vertical angles.

Prove: $\angle ABE \cong \angle CBD$

EXPLORE

Proof Prep

Recommended group size: 2

The Point

To do the *rewrite, draw,* and *state* steps for a proof.

Look and Listen...

- For students who do not label their figures or do not use those labels in the *Given* and *Prove.*

Ask...

- How can you tell what information to include in your figure?

For Groups That Finish Early

Do the *rewrite, draw,* and *state* steps for the following theorem: "Supplements of the same angle are congruent."

EXPLORE: PROOF PREP

Do the *rewrite, draw,* and *state* steps for a proof of the following theorem.

Two coplanar lines that are perpendicular to the same line are parallel.

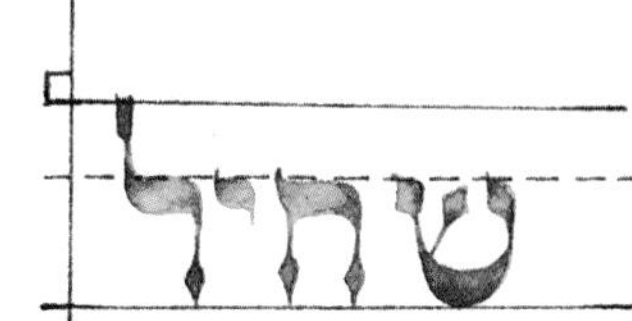

The calligraphy sample at the right, which shows Hebrew letters, may help you with the *draw* step. Don't worry about finishing the proof—you don't have quite enough information to complete it at this point. Compare your setup with those of other students, and decide which seems best.

Alert

Students may include some of the information in the conclusion of a conjecture (the *prove* part) in their figure. You may want to remind them that they should only *draw* the information in the hypothesis of the statement by showing a concrete example, such as "If you're trying to *prove* that two angles are congruent, you can't mark that they *are* congruent in your figure."

REFLECT

1. In your own words, give a definition of *alternate exterior angles.*
2. Why is it important not to illustrate the conclusion when you are drawing a figure for use in a proof?
3. A transversal is a line that intersects two coplanar lines at two different points. What happens when a line intersects two coplanar lines at the *same* point? Sketch the situation. What type(s) of angles are formed?

Exercises

CORE

Getting Started Name each of the following in the figure at the right.

1. alternate interior angles
2. alternate exterior angles
3. same-side interior angles
4. corresponding angles
5. vertical angles
6. When two nonintersecting lines in a plane are intersected by a transversal, how many pairs of corresponding angles are formed? alternate interior angles? alternate exterior angles?
7. Think about the location of corresponding angles. How is this name descriptive of their location? Answer the same question for alternate interior and alternate exterior angles.
8. Part of a calligraphy guidesheet is shown at the right. Name all transversals, and identify the pair(s) of lines for which they are transversals.

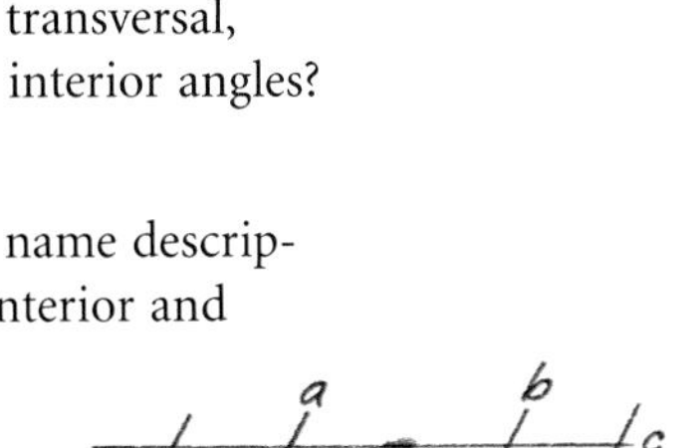

9. Choose the term in the group of terms below that does not belong, and explain why.

   alternate interior, corresponding, transversal, alternate exterior

Do the *rewrite, draw,* and *state* steps for the proof of each theorem.

10. Right angles are congruent.
11. If M is the midpoint of $\overline{AB}$, $AM = \frac{1}{2}AB$.

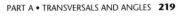

Ongoing Assessment

Self-Assessment Exercises 1, 3, 5, 9, 11, 13

Embedded Assessment Reflect 2; Exercises 6, 7, 10

Vocabulary
Practice/Skills
Review
Math Reasoning
Problem Solving
Challenge

Follow Up

Ask students to show their results from the **Explore** on the overhead or board.

Possible Answer

Rewrite: If two coplanar lines are perpendicular to the same line, then they are parallel.

Draw:

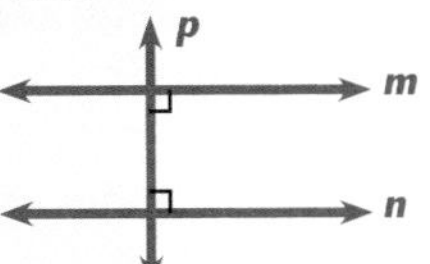

State: Given: m and n are coplanar; $m \perp p$; $n \perp p$.

Prove: $m \parallel n$

Journal

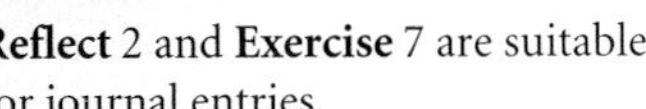

Reflect 2 and **Exercise** 7 are suitable for journal entries.

REFLECT

Possible Answers

1. Two angles on the exterior of a pair of lines and on opposite sides of the transversal.
2. Because you may look at the figure and think that you have already shown that this information is true.
3. Three lines intersect at the same point; vertical angles (and linear pairs) are formed.

Part A Exercises

Exercise Notes

Core

12. Students graph linear equations on a coordinate plane and identify a transversal. You might take this opportunity to review slope-intercept form and the fact that coplanar lines with the same slope are parallel.
13. Shows alternate interior angles in the path of light in a periscope. In Part C, Exercise 13, students use parallel lines and the properties of reflection to explain how a periscope works.

Parallel Lines and Transversals

More Math Reasoning

26. Encourages students to think three-dimensionally. This exercise shows why it is necessary to include *coplanar* in the definition of *transversal.*

Exercise Answers

Core

1. $\angle 3$ and $\angle 7$; $\angle 2$ and $\angle 6$.

2. $\angle 4$ and $\angle 8$; $\angle 1$ and $\angle 5$.

3. $\angle 2$ and $\angle 3$; $\angle 7$ and $\angle 6$.

4. $\angle 4$ and $\angle 2$; $\angle 3$ and $\angle 1$; $\angle 5$ and $\angle 7$; $\angle 6$ and $\angle 8$.

5. $\angle 4$ and $\angle 6$; $\angle 3$ and $\angle 5$; $\angle 2$ and $\angle 8$; $\angle 1$ and $\angle 7$.

6. Corresponding: 4; Alternate interior: 2; Alternate exterior: 2.

7. Possible answer: Corresponding: The angles are in the same relative position where the transversal intersects each line; Alternate interior: On opposite sides of the transversal in the interior of the figure, but not a linear pair; Alternate exterior: On opposite sides of the transversal on the exterior of the figure, but not a linear pair

8. *a* and *b* are transversals for *c* and *d*, *c* and *e*, and *d* and *e*; *c*, *d*, and *e* are transversals for *a* and *b*.

9. Transversal; A line, not an angle.

10. *Rewrite:* If two angles are right angles, then they are congruent. *Draw:*

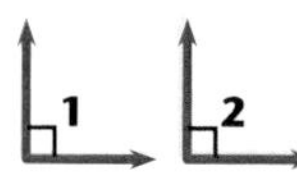

State: Given: $\angle 1$ and $\angle 2$ are right angles; *Prove:* $\angle 1 \cong \angle 2$

11. *Rewrite:* Leave as is; *Draw:*

State: Given: M is the midpoint of $\overline{AB}$; *Prove:* $AM = \frac{1}{2}AB$

12–18, 24–28. See Additional Answers p. T214.

Algebra | Functions | Discrete Math | Probability | Data/Statistics

P **12.** Graph each of the equations below on a coordinate plane. Then identify the equation of the line that is a transversal to the other two.

$y = 2x + 4$ $\qquad$ $y = -\frac{1}{2}x + 2$ $\qquad$ $y = 2x - 1$

P **13.** **Periscope Problem #1** In a periscope, a pair of mirrors are mounted parallel to each other, as shown. The path of the reflected light becomes a transversal. Name a pair of alternate interior angles.

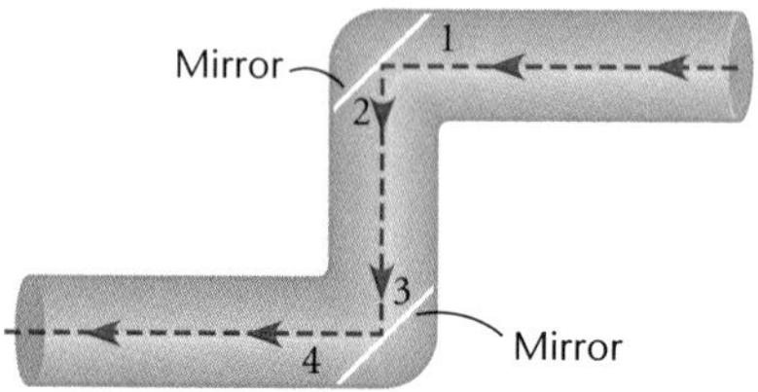

LOOK BACK

R **Write a conditional statement with each of the following sets of characteristics. [2-1]**

14. The conditional is true, and its inverse is false.

15. The conditional and its inverse, converse, and contrapositive are all false.

R **For each measure of $\angle A$, give the measure of its complement and its supplement. [3-3]**

16. $m\angle A = 42°$ $\qquad$ **17.** $m\angle A = 88°$ $\qquad$ **18.** $m\angle A = 32.4°$

MORE PRACTICE

P **Name each of the following in the figure at the right.**

19. alternate interior angles
$\angle 5$ and $\angle 3$; $\angle 4$ and $\angle 6$

20. alternate exterior angles
$\angle 8$ and $\angle 2$; $\angle 1$ and $\angle 7$

21. same-side interior angles
$\angle 3$ and $\angle 6$; $\angle 4$ and $\angle 5$

22. corresponding angles
$\angle 8$ and $\angle 4$; $\angle 5$ and $\angle 1$; $\angle 7$ and $\angle 3$; $\angle 6$ and $\angle 2$

23. vertical angles
$\angle 1$ and $\angle 3$; $\angle 2$ and $\angle 4$; $\angle 6$ and $\angle 8$; $\angle 5$ and $\angle 7$

P **Do the *rewrite, draw,* and *state* steps for the proof of each theorem.**

24. Two perpendicular lines form four right angles.

25. Two angles that are supplementary to the same angle are congruent.

Key

V Vocabulary
P Practice/Skills
R Review
MR Math Reasoning
PS Problem Solving
C Challenge

Technology Note

When using software to measure angles in the **Explore** on page 221, students need to mark a point on each side and at the vertex. Students may try to do this by simply placing points "on" the lines or "at" the points of intersection. In many cases, software requires them to *construct* points on objects and points of intersection. They may need to be shown how to use the Construction option to do this.

MORE MATH REASONING

26. Suppose line m intersects lines n and p at two different points, but is *not* a transversal. Explain how this is possible.

27. Crossing the Cube List all the pairs of lines through vertices of the cube for which $\overleftrightarrow{BH}$ is a transversal.

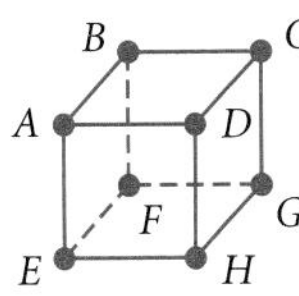

28. Do the *rewrite, draw,* and *state* steps for a proof of the following statement.

Angle congruence is transitive.

(Hint: The Transitive Property of Equality is: If $a = b$ and $b = c$, then $a = c$.)

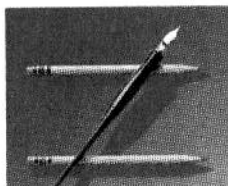

3-4 PART B Parallel Lines, Transversals, and Angles

← CONNECT → ***You've worked with parallel lines before. Now you will look at what happens when a transversal intersects two parallel lines.***

On calligraphy guidesheets, you see many parallel lines crossed by transversals. If you look closely at the angles formed by these lines, you may notice some consistent patterns. In the following Explore, you will check to see whether these relationships are always true.

EXPLORE: PARALLEL CROSSING

MATERIALS

Protractor, Straightedge
Geometry software (optional)

Use geometry software or the opposite edges of a straightedge to draw two parallel lines. Draw a transversal through the two lines.

Measure the various angles, and make as many conjectures as you can about the angles that are congruent and supplementary in your figure. (You may want to check to be sure that your conjectures hold for the calligraphy guidesheet at the right.)

Student Resources

- **Alternative Lessons 3-4B**
- **Laboratory Manual 3-4B**
- Technology Lab Manual
- **Practice 3-4B**
- **Study Guide and Journal 3-4B**
- **Guía de estudios y Diario 3-4B**
- **Multilingual Handbook**
- **More Look Ahead 3-4B**
- SAT Preparation

Media Resources

- **Transparency FFM 3-4B**
- Transparency AE
- Teaching Transparency
- **AWSMTest and practice software**
- AWSM Videodisc

PART B At a Glance

Objective
To see relationships among angles formed when a transversal intersects two parallel lines.

Development
In the **Explore,** students identify congruent and supplementary angles formed when parallel lines are cut by a transversal.

Then, in **What Do You Think?,** students see two different ways to support a theorem they discovered in the **Explore.**

Suggested Materials
Student Protractor, straightedge, geometry software

First Five Minutes
Transparency FFM 3-4B

Sketch two lines cut by a transversal and label the angles formed. Then list the pairs of alternate interior, alternate exterior, same-side interior, and corresponding angles.

Motivate
Ask...
- We'll be investigating postulates and theorems about parallel lines and transversals. Why do we need postulates?

EXPLORE

Parallel Crossing
Recommended group size: 4

The Point
To discover relationships for alternate interior, alternate exterior, corresponding, and same-side interior angles when lines are parallel.

Look and Listen...
- For students who are not making conjectures that involve alternate interior, corresponding, and other angles.

Ask...
- Can you state some of your results using the definitions in 3-4 Part A?

Parallel Lines and Transversals

For Groups That Finish Early
List all the pairs of angles in your diagram that you know are congruent or supplementary from previous knowledge.

Follow Up
Ask students to state each of their conjectures in *if-then* form.

Possible Answer
When parallel lines are cut by a transversal, alternate interior, alternate exterior, and corresponding angles are congruent, and same-side interior angles are supplementary.

WHAT DO YOU THINK?

Shows two different ways to support the theorem "If parallel lines are cut by a transversal, then the corresponding angles are congruent." Mike uses a transformational approach; Kimiko uses a synthetic one.

Asks students to look for other transformations that might help to support conjectures.

Possible Answer

1. Rotation. The center of the rotation is the midpoint of the segment on the transversal between the parallel lines, and the angle of rotation is 180°.

TRY IT

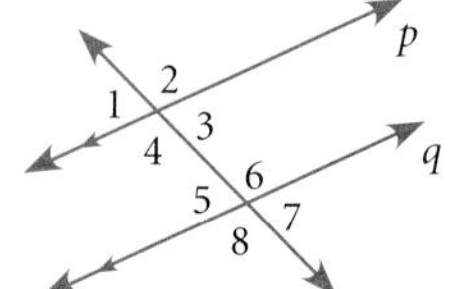

a. If $p \parallel q$ and $m\angle 1 = 72°$, find the measures of all other angles in the figure.
$m\angle 1 = m\angle 3 = m\angle 5 = m\angle 7 = 72°$;
$m\angle 2 = m\angle 4 = m\angle 6 = m\angle 8 = 108°$

We can now summarize the angle relationships for parallel lines that are cut by a transversal. Notice that we have to assume that one of the conjectures is true. The others can be proved, but their proofs rely on the truth of the postulate.

POSTULATE

If parallel lines are cut by a transversal, then the alternate interior angles are congruent.

THEOREMS

If parallel lines are cut by a transversal, then the corresponding angles are congruent.

If parallel lines are cut by a transversal, then the alternate exterior angles are congruent.

If parallel lines are cut by a transversal, then the same-side interior angles are supplementary.

WHAT DO YOU THINK?

Kimiko and Mike's teacher asked the class to give evidence to support the theorem "If parallel lines are cut by a transversal, then the corresponding angles are congruent."

Mike thinks . . .

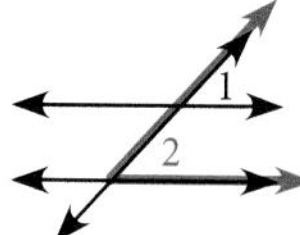

I'll draw a picture of two parallel lines with a transversal. If I trace ∠2, and then translate it up along the transversal, I can see it's congruent to ∠1. I can do the same thing for any pair of corresponding angles. SO I can use a translation to support this theorem.

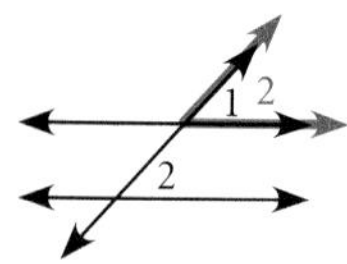

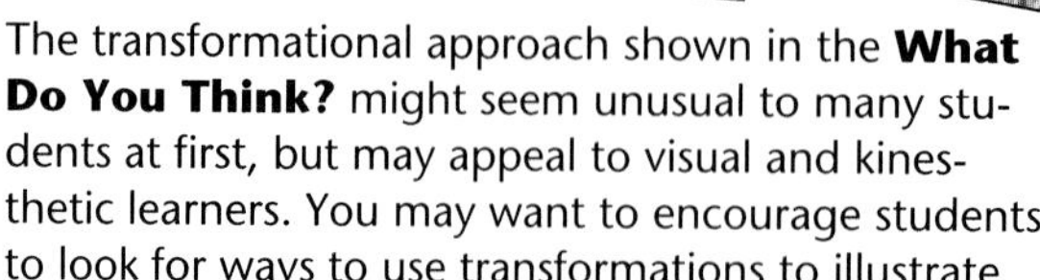

The transformational approach shown in the **What Do You Think?** might seem unusual to many students at first, but may appeal to visual and kinesthetic learners. You may want to encourage students to look for ways to use transformations to illustrate conjectures.

Kimiko thinks . . .

First, I'll draw a picture of two parallel lines with a transversal. I know that vertical angles are congruent, so $\angle 1 \cong \angle 3$. A postulate says that alternate interior angles of parallel lines are congruent, so $\angle 3 \cong \angle 2$. And if $\angle 1 \cong \angle 3$ and $\angle 3 \cong \angle 2$, then $\angle 1$ must be congruent to $\angle 2$. I can do the same thing for any pair of corresponding angles, so corresponding angles must be congruent.

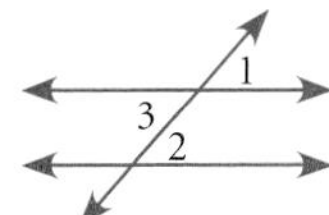

1. In the preceding situation, Mike used a translation to support the theorem about corresponding angles. Which transformation(s) could be used to support the theorem about alternate exterior angles?

REFLECT

1. Suppose two parallel lines are cut by a transversal that is not perpendicular to the lines. How many different measures are there among the angles formed? What is the relationship among these measures? Explain.
2. Justify the statement "If one of two parallel lines is perpendicular to a transversal, then so is the other."

Exercises

CORE

Getting Started Find the measures of all the numbered angles in the figure for each value of $m\angle 1$.

1. $m\angle 1 = 41°$ **2.** $m\angle 1 = 105°$

3. In the figure, $m\angle 1 = x$. Find the measures of all other angles in terms of x. Then determine whether this statement is true or false: "If two parallel lines are cut by a transversal, the angles in any pair of angles formed are either congruent or supplementary." Explain.

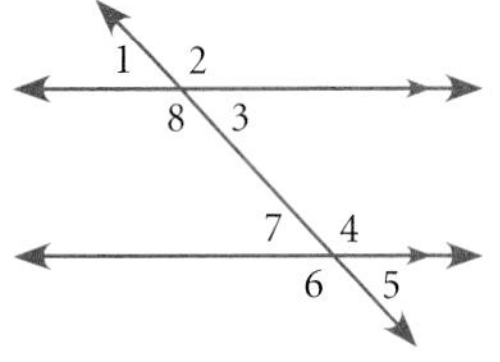

Ongoing Assessment

Vocabulary
Practice/Skills
Review
Math Reasoning
Problem Solving
Challenge

Self-Assessment Exercises 1, 2, 5, 7, 11, 12

Embedded Assessment Reflect 2; Exercises 3, 9, 10

Journal

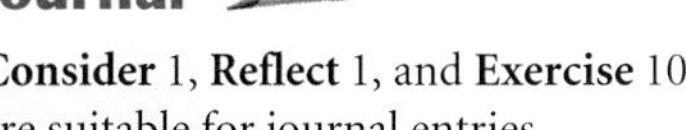

Consider 1, **Reflect** 1, and **Exercise** 10 are suitable for journal entries.

REFLECT

Possible Answers

1. There are two different angle measures, and they add to 180°.

2. The known perpendicular lines form a 90° angle. This means that a corresponding angle where the other parallel line intersects the transversal also measures 90°, so it is a right angle, and the lines are perpendicular.

Part B Exercises

Exercise Notes

Core

5. and 6. Give students practice in the *draw* and *state* steps for proof.

8. and 9. Apply angles formed by parallel lines and transversals to calligraphy.

Look Ahead

13. and 14. These exercises preview ways to prove that lines are parallel (introduced in 3-4 Part C).

More Math Reasoning

21. Students see whether "is parallel to" is a reflexive, symmetric, and transitive relationship.

Exercise Answers

Core

1. $m\angle 1 = m\angle 3 = m\angle 5 = m\angle 7 = 41°$; $m\angle 2 = m\angle 4 = m\angle 6 = m\angle 8 = 139°$

2. $m\angle 1 = m\angle 3 = m\angle 5 = m\angle 7 = 105°$; $m\angle 2 = m\angle 4 = m\angle 6 = m\angle 8 = 75°$

3. $m\angle 1, 3, 5, 7 = x$; $m\angle 2, 4, 6, 8 = (180 - x)°$; T: The angles with measure $x°$ are congruent to each other, and the angles that measure $(180 - x)°$ are congruent to each other. The angles measuring $x°$ and $(180 - x)°$ are supplements to each other. Thus, in picking two angles, the second will be either congruent to the first or supplementary to the first.

Parallel Lines and Transversals

4. Rotate 180° around the midpoint of the segment of the transversal between the lines. The angles will overlap exactly.

5. *Draw:*

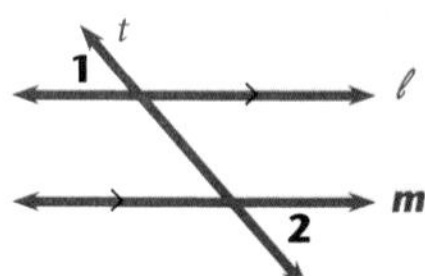

State: Given: $\ell \parallel m$, *t* is a transversal; *Prove:* $\angle 1 \cong \angle 2$

6. *Draw:*

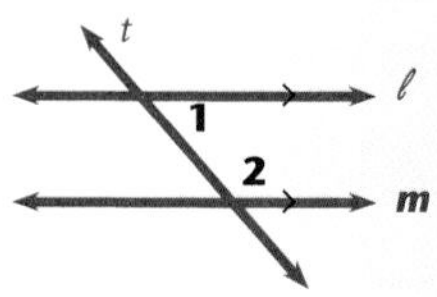

State: Given: $\ell \parallel m$, *t* is a transversal; *Prove:* $m\angle 1 + m\angle 2 = 180°$

7. 76°

8. Possible answer: The horizontal parallel lines indicate the heights of the letters and the slanted "vertical" lines (which are also parallel and evenly spaced) are the transversals.

9. a. Check students' art.

b. $m\angle 1 = 45°$, $m\angle 2 = 135°$

10. 100°; Consider the original and final paths/directions to be parallel lines and the line between angles *A* and *B* as a transversal; then $\angle B$ is the alternate interior angle of $\angle A$.

11. If the trenches are parallel and the pipeline crossing the street is a transversal, then the two angles are same-side interior angles, and Damaso's angle should measure $180° - 120° = 60°$.

12. a. iv **b.** iii

c. i

Look Ahead

13. Inverse: If two angles are not supplementary to the same angle, then they are not congruent. Converse: If two angles are congruent, then they are supplementary to the same angle. Contrapositive: If two angles are not congruent, then they are not supplementary to the same angle.

MR **4.** Explain how you could use a transformation to support the postulate that parallel lines have congruent alternate interior angles.

P **Do the *draw* and *state* steps for the proof of each theorem.**

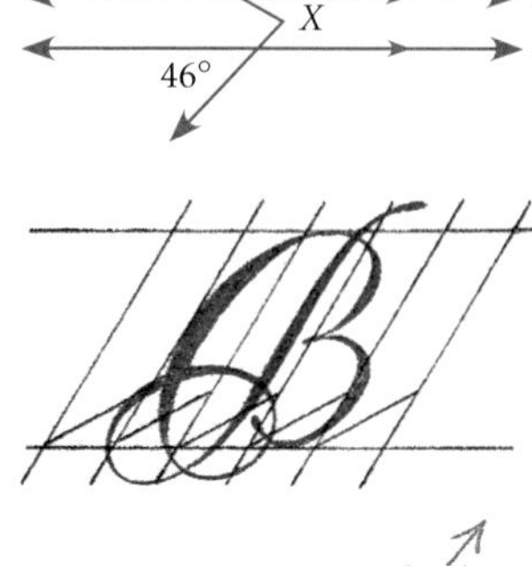

5. If parallel lines are cut by a transversal, then the alternate exterior angles are congruent.

6. If parallel lines are cut by a transversal, then the same-side interior angles are supplementary.

PS **7.** In the figure above, $r \parallel s$. Find the measure of $\angle X$. (Hint: Draw a line through the vertex of $\angle X$, parallel to lines *r* and *s*. Which postulate permits this?)

P **8.** Describe the calligraphy worksheet at the right in terms of parallel lines and transversals.

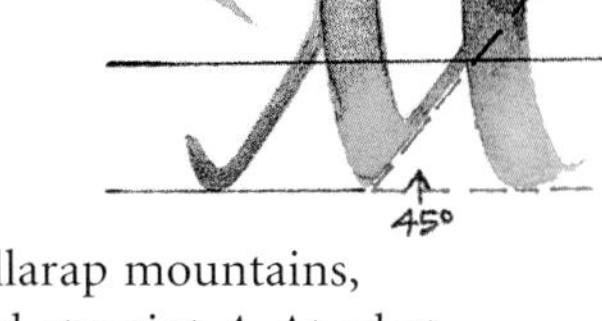

P **9. The Calligraphy Angle** When forming italic letters in calligraphy, the angle shown should be 45°.
a. Make a few italic letter *M*'s of your own.
b. Give the measure of the numbered angles.

PS **10. Road Work** While making a road through the remote Lellarap mountains, the construction team must put a turn of 100° in the road at point *A*. At what angle should the team put the turn at point *B* so that the road will head back in its original direction? Explain your answer.

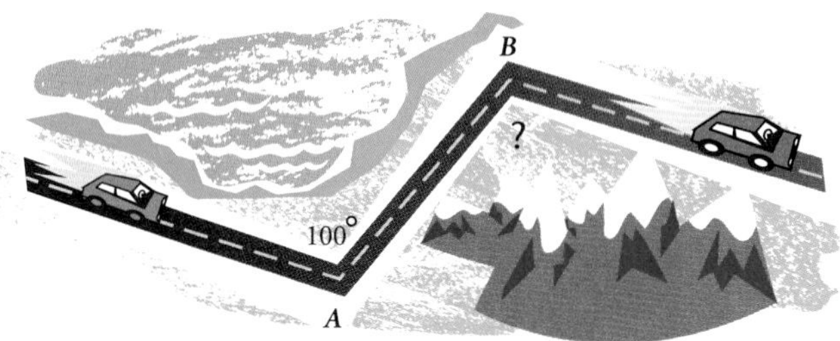

PS **11. They Can't Miss** Sue and Damaso are laying sections of pipe in trenches on opposite sides of Dartanian Street. Both are ready to start the section of pipe that will cross the street. Sue has placed her first section of pipe as shown. At what angle should Damaso place his first section so they will meet in a line? Explain. What are you assuming about the trenches?

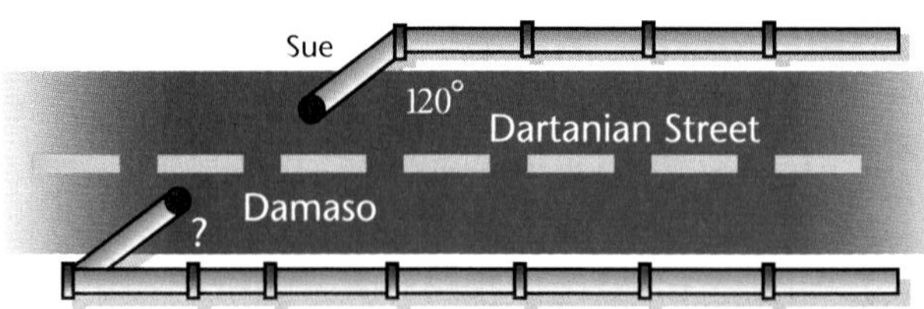

Key

V Vocabulary
P Practice/Skills
R Review
MR Math Reasoning
PS Problem Solving
C Challenge

12. Justify statements **a, b,** and **c** in the flow proof with a reason from the list below.

If two parallel lines are cut by a transversal, then the alternate exterior angles are congruent.

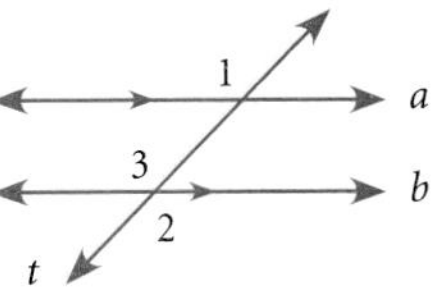

Given: Parallel lines *a* and *b* are cut by transversal *t*.

Prove: $\angle 1 \cong \angle 2$

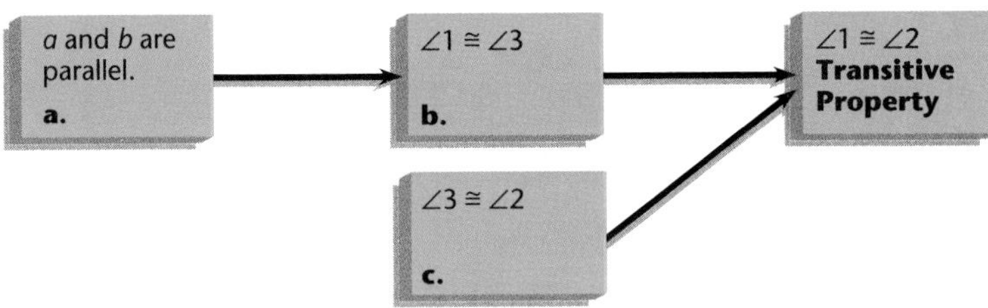

i. Vertical angles are congruent.
ii. If lines are parallel, their alternate interior angles are congruent.
iii. If lines are parallel, their corresponding angles are congruent.
iv. Given information

LOOK AHEAD

13. Write the inverse, converse, and contrapositive of the statement "If two angles are supplementary to the same angle, then they are congruent."

14. Draw an acute angle $\angle MNP$. Then use a compass and straightedge to construct $\angle JKL$ so that $\angle JKL \cong \angle MNP$.

MORE PRACTICE

Find the measures of all the numbered angles for each value of $m\angle 1$.

15. $m\angle 1 = 160°$

16. $m\angle 1 = 35°$

17. $m\angle 1 = 82.5°$

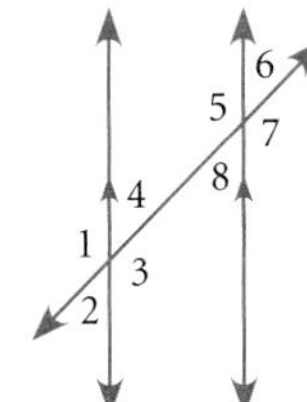

14.

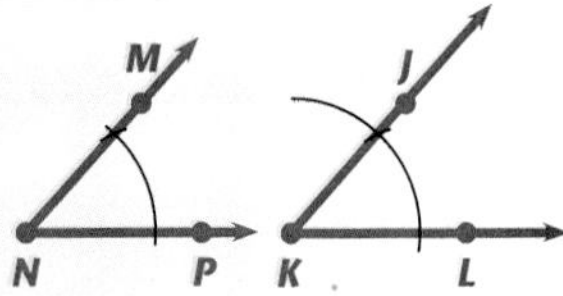

More Practice

15. $m\angle 1, 3, 5, 7 = 160°$; $m\angle 2, 4, 6, 8 = 20°$

16. $m\angle 1, 3, 5, 7 = 35°$; $m\angle 2, 4, 6, 8 = 145°$

17. $m\angle 1, 3, 5, 7 = 82.5°$; $m\angle 2, 4, 6, 8 = 97.5°$

18. 124°

19. *Draw:*

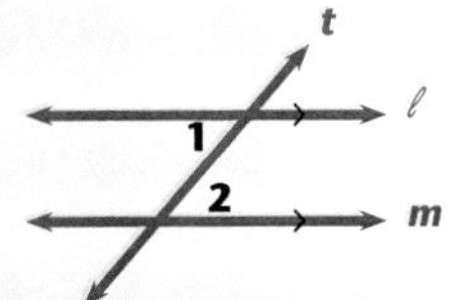

State: Given: $\ell \parallel m$, *t* is a transversal, and $\angle 1$ and $\angle 2$ are alternate interior angles; *Prove:* $\angle 1 \cong \angle 2$

More Math Reasoning

20. a. *Draw:*

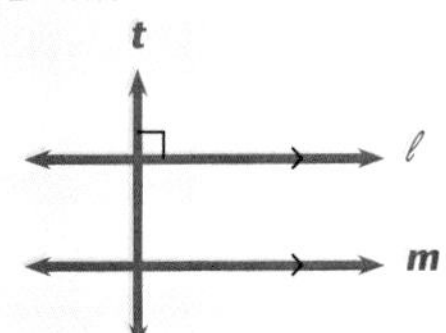

State: Given: $\ell \parallel m$, *t* is a transversal, and $\ell \perp t$; *Prove:* $m \perp t$

b. Yes; Corresponding angles are congruent.

21. a. No; Definition says parallel lines are coplanar lines that do not intersect.

b. Yes; Coplanarity and non-intersection are both symmetric.

c. Yes; If *m* and *n* have no common point(s) and if *n* and *p* have no common point(s), then *m* and *p* have no common points.

22. $m\angle 1, 2, 4, 6, 8, 10 = 96°$; $m\angle 3, 5, 7, 9, 11, 14 = 84°$; $m\angle 12, 13, 15, 16 = 48°$

Parallel Lines and Transversals

PART C At a Glance

Objective

To find ways to use angles formed by transversals to prove lines parallel.

Development

In the **Explore,** students discover that the converses of the postulate and theorems from 3-4 Part B are true. Then they see that these converses are ways to show that lines are parallel.

Suggested Materials

Student Compass, straightedge, protractor

First Five Minutes

Transparency FFM 3-4C

Sketch an angle. Then use a compass and straightedge to construct an angle congruent to it.

Motivate

Ask...

- If a statement is true, is its converse always true?
- How can we write a conditional statement and its true converse as a single statement?

PS **18.** In the figure, $a \parallel b$. Find the measure of $\angle X$.

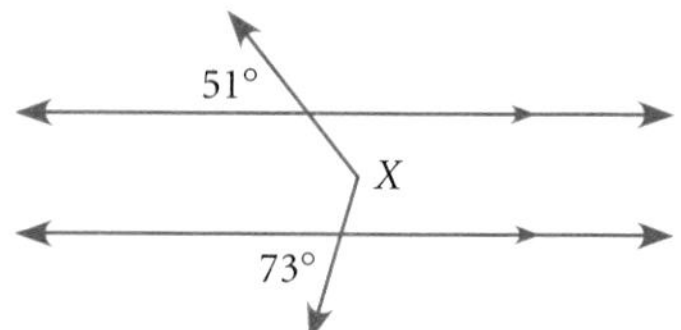

P **19.** Do the *draw* and *state* steps for the proof of the following theorem.

If parallel lines are cut by a transversal, then the alternate interior angles are congruent.

MORE MATH REASONING

MR **20.** Lynn says, "If one of two parallel lines is perpendicular to a transversal, then the other one is too."
- **a.** Do the *draw* and *state* steps for a proof of this statement.
- **b.** Tell whether or not Lynn is correct, and why.

MR **21.** Consider the relation "is parallel to."
- **a.** Is a line parallel to itself? (In other words, is there a Reflexive Property for *parallel*?) Explain.
- **b.** If $m \parallel n$, is $n \parallel m$? (Is there a Symmetric Property for *parallel*?) Explain.
- **c.** If $m \parallel n$ and $n \parallel p$, is $m \parallel p$? (Is there a Transitive Property for *parallel*?) Explain.

MR **22.** In the figure, $a \parallel b$, and $c \parallel d$. Calculate the measure of each numbered angle.

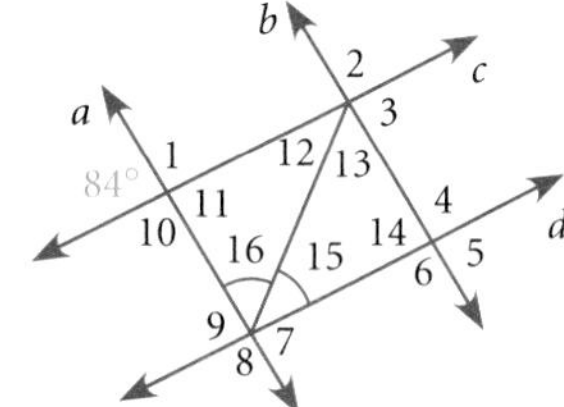

3-4 PART C Proving Lines Parallel

← CONNECT → ***You've explored properties of the angles formed when two parallel lines are cut by a transversal. Now you will investigate the converses of these properties to find ways to show that lines are parallel.***

You have discovered and used several of the relationships about angles formed by parallel lines and a transversal. But suppose you want to make a calligraphy worksheet. How can you be sure that your lines are parallel? In the following Explore, you will see if the converses of some of the statements about angles and parallel lines are true as well.

Key

- V Vocabulary
- P Practice/Skills
- R Review
- MR Math Reasoning
- PS Problem Solving
- C Challenge

EXPLORE: CONVERSELY . . .

MATERIALS

Compass
Straightedge
Protractor

1. Use a straightedge to draw two intersecting lines, *a* and *b*. Label an angle at their intersection $\angle 1$. Select a point *X* on line *a*. Construct an alternate interior angle at *X* congruent to $\angle 1$, using a compass and straightedge. Extend the side of the new angle, and label it line *c*. What seems to be true about lines *c* and *b*?

2. Repeat the steps above, but this time construct a congruent corresponding angle. Are the lines parallel?

3. There are two other theorems about the angles formed by parallel lines.
- If parallel lines are cut by a transversal, then the alternate exterior angles are congruent.
- If parallel lines are cut by a transversal, then the same-side interior angles are supplementary.

Investigate the converses of these theorems. Use a figure like the one in the photo to begin your investigations. You may use a protractor to draw the angles.

4. Write your conjectures in if-then form. Are all of them converses of the postulate and theorems about the angles formed by parallel lines?

TRY IT

y Congruent
ate Interior Angles;
y Congruent
sponding Angles;
y Congruent
ate Interior Angles.
le answer:
$\angle 1 \cong \angle 2$, $\angle 1 \cong \angle 4$,
$1 + m\angle 3 = 180°$

a. List the pairs of parallel lines in the figure at the right. Explain how you *know* the lines are parallel.

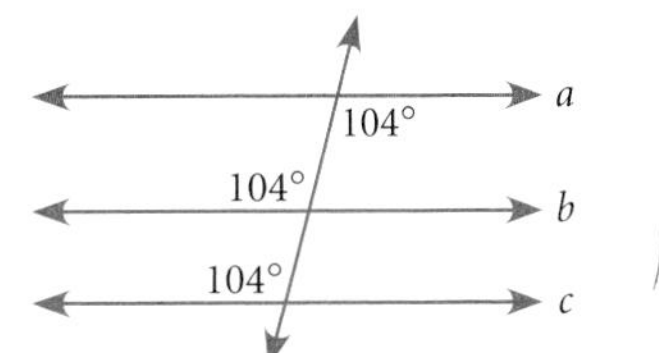

b. A contractor wants to guarantee that the new street she is marking off is parallel to Douglass Street. She finds that $m\angle 1 = 45°$. Give three different ways that she can use angles to be sure that the new street is parallel to Douglass Street.

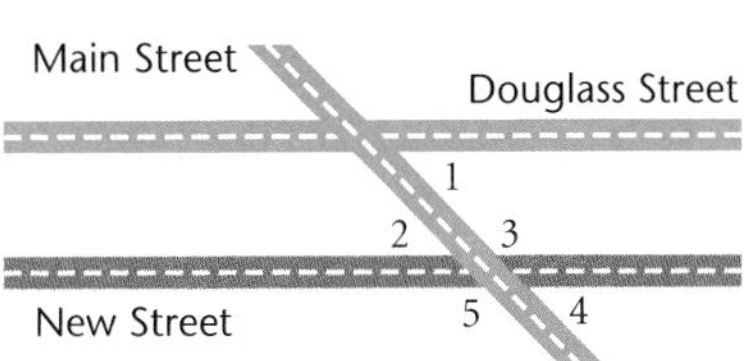

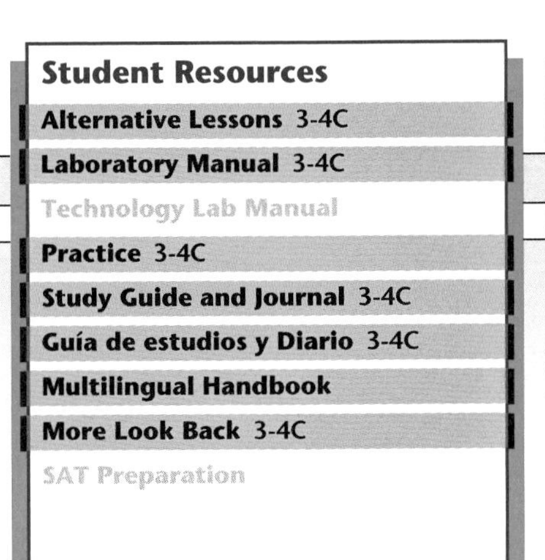

Student Resources

- **Alternative Lessons** 3-4C
- **Laboratory Manual** 3-4C
- Technology Lab Manual
- **Practice** 3-4C
- **Study Guide and Journal** 3-4C
- **Guía de estudios y Diario** 3-4C
- **Multilingual Handbook**
- **More Look Back** 3-4C
- SAT Preparation

Media Resources

- **Transparency FFM** 3-4C
- Transparency AE
- Teaching Transparency
- **AWSMTest and practice software**
- AWSM Videodisc

EXPLORE

Conversely...

Recommended group size: 4

The Point
To discover that the converses of the postulates and theorem from 3-4 Part B are also true; that is, if corresponding angles are congruent, lines are parallel, and so on.

Look and Listen...
- For students who are unsure where to draw the alternate interior angle in Step 1.

Ask...
- Is it easier to see where to draw the angle if you write its number in the proper position *before* doing the construction?

For Groups That Finish Early
Sketch two parallel lines cut by two parallel transversals. Then use markings to show all the congruent angles formed.

Follow Up
Ask students to state each of their conjectures in *if-then* form. Then have them explain what they can show by using these conjectures.

Possible Answers

1. They are parallel.

2. They are parallel.

3. Both converses are true.

4. If two lines are cut by a transversal so that a pair of
- alternate interior angles are congruent, then the lines are parallel.
- alternate exterior angles are congruent, then the lines are parallel.
- corresponding angles are congruent, then the lines are parallel.
- same-side interior angles are supplementary, then the lines are parallel.

All of the above are converses of a postulate or theorem about the angles formed by parallel lines and a transversal.

Parallel Lines and Transversals

Journal

Reflect 1 and **Exercise** 13 are suitable for journal entries.

REFLECT

Possible Answers

1. Three. One angle at one of the four points of intersection can be a corresponding angle for both pairs of lines.
2. No. Vertical angles are always congruent.

Part C Exercises

Exercise Notes

Core

13. Students use properties of parallel lines to explain how a periscope works.

16. Students use their knowledge of the properties of parallel lines to devise a construction technique. You may want to have a few students present their techniques to the class.

More Math Reasoning

27. Students fill in blanks in a paragraph proof of one of the theorems they discovered in this Part's **Explore.**

Exercise Answers

Core

1. Corresponding angles are congruent.
2. Alternate interior angles are congruent.
3. Same-side interior angles are supplementary.
4. $a \parallel c$; Corresponding Angles Theorem
5. $a \parallel b$; Alternate Interior Angles Postulate
6. $b \parallel c$; Same-side Interior Angles Theorem
7. $a \parallel c$; Alternate Interior Angles Postulate
8. $b \parallel c$; Corresponding Angles Theorem

The following statements give ways to prove that lines are parallel. They are all converses of the statements that you learned about parallel lines.

POSTULATE

If two lines are cut by a transversal so that a pair of alternate interior angles are congruent, then the lines are parallel.

THEOREMS

If two lines are cut by a transversal so that a pair of corresponding angles are congruent, then the lines are parallel.

If two lines are cut by a transversal so that a pair of alternate exterior angles are congruent, then the lines are parallel.

If two lines are cut by a transversal so that a pair of same-side interior angles are supplementary, then the lines are parallel.

REFLECT

1. If two lines are cut by two transversals, what is the smallest number of angles that you need to measure to make sure the lines are parallel *and* the transversals are parallel?
2. Can you tell whether lines x and y are parallel from the given information? Why or why not?

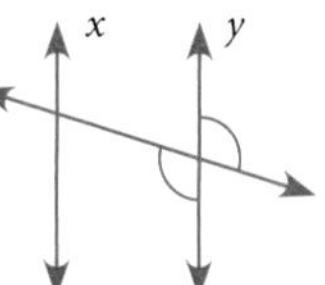

Exercises

CORE

P **Getting Started** **For each figure, give a reason why line ℓ is parallel to line m.**

1. 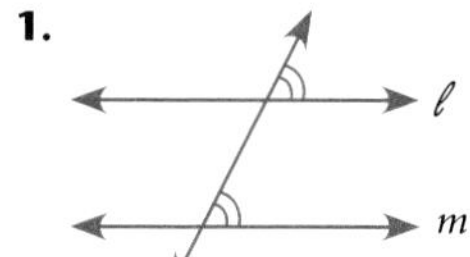

2. 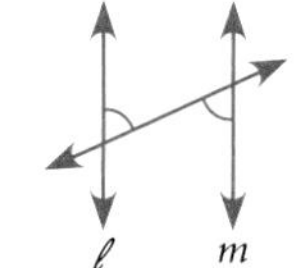

3. 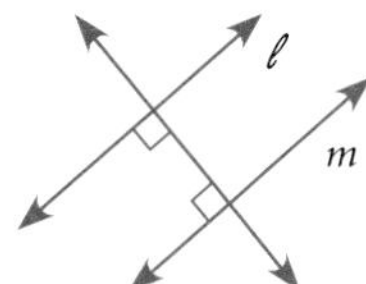

Key

- V Vocabulary
- P Practice/Skills
- R Review
- MR Math Reasoning
- PS Problem Solving
- C Challenge

Use the given information to decide which lines are parallel. Justify your answers with a theorem or postulate.

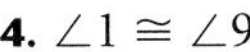

4. $\angle 1 \cong \angle 9$ **5.** $\angle 3 \cong \angle 6$

6. $m\angle 8 + m\angle 10 = 180°$ **7.** $\angle 4 \cong \angle 9$

8. $\angle 8 \cong \angle 12$ **9.** $\angle 1 \cong \angle 8$

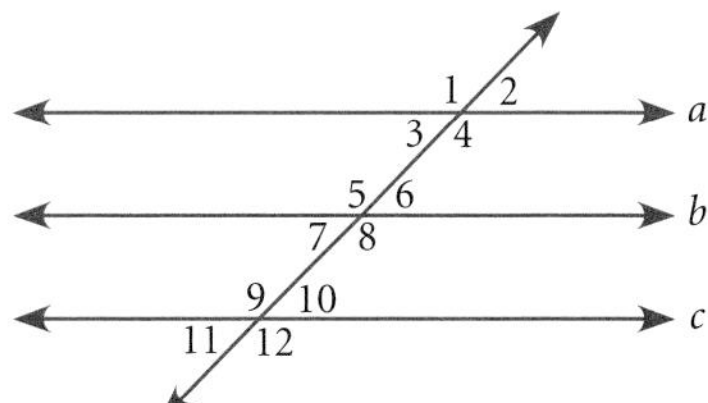

Find the value of *x* for which *s* || *t*.

10. $m\angle 2 = 2x°$, $m\angle 3 = 4x°$ $x = 30°$

11. $m\angle 1 = 2x°$, $m\angle 6 = 136°$ $x = 68°$

12. $m\angle 1 = 3x°$, $m\angle 5 = 60°$ $x = 40°$

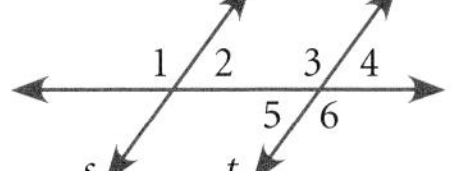

13. Periscope Problem #2 The mirrors in a periscope are mounted parallel to each other, as shown. Because the angle of incidence of a light ray is congruent to the angle of reflection, $\angle 1 \cong \angle 2$.

Explain why the light entering the periscope is parallel to the light leaving the periscope. (Hint: What is the transversal for these light rays?)

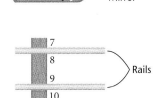

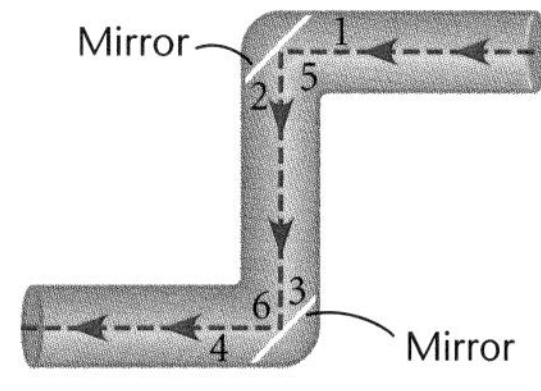

14. Geometry Training The rails of a railroad track must always be parallel. Assume that $\angle 8$ is a right angle. List all the possible ways to check that the rails are parallel by measuring one of the other numbered angles.

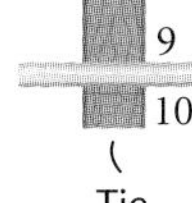

15. Do the *draw* and *state* steps for the proof of the following.

If two lines are cut by a transversal so that a pair of corresponding angles are congruent, then the lines are parallel.

16. Write a procedure for constructing a line parallel to a line ℓ through a point P not on line ℓ. Then copy the figure and show your construction.

LOOK BACK

In Exercises 17 and 18, write each biconditional as two conditional statements. [2-2]

17. An angle is acute if and only if it measures less than 90°.

18. A chemical reaction is exothermic if and only if it releases heat.

19. Draw an obtuse angle, $\angle ABC$. Then use a compass and straightedge to construct $\overrightarrow{BD}$, the angle bisector of $\angle ABC$. [3-3]

Ongoing Assessment

Self-Assessment Exercises 1–11 odd, 15

Embedded Assessment Try It b; Reflect 1; Exercises 6, 12, 16

9. $a \parallel b$; Alternate Exterior Angles Theorem

13.

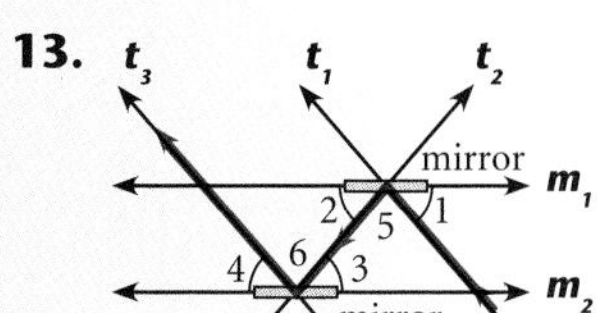

Let $m_1 \parallel m_2$ be the mirror's orientation lines, and t_1, t_2, and t_3 be transversals where the light path is as shown. Along the transversals, $\angle 1 \cong \angle 2$ (angle of incidence $\cong$ angle of reflection). Then $\angle 2$ and $\angle 3$ are alternate interior angles of m_1 and m_2 (where $m_1 \parallel m_2$) so $\angle 2 \cong \angle 3$. But $\angle 3 \cong \angle 4$ (angle of incidence $\cong$ angle of reflection). Then $m\angle 1 + m\angle 5 + m\angle 2 = 180° = m\angle 3 + m\angle 6 + m\angle 4$ implies $m\angle 5 = m\angle 6$ since $\angle 1 \cong \angle 2 \cong \angle 3 \cong \angle 4$. Since $\angle 5$ and $\angle 6$ are alternate interior angles with t_2 as the transversal, $t_1 \parallel t_3$, i.e., the light rays entering and leaving the periscope are parallel.

14. If $m\angle 9 = 90°$, the rails are parallel because same-side interior angles are supplementary. If $m\angle 10 = 90°$, the rails are parallel because corresponding angles are congruent.

15. *Draw:*

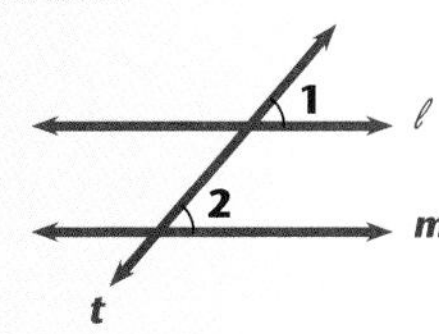

State: Given: Transversal cuts ℓ and m such that the corresponding angles 1 and 2 are congruent; *Prove:* $\ell \parallel m$

16. Draw ℓ and P not on ℓ. Draw m through P. Use congruent angle construction to draw n so corresponding angles are congruent.

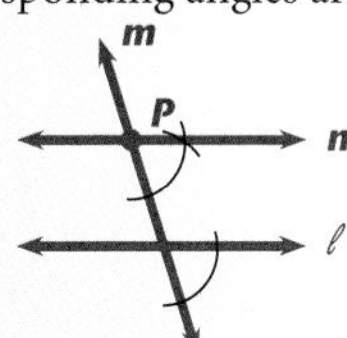

Look Back

17. If an angle is acute, then it measures less than 90°. If an angle measures less than 90°, then it is acute.

Parallel Lines and Transversals

18. If a chemical reaction is exothermic, then it releases heat. If a chemical reaction releases heat, then it is exothermic.

19.

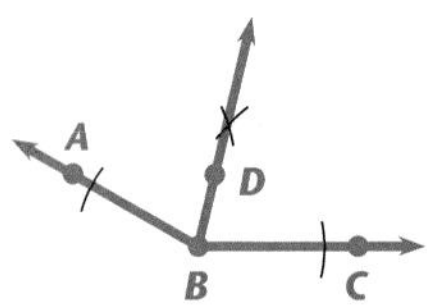

More Practice

20. $\overleftrightarrow{AB} \parallel \overleftrightarrow{DC}$ by Alternate Interior Angles

21. $c \parallel d$ by Alternate Exterior Angles

22. $\overleftrightarrow{QR} \parallel \overleftrightarrow{NP}$ by Corresponding Angles

23. $y = 0$; $x = 118$

24. $y = 15$; $x = 45$

25. $x = 3$; $y = -20$

More Math Reasoning

26. Possible answer:

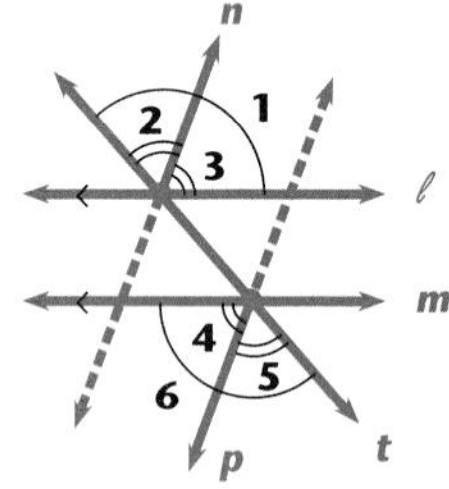

The bisectors are parallel. From the figure: $\ell \parallel m$ and t is a transversal. $\angle 1 \cong \angle 6$ because they are alternate exterior angles. Bisect $\angle 1$ with n, getting $\angle 2 \cong \angle 3$; Bisect $\angle 6$ with p, getting $\angle 4 \cong \angle 5$. $\angle 2 \cong \angle 3 \cong \angle 4 \cong \angle 5$ since each is (in measure) one-half of congruent angles 1 or 6. Consider the lines of bisection n and p and their transversal, t. $\angle 2$ and $\angle 5$ are alternate exterior angles, and, since they are congruent, $n \parallel p$, i.e., the bisectors are parallel.

27. a. Definition of *linear pair*

b. Linear-Pair Postulate

c. Supplementary angles

d. Congruent **e.** Congruent

MORE PRACTICE

P **Use the given information to decide which lines are parallel. Justify your answers with a theorem or postulate.**

20.

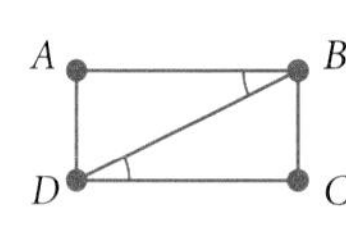

21.

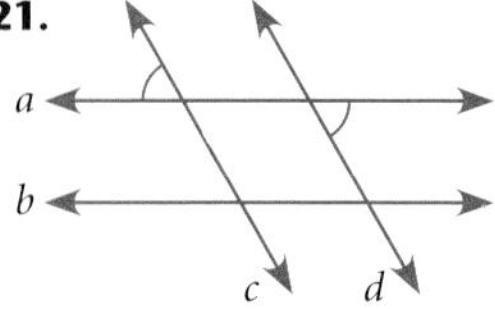

22.

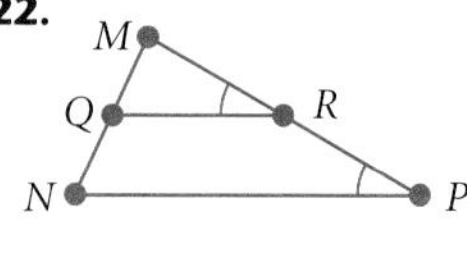

P **Find the values of *x* and *y* for which *m* || *n*.**

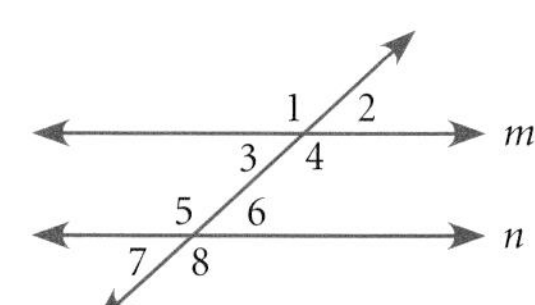

23. $m\angle 1 = (x + y)°$, $m\angle 4 = (x - y)°$, and $m\angle 8 = 118°$

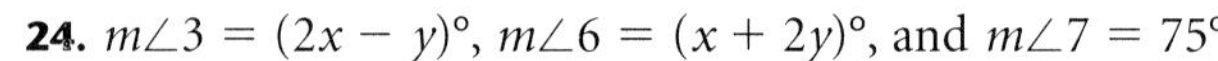

24. $m\angle 3 = (2x - y)°$, $m\angle 6 = (x + 2y)°$, and $m\angle 7 = 75°$

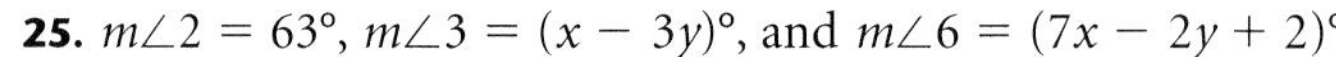

25. $m\angle 2 = 63°$, $m\angle 3 = (x - 3y)°$, and $m\angle 6 = (7x - 2y + 2)°$

MORE MATH REASONING

PS **26.** Use a straightedge to draw two parallel lines and a transversal. Then use a protractor to bisect a pair of alternate exterior angles. Write a statement about these bisectors, and explain why the statement is true.

> **Problem-Solving Tip**
>
> Use deductive reasoning.

MR, C **27.** The proof below is shown in paragraph form. Fill in the blanks to complete the proof.

Given: $\angle 1$ is supplementary to $\angle 2$.

Prove: $g \parallel h$

Proof: We are given that $\angle 1$ and $\angle 2$ are supplementary. $\angle 2$ and $\angle 3$ are a linear pair, by the **a.** ____. This means that they are supplementary, by the **b.** ____. $\angle 1$ and $\angle 3$ are both **c.** ____ to $\angle 2$, and supplements of the same angle are **d.** ____. $\angle 1$ and $\angle 3$ are corresponding angles, by the definition of corresponding angles. Therefore, since a pair of corresponding angles are **e.** ____, we know $g \parallel h$.

Key

- V Vocabulary
- P Practice/Skills
- R Review
- MR Math Reasoning
- PS Problem Solving
- C Challenge

3-4 PART D Making Connections

← CONNECT → ***Examples of parallel lines are everywhere, both in nature and in manufactured objects. You've explored parallel lines and the angles formed when they are intersected by transversals.***

In the following Explore, you will see how our results about parallel lines, transversals, and angles can be used to create your own calligraphy worksheet.

EXPLORE: GETTING THE RIGHT ANGLE

MATERIALS

Protractor
Straightedge

In the calligraphy worksheet at the right, the measure of the alternate interior angles determines the slant of the letters created.

1. Create your own calligraphy worksheet by experimenting with different measures for the alternate interior angles. Find an angle that you think makes the best-looking letters. Set up a section of your worksheet using this angle, and use this section to write your name.
2. On this section of your worksheet, mark a set of parallel lines and a transversal. Label some points, so that you can list the pairs of corresponding angles, alternate interior angles, alternate exterior angles, and same-side interior angles. Give the measures of all the angles on your worksheet.

REFLECT

1. All of the facts you have learned about the angles formed by parallel lines and transversals have true converses. Give an example of a true statement about parallel lines that has a false converse.
2. Write a summary of the theorems and postulates about parallel lines and transversals. Illustrate each with a sketch.

Student Resources

- Alternative Lessons
- **Laboratory Manual** 3-4D
- Technology Lab Manual
- **Practice** 3-4D
- **Study Guide and Journal** 3-4D
- **Guía de estudios y Diario** 3-4D
- **Multilingual Handbook**
- **More Look Back** 3-4D
- SAT Preparation

Media Resources

- **Transparency FFM** 3-4D
- Transparency AE
- Teaching Transparency
- **AWSMTest and practice software**
- AWSM Videodisc

PART D At a Glance

Objective

To use parallel lines and transversals to design a calligraphy worksheet.

Development

In the **Explore,** students use parallel lines and transversals to design a calligraphy worksheet.

Suggested Materials

Student Protractor, straightedge

First Five Minutes

Transparency FFM 3-4D

List as many definitions, postulates, and theorems as you can about the angles formed by two lines and a transversal.

EXPLORE

Getting the Right Angle

Recommended group size: 2

The Point

To design a calligraphy worksheet using parallel lines, transversals, and their angles.

Look and Listen...

- For students who do not see how to use the transversals to guide the slant of their letters.

Ask...

- Which up or down strokes of the letter should follow the slant?

For Groups That Finish Early

Sketch a section of a calligraphy worksheet where the "horizontal" lines are *not* parallel. Make parallel transversals to guide your writing. Use this worksheet to write a sentence. What might this worksheet be used for?

Follow Up

Ask students to give the measures of their "best" angle from Step 1 and tabulate the responses. If responses tend to be similar, you may want to have a discussion about why this is so.

Possible Answers

Check students' art.

Parallel Lines and Transversals

Portfolio

Have students select items from their work that demonstrate their understanding of the material in 3-4.

You may wish to have students include their best first three steps for a deductive proof, an **Exercise** showing a real-world application of parallel lines, and an **Exercise** that they found interesting or challenging.

REFLECT

Possible Answers

1. If two lines are parallel, then they do not intersect. The converse is false because skew lines do not intersect.
2. Students' lists should include the postulates and theorems listed on pages 222 and 228.

Self-Assessment

Exercise Notes

10. Students use algebra to find a value of a variable that makes lines parallel.

14. Shows an application of parallel lines in optics.

Self-Assessment Answers

11. $\angle VXW \cong \angle YXZ$ and $\angle VXY \cong \angle WXZ$ because they are vertical angles.

12. $\angle YXV$ and $\angle VXW$, $\angle YXZ$ and $\angle ZXW$, $\angle VXW$ and $\angle WXZ$, $\angle VXY$ and $\angle YXZ$ because they are linear pairs.

14. $\angle 1 \cong \angle 3$, each of measure 45° (Corresponding angles of parallel air lines); $m\angle 2 = m\angle 4 = 110°$ (Corresponding angles of parallel water lines); $m\angle 5 = m\angle 6$ (Corresponding angles of parallel water lines); $m\angle 7 = m\angle 8$ (Corresponding angles of parallel air lines); If water surface $\|$ dotted line, then $m\angle 7 = m\angle 8 = 180° - m\angle 1 = 135°$. If water surface and bottom are parallel, then $m\angle 5 = m\angle 6 = 180° - m\angle 2$, or 70°.

15. Check students' answers.

Self-Assessment

P **Determine whether each statement is true or false. If a statement is false, explain why.**

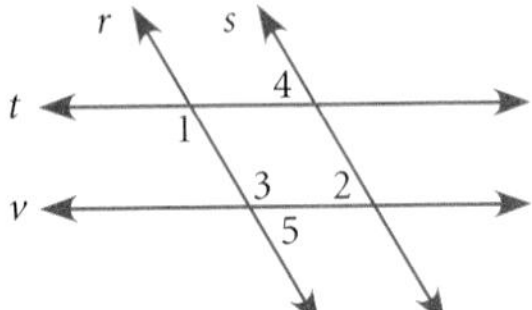

1. $\angle 1$ and $\angle 3$ are alternate interior angles. T
2. If $t \| v$, then $m\angle 2 + m\angle 5 = 180°$. F; $\angle 2 \cong \angle 5$
3. If $\angle 2 \cong \angle 4$, then $t \| v$. T
4. If $t \| v$, $r \| s$, and $m\angle 4 = 24°$, then $m\angle 3 = 24°$. F; $m\angle 3 = 156°$

P **Use the given information to name the lines (if any) that are parallel.**

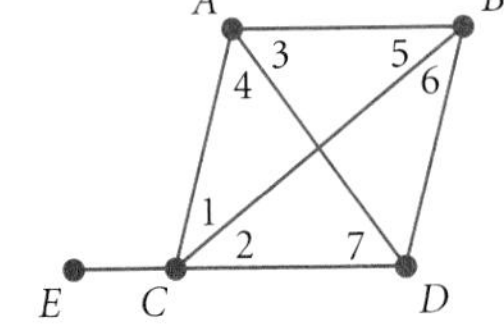

5. $\angle 3 \cong \angle 7$ $\overleftrightarrow{AB} \| \overleftrightarrow{CD}$
6. $\angle 2 \cong \angle 6$ Possibly none
7. $\angle 2 \cong \angle 3$ Possibly none
8. $\angle ACE \cong \angle BDC$ $\overleftrightarrow{AC} \| \overleftrightarrow{BD}$
9. $m\angle ACD + m\angle BDC = 180°$ $\overleftrightarrow{AC} \| \overleftrightarrow{BD}$

P **10.** Suppose $m\angle 2 = (3x + 10)°$ and $m\angle 5 = (x + 28)°$. Find the value for x for which $\overline{AB} \| \overline{CD}$. $x = 9$

R **Use the figure at the right to answer each question. [3-3]**

11. Name two pairs of congruent angles. Explain why they are congruent.
12. Name four pairs of supplementary angles. Explain why they are supplementary.

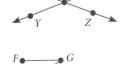

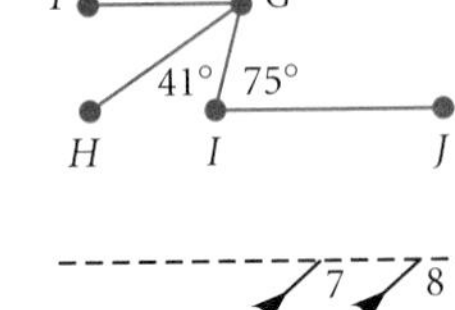

P **13.** In the figure at the right, $\overline{FG} \| \overline{IJ}$. $m\angle FGH =$ ____. (a)
(a) 34° (b) 41° (c) 45° (d) 75° (e) 116°

P *Science* **14. Refract Facts** Because light travels at different speeds in air and water, light rays are refracted (bent) when they go from one medium to the other. Light rays are bent by the same amount, so if they are parallel in the water, they are also parallel in the air. In the figure at the right, $m\angle 1 = 45°$ and $m\angle 2 = 110°$. Find the measures of all other numbered angles.

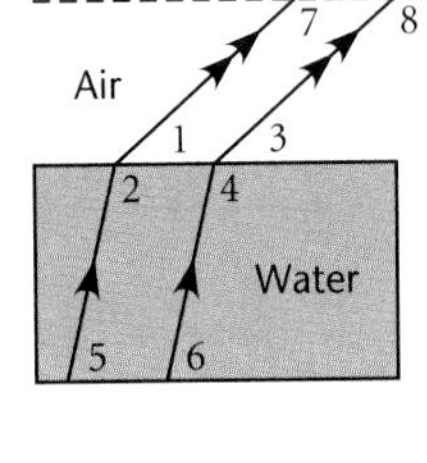

PS **15. Handwriting Analysis** Write a few words on your paper. Then measure the angle of inclination (angle to the right of vertical) of your handwriting. Get writing samples from two other people. What is the range of their angles of inclination? Do any of the samples have a "negative" angle of inclination? What is the average angle of inclination?

Angle of inclination

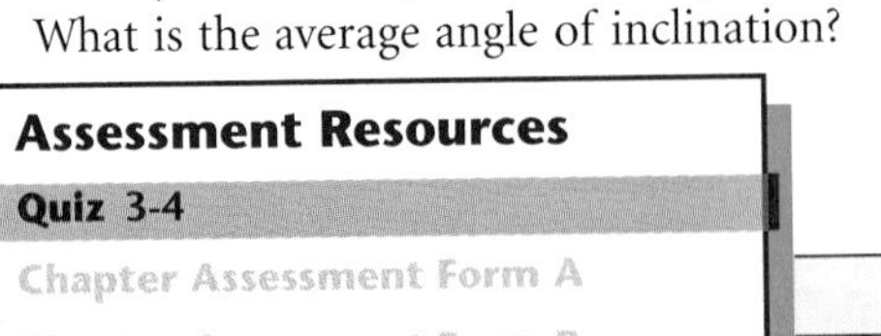

Assessment Resources

- Quiz 3-4
- Chapter Assessment Form A
- Chapter Assessment Form B
- Chapter Alternative Assessment
- Mid-Year Assessment
- End-of-Year Assessment
- AWSMTest and practice software

Ongoing Assessment

Self-Assessment Self-Assessment Exercises

Embedded Assessment Explore Step 2; Reflect and 2

Chapter 3 Review

In Chapter 3, you learned about angles, bearings, translations, and vectors. You investigated rotations and rotational symmetry and explored the assumptions that may be made about angles and distances in a figure. You also explored the relationships between pairs of angles and between the angles formed by two parallel lines and a transversal.

KEY TERMS

acute angle [3-1]	half-turn [3-2]	same-side interior angles [3-4]
alternate exterior angles [3-4]	linear pair [3-3]	supplementary angles [3-3]
alternate interior angles [3-4]	obtuse angle [3-1]	translation [3-1]
angle bisector [3-3]	opposite rays [3-1]	translation vector [3-1]
bearing [3-1]	point symmetry [3-2]	transversal [3-4]
complementary angles [3-3]	right angle [3-1]	vector sum [3-1]
corresponding angles [3-4]	rotation [3-2]	vector [3-1]
equal vectors [3-1]	rotational symmetry [3-2]	vertical angles [3-3]

Determine whether each statement is true or false. If the statement is false, change the underlined word or phrase to make it true.

1. A vector is a directed line segment. T
2. The measure of an acute angle is greater than 90° but less than 180°. F; Obtuse
3. If a figure can be rotated onto itself through an angle of 180°, it has point symmetry. T
4. Complementary angles are angles whose measures add up to 180°. F; Supplementary
5. A transversal is a line that intersects two coplanar lines in two different points. T

CONCEPTS AND APPLICATIONS

Name each of the following, using the figure at the right. [3-1]

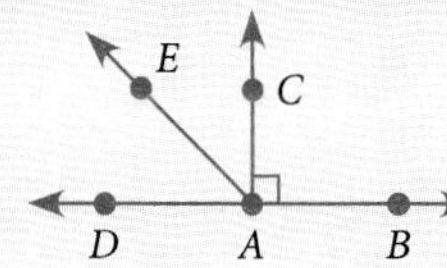

6. two opposite rays $\overrightarrow{AD}$, $\overrightarrow{AB}$
7. one acute angle, one obtuse angle, and one right angle Possible answer: $\angle DAE$, $\angle EAB$, $\angle CAB$
8. a point in the interior of $\angle DAC$ E

Vocabulary
Practice/Skills
Review
Math Reasoning
Problem Solving
Challenge

Chapter 3 Review

Journal

Students can identify **Key Terms** that they do not understand, and look up the definitions in the indicated section or in the glossary. Non-English-speaking students may want to use the *Multilingual Handbook.*

Vocabulary exercises and the **Self-Evaluation** are useful journal entries.

Review Answers

9. No; The distance from P to the lake and to the mountain.

10. $\overrightarrow{AB}$: Length $= \sqrt{6^2 + 2^2} = \sqrt{40}$; Direction $\approx 18°$; $\overrightarrow{CD}$: Length $= \sqrt{(-6)^2 + (-4)^2} = \sqrt{52}$; Direction $\approx 214°$; $\overrightarrow{EF}$: Length $= \sqrt{2^2 + (-4)^2} = \sqrt{20}$; Direction $\approx 297°$

11. Yes; 90°, 180°, 270°

12. Yes; 180° **13.** No

14. $m\angle AOD - m\angle BOC = m\angle AOB + m\angle COD$; $130° - 40° = 90°$; Since $\angle AOB \cong \angle COD$, each has measure 45°.

15. $m\angle AOD = m\angle AOB + m\angle BOC + m\angle COD$; $5x° = (x + 10)° + 40° + 2x° = (3x + 50)°$, so $x = 25$; $m\angle AOB = (x + 10)° = 35°$; $m\angle COD = 2x° = 50°$.

16. $m\angle 1 = 60°$; $m\angle 2 = 30°$; $m\angle 3 = 30°$; $m\angle 4 = 85°$;

17.

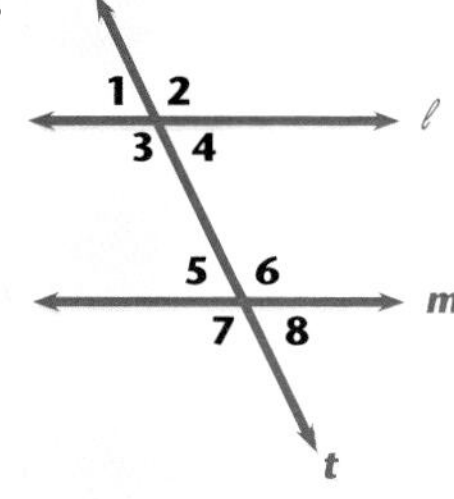

Show for example that $\angle 3 \cong \angle 6$, $\angle 1 \cong \angle 8$ or $\angle 1 \cong \angle 5$, or that $m\angle 3 + m\angle 5 = 180°$.

18. F; Three (noncollinear) points determine a plane (Plane Postulate).

19. T; Points-Existence Postulate

20. $a \parallel b$; Alternate interior angles are congruent.

21. $a \parallel b$; Alternate interior angles are congruent.

22. No parallel lines

23. Check students' answers.

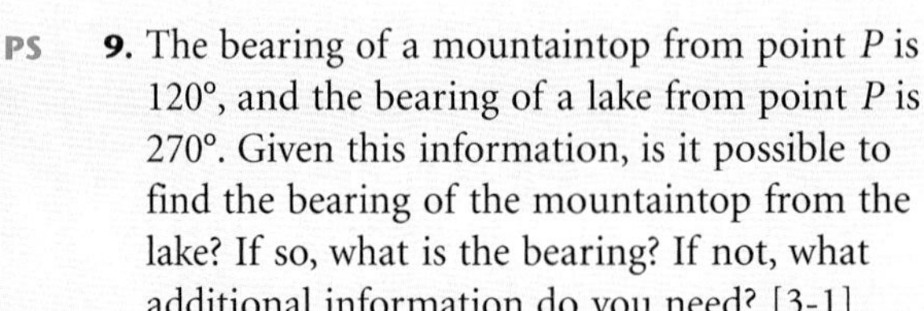

PS **9.** The bearing of a mountaintop from point P is 120°, and the bearing of a lake from point P is 270°. Given this information, is it possible to find the bearing of the mountaintop from the lake? If so, what is the bearing? If not, what additional information do you need? [3-1]

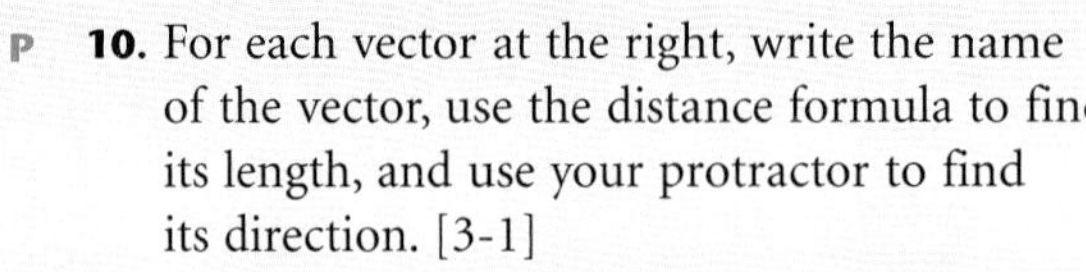

P **10.** For each vector at the right, write the name of the vector, use the distance formula to find its length, and use your protractor to find its direction. [3-1]

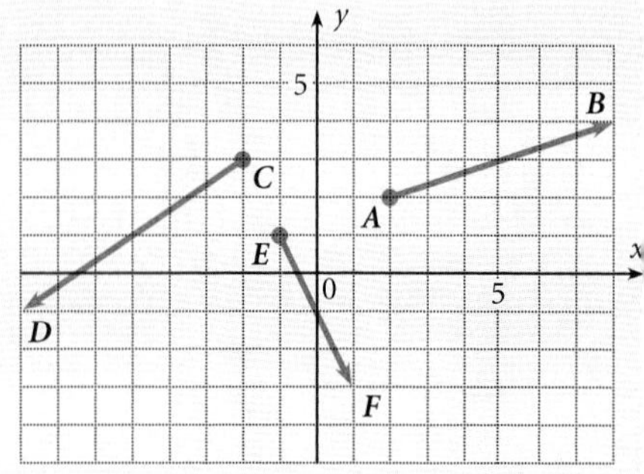

P **Determine which of the designs below have rotational symmetry. For those that have rotational symmetry, give the direction and number of degrees of all clockwise rotations of less than 360° that map the figure onto itself. [3-2]**

11.

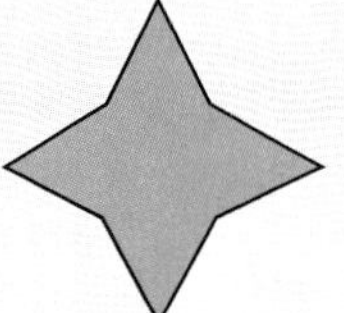

12.

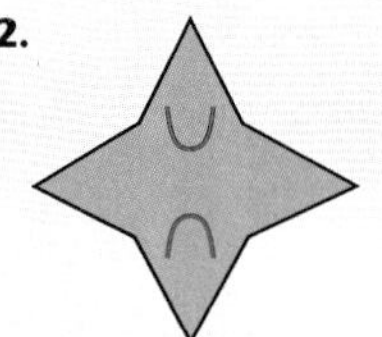

13.

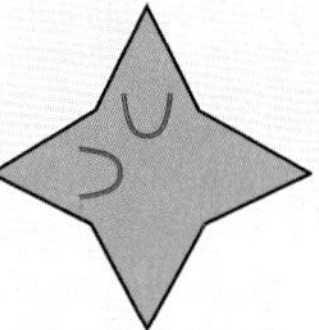

P **In each of the following, write and solve an equation to find the measures of $\angle AOB$ and $\angle COD$. [3-3]**

14. $m\angle AOB = m\angle COD$, $m\angle BOC = 40°$, and $m\angle AOD = 130°$.

15. $m\angle AOB = (x + 10)°$, $m\angle BOC = 40°$, and $m\angle COD = 2x°$, $m\angle AOD = 5x°$.

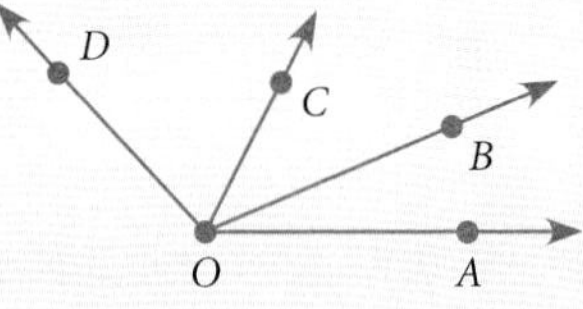

P **16.** Find the measures of the numbered angles in the figure at the right. [3-3]

MR **17.** Write a summary of the relationships among the angles formed by a transversal that intersects two parallel lines. Sketch and mark a figure to illustrate each relationship.

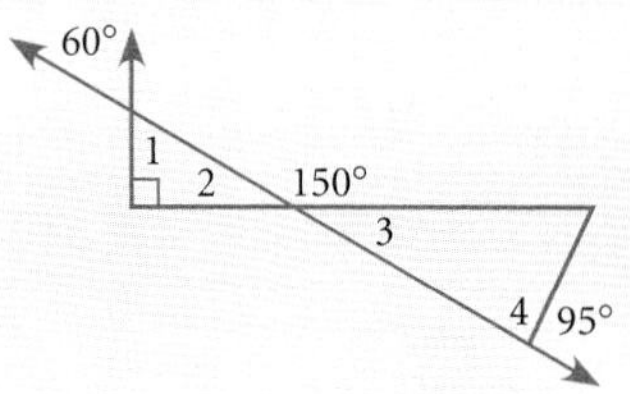

R **Determine whether each statement is true or false. If true, state the postulate that justifies it. [2-2]**

18. The noncollinear points A, B, and C are contained in two different planes.

19. Space contains at least one point not in plane A.

Student Resources

- Alternative Lessons
- Laboratory Manual
- Technology Lab Manual
- Practice
- **Study Guide and Journal** Ch 3
- **Guía de estudios y Diario** Ch 3
- **Multilingual Handbook**
- More Look Ahead
- **SAT Preparation**

Media Resources

- Transparency FFM
- Transparency AE
- Teaching Transparency
- **AWSMTest and practice software**
- AWSM Videodisc

In each figure, determine which, if any, of the lines must be parallel. Justify each answer with a theorem or postulate. [3-4]

20. 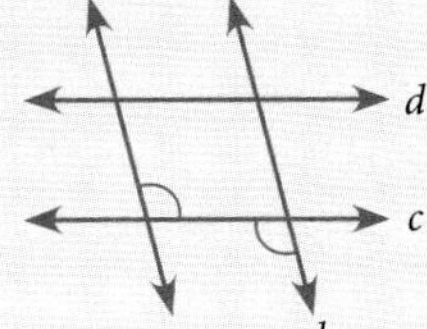

21. 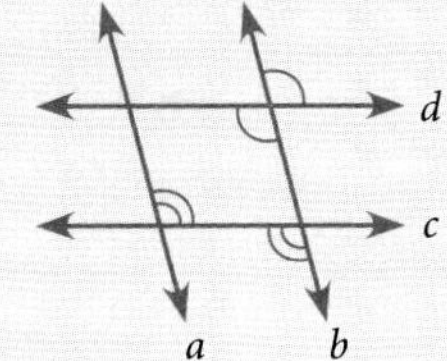

22. 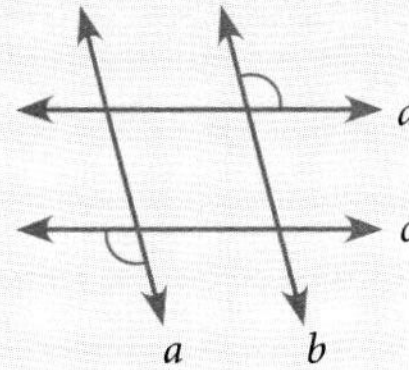

CONCEPTS AND CONNECTIONS

23. Geography Choose two cities in the United States. Sketch a route between the two cities, using at least four straight segments. Each segment should join two large cities. Describe the route, using the language of translations and vectors. Name the translation vector for each segment, and estimate the length and direction of each vector. Then describe the route using the language of bearings; for each segment, estimate the bearing of the second city from the first.

SELF-EVALUATION

Write a paragraph summarizing the main facts about angles covered in Chapter 3. Be sure to include concepts related to bearings, vectors, rotations, angle pairs, and transversals. Describe any topics that you found difficult, and describe how you plan to review those topics.

Chapter 3 Assessment

TEST

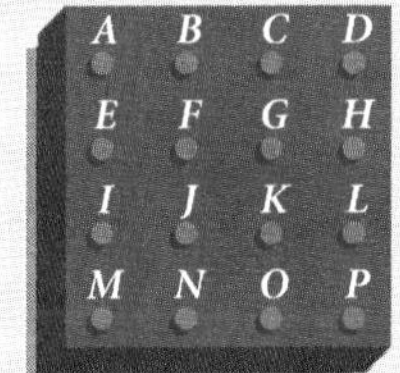

1. Which points on the grid at the right have a bearing greater than 090 and less than 180 from point B? G, H, K, L, O, P

2. Which point on the grid has a bearing of 045 from J and 090 from B? D

3. What is the image of the point $(-2, 1)$ under the translation with vector <2, 5> followed by the translation with vector <−2, 3>? What is the vector for the single translation that is equivalent to the two translations given? $(-2, 9)$; <0, 8>

sessment Resources

iz

apter 3 Assessment Form A

apter 3 Assessment Form B

apter 3 Alternative Assessment

d-Year Assessment

d-of-Year Assessment

VSMTest Chapter 3

Ongoing Assessment

Self-Assessment Chapter 3 Review and Self-Evaluation

Embedded Assessment Chapter 3 Performance Task

Test Chapter 3 Test

Chapter 3 Assessment

Portfolio

Students may select items that represent their mathematical understanding of the ideas in Chapter 3 and that illustrate the effort they have put forth on this chapter.

A rubric for assessing portfolios is included in the introduction to the Teacher's Edition.

Assessment Answers

4. No; True only when the vectors are collinear rays, in the same direction.

7. The segment with endpoints $(12, 2)$ and $(7, -3)$

9. Conditional: T
Inverse: If it isn't raining, then it isn't cloudy: F
Converse: If it is cloudy, then it is raining: F
Contrapositive: If it is not cloudy, then it is not raining: T.

10. Yes; 45°, 90°, 135°, 180°, 225°, 270°, 315°

16. Yes; Points on a line are collinear and relative positions are accurate.

17. No; One cannot assume exact measurements or relative sizes of figures.

18. No; One cannot assume exact measurements or relative sizes of figures.

19. $m\angle 1, \angle 3, \angle 5, \angle 7 = 50°$; $m\angle 2, \angle 4, \angle 6 = 130°$.

20. Two; All vertical-angle pairs are congruent, creating one angle measure and its supplement; then, since there are two sets of parallel lines, matching alternate interior, alternate exterior and/or corresponding angles shows that every angle can be matched with (is congruent to) either the initial vertical angles or to their supplement.

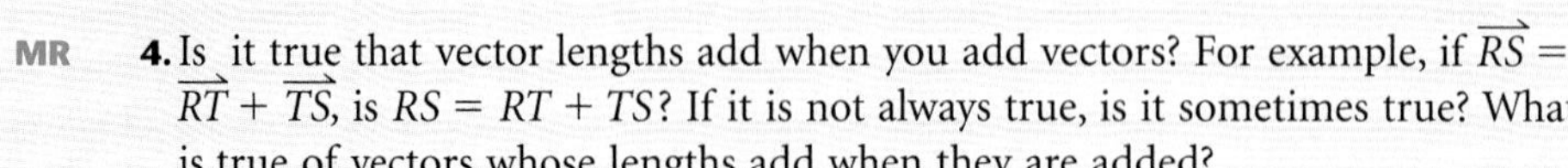

21. If two lines (the "line" where the trapeze is hung and the trapeze bar itself) are cut by a transversal (the "rope") so that a pair of same-side interior angles ($\angle 1$ and $\angle 2$) are supplementary (given), then the lines are parallel (in this case, horizontal).

22. If alternate interior, alternate exterior, or corresponding angles are congruent, or if same-side interior angles are supplementary.

MR **4.** Is it true that vector lengths add when you add vectors? For example, if $\overrightarrow{RS} = \overrightarrow{RT} + \overrightarrow{TS}$, is $RS = RT + TS$? If it is not always true, is it sometimes true? What is true of vectors whose lengths add when they are added?

P **Using the vector $\overrightarrow{SS'}$ as a translation vector, find the coordinates of the translation image of each of the following.**

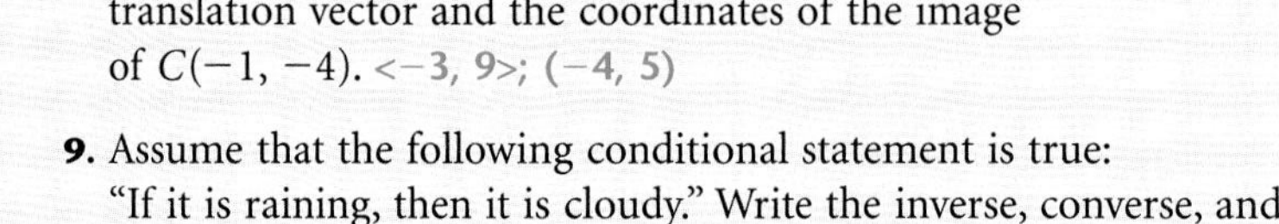

5. the point X (3, −2)

6. the point (u, v) The point $(u + 6, v - 1)$

7. the segment with endpoints (6, 3) and (1, −2)

P **8.** The translation image of $A(3, -7)$ is $B(0, 2)$. Give the translation vector and the coordinates of the image of $C(-1, -4)$. <−3, 9>; (−4, 5)

P **9.** Assume that the following conditional statement is true: "If it is raining, then it is cloudy." Write the inverse, converse, and contrapositive, and determine which of these, if any, are also true.

P **Determine whether each figure has rotational symmetry. For those that have rotational symmetry, give the number of degrees of all clockwise rotations of less than 360° that map the figure onto itself.**

10.

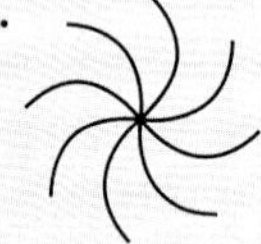

11.

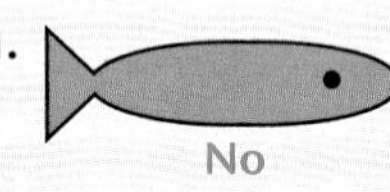

No

12.

Yes; 180°

P **13.** Find the measure of an angle whose supplement is four times its complement. 60°

P **14.** In the figure below, $m\angle AOB = (2x + 10)°$, $m\angle BOC = (4x - 20)°$, and $m\angle AOC = 110°$. Write and solve an equation to find $m\angle AOB$ and $m\angle BOC$.
$2x + 10 + 4x - 20 = 110$, $m\angle AOB = 50°$; $m\angle BOC = 60°$

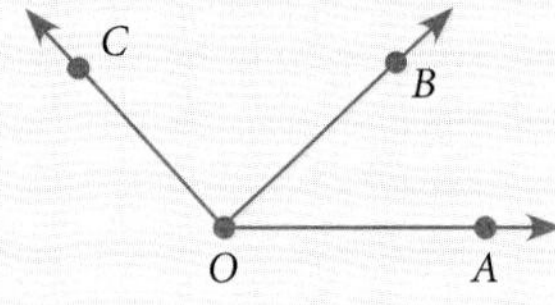

P **15.** Suppose that $\angle A$ and $\angle B$ are complementary angles, $\angle B$ and $\angle C$ are vertical angles, $\angle C$ and $\angle D$ are supplementary angles, and $\angle D$ and $\angle E$ are vertical angles. Which of the following must be true?

a. $m\angle E + m\angle C = 180°$ Yes
b. $m\angle B + m\angle C = 90°$ No
c. $m\angle C + m\angle A = 90°$ Yes
d. $\angle B \cong \angle D$ No

236 CHAPTER 3 • ASSESSMENT

Key

V Vocabulary
P Practice/Skills
R Review
MR Math Reasoning
PS Problem Solving
C Challenge

Determine which of the following may be assumed from the figure at the right. Explain.

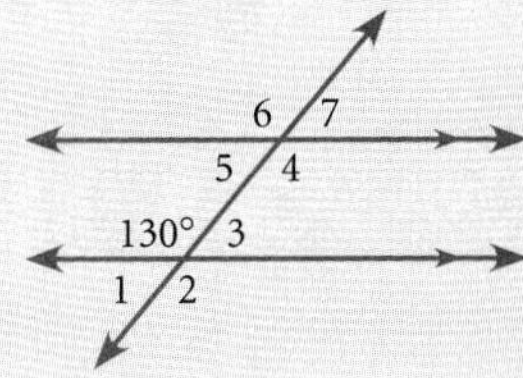

16. Point B is between points A and C.

17. $\angle DAC \cong \angle DCA$

18. $DA > CA$

19. Find the measure of each of the numbered angles in the figure below.

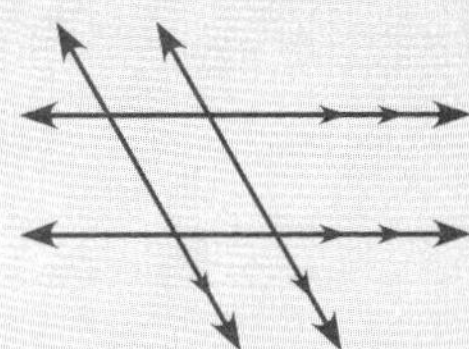

20. How many different measures are there among the angles in the figure below? Explain your answer.

21. Eddie is standing on a trapeze. When the trapeze swings sideways, $\angle 1$ and $\angle 2$ are supplementary. Why does the bar on which Eddie stands remain horizontal? Justify your answer with a theorem or postulate.

22. Write a summary of ways to show that two lines intersected by a transversal are parallel. Sketch and mark a figure to illustrate each method.

PERFORMANCE TASK

Draw a large figure showing two parallel lines and a transversal that intersects them. Then use a compass and straightedge to construct the bisector of each alternate interior angle. Repeat the construction, beginning with a different transversal. Make a conjecture about the pairs of angle bisectors you constructed, and give a deductive argument that shows why your conjecture is true.

Performance Task

Answer

The angle bisectors are parallel. Each pair of alternate interior angles for the original lines is congruent, so the angles formed by their bisectors are also congruent. Since pairs of these angles are alternate interior angles for the bisectors, the bisectors are parallel.

Suggested Scoring Rubric

Level 4 Full Accomplishment

- Shows full understanding of the properties of angles formed by parallel lines and transversals.
- Constructions are accurate, and the conjecture is correct.
- Deductive justification uses general angle measures and refers explicitly or implicitly to the Multiplication Property of Equality.

Level 3 Substantial Accomplishment

- Shows essential grasp of the properties of angles formed by parallel lines and transversals.
- Constructions are generally accurate, and the conjecture is correct.
- Deductive justification may involve specific angle measures instead of general ones.

Level 2 Partial Accomplishment

- Shows partial grasp of the properties of angles formed by parallel lines and transversals.
- Constructions may be incomplete or inaccurate, but the conjecture is correct.
- Deductive justification is unclear or vague.

Level 1 Little Accomplishment

- Shows little or no grasp of the properties of angles formed by parallel lines and transversals.
- Constructions are incomplete or inaccurate, and the conjecture is incorrect.

4

Chapter 4 Triangles

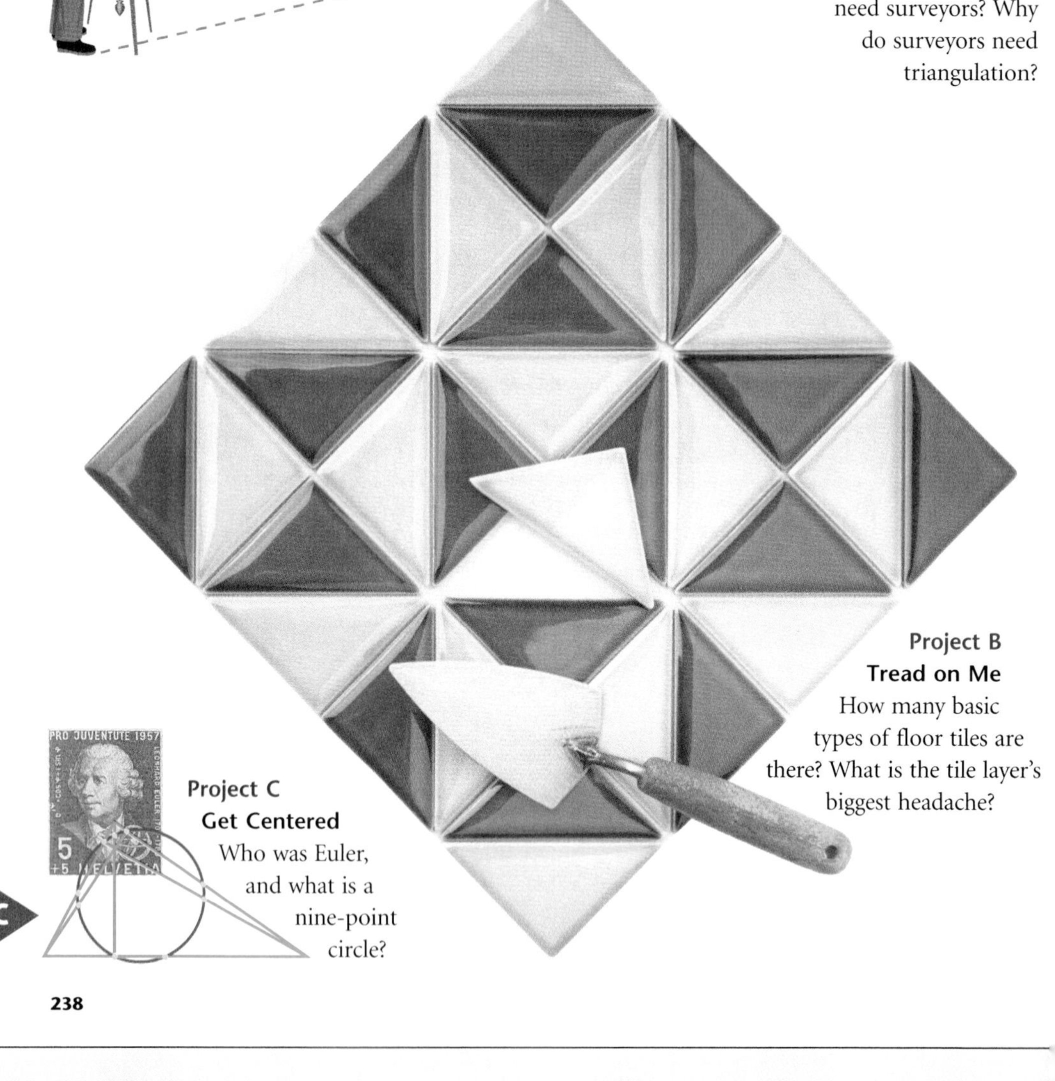

Project A
This Land Is My Land
Why do landowners need surveyors? Why do surveyors need triangulation?

Project B
Tread on Me
How many basic types of floor tiles are there? What is the tile layer's biggest headache?

Project C
Get Centered
Who was Euler, and what is a nine-point circle?

238

A

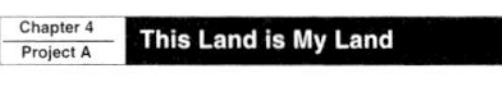

Do a Field Survey

Find the distance between two points that you cannot walk between.

- Did you know that most modern topographic maps are made by putting aerial photographs in computerized plotters?
- Don't you wonder how inaccessible distances are measured?
- How does this connect to Chapter 4? You can "survey" using **congruent triangles**.

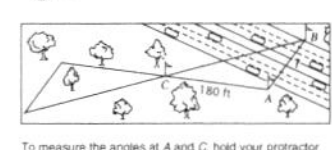

To measure the angles at *A* and *C*, hold your protractor in a plane parallel to the ground. You may need to take several protractor readings to be sure of your angle measure.

Expand Your Vocabulary

transit	bench mark	geodesy
tripod	triangulation	cartography
parallax	field survey	scribing

Project Guidelines

Investigate

- Read about surveying in an encyclopedia or geography book.
- Interview a surveyor, city planner, or real estate appraiser.

Set Your Direction

- Decide on a general location for your survey. Try to work on level ground.
- Decide what distance you'll find, for instance, the distance across a freeway or river.

Make a Plan

- Make a calendar for each day's work. Check in with your group and with your teacher.
- You'll need:
  large protractor measuring tape

Collect and Organize Your Information

- Draw a simple sketch of the survey site.
- Choose or set up landmarks *A* and *B* at the ends of the distance you will measure.
- Choose a third point *C* so that *AC* is measurable.
- By sighting lines between landmarks, measure the angles at *A* and *C*.
- Build a triangle congruent to $\triangle ABC$, all of whose sides are measurable.

Carry Out Your Plan

- Find *AB* by measuring the corresponding side of your new triangle.
- Tell what postulate or theorem justifies your answer.
- Document the steps in your procedure.

Look Back

- Who might need to know the measurement you found?
- How would a surveyor have found this distance? How else might *you* have found it?
- If one of your angles was in error by 5°, how much difference would that have made? What other sources of error are there in your survey?
- Why was it helpful to work on level ground?
- What could you have done differently?

C

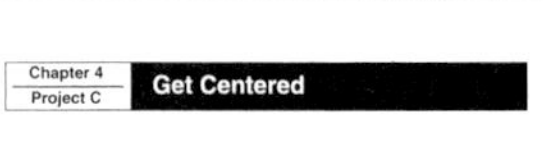

Draw Special Circles

Use a compass and straightedge to draw special circles related to triangles.

- Did you know that the vertices of a triangle determine a circle?
- Don't you wonder if a circle can fit perfectly inside a triangle?
- How does this connect to Chapter 4? You can generate unique circles from special points on and in a **triangle.**

Helvetia is the Latin name for Switzerland, where Leonhard Euler lived and worked.

Expand Your Vocabulary

incenter	inscribed circle
orthocenter	circumscribed circle
circumcenter	nine-point circle

Project Guidelines

Investigate

- Study the contributions of Leonhard Euler, Jean Victor Poncelet, and Charles Brianchon.
- Read about circumcenters and incenters in a math dictionary.
- Draw the altitudes, perpendicular bisectors, and angle bisectors of several triangles. Find their intersections with the sides and with each other.
- Experiment with the points of intersection. Fit circles to some of the points. Look for relationships that identify their centers.

Set Your Direction

- Decide whether you will experiment by hand or use a computer.
- Will you test your results on triangles of different types?

Make a Plan

- You'll need a compass and straightedge.• Make a calendar for each day's work. Check in with your group and with your teacher.
- Schedule time for library research, for work with construction tools or at a computer, and for writing up your presentation.

Collect and Organize Your Information

- Find a circle that passes perfectly through the vertices of a triangle. Locate its center.
- Find a circle that fits perfectly inside a triangle. Locate its center.
- Fit a circle to the midpoints of the sides of a triangle and the feet of its altitudes. What other relationship does the circle have to the altitudes? Can you find its center?

Carry Out Your Plan

- Write up your results telling how many special circles you found.
- Give steps for constructing each circle. Illustrate your report with constructions for each step.
- Tell why you think the constructions work and whether you think they work for all triangles.

Look Back

- Did you uncover any practical applications for the circles you drew?

GLENN GARLAND

Math came easily to me in high school. I enjoy technical and scientific things.

Today I use geometry and trigonometry to coordinate land and construction projects. For example, to get oriented, I find x-, y-, and z-coordinates of two control points on the ground. In the end, a massive project is complete, and I was a part of it.

Glenn Garland
Surveyor/Engineer
Kirkham Michael & Associates
Englewood, Colorado

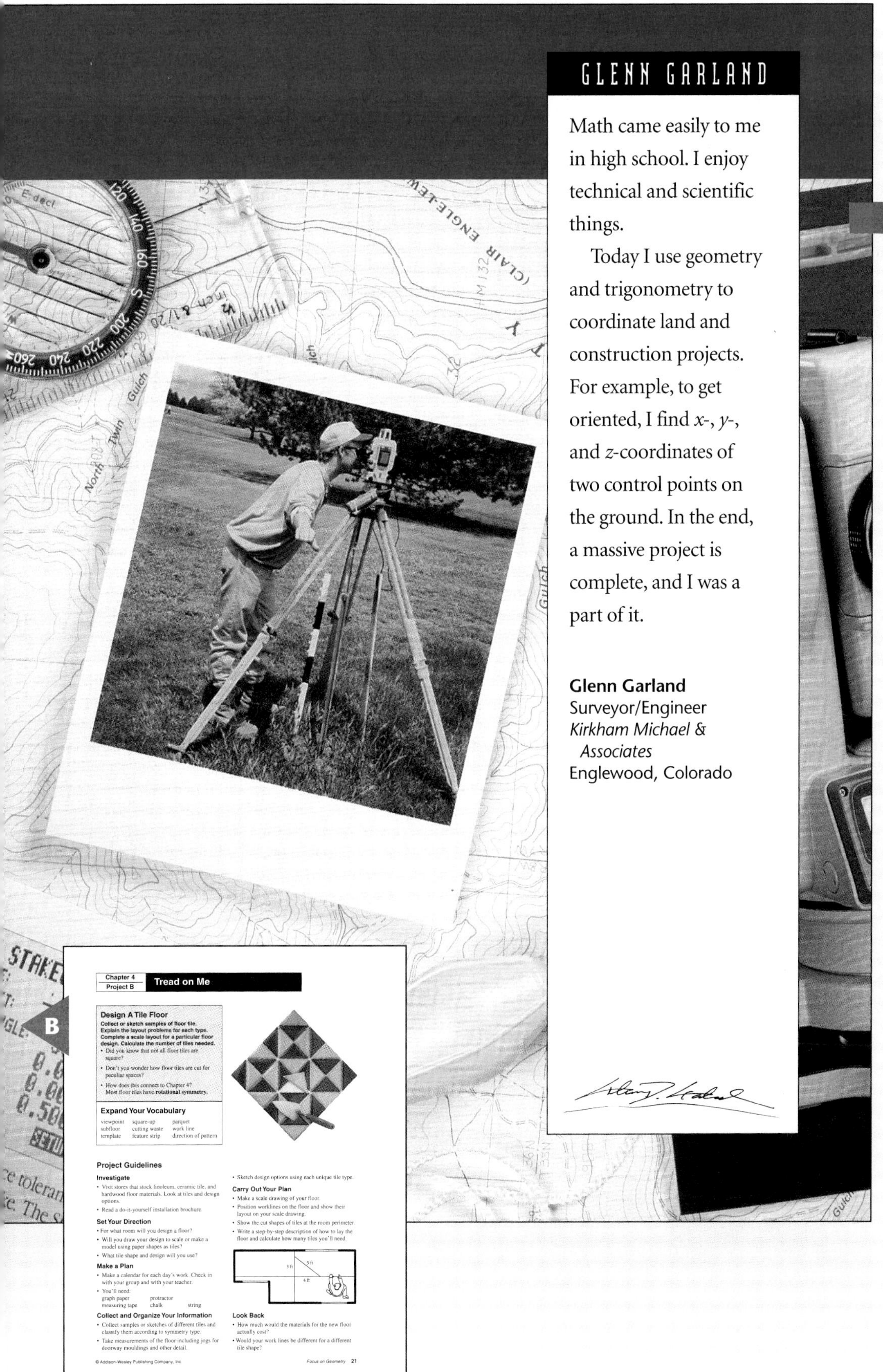

Chapter 4 Project B

Tread on Me

Design A Tile Floor

Collect or sketch samples of floor tile. Explain the layout problems for each type. Complete a scale layout for a particular floor design. Calculate the number of tiles needed.

- Did you know that not all floor tiles are square?
- Don't you wonder how floor tiles are cut for peculiar spaces?
- How does this connect to Chapter 4? Most floor tiles have **rotational symmetry.**

Expand Your Vocabulary

viewpoint	square-up	parquet
subfloor	cutting waste	work line
template	feature strip	direction of pattern

Project Guidelines

Investigate

- Visit stores that stock linoleum, ceramic tile, and hardwood floor materials. Look at tiles and design options.
- Read a do-it-yourself installation brochure.

Set Your Direction

- For what room will you design a floor?
- Will you draw your design to scale or make a model using paper shapes as tiles?
- What tile shape and design will you use?

Make a Plan

- Make a calendar for each day's work. Check in with your group and with your teacher.
- You'll need:
  graph paper, protractor, measuring tape, chalk, string

Collect and Organize Your Information

- Collect samples or sketches of different tiles and classify them according to symmetry type.
- Take measurements of the floor including jogs for doorway mouldings and other detail.
- Sketch design options using each unique tile type.

Carry Out Your Plan

- Make a scale drawing of your floor.
- Position worklines on the floor and show their layout on your scale drawing.
- Show the cut shapes of tiles at the room perimeter.
- Write a step-by-step description of how to lay the floor and calculate how many tiles you'll need.

Look Back

- How much would the materials for the new floor actually cost?
- Would your work lines be different for a different tile shape?

Focus on Geometry 21

Biographical Note

Glenn Garland graduated from Miramonte High School in Orinda, CA. He took Algebra, Geometry, Trigonometry, and Precalculus.

Chapter 4

Overview

Triangles

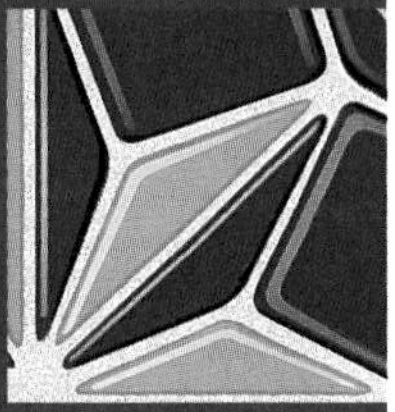

4-1 Tessellations and Triangles

Triangles are important in the structures of buildings and in the art forms that decorate them. You will learn about some of the properties of triangles, and see how these properties relate to tessellations.

4-2 Deductive Proof with Triangles

Logical reasoning is used by most people every day. You are asked to demonstrate this kind of reasoning whenever someone says, "Is that so? Prove it!" You will now explore more properties of triangles, and continue to develop skills for deductive proof.

4-3 Properties of Special Triangles

Special triangles and the lines associated with them are important in industries that need structural stability in their products. You will discover some additional properties of special triangles and explore segments associated with triangles.

CHAPTERS

Chapter 4 Planning Guide

The following ancillaries are recommended for each course level. The additional resources, *Technology Lab Manual, Study Guide and Journal, Multilingual Handbook,* and *Assessment,* are recommended for all levels.

	Comprehensive Course	Core Course	Informal Course
4-1 Part A	▲	▲	▲
Alternative Lessons			▲
Laboratory Manuals	▲	▲	▲
Practice			▲
More Look Ahead		▲	▲
4-1 Part B	▲	▲	▲
Alternative Lessons			▲
Laboratory Manuals	▲	▲	▲
Practice			▲
More Look Back		▲	▲
4-1 Part C	▲	▲	▲
More Look Back		▲	▲
Quiz 4-1	▲	▲	▲
4-2 Part A	▲	▲	▲
Alternative Lessons			▲
Laboratory Manuals	▲	▲	▲
Practice			▲
More Look Back		▲	▲
4-2 Part B	▲	▲	▲
Alternative Lessons			▲
Laboratory Manuals	▲	▲	▲
Practice			▲
More Look Ahead		▲	▲
4-2 Part C	▲	▲	
Alternative Lessons			
Laboratory Manuals	▲	▲	
Practice			
More Look Back		▲	
4-2 Part D	▲	▲	
Alternative Lessons			
Laboratory Manuals	▲	▲	
Practice			
More Look Ahead		▲	
4-2 Part E	▲	▲	▲
More Look Back		▲	▲
Quiz 4-2	▲	▲	▲
4-3 Part A	▲	▲	▲
Alternative Lessons			▲
Laboratory Manuals	▲	▲	▲
Practice			▲
More Look Ahead		▲	▲
4-3 Part B	▲	▲	▲
Alternative Lessons			▲
Laboratory Manuals	▲	▲	▲
Practice			▲
More Look Back		▲	▲
4-3 Part C	▲	▲	▲
Alternative Lessons			▲
Laboratory Manuals	▲	▲	▲
Practice			▲
More Look Ahead		▲	▲
4-3 Part D	▲	▲	▲
Alternative Lessons			▲
Laboratory Manuals	▲	▲	▲
Practice			▲
More Look Back		▲	▲
4-3 Part E	▲	▲	▲
More Look Back		▲	▲
Quiz 4-3	▲	▲	▲

BIBLIOGRAPHY

Reading for Students

Visions of Symmetry: Notebooks, Periodic Drawings, and Related Work of M. C. Escher, Doris Schattschneider. © 1990 Doris Schattschneider. Available through Dale Seymour Publications (NS22345).

Videos

The Alhambra Past and Present: A Geometer's Odyssey, Lorraine Foster. Available through Dale Seymour Publications (NS22388).

Teacher Resources

Introduction to Tessellations, Dale Seymour and Jill Britton. Dale Seymour Publications, 1989 (NS07901).

Tessellation Teaching Masters, Dale Seymour. Dale Seymour Publications, 1989 (NS07900).

4-1

Tessellations and Triangles

SUPERLESSON AT A GLANCE

Superlesson Goal

Students will investigate properties of the measures of interior and exterior angles of a triangle.

Management Guide

	Topic	Objectives	Key Terms	New Ideas	Materials
Part A	Angles Inside the Triangle	To find that the sum of the measures of the interior angles of a triangle is 180°.	Tessellation, triangle, scalene, isosceles, equilateral, equiangular, acute, obtuse, and right triangles	Classifying triangles by side lengths and angle measures. The sum of the measures of the interior angles of a triangle is 180°.	**Student** Straightedge, scissors, paper
Part B	Angles Outside the Triangle	To discover that the measure of an exterior angle is equal to the sum of the measures of its remote interior angles.	Exterior angle, remote interior angle, adjacent interior angle, corollary	The measure of an exterior angle is equal to the sum of its remote interior angles and greater than the measure of either one.	**Student** Ruler, protractor, geometry software
Part C	Making Connections	To use angle measures of triangles to see why congruent triangles tessellate a plane.	In Making Connections, students apply and synthesize key terms and new ideas.		**Student** Paper, straightedge, scissors, protractor

Pacing Chart (45-Minute Periods)

	Comprehensive Course	Core Course	Informal Course
Part A	1	1	1
Part B	1	1	1
Part C	1	1	1
TOTAL periods for Superlesson	3	3	3

NCTM Standards

Mathematics as Problem Solving

Mathematics as Communication

Mathematics as Reasoning

Mathematical Connections

Geometry from a Synthetic Perspective

Social Science/History | Fine Arts/Literature

4-1 Tessellations and Triangles

Miles of Tiles

For centuries, geometric figures have been a part of art and architecture. Mosaics—designs composed of many small tiles set in clay or plaster—were used by the Sumerians in architectural surfaces as early as 4000 B.C. These tiles served not only as artistic decorations, but also as part of the structure.

The Persians showed that they were masters of tile decoration by covering buildings with mosaics. Construction on the Madrasah on Reghistan in Samarkand (in what is now Uzbekistan) began in 1420 A.D. Perhaps the most elaborate example of tiled architecture was created for a temple in Isfahan, the construction of which began in 1602.

Lutfallah Mosque, Isfahan, Iran

Masjia-E Shah, Isfahan, Iran

The Romans also used tiles, called *tesserae*, in buildings, floors, and roads. A fort called Vollubilis stood at the edge of the Roman Empire in what is now Morocco. Stunning mosaics cover the floor of the fort.

Artists from the areas around Egypt, Turkey, and Spain also used patterns of geometric figures as decorations. Even today, artists and architects use simple geometric figures, and the patterns created by fitting the figures together, in their design of modern structures.

?

1. A *tessellation* is a repeating pattern that completely fills up a plane region. What Roman (Latin) word is the root word for tessellation?
2. Identify two tessellations in your classroom. What geometric figures are used in these tessellations?
3. Name some common geometric figures that can be used to tessellate (fill up) a region.

More About Tessellations

Islamic peoples ruled parts of Spain from A.D. 711 to 1492. Muslim artists did not depict living creatures in art or architecture. Instead, they used a stunning array of decorative patterns, including tessellations. M. C. Escher visited the Alhambra in 1936, and he found in these patterns a source of inspiration for his own art. The decorations on the walls of the Alhambra show all 17 possible two-dimensional "wallpaper patterns." We will investigate wallpaper patterns in Chapter 10.

Where Are We Now?

Students are familiar with angle measurement and special relationships between angle pairs.

Where Are We Going?

In 4-1, students will see that the sum of the measures of the interior angles of a triangle is 180°. This theorem has immediate applications and is needed for several other theorems, including the SAA triangle-congruence theorem in 4-2, and in finding the sum of the measures of the interior angles of any polygon in 6-1.

Students also discover that the measure of an exterior angle of a triangle is equal to the sum of the measures of its remote interior angles.

Possible Answers

1. Tesserae
2. Tiles on the floor (squares), panels on the ceiling (squares or rectangles).
3. Squares, rectangles, equilateral triangles, and so on.

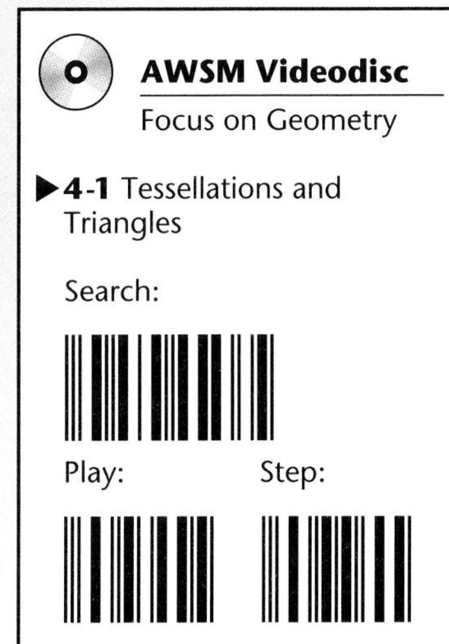

4-1

Algebra	Functions	Discrete Math	Probability	Data/Statistics

Tessellations and Triangles

PART A At a Glance

Objective

To find that the sum of the measures of the interior angles of a triangle is 180°.

Development

First, students see the definition of tessellations.

In the **Explore,** students discover the Triangle Angle-Sum Theorem and see how to use tessellations to support their conjectures.

Students are then introduced to ways to classify triangles.

Suggested Materials

Student Straightedge, scissors, paper

Key Terms

Tessellation, triangle, scalene, isosceles, equilateral, equiangular, acute, obtuse, and right triangles

First Five Minutes

Transparency FFM 4-1A

Read the material on page 242. Then sketch $\triangle JKL$ and list all other ways to name this triangle. *$\triangle JLK$, $\triangle KLJ$, $\triangle KJL$, $\triangle LJK$, and $\triangle LKJ$*

Motivate

Ask...

- Sketch a figure in which $\overrightarrow{BA}$ and $\overrightarrow{BE}$ are opposite rays, $\angle ABC$, $\angle CBD$, and $\angle DBE$ are coplanar, and D is in the interior of $\angle CBE$. What is the sum of the measures of these angles? How do you know?

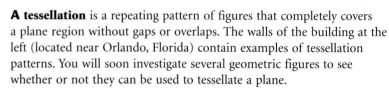

4-1 PART A Angles Inside the Triangle

← CONNECT → ***You have worked with angles and triangles before. Now you will learn some ways to classify triangles. You will also discover a useful fact about the angles of a triangle.***

A tessellation is a repeating pattern of figures that completely covers a plane region without gaps or overlaps. The walls of the building at the left (located near Orlando, Florida) contain examples of tessellation patterns. You will soon investigate several geometric figures to see whether or not they can be used to tessellate a plane.

We will begin with triangles. Although you are already familiar with triangles, it is important for everyone to use the same terms.

A **triangle** is a figure formed by three line segments that connect three noncollinear points.

The figure below illustrates some vocabulary commonly associated with triangles.

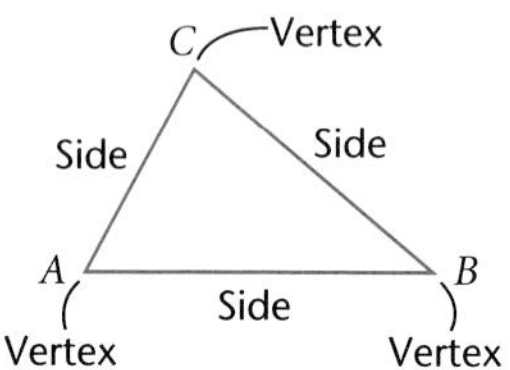

A triangle is named using its vertices and a $\triangle$ symbol. For example, the triangle shown can be named $\triangle ABC$.

In the following Explore, you will investigate an important property of the angles of a triangle.

EXPLORE: THE THIRD DEGREE!

MATERIALS

Straightedge
Scissors
Paper

1. Use a straightedge to draw a large triangle. Cut out your triangle. Label the angle that appears to have the largest measure ∠1, and label the others ∠2 and ∠3. Label the angles on the front and the back of your triangle.
2. Fold ∠1 so that its vertex touches the opposite side of the triangle; the fold should look parallel to that side. Then fold ∠2 and ∠3 inward so that they touch the vertex of ∠1. Your triangle should now look something like an envelope.
3. Make a conjecture about the sum of the measures of the angles in a triangle. Explain how folding the triangle illustrates your conjecture. Compare your conjecture with those made by your classmates. Does the sum depend on the size or shape of the triangle?
4. Does the tessellation at the right formed by congruent triangles support your conjecture about the angles of a triangle? If so, how?

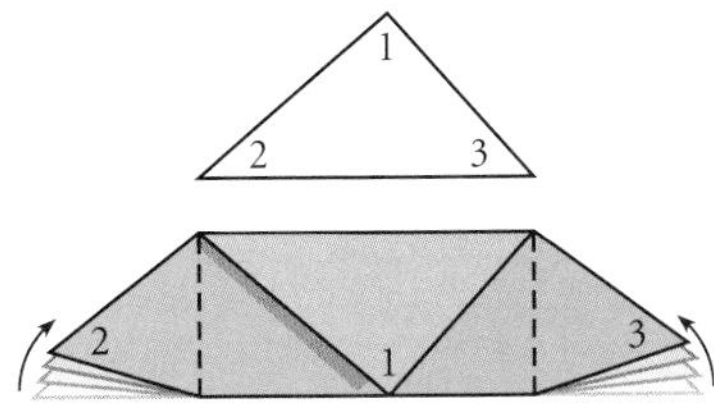

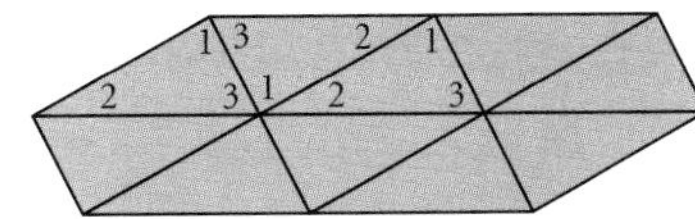

TRY IT

a. Two angles of a triangle measure 40° and 58°. What is the measure of the third angle? 82°

Earlier you saw that an angle can be classified by its measure. Triangles can also be classified in several ways.

TRIANGLE CLASSIFICATION BY SIDES

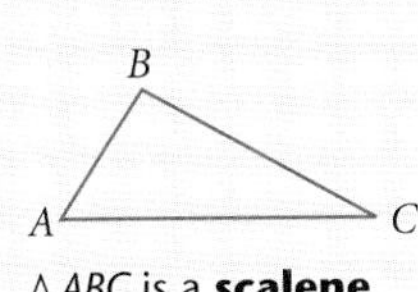

$\triangle ABC$ is a **scalene triangle.** No two of its sides are congruent.

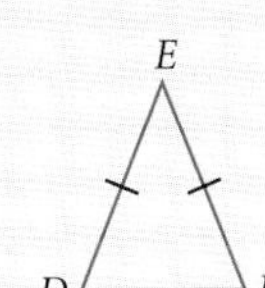

$\triangle DEF$ is an **isosceles triangle.** At least two of its sides are congruent.

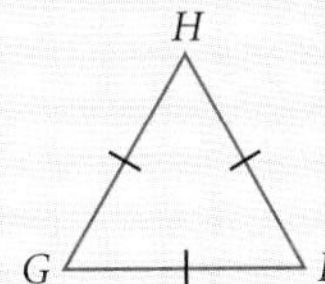

$\triangle GHI$ is an **equilateral triangle.** All of its sides are congruent.

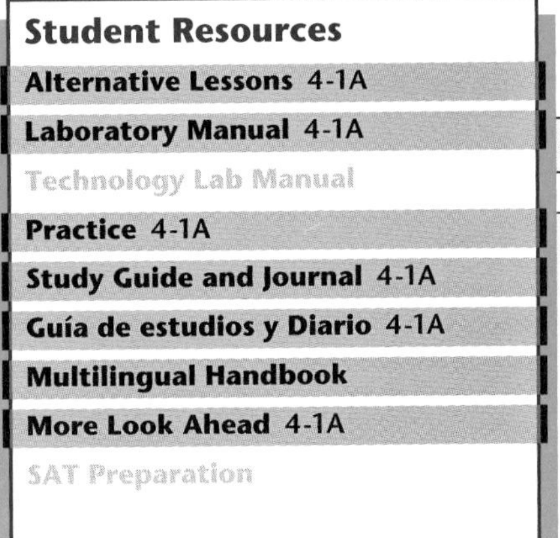

Student Resources
- Alternative Lessons 4-1A
- Laboratory Manual 4-1A
- Technology Lab Manual
- Practice 4-1A
- Study Guide and Journal 4-1A
- Guía de estudios y Diario 4-1A
- Multilingual Handbook
- More Look Ahead 4-1A
- SAT Preparation

Media Resources
- Transparency FFM 4-1A
- Transparency AE 4-1A
- Teaching Transparency
- AWSMTest and practice software
- AWSM Videodisc

EXPLORE

The Third Degree!

Recommended group size: 4

The Point

To discover the Triangle Angle-Sum Theorem.

Look and Listen...

- For students who do not understand how to label the angles.

Ask...

- Have you marked each angle with the same number on both sides of your paper triangle?

For Groups That Finish Early

The horizontal lines in the tessellation shown on page 243 are parallel. Is there a way to use a theorem about angles formed by parallel lines to support your conjecture about the measures of the angles in a triangle? **∠2 is a same-side interior angle to the angle formed by ∠1 and ∠3, so $m\angle 1 + m\angle 2 + m\angle 3 = 180°$.**

Follow Up

Ask students to summarize their results about the sum of the measures of the interior angles in a triangle and to give evidence to support their conjecture.

Possible Answers

3. The sum of the measures of the angles is 180°; this does not depend on the size or shape of the triangle.

4. Because ∠1, ∠2, and ∠3 lie on a straight line, the sum of their measures should be 180°.

Algebra	Functions	Discrete Math	Probability	Data/Statistics

Tessellations and Triangles

ALTERNATE EXAMPLES

Classify each triangle, using both angle and side classification.

1. 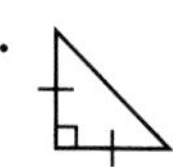

Right, isosceles

2. 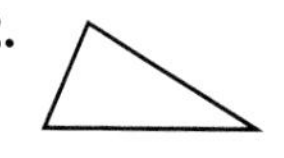

Acute, scalene

3. 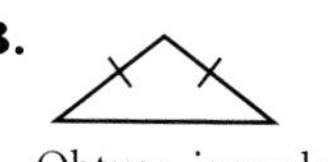

Obtuse, isosceles

4. 

Equiangular, equilateral

The sides and angles of an isosceles triangle have special names, as shown at the right.

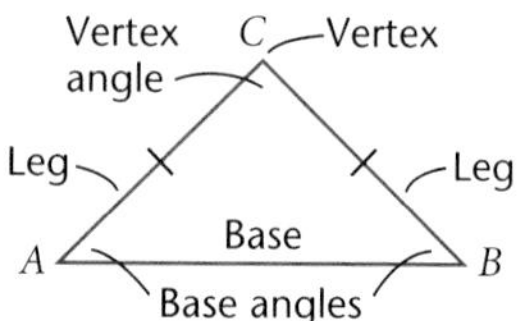

TRIANGLE CLASSIFICATION BY ANGLES

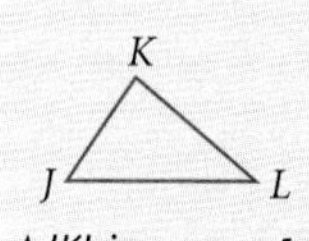

$\triangle JKL$ is an **acute triangle.** All of its angles are acute.

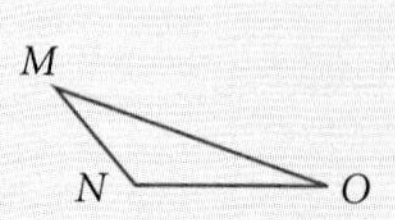

$\triangle MNO$ is an **obtuse triangle.** It has one obtuse angle.

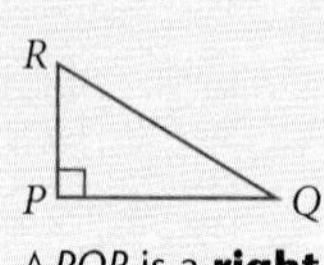

$\triangle PQR$ is a **right triangle.** It has one right angle.

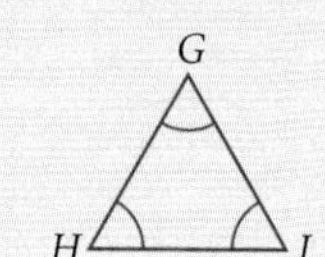

$\triangle GHI$ is an **equiangular triangle.** All of its angles have the same measure.

You may notice that $\triangle GHI$ also appears to be equilateral. The fact that a triangle is equilateral if and only if it is equiangular is important, and you will soon investigate this further.

The sides of a right triangle also have special names, as shown at the right.

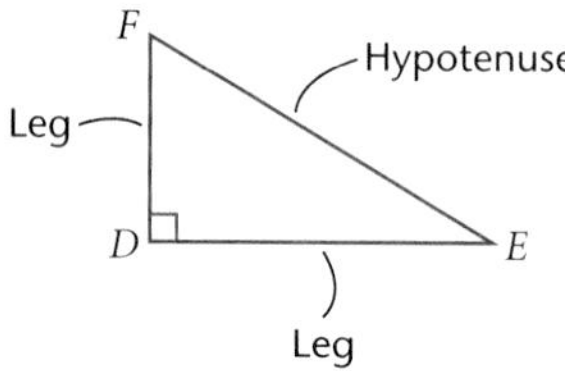

EXAMPLES

Classify each triangle using both angle and side classification.

1. 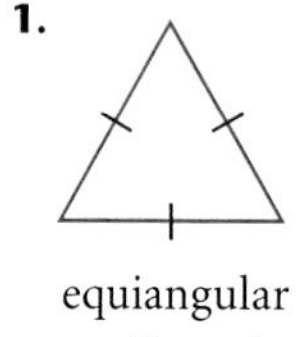

equiangular equilateral

2. obtuse scalene

3. 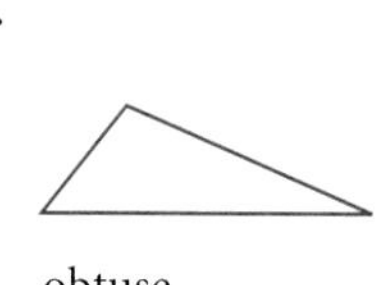

right scalene

4. 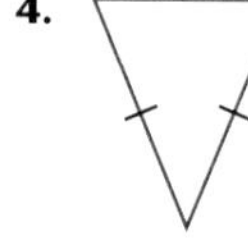

acute isosceles

TRY IT

b. 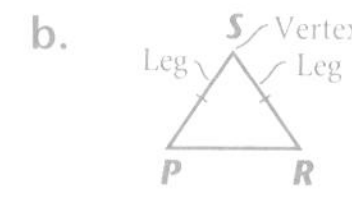

c.
H
Hypotenuse
Leg
F
G
Leg

b. Draw an isosceles triangle, $\triangle PRS$, with base $\overline{PR}$. Name the legs and the vertex angle. Vertex $\angle S$; Legs $\overline{SP}$ and $\overline{SR}$.

c. Draw a right triangle, $\triangle FGH$, with right angle $\angle F$. Name the hypotenuse and the legs. Hypotenuse $\overline{HG}$; Legs $\overline{FH}$ and $\overline{FG}$.

The property you investigated in the Explore can be proved, so we state it as a theorem. You will be asked to justify this theorem in Exercise 18.

TRIANGLE ANGLE-SUM THEOREM

The sum of the measures of the angles of a triangle is 180°.

1. What does the Triangle Angle-Sum Theorem tell you about the measures of each angle in an equiangular triangle?

REFLECT

1. Is it possible for a triangle to have more than one obtuse angle? more than one right angle? more than one acute angle? Explain each of your answers.
2. Explain why an acute triangle cannot be an obtuse triangle.
3. Which angle in a right triangle has the largest measure? Why? What does this tell you about the other two angles?

Exercises

CORE

Getting Started **Name and classify each triangle, using both angle and side classification.**

1. 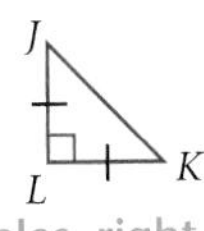

Isosceles, right

2. 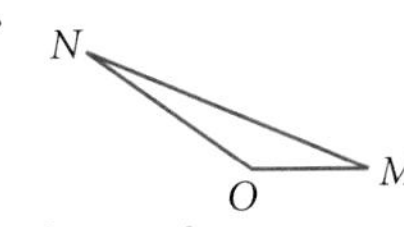

Scalene, obtuse

3. 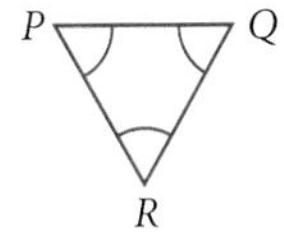

Equilateral, equiangular

4. 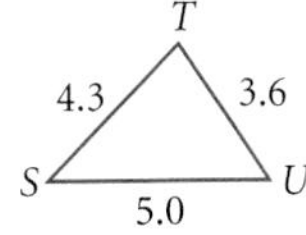

Scalene, acute

5. List all the possible names for the triangle at the right.
$\triangle LMN$, $\triangle LNM$, $\triangle MLN$, $\triangle MNL$, $\triangle NLM$, $\triangle NML$.

Is it possible for each of the following types of triangles to exist? If so, sketch an example. If not, explain why not.

6. obtuse isosceles
7. right equilateral
8. right scalene

Ongoing Assessment

Vocabulary
Practice/Skills
Review
Math Reasoning
Problem Solving
Challenge

Self-Assessment Exercises 1–17 odd

Embedded Assessment Reflect 3; Exercises 4, 8, 12, 16

Possible Answer

1. Since the three angles are congruent and their measures add up to 180°, each angle measures 60°.

Journal 

Explore Step 3 and **Reflect** 1 and 2 are suitable for journal entries.

REFLECT

Possible Answers

1. A triangle cannot have more than one obtuse or right angle, because the sum of the measures of its angles would exceed 180°. A triangle must have at least two acute angles, and may have three.
2. In an acute triangle, all of the angles are acute.
3. The right angle has the largest measure; since the sum of the measures of the other two must be 90°, each must measure less than 90°. Therefore, the other angles are acute.

Part A Exercises

Exercise Notes

Core

18. Connects theorems about parallel lines to the Triangle Angle-Sum Theorem. The connection between this theorem and properties of parallel lines resurfaces when we explore non-Euclidean geometry in Chapter 12. There, students see that the fact that the sum of the angle measures in a triangle is 180° depends on the Parallel Postulate.

Look Ahead

These exercises review properties of linear pairs that are needed to support the Exterior Angle Theorem in 4-2 Part B.

More Math Reasoning

32. Students see that when two triangles have two pairs of congruent angles, the third pair is also congruent.

4-1

Tessellations and Triangles

Exercise Answers

Core

6. Yes;

7. No; Every angle of an equilateral triangle is 60°, but a right triangle has a 90° angle.

8. Yes;

9. a. B, C, D, E, V, W, X, Y

b. $G, H, I, J, L, Q, R, S, T$

c. H, L, M, N, O, R **d.** $\frac{3}{4}$

10. 31°; Triangle Angle-Sum Theorem.

15. $m\angle A = 53°$, $m\angle B = 24°$, $m\angle C = 103°$

16. 9 m; The legs of an isosceles triangle have the same length.

17. $m\angle 1 = 90° - m\angle 2$

18. Since they are alternate interior angles, $m\angle 1 = m\angle 4$ and $m\angle 3 = m\angle 5$. Therefore, since $m\angle 4 + m\angle 2 + m\angle 5 = 180°$ by the Angle-Addition and Linear-Pair Postulates, $m\angle 1 + m\angle 2 + m\angle 3 = 180°$ by substitution.

More Practice

22. Yes;

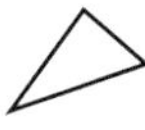

23. Yes;

24. Yes;

25. Scalene

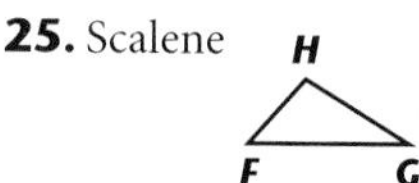

26. Obtuse, scalene

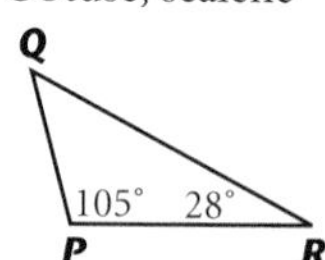

More Math Reasoning

32. Yes; Let a be the sum of the measures of the two angles in each triangle that we know are congruent to angles in the other. Then each of the third angles has to have measure $180° - a$, by the Triangle Angle-Sum Theorem.

Algebra | Functions | Discrete Math | Probability | Data/Statistics

P **9.** $\overline{FP}$ is one side of a triangle on the grid. List the possibilities for the third vertex if the triangle is of the following type.
a. obtuse **b.** right **c.** isosceles
d. Suppose the third vertex of the triangle is chosen randomly from the points shown in red. What is the probability that the triangle will be a right triangle?

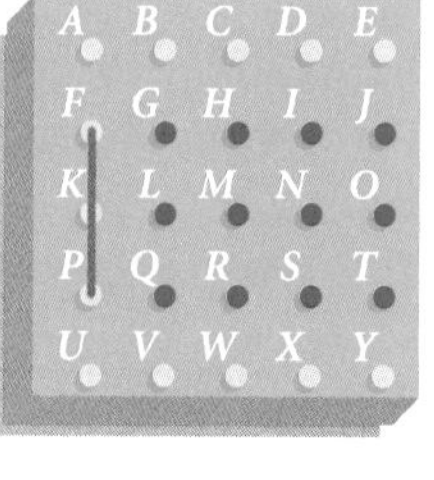

P **10.** A surveyor measured two angles of a triangular lot as shown. What is the measure of the third angle? What theorem justifies your answer?

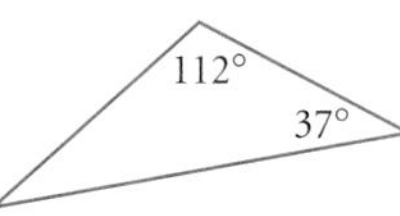

P **Find the measure of ∠1 in each figure.**

11. 68°

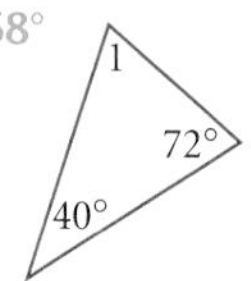

12. 33°

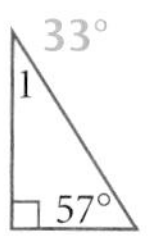

13. 58°

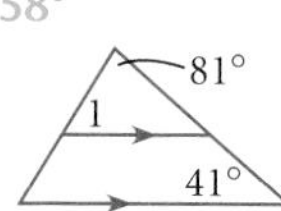

14. 80°

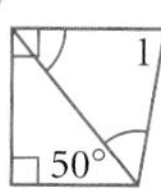

P **15.** In $\triangle ABC$, $m\angle A = (x + 20)°$, $m\angle B = (2x - 42)°$, and $m\angle C = (3x + 4)°$. Find the measure of each angle.

P **16. Shingle Minded** A carpenter is building a roof frame. The cross section of the frame is an isosceles triangle, as shown. What is the length of the other leg of the roof frame? How do you know?

Careers

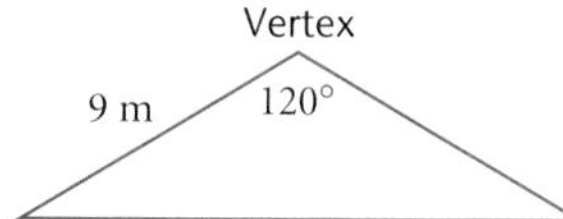

P **17.** The measure of one of the acute angles in a right triangle depends on the measure of the other. Suppose ∠1 and ∠2 are the acute angles of a right triangle. Write an equation for $m\angle 1$ in terms of $m\angle 2$.

MR **18. Justify It** Explain how the properties of parallel lines can be used to justify the Triangle Angle-Sum Theorem. Assume $\overline{RS} \parallel \overline{AB}$.

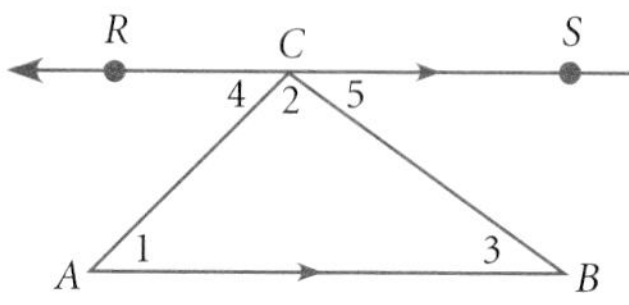

LOOK AHEAD

R **19.** If ∠1 and ∠2 are supplementary, what is the measure of ∠3? 35°

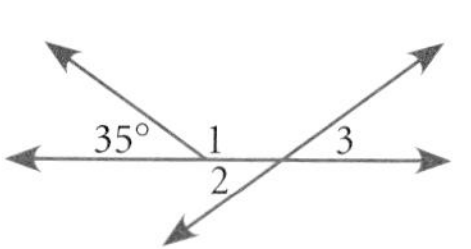

R **Use the figure at the right to find $m\angle 1$ in each of the following.**

20. $m\angle 1 = (x - 20)°$, and $m\angle 2 = (4x + 20)°$. 16°

21. The measure of ∠2 is 60° more than the measure of ∠1. 60°

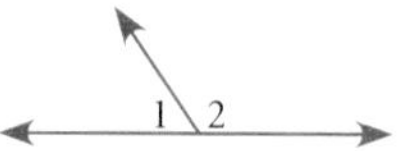

Key

V Vocabulary
P Practice/Skills
R Review
MR Math Reasoning
PS Problem Solving
C Challenge

MORE PRACTICE

Is it possible for each of the following types of triangles to exist? If so, sketch an example. If not, explain why not.

22. acute scalene **23.** isosceles equiangular **24.** scalene right

Draw and classify each triangle.

25. $\triangle FGH$ with $FG \neq GH \neq FH$ **26.** $\triangle QPR$ with $m\angle P = 105°$ and $m\angle R = 28°$

Find the measure of $\angle 1$ in each figure.

27. 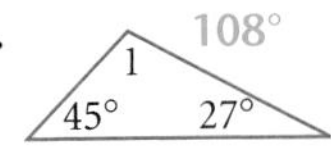

108°

28. 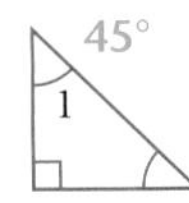

45°

29. 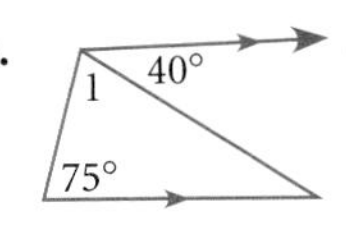

65°

30. 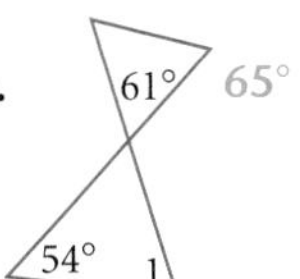

65°

MORE MATH REASONING

31. The coordinates of the vertices of $\triangle ABC$ are $A(3, 3)$, $B(-1, 6)$, and $C(-4, 2)$.

a. Classify the triangle by its angles and by its sides. Right, isosceles

b. How many points with integer coordinates lie in the interior of the triangle? 12

32. Roshawn wrote the following statement in her journal.

If two angles of one triangle are congruent to two angles in another triangle, then the third pair of angles also has to be congruent.

Do you agree? Explain.

4-1 PART B Angles Outside the Triangle

← CONNECT → ***You have learned about the sum of the measures of the angles inside a triangle. Now you will discover some relationships between angles inside and outside a triangle.***

You'll see that figures that tessellate a plane have particular measures for their interior and exterior angles. An **exterior angle** of a triangle is formed by extending one of the sides of the triangle.

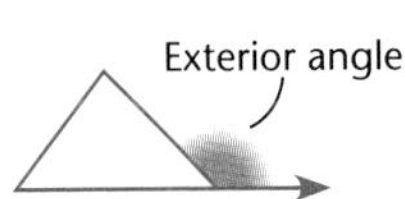

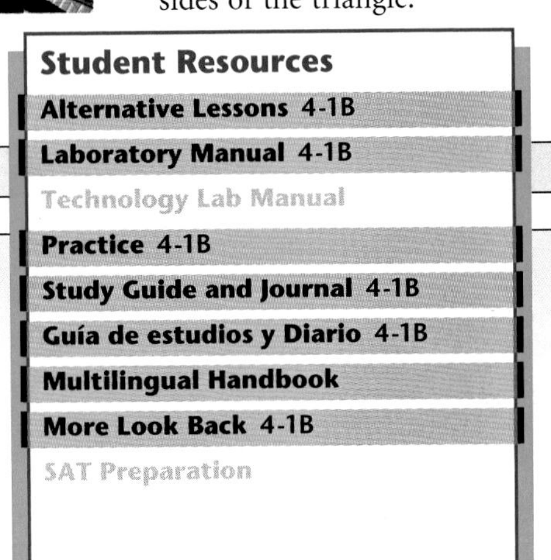

Student Resources
Alternative Lessons 4-1B
Laboratory Manual 4-1B
Technology Lab Manual
Practice 4-1B
Study Guide and Journal 4-1B
Guía de estudios y Diario 4-1B
Multilingual Handbook
More Look Back 4-1B
SAT Preparation

Media Resources

Transparency FFM 4-1B

Transparency AE

Teaching Transparency

AWSMTest and practice software

AWSM Videodisc

PART B At a Glance

Objective

To discover that the measure of an exterior angle is equal to the sum of the measures of its remote interior angles.

Development

First, students see terminology for interior and exterior angles of a triangle.

Then, in the **Explore,** students discover that the measure of an exterior angle of a triangle is equal to the sum of the measures of its remote interior angles.

Suggested Materials

Student Ruler, protractor, geometry software

Key Terms

Exterior angle, remote interior angle, adjacent interior angle, corollary

First Five Minutes

Transparency FFM 4-1B

Read the paragraphs at the bottom of page 247 and the top of page 248. Then do **Try It a** and **b.**

Motivate

Ask...

- What is the relationship between an exterior angle of a triangle and its remote interior angles?
- In the figure at the top of page 248, which seems larger, the measure of an exterior angle or the measure of either of its remote interior angles? Is this always true? Explain why or why not.

Tessellations and Triangles

Note: In the following **Explore,** some students may prefer to use a compass to construct the equilateral triangle.

EXPLORE

What's My Angle?

Recommended group size: 4

The Point

To see inductive support for the Triangle Angle-Sum Theorem, and to discover that the measure of an exterior angle of a triangle is equal to the sum of the measures of its remote interior angles.

Look and Listen...

- For students who are not reaching conclusions because their measurements are inexact.

Ask...

- If you assume that your measurements are only approximate, do you see any patterns?

For Groups That Finish Early

Draw a four-sided figure and an exterior angle at one vertex. Can you find a relationship between the measure of the exterior angle and the measures of its three remote interior angles? **The sum of the measures of the remote interior angles is 180° greater than the measure of the exterior angle.**

Follow Up

Ask students to state their conjecture from Step 4 in *if-then* form.

Possible Answers

3. The sums of the measures of the interior angles in each triangle is 180°; each angle in the equilateral triangle measures 60°.

4. The measure of an exterior angle of a triangle is equal to the sum of the measures of its remote interior angles.

$\triangle ABC$ has each side extended to form the exterior angles $\angle 1$, $\angle 2$, and $\angle 3$. The interior angle in a linear pair with exterior $\angle 1$, $\angle CAB$, is called its **adjacent interior** angle. $\angle CBA$ and $\angle ACB$ are the **remote interior** angles of exterior $\angle 1$.

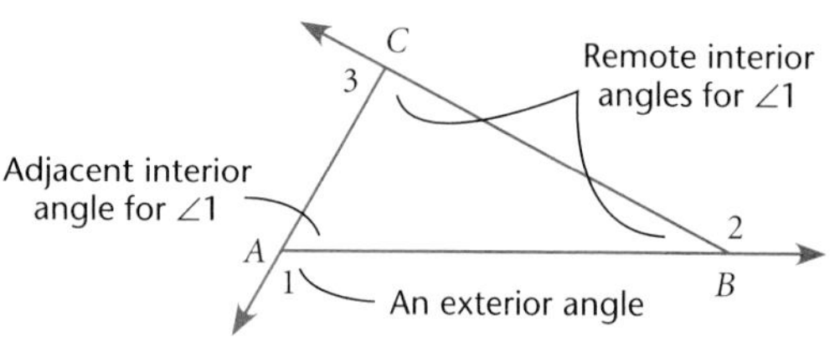

TRY IT

a. Name the exterior angles in the figure at the right. $\angle 1$, $\angle 2$, $\angle 3$

b. Name the remote interior angles for $\angle 3$. $\angle 4$, $\angle 5$

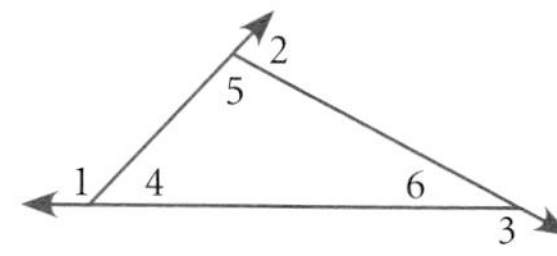

Earlier you found angle relationships formed by parallel lines and transversals. In this Explore, you will explore angle relationships in triangles.

EXPLORE: WHAT'S MY ANGLE?

MATERIALS

Ruler
Protractor
Geometry software (optional)

1. Use geometry software or a straightedge to draw an equilateral triangle. Draw an extension of one side. Measure the four angles formed by your figure.
2. Repeat Step 1 using an isosceles triangle, a right triangle, a scalene triangle, and an obtuse triangle.

Problem-Solving Tip

You may want to make a table to organize your data.

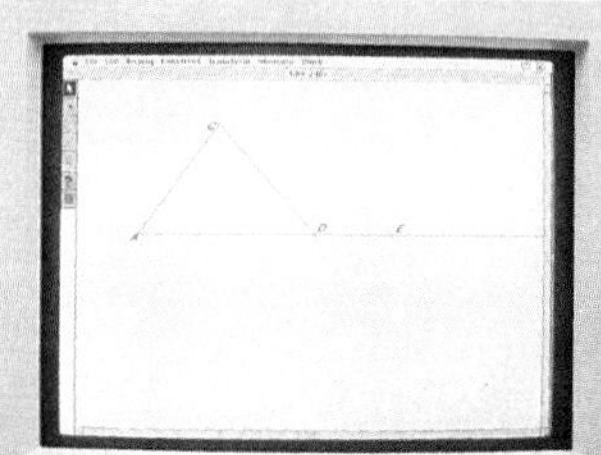

3. How does your data confirm the Triangle Angle-Sum Theorem? How does it show that equilateral triangles are also equiangular?
4. An important conclusion about triangles relates an exterior angle to its two remote interior angles. State this conclusion, and justify it deductively. (Hint: If you're stuck, try using the Triangle Angle-Sum Theorem.)

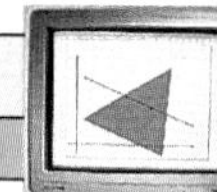

Technology Note

If students use software for this **Explore,** successive triangles may be labeled differently. This can confuse students when they organize their results in a table. You may want to have them consider the exterior angle $\angle 1$, its adjacent interior angle $\angle 2$, and the other two angles $\angle 3$ and $\angle 4$, regardless of how the software labels the points.

1. From the evidence you gathered above, what seems to be true about the acute angles of a right triangle? How does the Triangle Angle-Sum Theorem support this conjecture?

Shows that the acute angles of a right triangle are complementary.

Possible Answer

1. The angles are complementary. The three angle measures sum to 180°, so if one measure is 90°, the other two must sum to 90°.

TRY IT

c. Complete the table for the triangle shown.

$m\angle 1$	$m\angle 2$	$m\angle 3$	$m\angle 4$
83°	40°		
	84°		148°
	71°	54°	

Some of the conjectures you may have made suggest the following theorems.

EXTERIOR ANGLE THEOREM

The measure of an exterior angle of a triangle is equal to the sum of the measures of its remote interior angles.

This theorem leads directly to another one. A theorem that follows immediately from another is called a **corollary** of the original theorem.

EXTERIOR ANGLE INEQUALITY THEOREM

The measure of an exterior angle of a triangle is greater than the measure of either of its remote interior angles.

THEOREMS ABOUT ANGLES IN SPECIAL TRIANGLES

Each angle of an equilateral triangle measures 60°.

The acute angles of a right triangle are complementary.

Research Note

Students who get frustrated by a nonroutine problem will often just quit. They assume automatically that getting stuck is a sign to stop or ask for help, rather than a normal part of problem-solving.

If problem-solvers become aware of their emotional reactions, they may improve their ability to control their automatic responses to problems...[and] chances for success. (Douglas B. McLeod, "Affective Issues in Problem Solving," *Journal for Research in Mathematics Education,* Vol. 19, No. 2, p. 137. © 1988 NCTM.)

4-1

Tessellations and Triangles

Journal 

Explore Step 4, **Reflect** 1, and **Exercise** 16 are suitable for journal entries.

REFLECT

Possible Answers

1. The Exterior Angle Theorem states that the measure of an exterior angle is equal to the sum of the measures of its remote interior angles. Therefore, it follows that its measure must be greater than the measure of either of the remote interior angles.
2. No. This would mean that it has two obtuse interior angles.

TRY IT

Answers

c.

$m\angle 1$	$m\angle 2$	$m\angle 3$	$m\angle 4$
83°	40°	57°	97°
32°	84°	64°	148°
55°	71°	54°	125°

Part B Exercises

Exercise Notes

Look Back

18. Reviews mean, median, and mode in a social science context.

More Math Reasoning

25. Provides another way to support the Triangle Angle-Sum Theorem. Students may benefit from seeing that there are several different ways to confirm a conjecture.

26. Reviews bearings. Students will need to use facts about angles formed by parallel lines, the Triangle Angle-Sum Theorem, and the Exterior Angle Theorem to find a bearing.

Exercise Answers

Core

4–7.

$m\angle 5$	$m\angle 6$	$m\angle 7$	$m\angle 8$
104°	76°	33°	71°
108°	72°	8°	100°
137°	43°	68°	69°
156°	$x°$	$(2x+31)°$	$(4x-19)°$

8. $m\angle 1 = 48°$, $m\angle 2 = 32°$, $m\angle 3 = 80°$, $m\angle 4 = 42°$

REFLECT

1. Explain why the Exterior Angle Inequality Theorem is a corollary of the Exterior Angle Theorem.
2. Can a triangle ever have more than one acute exterior angle? Explain why or why not.

Exercises

CORE

P **Getting Started** **In each figure, name the remote interior angles for $\angle 1$.**

1. 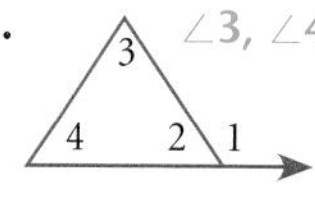 $\angle 3$, $\angle 4$

2. $\angle 2$, $\angle 4$

3. $\angle 2$, $\angle 3$

P **Complete the table for the triangle shown.**

	$m\angle 5$	$m\angle 6$	$m\angle 7$	$m\angle 8$
4.	104°		33°	
5.		72°		100°
6.		43°	68°	
7.		$x°$	$(2x + 31)°$	$(4x - 19)°$

P 8. Find the measures of $\angle 1$, $\angle 2$, $\angle 3$, and $\angle 4$ in the figure at the right.

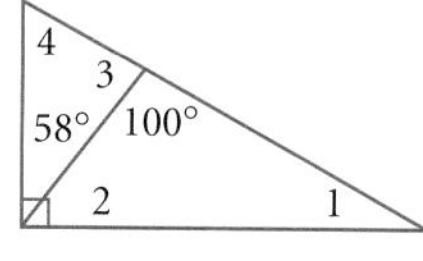

V 9. Determine whether the following statement is true or false. If it is false, change the underlined phrase to make it true.

The measure of an exterior angle of a triangle is equal to the sum of the measures of its <u>adjacent interior</u> angles.

P 10. **Brace Your Shelf!** The brace $\overline{JK}$ is fastened to the wall and the shelf shown at the right. Which angle has the greater measure, $\angle LJK$ or $\angle MKJ$? Justify your answer.

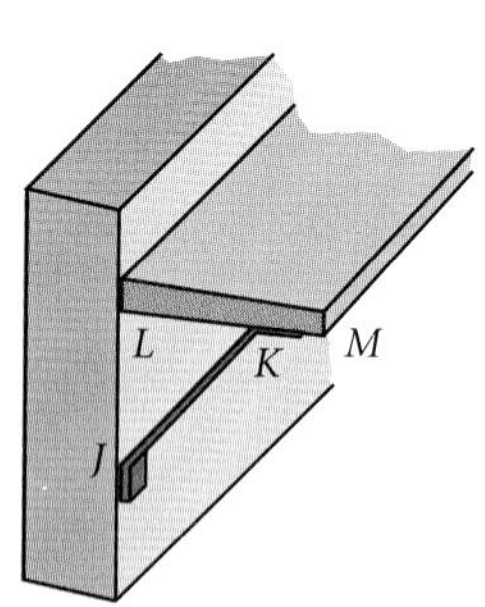

P 11. The measures of the acute angles of a right triangle are in the ratio 1:2. What is the measure of the smallest angle of the triangle? 30°

Key

V Vocabulary
P Practice/Skills
R Review
MR Math Reasoning
PS Problem Solving
C Challenge

Diversity Issues

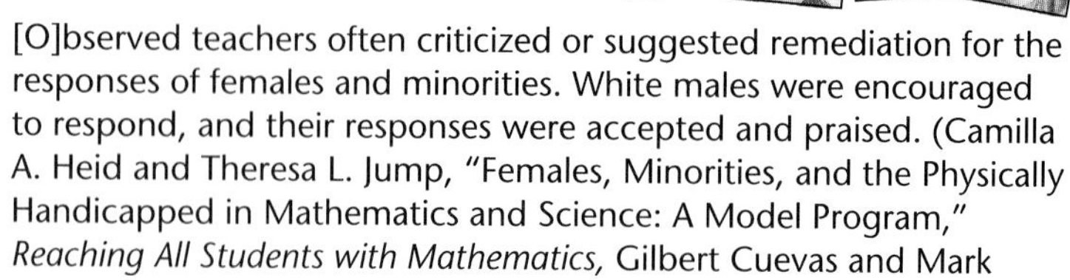

[O]bserved teachers often criticized or suggested remediation for the responses of females and minorities. White males were encouraged to respond, and their responses were accepted and praised. (Camilla A. Heid and Theresa L. Jump, "Females, Minorities, and the Physically Handicapped in Mathematics and Science: A Model Program," *Reaching All Students with Mathematics,* Gilbert Cuevas and Mark Driscoll, eds., p. 169. © 1993 NCTM.)

12. If the measures of the exterior angles of the acute angles of a right triangle are $(6x + 23)°$ and $(4x + 17)°$, find the measures of the acute angles. 19°, 71°

$\triangle BCD$ is a right triangle.

13. If $m\angle 1 = 18°$, find $m\angle 2$. 72°

14. If $m\angle 4 = 150°$ and $m\angle 3 = 130°$, find $m\angle ACD$. 20°

15. If $m\angle 1 = 20°$, find $m\angle 3$. 110°

16. A Leaning Ladder A ladder is leaning against a wall. As the foot of the ladder (point B) slides on the ground away from the wall, the top slides down the wall. If $\overline{AB}$ represents the ladder, then the measures of $\angle 1$, $\angle 2$, $\angle 3$, and $\angle 4$ change as the ladder slides.

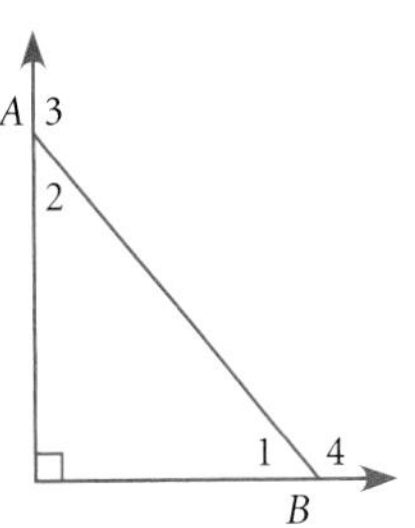

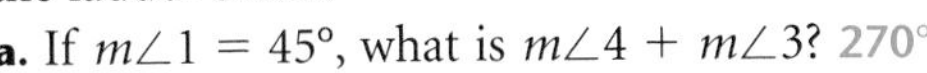

a. If $m\angle 1 = 45°$, what is $m\angle 4 + m\angle 3$? 270°
b. If $m\angle 1 = 40°$, what is $m\angle 4 + m\angle 3$? 270°
c. If $m\angle 1 = 35°$, what is $m\angle 4 + m\angle 3$? 270°
d. Make a conjecture about $m\angle 4 + m\angle 3$. Write a statement explaining how you made your conjecture.

LOOK BACK

17. Do the *rewrite, draw,* and *state* steps for a proof of the Exterior Angle Theorem. [3-4]

18. Find the mean, median, and mode of the unemployment rates in the data set given below. Where necessary, round answers to the nearest tenth. [Previous course]

Unemployment Rate in the Civilian Labor Force

Month	5/91	6/91	7/91	8/91	9/91	10/91	11/91	12/91	1/92	2/92	3/92	4/92
Rate (%)	6.8	6.9	6.8	6.8	6.8	6.9	6.9	7.1	7.1	7.3	7.3	7.2

MORE PRACTICE

19. Find the measure of $\angle ABC$. 45°

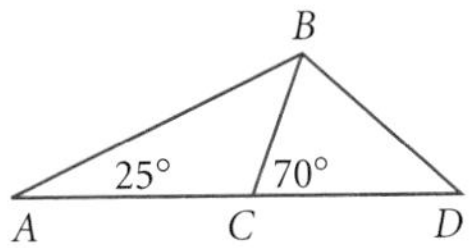

20. If $m\angle 1 = m\angle 2$, find $m\angle 3$. 155°

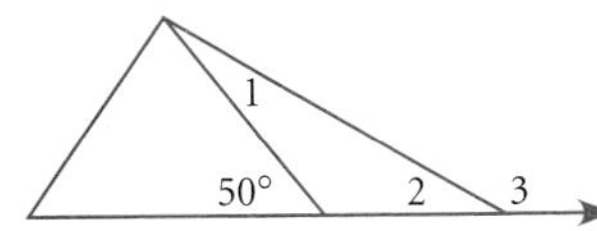

Ongoing Assessment

Self-Assessment Exercises 1–15 odd

Embedded Assessment Try It c; Reflect 1; Exercises 8, 12, 16

9. F; Remote interior angles.

10. $\angle MKJ$ has the greater measure because of the Exterior Angle Inequality Theorem. ($\angle LJK$ is a remote interior angle for $\angle MKJ$.)

16. d. $m\angle 4 + m\angle 3 = 270°$. In the previous three problems, $m\angle 4 + m\angle 3 = 270°$ even though $m\angle 1$ changed.

Look Back

17. *Rewrite:* If an angle is an exterior angle of a triangle, then its measure is equal to the sum of the measures of its remote interior angles.

Draw:

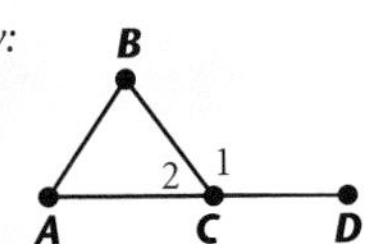

State: Given: $\angle 1$ is an exterior angle. *Prove:* $m\angle 1 = m\angle A + m\angle B$

18. The mean is 7.0, the median is 6.9, the mode is 6.8.

More Practice

21–24.

$m\angle 1$	$m\angle 2$	$m\angle 3$	$m\angle 4$
15°	136°	44°	29°
22°	119°	61°	39°
20°	143°	37°	17°
$(x - 20)°$	100°	$(180 - 2x)°$	$(2x - 50)°$

More Math Reasoning

25. By properties of parallel lines, $m\angle 1 = m\angle 5$ and $m\angle 2 = m\angle 4$. Therefore, since $m\angle 3 + m\angle 4 + m\angle 5 = 180°$ (by the Angle-Addition and Linear-Pair Postulates), $m\angle 3 + m\angle 2 + m\angle 1 = 180°$ by substitution.

Tessellations and Triangles

PART C At a Glance

Objective

To use angle measures of triangles to see why congruent triangles tessellate a plane.

Development

In the **Explore,** students see that any triangle tessellates a plane, and they use the Triangle Angle-Sum Theorem to help justify this result.

Suggested Materials

Student Paper, straightedge, scissors, protractor

First Five Minutes

Transparency FFM 4-1C

Write a brief summary of theorems about measures of interior and exterior angles of triangles.

EXPLORE

Tessellation Station

Recommended group size: 4

The Point

To discover that any triangle can tessellate a plane, and to use the Triangle Angle-Sum Theorem to justify that conjecture.

Look and Listen...

- For students who are finding it difficult to make a tessellation pattern.

Ask...

- Will it help to arrange a few of the triangles along a line?

For Groups That Finish Early

Can you make a tessellation pattern where the triangles do not lie along a straight line? If so, sketch such a pattern. Yes

P **Complete the table for the triangle shown.**

	$m\angle 1$	$m\angle 2$	$m\angle 3$	$m\angle 4$
21.	15°		44°	
22.		119°		39°
23.			37°	17°
24.	$(x - 20)°$		$(180 - 2x)°$	$(2x - 50)°$

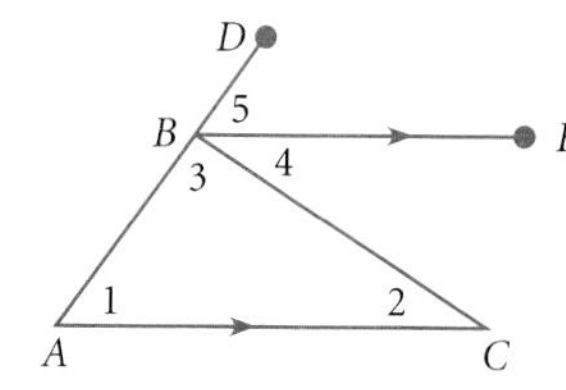

MORE MATH REASONING

MR **25.** If $\overline{AC} \parallel \overline{BE}$, explain how the figure at the right shows that $m\angle 1 + m\angle 2 + m\angle 3 = 180°$.

PS **26. Stable Bearings** A scout group hikes from camp (A) to a riding stable and then to a road—illustrated by $\triangle ABC$ in the figure below. An observation tower lies on the extension of segment $\overline{AC}$. What is the bearing of the riding stable from the observation tower? 210

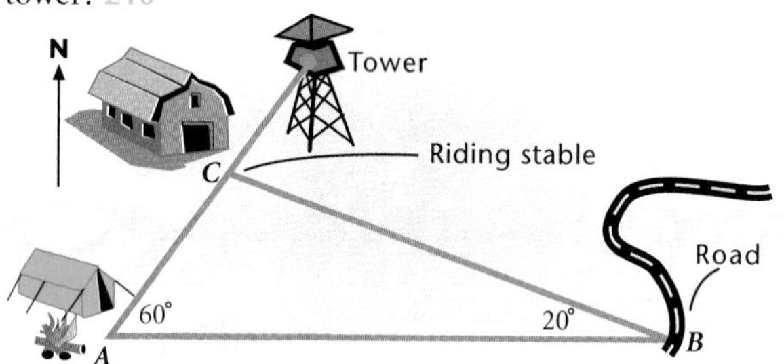

4-1 PART C Making Connections

← CONNECT → ***Triangles are important in the structures of buildings and in the art forms that decorate them. You have learned about some of the properties of triangles. Now you will explore how these properties relate to tessellations.***

The angle properties for triangles that you have become familiar with will help you in the following Explore when you investigate whether or not congruent triangles can tessellate a plane.

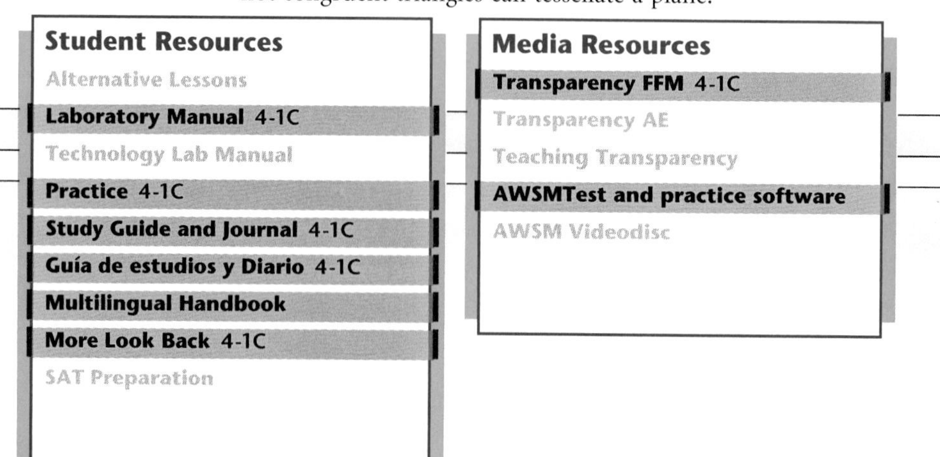

Student Resources
Alternative Lessons
Laboratory Manual 4-1C
Technology Lab Manual
Practice 4-1C
Study Guide and Journal 4-1C
Guía de estudios y Diario 4-1C
Multilingual Handbook
More Look Back 4-1C
SAT Preparation
Media Resources
Transparency FFM 4-1C
Transparency AE
Teaching Transparency
AWSMTest and practice software
AWSM Videodisc

EXPLORE: TESSELLATION STATION

MATERIALS

Paper
Straightedge
Scissors
Protractor (optional)

1. Do you think *any* triangle can be used to tessellate a plane? Make an "educated guess" before continuing.
2. Fold a sheet of paper in half three times. Then use a straightedge to draw a scalene triangle on the folded paper. Cut out the triangle to make eight congruent copies. Now try to create a tessellation with the triangles.
3. Compare your tessellation with those of classmates. See if all of the different types of triangles you used formed tessellations.
4. A *tessellation vertex* is a point in a tessellation where several of the figures meet. Use your knowledge of rotations to determine what the sum of the angles at a tessellation vertex must be so that there are no gaps or overlaps in the pattern.
5. Look at a tessellation vertex in one of your triangle tessellations. Find the sum of all of the angles that meet at a vertex. (Hint: Label the angles of the triangles as shown at the right.)
6. Can any triangle be used to tessellate a plane? Justify your answer.

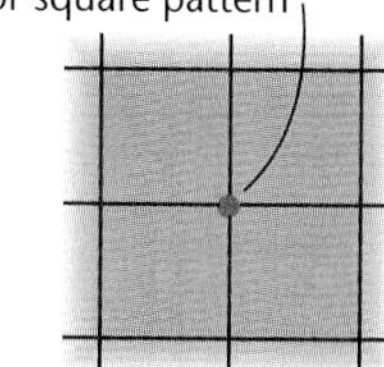

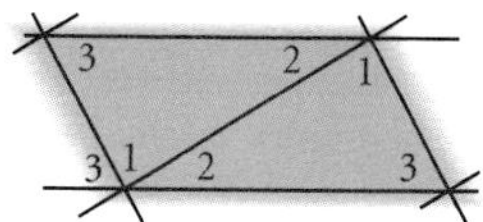

REFLECT

1. Explain how triangle tessellation patterns illustrate the following two theorems.
   a. the Triangle Angle-Sum Theorem
   b. the Exterior Angle Theorem
2. Prepare a summary of the different types of triangles you have learned about. Draw and label each type.

Self-Assessment

Is it possible for each of the following types of triangles to exist? If so, sketch an example. If not, explain why not.

1. right isosceles
2. right equilateral
3. obtuse isosceles

Vocabulary
Practice/Skills
Review
Math Reasoning
Problem Solving
Challenge

Follow Up

Ask students whether any triangle can tessellate a plane, and, if so, to explain why.

Possible Answers

5. 360°

6. Yes. The sum of all the angles at a vertex must be 360°. This can be done with any $\triangle ABC$ by arranging six triangles at a vertex with $\angle A$, $\angle B$, and $\angle C$ alternating. $m\angle A + m\angle B + m\angle C = 180°$, and there are two of each type at the vertex, so the sum is exactly 360°.

Portfolio

Have students select items from their work that demonstrate their understanding of the material in 4-1.

You may wish to have students include their favorite **Exercise** involving the Triangle Angle-Sum Theorem, favorite real-world application of any of the theorems, and an **Exercise** that they found challenging.

REFLECT

Possible Answers

1. a. A pattern like the one shown for Step 5 in the **Explore** illustrates the Angle-Sum Theorem; the three angles lie on a line, so their measures sum to 180°.

b. The pattern also illustrates the Exterior Angle Theorem. The measure of the exterior angle for $\angle 2$ equals $m\angle 1 + m\angle 3$, and this is also the sum of the remote interior angle measures.

2. Students should discuss acute, right, obtuse, equiangular, scalene, isosceles, and equilateral triangles.

Self-Assessment

Exercise Notes

10. Students find the mean, median, and mode of a data set.

Algebra | Data/Statistics | Logic/Reasoning | Social Science/History

Tessellations and Triangles

16. Students use a tessellation vertex to justify the Triangle Angle-Sum Theorem and the Exterior Angle Theorem.

Self-Assessment Answers

1. Yes;

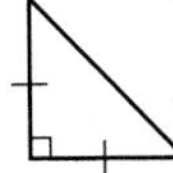

2. No; Every angle of an equilateral triangle is 60° but a right triangle has a 90° angle.

3. Yes;

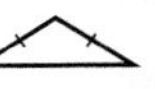

9. *Rewrite:* If a triangle is a right triangle, then its acute angles are complementary.
State: Given: $\triangle ABC$ is a right triangle, $\angle A$ is a right angle. *Prove:* $m\angle B + m\angle C = 90°$.

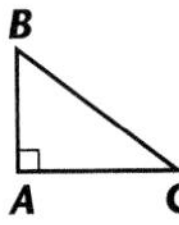

10. The mean is 65.8; The median is 71; The mode is 71.

11. A triangle cannot have those angle measures. Solving gives $x = 30$, but this would give the $(2x - 70)°$ angle a negative measure.

12. $m\angle 1 + m\angle 3 = 120°$ by the Exterior Angle Theorem.

13. Possible answer: $m\angle 2 = 60°$ by the Linear Pair Postulate.

14. Not possible; Possible answer: All that can be said about $\angle 3$ is that $m\angle 3 = 120° - m\angle 1$, and that is not enough to determine a unique value for $m\angle 3$.

15. No; By the Exterior Angle Inequality Theorem, the measure of an exterior angle is greater than the measure of either of the two remote interior angles. Therefore an exterior angle cannot be congruent to a remote interior angle.

P **Complete each statement with *always, sometimes,* or *never.* Give an explanation for each answer.**

4. A triangle with two complementary acute angles is ___ a right triangle. Always

5. An isosceles triangle is ___ a right triangle. Sometimes

6. A triangle with an obtuse angle is ___ a right triangle. Never

7. A triangle with two sides congruent is ___ equilateral. Sometimes

P **8.** In the figure at the right, $m\angle 1 + m\angle 2 + m\angle 3 - m\angle 4 =$ (c)
(a) $m\angle 1$ (b) $m\angle 2$
(c) $m\angle 3$ (d) $m\angle 4$
(e) 180°

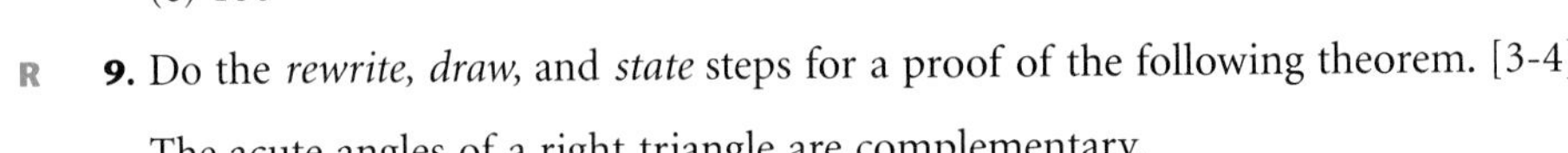

R **9.** Do the *rewrite, draw,* and *state* steps for a proof of the following theorem. [3-4]
The acute angles of a right triangle are complementary.

R **10.** Find the mean, median, and mode of the temperatures in the data set given below. Where necessary, round your answers to the nearest tenth. [Previous course]

Social Science

Average High Temperature in April

City	Quebec	Mexico City	Sydney	Hamilton (Bermuda)	Moscow	Cairo
Temp. (°F)	45	78	71	71	47	83

P, MR **11.** Can a triangle have angle measures of $(x + 40)°$, $(2x - 70)°$, and $(3x + 30)°$? If so, what is the value of x? If not, explain why not.

P **12.** In the figure at the right, find $m\angle 1 + m\angle 3$. Justify your answer with a theorem.

P **13.** Find the measure of $\angle 2$. Justify your answer.

MR **14.** Find the measure of $\angle 3$ if possible. Write an explanation of your thinking.

MR **15.** Can an exterior angle of a triangle be congruent to a remote interior angle? Explain.

C **16.** Explain how the triangular tessellation pattern at the right can be used to justify the Triangle Angle-Sum Theorem and the Exterior Angle Theorem. (Hint: The tessellation vertex shown will help in both explanations.)
See Additional Answers p. T254.

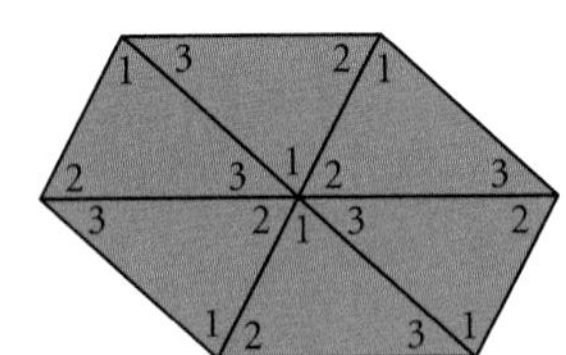

Assessment Resources

Quiz 4-1
Chapter Assessment Form A
Chapter Assessment Form B
Chapter Alternative Assessment
Mid-Year Assessment
End-of-Year Assessment
AWSMTest and practice software

Ongoing Assessment

Self-Assessment Self-Assessment Exercises

Embedded Assessment Reflect 1, 2

ADDITIONAL ANSWERS

4-1 Part C Self-Assessment

16. In the picture, $\angle 1$, $\angle 2$, and $\angle 3$ form a straight line at the tessellation vertex. Therefore $m\angle 1 + m\angle 2 + m\angle 3 = 180°$. Also in the picture at the tessellation vertex, $\angle 1$ and $\angle 2$ form the exterior angle of $\angle 3$, $\angle 3$ and $\angle 1$ form the exterior angle of $\angle 2$, and $\angle 2$ and $\angle 3$ form the exterior angle of $\angle 1$.

4-3 Part C Exercises

More Practice

20. Circle with radius 2 cm and center at point X.

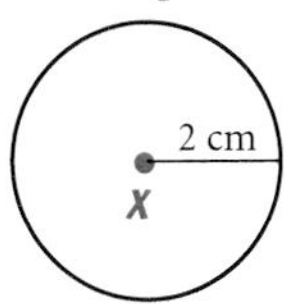

21. Sphere with radius 3 in. and center at point K.

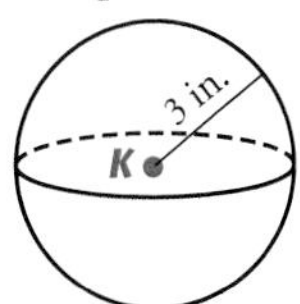

22. Cylinder with radius 1 m and the line S as the center.

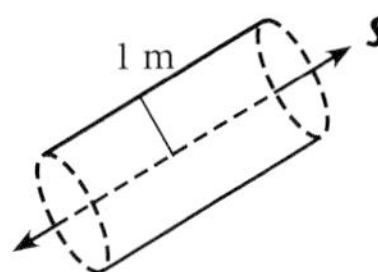

More Math Reasoning

26. Draw $\overline{OB}$ and $\overline{AP}$, and call the point of their intersection C. The key is at the intersection of $\overline{AB}$ and the bisector of $\angle ACB$. The key is on $\overline{AB}$ and, by the definition of an *angle bisector*, equidistant from lines $\overleftrightarrow{CB} = \overleftrightarrow{OB}$ and $\overleftrightarrow{CA} = \overleftrightarrow{PA}$.

4-3 Part C Exercises

27. Possible answer:

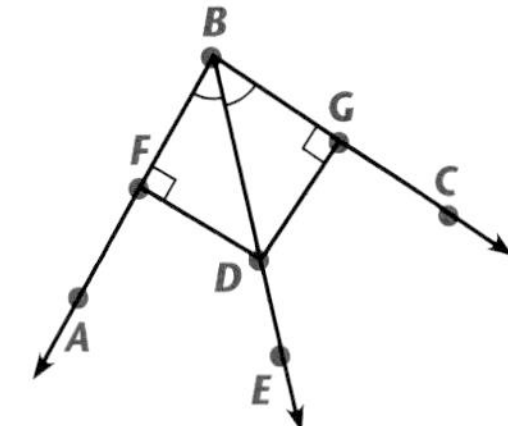

Given: $\overrightarrow{BE}$ is the angle bisector of $\angle ABC$, D lies on $\overrightarrow{BE}$.
Prove: D is equidistant from $\overrightarrow{BA}$ and $\overrightarrow{BC}$.
Proof: Draw $\overline{DF} \perp \overrightarrow{BA}$ and $\overline{DG} \perp \overrightarrow{BC}$. By the definition of *distance from a point to a line*, DF is the distance from D to $\overrightarrow{BA}$ and DG is the distance from D to $\overrightarrow{BC}$. Since $\overrightarrow{BE}$ is the angle bisector of $\angle ABC$, $\angle ABE \cong \angle CBE$. $\overline{BD} \cong \overline{BD}$ by the Reflexive Property. $\angle BFD \cong \angle BGD$ because right angles are congruent. $\triangle BFD \cong \triangle BGD$ by the SAA postulate. $\overline{FD} \cong \overline{GD}$ by CPCTC, so D is equidistant from the sides of the angle.

4-2

Deductive Proof with Triangles

SUPERLESSON AT A GLANCE

Superlesson Goal

Students will explore the conditions necessary for two triangles to be congruent and complete deductive proofs using the fact that corresponding parts of congruent triangles are congruent.

Management Guide

	Topic	Objectives	Key Terms	New Ideas	Materials
Part A	Correspondence and Congruence	To identify corresponding parts of congruent triangles.	Congruent triangles, correspondence, congruence correspondence	Correspondence. Setting up congruence correspondences. Definition of congruent triangles.	**Student** Ruler, protractor
Part B	Congruent Triangles	To use SSS, SAS, ASA, and SAA to show that triangles are congruent.	Opposite, included	Showing that triangles are congruent by using congruence postulates and theorems.	**Student** Ruler, protractor, compass
Part C	Organizing a Proof	To see different ways to organize a proof.	Flow proof, paragraph proof, two-column proof	Using different formats to organize a proof. Filling in missing statements or reasons to complete a proof.	
Part D	Corresponding Parts	To show that sides or angles are congruent because they are corresponding parts of congruent triangles.	Reflexive, symmetric, transitive	Showing sides and angles are congruent because they are corresponding parts of congruent triangles.	
Part E	Making Connections	To use triangle congruence to solve a real-world problem.	In Making Connections, students apply and synthesize key terms and new ideas.		

Pacing Chart (45-Minute Periods)

	Comprehensive Course	Core Course	Informal Course
Part A	1	1	1
Part B	1	1	2
Part C	1	2	0
Part D	1	2	0
Part E	1	1	1*
TOTAL periods for Superlesson	5	7	4

*Material on proof in this part may be omitted or downplayed in an Informal Course.

NCTM Standards

Mathematics as Problem Solving

Mathematics as Communication

Mathematics as Reasoning

Mathematical Connections

Geometry from a Synthetic Perspective

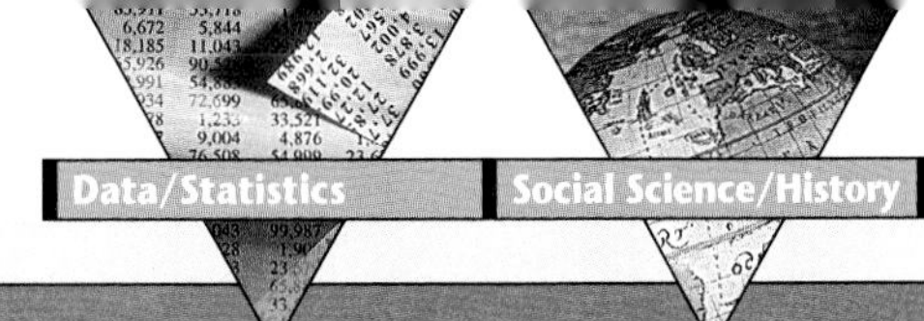

4-2 Deductive Proof with Triangles

Travels with Napoleon

Napoleon Bonaparte (1769–1821) ruled France from 1799 to 1815. During that period, his armies fought battles across Europe and North Africa. One of the most disastrous of these campaigns was Napoleon's invasion of Russia in the winter of 1812–1813. That winter was an especially harsh one in Europe. Although over 400,000 soldiers entered Russia as part of Napoleon's Grand Army, less than 10,000 made it back.

In 1862, a French engineer named Charles Minard created a graph to illustrate the terrible effect of the weather on Napoleon's troops. A simplified version of the graph is shown here.

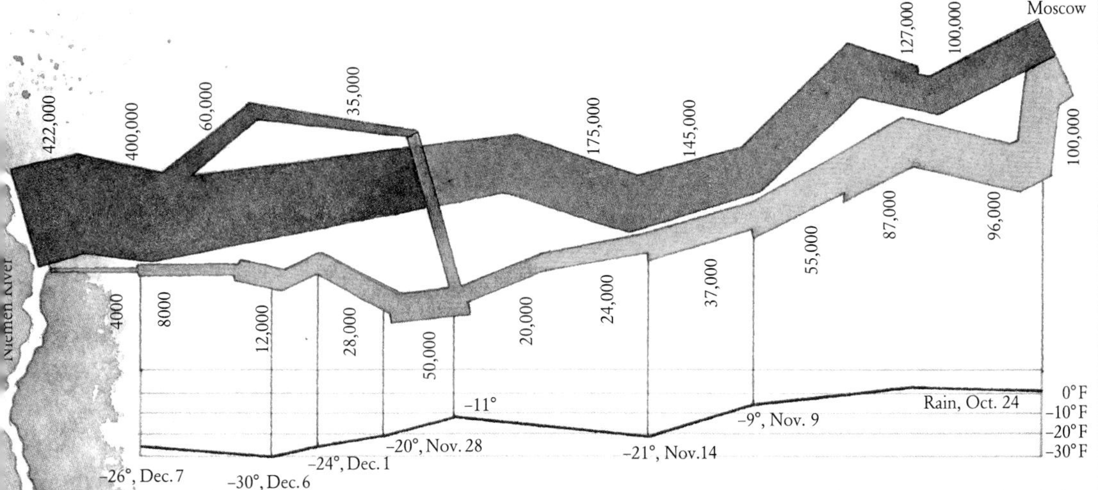

The wide band across the map of Europe shows the army moving toward Moscow; the width of the band is proportional to the number of soldiers in the army. The thinner band shows the return trip. Minard also added a line graph showing the sub-zero temperatures of the return trip. As the temperature plunges, the band representing the number of survivors becomes even thinner.

It is said that during one of Napoleon's campaigns, he needed to determine the distance across a river. One of his officers solved the problem using only a flagpole. As you learn more about congruent triangles, you will discover how his method worked.

?

1. **Did Napoleon's army lose a greater number of soldiers on the way to Moscow or on the way back? In which direction did Napoleon's army lose a greater percentage of soldiers? Explain your ideas.**
2. **Describe some ways geometry can be used to find an unknown distance.**

Where Are We Now?

Students are familiar with some basic properties of triangles, and have seen several ways to prove angles congruent. They have also become familiar with three steps of our five-step process for deductive proof and done informal justification of conjectures.

Where Are We Going?

In 4-2, students will see different ways to prove triangles congruent. Ideas of congruence and correspondence are important throughout the course, and these topics have many parallels to similar triangles seen in Chapter 7.

Students also see different structures for organizing proofs, and they complete proofs by filling in statements and reasons. This continues their preparation for deductive proof; in Chapter 5 the students will *plan* proofs, and in Chapter 6 they will *demonstrate* proofs on their own.

Possible Answers

1. Napoleon's army lost a greater number of soldiers on the way to Moscow, but a greater percentage on the way back.
2. If coordinates are known, the distance formula can be used; an unknown side length of an equiangular triangle is equal to a known side length.

More About Napoleon

Napoleon Bonaparte (1769–1821) became a general in the French Army during the period following the French Revolution. After campaigns in Italy and Egypt, he returned to France in 1799 and came to power in a *coup d'état.* By 1810, his military and political victories had made France the dominant power in Europe. The disastrous invasion of Russia destroyed his army, and he was deposed and exiled to the island of Elba in 1814. Napoleon escaped and returned to power in 1815, but was finally defeated at Waterloo and exiled to the island of St. Helena.

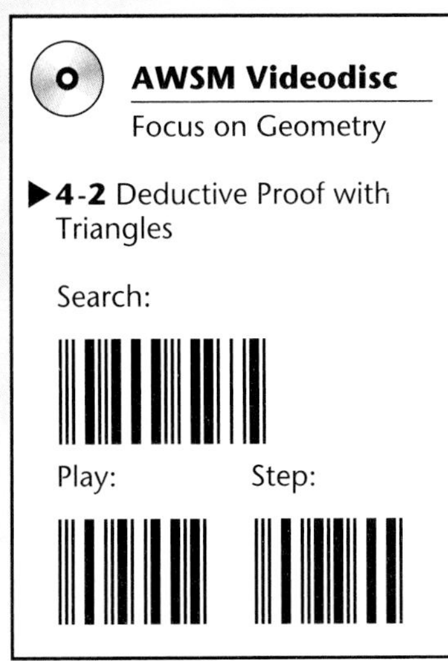

Deductive Proof with Triangles

PART A At a Glance

Objective

To identify corresponding parts of congruent triangles.

Development

In **Consider** questions, students see that differently oriented figures can be congruent.

In the **Explore,** they set up a congruence correspondence for two triangles and see how a congruence statement identifies congruent corresponding parts.

Suggested Materials

Student Ruler, protractor

Key Terms

Congruent triangles, correspondence, congruence correspondence

First Five Minutes

Transparency FFM 4-2A

Read the paragraph above the **Consider** on page 256 and answer **Consider** 1 and 2.

Motivate

Ask...

- If two triangles are congruent, what can you say about their sides? their angles?

Possible Answers

1. The first and third pairs are congruent.
2. First pair: rotation; third pair: reflection.

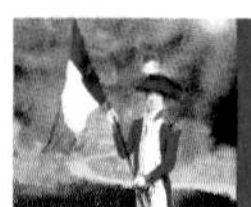

4-2 PART A Correspondence and Congruen

← CONNECT → *You've discovered many facts about angles and sides in individual triangles. Now you will begin to investigate pairs of triangles.*

As you've seen when creating tessellations, it's helpful to be able to recognize congruent figures in different orientations.

1. **Determine whether each pair of figures below is congruent. Explain your answers.**

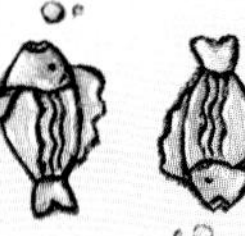

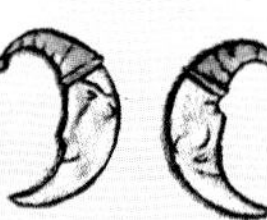

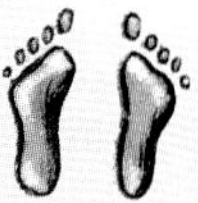

2. **For the pairs of congruent figures, what transformation(s) is (are) necessary to move one figure so that it coincides with the other?**

Congruent figures can be slid, flipped, and turned until they overlap exactly. It is important to match up parts correctly when you work with congruent triangles.

EXPLORE: FINDING THE RIGHT MATCH

MATERIALS

Ruler
Protractor

1. The two triangles below are congruent. Using whatever measurement tools you need, list all of the parts (angles and segments) of the triangles that are congruent. How many pairs of congruent parts do two congruent triangles have?

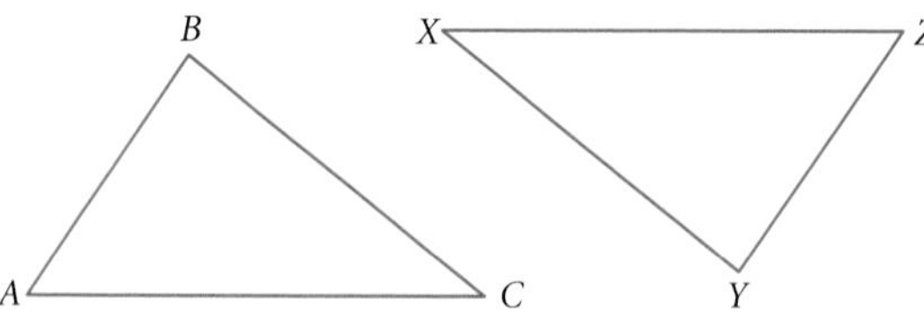

Alert

Students may be confused by the use of *corresponding* in different contexts: (1) when matching up parts of figures and (2) in lines cut by a transversal. It may help them if you point out this potential confusion and show examples of corresponding angles in each of these contexts.

2. Using your list of congruent parts as a guide, identify the vertices of the two triangles that match up with one another.
3. Complete the following congruence statement in a way that shows the congruent parts of the triangles. $\triangle ABC \cong \triangle$___. What does the order of the letters tell you about the congruent parts of the triangles?
4. Suppose $\triangle JKL \cong \triangle PQR$. List all pairs of sides and angles that must be congruent.

TRY IT

a. Write a congruence statement for the triangles shown. $\triangle MNO \cong \triangle TUS$

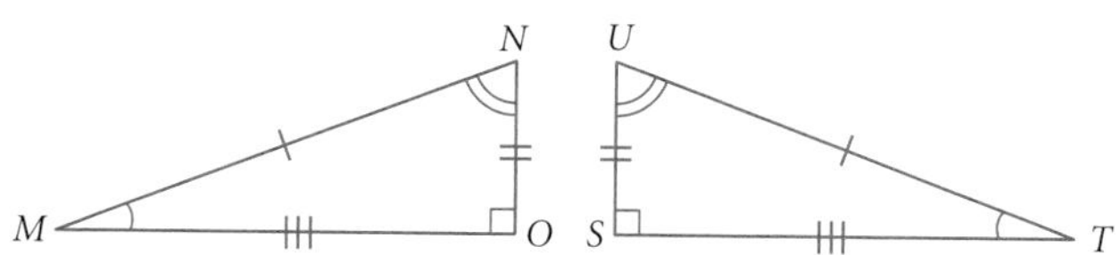

To write a useful congruence statement, you need to match up the vertices correctly to make a *correspondence.*

DEFINITIONS

A **correspondence** between two geometric figures is any way of pairing up their vertices. A **congruence correspondence** matches the vertices so that all pairs of corresponding parts are congruent.

The symbol for *corresponds to* is $\leftrightarrow$. One congruence correspondence between the two triangles below is $\triangle ABC \leftrightarrow \triangle RST$. The order of the letters in the correspondence statement specifies the corresponding sides and corresponding angles.

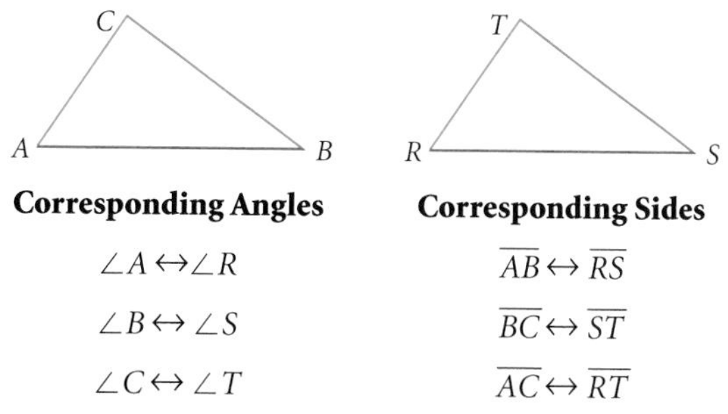

Corresponding Angles	Corresponding Sides
$\angle A \leftrightarrow \angle R$	$\overline{AB} \leftrightarrow \overline{RS}$
$\angle B \leftrightarrow \angle S$	$\overline{BC} \leftrightarrow \overline{ST}$
$\angle C \leftrightarrow \angle T$	$\overline{AC} \leftrightarrow \overline{RT}$

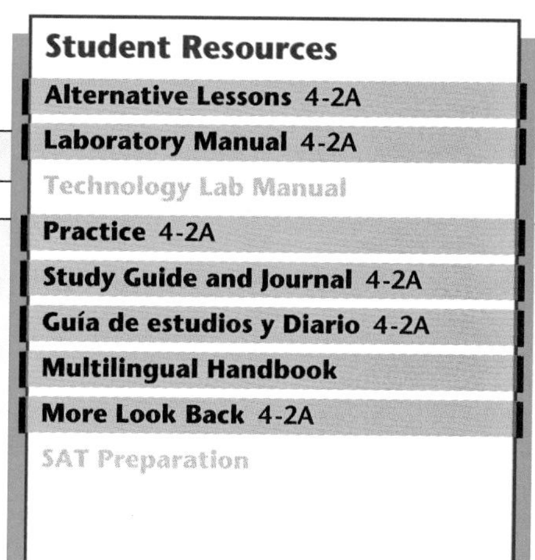

Student Resources

- Alternative Lessons 4-2A
- Laboratory Manual 4-2A
- Technology Lab Manual
- Practice 4-2A
- Study Guide and Journal 4-2A
- Guía de estudios y Diario 4-2A
- Multilingual Handbook
- More Look Back 4-2A
- SAT Preparation

Media Resources

- Transparency FFM 4-2A
- Transparency AE
- Teaching Transparency
- AWSMTest and practice software
- AWSM Videodisc

EXPLORE

Finding the Right Match

Recommended group size: 2

The Point

To set up a congruence correspondence between two triangles; to see how a congruence statement shows congruent corresponding parts.

Look and Listen...

- For students who do not see that the order of the letters shows the correspondence.

Ask...

- How can you show which vertex in $\triangle XYZ$ corresponds to A?

For Groups That Finish Early

Suppose $\triangle DEF \cong \triangle GHI$, and each triangle is isosceles with vertices D and G, respectively. Write another true congruence statement that begins $\triangle DEF \cong$ ______.

Follow Up

Ask students to explain how to write a congruence correspondence and to explain how the notation works.

Possible Answers

1. 6
2. A matches with Z, B with Y, and C with X.
3. $\triangle ABC \cong \triangle ZYX$. The first vertex listed for the first triangle corresponds to the first vertex listed for the second, and so on.
4. $\overline{JK} \cong \overline{PQ}$, $\overline{KL} \cong \overline{QR}$, $\overline{JL} \cong \overline{PR}$, $\angle J \cong \angle P$, $\angle K \cong \angle Q$, $\angle L \cong \angle R$

4-2 Deductive Proof with Triangles

Journal 

Reflect 1 and 2 are suitable for journal entries.

REFLECT

Possible Answers

1. In a transformation, each vertex point on the pre-image has a corresponding point on the image.
2. A correspondence is a one-to-one pairing. *Congruent* means having the same size. A congruence correspondence is a way to pair vertices of a figure so that congruent parts are matched.

Up until now, we have simply stated that congruent triangles "have the same shape." Now we are ready to give a more useful definition.

> **DEFINITION**
>
> Two triangles are **congruent triangles** if and only if all of their corresponding parts are congruent.

REFLECT

1. Have you ever used the idea of correspondence to match up vertices of figures before? Explain. (Hint: Think about transformations.)
2. Explain the difference between congruence and correspondence.

Part A Exercises

Exercise Notes

Core

19. Asks students to explain why interchangeable (congruent) parts are important in industry.

More Math Reasoning

33. Students need to list all of the permutations of three letters. You may want to encourage them to find an organized way to do this.

Extension: How many ways can you arrange n distinct items? $n \times (n-1) \times (n-2) \times \cdots \times 1$

You may want to take this opportunity to show or remind students that this is $n!$.

Exercise Answers

Core

3. Possible answer: $\angle X \leftrightarrow \angle U$, $\angle Y \leftrightarrow \angle V$, $\angle Z \leftrightarrow \angle W$, $\overline{XY} \leftrightarrow \overline{UV}$, $\overline{YZ} \leftrightarrow \overline{VW}$, $\overline{ZX} \leftrightarrow \overline{WU}$

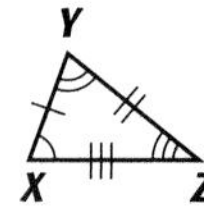

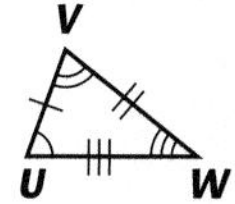

4. $\triangle JLK \cong \triangle MPN$, $\triangle KLJ \cong \triangle NPM$, $\triangle KJL \cong \triangle NMP$, $\triangle LJK \cong \triangle PMN$, $\triangle LKJ \cong \triangle PNM$

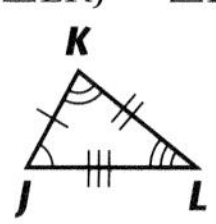

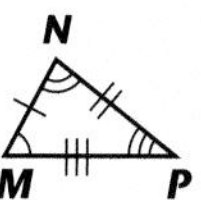

Exercises

CORE

P **Getting Started Give a congruence correspondence for each figure. Use the symbol ≅ to write the congruence.**

1.

$\triangle DEF \cong \triangle XZY$

2.

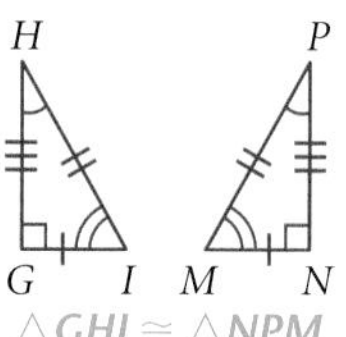

$\triangle GHI \cong \triangle NPM$

P 3. Draw $\triangle XYZ$ and $\triangle UVW$ so that $\triangle XYZ \cong \triangle UVW$. Mark the congruent parts. List the pairs of corresponding congruent parts.

P 4. Draw and mark triangles for the congruence $\triangle JKL \cong \triangle MNP$. Rewrite the congruence in five other ways.

P **Suppose $\triangle RST \cong \triangle LMO$. Complete each statement.**

5. $m\angle R =$ ___ $m\angle L$ 6. $\angle O \cong$ ___ $\angle T$ 7. $\overline{LM} \cong$ ___ $\overline{RS}$

P 8. Write congruence statements for the triangles in the figure that appear to be congruent.

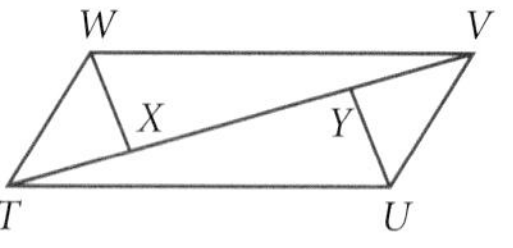

Key

- V Vocabulary
- P Practice/Skills
- R Review
- MR Math Reasoning
- PS Problem Solving
- C Challenge

Diversity Issues

Visual learners may find it easy to identify congruence correspondences in triangles that are reflections and rotations of one another, but other students may not. You may want to help students who have difficulty in this area by cutting out a pair of congruent triangles and showing correspondences for a variety of orientations and positions.

In the figure, $\triangle ABC \cong \triangle EDC$. Find each measure.

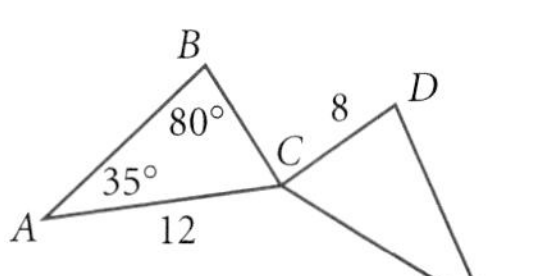

9. $m\angle D =$ ___ 80° **10.** $CE =$ ___ 12

11. $m\angle DCE =$ ___ 65° **12.** $BC =$ ___ 8

In the figure, $\triangle TUV \cong \triangle WZY$. Find each measure.

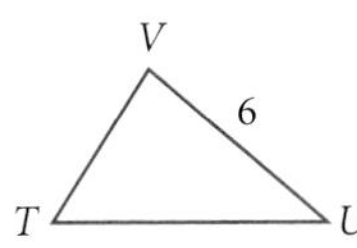

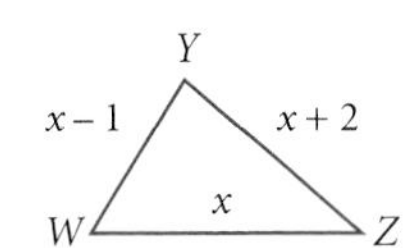

13. $YZ =$ ___ 6 **14.** $WY =$ ___ 3

15. $VT =$ ___ 3 **16.** $TU =$ ___ 4

17. The quilt shown at the right is made by sewing together triangular shapes. How many different noncongruent shapes are used? Two

18. Plot the points $M(2, 3)$, $N(6, 3)$, $P(8, 7)$, and draw $\triangle MNP$. Reflect $\triangle MNP$ across the y-axis, and label the image $\triangle RST$, so that $\triangle MNP \cong \triangle RST$. Give the coordinates of R, S, and T.

19. Mass Production Suppose that an automobile company manufactures triangular plastic safety-belt guides for its cars. All of the triangular guides are congruent.

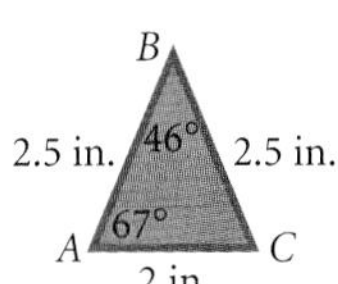

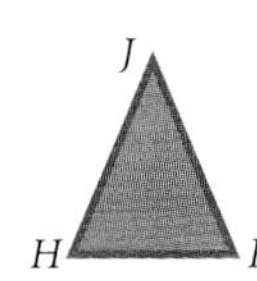

a. If $\triangle ABC$ has the measures shown and $\triangle ABC \cong \triangle HJK$, find the measure of each angle and the length of each side of $\triangle HJK$.

b. Why might the company producing these cars want to be sure that all of these parts are congruent?

LOOK BACK

20. Copy point P and line m. Use a compass and straightedge to construct a line through P that is parallel to m. [3-4]

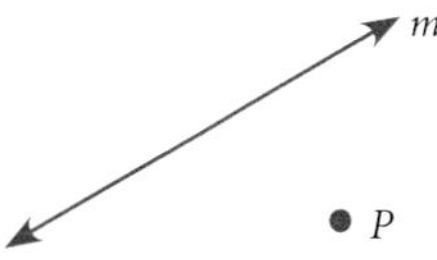

In each of the following, use the given information to find $m\angle C$. [4-1]

21. $m\angle A = 34°$, and $\angle A \cong \angle B$. 112°

22. $\triangle ABC$ is equilateral. 60°

23. $m\angle A = (x + 32)°$, $m\angle B = (2x - 11)°$, and $m\angle C = (3x + 21)°$. 90°

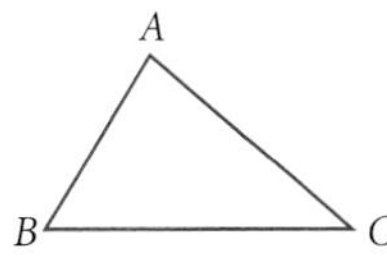

8. $\triangle TXW \cong \triangle VYU$, $\triangle TYU \cong \triangle VXW$, $\triangle TWV \cong \triangle VUT$

18. $R(-2, 3)$, $S(-6, 3)$, $T(-8, 7)$

19. a. $HJ = 2.5$ in., $JK = 2.5$ in., $HK = 2$ in., $m\angle H = 67°$, $m\angle K = 67°$, $m\angle J = 46°$

b. Possible answer: So that each part can fit in any car they produce.

Look Back

20.

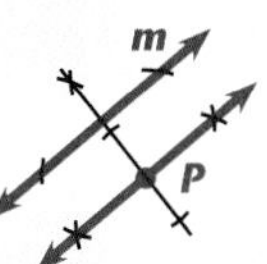

More Practice

24.

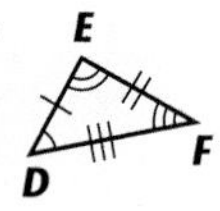

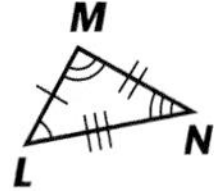

a. No; Possible answer: $DE \neq LN$

b. Yes; All their corresponding parts are congruent.

c. Yes; All their corresponding parts are congruent.

More Math Reasoning

32. Isosceles; $\overline{AB} \cong \overline{CB}$ from the congruence correspondence $\triangle ABC \cong \triangle CBA$, so $\triangle ABC$ is isosceles by definition.

Ongoing Assessment

Self-Assessment Exercises 1, 5–17 odd, 18

Embedded Assessment Explore Step 4; Exercises 2, 10, 19

Deductive Proof with Triangles

PART B At a Glance

Objective

To use SSS, SAS, ASA, and SAA to show that triangles are congruent.

Development

In the **Explore,** students discover patterns of three pairs of congruent parts that always result in congruent triangles. Then the SSS, SAS, ASA, and SAA postulates are formally stated.

Suggested Materials

Student Ruler, protractor, compass

Key Terms

Opposite, included

First Five Minutes

Transparency FFM 4-2B

Suppose $\triangle RTS \cong \triangle XWY$. List all of the pairs of corresponding congruent parts. $\overline{RT} \cong \overline{XW}$, $\overline{TS} \cong \overline{WY}$, $\overline{RS} \cong \overline{XY}$, $\angle R \cong \angle X$, $\angle T \cong \angle W$, and $\angle S \cong \angle Y$

Motivate

Ask...

- Suppose you know that one side of an equilateral triangle is congruent to a side of another equilateral triangle. Can you conclude that the two triangles are congruent? Explain.

MORE PRACTICE

P **24.** Draw a scalene triangle, $\triangle DEF$, congruent to $\triangle LMN$ ($\triangle DEF \cong \triangle LMN$).
  a. Is $\triangle DEF \cong \triangle LNM$? Why or why not?
  b. Is $\triangle FED \cong \triangle NML$? Why or why not?
  c. Is $\triangle EDF \cong \triangle MLN$? Why or why not?

P **$\triangle ABC \cong \triangle RST$. Complete each statement.**

25. $\overline{AC} \cong$ $\overline{RT}$ **26.** $m\angle ABC =$ $m\angle RST$ **27.** $m\angle TSR =$ $m\angle CBA$

P **$\triangle FGH \cong \triangle JIH$. Find each measure.**

28. $m\angle G =$ ___ $63°$ **29.** $IJ =$ ___ 9.1

30. $m\angle GFH =$ ___ $27°$ **31.** $FH =$ ___ 8.1

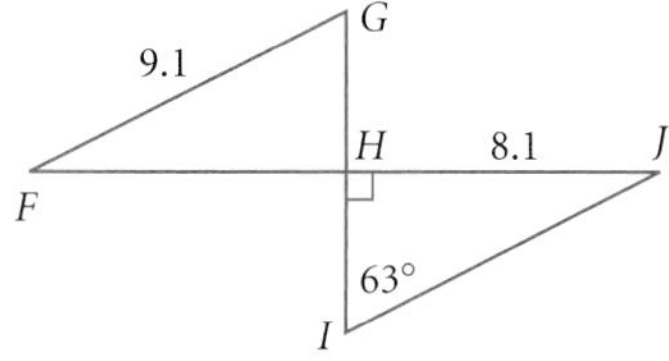

MORE MATH REASONING

MR **32.** If $\triangle ABC \cong \triangle CBA$, what type of triangle is $\triangle ABC$? Explain your answer.

C, PS **33.** Scalene triangle $\triangle PQR$ is congruent to a triangle with vertices S, T, and U, but the congruence correspondence is not necessarily in that order. If you complete the congruence statement $\triangle PQR \cong \triangle$___ by writing S, T, and U in a random order, what is the probability you will write a true congruence statement? $\frac{1}{6}$

4-2 PART B Congruent Triangles

← CONNECT → ***You've seen what is needed to establish congruence of triangles. Now you will investigate some shortcuts for proving triangles congruent.***

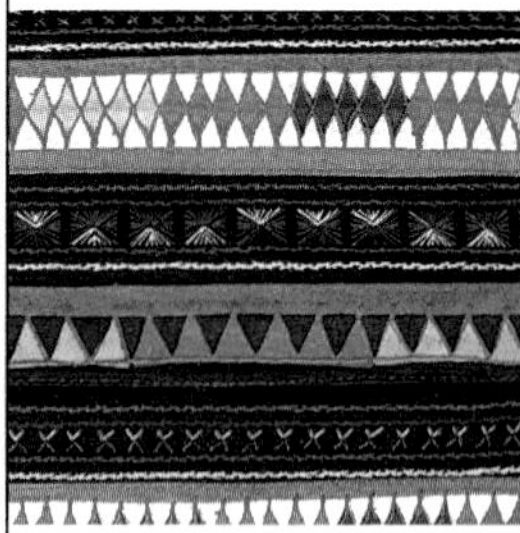

This textile pattern from Thailand contains many sets of congruent triangles. You know that two congruent triangles have six pairs of corresponding congruent parts: three pairs of sides and three pairs of angles.

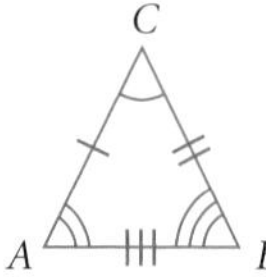

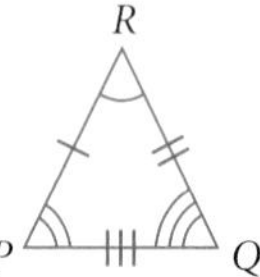

Key

V Vocabulary
P Practice/Skills
R Review
MR Math Reasoning
PS Problem Solving
C Challenge

History Connection

Sonya Kovalevsky (1850–1891) may have been the greatest female mathematical genius of the past two centuries. Born in Russia, she traveled to Germany in 1869, where she studied mathematics at the University of Heidelberg and earned a doctorate from the University of Göttingen in 1874. Her primary areas of work were in analysis and mathematical physics.

Do you really need to know *all six* of these congruences to conclude that two triangles are congruent? Are there some shortcuts? To help investigate this question in the following Explore, you will need to become familiar with some new terms.

You can describe the parts of a triangle by their relative position as follows.

$\angle R$ is *opposite* side $\overline{ST}$.

$\overline{RT}$ is *opposite* $\angle S$.

$\angle S$ is *included* between $\overline{RS}$ and $\overline{ST}$.

$\overline{RT}$ is *included* between $\angle R$ and $\angle T$.

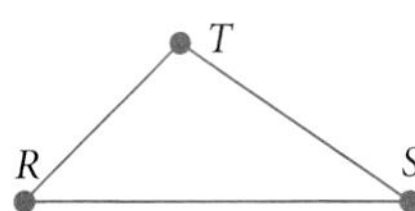

EXPLORE: WHAT DO YOU NEED TO KNOW?

MATERIALS

Ruler
Protractor
Compass (optional)

Work in pairs. In Steps 1–5, alternate roles so that each of you has a chance to draw the initial triangle.

1. Draw a triangle. Measure *two sides* and their *included angle.* Then tell your partner just those three measurements, and have him draw a triangle with those characteristics. Compare your triangles to see whether or not they are congruent.
2. Repeat the process with a new triangle, but this time tell your partner the measures of *two angles* and their *included side.* Compare your triangles for congruence.
3. This time, tell your partner the measures of all *three angles* of your triangle. Compare your triangles for congruence.
4. Now, tell your partner the measures of *two angles* and a *side opposite* one of the angles. Compare your triangles for congruence.
5. Tell your partner the measure of all *three sides* of your triangle. (Hint: Making this triangle might be a bit tougher; use the figure at the right as a hint.) Compare your triangles for congruence.
6. List any conditions you discovered that seem to guarantee congruent triangles.

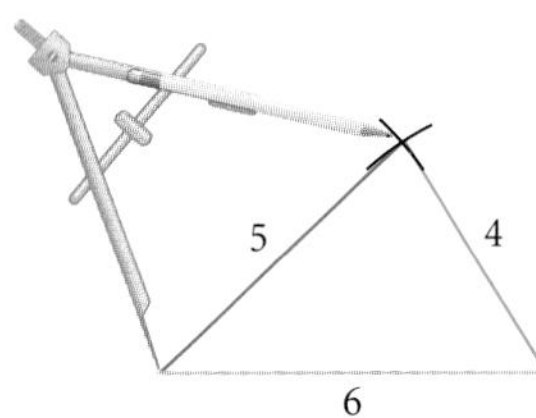

Student Resources

- Alternative Lessons 4-2B
- Laboratory Manual 4-2B
- Technology Lab Manual
- Practice 4-2B
- Study Guide and Journal 4-2B
- Guía de estudios y Diario 4-2B
- Multilingual Handbook
- More Look Ahead 4-2B
- SAT Preparation

Media Resources

- Transparency FFM 4-2B
- Transparency AE
- Teaching Transparency
- AWSMTest and practice software
- AWSM Videodisc

EXPLORE

What Do You Need to Know?

Recommended group size: 2

The Point

To discover ways to show that triangles are congruent using three pairs of corresponding congruent parts.

Look and Listen...

- For students who are having difficulty drawing their partner's SSS triangle. Suggest that they start by drawing one side. Then they can use a compass to make arcs from the endpoints of the first side, using the lengths of each of the other sides. The point where the arcs intersect is the third vertex of the triangle.
- For students who are assuming that the triangles are congruent without measurement.

Ask...

- According to the definition of congruent triangles, what do you need to know to be able to conclude that two triangles are congruent? Have you checked all of these?

For Groups That Finish Early

Investigate the possibility that only two pairs of parts are enough to guarantee congruent triangles: two sides, two angles, or a side and an angle. Will any of these patterns guarantee that the triangles are congruent? No

Follow Up

Ask students to summarize the patterns of three pairs of congruent parts that guarantee congruent triangles.

Possible Answers

1. Yes
2. Yes
3. No
4. Yes
5. Yes
6. SAS, ASA, SAA, and SSS patterns guarantee triangle congruence. (AAA does not.)

You have just explored four ways to show that triangles are congruent using only three pairs of corresponding congruent parts.

SIDE-SIDE-SIDE CONGRUENCE POSTULATE (SSS)

If each of the three sides of one triangle are congruent to the sides of another triangle, then the two triangles are congruent.

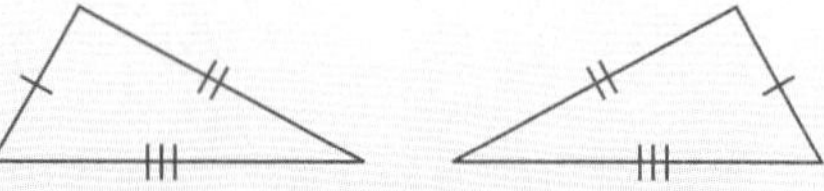

SIDE-ANGLE-SIDE CONGRUENCE POSTULATE (SAS)

If two sides and the included angle of one triangle are congruent to two sides and the included angle of another triangle, then the two triangles are congruent.

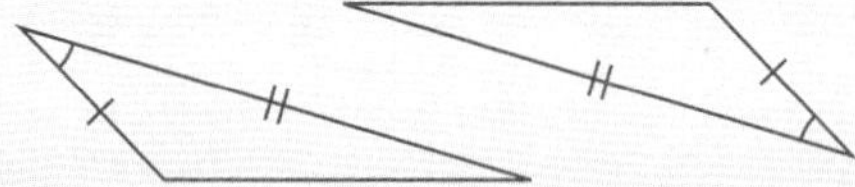

ANGLE-SIDE-ANGLE CONGRUENCE POSTULATE (ASA)

If two angles and the included side of one triangle are congruent to two angles and the included side of another triangle, then the two triangles are congruent.

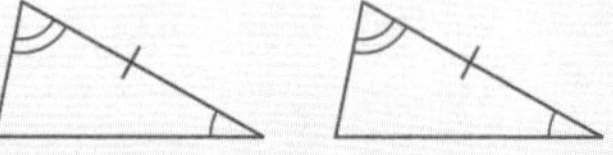

SIDE-ANGLE-ANGLE CONGRUENCE POSTULATE (SAA)

If two angles and a side opposite one of them in one triangle are congruent to the corresponding parts of another triangle, then the two triangles are congruent.

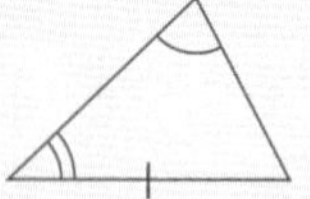

Technology Note

You may wish to have students use geometry software to confirm their results to the **Explore** on page 261. By using software to construct two congruent angles included between two pairs of congruent sides, they can see that all sides and angles of the completed triangles are congruent. You might have students first do the **Explore** without software to preserve its interactive aspects.

TRY IT

If possible, write a congruence statement for each pair of triangles. Then name the triangle-congruence postulate that applies. If the triangles are not congruent, say so.

a.

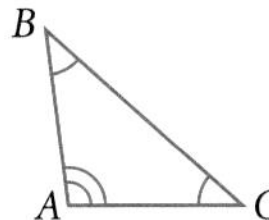

M O N

$\triangle ABC$ may be congruent to $\triangle OMN$. More information is needed.

b. D 20° P 130° Q 20° 130° E F R

$\triangle DEF \cong \triangle RQP$; SAA Postulate

REFLECT

1. If you use the definition of congruent triangles to show that two triangles are congruent, how many pairs of corresponding congruent parts do you need to have? How many pairs do each of the postulates require?
2. A welder must make two congruent triangular steel frames. She does this without ever measuring an angle. How? Which postulate is she using?

Exercises

CORE

Getting Started In each of the following, name the required angle or side.

1. the side opposite $\angle MPN$ $\overline{MN}$
2. the angle opposite $\overline{QN}$ $\angle QMN$
3. the included side for $\angle QMP$ and $\angle QPM$ $\overline{MP}$
4. the included angle for $\overline{QP}$ and $\overline{PM}$ $\angle QPM$

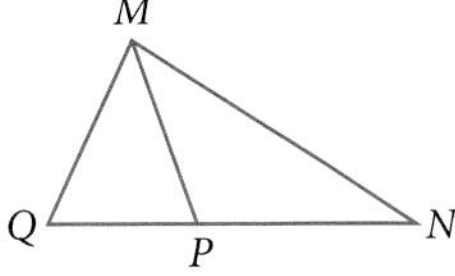

If possible, write a congruence statement for each pair of triangles. Then name the triangle-congruence postulate that applies. If the triangles are not congruent, say so.

5.

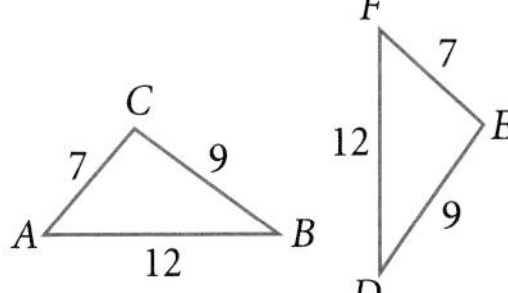

6.

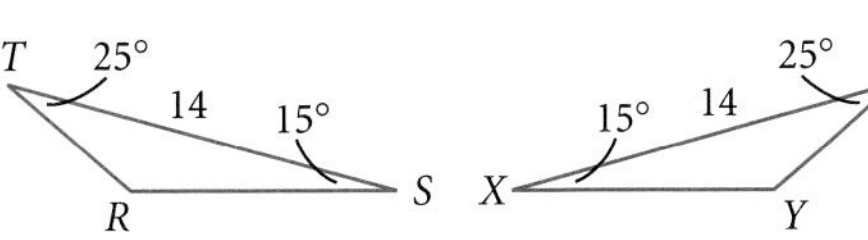

Journal

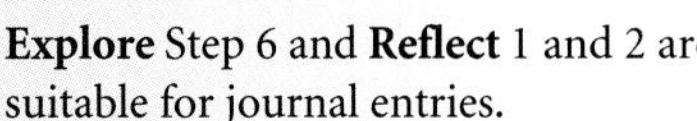

Explore Step 6 and **Reflect** 1 and 2 are suitable for journal entries.

REFLECT

Possible Answers

1. The definition requires six pairs of corresponding congruent parts, the postulates only three.
2. If she uses three pairs of congruent sides, the triangles are congruent by SSS.

Part B Exercises

Exercise Notes

Core

14. Shows students why there is no AAA congruence postulate.

15. Reviews *rewrite, draw,* and *state* steps.

Look Ahead

These exercises review skills needed in deductive proofs. In 4-2 Part C, students see different ways to write a proof and fill in missing statements and reasons to complete proofs.

Exercise Answers

Core

5. $\triangle ABC \cong \triangle FDE$; SSS Postulate
6. $\triangle RST \cong \triangle YXZ$; ASA Postulate
7. $\triangle PQR \cong \triangle KJH$; SAS Postulate
8. $\triangle ABC \cong \triangle DEC$; SAS Postulate
9. $\triangle URS \cong \triangle STU$; SSS Postulate
10. SAS;

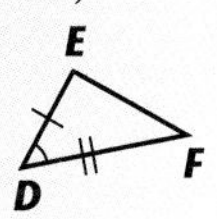

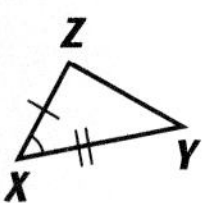

11. Yes; SAA Postulate
12. Yes; SAS Postulate
13. Yes; SAA Postulate
14.

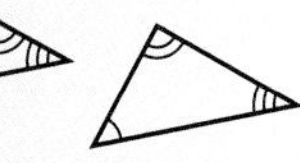

Ongoing Assessment

Self-Assessment Exercises 1–15 odd

Embedded Assessment Explore Step 6; Reflect 2; Exercises 6, 8, 16

Vocabulary
Practice/Skills
Review
Math Reasoning
Problem Solving
Challenge

4-2

Deductive Proof with Triangles

15.

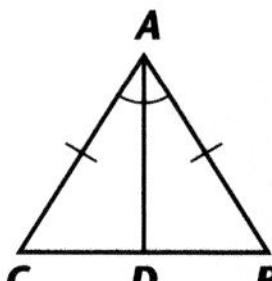

Given: $\overline{CA} \cong \overline{AB}$, D is on $\overline{BC}$, $\angle CAD \cong \angle DAB$
Prove: D is the midpoint of $\overline{BC}$

16. Yes; SSS Postulate

Look Ahead

17.

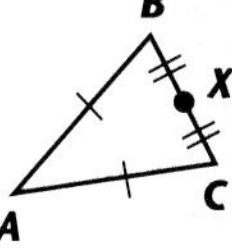

18. Right angles are congruent

19. Vertical angles are congruent

20. Supplements of congruent angles are congruent.

More Practice

21. $\triangle ABC \cong \triangle DEF$; SAS Postulate

22. $\triangle GHI \cong \triangle JKL$ or $\triangle LJK$; ASA Postulate

23. $\triangle ABC \cong \triangle DEC$; SAA Postulate

24. $\triangle ABC \cong \triangle DEC$; SAS Postulate

25. $\triangle ABC$ may not be congruent to $\triangle DEC$.

More Math Reasoning

26. (8, 5), (8, −1)

27. *Rewrite:* If two line segments are the two diagonals on a face of a cube, then they are congruent.
Draw:

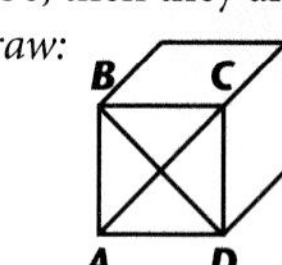

State: Given: $\overline{AC}$ and $\overline{BD}$ are the two diagonals on a face of a cube.
Prove: $\overline{AC} \cong \overline{BD}$.

SAS justifies the conclusion, $\triangle ABC \cong \triangle CDB$.

P **If possible, write a congruence statement for each pair of triangles. Then name the triangle-congruence postulate that applies. If the triangles are not congruent, say so.**

7.

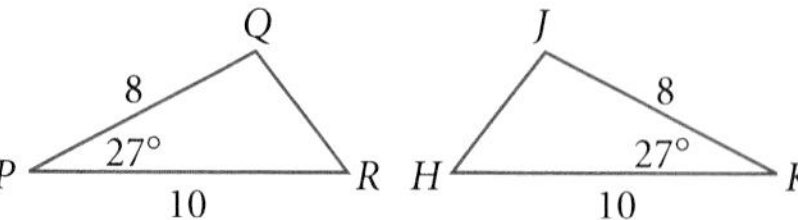

8.

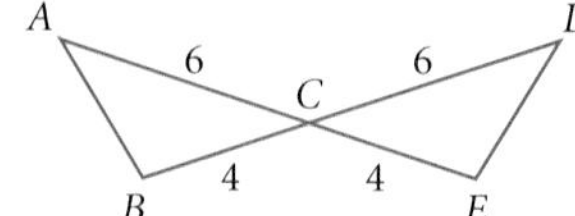

9.

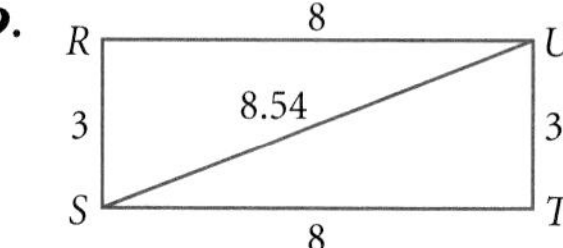

P **10.** If $\overline{DE} \cong \overline{XZ}$, $\overline{DF} \cong \overline{XY}$, and $\angle D \cong \angle X$, which triangle-congruence postulate (if any) can you use to show that $\triangle DEF \cong \triangle XZY$? Explain your answer with a sketch.

P **Under the conditions stated, are the triangles $\triangle GHJ$ and $\triangle MNO$ congruent? If so, write the congruence statement and name the congruence postulate that justifies it.**

11. $\overline{GH} \cong \overline{MN}$, $\angle J \cong \angle O$

12. $\overline{GH} \cong \overline{MN}$, $\overline{HJ} \cong \overline{NO}$

13. $\angle G \cong \angle M$, $\overline{HJ} \cong \overline{NO}$

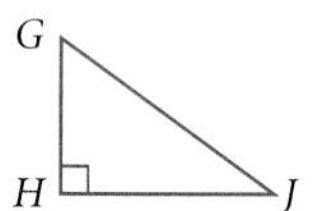

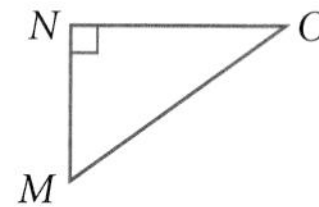

MR **14.** Show that there is no Angle-Angle-Angle (AAA) Postulate by drawing two noncongruent triangles with three pairs of congruent corresponding angles.

P **15.** For the following statement, *draw* and label a figure to represent the hypothesis, and *state* what is given and what is to be proved.

If $\overline{CA} \cong \overline{AB}$, D is on $\overline{BC}$, and $\angle CAD \cong \angle DAB$, then D is the midpoint of $\overline{BC}$.

MR **16.** **Peddle the Metal** Ehlers Steel Co. needs to sell some of its 20-in.-long steel tubing. Wheelright Bicycle Manufacturers have a bicycle frame design featuring one equilateral triangle, and the triangles in all of their bicycle frames must be congruent. Ehlers's sales representative calls up Wheelright and says, "If you buy our tubing, we will guarantee that all of the triangles you make out of it will be equilateral and exactly the same size! You'll never have to measure another angle again!" Assuming that all of Ehlers's tubes are exactly 20 in. long, is their guarantee valid? Why?

Key

- V Vocabulary
- P Practice/Skills
- R Review
- MR Math Reasoning
- PS Problem Solving
- C Challenge

LOOK AHEAD

17. *Draw* a figure and mark the given information.

Given: $\triangle ABC$ with $\overline{AB} \cong \overline{AC}$ and X the midpoint of $\overline{BC}$

Use the figure below to give a reason that justifies each statement.

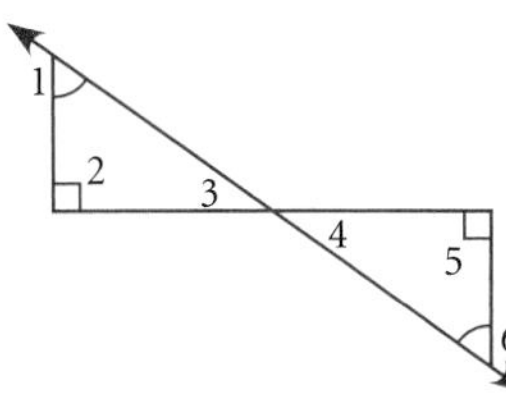

18. $\angle 2 \cong \angle 5$

19. $\angle 3 \cong \angle 4$

20. $\angle 1 \cong \angle 6$

MORE PRACTICE

If possible, write a congruence statement for each pair of triangles. Then name the triangle-congruence postulate that applies. If the triangles are not congruent, say so.

21.

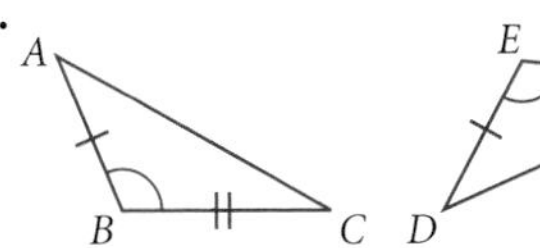

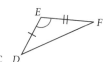

22.

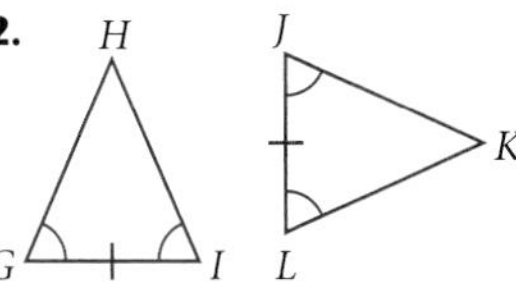

Under the conditions stated, are the triangles $\triangle ABC$ and $\triangle DEC$ congruent? If so, write the congruence statement, and name the congruence postulate that justifies it.

23. $\overline{AB} \cong \overline{DE}$, $\angle A \cong \angle D$

24. $\overline{AC} \cong \overline{DC}$, $\overline{BC} \cong \overline{EC}$

25. $\angle B \cong \angle E$, $\angle A \cong \angle D$

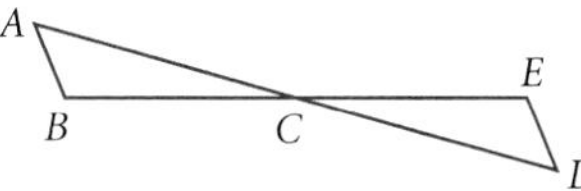

MORE MATH REASONING

26. Find all possible coordinates for point T so that $\triangle MNP \cong \triangle RST$ if the coordinates of the other points are $M(-2, 4)$, $N(1, 4)$, $P(1, 7)$, $R(5, 2)$, and $S(8, 2)$.

27. *Rewrite* the following statement, *draw* and label a figure that represents the statement, and *state* the Given and Prove.

Statement: The two diagonals on a face of a cube are congruent.

What triangle-congruence postulate justifies the conclusion to this statement?

Deductive Proof with Triangles

PART C At a Glance

Objective

To see different ways to organize a proof.

Development

First, students see an **Example** of a complete proof in paragraph form. Then, **What Do You Think?** illustrates two-column and flow-proof formats for the same proof.

In the **Explore,** students fill in reasons to complete a paragraph proof and then rewrite the proof in the other formats.

Key Terms

Flow proof, paragraph proof, two-column proof

First Five Minutes

Transparency FFM 4-2C

Briefly describe the *rewrite*, *draw*, and *state* steps for a deductive proof.
Rewrite—write conjecture in *if-then* form; *draw*—illustrate and label the hypothesis; *state*—write the *Given* and *Prove* using the labels from the figure.

Motivate

Ask...

- Why is it important to be able to prove conjectures?

MR, C **28.** Fill in the missing reasons in the flow chart to complete the following proof.

Given: M is the midpoint of $\overline{AB}$, $\angle A$ is a right angle, and $\angle B$ is a right angle.

Prove: $\triangle AMC \cong \triangle BMD$

Proof:

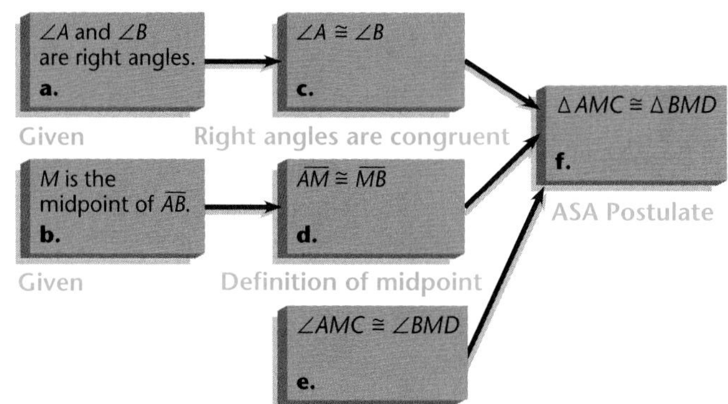

Given — Right angles are congruent — Given — Definition of midpoint — Vertical angles are congruent — ASA Postulate

4-2 PART C Organizing a Proof

← CONNECT → ***You've seen many situations in which you need to organize facts to draw a correct conclusion. Now you will review our five-step process for deductive proof and learn about ways to write out a proof.***

A proof is a sequence of true facts (statements) placed in a logical order. To convince others that a proof is valid, we supply a reason to justify each statement. The reasons that can be used for justifying statements are the following:

- the hypothesis (given information) and information that can be assumed from a figure
- definitions
- postulates and algebraic properties
- theorems that have already been proved

Key

- V Vocabulary
- P Practice/Skills
- R Review
- MR Math Reasoning
- PS Problem Solving
- C Challenge

You've already been introduced to five steps for preparing a proof: *rewrite, draw, state, plan,* and *demonstrate.* In Chapters 5 and 6, you will gradually become more familiar with the last two steps of this process. In the rest of this chapter, you will be completing proofs that have been started for you.

In the following example, we illustrate a complete proof so that you can become more familiar with how one looks.

EXAMPLE

Prove the following: If $\overline{AC}$ and $\overline{BD}$ bisect each other at *M*, then $\triangle AMB \cong \triangle CMD$.

Rewrite: (The statement is already in if-then form.)

Draw:

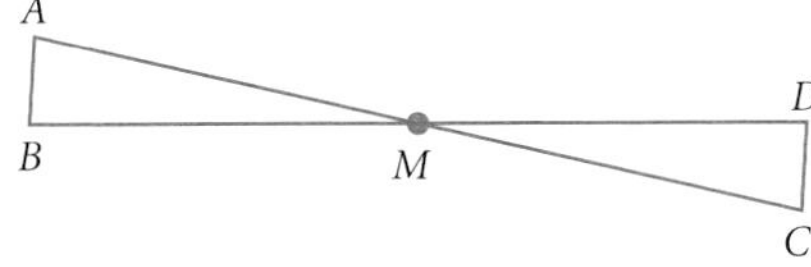

State: *Given:* $\overline{AC}$ and $\overline{BD}$ bisect each other at *M*.

Prove: $\triangle AMB \cong \triangle CMD$

Plan: Bisect means "cut in half," so we have two pairs of congruent segments crossing at *M*. Their included angles are vertical angles, so the angles are congruent. We can use the SAS Postulate to show that the triangles are congruent.

Proof: We are given that $\overline{AC}$ and $\overline{BD}$ bisect each other at *M*. Therefore, $\overline{AM} \cong \overline{MC}$, and $\overline{BM} \cong \overline{MD}$, by the definition of *bisect*. $\angle AMB \cong \angle CMD$ because vertical angles are congruent. Therefore, $\triangle AMB \cong \triangle CMD$ by the SAS Postulate.

You will become familiar with three different formats for demonstrating a deductive proof. In the example, we used paragraph form. This is one of the most common ways to write out a proof.

A two-column format can also be used to organize your thinking. In two-column format, statements appear in a column on the left and the reasons are in a column on the right. We can also write a proof in flow-proof format. In this format, statements and reasons are given in boxes and linked by arrows.

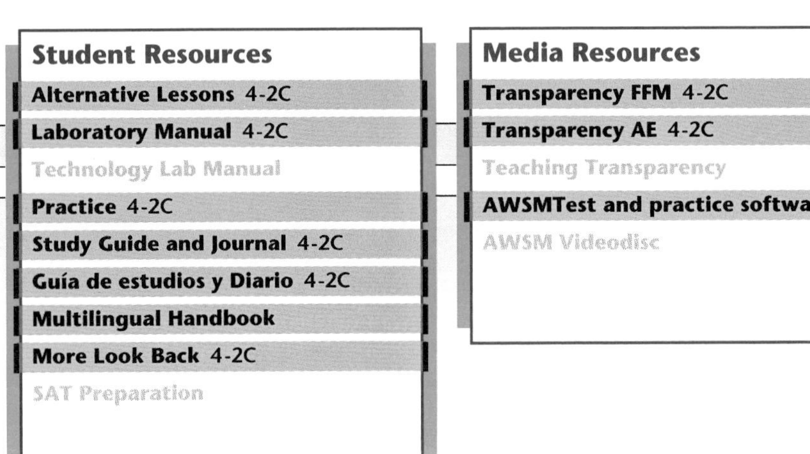

Student Resources

- Alternative Lessons 4-2C
- Laboratory Manual 4-2C
- Technology Lab Manual
- Practice 4-2C
- Study Guide and Journal 4-2C
- Guía de estudios y Diario 4-2C
- Multilingual Handbook
- More Look Back 4-2C
- SAT Preparation

Media Resources

- Transparency FFM 4-2C
- Transparency AE 4-2C
- Teaching Transparency
- AWSMTest and practice software
- AWSM Videodisc

ALTERNATE EXAMPLE

Prove the following:

If *m* and *n* are both perpendicular to transversal *t*, then $m \parallel n$.

Rewrite: (The statement is already in *if-then* form.)

Draw:

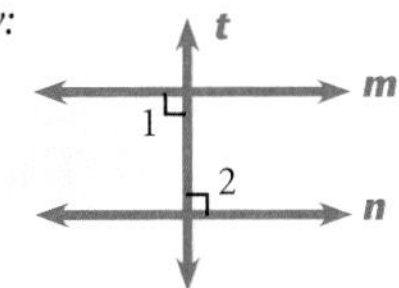

State: Given: m and *n* are both perpendicular to transversal *t*.

Prove: $m \parallel n$

Plan: Show that $\angle 1$ and $\angle 2$ are congruent; then show that $m \parallel n$ because alternate interior angles are congruent.

Demonstrate: We are given that $m \perp t$ and $n \perp t$. $\angle 1$ and $\angle 2$ are right angles because perpendicular lines form four right angles, so $\angle 1 \cong \angle 2$ because all right angles are congruent. $\angle 1$ and $\angle 2$ are alternate interior angles for *m* and *n*, so $m \parallel n$ because a pair of alternate interior angles are congruent.

4-2

Deductive Proof with Triangles

WHAT DO YOU THINK?

Illustrates the proof from the **Example** in two-column and flow-proof formats.

Note: Students may believe that, although there are many different ways to show a proof, there is only one correct sequence of steps. You may want to show them that the proof in two-column form could have been correctly started with Step 4.

Possible Answer

1. Answers will differ. Some students may find the paragraph format easiest because it is most like natural language; some may prefer the two-column form because its linear format is an easy structure to read; some may like the flow proof because connections between steps are clearly shown.

EXPLORE

Convince Me!

Recommended group size: 2

The Point

To fill in missing reasons in a paragraph proof, and to present the proofs in each of the other two formats as well.

Look and Listen...

- For students who are having difficulty identifying some of the reasons. You may need to prompt them with appropriate questions, for example, "What do you know about supplements of congruent angles?"
- For students who do not understand how to show the dependence of steps, especially in the flow-proof format.

WHAT DO YOU THINK?

Write out the *demonstrate* step for the preceding proof, using the format you think is clearest.

Atiba thinks . . .

I like the flow-proof format. I think it's the best way to show where each step comes from.

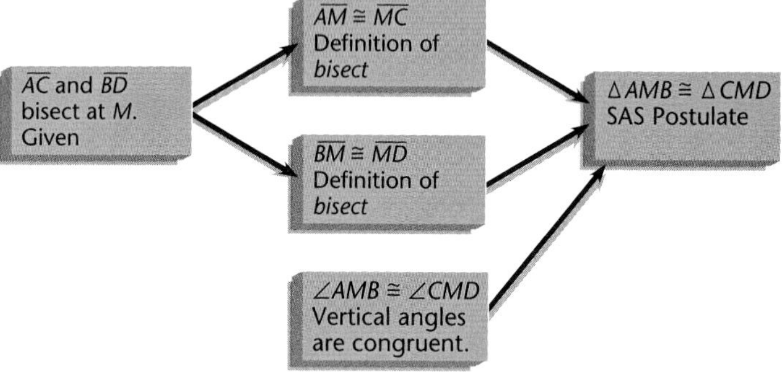

Heather thinks . . .

I'll use the two-column format since it's easy to read and clearly shows the reason for each statement.

Statements	Reasons
1. $\overline{AC}$ and $\overline{BD}$ bisect each other at M.	**1.** Given
2. $\overline{AM} \cong \overline{MC}$	**2.** Definition of *bisect*
3. $\overline{BM} \cong \overline{MD}$	**3.** Definition of *bisect*
4. $\angle AMB \cong \angle CMD$	**4.** Vertical angles are congruent.
5. $\triangle AMB \cong \triangle CMD$	**5.** SAS Postulate

CONSIDER

1. Which of the three proof formats presented do you find the easiest to understand? Why?

Research Note

Harbeck and Summa investigated the effect of the flow proof format versus the two-column proof format....[T]here were no significant differences in achievement or critical thinking ability. Van Akin studied the paragraph format versus the two-column format and also discovered no significant difference in achievement on geometry facts or ability to reason logically. (Phares G. O'Daffer and Bruce Thornquist, "Critical Thinking, Mathematical Reasoning, and Proof," *Research Ideas for the Classroom: High School Mathematics,* NCTM Research Interpretation Project, Patricia S. Wilson, ed., p. 52. © 1993 NCTM.)

EXPLORE: CONVINCE ME!

1. Copy the figure and mark the congruent parts. Then fill in the missing reasons to complete the paragraph proof below.

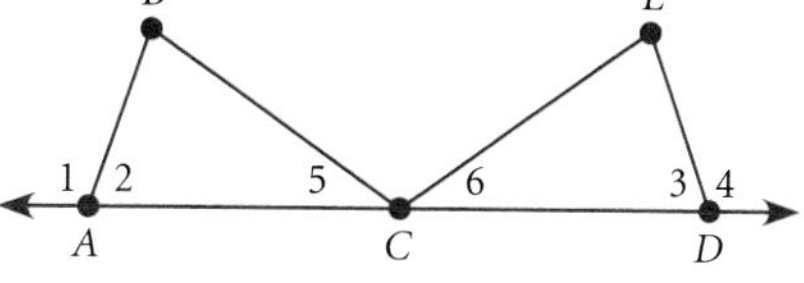

Given: $\angle 1 \cong \angle 4$
$\overline{AC} \cong \overline{CD}$
$\angle 5 \cong \angle 6$

Prove: $\triangle ABC \cong \triangle DEC$

Proof: $\angle 1$ and $\angle 2$ form a linear pair, as do $\angle 3$ and $\angle 4$. Thus, $\angle 1$ is supplementary to $\angle 2$, and $\angle 3$ is supplementary to $\angle 4$ because **a.** ____. The **b.** ____ tells us that $\angle 1 \cong \angle 4$. Therefore, $\angle 2 \cong \angle 3$ because **c.** ____. We also know that $\overline{AC} \cong \overline{CD}$, and $\angle 5 \cong \angle 6$ from **d.** ____. Therefore, we can conclude that $\triangle ABC \cong \triangle DEC$ by the **e.** ____ Postulate.

2. Put your paragraph proof into two-column form.

3. Show the same proof as a flow proof.

TRY IT

a. Complete the following two-column proof by choosing a reason for each statement from the Scrambled Reasons' list.

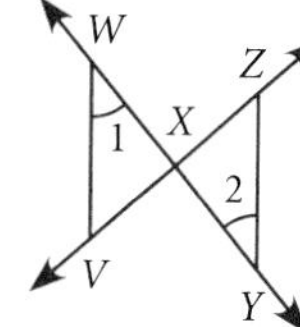

Given: X is the midpoint of $\overline{VZ}$.
$\angle 1 \cong \angle 2$

Prove: $\triangle VXW \cong \triangle ZXY$

Proof:

Statements	Reasons	Scrambled Reasons
1. X is the midpoint of $\overline{VZ}$.	**1.**	**a.** Supplements of congruent angles are congruent.
2. $\overline{VX} \cong \overline{XZ}$	**2.**	**b.** Given
3. $\angle WXV \cong \angle YXZ$	**3.**	**c.** SAA Postulate
4. $\angle 1 \cong \angle 2$	**4.**	**d.** Definition of *midpoint*
5. $\triangle VXW \cong \triangle ZXY$	**5.**	**e.** Vertical angles are congruent.
		f. Right angles are congruent.

1. (b), 2. (d), 3. (e), 4. (b), 5. (c)

Ask...

- What facts does the conclusion that $\angle 2 \cong \angle 3$ depend on? How do you show this in a flow proof? a two-column proof?

For Groups That Finish Early

Change the *Given* information so that the triangles could be proved congruent by a different congruence postulate.

Follow Up

Have students share their reasons to justify the statements in Step 1. Then have groups present the proof in the other formats.

Possible Answers

1. a. The angles in a linear pair are supplementary.

b. Given information.

c. Supplements of congruent angles are congruent.

d. Given information.

e. ASA

2.

Statements	Reasons
1. $\angle 1$ and $\angle 2$ are supp.; $\angle 3$ and $\angle 4$ are supp.	1. Angles in a linear pair are supplementary.
2. $\angle 1 \cong \angle 4$	2. Given
3. $\angle 2 \cong \angle 3$	3. Supplements of congruent angles are congruent.
4. $\overline{AC} \cong \overline{CD}$	4. Given
5. $\angle 5 \cong \angle 6$	5. Given
6. $\triangle ABC \cong \triangle DEC$	6. ASA Postulate

3. See Additional Answers p. T284.

4-2

Deductive Proof with Triangles

Journal

Reflect 1 and 2 and **Exercise** 3 are suitable for journal entries.

REFLECT

Possible Answers

1. Paragraph proofs sound more natural but may not look well organized. Flow proofs show which steps follow from others but may look confusing. Two-column proofs are easy to set up but may not show the flow of the proof well.
2. It gives students a consistent way to organize their thoughts; it may be faster to grade.

Part C Exercises

Exercise Notes

Core

3. Shows that triangles are stable, but figures with a greater number of sides are not. This explains the triangular supports seen in many structures. You may want to have students actually construct these figures with sticks and fasteners and contrast their stability.

   Extension: Which congruence postulate explains why these triangles are rigid? **SSS; triangles with fixed side lengths can have only one shape.**

6. Includes coordinates in a triangle-congruence justification. This previews coordinate proof in 6-2.

More Math Reasoning

19. and 20. Students identify missing information needed to be able to do a proof.

REFLECT

1. What are some advantages and disadvantages of each of the three proof formats you have worked with?
2. Although most proofs written by mathematicians are in paragraph form, modern geometry books have primarily used the two-column format. Why do you think this has been the case?

Exercises

CORE

P **1. Getting Started** Make a list of everything you know that must be true about the figure at the right.

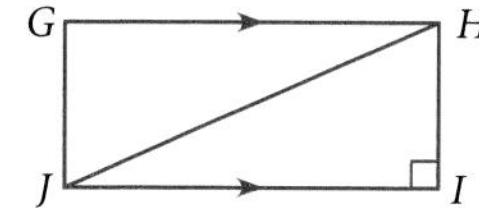

P **2.** Rewrite the following paragraph proof in two-column format.

Given: $\triangle ABC$ and $\triangle XYZ$ are right triangles with right angles $\angle A$ and $\angle X$. $\overline{AB} \cong \overline{XY}$, and $\angle B \cong \angle Y$.

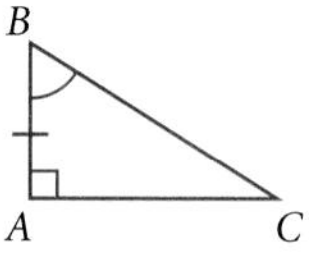

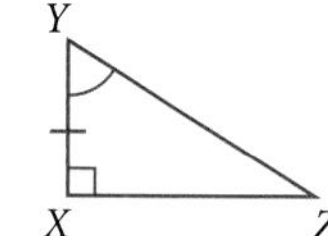

Prove: $\triangle ABC \cong \triangle XYZ$

Proof: The given information tells us that $\overline{AB} \cong \overline{XY}$ and that $\angle A$ and $\angle X$ are right angles. $\angle A \cong \angle X$ because all right angles are congruent. We are also given that $\angle B \cong \angle Y$. Therefore, $\triangle ABC \cong \triangle XYZ$ by the ASA Postulate.

MR **3. Brace Yourself** If a rectangle is made of wooden rods and hinges, it can collapse as shown.

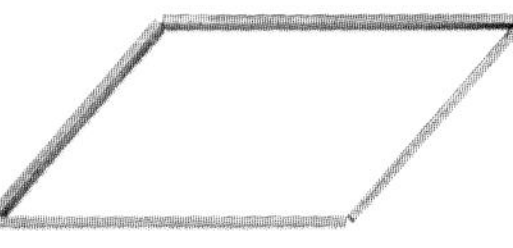

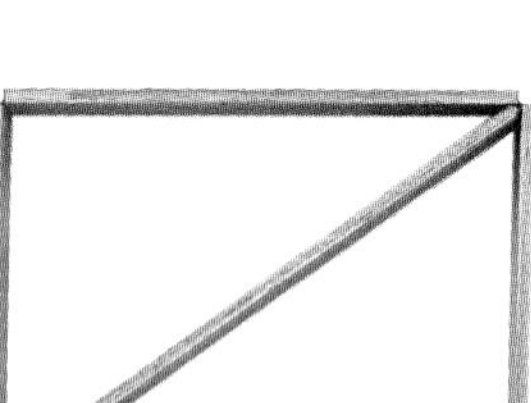

However, adding another wooden rod to form the diagonal of the figure makes the rectangle stable. What is true about the stability of triangles that is not true about figures with a greater number of sides? Why are triangular supports often seen in bridges, towers, and other large structures?

Key

- V Vocabulary
- P Practice/Skills
- R Review
- MR Math Reasoning
- PS Problem Solving
- C Challenge

4. a. Complete the following proof by choosing a reason for each statement from the Scrambled Reasons' list.

Given: F is the midpoint of $\overline{DH}$ and $\overline{EG}$.

Prove: $\triangle DFE \cong \triangle HFG$

Proof:

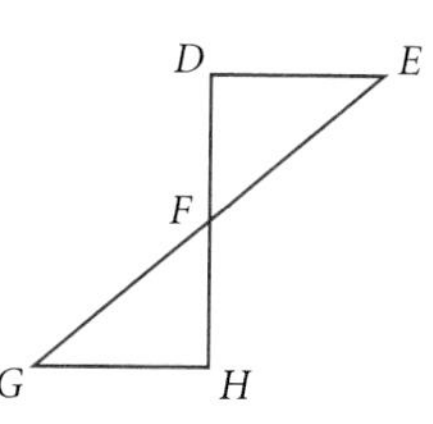

Statements	Reasons	Scrambled Reasons
1. F is the midpoint of $\overline{DH}$ and $\overline{EG}$.	**1.**	**a.** Vertical angles are congruent.
2. $\overline{DF} \cong \overline{HF}$	**2.**	**b.** Definition of *midpoint*
3. $\overline{EF} \cong \overline{GF}$	**3.**	**c.** Given
4. $\angle HFG \cong \angle DFE$	**4.**	**d.** SAS Postulate
5. $\triangle DFE \cong \triangle HFG$	**5.**	

b. Rewrite the proof in flow-proof format.
c. Which format do you think works better for this proof? Justify your choice.

5. Fill in the missing statements and reasons to complete the following two-column proof.

Given: $\overline{PQ} \parallel \overline{RS}$, $\overline{PQ} \cong \overline{RS}$

Prove: $\triangle PQS \cong \triangle RSQ$

Proof:

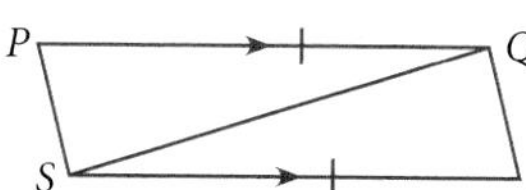

Statements	Reasons
1. $\overline{PQ} \cong \overline{RS}$	**1.**
2. $\overline{SQ} \cong \overline{SQ}$	**2.** Reflexive Property
3. $\overline{PQ} \parallel \overline{RS}$	**3.**
4.	**4.** If two parallel lines are cut by a transversal, the alternate interior angles are congruent.
5.	**5.** SAS Postulate

6. The vertices of triangles $\triangle ABC$ and $\triangle DEF$ are $A(2, 3)$, $B(5, 7)$, $C(8, -2)$, $D(-1, 3)$, $E(3, 6)$, and $F(-6, 9)$. Can you conclude that $\triangle ABC \cong \triangle DEF$? Justify your answer.

Ongoing Assessment

Self-Assessment Exercises 1, 4, 5

Embedded Assessment Reflect 1; Exercises 2, 3, 7

Exercise Answers

Core

1. Possible answer: $\overline{GH} \parallel \overline{JI}$, $\angle GHJ \cong \angle IJH$, $\angle HIJ$ is a right angle, $m\angle HGJ + m\angle GJI = 180°$, $\angle GHI$ is a right angle.

2.

Statements	Reasons
1. $\overline{AB} \cong \overline{XY}$	**1.** Given
2. $\angle A \cong \angle X$	**2.** Right angles are congruent
3. $\angle B \cong \angle Y$	**3.** Given
4. $\triangle ABC \cong \triangle XYZ$	**4.** ASA Postulate

3. Possible answer: The lengths of its sides determine the shape of the triangle. This is not true about figures with a greater number of sides. Triangular supports are often seen because they are stable.

4. a. 1. (c), 2. (b), 3. (b), 4. (a), 5. (d)

b. See Additional Answers p. T284.

c. Check students' answers.

5. Reason 1: Given
Reason 3: Given
Statement 4: $\angle PQS \cong \angle RSQ$
Statement 5: $\triangle PQS \cong \triangle RSQ$

6. Yes; $AB = DE = 5$, $BC = EF = 3\sqrt{10}$, $CA = FD = \sqrt{61}$, so by the SSS Postulate, $\triangle ABC \cong \triangle DEF$

Algebra | Functions | Discrete Math | Probability | Data/Statistics

Deductive Proof with Triangles

7. Reason 1: Given
Reason 2: If two parallel lines are cut by a transversal, the alternate interior angles are congruent.
Reason 3: Given
Reason 4: If two parallel lines are cut by a transversal, the alternate interior angles are congruent.
Statement 5: $\overline{JL} \cong \overline{KM}$
Statement 6: $\triangle JLK \cong \triangle MKL$
Reason 6: SAA Postulate

Look Back

11. 109° **12.** 153°

13. 123°

More Practice

15. Reason 1. Given
Reason 2. Given
Reason 3. Given
Reason 4. SSS Postulate

16. 1. (c), 2. (e), 3. (f), 4. (c), 5. (d), 6. (b), 7. (a)

More Math Reasoning

17. a.

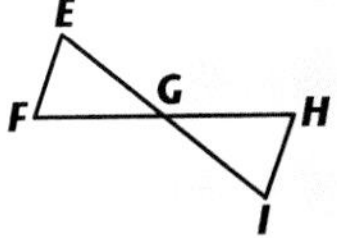

b. $\overline{EG} \cong \overline{GI}$ and $\overline{FG} \cong \overline{GH}$ by the definition of *midpoint.* $\angle EGF \cong \angle IGH$ because vertical angles are congruent. Thus, $\triangle EFG \cong \triangle IHG$ by SAS.

18. a. $x = 30$

b. $m\angle R = m\angle U = 80°$, $RS = UV = 70$, $RT = UW = 36$

c. $\triangle RST \cong \triangle UVW$ by the SAS Postulate.

19. a. Possible answer: X bisects $\overline{VY}$ and $\overline{WZ}$.

b. Possible answer: Show that $\overline{WX} \cong \overline{ZX}$, $\overline{YX} \cong \overline{VX}$ and $\angle WXV \cong \angle ZXY$ to show that $\triangle WXV \cong \triangle ZXY$ by SAS Postulate.

20. a. Possible answer: $\overline{WZ} \cong \overline{YV}$

b. Possible answer: Show that $\overline{WV} \cong \overline{YZ}$ and then prove that $\triangle VZY \cong \triangle ZVW$ by the SSS Postulate.

P, MR **7.** Fill in the missing statements and reasons to complete the following proof.

Given: $\overline{JK} \parallel \overline{LM}$
$\overline{JL} \parallel \overline{KM}$
$\overline{JL} \cong \overline{KM}$

Prove: $\triangle JLK \cong \triangle MKL$

Proof:

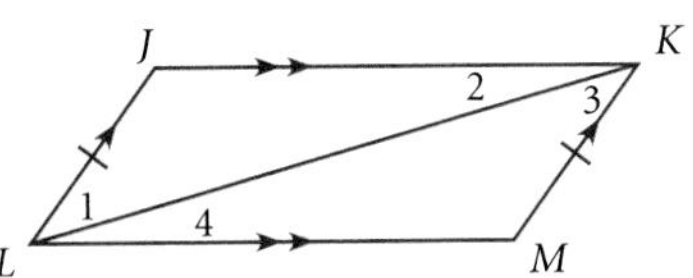

Statements	Reasons
1. $\overline{JK} \parallel \overline{LM}$	1.
2. $\angle 2 \cong \angle 4$	2.
3. $\overline{JL} \parallel \overline{KM}$	3.
4. $\angle 1 \cong \angle 3$	4.
5.	5. Given
6.	6.

LOOK BACK

R **8.** Name all points on the grid with a bearing of 090 from point I. [3-1] J, K, L

R **9.** Name all points on the grid whose bearing from point D is greater than 180. [3-1] A, B, C, E, F, G, I, J, K, M, N, O

R **10.** What is the probability that a grid point randomly chosen from points A through O has a bearing greater than 315 from point P? [3-1] $\frac{1}{5}$

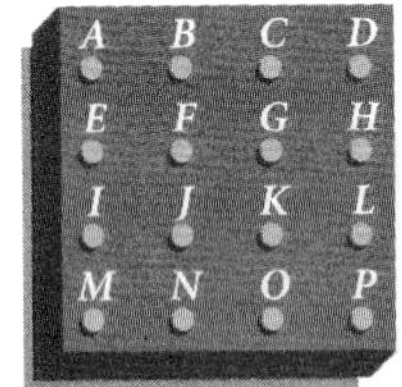

R **Complete the table for the triangle shown. [4-1]**

	$m\angle 1$	$m\angle 2$	$m\angle 3$
11.	146°		37°
12.		81°	72°
13.	161°	38°	

R **14.** If $30° < m\angle 6 < 45°$, what measures are possible for $\angle 5$? [3-3] $135° < m\angle 5 < 150°$

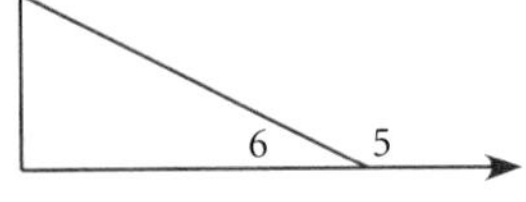

Key

V Vocabulary
P Practice/Skills
R Review
MR Math Reasoning
PS Problem Solving
C Challenge

MORE PRACTICE

15. Fill in the missing reasons to complete the following proof.

Given: $\overline{AC} \cong \overline{ED}$
$\overline{AB} \cong \overline{EF}$
$\overline{BC} \cong \overline{FD}$

Prove: $\triangle ABC \cong \triangle EFD$

Proof:

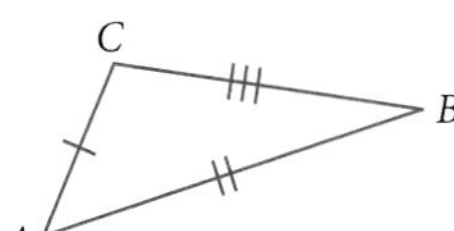

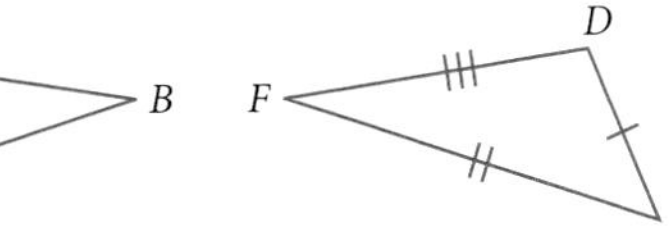

Statements	Reasons
1. $\overline{AC} \cong \overline{ED}$	**1.**
2. $\overline{AB} \cong \overline{EF}$	**2.**
3. $\overline{BC} \cong \overline{FD}$	**3.**
4. $\triangle ABC \cong \triangle EFD$	**4.**

16. Complete the following proof by choosing a reason for each statement from the Scrambled Reasons' list.

Given: J is the midpoint of $\overline{HL}$.
$\angle 1 \cong \angle 2$

Prove: $\triangle HIJ \cong \triangle LKJ$

Proof:

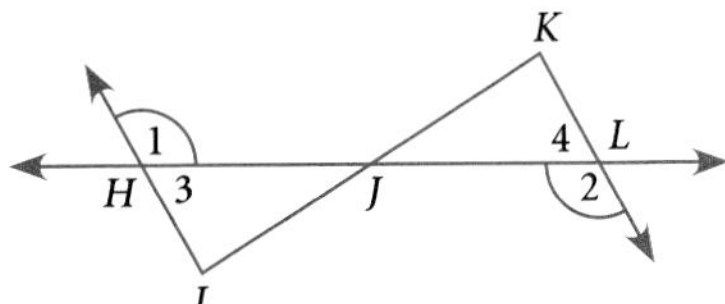

Statements	Reasons	Scrambled Reasons
1. J is the midpoint of $\overline{HL}$.	**1.**	**a.** ASA Postulate
2. $\overline{HJ} \cong \overline{JL}$	**2.**	**b.** Vertical angles are congruent.
3. $\angle 1$ and $\angle 3$ are supplementary. $\angle 2$ and $\angle 4$ are supplementary.	**3.**	**c.** Given
		d. Supplements of congruent angles are congruent.
4. $\angle 1 \cong \angle 2$	**4.**	**e.** Definition of *midpoint*
5. $\angle 3 \cong \angle 4$	**5.**	**f.** Linear pairs are supplementary.
6. $\angle HJI \cong \angle LJK$	**6.**	
7. $\triangle HIJ \cong \triangle LKJ$	**7.**	

Deductive Proof with Triangles

Part D At a Glance

Objective

To show that sides or angles are congruent because they are corresponding parts of congruent triangles.

Development

In the **Explore,** students unscramble statements and write reasons for a proof. The final step in the proof shows that two corresponding sides of the triangles are congruent because the triangles have been proven congruent.

The reflexive, symmetric, and transitive properties of congruence are presented. Students use the reflexive property to prove a shared side congruent in a **Try It.**

Key Terms

Reflexive, symmetric, transitive

First Five Minutes

Transparency FFM 4-2D

Suppose that $\angle J \cong \angle P$, $\angle K \cong \angle Q$, and $\overline{JL} \cong \overline{PS}$. Sketch triangles satisfying these conditions, and write and justify a congruence statement. Then list other parts of the triangles that must also be congruent.

Motivate

Ask...

- How many pairs of congruent parts are needed to prove two triangles congruent?
- If you know that two triangles are congruent, how many pairs of congruent parts can you list?

MORE MATH REASONING

MR, C **17.** *Given:* G is the midpoint of $\overline{FH}$, and G is the midpoint of $\overline{EI}$. E is not on $\overleftrightarrow{FH}$.

Prove: $\triangle EFG \cong \triangle IHG$

a. *Draw* and label a figure for this proof.
b. Develop a *plan* for the proof. Then *demonstrate* the proof using any format.

MR **18.** Consider triangles $\triangle RST$ and $\triangle UVW$, where $\angle R \cong \angle U$, $m\angle R = (2x + 20)°$, $m\angle U = (x + 50)°$, $RS = 2x + 10$, $UV = 3x - 20$, $RT = x + 6$, and $UW = 2x - 24$.
a. Determine the value of x.
b. Determine the measures of the given sides and angles.
c. Explain why $\triangle RST$ is or is not congruent to $\triangle UVW$.

MR **Use the figure at the right for Exercises 19 and 20.**

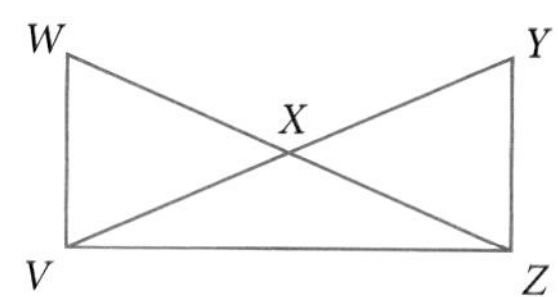

19. a. What additional information do you need to be able to prove $\triangle WXV \cong \triangle ZXY$?
b. Assuming this information, write a *plan* for the proof.

20. a. What additional information do you need to be able to prove $\triangle VZY \cong \triangle ZVW$?
b. Assuming this information, write a *plan* for the proof.

4-2 PART D Corresponding Parts

← CONNECT → ***You know that three pairs of congruent parts may be enough to prove two triangles congruent and that the triangles have six pairs of corresponding parts. Now you will connect these ideas to get "bonus information" when proving two triangles congruent.***

Congruent triangles can be found in everyday structures ranging from skyscrapers to fences. They are also useful in mathematics. In fact, proving that two triangles are congruent does not have to be the final step in a proof. As you will see, showing that triangles are congruent can be an important stepping stone to proving other things.

Key

- V Vocabulary
- P Practice/Skills
- R Review
- MR Math Reasoning
- PS Problem Solving
- C Challenge

Tips from Teachers

This might be a good place to review the problem-solving technique of working backward, since it is often helpful when doing a proof. The following problem can be used to illustrate this technique. Three customers in succession enter a fruit store and buy half of the apples in the store plus two additional apples. After these sales, one apple remains. How many were there at the start? 36

EXPLORE: ONE STEP BEYOND

1. Rearrange the statements for the following proof so that they form a logical sequence. Then write a reason to justify each statement.

Problem-Solving Tip

It may be helpful to work backwards.

Given: $\overline{AE} \cong \overline{CE}$
$\angle ABE \cong \angle CDE$
$\angle AEB$ and $\angle CED$ are right angles.

Prove: $\overline{AB} \cong \overline{CD}$

Statements:

a. $\angle AEB \cong \angle CED$ **b.** $\overline{AE} \cong \overline{CE}$ **c.** $\angle AEB$ and $\angle CED$ are right angles.
d. $\angle ABE \cong \angle CDE$ **e.** $\overline{AB} \cong \overline{CD}$ **f.** $\triangle AEB \cong \triangle CED$

2. Explain how you used the next-to-last step of the proof to get to the last step. What reason justified the final step in the proof, and why did it work?
3. Compare your proof with that of a classmate. If there are differences, decide whether both versions of the proof are correct or whether you need to correct one or both of your proofs.

If you can prove that two triangles are congruent (usually by showing that three pairs of corresponding parts are congruent), you know from the definition of congruence that all six pairs of corresponding sides and angles are congruent.

Corresponding **P**arts of **C**ongruent **T**riangles are **C**ongruent.

This fact is used so often that you may find it helpful to refer to it as CPCTC. Notice how CPCTC is used in the last step of the following flow proof.

Student Resources
- Alternative Lessons 4-2D
- Laboratory Manual 4-2D
- Technology Lab Manual
- Practice 4-2D
- Study Guide and Journal 4-2D
- Guía de estudios y Diario 4-2D
- Multilingual Handbook
- More Look Ahead 4-2D
- SAT Preparation

Media Resources
- Transparency FFM 4-2D
- Transparency AE 4-2D
- Teaching Transparency
- AWSMTest and practice software
- AWSM Videodisc

EXPLORE

One Step Beyond

Recommended group size: 2

The Point

To rearrange statements and fill in reasons for a proof whose last step involves showing that two sides of a triangle are congruent because they are corresponding parts of congruent triangles.

Look and Listen...
- For students who think that the final step of the proof must show that two triangles are congruent.

Ask...
- What are you trying to prove?

For Groups That Finish Early

Rewrite the proof in flow-proof or two-column format.

Follow Up

Ask students to present their completed proof. You may want to emphasize that proving triangles congruent allows you to conclude that their corresponding parts are congruent.

Possible Answers

1. c. $\angle AEB$ and $\angle CED$ are right angles; given.

a. $\angle AEB \cong \angle CED$; right angles are congruent.

b. $\overline{AE} \cong \overline{CE}$; given.

d. $\angle ABE \cong \angle CDE$; given.

f. $\triangle AEB \cong \triangle CED$; SAA.

e. $\overline{AB} \cong \overline{CD}$; definition of *congruent triangles.*

2. By proving the triangles congruent, we can conclude that each pair of corresponding sides (and angles) is congruent by the definition of congruent triangles.

Deductive Proof with Triangles

ALTERNATE EXAMPLE

Given: $\triangle ABC$ is isosceles, with $\overline{AB} \cong \overline{CB}$.

D is the midpoint of $\overline{AC}$.

Prove: $\angle A \cong \angle C$

Proof: We are given that D is the midpoint of $\overline{AC}$, so $\overline{AD} \cong \overline{DC}$ by the definition of *midpoint*. $\overline{AB} \cong \overline{CB}$ from given information. $\overline{BD} \cong \overline{BD}$ because a segment must have the same length as itself (the Reflexive Property). Therefore, $\triangle ABD \cong \triangle CBD$ by SSS, and $\angle A \cong \angle C$ by CPCTC.

Note: This **Alternate Example** is a preview of the Isosceles Triangle Theorem, which is developed in 4-3 Part A.

EXAMPLE

Given: $\overline{XY} \cong \overline{ZW}$
$\overline{YZ} \cong \overline{WX}$

Prove: $\overleftrightarrow{WX} \parallel \overleftrightarrow{YZ}$

Proof:

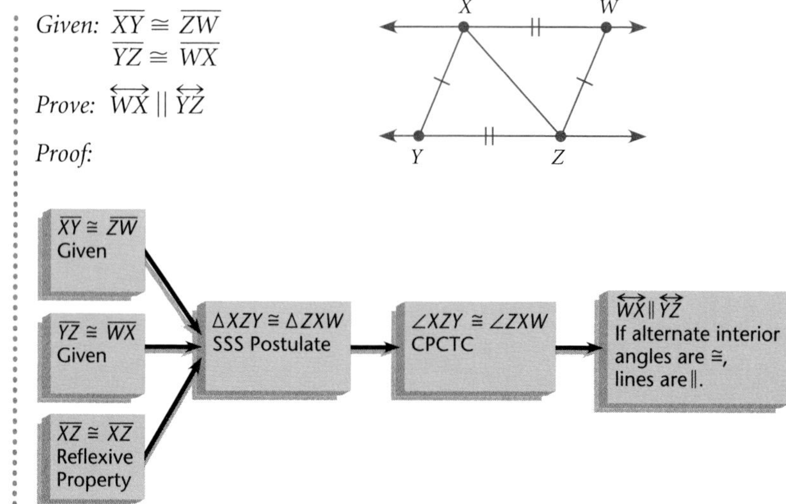

In this example, segment $\overline{XZ}$ is a part of both triangles that we want to prove congruent. To show that a side (or angle) shared by two triangles is congruent to itself, we use the Reflexive Property for congruence. This property, which is related to the Reflexive Property in algebra, says that a figure is congruent to itself. We can also use the Symmetric and Transitive Properties for congruence in proofs.

Properties of Congruence	Examples
• Reflexive Property	$\overline{AB} \cong \overline{AB}$
• Symmetric Property	If $\angle 1 \cong \angle 2$, then $\angle 2 \cong \angle 1$.
• Transitive Property	If $\overline{WX} \cong \overline{XY}$ and $\overline{XY} \cong \overline{YZ}$, then $\overline{WX} \cong \overline{YZ}$.

TRY IT

a. In the figure at the right, how can you prove that the triangles are congruent by using the SAS Postulate?

b. Which additional pairs of sides and angles could you then prove congruent by using CPCTC?

a. Given: $\overline{ST} \cong \overline{UT}$, and $\angle VTS \cong \angle VTU$ because they are right angles. $\overline{VT} \cong \overline{VT}$ by the Reflexive Property. Now use the SAS Postulate.

b. $\overline{SV}$ and $\overline{UV}$, $\angle VST$ and $\angle VUT$, $\angle SVT$ and $\angle UVT$

REFLECT

1. Do you think the definition of congruent triangles is often used to prove that two triangles are congruent? Why or why not?
2. Is $\triangle ABC \cong \triangle ABC$? Explain your reasoning.

Exercises

CORE

1. **Getting Started** **a.** Write a triangle-congruence statement for the triangles shown in the figure at the right. $\triangle ABC \cong \triangle RST$

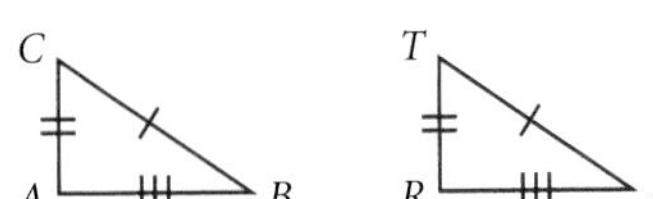

   b. Which congruence postulate can be used to prove the triangles are congruent? SSS Postulate

   c. Once you prove the triangles are congruent, how can you show that $\angle C \cong \angle T$? Use CPCTC

Determine whether each statement is true or false. If the statement is false, change the underlined word or phrase to make it true.

2. The statement $\overline{RS} \cong \overline{RS}$ can be justified by the <u>Symmetric</u> Property. F; Reflexive

3. If $\overline{VW} \cong \overline{XY}$, then $\overline{XY} \cong \overline{VW}$ by the <u>Transitive</u> Property. F; Symmetric

4. Fill in the missing reasons to complete the following proof.

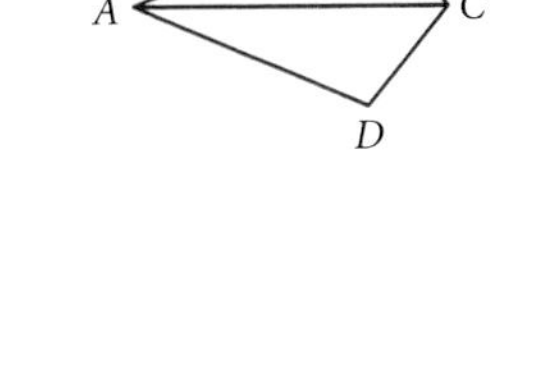

Given: $\overrightarrow{AC}$ bisects $\angle BAD$, and $\overrightarrow{CA}$ bisects $\angle BCD$.

Prove: $\overline{AD} \cong \overline{AB}$

Proof:

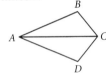

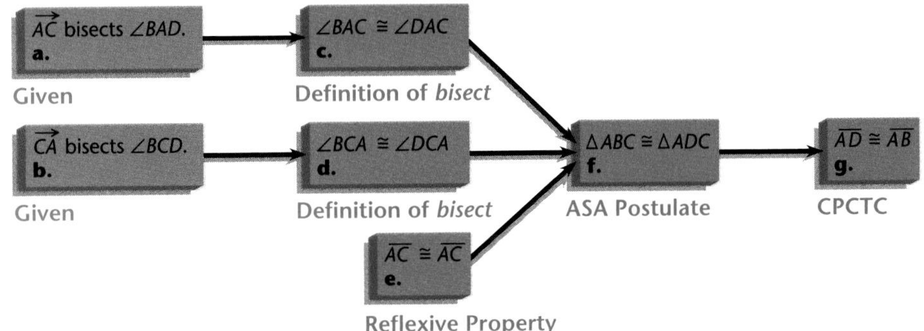

Journal

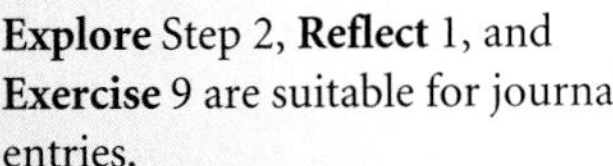

Explore Step 2, **Reflect** 1, and **Exercise** 9 are suitable for journal entries.

REFLECT

Possible Answers

1. No. It requires the use of six pairs of congruent parts, and the postulates use only three.
2. Yes. One justification: Each side is congruent to itself by the Reflexive Property, so the triangles are congruent by SSS.

Part D Exercises

Exercise Notes

Core

9. Asks students to explain a solution method for a real-world problem. The solution uses the idea of corresponding parts.

10. Students develop the construction for a perpendicular to a point on a given line. You may want to review this construction with the class when going over homework.

Look Ahead

12–16. Review terminology needed in 4-3.

17–19. Review the idea of perimeter. Students work with perimeter in 5-1 Part A.

More Math Reasoning

22. Students use their knowledge of geometry to translate a textbook page written in a fictitious language. You might use this exercise to lead a class discussion of mathematics as a universal language. You might also want to encourage students to bring in textbooks in different languages and see if the class can translate passages from those texts.

y

Vocabulary
Practice/Skills
Review
R Math Reasoning
; Problem Solving
Challenge

Ongoing Assessment

Self-Assessment Exercises 1–7 odd, 8, 11

Embedded Assessment Reflect 1; Exercises 4, 6, 9

Deductive Proof with Triangles

Exercise Answers

Core

5. Possible Answer:

Statements	Reasons
1. e	**1.** Given
2. b	**2.** Given
3. c	**3.** Reflexive property
4. a	**4.** SSS
5. d	**5.** CPCTC

6. a. Reason 1: Given
Statement 2: $\overline{US} \cong \overline{US}$
Statement 3: $\angle RUS \cong \angle TSU$
Reason 3: Given
Reason 4: SAS Postulate
Statement 5: $\angle SUT \cong \angle USR$
Reason 5: CPCTC
Reason 6: If alternate interior angles are congruent, the lines are parallel.

b. See Additional Answers p. T284.

7.

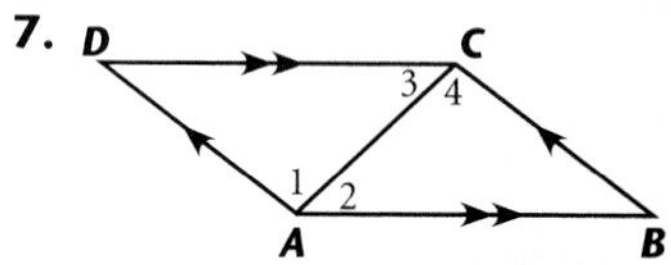

a. $\angle 2$ **b.** $\angle 1$

c. If two parallel lines are cut by a transversal, the alternate interior angles are congruent.

d. Reflexive Property

e. $\triangle CBA$

f. The ASA Postulate

g. CPCTC

8. The triangles are congruent by the SAS Postulate. The fences are congruent by CPCTC, so they are the same length.

9. 18 ft; Helen set up two congruent triangles. She knows they are congruent by SAS. By CPCTC, the hole is 18 ft wide.

P, MR **5.** Arrange the scrambled statements for the following proof in a logical order. Then give a reason for each statement.

Given: $\overline{EH} \cong \overline{GH}, \overline{EF} \cong \overline{GF}$

Prove: $\angle GFH \cong \angle EFH$

Proof:

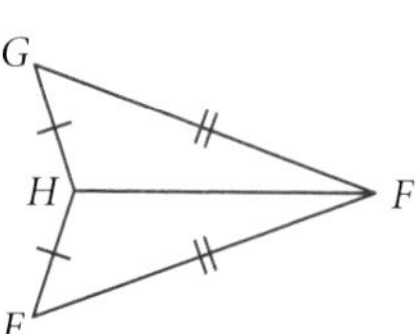

Statements	Reasons	Scrambled Statements
1.	**1.**	**a.** $\triangle GFH \cong \triangle EFH$
2.	**2.**	**b.** $\overline{EF} \cong \overline{GF}$
3.	**3.**	**c.** $\overline{HF} \cong \overline{HF}$
4.	**4.**	**d.** $\angle GFH \cong \angle EFH$
5.	**5.**	**e.** $\overline{EH} \cong \overline{GH}$

P, MR **6. a.** Fill in the missing statements and reasons to complete the following proof.

Given: $\overline{RU} \cong \overline{ST}$
$\angle RUS \cong \angle TSU$

Prove: $\overline{RS} \parallel \overline{UT}$

Proof:

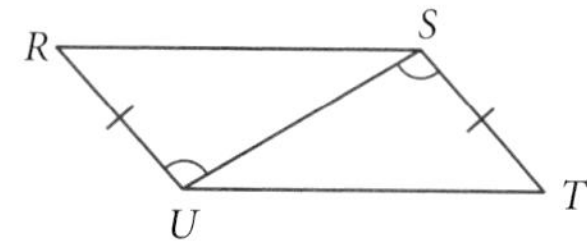

Statements	Reasons
1. $\overline{RU} \cong \overline{ST}$	**1.**
2.	**2.** Reflexive Property
3.	**3.**
4. $\triangle RSU \cong \triangle TUS$	**4.**
5.	**5.**
6. $\overline{RS} \parallel \overline{UT}$	**6.**

b. Rewrite the completed proof in flow-proof format.

P, MR **7.** Copy and mark the figure. Then complete the following proof.

Given: $\overline{AD} \parallel \overline{BC}, \overline{AB} \parallel \overline{DC}$

Prove: $\overline{AD} \cong \overline{BC}$

Proof: Since it is given that $\overline{AD} \parallel \overline{BC}$ and $\overline{AB} \parallel \overline{DC}$, $\angle 3 \cong$ **a.** ___, and $\angle 4 \cong$ **b.** ___ because **c.** ___. $\overline{AC}$ is a shared side, and $\overline{AC} \cong \overline{AC}$ because of the **d.** ___. $\triangle ADC \cong \triangle$ **e.** ___ by **f.** ___. Finally, $\overline{AD} \cong \overline{BC}$ by **g.** ___.

Key

V Vocabulary
P Practice/Skills
R Review
MR Math Reasoning
PS Problem Solving
C Challenge

8. A surveyor concludes that the fences shown are the same length. How can he make this conclusion?

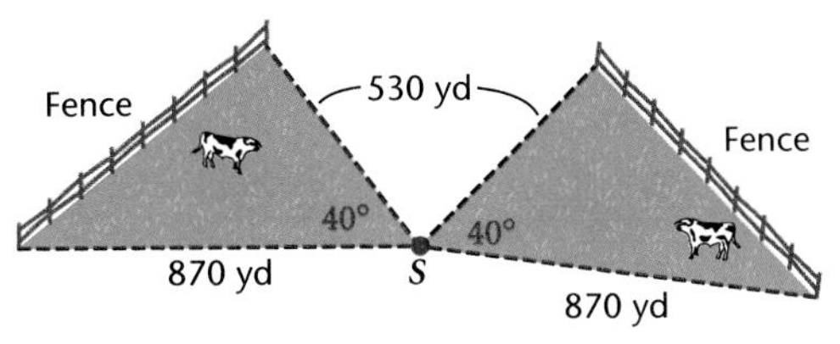

9. Street Repairs Helen's crew is doing some repairs, and they have dug up some asphalt on a street. The crew needs to cover the hole at night, but it is too wide to measure directly. Helen sets up two intersecting metal rods and then places a third rod across the other two as shown. How wide is the hole? Explain how Helen solved the problem.

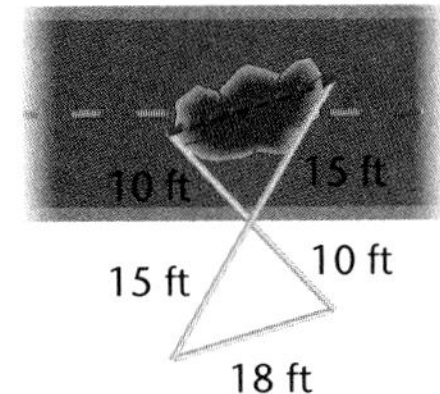

10. A New Construction The first two steps of the construction of a line perpendicular to a point on a given line are shown below.

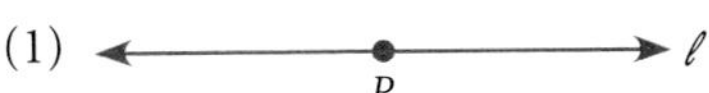

(2) A P B ℓ

a. Explain how to complete the construction.

b. Draw line m and point K on m. Then use a compass and straightedge to construct line n perpendicular to m at K.

11. *Given:* $\overline{MP}$ and $\overline{NQ}$ bisect each other at O. Find the measure of $\angle N$. Explain your reasoning.

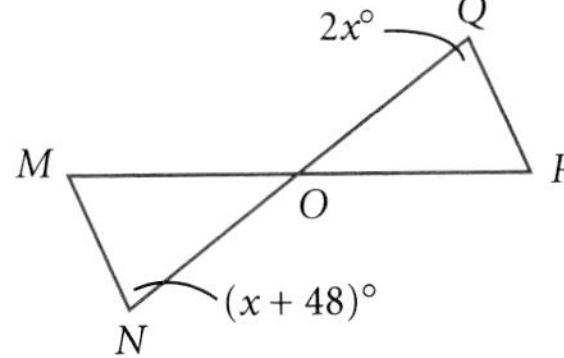

LOOK AHEAD

12. Name the hypotenuse of $\triangle ABD$. $\overline{AB}$ **13.** Name the vertex angle of $\triangle ADC$. $\angle ADC$

14. Name the legs of $\triangle ADC$. $\overline{AD}$, $\overline{CD}$ **15.** Name the legs of $\triangle ABD$. $\overline{AD}$, $\overline{DB}$

16. Name the base angles of $\triangle ADC$. $\angle DAC$, $\angle DCA$

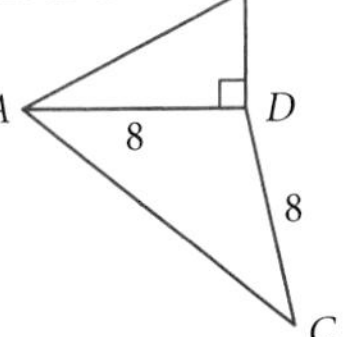

For each figure described, find the perimeter (distance around).

17. A rectangle with length 20 cm and width 11 cm. 62 cm

18. An equilateral triangle with side length $3\frac{1}{6}$ in. $9\frac{1}{2}$ in.

19. An isosceles triangle with base length 8.1 in. and leg length 6.5 in. 21.1 in.

10. a. Draw part of the arc of a circle with center at A such that it is directly above P. Without changing the compass width, draw another arc with center at B such that it intersects the first arc. Mark the point of intersection Q. Then $\overleftrightarrow{PQ}$ is perpendicular to ℓ.

b.

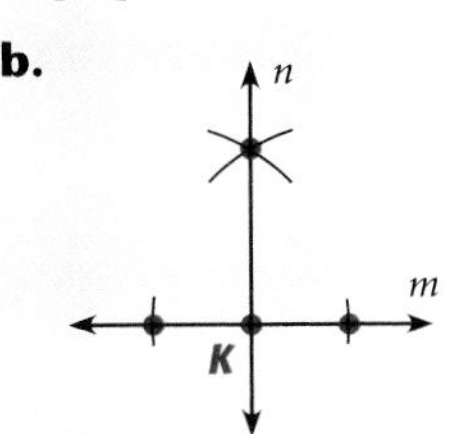

11. $\angle N = 96°$; $\overline{OP} \cong \overline{OM}$ and $\overline{OQ} \cong \overline{ON}$ by the definition of *bisect*. $\angle MON \cong \angle POQ$ because vertical angles are congruent. $\triangle MON \cong \triangle POQ$ by the SAS Postulate. $\angle N \cong \angle Q$ by CPCTC. Therefore $x + 48 = 2x$. Solving the equation gives $x = 48$. Then $m\angle N = (x + 48)° = 96°$.

Deductive Proof with Triangles

More Practice

20. Reason 1: Given
Statements 2 and 3: $\angle 1 \cong \angle 2$; E is the midpoint of $\overline{BC}$
Reason 4: Definition of *midpoint*
Statement 5: $\triangle CDE \cong \triangle EFB$
Reason 5: SAS Postulate
Reason 6: CPCTC

21. a. The Reflexive Property
b. Given information
c. Given information
d. *ABC* **e.** *CDA*
f. The SAA Postulate
g. CPCTC

More Math Reasoning

22. $\overline{AB} \cong \overline{BC}$; Given
$\overline{BD} \cong \overline{BD}$; Reflexive Property
$\angle ABD \cong \angle DBC$; Right angles are congruent
$\triangle ABD \cong \triangle CBD$; SAS
$\angle A \cong \angle C$; CPCTC

MORE PRACTICE

P, MR **20.** Fill in the missing statements and reasons to complete the following proof.

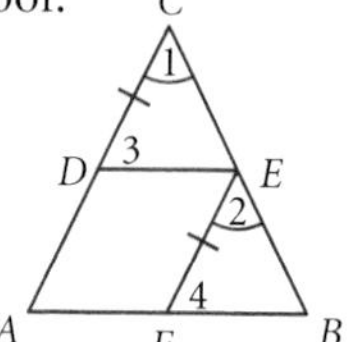

Given: E is the midpoint of $\overline{BC}$, $\angle 1 \cong \angle 2$, and $\overline{CD} \cong \overline{EF}$.

Prove: $\angle 3 \cong \angle 4$

Proof:

Statements	Reasons
1. $\overline{CD} \cong \overline{EF}$	**1.**
2.	**2.** Given
3.	**3.** Given
4. $\overline{CE} \cong \overline{BE}$	**4.**
5.	**5.**
6. $\angle 3 \cong \angle 4$	**6.**

P, MR **21.** Copy and mark the figure. Then complete the following proof.

Given: $\angle 1 \cong \angle 4$, $\angle B \cong \angle D$

Prove: $\overline{AD} \cong \overline{BC}$

Proof: $\overline{AC}$ is congruent to itself by **a.** ____. $\angle 1 \cong \angle 4$ by the **b.** ____. $\angle B \cong \angle D$, also by the **c.** ____. Therefore, $\triangle$ **d.** ____ $\cong \triangle$ **e.** ____ by **f.** ____. Therefore, sides $\overline{AD}$ and $\overline{BC}$ are congruent by **g.** ____.

MORE MATH REASONING

C, MR **22. Dig This!** An archaeologist digging near the lost city of Ecneurgnoc discovers the ancient textbook page shown below. Translate the page into English as completely as you can.

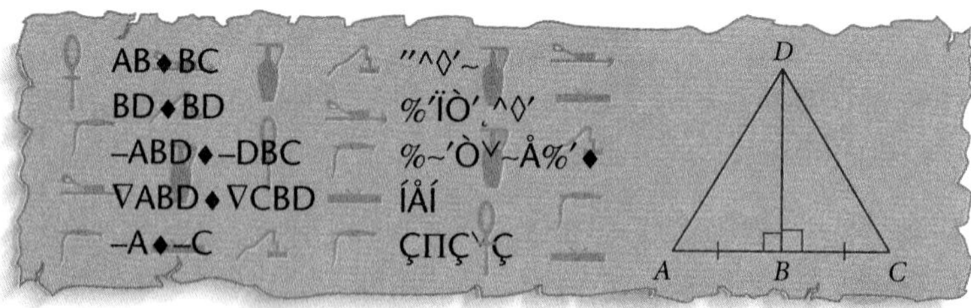

Key

V Vocabulary
P Practice/Skills
R Review
MR Math Reasoning
PS Problem Solving
C Challenge

4-2 PART E Making Connections

← CONNECT → *Most people use logical reasoning every day. You are asked to demonstrate such reasoning whenever someone says, "Is that so? Prove it!" You have explored more properties of triangles and continued to develop skills for deductive proof.*

The real test of understanding comes when you have to use your knowledge to solve a problem in a new situation. In the following Explore, you will look at a real problem that confronted Napoleon's troops.

EXPLORE: A CONGRUENT CROSSING

It is said that Napoleon once needed to find the distance across a river. One of his officers solved the problem by using geometry.

He placed a flagpole vertically at the edge of the riverbank and stood an arm's length away. He held the pole firmly with one hand while sliding the other hand to a position on the pole so that his line of sight with his hand was in line with the opposite riverbank.

Keeping the same angle of sight and his hands in the same position, he turned to sight a rock on his side of the riverbank. (Note: Lengths in the drawing are affected by perspective.)

1. *Draw* a figure that represents the problem. Label the figure. *State* the Given and Prove.
2. Name the corresponding sides and angles. Explain how you identified them.
3. Mark any parts that you know are congruent. Explain why each pair of parts is congruent.
4. How did Napoleon's officer determine the distance across the river? Write an explanation of the method he used.

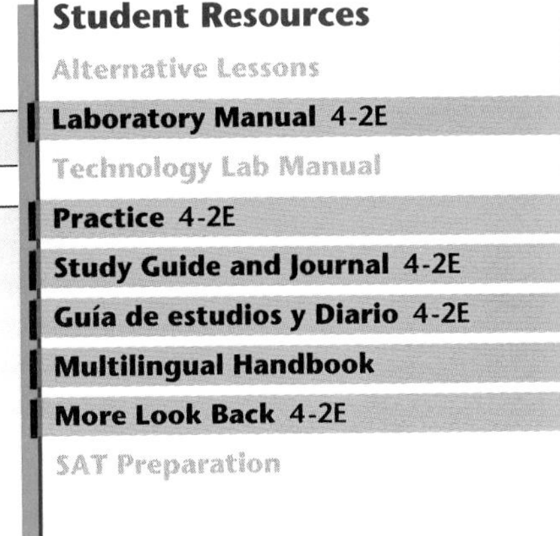

Student Resources

- Alternative Lessons
- Laboratory Manual 4-2E
- Technology Lab Manual
- Practice 4-2E
- Study Guide and Journal 4-2E
- Guía de estudios y Diario 4-2E
- Multilingual Handbook
- More Look Back 4-2E
- SAT Preparation

Media Resources

- Transparency FFM 4-2E
- Transparency AE
- Teaching Transparency
- AWSMTest and practice software
- AWSM Videodisc

PART E At a Glance

Objective

To use triangle congruence to solve a real-world problem.

Development

In the **Explore,** students use congruent triangles to find the width of a river.

First Five Minutes

Transparency FFM 4-2E

In your own words, explain the meaning of "Corresponding parts of congruent triangles are congruent." How is it used to show sides or angles congruent?

EXPLORE

A Congruent Crossing

Recommended group size: 4

The Point

To use triangle congruence to find the width of a river.

Look and Listen...

- For students who have difficulty visualizing the triangles formed.

Ask...

- The bottom of the flagpole is a vertex in both triangles. What are the other vertices of the triangle that crosses the river? the triangle on the riverbank?
- What kind of angle does the flagpole make with the ground?

For Groups That Finish Early

How accurate do you think this method is? What might be some causes of inaccuracy in the method? **Flagpole not exactly perpendicular; not keeping a consistent line of sight; distance to the rock not accurately measured.**

Follow Up

Ask students to explain how the officer found the river's width.

4-2

Deductive Proof with Triangles

Possible Answers

1. *Draw:* See below.

State: Given: $\angle RFO \cong \angle VFO$

$\angle FOR$ and $\angle FOV$ are right angles.

Prove: $\overline{OR} \cong \overline{OV}$

2. $\angle RFO \leftrightarrow \angle VFO$, $\angle FOR \leftrightarrow \angle FOV$, $\angle R \leftrightarrow \angle V$, $\overline{FR} \leftrightarrow \overline{FV}$, $\overline{FO} \leftrightarrow \overline{FO}$, $\overline{OR} \leftrightarrow \overline{OV}$.

3.

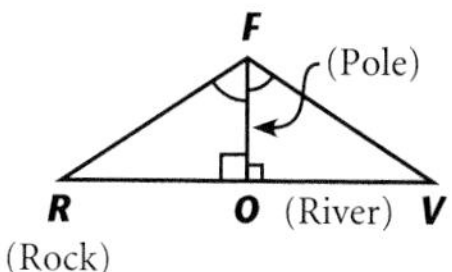

$\angle RFO \cong \angle VFO$ because the angle of sight is the same. $\angle FOR \cong \angle FOV$ because right angles are congruent. Also, $\overline{FO} \cong \overline{FO}$ because of the Reflexive Property.

4. He measured the distance to the rock. $\triangle FOR \cong \triangle FOV$ by ASA, so $\overline{OR} \cong \overline{OV}$—distance to rock equals distance across river.

Portfolio

Have students select items from their work that demonstrate their understanding of the material in 4-2.

You may wish to have students include their favorite fill-in proof, proofs presented in two different formats, and a real-world application of congruent triangles.

REFLECT

1. Explain and illustrate each of the triangle-congruence postulates.
2. The definition of congruent triangles can be written as a biconditional statement.
   a. Write the definition in biconditional form.
   b. Break the definition into two conditional statements.
   c. One of the two conditionals is used much more frequently than the other. Identify the one that is rarely used, and explain why this is so.
3. Describe a situation in which triangle congruence can be used to find an unknown distance. Explain your method.

Self-Assessment

P **Complete each statement in Exercises 1–4 with *always, sometimes,* or *never.* Explain your answers.**

1. Two triangles are ___ congruent if two sides and the included angle of one are congruent to two sides and the included angle of the other. Always
2. An equilateral triangle is ___ congruent to a right triangle. Never
3. If three angles of a triangle are congruent, then the triangle is ___ scalene. Never
4. If two triangles are congruent, the corresponding parts are ___ congruent. Always

P 5. Which of the following is *not* a triangle-congruence postulate? (c)
(a) SSS (b) SAS (c) AAA (d) SAA (e) ASA

P **Use each set of given information and the figures below to state a postulate or theorem that proves $\triangle ABC \cong \triangle RST$.**

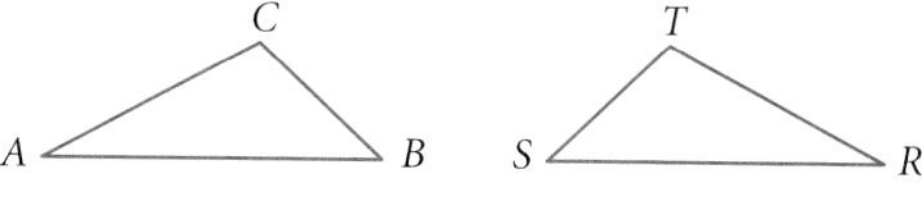

6. *Given:* $\angle A \cong \angle R$, $\overline{AB} \cong \overline{RS}$, $\angle B \cong \angle S$
   ASA Postulate
7. *Given:* $\angle C$ and $\angle T$ are right angles, $\overline{AB} \cong \overline{RS}$, and $\angle A \cong \angle R$.
   SAA Postulate
8. *Given:* $\angle C \cong \angle T$, $\overline{AC} \cong \overline{RT}$, $\overline{CB} \cong \overline{TS}$
   SAS Postulate

PS 9. **Bridging the Gap** Three bridges have been built to connect island *M* to cities *S* and *T*, and *S* and *T* to one another. Bridges parallel to these need to be built to connect *S* and *T* to island *N*. How long should bridges $\overline{NS}$ and $\overline{NT}$ be? Justify your answer.

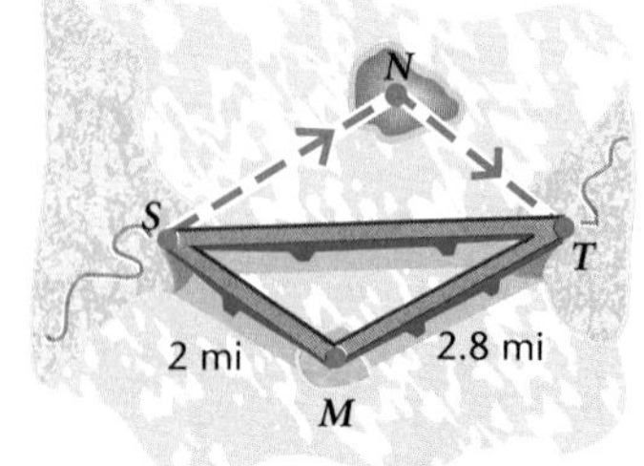

Key

V Vocabulary
P Practice/Skills
R Review
MR Math Reasoning
PS Problem Solving
C Challenge

Tips from Teachers

After students do the *Explore,* you may want to set up a model for it somewhere on the school grounds. You would need to have a "flagpole," a "rock," and an imaginary river. You could mark and measure the distance to some inaccessible spot beforehand and have groups test the method to see how accurate it is.

R **10.** Write a description of how CPCTC is used to prove a pair of sides or angles congruent.

R **Use a protractor to find the bearing from the control tower to each of the following. [3-1]**

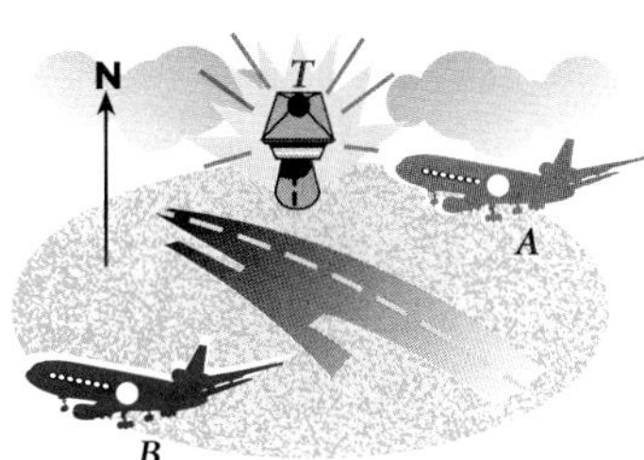

11. Airplane A 110

12. Airplane B 210; they differ by 180°.

R **13.** Find the bearing from Airplane A to Airplane B. How does this compare to the bearing from Airplane B to Airplane A? [3-1] 240

R **In each of the following, use the figure at the right and the given information to find $m\angle C$. [4-1]**

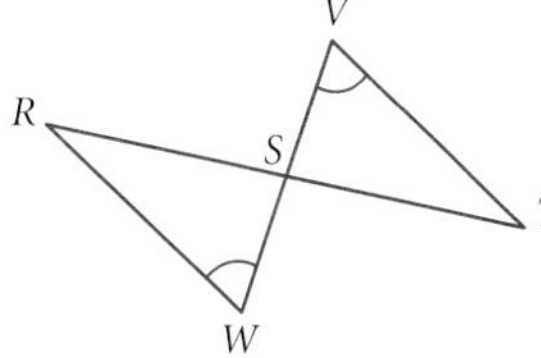

14. $m\angle A = 51°$, $m\angle B = 81°$ 48°

15. $m\angle A = 87°$, $\angle A \cong \angle B$ 6°

16. $m\angle A = (x + 54)°$, $m\angle B = (7x - 5)°$, $m\angle C = (51 - 3x)°$ 3°

R **17.** Complete the following proof.

Given: $\angle W \cong \angle V$
S is the midpoint of $\overline{RT}$.

Prove: $\triangle WSR \cong \triangle VST$

Proof: S is the midpoint of $\overline{RT}$, so $\overline{RS} \cong \overline{ST}$ by the **a.** ____. Since **b.** ____, $\angle WSR \cong \angle VST$. $\angle W \cong \angle V$, from the **c.** ____. Therefore, we can conclude that $\triangle WSR \cong \triangle VST$ by the **d.** ____ Postulate.

R **18.** *Given:* $\overline{AB} \cong \overline{CD}$
$\angle 1 \cong \angle 2$

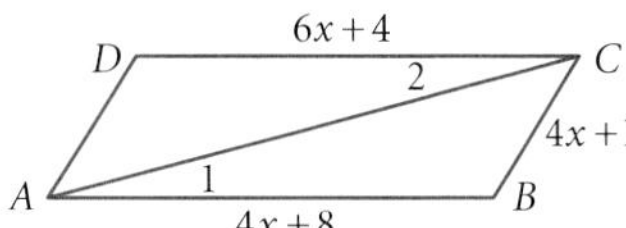

Find the length of $\overline{AD}$. Write a short paragraph to explain your reasoning.

19. *Given:* $\overline{EG} \perp \overline{FH}$, and G is the midpoint of $\overline{FH}$.

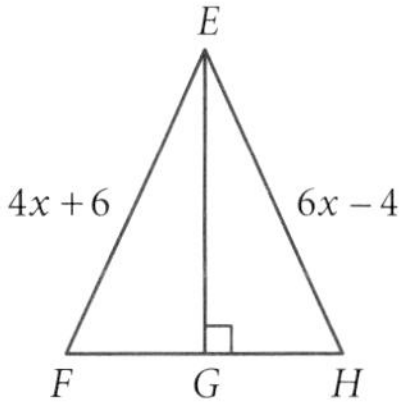

Find the length of $\overline{EH}$. Write a short paragraph to explain your reasoning.

Assessment Resources

Quiz 4-2
Chapter Assessment Form A
Chapter Assessment Form B
Chapter Alternative Assessment
Mid-Year Assessment
End-of-Year Assessment
IWSMTest and practice software

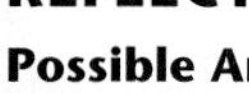

Ongoing Assessment

Self-Assessment Self-Assessment Exercises

Embedded Assessment Explore Step 4; Reflect 1, 2

REFLECT

Possible Answers

1. Students should explain and illustrate SSS, SAS, ASA, and SAA.

2. a. Triangles are congruent if and only if all pairs of corresponding angles and sides are congruent.

b. If triangles are congruent, then all pairs of corresponding angles and sides are congruent.

If all pairs of corresponding angles and sides are congruent, then the triangles are congruent.

c. The first (CPCTC) is used more frequently. The second is inefficient because of SSS, SAS, ASA, and SAA.

3. Students may describe a method similar to that in the **Explore** on page 281 or **Exercise** 9 on page 279.

Self-Assessment

Exercise Notes

18. and 19. Students show that two triangles are congruent. Then they use algebra to find the length of a missing side.

21. Reviews the construction method for a perpendicular to a point on a given line developed in 4-2 Part D, Exercise 10.

Self-Assessment Answers

9. $NS = 2.8$ mi, $NT = 2$ mi; $\triangle NST \cong \triangle MTS$ by ASA.

10. Possible answer: Prove triangles congruent, then any corresponding sides or angles are also congruent.

17. a. Definition of *midpoint*

b. Vertical angles are congruent.

c. Given information

d. SAA

Deductive Proof with Triangles

18. 9; $\overline{AC} \cong \overline{AC}$ by the Reflexive Property. $\triangle ABC \cong \triangle CDA$ by the SAS Postulate. Therefore $\overline{AD} \cong \overline{CB}$ by CPCTC, so $AD = 4x + 1$. Since $\overline{AB} \cong \overline{CD}$ is given, $6x + 4 = 4x + 8$. Solve for x to get $x = 2$. So $AD = 4x + 1 = 9$.

19. 26; $\overline{FG} \cong \overline{GH}$ by the definition of midpoint. $\overline{EG} \cong \overline{EG}$ by the Reflexive Property. $\angle FGE$ and $\angle HGE$ are right angles because $\overline{EG} \perp \overline{FH}$. $\angle FGE \cong \angle HGE$ because right angles are congruent. $\triangle FGE \cong \triangle HGE$ by the SAS Postulate. $\overline{FE} \cong \overline{HE}$ by CPCTC. Therefore, $4x + 6 = 6x - 4$. Solve for x to get $x = 5$. So $EH = 6x - 4 = 26$.

20. a. Reason 1: Given
Reason 2: If two parallel lines are cut by a transversal, the alternate interior angles are congruent.
Statement 3: $\angle S \cong \angle U$
Statement 4: $\overline{RT} \cong \overline{RT}$
Statement 5: $\triangle URT \cong \triangle STR$
Reason 5: SAA Postulate
Statement 6: $\overline{RS} \cong \overline{TU}$
Reason 6: CPCTC

b. Possible answer: Since it is given that $\overline{RU} \parallel \overline{ST}$, $\angle URT \cong \angle STR$ because if two parallel lines are cut by a transversal, the alternate interior angles are congruent. We are given $\angle S \cong \angle U$. $\overline{RT} \cong \overline{RT}$ by the Reflexive Property. So $\triangle URT \cong \triangle STR$ by the SAA Postulate. Therefore, $\overline{RS} \cong \overline{TU}$ by CPCTC.

c. See Additional Answers p. T284.

21. See Additional Answers p. T284.

Logic/Reasoning

P, MR **20. a.** Complete the following proof.

Given: $\overline{RU} \parallel \overline{ST}$, $\angle S \cong \angle U$

Prove: $\overline{RS} \cong \overline{TU}$

Proof:

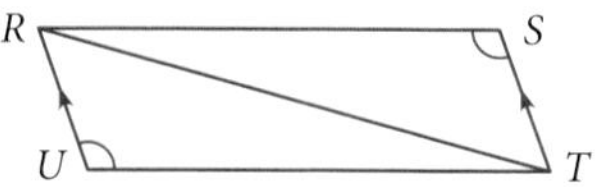

Statements	Reasons
1. $\overline{RU} \parallel \overline{ST}$	**1.**
2. $\angle URT \cong \angle STR$	**2.**
3.	**3.** Given
4.	**4.** Reflexive Property
5.	**5.**
6.	**6.**

b. Rewrite your proof in paragraph format.
c. Rewrite your proof in flow-proof format.

P, MR **21. a.** Draw line s and point D on s. Then construct line t perpendicular to s at D, using the construction technique you developed in Exercise 10 on page 279.
b. Mark the segments on your construction that must be congruent. Then explain why the construction works.

P, MR **22.** Supply reasons to complete the following proof.

Given: $\overline{AC}$ and $\overline{BD}$ bisect each other.

Prove: $\overline{AD} \parallel \overline{BC}$

Proof:

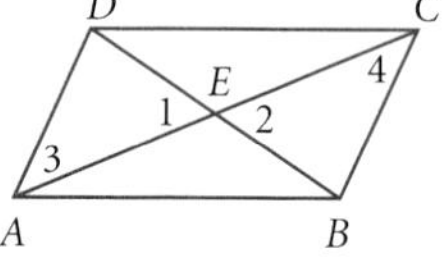

Statements	Reasons
1. $\overline{AC}$ and $\overline{BD}$ bisect each other.	**1.**
2. $\overline{AE} \cong \overline{CE}$, $\overline{DE} \cong \overline{BE}$	**2.**
3. $\angle 1 \cong \angle 2$	**3.**
4. $\triangle AED \cong \triangle CEB$	**4.**
5. $\angle 3 \cong \angle 4$	**5.**
6. $\overline{AD} \parallel \overline{BC}$	**6.**

See Additional Answers p. T284.

Key

- **V** Vocabulary
- **P** Practice/Skills
- **R** Review
- **MR** Math Reasoning
- **PS** Problem Solving
- **C** Challenge

4-2 Part C Explore

3.

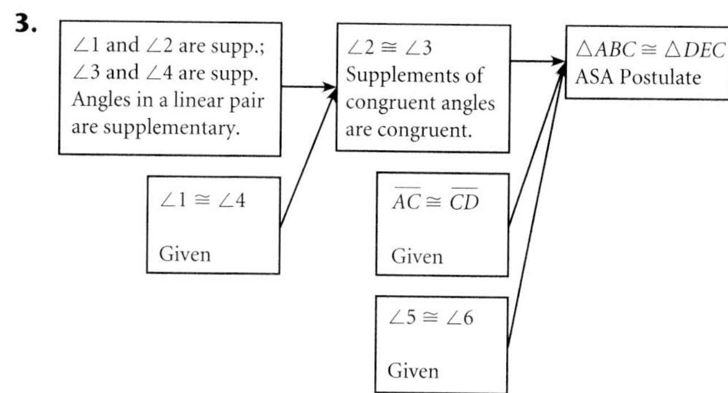

4-2 Part C Exercises

4. b.

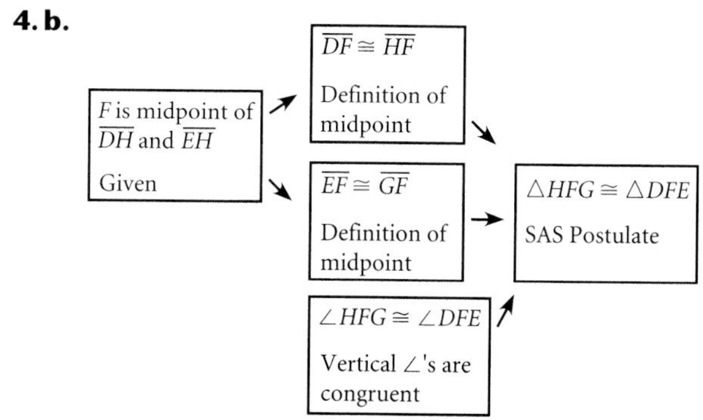

4-2 Part D Exercises

6. b.

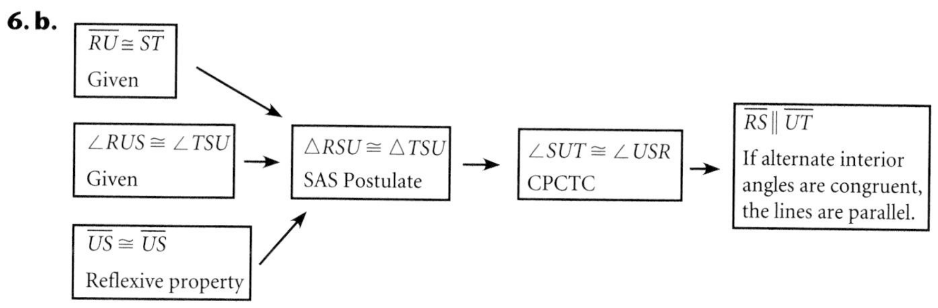

4-2 Part E Self-Assessment

20. c.

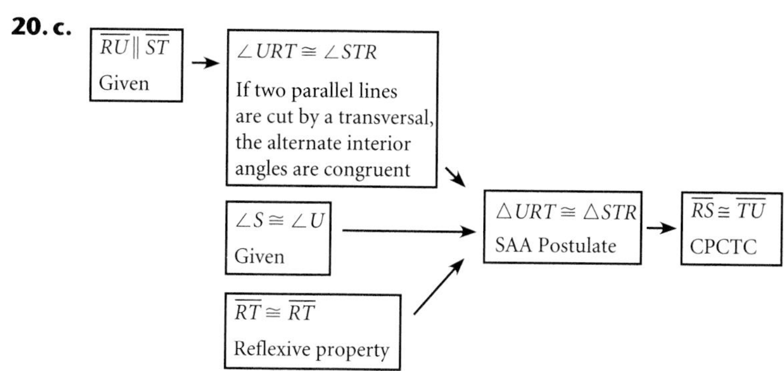

4-2 Part E Self-Assessment

21. a.

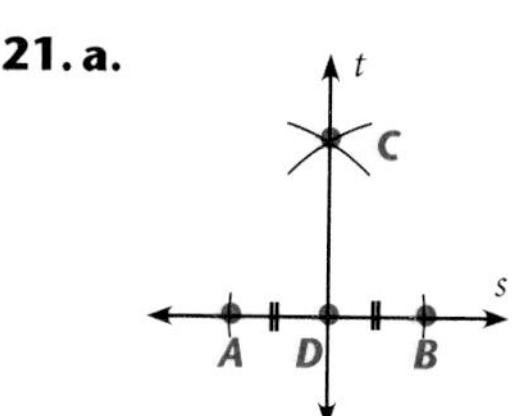

b. $\overline{AD} \cong \overline{DB}$ and $\overline{AC} \cong \overline{BC}$ because each pair was made with the same compass settings. $\overline{DC} \cong \overline{DC}$, so $\triangle ADC \cong \triangle BDC$ by SSS. Since $\angle ADC \cong \angle BDC$ (CPCTC) and they are supplementary, each must be a right angle. Therefore, $s \perp t$.

22. Reasons
1: Given
2: Definition of *bisect*
3: Vertical angles are congruent.
4: SAS Postulate
5: CPCTC
6: If alternate interior angles are congruent, the lines are parallel.

4-3

Properties of Special Triangles

SUPERLESSON AT A GLANCE

Superlesson Goal

Students will explore isosceles and right triangles, and see uses of auxiliary lines in proofs.

Management Guide

	Topic	Objectives	Key Terms	New Ideas	Materials
Part A	Isosceles Triangles	To use the Isosceles Triangle Theorem and its converse.	Auxiliary line	Isosceles triangle base angles are congruent. In a triangle, sides opposite congruent angles are congruent. Auxiliary lines.	**Student** Paper, ruler, scissors, protractor
Part B	Right Triangles	To use congruence theorems for right triangles, and to see there is no SSA congruence.		Using right-triangle congruence theorems.	**Student** Ruler, protractor, compass
Part C	Perpendiculars, Bisectors, and Locus	To find sets of points satisfying given conditions.	Locus	Locus. Points on the perpendicular bisector of a segment are equidistant from its endpoints. Points on the bisector of an angle are equidistant from its sides.	**Student** Paper, ruler, protractor
Part D	Lines Associated with Triangles	To see special lines in triangles, and to find that the centroid of a triangle is its center of balance.	Angle bisector, perpendicular bisector, altitude, median of a triangle, concurrent lines, centroid	Special lines associated with triangles. Centroid, center of balance (gravity).	**Student** Cardboard, scissors, ruler, pencil
Part E	Making Connections	To use centroids to estimate the center of balance of a bicycle frame.	In Making Connections, students apply and synthesize key terms and new ideas.		**Student** Ruler, geometry software

Pacing Chart (45-Minute Periods)

	Comprehensive Course	Core Course	Informal Course
Part A	1	1	1*
Part B	1	1	1*
Part C	1	2	2
Part D	1	2	2
Part E	1	1	1
TOTAL periods for Superlesson	5	7	7

*Material on proof in this part may be omitted or downplayed in an Informal Course.

NCTM Standards

Mathematics as Problem Solving

Mathematics as Communication

Mathematics as Reasoning

Mathematical Connections

Geometry from a Synthetic Perspective

4-3 Properties of Special Triangles

PEDALING THROUGH GEOMETRY

A Frenchman named de Sivrac invented the first bicycle around 1790. This bike, called the *célerifère*, had heavy, cart-like wheels. There was no way to steer it, and it had no pedals—the rider pushed it along with his or her feet.

In 1870, James Starley patented the first lightweight, all-metal bicycle. Its wire-spoked wheels were a great improvement over the heavy wheels used earlier. To increase the speed of the bicycle, the pedals were attached to a large front wheel. These "penny farthings" became the most popular type of bicycle, despite the difficulties of getting on, staying on, and figuring out how to get off at the end of the ride.

Today's bicycles have come a long way from these early designs. The most important part of a modern bicycle is the frame. Two popular frames are shown here.

The measurements of the tube lengths, seat angle, and head (or steering post) angle are referred to as the *frame geometry*. In addition to the seat and head angle, there is another important angle that can be called the *human angle*.

The properties of the frame geometry determine the bicycle's responsiveness, traction, and shock absorption.

Penny farthing

Racing bike

Mountain bike

?

1. Why do you think early bicycles with wagon-type wheels were called "boneshakers"?
2. Why did the large front wheel of a penny farthing increase the speed of the bicycle?
3. Why do you think triangles are used in bicycle frames?

285

More About Bicycles

The bicycle may be the most efficient machine yet devised for converting human power into motion. The cycling speed record for 200 m (with a flying start) is 65.484 mi/hr, achieved by Fred Markham in 1986. This is almost three times as fast as the world record for the 200-m run (approximately 22.8 mi/hr, Pietro Mennea, 1979). The 1-hr speed record for a human on a bicycle is 46.96 mi/hr (Pat Kinch, 1990), more than three times as fast as the comparable running record of 13.1 mi/hr (Arturo Barrios, 1991).

Where Are We Now?

Students have used congruence postulates to show that triangles are congruent, worked with three methods for presenting a proof, and filled in statements and reasons to complete proofs.

Where Are We Going?

In 4-3, students learn properties of isosceles triangles and congruence theorems for right triangles. The properties of isosceles triangles are used frequently in the course, and right triangles are the main focus of 5-3 and 7-3.

Students are also introduced to locus, and they see angle bisectors, medians, perpendicular bisectors, and altitudes of triangles. These are used as auxiliary lines in proofs. In Chapter 6, when students do their own proofs with quadrilaterals, they will need to use auxiliary lines.

Possible Answers

1. The heavy spokes did not flex when the bicycles hit a bump. Therefore, little of the impact was absorbed before it reached the rider.
2. These bicycles had no gears, so one turn of the pedals equaled one turn of the wheel. The larger the wheel, the farther one turn of the pedals would take you.
3. They are rigid, so they provide strong support for the bicycle.

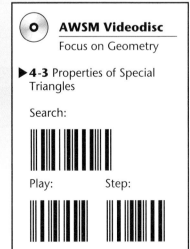

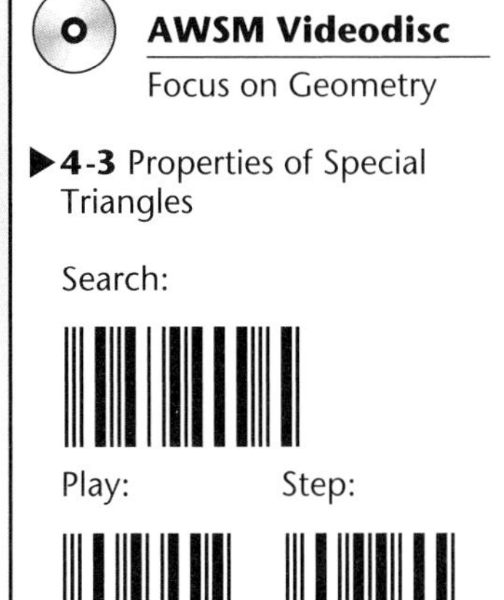

Properties of Special Triangles

PART A At a Glance

Objective

To use the Isosceles Triangle Theorem and its converse.

Development

In the **Explore,** students cut and fold paper to discover the Isosceles Triangle Theorem and its converse.

Then, in an **Example,** students see the proof of the Isosceles Triangle Theorem. This introduces them to the idea of an auxiliary line.

Suggested Materials

Student Paper, ruler, scissors, protractor

Key Terms

Auxiliary line

First Five Minutes

Transparency FFM 4-3A

Sketch a triangle with exactly one line of symmetry. What type of triangle does it appear to be? **Isosceles.**

Motivate

Ask...

- Is an isosceles triangle the only type of triangle that has a line of symmetry? **An equilateral triangle has 3 lines of symmetry.**

EXPLORE

The Isosceles Have It!

Recommended group size: 4

The Point

To discover the Isosceles Triangle Theorem and its converse.

Look and Listen...

- For students who do not see many properties of the fold in their triangle.

Ask...

- Does the fold bisect any parts of the triangle?

4-3 PART A Isosceles Triangles

← CONNECT → ***You are already familiar with different types of triangles. Now you will discover some special properties of isosceles triangles and see how these can be used in deductive arguments.***

There are many types of bicycles. However, some of them have distinguishing features. For example, as shown in the illustrations on the previous page, the nonhorizontal top tube is characteristic of a mountain bike.

Some triangles also have "special features." For example, an equilateral triangle has three congruent sides, and an isosceles triangle (shown at the right) has at least two congruent sides. You will investigate some special characteristics of these triangles in the following Explore.

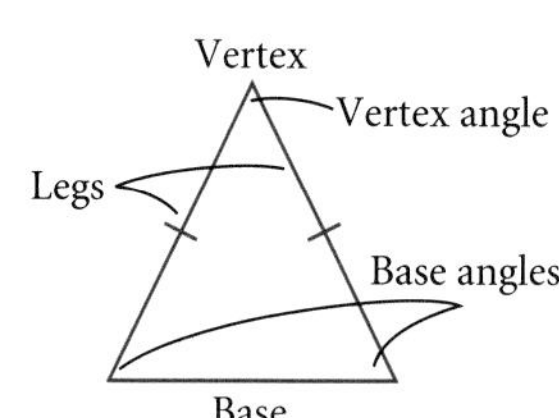

EXPLORE: THE ISOSCELES HAVE IT!

MATERIALS

Paper
Ruler
Scissors
Protractor

1. Draw an isosceles triangle on a sheet of paper. Then cut out your triangle and fold it so that the two legs match up. What can you say about the base angles of the triangle? Write a conjecture in if-then form.
2. State the converse of your conjecture from Step 1. See whether the converse is true by cutting and folding triangles with the appropriate characteristics.
3. Look at the folds made in your cutout triangles. What transformation do these folds suggest? Make as many conjectures as you can about the segment determined by the fold. Compare your conjectures with those of your classmates.

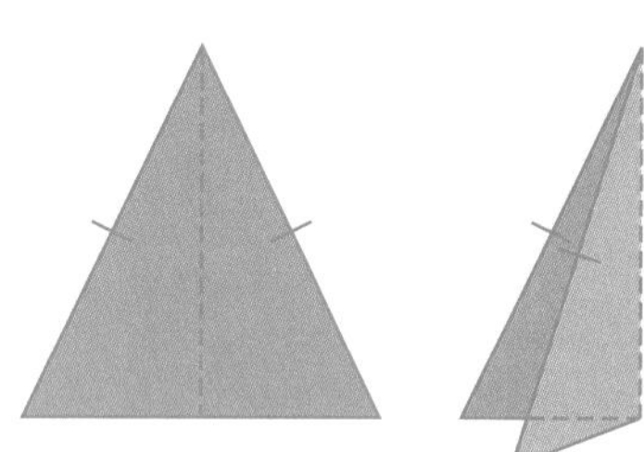

The properties of isosceles triangles that you have discovered are useful in finding unknown side lengths and angle measures.

History Connection

Euclid's proof of the Isosceles Triangle Theorem is somewhat subtle. In the Middle Ages, students often studied geometry by memorizing Euclid's proofs. Because some students found it difficult to get past the Isosceles Triangle theorem, it earned the name *Pons asinorum*—Latin for "Bridge of Asses."

TRY IT

a. In isosceles triangle $\triangle ABC$, $\overline{AB} \cong \overline{BC}$. What else must be true? $\angle A \cong \angle C$

b. In $\triangle MNO$, $\angle M \cong \angle N$. Find the lengths of sides $\overline{MO}$ and $\overline{NO}$. (Hint: What do you know about these sides?) 62

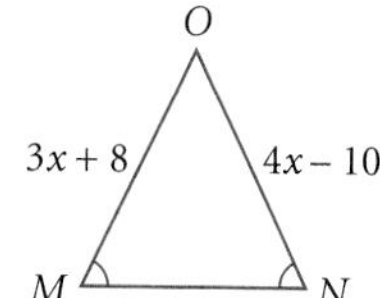

You have explored an important theorem about isosceles triangles and have seen that its converse is also true. We now state these theorems and a second pair of theorems that will be important "helpers" in upcoming proofs.

ISOSCELES TRIANGLE THEOREM

If two sides of a triangle are congruent, then the angles opposite those sides are congruent.

CONVERSE OF THE ISOSCELES TRIANGLE THEOREM

If two angles of a triangle are congruent, then the sides opposite those angles are congruent.

UNIQUE BISECTOR THEOREMS

Every segment has a unique midpoint.

Every angle has a unique ray that bisects it.

1. State the Isosceles Triangle Theorem and its converse as a single biconditional statement.

If a conjecture is called a *theorem,* we must be able to prove it. Watch for the "trick" in the following proof of the Isosceles Triangle Theorem. It is a technique that will be useful in many proofs.

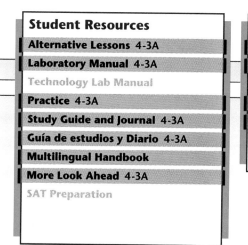

For Groups That Finish Early

Which properties of a geometric figure remain the same when the figure is reflected over a line? How do these properties support one or both of your conjectures?

Follow Up

Ask students to state their conjectures and explain how the properties of reflections support those conjectures.

Possible Answers

1. If two sides of a triangle are congruent, then its opposite (base) angles are congruent.
2. If two angles of a triangle are congruent, then the sides opposite the angles are also congruent; true.
3. The folds suggest reflections. The fold is a line of reflection and a line of symmetry, it is perpendicular to the base, it bisects the base, and it bisects the vertex angle.

(Note: Reflections preserve side lengths and angle measures. Students can use this idea to help support their conjectures about base angles in an isosceles triangle.)

Possible Answer

1. Two sides of a triangle are congruent if and only if their opposite angles are congruent.

Student Resources

- Alternative Lessons 4-3A
- Laboratory Manual 4-3A
- Technology Lab Manual
- Practice 4-3A
- Study Guide and Journal 4-3A
- Guía de estudios y Diario 4-3A
- Multilingual Handbook
- More Look Ahead 4-3A
- SAT Preparation

Media Resources

- Transparency FFM 4-3A
- Transparency AE 4-3A
- Teaching Transparency
- AWSMTest and practice software
- AWSM Videodisc

4-3

Properties of Special Triangles

ALTERNATE EXAMPLE

Prove: If two sides of a triangle are congruent, then the angles opposite those sides are congruent.

Given: In $\triangle JKL$, $\overline{JK} \cong \overline{JL}$.

Prove: $\angle K \cong \angle L$.

Plan: Add an *auxiliary segment* $\overline{JM}$, the angle bisector of $\angle J$. Then prove that $\triangle JKM \cong \triangle JLM$ by SAS. Use CPCTC to prove $\angle K \cong \angle L$.

Proof: We can draw $\overline{JM}$, the angle bisector of $\angle J$, because every angle has a unique bisector. $\angle KJM \cong \angle LJM$ by the definition of angle bisector. $\overline{JM} \cong \overline{JM}$ by the Reflexive Property. From the given information, $\overline{JK} \cong \overline{JL}$. Therefore, $\triangle JKM \cong \triangle JLM$ by SAS. This means that $\angle K \cong \angle L$ by CPCTC.

Possible Answers

2. It divided the original triangle into two triangles that can be proven congruent. CPCTC can then be used on corresponding parts of those triangles.
3. The line from the vertex to the midpoint of the base seems to be a line of symmetry for the isosceles triangle.

EXAMPLE

Prove: If two sides of a triangle are congruent, then the angles opposite those sides are congruent.

Given: In $\triangle XYZ$, $\overline{XZ} \cong \overline{YZ}$.

Prove: $\angle X \cong \angle Y$

Plan: Add an *auxiliary segment* $\overline{ZM}$ from Z to M, the midpoint of $\overline{XY}$. Then prove that the two triangles formed are congruent by the SSS Congruence Postulate, and use CPCTC to show that the base angles are congruent.

Proof:

Statements	Reasons
1. Draw M, the midpoint of $\overline{XY}$.	**1.** Every segment has a unique midpoint.
2. Draw $\overline{ZM}$.	**2.** Two points determine a line.
3. $\overline{XM} \cong \overline{MY}$	**3.** Definition of *midpoint*
4. $\overline{ZM} \cong \overline{ZM}$	**4.** Reflexive Property
5. $\overline{XZ} \cong \overline{YZ}$	**5.** Given
6. $\triangle XMZ \cong \triangle YMZ$	**6.** SSS Postulate
7. $\angle X \cong \angle Y$	**7.** CPCTC

An **auxiliary line** is a line (or part of a line) added to a figure. You can add lines and points to a figure as long as you can show that they actually exist. Notice how this was done in Steps 1 and 2 of the proof in the preceding example.

2. How did the addition of an auxiliary line help prove the Isosceles Triangle Theorem?

3. Does the auxiliary line in the proof, shown in the example, remind you of something you saw in the Explore? Explain.

You will be asked to prove the converse of the Isosceles Triangle Theorem in Exercise 16.

REFLECT

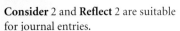

1. Use the Isosceles Triangle Theorem to explain why an equilateral triangle must be equiangular.
2. a. You cannot assume that the angle bisector of an angle of a triangle intersects the opposite side at its midpoint. Why not?
   b. Does the angle bisector of the vertex angle of an isosceles triangle intersect the base at its midpoint? Explain.
3. Maritza says, "If an isosceles triangle is obtuse, the vertex angle has to be the obtuse angle." Is she right? If so, justify her statement. If not, provide a counterexample.

Exercises

CORE

Getting Started **Give a reason to justify each statement.**

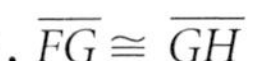

1. $\overline{FG} \cong \overline{GH}$
2. $\angle F \cong \angle H$
3. $\triangle FGH$ is isosceles.

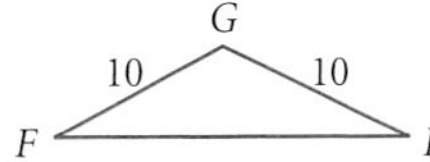

Use the information in the figures to find the following.

4. $m\angle A$ 110°
5. $m\angle D$ 25°
6. $m\angle G$ 60°
7. YZ 19

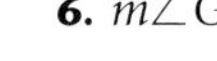

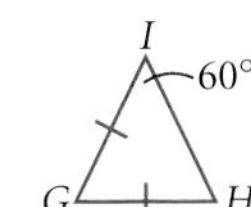

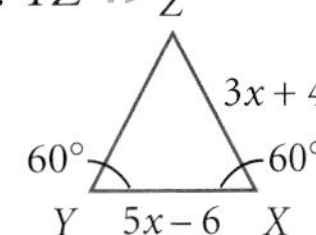

Z, $3x + 4$, 60°, 60°, Y, $5x - 6$, X

Use the figure at the right in Exercises 8–10.

C, A D E B

8. *Given:* $\triangle ABC$ is isosceles, with base $\overline{AB}$.
   a. Name the congruent sides. $\overline{AC}, \overline{BC}$
   b. Name the congruent angles. $\angle CAB, \angle CBA$
   c. What theorem guarantees that the angles are congruent? Isosceles Triangle Theorem
9. *Given:* $\angle CDE \cong \angle CED$
   a. Name the congruent sides in $\triangle DEC$.
   b. What theorem guarantees that the sides are congruent?
10. If $\triangle ABC$ is isosceles with base $\overline{AB}$, and $\overline{AD} \cong \overline{BE}$, is $\triangle DCE$ isosceles? Explain.
11. $\triangle RST$ is isosceles with base $\overline{RS}$. Draw $\triangle RST$, and mark the congruent sides. If $RT = 5x - 4$, $ST = 3x + 4$, and $RS = 2x + 9$, find the lengths of the sides of the triangle.

Ongoing Assessment

Vocabulary
Practice/Skills
Review
Math Reasoning
Problem Solving
Challenge

Self-Assessment Exercises 1–15 odd

Embedded Assessment Consider 2; Exercises 6, 8, 12, 16

Journal

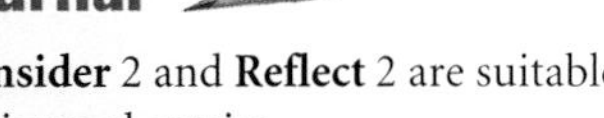

Consider 2 and **Reflect** 2 are suitable for journal entries.

REFLECT

Possible Answers

1. Suppose $\triangle ABC$ is equilateral. Since $\overline{BC} \cong \overline{AC}$, we know $\angle A \cong \angle B$; since $\overline{AC} \cong \overline{AB}$, we know $\angle B \cong \angle C$. Therefore, $\angle A \cong \angle B \cong \angle C$.
2. a. An angle bisector is only guaranteed to divide the angle into congruent halves, not the opposite side.
   b. Yes. It divides the isosceles triangles into two smaller triangles that can be proved congruent by SAS. By CPCTC, the segments created on the base by the angle bisector are congruent, so the point of intersection of the base and angle bisector is the midpoint of the base.
3. Yes. Base angles of an isosceles triangle are congruent. If one of the base angles were obtuse, the other would be also, and the sum of the measures of the angles of the triangle would exceed 180°.

Part A Exercises

Exercise Notes

Core

12. Students use the Triangle Angle-Sum Theorem and the converse of the Isosceles Triangle Theorem to solve a real-world problem.

15. History Note: Napoleon had a great interest in mathematics. He once said, "The advancement and perfection of mathematics are intimately connected with the prosperity of the state."

16. Students complete a proof of the Isosceles Triangle Theorem's converse.

Look Ahead

These exercises apply triangle-congruence postulates to right triangles. In 4-3 Part B, students will see triangle-congruence theorems that apply specifically to right triangles.

Properties of Special Triangles

Exercise Answers

Core

1. $\overline{FG}$ and $\overline{GH}$ have the same length.

2. Isosceles Triangle Theorem

3. Definition of an *isosceles triangle*

9. a. $\overline{CD}$, $\overline{CE}$

b. Converse of the Isosceles Triangle Theorem.

10. Yes; $\overline{AC} \cong \overline{BC}$ since $\triangle ABC$ is isosceles. $\angle A \cong \angle B$ by the Isosceles Triangle Theorem. We are given $\overline{AD} \cong \overline{BE}$. Therefore $\triangle ACD \cong \triangle BCE$ by SAS. So $\overline{DC} \cong \overline{EC}$ by CPCTC. Then $\triangle DCE$ is isosceles by definition.

11. $RS = 17$, $RT = ST = 16$

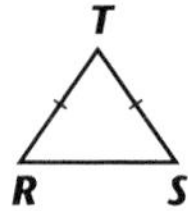

12. 48 ft; The angle at the top is also 45° by the Triangle Angle-Sum Theorem. The side of the building is congruent to the 48 ft portion of the ground by the converse of the Isosceles Triangle Theorem. So the height of the building is 48 ft.

13. *Given:* $\angle 2 \cong \angle 4$
Prove: $\triangle XYZ$ is isosceles.
Proof: 1. (b), Given; 2. (e), Vertical angles are congruent; 3. (a), Transitive Property; 4. (d), Isosceles Triangle Theorem Converse; 5. (c), Definition of *isosceles.*

14. One (unless it is equilateral)

16.

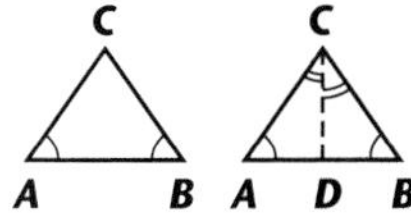

Reason 2: Definition of *bisect*
Statement 3. $\overline{CD} \cong \overline{CD}$
Statement 4. $\angle A \cong \angle B$
Statement 5. $\triangle ADC \cong \triangle BDC$
Reason 5. SAA Postulate
Reason 6. CPCTC

PS, MR **12. Steep Thinking** A surveyor is curious about the height of a tall building. Using an ordinary protractor, he finds that the top of the building and the ground make a 45° angle when the protractor is 48 ft away from the base of the building. How tall is the building? Explain the reasoning you used to solve this problem.

P, MR **13.** Write the Given and Prove for the following proof. Then arrange the statements in a logical order, and give a reason for each statement.

If $\angle 2 \cong \angle 4$, then $\triangle XYZ$ is isosceles.

Given: ____

Prove: ____

Proof:

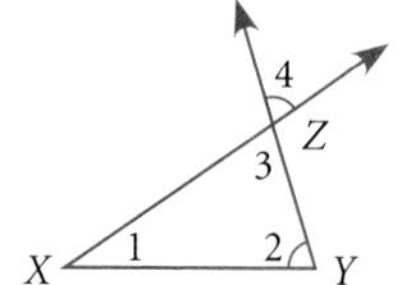

Statements	Reasons	Scrambled Statements
1.	**1.**	**a.** $\angle 2 \cong \angle 3$
2.	**2.**	**b.** $\angle 2 \cong \angle 4$
3.	**3.**	**c.** $\triangle XYZ$ is isosceles.
4.	**4.**	**d.** $\overline{XY} \cong \overline{XZ}$
5.	**5.**	**e.** $\angle 4 \cong \angle 3$

P **14.** Draw three different isosceles triangles. For each, illustrate all the lines of symmetry that reflect the triangle onto itself. How many lines of symmetry does an isosceles triangle have?

MR History **15. Napoleon's Conjecture** Napoleon is said to have made a conjecture about triangles suggested by the steps below. See if you can discover the conjecture he made.

Start with a triangle $\triangle ABC$. Using each of its sides as a base, construct isosceles triangles whose base angles are 30°. Connect the vertices of the isosceles triangles to form $\triangle DEF$ as shown. $\triangle DEF$ is equilateral

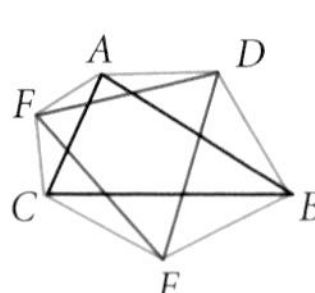

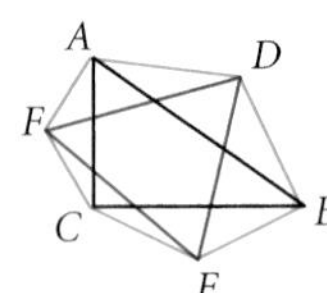

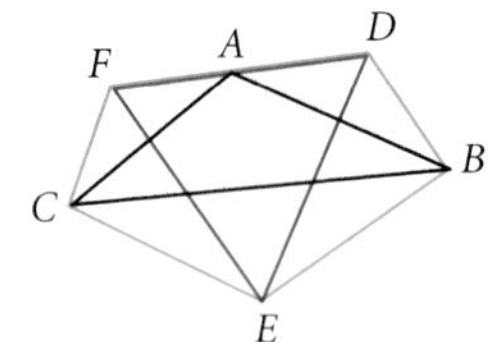

Key

V Vocabulary
P Practice/Skills
R Review
MR Math Reasoning
PS Problem Solving
C Challenge

16. Proving the Converse *Draw* a figure to represent the Given information. Then add the auxiliary line discussed in the *plan*. Finally, complete the proof below.

Prove: If two angles of a triangle are congruent, then the sides opposite the angles are congruent.

Given: $\triangle ABC$ with $\angle A \cong \angle B$ *Prove:* $\overline{AC} \cong \overline{BC}$

Plan: Draw an auxiliary ray that bisects $\angle C$. Prove that the two triangles formed are congruent, and then use CPCTC.

Proof:

Statements	Reasons
1. Draw $\overrightarrow{CD}$, the angle bisector of $\angle C$ that intersects $\overline{AB}$ at D.	**1.** Every angle has a unique ray that bisects it.
2. $\angle ACD \cong \angle BCD$	**2.**
3.	**3.** Reflexive Property
4.	**4.** Given
5.	**5.**
6. $\overline{AC} \cong \overline{BC}$	**6.**

LOOK AHEAD

Name the triangle-congruence condition that could be used to show $\triangle ABC \cong \triangle RST$.

17. $\overline{BC} \cong \overline{ST}$, $\overline{AB} \perp \overline{BC}$, $\overline{RS} \perp \overline{ST}$, and $\overline{AB} \cong \overline{RS}$. SAS Postulate

18. $\overline{AC} \cong \overline{RT}$, $\angle C \cong \angle T$, $m\angle B = 90°$, and $m\angle S = 90°$. SAA Postulate

19. $\overline{AB} \cong \overline{RS}$, $\overline{AB} \perp \overline{BC}$, $\overline{RS} \perp \overline{ST}$, and $\angle A \cong \angle R$. ASA Postulate

20. $\overline{AB} \cong \overline{RS}$, $\angle C \cong \angle T$, $m\angle B = 90°$, and $m\angle S = 90°$. SAA Postulate

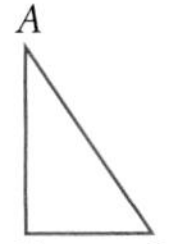

MORE PRACTICE

Use the information in the figures to find the following.

21. $m\angle A$ 80°

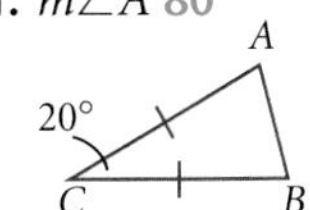

22. $m\angle D$ 18.5°

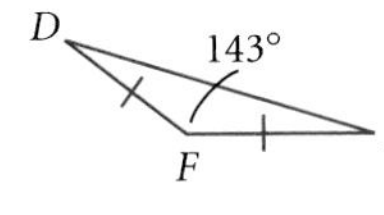

23. $m\angle H$ 45°

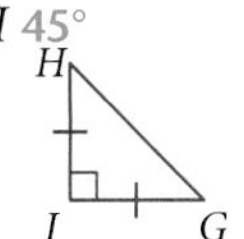

24. XZ 3

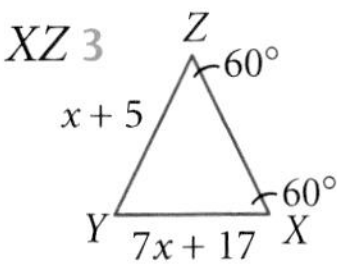

More Math Reasoning

25. Draw a straight line. Set the compass on the line at a point A and draw an arc which intersects the line at a point B and sweeps wide to one side. Move the compass to B and draw another arc which intersects the first one at a point C. $\triangle ABC$ is equilateral because all sides are the same length.

27. Yes; The road and the two lines of sight form an isosceles triangle.

Properties of Special Triangles

PART B At a Glance

Objective

To use congruence theorems for right triangles, and to see that there is no SSA congruence.

Development

First, students see the LL, HA, and LA congruence theorems for right triangles.

Then, in the **Explore,** students discover that there is no SSA congruence postulate. They also see that SSA *does* work for right triangles. This leads to the HL congruence theorem.

Suggested Materials

Student Ruler, protractor, compass

First Five Minutes

Transparency FFM 4-3B

List all of the triangle-congruence postulates, and give a sketch to illustrate each.

Motivate

Ask...

- Suppose you know that the two legs of one right triangle are congruent to the legs of another right triangle. Are the triangles congruent? Justify your answer.

MORE MATH REASONING

PS **25.** Construct an equilateral triangle with a compass and straightedge. Explain the method that you used, and explain why it works.

MR **26.** In $\triangle ABC$, $AB = 9 - 2x$, $AC = 4x$, and $BC = x + 3$. Find all values of x that make $\triangle ABC$ isosceles. 2, 1.5, 1

C **27. A Futuristic Bike** Karl tells a friend that he can use the gadgets on his new bike to find out how far away from the road a satellite tracking station is located. Karl explains that the bike's angle locator and odometer (the device that measures the distance traveled) will help him determine the distance to the tracking station.

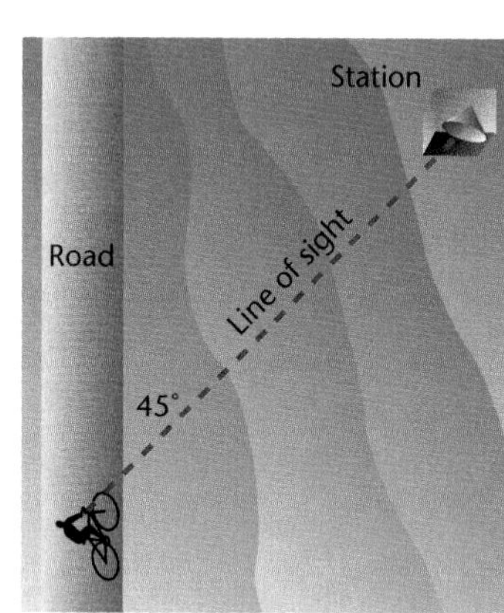

Karl says, "I'll keep checking the angle between the road and my line of sight to the station until I get a 45° angle. Then, I'll set the odometer to zero and ride down the road until the angle between the road and the line of sight to the station is a right angle. The odometer reading at that time will be the distance to the station."

Is Karl right? Explain.

4-3 PART B Right Triangles

← CONNECT → ***You've seen right triangles before, and you're familiar with several ways to prove triangles congruent. Now you will explore special congruence properties for right triangles and investigate whether or not there is a Side-Side-Angle congruence postulate.***

If you need to prove that two right triangles are congruent, you can use any of the triangle-congruence postulates that you've seen so far. However, there are some additional methods that apply only to right triangles. You will see that most of these are simply special cases of the postulates you already know.

Key

- **V** Vocabulary
- **P** Practice/Skills
- **R** Review
- **MR** Math Reasoning
- **PS** Problem Solving
- **C** Challenge

Research Note

Often, students do not realize that a mathematical statement is said to be correct only if it is correct in each and every conceivable instance in which the assumptions are satisfied. (Tommy Dreyfus and Nurit Hadas, "Euclid May Stay—and Even Be Taught," *Learning and Teaching Geometry, K–12, 1987 Yearbook,* Mary Montgomery Lindquist and Albert P. Shulte, eds., p. 49. © 1987 NCTM.)

LEG-LEG CONGRUENCE THEOREM (LL)

If the legs of a right triangle are congruent to the legs of another right triangle, then the two triangles are congruent.

Right triangles $\triangle ABC$ and $\triangle FGH$ are congruent by LL.

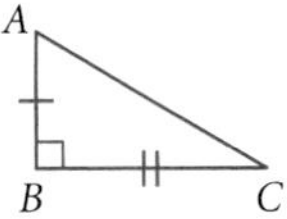

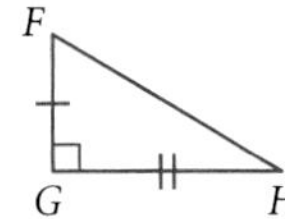

HYPOTENUSE-ACUTE-ANGLE CONGRUENCE THEOREM (HA)

If the hypotenuse and an acute angle of one right triangle are congruent to the hypotenuse and an acute angle of another right triangle, then the two triangles are congruent.

Right triangles $\triangle HIJ$ and $\triangle RST$ are congruent by HA.

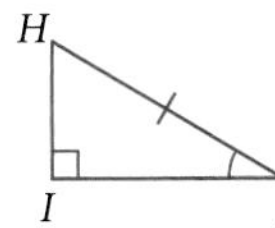

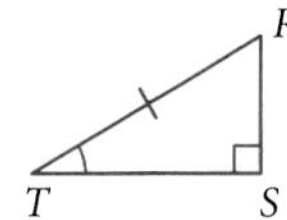

LEG-ACUTE-ANGLE CONGRUENCE THEOREM (LA)

If one leg and one acute angle of a right triangle are congruent to the corresponding leg and acute angle of another right triangle, then the two triangles are congruent.

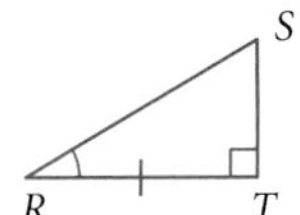

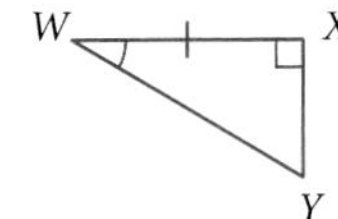

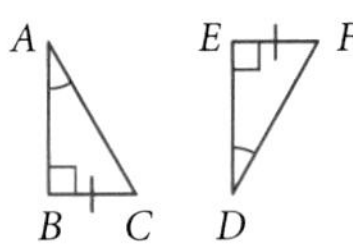

Right triangles $\triangle RST$ and $\triangle WXY$ are congruent by LA. $\triangle ABC$ and $\triangle DEF$ are also congruent by LA.

1. Which congruence theorem that applies to all triangles can be used instead of HA? Illustrate your answer.

Shows that some of the right-triangle congruence theorems are simply special cases of the general congruence postulates.

Possible Answer

1. The SAA postulate.

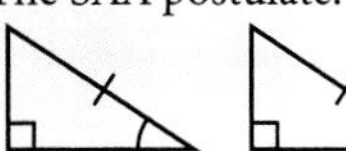

Student Resources

- Alternative Lessons 4-3B
- Laboratory Manual 4-3B
- Technology Lab Manual
- Practice 4-3B
- Study Guide and Journal 4-3B
- Guía de estudios y Diario 4-3B
- Multilingual Handbook
- More Look Back 4-3B
- SAT Preparation

Media Resources

- Transparency FFM 4-3B
- Transparency AE 4-3B
- Teaching Transparency
- AWSMTest and practice software
- AWSM Videodisc

Algebra	Functions	Discrete Math	Probability	Data/Statistics

Properties of Special Triangles

EXPLORE

The Case of the Ambiguous Triangle

Recommended group size: 4

The Point

To see that there is no SSA congruence for triangles, and to discover the HL congruence theorem for right triangles.

Look and Listen...

- For students who do not find two triangles in Step 1.
- For students who are having difficulty using a compass to measure the third side.

Ask...

- If you put the tip of the compass at B and swing an arc, in how many places does the arc intersect the other side of $\angle A$? What does this mean?

For Groups That Finish Early

Suppose $\angle A$ has a measure of 30°, and $AB = 5$. In the situation where $\overline{BC}$ "fits perfectly," find the measures of all other angles and sides. Is there any special relationship between BC and AB? $BC = \frac{1}{2}AB$; 30°–60°–90° △

Follow Up

Ask students if there is an SSA postulate for all triangles. If not, does SSA seem to work in some situations?

Possible Answers

1. No. Two different triangles satisfy these conditions.
2. There is no way to construct such a triangle.
3. Second side too short—no triangle. Second side "just right"—one triangle (a right triangle). Second side longer than the one for a right triangle but shorter than the first side—two triangles. Second side longer than the first side—one triangle.
4. SSA works for right triangles.

You're familiar with the SAS Congruence Postulate, which uses two sides and an included angle. In the following Explore, you will investigate whether or not there is a Side-Side-Angle (SSA) Congruence Postulate, where the known angle is not the included angle.

EXPLORE: THE CASE OF THE AMBIGUOUS TRIANGLE

MATERIALS

Ruler
Protractor
Compass

1. Draw $\angle A$ with measure 30°. Along one side of $\angle A$, locate point B, 5 in. from A. Now complete $\triangle ABC$ with a segment $\overline{BC}$ that is $3\frac{1}{2}$ in. long. Compare your triangle with those made by your classmates. Are they all congruent? Do you think there is an SSA congruence postulate?
2. Repeat Step 1, but this time complete $\triangle ABC$ with a segment $\overline{BC}$ that is 2 in. long. Explain what this tells you about triangles with a 30° angle, a 5-in. side, and a 2-in. side opposite the angle.
3. Explore what is happening by experimenting with different lengths for $\overline{BC}$. Are there different ways the arc can intersect the side? Find all the possibilities, and draw a sketch of each. Make any conjectures you can.
4. In what case does SSA "work"—that is, when did you get just one triangle? Make a conjecture that describes this situation.

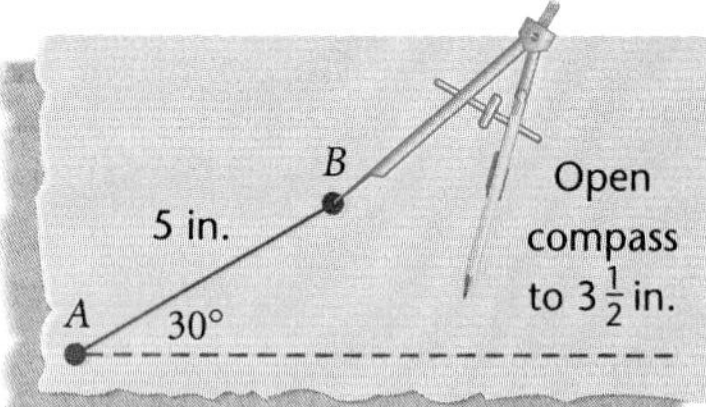

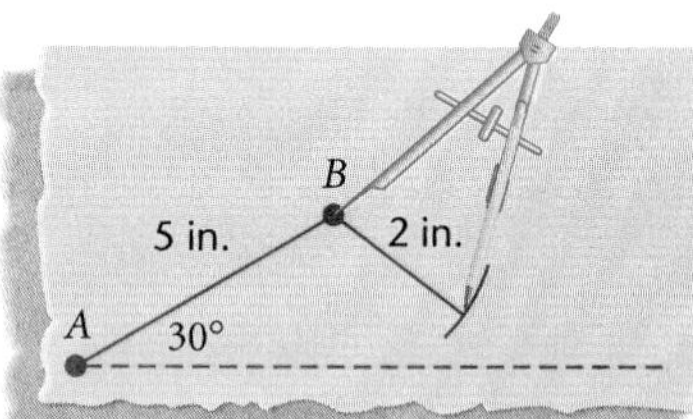

Although SSA does not work for triangles in general, the right-triangle version does work. This is the HL Congruence Theorem for right triangles.

HYPOTENUSE-LEG CONGRUENCE THEOREM (HL)

If the hypotenuse and a leg of one right triangle are congruent to the hypotenuse and a leg of another right triangle, then the two triangles are congruent.

Alert

Students may object to the HL theorem because, in the *Explore,* the given angle was acute, not right. You may want to show them that HL does work by sketching $\triangle ABC$ with $m\angle A = 90°$, $AB = 5$, and $BC = 6$. There is only one possibility in this situation with any $BC > 5$. If $BC \leq 5$, no triangle is possible. The two-triangle situation is not possible for right triangles.

EXAMPLE

Given: $\overline{SR} \perp \overline{RT}$, $\overline{XT} \perp \overline{TR}$, $\overline{ST} \cong \overline{XR}$

Prove: $\triangle RST \cong \triangle TXR$

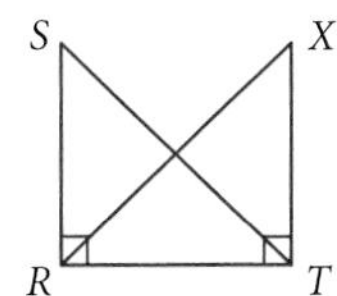

We can separate the overlapping triangles from the figure and mark the congruent parts.

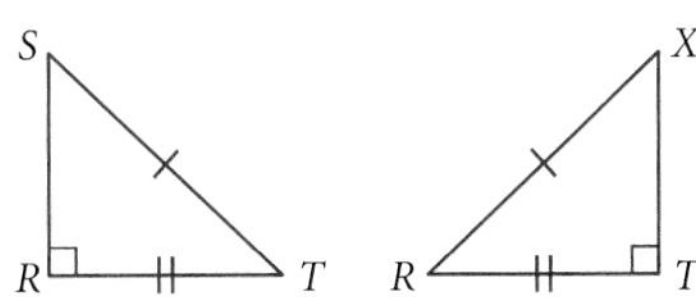

Proof: Since the given information tells us that $\overline{SR} \perp \overline{RT}$, and $\overline{XT} \perp \overline{TR}$, then $\angle SRT$ and $\angle XTR$ are right angles because perpendicular lines form right angles. $\triangle RST$ and $\triangle TXR$ are right triangles by the definition of *right triangle.* We are given that the triangles have congruent hypotenuses, $\overline{ST}$ and $\overline{XR}$, and the shared leg $\overline{RT}$ is congruent to itself by the Reflexive Property. It follows from the HL Theorem that $\triangle RST \cong \triangle TXR$.

REFLECT

1. What must you know before you use LL, LA, HA, or HL to prove triangles congruent?
2. Why is there no Side-Side-Angle congruence condition for triangles?

Exercises

CORE

Getting Started Name the right-triangle congruence theorem that shows why the triangles in each pair are congruent. If the triangles are not necessarily congruent, explain why.

1.  **2.** 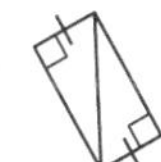 **3.**  **4.** 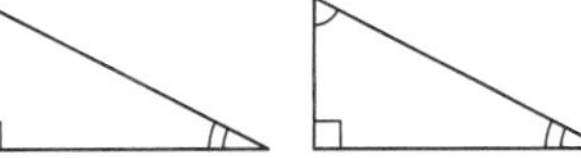

ALTERNATE EXAMPLE

Given: $\overline{SR} \perp \overline{RT}$, $\overline{XT} \perp \overline{RT}$, $\angle S \cong \angle X$

Prove: $\triangle RST \cong \triangle TXR$

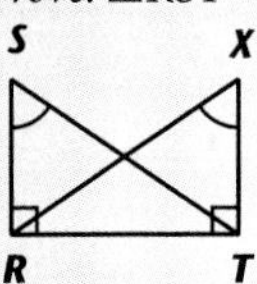

Proof: The given information states that $\overline{SR} \perp \overline{RT}$ and $\overline{XT} \perp \overline{RT}$. $\angle SRT$ and $\angle XTR$ are right angles, since perpendicular lines form right angles. $\triangle RST$ and $\triangle TXR$ are right triangles by definition. $\angle S \cong \angle X$ (given) and $\overline{RT} \cong \overline{RT}$ (Reflexive), so $\triangle RST \cong \triangle TXR$ by the LA theorem.

Journal

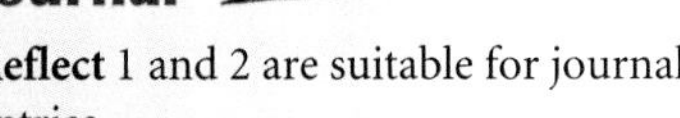

Reflect 1 and 2 are suitable for journal entries.

REFLECT

Possible Answers

1. The triangles involved must be right triangles.
2. In some situations, two triangles can be shaped differently even though two sides and a non-included angle in the first triangle are congruent to the corresponding parts in the second triangle.

Ongoing Assessment

Vocabulary
Practice/Skills
Review
Math Reasoning
Problem Solving
Challenge

Self-Assessment Exercises 1–11 odd

Embedded Assessment Reflect 2; Exercises 6, 8, 10

Algebra	Functions	Discrete Math	Probability	Data/Statistics

Properties of Special Triangles

Part B Exercises

Exercise Notes

Core

10. Connects topics of this part to astronomy.

Science Note: At its brightest, Venus is the third-brightest object seen from the earth after the sun and the moon. It is about 16 times as bright as Sirius, the brightest star.

11. Shows right triangles in a construction application.

More Math Reasoning

22. Students prove a property of the diagonals of a rectangle. This proof requires the use of auxiliary lines, and previews topics in Chapter 6.

Exercise Answers

Core

1. HL Theorem **2.** HL Theorem

3. HA Theorem

4. The triangles are not necessarily congruent because three pairs of congruent angles does not imply that the triangles are congruent.

5. $\overline{WX} \cong \overline{ZY}$ or $\overline{ZX} \cong \overline{WY}$

6. $\overline{WX} \cong \overline{ZY}$ and $\overline{ZX} \cong \overline{WY}$

7. $\overline{WX} \cong \overline{ZY}$ and $\angle ZWX \cong \angle WZY$, or $\overline{ZX} \cong \overline{WY}$ and $\angle WZX \cong \angle ZWY$ (both), or $\overline{WX} \cong \overline{ZY}$ and $\angle WZX \cong \angle ZWY$ or $\overline{ZX} \cong \overline{WY}$ and $\angle ZWX \cong \angle WZY$ (LA only).

8. a. Given information

b. Definition of *perpendicular*

c. Definition of a *right triangle*

d. Given information

e. Definition of *midpoint*

f. Reflexive Property

g. LL **h.** CPCTC

i. Definition of an *isosceles triangle*

P **Given that $\angle X$ and $\angle Y$ are right angles, state the pairs of corresponding parts that are needed to establish that $\triangle WXZ \cong \triangle ZYW$ by the given method. List all possible pairs of corresponding parts for each.**

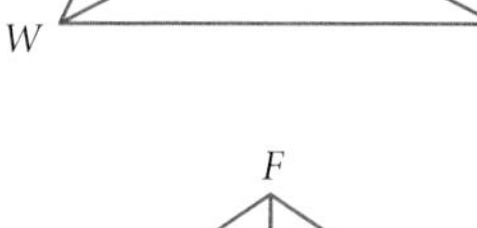

5. HL **6.** LL or SAS **7.** LA or ASA

P, MR **8.** Complete the following proof.

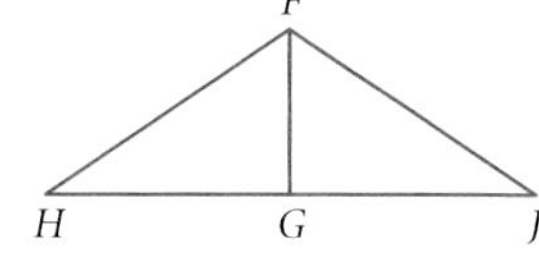

Given: $\overline{FG} \perp \overline{HJ}$
G is the midpoint of $\overline{HJ}$.

Prove: $\triangle HFJ$ is isosceles.

Proof: The **a.** ___ tells us that $\overline{FG} \perp \overline{HJ}$. Therefore, $\angle FGH$ and $\angle FGJ$ are right angles by the **b.** ___, and $\triangle FGH$ and $\triangle FGJ$ are right triangles by the **c.** ___. G is the midpoint of $\overline{HJ}$ from the **d.** ___, so $\overline{HG} \cong \overline{JG}$ by the **e.** ___. $\overline{FG} \cong \overline{FG}$ because of the **f.** ___. Therefore, $\triangle FGH \cong \triangle FGJ$ by the **g.** ___ Theorem. Since the triangles are congruent, $\overline{FH} \cong \overline{FJ}$ by **h.** ___. Finally, $\triangle HFJ$ is isosceles by the **i.** ___.

P, MR **9.** Complete the following proof.

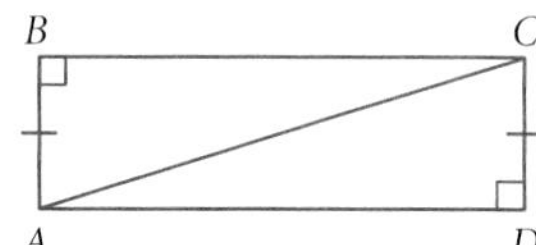

Given: $\angle B$ and $\angle D$ are right angles, and $\overline{AB} \cong \overline{CD}$.

Prove: $\triangle ABC \cong \triangle CDA$

Proof:

Statements	Reasons
1. $\angle B$ and $\angle D$ are right angles.	**1.**
2. $\triangle ABC$ is a right triangle. $\triangle CDA$ is a right triangle.	**2.**
3.	**3.** Given
4.	**4.**
5. $\triangle ABC \cong \triangle CDA$	**5.**

MR Science **10. Looking for Planets** Because Venus is nearer to the sun than the earth is, it always appears just above the horizon. The best time to see this planet is in the morning or evening when it is at a *maximum elongation,* as shown. At these positions, Venus is at its greatest distance from the horizon.

If we assume that Venus's orbit is perfectly circular, $\overline{SV_1} \cong \overline{SV_2}$. Explain why $\triangle SV_1E \cong \triangle SV_2E$.

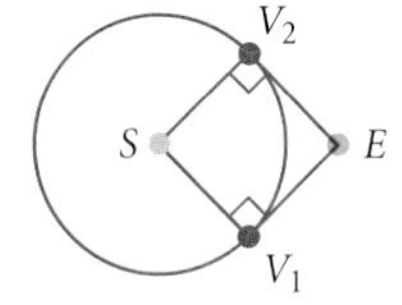

At V_1, Venus is at maximum eastern elongation.
At V_2, Venus is at maximum western elongation.

Key

V Vocabulary
P Practice/Skills
R Review
MR Math Reasoning
PS Problem Solving
C Challenge

11. King-Post Truss One method of supporting the rafters of a roof is called a *king-post truss.* Assume rafter $\overline{AB} \cong$ rafter $\overline{CB}$, brace $\overline{DH}$ is placed at the midpoint of $\overline{AB}$, brace $\overline{HF}$ is placed at the midpoint of $\overline{BC}$, E is the midpoint of $\overline{AH}$, G is the midpoint of $\overline{CH}$, $\overline{DE} \perp \overline{AH}$, $\overline{BH} \perp \overline{AC}$, and $\overline{FG} \perp \overline{HC}$.

a. State congruences for three pairs of right triangles.

b. Support each congruence with a congruence theorem.

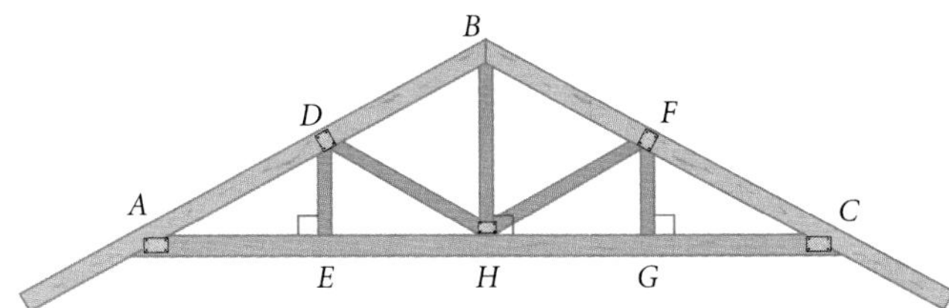

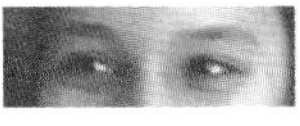

LOOK BACK

For each of the following transformations, copy $\triangle ABC$, and draw the image $\triangle A'B'C'$.

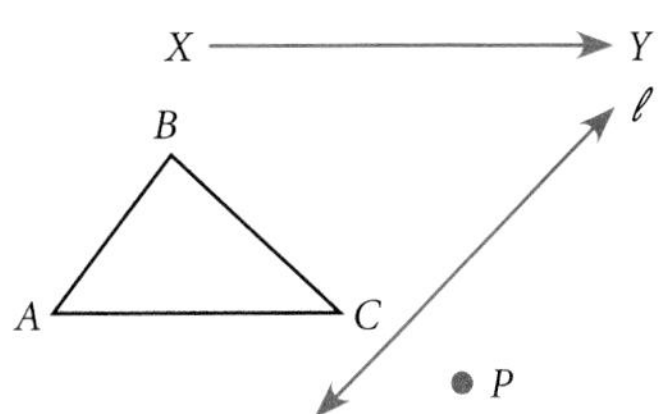

12. a 45° clockwise rotation around point P [3-2]

13. a reflection over line ℓ [1-4]

14. a translation with translation vector $\overrightarrow{XY}$ [3-1]

15. Complete the following proof. [3-4, 4-2]

Given: $\overline{VW} \cong \overline{ZY}$, $\overline{VW} \parallel \overline{ZY}$

Prove: $\triangle XVW \cong \triangle XZY$

Proof:

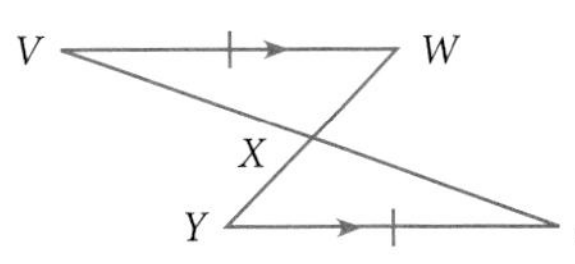

Statements	Reasons
1. $\overline{VW} \cong \overline{ZY}$	**1.**
2.	**2.** Vertical angles are congruent.
3. $\overline{VW} \parallel \overline{ZY}$	**3.**
4. $\angle WVX \cong \angle YZX$	**4.**
5.	**5.**

9. Reason 1: Given
Reason 2: Definition of a *right triangle*
Statement 3: $\overline{AB} \cong \overline{CD}$
Statement 4: $\overline{AC} \cong \overline{AC}$
Reason 4: Reflexive Property
Reason 5: HL Theorem

10. $\angle V_1$ and $\angle V_2$ are right angles, so $\triangle SV_1E$ and $\triangle SV_2E$ are right triangles by the definition of *right triangles.* $\overline{SE} \cong \overline{SE}$ by the Reflexive Property. We are given that $\overline{SV_1} \cong \overline{SV_2}$. Therefore, $\triangle SV_1E \cong \triangle SV_2E$ by the HL Theorem.

11. a. Possible answer:
$\triangle ABH \cong \triangle CBH$,
$\triangle ADE \cong \triangle HDE$,
$\triangle HFG \cong \triangle CFG$

b. HL Theorem, LL Theorem, LL Theorem, respectively.

Look Back

12.

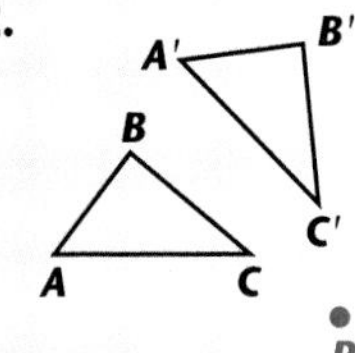

13.

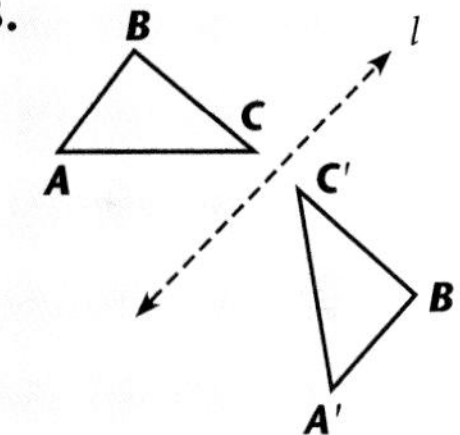

14.

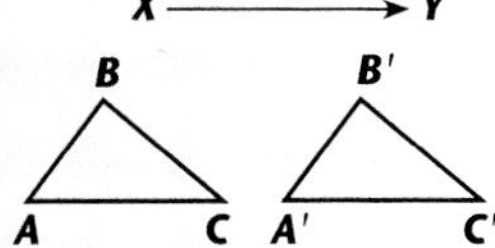

15. Reason 1: Given
Statement 2: $\angle YXZ \cong \angle WXV$
Reason 3: Given
Reason 4: If two parallel lines are cut by a transversal, the alternate interior angles are congruent.
Statement 5: $\triangle XVW \cong \triangle XZY$
Reason 5: SAA Postulate

Properties of Special Triangles

More Practice

19. Statement 1: $\angle EDF$ and $\angle CFD$ are right angles
Reason 1: Given
Reason 2: Definition of a *right triangle*
Reason 3: Given
Statement 4: $\overline{FD} \cong \overline{FD}$
Reason 5: HL Theorem
Statement 6: $\overline{DE} \cong \overline{FC}$
Reason 6: CPCTC

More Math Reasoning

20. They both measure 45°; The acute angles are complementary, and by the Isosceles Triangle Theorem, they are congruent. It follows that they each measure 45°.

21. Possible answer: So that we do not conclude that triangles like those below are congruent.

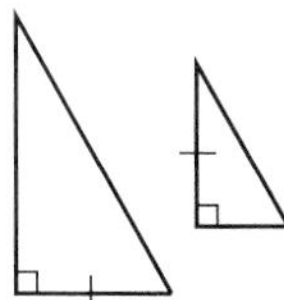

22. Possible answer:
Given: ABCD is a rectangle

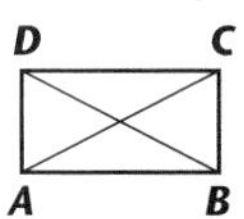

Prove: $\overline{AC} \cong \overline{BD}$
Proof: $\overline{AC} \cong \overline{AC}$ by the Reflexive Property. $\angle CDA$ and $\angle BAD$ are right angles (given). Each measures 90°, by definition, so these same side interior angles are supplementary, and $\overline{AD} \parallel \overline{BC}$. Thus, alternate interior angles are congruent, and $\angle DCA \cong \angle BAC$. $\triangle DCA$ and $\triangle BAC$ are right triangles, by definition, and $\triangle DCA \cong \triangle BAC$ by HA. $\overline{DA} \cong \overline{BC}$ by CPCTC. $\overline{AB} \cong \overline{AB}$ by the Reflexive Property. Therefore, right triangles $\triangle ABC$ and $\triangle BAD$ are congruent by LL, and diagonal $\overline{AC}$ is congruent to diagonal $\overline{BD}$ by CPCTC.

MORE PRACTICE

P **In each of the following, name the right-triangle congruence theorem that shows that $\triangle SQR \cong \triangle TQP$. If the triangles are not necessarily congruent, explain why.**

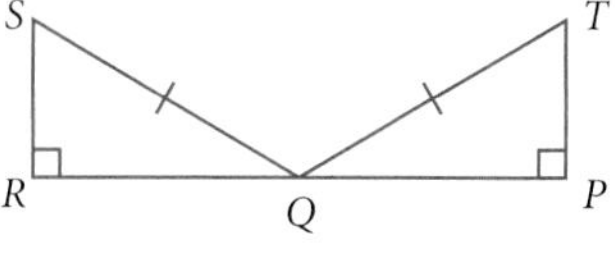

16. Q is the midpoint of $\overline{RP}$. HL Theorem

17. $\overline{RS} \cong \overline{TP}$ HL Theorem

18. $\angle S \cong \angle T$ HA Theorem

P, MR **19.** Complete the following proof.

Given: $\overline{DC} \cong \overline{FE}$
$\angle EDF$ and $\angle CFD$ are right angles.

Prove: $\overline{DE} \cong \overline{FC}$

Proof:

Statements	Reasons
1.	**1.**
2. $\triangle CFD$ is a right triangle. $\triangle EDF$ is a right triangle.	**2.**
3. $\overline{DC} \cong \overline{FE}$	**3.**
4.	**4.** Reflexive Property
5. $\triangle DFC \cong \triangle FDE$	**5.**
6.	**6.**

MORE MATH REASONING

MR **20.** The figure at the right shows an isosceles right triangle. Make a conjecture about the acute angles of an isosceles right triangle. Explain your reasoning.

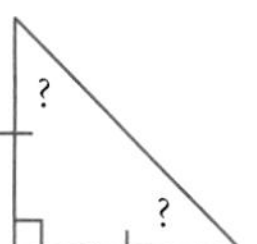

C **21.** Explain why the word *corresponding* is important in the LA congruence theorem.

MR **22.** All four angles in a rectangle are right angles. Prove that the diagonals of a rectangle are congruent.

Key

V Vocabulary
P Practice/Skills
R Review
MR Math Reasoning
PS Problem Solving
C Challenge

4-3 PART C Perpendiculars, Bisectors, and Locus

← CONNECT → *You're already familiar with angle bisectors and segment bisectors. Now you will investigate their special properties and see how they are related to the idea of locus.*

Many geometry problems can be solved by finding the set of points that satisfy certain conditions.

DEFINITION

A **locus** is the set of all the points that satisfy a given condition.

EXAMPLE

Determine the locus of points in a plane 2 in. from a given point Q.

Step 1: Plot point Q and several other points that are 2 in. from Q (points A–H).

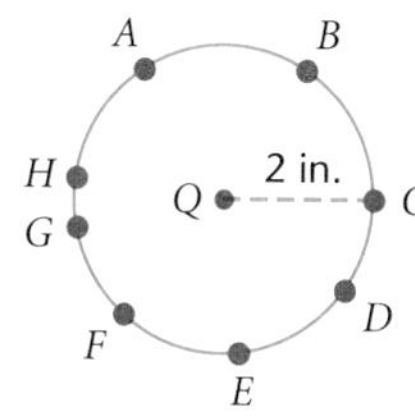

Step 2: Draw a figure that contains these points. The figure is a circle with radius 2 in.

Step 3: Check: Does every point on the figure satisfy the given condition? *(Yes)* Are there any points that satisfy the condition that are not on the figure? *(No)*

Therefore, the locus of all points in a plane 2 in. from a given point Q is a circle with radius 2 in. and center at point Q.

TRY IT

a. Describe the locus of points *in space* that are 2 in. from a given point C. The sphere with radius 2 in. and center at point C.

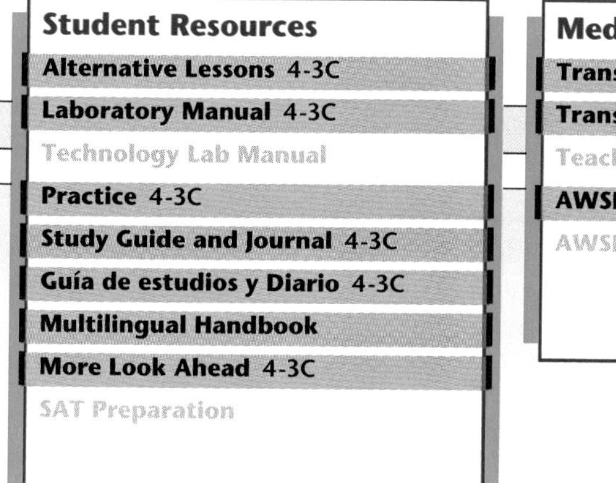

Student Resources
- Alternative Lessons 4-3C
- Laboratory Manual 4-3C
- Technology Lab Manual
- Practice 4-3C
- Study Guide and Journal 4-3C
- Guía de estudios y Diario 4-3C
- Multilingual Handbook
- More Look Ahead 4-3C
- SAT Preparation

Media Resources
- Transparency FFM 4-3C
- Transparency AE 4-3C
- Teaching Transparency
- AWSMTest and practice software
- AWSM Videodisc

PART C At a Glance

Objective

To find sets of points satisfying given conditions.

Development

Students see the definition of locus, and, in an **Example** and **Try It,** find some simple loci.

In the **Explore,** students discover that points on the perpendicular bisector of a segment are equidistant from the segment's endpoints, and that points on the bisector of an angle are equidistant from the angle's sides. They use these properties to solve a practical problem.

Suggested Materials

Student Paper, ruler, protractor

Key Terms

Locus

First Five Minutes

Transparency FFM 4-3C

Read the definition of *locus* and the **Example** on page 299. Then do **Try It a.**

Motivate

Ask...

- How do you determine the distance from a point to a line?
- Suppose two cities share the cost of a new airport that serves both cities. Why might it be important for the airport to be equally distant from each city? Is it possible that the best location for the airport may not be equally distant from the cities? Why?

ALTERNATE EXAMPLE

Transparency AE 4-3C

4-3

Properties of Special Triangles

Algebra | Functions | Discrete Math | Probability | Data/Statistics

EXPLORE

Build It There!

Recommended group size: 4

The Point

To discover that points on the perpendicular bisector of a segment are equidistant from the segment's endpoints and that points on the bisector of an angle are equidistant from the angle's sides.

Look and Listen...

- For students who have difficulty seeing that points on the angle bisector are equidistant from its sides in Step 3.

Ask...

- If you select a point on the bisector, how do you find the distance from that point to a side of the angle? (Hint: How do you find the distance from a point to a line?)

For Groups That Finish Early

Explain why there is only one possible place for the tower.

Follow Up

Ask students to describe the following.

1. The locus of points equidistant from two given points.
2. The locus of points equidistant from the sides of an angle.

Possible Answers

1. Points on the fold are equidistant from A and B.
2. The locus of points in a plane equidistant from two given points is the perpendicular bisector of the segment joining the given points.
3. The locus of points equidistant from the sides of an angle is the angle bisector of the angle.
4. The tower should be at the point of intersection of the angle bisector of the highways and the perpendicular bisector of the segment joining the towns.

EXPLORE: BUILD IT THERE!

MATERIALS

Paper
Ruler
Protractor

A contractor has been commissioned to set up a transmitting tower. The tower must be equidistant from two towns, Wilbur and Clay Center, and must also be equidistant from two highways, Hwy 6 and Hwy 81.

After you complete Steps 1–3, you will be able to help the contractor identify the location for the tower.

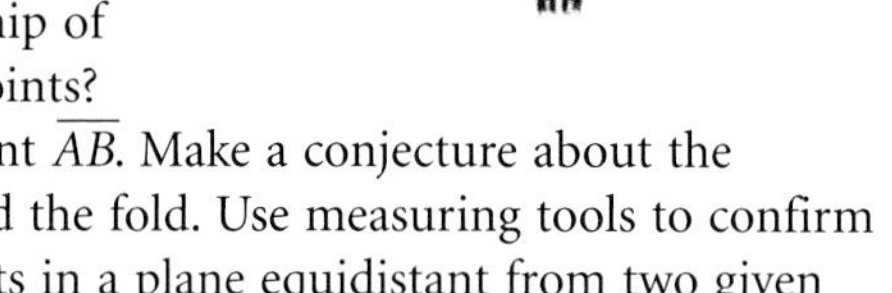

1. Draw points A and B on a sheet of paper. Fold the paper so that one point is reflected onto the other. What is the relationship of any point on the fold to these two points?
2. Use your straightedge to draw segment $\overline{AB}$. Make a conjecture about the relationship between the segment and the fold. Use measuring tools to confirm your ideas. What is the locus of points in a plane equidistant from two given points?
3. Draw an angle on a sheet of paper, and fold the paper so that one side of the angle is reflected onto the other. Make a conjecture about how the fold divides the angle. Then investigate the distances of the points on the fold from the two sides. Make a conjecture about the locus of points equidistant from the sides of an angle.
4. Find the location where the contractor should build the tower.

In the Explore, you used the perpendicular bisector of a segment. Although you have seen this term before, a quick reminder of its definition may be helpful.

A **perpendicular bisector** of a segment is a line, ray, segment, or plane that is perpendicular to the segment and divides it into two congruent segments. In the figure at the right, line m is the perpendicular bisector of $\overline{AB}$.

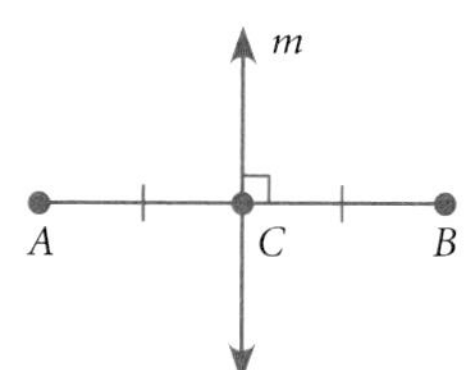

The next theorem states the relationship between any point on a perpendicular bisector and any point equidistant from two given points.

Tips from Teachers

Students may have difficulty understanding why the plural of *locus* is *loci*. You may want to explain that many words with Latin origins have singular versions that end in *us*, and plurals that end in *i*. (Example: *alumnus–alumni*.) This pattern holds true in Latin for many masculine words. The general pattern for feminine words follows: singular—*a*, plural—*ae*. (Example: *alumna–alumnae*.)

THEOREM

A point is on the perpendicular bisector of a segment if and only if it is equidistant from the endpoints of the segment.

A similar theorem describes the relationship between points on an angle bisector and the sides of the angle.

THEOREM

A point is on the angle bisector of an angle if and only if it is equidistant from the sides of the angle.

REFLECT

1. Explain why point S on the perpendicular bisector of $\overline{RT}$ must be equidistant from points R and T.
2. Suppose $m\angle NMP = 148°$, and point L is equidistant from rays $\overrightarrow{MN}$ and $\overrightarrow{MP}$. Find $m\angle NML$. Explain your reasoning.
3. Describe and illustrate the difference between a bisector of a segment and a perpendicular bisector of a segment.

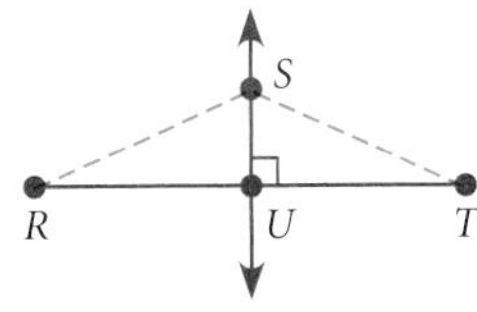

Exercises

CORE

1. **Getting Started** Follow the steps below to find the locus of all the points on a coordinate plane that are 3 units from the line $y = 2$.
   a. Choose any point on the line $y = 2$. Plot the point 3 units above this point and the point 3 units below it.
   b. Repeat **1a** at different points along the line until you recognize the solution.
   c. Complete the sketch of the locus.
   d. Use equations to describe the locus.

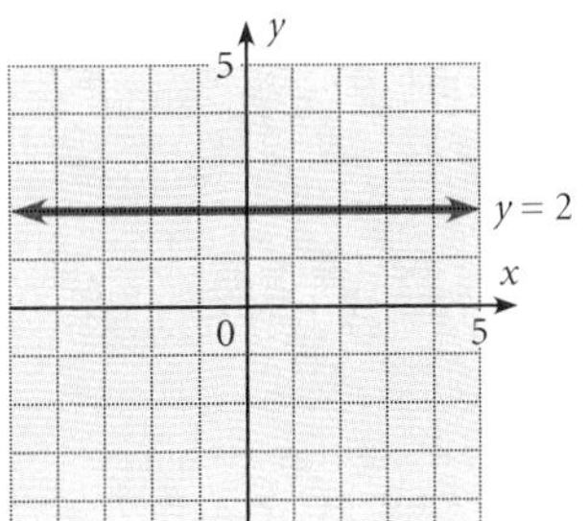

Journal

Reflect 1 and 2 and **Exercise** 14 are suitable for journal entries.

REFLECT

Possible Answers

1. Suppose S is not on $\overline{RT}$. Let U be the midpoint of $\overline{RT}$. Then $\triangle RUS \cong \triangle TUS$ by LL, and $RS = TS$. If S is on $\overline{RT}$, it must be the midpoint and is equidistant by definition.
2. 74°; If L is equidistant from $\overrightarrow{MN}$ and $\overrightarrow{MP}$, it is on the angle bisector.
3. A bisector divides a segment or angle into two parts with equal measures. A perpendicular bisector divides a segment into two parts with equal lengths and is perpendicular to the segment.

Part C Exercises

Exercise Notes

Core

9–11. Students explore loci on a coordinate plane.

13. and 14. Students are to solve application problems similar to the one in the **Explore,** and give a written explanation of their method.

Look Ahead

These exercises review definitions and constructions related to medians, altitudes, angle bisectors, and perpendicular bisectors. These will be related to triangles in 4-3 Part D.

More Math Reasoning

27. Students give a deductive justification of the discovery that points on the bisector of an angle are equidistant from the angle's sides.

y

Vocabulary
Practice/Skills
Review
Math Reasoning
Problem Solving
Challenge

Ongoing Assessment

Self-Assessment Exercises 1–13 odd

Embedded Assessment Reflect 2; Exercises 2, 6, 8, 14

Properties of Special Triangles

Exercise Answers

Core

1. a–c. Possible answer:

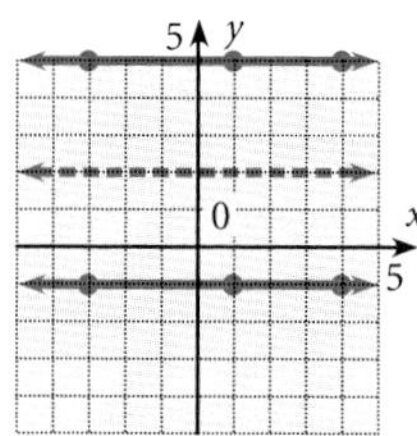

d. $y = 5$, $y = -1$

2. Circle with radius 3 in. and center at point A.

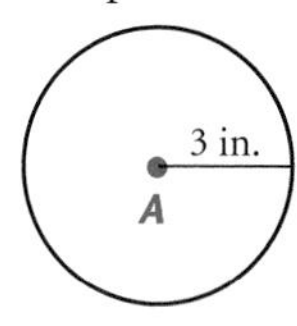

3. Two lines parallel to m, each 8 cm away.

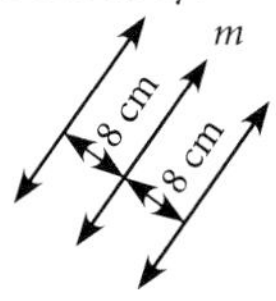

4. Two line segments 1 in. directly above and below $\overline{XY}$ and two half circles connecting the line segments with radius 1 in. and centers at X and Y.

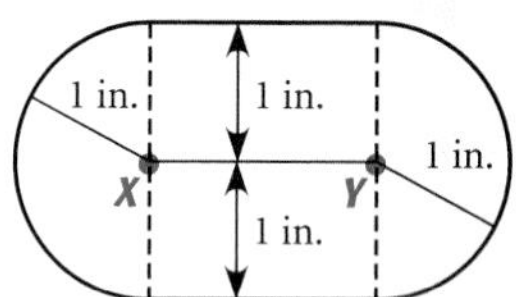

7. The angle bisector

8. The perpendicular bisector

9. It is the line with slope 1 passing through the origin.

10.

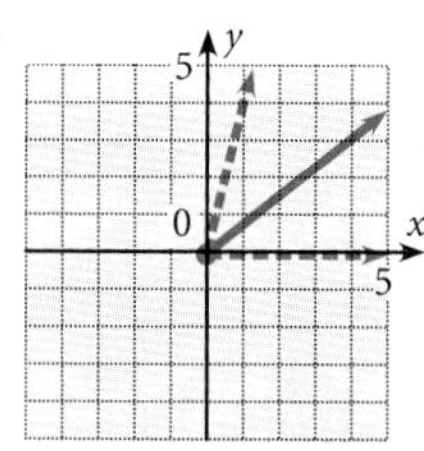

P **Describe each locus of points in a plane. Give a sketch to illustrate each answer.**

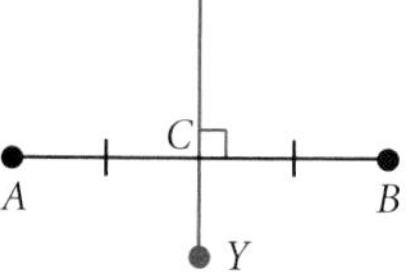

2. the locus of points 3 in. from point A

3. the locus of points 8 cm from line m

4. the locus of points 1 in. from segment $\overline{XY}$

P **5.** In the figure at the right, $\overline{XY}$ is a perpendicular bisector of $\overline{AB}$. If $AX = 10x - 4$ and $BX = 4x + 8$, find x. 2

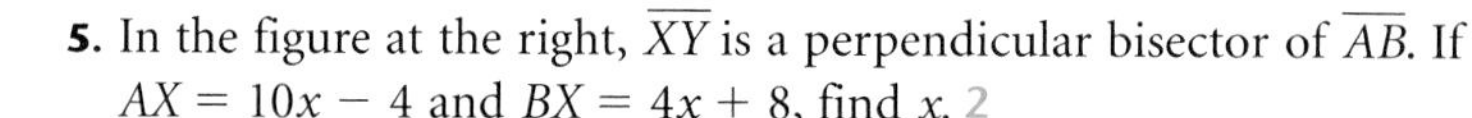

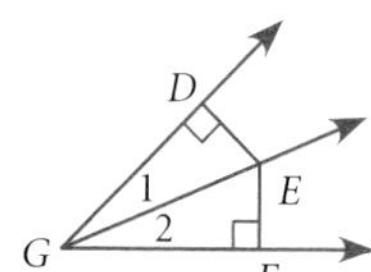

P **6.** If $\angle 1 \cong \angle 2$, $EF = 2x + 8$, and $ED = 6x - 8$, find x. 4

V **Write the word or phrase that correctly completes each statement.**

7. The locus of points equidistant from the sides of an angle is ____.

8. The locus of points equidistant from the endpoints of a segment is ____.

P **9.** Describe the locus of points in a plane that satisfies the equation $y = x$.

P **10.** Sketch the locus of points in a plane equidistant from the sides of the angle determined by the positive x-axis and the line $y = 4x$ in the first quadrant.

P **11.** Sketch the locus of points in a plane equidistant from the lines $y = 8$ and $y = 2$.

P, MR **12.** Fill in the missing statements and reasons to complete the proof of the following.

If a point is on the perpendicular bisector of a line segment, then it is equidistant from the endpoints of the segment.

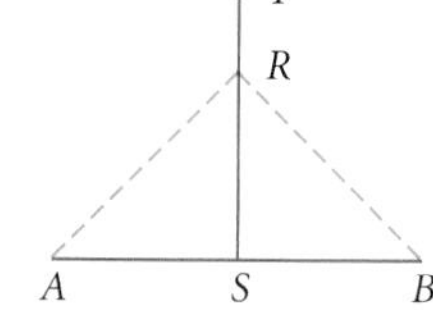

Given: $\overline{TS}$ is a perpendicular bisector of $\overline{AB}$, and R lies on $\overline{TS}$.

Prove: $\overline{RA} \cong \overline{RB}$

Proof:

Statements	Reasons
1. $\overline{TS}$ is a perpendicular bisector of $\overline{AB}$; R lies on $\overline{TS}$.	**1.**
2. Draw $\overline{AR}$ and $\overline{BR}$.	**2.** Two points determine a line.
3. $\overline{AS} \cong \overline{SB}$	**3.**
4. $\overline{TS} \perp \overline{AB}$	**4.**
5. $\angle RSA$ and $\angle RSB$ are right angles.	**5.**
6.	**6.** Definition of *right triangle*
7. $\overline{RS} \cong \overline{RS}$	**7.**
8. $\triangle RSA \cong \triangle RSB$	**8.**
9. $\overline{RA} \cong \overline{RB}$	**9.**

Key

V Vocabulary
P Practice/Skills
R Review
MR Math Reasoning
PS Problem Solving
C Challenge

13. A power substation is to be located along a power line and must be equidistant from the two cities shown.

Where should the substation be located? Make a sketch to show your answer. Explain the reasoning you used to find the location.

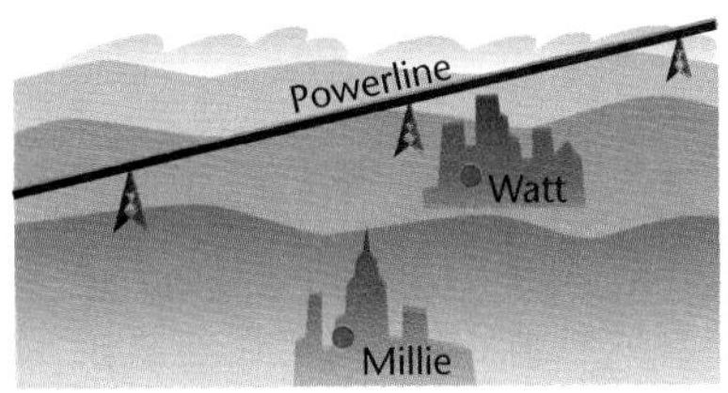

14. Buried Treasure The figure on the right is a partial map of "Treasure Island." A buried treasure is equidistant from the two straight shorelines, $\overline{FG}$ and $\overline{FH}$, and equidistant from two trees, J and K. Make a sketch of the map and locate the treasure. Write a note explaining your method.

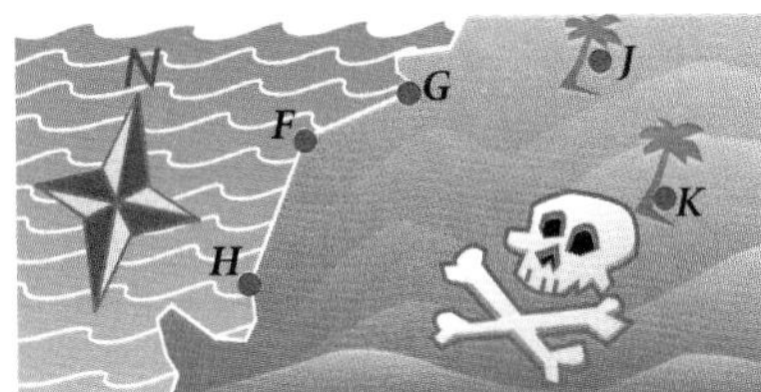

LOOK AHEAD

Name each of the following in the figure at the right.

15. an angle bisector $\overrightarrow{TU}$

16. a perpendicular bisector $\overline{WY}$

17. perpendicular lines $\overleftrightarrow{VZ} \perp \overleftrightarrow{WY}$

18. a midpoint X

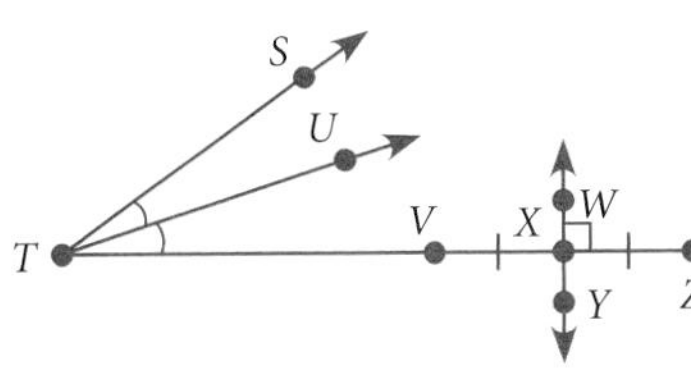

19. Draw a large triangle, $\triangle ABC$. Then construct the midpoint of each side of $\triangle ABC$, using a compass and straightedge.

MORE PRACTICE

Describe each locus of points. Give a sketch to illustrate each answer.

20. the locus of points in a plane 2 cm from point X

21. the locus of points in space 3 in. from point K

22. the locus of points in space 1 m from line s

Find the missing value in each statement. Assume that $\overline{DF} \perp \overline{BC}$, $\overline{DE} \cong \overline{EF}$, and $\overline{AE} \cong \overline{BE}$.

23. If $AD = 10$, then $BF =$ ____. 10

24. If $DC = 12x - 3$ and $FC = 21$, then $x =$ ____. 2

25. If $BD = 5x$ and $AD = 7x - 8$, then $AD =$ ____. 20

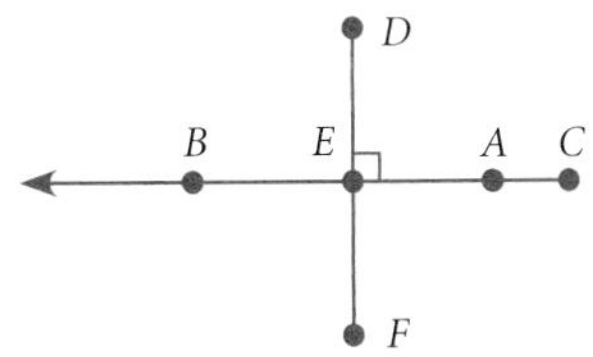

11.

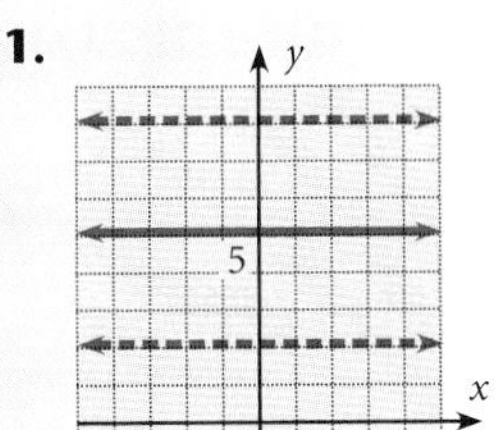

12. Reason 1: Given
Reason 3: Definition of *bisect*
Reason 4: Definition of *perpendicular bisector*
Reason 5: Definition of *perpendicular*
Statement 6: $\triangle RSA$ and $\triangle RSB$ are right triangles
Reason 7: Reflexive Property
Reason 8: LL Theorem
Reason 9: CPCTC

13.

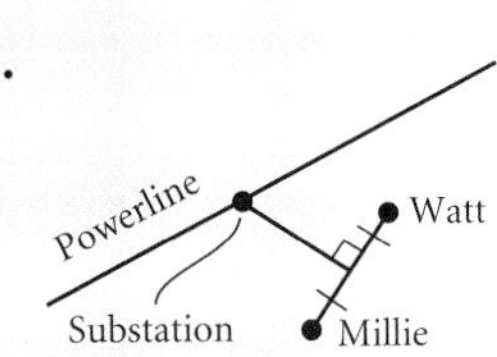

Draw the line segment from Millie to Watt. Draw the perpendicular bisector of that line segment until it intersects with the power line. This is where the substation should be: It lies on the perpendicular bisector, so it is equidistant from the two cities.

14.

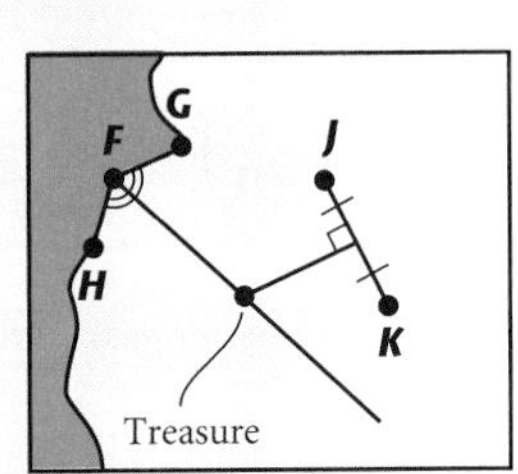

Draw the line segment $\overline{JK}$. Draw the perpendicular bisector of $\overline{JK}$. Draw the angle bisector of $\angle HFG$. Mark the intersection of the two bisectors. This is where the treasure is, since the intersection is equidistant from J and K and equidistant from $\overline{FG}$ and $\overline{FH}$.

Look Ahead

19. Possible answer:

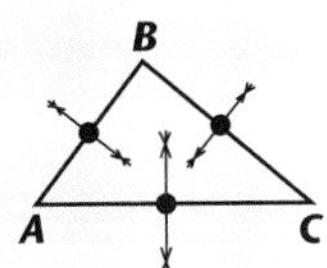

20–22. and 26–27.
See Additional Answers p. T254.

Properties of Special Triangles

PART D At a Glance

Objective

To see special lines in triangles, and to find that the centroid of a triangle is its center of balance.

Development

First, students see the definitions of *angle bisectors, medians, altitudes,* and *perpendicular bisectors* in triangles.

In the **Explore,** students find the center of balance of a triangle. Then they draw the medians of the triangle and discover that its balance point is the point of intersection of the medians. Finally, they see that this point (the centroid) is at two-thirds of the distance from each vertex to the midpoint of the opposite side.

Suggested Materials

Student Cardboard, scissors, ruler, pencil

Key Terms

Angle bisector, perpendicular bisector, altitude, median of a triangle, concurrent lines, centroid

First Five Minutes

Transparency FFM 4-3D

Draw a large triangle, and construct the bisector of each of its angles, using a compass and straightedge.

Motivate

Ask...

- What do you think *center of balance* means? Where is the center of balance of a circle? How could you find the center of balance of a square?

MORE MATH REASONING

PS **26. A Key Question** A group of campers was playing a game that gave clues to the location of various objects. The clues for finding a key were as follows.

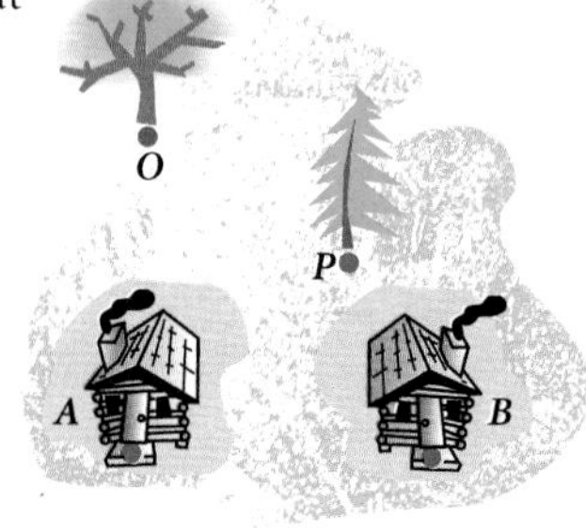

- The key is equidistant from the segments joining cabin A to pine tree P and cabin B to oak tree O.
- The key is on the segment connecting cabin A and cabin B.

To win the game, you must give a written description of the precise location of the key. Describe the method you will use to find the key, and explain why the method works.

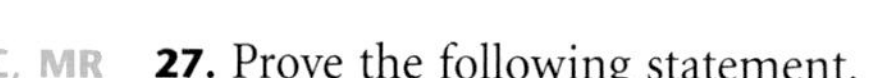

C, MR **27.** Prove the following statement.

If a point is on the angle bisector of an angle, then it is equidistant from the sides of the angle.

4-3 PART D Lines Associated with Triangles

← CONNECT → ***You've already learned about bisectors and perpendiculars. Now you will explore properties of bisectors and perpendiculars when they are contained in triangles.***

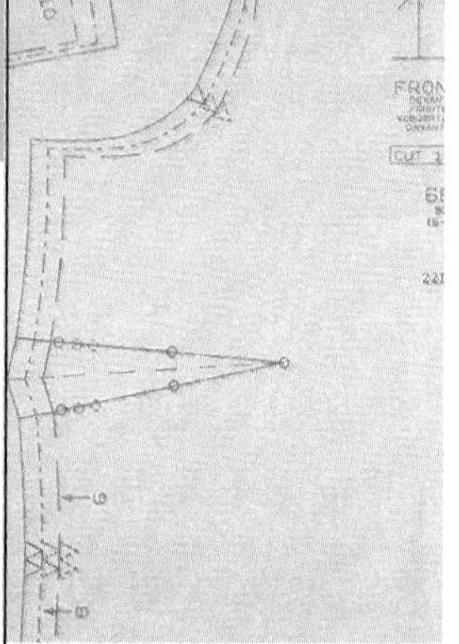

Segments that bisect sides and angles in triangles have some important properties. They are also useful choices for auxiliary lines in proofs.

The fabric pattern at the left illustrates an angle bisector. The bisector of an angle is a ray. However, when an angle bisector is used in a triangle, we restrict the ray to a segment. One endpoint of the segment is a vertex and the other endpoint is on the side opposite the bisected angle.

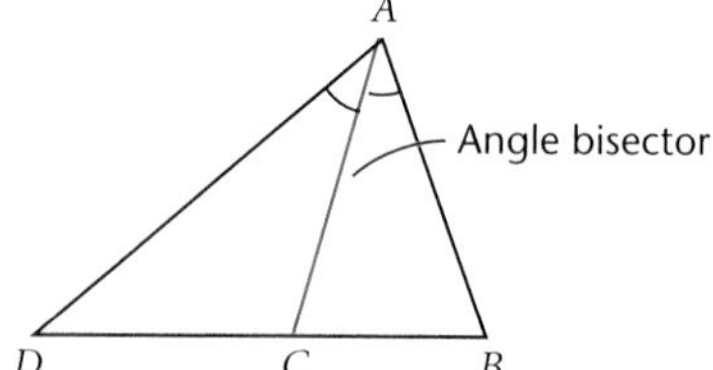

$\overline{AC}$ is an angle bisector of $\triangle ABD$ from vertex A to side $\overline{DB}$.

Key

V	Vocabulary
P	Practice/Skills
R	Review
MR	Math Reasoning
PS	Problem Solving
C	Challenge

Alert

Students may have difficulty drawing these segments in an obtuse triangle (as seen in the *Try It* on page 306). You might remind them that each side of a triangle is a line segment and that the line containing this segment can be drawn.

A **median** of a triangle is a segment whose endpoints are a vertex and the midpoint of the opposite side.

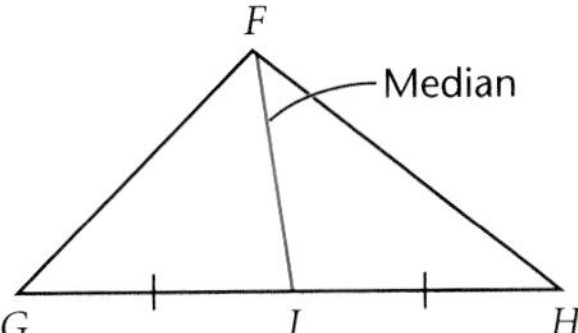

$\overline{FJ}$ is a median of $\triangle FGH$ from vertex F to side $\overline{GH}$.

An **altitude** of a triangle is a perpendicular segment drawn from a vertex to the line that contains the opposite side.

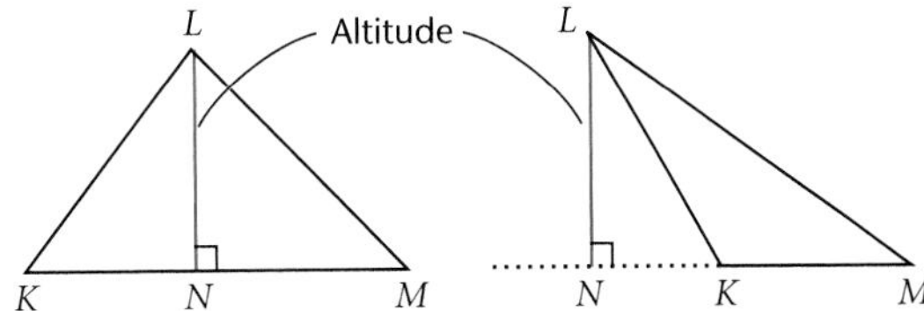

In the two triangles, $\overline{LN}$ is an altitude of $\triangle KLM$ from vertex L.

As seen in the figure on the right above, an altitude may lie outside the triangle. It may also be a side of the triangle.

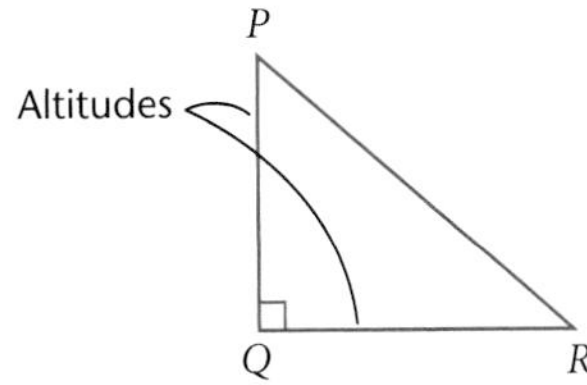

In $\triangle PQR$, $\overline{PQ}$ is the altitude from vertex P, and $\overline{RQ}$ is the altitude from vertex R.

A **perpendicular bisector** of a side of a triangle is a line perpendicular to a side through the midpoint of the side.

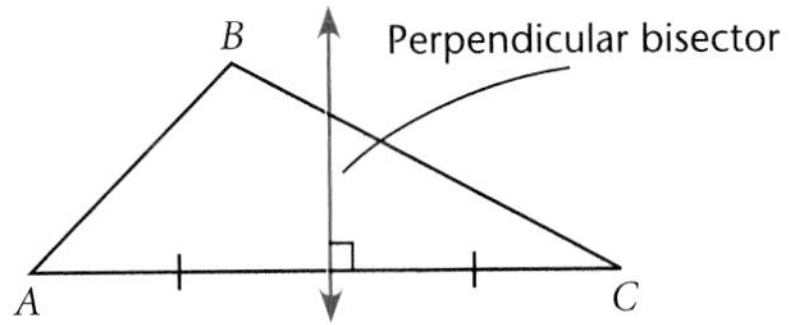

A perpendicular bisector of $\overline{AC}$ in $\triangle ABC$ is shown.

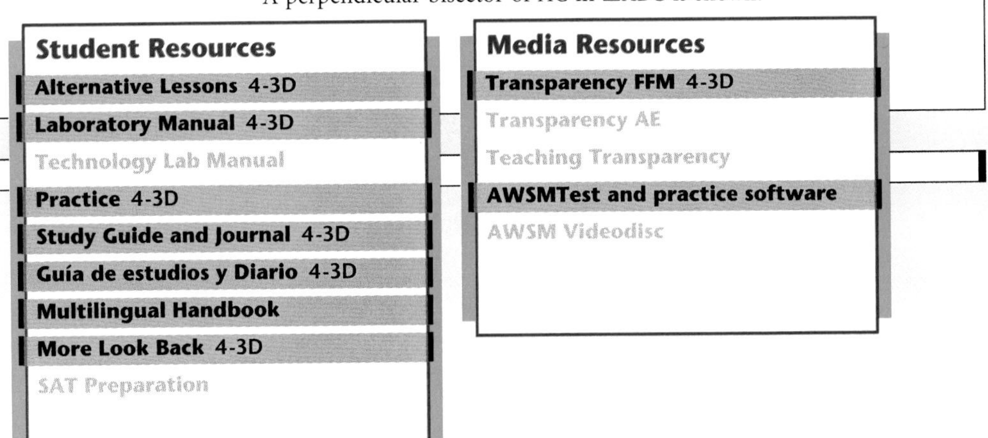

Student Resources

- Alternative Lessons 4-3D
- Laboratory Manual 4-3D
- Technology Lab Manual
- Practice 4-3D
- Study Guide and Journal 4-3D
- Guía de estudios y Diario 4-3D
- Multilingual Handbook
- More Look Back 4-3D
- SAT Preparation

Media Resources

- Transparency FFM 4-3D
- Transparency AE
- Teaching Transparency
- AWSMTest and practice software
- AWSM Videodisc

4-3

Algebra	Functions	Discrete Math	Probability	Data/Statistics

Properties of Special Triangles

EXPLORE

Balancing Act

Recommended group size: 2

The Point

To see that the center of balance of a triangle is the point of intersection of its medians, and to find that the centroid is two-thirds of the distance from each vertex to the midpoint of the opposite side.

Look and Listen...

- For students with triangles whose sides are not straight. (This causes inaccuracy in finding the center of balance and difficulties in finding midpoints.)
- For students who do not see a relationship in the segment lengths in Step 4.

Ask...

- Does the centroid divide each median in the same way?

For Groups That Finish Early

Draw a triangle, and construct all of its angle bisectors, altitudes, and perpendicular bisectors. Do each of these sets of segments meet at a common point? **Yes**

Follow Up

Ask students to summarize their conclusions about the centroid of a triangle.

Possible Answers

2. The centroid is at the point of intersection of the medians.

3. The centroid is again the point of intersection of the medians.

4. The centroid is two-thirds of the distance from each vertex to the midpoint of the opposite side.

TRY IT

a. Draw an obtuse triangle $\triangle XYZ$ with obtuse angle $\angle Z$. Draw the median, angle bisector, and altitude from $\angle X$.

b. Draw an isosceles triangle $\triangle FGH$. Draw the median, angle bisector, and altitude from the vertex angle, $\angle G$, to the base.

In the following Explore, you will investigate some special properties of the medians of a triangle.

EXPLORE: BALANCING ACT

MATERIALS

Cardboard
Scissors
Ruler
Pencil

1. Cut a triangle out of cardboard. Then find the "center of balance" of the triangle by balancing it on the eraser of a pencil. Mark the center of balance. This point is the *centroid* of the triangle.
2. Using a ruler to help you find the midpoints of the sides, draw all three medians of your triangle. Mark the point of intersection of the medians. What is the relationship between this point and the centroid?
3. Repeat the process with a different triangle. Do all three medians still meet at one point? Is this point the centroid of the triangle?
4. The point of intersection of the three medians divides each median into two segments. Measure the two segments of each median in both of your triangles. Make a conjecture about your results.

If three or more coplanar lines intersect at the same point, they are **concurrent lines.** The point of intersection is the **point of concurrency.**

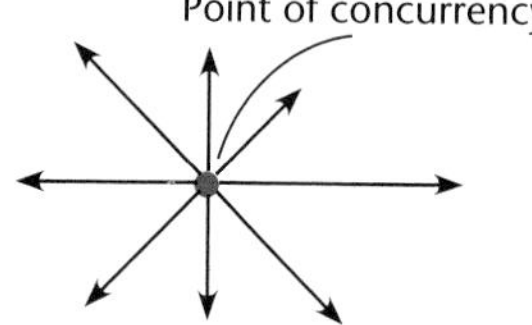

The point of concurrency of the medians of any triangle is called the **centroid.** The centroid is important because it is the *center of balance* (or *center of gravity*) of the triangle. You may also have discovered the following fact about centroids.

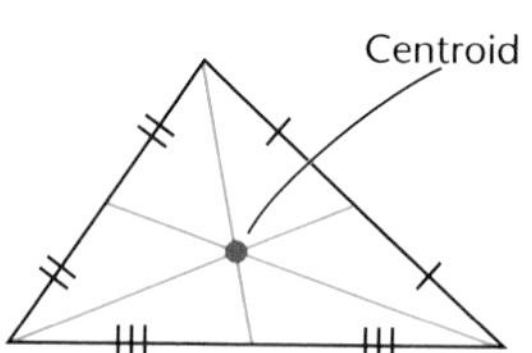

Careers Connection

Mary Ross, a direct descendant of a Cherokee chief, is an engineer whose work in aerospace was important in the development of the Agena rocket. This rocket, a predecessor to the Titan rockets used to send humans to the moon, was an important part of the space program. Ross also participated in the conceptualizing of flyby missions to Venus and Mars.

THEOREM

The centroid of a triangle is located two-thirds of the distance from each vertex to the midpoint of the opposite side.

REFLECT

1. Use the figures below and the idea of a center of balance to explain why the centroid of a triangle is farther from the vertex than it is from the opposite side.

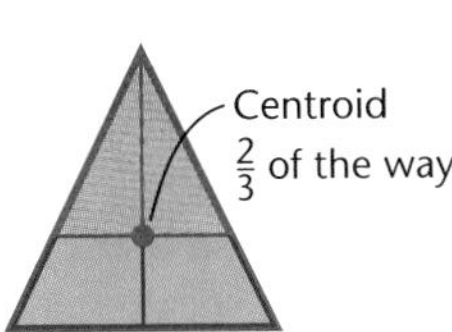

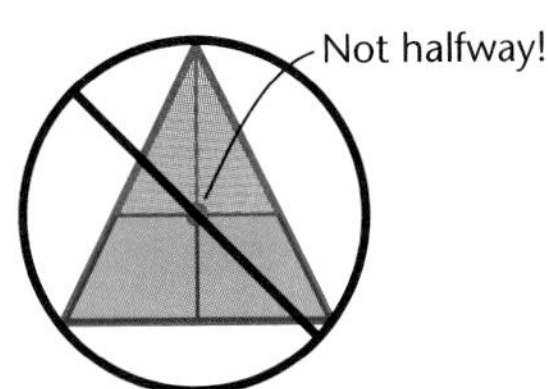

2. Is it possible for a segment to be both a median and an altitude of a triangle? Explain your answer with a sketch.
3. When is an altitude in the exterior of a triangle? a side of a triangle? Illustrate your answers.

Exercises

CORE

Getting Started Use the figure at the right for Exercises 1–4.

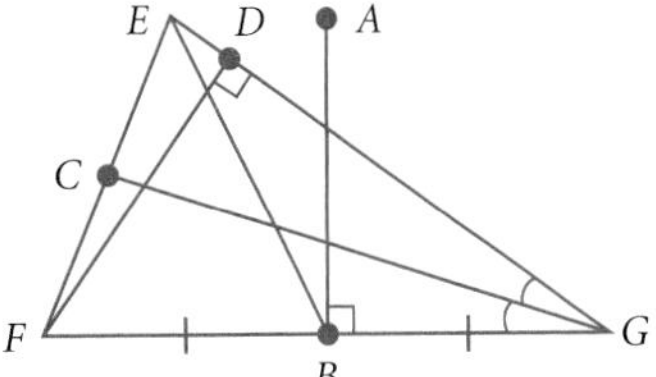

1. Name an angle bisector in $\triangle EFG$. $\overline{CG}$
2. Name a median in $\triangle EFG$. $\overline{EB}$
3. Name a perpendicular bisector in $\triangle EFG$. $\overline{AB}$
4. Name an altitude in $\triangle EFG$. $\overline{DF}$
5. Carefully draw an isosceles triangle. Then draw the altitude, the median, and the angle bisector from the vertex to the base. Make any conjectures that you can. Explain why your conjectures must be true.
6. From the four terms below, choose the term that does not belong, and explain why.

median, centroid, angle bisector, altitude

Ongoing Assessment

Vocabulary
Practice/Skills
Review
Math Reasoning
Problem Solving
Challenge

Self-Assessment Exercises 1, 2, 3, 7, 9, 11, 12

Embedded Assessment Reflect 3; Exercises 4, 6, 13, 14

Journal

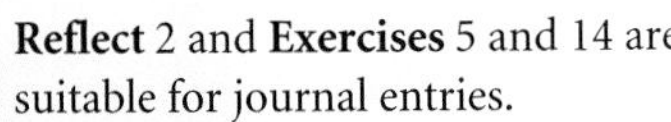

Reflect 2 and **Exercises** 5 and 14 are suitable for journal entries.

REFLECT

Possible Answers

1. As you go from a vertex to the opposite side, the triangle gets wider. Therefore, the center of balance is closer to the opposite side.
2. Yes. Sketches should show a median/altitude between two congruent sides.
3. An altitude is in the exterior of a triangle when the triangle is obtuse and the altitude is not drawn from the vertex of the obtuse angle. It is a side of a right triangle if it is not drawn from the vertex of the right angle.

TRY IT

Answers

a.

X, Y, Z; Median; Altitude; Angle bisector

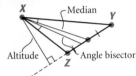

b.

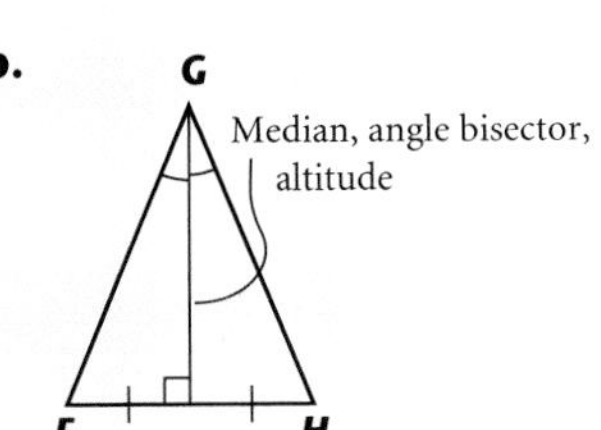

Part D Exercises

Exercise Notes

Core

5. Students see that the altitude, median, and angle bisector from the vertex of an isosceles triangle are the same segment.

13. Shows how ancient architects applied properties of special segments in isosceles triangles to make a leveling tool.

More Math Reasoning

24. Students discover the Euler line.

Properties of Special Triangles

Exercise Answers

Core

5.

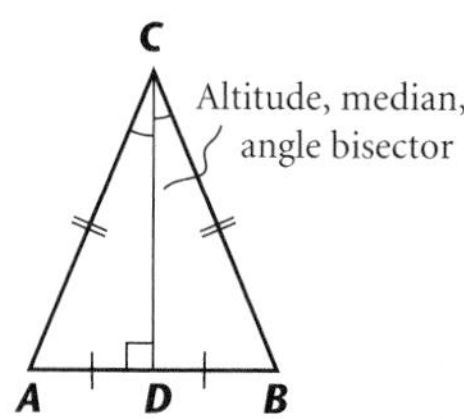

The altitude, the median, and the angle bisector are the same line segment. Suppose $\overline{CD}$ is the altitude, then $\overline{CD} \perp \overline{AB}$ by definition of *altitude,* and $\triangle CDA$ and $\triangle CDB$ are right triangles. $\overline{CA} \cong \overline{CB}$ because $\triangle ABC$ is an isosceles triangle and C is the vertex. $\overline{CD} \cong \overline{CD}$ by the Reflexive Property. So $\triangle ACD \cong \triangle BCD$ by the HL Theorem. Therefore $\angle ACD \cong \angle BCD$ and $\overline{AD} \cong \overline{BD}$ by CPCTC. So we can conclude $\overline{CD}$ is also the angle bisector and median from the vertex angle.

6. Centroid does not belong. The centroid is a point while the median, angle bisector, and altitude are line segments.

10. Since it lies on all three angle bisectors, the point of concurrency is equidistant from any two sides and is therefore equidistant from all sides.

11. Since it lies on all three perpendicular bisectors, the point of concurrency is equidistant from any pair of vertices and therefore is equidistant from all vertices.

P **In $\triangle TUV$, $\overline{UX}$ and $\overline{TW}$ are medians, $TY > YW$, and $UY > YX$.**

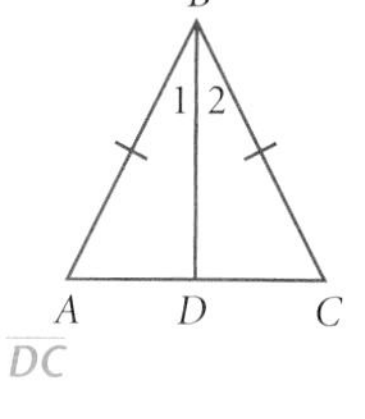

7. If $TY = 48$, find YW. 24

8. If $YX = 3.5$, find UX. 10.5

P **9.** If $TY = 8x - 12$ and $YW = 2x$, find the following.

a. x 3 **b.** YW 6 **c.** TY 12 **d.** TW 18

MR **10.** Explain why the point of concurrency of the angle bisectors of the sides of a triangle is equidistant from all the sides of the triangle.

MR **11.** Explain why the point of concurrency of the perpendicular bisectors of the sides of a triangle is equidistant from all the vertices of the triangle.

P, MR **12.** Fill in the missing statements and reasons in the proof to prove that the median from the vertex to the base of an isosceles triangle is also the angle bisector.

Given: Isosceles $\triangle ABC$ with $\overline{AB} \cong \overline{BC}$
$\overline{BD}$ is a median from the vertex B to base $\overline{AC}$.

Prove: $\angle 1 \cong \angle 2$

Proof:

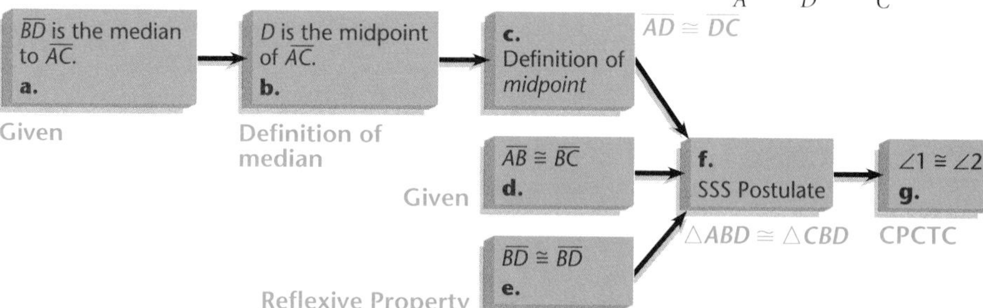

MR History **13. Do Your Level Best** In carpentry and other trades, it is often important to make sure that something is exactly horizontal. The leveling instrument shown is similar to some Egyptian artifacts. An instrument like this may have been used in the building of the pyramids.

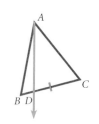

$\triangle ABC$ is isosceles, and the midpoint of $\overline{BC}$ is marked. A string with a weight is attached to the vertex. The string meets the base $\overline{BC}$ at point D.

a. If the surface on which $\overline{BC}$ rests is perfectly horizontal, where will the weight hang? Why?

b. When $\overline{BC}$ is horizontal, what is true about $\triangle ADB$ and $\triangle ADC$? Justify your answer.

Key

- V Vocabulary
- P Practice/Skills
- R Review
- MR Math Reasoning
- PS Problem Solving
- C Challenge

14. Cart Capers A cart manufacturer is interested in making a cart whose body is a triangular prism. Side views of two designs are shown at the right.

a. Copy each figure and find the center of gravity of each of their triangular cross sections.

b. The lower the center of gravity, the more stable a cart is. Which design seems to be more stable? List other advantages and disadvantages of each design.

LOOK BACK

15. In the figure at the right, $m \parallel n$ and $s \parallel t$. Find the measures of the numbered angles. [3-4]

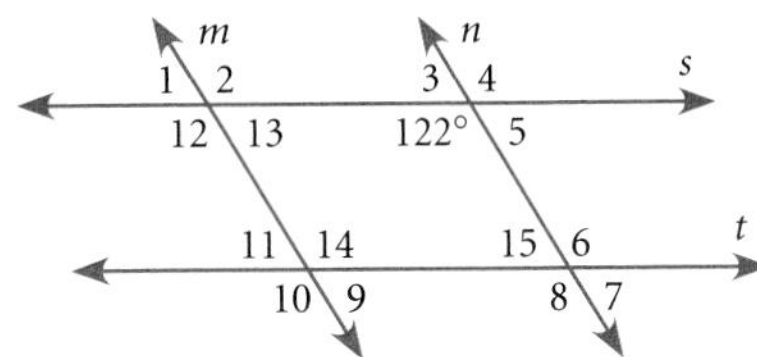

16. Complete the following proof. [3-4, 4-2]

Given: $\angle SVT \cong \angle UTV$

$\overline{SV} \cong \overline{UT}$

Prove: $\overleftrightarrow{ST} \parallel \overleftrightarrow{UV}$

Proof:

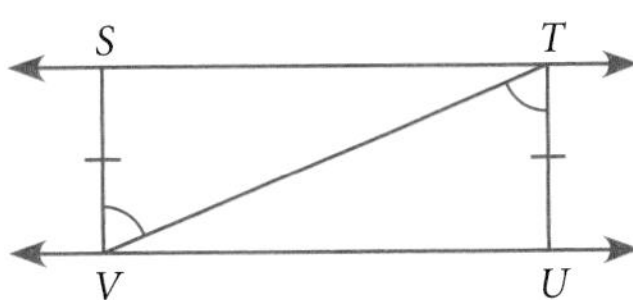

Statements	Reasons
1. $\angle SVT \cong \angle UTV$	**1.**
2.	**2.** Given
3.	**3.** Reflexive Property
4. $\triangle SVT \cong \triangle UTV$	**4.**
5.	**5.** CPCTC
6. $\overleftrightarrow{ST} \parallel \overleftrightarrow{UV}$	**6.**

MORE PRACTICE

17. Name an angle bisector in $\triangle MHI$. $\overline{HJ}$

18. Name a median in $\triangle MHI$. $\overline{LI}$

19. Name a perpendicular bisector in $\triangle MHI$. $\overline{LK}$

20. Name an altitude in $\triangle MHI$. $\overline{MG}$

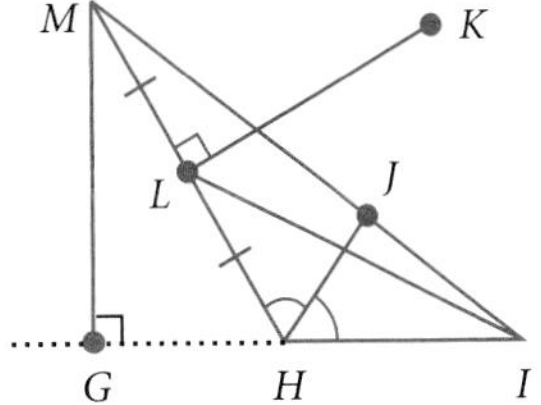

13. a. The string will meet the base at the midpoint. Since $\overline{BC}$ is horizontal and $\overline{AD}$ is vertical, $\overline{AD} \perp \overline{BC}$. Therefore $\overline{AD}$ is the altitude from A, but we know from a previous problem that the altitude of an isosceles triangle from the vertex is also the median. So D is at the midpoint of $\overline{BC}$.

b. $\triangle ADB$ and $\triangle ADC$ are congruent. $\overline{AD} \cong \overline{AD}$ by the Reflexive Property. $\overline{AB} \cong \overline{AC}$ because $\triangle ABC$ is isosceles and A is the vertex. By part **a,** D is the midpoint of $\overline{BC}$, so $\overline{BD} \cong \overline{DC}$. Therefore $\triangle ADB \cong \triangle ADC$ by the SSS Postulate.

14. a. The center of gravity of cart A is $\frac{4}{3}$ ft above the midpoint of the base. The center of gravity of cart B is 2 ft above the midpoint of the base.

b. Cart A seems to be more stable; Possible answers: Cart A is shorter in height, so it can move easily under things. Cart B is shorter in length, so it has a smaller turning radius and is more maneuverable.

Look Back

15. $m\angle 1$, $m\angle 3$, $m\angle 5$, $m\angle 7$, $m\angle 9$, $m\angle 11$, $m\angle 13$, $m\angle 15 = 58°$; $m\angle 2$, $m\angle 4$, $m\angle 6$, $m\angle 8$, $m\angle 10$, $m\angle 12$, $m\angle 14 = 122°$

16. Reason 1: Given
Statement 2: $\overline{SV} \cong \overline{UT}$
Statement 3: $\overline{VT} \cong \overline{VT}$
Reason 4: SAS Postulate
Statement 5: $\angle TVU \cong \angle VTS$
Reason 6: If alternate interior angles are congruent, the lines are parallel.

More Math Reasoning

23. An equilateral triangle; Then the earlier results for isosceles triangles apply three times, with each of the angles in turn taken as the vertex.

24. a. Points of concurrency of medians, altitudes, and perpendicular bisectors.

b. If M, A, and P are the concurrency points of the medians, altitudes, and perpendicular bisectors, respectively, then M lies between A and P, and $MP = \frac{1}{2}MA$.

Algebra	Functions	Discrete Math	Probability	Data/Statistics

Properties of Special Triangles

PART E At a Glance

Objective

To use centroids to estimate the center of balance of a bicycle frame.

Development

In the **Explore,** students see how to use centroids to find the approximate center of balance of a bicycle frame. They use their knowledge to design a frame with a lower center of balance.

Suggested Materials

Student Ruler, geometry software

First Five Minutes

Transparency FFM 4-3E

Sketch a triangle. Use a ruler to find the approximate location of its centroid.

EXPLORE

Frame It!

Recommended group size: 4

The Point

To find the approximate center of balance of a bicycle frame, and to design a similar frame with a lower center of balance.

Look and Listen...

- For students who do not see a way to estimate the center of balance of the entire frame.

Ask...

- If you draw a segment that joins the two centroids, would it help you make a guess about the location of the centroid of the whole frame?

For Groups That Finish Early

Sketch an irregular figure with five sides. Describe a way to find its approximate center of gravity. Divide the figure into three triangular regions, and find the centroid of each. Sketch a triangle with these centroids as its vertices, and find the centroid of this triangle. This is the centroid of the figure.

P **In $\triangle PQR$, $\overline{PS}$ and $\overline{RT}$ are medians. $UR > UT$, and $UP > US$.**

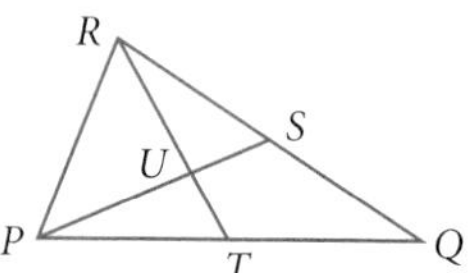

21. If $RT = 24$, find RU. 16 **22.** If $US = 15$, find UP. 30

MORE MATH REASONING

MR **23.** There is a type of triangle in which every angle bisector is also a median, an altitude, and a perpendicular bisector. What type of triangle is it? Explain.

C **24. The Euler Line** Draw a large acute scalene triangle and construct the point of concurrency of the medians. Then construct the points of concurrency of the altitudes, angle bisectors, and perpendicular bisectors.

a. Which three of these points are collinear?

b. The line that contains the three collinear points is called the Euler line. Make a conjecture about how the three points of concurrency divide the Euler line.

4-3 PART E Making Connections

← CONNECT → ***Special triangles and the lines associated with them are important in industries that need structural stability in their products. You've discovered some properties of special triangles and explored some special segments associated with triangles.***

This bicycle was built for paratroopers in World War II. It features a folding frame. In the following Explore, you will see how the properties of triangles and the lines associated with them can be used to investigate the structure of a bicycle frame.

Key

V Vocabulary
P Practice/Skills
R Review
MR Math Reasoning
PS Problem Solving
C Challenge

Technology Note

If your software has coordinate capabilities, you may want to make use of this in the **Explore** on Page 311. Have students place the triangles on a graph, find centroids, draw the segment joining these, and construct its midpoint to approximate the frame's centroid. Have students label the centroid's coordinates and see how the y-value changes as they drag vertices of the triangles.

EXPLORE: FRAME IT!

MATERIALS

Ruler
Geometry software (optional)

A bicycle frame contains the two triangles shown in the figure. (Note: The tip of the triangle at point *B* is actually cut off, but you may assume that the triangle is complete.)

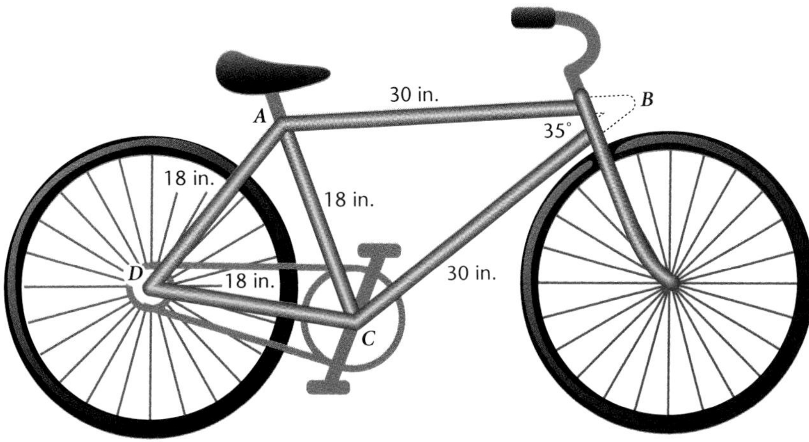

1. Find the measures of all angles in the two triangles. Explain your reasoning.
2. Copy the figure, using pencil and paper or geometry software. Find the center of gravity of each of the two triangles.
3. Estimate the center of gravity of the entire frame. Explain your method.
4. Suppose you want the bicycle to have a lower center of gravity. Describe one way you might modify the bicycle frame to achieve a lower center of gravity. Try your new design by sketching it or using geometry software to see whether or not it actually lowers the center of gravity.

REFLECT

1. The HL, LL, LA, and HA triangle-congruence theorems only require two pairs of congruent parts instead of the three needed in ASA, SAS, SSS, and SAA. Explain why.
2. List as many properties of isosceles triangles as you can. Provide a sketch for each property.
3. Is it possible for an altitude of a triangle to be on a side of the triangle? in the interior of the triangle? in the exterior of the triangle? Support your answers with drawings. What are the possibilities for the medians of a triangle? Explain.

Student Resources
Alternative Lessons
Laboratory Manual 4-3E
Technology Lab Manual
Practice 4-3E
Study Guide and Journal 4-3E
Guía de estudios y Diario 4-3E
Multilingual Handbook
More Look Back 4-3E
SAT Preparation

Media Resources
Transparency FFM 4-3E
Transparency AE
Teaching Transparency
AWSMTest and practice software
AWSM Videodisc

Follow Up

Ask students to explain how they approximated the center of gravity of the frame and how they would adjust the frame to lower its center of gravity.

Possible Answers

1. $\triangle ADC$ is equilateral, so $m\angle D = m\angle DAC = m\angle ADC = 60°$. $\angle BAC$ and $\angle BCA$ are base angles of isosceles $\triangle BAC$, so they have equal measures. $m\angle BAC = m\angle BCA = \frac{1}{2}(180 - 35) = 72.5°$.
2. Students should draw medians to find the center of gravity.
3. One possible approximation: the midpoint of the segment joining the centroids of the two triangles.
4. One possibility: Change the top bar so it angles downward from seat to handlebars.

Portfolio

Have students select items from their work that demonstrate their understanding of the material in 4-3.

You may wish to have students include a fill-in proof, an **Exercise** where they used the idea of locus to solve a real-world problem, and an **Exercise** or **Reflect** question they found interesting or challenging.

REFLECT

Possible Answers

1. In right triangles, the right angles are also congruent. In many cases, this is the "third pair" of congruent parts.
2. Two sides are congruent; the base angles are congruent; the median, altitude, angle bisector, and perpendicular bisector from the vertex to the base are the same segment; this segment is a line of symmetry for the triangle.
3. Two of the altitudes of a right triangle are on a side of the triangle; two of the altitudes of an obtuse triangle are in the exterior of the triangle. Since any median has one endpoint on a vertex and the other on a side, medians are always in the interior of a triangle.

Properties of Special Triangles

Self-Assessment

Exercise Notes

6. Similar to multiple-choice questions on standardized tests.

15. Shows connections between right-triangle congruence theorems and congruence postulates for general triangles.

16. Students use loci to solve a real-world problem.

Self-Assessment Answers

7. Line parallel to ℓ and m, halfway between ℓ and m.

8. The perpendicular bisector of the line segment $\overline{PQ}$.

9. The angle bisector of $\angle RPQ$.

13. Reason 1: Given
Statement 2: $\angle 1 \cong \angle 2$
Statement 3: $\overline{BD} \cong \overline{BD}$
Reason 4: SAS Postulate
Reason 5: CPCTC
Statement 6: $\angle DAC \cong \angle DCA$
Reason 6: Isosceles Triangle Theorem

14. a. Given information

b. Definition of *right triangles*

c. Reflexive Property

d. $\overline{XW} \cong \overline{ZW}$

e. $\triangle WYX \cong \triangle WYZ$

f. CPCTC

g. Y is the midpoint of $\overline{XZ}$

Self-Assessment

P **State a congruence postulate or theorem that justifies each of the following.**

1. $\triangle WZY \cong \triangle YXW$ HL Theorem

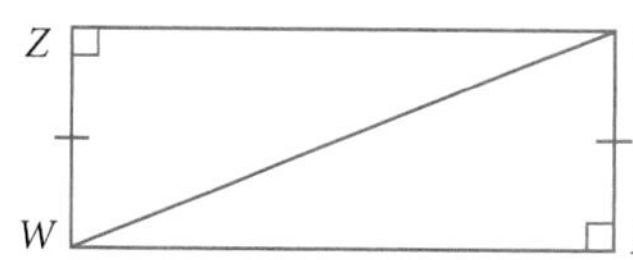

2. $\triangle STV \cong \triangle UTV$ HL Theorem

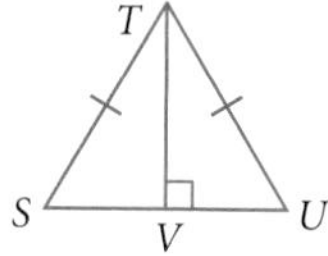

3. $\triangle LMN \cong \triangle NPL$ HA Theorem

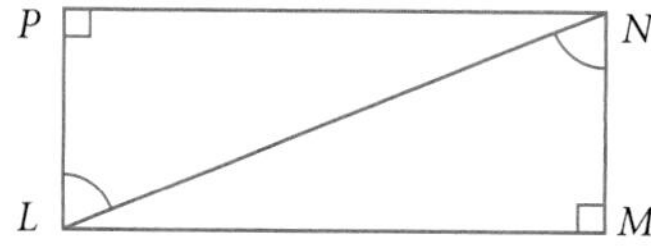

4. $\triangle GHK \cong \triangle JHI$ LA Theorem

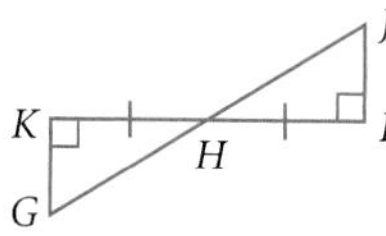

PS **5.** In $\triangle XYZ$, $m\angle Y = (4x - 10)°$, and $m\angle Z = (53 - 3x)°$. If $\triangle XYZ$ is isosceles with base $\overline{YZ}$, find $m\angle X$. 128°

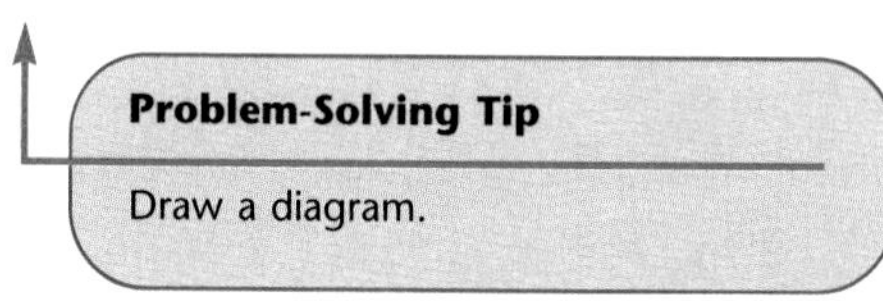

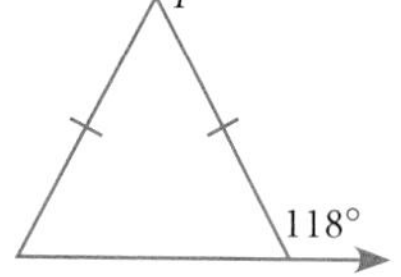

P **6.** Which of the following is $m\angle F$? (a)
(a) 56° (b) 59° (c) 62° (d) 118°

P **Describe and draw the locus of points in a plane that satisfies the given condition.**

7. equidistant from lines ℓ and m

8. equidistant from P and Q

9. equidistant from the sides of $\angle RPQ$

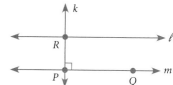

R **Name the translation image of each figure for the given transformation. [1-4, 3-1, 3-2]**

10. the image of point A under a translation with vector $\overrightarrow{EG}$ C

11. the image of segment $\overline{BC}$ under a reflection over line $\overleftrightarrow{EH}$ JK

12. the image of $\triangle EFJ$ after a 180° clockwise rotation about point J $\triangle ONJ$

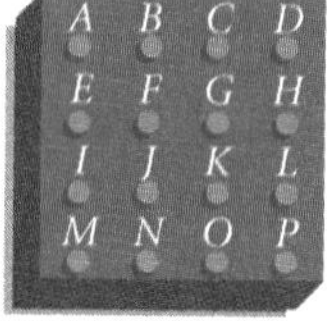

Key

V Vocabulary
P Practice/Skills
R Review
MR Math Reasoning
PS Problem Solving
C Challenge

13. Complete the following proof.

Given: $\triangle ABC$ is isosceles, $\overline{AB} \cong \overline{BC}$, $\angle 1 \cong \angle 2$.

Prove: $\angle DAC \cong \angle DCA$

Proof:

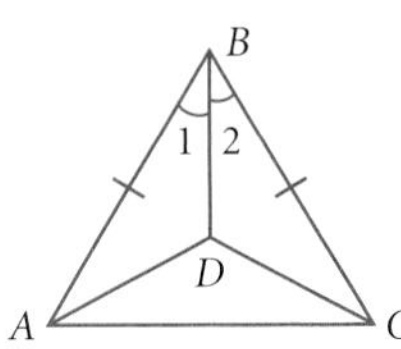

Statements	**Reasons**
1. $\overline{AB} \cong \overline{BC}$	**1.**
2.	**2.** Given
3.	**3.** Reflexive Property
4. $\triangle ADB \cong \triangle CDB$	**4.**
5. $\overline{AD} \cong \overline{CD}$	**5.**
6.	**6.**

14. Complete the following proof. [4-2]

Given: $\angle WYX$ and $\angle WYZ$ are right angles. $\overline{XW} \cong \overline{ZW}$

Prove: Y is the midpoint of $\overline{XZ}$.

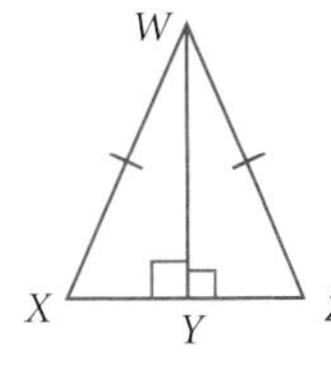

Proof: The **a.** ___ tells us that $\angle WYX$ and $\angle WYZ$ are right angles. Therefore, $\triangle WYX$ and $\triangle WYZ$ are right triangles by the **b.** ___. $\overline{WY} \cong \overline{WY}$ because of the **c.** ___. **d.** ___ from the given information. Therefore, **e.** ___ by the HL congruence theorem. Since the triangles are congruent, $\overline{XY} \cong \overline{YZ}$ by **f.** ___. Finally, **g.** ___ by the definition of midpoint.

15. Name the right-triangle congruence theorem that is a "special case" of each of the following. Explain your answers with an illustration. In some cases, there may be more than one right-triangle theorem; in others, there may not be any.

a. SAS **b.** ASA **c.** SSS **d.** SAA

16. Just Resting A rest shelter is to be built along a bike trail equidistant from the city park and the post office. Copy the figure, and find the location for the shelter. Write a description of the method you used to solve the problem.

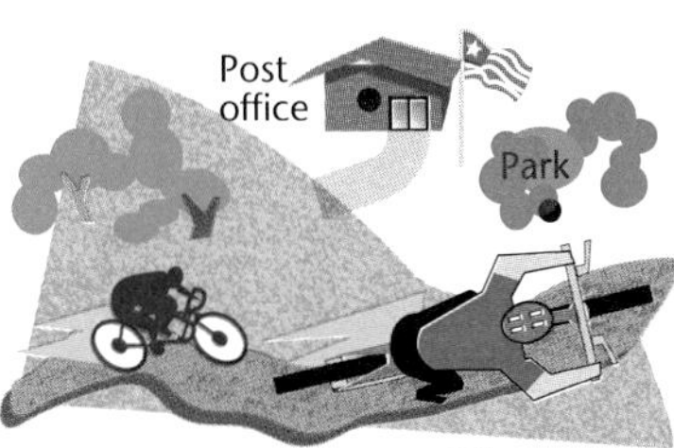

15. a. LL

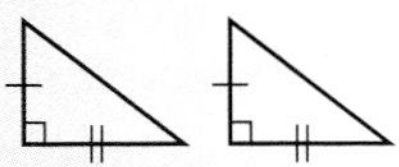

b. LA

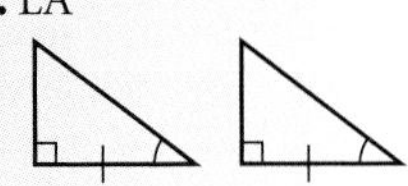

c. None

d. HA

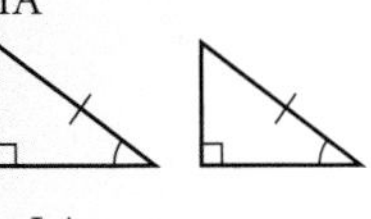

or LA

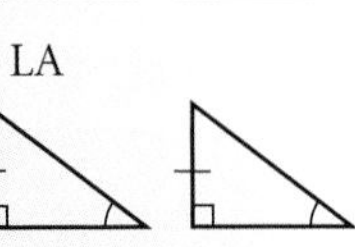

16. Draw the line segment from the post office to the park. Draw the perpendicular bisector of the line segment until it intersects the bike path. This is where the rest shelter should be built.

ssessment Resources

iz 4-3

hapter Assessment Form A

hapter Assessment Form B

hapter Alternative Assessment

id-Year Assessment

nd-of-Year Assessment

WSMTest and practice software

Ongoing Assessment

Self-Assessment Self-Assessment Exercises

Embedded Assessment Reflect 1, 2, 3

Chapter 4 Review

Journal

Students can identify **Key Terms** that they do not understand, and look up the definitions in the indicated section or in the glossary. Non-English-speaking students may want to use the *Multilingual Handbook.*

Vocabulary exercises and the **Self-Evaluation** are useful journal entries.

Review Answers

8. 242

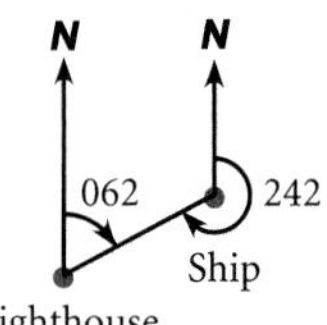

11. The LL Theorem is a special case of the SAS Postulate, where the legs of the right triangle are the sides and the right angle is the angle.

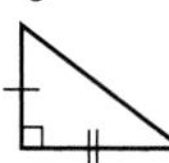
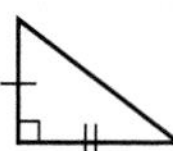

The HA Theorem is a special case of the SAA Postulate, where the hypotenuse is the side, an acute angle is the first angle and the right angle is the second angle.

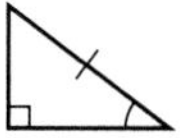
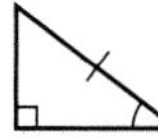

In some cases, the LA Theorem is a special case of the ASA Postulate where the right angle corresponds to an angle, the leg corresponds to the side, and the angle adjacent to the leg corresponds to the other angle in the postulate.

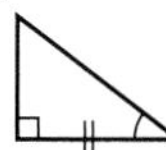
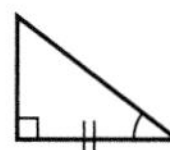

In other cases, the LA Theorem is a special case of the SAA Postulate, where the leg is the side, the right angle is the first angle and the acute angle opposite the leg is the other angle.

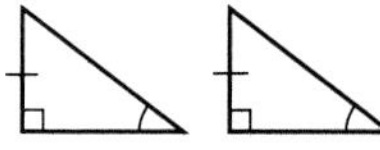

Chapter 4 Review

Triangles are important building blocks in geometry. In Chapter 4, you learned how to classify triangles, and you explored properties of different types of triangles. You also took a closer look at the idea of congruence and how it relates to triangles. By investigating congruent triangles, you were also able to further develop your proof skills.

KEY TERMS

acute triangle [4-1]	corollary [4-1]	obtuse triangle [4-1]
adjacent interior angle [4-1]	correspondence [4-2]	perpendicular bisector [4-3]
altitude [4-3]	equiangular triangle [4-1]	point of concurrency [4-3]
auxiliary line [4-3]	equilateral triangle [4-1]	remote interior angle [4-1]
base angle [4-1]	exterior angle [4-1]	right triangle [4-1]
centroid [4-3]	hypotenuse [4-1]	scalene triangle [4-1]
concurrent lines [4-3]	isosceles triangle [4-1]	tessellation [4-1]
congruence correspondence [4-2]	leg [4-1]	triangle [4-1]
congruent triangles [4-2]	locus [4-3]	vertex angle [4-1]
	median [4-3]	

V **Write the word or phrase that correctly completes each statement.**

1. The side opposite the right angle of a right triangle is the ____. Hypotenuse

2. The point of concurrency of the ____ of a triangle is the centroid. Medians

3. A ____ triangle is one in which two sides are congruent. Isosceles

4. A ____ is the set of points satisfying a given condition. Locus

CONCEPTS AND APPLICATIONS

P **Find the measure of ∠1 in each figure. [4-1]**

5. 89°

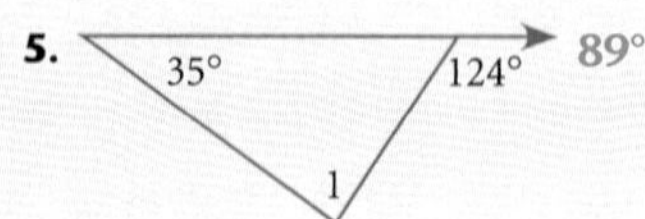

6. 8°

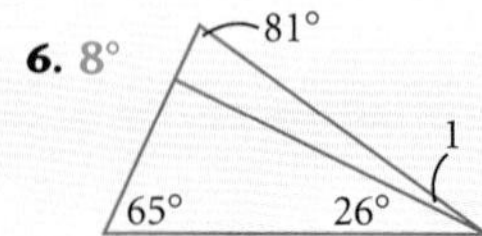

Key

V Vocabulary
P Practice/Skills
R Review
MR Math Reasoning
PS Problem Solving
C Challenge

7. A triangle has angles that measure $(4x + 50)°$, $2x°$, and $(x + 39)°$. Find the measures of the angles of the triangle. [4-1] 102°, 26°, 52°

8. If the bearing from a lighthouse to a ship is 062, what is the bearing from the ship to the lighthouse? Provide a sketch to illustrate your answer. [3-1]

If possible, write a congruence statement for each pair of triangles. Then name the congruence postulate that applies. If the triangles are not congruent, say so. [4-2]

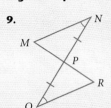

9. $\triangle MNP \cong \triangle RQP$; ASA Postulate

10. 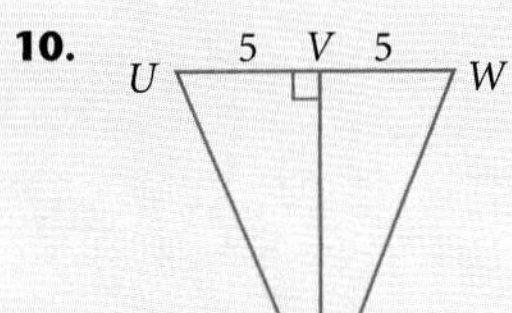

$\triangle UVX \cong \triangle WVX$; SAS Postulate

11. Write a summary describing how the LL, HA, and LA theorems for proving right triangles congruent are just special cases of the congruence postulates for all triangles. Provide a sketch to illustrate each case. [4-3]

12. Complete the following proof. [4-2]

Given: $\angle 1 \cong \angle 2$, and $\overline{DB}$ is perpendicular to $\overline{AC}$.

Prove: $\triangle ABD \cong \triangle CBD$

Statements	Reasons
1. $\angle 1 \cong \angle 2$	1.
2. $\angle DAB$ is supplementary to $\angle 1$, and $\angle DCB$ is supplementary to $\angle 2$.	2.
3. $\angle DAB \cong \angle DCB$	3.
4.	4. Reflexive Property
5. $\angle ABD$ and $\angle CBD$ are right angles.	5.
6. $\angle ABD \cong \angle CBD$	6.
7.	7.

13. A water tower is to be built equidistant from Highway 381 and Interstate 50. The tower must also be equidistant from the towns of Carterville and Ely. Copy the figure at the right, and indicate where the water tower should be built. Explain why your location for the tower works. [4-3]

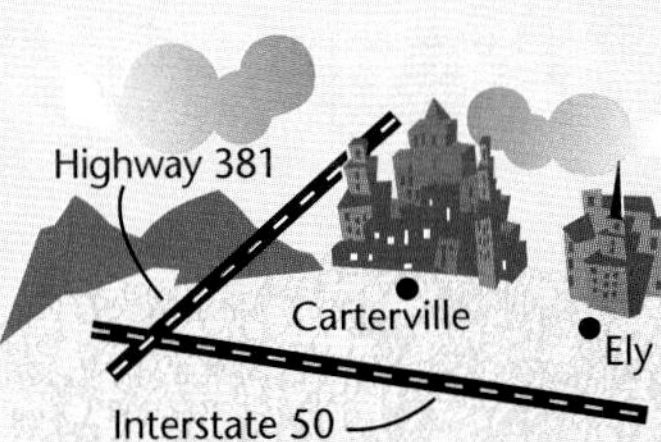

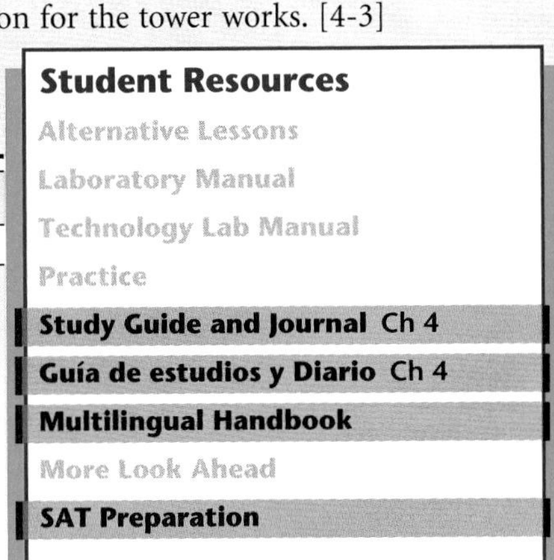

Student Resources
Alternative Lessons
Laboratory Manual
Technology Lab Manual
Practice
Study Guide and Journal Ch 4
Guía de estudios y Diario Ch 4
Multilingual Handbook
More Look Ahead
SAT Preparation

Media Resources
Transparency FFM
Transparency AE
Teaching Transparency
AWSMTest and practice software
AWSM Videodisc

12. Reason 1: Given
Reason 2: Linear-Pair Postulate
Reason 3: Supplements of congruent angles are congruent.
Statement 4: $\overline{DB} \cong \overline{DB}$
Reason 5: Definition of *perpendicular*
Reason 6: Right angles are congruent
Statement 7: $\triangle ABD \cong \triangle CBD$
Reason 7: SAA Postulate

13. Draw the line segment from Carterville to Ely. Draw the perpendicular bisector. Any point on the bisector is equidistant from Carterville and Ely. Draw the angle bisector of the angle formed at the intersection of Highway 381 and Interstate 50. Any point on this bisector is equidistant from the two highways. Therefore the point of intersection of the two bisectors is where the water tower is to be built.

15. It is not possible to create a tessellation with any two triangles.

Chapter 4 Assessment

Portfolio

Students may select items that represent their mathematical understanding of the ideas in Chapter 4 and that illustrate the effort that they put into this chapter.

A rubric for assessing portfolios is included in the introduction to the Teacher's Edition.

Assessment Answers

3. Draw the perpendicular bisector of the bike path. Any point on the bisector is equidistant from the endpoints of the bike path. Draw the perpendicular bisector of the line segment from Building *A* to Building *B*. Any point on this bisector is equidistant from Buildings *A* and *B*. Therefore, the point where the two bisectors intersect is where the phone should be.

4. 0 

5. 1 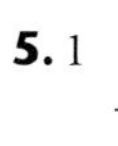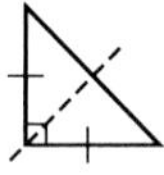

6. 3 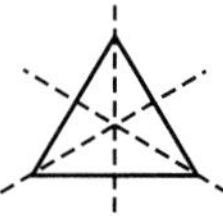

7. Reason 2: Two points determine a line.
Reason 3: If two parallel lines are cut by a transversal, the alternate interior angles are congruent.
Statement 4: $\overline{MK} \cong \overline{MK}$
Reason 5: ASA Postulate
Statement 6: $\angle J \cong \angle L$

8. Two pairs of sides and a pair of non-included angles may be congruent without the triangles being congruent.

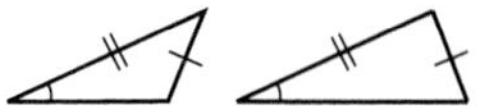

10. Two lines parallel to *t*, each 4 cm away from *t*.

P **14.** $\angle ABC$ is the vertex of isosceles triangle $\triangle ABC$. $\overline{AP}$, $\overline{BR}$, and $\overline{CN}$ are medians of $\triangle ABC$. Find *BN* and *BQ*. [4-3]
BN = 6.5, *BQ* = 8

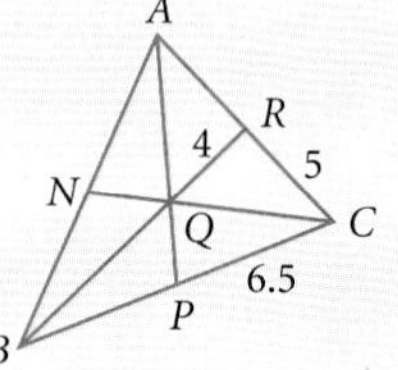

CONCEPTS AND CONNECTIONS

MR **15. Art** Tessellations are found in the art of many cultures. Some of the most beautiful tessellations are those that contain more than one geometric figure. Create a tessellation using congruent copies of *two different* triangles. Use color or shading to distinguish the triangles from each other. Based on your work, do you think it is possible to create a tessellation from *any* two given triangles? Why or why not?

Fine Arts

SELF-EVALUATION

Write a summary of the most important facts about triangles that you learned in Chapter 4. Include in your summary all of the methods you have learned for showing that two triangles are congruent. Provide a sketch to illustrate each postulate or theorem.

Chapter 4 Assessment

TEST

P **1.** Find $m\angle WZY$ and $m\angle WYX$.
$m\angle WZY = 78°$, $m\angle WYX = 61°$

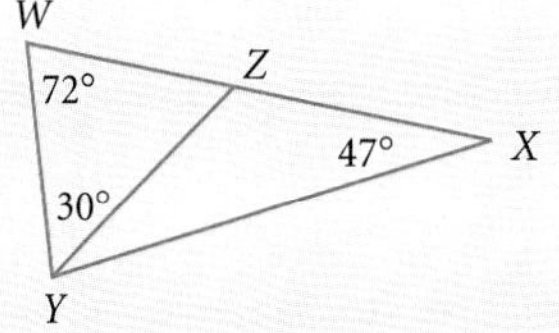

2. Find *AB* and *ED*.
AB = 10, *ED* = 8

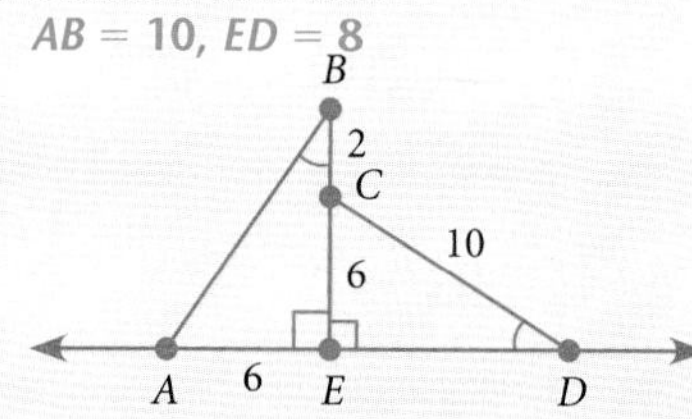

PS **3.** An architect is designing a park for a large apartment complex. The park includes a straight bike path. It is required that a pay phone be located equidistant from the endpoints of the bike path. The architect would also like the pay phone to be equidistant from Buildings *A* and *B*. Where should the phone be located? Explain.

Careers

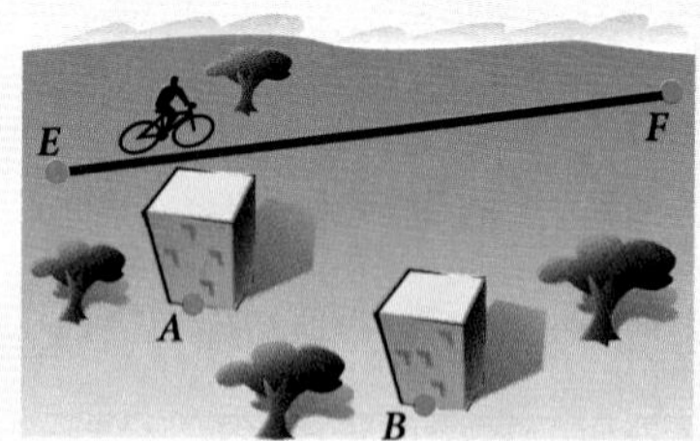

Assessment Resources

- Quiz
- Chapter 4 Assessment Form A
- Chapter 4 Assessment Form B
- Chapter 4 Alternative Assessment
- Mid-Year Assessment
- End-of-Year Assessment
- AWSMTest Chapter 4

Ongoing Assessment

Self-Assessment Chapter 4 Review and Self-Evaluation

Embedded Assessment Chapter 4 Performance Task

Test Chapter 4 Test

How many lines of symmetry do each of the following types of triangles have? Provide a sketch with each answer.

4. scalene triangle **5.** isosceles right triangle **6.** equilateral triangle

7. Complete the following proof.

Given: In the figure, $\overline{JK} \parallel \overline{LM}$ and $\overline{JM} \parallel \overline{KL}$

Prove: $\angle J \cong \angle L$

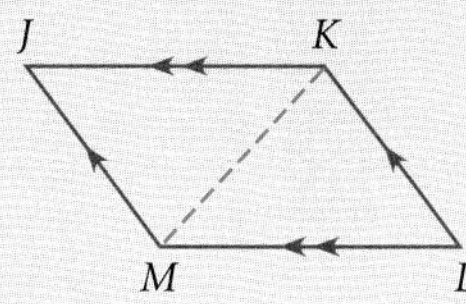

Statements	**Reasons**
1. $\overline{JK} \parallel \overline{LM}$ and $\overline{JM} \parallel \overline{KL}$	**1.** Given
2. Draw $\overline{KM}$.	**2.**
3. $\angle KML \cong \angle JKM$ $\angle LKM \cong \angle JMK$	**3.**
4.	**4.** Reflexive Property
5. $\triangle JMK \cong \triangle LKM$	**5.**
6.	**6.** CPCTC

8. Write a brief explanation of why there is no SSA postulate for triangle congruence. Use a figure to illustrate your explanation.

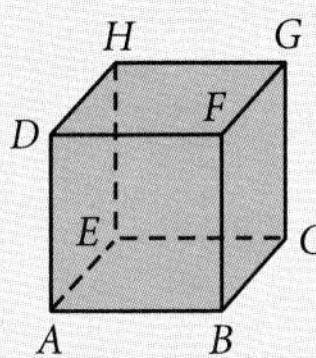

9. Suppose you form right triangles using the vertices of the cube at the right as vertices of the triangles. How many such triangles can be formed that lie on the faces of the cube? 24

10. Describe the locus of points in a plane 4 cm from line *t*.

11. Line *m* is parallel to line *n*. What are the measures of $\angle 1$ and $\angle 2$? $m\angle 1 = 40°$, $m\angle 2 = 34°$

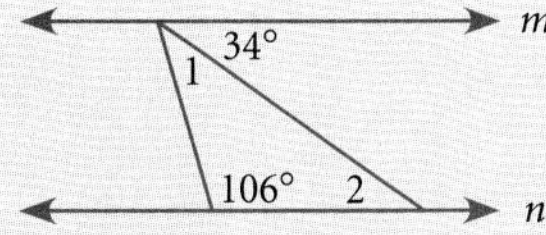

PERFORMANCE TASK

The *circumcenter* of a triangle is the point of concurrency of the perpendicular bisectors of the sides of the triangle. For what type of triangle does the circumcenter lie in the interior of the triangle? in the exterior of the triangle? on the triangle? Investigate these questions by drawing several different triangles. Use a compass and straightedge to find the circumcenter of each. After investigating various possibilities, use your results to make a conjecture.

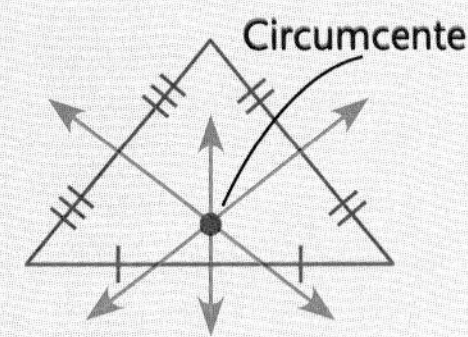

Performance Task

Answer

The circumcenter of an obtuse triangle is in its exterior; the circumcenter of a right triangle is on the triangle; the circumcenter of an acute triangle is in its interior.

Suggested Scoring Rubric

Level 4 Full Accomplishment

- Shows full understanding of the idea of a point of concurrency.
- Constructions are accurate and show that many different types of triangles have been investigated.
- Results of the investigation are summed up in three correct conjectures.

Level 3 Substantial Accomplishment

- Shows essential grasp of the idea of a point of concurrency.
- Constructions are accurate and show that several different types of triangles have been investigated.
- All conjectures are correct, but some may be redundant (e.g., the results for both acute and equilateral triangles are stated).

Level 2 Partial Accomplishment

- Shows partial grasp of the idea of a point of concurrency.
- Constructions may be incomplete or inaccurate and/or show that only a few types of triangles have been investigated.
- Some conjectures are incorrect.

Level 1 Little Accomplishment

- Shows little or no grasp of the idea of a point of concurrency.
- Constructions are incomplete or inaccurate; only one or two different types of triangles have been investigated.
- Some or all conjectures are incorrect.

5

Chapter 5 Area

Chapter 5 Project A: How Dry I Am

Plan a Garden

Lay out a garden and plan its irrigation system.

- Did you know that an inch of rain will penetrate 12 in. in sandy soil but only 4 or 5 in. in clay soil?
- Don't you wonder how to prevent wasteful water runoff?
- How does this connect to Chapter 5?
  The **area** of a garden determines the length of irrigation hoses.

Expand Your Vocabulary

loam, shutoff valve, hose bibb, runoff, horticulture, PVC pipe, sprinkler heads and risers, drip emitters

Project Guidelines

Investigate

- Read about sprinkler- and drip-irrigation in a garden book or in a manufacturer's pamphlet from a garden supply store.
- Read about watering gardens in a garden book written for your geographical region.

Set Your Direction

- Will you plan a vegetable or a flower garden?
- Will you plan for a sprinkler or drip-irrigation system?

Make a Plan

- Make a calendar for each day's work. Check in with your group and with your teacher.
- Decide what you'll need. Some tools to gather:
  measuring tape, graph paper, calculator (optional)

Collect and Organize Your Information

- Take measurements and mark them on a sketch of the garden.
- Estimate water needs. Plan a schedule suited to soil and plant types and to your irrigation system.
- Calculate the amount of water needed per square foot for a given period of time.

Carry Out Your Plan

- Make a scale drawing of the garden. Show the locations of water sources. Show branch lines and the locations of sprinkler heads or drip emitters.
- Calculate the total lengths of all irrigation lines.
- Tell why the plan will be adequate for the needs of the garden.

Look Back

- What would it actually cost to plant the garden and to install the irrigation system? Could you do all the work yourself?
- Would your planning steps be the same for a garden ten times as big?

 Focus on Geometry 25

A

Project A
How Dry I Am
How much water does a garden need? Are you ready to grow your own food?

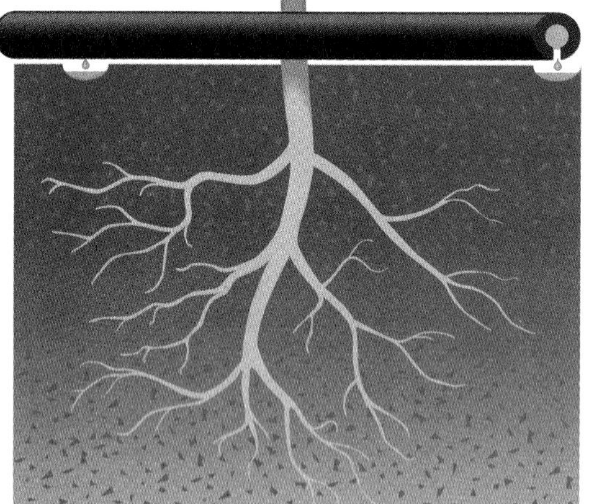

Project B
Stick to It
If you break a stick in two places, what are the chances that the pieces will form a triangle?

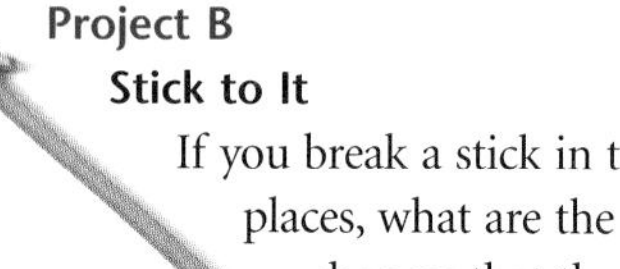

Project C
The Dots Have It
How are the paintings of Georges Seurat like a four-color printing process?

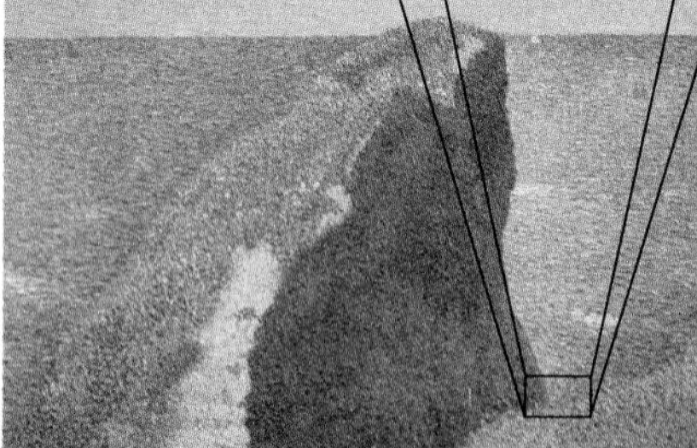

318

Chapter 5 Project C: The Dots Have It

Paint a Digital Picture

Translate a continuous-tone photograph into pointillist art made of individual dots.

- Did you know that color mixing with paint is different from color mixing with light?
- Don't you wonder how a TV screen makes a color image?
- How does this connect to Chapter 5?
  The clarity of detail in a pointillist picture or in a TV screen image depends on the number of dots in a given **area.**

Expand Your Vocabulary

pixel, optical mixing, resolution, mosaic, digital image, primary color, pointillism, monochromatic, continuous tone

The larger images show higher resolution and the details show lower resolution.

Project Guidelines

Investigate

- Look at reproductions of works by Georges Seurat and Paul Signac in an art history book.
- Read about TV image production in an encyclopedia or in a video production handbook.
- Use a magnifier to look at color reproductions in a magazine or newspaper.

Set Your Direction

- Will you make your own pointillist art with paint dots? with a computer? Will you make a mosaic with paper bits?
- Will it be in color? in black-and-white?

Make a Plan

- Make a calendar for each day's work. Check in with your group and with your teacher.
- Decide what you'll need. Some tools to gather:
  magnifier, graph paper, art materials or computer

Collect and Organize Your Information

- Interview an artist, printer, or video technician.
- Choose a photograph to "digitalize."
- Make a sketch or tracing of the photo showing light and dark patterns.
- Experiment with primary color "pixels" to achieve the effect you want.

Carry Out Your Plan

- Transfer your sketch to graph paper. Adjust the outlines of the sketch to follow the grid lines.
- Decide which colors or gray tones to use in each square.
- In a paragraph, tell how an area covered with different colors "adds up" to the general impression.

Look Back

- What did Seurat and Signac do to get high resolution in their paintings?
- If you wanted a higher resolution picture, what would you have to do?

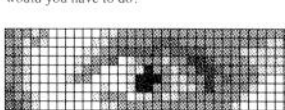

 Focus on Geometry 29

C

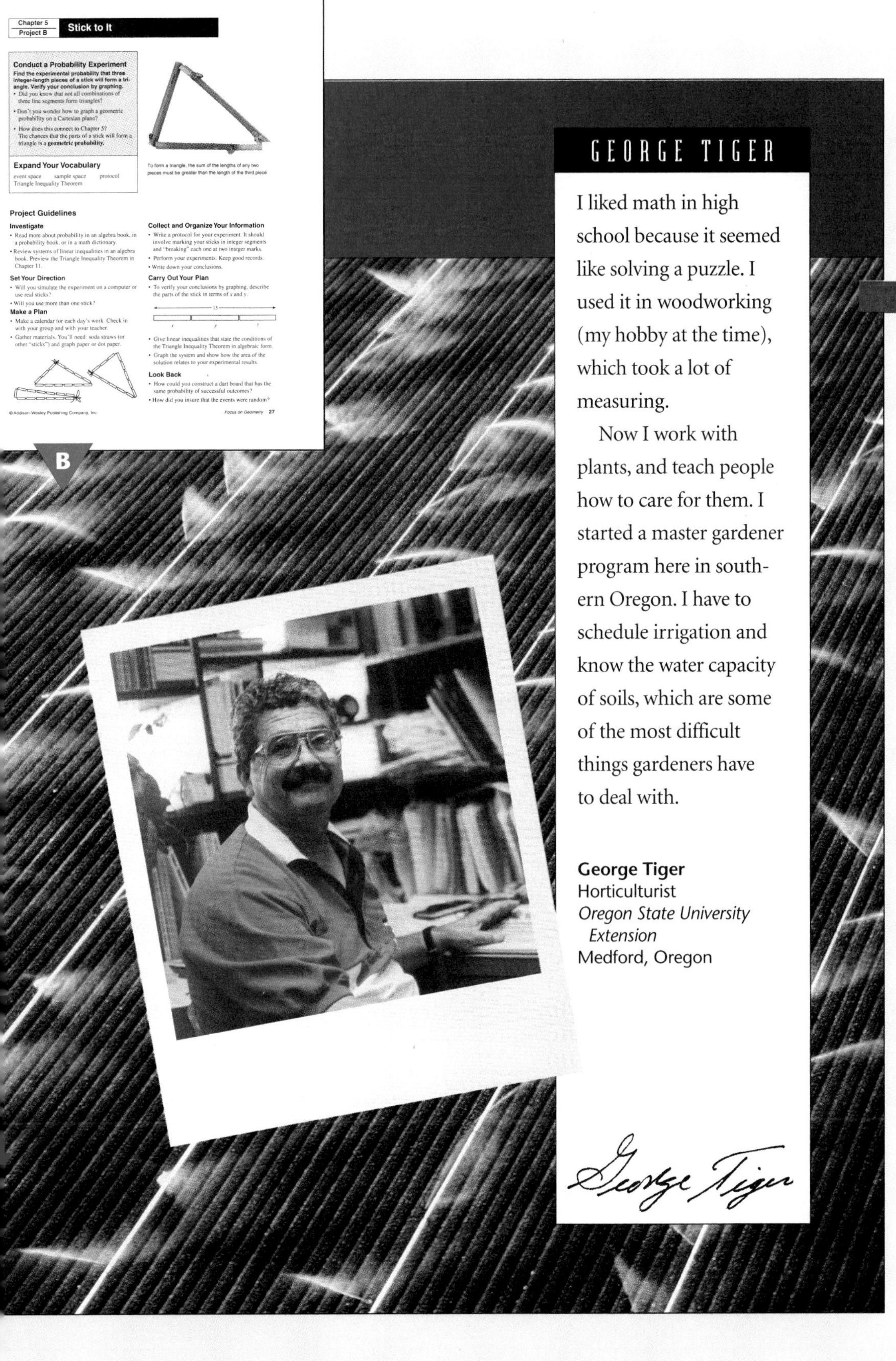

Chapter 5
Project B

Stick to It

Conduct a Probability Experiment

Find the experimental probability that three integer-length pieces of a stick will form a triangle. Verify your conclusion by graphing.

- Did you know that not all combinations of three line segments form triangles?
- Don't you wonder how to graph a geometric probability on a Cartesian plane?
- How does this connect to Chapter 5? The chances that the parts of a stick will form a triangle is a **geometric probability.**

Expand Your Vocabulary

event space sample space protocol
Triangle Inequality Theorem

To form a triangle, the sum of the lengths of any two pieces must be greater than the length of the third piece.

Project Guidelines

Investigate

- Read more about probability in an algebra book, in a probability book, or in a math dictionary.
- Review systems of linear inequalities in an algebra book. Preview the Triangle Inequality Theorem in Chapter 11.

Set Your Direction

- Will you simulate the experiment on a computer or use real sticks?
- Will you use more than one stick?

Make a Plan

- Make a calendar for each day's work. Check in with your group and with your teacher.
- Gather materials. You'll need: soda straws (or other "sticks") and graph paper or dot paper.

Collect and Organize Your Information

- Write a protocol for your experiment. It should involve marking your sticks in integer segments and "breaking" each one at two integer marks.
- Perform your experiments. Keep good records.
- Write down your conclusions.

Carry Out Your Plan

- To verify your conclusions by graphing, describe the parts of the stick in terms of x and y.

- Give linear inequalities that state the conditions of the Triangle Inequality Theorem in algebraic form.
- Graph the system and show how the area of the solution relates to your experimental results.

Look Back

- How could you construct a dart board that has the same probability of successful outcomes?
- How did you insure that the events were random?

© Addison-Wesley Publishing Company, Inc. *Focus on Geometry* 27

GEORGE TIGER

I liked math in high school because it seemed like solving a puzzle. I used it in woodworking (my hobby at the time), which took a lot of measuring.

Now I work with plants, and teach people how to care for them. I started a master gardener program here in southern Oregon. I have to schedule irrigation and know the water capacity of soils, which are some of the most difficult things gardeners have to deal with.

George Tiger
Horticulturist
Oregon State University Extension
Medford, Oregon

Biographical Note

George Tiger graduated from Stayton High School in Stayton, OR. He took Algebra and Geometry, the only offerings.

Chapter 5

Overview

Area

5-1 Understanding and Applying Area

The area and perimeter of simple geometric figures have important applications in everyday situations and in algebra. You will calculate area and perimeter, and see how area is related to algebra and probability.

5-2 Derivations of Area Formulas

The ability to calculate area accurately has been important for hundreds of years. Now you will see where area formulas come from, and why they work. You will also plan logical arguments using area.

5-3 The Pythagorean Theorem

The Pythagorean Theorem enables you to find an unknown side length in a right triangle. This theorem is useful in architecture, surveying, and other fields. You will learn about the history and applications of the Pythagorean Theorem, and see why the theorem is true.

CHAPTERS

320

Chapter 5 Planning Guide

The following ancillaries are recommended for each course level. The additional resources, *Technology Lab Manual, Study Guide and Journal, Multilingual Handbook,* and *Assessment,* are recommended for all levels.

	Comprehensive Course	Core Course	Informal Course
5-1 Part A	▲	▲	▲
Alternative Lessons			▲
Laboratory Manuals	▲	▲	▲
Practice			▲
More Look Ahead		▲	▲
5-1 Part B	▲	▲	▲
Alternative Lessons			▲
Laboratory Manuals	▲	▲	▲
Practice			▲
More Look Back		▲	▲
5-1 Part C	▲	▲	▲
Alternative Lessons			▲
Laboratory Manuals	▲	▲	▲
Practice			▲
More Look Ahead		▲	▲
5-1 Part D	▲	▲	▲
Alternative Lessons			▲
Laboratory Manuals	▲	▲	▲
Practice			▲
More Look Back		▲	▲
5-1 Part E	▲	▲	▲
More Look Back		▲	▲
Quiz 5-1	▲	▲	▲
5-2 Part A	▲	▲	▲
Alternative Lessons			▲
Laboratory Manuals	▲	▲	▲
Practice			▲
More Look Back		▲	▲
5-2 Part B	▲	▲	▲
Alternative Lessons			▲
Laboratory Manuals	▲	▲	▲
Practice			▲
More Look Ahead		▲	▲
5-2 Part C	▲	▲	
Alternative Lessons			
Laboratory Manuals	▲	▲	
Practice			
More Look Back		▲	
5-2 Part D	▲	▲	▲
More Look Back		▲	▲
Quiz 5-2	▲	▲	▲
5-3 Part A	▲	▲	▲
Alternative Lessons			▲
Laboratory Manuals	▲	▲	▲
Practice			▲
More Look Ahead		▲	▲
5-3 Part B	▲	▲	▲
Alternative Lessons			▲
Laboratory Manuals	▲	▲	▲
Practice			▲
More Look Ahead		▲	▲
5-3 Part C	▲	▲	▲
Alternative Lessons			▲
Laboratory Manuals	▲	▲	▲
Practice			▲
More Look Back		▲	▲
5-3 Part D	▲	▲	▲
Alternative Lessons			▲
Laboratory Manuals	▲	▲	▲
Practice			▲
More Look Ahead		▲	▲
5-3 Part E	▲	▲	▲
More Look Back		▲	▲
Quiz 5-3	▲	▲	▲

BIBLIOGRAPHY

Teacher Resources

Taxicab Geometry, Eugene F. Krause. Addison-Wesley, 1975 (03934).

Geometric Design: Step by Step, Dale Seymour. Dale Seymour Publications, 1988 (NS07802).

Reading for Teachers

Geometry in Architecture, William Blackwell. Key Curriculum Press, 1984.

Videos

The Theorem of Pythagoras, Project Mathematics!—California Institute of Technology. Available through Dale Seymour Publications (NS02090).

5-1

Understanding and Applying Area

SUPERLESSON AT A GLANCE

Superlesson Goal

Students will calculate areas of simple figures and see how area connects with algebra and geometric probability.

Management Guide

	Topic	Objectives	Key Terms	New Ideas	Materials
Part A	Area and Perimeter	To review areas of simple figures, and to apply the Area-Addition Postulate.	Area, polygon, polygonal region, perimeter	Areas and perimeters of rectangles, squares, and triangles. Using the Area-Addition Postulate to find areas of polygonal regions.	**Student** Graph paper, geometry software
Part B	Polynomials and Area	To see how products of binomials can be used to model areas of rectangles, and to use this connection to help factor algebraic expressions.		Representing monomials with square and rectangular tiles. Factoring expressions by arranging tiles. Using quadratic expressions to model areas.	**Student** Algebra tiles (or graph paper and scissors)
Part C	The Quadratic Formula and Area	To use the quadratic formula to solve problems involving area.	Quadratic equation, quadratic formula	Solving quadratic equations by using the quadratic formula.	
Part D	Area and Probability	To solve probability problems involving area and perimeter ratios.	Geometric probability	Solving geometric probability problems. Designing problems to match a given probability.	
Part E	Making Connections	To use knowledge of the areas of figures to design a game with a given probability of winning.	In Making Connections, students apply and synthesize key terms and new ideas.		

Pacing Chart (45-Minute Periods)

	Comprehensive Course	Core Course	Informal Course
Part A	1	1	1
Part B	1	2	2
Part C	1	2	2
Part D	1	1	1
Part E	1	1	1
TOTAL periods for Superlesson	5	7	7

NCTM Standards

Mathematics as Problem Solving

Mathematics as Communication

Mathematics as Reasoning

Mathematical Connections

Algebra

Geometry from an Algebraic Perspective

Probability

5-1 Understanding and Applying Area

HURRY, HURRY, STEP RIGHT UP!

"Ladies and gentlemen, children of all ages! Join me on a thrilling adventure under the big top, a journey to a world like no other." This ringmaster's announcement signals the start of the Ringling Brothers and Barnum & Bailey Circus. This circus presents two shows a day, and travels to 52 cities and towns across the country. It had its origins over a century ago.

In the late 1800s and early 1900s, circuses captivated audiences across America. People looked forward to the thrilling and exotic circus acts and the games of chance. In 1909, there were 98 touring circuses in the United States.

In the 1940s, circus attendance was at an all-time high. But the circus was competing with the phonograph, movies, radio, and later, television for people's entertainment time and money. The circus suffered a steady decline in attendance. Today there are only about half a dozen circuses still traveling the country and performing under canvas tents.

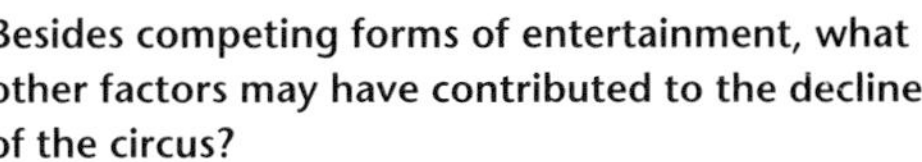

Besides competing forms of entertainment, what other factors may have contributed to the decline of the circus?

The words *circus* and *circle* both have their origins in the Greek word *kirkos,* meaning *ring.* Explain the relationship between the words *circus* and *circle.*

3. How might calculations of area and perimeter be important to a circus?

More About Circuses

In the late 1800s, before a circus came to an American town, it staged an intense advertising campaign. Flyers and posters not only enticed people to come to the show, but also belittled competing circuses that were performing nearby. The circus also staged a huge parade to advertise its arrival. The parade included bugle brigades, flag bearers, horses, and exotic animals in elaborately decorated cages. It usually ended with the famous steam calliope.

Where Are We Now?

Students are probably familiar with calculating the areas of simple geometric figures from earlier mathematics courses.

Where Are We Going?

In 5-1, students will review areas and perimeters of simple figures. They will see connections to algebraic expressions, factoring trinomials, and geometric probability.

In 5-2, having reviewed and extended their understanding of area, students will use deductive reasoning to justify area formulas for several figures, including important quadrilaterals.

Possible Answers

1. Increasing expenses; people are more concerned about the treatment of animals; people are more familiar with exotic animals from television; a less glamorous or exotic image.
2. Circuses (and earlier forms of entertainment) presented their shows in oval or circular arenas.
3. Might need to know the dimensions of a stage, distance around a track for horses, and so on.

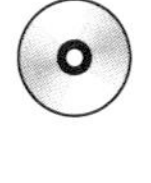

AWSM Videodisc

Focus on Geometry

▶ **5-1** Understanding and Applying Area

Search:

Play:

Step:

Understanding and Applying Area

PART A At a Glance

Objective

To review areas of simple figures, and to apply the Area-Addition Postulate.

Development

Students first review areas of rectangles, squares, and triangles. The Area-Addition Postulate is presented.

In the **Explore,** students see that area and perimeter are independent quantities, and they find that the rectangle with the largest area for a given perimeter is a square. Students will confirm this result algebraically in 11-2.

Suggested Materials

Student Graph paper, geometry software

Key Terms

Area, polygon, polygonal region, perimeter

First Five Minutes

Transparency FFM 5-1A

Review the area formulas of rectangles, squares, and triangles presented on page 322. Then calculate each of the following.

1. The area of a square with side lengths of 4 cm. **16 cm²**

2. The area of a rectangle with width 5.2 in. and length 8.5 in. **44.2 in.²**

3. The area of a triangle with a base length of 11 cm and a height of $6\frac{1}{2}$ cm. **$35\frac{3}{4}$ cm²**

Motivate

Ask...

- What does the area of a figure measure? the perimeter?
- If you planned to buy a piece of farmland, why would you want to know its area? Why might you want to know its perimeter?

5-1 PART A Area and Perimeter

← CONNECT → *You already know how to find the area and perimeter of some geometric figures. Now you will explore some familiar formulas and begin to extend the ideas of area and perimeter to more complicated figures.*

The figure below shows that the **area** of a rectangle can be found by counting unit squares, or—more quickly—by multiplying the length of the rectangle by its width.

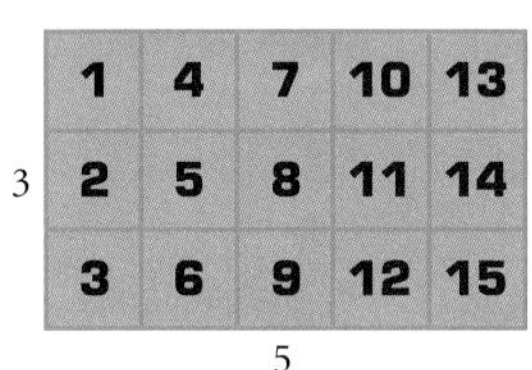

Since there are 3 rows of 5 squares, $A = \ell w = 3 \times 5 = 15$ square units.

Because a square is a rectangle whose length and width are equal, the area of a square is equal to the square of the length of one of its sides.

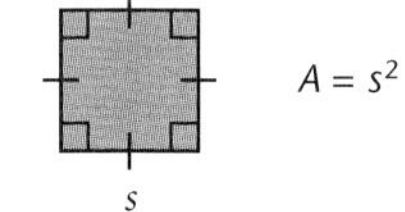

$A = s^2$

The area formula for a triangle may also be familiar to you. The area of a triangle is one-half the product of the length of the base and the height.

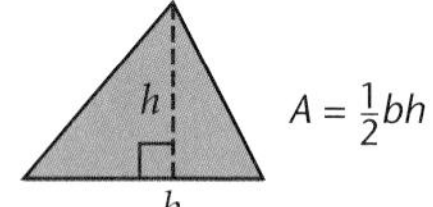

$A = \frac{1}{2}bh$

In 5-2, we will bring area formulas into our deductive system. You will see why these and other area formulas work. For now, we'll assume that a few basic formulas are valid, so that we can explore some connections between area, perimeter, algebra, and probability.

The following definition and postulates provide a foundation for studying area. Most of the figures you will be working with are **polygons.** As you'll see, a polygon is a many-sided plane figure whose sides are line segments.

DEFINITION

A **polygonal region** consists of a polygon and its interior.

A polygonal region can always be divided into nonoverlapping triangular regions as shown.

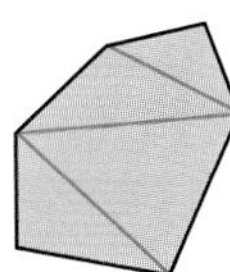

AREA POSTULATES

For every polygonal region, there is a unique positive number called the *area* of the region.

If two polygonal regions are congruent, then they have equal areas.

AREA-ADDITION POSTULATE

The area of a polygonal region is the sum of the areas of all of its nonoverlapping parts.

The Area-Addition Postulate helps you calculate the areas of complicated regions. You can find the area of a polygonal region by dividing it into convenient triangles and rectangles and adding their areas.

EXAMPLE

Find the area of the figure at the right.

To find the area of the figure, add the area of the rectangle to the area of the triangle.

area of figure = area of rectangle + area of triangle

$= 6 \cdot 15 + \frac{1}{2} \cdot 15 \cdot 4$

$= 90 + 30$

$= 120 \text{ cm}^2$

Another measure of a figure is its **perimeter**—the distance around the figure. Remember that perimeter and area measure different things. Perimeter is a distance, so it is measured in linear units (for example, inches or centimeters). Area is measured in square units (for example, square feet or square meters).

Note: The Area-Addition Postulate applies to adjacent polygonal regions and nonintersecting polygonal regions. It does not apply to regions that share interior points.

ALTERNATE EXAMPLE

Find the area of the figure below.

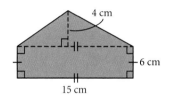

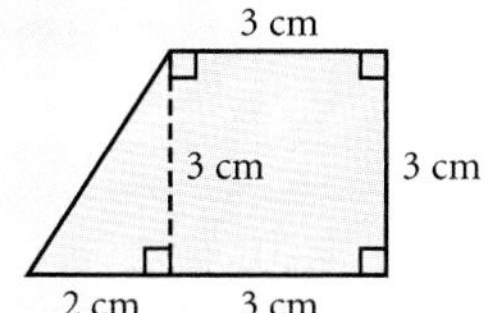

To find the area of the figure, add the area of the square to the area of the triangle.

Area of figure = Area of triangle + Area of square

$= \frac{1}{2} \cdot 2 \cdot 3 + 3^2$

$= 3 + 9$

$= 12 \text{ cm}^2$

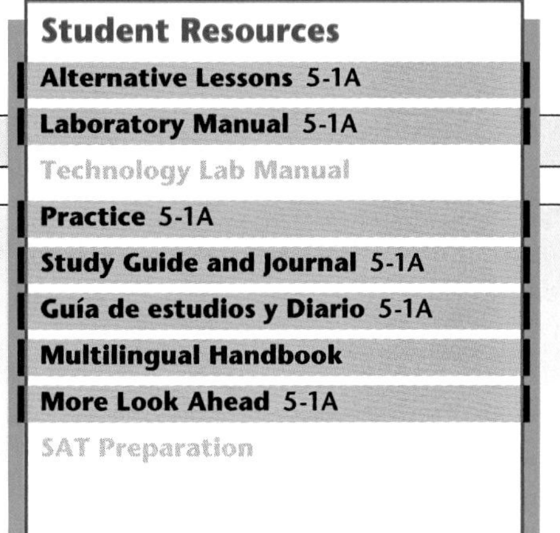

Student Resources
Alternative Lessons 5-1A
Laboratory Manual 5-1A
Technology Lab Manual
Practice 5-1A
Study Guide and Journal 5-1A
Guía de estudios y Diario 5-1A
Multilingual Handbook
More Look Ahead 5-1A
SAT Preparation

Media Resources

- Transparency FFM 5-1A
- Transparency AE 5-1A
- Teaching Transparency
- AWSMTest and practice software
- AWSM Videodisc

Understanding and Applying Area

EXPLORE

Perimeter vs. Area

Recommended group size: 4

The Point
To discover that area and perimeter are independent quantities, and to find that the rectangle with the largest area for a given perimeter is a square.

Look and Listen...

- For students who do not see that 4 × 3 and 3 × 4 rectangles are equivalent.
- For students who are not using an area value that is a perfect square. They may not see that the best rectangle is a square.

Ask...

- Do the side lengths of the rectangles have to be integers?

For Groups That Finish Early
Does the area of a *square* depend on its perimeter? Explain.

Follow Up
Have students characterize the rectangles with the largest and smallest areas for a given perimeter. Ask if the area or the perimeter of a rectangle tells you anything about the other quantity.

Possible Answers

3. A square has the greatest area for a given perimeter; there is no rectangle with the least area.
4. In general, area and perimeter are independent. For some figures (square, circle), they do depend on each other.

Journal

Reflect 1 and 5 and **Exercise** 14 are suitable for journal entries.

Algebra | Functions | Discrete Math | Probability | Data/Statistics

EXPLORE: PERIMETER vs. AREA

MATERIALS

Graph paper
Geometry software (optional)

1. Use geometry software or graph paper to draw three noncongruent rectangles with the same area. Find their perimeters, and record your data.
2. Draw three different rectangles with the same perimeter. Find their areas, and record your data.
3. What type of rectangle has the largest area for any given perimeter? What type has the smallest area for any given perimeter (assuming the side lengths are whole numbers)? Make conjectures and compare your results with those of your classmates.
4. Does the area of a figure depend on its perimeter? Does the perimeter of a figure depend on its area? Explain.

TRY IT

Find the perimeter and area of each figure.

a.

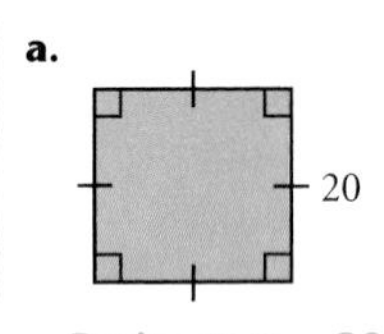

Perimeter = 80;
Area = 400

b.

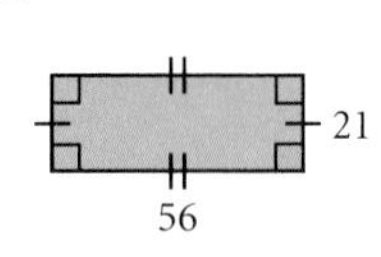

Perimeter = 154;
Area = 1176

c.

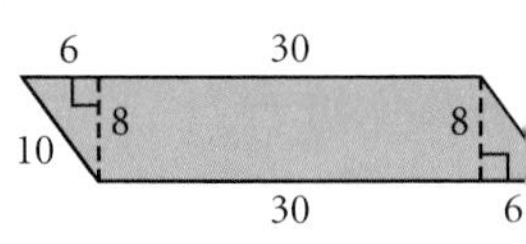

Perimeter = 92;
Area = 288

REFLECT

1. Explain the difference between perimeter and area.

Describe a way to find the area of each figure. Assume that you can measure any lengths that you wish.

2.

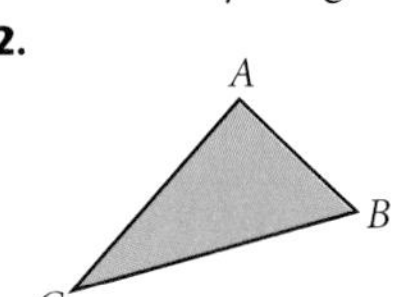

3.

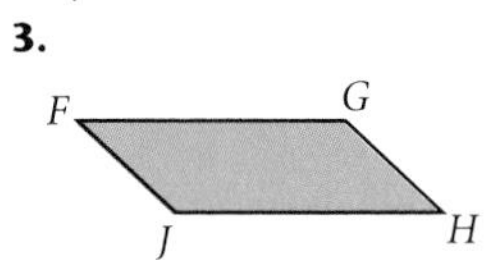

4.

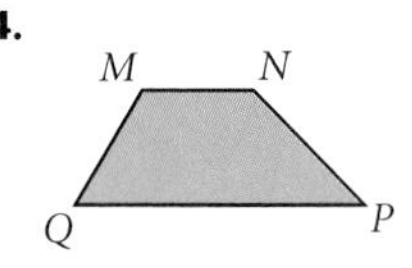

5. Soraya says, "If I have a ruler and a protractor, I know I can find the area of any polygonal region." Is this true? If so, how can Soraya justify her claim? If not, explain why not.

Technology Note

In the **Explore,** students must construct different rectangles with the *same* perimeter or area. When using geometry software to do this, it may be easiest if students first draw two rectangles and take measurements. Then, to adjust the perimeter or area of the second so that it is the same as that of the first, students will need to drag two vertices alternately.

Exercises

CORE

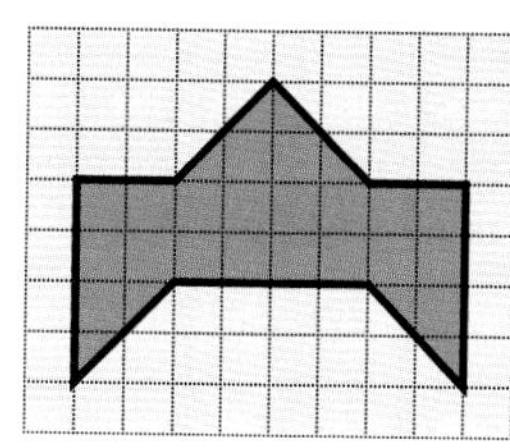

1. **Getting Started** Find the area of the figure. Each square on the grid has an area of 1 square unit. 24

Find the perimeter and area of each figure.

2. 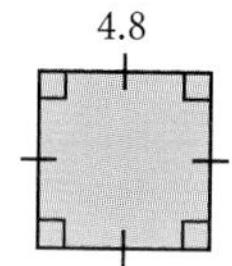

Perimeter = 19.2; Area = 23.04

3. 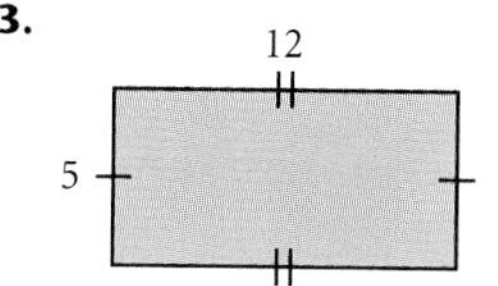

Perimeter = 34; Area = 60

4. 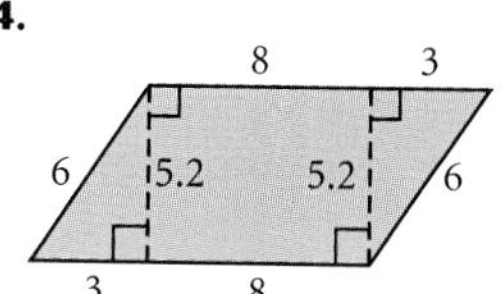

Perimeter = 34; Area = 57.2

5. 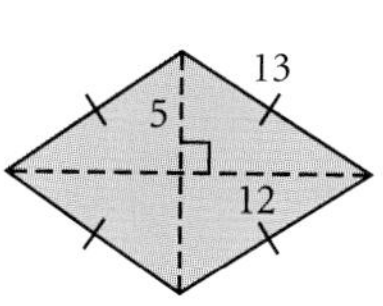

Perimeter = 52; Area = 120

6. 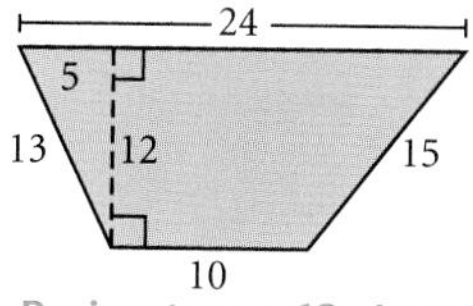

Perimeter = 62; Area = 204

The area of Figure A is 28 square units, the area of Figure B is 32 square units, the area of Figure C is 19 square units, and the area of Figure D is 25 square units. Find the following areas. (Hint: Recall that ∪ means the union of two sets.)

7. the area of Figure A ∪ Figure C
8. the area of Figure B ∪ Figure D
9. the area of Figure A ∪ Figure D

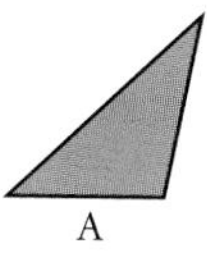
A
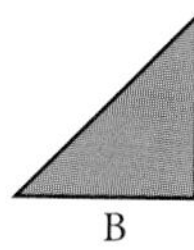
B
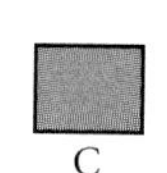
C
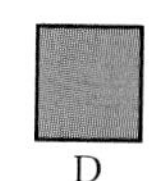
D

10. What postulate are you using in calculating the areas in Exercises 7–9?
11. What is the difference between 100 cm and 100 cm^2? Illustrate your answer.
12. Write the word or phrase that correctly completes the following statement.

    A polygonal region can be divided into nonoverlapping ____ regions.

13. Find formulas for the perimeter of a rectangle and the perimeter of a square.
14. **Remodeling the Kitchen** A rectangular kitchen measures 120 ft^2. The floor is to be covered with square tiles measuring 6 in. by 6 in. How many tiles will it take to cover the floor? Assume only whole tiles are used. Give a short, written description of how you solved this problem.

Ongoing Assessment

Vocabulary
Practice/Skills
Review
Math Reasoning
Problem Solving
Challenge

Self-Assessment Exercises 1–15 odd

Embedded Assessment Explore Step 4; Exercises 4, 8, 14, 16

REFLECT

Possible Answers

1. The perimeter measures distance around a figure; the area measures enclosed space.
2. Measure one side of the triangle and the length of the altitude to that side; use $A = \frac{1}{2}bh$.

3. and 4. Split the figure into two triangles. Then find the area of each triangle (as described in the answer to **2** above) and add.

5. This is true. She can divide the region into triangular regions. Using the protractor, she can sketch an altitude of each triangle. Then she can use the ruler to measure the base and height of each triangle, calculate each area, and add the individual areas together. (Note: If measurements are inexact, answers will be approximations.)

Part A Exercises

Exercise Notes

Core

15. Students find the area of a region on a coordinate plane. In 5-2 Part C, they will approximate areas of regions under curves on a coordinate plane.

Look Ahead

These exercises review algebra terminology used in 5-1 Part B.

More Math Reasoning

29. Introduces the idea of a limit. This concept is an underpinning of calculus and is important in the development of the area formula for a circle in 8-1 Part D.

Exercise Answers

Core

7. 47 square units
8. 57 square units
9. 53 square units
10. Area-Addition Postulate
11. The units are different; A perimeter could be represented by 100 cm, whereas an area could be represented by 100 cm^2.
12. Triangular

5-1

Understanding and Applying Area

13. Rectangle $= 2l + 2w$;
Square $= 4s$

14. 480 tiles; Divide 120 ft^2 by the area of one tile, which is 0.25 ft^2.

15. Area = 49

16. Possible answer:

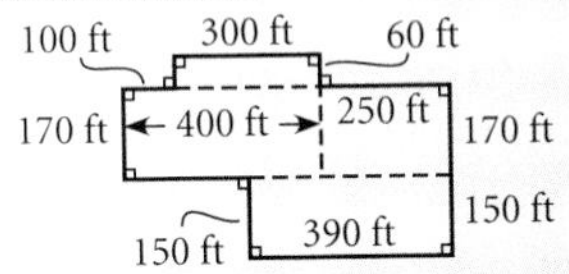

Total fencing = $6880

17. Diamond $= \frac{1}{2}(70 \cdot 120)$ cm^2 = 4200 cm^2;
Each triangle $= \frac{1}{2}(35 \cdot 60)$ cm^2 = 1050 cm^2

More Practice

22. 144.15 in.^{2} **23.** 50.41 m^2

24. 864 in.^{2} or 6 ft^2

25. 20.35 cm^2 **26.** 126 ft^2

27. 24

More Math Reasoning

28. a. Area A ∪ B = area A + area B − intersecting area of A and B.

b. Area A ∪ B = area A + area B − area A ∩ B

29. a. Blue triangles: 1, 3, 6, 10, 15,... add 2, add 3, add 4, add 5,... white triangles: 0, 1, 3, 6, 10,... add 1, add 2, add 3, add 4,...

b. 21:15, 28:21, 36:28

c. $\frac{n+1}{n-1}$

d. The limit is 1.

Algebra | Functions | Discrete Math | Probability | Data/Statistics

P **15.** Find the area of a figure on the coordinate plane that is bounded by the x-axis, the line $y = 2x$, and the line $x = 7$.

PS **16. Okay, Corral It!** A horse rancher has to divide this parcel of land into four rectangular fenced regions. Corral fencing costs $8.00 per foot. Sketch a way to divide the land, and include the dimensions in your sketch. How much does the fencing cost?

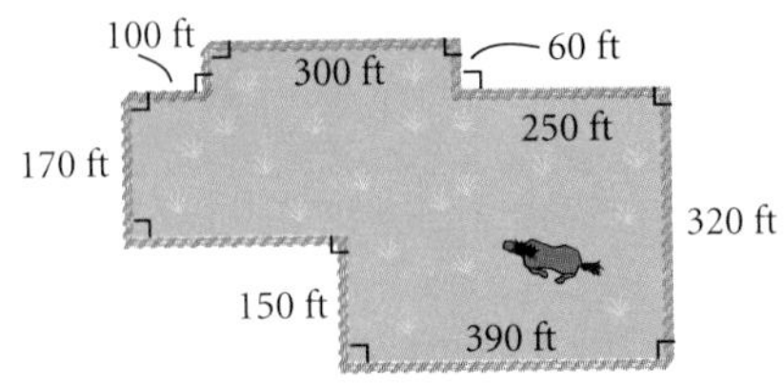

PS **17.** A stained-glass window has a central red diamond with four green triangles on its sides. Find the area of the red region and the area of each of the green triangles. Explain how you found the areas.

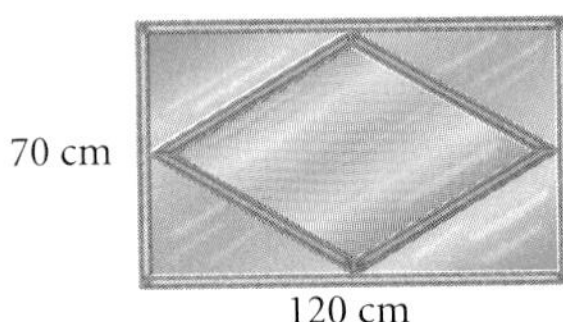

LOOK AHEAD

P **Identify each of these polynomials as a monomial (one term), a binomial (two terms), or a trinomial (three terms).**

18. $3x^2$ Monomial **19.** $4y + 7$ Binomial **20.** $2x^3y^2z^4$ Monomial **21.** $x^2 + y^2 + z^2$ Trinomi

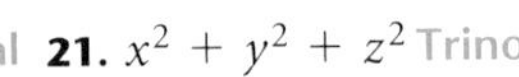

MORE PRACTICE

P **Find the area of each figure.**

22.

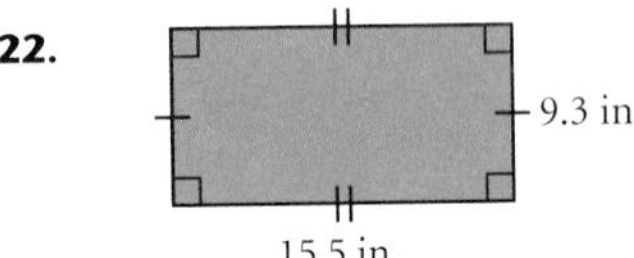

23.

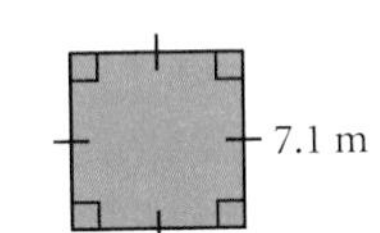

24.

3 ft

48 in.

25.

2 cm
1 cm
4.3 cm
4.7 cm
3 cm

26.

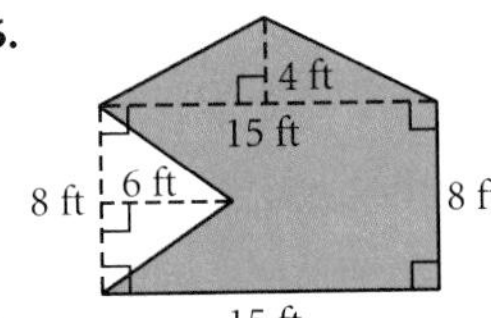

27.

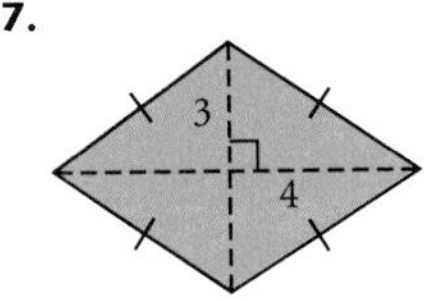

MORE MATH REASONING

MR **28.** Suppose that Figure A and Figure B are overlapping polygons.
a. Describe a method for finding the area of A ∪ B.
b. Write a formula for finding the area of A ∪ B. (Hint: The intersection of A and B is written A ∩ B.)

Key

V Vocabulary
P Practice/Skills
R Review
MR Math Reasoning
PS Problem Solving
C Challenge

29. Triangular "checkerboards" of different sizes are shown below. Notice that the ratio of the blue area to the white area seems to decrease as the number of triangles on the board increases.

a. Identify a pattern in the numbers of blue and white triangles. Do these patterns continue?

b. Find the ratios for the next few checkerboards.

c. Write a formula for the number of blue triangles on a board that has n triangles on a side.

d. Does the ratio of blue to white triangles seem to approach a particular value? If so, what is this value? (Note: A value that a sequence or graph approaches is called a *limit*.)

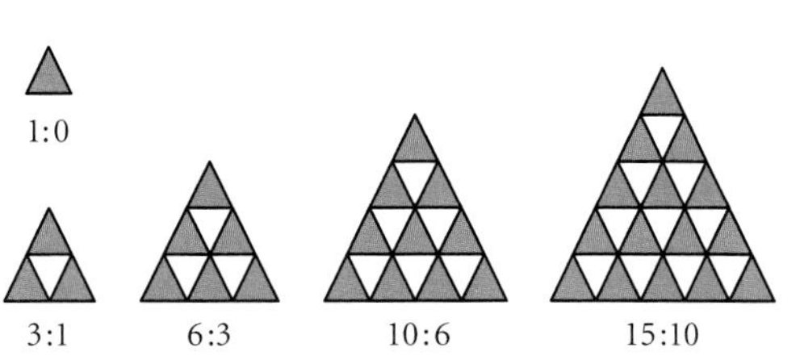

5-1 PART B Polynomials and Area

← CONNECT → *You have learned about polynomials in previous math courses. Now you will connect algebra and geometry by looking at polynomials and area.*

There are connections between mathematics and art, science, business, and nature. There are also connections between different areas of mathematics. Connections between numbers, equations, graphs, and geometric figures show the relationship between algebra and geometry.

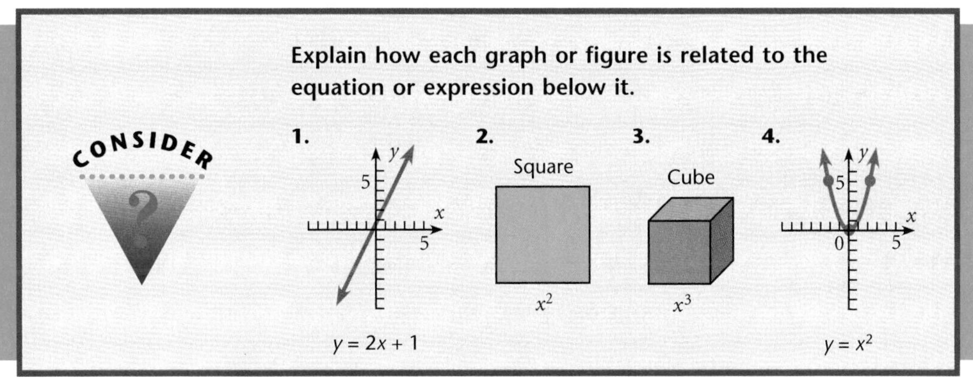

CONSIDER
Explain how each graph or figure is related to the equation or expression below it.
1.
2.
3.
4.
Square
Cube
y = 2x + 1
x²
x³
y = x²

Student Resources

- Alternative Lessons 5-1B
- Laboratory Manual 5-1B
- Technology Lab Manual
- Practice 5-1B
- Study Guide and Journal 5-1B
- Guía de estudios y Diario 5-1B
- Multilingual Handbook
- More Look Back 5-1B
- SAT Preparation

Media Resources

- Transparency FFM 5-1B
- Transparency AE 5-1B
- Teaching Transparency
- AWSMTest and practice software
- AWSM Videodisc

PART B At a Glance

Objective

To see how products of binomials can be used to model areas of rectangles, and to use this connection to help factor algebraic expressions.

Development

Students see how squares and rectangles (algebra tiles) are used to represent algebraic expressions.

Then, in the **Explore,** students discover how this geometric model can be used to multiply binomials and factor trinomials.

Suggested Materials

Student Algebra tiles (or graph paper and scissors)

First Five Minutes

Transparency FFM 5-1B

Read the first paragraph on page 327. Then answer **Consider** questions 1–4.

Motivate

Ask...

- What are some connections between algebra and geometry that you've seen?

Shows connections between algebra and geometry.

Possible Answers

1. The line is a graph of the equation.

2. The area of the square is x^2.

3. The volume of the cube is x^3.

4. The curve (parabola) is a graph of the equation.

5-1

Understanding and Applying Area

ALTERNATE EXAMPLES

Use squares and rectangles to represent each algebraic expression.

1. $x + 2$

Use a rectangle and two unit squares.

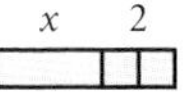

2. Transparency AE 5-1B

EXPLORE

The Tile Factor

Recommended group size: 2

The Point

To see how algebra tiles can be used to express the product of a binomial and factor a trinomial.

Look and Listen...

- For students who do not see that the area of the rectangle in Steps 1 and 2 is the sum of the expressions representing the tiles.

Ask...

- What is the area of a large square? a rectangle? a small square?
- Copy the figure. If you label each square or rectangle with an x^2, x, or 1, how can you find its total area?

For Groups That Finish Early

Use squares and rectangles to show how to factor $4x^2 + 16x + 15$.

(2x + 5)(2x + 3)

Follow Up

Ask students to explain how algebra tiles (squares and rectangles) can be used to

1. multiply algebraic expressions

2. factor expressions

We can multiply two binomials, like $(x + 3)$ and $(x + 5)$, geometrically. The process we will use is related to finding the area of a rectangle.

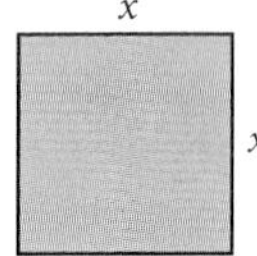

In this method, squares and rectangles model algebraic expressions.

The area of this large square is x^2, so a square of this size "equals" x^2.

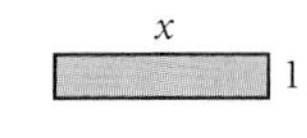

This rectangle has length x and width 1, so it has an area of x.

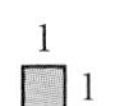

This small square has area 1. It is called the *unit square.*

EXAMPLES

Use squares and rectangles to represent each algebraic expression.

1. $x + 3$

Use an x rectangle and three unit squares.

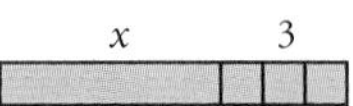

2. $(x + 3)(x + 5)$

Start by measuring a horizontal segment of length $(x + 3)$. Use tick marks to mark lengths.

Add a vertical segment of length $(x + 5)$, as shown below on the left. Then extend the tick marks vertically and horizontally to complete the figure.

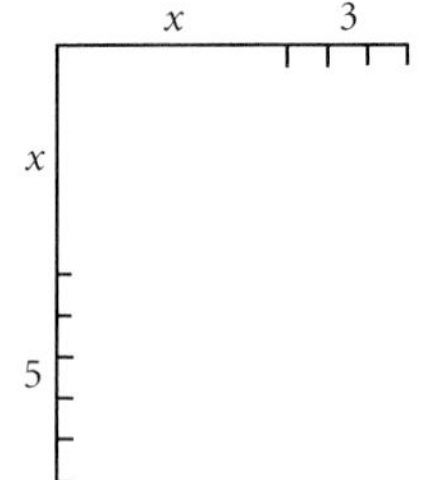

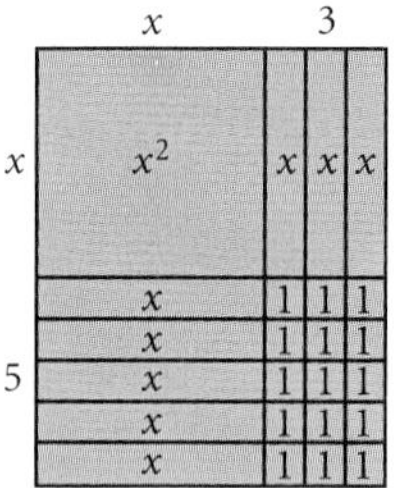

You can count squares and rectangles to see that the area of the large rectangle is $x^2 + 8x + 15$.

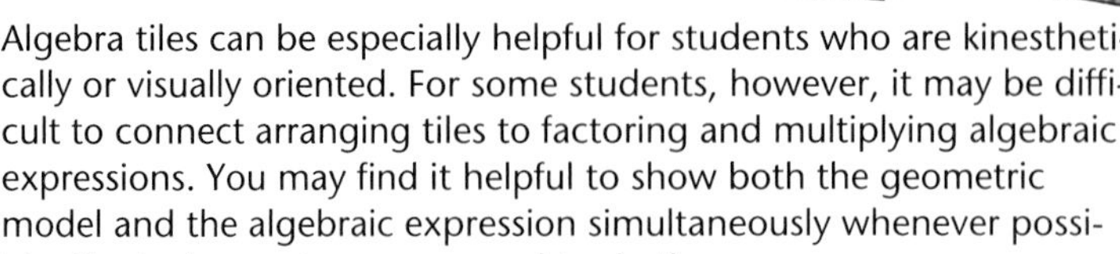

Diversity Issues

Algebra tiles can be especially helpful for students who are kinesthetically or visually oriented. For some students, however, it may be difficult to connect arranging tiles to factoring and multiplying algebraic expressions. You may find it helpful to show both the geometric model and the algebraic expression simultaneously whenever possible. Students may be encouraged to do the same.

In the following Explore, you will investigate the connection between multiplying binomials geometrically and factoring trinomials.

EXPLORE: THE TILE FACTOR

MATERIALS

Algebra tiles (or graph paper and scissors)

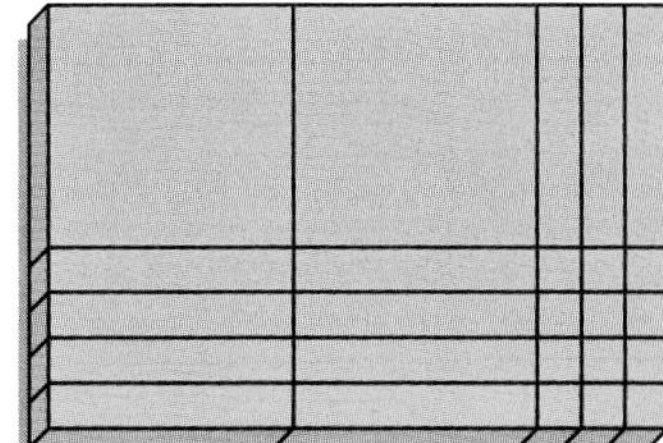

1. Use squares and rectangles to represent $(x + 4)(x + 1)$. What is the area of the overall rectangle? Explain why this area is the product of $(x + 4)$ and $(x + 1)$.
2. What is the area of the large rectangle shown at the right? What product does it represent?
3. Suppose you want to use squares and rectangles to factor instead of multiply. Use algebra tiles to represent (or cut out graph paper to make) one x^2 square, eight x rectangles, and twelve unit squares. Arrange these into a rectangle to represent the expression $x^2 + 8x + 12$. Sketch your rectangle, and explain how it shows the factorization of $x^2 + 8x + 12$.
4. Write a paragraph explaining how to use squares and rectangles to factor trinomials.

TRY IT

a. Use squares and rectangles to multiply the binomials $(x + 4)$ and $(x + 2)$.

b. Use squares and rectangles to factor $x^2 + 7x + 10$.

REFLECT

1. Explain why finding the area of a rectangle that is $(x + 2)$ units by $(x + 6)$ units also finds the product of $(x + 2)$ and $(x + 6)$.
2. When using squares and rectangles to multiply or factor, does it matter what length you use to represent x? Why or why not?
3. Use squares and rectangles to explain why $(x + 2)^2 \neq x^2 + 4$. Provide a sketch with your explanation.

Possible Answers

1. $x^2 + 5x + 4$
2. $2x^2 + 11x + 12$; $(2x + 3)(x + 4)$
3. $x^2 + 8x + 12 = (x + 6)(x + 2)$

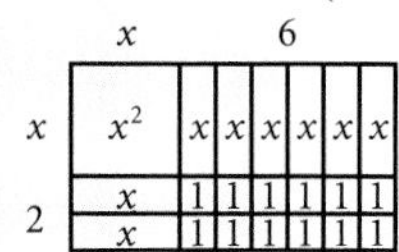

4. Arrange squares and rectangles that represent the expression into a large rectangle. Dimensions of the large rectangle show factorization.

Journal

Explore Step 4, **Reflect** 1, and **Exercise** 13 are suitable for journal entries.

REFLECT

Possible Answers

1. A rectangle's area is the product of its length and width.
2. No. Regardless of the length of the x rectangle, arrangements that represent products will have the same dimensions.
3. $(x + 2)^2 = x^2 + 4x + 4$

TRY IT

Answers

a. $x^2 + 6x + 8$

b. $(x + 5)(x + 2)$

Alert

It is important that students think of x as a variable length. (Using the figure on page 328, some may assume that $x \approx 5$.) You may need to explain that we had to choose a length for x to make our model, but we could have chosen *any* length. If time permits, you may want to use two sets of tiles with different "x-values" to show that $x^2 + 3x + 2$ has the same arrangement for both.

Understanding and Applying Area

Part B Exercises

Exercise Notes

Core

13. Reminds students of a common algebraic error. They use tiles to show why the square of a binomial is not the sum of the squares of its individual terms.

More Math Reasoning

34. Asks students to visualize and sketch figures in three dimensions that represent algebraic expressions.

Extension: Ask whether they can think of a usable geometric model to represent expressions with x^4 (or higher-order) terms.

35. Students work with triangular numbers.

Exercise Answers

Core

1. a–c.

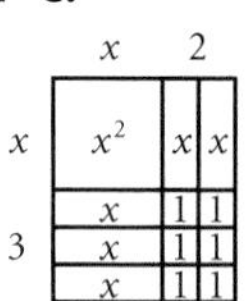

2. x 1 1 1 1

3. x 1 1 1 1 1 1

4. x^2 x x

5.

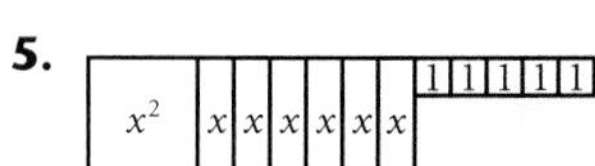

7.

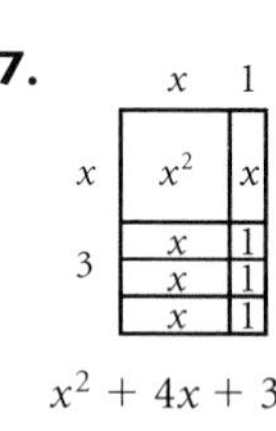

$x^2 + 4x + 3$

Algebra | Functions | Discrete Math | Probability | Data/Statistics

Exercises

CORE

P **1. Getting Started** By following these steps, use squares and rectangles to represent the product $(x + 2)(x + 3)$.

a. Draw a horizontal segment of length $(x + 2)$. Use tick marks to mark the lengths of the x rectangle and the unit squares.

b. Add a vertical segment of length $(x + 3)$ perpendicular to the horizontal segment, using tick marks to mark off the lengths. Be sure to be consistent with the lengths you used in **1a.**

c. Extend the tick marks vertically and horizontally to complete the figure.

P **Use squares and rectangles to represent each expression.**

2. $x + 4$ **3.** $x + 6$ **4.** $x^2 + 2x$ **5.** $x^2 + 6x + 5$

P **6.** Write out the product illustrated by the squares and rectangles at the right. $(x + 2)(x + 6)$

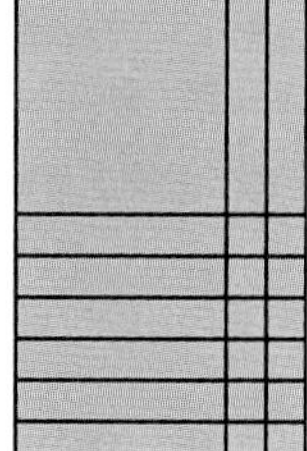

P **Use squares and rectangles to represent each product, and then write the product algebraically.**

7. $(x + 1)(x + 3)$ **8.** $(x + 3)(2x + 1)$ **9.** $(2x)(3x + 5)$

P **Factor each trinomial, using squares and rectangles. Provide a sketch, and give an algebraic answer.**

10. $x^2 + 4x + 3$ **11.** $x^2 + 8x + 15$ **12.** $2x^2 + 7x + 6$

MR **13. Is This Right?** A student answered a test question as shown.

Question: Factor $x^2 + 16$. Answer: $(x + 4)(x + 4)$

Use squares and rectangles to show whether or not this is the correct answer. If it is not, give your response to the question, and explain why the student may have made this error.

P **14.** Suppose that a rectangle has an area of $x^2 + 6x + 8$. If its length is $x + 4$, what is its width? $x + 2$

PS **15.** A rectangular field is two kilometers longer than it is wide.

a. Use squares and rectangles to find the area of the field in terms of w, its width.

b. If the field has an area of fifteen square kilometers, find its length and its width.

Key

V Vocabulary
P Practice/Skills
R Review
MR Math Reasoning
PS Problem Solving
C Challenge

16. Cubicle Equations A business has a square floor space for offices, with an area of 1600 ft^2.

a. What are the dimensions of the office space? 40 ft × 40 ft

b. If the average worker has a 50-ft^2 office, how many workers are there? 32

c. Heidi and Cristina, two industrial engineers, come up with a new design for the building space that increases the width of the available office space by 5 ft and the length by 10 ft. What are the dimensions of the new office space? Width = 45 ft, length = 50 ft

d. If the average space per worker stays the same, how many workers can use the new space? Explain how you found your answer. 45

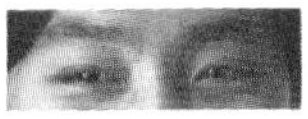

LOOK BACK

Use the given information to determine which lines are parallel. Justify your answers with a theorem or postulate. [3-4]

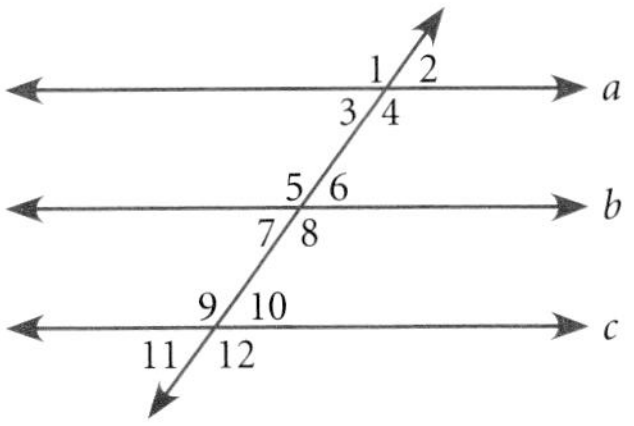

17. $\angle 1 \cong \angle 10$

18. $\angle 4 \cong \angle 8$

19. $m\angle 3 + m\angle 9 = 180°$

20. $\angle 5 \cong \angle 9$

21. $\angle 1 \cong \angle 8$

Write the congruence correspondence for each pair of triangles. Give the postulate or theorem that proves each pair of triangles congruent. [4-2]

22.

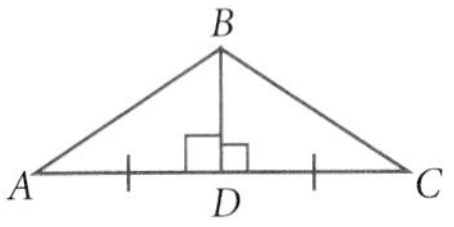

$\triangle ADB \cong \triangle CDB$; SAS Postulate OR LL Theorem

23.

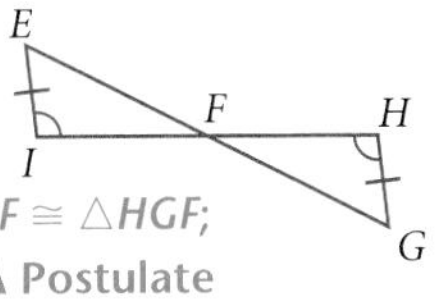

$\triangle IEF \cong \triangle HGF$; SAA Postulate

24.

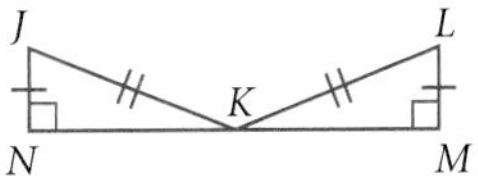

$\triangle KJN \cong \triangle KLM$; HL for right triangles

MORE PRACTICE

Use squares and rectangles to represent each expression.

25. $2x + 7$

26. $x^2 + 5$

27. $x^2 + 5x + 3$

Use squares and rectangles to represent each product, and then write the product algebraically.

28. $(x + 2)(x + 5)$

29. $(3x + 2)(x + 1)$

30. $(5)(2x + 3)$

Factor each trinomial by using squares and rectangles. Provide a sketch, and give an algebraic answer.

31. $x^2 + 4x + 3$

32. $x^2 + 8x + 15$

33. $2x^2 + 11x + 5$

Ongoing Assessment

Self-Assessment Exercises 1–11 odd, 14

Embedded Assessment Exercises 8, 12, 13, 15, 16

8.

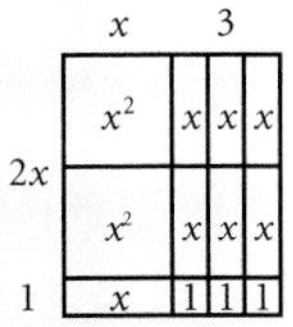

$2x^2 + 7x + 3$

9.

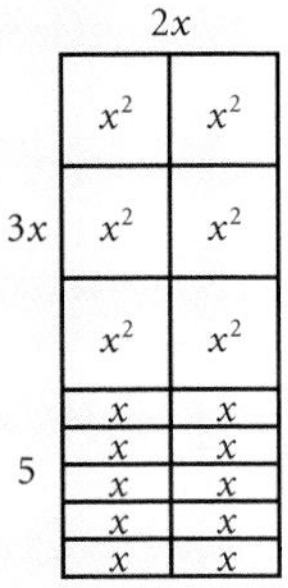

$6x^2 + 10x$

10.

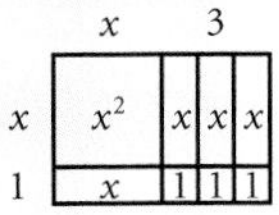

$(x + 3)(x + 1)$

11.

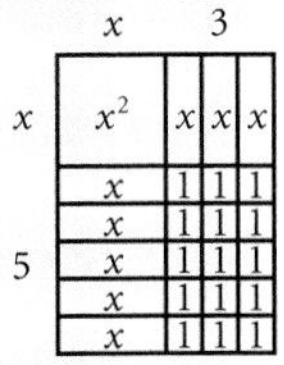

$(x + 3)(x + 5)$

12.

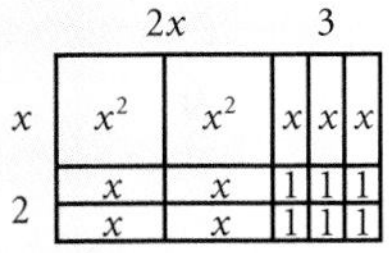

$(2x + 3)(x + 2)$

13. The answer is incorrect. By using squares and rectangles, we see that $(x + 4)^2 = x^2 + 8x + 16$.

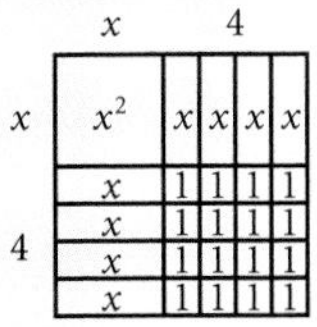

The student tried to distribute an exponent—this is not valid.

15. a. $2w + w^2$

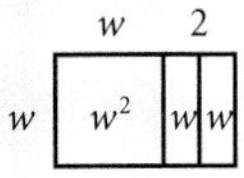

b. $w = 3$ km; $l = 5$ km

17–21., 25–35. See Additional Answers p. T344.

Algebra | Functions | Discrete Math | Probability | Data/Statistics

Understanding and Applying Area

PART C At a Glance

Objective

To use the quadratic formula to solve problems involving area.

Development

First, students see the quadratic formula used in an **Example** and practice applying it in a **Try It.**

Then, in the **Explore,** they use the quadratic formula to find the dimensions for a circus poster that satisfy certain area requirements.

Key Terms

Quadratic equation, quadratic formula

First Five Minutes

Transparency FFM 5-1C

Read the paragraphs at the bottom of page 332 and page 333 through the **Example.** Then use the quadratic formula to solve

$x^2 - 7x + 6$

Use factoring to check your solution.
$x = 6, x = 1$

Motivate

Ask...

- When you have more than one technique available to solve a problem, how do you decide which one to use?

MORE MATH REASONING

MR, C **34.** Suppose you want to apply our geometric multiplication technique to algebraic expressions that have x^3 terms. You'll need three-dimensional figures! Use solids to illustrate each of the following expressions.

a. x^3 **b.** x^2 **c.** x **d.** 1

e. Can you easily multiply $(x + 1)(x + 2)(x + 3)$ using the figures you have developed? Why or why not?

MR, PS **35.** Count the dots in each dot-triangle. Describe any patterns that you see.

What happens if you add two consecutive numbers from the triangle sequence? Why do you think this is true?

5-1 PART C The Quadratic Formula and Area

← CONNECT → ***You've solved quadratic equations before. Now you will use the quadratic formula to solve problems involving area.***

Any equation that can be put into the form $ax^2 + bx + c = 0$ is a **quadratic equation.**

You may be able to solve a quadratic equation quickly by factoring, as in the following example.

Solve: $x^2 + 3x - 10 = 0$

$(x + 5)(x - 2) = 0$	Factor the trinomial.
$x + 5 = 0$ *or* $x - 2 = 0$	If the product of two quantities is zero, one of them must be zero.
$x = -5$ *or* $x = 2$	Solve the two equations.

Key

V Vocabulary
P Practice/Skills
R Review
MR Math Reasoning
PS Problem Solving
C Challenge

Alert

When using the quadratic formula, students often forget that the $-b$ term is also divided by the $2a$. You may need to remind them of this frequently. Many teachers state the formula as "The opposite of b plus or minus the square root of b^2 minus $4ac$ all over $2a$."

Most quadratics cannot easily be solved by factoring. Fortunately, there is a formula that can always be used to find the solutions to a quadratic equation, if any exist.

THE QUADRATIC FORMULA

The solutions to the equation $ax^2 + bx + c = 0$ (where $a \neq 0$) are given by the following.

$$x = \frac{-b \pm \sqrt{b^2 - 4ac}}{2a}$$

EXAMPLE

Solve: $2x^2 - 4x - 5 = 0$. Round answers to the nearest hundredth.

Use the quadratic formula with $a = 2$, $b = -4$, and $c = -5$.

$$x = \frac{-(-4) \pm \sqrt{(-4)^2 - 4(2)(-5)}}{2(2)}$$

$$x = \frac{4 \pm \sqrt{16 + 40}}{4}$$

$$x = \frac{4 \pm \sqrt{56}}{4} = \frac{4 \pm 2\sqrt{14}}{4} = \frac{2 \pm \sqrt{14}}{2}$$

A calculator gives approximate solutions of $x = \frac{2 + \sqrt{14}}{2} \approx 2.87$, and $x = \frac{2 - \sqrt{14}}{2} \approx -0.87$.

TRY IT

a. Solve $x^2 + 2x = 10$. Round answers to the nearest hundredth. (Hint: Be sure to get one side of the equation equal to zero before applying the quadratic formula!) $x \approx -4.32$, $x \approx 2.32$

1. Iliana used the quadratic formula to find the dimensions of a rectangle. When she solved for its length, she came up with two solutions, one positive and one negative. Why did this happen, and what should she do next?

Student Resources

- **Alternative Lessons** 5-1C
- **Laboratory Manual** 5-1C
- Technology Lab Manual
- **Practice** 5-1C
- **Study Guide and Journal** 5-1C
- **Guía de estudios y Diario** 5-1C
- **Multilingual Handbook**
- **More Look Ahead** 5-1C
- SAT Preparation

Media Resources

- **Transparency FFM** 5-1C
- **Transparency AE** 5-1C
- Teaching Transparency
- **AWSMTest and practice software**
- AWSM Videodisc

ALTERNATE EXAMPLE

Solve $3x^2 - 2x - 6 = 0$. Round answers to the nearest hundredth.

Use the quadratic formula with $a = 3$, $b = -2$, and $c = -6$.

$$x = \frac{-(-2) \pm \sqrt{(-2)^2 - 4(3)(-6)}}{2(3)}$$

$$x = \frac{2 \pm \sqrt{4 + 72}}{6}$$

$$x = \frac{2 \pm \sqrt{76}}{6} = \frac{2 \pm 2\sqrt{19}}{6} = \frac{1 \pm \sqrt{19}}{3}$$

A calculator gives approximate solutions of $x = \frac{1 + \sqrt{19}}{3} \approx 1.79$ or $x = \frac{1 - \sqrt{19}}{3} \approx -1.12$.

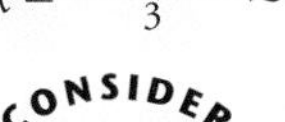

Possible Answer

1. The quadratic formula may give two solutions for a quadratic equation. Both are valid solutions to the equation, but one may not make sense in the context of the problem. In this case, since a length cannot be negative, she should disregard the negative answer and use the positive one.

5-1

Understanding and Applying Area

EXPLORE

Circus Giganticus

Recommended group size: 4

The Point

To use the quadratic formula to find dimensions of a circus poster that satisfy given conditions.

Look and Listen...

- For students who have difficulty writing an equation to represent the problem.
- For students who forget that one side of the equation must be set to zero before using the quadratic formula.
- For students who forget to add both borders to the dimensions of the square.

Ask...

- Have you drawn a picture and labeled its dimensions?

For Groups That Finish Early

Solve this problem for a poster with a border of 2 in. on all sides. Can you solve this problem *without* using the quadratic formula? **30.64 in. on a side; solve by taking the square root of both sides of $(x + 4)^2 = 1200$.**

Follow Up

Ask students to give their dimensions for the poster and show their solution method. If they used the quadratic formula, ask why they chose this method.

Possible Answers

1. Dimensions are $x + 6$ by $x + 4$.
2. Dimensions: 35.7 in. by 33.7 in. Area of photo ≈ 879.4 in.^{2}

Journal 

Consider 1 and **Reflect** 1 are suitable for journal entries.

In the following Explore, you will see how the quadratic formula can be used in a problem-solving situation.

EXPLORE: CIRCUS GIGANTICUS

Circus Giganticus is producing posters for its next tour. The posters must have an area of 1200 in^2. The designers have planned for a square image surrounded by a border 3 in. wide on the left and right and 2 in. wide on the top and bottom.

1. Use x to represent the side length of the square photograph. Write expressions for the length and width of the poster in terms of x.
2. What should the dimensions of the poster be? What should the area of the photograph be? Round your answers to the nearest tenth.

Problem-Solving Tip

Write an equation that represents the real-world situation.

3. Compare your methods and your results with those of your classmates.

The quadratic formula is an important algebraic tool because it finds all possible solutions for any quadratic equation. It requires some computation and simplification, however, so it may take more time than solving by factoring. You should be familiar with both methods so that you can choose the most appropriate one.

REFLECT

1. Describe the advantages and disadvantages of using the quadratic formula to solve a quadratic equation.
2. In general, how many solutions are there to a quadratic equation?

Alert

Students often have a hard time using a single variable to represent a situation with two quantities. For example, in the *Explore*, they may try to use variables for both the length and the width. It may help to remind them that it is much easier to solve equations with only one variable.

Exercises

CORE

1. Getting Started Follow these steps to solve $x^2 + 4x = 7$.
- **a.** Write the equation in the form $ax^2 + bx + c = 0$.
- **b.** Find the a, b, and c values. Substitute these values into the quadratic formula.
- **c.** If possible, simplify the square root.
- **d.** If possible, simplify the fraction. You now have exact solutions to the equation.
- **e.** Use your calculator to write the approximate solutions to the nearest hundredth.

Solve each equation. Round answers to the nearest hundredth.

2. $x^2 + 4x - 6 = 0$ $x \approx -5.16$, $x \approx 1.16$

3. $x^2 - 3x = 4$ $x = 4$, $x = -1$

4. $2x^2 - 9x + 7 = 0$ $x = 3.5$, $x = 1$

5. $-3x^2 + 5x + 1 = 0$ $x \approx 1.85$, $x \approx -0.18$

6. $1.3x^2 = -2.7x + 11.1$ $x \approx -4.14$, $x \approx 2.06$

7. $x^2 + 2x - 5 = 0$ $x = \approx -3.45$, $x \approx 1.45$

8. Determine whether the following statement is true or false. If the statement is false, change the underlined words to make it true.

You can use the quadratic <u>equation</u> to solve a quadratic <u>formula</u>.

9. Carnival Canopy The carnival at a circus operates under a tent with a rectangular base that is 18 ft longer than it is wide. If the total area under the tent is 7663 ft^2, what are the length and width of the tent?

10. The first mathematical work published in the Americas was the *Sumario Compendioso* (1556), by Juan Diez. It featured the following problem.

A man takes passage on a ship and asks the ship's master what he has to pay. [T]he master replies: "[The price] will be the number of pesos which, multiplied by itself and added to the number, gives 1260."

- **a.** This problem can be represented by the quadratic equation $x^2 + x = 1260$. Explain why this equation represents the problem.
- **b.** How many pesos does the man pay for the trip?

11. The length of a rectangular basketball court is 6 ft shorter than twice its width.
- **a.** Find the length of the court in terms of w, its width. Length $= 2w - 6$
- **b.** Find its area in terms of its width. Area $= (2w - 6)w$
- **c.** If the area of the court is 4700 ft^2, find its length and width. Width $= 50$; length $= 94$

REFLECT

Possible Answers

1. Advantages: The formula is guaranteed to find all solutions. Disadvantages: The calculations involve radicals and fractions.

2. There may be 2, 1, or 0 different real-number solutions. Students usually see quadratics with two different solutions.

Part C Exercises

Exercise Notes

Core

8. Students often confuse the terms *formula* and *equation*. This exercise reminds them that there is a difference between the two.

10. Students may be surprised to find that "word problems" have been challenging mathematicians for hundreds of years!

Look Ahead

13. Previews the geometric probability seen in 5-1 Part D.

14–17. Review basic skills needed in 5-1 Part D.

More Math Reasoning

23. A rough algebraic model of a business situation. Although the model is simple, it does simulate profits being low when the price of an item is too low (not enough revenue) or too high (decreased demand).

Exercise Answers

Core

1. a. $x^2 + 4x - 7 = 0$

b. $a = 1$, $b = 4$, $c = -7$

$$x = \frac{-4 \pm \sqrt{(4)^2 - 4(1)(-7)}}{2(1)}$$

c. $x = \dfrac{-4 \pm 2\sqrt{11}}{2}$

d. $x = -2 \pm \sqrt{11}$

e. $x \approx -5.32$, $x \approx 1.32$

8. Use the quadratic formula to solve a quadratic equation.

9. Length = 97 ft; width = 79 ft

ey

Vocabulary
Practice/Skills
Review
Math Reasoning
Problem Solving
Challenge

Ongoing Assessment

Self-Assessment Exercises 1–11 odd

Embedded Assessment Explore Step 2; Exercises 2, 6, 10, 12

Algebra | Functions | Discrete Math | Probability | Data/Statistics

Understanding and Applying Area

10. a. If x represents the amount the man must pay, x^2 is the number multiplied by itself, so $x^2 + x$ is the number multiplied by itself and added to the number.

b. The man must pay 35 pesos.

12. a. Length $= 50 + 2x$; Width $= 25 + 2x$

b. Area $= 4x^2 + 150x + 1250$; multiplied length and width.

c. The width of the walkway is 6 ft.

More Math Reasoning

22. $t \approx 4.05$ sec; Set $h = 0$, use the quadratic formula, and discard the negative solution.

23. a. The maximum price is \$30 and the minimum price is \$6.25.

b. The model is reasonable. Too low a price means a loss on each set sold; too high a price keeps customers from buying.

PS **12. Quadratic-Sized Pool** A rectangular swimming pool is 50 ft long and 25 ft wide. There is a walkway x ft wide surrounding the pool.
a. Find the length and width of the pool with the walkway in terms of x.
b. Find the area of the pool with the walkway in terms of x. Explain how you found this expression.
c. If the total area of the pool and the walkway is 2294 ft^2, what is the width of the walkway?

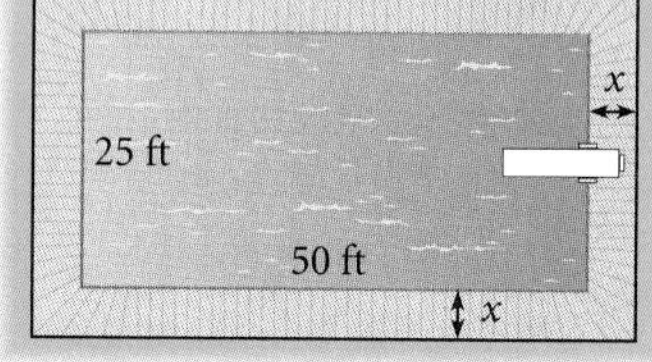

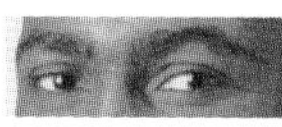

LOOK AHEAD

P **13.** What fractional part of the interior of the square shown is colored as follows?
a. solid red $\frac{3}{8}$ **b.** solid white $\frac{1}{4}$
c. striped $\frac{3}{8}$ **d.** solid red or solid white $\frac{5}{8}$

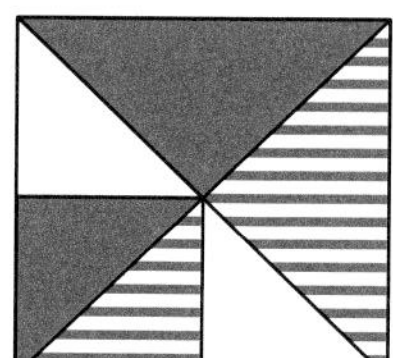

P **Express each fraction in lowest terms. Then convert the fraction to an equivalent decimal and percentage. When necessary, round decimals to the nearest hundredth and percentages to the nearest one percent.**

14. $\frac{3}{5}$ $\frac{3}{5}$; 0.6, 60% **15.** $\frac{8}{12}$ $\frac{2}{3}$; 0.67, 67% **16.** $\frac{26}{56}$ $\frac{13}{28}$; 0.46, 46% **17.** $\frac{36}{90}$ $\frac{2}{5}$; 0.4, 40%

MORE PRACTICE

P **Solve each equation. Round answers to the nearest hundredth.**

18. $x^2 + 6x + 5 = 0$ $x = -5,\ x = -1$
19. $3x^2 - 10x + 2 = 0$ $x \approx 0.21,\ x \approx 3.12$
20. $-2.3x^2 + 3.4 = 0.8x$ $x \approx 1.05,\ x \approx -1.40$
21. $4.4x^2 = 16.7$ $x \approx -1.95,\ x \approx 1.95$

MORE MATH REASONING

PS, C Science **22. What Goes Up . . .** If you throw a ball upward off a 100-ft building at 40 ft/sec, the equation below gives its approximate height t seconds after it is thrown.

$h = -16t^2 + 40t + 100$

When will the ball hit the ground? Explain how you found your answer. (Assume the ball does not hit the building on the way down.)

Key
V Vocabulary
P Practice/Skills
R Review
MR Math Reasoning
PS Problem Solving
C Challenge

23. Quest for Profit Elisa, the owner of a game store, finds that the total monthly profit generated by *Space Quest* depends on the price she charges for the game. She finds that a graph of profit (y) as a function of price (x) approximately follows the equation below.

$y = -4x^2 + 145x - 750$

a. Find the maximum and minimum prices that Elisa can charge so that *Space Quest* will make a (positive) profit.

b. Is this function a reasonable model for a real-world situation? Investigate the graph of the function. What happens when the price is low? high? How might this happen in a real situation?

5-1 PART D Area and Probability

← CONNECT → ***You may have studied probability using coins, dice, or random numbers. Now you will see how geometry and probability are related.***

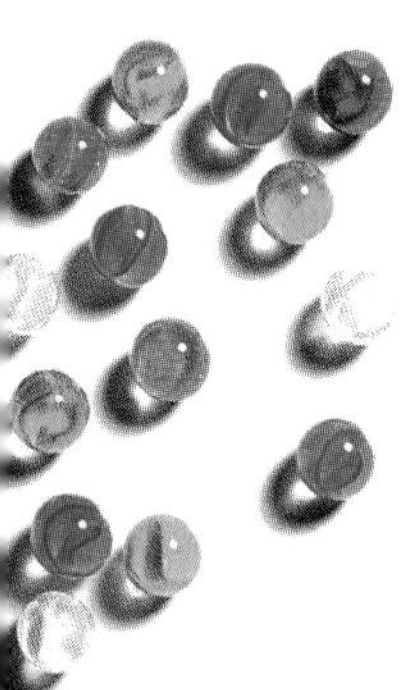

The probability of an event measures how likely it is to happen. If we conduct an experiment with n equally likely outcomes, and m of those are "successful" outcomes, then the probability of a success is $\frac{m}{n}$. For example, if there are 6 green marbles in a bag with a total of 24 marbles, the probability that you will shake a green marble into your hand is $\frac{6}{24} = \frac{1}{4} = 0.25$, or 25%.

Notice that a probability may be expressed as a fraction, a decimal, or a percent.

TRY IT

a. What is the probability of throwing a one or a six on one toss of a die? Express your answer as a fraction. $\frac{1}{3}$

b. A hotel has 14 rooms on the first floor, 12 on the second, and 15 on the third. If you are assigned a hotel room at random, what is the probability that it will be on the third floor? Express your answer in decimal form. ≈ 0.37

PART D At a Glance

Objective

To solve probability problems involving area and perimeter ratios.

Development

Students are introduced to the idea of geometric probability.

In the **Explore,** students use simple geometric figures to design targets for a carnival game that yield a given probability of winning.

Key Terms

Geometric probability

First Five Minutes

Transparency FFM 5-1D

Read the first two paragraphs on page 337 and do **Try It a** and **b.**

Motivate

Ask...

- If you assume that darts are thrown randomly at a target, how would you calculate the probability that a dart will land on the bull's-eye?

Student Resources

- **Alternative Lessons 5-1D**
- **Laboratory Manual 5-1D**
- Technology Lab Manual
- **Practice 5-1D**
- **Study Guide and Journal 5-1D**
- **Guía de estudios y Diario 5-1D**
- **Multilingual Handbook**
- **More Look Back 5-1D**
- SAT Preparation

Media Resources

- **Transparency FFM 5-1D**
- **Transparency AE 5-1D**
- Teaching Transparency
- **AWSMTest and practice software**
- AWSM Videodisc

Understanding and Applying Area

ALTERNATE EXAMPLE

Find the probability that a randomly chosen point inside the figure shown lies in a blue region.

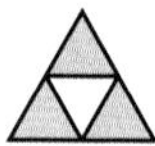

The figure is divided into four regions with equal areas. Three of them are blue, so the probability that a randomly selected point will be in a blue region is $\frac{3}{4} = 0.75 = 75\%$.

EXPLORE

Targeting Probability

Recommended group size: 4

The Point

To use geometric probability to design targets for a carnival game.

Look and Listen...

- For students who are designing targets where the ratio of the shaded area to the unshaded area is 1:4. (To get a probability of $\frac{1}{4}$, the ratio must be 1:3.)

Ask...

- Is the probability of winning the ratio of shaded area to unshaded area or the ratio of the shaded area to the total area?

For Groups That Finish Early

Give dimensions for the shaded region in each target so that the probability of winning is $\frac{1}{8}$.

Follow Up

Ask students to present their target designs and to explain why the probability of winning is $\frac{1}{4}$.

In **geometric probability,** the probability of an event is determined by comparing the areas (or perimeters, angle measures, or other measures) of the "successful" regions to the total area of the figure. (When working with geometric probability, assume that figures that appear congruent are congruent.)

EXAMPLE

Find the probability that a randomly chosen point inside the figure shown will lie in a blue region.

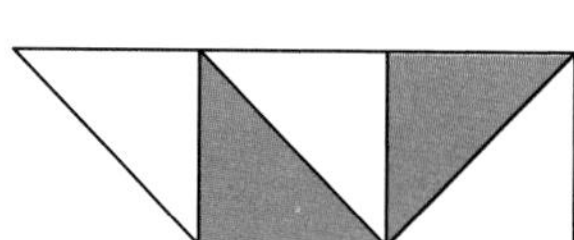

The figure is divided into five regions of equal area. Two of the regions are blue, so the probability that a randomly selected point will be in a blue region is $\frac{2}{5} = 0.4 = 40\%$.

TRY IT

c. In an air hockey game, you score a goal when the puck goes into an opening at your opponent's end of the table.

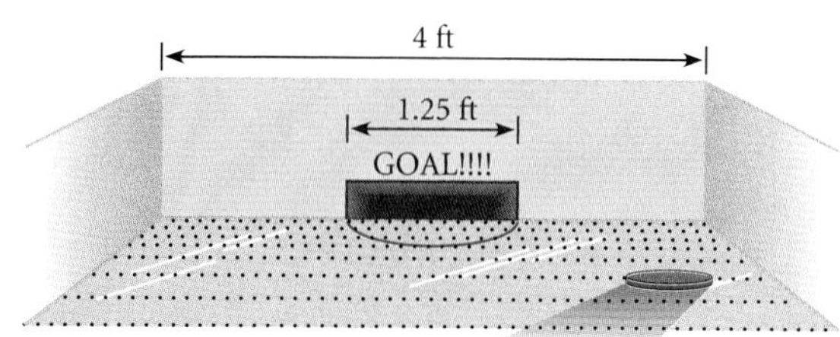

If you shoot the puck randomly and your opponent doesn't stop it, what's the probability that you will score a goal? (Don't consider the size of the puck.) 0.3125

d. Your baby sister throws your favorite cassette toward the wall with the open window, as shown. Assuming she throws the tape randomly, what is the probability that it will go out the window? $\frac{1}{12} \approx 0.083$

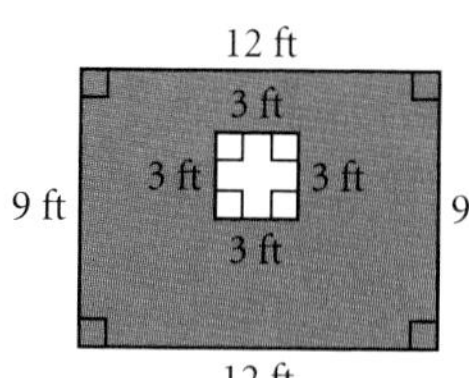

You now know how to calculate geometric probabilities for figures that are given. In the following Explore, you'll reverse this process and design figures that result in a specific geometric probability.

Probability Connection

Students may have a difficult time seeing how to find the probability of successive independent events, as in Step 2 of the **Explore.** A probability tree diagram can be a useful tool for finding probabilities of compound independent events. The probabilities can be calculated by branching on the different outcomes and multiplying the probabilities of each branch.

EXPLORE: TARGETING PROBABILITY

The targets at the right are used in a carnival dart-throwing contest. A contestant wins a stuffed dog if his dart hits the shaded region. Although the contestants hit the target every time, the darts are old and difficult to aim, so you may assume that the game is random. For the carnival to make a profit, the owner wants the probability of winning the game to be $\frac{1}{4}$.

1. Give dimensions for the shaded regions in each target so that the probability of winning is $\frac{1}{4}$.
2. Suppose a person plays the game twice in a row. What is the probability that he or she will win both times? Explain your reasoning.

a.

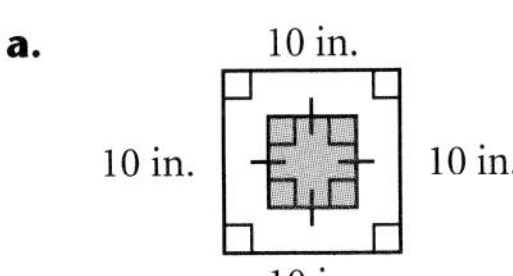

b.

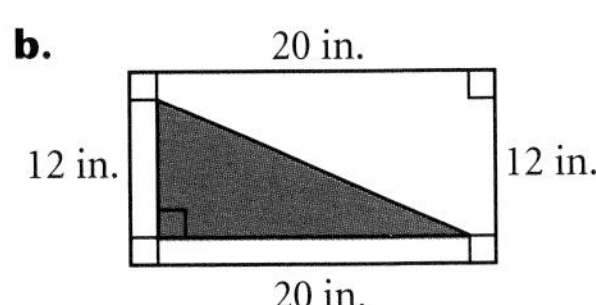

c.

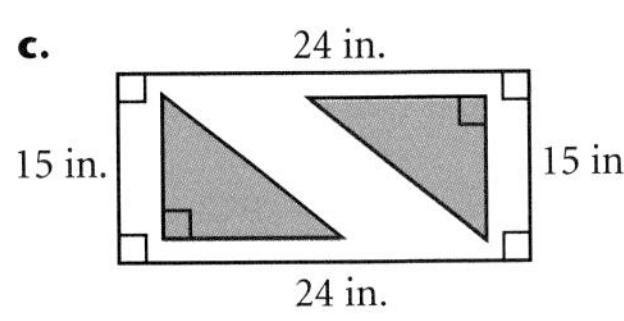

Possible Answers

1. **a.** Inner square: 5 in. × 5 in.
   b. Right triangle: 10 in. height, 12 in. base.
   c. Each right triangle: 9 in. height, 10 in. base.
2. The probability of winning twice in a row is $\frac{1}{16}$; $\frac{1}{4}$ of the people playing the game will win the first time, and $\frac{1}{4}$ of that $\frac{1}{4}$ will also win the second.

Journal

Reflect 2 and **Exercise** 9 are suitable for journal entries.

REFLECT

1. If a rectangle is divided into six congruent regions and three of them are shaded, what is the probability that you will randomly pick a point in the shaded area? Does it matter which three regions are shaded?
2. Describe one underlying assumption you make when using geometric probability. When is it inappropriate to use geometric probability in a situation involving areas?

Possible Answers

1. $\frac{1}{2}$; no.
2. You are assuming that the event (dart landing on a target, etc.) is truly random. It is inappropriate to use geometric probability when the event is not random. For example, the assumption of randomness would be invalid for a skilled archer shooting at a target, whose arrows are more likely to land near the bull's-eye than near the edge of the target.

Exercises

CORE

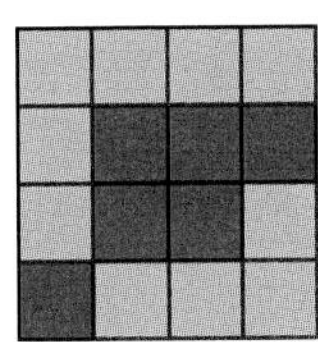

1. **Getting Started** Find the probability that a randomly chosen point inside the figure shown will lie in a red region. Express your answer as a fraction. $\frac{3}{8}$
2. You are designing a new target that is a square inside a 16′ × 9′ rectangle. What size should the square be if you want the following probabilities of winning the game?
   a. $\frac{1}{36}$ 2 ft × 2 ft **b.** $\frac{1}{16}$ 3 ft × 3 ft **c.** 0.25 6 ft × 6 ft
3. What is the probability that you will get a star when you spin the spinner at the right? Express your answer as a fraction. $\frac{1}{4}$

Part D Exercises

Exercise Notes

Core

9.b. It is important for students to understand that probability techniques should only be used when an event is random or approximately random, and for them to begin questioning the assumption of randomness.

ey

Vocabulary
Practice/Skills
Review
R Math Reasoning
S Problem Solving
Challenge

Ongoing Assessment

Self-Assessment Exercises 1, 3, 5, 7, 11

Embedded Assessment Reflect 1; Exercises 2, 4, 6, 9

Understanding and Applying Area

More Math Reasoning

20. Students use basic principles of combinations of numbers to discover how many different area codes are possible with the current system.

Extension: Car licenses might have two letters followed by four digits. Which of the following states could use this system? (Figures are 1991 estimated registrations.)

California: 17.2 million cars

Ohio: 8.5 million cars

Georgia: 5.6 million cars

Massachusetts: 3.7 million cars

Georgia and Massachusetts. 6.76 million different combinations are possible.

Exercise Answers

Core

4. 0.33 **5.** 0.25

6. 0.18 **7.** 0.17

8. Exercise 4; The probability of success is highest.

9. a. 0.05

b. The skydiver will hit the target with higher probability because aim becomes better with practice.

10. $\frac{5}{9}$

11. Michigan ≈ 0.59; Indiana ≈ 0.04; Illinois ≈ 0.05; Wisconsin ≈ 0.32

More Practice

16. 0.18 **17.** 0.28

18. 0.23

More Math Reasoning

19. d. It does not make a difference if the pieces are arranged differently, as long as they do not overlap. Each piece still has the same area.

P **In a carnival game, you must hit the shaded area on a target with a dart to win a prize. Assume that all of your darts hit the target randomly. What is the probability that you will hit the shaded area for each of the regions? Express your answer as a decimal rounded to the nearest hundredth.**

4.

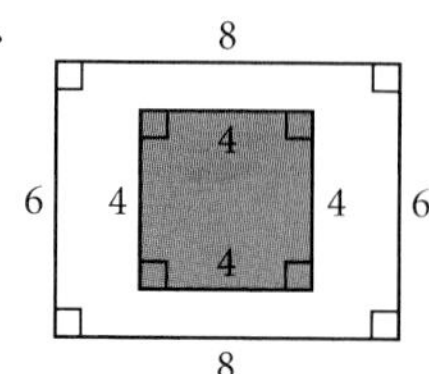

5.

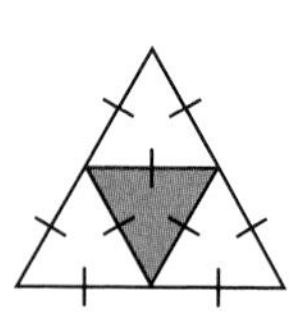

6.

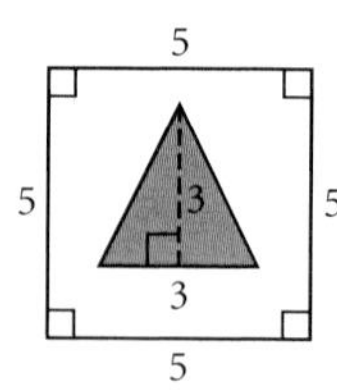

7.

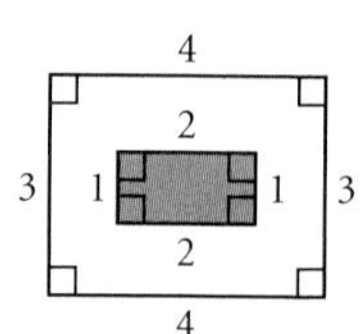

MR **8.** Which of the targets in Exercises 4–7 would you choose to throw at? Why?

MR **9. Right on Target** A skydiver is trying to land on the cross-shaped target. Assume that the diver is certain to land at a random point somewhere in the surrounding 10-m × 10-m square.

a. Find the probability that the diver will hit the target. Express your answer as a decimal rounded to the nearest hundredth.

b. If the skydiver is a professional who has made this jump hundreds of times, do you think his actual probability will be higher or lower than this? Explain your reasoning.

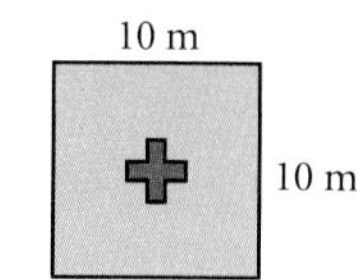

All edges of the target are 1 m long. All angles are right angles.

PS **10. Lost Dogie** A rancher realizes that a calf has been left behind in the round-up. She goes to look for the calf, which is somewhere in the fenced square area shown. She can only search the green area before sundown. What is the probability that she will find the calf before sundown? Express your answer as a fraction in lowest terms.

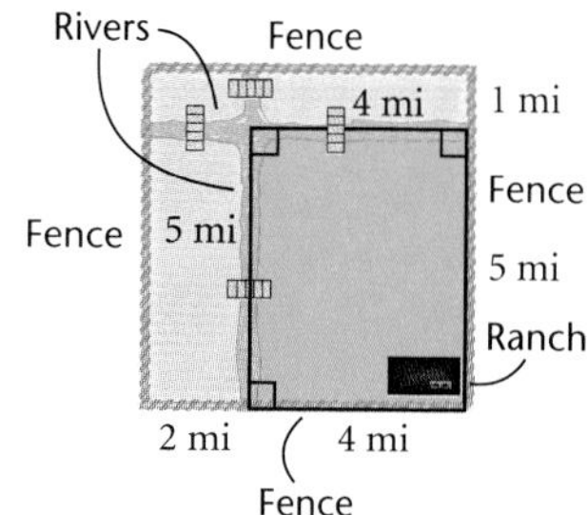

P **11. Water Bottle** A child on a boat sealed a message inside a corked bottle and set it afloat in the center of Lake Michigan. The states around Lake Michigan and the approximate lengths of their shorelines are shown.

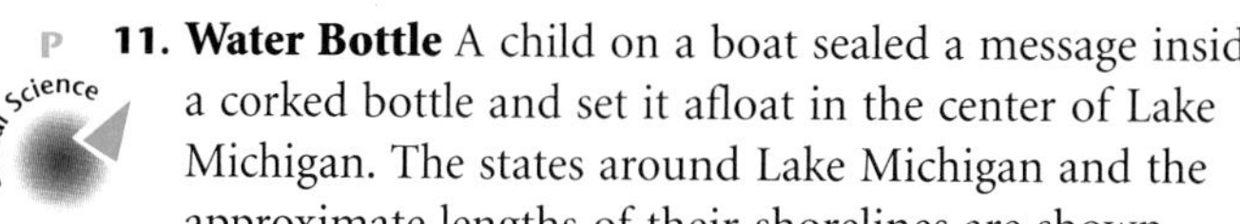

Assume that the bottle lands randomly on the shoreline of Lake Michigan. What is the probability that it will land in each state? Express your answer as a decimal rounded to the nearest hundredth.

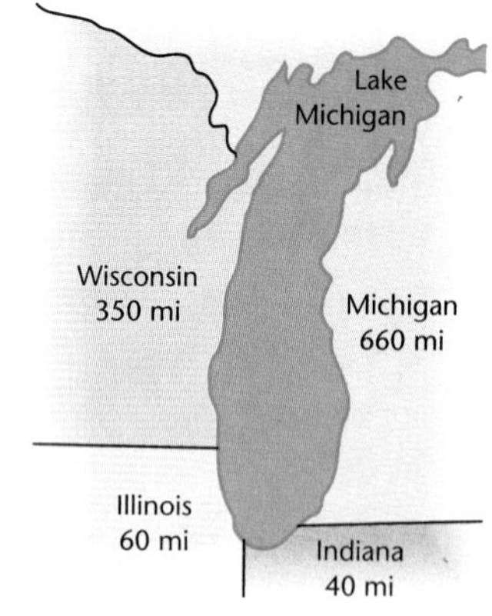

Key

V Vocabulary

P Practice/Skills

R Review

MR Math Reasoning

PS Problem Solving

C Challenge

LOOK BACK

For each measure of $\angle 1$, find the measure of its complement and its supplement. [3-3]

12. $m\angle 1 = 21°$ Complement = 69°; Supplement = 159°

13. $m\angle 1 = 84°$ Complement = 6°; Supplement = 96°

14. $m\angle 1 = 33.5°$ Complement = 56.5°; Supplement = 146.5°

15. $m\angle 1 = 48\frac{2}{3}°$ Complement = $41\frac{1}{3}°$; Supplement = $131\frac{1}{3}°$

MORE PRACTICE

In a carnival game, you must toss a penny into the hole in a target to win a prize. Assuming that you toss the penny onto the target randomly, what is the probability that you will win a prize for each of the following targets? Express your answers in decimal form rounded to the nearest hundredth.

16.

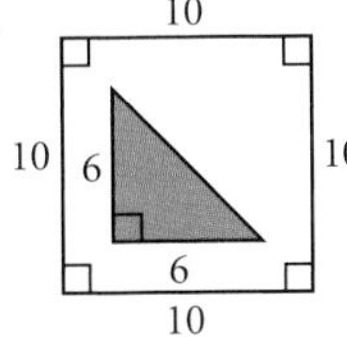

17.

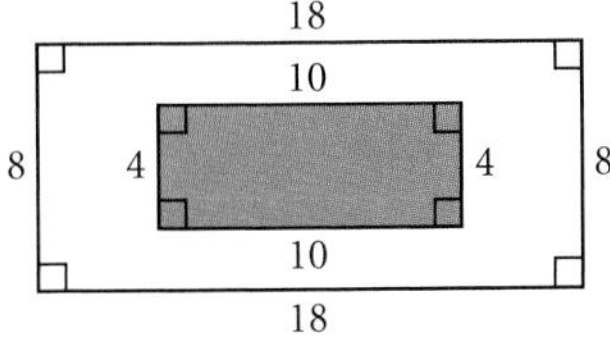

18.

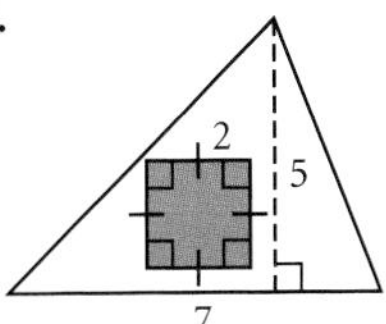

MORE MATH REASONING

19. Suppose you arrange seven tangram pieces into a perfect square as shown. If a fly lands on your tangram, what is the probability that it will land on each of the following pieces? (Hint: Trace and cut out the figure, or use an actual tangram to see the relationships of the various pieces.)

a. the parallelogram $\frac{1}{8}$

b. the medium-sized triangle $\frac{1}{8}$

c. one of the large triangles $\frac{1}{2}$

d. Does it make a difference in your answers if you arrange your tangram pieces differently? Explain why the arrangement of the pieces does or does not make a difference.

20. Long Distance Telephone area codes in the United States and Canada consist of three digits. The first digit of the code can be any number from 2 through 9, and the second digit is either 0 or 1. The third digit can be any number.

If an area code is selected randomly from all of the possible codes, what is the probability of each of the following? Express your answers in decimal form rounded to the nearest hundredth.

a. the first digit of the area code is 3 0.13

b. the third digit is 4 or 5 0.20

c. the first two digits are 3–0 0.06

d. How many different area codes can be made using this system? Explain how you found your answer. $8 \cdot 2 \cdot 10 = 160$

5-1

Understanding and Applying Area

PART E At a Glance

Objective

To use knowledge of the areas of figures to design a game with a given probability of winning.

Development

In the **Explore,** students design a game where the probability of winning is 20%. They find how much it should cost to play if the game is to make a profit.

First Five Minutes

Transparency FFM 5-1E

Give a brief summary of the different ways that area calculations are used in 5-1. Use sketches to help show your ideas.

EXPLORE

Carnival Calculations

Recommended group size: 4

The Point

To design a game with a 20% chance of winning, and to decide what to charge to make a profit.

Look and Listen...

- For students who do not understand how to calculate expected profit.

Ask...

- If ten people play the game, how much money do you take in if each pays 50¢? How many prizes would you expect to give away? How much should each prize cost if you are to break even?

For Groups That Finish Early

Suppose you own the carnival. What information would you need before deciding how much to charge to play a game and how much to spend for prizes? **Estimates of how many people play, how that number is affected by costs and prizes, and so on.**

Algebra | Functions | Discrete Math | Probability | Data/Statistics

5-1 PART E Making Connections

← CONNECT → *The areas and perimeters of simple geometric figures have important applications in everyday situations and in algebra. You've calculated areas and perimeters, and seen how areas are related to algebra, probability, and problem solving.*

In the following Explore, you will see how the ideas of area and geometric probability can be helpful in designing a carnival game of chance. You will also see how probability can be useful in making some related business decisions.

EXPLORE: CARNIVAL CALCULATIONS

In a carnival game, ping-pong balls are tossed onto a large, horizontal, square area. There are ten congruent triangular holes. A person who tosses a ball so that it falls into a hole wins a prize. (He does not win if the ball bounces into the target.)

1. If the ping-pong balls are thrown randomly, there should be a 20% probability of throwing a ball into a hole. Make a sketch of your design of the game. Include the dimensions of the figures in your sketch. Compare your design with those of your classmates.
2. Suppose you charge 50 cents to play your game (one toss). How much should the prizes be worth if you want to expect to break even at the end of the day? How much should the prizes be worth if you want to expect to have a profit at the end of the day? Why?

REFLECT

1. Explain how to find the probability of randomly hitting the shaded portion of a target.
2. Use sketches and words to show how the product of two binomials is connected to the idea of area.
3. What is the difference between yards and square yards? Explain when it is appropriate to use each unit.

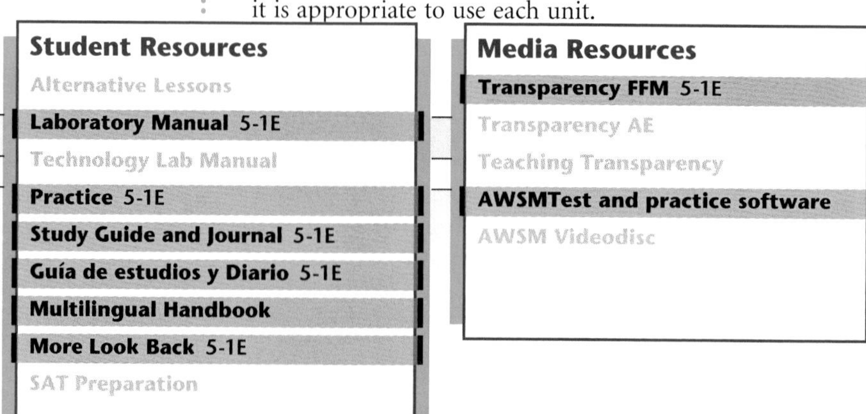

Student Resources

- Alternative Lessons
- **Laboratory Manual 5-1E**
- Technology Lab Manual
- **Practice 5-1E**
- **Study Guide and Journal 5-1E**
- **Guía de estudios y Diario 5-1E**
- **Multilingual Handbook**
- **More Look Back 5-1E**
- SAT Preparation

Media Resources

- **Transparency FFM 5-1E**
- Transparency AE
- Teaching Transparency
- **AWSMTest and practice software**
- AWSM Videodisc

Self-Assessment

Find the area of each figure.

1. 64

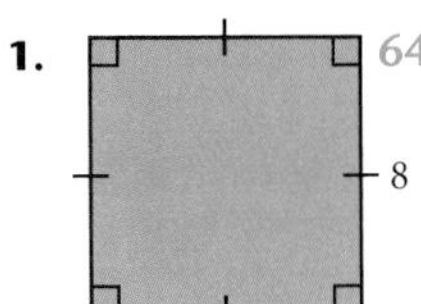

2. 6.75

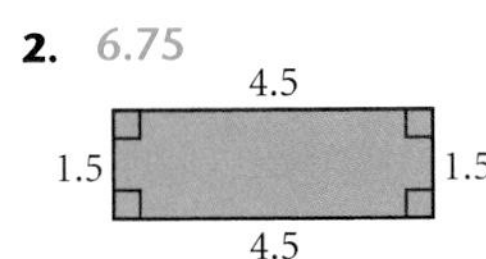

3. 8.4

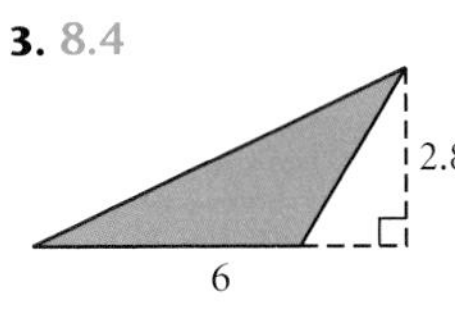

4. 120

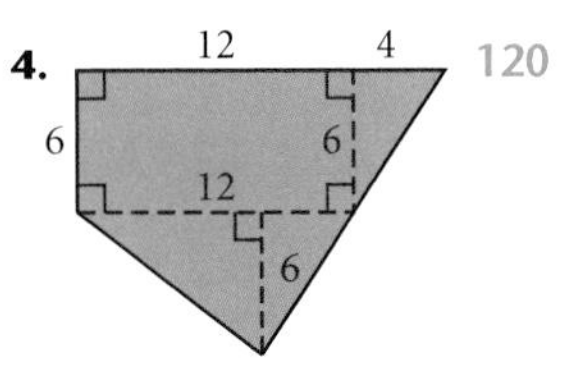

Find the perimeter of each figure.

5. 76

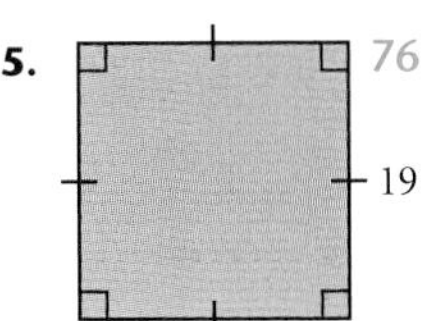

6. 19.8

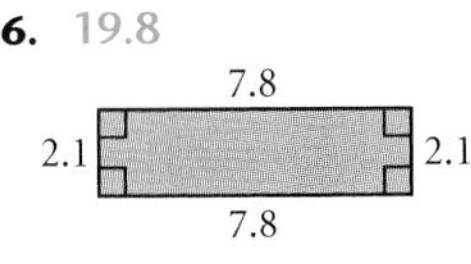

7. 15.42

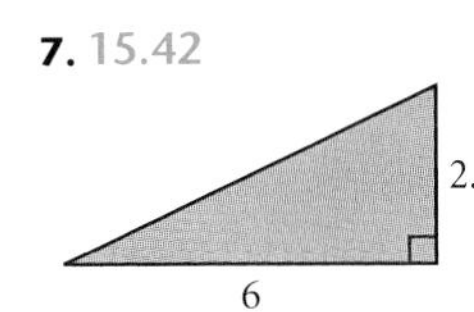

8. 50.8

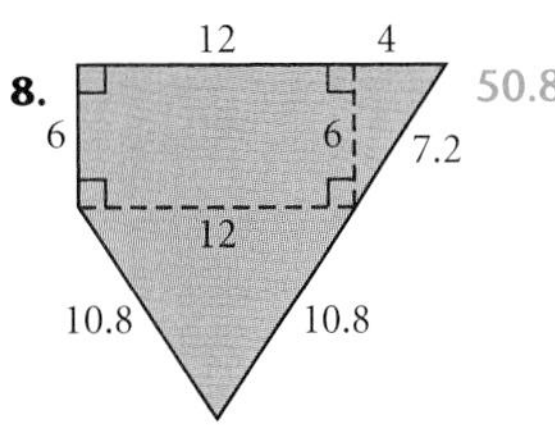

Use squares and rectangles for Exercises 9 and 10.

9. Multiply $(x + 2)$ and $(x + 3)$.

10. Factor $x^2 + 6x + 8$.

11. Solve $x^2 + 3x - 2 = 0$ using the quadratic formula.

12. Complete the following proof. [4-2]

Given: $\overline{RU} \cong \overline{TS}$, $\overline{RS} \cong \overline{TU}$

Prove: $\overline{RS} \parallel \overline{TU}$

Proof:

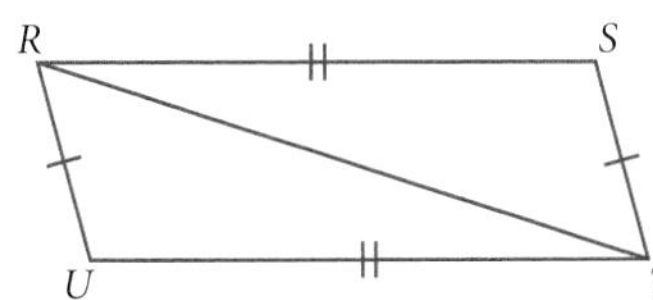

Statement	Reason
1. $\overline{RU} \cong \overline{TS}$	**1.**
2. $\overline{RS} \cong \overline{TU}$	**2.**
3.	**3.** Reflexive Property
4.	**4.**
5. $\angle UTR \cong \angle SRT$	**5.**
6.	**6.**

Follow Up

Ask students to show their finished designs and to state how much their prizes will be worth.

Possible Answers

1. For example: a 10-ft × 10-ft square with 10 right isosceles triangular holes with 2-ft legs.

2. \$2.50 is the break-even point. If the prizes cost less than this, you can expect a profit. For each play of the game, you earn 50¢. There is a 20% probability of having to give away a prize. Break even:

$0.20 \times (\text{prize value}) = \$\,0.50$, so prize value $= \frac{0.50}{0.20} = 2.50$.

Portfolio

Have students select items from their work that demonstrate their understanding of the material in 5-1.

You may wish to have students include an **Exercise** where they used squares and rectangles to multiply/factor, their best solution to a problem involving probability, and a game they designed that uses probabilities.

REFLECT

Possible Answers

1. Find the ratio of the area of the shaded region to the total area of the target.

2. If one binomial is considered the length of a rectangle and the other the width, their product is the area of the rectangle.

3. Yards measure length; square yards measure area. It is appropriate to use the first to measure distance, the second to measure enclosed space.

y

Vocabulary
Practice/Skills
Review
Math Reasoning
Problem Solving
Challenge

5-1

Understanding and Applying Area

Self-Assessment

Exercise Notes

16. Similar to multiple-choice questions on standardized tests.

17. Shows how bar graphs can be misleading if both the length and width of the bar are doubled when the statistic involved doubles.

19. Combines many of the concepts in 5-1.

Extension: Students may not have seen probabilities expressed in terms of variables. You may want to graph the resulting probability function on a graphing utility, using an appropriate range. The probability of winning increases from $x = 0$ to $x \approx 4.47$, where the probability of winning is a shade over 50%.

Self-Assessment Answers

9. $x^2 + 5x + 6$

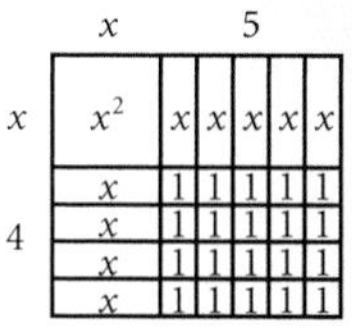

10. $(x + 2)(x + 4)$

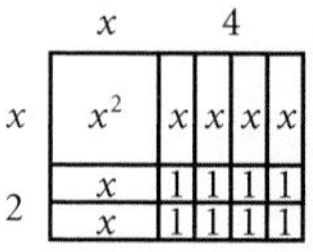

11. $x \approx -3.56$, $x \approx 0.56$

12. 1. Given
2. Given
3. $\overline{RT} \cong \overline{RT}$
4. $\triangle RUT \cong \triangle TSR$; SSS Postulate
5. CPCTC
6. $\overline{RS} \parallel \overline{TU}$; Alternate Interior Angles

17. a. The 1990 bar is wider than the 1980 bar, as well as taller.

b. The bars should be the same width so that their areas are proportional.

R **Find the measures of all of the numbered angles for each measure of $\angle 1$. [3-4]**

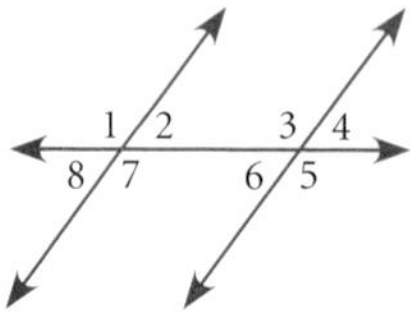

13. $m\angle 1 = 95°$ $m\angle 2, 4, 6, 8 = 85°$; $m\angle 3, 5, 7 = 95°$

14. $m\angle 1 = 49°$ $m\angle 2, 4, 6, 8 = 131°$; $m\angle 3, 5, 7 = 49°$

15. $m\angle 1 = 99.2°$ $m\angle 2, 4, 6, 8 = 80.8°$; $m\angle 3, 5, 7 = 99.2°$

P **16.** What is the probability of a randomly thrown dart hitting the triangular target on the rectangular background? (d)

(a) $\frac{1}{2}$ (b) $\frac{1}{3}$ (c) $\frac{1}{4}$ (d) $\frac{1}{8}$ (e) $\frac{1}{10}$

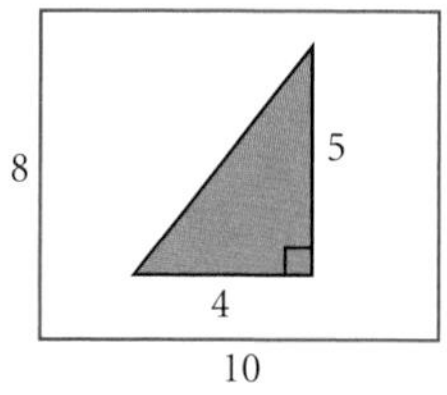

MR Social Science **17.** According to the 1993 *Information Please Almanac,* per-capita personal income in the United States grew from \$9910 in 1980 to \$18,696 in 1990. Suppose an organization published the graph at the right to illustrate this data.

a. Do you think the graph at the right is an accurate representation of the data? If so, why? If not, how is it misleading?

b. Explain how this graph was made. If you feel the graph is misleading, explain how it should be drawn to represent the data accurately.

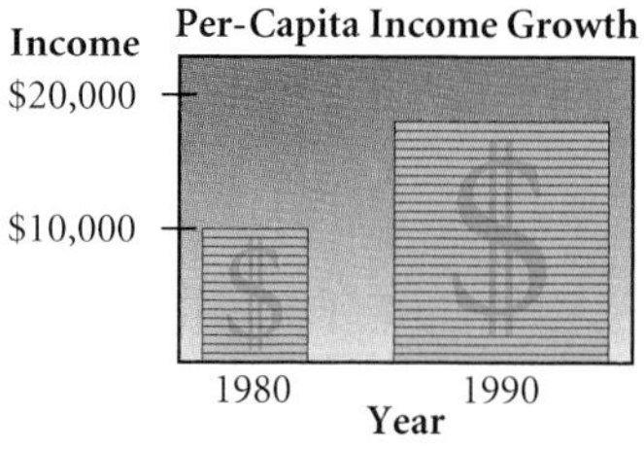

PS **18. Free Game!** At the end of a miniature golf game, you hit your golf ball up a ramp and into an 8-ft square target. If you hit the rectangular target, you win one free game. If you hit the triangular target, you win two free games. Assuming that the golf ball hits the target randomly and that the size of the ball doesn't affect the outcome, find each probability. Express your answers in decimal form rounded to the nearest hundredth.

a. the probability that you win one free game 0.16

b. the probability that you win two free games 0.06

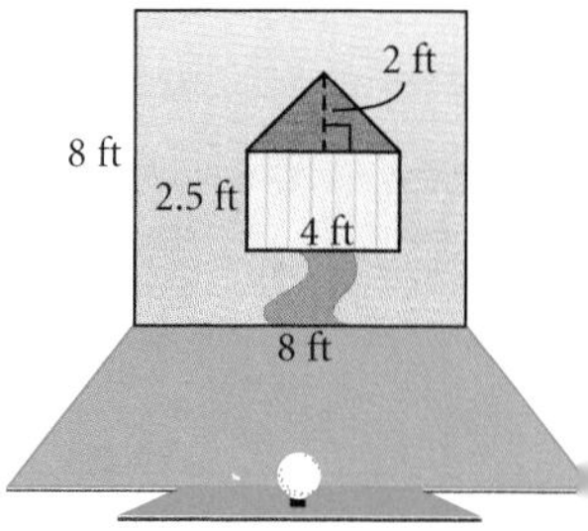

PS, C **19. Mathematical Darts** At a convention of Math Lovers Unite!, Keisha set up a carnival game. She used squares and rectangles to represent $(x + 5)(x + 4)$. A contestant who threw a dart and hit one of the x-sized rectangles won a prize. This was an interesting game, because the probability of winning depended on the value of x. Find the probability of winning in terms of x. Write a brief explanation of the method you used to solve the problem. See Additional Answers p. T344.

Assessment Resources

Quiz 5-1
Chapter Assessment Form A
Chapter Assessment Form B
Chapter Alternative Assessment
Mid-Year Assessment
End-of-Year Assessment
AWSMTest and practice software

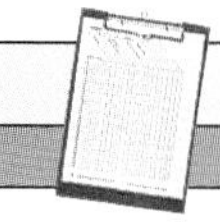

Ongoing Assessment

Self-Assessment Self-Assessment Exercises

Embedded Assessment Reflect 1, 2, 3

ADDITIONAL ANSWERS

5-1 Part B Exercises

Look Back

17. This pair of angles does not help determine if a and c are parallel.

18. Line a parallel to line b because corresponding angles are congruent.

19. $a \parallel c$ because same-side interior angles are supplementary.

20. $b \parallel c$ because corresponding angles are congruent.

21. $a \parallel b$ because alternate exterior angles are congruent.

More Practice

25. x x 1 1 1 1 1 1 1 1

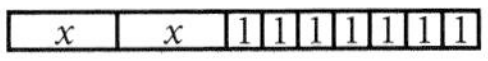

26. x^2 1 1 1 1 1

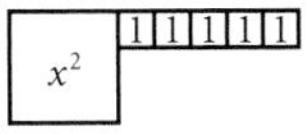

27. x^2 x x x x x 1 1 1

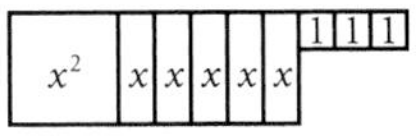

28. x 2; x 5

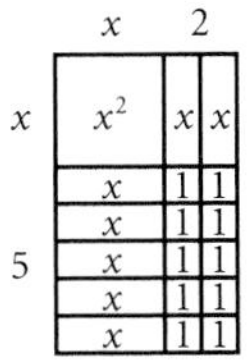

$x^2 + 7x + 10$

29. $3x$ 2; x 1

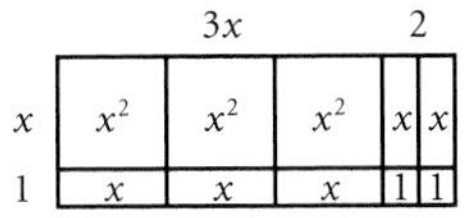

$3x^2 + 5x + 2$

30. 5; $2x$ 3

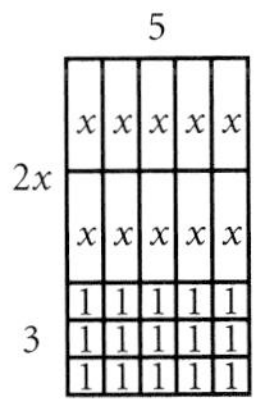

$10x + 15$

31. x 3; x 1

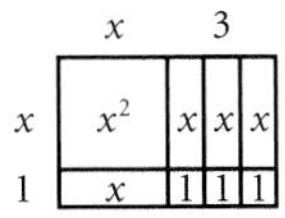

$(x + 3)(x + 1)$

5-1 Part B Exercises

32. x 3; x 5

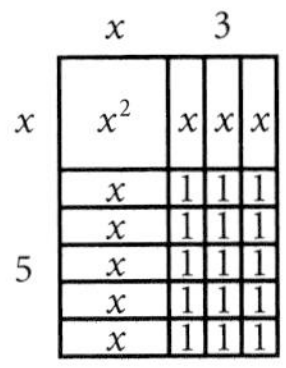

$(x + 3)(x + 5)$

33. x 5; $2x$ 1

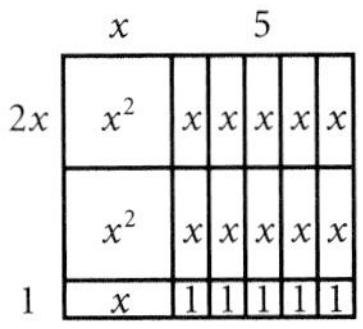

$(x + 5)(2x + 1)$

More Math Reasoning

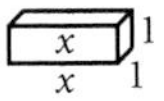

34. a. x^3; x, x, x **b.** x^2; x, x, 1

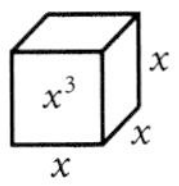

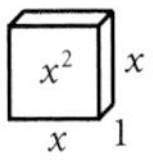

c. x; x, 1, 1 **d.** 1; 1, 1, 1

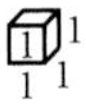

e. This would be a cube with sides $(x + 1)$, $(x + 2)$, and $(x + 3)$. This method would not be convenient on paper, but it could be used with real cubes and boxes.

35. 3, 6, 10: Add 3, add 4; The sum is a perfect square $\frac{(n)(n+1)}{2} + \frac{(n-1)(n)}{2} = n^2$.

5-1 Part E Self-Assessment

19. $\frac{9x}{x^2 + 9x + 20}$

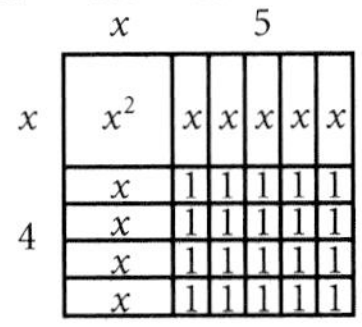

x 5; x 4

The total area is $x^2 + 9x + 20$, and the winning area is $9x$.

5-2

Derivations of Area Formulas

SUPERLESSON AT A GLANCE

Superlesson Goal

Students will discover and use area formulas for triangles and quadrilaterals, and as they provide justifications for these formulas, they will develop their skills in planning a deductive proof.

Management Guide

	Topic	Objectives	Key Terms	New Ideas	Materials
Part A	Assumptions About Area	To discover and use area formulas for a square, parallelogram, and triangle.	Quadrilateral, parallelogram, rectangle, square	Justification of area formulas. Areas of parallelograms.	**Student** Paper, scissors
Part B	Planning a Proof	To derive and use area formulas for a rhombus and trapezoid, and to develop skills in planning deductive proofs.	Rhombus, trapezoid	Areas of rhombuses and trapezoids.	
Part C	The Area Under a Curve	To use trapezoids to estimate the area under a curve.		Areas under graphs of algebraic equations. Estimating areas of non-polygonal regions.	**Student** Graph paper
Part D	Making Connections	To use areas of quadrilaterals and triangles to find areas of irregular regions.	In Making Connections, students apply and synthesize key terms and new ideas.		**Student** Graph paper, compass

Pacing Chart (45-Minute Periods)

	Comprehensive Course	Core Course	Informal Course
Part A	1	1	1
Part B	1	1	1*
Part C	1	1	0
Part D	1	1	1
TOTAL periods for Superlesson	4	4	3

*Material on proof in this part may be omitted or downplayed in an Informal Course.

NCTM Standards

Mathematics as Problem Solving

Mathematics as Communication

Mathematics as Reasoning

Mathematical Connections

Algebra

Functions

Geometry from a Synthetic Perspective

Geometry from an Algebraic Perspective

Conceptual Underpinnings of Calculus

5-2 Derivations of Area Formulas

AZTEC AREA

Tenochtitlán, on the site of present-day Mexico City, was the capital of the Aztec civilization. This spectacular city featured huge pyramids and magnificent palaces. Two aqueducts brought in fresh water, and three drawbridges connected the island city to the mainland. In the 1400s, the population of Tenochtitlán may have been as large as 300,000—greater than that of any European city at the time.

This civilization had many "modern" features. For example, Aztec landowners paid property taxes. These taxes were based on records that gave the property's boundaries, area, and market value. Aztec farms usually had irregular shapes. Although these areas were not simple to calculate, Aztec measurements were very accurate.

In the Aztec civilization, length was measured in *quahuitls,* which were about 2.5 m long. Area was measured in square *quahuitls.* Aztec officials measured and recorded the dimensions of the property and may have sketched small scale drawings.

A recent comparison of Aztec land records to those made later by the Spanish showed that the Aztec records were more accurate. One reason for this might have been the Aztec expertise in planning cities and building pyramids—tasks that require very precise measurements.

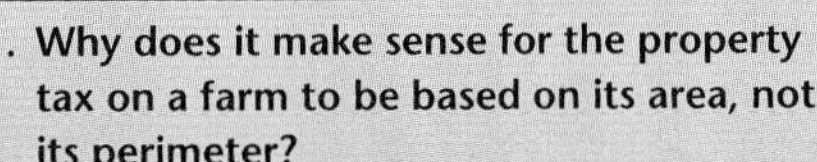

1. **Why does it make sense for the property tax on a farm to be based on its area, not its perimeter?**
2. **Give some reasons why Aztec farms might have had irregular shapes.**
3. **Why might the Aztecs have needed precise measurements to build their pyramids?**

Where Are We Now?

Students have used area formulas for simple geometric figures and seen connections between areas and algebraic concepts.

Where Are We Going?

In 5-2 students will discover and use area formulas for triangles and quadrilaterals. They use deductive reasoning to show why these formulas work. In this context, students develop their skills at writing a *plan* for a deductive proof. In Chapter 6, students will complete all five steps of deductive proofs on their own.

Possible Answers

1. The area is a much better indicator of how much food the land can produce.
2. Rough, mountainous terrain or rivers may have made irregular shapes necessary.
3. Precise measurements were needed to have accurate side lengths, slopes of sides and staircases, and so on.

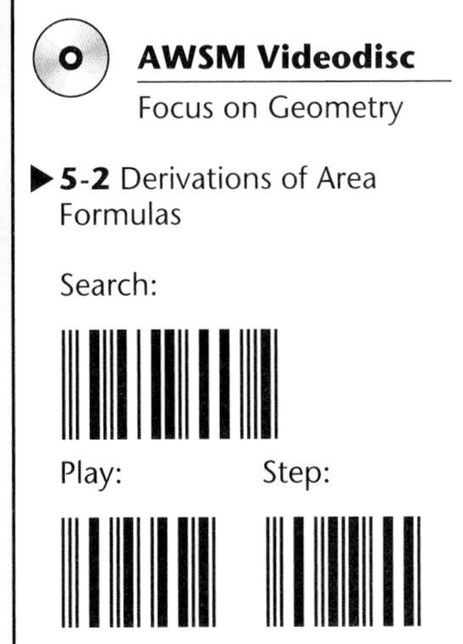

More About the Aztec Civilization

The Aztec civilization had the greatest population density in Mesoamerican history. Some of the most impressive Aztec technical achievements are seen in the agricultural techniques they developed to feed that population. Their method of reclaiming swamps and colonizing lakes was called *chiampa.* By digging drainage ditches, constructing artificial land from mud and vegetation, and erecting masonry dams, the Aztecs turned 300,000 acres into arable land.

Derivations of Area Formulas

PART A At a Glance

Objective

To discover and use area formulas for a square, parallelogram, and triangle.

Development

Students see formal definitions of *quadrilateral, parallelogram, rectangle,* and *square.* Then, in **Consider** questions, students use the area formula for a rectangle to justify the result for a square.

In the **Explore,** students continue to discover and justify area formulas, finding results for a parallelogram and a triangle.

Suggested Materials

Student Paper, scissors

Key Terms

Quadrilateral, parallelogram, rectangle, square

First Five Minutes

Transparency FFM 5-2A

Write your own definitions of *quadrilateral, parallelogram, rectangle,* and *square.*

Motivate

Ask...

- Read the formal definitions of *quadrilateral, parallelogram, rectangle,* and *square* on page 346. Do these definitions differ from your informal ideas of these figures? If so, how?

Note: The suitcase icon appears throughout the text whenever a new area formula is derived. It reminds students of the formulas they "carry with them."

5-2 PART A Assumptions About Area

← CONNECT → ***You already know how to find the areas of some figures. Now you are ready to derive and use formulas for the areas of a square, triangle, and parallelogram.***

The photo at the left shows the present-day site of an Aztec ruin. You will see how the Aztecs may have used area formulas and will see how we can incorporate these formulas into our deductive system.

The figures below are familiar, but we need to give some formal definitions before looking at their areas.

DEFINITIONS

A **quadrilateral** is a polygon with four sides.

A **parallelogram** is a quadrilateral with two pairs of parallel sides.

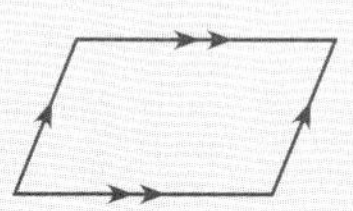

A **rectangle** is a quadrilateral with four right angles.

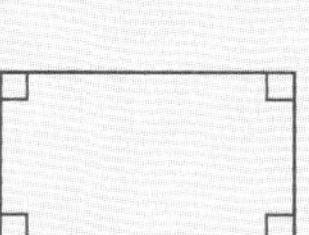

A **square** is a quadrilateral with four right angles and four congruent sides.

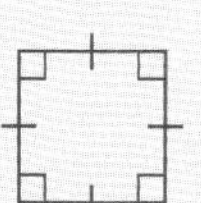

You may know that squares and rectangles are parallelograms. The opposite sides of all parallelograms (including squares and rectangles) are congruent. You will justify properties of parallelograms deductively in Chapter 6.

The idea that the area of a rectangle is its length times its width makes sense when you see a rectangle on a grid.

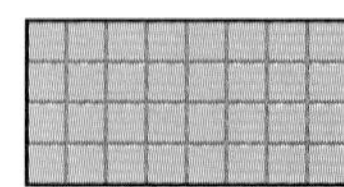

8 units × 4 units = 32 square units

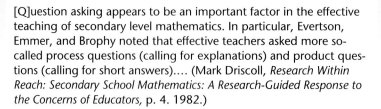

Research Note

[Q]uestion asking appears to be an important factor in the effective teaching of secondary level mathematics. In particular, Evertson, Emmer, and Brophy noted that effective teachers asked more so-called process questions (calling for explanations) and product questions (calling for short answers).... (Mark Driscoll, *Research Within Reach: Secondary School Mathematics: A Research-Guided Response to the Concerns of Educators,* p. 4. 1982.)

When you accept the area result for a rectangle ($A = \ell w$), you can use it to find the areas of other figures. The "area suitcase" will fill up as you discover how to calculate the areas of more figures. Once you have derived a formula, you can use it to develop others. (Remember our deductive system!)

CONSIDER

1. Assuming that the area of a rectangle is ℓw, what is the area of a square of side s? Justify your answer.
2. Do you think that the area formula for a rectangle is a postulate or a theorem? What about your result for a square? Explain.

In the following Explore, you will discover how to find the areas of a parallelogram and a triangle.

EXPLORE: IN THE AREA

MATERIALS

Paper, Scissors

1. Cut out a paper parallelogram, and label a base and height as shown on the left below. By cutting and rearranging pieces, use the area formula for a rectangle to help find the area formula for a parallelogram in terms of the length of the base and the height. Give an illustrated explanation of your result.

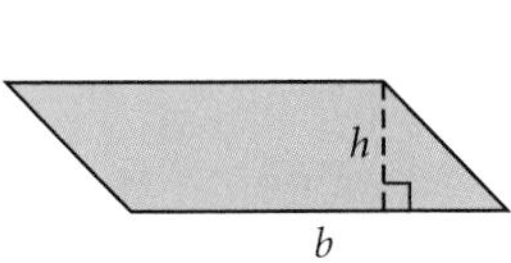

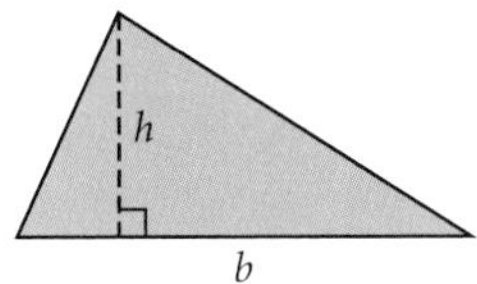

2. Now show why the area formula for a triangle works. Cut out or sketch a triangle as shown on the right above. Then look for a way to apply the area formula for a parallelogram or rectangle, so that you can find the triangle's area formula in terms of the length of the base and the height. Be creative!

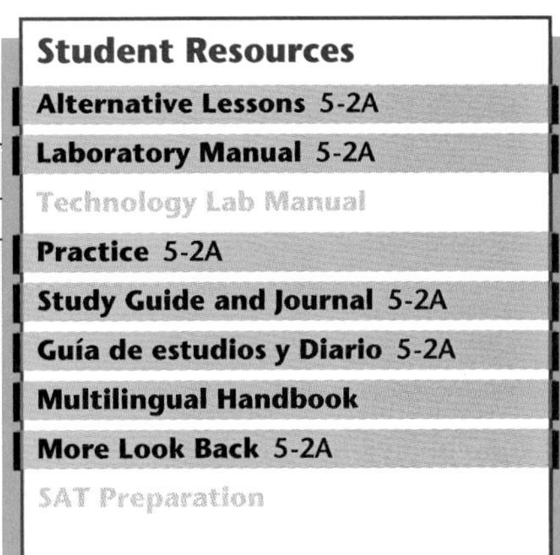

Student Resources

- Alternative Lessons 5-2A
- Laboratory Manual 5-2A
- Technology Lab Manual
- Practice 5-2A
- Study Guide and Journal 5-2A
- Guía de estudios y Diario 5-2A
- Multilingual Handbook
- More Look Back 5-2A
- SAT Preparation

Media Resources

- Transparency FFM 5-2A
- Transparency AE
- Teaching Transparency
- AWSMTest and practice software
- AWSM Videodisc

CONSIDER

Possible Answers

1. ℓ and w are both s; $\ell w = s^2$.
2. We assume the area formula for a rectangle; it is a postulate. We use the postulate to justify the result for a square; it is a theorem.

EXPLORE

In the Area

Recommended group size: 4

The Point

To justify the parallelogram and triangle area formulas.

Look and Listen...

- For students who do not see how to develop the triangle area formula in Step 2.

Ask...

- Would it help to cut out two congruent triangles?

For Groups That Finish Early

Suppose that we assume the area formula for a triangle as a postulate. Could you justify the formula for a rectangle by starting with the triangle formula? If so, how? **Divide it into two right triangles; it has twice the area of each.**

Follow Up

Ask students to present their results and explain how they found them.

Possible Answers

1. $A = bh$, the same as the area of a rectangle with this base and height.

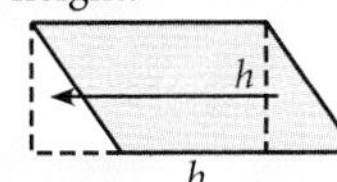

2. Place a duplicate triangle as shown to form a parallelogram. The area of one triangle is half the area of the parallelogram; $A = \frac{1}{2}bh$.

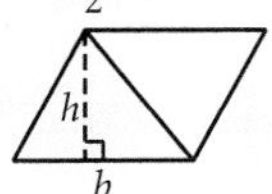

5-2

Derivations of Area Formulas

Journal

Consider question 1 and **Reflect** 1 are suitable for journal entries.

REFLECT

Possible Answers

1. a. Draw a rectangle. Show that a triangle whose base is on one side of the rectangle and whose third vertex is on the opposite side has half the area of the rectangle.

b. Draw a parallelogram. Show that the diagonal cuts it into two triangles with the same base and height. Each triangle has half the area of the parallelogram.

2. a. The length of a side.

b. The length and the width.

c. The base length and the height.

TRY IT

Find the area of each figure.

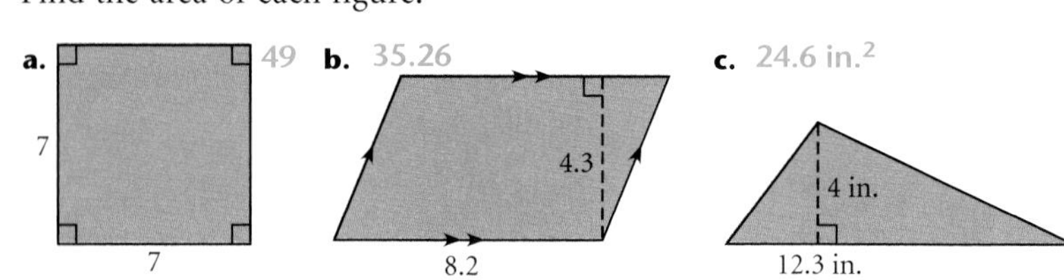

The area results that you investigated in the preceding Explore are summarized in the following list.

POSTULATE

The area of a rectangle is the product of its length (ℓ) and width (w).

$A = \ell w$

THEOREMS

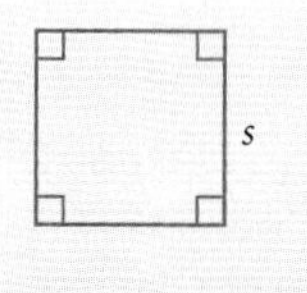

The area of a square is the square of its side length (s).

$A = s^2$

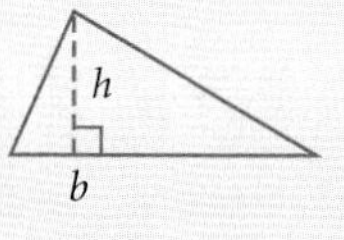

The area of a triangle is half the product of its base length (b) and corresponding height (h).

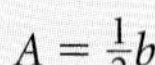

$A = \frac{1}{2}bh$

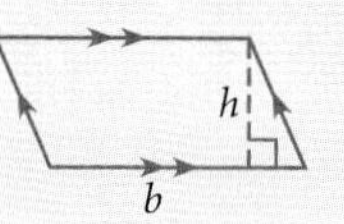

The area of a parallelogram is the product of its base length (b) and height (h).

$A = bh$

REFLECT

1. Describe a way to justify that the area of a triangle is $\frac{1}{2}bh$ by using the following.
   a. the area formula for a rectangle
   b. the area formula for a parallelogram
2. State the information necessary to find the area of each figure.
   a. a square **b.** a rectangle **c.** a triangle

Careers Connection

Dr. Shirley Jackson is a preeminent African-American physicist. She earned a Ph.D. in physics from MIT, and has worked at AT&T Bell Labs, where she did research on gases, films, and semiconductors. She is currently a professor at Rutgers University. Throughout her career, she has helped women and members of minority groups pursue scientific studies.

Exercises

CORE

Getting Started Find the area of each figure.

1. 11.04 in.^{2}

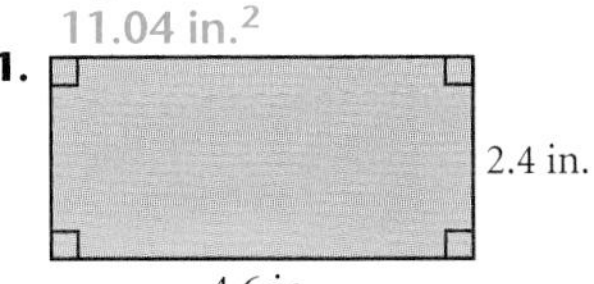

2. 1218 cm^2

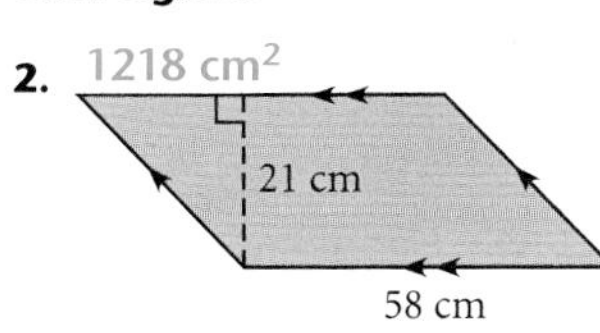

3. 5.4 ft^2

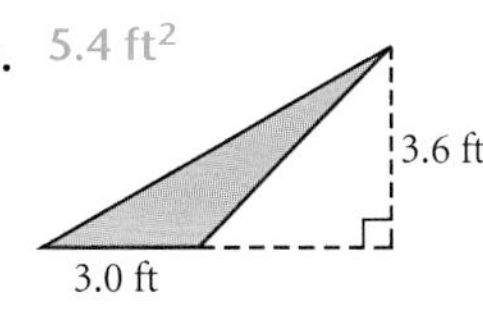

Suppose the figures shown represent irregularly shaped Aztec farms. Find the area of each farm.

4. 78

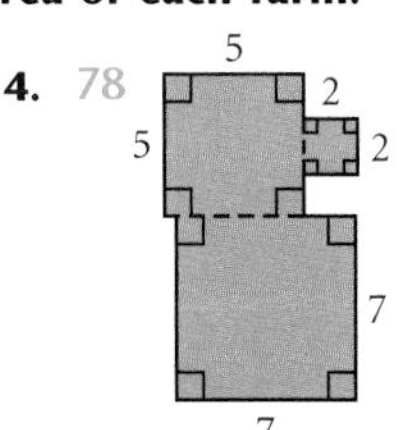

5. 166.25

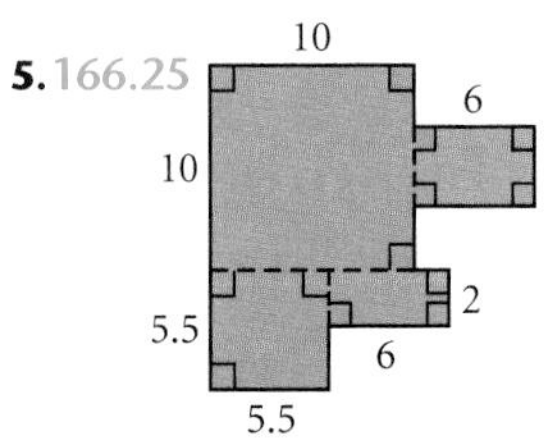

6. 145.8

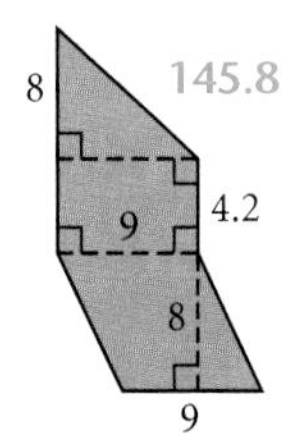

Find each of the following.

7. the area of a right triangle with legs of length 1.8 m and 3.2 m 2.88 m^2

8. the base length of a parallelogram with $A = 5.4$ in.^{2} and $h = 1.5$ in. 3.6 in.

9. the length of a side of a square with $A = 2.89$ cm^2 1.7 cm

10. Poetry Reading In an early reading of his poem, *The Thorn,* William Wordsworth (1770–1850) included these lines about a pond. 6 ft^2

I've measured it from side to side:
'Tis three feet long, and two feet wide.

If the pond's surface is rectangular, what is its area?

From each group of terms, choose the term that does not belong, and explain why. Can you think of more than one possible answer?

11. quadrilateral, parallelogram, rectangle, square

12. right triangle, obtuse triangle, rectangle, square

13. If a quart of varnish covers 125 ft^2, how many quarts must you buy to apply two coats to a rectangular floor that is 12 ft by 14 ft? Explain.

Problem-Solving Tip

Check to see if your answer makes sense.

Part A Exercises

Exercise Notes

Core

13. Students apply area to solve a practical problem. They are also reminded that answers to actual problems must make sense—you cannot buy 2.688 quarts of varnish in a store!

More Math Reasoning

32. Students discover Pick's Theorem.

Exercise Answers

Core

11. Possible answer: Quadrilateral does not belong because it is a type of figure, whereas the others are types of quadrilaterals.

12. Possible answer: Obtuse triangle does not belong because the area cannot be found by the lengths of two appropriate sides.

13. 3 (2.7 rounded up)

Ongoing Assessment

Vocabulary
Practice/Skills
Review
Math Reasoning
Problem Solving
Challenge

Self-Assessment Exercises 1–17 odd

Embedded Assessment Reflect 1; Exercises 2, 6, 14, 16

Derivations of Area Formulas

14. Minimum = 2000 mi²;
Maximum = 3000 mi²

Look Back

19. a. *L, M, Q, R, V, W*

b. *F, K, P, U, I, N, S, X*

c. *P, S* **d.** $\frac{3}{10}$

20. $(x + 3)(x + 2)$

	x	3
x	x^2	x x x
2	x x	1 1 1 1 1 1

21. $(x + 5)(x + 2)$

	x	5
x	x^2	x x x x x
2	x x	1 1 1 1 1 1 1 1 1 1

22. $(x + 4)(x + 2)$

	x	4
x	x^2	x x x x
2	x x	1 1 1 1 1 1 1 1

PS **14.** The photo at the right shows an Aztec bowl. Aztec agriculture supported a population of 1,000,000 to 1,500,000 people at a population density of 500 people/mi². Find minimum and maximum values for the area these people lived in.

History

P **What is the probability that a randomly chosen point in each figure will lie in the shaded region? Express your answers as decimals rounded to the nearest hundredth.**

15. 0.6

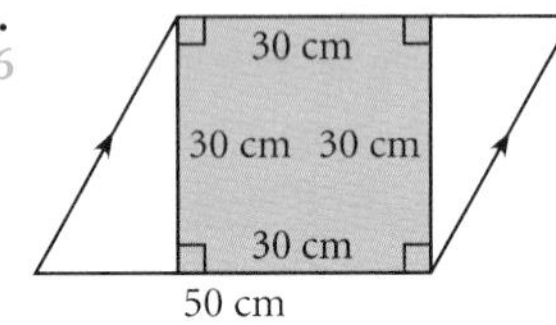

16. 0.47

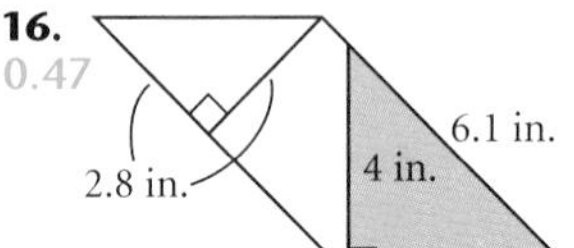

17. 0.5

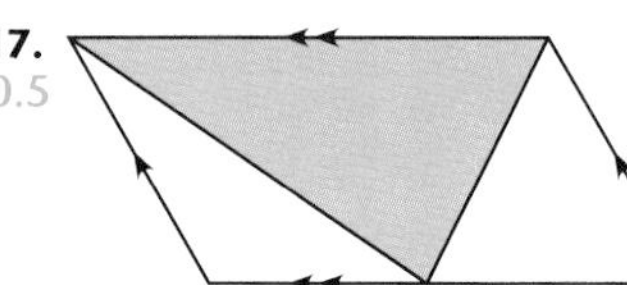

PS **18. Skylight** The glass ceiling of a building has metal supports that divide it into parallelogram-shaped regions. What is the area of each of the regions? 40 ft²

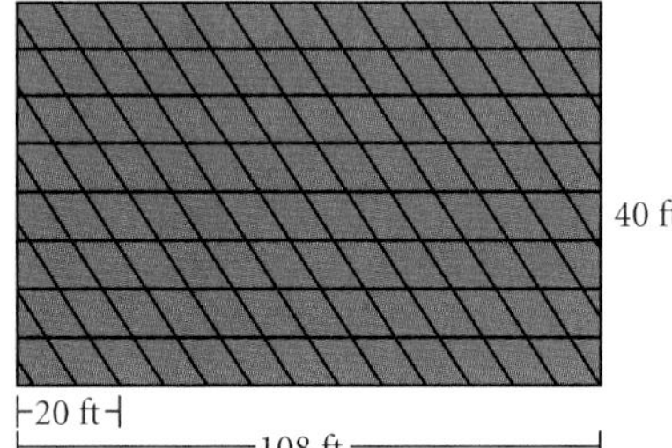

LOOK BACK

R **19.** $\overline{AD}$ is one side of a triangle on the grid. List the possibilities for the third vertex if the triangle is of the following type. [4-1]

a. acute **b.** right **c.** isosceles

d. Suppose the third vertex of the triangle is chosen randomly from the points shown in red. What is the probability that the triangle will be obtuse? Express your answer as a fraction.

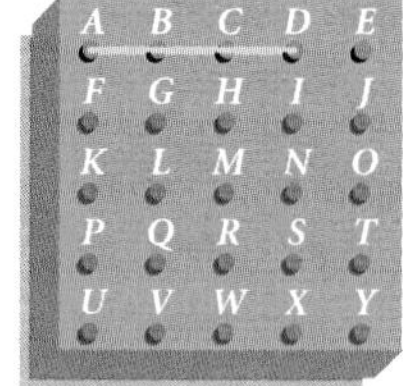

R **Factor each trinomial, using squares and rectangles. Provide a sketch, and give an algebraic answer. [5-1]**

20. $x^2 + 5x + 6$ **21.** $x^2 + 7x + 10$ **22.** $x^2 + 6x + 8$

Key

V Vocabulary
P Practice/Skills
R Review
MR Math Reasoning
PS Problem Solving
C Challenge

MORE PRACTICE

Find the area of each figure.

23. 34.04 cm^2

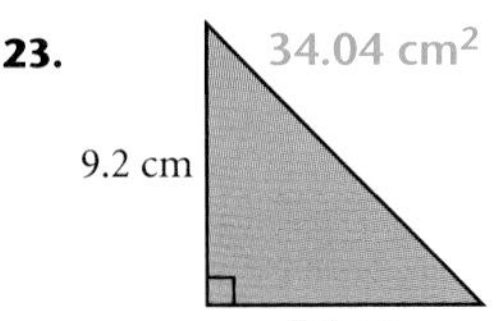

24. 3.9 $in.^2$

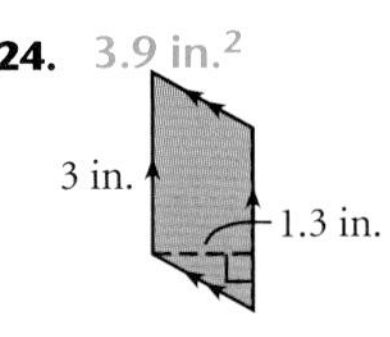

25. 3000 ft^2

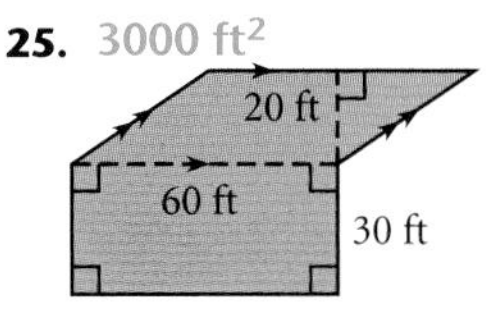

26. 46.08 m^2

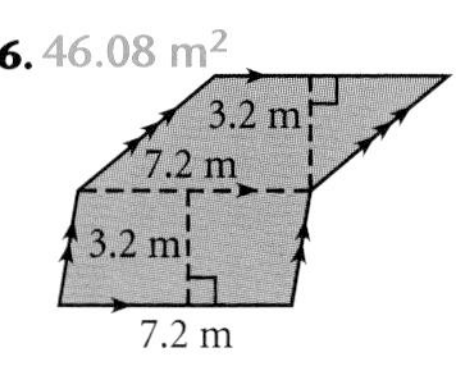

Find each of the following.

27. the height of a parallelogram whose area is 62 cm^2 and whose base length is 11.2 cm 5.54 cm

28. the length of a side of a square whose area is 84.64 ft^2 9.2 ft

29. the height of a triangle whose base length is 4 in. and whose area is 23 $in.^2$ 11.5 in.

30. the base length of a parallelogram whose area is 48 m^2 and whose height is half its base length ≈ 9.80 m

MORE MATH REASONING

31. Some of the earliest human artists traced their hands with paint on cave walls. The photograph at the right shows aboriginal art from a cave in Australia.

Trace your hand on graph paper and estimate its area.

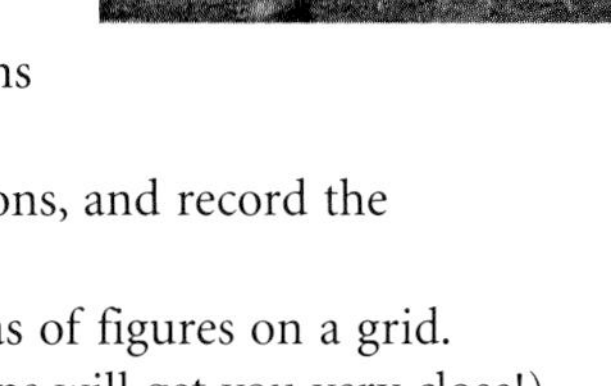

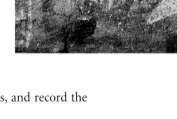

32. Pick's Theorem Use a geoboard or dot paper and the following steps to discover Pick's Theorem.

a. Draw three different triangles and three different rectangles on a geoboard or dot paper. (Vertices should be at grid points.)

b. Find X, the number of grid points inside each figure.

c. Find Y, the number of grid points on the perimeter of each figure.

d. Make a table to record your results. Label the columns of your table X, Y, $\frac{1}{2}X$, $\frac{1}{2}Y$, and Area of Polygon.

e. Use area formulas to calculate the areas of the polygons, and record the results of your calculations.

f. Use your table to discover a formula to calculate areas of figures on a grid. (Hint: The sum of the values from two of the columns will get you very close!) This formula is known as Pick's Theorem.

More Math Reasoning

31. Check students' answers.

32. Possible answers

a.

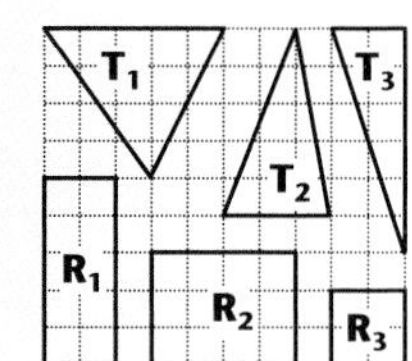

b–e.

	X	Y	$\frac{1}{2}X$	$\frac{1}{2}Y$	A
T_1	7	8	$3\frac{1}{2}$	4	10
T_2	6	5	3	$2\frac{1}{2}$	$7\frac{1}{2}$
T_3	2	10	1	5	6
R_1	4	14	2	7	10
R_2	6	14	3	7	12
R_3	1	8	$\frac{1}{2}$	4	4

f. $A = X + \frac{1}{2}Y - 1$

5-2

Derivations of Area Formulas

PART B At a Glance

Objective

To derive and use area formulas for a rhombus and trapezoid and to develop skills in planning deductive proofs.

Development

First, students see definitions of *rhombus* and *trapezoid.*

Next, an **Example** shows students a *plan* for a proof.

In the **Explore,** students put these ideas together to discover the area formula for a trapezoid and *plan* a proof to justify their result.

Key Terms

Rhombus, trapezoid

First Five Minutes

Transparency FFM 5-2B

Read the definitions of *rhombus* and *parallelogram* on page 352. Then do **Try It a–e.**

Motivate

Ask...

- How are trapezoids similar to parallelograms? How are they different? **Both have parallel sides, but the trapezoid has only one pair.**

5-2 PART B Planning a Proof

← CONNECT → *You already know several area formulas. Now you will learn how to find the areas of trapezoids and rhombuses. You will also begin to write your own plans for deductive proofs.*

The definitions of two important types of quadrilaterals are given below.

DEFINITIONS

A **rhombus** is a quadrilateral with four congruent sides.

A **trapezoid** is a quadrilateral with exactly one pair of parallel sides. The parallel sides are the *bases* of the trapezoid, and the nonparallel sides are its *legs*.

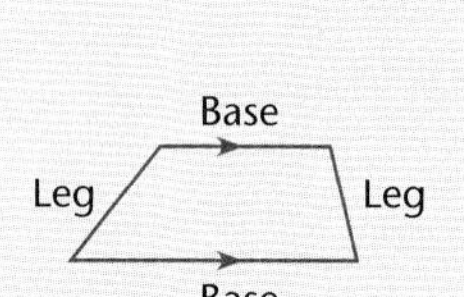

Like rectangles and squares, all rhombuses are parallelograms.

TRY IT

Classify each quadrilateral as a square, rectangle, rhombus, parallelogram, or trapezoid. Some figures may be classified in more than one way.

a. 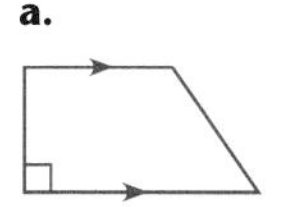

b. 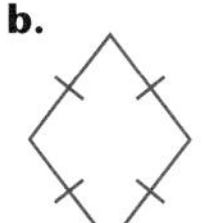

c. 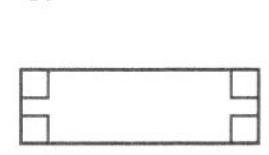

d. 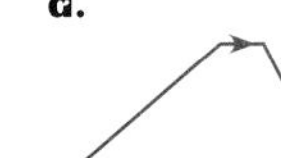

e. 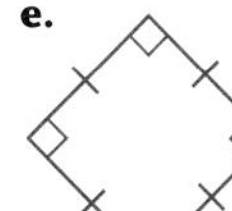

a. Trapezoid; **b.** Rhombus, parallelogram; **c.** Rectangle, parallelogram; **d.** Trapezoid; **e.** Square, rectangle, rhombus, parallelogram

Making a *plan* is the fourth step in our five-step process for deductive proof. In the *plan* illustrated in the following example, notice the importance of adding an auxiliary line to the figure.

Alert

This is a crucial step along the road to proof and one that is often challenging for students. As they start to plan proofs, you might routinely ask them questions such as "What are the given facts?" "What is it we need to prove?" "What information do we need to make this conclusion?" Students may internalize these prompts and ask themselves similar questions.

EXAMPLE

Write a *plan* for proving that all rhombuses are parallelograms.

Rewrite: If a quadrilateral is a rhombus, then it is a parallelogram.

Draw:

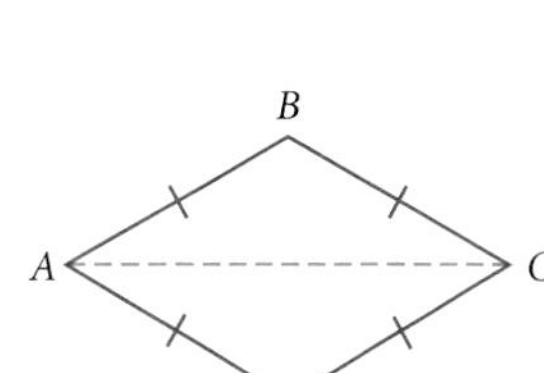

State: *Given:* Quadrilateral *ABCD* is a rhombus.

Prove: *ABCD* is a parallelogram.

Plan: To show that the rhombus is a parallelogram, we must show that $\overline{AB} \parallel \overline{CD}$ and $\overline{AD} \parallel \overline{BC}$. Adding diagonal $\overline{AC}$ provides a transversal to help prove lines parallel.

$\overline{AC}$ splits the rhombus into two triangles. We can show that $\triangle ABC \cong \triangle CDA$ by SSS.

$\angle BAC \cong \angle DCA$, and $\overline{AB} \parallel \overline{CD}$ since alternate interior angles are congruent. Also, $\angle BCA \cong \angle DAC$, so $\overline{AD} \parallel \overline{BC}$, and *ABCD* is a parallelogram.

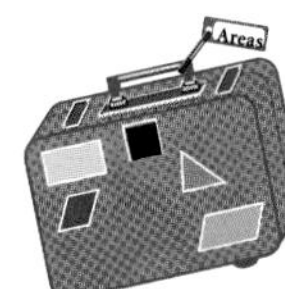

Since every rhombus is a parallelogram, you can find the area of a rhombus by using $A = bh$.

In the following Explore, you'll see how to calculate the area of a trapezoid. You will also write a *plan* to justify your result.

EXPLORE: FROM TRIANGLES TO TRAPEZOIDS

1. The area of a trapezoid with base lengths b_1 and b_2 and height h can be found by using what you have learned about the area of a triangle. Use the figure at the right to help find the formula for the area of a trapezoid.
2. Write a *plan* describing how you might prove your result from Step 1. Compare your *plan* with those developed by your classmates.

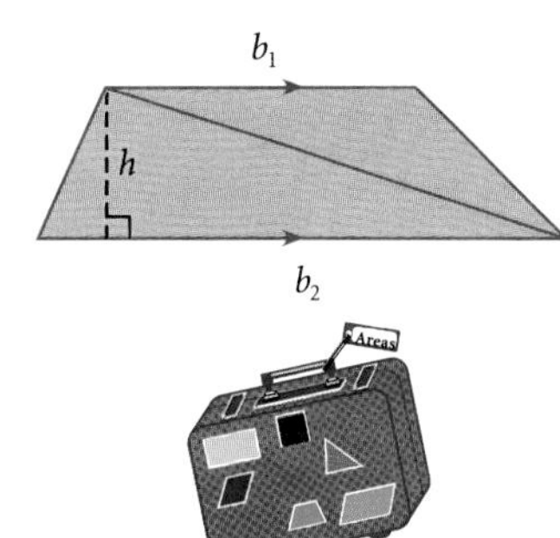

Student Resources

- Alternative Lessons 5-2B
- Laboratory Manual 5-2B
- Technology Lab Manual
- Practice 5-2B
- Study Guide and Journal 5-2B
- Guía de estudios y Diario 5-2B
- Multilingual Handbook
- More Look Ahead 5-2B
- SAT Preparation

Media Resources

- Transparency FFM 5-2B
- Transparency AE 5-2B
- Teaching Transparency
- AWSMTest and practice software
- AWSM Videodisc

ALTERNATE EXAMPLE

Transparency AE 5-2B

EXPLORE

From Triangles to Trapezoids

Recommended group size: 4

The Point

To discover and justify the area formula for a trapezoid.

Look and Listen...

- For students who do not see that the height of the obtuse triangle is also *h*.
- For students who need hints to begin their *plan* for proof. You might suggest adding an auxiliary line as the first step in their *plan*.

Ask...

- How do you draw the altitude to b_1 in the obtuse triangle?
- Can you simplify your result by factoring?

For Groups That Finish Early

Suppose you draw a triangle whose base is b_2 and whose third vertex is on b_1. What is the probability that a randomly selected point inside the trapezoid will also be inside the triangle? $\frac{b_2}{b_1 + b_2}$

Follow Up

Ask students to share their results and to briefly explain their justification plan.

Possible Answers

1. $A = \frac{1}{2}(b_1 + b_2)h = \frac{(b_1 + b_2)h}{2}$
2. To a trapezoid with height h and bases b_1 and b_2, add an auxiliary line, a diagonal of the trapezoid. This divides the trapezoid into two triangles. Their areas are $\frac{1}{2}b_1h$ and $\frac{1}{2}b_2h$.

$$A = \frac{1}{2}b_1h + \frac{1}{2}b_2h = \frac{1}{2}h(b_1 + b_2) = \frac{1}{2}(b_1 + b_2)h$$

Derivations of Area Formulas

Journal

Reflect 1 and 2 are suitable for journal entries.

REFLECT

Possible Answers

1. A trapezoid cannot be a parallelogram. By definition, a trapezoid has only one pair of parallel sides.

2. The *rewrite* and *state* steps make the starting point and goal of the proof clear and may therefore help you find a strategy. The *draw* step provides a figure that may suggest auxiliary lines, possible congruent figures, parallel lines, and so on, that can be important intermediate steps in a proof.

3. Find the area of the trapezoid, and subtract the area of the "missing" triangle; 130 units^2.

TRY IT

Find the area of each trapezoid.

f.

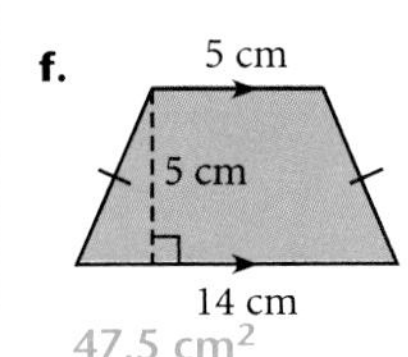

47.5 cm^2

g.

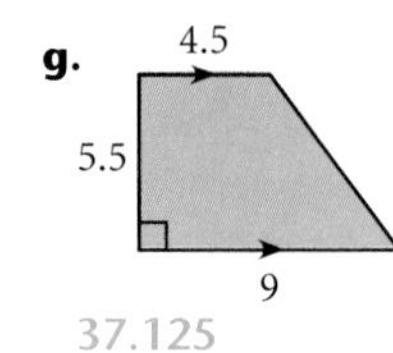

37.125

h.

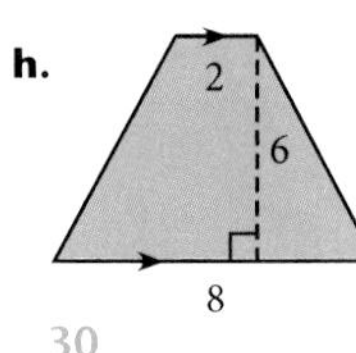

30

THEOREM

The area of a trapezoid is the product of half the sum of the bases (b_1 and b_2) and the height (h). $A = \frac{b_1 + b_2}{2}h$

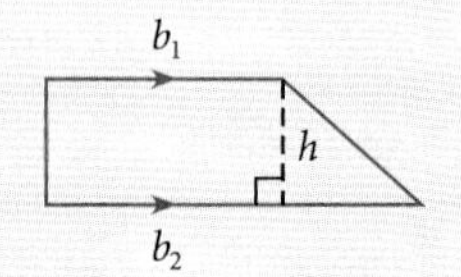

REFLECT

1. Can a trapezoid be a parallelogram? Explain.
2. How might the *rewrite, draw,* and *state* steps be helpful in planning a proof?
3. Write a *plan* for finding the area of the shaded region. Then calculate the area.

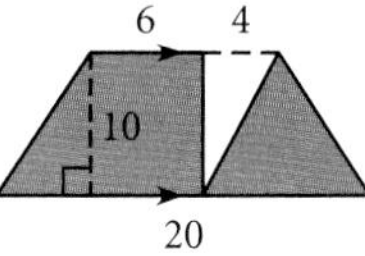

Part B Exercises

Exercise Notes

Core

12. Students find an area formula for a kite.

13. Students use Heron's formula to find the area of a triangular plot of land.

Look Ahead

16. Students find the area under a graph on a coordinate plane. In 5-2 Part C, they will approximate areas under curves on the coordinate plane.

More Math Reasoning

24. Some students may remember the area formula for a trapezoid more easily if they think of it as the average of the bases times the height.

Exercises

CORE

P **Getting Started** **Find the area of each figure.**

1.

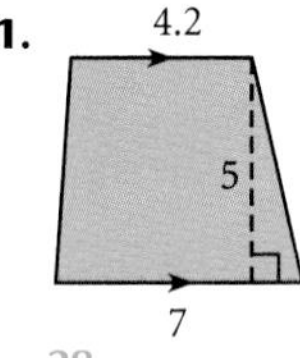

28

2.

105.6

3.

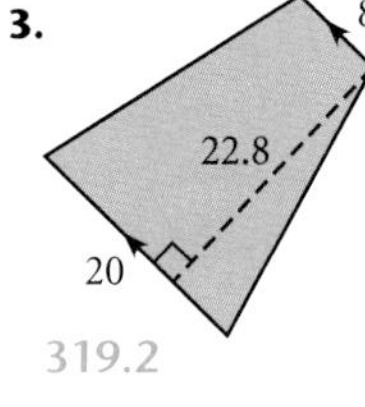

319.2

4.

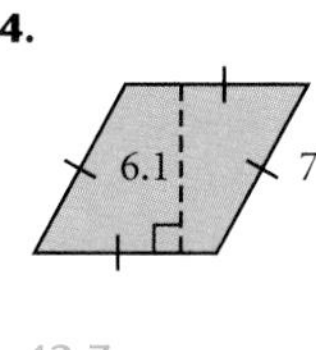

42.7

P **Find the area of each trapezoid.**

5. base lengths = 10 in. and 12 in., height = 5 in. 55 in.^{2}

6. base lengths = 6 ft and 10 ft, height = 7 ft 56 ft.^{2}

Key

V Vocabulary
P Practice/Skills
R Review
MR Math Reasoning
PS Problem Solving
C Challenge

History Connection

The Ahmes (Rhind) papyrus is an important source of knowledge about the mathematics that existed in Egypt about 4000 years ago. In it, the areas of an isosceles triangle and a trapezoid are found using calculations similar to the formulas we use today. In both cases, the scribe suggests that these calculations can be justified by rearranging pieces of the figure to form a rectangle.

7. The area of a trapezoid is 84 square units. The length of one base is 8 units, and the length of the other base is 16 units. Find the height of the trapezoid. 7 units

8. The area of a trapezoid is 45 square units. The height is 5 units, and one of the bases is 8 units. Find the length of the other base. 10 units

Write the word or phrase that correctly completes each statement.

9. A ___ is a quadrilateral with four congruent sides. Rhombus

10. If exactly two sides of a quadrilateral are parallel, then the quadrilateral is a ___. Trapezoid

11. Find two pairs of triangles that have equal areas in the figure at right. For each pair, *plan* a proof to show that their areas are equal.

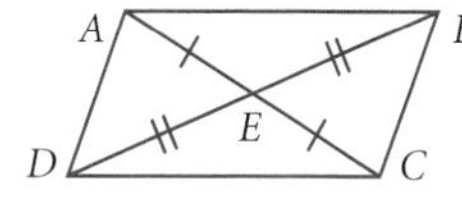

12. **Go Measure a Kite** A **kite** is a quadrilateral with two distinct pairs of adjacent, congruent sides. What is the area of a kite with diagonals of lengths a and b? *Plan* a logical argument to justify your area formula.

13. **Heron's Formula** Heron was a first-century Greek mathematician who discovered a formula for the area of a triangle by using only the lengths of its three sides. The area of any triangle with side lengths a, b, and c, is

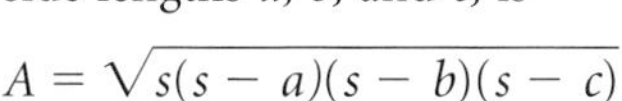

$$A = \sqrt{s(s-a)(s-b)(s-c)}$$

where s is the semiperimeter (half the perimeter) of the triangle.

A surveyor needs to measure the area of the plot of land at the right.

a. Find the area of the plot of land by using Heron's Formula.

b. Why might it be good to have two different ways to find the area of a triangle? (Hint: Suppose the surveyor can only measure lengths by using ropes.)

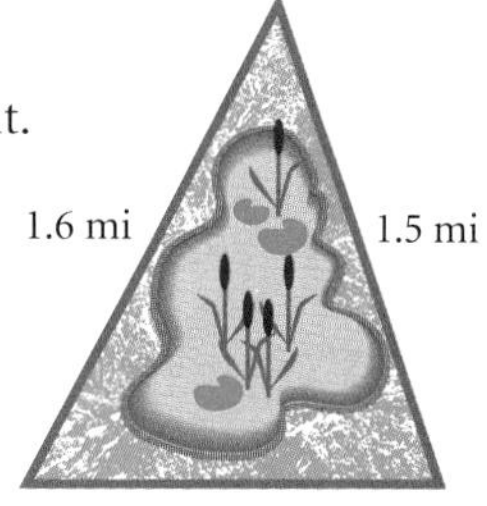

14. *Plan* a logical argument to show that congruent triangles have equal areas.

15. **Metallic Rhombuses** When bonded in metallic form, magnesium atoms form close-packed planes of atoms, as shown. The radius of a magnesium atom is 1.6×10^{-7} mm.

a. Assuming each atom has the same radius, explain why the figure joining the centers of the atoms as shown must be a rhombus.

b. Using the value of h given, find the area of the rhombus.

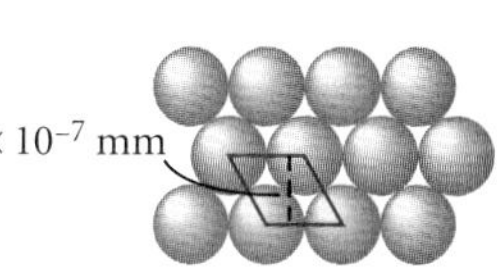

Exercise Answers

Core

11. Possible answer: $\triangle DEC$ and $\triangle BEA$ have equal areas, as do $\triangle ADE$ and $\triangle CBE$. For each pair, construct the altitudes and use SAS to show congruence of triangles. Use CPCTC to show congruence of the altitudes and of the corresponding bases.

12. $\frac{ab}{2}$; Show that diagonals are perpendicular, and that one diagonal bisects the other. Then add the areas of the four internal triangles.

13. a. 0.91 mi^2

b. Possible answer: Finding the area in two different ways provides a check; it may not be possible to use one of the methods.

14. Possible answer: First show that the bases are equal and the heights are equal.

15. a. Each side length is equal to two radii.

b. 9.0×10^{-14} mm^2

Ongoing Assessment

Self-Assessment Exercises 1–15 odd

Embedded Assessment Explore Step 1; Exercises 4, 6, 8, 14

Derivations of Area Formulas

Look Ahead

16. 130; Sum the area of one large rectangle and one trapezoid.

More Math Reasoning

24. Yes; $A = \frac{(b_1 + b_2)}{2}h$

25. Short base = 4; Long base = 8; Height = 11

26. a. Each of the triangles has the same area because they are all congruent.

b. △2 and △4 have the same area and △1 and △3 have the same area because each of the pairs of triangles are congruent.

c. None of the triangles need have the same area because the lengths of the sides of the trapezoid are all different, and so the bases of the triangles are not congruent.

LOOK AHEAD

P **16.** Find the area of the shaded region at the right. Explain your method.

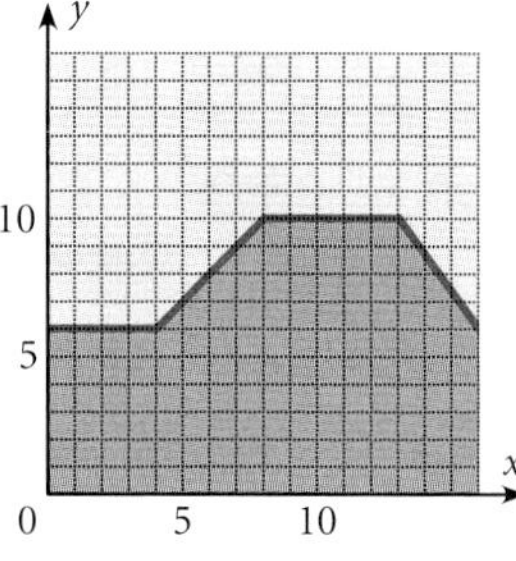

MORE PRACTICE

P **Find the area of each figure.**

17.

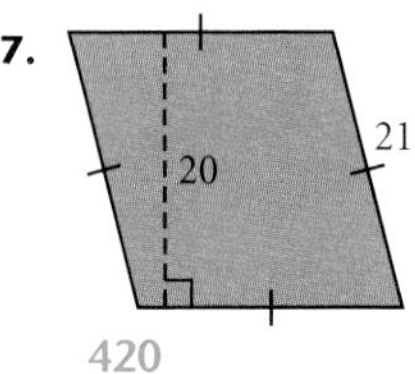

420

18.

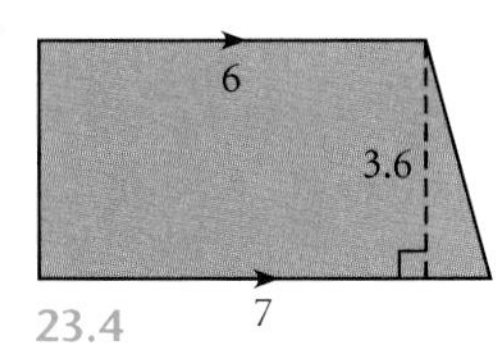

23.4

19.

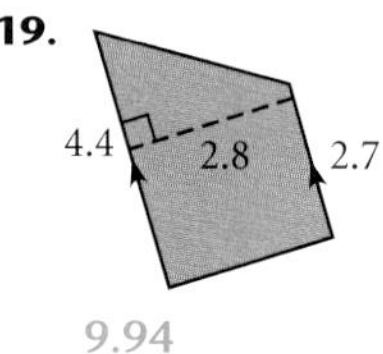

9.94

P **Find the area of each trapezoid.**

20. base lengths = 6 in. and 8 in., height = 4 in. 28 in.^{2}

21. base lengths = 11 m and 16 m, height = 5 m 67.5 m^2

22. base lengths = 5.4 cm and 8.8 cm, height = 12.1 cm 85.91 cm^2

P **23.** The area of a trapezoid is 25 m^2. The height is 4 m, and one of the base lengths is 3 m. Find the length of the other base. 9.5 m

MORE MATH REASONING

MR **24.** Darrell says, "The area of a trapezoid is equal to the average of its base lengths times its height." Is he correct? Why?

PS **25. Algebra Trapezoid** The area of a trapezoid is 66 square units. The length of its longer base is 4 units longer than the length of its shorter base, and its height is 7 units longer than the length of its shorter base. Find the length of each base and the height of the trapezoid.

MR, C **26.** A quadrilateral is divided into four triangles as shown. For each type of quadrilateral, which of the four triangles, if any, must be of equal area? Give a convincing argument in each case.

a. square

b. parallelogram

c. trapezoid

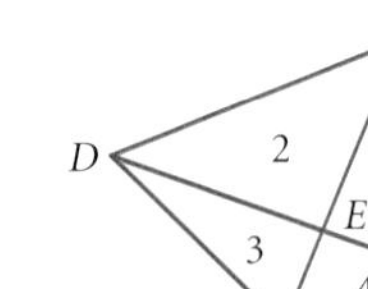

Key

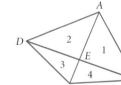

V Vocabulary
P Practice/Skills
R Review
MR Math Reasoning
PS Problem Solving
C Challenge

5-2 PART C

The Area Under a Curve

← CONNECT → *Scientists and engineers often need to calculate the areas of figures with irregular or curved surfaces. Now that you know how to find the areas of many geometric figures, you will expand your study of area to more complex figures.*

Finding the area under a curve is important in higher mathematics, and the technique has many practical applications. For example, the amount of glass needed for the front of the supermarket shown is approximately equal to the area under the curved roof.

The shaded regions below show the areas between the curve and the x-axis for graphs that are related to two useful mathematical equations.

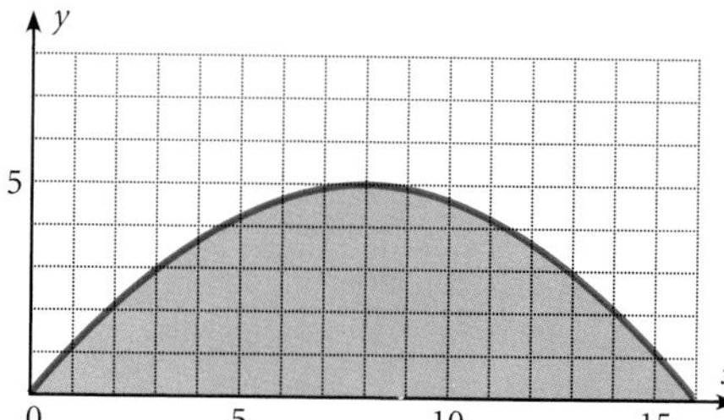

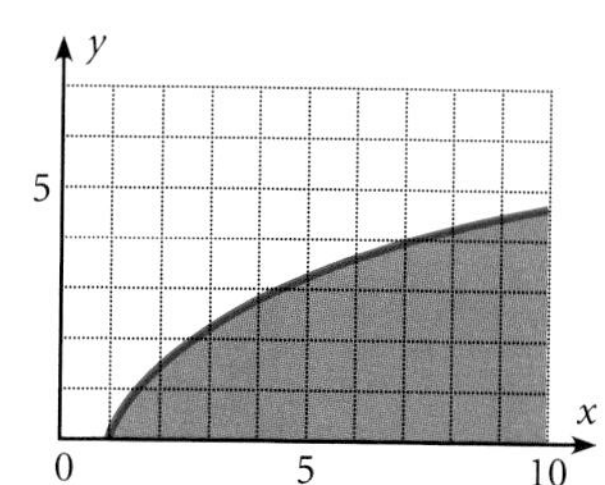

CONSIDER

1. Using what you already know, how could you find an approximation for the area of the shaded regions above?

In the following Explore, you will find a way to approximate the area under $y = x^2$ between $x = 0$ and $x = 6$. You will also begin to look for ways to generalize your method.

Student Resources

- Alternative Lessons 5-2C
- Laboratory Manual 5-2C
- Technology Lab Manual
- Practice 5-2C
- Study Guide and Journal 5-2C
- Guía de estudios y Diario 5-2C
- Multilingual Handbook
- More Look Back 5-2C
- SAT Preparation

Media Resources

- Transparency FFM 5-2C
- Transparency AE 5-2C
- Teaching Transparency
- AWSMTest and practice software
- AWSM Videodisc

PART C At a Glance

Objective

To use trapezoids to estimate the area under a curve.

Development

First, students become familiar with the idea of the area under a curve. In the **Explore,** they develop their own methods for approximating the area under a curve.

Finally, they are shown the trapezoidal method for approximating the area under a curve.

Suggested Materials

Student Graph paper

First Five Minutes

Transparency FFM 5-2C

Read the paragraphs on page 357 and answer the **Consider** question at the bottom of the page.

Motivate

Ask...

- With your current knowledge, do you think you can find the exact area underneath a curve? Why or why not? **No; all figures for which we can calculate areas have straight sides, so these can only approximate the area under a curve.**

CONSIDER

Possible Answer

1. Count grid squares, estimate areas of partially shaded squares. Draw triangles, rectangles, and other figures to fill as much of the area under the curve as possible. Add their areas.

Derivations of Area Formulas

EXPLORE

The Area Underneath

Recommended group size: 4

The Point
To devise a method for approximating the area under a curve.

Look and Listen...

- For students who have trouble sketching the graph and/or do not remember right-hand and bottom region boundaries.
- For students who use trapezoids and have trouble seeing that the heights of the trapezoids are horizontal.

Ask...

- Would it help to make a table of values from $x = 0$ to $x = 6$?

For Groups That Finish Early
Use a second method to approximate the area under this curve. Which was faster? Which might be more accurate?

Follow Up
Ask different students to explain their methods. Then collect all the answers for the area. You may want to compare the average of these to the actual answer.

Possible Answers

2. Possible methods: Counting grid squares, inscribing or circumscribing rectangles or trapezoids, filling the area with figures of different sizes. (Actual answer: 72 units^2)
3. If students filled the region with figures, they could get a better estimate by using smaller figures.
4. A method that does not rely on counting and that can be applied in all situations is preferable.

ALTERNATE EXAMPLE

Transparency AE 5-2C

EXPLORE: THE AREA UNDERNEATH

MATERIALS

Graph paper

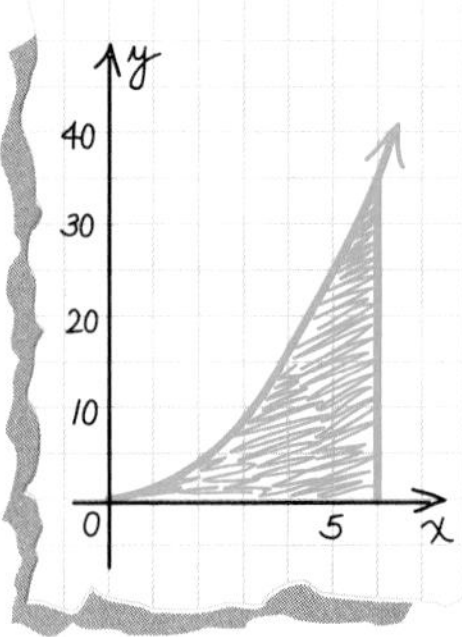

1. Draw the graph of $y = x^2$ on a sheet of graph paper. Start at $x = 0$, and end at $x = 6$. Draw a vertical line down to the x-axis from your last point. Lightly shade the region under the curve.
2. Devise a method for finding the approximate area under this curve. Write an explanation of your method, and give your approximation for the area.
3. If you needed to use your method to find a more accurate answer, could you do it? How?
4. Compare your approximation and your method with classmates. Discuss whether some methods are more efficient or accurate than others. Which method would you use to find the area under this curve from $x = 0$ to $x = 60$? Explain your choice.

Although many methods give good approximations for the area under a curve, mathematicians have a method that is especially powerful.

To use this method, we pretend the region is a polygon and then break it down into pieces we can deal with. The pieces we'll use are trapezoids with vertical bases and equal heights along the x-axis.

The slanted line of the trapezoid follows the curve as well as it can, but doesn't exactly match it, so our answer is only an approximation.

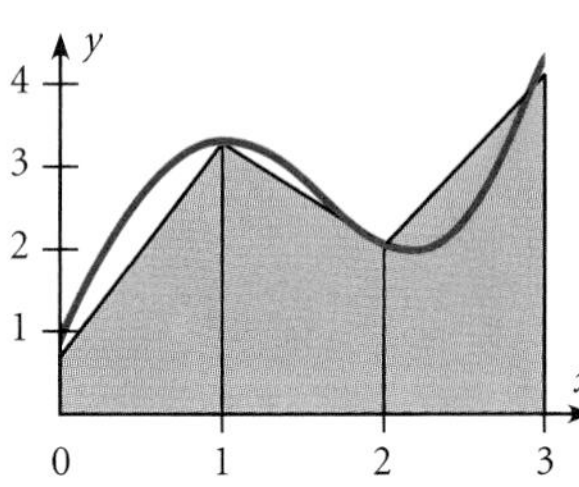

EXAMPLE

Find the approximate area between the positive x-axis and the graph of $y = 2\sqrt{x}$ from $x = 0$ to $x = 3$.

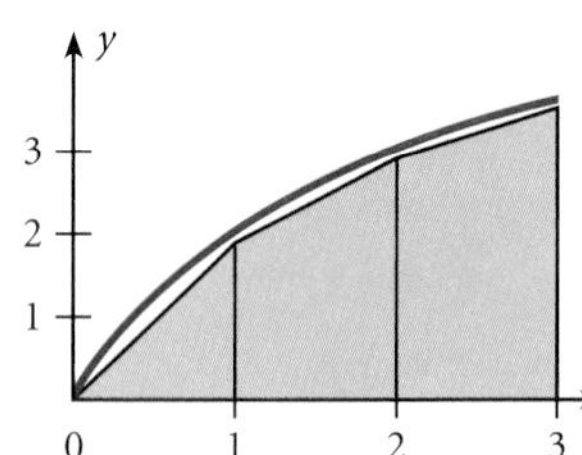

Tips from Teachers

Finding the area under a curve is a central idea in the study of calculus. Once your students feel comfortable with the concept, you may want to tell them that they are actually studying an important topic in calculus. Students who are familiar with some of the topics in future math courses may feel less intimidated by those courses.

- Sketch a graph of the curve (see page 358).
- Choose a convenient height for the trapezoids. In this example, we will choose 1 unit. Remember that these trapezoids have their heights along the x-axis.
- Find the two bases of each trapezoid by substituting the x-values at the two ends of the trapezoid into the equation $y = 2\sqrt{x}$. The y-values give the bases of the trapezoids. Results are shown in the table.

First trapezoid	$x = 0$ $x = 1$	$y = 2\sqrt{0} = 0$ (left base) $y = 2\sqrt{1} = 2$ (right base)
Second trapezoid	$x = 1$ $x = 2$	$y = 2\sqrt{1} = 2$ (left base) $y = 2\sqrt{2} \approx 2.8$ (right base)
Third trapezoid	$x = 2$ $x = 3$	$y = 2\sqrt{2} \approx 2.8$ (left base) $y = 2\sqrt{3} \approx 3.5$ (right base)

- Now calculate the areas of the trapezoids, and add them.

$$\text{Area under the curve} \approx \frac{0+2}{2}(1) + \frac{2+2.8}{2}(1) + \frac{2.8+3.5}{2}(1) = 1 + 2.4 + 3.15 = 6.55$$

2. How could you use the trapezoid method to get a better estimate for the area under the curve in the example?

REFLECT

1. Could you choose a geometric figure other than a trapezoid to find the approximate area under a curve? If so, which figure? What are the advantages and disadvantages of using this figure?
2. Describe how you could find the area between the two curves shown in the figure at the right.

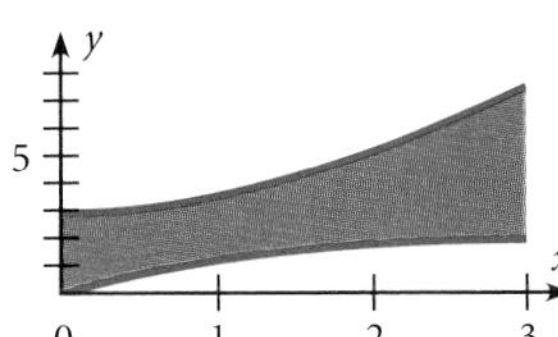

Develops the idea that smaller partitions give a better approximation for the area underneath a curve.

Possible Answer

2. Use trapezoids whose heights are less than 1.

Journal 

Consider question 2 and **Reflect** 1 and 2 are suitable for journal entries.

REFLECT

Possible Answers

1. A rectangle could be used. Calculations are easier, but if trapezoids and rectangles of the same width are used, trapezoids will give an approximation that is at least as good and usually better.
2. Approximate the area between each curve and the x-axis. Then subtract the area under the lower curve from the area under the higher curve.

Diversity Issues

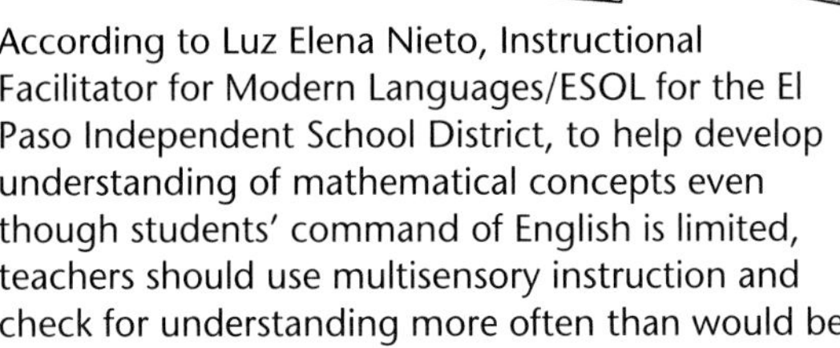

According to Luz Elena Nieto, Instructional Facilitator for Modern Languages/ESOL for the El Paso Independent School District, to help develop understanding of mathematical concepts even though students' command of English is limited, teachers should use multisensory instruction and check for understanding more often than would be usual for fluent English speakers.

Derivations of Area Formulas

Part C Exercises

Exercise Notes

Core

2. Students see that smaller trapezoids lead to a closer area approximation.

4. Students find the area of an irregularly shaped region that is not on a grid.

More Math Reasoning

13. Students see that the area under a rate-time graph is equal to the distance traveled. The idea that the area under a curve has a real-world interpretation shows students why the study of this topic is important.

14. The Koch Snowflake is an example of a fractal and could serve as an introduction to this area of study. Students may find the "paradox" that a figure can have a finite area and an infinite perimeter interesting to unravel. Fractals are studied more extensively in Chapter 12.

Exercise Answers

Core

1. a, d.

$x = 0$	$y = 0$
$x = 1$	$y = \frac{1}{2}$
$x = 2$	$y = 2$
$x = 3$	$y = 4.5$
$x = 4$	$y = 8$

b, c.

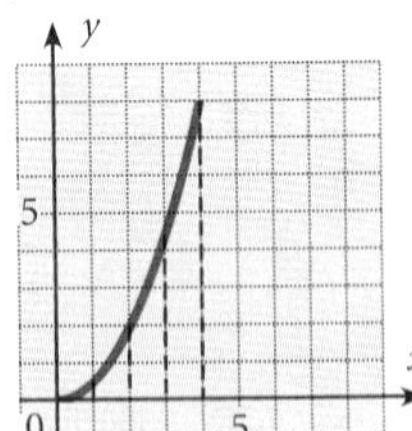

e. First area = 0.25;
Second area = 1.25;
Third area = 3.25;
Fourth area = 6.25

f. 11

Exercises

CORE

P **1. Getting Started** Follow these steps to find the approximate area between the positive x-axis and the graph of $y = \frac{1}{2}x^2$ from 0 to 4.

a. Make a table of ordered pairs, using the x-values 0, 1, 2, 3, and 4.

b. Use the table to sketch the graph on graph paper.

c. Divide the graph into trapezoids of height 1.

d. Find the lengths of the left and right bases for each trapezoid. (Hint: You should already have calculated these!)

e. Calculate the area of each trapezoid.

f. Find the approximate total area by finding the sum of the areas of the trapezoids.

P **2.** Repeat Exercise 1, but now approximate the area between the positive x-axis and the graph of $y = \frac{1}{2}x^2$ from 0 to 4 by using trapezoids of height 2. Which approximation do you think is closer to the actual area? Explain why you feel this method is more accurate.

P **3. a.** Find the approximate area of the shaded region between the x-axis and the curve shown from $x = 0$ to $x = 6$. Use trapezoids of height 1.

b. Suppose a point is selected randomly from the rectangle shown in blue. What is the approximate probability that the point will lie in the shaded region?

PS, MR **4. As Big As Texas** How can you find the approximate area of the state of Texas? Texas doesn't have perfectly straight borders, so you'll need to use some creativity.

Social Science

a. Copy or trace the map of Texas. Draw and measure adjacent trapezoids that "fill" the interior. Estimate the area of Texas by finding the sum of the areas of the trapezoids.

b. How could you get a more accurate approximation of the area? Explain.

c. Alaska's area is about 2.18 times larger than the area of Texas. Approximate the area of Alaska.

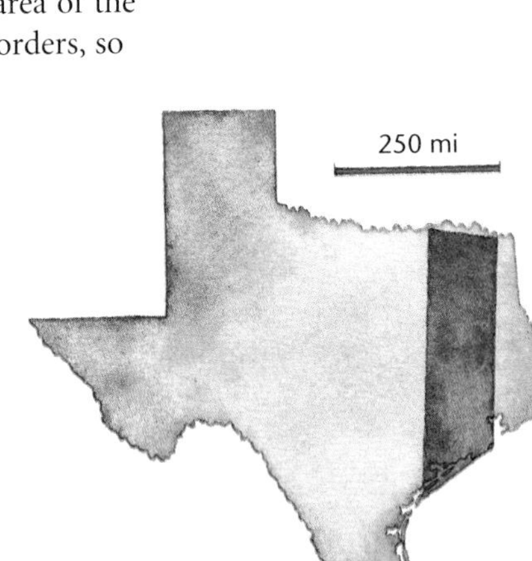

Key

V Vocabulary
P Practice/Skills
R Review
MR Math Reasoning
PS Problem Solving
C Challenge

LOOK BACK

In $\triangle ABC$, $\overline{BF}$ and $\overline{AE}$ are medians. $BD > DF$, and $AD > DE$. [4-3]

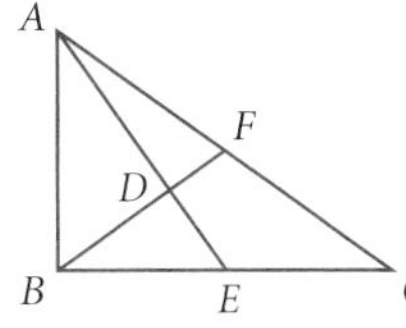

5. If $BD = 38$, find DF. 19

6. If $DE = 11$, find AE. 33

7. If $AD = 6x - 16$ and $DE = 2x$, find the following.

a. x 8 **b.** AD 32 **c.** DE 16 **d.** AE 48

Solve each equation. Give answers to the nearest hundredth. [5-1]

8. $x^2 + 2x - 5 = 0$
$x \approx -3.45$, $x \approx 1.45$

9. $x^2 - 4x = 3$
$x \approx -0.65$, $x \approx 4.65$

10. $2x^2 - 6x + 3 = 0$
$x \approx 0.63$, $x \approx 2.37$

MORE PRACTICE

11. Find the approximate area between the positive x-axis and the graph of the equation $y = \frac{1}{4}x^3$ from 0 to 3, using the trapezoid method. Use trapezoids of height 1. 5.625

12. Find the approximate area between the positive x-axis and the graph of the equation $y = 4\sqrt{x}$ from 0 to 4, using the trapezoid method. Use trapezoids of height 2. 19.31

MORE MATH REASONING

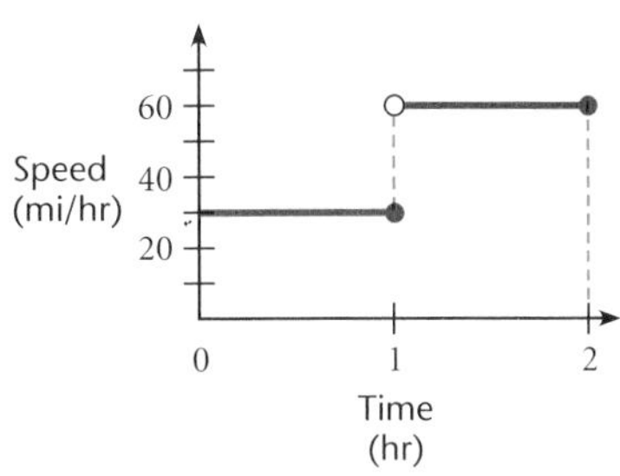

13. Explain what the area under this graph tells you about the trip it represents. (Hint: Find the area under the graph. Then think about the two parts of the trip.)

14. The Koch Snowflake The Koch Snowflake begins with an equilateral triangle. Then, in the middle third of each segment, a new equilateral triangle is built. Each successive figure is made in the same way. The Koch Snowflake results when this process is repeated forever.

a. Each stage of the snowflake can be contained in the same circle. What does this tell you about the area of the Koch Snowflake?

b. What is the change in the perimeter of the snowflake each time a new set of triangles is added?

c. Write a brief paragraph about the Koch Snowflake using the words *finite* and *infinite* to describe its area and perimeter.

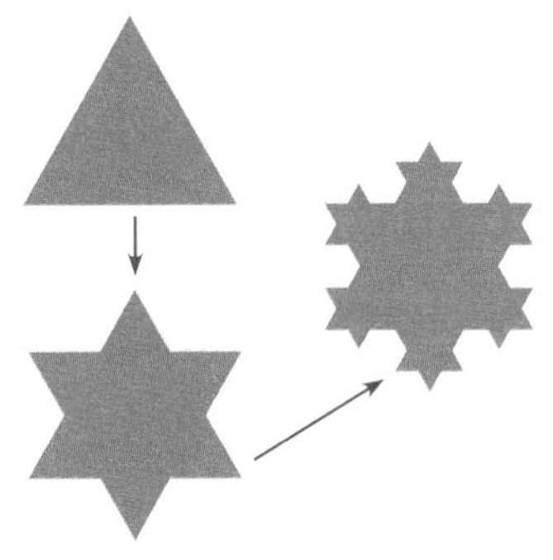

Ongoing Assessment

Self-Assessment Exercises 1, 3

Embedded Assessment Consider 2; Exercises 2, 4

2. Approximate area = 12. The area in Exercise 1 is closer to the actual area. The more sections used to approximate the area, the less error there will be.

3. a. Approximate area = 36.5

b. 0.34

4. a.

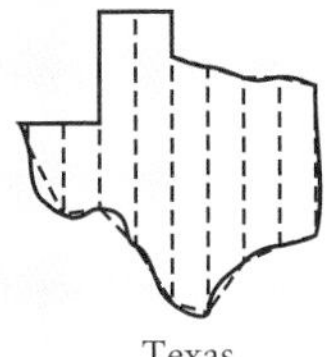

Texas

Approximate area = 260,000 mi^2

b. Divide the state up into more trapezoids.

c. 570,000 mi^2

More Math Reasoning

13. Area = 90. Possible answer: The area under the speed/time graph is the distance traveled.

14. a. The area of the Koch snowflake is less than the area of the circle.

b. The perimeter increases.

c. Possible answer: The area of the Koch snowflake is finite because it is less than the area of a particular circle. The perimeter is infinite.

5-2

Derivations of Area Formulas

PART D At a Glance

Objective

To use areas of quadrilaterals and triangles to find areas of irregular regions.

Development

In the **Explore,** students find the areas of irregularly shaped regions that model Aztec farms.

Suggested Materials

Student Graph paper, compass

First Five Minutes

Transparency FFM 5-2D

List the quadrilaterals you have studied and the area formula for each. Then describe two ways to find the area under a curve.

EXPLORE

Aztec Agriculture

Recommended group size: 4

The Point

To find area measurements for irregular regions.

Look and Listen...

- For students who are having difficulty using a compass to help draw the regions.
- For students who do not see how to find exact areas.

Ask...

- Can you divide the figures into regions for which you can find areas?

For Groups That Finish Early

Compare your estimates of the area of each field to the exact areas, and find the percent error.

Follow Up

Ask students to present their approximate and exact solution methods for one field. If students used different methods, you might discuss the strengths of each.

5-2 PART D Making Connections

← CONNECT → ***The ability to calculate areas accurately has been important for hundreds of years. You have examined area formulas and why they work. You've also planned logical arguments using area.***

There are several ways to find the area of a region, from counting squares to using the trapezoidal method. The Aztecs made accurate area calculations over 500 years ago. The photo at the left shows a piece of Aztec pottery.

In the following Explore, you will make scale drawings and calculate the areas of some irregularly shaped farms like those seen in Aztec records.

EXPLORE: AZTEC AGRICULTURE

MATERIALS

Graph paper
Compass

The Aztec fields on the left below have been drawn to scale, and measurements are shown in *quahuitls.* (A *quahuitl* was about 2.5 m long.)

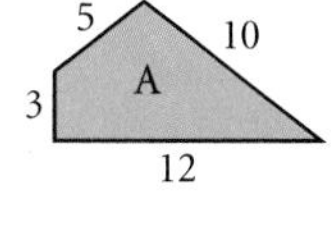

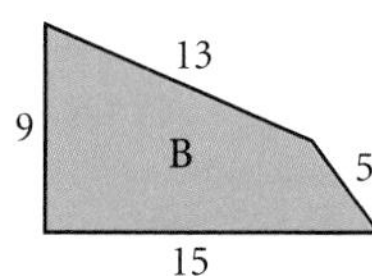

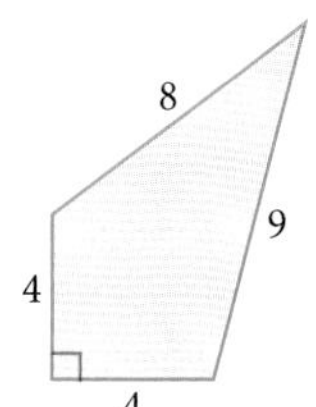

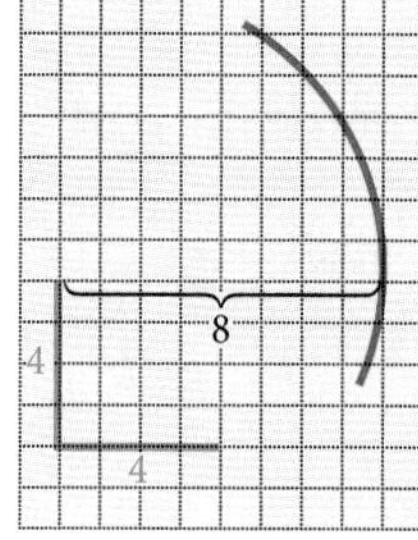

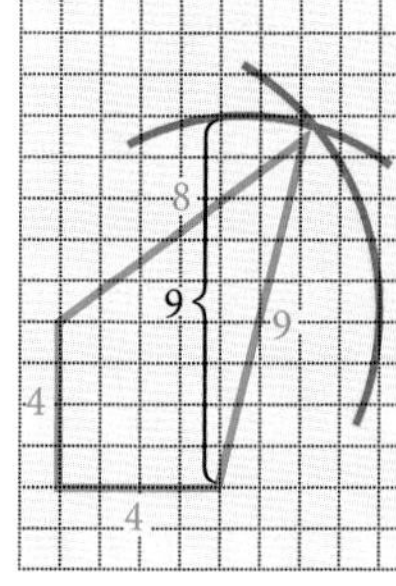

1. Make a careful drawing of Fields A and B on graph paper. Use one square of the paper to represent one square *quahuitl.* You may need to use a compass to locate the intersections of some sides, as shown by the series of figures above on the right.
2. Estimate the area of each field. Write a brief explanation of how you arrived at your estimates.
3. Find the exact area of each field. Write a brief explanation of how you found these.

Student Resources

- Alternative Lessons
- Laboratory Manual 5-2D
- Technology Lab Manual
- Practice 5-2D
- Study Guide and Journal 5-2D
- Guía de estudios y Diario 5-2D
- Multilingual Handbook
- More Look Back 5-2D
- SAT Preparation

Media Resources

- Transparency FFM 5-2D
- Transparency AE
- Teaching Transparency
- AWSMTest and practice software
- AWSM Videodisc

REFLECT

1. Summarize the area formulas you have learned. Draw a sketch to illustrate each.
2. How many of the area formulas do you really need to memorize? Show how you can deduce area formulas from the rectangle formula.
3. When can you use area formulas to find the exact area of a region? When is it impossible to use the formulas to find the exact area?
4. Describe some different ways to find the areas of irregular figures. Give a brief summary of each method, and explain how it works.

Self-Assessment

Find the area of each figure.

1. 38.08 cm²

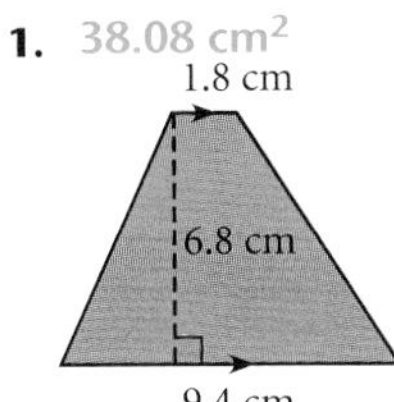

2. 2440 ft²

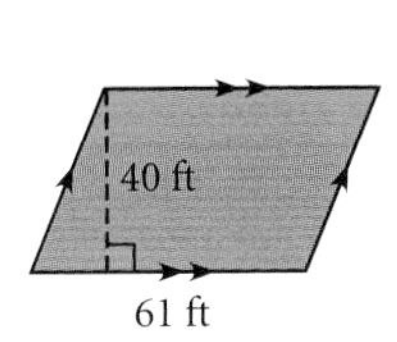

3. 22.04 in.²

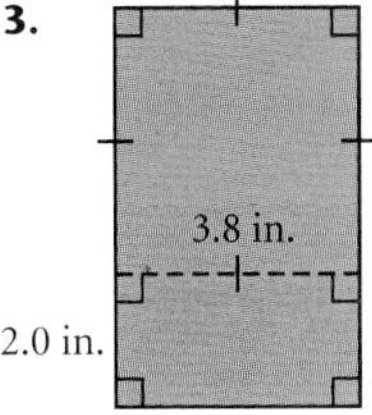

4. 13.1

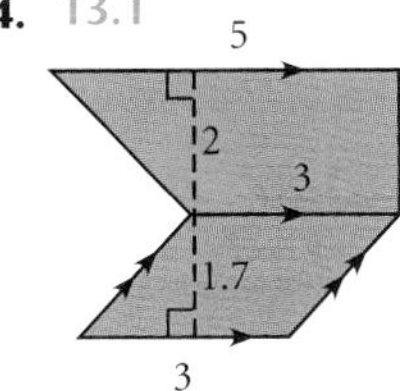

In Exercises 5–7, suppose *C* is the centroid of $\triangle MNP$. Point *C* is 4 cm from *M* and 6 cm from *N*. [4-3]

5. If R is the midpoint of $\overline{NP}$, find RC. Explain how you found your answer.
6. If S is the midpoint of $\overline{MP}$, find NS. Again, explain your solution method.
7. Use a ruler to draw $\triangle MNP$ that has these characteristics.
8. **Aztec Pyramid** The central pyramid in Tenochtitlán has a square base that is 97 m on a side. Find the area of the base of the pyramid. (A similar pyramid in Chichen Itza is shown at the right.)

9. The length of Colorado, a rectangular state, is approximately 100 mi greater than its width. Colorado's area is 103,730 mi². Find the approximate length and width of Colorado. Round your answers to the nearest mile. If you used algebra to help solve this problem, explain how you used it. [5-1]

Vocabulary
Practice/Skills
Review
Math Reasoning
Problem Solving
Challenge

Possible Answers

2–3. (Exact answers given.)
A: 42 quahuitl²; B: 84 quahuitl²

Portfolio

Have students select items from their work that demonstrate their understanding of the material in 5-2.

You may wish to have students include their best *plan* for a proof, an **Exercise** where they approximated an area, and an interesting **Reflect** question.

REFLECT

Possible Answers

1. Rectangle = ℓw, Square = s^2, Triangle = $\frac{1}{2}bh$, Parallelogram = bh, Rhombus = bh, Trapezoid = $\frac{1}{2}(b_1 + b_2)h$.

2. None. Rectangle: square counting implies formula. Square: special rectangle. Parallelogram: rearranged rectangle. Triangle: half of a parallelogram. Rhombus: special parallelogram. Trapezoid: two triangles with same height, different bases.

3. We can use area formulas to find the exact area of any polygonal region if we can find the necessary length measurements. If the region is not polygonal, we cannot use formulas (yet).

4. Divide into figures whose areas can be found; draw on grid and count squares; use trapezoidal method for area under a curve, and so on.

Self-Assessment

Exercise Notes

16. Students "simulate" a software experiment to see that the area of any triangle with a given base and height is always the same.

17. Students apply formulas learned in 5-2 to geometric probability.

Algebra | Probability | Logic/Reasoning | Functions

Derivations of Area Formulas

Self-Assessment Answers

5. $RC = 2$ cm; $\overline{MR}$ is a median. C is two-thirds the length of $\overline{MR}$ away from M on $\overline{MR}$. Therefore $RC = \frac{1}{2}MC$.

6. $NS = 9$ cm; $\overline{NS}$ is a median. C is two-thirds the length of $\overline{NS}$ away from N on $\overline{NS}$. Therefore $NS = \frac{3}{2}NC$.

7.

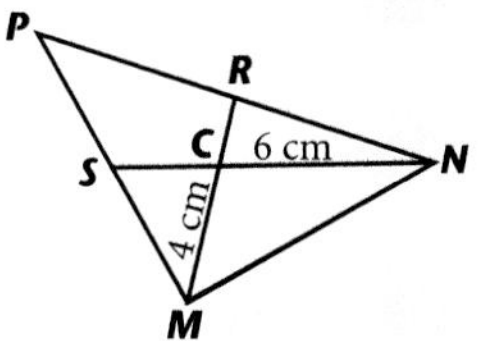

8. 9409 m^2

9. Width: 276 miles; Length: 376 miles; Solve the equation $(w)(w + 100) = 103{,}730$.

11. Possible answer: Use LL for two right triangles where the diagonals are the hypotenuses. Use CPCTC to show that diagonals are congruent.

12. Bags of fertilizer = 30; Bags of seed = 50

13. 50

14.

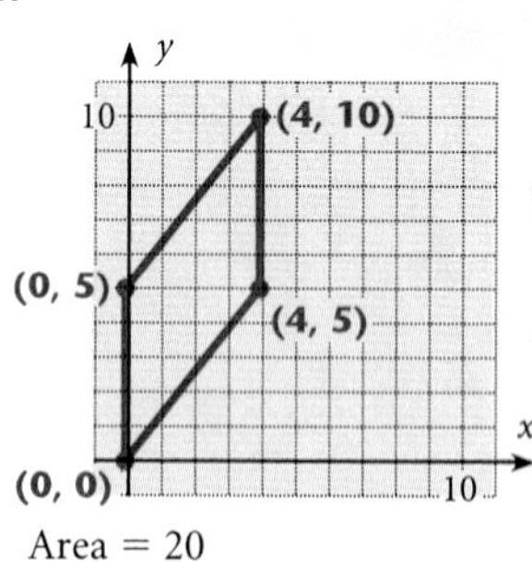

Area = 20

15. and 16.

See Additional Answers p. T364.

P **10.** In the figure at the right, the area of trapezoid $ABCD$ is 16 square units. Rectangle $ABCE$ and $\triangle AED$ have equal areas. $DC =$ (d)

(a) 2 (b) 3 (c) 4
(d) 6 (e) 8

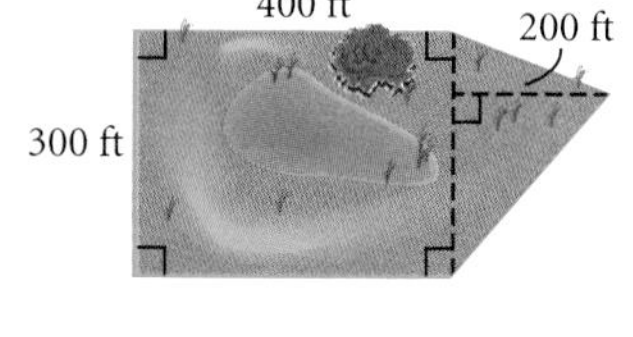

MR **11.** *Plan* a logical argument to show that the diagonals of a square are congruent.

PS **12. Fields of Green** A bag of fertilizer covers 5000 ft^2. A bag of grass seed covers 3000 ft^2. How many bags of each are needed to cover this plot of land?

400 ft
200 ft
300 ft

P **13.** Find the approximate area between the x-axis and the curve shown, from $x = 0$ to $x = 16$. Use trapezoids of height 4.

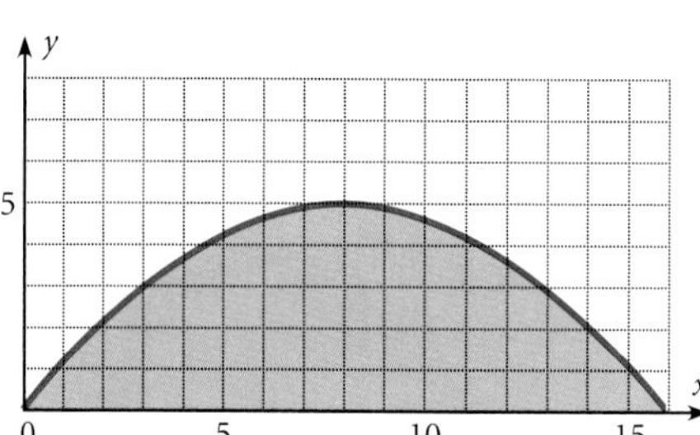

P **Draw a quadrilateral whose vertices have the following coordinates. Then find the area of the quadrilateral.**

14. (0, 0), (4, 5), (4, 10), (0, 5)

15. (−4, 3), (6, 3), (10, 8), (0, 8)

MR, C **16. Does Not Compute** The computer screen shows two parallel lines. Points A and B do not move. Point C moves along its line from the left side of the screen to the right. What will happen to the numbers showing the area and perimeter of triangle $\triangle ABC$? Explain your reasoning.

PS **17.** Suppose the trapezoid and parallelogram shown are cultivated fields on a rectangular plot of land. A raindrop falls randomly on the plot of land. What is the probability that it will land on one of the cultivated fields? Express your answer in decimal form rounded to the nearest hundredth. 0.16

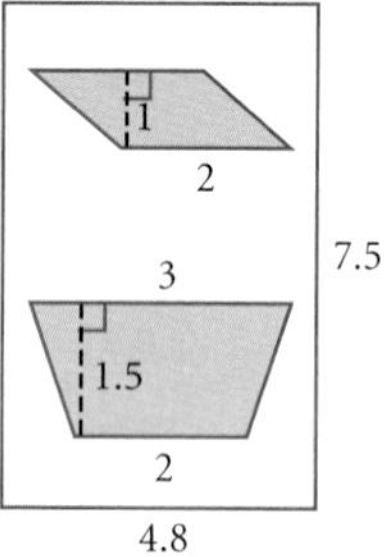

Assessment Resources

- **Quiz 5-2**
- Chapter Assessment Form A
- Chapter Assessment Form B
- Chapter Alternative Assessment
- Mid-Year Assessment
- End-of-Year Assessment
- **AWSMTest and practice software**

Ongoing Assessment

Self-Assessment Self-Assessment Exercises

Embedded Assessment Reflect 1, 2, 4

5-2 Part D Self-Assessment

15.

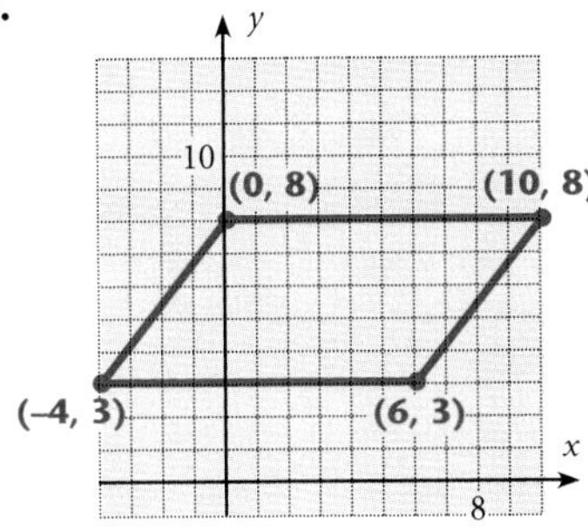

Area = 50

16. The perimeter will get smaller until C is directly above the midpoint of A and B, after which it will increase again. The area will remain constant, since neither the base nor the height will be changing.

5-3 Part A Explore

1. c^2

2. $\frac{ab}{2}$

3. A small square remains in the interior; its area is $(b - a)^2$.

4. $(b - a)^2 + 4\left(\frac{ab}{2}\right) = c^2$

$b^2 - 2ab + a^2 + 2ab = c^2$

$b^2 + a^2 = c^2$

5. Draw a large square of side length c. Draw four congruent right triangles with hypotenuses on sides of the large square; label the lengths of their longer legs b and shorter legs a. This forms a small square in the center of the large square. Using the Area-Addition Postulate, set the area of the large square equal to the sum of the areas of the triangles plus the small square. Simplifying leads to the Pythagorean Theorem.

5-3

The Pythagorean Theorem

SUPERLESSON AT A GLANCE

Superlesson Goal

Students will apply the Pythagorean Theorem and its converse. They will also use the Pythagorean Theorem to develop patterns of side lengths in 30°-60°-90° and 45°-45°-90° triangles and to justify the distance formula.

Management Guide

	Topic	Objectives	Key Terms	New Ideas	Materials
Part A	The Pythagorean Theorem	To use the Pythagorean Theorem, and to understand a deductive justification of the theorem.	Pythagorean triple	Solving for missing side lengths in right triangles. Pythagorean triples.	
Part B	Special Right Triangles	To discover and apply patterns of side lengths in 30°-60°-90° and 45°-45°-90° triangles.		Patterns of side lengths in 30°-60°-90° and 45°-45°-90° triangles.	
Part C	The Distance Formula Revisited	To use the Pythagorean Theorem to justify the distance formula, and to explore the equation of a circle.		Using an equation to describe a locus of points.	**Teacher** String tied to an overhead pen/piece of chalk
Part D	The Converse of the Pythagorean Theorem	To discover that the converse of the Pythagorean Theorem is true, and to discover inequalities that can be used to classify triangles.		Using side lengths to determine whether a triangle is right, acute, or obtuse.	**Student** Paper, ruler, scissors, geometry software
Part E	Making Connections	To discover Pythagorean patterns in a Babylonian tablet.	In Making Connections, students apply and synthesize key terms and new ideas.		

Pacing Chart (45-Minute Periods)

	Comprehensive Course	Core Course	Informal Course
Part A	1	1	1*
Part B	1	1	1
Part C	1	1	1
Part D	1	1	1*
Part E	1	1	1
TOTAL periods for Superlesson	5	5	5

*Material on proof in this part may be omitted or downplayed in an Informal Course.

NCTM Standards

Mathematics as Problem Solving

Mathematics as Communication

Mathematics as Reasoning

Mathematical Connections

Algebra

Geometry from a Synthetic Perspective

Geometry from an Algebraic Perspective

5-3 The Pythagorean Theorem

IT'S ALL BABYLONIAN TO ME

Four thousand years ago, the Babylonian civilization thrived in the Middle East area bounded by the Tigris and Euphrates Rivers. Using clay tablets and a pointed tool called a stylus to do their calculations, Babylonian students learned the same right-triangle theorem we study today. But they didn't call their theorem the "Pythagorean Theorem" because Pythagoras was not born for another thousand years. The theorem was probably so named because he was the first to prove it. He was certainly not the first to use it!

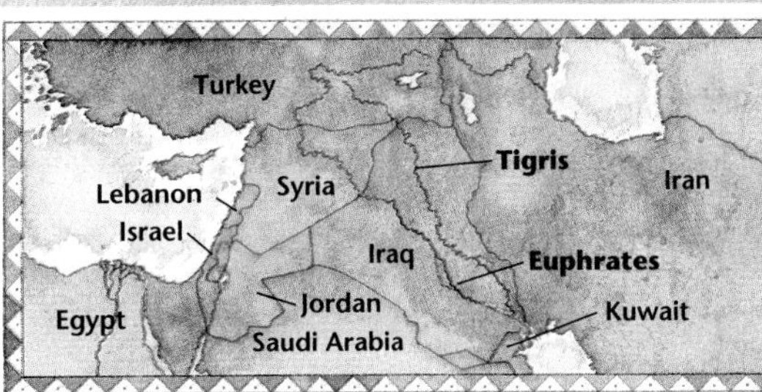

In modern times, a remarkable Babylonian tablet, called Plimpton 322, was discovered. It had survived undamaged underground for 4000 years. Ironically, someone dropped it and a piece broke off. Nobody knows the whereabouts of the missing piece, but the remaining portion lists columns of numbers showing the Babylonians' knowledge of relationships in right triangles. This tablet is now on display at Columbia University in New York.

1. **The Babylonians based some of their mathematics on the number 60. Describe a current system of measurement in which the number 60 is important.**
2. **How do you think the Babylonians might have discovered the right-triangle theorem now known as the Pythagorean Theorem?**

365

More About Cuneiform

The Sumerian people dominated Mesopotamia for most of the era between 4000 and 2000 B.C. Between 3500 and 3000 B.C., cuneiform writing was developed in the region. Clay tablets were used to record business contracts, historical and legal documents, mathematical and astronomical works, and poetry and literature, including the oldest known heroic tale. Hundreds of thousands of these tablets have been found by archaeologists.

Where Are We Now?

Students have developed area formulas for several different figures and are becoming more familiar with deductive justification of conjectures.

Where Are We Going?

In 5-3 students will see many different ways to justify the Pythagorean Theorem. These rely on the area formulas developed in 5-2. They then use the Pythagorean Theorem to find patterns of side lengths in 30°- 60°- 90° and 45°- 45°- 90° triangles, and to justify the distance formula and the equation of a circle.

The Pythagorean Theorem has applications throughout the course, and is especially important in 7-3, when students study trigonometry.

Possible Answers

1. Hours and minutes are subdivided into sixtieths.
2. The Pythagorean Theorem was probably discovered by observing patterns.

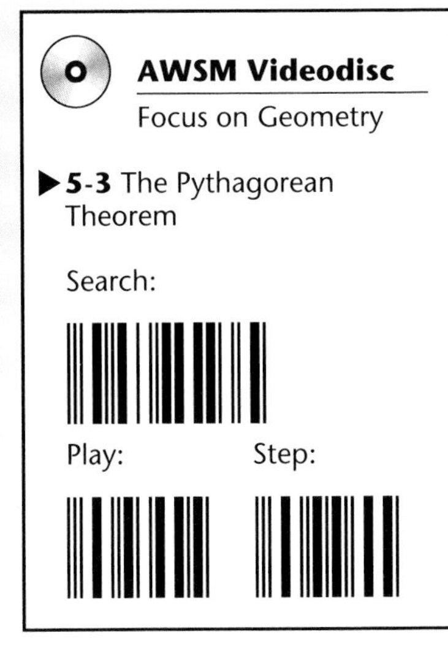

5-3

The Pythagorean Theorem

PART A At a Glance

Objective

To use the Pythagorean Theorem, and to understand a deductive justification of the theorem.

Development

First, students see the Pythagorean Theorem.

Then, in the **Explore,** students justify the theorem, using the Bhaskara proof.

Key Terms

Pythagorean triple

First Five Minutes

Transparency FFM 5-3A

Simplify each of the following radicals.

1. $\sqrt{16}$ 4 **2.** $\sqrt{81}$ 9

3. $\sqrt{72}$ $6\sqrt{2}$ **4.** $\sqrt{28}$ $2\sqrt{7}$

Motivate

Ask...

- If we are given the lengths of any two sides of a right triangle, can there be more than one way to complete the triangle? **No. This can be shown by drawing possibilities on grid paper or by realizing that the HL and LL theorems imply that there is only one such triangle.**
- Do the lengths of two sides of a right triangle determine the length of the third side? **Yes**

ALTERNATE EXAMPLES

Transparency AE 5-3A

5-3 PART A The Pythagorean Theorem

← CONNECT → ***Your knowledge of area gives you the background needed to prove the Pythagorean Theorem. You will investigate one proof of the theorem and use it to calculate side lengths in a right triangle.***

Yale Babylonian Collection

The photograph at the left shows a portion of a Babylonian tablet. The marks on the tablet suggest that the Babylonians studied properties of right triangles.

The Pythagorean Theorem describes a special relationship between the lengths of the sides of a right triangle. It can be used to calculate the length of any side of a right triangle when the lengths of the other two sides are known.

PYTHAGOREAN THEOREM

In a right triangle, the square of the length of the hypotenuse is equal to the sum of the squares of the lengths of the legs.

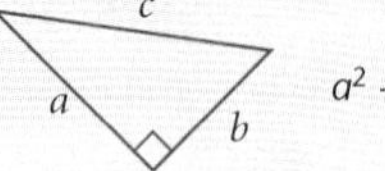

$a^2 + b^2 = c^2$

EXAMPLES

The lengths of two sides of right triangle $\triangle STU$ are given. Find the length of the third side.

1. $ST = 3$, $TU = 4$

$$ST^2 + TU^2 = SU^2$$
$$3^2 + 4^2 = SU^2$$
$$25 = SU^2$$
$$5 = SU$$

2. $ST = 7$, $SU = 10$

$$ST^2 + TU^2 = SU^2$$
$$7^2 + TU^2 = 10^2$$
$$49 + TU^2 = 100$$
$$TU^2 = 51$$
$$TU = \sqrt{51} \approx 7.14$$

There are more than 370 known proofs of the Pythagorean Theorem. One of the most famous proofs is based on a cleverly drawn figure. The proof is attributed to Bhaskara, a Hindu mathematician of the twelfth century, who accompanied the proof with a single word—"Behold!"

Research Note

Research on confidence in learning mathematics indicates that there are substantial differences between males and females in this dimension.... In general, males tend to be more confident than females, even when females may have better reasons (based on their performance) to feel confident. (Douglas B. MacLeod and Michele Ortega, "Affective Issues in Mathematics Education," *Research Ideas for the Classroom: High School Mathematics,* NCTM Research Interpretation Project, Patricia S. Wilson, ed., p. 27. © 1993 NCTM.)

Logic/Reasoning | Industry/Careers | Science/Health | Social Science/History | Fine Arts/Literature

EXPLORE: BEHOLD! THE BHASKARA PROOF

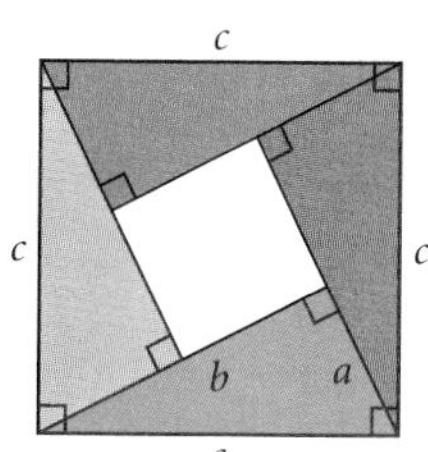

1. What is the area of the large square?
2. What is the area of each of the right triangles?
3. What figure remains in the interior of the figure? What is its area? (Hint: What is the length of one of its sides in terms of *a* and *b*?)
4. Use the Area-Addition Postulate, and then simplify your equation to "behold" the Pythagorean Theorem.
5. Write out a *plan* for the Bhaskara proof.

There are some special sets of positive integers that "work" in the Pythagorean Theorem. For instance, as you saw in Example 1, if the lengths of the legs of a right triangle are 3 and 4, the length of its hypotenuse is 5. The set of numbers 3, 4, 5 is a **Pythagorean triple.** It is useful to recognize sets of numbers that are Pythagorean triples.

TRY IT

Find the length of the missing side in each triangle. Then identify the corresponding Pythagorean triple.

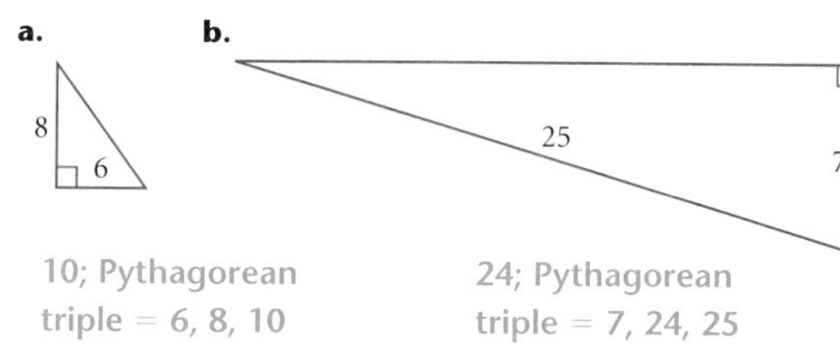

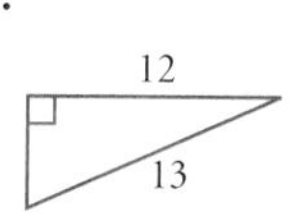

10; Pythagorean triple = 6, 8, 10

24; Pythagorean triple = 7, 24, 25

5; Pythagorean triple = 5, 12, 13

REFLECT

1. People had been using the Pythagorean Theorem long before Pythagoras proved it. Why is the proof of any theorem important?
2. Describe how the areas of the three large squares are related. How is this figure related to the Pythagorean Theorem?

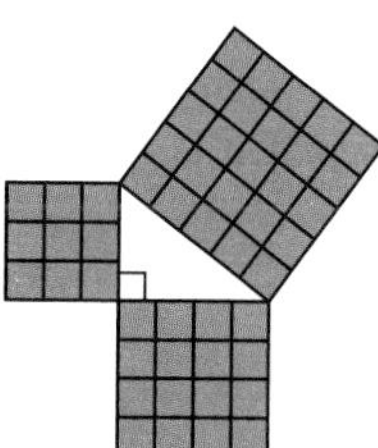

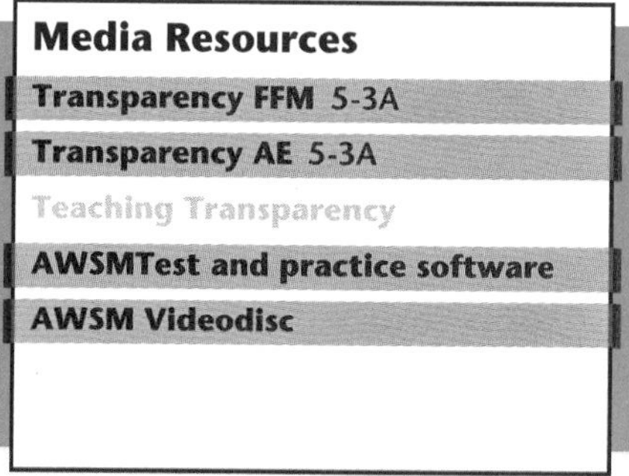

Student Resources
- Alternative Lessons 5-3A
- Laboratory Manual 5-3A
- Technology Lab Manual
- Practice 5-3A
- Study Guide and Journal 5-3A
- Guía de estudios y Diario 5-3A
- Multilingual Handbook
- More Look Ahead 5-3A
- SAT Preparation

Media Resources
- Transparency FFM 5-3A
- Transparency AE 5-3A
- Teaching Transparency
- AWSMTest and practice software
- AWSM Videodisc

EXPLORE

Behold! The Bhaskara Proof

Recommended group size: 2

The Point

To justify the Pythagorean Theorem.

Look and Listen...

- For students who are having difficulty simplifying algebraic expressions.
- For students who do not see that the side length of the small center square is $b - a$.

Ask...

- Would it help you to mark all of the short legs of the right triangles with their length, *a*?

For Groups That Finish Early

Using the top right triangle as a pre-image, describe how to generate each of the other triangles with a clockwise rotation. Specify the center and angle for each. **Center of each is center of large square; angles are 90°, 180°, 270°.**

Follow Up

Ask students to explain their proofs to the class.

Possible Answers

See Additional Answers p. T364.

Journal 

Reflect 1 and 2 and **Exercise** 12 are suitable for journal entries.

REFLECT

Possible Answers

1. A proof shows that a conjecture is always true.
2. The area of the large square is equal to the sum of the two small squares. Since the side lengths of the squares are the lengths of the sides of the triangles, this illustrates the Pythagorean Theorem.

Algebra	Functions	Discrete Math	Probability	Data/Statistics

The Pythagorean Theorem

Part A Exercises

Exercise Notes

Core

11. and 12. Illustrate ancient Chinese awareness of the concept of the Pythagorean Theorem.

Look Ahead

18–20. Review skills for simplification of radicals needed in 5-3 Part B.

21–23. Preview work with 45°-45°-90° right triangles in 5-3 Part B.

More Math Reasoning

33. Illustrates a proof of the Pythagorean Theorem devised by President Garfield.

Exercise Answers

Core

11. Possible answer: Find the area of the large square, the four right triangles, and the small square. Express and simplify the area of the small square in terms of the areas of the right triangles and large square.

12. Possible answer: This is an application of the Pythagorean Theorem: $3^2 + 4^2 = 5^2$

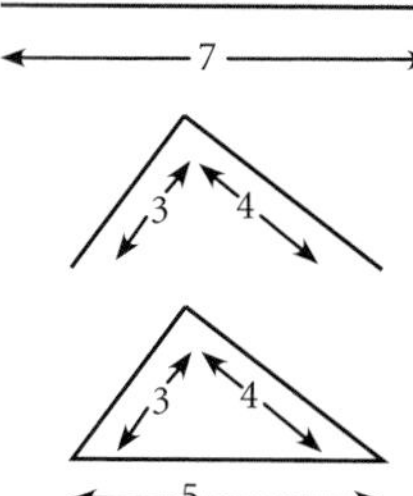

15. 14.8 ft

16. Pythagorean triple

17. a. They have the same area.

b. The parallelogram has a larger perimeter and therefore will cost more to fence.

c. The rectangle; The area is the same as the parallelogram and the perimeter is smaller.

Exercises

CORE

P **1. Getting Started** Follow these steps to find the length of $\overline{AB}$. Express your answer as a radical in simplest form and as a decimal approximation rounded to the nearest hundredth.

a. What are the lengths of the legs? 2, 4

b. Square the lengths of the legs, and find the sum. 20

c. To find AB, take the positive square root of your answer, and simplify. $2\sqrt{5}$

d. Use a calculator to find the decimal equivalent. Round to the nearest hundredth. 4.47

P **Find the length of the missing side in each triangle. Express it as a radical in simplest form (if possible) and as a decimal approximation rounded to the nearest hundredth.**

2. 17

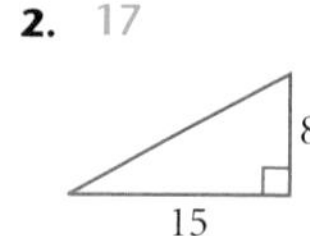

3. 12

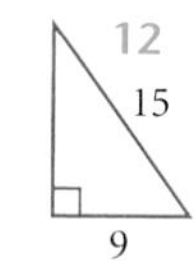

4. $3\sqrt{2}$, 4.24

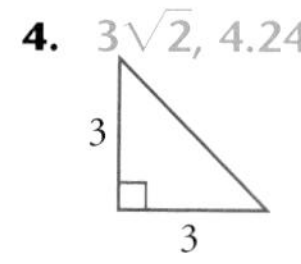

5. $2\sqrt{14}$, 7.48

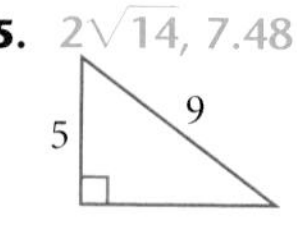

P **Use the figure at the right to complete the following.**

6. $p = 7$, $q = 24$, $r =$ 25

7. $p = 15$, $r = 25$, $q =$ 20

8. $p = 2\sqrt{3}$, $r = 6$, $q =$ $2\sqrt{6}$

9. $p = \sqrt{3}$, $q = \sqrt{2}$, $r =$ $\sqrt{5}$

10. $r = 6.7$, $q = 3.9$, $p =$ 5.45

MR History **11.** Write a *plan* for a proof of the Pythagorean Theorem that uses the figure at the right. (This figure is similar to one seen in the *Chóu-peï*, an ancient Chinese text. The author and date are unknown, but the book probably records ideas from about 1100 B.C.)

MR History **12.** A passage from the *Chóu-peï* reads, "Break the line and make the breadth 3, the length 4; then the distance between the corners is 5." Explain the meaning of this excerpt. Illustrate your answer with a sketch.

P, MR **13. The Secret of Horror Lake** It's forty-three miles from Fearville to Frighton, and it's twenty-two miles from Scare City to Fearville. No one knows how wide Horror Lake is. Find the distance across the lake to the nearest mile, and explain your method. 37 miles

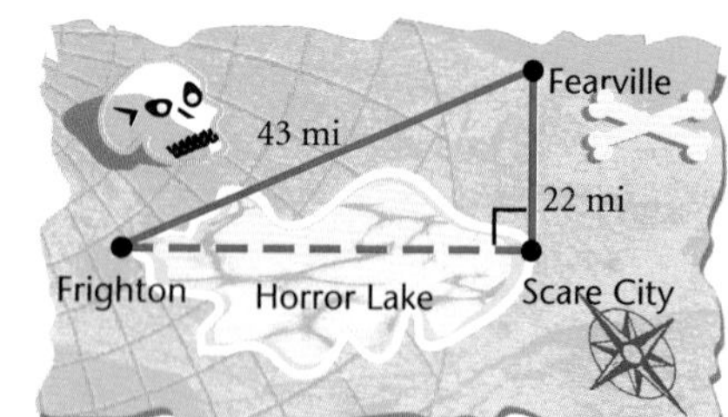

P **14.** Find the length of the longest segment that can be drawn on an $8\frac{1}{2}'' \times 11''$ sheet of paper. 13.90″

Key

V Vocabulary
P Practice/Skills
R Review
MR Math Reasoning
PS Problem Solving
C Challenge

15. Window Washing The base of a 16-ft ladder is placed 6 ft from a wall. How far up the wall will the ladder reach? Round your answer to the nearest tenth of a foot.

16. Write the word or phrase that correctly completes the following statement.

If the sum of the squares of two positive integers is equal to the square of a third positive integer, then the three integers are a(n) ____.

17. A farmer can choose to fence off some of his land as a parallelogram or a rectangle, as shown.

a. Which figure gives the larger area?

b. Which figure costs more to fence?

c. If you were the farmer, which figure would you choose for the field? Explain your decision.

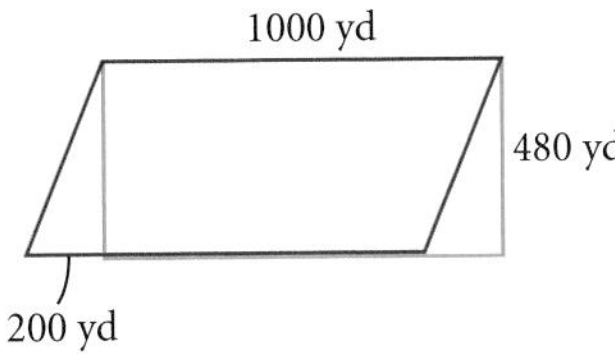

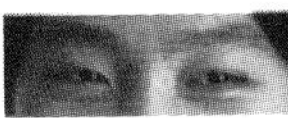

LOOK AHEAD

Write each radical in simplest form. Then express the radical as a decimal. Round answers to the nearest hundredth.

18. $\sqrt{25}$ 5 **19.** $\sqrt{20}$ $2\sqrt{5}$, 4.47 **20.** $\frac{7}{\sqrt{3}}$ $\frac{7}{3}\sqrt{3}$, 4.04

Find the length of the diagonal of a square with each of the following side lengths.

21. 3 4.24 **22.** 8 11.31 **23.** $2\sqrt{5}$ $2\sqrt{10} \approx 6.22$

MORE PRACTICE

Find the length of the unknown side in each triangle. Express it as a radical in simplest form (if possible) and as a decimal approximation rounded to the nearest hundredth.

24.

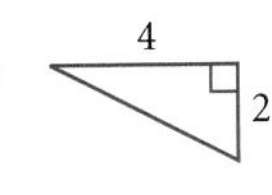

$2\sqrt{5}$, 4.47

25.

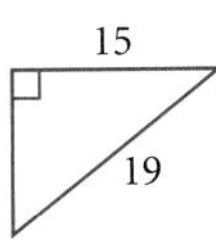

$2\sqrt{34}$, 11.66

26.

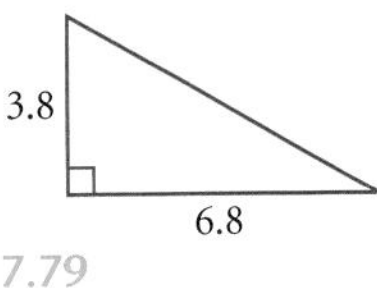

7.79

Use the figure at the right to complete the following.

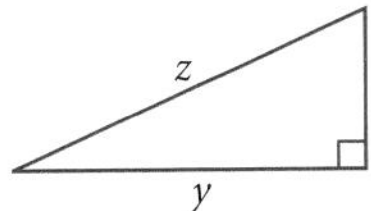

27. $x = 6, y = 8, z =$ 10 **28.** $y = 5\sqrt{5}, z = 15, x =$ 10

29. $x = \sqrt{10}, z = \sqrt{15}, y =$ $\sqrt{5}$ **30.** $x = 4.4, y = 6.2, z =$ 7.60

More Math Reasoning

31. Possible answer: Starting with a line segment whose length is taken as 1 unit, construct a ray perpendicular to the segment, originating from one of its endpoints. With the compass, mark off on the ray a second segment congruent to the first. Connect the two distant endpoints; this third segment has length $\sqrt{2}$. Starting with this third segment, again construct a perpendicular segment of length 1 and connect the distant endpoints; the last segment has length $\sqrt{3}$.

32. $\sqrt{2}$: $\overline{AG}$
$\sqrt{3}$: not possible
$\sqrt{4} = 2$: $\overline{AC}$ or $\overline{AK}$
$\sqrt{5}$: $\overline{AH}$ or $\overline{AL}$
$\sqrt{6}$: not possible
$\sqrt{7}$: not possible
$\sqrt{8}$: $\overline{AM}$
$\sqrt{9} = 3$: $\overline{AD}$
$\sqrt{10}$: $\overline{AI}$

33. Area of trapezoid in terms of its exterior dimensions $= (a + b)(a + b)\frac{1}{2}$. Area of trapezoid in terms of the areas of the interior triangles $= \frac{1}{2}ab + \frac{1}{2}ab + \frac{1}{2}c^2$. Set the areas equal:
$(a + b)(a + b)\frac{1}{2} = \frac{1}{2}ab + \frac{1}{2}ab + \frac{1}{2}c^2$
$(a^2 + b^2 + 2ab)\frac{1}{2} = \frac{1}{2}(ab + ab + c^2)$
$a^2 + b^2 + 2ab = 2ab + c^2$
$a^2 + b^2 = c^2$

Ongoing Assessment

Self-Assessment Exercises 1, 3, 5, 7, 9, 13, 14, 15, 16

Embedded Assessment Try It a; Exercises 4, 10, 11, 17

The Pythagorean Theorem

PART B At a Glance

Objective

To discover and apply patterns of side lengths in 30°-60°-90° and 45°-45°-90° triangles.

Development

Students are introduced to 30°-60°-90° and 45°-45°-90° triangles.

In the **Explore,** students use the Pythagorean Theorem to discover the special side-length relationships in these triangles.

First Five Minutes

Transparency FFM 5-3B

Read the paragraphs at the bottom of page 370. Then answer **Consider** questions 1 and 2 at the top of page 371.

Motivate

Ask...

- How many side lengths of an isosceles right triangle do you need to know before you can find the lengths of all of the other sides? **One**

Possible Answers

1. The base angles are congruent and complementary, so each measures 45°. 45°-45°-90° describes the angle measures.
2. 30°-60°-90°

MORE MATH REASONING

C, PS **31.** Given a segment of length 1, describe how to construct a segment with length $\sqrt{2}$ by using a compass and straightedge. Then describe how to construct a segment with length $\sqrt{3}$ by using a compass and straightedge.

PS **32.** Assume the distance from A to B is one unit. If possible, find segments on the grid with one endpoint at A that have lengths $\sqrt{2}$, $\sqrt{3}$, $\sqrt{4}$, $\sqrt{5}$, $\sqrt{6}$, $\sqrt{7}$, $\sqrt{8}$, $\sqrt{9}$, and $\sqrt{10}$. (Hint: Three of these are not possible.)

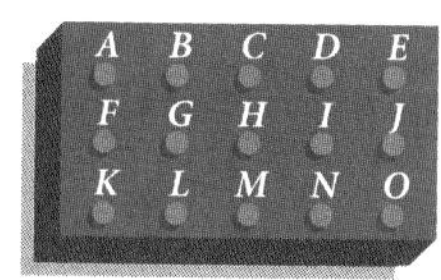

MR, C **33.** **A Presidential Proof** James A. Garfield, the 20th president of the United States, is also known for his original proof of the Pythagorean Theorem. Using his drawing (shown at the right) and your knowledge of area, reproduce his proof of the Pythagorean Theorem. (Hint: Write the area of trapezoid $PQTS$ two different ways.)

History

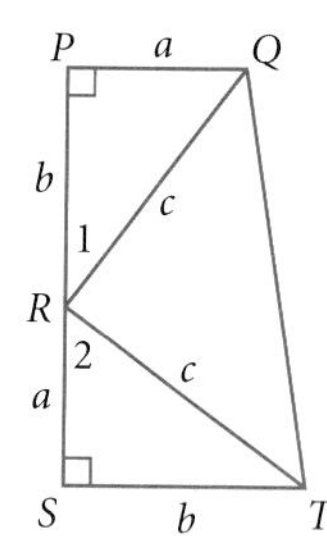

5-3 PART B Special Right Triangles

← CONNECT → ***You have justified the Pythagorean Theorem. Now you will use it to identify patterns in the side lengths of special right triangles.***

There are two types of right triangles that occur so often that they deserve special attention.

The first type of special triangle is an isosceles right triangle. One way to make an isosceles right triangle is to cut a square in half.

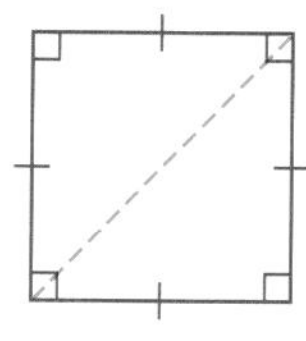
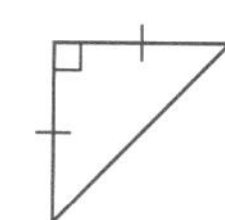
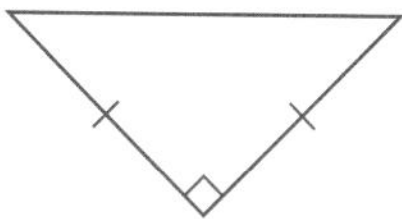
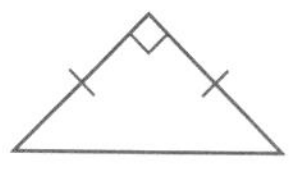

The three triangles on the right in the above figure are isosceles right triangles.

Key

- V Vocabulary
- P Practice/Skills
- R Review
- MR Math Reasoning
- PS Problem Solving
- C Challenge

You can make the second type of special right triangle by cutting an equilateral triangle in half.

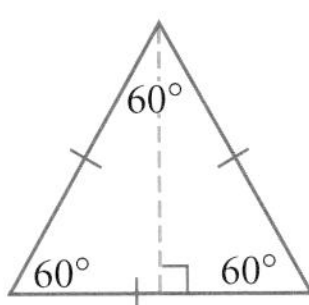

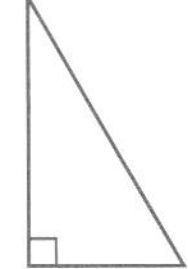
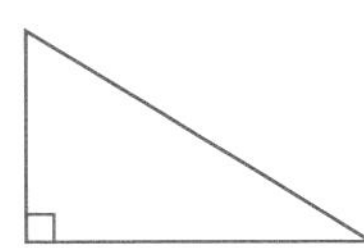
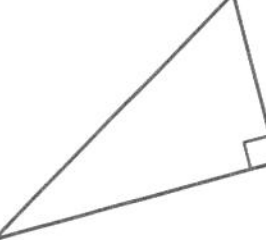

1. An isosceles right triangle is called a 45°-45°-90° triangle. Why?
2. What are the measures of the angles of half an equilateral triangle (as shown above)? Name this type of triangle, using the measures of the three angles.

Since the Pythagorean Theorem applies to all right triangles, it also applies to these special right triangles.

EXPLORE: RIGHT RATIOS

For this Explore, leave all measurements in simplest radical form.

1. Sketch a 45°-45°-90° triangle, and choose a whole number for the lengths of its legs (a sample triangle is shown). Then use the Pythagorean Theorem to find the length of its hypotenuse. Simplify your result. Repeat this process for several different triangles, and make a conjecture about the sides of 45°-45°-90° triangles.

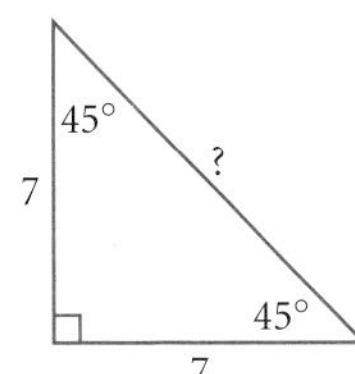

Problem-Solving Tip

Make a table, and look for a pattern in your results.

2. Sketch an equilateral triangle, and choose a whole number for the lengths of its sides. Make a 30°-60°-90° triangle by dividing the triangle in half (a sample triangle is shown). Find the length of the unknown leg by using the Pythagorean Theorem, and simplify your result. Repeat this process for several different triangles, and make a conjecture about the sides of 30°-60°-90° triangles.

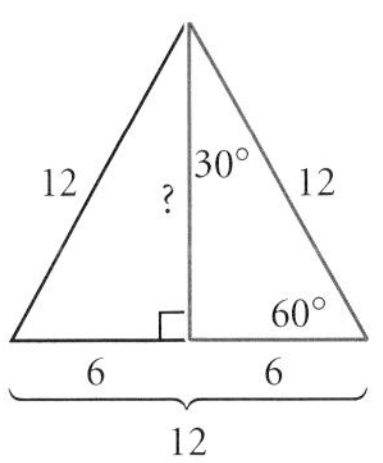

Student Resources

- Alternative Lessons 5-3B
- Laboratory Manual 5-3B
- Technology Lab Manual
- Practice 5-3B
- Study Guide and Journal 5-3B
- Guía de estudios y Diario 5-3B
- Multilingual Handbook
- More Look Ahead 5-3B
- SAT Preparation

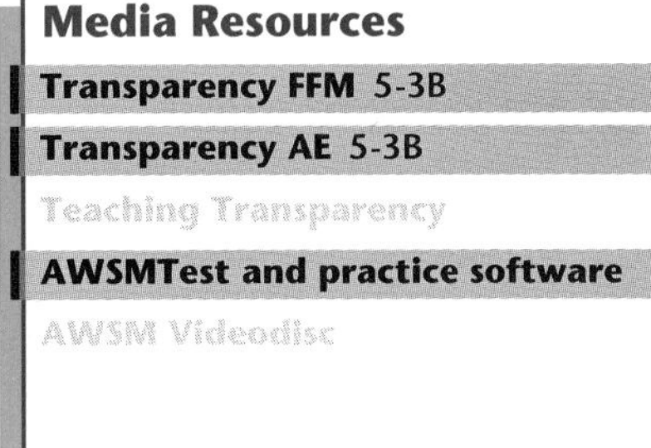

Media Resources

- Transparency FFM 5-3B
- Transparency AE 5-3B
- Teaching Transparency
- AWSMTest and practice software
- AWSM Videodisc

EXPLORE

Right Ratios

Recommended group size: 4

The Point

To use the Pythagorean Theorem to discover ratios of side lengths in 45°-45°-90° and 30°-60°-90° triangles.

Look and Listen...

- For students who use their calculators to find the measures of the sides. They will not be able to see all of the patterns.
- For students who do not see that they are looking for a leg, rather than a hypotenuse, in Step 2.

Ask...

- In 45°-45°-90° triangles, what do you notice about the length of the hypotenuse compared to the lengths of the legs?
- Suppose that you are given the length of the leg opposite the 30° angle in a 30°-60°-90° triangle. Can you use patterns in your results to find the lengths of the other sides?

For Groups That Finish Early

Repeat Step 1, using ℓ for the length of a leg, and repeat Step 2, using 2ℓ as the side length of the equilateral triangle. Express your results in terms of ℓ. ℓ-ℓ-$\ell\sqrt{2}$; ℓ-$\ell\sqrt{3}$-2ℓ

Follow Up

Ask students to describe the patterns they observed in the side lengths of 45°-45°-90° triangles and 30°-60°-90° triangles.

Possible Answers

1. Length of the hypotenuse is $\sqrt{2}$ times the length of a leg.
2. Length of the side opposite the 30° angle is half the length of the hypotenuse; length of the side opposite the 60° angle is $\sqrt{3}$ times as long as the side opposite the 30° angle.

The Pythagorean Theorem

ALTERNATE EXAMPLES

Find the lengths of the missing sides in each triangle. Express each as a radical in simplest form (if possible) and as a decimal approximation rounded to the nearest hundredth.

1.

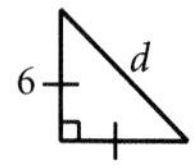

$d = 6\sqrt{2} \approx 8.49$

2.

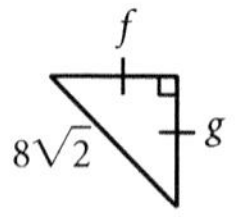

$f = g = 8$

3.

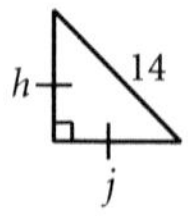

$h = j = \frac{14}{\sqrt{2}} = 7\sqrt{2} \approx 9.90$

EXAMPLES

Find the lengths of the unknown sides in each triangle. Express each as a radical in simplest form (if possible) and as a decimal approximation rounded to the nearest hundredth.

1.

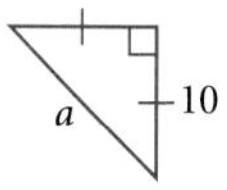

$a = 10\sqrt{2} \approx 14.14$

2.

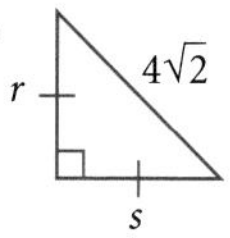

$r = s = 4$

3.

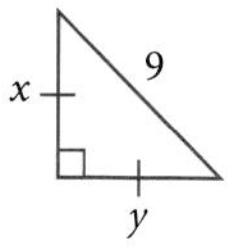

$x = y = \frac{9}{\sqrt{2}} \approx 6.36$

In Example 3, we had the expression $\frac{9}{\sqrt{2}}$. To put this expression in simplest form, we must clear the radicals from the denominator as follows:

$$\frac{9}{\sqrt{2}} \times \frac{\sqrt{2}}{\sqrt{2}} = \frac{9\sqrt{2}}{2}$$

Notice there are no radicals in the denominator of the simplified expression.

TRY IT

Find the length of the unknown sides in each triangle. Express each as a radical in simplest form (if possible) and as a decimal approximation rounded to the nearest hundredth.

a. $y = 4\sqrt{3} \approx 6.93$, $z = 8$
b. $x = 10$, $y = 10\sqrt{3} \approx 17.32$
c. $x = 5$, $z = 10$
d. $x = 2.77$, $z = 5.54$

	x	y	z
a.	4	___	___
b.	___	___	20
c.	___	$5\sqrt{3}$	___
d.	___	4.8	___

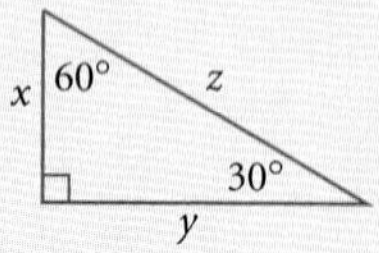

The results you have discovered about special right triangles are summarized below.

45°-45°-90° TRIANGLE THEOREM

In a 45°-45°-90° triangle, the hypotenuse is $\sqrt{2}$ times as long as either leg. The ratios of the side lengths can be written ℓ-ℓ-$\ell\sqrt{2}$.

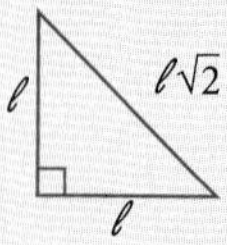

30°-60°-90° TRIANGLE THEOREM

In a 30°-60°-90° triangle, the hypotenuse is twice as long as the shorter leg (the leg opposite the 30° angle), and the longer leg (opposite the 60° angle) is $\sqrt{3}$ times as long as the shorter leg. The ratios of the side lengths can be written ℓ-$\ell\sqrt{3}$-2ℓ.

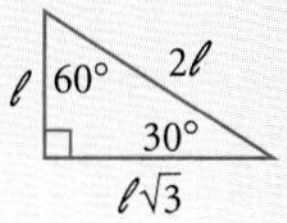

REFLECT

1. Why do 45°-45°-90° triangles have two sides with the same length? Be sure to support your answer with a theorem.
2. Explain why the length of the shorter leg of a 30°-60°-90° triangle is half the length of the hypotenuse.
3. If a square has sides that are *s* units long, what are the lengths of its diagonals? Why?

Exercises

CORE

Getting Started **The length of one side of each triangle is given. Find the lengths of the other two sides in simplest radical form.**

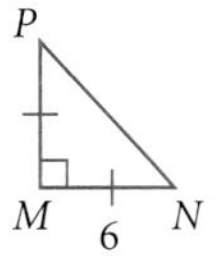

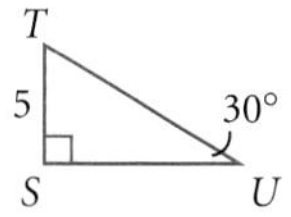

1. $MN = 6$ $PM = 6$, $PN = 6\sqrt{2}$
2. $ST = 5$ $SU = 5\sqrt{3}$, $TU = 10$

Find the lengths of the unknown sides in each triangle. Express each as a radical in simplest form (if possible) and as a decimal approximation rounded to the nearest hundredth.

	a	*b*	*c*
3.	3	___	___
4.	___	___	$6\sqrt{2}$
5.	___	4.6	___
6.	___	___	5

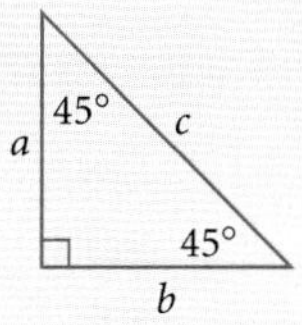

3. $b = 3$, $c = 3\sqrt{2} = 4.24$
4. $a = 6$, $b = 6$
5. $a = 4.6$, $c = 6.51$
6. $a = \frac{5}{2}\sqrt{2} = 3.54$, $b = \frac{5}{2}\sqrt{2} = 3.54$

Journal

Reflect 2 and 3 and **Exercise** 19 are suitable for journal entries.

REFLECT

Possible Answers

1. Since two angles are congruent, their opposite sides must be congruent by the converse of the Isosceles Triangle Theorem.
2. A 30°-60°-90° triangle can be made by drawing the angle bisector from one vertex of an equilateral triangle. Using triangle-congruence postulates, you can show that this segment is also a median; it divides the side it intersects into segments half the length of a side of the original equilateral triangle.
3. $s\sqrt{2}$; the diagonal of a square divides it into two 45°-45°-90° triangles.

Part B Exercises

Exercise Notes

Core

19. Students apply properties of special right triangles to explore a city-planning problem. This problem presents two alternative plans, each of which has advantages. Students do not identify the "right" plan, but find the strengths of each.

21. Students find a formula for the area of an equilateral triangle.

Look Ahead

These exercises review distances between points on a coordinate plane. Students will use the Pythagorean Theorem to justify the distance formula in 5-3 Part C.

More Math Reasoning

33–35. Give students experience with coordinates of points on a unit circle. This topic is important in trigonometry courses.

y

Vocabulary
Practice/Skills
Review
Math Reasoning
Problem Solving
Challenge

Ongoing Assessment

Self-Assessment Exercises 1–17 odd, 18

Embedded Assessment Explore Steps 1, 2; Exercises 6, 8, 19

5-3

The Pythagorean Theorem

Exercise Answers

Core

11. By the 45°-45°-90° Theorem, $90\sqrt{2} \approx 127.28$ ft.

19. Possible answers:

a. The perpendicular parking design allows more cars to be parked because it minimizes the curb width of each space. The angle parking requires 9.2 ft per space.

b. The angled spaces are easier for drivers to maneuver in and out of.

20. Possible answer:

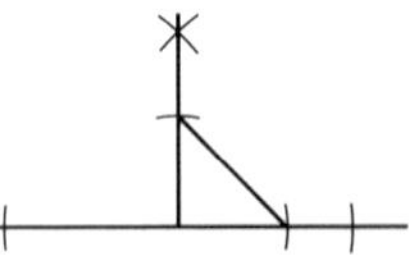

21. $\frac{s^2\sqrt{3}}{4}$

Look Ahead

22. 5

23. 10.05

24. 8.06

25. 7.00

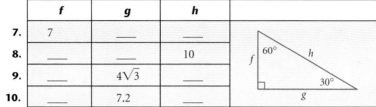

Algebra | Functions | Discrete Math | Probability | Data/Statistics

P **Find the lengths of the unknown sides in each triangle. Express each as a radical in simplest form (if possible) and as a decimal approximation rounded to the nearest hundredth.**

	f	g	h
7.	7	___	___
8.	___	___	10
9.	___	$4\sqrt{3}$	___
10.	___	7.2	___

(Triangle with legs f and g, hypotenuse h; angles 60° and 30°.)

7. $g = 7\sqrt{3} = 12.12$, $h = 14$
8. $f = 5$, $g = 5\sqrt{3} = 8.66$
9. $f = 4$, $h = 8$
10. $f = 4.16$, $h = 8.31$

P, MR **11. You're Out!** A baseball diamond is a square with consecutive bases 90 ft apart. About how far does a catcher have to throw the baseball to catch a runner trying to steal second base? Explain how you solved this problem.

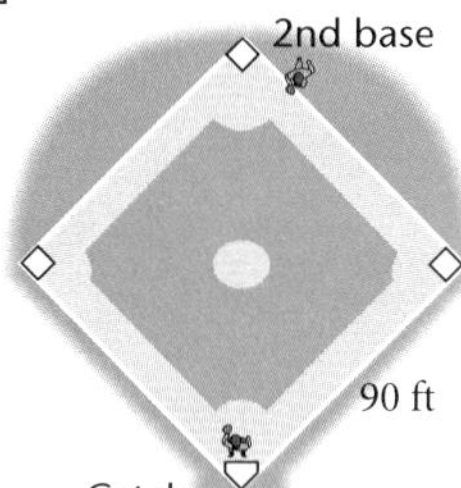

P **Find the area of each figure.**

12. 34.15

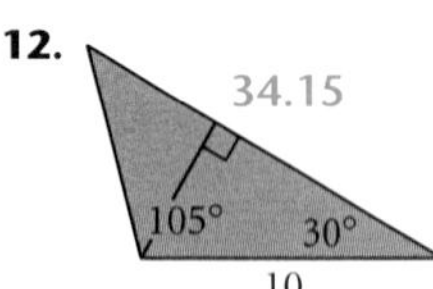

13. 389.71

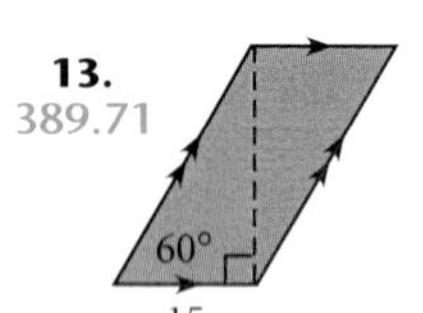

14. 249.42

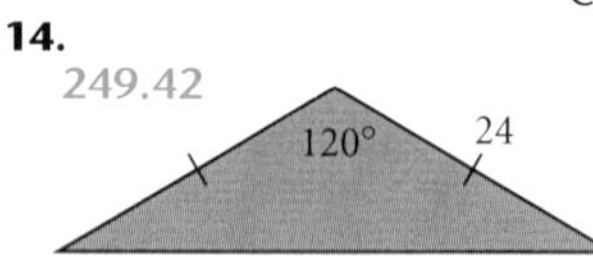

P **Find the lengths of the diagonals of a square with the following side lengths. Express your answers in simplest radical form.**

15. 10 $10\sqrt{2}$ **16.** $8\sqrt{2}$ 16 **17.** $22\sqrt{6}$ $44\sqrt{3}$

P **18.** Suppose that parallel rays of light pass through the center and the tip of the lens shown. After they are bent by the lens, the rays cross at focal point *F*. Find *FL* to the nearest tenth of a centimeter. 12.1 cm

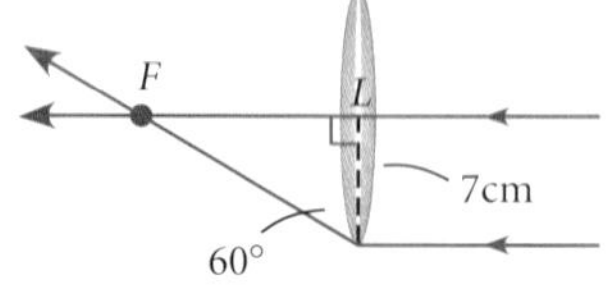

PS **19. Parallel Parking** As a city planner, you are designing parking for a downtown area. You are considering the two designs shown. In each design, the distance between the lines is 8 ft.

a. Which design allows more cars to be parked along a 200-ft block? Explain.

b. What advantages might the other design have?

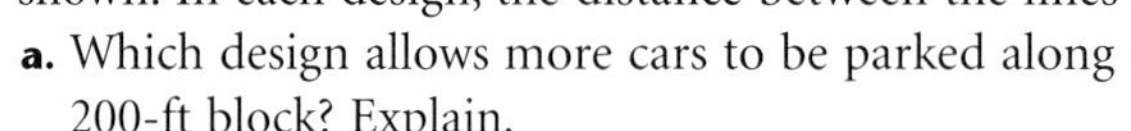

Perpendicular parking

P **20.** Use a compass and straightedge to construct an isosceles right triangle and a 30°-60°-90° triangle.

21. Find a formula for the area of an equilateral triangle in terms of *s*, the length of a side of the triangle.
MR, C

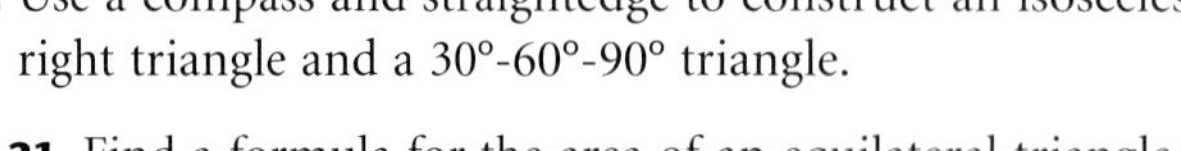

Angle parking

Key

- V Vocabulary
- P Practice/Skills
- R Review
- MR Math Reasoning
- PS Problem Solving
- C Challenge

LOOK AHEAD

Find the distance between each pair of points.

22. (0, 3) and (3, 7)

23. (2, 3) and (1, −7)

24. (−5, −3) and (−1, 4)

25. (2.2, −1.3) and (−4.7, −2.5)

MORE PRACTICE

Find the lengths of the unknown sides in each triangle. Express each as a radical in simplest form and as a decimal approximation rounded to the nearest hundredth.

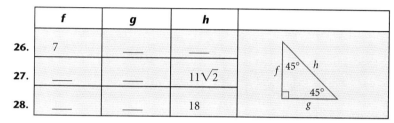

	f	*g*	*h*	
26.	7	___	___	
27.	___	___	$11\sqrt{2}$	
28.	___	___	18	

26. $g = 7$, $h = 7\sqrt{2} = 9.90$

27. $f = 11$, $g = 11$

28. $f = 9\sqrt{2} = 12.73$, $g = 9\sqrt{2} = 12.73$

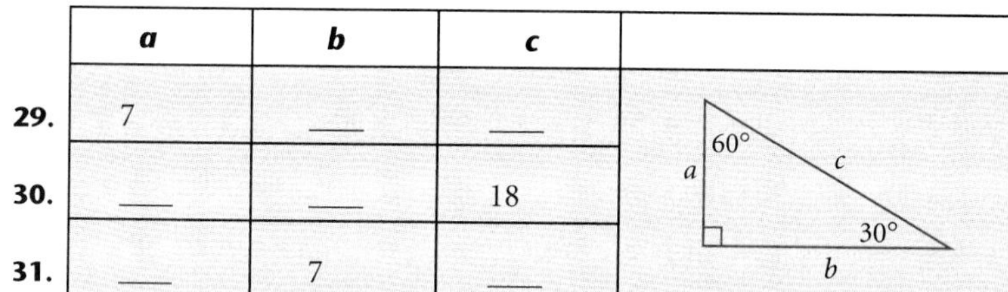

	a	*b*	*c*	
29.	7	___	___	
30.	___	___	18	
31.	___	7	___	

29. $b = 7\sqrt{3} = 12.12$, $c = 14$

30. $a = 9$, $b = 9\sqrt{3} = 15.59$

31. $a = \frac{7}{3}\sqrt{3} = 4.04$, $c = \frac{14}{3}\sqrt{3} = 8.08$

MORE MATH REASONING

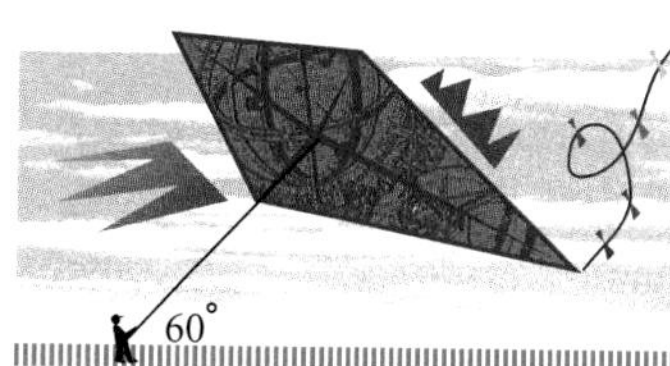

32. A kite string is 200 ft long, and the angle the string makes with the ground is 60°. How high is the kite?
173.21 ft

Find the coordinates of point *P* on each circle. The radius of each circle is 1.

33.

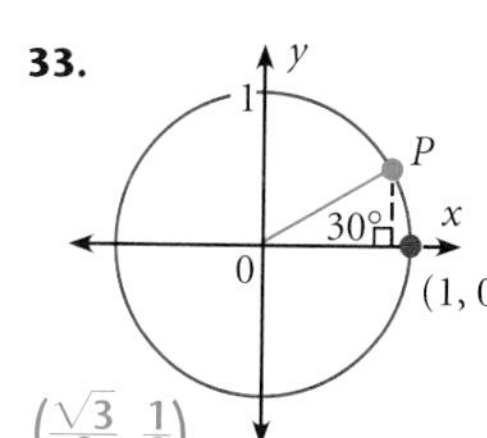

$\left(\frac{\sqrt{3}}{2}, \frac{1}{2}\right)$

34.

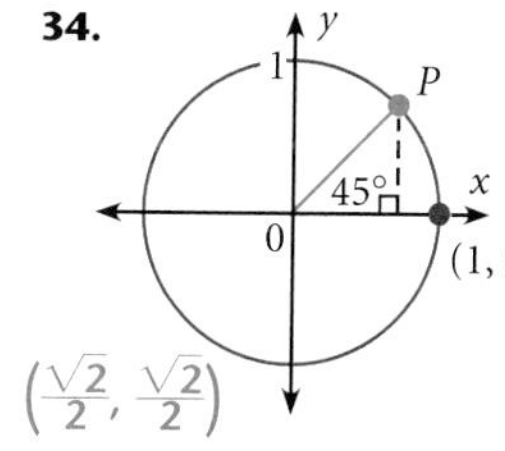

$\left(\frac{\sqrt{2}}{2}, \frac{\sqrt{2}}{2}\right)$

35.

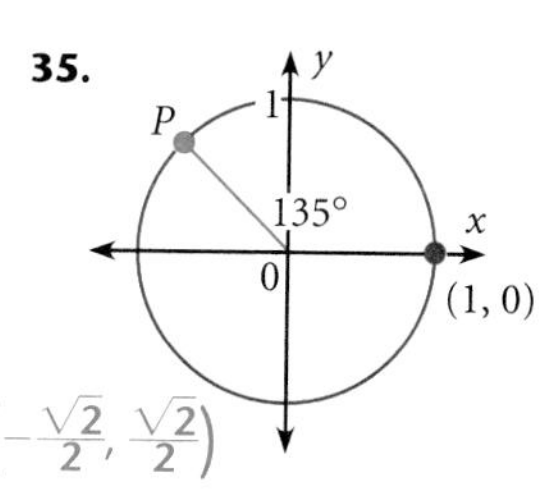

$\left(-\frac{\sqrt{2}}{2}, \frac{\sqrt{2}}{2}\right)$

The Pythagorean Theorem

PART C At a Glance

Objective

To use the Pythagorean Theorem to justify the distance formula, and to explore the equation of a circle.

Development

In the **Explore,** students use the Pythagorean Theorem to show why the distance formula works.

Students then see that applying the distance formula to points on a circle leads to an equation for a circle.

Suggested Materials

Teacher String tied to an overhead pen/piece of chalk

First Five Minutes

Transparency FFM 5-3C

Find the distance between each pair of points below.

1. $A(5, -8)$, $B(-7, -3)$ 13

2. $A(-9.3, 8.1)$, $B(-2.2, 5.4)$ ≈ 7.60

Motivate

Ask...

- When is it unnecessary to use the distance formula to find the distance between two points on a coordinate plane? **When they have the same *x*- or *y*-coordinate.**

EXPLORE

Going the Distance

Recommended group size: 2

The Point

To use the Pythagorean Theorem to justify the distance formula.

Look and Listen...

- For students who do not see the (right) triangle.

Ask...

- What type of triangle do you get if you join *A*, *B*, and *C*?

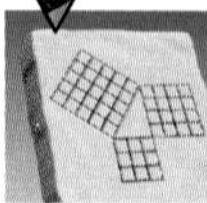

5-3 PART C The Distance Formula Revisited

← CONNECT → ***You've already used the distance formula, but now you can justify why it works. You will also investigate the standard form for the equation of a circle.***

The formula for the distance between two points in a plane and the Pythagorean Theorem are the same thing written in two different ways. You will investigate this in the following Explore.

EXPLORE: GOING THE DISTANCE

Use the figure at the right and the Pythagorean Theorem to explain why the distance formula works. Use your explanation to write a *plan* for a proof of the distance formula.

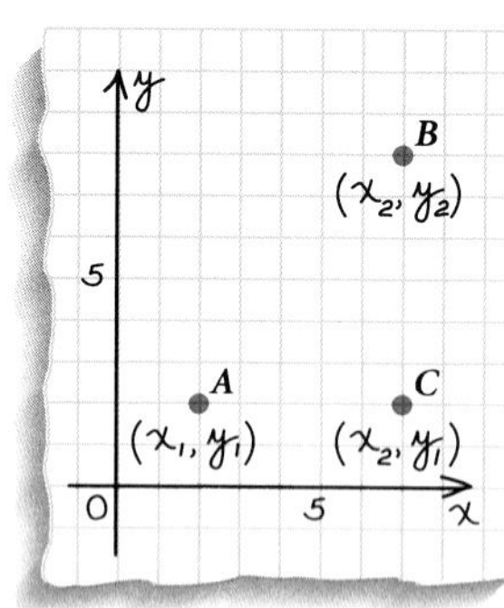

TRY IT

Find the distance between each pair of points.

a. (22, 4) and (2, 1) $\sqrt{409}$

b. (26, 0) and (6, 5) $5\sqrt{17}$

A circle is the locus of points in a plane that are equidistant from a given point. Let's see what happens when we use the distance formula to help attach numbers to those characteristics.

One way to draw a circle with a radius of *r* is to use a string and a pencil. Since the string is *r* units long, all points on the circle are *r* units away from the center.

r

Tips from Teachers

You may want to demonstrate how to use a string to draw a circle on the overhead or chalkboard. Students can explain how the string models the radius of the circle.

Research Note

Comprehension and retention are greater when teachers and students connect new information with previous knowledge. (U.S. Department of Education, *What Works: Research About Teaching and Learning,* p. 36. 1986)

Let's put a coordinate system on this circle. The most convenient place for the center is (0, 0). Any point whose (x, y) coordinates are on the circle must be r units away from (0, 0).

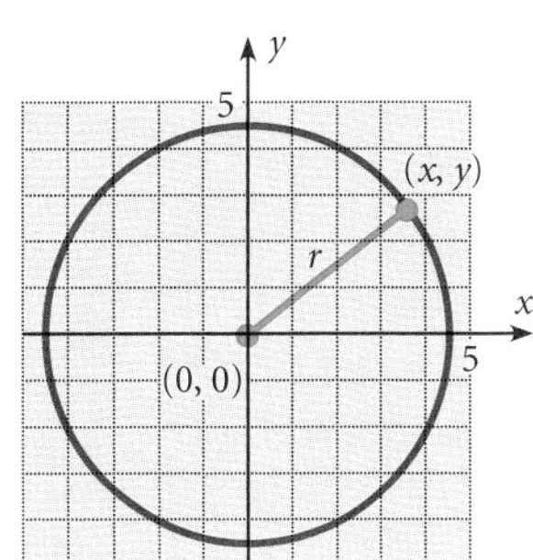

The distance from (x, y) to (0, 0) is r, so we have the following.

$\sqrt{(x - 0)^2 + (y - 0)^2} = r$

Simplifying gives $\sqrt{x^2 + y^2} = r$.

Finally, we square both sides to get the result shown below.

EQUATION OF A CIRCLE

The circle with radius r and center (0, 0) has the equation $x^2 + y^2 = r^2$.

TRY IT

What is the radius of each of the following circles?

c. $x^2 + y^2 = 9$ 3 **d.** $x^2 + y^2 = 121$ 11 **e.** $x^2 + y^2 = 21$ $\sqrt{21}$

EXAMPLE

Sketch a graph of the circle whose equation is $x^2 + y^2 = 16$.

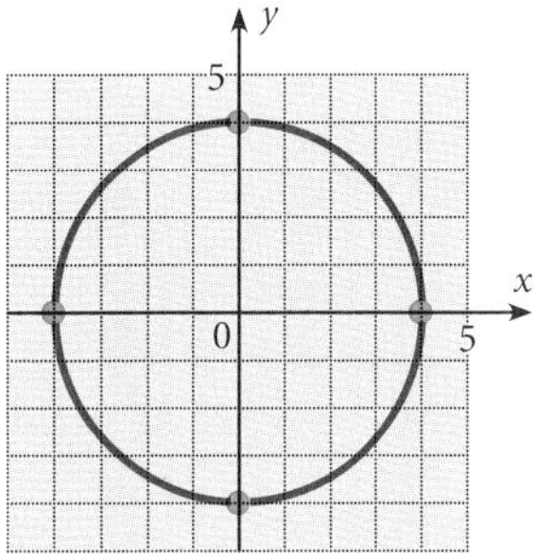

The center of the circle is (0, 0). Since $r^2 = 16$, the radius of the circle is 4. The points that are directly above, below, left, and right of the center are (0, 4), (0, −4), (−4, 0), and (4, 0). We can draw a smooth curve that connects these points.

REFLECT

1. Explain the connection between the distance formula and the Pythagorean Theorem.
2. Why do the points that satisfy the equation $x^2 + y^2 = 25$ form a circle whose center is at the origin and whose radius is 5?

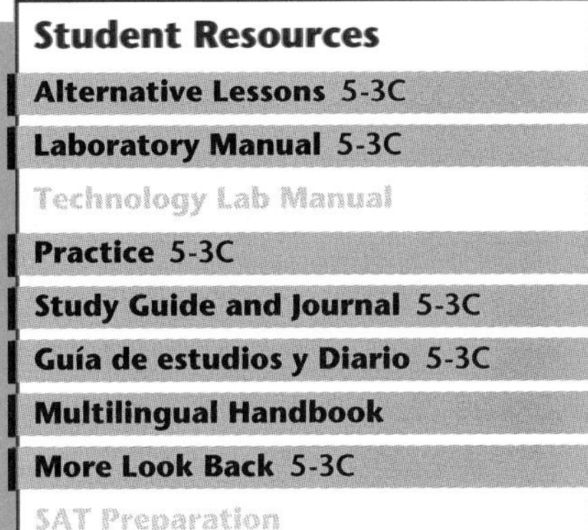

Student Resources
Alternative Lessons 5-3C
Laboratory Manual 5-3C
Technology Lab Manual
Practice 5-3C
Study Guide and Journal 5-3C
Guía de estudios y Diario 5-3C
Multilingual Handbook
More Look Back 5-3C
SAT Preparation

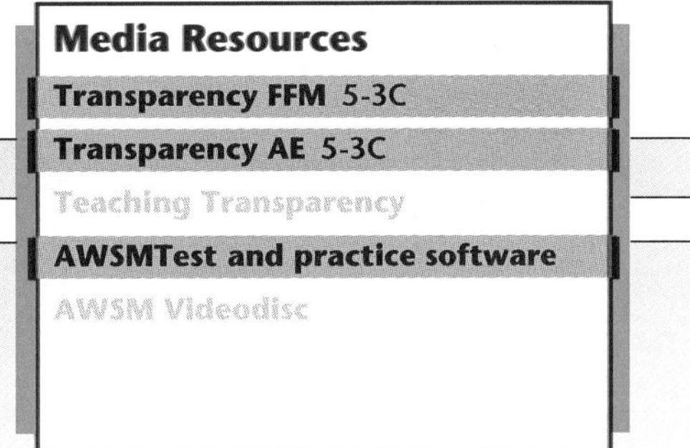

For Groups That Finish Early

List all points with integer coordinates 5 units from (1, 1). (6, 1), (1, 6), (1, −4), (−4, 1), (4, 5), (5, 4), (−2, 5), (−3, 4), (−2, −3), (−3, −2), (4, −3), (5, −2).

Follow Up

Ask students to explain the connection between the Pythagorean Theorem and the distance formula.

Possible Answers

By drawing a right triangle whose hypotenuse joins the points, we see that the distance formula is the Pythagorean Theorem applied to points on a coordinate plane.

Plan: Sketch two points with coordinates (x_1, y_1) and (x_2, y_2). Add a point at (x_2, y_1). Sketch the right triangle containing the points. Apply the Pythagorean Theorem to find the distance from (x_1, y_1) to (x_2, y_2). The result is the distance formula.

ALTERNATE EXAMPLE

Sketch a graph of the circle whose equation is $x^2 + y^2 = 9$.

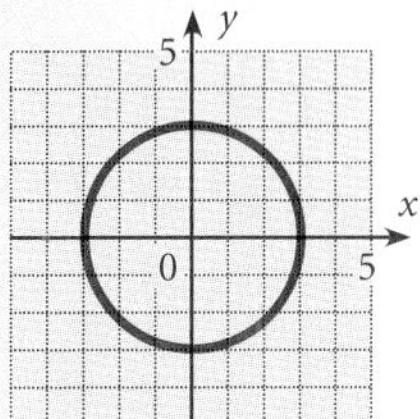

The center of the circle is (0, 0). Since $r^2 = 9$, the radius of the circle is 3. The points directly above, below, left, and right of the center are (0, 3), (0, −3), (−3, 0), and (3, 0). Draw a smooth curve to connect these points.

Journal

Reflect 1 and 2 are suitable for journal entries.

REFLECT

Possible Answers

1. The distance formula is the Pythagorean Theorem applied to points on a coordinate plane.
2. If point (x, y) is 5 units from (0, 0), then by the distance formula, $\sqrt{(x - 0)^2 + (y - 0)^2} = 5$. Squaring both sides gives $x^2 + y^2 = 25$.

The Pythagorean Theorem

Part C Exercises

Exercise Notes

Core

13. Students write an equation that models the orbit of the earth around the sun.

More Math Reasoning

24. Students use an algebraic inequality to describe the locus of points inside a circle.

25. Students substitute an x-value into their equation for the earth's orbit from Exercise 13. They must realize that there are two valid y-values in this situation.

Extension: You may want to have students sketch a graph of the equation for the earth's motion, using an appropriate scale, and locate these points on the graph. You might also ask what is at the origin of the graph, and from what perspective we are observing the orbit. **The sun; directly "above" or "below" the sun.**

Exercise Answers

Core

7. $x^2 + y^2 = 1$

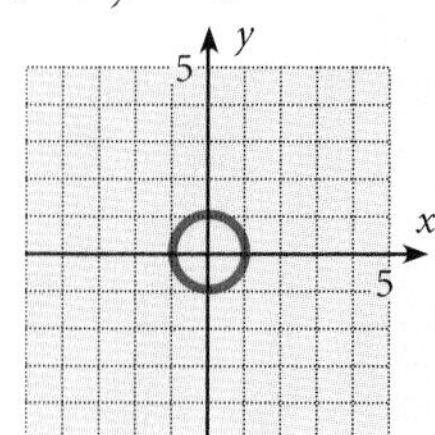

8. $x^2 + y^2 = 9$

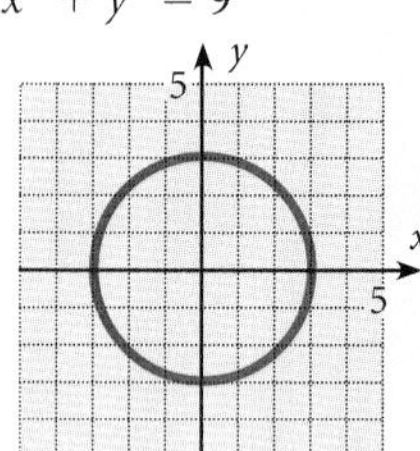

9. $x^2 + y^2 = 100$

10. a. Yes; $d \approx 98.86$ yards

b. $x^2 + y^2 = 22{,}500$

Exercises

CORE

P **Getting Started Find the distance between each pair of points. Express your answers as decimal approximations rounded to the nearest hundredth.**

1. $(-4, 9)$ and $(-4, -12)$ 21

2. $(4, -3)$ and $(2, 7)$ 10.20

3. $(-3, -2)$ and $(1, -6)$ 5.66

4. $(17.2, 27.5)$ and $(27.2, 22.4)$ 11.23

P **Find the distance between each pair of points.**

5. (c, d) and (d, c), where $d > c$ $(d - c)\sqrt{2}$

6. (q, q) and $(-q, -q)$, where $q > 0$ $2q\sqrt{2}$

P **Write an equation for a circle with center at (0, 0) and the given radius. Then sketch a graph of the circle.**

7. $r = 1$

8. $r = 3$

P **9.** Give an equation for the locus of points in the coordinate plane 10 units from (0, 0).

PS **10. Going Swimming** Alicia can swim one hundred and fifty yards in two minutes. She begins her swim at (0, 0).

a. A raft is located at the point (62, 77). Can she reach the raft in two minutes? Explain.

b. Write an equation for the locus of points one hundred and fifty yards from her starting point.

MR **11.** When the rotor of a helicopter spins very quickly, it looks like a disk. Explain why this happens.

P History **12. Big Babylon** Around the year 600 B.C., Babylon, the capital of Babylonia, was the largest city in the world. It covered an area of 2500 acres. If one acre is approximately equivalent to 1.56×10^{-3} mi^2, find the area of Babylon in square miles.

P Science **13.** The earth's orbit around the sun is nearly circular. The radius of the orbit is approximately 9.3×10^7 mi. Assuming the center of the sun is located at (0, 0) in the figure at the right, write an equation for the orbit of the earth around the sun.

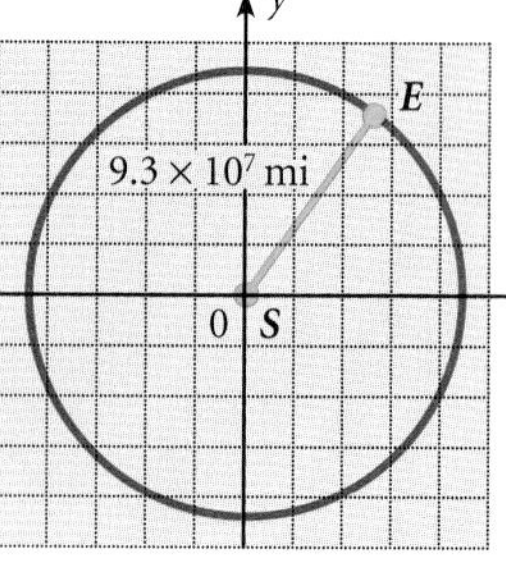

MR **14.** *Plan* a proof to show that the points $(-x, 0)$ and $(x, 0)$ are equidistant from $(0, y)$.

Key

V Vocabulary
P Practice/Skills
R Review
MR Math Reasoning
PS Problem Solving
C Challenge

LOOK BACK

15. Fill in the missing reasons to complete the proof. [4-2, 4-3]

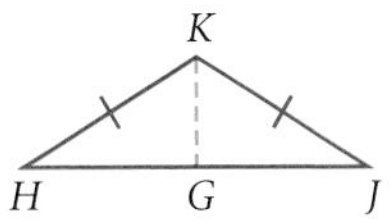

Given: $\triangle KHJ$ is isosceles, with $\overline{KH} \cong \overline{KJ}$.
$\overline{KG}$ is the median from K to $\overline{HJ}$.

Prove: $\overline{KG}$ is the angle bisector of $\angle HKJ$.

Proof: The **a.** ____ tells us that $\overline{KH} \cong \overline{KJ}$. We know that $\overline{KG} \cong \overline{KG}$ by the **b.** ____. We also know that $\overline{KG}$ is the median from K to $\overline{HJ}$ from the **c.** ____, so G is the midpoint of $\overline{HJ}$ by the **d.** ____. Therefore, $\overline{HG} \cong \overline{GJ}$ by the **e.** ____. $\triangle KGH \cong \triangle KGJ$ by the **f.** ____, and $\angle HKG \cong \angle JKG$ by **g.** ____. Therefore, $\overline{KG}$ is the angle bisector of $\angle HKJ$ by the **h.** ____.

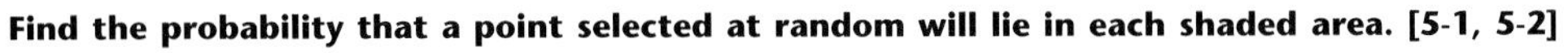

Find the probability that a point selected at random will lie in each shaded area. [5-1, 5-2]

16. $\frac{1}{2}$

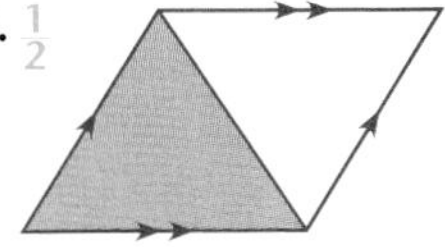

17. 0.44

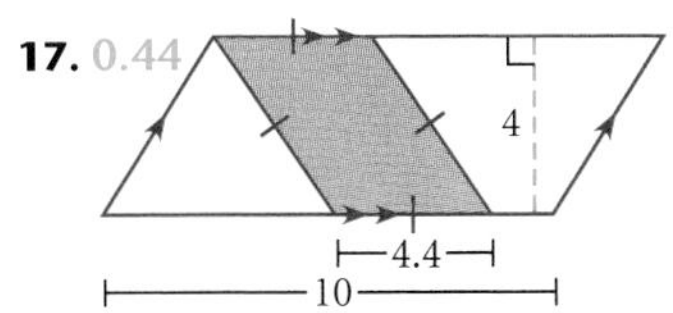

MORE PRACTICE

Find the distance between each pair of points. Express your answers as decimal approximations rounded to the nearest hundredth.

18. $(-7, 14)$; $(12, 14)$ 19

19. $(19.3, 9.1)$; $(9.7, 19.9)$ 14.45

20. $(5.2, 10.1)$; $(-5.2, -10.1)$ 22.72

Write an equation for a circle with center at (0, 0) and the given radius.

21. $r = 7$ $x^2 + y^2 = 49$

22. $r = \sqrt{21}$ $x^2 + y^2 = 21$

23. $r = 2$ $x^2 + y^2 = 4$

MORE MATH REASONING

24. Write an inequality to describe the locus of points that are no more than 5 units from (0, 0). Graph the inequality.

25. In Exercise 13, you wrote an equation for the orbit of the earth around the sun. Find the possible y-values for the position of the earth when its x-value is 5.0×10^7 mi.

26. Graph the triangle with vertices $A(4, 3)$, $B(8, 2)$, and $C(1, 1)$. Find the image of $\triangle ABC$ under a 180° clockwise rotation around (0, 0). Show that each point and its image are equidistant from (0, 0).

Ongoing Assessment

Self-Assessment Exercises 1–13 odd, except 11

Embedded Assessment Try It d, e; Exercises 4, 8, 10

11. Possible answer: Since the human eye is not quick enough to catch the rotor at any one point, the eye sees a collection of all the places the blade has been. This looks like a disk.

12. 3.9 mi^2

13. $x^2 + y^2 = (9.3 \times 10^7)^2 \approx 8.65 \times 10^{15}$

14. Possible answer: Construct two right triangles, one with vertices at (0, 0), (0, y) and (x, 0), the other with vertices at (0, 0), (0, y) and ($-x$, 0). Use the Pythagorean Theorem to show that the hypotenuses are equal.

Look Back

15. a. Given information

b. Reflexive Property

c. Given information

d. Definition of median

e. Definition of midpoint

f. SSS Postulate

g. CPCTC

h. Definition of angle bisector

More Math Reasoning

24. $x^2 + y^2 \leq 25$

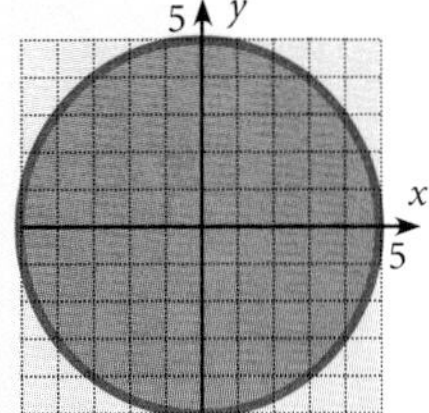

25. $y \approx \pm 7.84 \times 10^7$ mi

26.

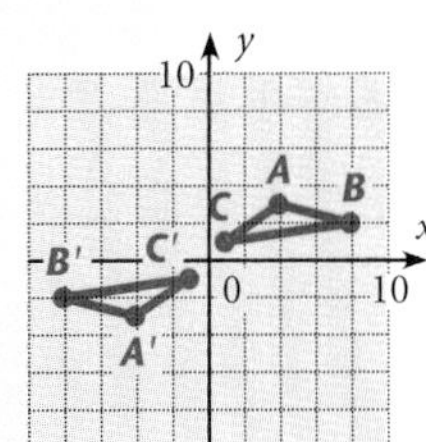

$CO = C'O = \sqrt{2}$;
$AO = A'O = 5$;
$BO = B'O = \sqrt{68} = 2\sqrt{17}$

PART D At a Glance

Objective

To discover that the converse of the Pythagorean Theorem is also true, and to discover inequalities that can be used to classify triangles as acute or obtuse.

Development

In the **Explore,** students discover two inequalities and an equation that they can use to classify triangles as acute, right, or obtuse. The converse of the Pythagorean Theorem is a part of this discovery.

Suggested Materials

Student Paper, ruler, scissors, geometry software

First Five Minutes

Transparency FFM 5-3D

What is a Pythagorean triple? List six different Pythagorean triples.

Motivate

Ask...

- What is the converse of the Pythagorean Theorem? Do you think this statement is also true?

EXPLORE

Conversely...(and More!)

Recommended group size: 4

The Point

To discover how side lengths can be used to decide whether a triangle is acute, right, or obtuse. The right-triangle case is the Pythagorean Converse.

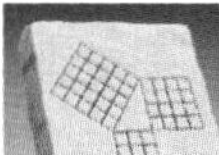

5-3 PART D The Converse of the Pythagorean Theo

← CONNECT → *You've seen that the Pythagorean Theorem holds for all right triangles. What if you aren't sure that a triangle is a right triangle? You will explore a method of testing the sides of a triangle to determine if it is right, acute, or obtuse.*

Like the Babylonians, the ancient Egyptians knew about properties of right triangles. The painting at the left shows Egyptian "rope stretchers" using what we now know as the converse of the Pythagorean Theorem. (You will take a closer look at this in Exercise 14.)

In the following Explore, you will investigate the converse of the Pythagorean Theorem.

EXPLORE: CONVERSELY . . . (AND MORE!)

MATERIALS

Paper, Ruler, Scissors
Geometry software (optional)

1. The table gives three different values for a and b. For each set of values, find three c values—one where $a^2 + b^2 = c^2$, one where $a^2 + b^2 < c^2$, and one where $a^2 + b^2 > c^2$. Be sure that c is greater than both a and b, but less than $a + b$.

	a	b	c
$a^2 + b^2 = c^2$	6	8	
$a^2 + b^2 < c^2$	6	8	
$a^2 + b^2 > c^2$	6	8	
$a^2 + b^2 = c^2$	5	12	
$a^2 + b^2 < c^2$	5	12	
$a^2 + b^2 > c^2$	5	12	
$a^2 + b^2 = c^2$	9	12	
$a^2 + b^2 < c^2$	9	12	
$a^2 + b^2 > c^2$	9	12	

Technology Note

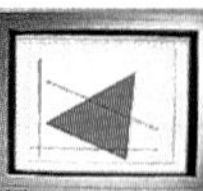

If you use software in this **Explore,** you may want to show students how to use the Preferences command to choose units and accuracy of measurements. In this **Explore,** lengths are most conveniently measured in centimeters. Also, when side lengths are rounded to the nearest tenth or unit, instead of the nearest hundredth, students may make inaccurate triangles that lead them to invalid conclusions.

2. Construct the triangles in your table using geometry software or by cutting strips of paper to the lengths of the sides. Are all of them right triangles? Explain.
3. Make a conjecture about the type of triangle that results for each of the following possibilities. (If you are using software, you may want to try a few more cases before making a conjecture.)
   a. $a^2 + b^2 = c^2$
   b. $a^2 + b^2 < c^2$
   c. $a^2 + b^2 > c^2$

Problem-Solving Tip

Look for a pattern before making a conjecture. Then check to see if your conjecture holds for the triangles in the table.

TRY IT

a. Is a triangle with sides 8, 15, and 17 a right triangle? If not, what type of triangle is it? Right
b. Is a triangle with sides 5, 6, and 8 a right triangle? If not, what type of triangle is it? Obtuse
c. Is a triangle with sides 4, 5, and 6 a right triangle? If not, what type of triangle is it? Acute

Based on your investigations in the preceding Explore, you may have made the following conjecture.

CONVERSE OF THE PYTHAGOREAN THEOREM

If the sum of the squares of the lengths of two sides of a triangle equals the square of the length of the third side, then the triangle is a right triangle and the longest side is the hypotenuse.

The inductive evidence shows that the converse of the Pythagorean Theorem seems to be true. Now we will prove it. Notice how we use the SSS Postulate in the proof.

Look and Listen...

- For students who do not choose appropriate c values.
- For students whose triangles are difficult to classify.

Ask...

- Is c greater than both a and b? Is c less than $a + b$?
- Might it help to choose a c value for the inequality that is farther from the one that satisfies the equation?

For Groups That Finish Early

Explain why c must be greater than either a or b.

Follow Up

Ask students to explain how they can use the side lengths to tell whether a triangle is right, acute, or obtuse.

Possible Answers

2. Triangles where $a^2 + b^2 = c^2$ are right triangles.
3. a. Right triangles.
   b. Obtuse triangles.
   c. Acute triangles.

Student Resources

- Alternative Lessons 5-3D
- Laboratory Manual 5-3D
- Technology Lab Manual
- Practice 5-3D
- Study Guide and Journal 5-3D
- Guía de estudios y Diario 5-3D
- Multilingual Handbook
- More Look Ahead 5-3D
- SAT Preparation

Media Resources

- Transparency FFM 5-3D
- Transparency AE
- Teaching Transparency
- AWSMTest and practice software
- AWSM Videodisc

The Pythagorean Theorem

Journal 

Explore Step 3, **Reflect** 2, and **Exercise** 10 are suitable for journal entries.

REFLECT

Possible Answers

1. Label the lengths of the shorter two sides a and b, and the length of the longest side c. If $a^2 + b^2 < c^2$, the triangle is obtuse. If $a^2 + b^2 = c^2$, the triangle is a right triangle. If $a^2 + b^2 > c^2$, the triangle is acute.
2. A triangle is a right triangle if and only if the square of the length of its longest side is equal to the sum of the squares of the lengths of its shorter sides.

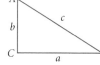

Given: $\triangle ABC$ with $a^2 + b^2 = c^2$

Prove: $\triangle ABC$ is a right triangle with hypotenuse c.

Plan: Show that any triangle whose side lengths satisfy the equation $a^2 + b^2 = c^2$ is congruent to a right triangle and is therefore a right triangle.

Proof: Draw a second triangle, $\triangle FGH$—a right triangle with legs a and b and hypotenuse h.

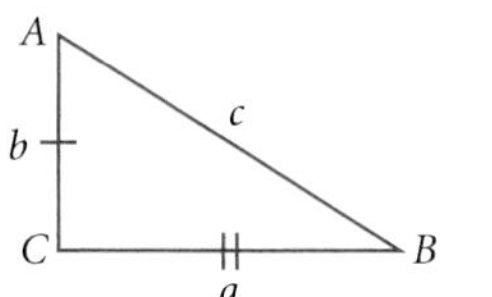

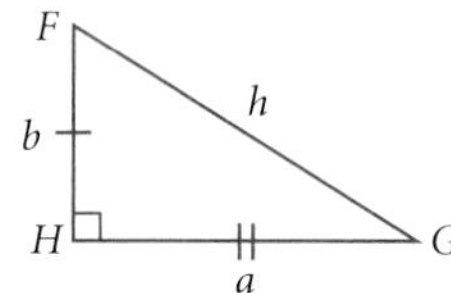

By the Pythagorean Theorem, $a^2 + b^2 = h^2$. We are given that $a^2 + b^2 = c^2$, so we can show by substitution that $h^2 = c^2$. Since both h and c are positive, $h = c$, and $\triangle ABC \cong \triangle FGH$ by SSS. Therefore, $\angle C \cong \angle H$ by CPCTC. $\angle H$ is a right angle, so it measures 90°. $\angle C$ must also measure 90°, by the definition of congruent angles, so $\angle C$ is also a right angle by the definition of right angles. Therefore, $\triangle ABC$ is a right triangle by the definition of right triangle, and c is its hypotenuse since it is opposite the right angle.

We summarize the inequalities related to the Pythagorean Theorem below.

> **PYTHAGOREAN INEQUALITY THEOREMS**
>
> If the sum of the squares of the lengths of two sides of a triangle is greater than the square of the length of the third side, then the triangle is acute.
>
> If the sum of the squares of the lengths of two sides of a triangle is less than the square of the length of the third side, then the triangle is obtuse.

REFLECT

1. If you know the side lengths of a triangle, how can you determine if it is a right triangle, an acute triangle, or an obtuse triangle?
2. State the Pythagorean Theorem and its converse as a biconditional.

Exercises

CORE

1. **Getting Started** Follow the steps to determine whether a triangle with side lengths 4, 5, and 7 is acute, obtuse, or right.
   a. Find the sum of the squares of the smaller side lengths. 41
   b. Find the square of the largest side length. 49
   c. Is the square of the largest side length less than the sum of the squares of the other sides? If so, the triangle is acute. If it is greater than the sum of the other squares, the triangle is obtuse. If it is equal to the sum of the other squares, the triangle is a right triangle. Obtuse

Given the following side lengths, classify each triangle as acute, obtuse, or right.

2. 3, 4, 5 Right
3. 10, 12, 15 Acute
4. 11, 11, 15 Acute
5. 4, $4\sqrt{3}$, 8 Right
6. 0.09, 0.40, 0.41 Right
7. $\frac{5}{12}$, 1, $1\frac{1}{12}$ Right

Find the values of x that will make each triangle an acute triangle.

8. 4, x, 7 $\sqrt{33} < x < \sqrt{65}$
9. 3, 6, x $3\sqrt{3} < x < 3\sqrt{5}$

10. Charles knows that a triangle with sides measuring 3, 4, and 5 units is a right triangle. He says that if you multiply all three side lengths by the same number, you will still have a right triangle. Do you agree with him? Explain why or why not.

11. **An Able Cable** You are raising a twenty-foot telephone pole with a cable. The cable hoist is fifteen feet from the pole. How can you ensure that the pole will be vertical? Explain.

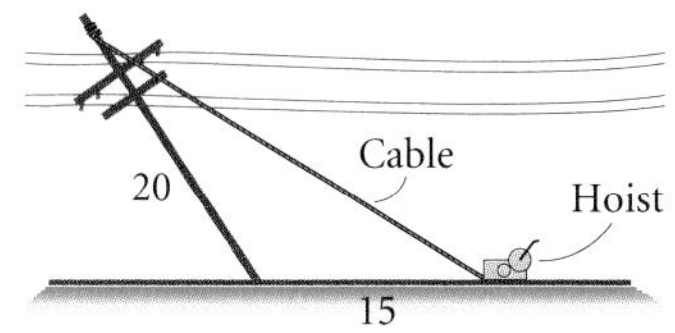

12. *Plan* a proof of the following statement: "If the side lengths of a triangle are 3, 3, and $3\sqrt{2}$, then the triangle is an isosceles right triangle."

13. Suppose you have computer software that draws straight line segments of any length and you can position the segments wherever you like. How can you use this software to draw a right angle?

14. **Knot a Bad Idea** Paintings in ancient Egyptian tombs depict people carrying ropes with equally spaced knots. These ropes may have been used by surveyors to make right angles and right triangles. Explain how a rope with 13 equally-spaced knots could be used to make a right triangle.

Part D Exercises

Exercise Notes

Core

13. and 14. Show that the Pythagorean Converse can be used to draw right angles. Exercise 14 shows how this idea may have been applied in ancient Egypt.

Look Ahead

15. Reviews properties of parallel lines. Students use these in 6-2 when proving properties of quadrilaterals.

16–20. Review types of quadrilaterals. Quadrilaterals are the main topic of Chapter 6.

More Math Reasoning

28. Students use algebra to show how formulas can be used to generate Pythagorean triples.

Extension: You may want to have students program a computer or calculator to use these formulas to generate a list of Pythagorean triples.

Exercise Answers

Core

10. Yes; If $a^2 + b^2 = c^2$, then $(ka)^2 + (kb)^2 = (kc)^2$.

11. The pole will be vertical when 25 feet of cable is extended.

12. Possible answer: Show that $3^2 + 3^2 = (3\sqrt{2})^2$, so the triangle is a right triangle. The lengths of two sides of the triangle are equal, which makes it isosceles.

13. Possible answer: Form lengths a, b, c where $a^2 + b^2 = c^2$.

14. The sides of the triangle will be 3, 4, and 5.

Ongoing Assessment

Vocabulary
Practice/Skills
Review
Math Reasoning
Problem Solving
Challenge

Self-Assessment Exercises 1–11 odd

Embedded Assessment Explore Step 3; Exercises 2, 6, 8, 14

The Pythagorean Theorem

Look Ahead

15. 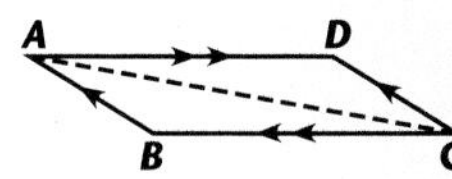

$\angle DAC \cong \angle BCA$, $\angle DCA \cong \angle BAC$ because alternate interior angles are congruent.

16. Possible answer: A parallelogram is a quadrilateral with two pairs of parallel sides.

17. Possible answer: A square is a quadrilateral with four right angles and four congruent sides.

18. Possible answer: A rectangle is a quadrilateral with four right angles.

19. Possible answer: A rhombus is a quadrilateral with four congruent sides.

20. Possible answer: A trapezoid is a quadrilateral with exactly one pair of parallel sides.

More Math Reasoning

27. Yes, since one can always multiply the numbers of the triple by a constant to obtain a new triple.

28. a. Possible answers:
$a = 3, b = 4, c = 5$
$a = 5, b = 12, c = 13$
$a = 21, b = 20, c = 29$
$a = 35, b = 12, c = 37$
$a = 9, b = 40, c = 41$

b. Possible answer: Algebra shows that $(m^2 - n^2)^2 + (2mn)^2 = (m^2 + n^2)^2$

Algebra | Functions | Discrete Math | Probability | Data/Statistics

LOOK AHEAD

MR **15.** *ABCD* is a parallelogram. Copy *ABCD*, and draw diagonal $\overline{AC}$. Then list any pairs of angles that you know are congruent, and explain why they are congruent.

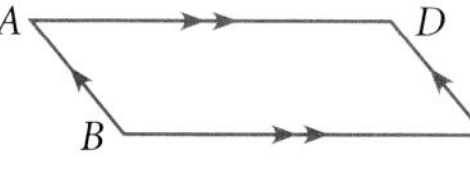

V **Define each of the following quadrilaterals in your own words.**

16. parallelogram **17.** square **18.** rectangle

19. rhombus **20.** trapezoid

MORE PRACTICE

P **Given the following side lengths, classify each triangle as acute, obtuse, or right.**

21. 20, 21, 29 Right **22.** 9, 12, 15 Right **23.** 9, 9, 13 Obtuse

24. 18, 18, $18\sqrt{2}$ Right **25.** $\frac{1}{3}, \frac{1}{4}, \frac{1}{5}$ Obtuse **26.** 4.3, 6.8, 10.1 Obtuse

MORE MATH REASONING

MR **27.** Malika claims that there are an infinite number of Pythagorean triples. Is she correct? Explain why you agree or disagree with her.

MR, C **28. Triple Play!** There is a simple way to create a long list of Pythagorean triples (a computer or programmable calculator can make it even easier). Choose any two positive integers *m* and *n*, with $m > n$. A Pythagorean triple (*a*, *b*, and *c*) will be given by the following equations:

$$a = m^2 - n^2$$

$$b = 2mn$$

$$c = m^2 + n^2$$

a. Generate a list of at least five Pythagorean triples using these formulas.
b. Why do these formulas work for generating Pythagorean triples?

MR **29.** Count the dots in each dot-square. Describe any patterns that you see. 4, 9, 16; 2^2, 3^2, 4^2

Key

V Vocabulary
P Practice/Skills
R Review
MR Math Reasoning
PS Problem Solving
C Challenge

5-3 PART E Making Connections

← CONNECT → ***The Pythagorean Theorem enables you to find an unknown side length in a right triangle. This is useful in architecture and other fields. You've learned about the history and applications of the Pythagorean Theorem and seen why the theorem is true.***

In the following Explore, you will investigate the Babylonian tablet known as Plimpton 322. You will do some archaeological detective work to find out what its numbers mean.

EXPLORE: TABLET TABULATIONS

Plimpton 322 contains columns of numbers written in base 60. Translated into base 10, the numbers are as follows.

119	169
3367	4825
4601	6649
65	97
319	481
2291	3541
799	1249
481	769
4961	8161
45	75

1. What is the significance of these numbers? What is their connection to the Pythagorean Theorem?
2. Add a third column to the table, and explain how you found the missing numbers.
3. If you were a scribe in ancient Babylonia, what other rows of numbers could you add to this list? (Give at least three more rows.)

Student Resources

Alternative Lessons
Laboratory Manual 5-3E
Technology Lab Manual
Practice 5-3E
Study Guide and Journal 5-3E
Guía de estudios y Diario 5-3E
Multilingual Handbook
More Look Back 5-3E
SAT Preparation

Media Resources

Transparency FFM 5-3E
Transparency AE
Teaching Transparency
AWSMTest and practice software
AWSM Videodisc

PART E At a Glance

Objective

To discover Pythagorean patterns in a Babylonian tablet.

Development

In the **Explore,** students investigate numbers from a Babylonian tablet. They discover that one column lists possible lengths for one leg of a right triangle, and the other lists the respective lengths of the hypotenuse. They then complete the table.

First Five Minutes

Transparency FFM 5-3E

List four formulas, equations, and/or inequalities used in 5-3 Parts A–D. Explain the meaning of each and how they are related.

EXPLORE

Tablet Tabulations

Recommended group size: 4

The Point
To discover the Pythagorean relationship between numbers on a Babylonian tablet.

Look and Listen...
- For students who do not see that the second column represents hypotenuse lengths.

Ask...
- Are you sure both columns represent lengths of legs?

For Groups That Finish Early
Starting with the Pythagorean triple 3, 4, 5, you can write other sets of Pythagorean triples by multiplying 3, 4, and 5 by the same number. What is the largest such triple for which your calculator can express all of the numbers without scientific notation?

Follow Up
Ask students to explain the meanings of the numbers in the table. Also, have them speculate on the possible uses of this table.

5-3

The Pythagorean Theorem

Possible Answers

1. The first column is the length of a leg of a right triangle; the second is the length of its hypotenuse.
2. By solving for a in $a^2 + b^2 = c^2$, we can complete the table. (Numbers are to be read as a column.)

   120, 3456, 4800, 72, 360, 2700, 960, 600, 6480, 60
3. 3, 4, 5; 5, 12, 13; 6, 8, 10; ...

Portfolio

Have students select items from their work that demonstrate their understanding of the material in 5-3.

You may wish to have students include a justification of the Pythagorean Theorem that they found interesting, their favorite **Exercise** that used the Pythagorean Theorem or its converse to solve a real-world problem, and an **Exercise** that involved the use of the Pythagorean Theorem in an algebraic setting.

Algebra | Functions | Discrete Math | Probability | Data/Statistics

REFLECT

1. If you know the lengths of all three sides of a triangle, what can you learn about the angles? Explain and illustrate your answer.
2. Use figures to show the ratios of the side lengths for special right triangles. Then explain why those ratios must be true for each type of triangle.
3. Explain how the figure at the right shows the relationship of the Pythagorean Theorem to the equation of a circle.

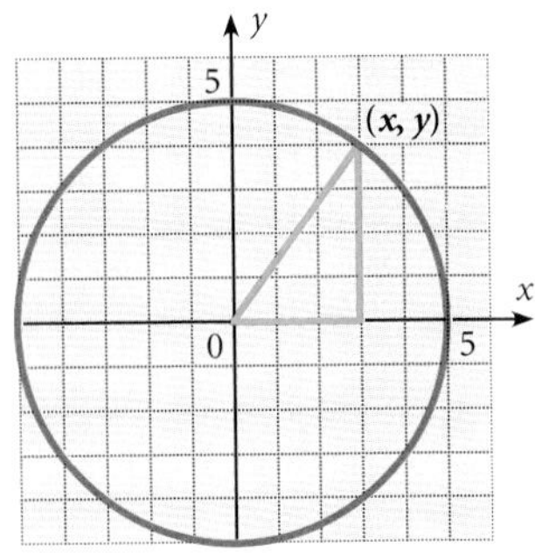

Self-Assessment

P **The shorter sides of a triangle are 6 cm and 8 cm long. Find a length for the longest side so that the triangle is**

1. a right triangle $c = 10$ cm　　2. an acute triangle $c < 10$ cm　　3. an obtuse triangle $c > 10$

P 4. If you hike 2 mi north, 5 mi east, 4 mi north, 7 mi east, then 1 mi south, what is the distance from your final location to the starting point? (b)

(a) $\sqrt{29}$ mi　(b) 13 mi　(c) 19 mi　(d) $\sqrt{150}$ mi　(e) not here

P **Find the probability that a point selected at random will be in the shaded area of each figure. [5-1, 5-2]**

5. 0.205

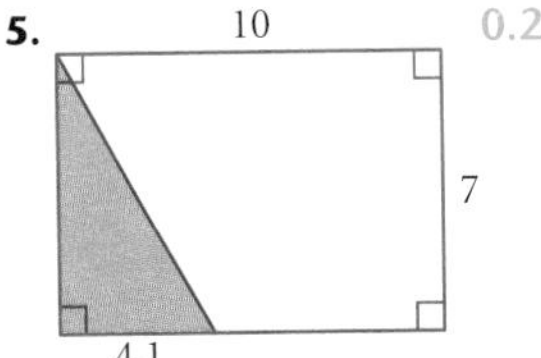

6. 0.261

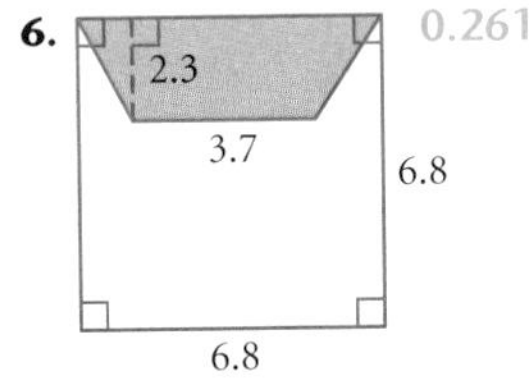

MR 7. **A Stable Shed** Leilani is building a rectangular frame for a wall of a shed. She knows that rectangles are unstable, so she wants to add a diagonal support to the frame. To the nearest centimeter, how long should the support be? Explain your answer.

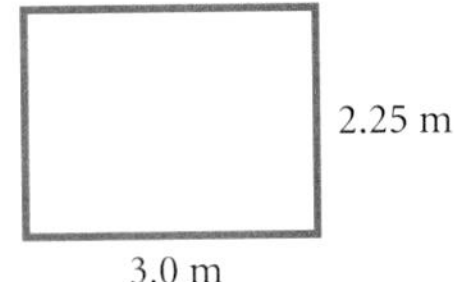

P 8. The point (6, −8) is on a circle with center (0, 0). Find the radius of the circle, and then write the equation of the circle. $x^2 + y^2 = 100$

Key

- V Vocabulary
- P Practice/Skills
- R Review
- MR Math Reasoning
- PS Problem Solving
- C Challenge

9. "A" Home Find the height of the A-frame home shown at the right. Round your answer to the nearest tenth of a foot. 34.6 ft

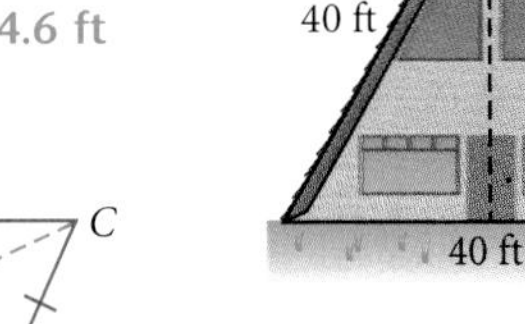

10. Complete the following proof. [4-2, 4-3]

Given: Quadrilateral $ABCD$ with $\overline{AB} \cong \overline{CD}$ and $\overline{BC} \cong \overline{AD}$

Prove: $\angle BAC \cong \angle DCA$

Proof:

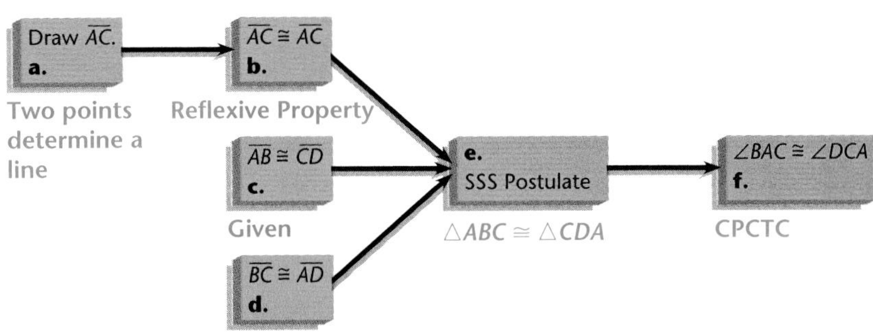

11. Find all possible lengths of segments whose endpoints are points on the 4×4 grid shown. (Assume the distance between adjacent vertical and horizontal points is 1.)

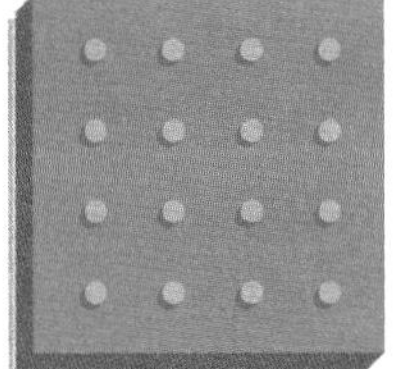

12. In the sequence of right triangles shown below, the original triangle (at the far right) is an isosceles right triangle with legs of length 1. Each additional right triangle is built with one leg on the hypotenuse of the preceding triangle and the other leg of length 1.

a. Find x. $\sqrt{7}$

b. If a dart is thrown randomly at this "target," what is the probability that it will hit the largest triangle? Express your answer as a decimal rounded to the nearest hundredth. 0.23

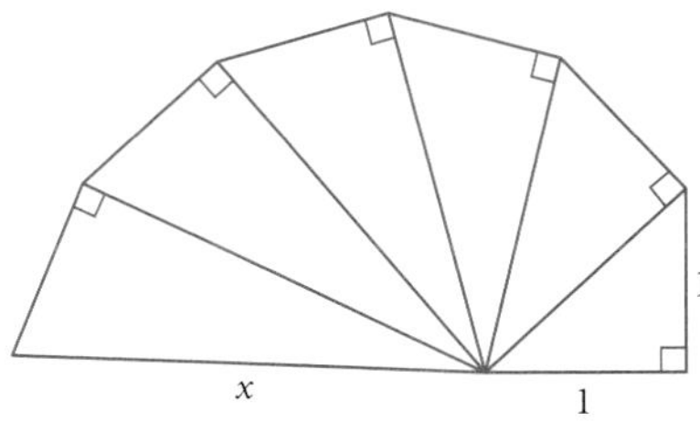
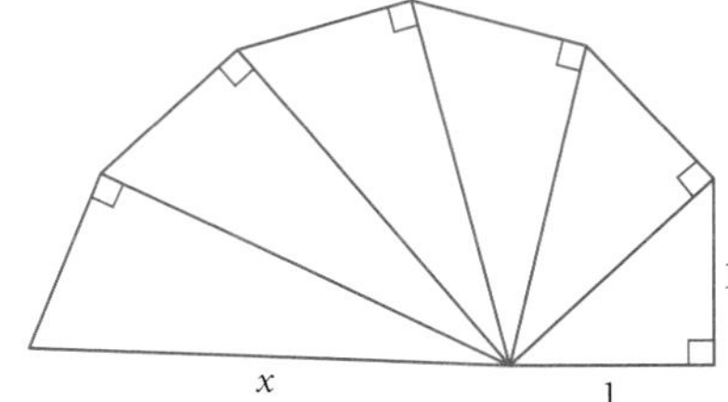

REFLECT

Possible Answers

1. You can use the converse of the Pythagorean Theorem and its related inequalities to determine whether the triangle is acute, right, or obtuse. If it is a right triangle, you can use the longest side (the hypotenuse) to identify the right angle.

2.

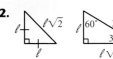

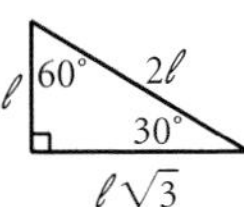

We can show that the first pattern is true by applying the Pythagorean Theorem to an isosceles right triangle; the second, by applying the theorem to half of an equilateral triangle.

3. By drawing the given triangle, we can see that the x-coordinate of the point represents the length of one leg of a right triangle, the y-coordinate represents the length of the other leg, and the radius represents the length of the hypotenuse. Therefore, for this point, $x^2 + y^2 = r^2$.

Self-Assessment

Exercise Notes

8. Students use the distance formula to find the radius of a circle; then they write an equation for the circle.

12. Students see a famous right-triangle "spiral." This exercise generates an interesting sequence of right-triangle side lengths.

Self-Assessment Answers

7. $\sqrt{300^2 + 225^2} = 375$ cm

11. $1, \sqrt{2}, 2, \sqrt{5}, 2\sqrt{2}, 3, \sqrt{10}, \sqrt{13}, 3\sqrt{2}$

ssessment Resources

iz 5-3

apter Assessment Form A

apter Assessment Form B

apter Alternative Assessment

d-Year Assessment

d-of-Year Assessment

VSMTest and practice software

Ongoing Assessment

Self-Assessment Self-Assessment Exercises

Embedded Assessment Reflect 1, 2, 3

Algebra | Functions | Discrete Math | Probability | Data/Statistics

Chapter 5 Review

Journal

Students can identify **Key Terms** that they do not understand, and look up the definitions in the indicated section or in the glossary. Non-English-speaking students may want to use the *Multilingual Handbook.*

Vocabulary exercises and the **Self-Evaluation** are useful journal entries.

Review Answers

11. $x^2 + 8x + 15$

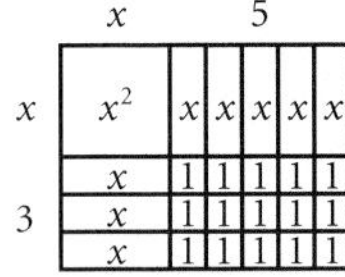

12. $(x + 10)(x + 2)$

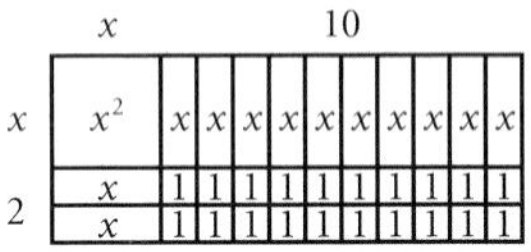

15. $AQ = 14$, $BN = 30$

16. Possible answer: Show that $\triangle JNK \cong \triangle LNM$ and $\triangle JNM \cong \triangle LNK$, using the SAS Postulate. Use CPCTC to show alternate interior angles congruent, so the sides are parallel.

20. Applying the Pythagorean Theorem to points on a coordinate plane gives the distance formula. Using the distance formula to find all points on a plane a given distance from the center point gives the equation for a circle.

Chapter 5 Review

The measurement of area is among the oldest and most common applications of mathematics. In Chapter 5, you learned how to determine and use areas of various polygonal regions. You also learned how to apply the concept of area to quadratic equations, geometric probability, and the proof of the Pythagorean Theorem.

KEY TERMS

area [5-1]	polygonal region [5-1]	rectangle [5-2]
geometric probability [5-1]	Pythagorean triple [5-3]	rhombus [5-2]
parallelogram [5-2]	quadratic equation [5-1]	square [5-2]
perimeter [5-1]	quadrilateral [5-2]	trapezoid [5-2]
polygon [5-1]		

V **Determine whether each statement is true or false. If the statement is false, change the underlined word or phrase to make it true.**

1. The area of a polygonal region is the sum of the areas of all of its <u>overlapping</u> parts. F; Non-overlapping

2. A <u>quadratic formula</u> is of the form $ax^2 + bx + c = 0$. F; Quadratic equation

3. A <u>parallelogram</u> is a quadrilateral with two pairs of parallel sides. T

4. A quadrilateral with four right angles is a <u>square.</u> F; Rectangle

CONCEPTS AND APPLICATIONS

P **Find the area of each figure. [5-1]**

5.

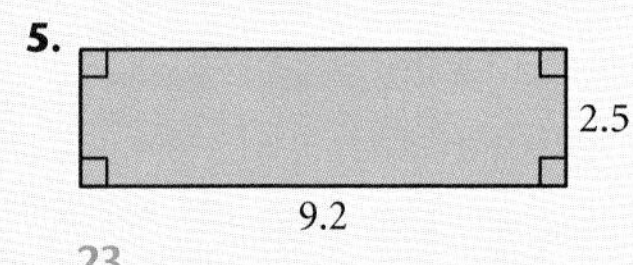

23

6.

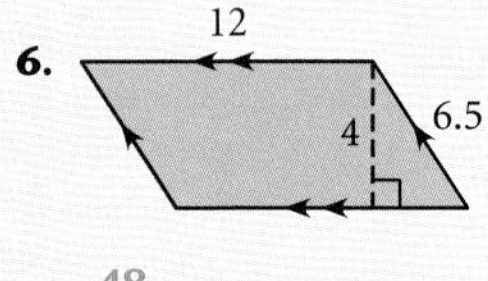

48

7.

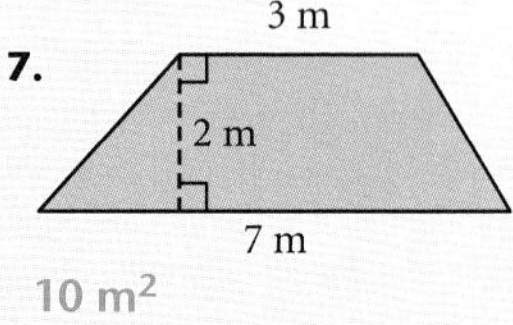

10 m²

P **Find the perimeter of each figure. [5-1, 5-2, 5-3]**

8. Rhombus *XYZW* $8\frac{1}{2}$ in.

X Y W Z $2\frac{1}{8}$ in.

9. 17.07 cm

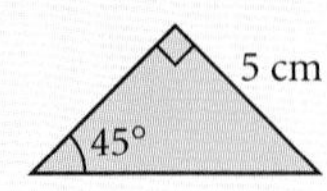

10. Square *RSTU* 288 m

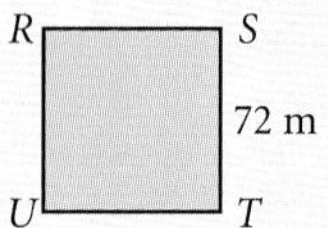

Key

V Vocabulary
P Practice/Skills
R Review
MR Math Reasoning
PS Problem Solving
C Challenge

Represent each of the following, using squares and rectangles. Provide a sketch, and give an algebraic answer. [5-1]

11. Multiply $(x + 5)$ and $(x + 3)$.

12. Factor $x^2 + 12x + 20$.

13. A hockey player's slap shot from 20 ft away from the goal will hit randomly within the outer rectangle. The identical shaded regions are that part of the open goal that the goalie cannot defend. [5-1]

a. What is the total area of the shaded regions? 6.25 ft^2

b. To the nearest hundredth, what is the probability that the shot will hit in the shaded regions, resulting in a score? 0.16

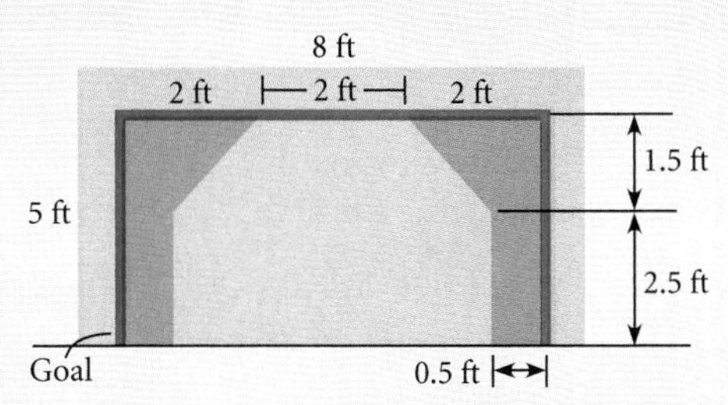

14. A 4″ × 5″ photograph is to be mounted within a mat of width x. [5-1]

a. What is the total area of the photograph and the mat in terms of x? $4x^2 + 18x + 20$ in.

b. If the total area is 40 in.^{2}, what is the width of the mat to the nearest tenth of an inch? 0.9

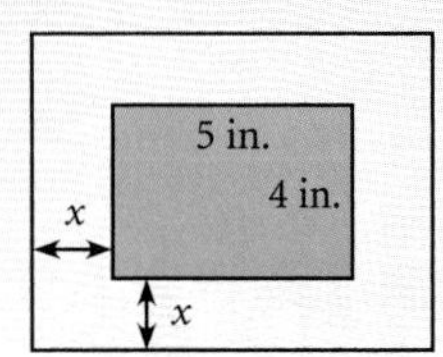

15. In $\triangle ABC$, $\overline{AM}$ and $\overline{BN}$ are medians and point Q is the centroid. $AM = 21$ and $QN = 10$. Find AQ and BN. [4-3]

16. The diagonals of quadrilateral $JKLM$ bisect each other. *Plan* a logical argument to show that $JKLM$ is a parallelogram. [5-2]

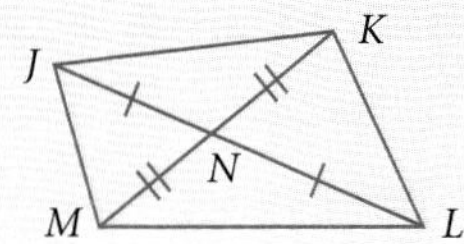

17. Find the approximate area between the x-axis and the graph of the equation $y = \sqrt{x}$ from $x = 0$ to 9, using the trapezoid method. Use trapezoids of height 3. [5-2] 17.04

18. What is the length of the cut where the sides of the picture frame are joined? [5-3] $4\sqrt{2}$ cm ≈ 5.66 cm

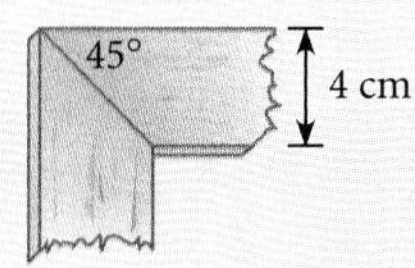

19. Find the length of the diagonal across a rectangular 20″ × 25″ television screen. [5-3] 32.0 in.

20. Write a summary of the relationships among the equation of a circle, the distance formula, and the Pythagorean Theorem. [5-3]

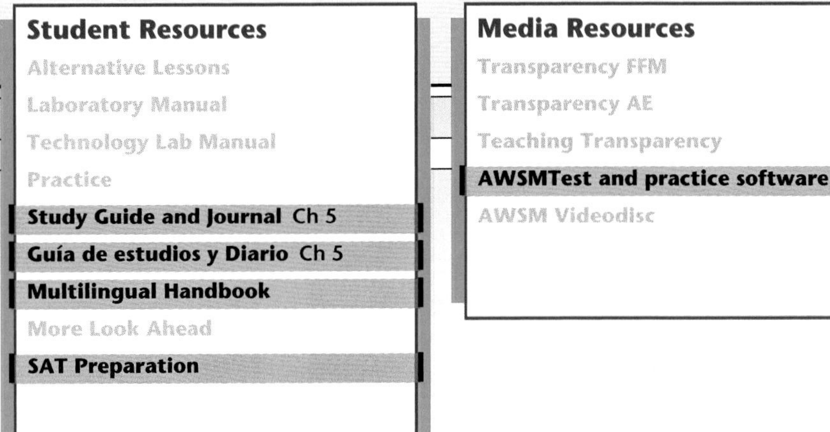

Student Resources
Alternative Lessons
Laboratory Manual
Technology Lab Manual
Practice
Study Guide and Journal Ch 5
Guía de estudios y Diario Ch 5
Multilingual Handbook
More Look Ahead
SAT Preparation
Media Resources
Transparency FFM
Transparency AE
Teaching Transparency
AWSMTest and practice software
AWSM Videodisc

21. Possible answer: The farmer will prefer a plan that maximizes the area.

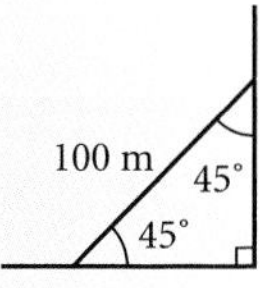

$$\text{Area} = \frac{1}{2}\left(\frac{100}{\sqrt{2}}\right)^2 = 2500\text{ m}^2$$

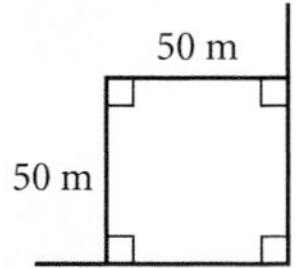

$$\text{Area} = (50)(50) = 2500\text{ m}^2$$

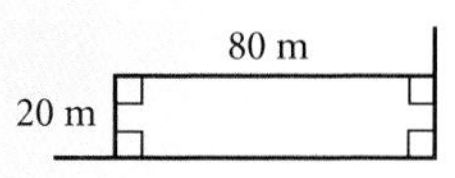

$$\text{Area} = (80)(20) = 1600\text{ m}^2$$

Chapter 5 Assessment

Portfolio

Students may select items that represent their mathematical understanding of the ideas in Chapter 5 and that illustrate the effort that they put into this chapter.

A rubric for assessing portfolios is included in the introduction to the Teacher's Edition.

Assessment Answers

7. $x^2 + 7x + 12$

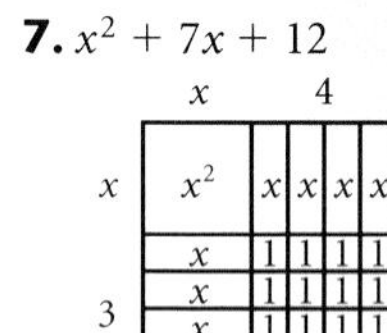

8. $(x + 6)(x + 1)$

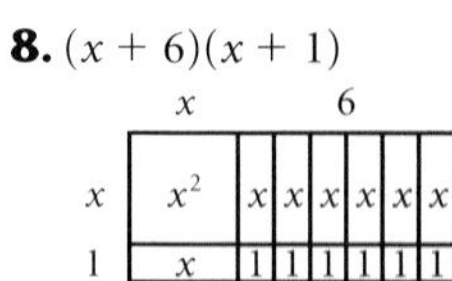

10. Possible answer: Use the ASA Postulate to show that the two triangles are congruent.

16. Find the sum of the squares of the lengths of the two shorter sides. If it is equal to, greater than, or less than the square of the length of the third side, then the triangle is a right triangle, an acute triangle, or an obtuse triangle, respectively.

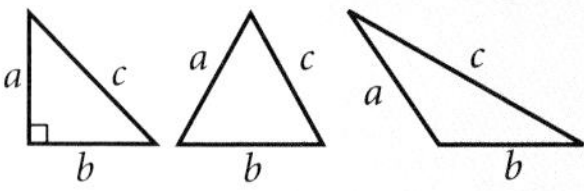

CONCEPTS AND CONNECTIONS

MR, PS **21. Construction** A farmer has 100 m of fencing to section off a corner of land for a new crop. One possible placement of the fence is shown. Make three other proposals for the placement of the fence. For each proposal, provide a sketch of the fence, showing as many dimensions as possible, and include information on the area of the fenced-off region. Which of your proposals do you think would be most appealing to the farmer? Why?

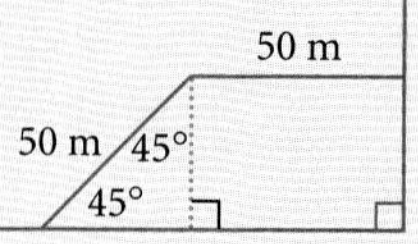

SELF-EVALUATION

Write a summary of the most important facts that you have learned from Chapter 5. Include facts about various quadrilaterals and right triangles as well as key formulas for determining areas and side lengths. Provide a sketch to illustrate each fact.

Chapter 5 Assessment

TEST

P **Find the area of each figure.**

1. $93\frac{1}{2}$ in.^{2} **2.** 39 **3.** 497 cm^2 **4.** 20 m^2

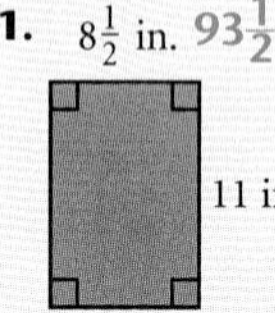

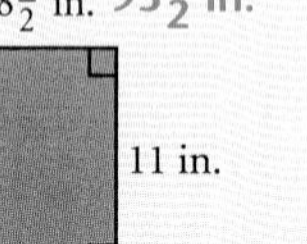

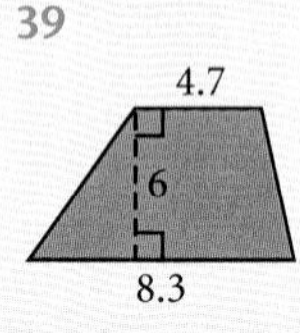

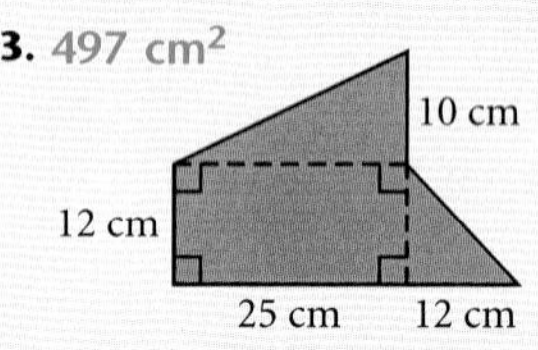

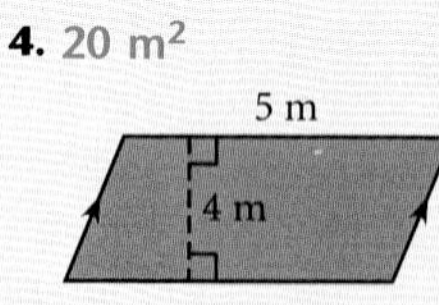

P **Find the length of each cable in the figure. Explain your method.**

5. Cable 1 $\sqrt{36^2 + 15^2} = 39$ m

6. Cable 2 72 m; 30°–60°–90° triangle

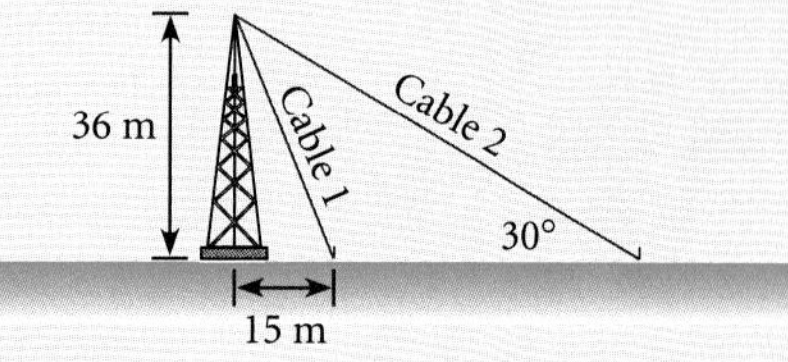

P **Represent each of the following using squares and rectangles. Provide a sketch, and give an algebraic answer.**

7. Multiply $(x + 4)$ and $(x + 3)$.

8. Factor $x^2 + 7x + 6$.

Assessment Resources

- Quiz
- Chapter 5 Assessment Form A
- Chapter 5 Assessment Form B
- Chapter 5 Alternative Assessment
- Mid-Year Assessment
- End-of-Year Assessment
- AWSMTest Chapter 5

Ongoing Assessment

Self-Assessment Chapter 5 Review and Self-Evaluation

Embedded Assessment Chapter 5 Performance Task

Test Chapter 5 Test

9. For what value of x will the area of the larger rectangle be three times that of the smaller one? 7.79

10. *Plan* a logical argument to show that a diagonal of a parallelogram divides it into two congruent triangles.

11. A slow-pitch softball pitcher with good control will always land her pitch within the outer rectangle in the figure. If the pitch lands within the shaded region, it is a strike.

a. What is the area of the shaded region? 208.25 in.^{2}

b. To the nearest hundredth, what is the probability that the pitch will be a strike? 0.35

12. Find the approximate area between the x-axis and the graph of the equation $y = x^2$ from $x = 0$ to 3, using the trapezoid method. Use trapezoids of height 1. 9.5

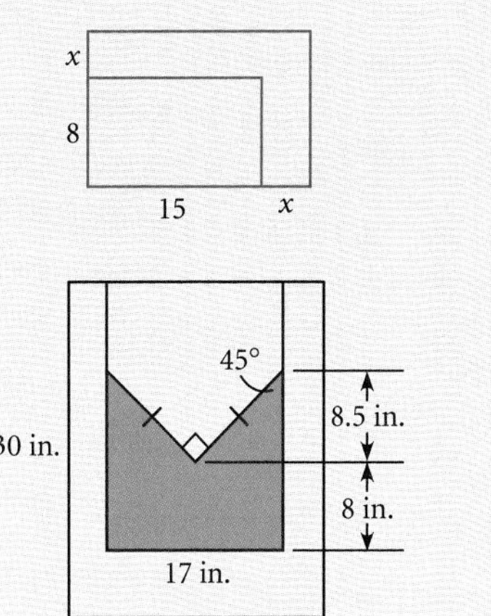

Find the perimeter of each figure.

13. Rhombus $GHIJ$ 16.8 m

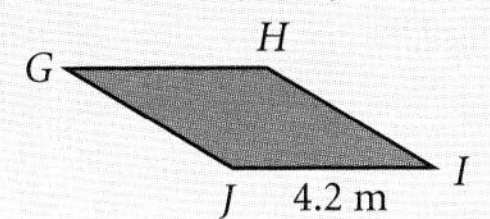

14. 9.46 in.

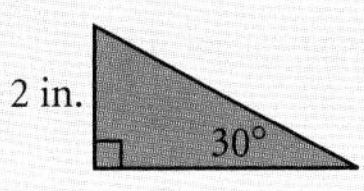

15. 27.31

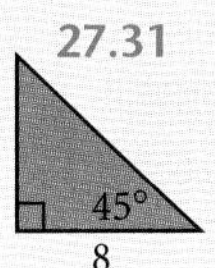

16. Write a summary of the methods for determining whether a triangle is right, acute, or obtuse when the lengths of its sides are known. Include sketches to illustrate the methods.

17. In $\triangle KLM$, $\overline{KW}$ and $\overline{LZ}$ are medians, $KW = 40$, and $LC = 12$. Find KC and LZ. $KC = \frac{80}{3}$, $LZ = 18$

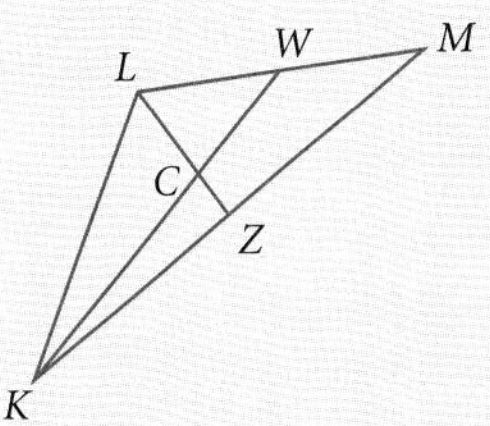

PERFORMANCE TASK

RSTU is a parallelogram, and *V* is any point in the interior of the parallelogram. Investigate how the area of the shaded region is related to the area of the parallelogram. Make a conjecture, and write a *plan* to justify your conjecture deductively.

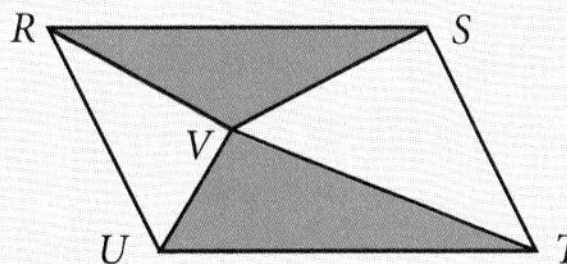

Performance Task

Answer

The area of the shaded triangles is half the area of the parallelogram.

Suggested Scoring Rubric

Level 4 Full Accomplishment

- Student makes correct conjecture that the sum of the areas of the triangles is half the area of the parallelogram.
- *Plan* for proof is valid, clear, and to the point. Uses idea that the sum of the heights of the two triangles must equal the height of the parallelogram.

Level 3 Substantial Accomplishment

- Student makes correct conjecture that the sum of the areas of the triangles is half the area of the parallelogram.
- Student may make the invalid assumption that the interior point is the point of intersection of the diagonals.
- *Plan* for proof is valid and uses idea that the sum of the heights of the two triangles must equal the height of the parallelogram. *Plan* may be vague in some areas or contain unnecessary information.

Level 2 Partial Accomplishment

- Student makes correct conjecture that the sum of the areas of the triangles is half the area of the parallelogram.
- Student may make the invalid assumption that the interior point is the point of intersection of the diagonals.
- *Plan* for proof is invalid.

Level 1 Little Accomplishment

- Student makes incorrect conjecture about the sum of the areas of the triangles.

6

Chapter 6 Polygons and Polyhedrons

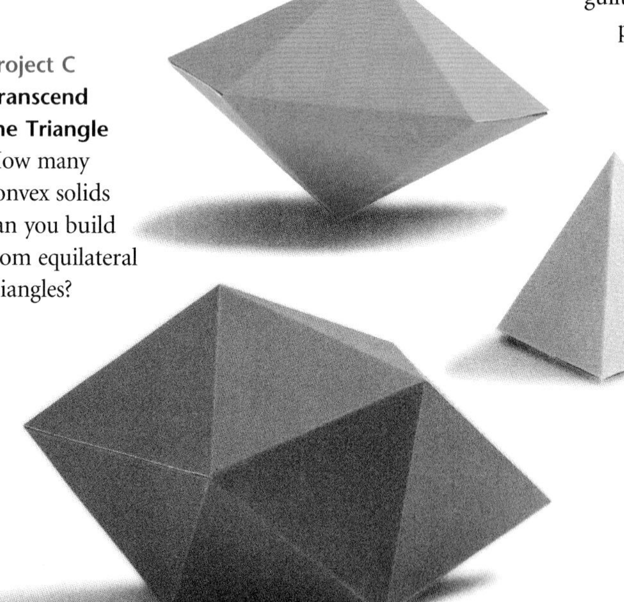

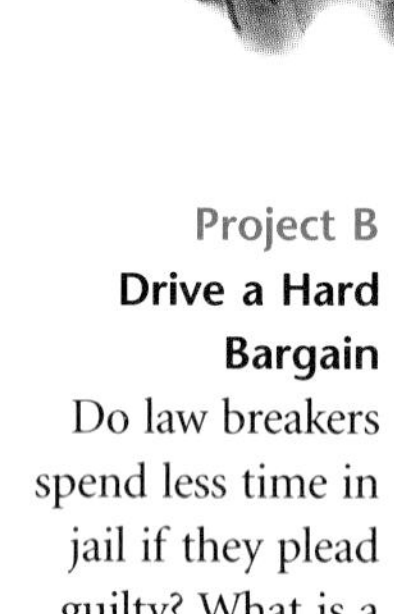

Project A

Model a Molecule

What are crystals, and how are they formed?

Project B

Drive a Hard Bargain

Do law breakers spend less time in jail if they plead guilty? What is a plea bargain?

Project C

Transcend the Triangle

How many convex solids can you build from equilateral triangles?

A

Chapter 6 / Project A **Model a Molecule**

Model a Common Crystal

Build a 3-D model or design a poster that shows the structure of a crystal substance.

- Did you know that graphite is a hexagonal mineral?
- Don't you wonder what the geometric structure of a diamond is?
- How does this connect to Chapter 6? Crystals have a **polyhedral** structure.

Expand Your Vocabulary

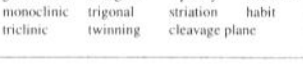

goniometer, tetragonal, lapidary, fracture, monoclinic, trigonal, striation, habit, triclinic, twinning, cleavage plane

Many amateur geologists have impressive collections of mineral and rock specimens. If you decide to go rock hunting, use a guide book, respect private and public property, and take a friend. Wear a helmet, and wear safety goggles if you chip or hammer rocks.

Project Guidelines

Investigate

- Visit a natural history museum. Look for symmetry in the exposed faces of rocks and minerals.
- Read about crystals in a high school chemistry book, in a geology book, or in an encyclopedia.
- Handle a crystal sample in a lapidary shop or in a hands-on museum exhibit.

Set Your Direction

- Which substance (or substances) will you study?
- Will you make a model of it from a paper net? from sticks and balls?
- Will you make a poster about crystal structure?

Make a Plan

- Make a calendar for each day's work. Check in with your group and with your teacher.
- Decide what you'll need. Some tools to gather: protractor, art or model materials

Collect and Organize Your Information

- Choose one or more crystal specimens to study.
- Use your protractor to measure the cleavage angle. Find the axis of symmetry.
- Determine some features of the crystal. For example, is it monoclinic or triclinic?
- Sketch out your poster or plan your model.

Carry Out Your Plan

- Finish your model or poster.
- Explain the features of the minerals you are showing and tell how they were formed.
- Explain how a geologist would distinguish this crystal from similar-looking rocks.

Look Back

- Why is it hard to see the symmetry in some mineral specimens?
- What practical applications for crystals did you learn about?
- What should you have done differently?

Focus on Geometry 31

C

Chapter 6 / Project C **Transcend the Triangle**

Model the Deltahedrons

Draw and assemble nets for the convex deltahedrons (solids whose sides are equilateral triangles).

- Did you know that not all deltahedrons are regular solids?
- Don't you wonder how many convex deltahedrons there are?
- How does this connect to Chapter 6? A deltahedron is one kind of **polyhedron.**

Expand Your Vocabulary

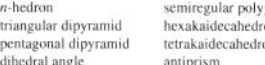

n-hedron, semiregular polygon, triangular dipyramid, hexakaidecahedron, pentagonal dipyramid, tetrakaidecahedron, dihedral angle, antiprism

This solid is a decahedron. The prefix *deca* is Greek, meaning 10 and the net for the decahedron has 10 equilateral triangles. The other eight convex deltahedrons also have names formed from Greek words that reveal the number of triangles in their nets.

Project Guidelines

Investigate

- Read more about polyhedrons and Euler's Theorem in a book about solid geometry.
- Experiment with nets of equilateral triangles to see which ones will fold into polyhedrons.

Set Your Direction

- Will you simply draw the nets and model the deltahedrons you discover?
- Or will you compare their symmetries and other interesting features as well?
- Will you display your models on a tray? as a mobile?

Make a Plan

- Make a calendar for each day's work. Check in with your group and with your teacher.
- Gather materials. You'll need: stiff paper, tape, craft knife or scissors, compass or protractor

Collect and Organize Your Information

- Draw nets for deltahedrons with 4, 6, 8, 10, 12, 14, 16, and 20 faces.
- Make tracings or copies of each net for reference.
- Cut out the equilateral triangle nets.
- ***Safety first:*** Be careful with sharp instruments.

Carry Out Your Plan

- Fold and tape your nets to form solids.
- Examine the model and the net of each deltahedron. Tell whether it is a regular polyhedron using Euler's Theorem.

Look Back

- Which of the deltahedrons might fill 3-D space without leaving any empty holes?
- Is there a way to tell from a net of triangles whether it will fold into a solid?
- Is there more than one configuration for a net that will fold into the same solid?

Focus on Geometry 35

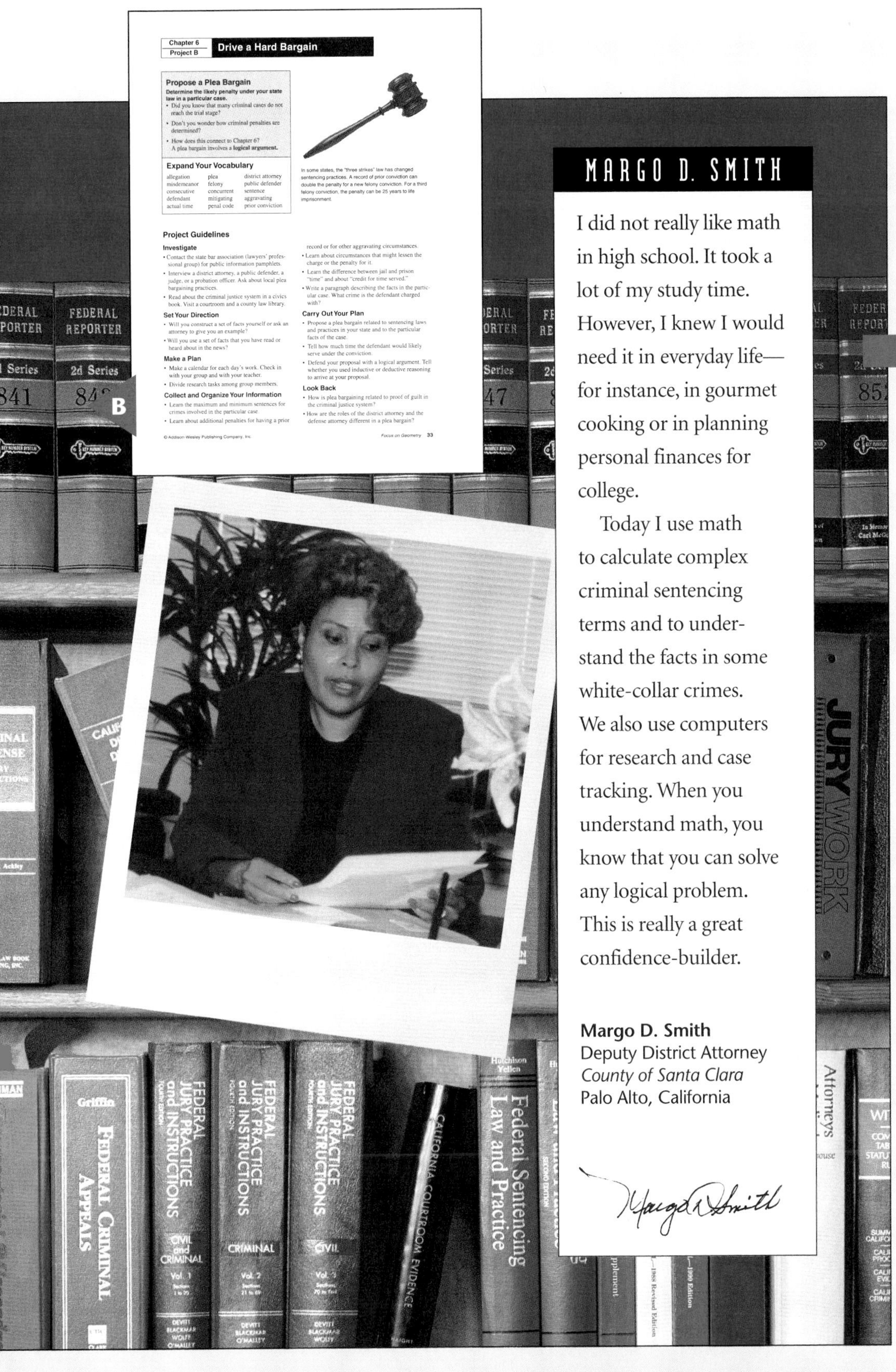

Chapter 6
Project B

Drive a Hard Bargain

Propose a Plea Bargain

Determine the likely penalty under your state law in a particular case.

- Did you know that many criminal cases do not reach the trial stage?
- Don't you wonder how criminal penalties are determined?
- How does this connect to Chapter 6?
  A plea bargain involves a **logical argument.**

Expand Your Vocabulary

allegation	plea	district attorney
misdemeanor	felony	public defender
consecutive	concurrent	sentence
defendant	mitigating	aggravating
actual time	penal code	prior conviction

In some states, the "three strikes" law has changed sentencing practices. A record of prior conviction can double the penalty for a new felony conviction. For a third felony conviction, the penalty can be 25 years to life imprisonment.

Project Guidelines

Investigate

- Contact the state bar association (lawyers' professional group) for public information pamphlets.
- Interview a district attorney, a public defender, a judge, or a probation officer. Ask about local plea bargaining practices.
- Read about the criminal justice system in a civics book. Visit a courtroom and a county law library.

Set Your Direction

- Will you construct a set of facts yourself or ask an attorney to give you an example?
- Will you use a set of facts that you have read or heard about in the news?

Make a Plan

- Make a calendar for each day's work. Check in with your group and with your teacher.
- Divide research tasks among group members.

Collect and Organize Your Information

- Learn the maximum and minimum sentences for crimes involved in the particular case.
- Learn about additional penalties for having a prior record or for other aggravating circumstances.
- Learn about circumstances that might lessen the charge or the penalty for it.
- Learn the difference between jail and prison "time" and about "credit for time served."
- Write a paragraph describing the facts in the particular case. What crime is the defendant charged with?

Carry Out Your Plan

- Propose a plea bargain related to sentencing laws and practices in your state and to the particular facts of the case.
- Tell how much time the defendant would likely serve under the conviction.
- Defend your proposal with a logical argument. Tell whether you used inductive or deductive reasoning to arrive at your proposal.

Look Back

- How is plea bargaining related to proof of guilt in the criminal justice system?
- How are the roles of the district attorney and the defense attorney different in a plea bargain?

MARGO D. SMITH

I did not really like math in high school. It took a lot of my study time. However, I knew I would need it in everyday life—for instance, in gourmet cooking or in planning personal finances for college.

Today I use math to calculate complex criminal sentencing terms and to understand the facts in some white-collar crimes. We also use computers for research and case tracking. When you understand math, you know that you can solve any logical problem. This is really a great confidence-builder.

Margo D. Smith
Deputy District Attorney
County of Santa Clara
Palo Alto, California

Biographical Note

Margo Smith graduated from Rossford High School in Rossford, Ohio. She took Algebra, Geometry, Algebra II, and Trigonometry.

Chapter 6

Overview

Polygons and Polyhedrons

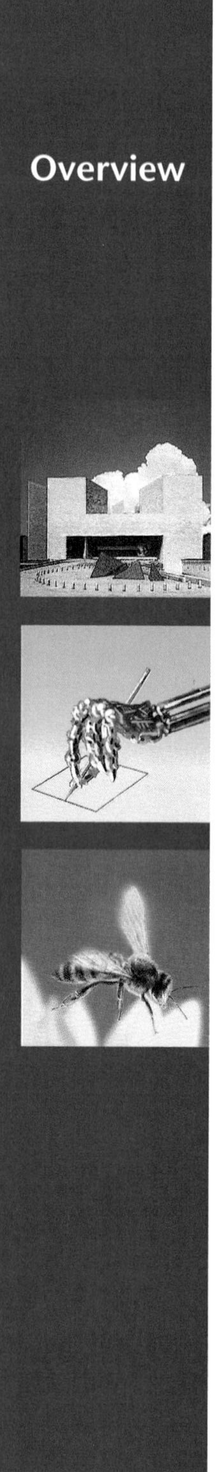

6-1 Polygons and Polyhedrons

Polyhedrons are present in both manufactured and naturally occurring objects. Now you will discover properties of polygons, and learn how polygons are related to polyhedrons. You will also explore some characteristics of polyhedrons.

6-2 Deductive Proof with Quadrilaterals

Knowledge of the properties of specific types of quadrilaterals is important in many professions, including carpentry and product design. You will investigate properties of several quadrilaterals and develop skills in demonstrating deductive proof.

6-3 Regular Polygons and Polyhedrons

Honeybees, gem cutters, and even the Greek philosopher, Plato, have found regular polygons and polyhedrons useful. You will investigate the properties of these figures.

CHAPTERS

394

Chapter 6 Planning Guide

The following ancillaries are recommended for each course level. The additional resources, *Technology Lab Manual, Study Guide and Journal, Multilingual Handbook,* and *Assessment,* are recommended for all levels.

	Comprehensive Course	Core Course	Informal Course
6-1 Part A	▲	▲	▲
Alternative Lessons			▲
Laboratory Manuals	▲	▲	▲
Practice			▲
More Look Ahead		▲	▲
6-1 Part B	▲	▲	▲
Alternative Lessons			▲
Laboratory Manuals	▲	▲	▲
Practice			▲
More Look Back		▲	▲
6-1 Part C	▲	▲	▲
Alternative Lessons			▲
Laboratory Manuals	▲	▲	▲
Practice			▲
More Look Ahead		▲	▲
6-1 Part D	▲	▲	▲
More Look Back		▲	▲
Quiz 6-1	▲	▲	▲
6-2 Part A	▲	▲	▲
Alternative Lessons			▲
Laboratory Manuals	▲	▲	▲
Practice			▲
More Look Ahead		▲	▲
6-2 Part B	▲	▲	▲
Alternative Lessons			▲
Laboratory Manuals	▲	▲	▲
Practice			▲

	Comprehensive Course	Core Course	Informal Course
More Look Back		▲	▲
6-2 Part C	▲	▲	▲
Alternative Lessons			▲
Laboratory Manuals	▲	▲	▲
Practice			▲
More Look Ahead		▲	▲
6-2 Part D	▲	▲	▲
Alternative Lessons			▲
Laboratory Manuals	▲	▲	▲
Practice			▲
More Look Back		▲	▲
6-2 Part E	▲	▲	
More Look Back		▲	
Quiz 6-2	▲	▲	
6-3 Part A	▲	▲	▲
Alternative Lessons			▲
Laboratory Manuals	▲	▲	▲
Practice			▲
More Look Back		▲	▲
6-3 Part B	▲	▲	▲
Alternative Lessons			▲
Laboratory Manuals	▲	▲	▲
Practice			▲
More Look Ahead		▲	▲
6-3 Part C	▲	▲	▲
More Look Back		▲	▲
Quiz 6-3	▲	▲	▲

BIBLIOGRAPHY

Teacher Resources

Build Your Own Polyhedra, Peter Hilton and Jean Pedersen. Addison-Wesley, 1988 (22060).

Polyhedra Primer, Peter Pearce and Susan Pearce. © 1978 by Peter Pearce and Susan Pearce. Available through Dale Seymour Publications (NS01335).

Reading for Teachers

Thinking Connections: Learning to Think and Thinking to Learn, David N. Perkins, Heidi Goodrich, Shari Tishman, Jill Mirman Owen. Addison-Wesley, 1994 (81998).

AI: The Tumultuous History of the Search for Artificial Intelligence, Daniel Crevier. © 1993 by Daniel Crevier. Published by BasicBooks, a division of HarperCollins Publishers, Inc.

6-1

Polygons and Polyhedrons

SUPERLESSON AT A GLANCE

Superlesson Goal

Students will explore properties of polygons and polyhedrons, including the measures of interior and exterior angles of polygons.

Management Guide

	Topic	Objectives	Key Terms	New Ideas	Materials
Part A	Exploring Quadrilaterals	To see relationships among different quadrilaterals, and to discover that the sum of their interior angle measures is 360°.	Diagonal, convex quadrilateral, concave quadrilateral	Using a "family tree" to show relationships among quadrilaterals. The sum of the measures of the interior angles of a quadrilateral is 360°.	**Student** Protractor, straightedge, geometry software
Part B	Exploring Polygons	To classify polygons and discover properties of the measures of their interior and exterior angles.	Polygon, diagonal of a polygon, convex polygon, concave polygon	Classifying polygons. The sum of the measures of the interior angles of an n-gon is $(n - 2)180°$; the sum of the measures of the exterior angles is 360°.	**Student** Straightedge, geometry software
Part C	Exploring Polyhedrons	To classify polyhedrons, and to discover Euler's Formula.	Polyhedron	Classifying polyhedrons. Euler's Formula.	**Teacher** Models of polyhedrons
Part D	Making Connections	To investigate which types of polygons will tessellate a plane.	In Making Connections, students apply and synthesize key terms and new ideas.		**Student** Paper, straightedge, scissors

Pacing Chart (45-Minute Periods)

	Comprehensive Course	Core Course	Informal Course
Part A	1	2	2
Part B	1	2	2
Part C	1	1	1
Part D	1	1	1
TOTAL periods for Superlesson	4	6	6

NCTM Standards

Mathematics as Problem Solving

Mathematics as Communication

Mathematics as Reasoning

Mathematical Connections

Discrete Mathematics

6-1 Polygons and Polyhedrons

GEOMETRIC CONSTRUCTION ZONE

Ieoh Ming Pei, a Chinese-born American architect, is noted for his beautifully-designed urban buildings and complexes. Pei's innovative East Building of the National Gallery of Art, in Washington, D.C., is an elegant triangular composition that is recognized as one of his finest achievements. Pei created urban projects, such as the Mile High Center in Denver, the Hyde Park Redevelopment in Chicago, and the Place Ville-Marie in Montreal. As the winner of a 1960 competition, Pei was chosen to design the airline terminal at John F. Kennedy International Airport. He also designed the New York City Convention Center, the John Hancock Tower in Boston, the Gateway office complex in Singapore, the Beijing Fragrant Hill Hotel, the Dallas Municipal Center, and the controversial glass pyramid for a courtyard at the Louvre Museum in Paris. Pei is noted for his bold, skillful arrangements of geometric figures. The pyramids, prisms, and tetrahedrons seen in his designs are all types of polyhedrons.

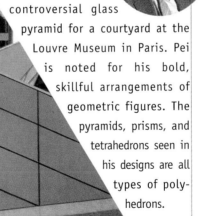

1. A pyramid and a cube are polyhedrons. A sphere and an egg are not. What do you think a polyhedron is?
2. Identify the two- and three-dimensional figures shown here in Pei's buildings.

Where Are We Now?

Students have discovered and used many different properties of triangles and quadrilaterals.

Where Are We Going?

In 6-1, students will review and extend their work on quadrilaterals and begin to explore polygons and polyhedrons. They will see how to classify these figures and investigate the measures of interior and exterior angles of polygons.

Students will use quadrilateral relationships in 6-2, where they prove properties of quadrilaterals. In 6-3, they will apply their knowledge of polygons and polyhedrons to regular polygons and polyhedrons.

Possible Answers

1. A three-dimensional figure with straight edges/polygonal sides.
2. Parallelograms, tetrahedrons, rectangles, rectangular solids.

More About Ieoh Ming Pei

I. M. Pei was born in Guangzhou, China, in 1917. He came to the United States to study architecture in 1935 and became a U.S. citizen in 1954. He began to develop his distinctive architectural style in the 1960s. Pei has designed many famous buildings, including the National Center for Atmospheric Research in Boulder, Colorado, and the John F. Kennedy Library in Boston.

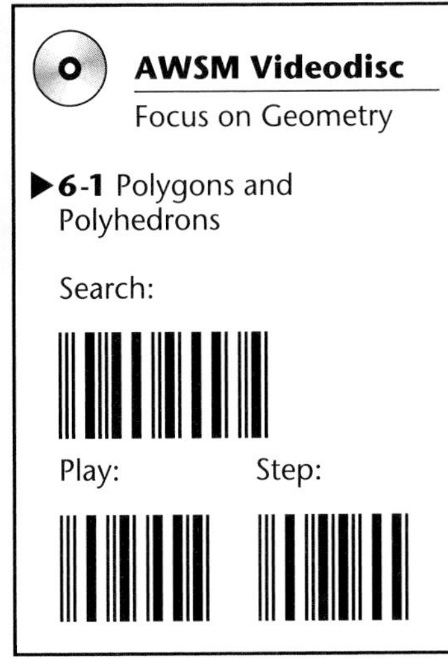

Algebra	Functions	Discrete Math	Probability	Data/Statistics

Polygons and Polyhedrons

PART A At a Glance

Objective

To see relationships among different quadrilaterals, and to discover that the sum of their interior angle measures is 360°.

Development

Students review definitions of familiar quadrilaterals. Then they see how the relationships among these quadrilaterals can be used to make a "family tree."

Next, in the **Explore,** students find that the sum of the measures of the interior angles of a convex quadrilateral is 360°.

Suggested Materials

Student Protractor, straightedge, geometry software

Key Terms

Diagonal, convex quadrilateral, concave quadrilateral

First Five Minutes

Transparency FFM 6-1A

Read the first two paragraphs on page 396. Then do **Try It a** and **b.**

Motivate

Ask...

- Are all squares rectangles? Yes
- Are some trapezoids squares? No
- Are all squares rhombuses? Yes

6-1 PART A Exploring Quadrilaterals

← CONNECT → *You've worked with the area of some special four-sided figures. Now you will investigate properties that hold for every quadrilateral.*

The surface of the pine cone at the left contains quadrilaterals. You know that a quadrilateral is a polygon with four sides. Some familiar quadrilaterals include squares, rectangles, parallelograms, and rhombuses.

We name a quadrilateral by listing its vertices in order. The quadrilateral at the right can be named *WXYZ, XWZY, YZWX,* or in several other ways. A **diagonal** of a quadrilateral is a line segment whose endpoints are opposite vertices.

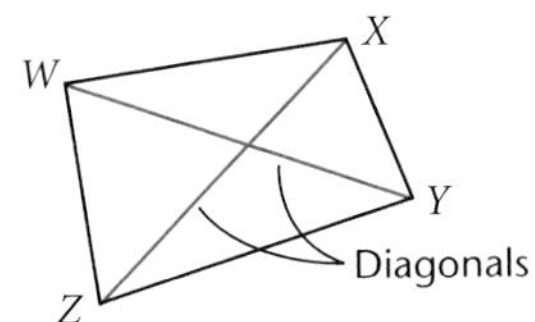

TRY IT

a. Possible answers: *DCBA, BADC, CDAB*

a. Name quadrilateral *ABCD* in three other ways.

b. Name the diagonals of *ABCD.* $\overline{DB}$, $\overline{AC}$

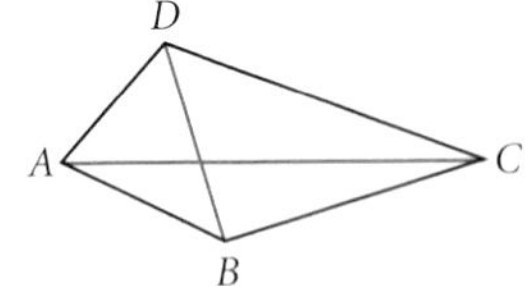

You already know about many special types of quadrilaterals. The definitions of some familiar ones are reviewed below.

DEFINITIONS

A **parallelogram** is a quadrilateral with two pairs of parallel sides.

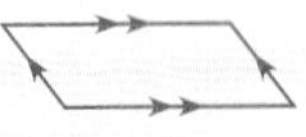

A **rectangle** is a quadrilateral with four right angles.

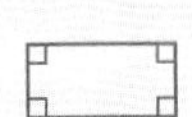

A **rhombus** is a quadrilateral with four congruent sides.

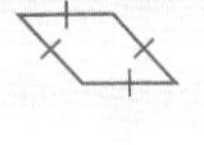

A **square** is a quadrilateral with four right angles and four congruent sides.

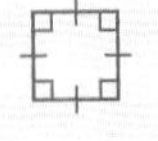

A **trapezoid** is a quadrilateral with exactly one pair of parallel sides.

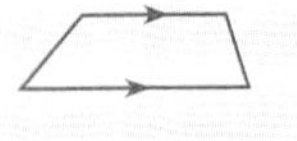

Research Note

When learning theorems, students often [incorporate] information contained in a specific diagram as part of a theorem (for instance, thinking that the exterior angle of a triangle must be obtuse because the diagram given with the theorem pictured an obtuse exterior angle). (Douglas H. Clements and Michael T. Battista, "Geometry and Spatial Reasoning," *Handbook of Research on Mathematics Teaching and Learning,* Douglas A. Grouws, ed., p. 448. © 1992 NCTM.)

The diagram below shows the relationships among these quadrilaterals. Each figure inherits all of the characteristics of the figure(s) above it that are connected to it.

A Quadrilateral Family Tree

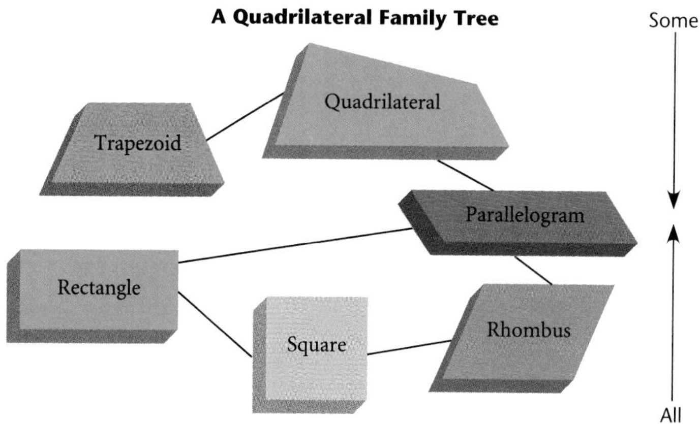

When you read the diagram downward, use the word *some* to note that "Some quadrilaterals are trapezoids," or "Some rhombuses are squares." When you read it upward, use the word *all* to note that "All squares are rectangles," or "All rhombuses are parallelograms." These properties can be proved, so you may use them as reasons in a deductive proof.

TRY IT

Possible answer: All tangles are parallelo- ms. All rectangles are adrilaterals. Some tangles are squares.

c. Classify the quadrilateral at the right. Rectangle

d. Use the quadrilateral family tree to write three true statements about this type of quadrilateral.

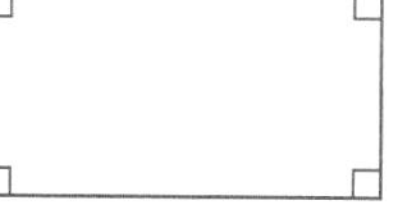

1. Explain why ***square*** is linked to both ***rhombus*** and ***rectangle*** in the quadrilateral family tree.

You have seen that there is an Angle-Sum Theorem for triangles. In the following Explore, you will investigate a similar theorem for quadrilaterals.

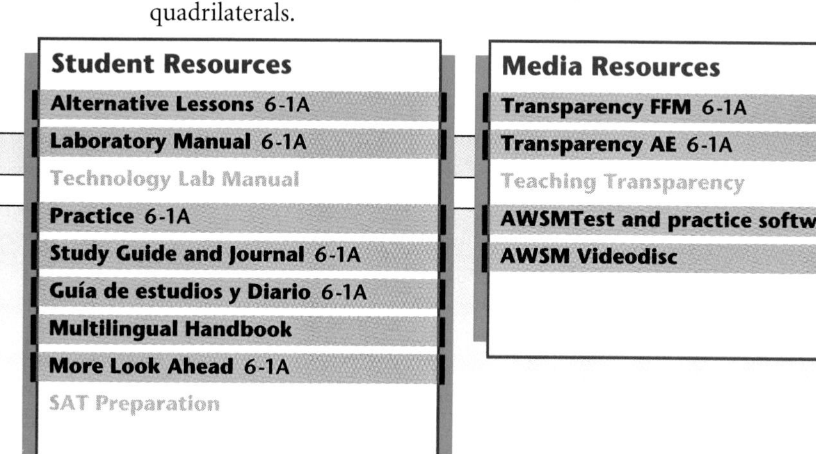

Student Resources
- Alternative Lessons 6-1A
- Laboratory Manual 6-1A
- Technology Lab Manual
- Practice 6-1A
- Study Guide and Journal 6-1A
- Guía de estudios y Diario 6-1A
- Multilingual Handbook
- More Look Ahead 6-1A
- SAT Preparation

Media Resources
- Transparency FFM 6-1A
- Transparency AE 6-1A
- Teaching Transparency
- AWSMTest and practice software
- AWSM Videodisc

Note: The quadrilateral family tree shows relationships that can be described by the words *all, some,* and *none.* Students should be familiar with the logical meanings of these terms from their work in Chapter 1.

Investigates how connections in the family tree show relationships among quadrilaterals.

Possible Answer

1. *Square* is linked to *rectangle* because both figures have four right angles. It is linked to *rhombus* because both figures have four congruent sides.

6-1

Polygons and Polyhedrons

Algebra | Functions | Discrete Math | Probability | Data/Statistics

EXPLORE

Quad Angles

Recommended group size: 4

The Point

To discover that the sum of the measures of the interior angles of a (convex) quadrilateral is 360°.

Look and Listen...

- For students who do not investigate figures with "dents" (concave figures).

Ask...

- What happens if you explore a quadrilateral with a "dent" in it?

For Groups That Finish Early

Draw a quadrilateral with a "dent." If you had to measure its interior "nonangle," how would you do it? What is the sum of the interior angle measures in this case? **Measure as an angle of rotation (subtract exterior angle measure from 360°). The sum of the interior angle measures is then 360°.**

Follow Up

Ask students to state the sum of the interior angle measures of a quadrilateral and give any exceptions to this rule.

Possible Answers

1–2. The sum of the interior angle measures of a quadrilateral is 360°.

3. A quadrilateral with a "dent" (*concave* quadrilateral) has only three measurable interior angles. The sum of its angle measures is not 360°.

ALTERNATE EXAMPLE

Transparency AE 6-1A

EXPLORE: QUAD ANGLES

MATERIALS

Protractor, Straightedge
Geometry software (optional)

1. Use a straightedge or geometry software to draw a quadrilateral. Use your protractor to measure each of the interior angles. Find the sum of the measures of the angles.
2. Repeat the process with different quadrilaterals. (You may wish to use the photograph at the right as one of these.) Use your results to state a conjecture. Compare your results with those of your classmates.
3. Can you find a quadrilateral for which your conjecture doesn't hold? Illustrate and explain.

EXAMPLE

Find the measures of the angles of the quadrilateral.

$x + (x + 40) + 2x + (x + 10) = 360$

$5x + 50 = 360$

$5x = 310$

$x = 62$

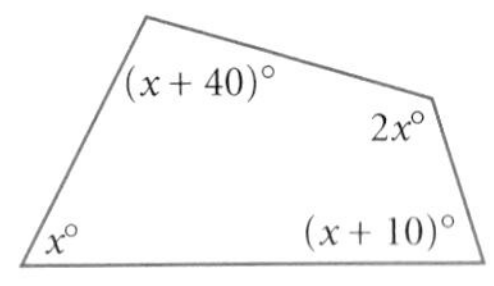

Substituting gives angle measures of 62°, 102°, 124°, and 72°.

The quadrilaterals that you will study are convex quadrilaterals. A quadrilateral is **convex** if each diagonal (excluding the endpoints) lies in the interior of the quadrilateral. It is **concave** if any diagonal lies in the exterior of the figure.

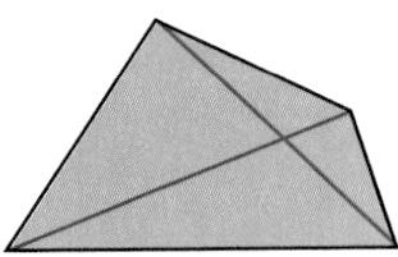

Convex quadrilateral

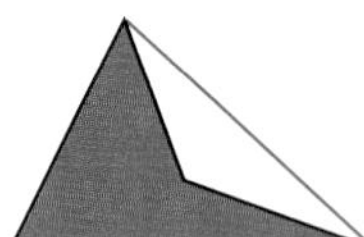

Concave quadrilateral

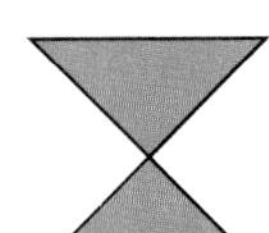

Not a quadrilateral

Alert

When investigating concave quadrilaterals in the *Explore*, students may not realize that there is no interior angle at the "dent." You may want to remind them that angle measures are between 0° and 180°. Students may also see that measuring this angle as an angle of rotation does give a total angle measure of 360° for the quadrilateral.

ANGLE-SUM THEOREM FOR QUADRILATERALS

The sum of the measures of the interior angles of a convex quadrilateral is 360°.

REFLECT

1. What types of quadrilaterals have parallel sides?
2. Describe some properties that rectangles and squares have in common.
3. It is possible to define a rectangle as a quadrilateral with four congruent angles. Explain why this definition is equivalent to the one we are using.

Exercises

CORE

P **Getting Started Use the figure at the right for Exercises 1 and 2.**

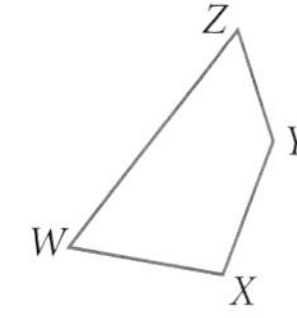

1. Name quadrilateral *WXYZ* in three other ways.
2. Name the diagonals of *WXYZ*.

P **Draw and classify the following quadrilaterals.**

3. a quadrilateral *ABCD* with $\overline{AB} \cong \overline{BC}$
4. a quadrilateral with all sides congruent that is not a square
5. a quadrilateral *QRST* with $\overline{QR} \parallel \overline{ST}$, and $\overline{QT}$ not parallel to $\overline{RS}$

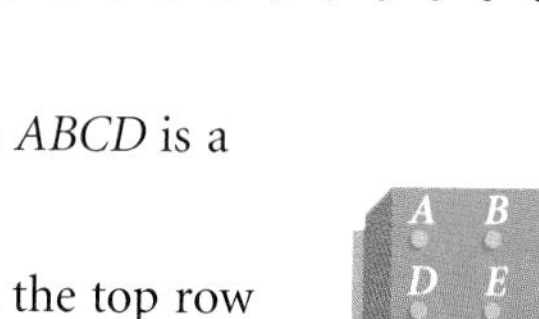

P 6. Give all possible classifications for each quadrilateral shown on the grid.

V 7. Determine whether the following statement is true or false. If the statement is false, change the underlined word to make it true.

If $\overline{AC}$ passes through the exterior of quadrilateral *ABCD*, then *ABCD* is a <u>concave</u> quadrilateral. T

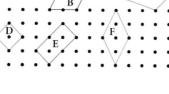

S 8. a. How many rectangles can be formed using two points from the top row of the grid and two points from the bottom row of the grid as vertices? 3

b. How many trapezoids can be formed in the same way? 4

A B C
D E F
G H I

Journal

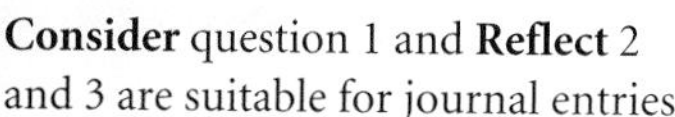

Consider question 1 and **Reflect** 2 and 3 are suitable for journal entries.

REFLECT

Possible Answers

1. Trapezoids have one pair of parallel sides; parallelograms, rhombuses, rectangles, and squares have two pairs.
2. Four right angles, opposite sides parallel. Students may also observe that opposite sides are congruent.
3. The interior angle measures of a quadrilateral sum to 360°. If the measures of these four angles are equal, each must measure 90°.

Part A Exercises

Exercise Notes

Core

17. and 18. Students work with cross-sections of three-dimensional figures. The ability to visualize cross-sections is especially important when students explore volumes in Chapter 9.

Look Ahead

These exercises preview work with polygons and their angles in 6-1 Part B.

More Math Reasoning

34. The definition of trapezoid is sometimes given as "a quadrilateral with at least one pair of parallel sides." In this exercise, students investigate how this definition would change the quadrilateral family tree.

Exercise Answers

Core

1. Possible answer: *ZYXW*, *XYZW*, *WZYX*
2. $\overline{ZX}$, $\overline{WY}$
3. Possible answer:

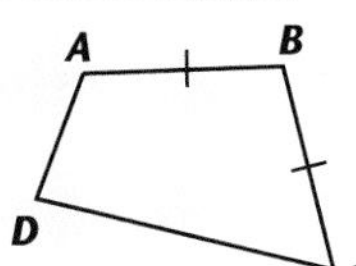

4.

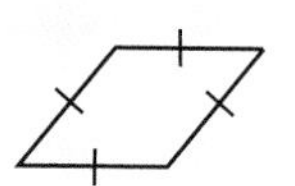

Key

Vocabulary
Practice/Skills
Review
Math Reasoning
Problem Solving
Challenge

Ongoing Assessment

Self-Assessment Exercises 1, 7–15 odd

Embedded Assessment Try It d; Explore Step 2; Exercises 4, 6, 14

Polygons and Polyhedrons

5.

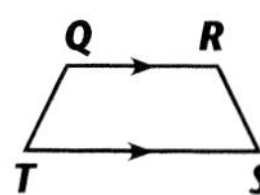

6. A: Trapezoid; B: Parallelogram; C: Parallelogram; D: Parallelogram, square, rectangle, rhombus; E: Rectangle, parallelogram; F: Rhombus, parallelogram

9. $m\angle 1 = 90°$; $m\angle 2 = 90°$; $m\angle 3 = 105°$; $m\angle 4 = 75°$. The sum of the measures should be 360°.

13. $x = 45$; $m\angle E = 100°$; $m\angle F = 135°$; $m\angle G = 45°$; $m\angle H = 80°$

14. $m\angle A = 90°$; $m\angle B = 120°$; $m\angle C = 60°$; $m\angle D = 90°$

15. $m\angle L = 52\frac{5}{7}°$; $m\angle K = 88\frac{3}{7}°$; $m\angle J = 113\frac{3}{7}°$; $m\angle M = 105\frac{3}{7}°$

16. $m\angle QRS = 60°$; $m\angle RSP = 90°$; $m\angle SPQ = 100°$; $m\angle PQR = 110°$

17. Triangle

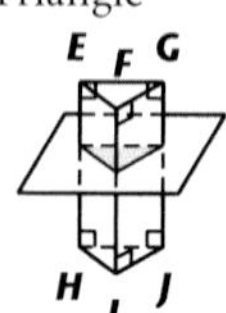

18. Rectangle

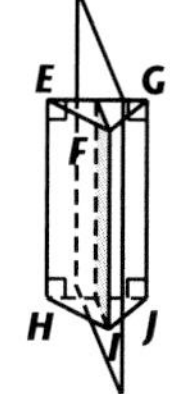

Look Ahead

19. Possible answer:

20. Possible answer:

21. Possible answer:

22. $m\angle UTS = 112°$; $m\angle RTS = 68°$; $m\angle S = 54°$; $m\angle R = 58°$

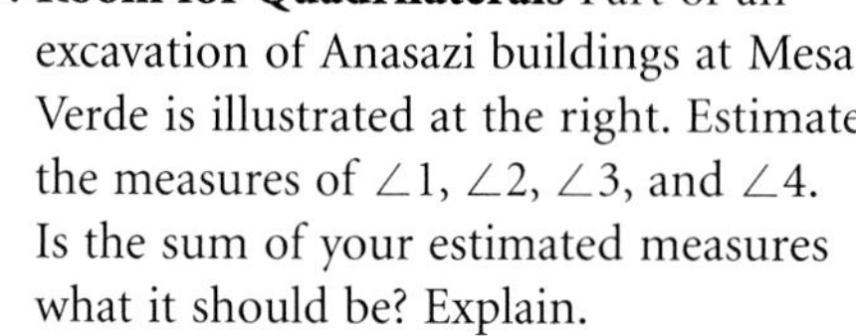

P History **9. Room for Quadrilaterals** Part of an excavation of Anasazi buildings at Mesa Verde is illustrated at the right. Estimate the measures of $\angle 1$, $\angle 2$, $\angle 3$, and $\angle 4$. Is the sum of your estimated measures what it should be? Explain.

P **If a quadrilateral is randomly selected from a set of five distinct quadrilaterals {square, rectangle, parallelogram, rhombus, trapezoid}, find the probability of the following.**

10. None of the quadrilateral's sides are parallel. 0

11. The quadrilateral is a parallelogram. $\frac{4}{5}$

12. All of the quadrilateral's sides are congruent. $\frac{2}{5}$

P **13.** Find x and measure the angles of quadrilateral $EFGH$.

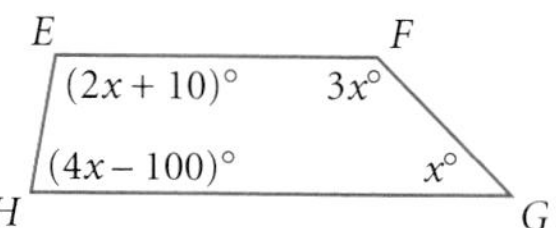

P **Find the measures of the angles of each quadrilateral.**

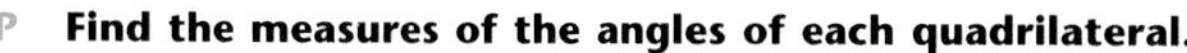

14.

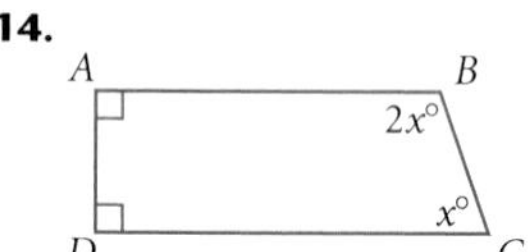

15.

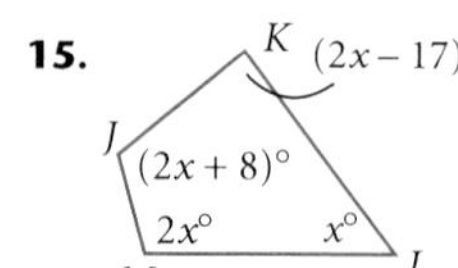

16.

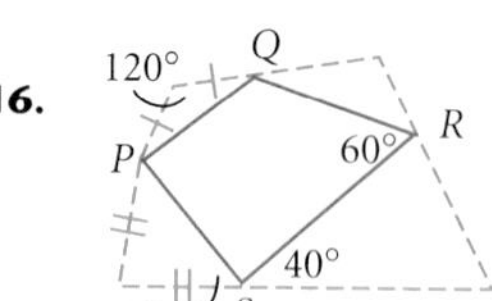

A **cross section** of a solid is the intersection of the solid and a plane. For example, the cross section produced by passing a plane through a cube as shown is a triangle.

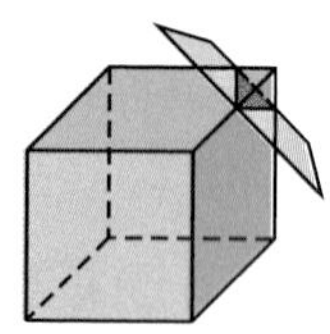

MR **Draw and classify the cross section of the solid shown at the right when it is cut by the following planes.**

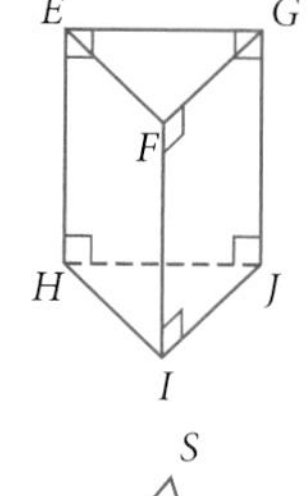

17. a plane parallel to $\triangle EFG$

18. the plane through F and I perpendicular to $\overline{EG}$

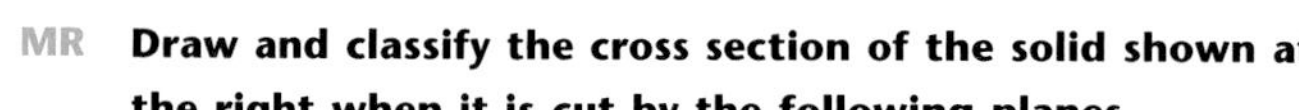

LOOK AHEAD

P **Sketch a polygon with the following number of sides.**

19. 5 sides **20.** 6 sides **21.** 8 sides

R **22.** Find the measure of the exterior angle and the measure of each interior angle in the figure.

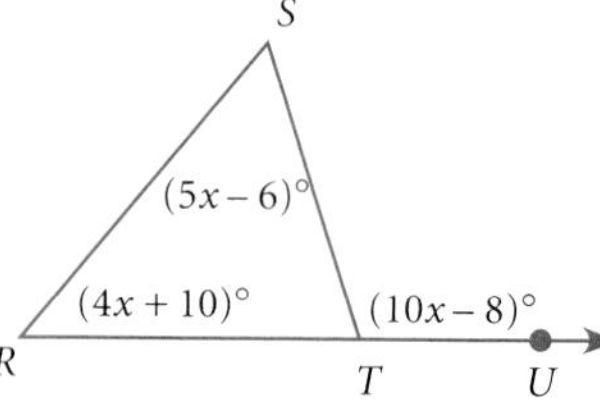

Key

- V Vocabulary
- P Practice/Skills
- R Review
- MR Math Reasoning
- PS Problem Solving
- C Challenge

MORE PRACTICE

Draw and classify the following quadrilaterals.

23. a quadrilateral with exactly two consecutive right angles

24. a quadrilateral *PQRS* with four right angles

Suppose a quadrilateral with the given vertices is drawn on the grid. Classify the quadrilateral.

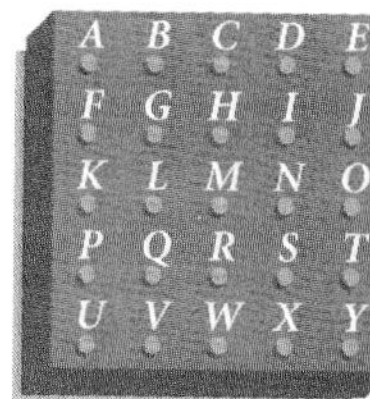

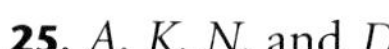

25. *A, K, N,* and *D*

26. *B, G, T,* and *E*

27. *U, L, O,* and *X*

28. *O, W, K,* and *C*

Find the measures of the angles of each quadrilateral.

29.

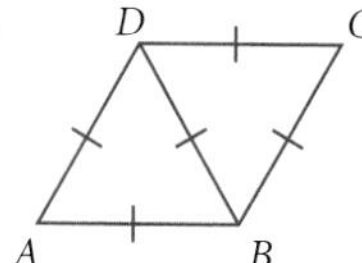

30.

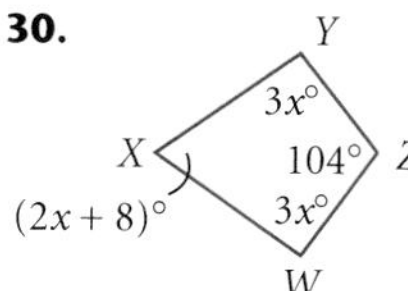

31.

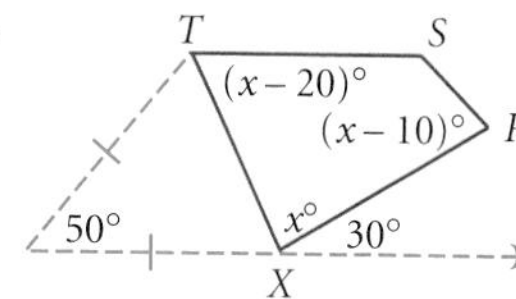

MORE MATH REASONING

32. Complete the following proof that all rectangles are parallelograms.

Given: *ABCD* is a rectangle.

Prove: *ABCD* is a parallelogram.

Proof:

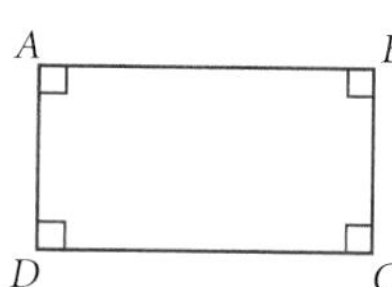

Statements	Reasons
1.	**1.** Given
2. $\angle A$, $\angle B$, $\angle C$, and $\angle D$ are right angles.	**2.**
3. $m\angle A = m\angle B = m\angle C = m\angle D = 90°$	**3.**
4. $\angle A$ and $\angle B$ are supplementary.	**4.**
5.	**5.** If two lines are cut by a transversal and the same-side interior angles are supplementary, then the lines are parallel.
6.	**6.** Definition of *supplementary*
7. $\overline{AB} \parallel \overline{DC}$	**7.**
8.	**8.**

More Practice

23. Possible answer: Trapezoid

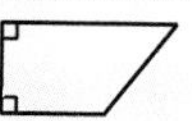

24. Possible answer: Rectangle

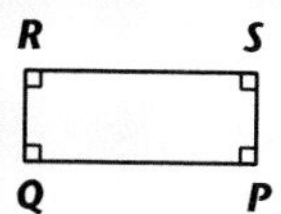

25. Rectangle **26.** Trapezoid

27. Parallelogram **28.** Square

29. $m\angle C = m\angle A = 60°$; $m\angle ADC = m\angle CBA = 120°$

30. $m\angle X = 70°$; $m\angle Y = 93°$; $m\angle Z = 104°$; $m\angle W = 93°$

31. $m\angle TXR = 85°$; $m\angle R = 75°$; $m\angle STX = 65°$; $m\angle S = 135°$

More Math Reasoning

32. Statement 1: *ABCD* is a rectangle.

Reason 2: Definition of a *rectangle*

Reason 3: Definition of *right angles*

Reason 4: Definition of *supplementary*

Statement 5: $\overline{AD} \parallel \overline{BC}$

Statement 6: $\angle A$ and $\angle D$ (or $\angle B$ and $\angle C$) are supplementary

Reason 7: If two lines are cut by a transversal and same-side interior angles are supplementary, then the lines are parallel.

Statement 8: *ABCD* is a parallelogram.

Reason 8: Definition of a *parallelogram*

33. d. Count the number of quadrilaterals with the given property. Divide that number by 5 to get the probability for one selection. Multiply that probability by itself to get the probability for two selections. Yes, they would be different if the first were not replaced.

34. All parallelograms would be trapezoids since parallelograms have two pairs of parallel sides.

Polygons and Polyhedrons

PART B At a Glance

Objective

To classify polygons and discover properties of the measures of their interior and exterior angles.

Development

Students see definitions of *polygon* and related terms, and learn how to classify polygons.

Then, in the **Explore,** they investigate the measures of the interior and exterior angles of different polygons. They find that there are consistent patterns for the interior and exterior angle measures.

Suggested Materials

Student Straightedge, geometry software

Key Terms

Polygon, diagonal of a polygon, convex polygon, concave polygon

First Five Minutes

Transparency FFM 6-1B

Sketch two convex polygons and two concave polygons, each with different numbers of sides.

Motivate

Ask...

- What is the definition of *polygonal region*?

PS, C **33. Quad Odds** If you randomly select a quadrilateral, replace it, and then select a second quadrilateral from a set of five distinct quadrilaterals {square, rectangle, rhombus, parallelogram, trapezoid}, what is the probability that both

a. will not have a pair of parallel sides? 0
b. will have at least three right angles? $\frac{4}{25}$
c. will be parallelograms? $\frac{16}{25}$
d. Explain how you calculated these probabilities. Would they be different if you did not replace the first quadrilateral?

MR **34.** Suppose a trapezoid was defined as a quadrilateral with at least one pair of parallel sides. How would this change affect the quadrilateral family tree? Explain your answer.

6-1 PART B Exploring Polygons

← CONNECT → *You've discovered some of the properties of four-sided polygons. Now you will investigate polygons that have more than four sides.*

A polygon is formed by fitting together segments end to end. The photograph at the left shows polygons in a basalt formation at Devil's Postpile National Monument in California.

We've already defined the term *polygon* informally. As you begin to study polygons in more detail, you will need the more complete definitions below.

DEFINITIONS

A **polygon** is a plane figure whose sides are three or more coplanar segments that intersect only at their endpoints (the vertices). Consecutive sides cannot be collinear, and no more than two sides can meet at any one vertex.

A **diagonal of a polygon** is a line segment whose endpoints are any two nonconsecutive vertices of the polygon.

A **convex polygon** is one in which each diagonal (except its endpoints) is in the interior of the polygon.

Key

V Vocabulary
P Practice/Skills
R Review
MR Math Reasoning
PS Problem Solving
C Challenge

Tips from Teachers

Students may remember the difference between *convex* and *concave* more easily if you explain that a concave object is "caved in."

Examples of figures that are and are not polygons are shown below. We will focus our investigations on convex polygons.

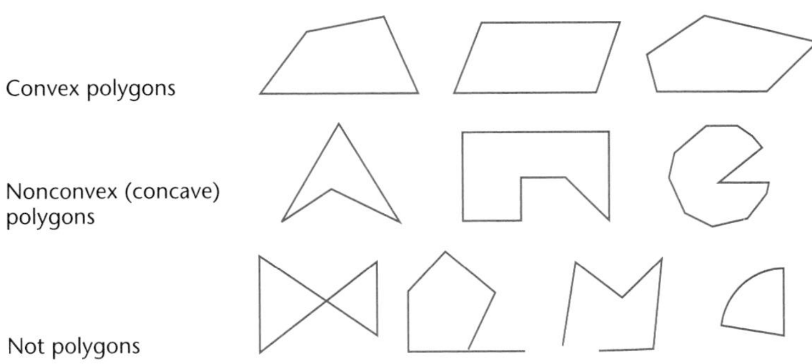

As with other figures, polygons are named using consecutive vertices. We classify a polygon by the number of sides it has. The following chart shows examples of some common polygons.

Classification of Polygons

Number of Sides	Polygon	Example	Number of Sides	Polygon	Example
3	Triangle (*tri* = three)		8	Octagon (*oct* = eight)	
4	Quadrilateral (*quadr* = four)		9	Nonagon (*non* = nine)	
5	Pentagon (*pent* = five)		10	Decagon (*dec* = ten)	
6	Hexagon (*hex* = six)		...	...	...
7	Heptagon (*hept* = seven)		n	n-gon	

Student Resources

- Alternative Lessons 6-1B
- Laboratory Manual 6-1B
- Technology Lab Manual
- Practice 6-1B
- Study Guide and Journal 6-1B
- Guía de estudios y Diario 6-1B
- Multilingual Handbook
- More Look Back 6-1B
- SAT Preparation

Media Resources

- Transparency FFM 6-1B
- Transparency AE 6-1B
- Teaching Transparency
- AWSMTest and practice software
- AWSM Videodisc

6-1

Algebra	Functions	Discrete Math	Probability	Data/Statistics

Polygons and Polyhedrons

EXPLORE

Divide and Conjecture

Recommended group size: 4

The Point

To discover that the sum of the measures of the interior angles of a convex n-gon is $(n - 2)180°$ and the sum of the measures of the exterior angles (one at each vertex) is 360°.

Look and Listen...

- For students who draw diagonals from more than one vertex.
- For students who do not see how the sequence of figures suggests a result for the sum of the exterior angle measures.

Ask...

- Think of the closed aperture of the camera as a tessellation vertex. What is the sum of the measures of the angles at a tessellation vertex?

For Groups That Finish Early

Identify the convex polygon with the least number of sides whose interior angle measures sum up to at least 1000°. **An octagon**

Follow Up

Ask students to summarize their results for Steps 4 and 5 and give a brief justification for each.

Possible Answers

2. The number of triangles is 2 less than the number of sides; for an n-gon, $n - 2$.

4. $S = (n - 2)180°$

5. The sum of the exterior angle measures (one at each vertex) is 360°. They are congruent to the angles that surround the center point in the final picture, which make a complete circle.

TRY IT

a. Possible answer: *ABCDEF*

a. Name the polygon at the right.

b. Classify the polygon. Hexagon

c. How many diagonals can be drawn from vertex *A*? 3

d. Is the polygon concave or convex? Convex

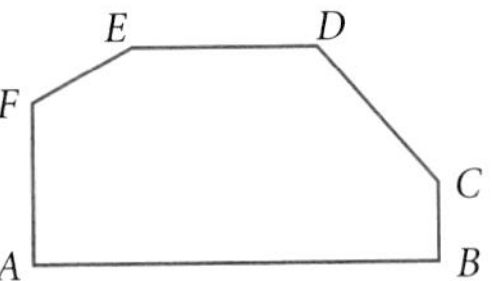

You have already found the sum of the measures of the interior angles for triangles and quadrilaterals. Now you will investigate the sum of the interior angles and the sum of the exterior angles of polygons.

EXPLORE: DIVIDE AND CONJECTURE

MATERIALS

Straightedge
Geometry software (optional)

1. Draw several convex polygons with different numbers of sides using a straightedge or geometry software. Draw all the diagonals from one vertex of each polygon.

2. In each case, how many triangles are formed? Find a relationship between the number of triangles and the number of sides. How many triangles are in an n-gon?

3. Use the triangles to help find the sum of the measures of the interior angles of each of your polygons.

4. What is the sum of the measures of the interior angles of an n-gon? Express your result as a function that gives S, the sum of the angle measures, in terms of n.

5. An exterior angle of a polygon is defined in the same way as an exterior angle for a triangle. The following sequence shows a "shrinking" heptagon with one exterior angle drawn at each vertex. As shown in the photograph, this is similar to how the aperture of a camera works.

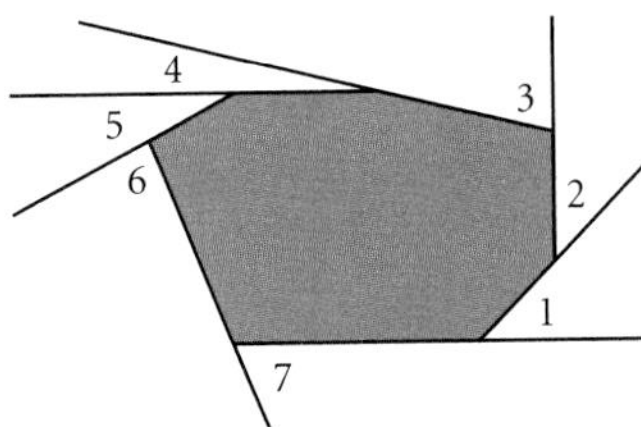

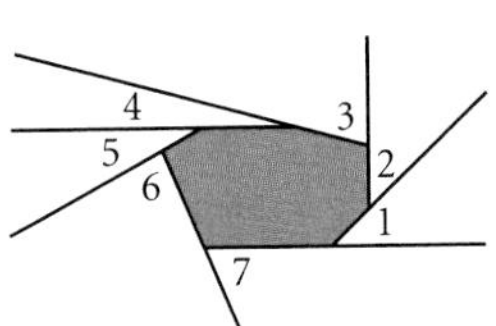

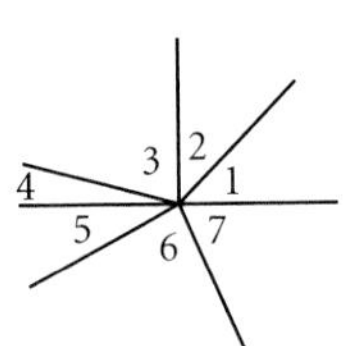

What does this sequence suggest about the sum of the measures of the exterior angles (one at each vertex) of a convex polygon? State a conjecture, and explain your reasoning.

Technology Note

If software is used in this **Explore,** it should be used primarily as a drawing tool. Students should make conjectures without first measuring the angles. After they make conjectures based on reasoning, students may use the measurement capabilities to check their results (especially the exterior-angle conjecture in Step 5).

Language Connection

Students may wonder why we have pentagons and hexagons, but not quadrigons. The word *gon* is Greek for angle, and the prefixes *penta-* and *hexa-* are also Greek. However, *lateral* and *quadr-* come from Latin.

EXAMPLES

Find the sum of the measures of the interior angles and exterior angles (one at each vertex) for each convex polygon.

1. a heptagon

interior angle sum $= (n - 2)180°$
$= (7 - 2)180°$
$= 900°$

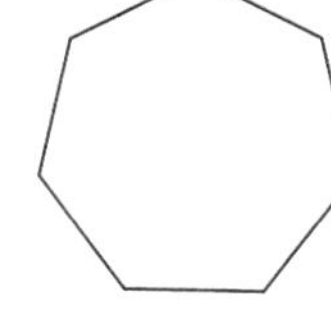

2. a 22-gon

interior angle sum $= (n - 2)180°$
$= (22 - 2)180°$
$= 3600°$

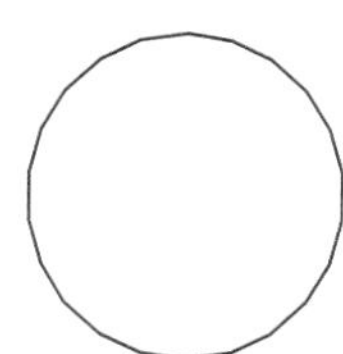

In both cases, the sum of the measures of the exterior angles is 360°.

Our results about the interior and exterior angles of a convex polygon are summarized below.

ANGLE-SUM THEOREM FOR POLYGONS

The sum of the measures of the interior angles of a convex polygon with n sides is given by $S = (n - 2)180°$.

EXTERIOR ANGLE THEOREM FOR POLYGONS

The sum of the measures of the exterior angles of a convex polygon (one at each vertex) is 360°.

REFLECT

1. How does the Angle-Sum Theorem for polygons compare with the Angle-Sum Theorem for quadrilaterals? Explain.

2. Janine said, "The Angle-Sum Theorem for polygons also applies to triangles, so we don't need the Triangle Angle-Sum Theorem any longer." Tien said, "That's true, but we couldn't have figured out the Angle-Sum Theorem for polygons without it!" Are the students' statements correct? Explain why or why not.

ALTERNATE EXAMPLES

Find the sum of the measures of the interior angles and exterior angles (one at each vertex) for each convex polygon.

1. A hexagon

Interior angle sum $= (n - 2)180°$
$= (6 - 2)180°$
$= 720°$

2. A 16-gon

Interior angle sum $= (n - 2)180°$
$= (16 - 2)180°$
$= 2520°$

In both cases, the sum of the measures of the exterior angles is 360°.

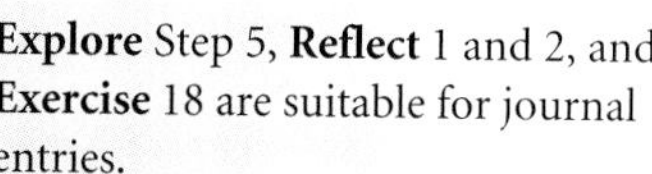

Journal

Explore Step 5, **Reflect** 1 and 2, and **Exercise** 18 are suitable for journal entries.

REFLECT

Possible Answers

1. The Angle-Sum Theorem for quadrilaterals is a special case of the theorem for polygons. If $n = 4$, $(n - 2)180° = 360°$.

2. Both statements are correct. The Triangle Angle-Sum Theorem is a special case of the general result for polygons. However, the reasoning used in the **Explore** to derive the general formula was based on dividing the polygon into triangles, each of which had a total interior angle measure of 180°.

Diversity Issues

According to Claudette Bradley, University of Alaska–Fairbanks, in a world of diverse populations, educators can no longer assume that students share common knowledge. A classroom teacher can create common experiences by introducing activities that allow students to observe and manipulate.

Algebra | Functions | Discrete Math | Probability | Data/Statistics

Polygons and Polyhedrons

Part B Exercises

Exercise Notes

Core

5. Students see that the prefixes used to classify polygons are also used in nonmathematical words.

13. Shows polygons occurring in nature.

More Math Reasoning

38. Students use inductive reasoning to find the total number of diagonals in an n-gon.

Exercise Answers

Core

1. (a) Octagon; (b) Pentagon; (c) Not a polygon; (d) Quadrilateral

2. (b); Each diagonal is in the interior.

3. Possible answer: *ABCDEF*, *DCBAFE*, *FEDCBA*; Hexagon

4. Possible answer:

5. Possible answer: Octopus—sea animal with 8 arms; Quadriceps—4 muscles in the upper leg; Quadraphonic—four-way sound in stereo.

9. a. 11 triangles; 4 pentagons; 1 hexagon; 6 quadrilaterals

b. Triangle, 180°; pentagon, 540°; hexagon, 720°; quadrilateral, 360°

c. 9

13. 540° (a pentagon)

Exercises

CORE

P **Getting Started Use the figures at the right for Exercises 1 and 2.**

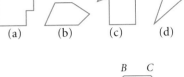

(a) (b) (c) (d)

1. Which of the figures at the right are polygons? Classify each polygon.

2. Which are convex polygons? Why?

P **3.** Name the polygon at the right in three different ways. Then classify the polygon.

B C A D F E

P **4.** Draw an equilateral hexagon that is not equiangular.

V **5.** Identify and define common words that begin with the prefixes *quadr* and *oct.*

V **Write the word or phrase that correctly completes each statement.**

6. A ___ has seven sides. Heptagon

7. An octagon is a polygon with ___ sides. 8

8. If a polygon has ___ sides, then it is a pentagon. 5

P **9.** The figure illustrates the facets cut on a stone. It is a view of the "crown" of the gem.

a. Identify all the different types of polygons that appear on the gem crown. How many of each type are there?

b. What is the sum of the measures of the interior angles for each type of polygon on the crown?

c. How many pairs of polygons appear to be congruent?

P **Find the sum of the measures of the interior and exterior angles (one at each vertex) for each convex polygon.**

10. a pentagon 540° interior, 360° exterior

11. a 14-gon 2160° interior, 360° exterior

12. an $(x + 2)$-gon $180x°$ interior, 360° exterior

P **13.** Science The electron microscope photograph at the right shows a magnification of aspirin. Find the sum of the measures of the angles for the outlined polygon.

Key

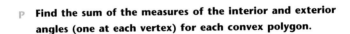

V Vocabulary
P Practice/Skills
R Review
MR Math Reasoning
PS Problem Solving
C Challenge

The sum of the measures of the interior angles of a convex polygon is given. Find the number of sides of the polygon.

14. 720° 6 **15.** 1800° 12 **16.** $(x - 1)360°$ $2x$

17. The John Hancock building in Boston (at the right) was designed by I. M. Pei. Identify the different types of polygons used in its design.

18. School Crossing A school-crossing sign is shown below. It has three right angles, and the other two angles are congruent. Find the measure of one of the non-right angles. Explain your method.

19. When using a public highway, vehicles that travel 25 mi/hr or less, such as farm equipment, must display a special sign. This sign is shown at the right. To form the polygonal sign, small equilateral triangles have been cut off each vertex of a larger equilateral triangle.

a. What is the sum of the measures of the interior angles of the sign? How do you know?

b. What is the measure of each interior angle of the sign?

LOOK BACK

Find the area of each figure. [5-2, 5-3]

20. 17.015

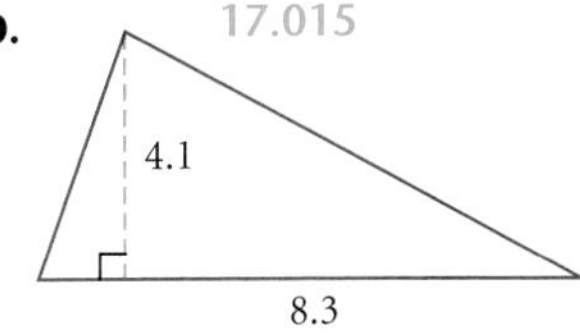

21. 40

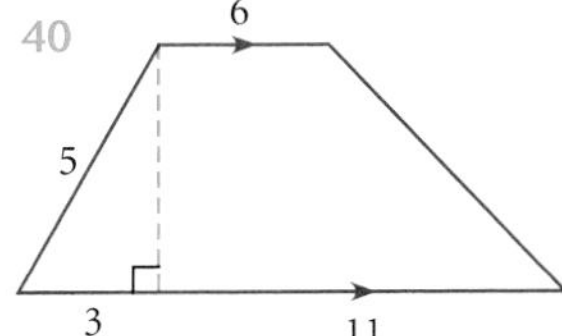

22. 50

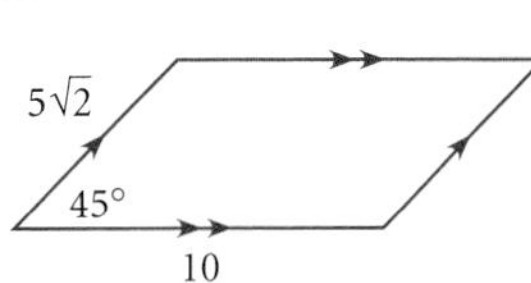

23. In the sequence of figures shown, how many cubes are needed to make a building with 10 steps? n steps? [1-2] 55; $\frac{n(n+1)}{2}$

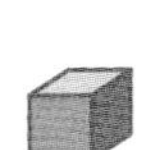

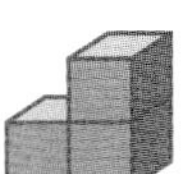

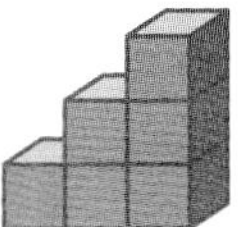

Ongoing Assessment

Self-Assessment Exercises 1–7 odd, 11–19 odd

Embedded Assessment Explore Steps 4, 5; Exercises 10, 14, 18

17. Triangles, rectangles

18. Possible answer: 135°, The sum of interior angles is $(n - 2)180° = (5 - 2)180° = 540°$. Let x be the measure of one non-right angle. $540° = 3(90°) + 2x$; $x = 135°$.

19. a. 720°; Use the Angle-Sum Theorem for $n = 6$.

b. 120°

Polygons and Polyhedrons

Look Back

24. Reason 1: Given

Reason 2: Definition of *perpendicular*

Reason 3: Right angles are congruent.

Reason 4: Definition of a *right triangle*

Statement 5: D is midpoint of $\overline{AB}$

Statement 6: $\overline{AD} \cong \overline{BD}$

Statement 7: $\overline{CD} \cong \overline{CD}$

Statement 8: $\triangle ADC \cong \triangle BDC$

Statement 9: $\overline{AC} \cong \overline{CB}$

Reason 9: CPCTC

More Practice

25. All; (a) Quadrilateral; (b) Hexagon; (c) Hexagon

26. (a) and (b); Each diagonal is in the interior.

27. Possible answer:

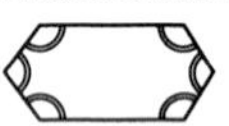

28. Possible answer:

29. Possible answer:

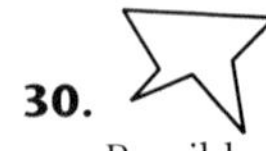

30. Possible answer:

31. Sum of interior angles = 1260°; Sum of exterior angles = 360°

32. Sum of interior angles = 2880°; Sum of exterior angles = 360°

33. Sum of the interior angles = $(2x - 4)180°$; Sum of exterior angles = 360°

More Math Reasoning

38. a. Quadrilateral: 4, 1, 2
Pentagon: 5, 2, 5
Hexagon: 6, 3, 9
Heptagon: 7, 4, 14
Octagon: 8, 5, 20
n-gon: n, $(n - 3)$, $\frac{n(n-3)}{2}$

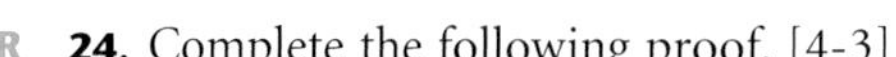

Algebra | Functions | Discrete Math | Probability | Data/Statistics

R **24.** Complete the following proof. [4-3]

Given: $\overline{AB} \perp \overline{CD}$, and D is the midpoint of $\overline{AB}$.

Prove: $\overline{AC} \cong \overline{CB}$

Proof:

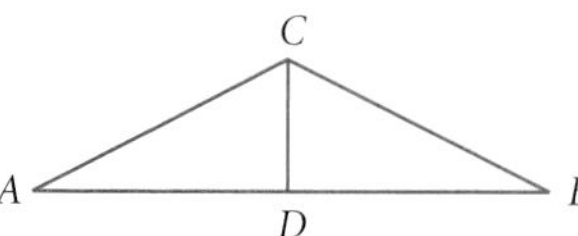

Statements	Reasons
1. $\overline{AB} \perp \overline{CD}$	**1.**
2. $\angle ADC$ and $\angle BDC$ are right angles.	**2.**
3. $\triangle ADC$ and $\triangle BDC$ are right triangles.	**3.**
4.	**4.** Given
5.	**5.** Definition of *midpoint*
6.	**6.** Reflexive Property
7.	**7.** LL Theorem
8.	**8.**

MORE PRACTICE

P **25.** Which of the figures at the right are polygons? Classify each polygon.

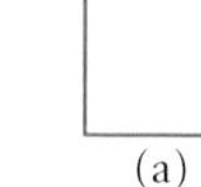
(a)

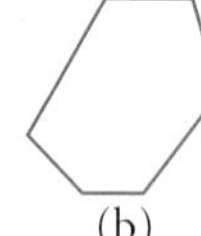
(b)

(c)

P **26.** Which figures at the right are convex polygons? Why?

P **27.** Draw an equiangular hexagon that is not equilateral.

P **28.** Draw an equilateral pentagon that is not equiangular.

P **29.** Draw a concave heptagon.

P **30.** Draw an equilateral, concave hexagon.

P **Find the sum of the measures of the interior and exterior angles (one at each vertex) for each convex polygon.**

31. a nonagon **32.** an 18-gon **33.** a $(2x - 2)$-gon

P **The sum of the measures of the interior angles of a convex polygon is given. Find the number of sides of the polygon.**

34. 540° 5 **35.** 1260° 9 **36.** $(x + 4)180°$ $x + 6$

Key

V Vocabulary
P Practice/Skills
R Review
MR Math Reasoning
PS Problem Solving
C Challenge

MORE MATH REASONING

37. The sum of the measures of the interior angles of a polygon is three times the sum of the measures of its exterior angles (one at each vertex). Classify the polygon. Octagon

38. A Diagonal Table Find the number of diagonals of an n-gon.

a. Copy the table shown. Draw each polygon and complete the table.

Polygon	Number of Vertices	Number of Diagonals from One Vertex	Total Number of Diagonals
Quadrilateral			
Pentagon			
Hexagon			
Heptagon			
Octagon			
n-gon			

b. Look for a relationship between the number of vertices and the number of diagonals from one vertex. What is this relationship for the n-gon? $n - 3$

c. Look for a relationship between the data in the first two columns and the total number of diagonals. Write the formula as $D =$ ___. $D = \frac{n(n-3)}{2}$

d. How many diagonals are in a 40-gon? 740

6-1 PART C Exploring Polyhedrons

← CONNECT → *You've drawn and made nets for many three-dimensional figures. Three-dimensional figures whose faces are polygons are polyhedrons. Now you will begin to investigate some properties of polyhedrons.*

As shown at the left, I. M. Pei's design of the East Building of the National Gallery of Art features a tetrahedron near the fountain. The gallery buildings themselves are prisms.

These three-dimensional figures, whose faces are triangles, rectangles, and other polygons, are examples of **polyhedrons**.

Student Resources

- **Alternative Lessons** 6-1C
- **Laboratory Manual** 6-1C
- Technology Lab Manual
- **Practice** 6-1C
- **Study Guide and Journal** 6-1C
- **Guía de estudios y Diario** 6-1C
- **Multilingual Handbook**
- **More Look Ahead** 6-1C
- SAT Preparation

Media Resources

- **Transparency FFM** 6-1C
- Transparency AE
- Teaching Transparency
- **AWSMTest and practice software**
- AWSM Videodisc

PART C At a Glance

Objective

To classify polyhedrons and find a relationship among their faces, edges, and vertices.

Development

First, students see the definition of *polyhedron* and learn how polyhedrons are classified.

Then, in the **Explore,** students see a relationship among the number of faces, edges, and vertices of a polyhedron. This relationship is formally stated as Euler's Formula.

Suggested Materials

Teacher Models of polyhedrons

Key Terms

Polyhedron

First Five Minutes

Transparency FFM 6-1C

Read the information about polyhedrons on pages 409 and 410 up to the **Try** It. Then do **Try It a–c.**

Motivate

Ask...

- What are the names of some polyhedrons that you are familiar with? **Cubes, pyramids, tetrahedrons, and rectangular solids have been discussed previously.**

Polygons and Polyhedrons

DEFINITION

A **polyhedron** is a solid whose faces are polygons.

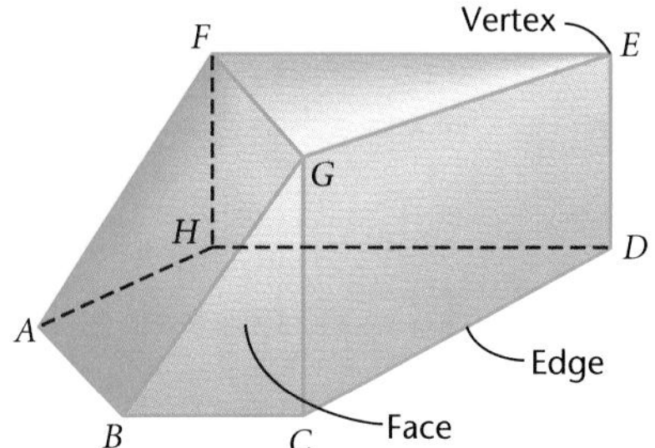

Faces are named in the same way as polygons. In the above figure, *ABCDH* is a pentagonal face.

TRY IT

The polyhedron shown is a cube with a corner cut off.

a. Name the triangular face of the polyhedron. *RST*

b. Name the face that includes *L*, *M*, and *Q* as vertices. *LMTRQ*

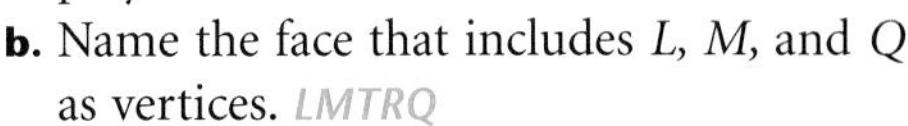

c. Find the number of faces, vertices, and edges of this polyhedron. 7 faces; 10 vertices; 15 edges

Polygons are classified by the number of sides they have. Similarly, polyhedrons are classified by the number of faces they have.

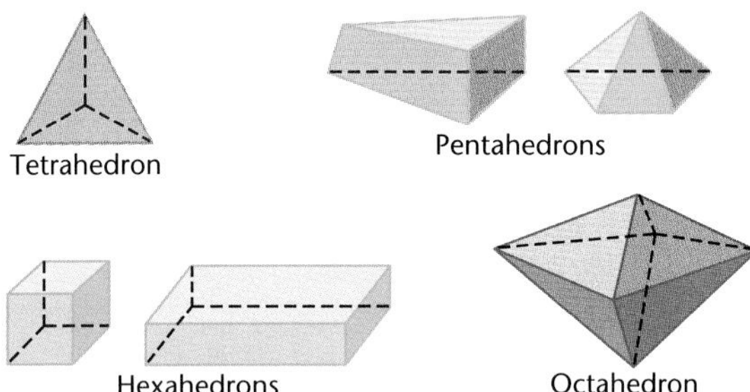

Other common polyhedrons include dodecahedrons, which have twelve faces, and icosahedrons, which have twenty.

Careers Connection

David R. Hedgeley, an African-American scientist, won the Space Act Award and a cash prize from NASA for his work in computer graphics. His programs allow many different types of computers to display three-dimensional shapes. The prize awarded Hedgeley was the largest ever given by NASA at that time.

In the following Explore, you will discover a relationship among the number of faces, edges, and vertices of a polyhedron.

EXPLORE: FACE FACTS

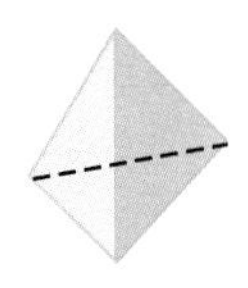
a.

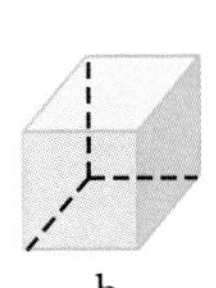
b.

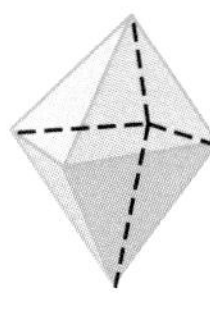
c.

d.

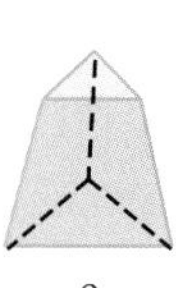
e.

1. Find the number of faces (F), vertices (V), and edges (E) of the polyhedrons shown above. Organize your data in a table.
2. There is a relationship among V, F, and E. Make a conjecture about this relationship, and write a formula to express your conjecture.
3. Check to see whether your conjecture holds for other polyhedrons illustrated elsewhere in this book.

1. Is there a relationship between the number of vertices and the number of sides of a polygon? If so, what is the relationship?

Leonhard Euler (1707–1783) was a Swiss mathematician who proved the formula you investigated in the Explore. This result is therefore known as Euler's Formula.

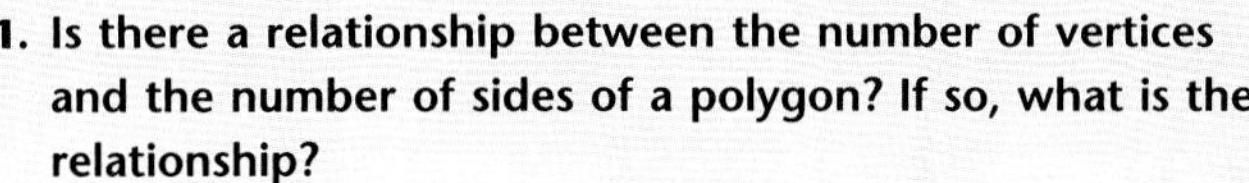

EULER'S FORMULA

For any polyhedron, the relationship among the number of faces (F), vertices (V), and edges (E) is $F + V - E = 2$.

You will have additional opportunities to work with Euler's Formula in the Exercises and in later chapters.

EXPLORE

Face Facts

Recommended group size: 2

The Point

To discover that
Faces + Vertices − Edges = 2
for any polyhedron (Euler's Formula).

Look and Listen...

- For students who are having difficulty counting faces, vertices, and edges correctly. (You may want to check their table entries to watch for this.)

Ask...

- Have you found a convenient way to keep track of the vertices and edges that you have and have not counted?
- Have you considered sums and differences of the numbers of faces, edges, and vertices?

For Groups That Finish Early

Sketch a cube with a rectangular "tunnel" through it. Does your result from Step 2 still hold? Yes

Follow Up

Ask students to give their formula from Step 2. If time permits, you might have them compare tables to make sure all students are counting vertices, faces, and edges correctly.

Possible Answers

1. **a.** 4 faces, 4 vertices, 6 edges
   b. 6 faces, 8 vertices, 12 edges
   c. 8 faces, 6 vertices, 12 edges
   d. 7 faces, 10 vertices, 15 edges
   e. 5 faces, 6 vertices, 9 edges
2. $F + V - E = 2$
3. The conjecture holds for all polyhedrons.

Possible Answer

1. A polygon has an equal number of sides and vertices.

Alert

Students may have difficulty remembering Euler's Formula. You may want to tell them that they can recreate it by sketching a cube in perspective and counting faces, vertices, and edges.

Tips from Teachers

You may want to provide students with supplies to make physical models of the polyhedrons they work with in the *Explore*. Gumdrops and toothpicks work well for this; there are also geometry manipulatives with sticks and connectors that can be used to construct polygons and polyhedrons.

Polygons and Polyhedrons

Journal

Reflect 1 and 2 and **Exercise** 15 are suitable for journal entries.

REFLECT

Possible Answers

1. There should be many hexahedral solids, including desks, books, boxes, etc.
2. Pentathlon, heptathlon, and decathlon (athletic contests made up of 5, 7, and 10 events), octopus, decade, etc.

Part C Exercises

Exercise Notes

Core

15. Students see why a methane molecule has the shape it does.

Look Ahead

These exercises review properties of parallel lines that will be important in 6-2.

More Math Reasoning

28–32. Involve cross-sections of polyhedrons and truncated polyhedrons. These exercises help students develop three-dimensional visualization skills.

Exercise Answers

Core

9. 4; Possible answer: You cannot enclose space with three polygons.

10. 4; Possible answer: Any three vertices are coplanar. At least four are needed to determine a three-dimensional polyhedron.

13. Possible answer:

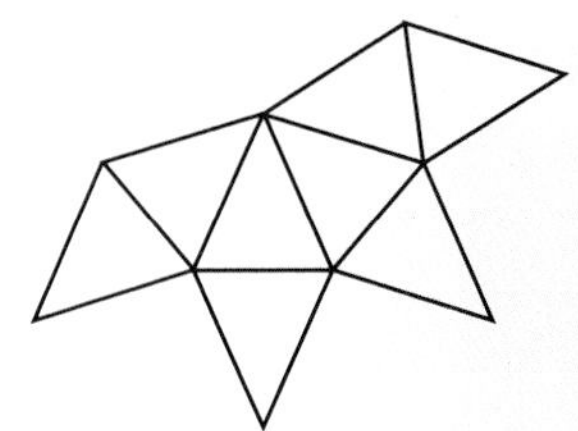

14. Nonahedron;
Area of base = 36 ft^2

REFLECT

1. Give examples of polyhedrons in your classroom. Classify each one by the number of faces.
2. It's helpful to remember prefixes when classifying polygons and polyhedrons. Give some examples of everyday words that begin with the same prefixes we use to classify polygons and polyhedrons.

Exercises

CORE

P **Getting Started Use the figure at the right for Exercises 1–4.**

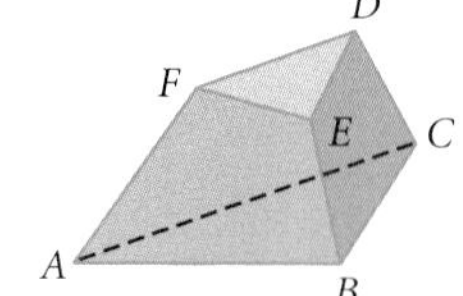

1. Name the faces of the polyhedron. *FABE, FED, EBCD, ACDF, ABC*
2. Classify the polyhedron. Pentahedron
3. Find the number of faces, vertices, and edges of the polyhedron. $F = 5$, $V = 6$, $E = 9$
4. Verify that Euler's Formula holds for the polyhedron. $5 + 6 - 9 = 2$

P **The polyhedron shown is a cube with each corner cut off. Use this polyhedron for Exercises 5–8.**

5. Classify faces 1 and 2. Face 1 is a triangle; Face 2 is an octagon
6. Name the vertices of face 1. *P, Q, V*
7. Name the sides of face 2. $\overline{PN}$, $\overline{NM}$, $\overline{MU}$, $\overline{UT}$, $\overline{TS}$, $\overline{SR}$, $\overline{RQ}$, $\overline{QP}$
8. How many faces, vertices, and edges does this polyhedron have? Does Euler's Formula hold? $F = 14$, $V = 24$, $E = 36$; Yes

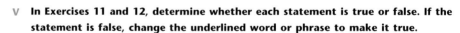

MR 9. What is the smallest number of faces a polyhedron can have? Why?

MR 10. What is the smallest number of vertices a polyhedron can have? Why?

V **In Exercises 11 and 12, determine whether each statement is true or false. If the statement is false, change the underlined word or phrase to make it true.**

11. A <u>tetrahedron</u> is a polyhedron with four faces. T
12. An octahedron has <u>six</u> faces. F; Eight

P 13. Sketch a net for the octahedron shown at the right.

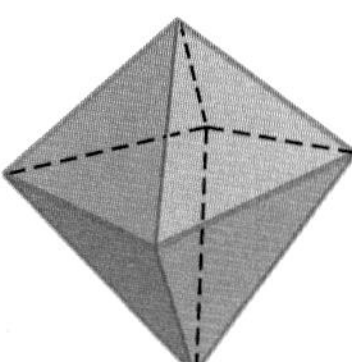

Key

- V Vocabulary
- P Practice/Skills
- R Review
- MR Math Reasoning
- PS Problem Solving
- C Challenge

14. An *obelisk* is a monument with a square base that tapers to a square pyramid at the top. A 3500-year-old Egyptian obelisk at Karnak is 80 ft tall and 6 ft long on each side of its base. Classify the obelisk, and calculate the area of its base.

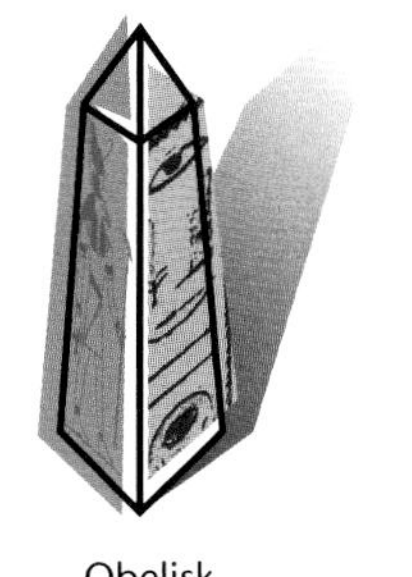
Obelisk

15. **Polyhedron Chemistry** A methane molecule has a carbon atom in the center and four hydrogen atoms around it, as shown in the perspective drawing at the right.
   a. If you connect the hydrogen atoms, what polyhedron results? Sketch the polyhedron, and show the locations of the carbon and hydrogen atoms.
   b. The hydrogen atoms in this molecule repel each other. Use this information to explain why a methane model has the shape it does.

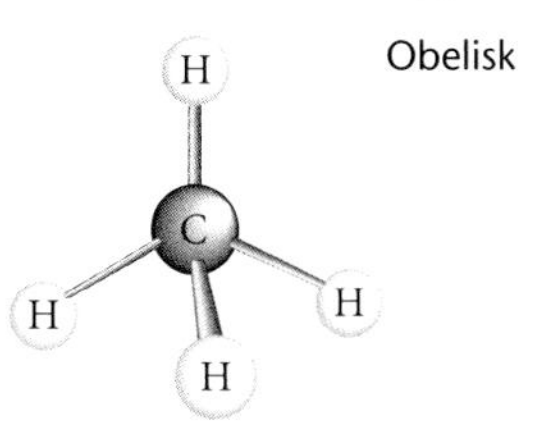

Describe a horizontal cross section of each polyhedron.

16. Triangle
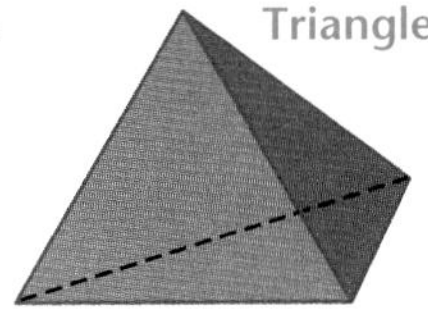
Tetrahedron

17. Quadrilateral
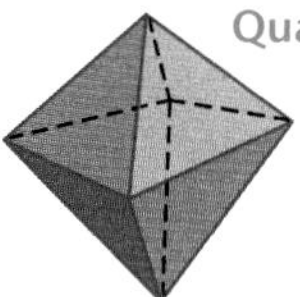
Octahedron

18. Square
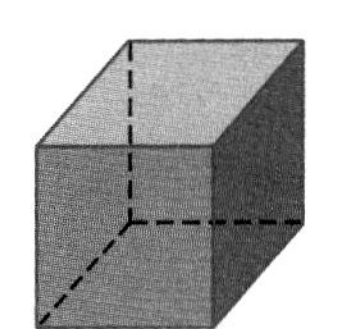
Hexahedron (cube)

19. **Animal, Vegetable, or Zircon?** Geologists are often asked to identify minerals found in geological explorations. The geometry of a mineral crystal is one way of identifying it. Draw your own simplified sketch of the zircon crystal shown in the photograph at the right. Then show that Euler's Formula holds for this crystal.

LOOK AHEAD

For each measure of $\angle A$, find the measures of the other angles of parallelogram *ABCD*. Justify each answer with a theorem or postulate.

20. $m\angle A = 107°$

21. $m\angle A = 64°$

22. $m\angle A = 138°$

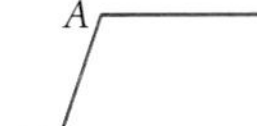
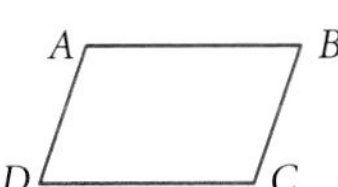

Ongoing Assessment

Self-Assessment Exercises 1–11 odd, 17, 19

Embedded Assessment Explore Step 2; Exercises 2, 8, 15, 18

15. a. Tetrahedron

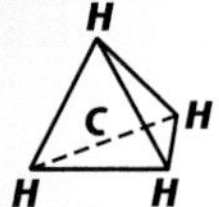

b. In a tetrahedron, the hydrogen atoms are as far away from each other as possible.

19. $F = 12$, $V = 10$, $E = 20$; $12 + 10 - 20 = 2$

Look Ahead

20. $m\angle C = 107°$—opposite angles in a parallelogram are congruent; $m\angle B = m\angle D = 73°$—consecutive angles in a parallelogram are supplementary.

21. $m\angle C = 64°$—opposite angles in a parallelogram are congruent. $m\angle B = m\angle D = 116°$—consecutive angles in a parallelogram are supplementary.

22. $m\angle C = 138°$—opposite angles are congruent. $m\angle B = m\angle D = 42°$—consecutive angles are supplementary.

More Practice

23. *HGFE, ABCD, AHGB, GFCB, FEDC, HEDA*

24. Hexahedron

25. $F = 6$, $V = 8$, $E = 12$; $6 + 8 - 12 = 2$

26.

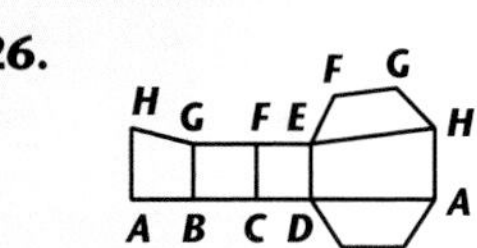

27. Rectangle

More Math Reasoning

28.

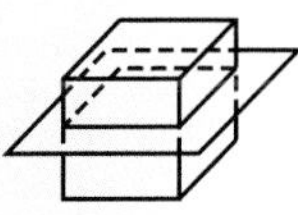

29. Possible answer:

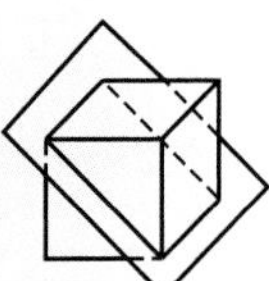

30–32. See Additional Answers p. T416.

Polygons and Polyhedrons

PART D At a Glance

Objective

To investigate which types of polygons will tessellate a plane.

Development

In the **Explore,** students see that any quadrilateral can tessellate a plane. They also investigate tessellations with other polygons.

Suggested Materials

Student Paper, straightedge, scissors

First Five Minutes

Transparency FFM 6-1D

Sketch three convex polygons, each with a different number of sides. Classify each, and give the sum of the measures of its interior angles and its exterior angles (one at each vertex).

EXPLORE

Plane Old Tessellations

Recommended group size: 4

The Point

To see that any congruent quadrilaterals can tessellate a plane, and to investigate other tessellations with polygons.

Look and Listen...

- For students who do not see that congruent quadrilaterals tessellate.

Ask...

- Have you tried different ways to arrange the quadrilaterals around a point?
- Have you tried concave quadrilaterals?
- In Step 3, are you checking to see whether any pentagon (hexagon, etc.) tessellates?

MORE PRACTICE

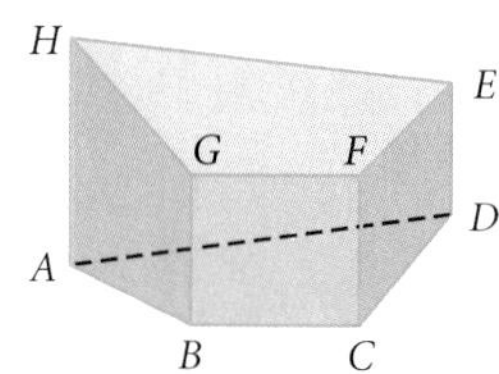

P **23.** Name the faces of the polyhedron at the right.

P **24.** Classify the polyhedron.

P **25.** Verify that Euler's Formula holds for this polyhedron.

P **26.** Sketch a net for the polyhedron.

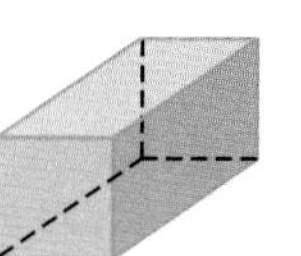

P **27.** Describe a horizontal cross section of the hexahedron shown at the right.

MORE MATH REASONING

MR, C **Draw a sketch to show how a plane can intersect a cube in each of the following cross sections.**

28. a square **29.** a rectangle

30. an isosceles triangle **31.** an equilateral triangle

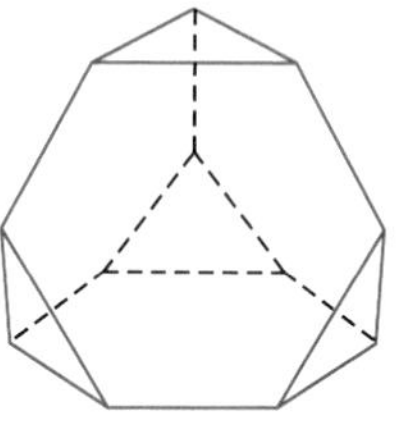

MR, PS **32.** Suppose a tetrahedron has all of its vertices cut off as shown.
a. What type of polyhedron is each piece that is cut off?
b. How many additional vertices and edges does cutting off the corners produce? Explain.
c. Show that Euler's Formula still holds for this truncated (cut-off) tetrahedron.
d. Sketch a net for the figure.

6-1 PART D Making Connections

← CONNECT → ***Polyhedrons are present in manufactured and natural objects. You have discovered properties of polygons and learned how polygons are related to polyhedrons. You've also explored characteristics of polyhedrons.***

As shown in the photo on page 415, I. M. Pei used tessellations in designing the glass pyramid at the Louvre Museum in Paris. In many of his other buildings, the faces of his polyhedrons contain triangle and square tessellations. Could Pei have used other figures? You will investigate this possibility in the following Explore.

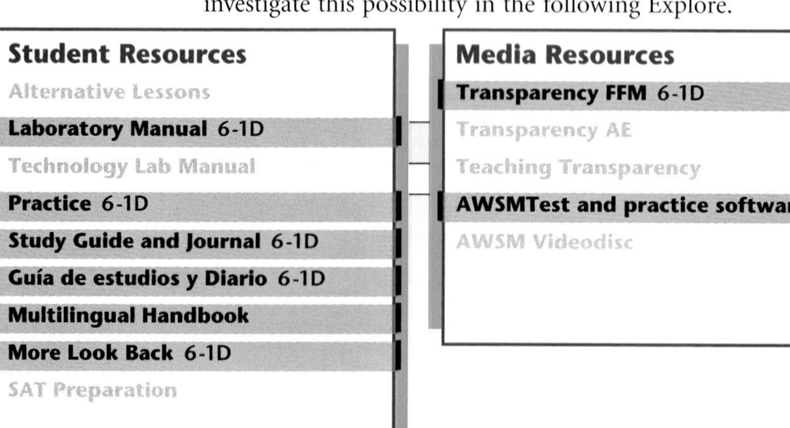

EXPLORE: PLANE OLD TESSELLATIONS

MATERIALS

Paper
Straightedge
Scissors

1. First, investigate whether any quadrilateral can tessellate a plane. Begin by folding a sheet of paper in half three times, drawing a quadrilateral on the paper, and cutting the folded sheet to make congruent quadrilaterals. Arrange the quadrilaterals to see if they tessellate the plane. Repeat the process with a different quadrilateral. Discuss your results with your classmates.
2. Make a conjecture about the quadrilaterals that will tessellate a plane. Explain why they tessellate.
3. You know that any triangle will tessellate a plane, and you have just investigated this possibility for quadrilaterals. Are there any other types of polygons that *always* tessellate a plane? Investigate pentagons, hexagons, and other polygons, and make a conjecture.

REFLECT

1. How are polygons and polyhedrons related? Give specific examples to support your ideas.
2. Explain how the classifications of polygons and polyhedrons are related. Give specific examples.
3. Explain why the sum of the measures of the interior angles of a polygon with n sides is $(n - 2)180°$. Use a sketch to illustrate your explanation.

Self-Assessment

1. Find x in the figure at the right. Then find the measure of each angle of $WXYZ$.

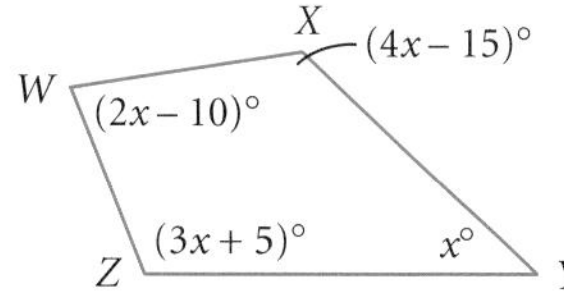

Find the sum of the measures of the interior and exterior angles (one at each vertex) for each polygon.

2. an octagon
3. a 15-gon

Vocabulary
Practice/Skills
Review
Math Reasoning
Problem Solving
Challenge

For Groups That Finish Early

Are there any polygons with more than 4 sides that tessellate? **Regular hexagons tessellate; some other convex pentagons and hexagons tessellate; some concave polygons will tessellate.**

Follow Up

Ask students to give their results for Step 2. If anyone found other polygonal tessellations, have them share these with the class.

Possible Answers

2. It is possible to tessellate the plane with any quadrilateral. Their angles sum to 360°; therefore, they can completely fill the space at a tessellation vertex.
3. No other type of polygon always tessellates a plane.

Portfolio

Have students select items from their work that demonstrate their understanding of the material in 6-1.

You may want students to include an **Exercise** where they calculated the sum of the measures of the interior angles of a polygon and an **Exercise** that involved a real-world application of polygons or polyhedrons.

REFLECT

Possible Answers

1. Polyhedrons are solids with polygonal faces.
2. The prefixes used are generally the same: pentagon/hedron, etc. However, quadrilateral and tetrahedron use different prefixes for "four."
3. The diagonals from one vertex divide it into $(n - 2)$ triangles. The sum of the interior angle measures for each is 180°.

6-1

Algebra | Logic/Reasoning | Discrete Math

Polygons and Polyhedrons

Self-Assessment

Exercise Notes

11–13. Students investigate a polyhedron made from two other polyhedrons. They see that Euler's Formula still holds despite the "loss" of some faces, edges, and vertices.

Self-Assessment Answers

1. $x = 38°$; $m\angle W = 66°$; $m\angle Z = 119°$; $m\angle Y = 38°$; $m\angle X = 137°$

2. Sum of interior angles = 1080°; Sum of exterior angles = 360°

3. Sum of interior angles = 2340°; Sum of exterior angles = 360°

4. 12 pentagons; 12 triangles; 24 quadrilaterals; 1 12-gon

5.

Type	Sum of Interior Angles
Pentagon	540°
Triangle	180°
Quadrilateral	360°
12-gon	1800°

10. Yes; Consider the triangles formed by the poles, their shadows, and the rays of the sun. The triangles are congruent by ASA or LA. The poles are the same height by CPCTC.

11. 3 new faces, 1 new vertex, 4 new edges

12. $F = 9$, $V = 9$, $E = 16$; $9 + 9 - 16 = 2$

13. Nonahedron

14. Possible answer:

15. Possible answer:

16. Not possible

P **The figure shows the top view of the facets on the crown of a gem.**

4. Identify all of the different types of polygons that appear on the gem crown. How many of each type are there?

5. What is the sum of the measures of the interior angles for each type of polygon on the crown of the gem?

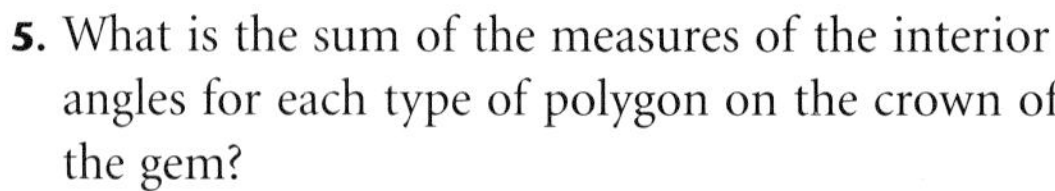

6. In the figure, $s + t + v + w = 470$. Therefore, $x =$ (c)
(a) 35 (b) 45 (c) 55 (d) 60 (e) 75

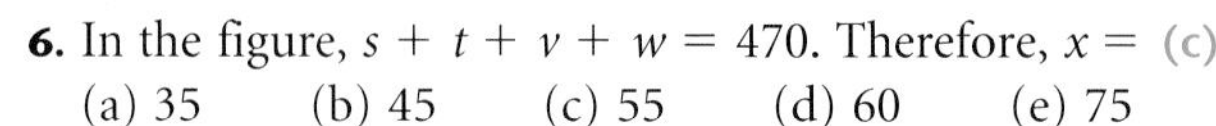

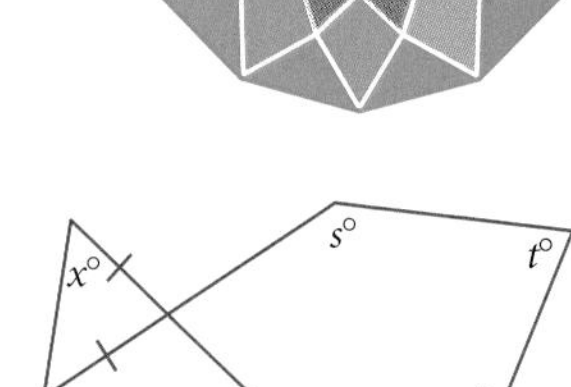

R **Find the area of each figure. [5-2]**

7. 33.64

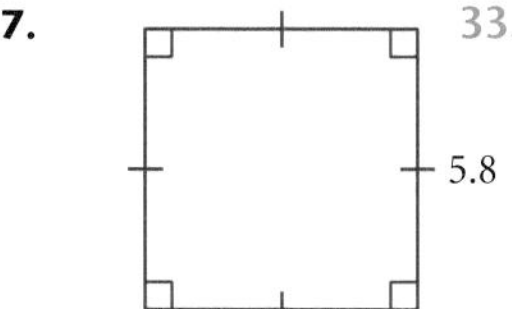

8. 360

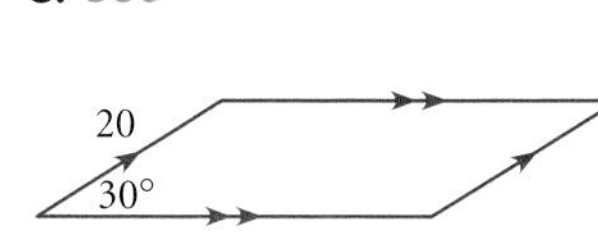

9. 600

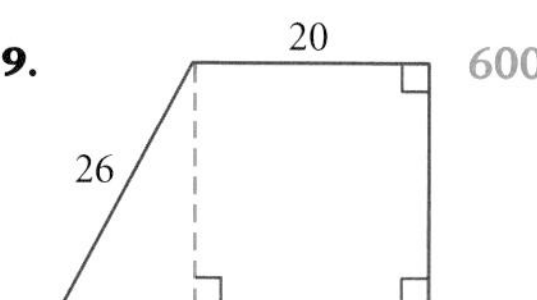

R, MR **10. Sun Day** When the sun is at a 41° angle as shown, a 24-ft-tall telephone pole casts a 27.6-ft-long shadow. The shadow of a nearby pole has the same length. Are the two poles the same height? Justify your answer. [4-3]

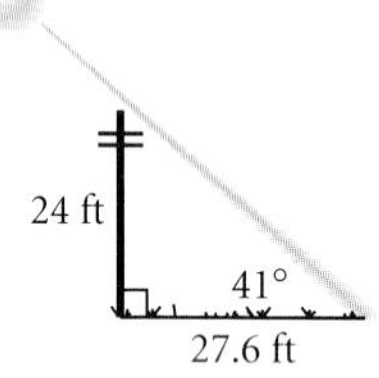

A pyramid with a square base is attached to a cube. The base of the pyramid is congruent to a face of the cube.

PS **11.** Compare the new polyhedron (cube + pyramid) to the cube. How many new faces, vertices, and edges were added by adding the pyramid?

P **12.** Show that Euler's Formula applies to the new polyhedron.

P **13.** Classify the new polyhedron.

P **Sketch each of the following, if possible. If it is not possible, say so.**

14. a concave quadrilateral

15. an equiangular pentagon that is not equilateral

16. a tetrahedron with six vertices

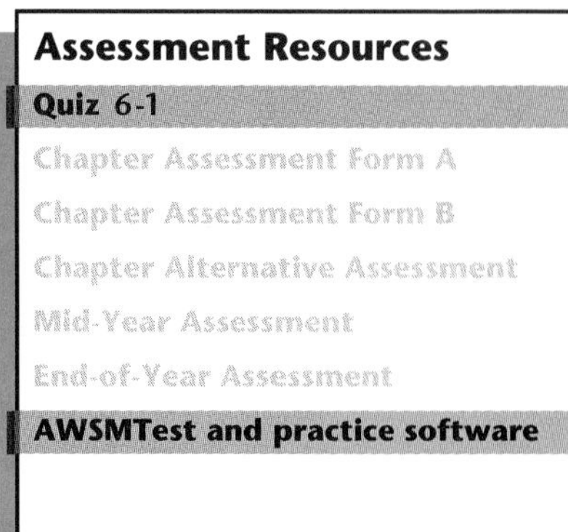

Assessment Resources

Quiz 6-1
Chapter Assessment Form A
Chapter Assessment Form B
Chapter Alternative Assessment
Mid-Year Assessment
End-of-Year Assessment
AWSMTest and practice software

Ongoing Assessment

Self-Assessment Self-Assessment Exercises

Embedded Assessment Explore Step 2; Reflect 2, 3

ADDITIONAL ANSWERS

6-1 Part C Exercises

30. Possible answer:

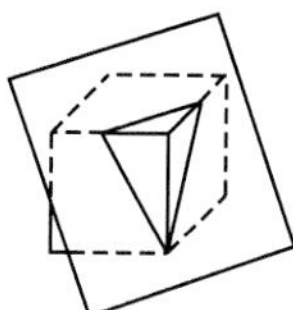

31. Possible answer:

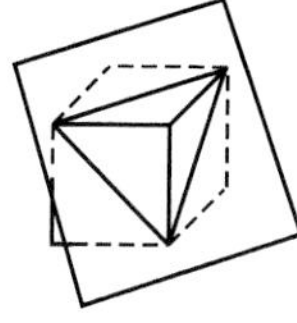

32. a. Tetrahedron

b. This creates 4 additional faces, 8 additional vertices, and 12 additional edges.

c. $F = 8$, $V = 12$, $E = 18$; $8 + 12 - 18 = 2$

d. Possible answer:

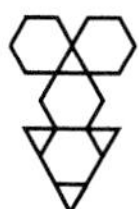

6-2 Part A Exercises

18. Possible answer:

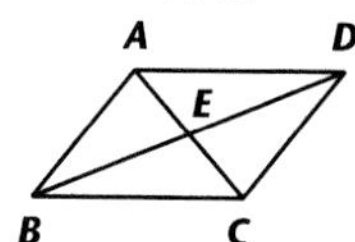

Given: $ABCD$ is a parallelogram.
Prove: $\overline{AC}$ and $\overline{BD}$ bisect each other.

Statement 1: $ABCD$ is a parallelogram.
Reason 1: Given

Statement 2: $\overline{AD} \parallel \overline{BC}$, $\overline{AB} \parallel \overline{CD}$
Reason 2: Definition of *parallelogram*

Statement 3: $\angle DBC \cong \angle BDA$, $\angle CDB \cong \angle ABD$
Reason 3: If parallel lines are cut by a transversal, the alternate interior angles are congruent.

Statement 4: $\overline{DB} \cong \overline{DB}$
Reason 4: Reflexive Property

Statement 5: $\triangle ABD \cong \triangle CDB$
Reason 5: ASA Postulate

6-2 Part A Exercises

18. (continued)

Statement 6: $\overline{AD} \cong \overline{BC}$
Reason 6: CPCTC

Statement 7: $\angle AED \cong \angle CEB$
Reason 7: Vertical angles are congruent.

Statement 8: $\triangle AED \cong \triangle CEB$
Reason 8: SAA Postulate

Statement 9: $\overline{AE} \cong \overline{EC}$, $\overline{BE} \cong \overline{ED}$
Reason 9: CPCTC

Statement 10: $\overline{AC}$ and $\overline{BD}$ bisect each other.
Reason 10: Definition of *bisect*

19. Statement 1: Draw $\overline{IL}$ so that $\overline{IL} \parallel \overline{HK}$.
Reason 1: There is exactly one line parallel to a given line through a point not on it.

Statement 2: Draw $\overline{HL}$
Reason 2: Two points determine a line.

Statement 3: $\overline{HI} \parallel \overline{LK}$
Reason 3: Definition of *trapezoid*

Statement 4: $\angle LHK \cong \angle HLI$, $\angle HLK \cong \angle LHI$
Reason 4: If parallel lines are cut by a transversal, alternate interior angles are congruent.

Statement 5: $\overline{HL} \cong \overline{HL}$
Reason 5: Reflexive Property

Statement 6: $\triangle LHK \cong \triangle HLI$
Reason 6: ASA Postulate

Statement 7: $\overline{IL} \cong \overline{HK}$
Reason 7: CPCTC

Statement 8: $\overline{HK} \cong \overline{IJ}$
Reason 8: Given

Statement 9: $\overline{IL} \cong \overline{IJ}$
Reason 9: Transitive Property

Statement 10: $\angle ILJ \cong \angle J$
Reason 10: Isosceles Triangle Theorem

Statement 11: $\angle K \cong \angle ILJ$
Reason 11: If two parallel lines are cut by a transversal, corresponding angles are congruent.

Statement 12: $\angle K \cong \angle J$
Reason 12: Transitive Property

6-2 Part A Exercises

Look Ahead

20. $\triangle ACD \cong \triangle CAB$; SSS Postulate

21. $\triangle EFG \cong \triangle IHG$; SAS Postulate

22. $\triangle WXY \cong \triangle YZW$; SAS Postulate

23. $4\sqrt{3}$ in.

More Practice

24. a. $\overline{TQ} \parallel \overline{SR}$, $\overline{TS} \parallel \overline{QR}$

b. $\overline{TQ} \cong \overline{SR}$, $\overline{TS} \cong \overline{QR}$

c. $\angle STQ$ and $\angle SRQ$, $\angle TQR$ and $\angle TSR$

d. $\angle RQT$ and $\angle QTS$, $\angle QRS$ and $\angle TSR$, $\angle SRQ$ and $\angle RQT$, $\angle QTS$ and $\angle TSR$

More Math Reasoning

28.

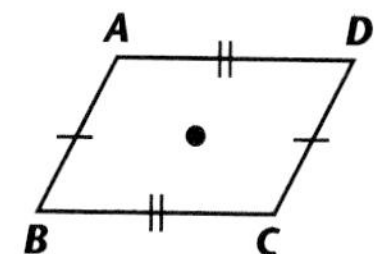

a. There are no lines of symmetry.

b. Yes; Rotate by 180°.

29. The computer is listing triangles where $\overline{BD}$ and $\overline{EC}$ are corresponding parts. It will check to see whether these triangles can be proved congruent.

6-2

Deductive Proof with Quadrilaterals

SUPERLESSON AT A GLANCE

Superlesson Goal

Students will write deductive proofs to justify statements about parallelograms, rhombuses, rectangles, and squares.

Management Guide

	Topic	Objectives	Key Terms	New Ideas	Materials
Part A	Proofs with Parallelograms	To discover and confirm properties of parallelograms.		Writing a complete deductive proof without guidance. Properties of parallelograms.	**Student** Ruler, protractor, geometry software
Part B	Proving Quadrilaterals Are Parallelograms	To investigate ways to show that quadrilaterals are parallelograms.		Using properties of quadrilaterals to determine whether or not they are parallelograms.	**Student** Ruler, protractor, graph paper, straws or sticks, geometry software
Part C	Proofs with Special Parallelograms	To investigate and confirm properties of diagonals of rectangles, rhombuses, and squares.		Properties of diagonals of rectangles, rhombuses, and squares.	**Student** Straws, scissors, thumbtacks, ruler
Part D	Quadrilaterals and Coordinate Proof	To use coordinate geometry in proofs about quadrilaterals.		Coordinate proof.	**Student** Graph paper **Teacher** Graph paper transparency
Part E	Making Connections	To discover and prove that the midpoints of the sides of a quadrilateral determine a parallelogram.	In Making Connections, students apply and synthesize key terms and new ideas.		**Student** Ruler, protractor, geometry software

Pacing Chart (45-Minute Periods)

	Comprehensive Course	Core Course	Informal Course
Part A	1	1	1*
Part B	1	1	1*
Part C	1	1	1*
Part D	1	1	1*
Part E	1	1	0
TOTAL periods for Superlesson	5	5	4

*Material on proof in this part may be omitted or downplayed in an Informal Course.

NCTM Standards

Mathematics as Problem Solving

Mathematics as Communication

Mathematics as Reasoning

Mathematical Connections

Geometry from a Synthetic Perspective

Geometry from an Algebraic Perspective

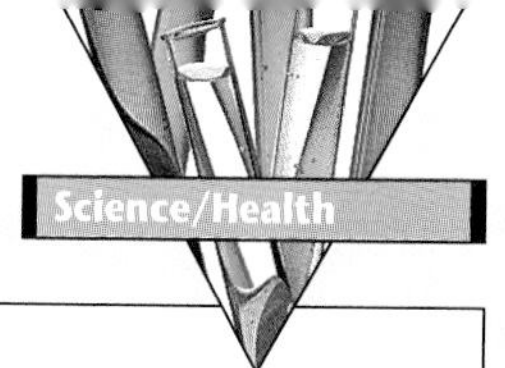

6-2 Deductive Proof with Quadrilaterals

TEcHno PRooFs

Researchers in the field of artificial intelligence (AI) explore ways to make computers simulate human thought. The following excerpt is from *AI: The Tumultuous History of the Search for Artificial Intelligence*, by Daniel Crevier. It describes a computer program developed in the 1950s by Herbert Gelernter to prove high school geometry theorems.

The Geometry Theorem Prover worked backward. One first described to it the theorem to prove. Much as a human being does, the program then started to build a chain of intermediate results leading back to known theorems or axioms.…[T]o figure out what steps might [work], the program looked at a drawing.…Gelernter had to enter a representational figure as a series of point coordinates.…Using these coordinates, the program was able to extract the same kind of information a human does…: Which sides are equal or parallel to each other? Are there any right angles? Are some angles equal to each other?

The figure shows a proof found by the Geometry Theorem Prover.

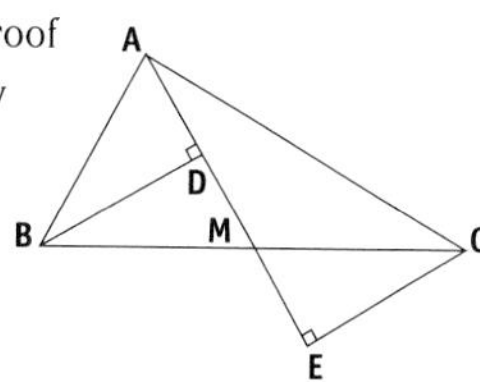

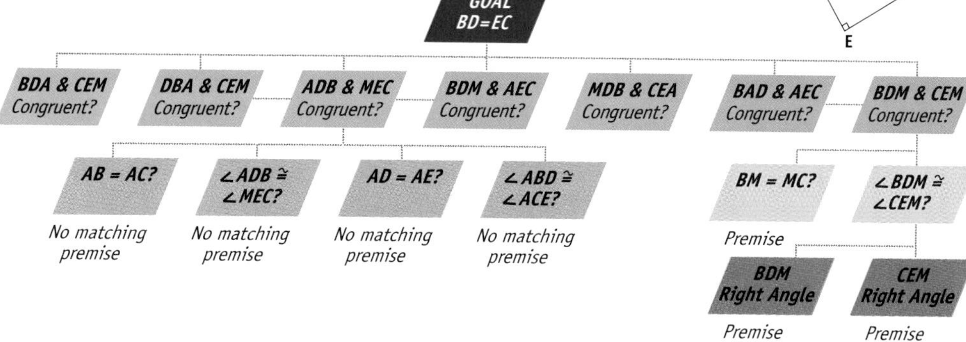

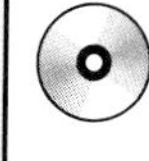

1. What strategies for proof did the Geometry Theorem Prover use that might be helpful to people when doing a proof?
2. The Geometry Theorem Prover could only prove theorems requiring ten steps or less. Why might this be true? Do you think computers could do longer proofs today?

More About Computer Proofs

In 1852, Thomas Guthrie conjectured that four colors were enough to shade any map on a plane or spherical surface so that no adjoining regions had the same color. This conjecture defied proof for over a century. In 1976, Kenneth Appel and Wolfgang Haken, of the University of Illinois, used a computer to prove the four-color theorem. They proved that there were only about 2000 different ways that regions could border one another, and then had the computer help show that each possibility could be colored with four colors.

Where Are We Now?

Students are familiar with properties of quadrilaterals and parallel lines, and with ways to prove triangles congruent. They have also practiced four of our five steps for deductive proof.

Where Are We Going?

In 6-2, students investigate properties of quadrilaterals. In this Superlesson, they complete all five steps of a deductive proof. They will complete proofs on their own through the rest of the text.

Possible Answers

1. Working backward, using a figure, looking for parallel sides, right angles, etc.
2. Longer proofs would require more memory and might have exceeded the capacity of the machine. Also, search processes for longer proofs might have taken a great deal of time. Today's computers have more memory and faster processing times, and can handle longer proofs.

AWSM Videodisc

Focus on Geometry

▶**6-2** Deductive Proof with Quadrilaterals

Search:

Play:

Step:

Deductive Proof with Quadrilaterals

PART A At a Glance

Objective

To discover and confirm properties of parallelograms.

Development

In the **Explore,** students discover as many properties of sides, angles, and diagonals of parallelograms as they can.

Then an **Example** shows a completed proof of one of the conjectures students may have made in the **Explore.** In the **Exercises** in this part, students do complete proofs on their own.

Suggested Materials

Student Ruler, protractor, geometry software

First Five Minutes

Transparency FFM 6-2A

Give a brief written summary of our five-step process for deductive proof. ***Rewrite*** **(in *if-then* form),** ***draw*** **(a figure and label parts),** ***state*** **(the** ***Given*** **and** ***Prove*****),** ***plan,*** ***demonstrate.***

Motivate

Ask...

- What are some of the formats used to *demonstrate* a proof? Give some strengths of each. **Paragraph proof (uses everyday language); Flow proof (shows how steps depend on each other); Two-column proof (consistent, easy-to-read format).**

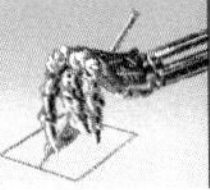

6-2 PART A Proofs with Parallelograms

← CONNECT → ***You've already investigated some properties of quadrilaterals. Now you will focus on the properties of one member of the family of quadrilaterals—the parallelogram.***

The fact that the opposite sides of a parallelogram are parallel gives it some special properties. In the following Explore, you will investigate the properties of the angles, sides, and diagonals of a parallelogram.

EXPLORE: PARALLELOGRAM PROBE

MATERIALS

Ruler, Protractor
Geometry software (optional)

1. Use geometry software or a ruler and protractor to draw several different parallelograms. Draw the diagonals of each parallelogram.
2. Measure the various parts of each parallelogram and its diagonals. Develop as many conjectures as you can about the angles, sides, and diagonals of parallelograms. Compare your results with those of your classmates.

Problem-Solving Tip

Check each of your conjectures by testing them on a new figure.

TRY IT

Find each of the following in parallelogram *MNOP*.

a. $m\angle PMN$ 135°
b. $m\angle NOP$ 135°
c. $m\angle OPM$ 45°
d. MP 7
e. OP 15
f. MQ 5.5
g. NQ 10.5

Technology Note

When using software to draw a parallelogram, students need to draw parallel sides. They may draw two adjacent sides and construct parallel lines as guidelines for the others. On some software, students can construct a quadrilateral, test whether opposite sides are parallel, and drag vertices to make adjustments.

While you've been exploring geometry facts, you've also been developing your ability to justify those facts with deductive proof. Remember the five-step process introduced on page 217. Now you will be doing all five steps on your own. The following example shows a complete proof of one of the conjectures you may have made in the preceding Explore.

EXAMPLE

Prove: The opposite angles of a parallelogram are congruent.

Rewrite: If a quadrilateral is a parallelogram, then its opposite angles are congruent.

Draw:

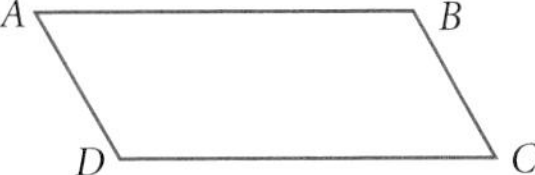

State:

Given: $ABCD$ is a parallelogram.

Prove: $\angle ABC \cong \angle CDA$ and $\angle DAB \cong \angle BCD$

Plan: Draw an auxiliary line segment, diagonal $\overline{AC}$. Show $\triangle ABC \cong \triangle CDA$ by ASA. Use CPCTC to show $\angle ABC \cong \angle CDA$. To prove that $\angle DAB \cong \angle BCD$, repeat the process, using diagonal $\overline{BD}$.

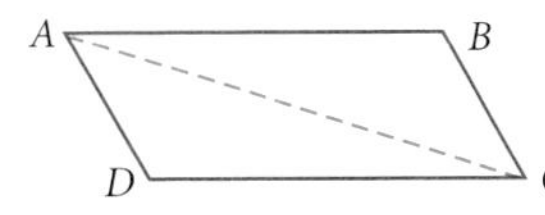

Demonstrate:

Statements	Reasons
1. Draw $\overline{AC}$.	**1.** Two points determine a line.
2. $ABCD$ is a parallelogram.	**2.** Given
3. $\overline{AB} \parallel \overline{DC}$ and $\overline{AD} \parallel \overline{BC}$	**3.** Definition of *parallelogram*
4. $\angle ACD \cong \angle CAB$ and $\angle DAC \cong \angle BCA$	**4.** If parallel lines are cut by a transversal, alternate interior angles are congruent.
5. $\overline{AC} \cong \overline{AC}$	**5.** Reflexive Property
6. $\triangle ABC \cong \triangle CDA$	**6.** ASA Postulate
7. $\angle ABC \cong \angle CDA$	**7.** CPCTC

To complete the proof, repeat Steps 1–6 using diagonal $\overline{BD}$ and the two triangles it forms to show that $\angle DAB \cong \angle BCD$.

Student Resources

- Alternative Lessons 6-2A
- Laboratory Manual 6-2A
- Technology Lab Manual
- Practice 6-2A
- Study Guide and Journal 6-2A
- Guía de estudios y Diario 6-2A
- Multilingual Handbook
- More Look Ahead 6-2A
- SAT Preparation

Media Resources

- Transparency FFM 6-2A
- Transparency AE 6-2A
- Teaching Transparency
- AWSMTest and practice software
- AWSM Videodisc

EXPLORE

Parallelogram Probe

Recommended group size: 4

The Point

To discover properties of the sides, angles, and diagonals of a parallelogram.

Look and Listen...

- For students who do not remember terms to describe geometric relationships.

Ask...

- What does *supplementary* mean? What does *bisect* mean?

For Groups That Finish Early

Take one of your conjectures and rewrite it in *if-then* form. Can you write a deductive justification for this conjecture?

Follow Up

Ask students to list all of the conjectures they made about parallelograms.

Possible Answer

2. Diagonals bisect each other, a diagonal divides the parallelogram into two congruent triangles, opposite sides are congruent, opposite angles are congruent, consecutive angles are supplementary.

ALTERNATE EXAMPLE

Transparency AE 6-2A

6-2

Deductive Proof with Quadrilaterals

Journal 

Explore Step 2 and **Reflect** 3 are suitable for journal entries.

REFLECT

Possible Answers

1. Rectangles, squares, and rhombuses.

2. 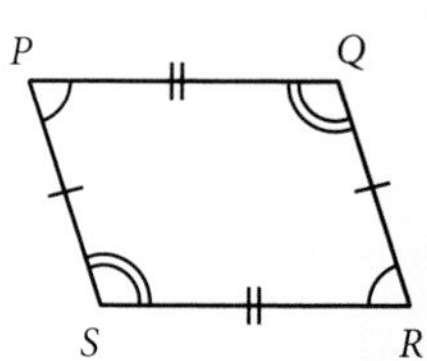

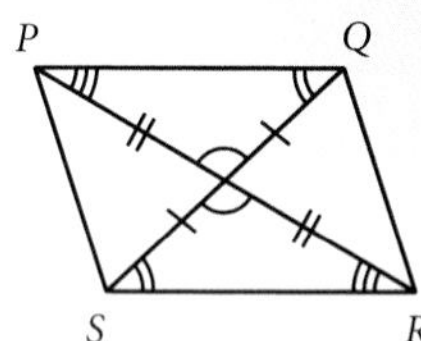

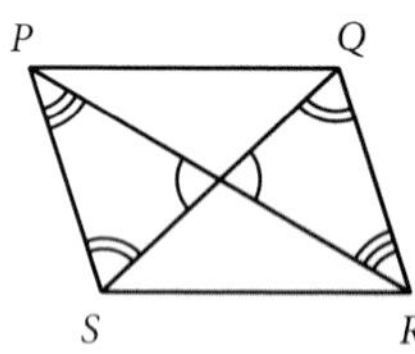

3. The diagonals divide the parallelogram into triangles, and these can be proved congruent with triangle congruence postulates.

Part A Exercises

Exercise Notes

Core

16–18. In these exercises, students prove properties of parallelograms.

19. In this exercise, students are introduced to isosceles trapezoids and prove that the base angles of an isosceles trapezoid are congruent.

Algebra | Functions | Discrete Math | Probability | Data/Statistics

Properties of parallelograms, including those properties you may have discovered in the preceding Explore, are summarized below. We proved one of the theorems in the example; you will have an opportunity to prove the others in the exercises.

PROPERTIES OF PARALLELOGRAMS

The opposite sides of a parallelogram are parallel (from the definition of a parallelogram).

The opposite angles of a parallelogram are congruent.

The opposite sides of a parallelogram are congruent.

The consecutive angles of a parallelogram are supplementary.

The diagonals of a parallelogram bisect each other.

REFLECT

1. Which special types of quadrilaterals also have the properties of parallelograms?
2. Draw a parallelogram and its diagonals. Mark all of the sides and angles that you know are congruent. (For clarity, you may want to draw more than one parallelogram.)
3. Why is drawing the diagonals of a parallelogram helpful in proving many of the parallelogram's properties?

Exercises

CORE

P **1. Getting Started** Using parallelogram *ABCD*, list all pairs of
   a. parallel sides $\overline{AB} \parallel \overline{DC}$, $\overline{AD} \parallel \overline{BC}$
   b. congruent sides $\overline{AB} \cong \overline{DC}$, $\overline{AD} \cong \overline{BC}$
   c. congruent angles $\angle D \cong \angle B$, $\angle A \cong \angle C$
   d. supplementary angles $\angle A$ and $\angle D$; $\angle A$ and $\angle B$; $\angle B$ and $\angle C$; $\angle C$ and $\angle D$

P **2.** Find the measures of all angles and the lengths of all sides of parallelogram *ABCD*.

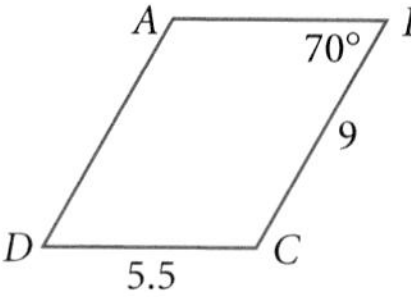

Key

V Vocabulary
P Practice/Skills
R Review
MR Math Reasoning
PS Problem Solving
C Challenge

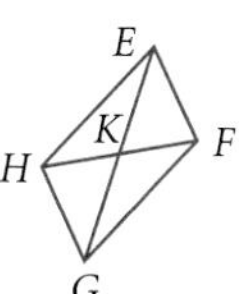

EFGH is a parallelogram. State a theorem that justifies each conclusion.

3. $\angle EHG \cong \angle EFG$

4. $\overline{EH} \cong \overline{FG}$

5. $\overline{HK} \cong \overline{KF}$

6. $\angle EHG$ is supplementary to $\angle HGF$.

WXYZ is a parallelogram. Complete each statement.

7. If $WX = 10$, $YZ =$ ___. 10

8. If $WY = 16$, $WV =$ ___. 8

9. If $m\angle XWZ = 102°$, $m\angle WZY =$ ___. 78°

10. If $m\angle XWZ = 87°$, $m\angle XYZ =$ ___. 87°

11. If $m\angle WZY = (2x + 12)°$ and $m\angle WXY = (5x - 36)°$, find $m\angle WXY$. $m\angle WXY = 44°$

12. If $WY = 4x - 14$ and $VY = x + 8$, find WV. $WV = 23$

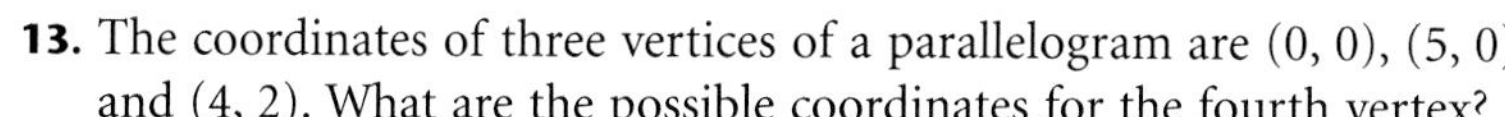

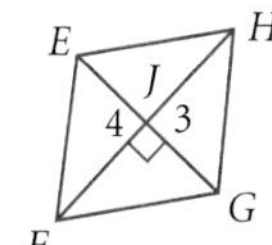

13. The coordinates of three vertices of a parallelogram are (0, 0), (5, 0), and (4, 2). What are the possible coordinates for the fourth vertex?

14. Quadrilateral $EFGH$ is a parallelogram. Find the lengths of all segments in the figure.

15. Shelf Size A carpenter needs to make a shelf so that its opposite sides have the same length. He finds a long board whose sides are parallel, and then makes two parallel cuts with his saw to make the shelf. Explain why this ensures that the opposite sides of the shelf have the same length.

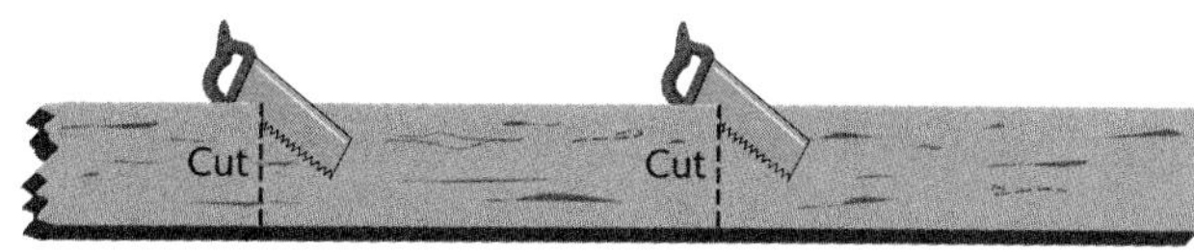

16. Prove that the opposite sides of a parallelogram are congruent.

Given: $ABCD$ is a parallelogram.

Prove: $\overline{AB} \cong \overline{CD}$, $\overline{BC} \cong \overline{AD}$

(Hint: Draw a diagonal.)

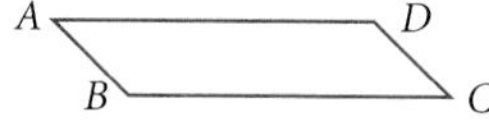

17. Prove that consecutive angles of a parallelogram are supplementary.

18. Prove that the diagonals of a parallelogram bisect each other.

19. An **isosceles trapezoid** is a trapezoid with congruent legs.

Given: $HIJK$ is an isosceles trapezoid with legs $\overline{HK} \cong \overline{IJ}$.

Prove: $\angle K \cong \angle J$

(Hint: Add segment $\overline{IL}$ parallel to $\overline{HK}$.)

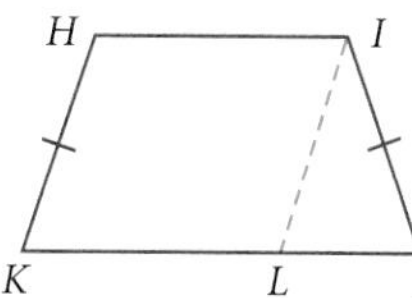

Ongoing Assessment

Self-Assessment Exercises 1–13 odd, 17

Embedded Assessment Reflect 2; Exercises 4, 10, 14, 18

Look Ahead

20–22. These exercises preview steps that will be important in proofs in 6-2 Part B.

23. Reviews special right triangles. Students will use properties of these triangles in 6-3.

More Math Reasoning

29. In this exercise, students analyze the strategy used by a computer program that proves geometry theorems. Analyzing methods of other problem-solvers may make students more aware of different strategies in problem-solving.

Exercise Answers

Core

2. $m\angle D = 70°$, $m\angle C = 110°$, $m\angle A = 110°$, $AD = 9$, $AB = 5.5$

3. The opposite angles of a parallelogram are congruent.

4. The opposite sides of a parallelogram are congruent.

5. The diagonals of a parallelogram bisect each other.

6. The consecutive angles of a parallelogram are supplementary.

13. (9, 2), (−1, 2), (1, −2)

14. $FG = HG = EH = EF = 5$; $JH = 4$; $EJ = 3$; $FH = 8$; $EG = 6$

15. The opposite sides of a parallelogram are congruent.

16. Statement 1: $ABCD$ is a parallelogram.
Reason 1: Given

Statement 2: Draw auxiliary line segment $\overline{AC}$.
Reason 2: Two points determine a line.

Statement 3: $\overline{AB} \parallel \overline{DC}$, $\overline{AD} \parallel \overline{BC}$
Reason 3: Definition of *parallelogram.*

Statement 4: $\angle DAC \cong \angle BCA$, $\angle ACD \cong \angle BAC$
Reason 4: If parallel lines are cut by a transversal, alternate interior angles are congruent.

Statement 5: $\overline{AC} \cong \overline{AC}$
Reason 5: Reflexive Property

Statement 6: $\triangle ADC \cong \triangle CBA$
Reason 6: ASA Postulate

Statement 7: $\overline{AB} \cong \overline{CD}$, $\overline{BC} \cong \overline{AD}$
Reason 7: CPCTC

Deductive Proof with Quadrilaterals

17. Possible answer:

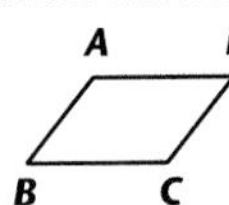

Given: $ABCD$ is a parallelogram.
Prove: Angle pairs $\angle A$ and $\angle B$, $\angle B$ and $\angle C$, $\angle C$ and $\angle D$, and $\angle D$ and $\angle A$ are supplementary.

Statement 1: $ABCD$ is a parallelogram.
Reason 1: Given

Statement 2: $\overline{AD} \parallel \overline{BC}$
Reason 2: Definition of *parallelogram*

Statement 3: $\angle A$ and $\angle B$ are supplementary.
Reason 3: Same-side interior angles of parallel lines are supplementary.

Use similar proof to show that other consecutive angles are supplementary.

18–24., 28., and 29.
See Additional Answers p. T416.

LOOK AHEAD

P **Write a congruence statement for each pair of triangles. Then name the postulate or theorem that allows you to conclude that they are congruent.**

20.

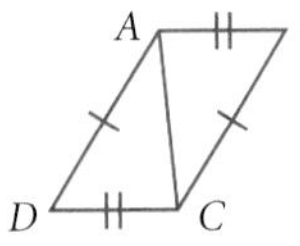

21.

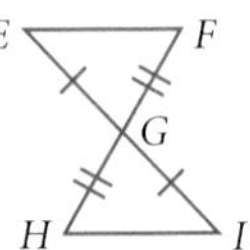

22.

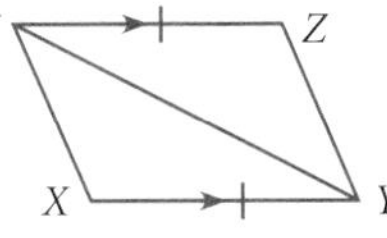

P **23.** Find the length of an altitude of an equilateral triangle with a side length of 8 in.

MORE PRACTICE

P **24.** Using parallelogram $QRST$, list all pairs of
a. parallel sides **b.** congruent sides **c.** congruent angles **d.** supplementary angles

P **Complete each statement for parallelogram *QRST*.**

25. If $m\angle SRP = 28°$, $m\angle T =$ ___ . 152°

26. If $QT = 14$, $SR =$ ___ . 14

27. If $m\angle TQR = 42°$, $m\angle TSR =$ ___ . 42°

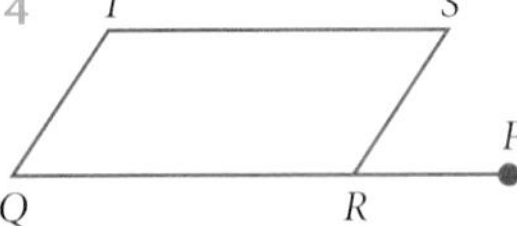

MORE MATH REASONING

MR **28.** Draw a parallelogram that is neither a rectangle nor a rhombus.
a. Draw and describe any lines of symmetry of the parallelogram.
b. Does the parallelogram have rotational symmetry? If so, locate the center of the rotation; then list all clockwise rotations of less than 360° that will rotate the parallelogram onto itself.

MR, C **29. Electromotive Reasoning** The figure and first "step" of the computer proof on page 417 are shown below. Explain the strategy the computer is using.

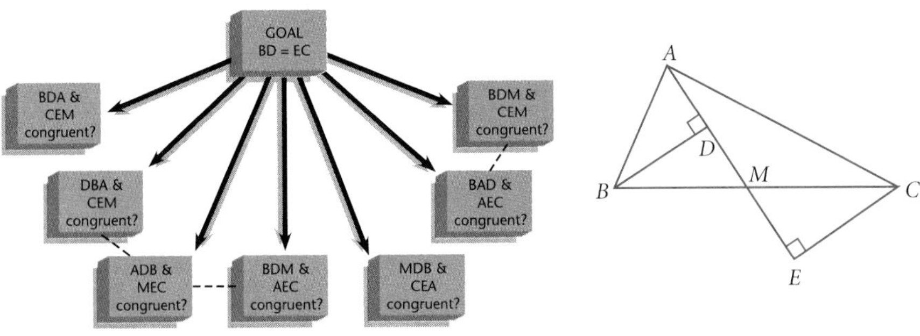

Key

V Vocabulary
P Practice/Skills
R Review
MR Math Reasoning
PS Problem Solving
C Challenge

Technology Note

In the **Explore** on page 423, students construct quadrilaterals with given characteristics. Using software to do this, they can draw a quadrilateral, measure sides/angles, and drag a vertex to make adjustments. (Tip: Keep a side horizontal.) To check for parallel sides, they can measure slopes or use property-checking capabilities.

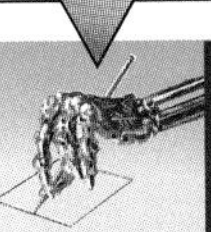

6-2 PART B Proving Quadrilaterals Are Parallelograms

← CONNECT → *You now know about many properties of parallelograms. Next you will investigate several ways to show that a quadrilateral is a parallelogram.*

You can be sure that a quadrilateral is a parallelogram if both pairs of opposite sides are parallel.

1. Why does showing that the opposite sides of a quadrilateral are parallel prove that the quadrilateral is a parallelogram?

In the following Explore, you will look for other characteristics that assure you that a quadrilateral is a parallelogram. These characteristics will be useful in subsequent proofs.

EXPLORE: AM I A PARALLELOGRAM?

1. State the converse of each of the four theorems about the properties of a parallelogram.
2. Investigate the converse of each theorem. You can draw and/or construct figures on graph paper, use straws or sticks to make models (as shown in the photograph at the right), or use geometry software.
3. Determine whether the converse of each theorem is true or false, and explain how you investigated it.
4. List all the ways that you know to show that a quadrilateral is a parallelogram. Compare your list with those of your classmates.

MATERIALS

Ruler, Protractor
Graph paper (optional)
Straws or sticks (optional)
Geometry software (optional)

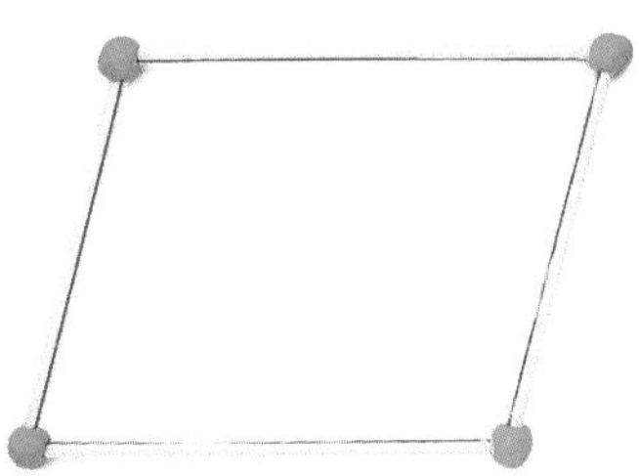

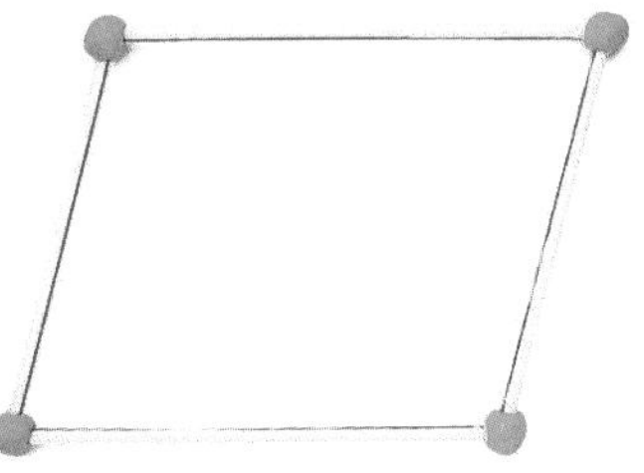

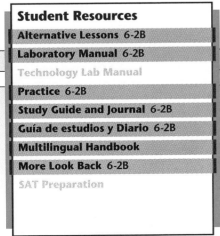

Student Resources
- Alternative Lessons 6-2B
- Laboratory Manual 6-2B
- Technology Lab Manual
- Practice 6-2B
- Study Guide and Journal 6-2B
- Guía de estudios y Diario 6-2B
- Multilingual Handbook
- More Look Back 6-2B
- SAT Preparation

Media Resources
- Transparency FFM 6-2B
- Transparency AE 6-2B
- Teaching Transparency
- AWSMTest and practice software
- AWSM Videodisc

PART B At a Glance

Objective
To investigate ways to show that quadrilaterals are parallelograms.

Development
In the **Explore,** students discover ways to show that a quadrilateral is a parallelogram.

One of the conjectures from the **Explore** is proved in an **Example.** Students are asked to prove others in **Exercises.**

Suggested Materials
Student Ruler, protractor, graph paper, straws or sticks, geometry software

First Five Minutes
Transparency FFM 6-2B

Read the opening paragraph on page 423. Then answer **Consider** question 1.

Motivate
Ask...
- Write the converse of the theorem "The opposite angles of a parallelogram are congruent." Do you think the converse is true? Explain.

Possible Answer

1. By definition, a quadrilateral with two pairs of parallel sides is a parallelogram.

EXPLORE

Am I a Parallelogram?
Recommended group size: 4

The Point
To discover ways to show that a quadrilateral is a parallelogram.

Deductive Proof with Quadrilaterals

Look and Listen...

- For students who are not writing the converses of the theorems from 6-2 Part A correctly. It is important that the hypotheses of the converses refer to a *quadrilateral,* not a *figure.* For example, "If the opposite angles of a *quadrilateral* are congruent...," is correct.

Ask...

- Have you rewritten the theorems from Part A in *if-then* form?

For Groups That Finish Early

Write a complete proof of one of your conjectures.

Follow Up

Ask students to list all of the ways to show that a quadrilateral is a parallelogram.

Possible Answers

1. If the opposite angles of a quadrilateral are congruent, then the quadrilateral is a parallelogram.

   If the opposite sides of a quadrilateral are congruent, then the quadrilateral is a parallelogram.

   If the consecutive angles of a quadrilateral are supplementary, then the quadrilateral is a parallelogram.

   If the diagonals of a quadrilateral bisect each other, then the quadrilateral is a parallelogram.

3. All of the converses are true.
4. See answer to Step 1.

ALTERNATE EXAMPLE

Transparency AE 6-2B

TRY IT

Determine whether each quadrilateral must be a parallelogram. Justify your answers.

a. 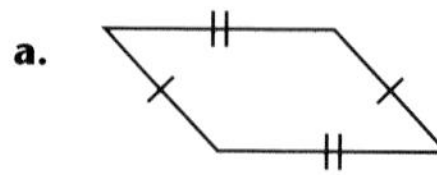

Parallelogram; Opposite sides are congruent.

b. 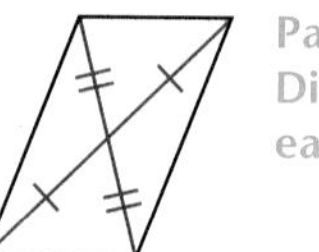

Parallelogram; Diagonals bisect each other.

c. 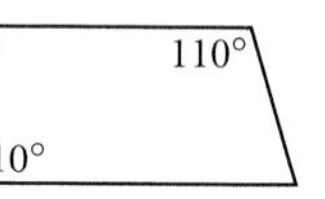

Parallelogram; Consecutive angles are supplementary.

d. 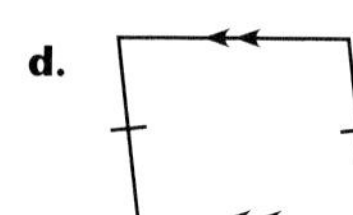

May not be a parallelogram; The congruent sides may not be parallel.

Although inductive investigations like the ones you did in the preceding Explore are important, we also want to be able to prove that what *usually* seems to work really *does* work under all circumstances. In the following Example, we will look at a proof of one of the conjectures you may have made in the Explore.

EXAMPLE

Prove: If the consecutive angles of a quadrilateral are supplementary, then the quadrilateral is a parallelogram.

Given: $\angle A$ and $\angle B$ are supplementary.
$\angle B$ and $\angle C$ are supplementary.
$\angle C$ and $\angle D$ are supplementary.
$\angle D$ and $\angle A$ are supplementary.

A D B C

Prove: $ABCD$ is a parallelogram.

Proof: $\angle A$ and $\angle B$ are same-side interior angles for $\overline{AD}$ and $\overline{BC}$. They are supplementary (from the given information). Therefore, $\overline{AD}$ and $\overline{BC}$ are parallel, because lines cut by a transversal are parallel if their same-side interior angles are supplementary. In the same way, $\overline{AB}$ and $\overline{DC}$ are parallel. Because $\overline{AD} \parallel \overline{BC}$ and $\overline{AB} \parallel \overline{DC}$, $ABCD$ is, by definition, a parallelogram.

You may have discovered that all of the converses of the parallelogram properties listed on page 420 are true. These methods of showing that a quadrilateral is a parallelogram are summarized below. One of these theorems was proved in the Example. You will have a chance to prove the others in the Exercises.

Careers Connection

Fumiko Yonezawa, a computational physicist at Keio University in Yokomana, Japan, uses mathematical models to study structures of solid matter. Her doctoral thesis was important in the development of a new approach to studying the structure of glasses. Her recent work has focused on how liquids become crystals or unstructured solids.

CONDITIONS FOR A PARALLELOGRAM

A quadrilateral is a parallelogram if both pairs of opposite sides are parallel (definition).

If both pairs of opposite angles of a quadrilateral are congruent, then the quadrilateral is a parallelogram.

If both pairs of opposite sides of a quadrilateral are congruent, then the quadrilateral is a parallelogram.

If the consecutive angles of a quadrilateral are supplementary, then the quadrilateral is a parallelogram.

If the diagonals of a quadrilateral bisect each other, then the quadrilateral is a parallelogram.

REFLECT

1. Can you conclude that a quadrilateral with one pair of congruent sides is a parallelogram? Explain or give a counterexample.
2. State the theorems about the properties of parallelograms and the conditions for parallelograms as biconditionals.

Exercises

CORE

P **Getting Started Determine whether each quadrilateral must be a parallelogram. Justify your answers.**

1. 95° 85° 85° 95°

2.

3.

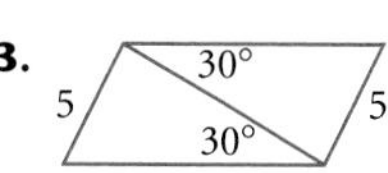

P **Given the following, determine whether quadrilateral *ABCD* must be a parallelogram. Justify your answers.**

4. $\overline{AE} \cong \overline{EC}, \overline{DE} \cong \overline{EB}$

5. $\angle ADC \cong \angle ABC$

6. $\overline{AB} \cong \overline{CD}, \overline{AD} \cong \overline{BC}$

7. $\overline{AB} \parallel \overline{CD}, \overline{AD} \parallel \overline{BC}$

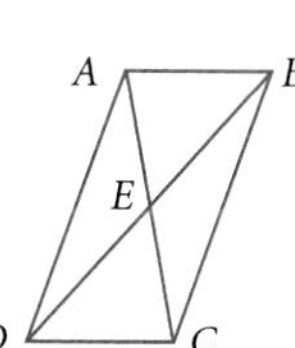

Key

Vocabulary
Practice/Skills
Review
MR Math Reasoning
PS Problem Solving
Challenge

Ongoing Assessment

Self-Assessment Exercises 1–17 odd

Embedded Assessment Reflect 1; Exercises 4, 8, 12, 16

Journal

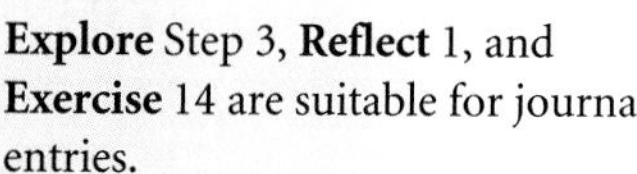

Explore Step 3, **Reflect** 1, and **Exercise** 14 are suitable for journal entries.

REFLECT

Possible Answers

1. No. For instance:

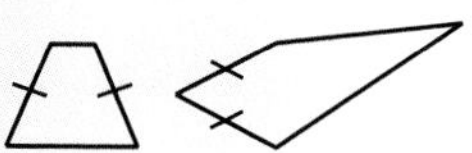

2. A quadrilateral is a parallelogram if and only if both pairs of opposite sides are congruent.

A quadrilateral is a parallelogram if and only if both pairs of opposite angles are congruent.

A quadrilateral is a parallelogram if and only if its consecutive angles are supplementary.

A quadrilateral is a parallelogram if and only if its diagonals bisect each other.

Part B Exercises

Exercise Notes

Core

14. and 15. Students use the concepts of this Part in real-world applications.

16. and 17. Students prove two of the conjectures from the **Explore.**

More Math Reasoning

30. Students prove a property of an isosceles trapezoid.

Exercise Answers

Core

1. Parallelogram; Both pairs of opposite angles are congruent.

2. Parallelogram; Both pairs of opposite sides are parallel.

3. May not be a parallelogram; The conditions for a parallelogram may not be satisfied.

4. Parallelogram; Diagonals bisect each other.

5. May not be a parallelogram; The conditions for a parallelogram may not be satisfied.

6. Parallelogram; Both pairs of opposite sides are congruent.

Deductive Proof with Quadrilaterals

7. Parallelogram; Both pairs of opposite sides are parallel.

8. Both pairs of opposite sides are congruent or both pairs of opposite sides are parallel.

9. Consecutive angles are supplementary.

10. Opposite sides of a parallelogram are congruent, so $4x = 20$ and $5y = 40$. Therefore, $x = 5$ and $y = 8$.

11. Opposite sides of a parallelogram are parallel, and if parallel lines are cut by a transversal the alternate interior angles are congruent. So $(3x + 6)° = 27°$ and $8y° = 64°$. Therefore, $x = 7$ and $y = 8$.

12. Consecutive angles are supplementary, so $(5x + y)° + (4x - y)° = 180°$. Therefore $9x = 180$ or $x = 20$. Opposite angles are congruent, so $(5x + y)° = 125°$. Substitute $x = 20$ to get $y = 25$.

14. Possible answer: The opposite sides are always congruent, so the footrests form parallelograms.

15. The quadrilaterals formed by the endpoints of the legs are parallelograms because the legs bisect each other.

16. Possible answer:

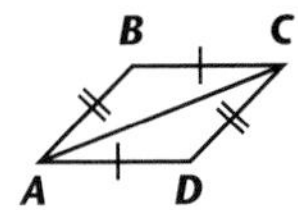

Given: $\overline{BC} \cong \overline{AD}$, $\overline{AB} \cong \overline{DC}$
Prove: $ABCD$ is a parallelogram.
Proof: Draw diagonal $\overline{AC}$ using two points to determine a line. $\overline{BC} \cong \overline{AD}$ and $\overline{AB} \cong \overline{DC}$ are given. $\overline{AC} \cong \overline{AC}$ by the Reflexive Property. $\triangle ABC \cong \triangle CDA$ by the SSS Postulate. $\angle BCA \cong \angle DAC$ and $\angle BAC \cong \angle DCA$ by CPCTC. Then $\overline{AD} \parallel \overline{BC}$ and $\overline{AB} \parallel \overline{DC}$ because lines cut by a transversal are parallel if their alternate interior angles are congruent. $ABCD$ is a parallelogram by definition.

17., 25–32.
See Additional Answers p. T178.

Algebra | Functions | Discrete Math | Probability | Data/Statistics

P **What information do you need in order to prove that *QRST* is a parallelogram using**

8. all four of its sides? **9.** consecutive angles?

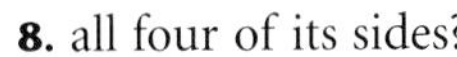

P **What values of *x* and *y* guarantee that each quadrilateral is a parallelogram? Justify your answers.**

10.

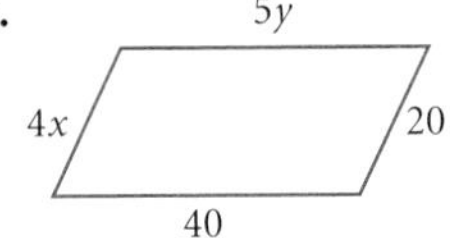

11.

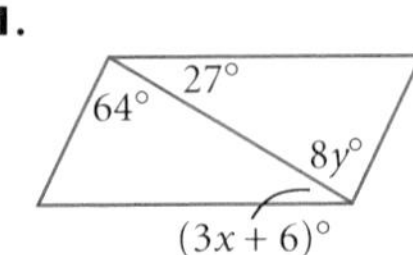

12.

(5x + y)°
(4x – y)°
125°

PS **13. The Harmony of the Grids** The three red points are vertices of a quadrilateral. If the fourth vertex is selected at random from the remaining grid points, what is the probability that the figure will be a parallelogram? $\frac{3}{22}$

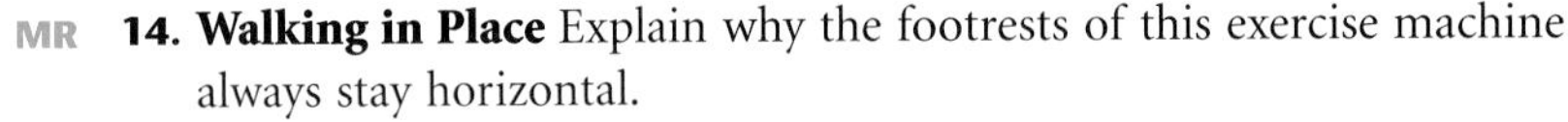

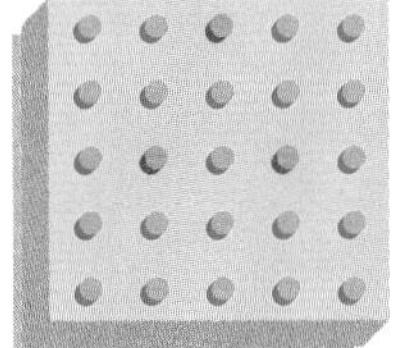

MR **14. Walking in Place** Explain why the footrests of this exercise machine always stay horizontal.

MR **15.** The seat of this director's chair is always parallel to the floor. Explain why this is the case.

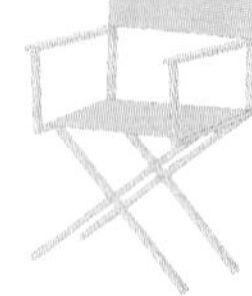

MR **16.** Prove: If both pairs of opposite sides of a quadrilateral are congruent, then the quadrilateral is a parallelogram.

MR **17.** Prove: If both pairs of opposite angles of a quadrilateral are congruent, then the quadrilateral is a parallelogram.

LOOK BACK

R **Find the length of the unknown side in each triangle. Express it as a radical in simplest form (if possible) and as a decimal approximation rounded to the nearest hundredth. [5-3]**

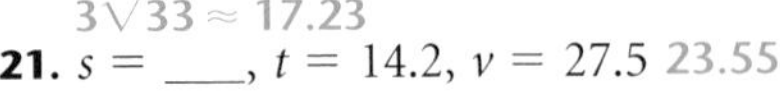

18. $s = 9$, $t = 12$, $v =$ ____ 15

19. $s = 8$, $t =$ ____, $v = 19$ $3\sqrt{33} \approx 17.23$

20. $s = 3\sqrt{2}$, $t = 7$, $v =$ ____ $\sqrt{67} \approx 8.19$

21. $s =$ ____, $t = 14.2$, $v = 27.5$ 23.55

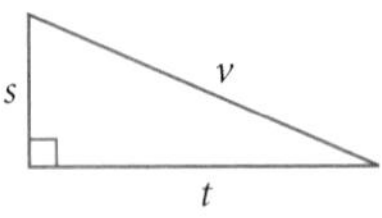

Key

V Vocabulary
P Practice/Skills
R Review
MR Math Reasoning
PS Problem Solving
C Challenge

R **Give the sum of the measures of the interior and exterior angles (one at each vertex) for each polygon. [6-1]**

22. a heptagon
Sum of interior angles = 900°;
Sum of exterior angles = 360°

23. a 16-gon
Sum of interior angles = 2520°;
Sum of exterior angles = 360°

24. an $(x + 5)$-gon
Sum of interior angles = $(x + 3)$ 180°;
Sum of exterior angles = 360°

MORE PRACTICE

P **Given the following, determine whether quadrilateral *JKLM* must be a parallelogram. Justify your answers.**

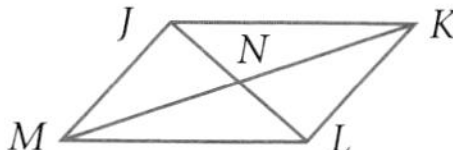

25. $\overline{JK} \cong \overline{LM}$, $\overline{JM} \cong \overline{LK}$

26. $\angle MJK \cong \angle MLK$, $\angle JML \cong \angle JKL$

27. $\overline{JN} \cong \overline{NL} \cong \overline{MN} \cong \overline{NK}$

28. $\overline{JK} \parallel \overline{LM}$, $\overline{JM} \cong \overline{LK}$

MORE MATH REASONING

R **29.** Prove the following theorem: If the diagonals of a quadrilateral bisect each other, then the quadrilateral is a parallelogram.

C **30.** Prove that the diagonals of an isosceles trapezoid (a trapezoid with congruent legs) are congruent. (Hint: See Exercise 19, page 421.)

R **31.** Draw an isosceles triangle, $\triangle ABC$, and mark any point, P, on the base. Draw line segments from P to the other sides of the triangle that are parallel to the legs. Prove that these segments form a parallelogram.

R **32.** Prove: If a quadrilateral is a parallelogram, then a diagonal divides it into two congruent triangles. Then prove the converse of this statement or disprove it by showing a counterexample.

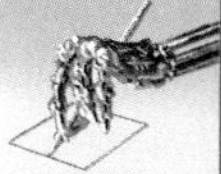

6-2 PART C Proofs with Special Parallelograms

← CONNECT → ***Quadrilaterals whose diagonals bisect each other are parallelograms. Now you will explore diagonal properties for special parallelograms.***

Since rhombuses, rectangles, and squares are special parallelograms, their diagonals have some unique characteristics. As you discover these, you will also see that these properties suggest ways to prove that a parallelogram *is* a rhombus, rectangle, or square.

Student Resources

- **Alternative Lessons 6-2C**
- **Laboratory Manual 6-2C**
- Technology Lab Manual
- **Practice 6-2C**
- **Study Guide and Journal 6-2C**
- **Guía de estudios y Diario 6-2C**
- **Multilingual Handbook**
- **More Look Ahead 6-2C**
- SAT Preparation

Media Resources

- **Transparency FFM 6-2C**
- **Transparency AE 6-2C**
- Teaching Transparency
- **AWSMTest and practice software**
- AWSM Videodisc

PART C At a Glance

Objective

To investigate and confirm properties of diagonals of rectangles, rhombuses, and squares.

Development

In the **Explore,** students investigate ways to use diagonals of a parallelogram to identify rectangles, rhombuses, and squares. (The proof of one of these methods is shown later in an **Example.**)

Then, in a **Consider** question, students state converses of their conjectures and decide whether these statements—about the properties of diagonals of special quadrilaterals—seem to be true.

Suggested Materials

Student Straws, scissors, thumbtacks, ruler

First Five Minutes

Transparency FFM 6-2C

Read the paragraph at the bottom of page 427. Then answer **Consider** questions 1–3 at the top of page 428.

Motivate

Ask...

- What properties do rectangles, rhombuses, and squares have because they are parallelograms? What other properties does each possess? **All: opposite sides parallel and ≅, opposite angles ≅, consecutive angles supplementary, diagonals bisect each other. Rectangles, squares: four right angles. Rhombuses, squares: four ≅ sides.**

Algebra	Functions	Discrete Math	Probability	Data/Statistics

Deductive Proof with Quadrilaterals

Reviews relationships between parallelograms, rectangles, rhombuses, and squares.

Possible Answers

1. Parallelograms, rectangles, and rhombuses

2–3. Parallelograms

EXPLORE

Draw Straws

Recommended group size: 4

The Point

To discover ways to use diagonals of a parallelogram to identify rectangles, rhombuses, and squares.

Look and Listen...

- For students who are mistakenly writing the converses of their discoveries in Step 3.
- For students who use congruent straws when exploring diagonals that are not necessarily congruent.

Ask...

- In this **Explore,** do you start with the figure and draw a conclusion about its diagonals, or do you start with the diagonals and draw a conclusion about the figure?

For Groups That Finish Early

A kite is a quadrilateral with two pairs of adjacent, congruent sides. Investigate the diagonals of a kite. Make any conjectures you can.

Follow Up

Ask students to list the diagonal relationships that they discovered.

Possible Answers

2. A parallelogram. (If the diagonals happen to be perpendicular, students may have a rhombus.)

Use the terms *parallelograms, rhombuses,* and *rectangles* to complete each statement. List all the terms that make the statement true.

1. All squares are ____. **2. All rhombuses are ____.**

3. All rectangles are ____.

In the following Explore, you will discover relationships between diagonals and special parallelograms.

EXPLORE: DRAW STRAWS

MATERIALS

Straws
Scissors
Thumbtacks
Ruler

1. You will need three straws—two that are the same length and one of a different length. Mark their midpoints.
2. Take two straws of different lengths. Cross them so that they bisect each other, and fasten them with a thumbtack. Place the straws on a sheet of paper, mark dots at the endpoints, and then use a straightedge to connect these points. What type of quadrilateral do you get?
3. Use the straws to find the type of quadrilateral that results for each combination below. In each case, be sure that the diagonals bisect each other.
   a. Diagonals are not perpendicular and not congruent.
   b. Diagonals are not perpendicular but are congruent.
   c. Diagonals are perpendicular but are not congruent.
   d. Diagonals are congruent and perpendicular.

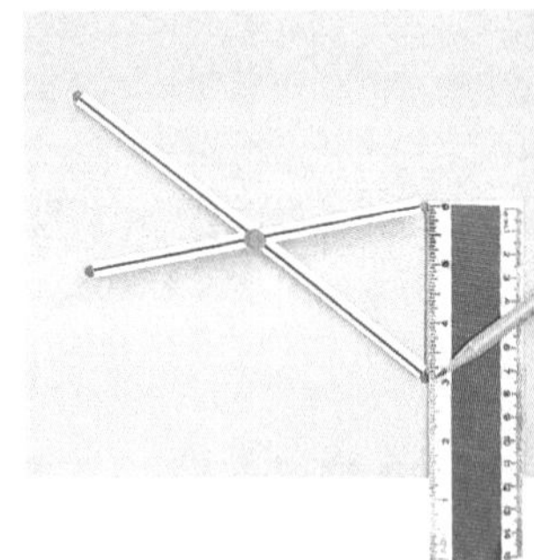

Write conditional statements to summarize your results.

4. State the converses of the theorems you discovered in the preceding Explore. Do you think the converses are true? Why or why not?

Diversity Issues

The manipulatives used in the **Explore** should appeal to kinesthetic learners. By pivoting the straws modeling the diagonals, they can get a feeling for how the position and size of the diagonals affect the shape of the quadrilateral.

TRY IT

Classify quadrilateral $VWXY$ using the given information.

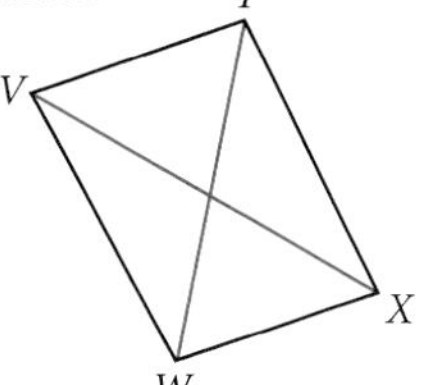

a. $\overline{VX}$ and $\overline{WY}$ bisect each other. Parallelogram

b. $\overline{VX}$ and $\overline{WY}$ bisect each other, and $\overline{VX} \perp \overline{WY}$. b. Rhombus

c. $\overline{VX}$ and $\overline{WY}$ bisect each other, and $\overline{VX} \cong \overline{WY}$. c. Rectangle

d. $\overline{VX}$ and $\overline{WY}$ bisect each other, $\overline{VX} \perp \overline{WY}$, and $\overline{VX} \cong \overline{WY}$. Square

EXAMPLE

Prove: If a parallelogram is a rectangle, then its diagonals are congruent.

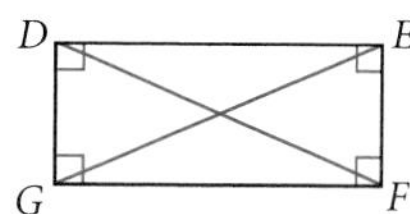

Given: Parallelogram $DEFG$ is a rectangle with diagonals $\overline{DF}$ and $\overline{GE}$.

Prove: $\overline{DF} \cong \overline{GE}$

Proof:

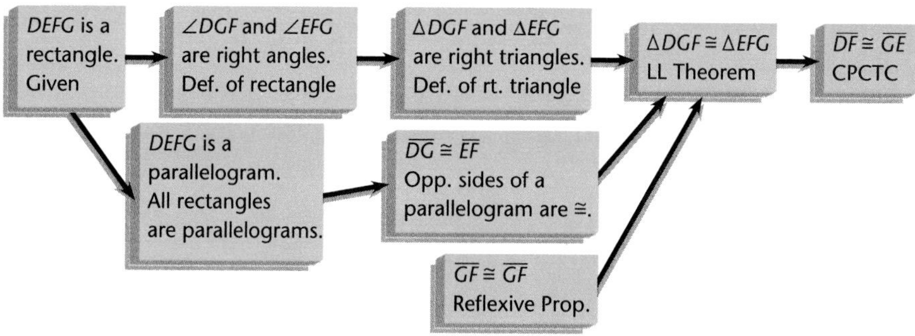

Your results from the Explore and their converses can be combined into the biconditional statements below.

THEOREMS ABOUT DIAGONALS OF SPECIAL PARALLELOGRAMS

A parallelogram is a rhombus if and only if its diagonals are perpendicular.

A parallelogram is a rectangle if and only if its diagonals are congruent.

A parallelogram is a square if and only if its diagonals are both perpendicular and congruent.

Research Note

Reported research that points out difficulties students have with proof suggests [that teachers]...[f]ocus on helping students to learn to begin proofs, combining both analysis and synthesis in the planning stages. (Phares G. O'Daffer and Bruce A. Thornquist, "Critical Thinking, Mathematical Reasoning, and Proof," *Research Ideas for the Classroom: High School Mathematics,* NCTM Research Interpretation Project, Patricia S. Wilson, ed., p. 53. © 1993 NCTM.)

3. a. A parallelogram

b. A rectangle

c. A rhombus

d. A square

If the diagonals of a parallelogram are congruent, then it is a rectangle.

If the diagonals of a parallelogram are perpendicular, then it is a rhombus.

If the diagonals of a parallelogram are both congruent and perpendicular, then it is a square.

Possible Answers

4. If a parallelogram is a rectangle, then its diagonals are congruent.

If a parallelogram is a rhombus, then its diagonals are perpendicular.

If a parallelogram is a square, then its diagonals are perpendicular and congruent.

All of these statements are true.

ALTERNATE EXAMPLE

Prove: If the diagonals of a parallelogram are perpendicular, then the parallelogram is a rhombus.

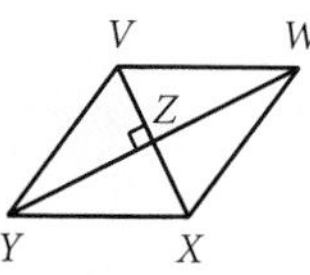

Given: In parallelogram $VWXY$, $\overline{VX} \perp \overline{WY}$.

Prove: $VWXY$ is a rhombus.

$\triangle VZY$ and $\triangle VZW$ are right triangles, by the definition of right triangles. $\overline{ZY} \cong \overline{ZW}$ because the diagonals of a parallelogram bisect each other. $\overline{VZ} \cong \overline{VZ}$ because of the Reflexive Property. Therefore, $\triangle VZY \cong \triangle VZW$ by LL, and $\overline{VY} \cong \overline{VW}$ by CPCTC. We can repeat these steps to show that $\overline{VW} \cong \overline{WX}$ and $\overline{WX} \cong \overline{YX}$. Since all of its sides are congruent, $VWXY$ is a rhombus.

Deductive Proof with Quadrilaterals

Journal

Explore Step 3, **Consider** question 4, and **Reflect** 1 are suitable for journal entries.

REFLECT

Possible Answers

1. The square inherits perpendicular diagonals from the rhombus, congruent diagonals from the rectangle, and bisecting diagonals from the parallelogram.
2. All four sides are congruent; the diagonals are perpendicular.
3.

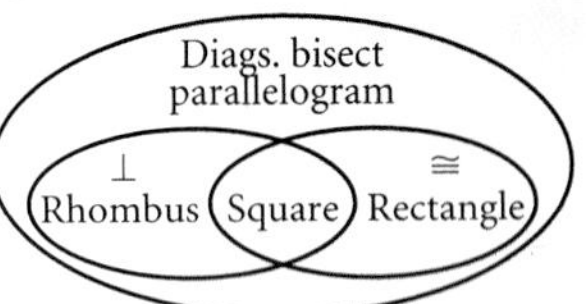

Part C Exercises

Exercise Notes

Core

5–12. Students may find this chart format helpful for seeing relationships between parallelograms.

25. Students use reflections to "construct" a rhombus.

Look Ahead

These exercises review geometry on a coordinate plane. In Part D, students will use coordinate geometry to justify conjectures.

More Math Reasoning

41. Students prove that certain diagonal characteristics produce a kite.

Exercise Answers

Core

5. Parallelogram, rectangle, rhombus, square
6. Parallelogram, rectangle, rhombus, square
7. Parallelogram, rectangle, rhombus, square
8. Parallelogram, rectangle, rhombus, square

REFLECT

1. A square is also a rhombus, a rectangle, and a parallelogram. What diagonal properties does the square inherit from each?
2. State two properties of a rhombus that do not hold true for all parallelograms.
3. Summarize the theorems about the diagonals of a parallelogram by filling in the Venn diagram with the names of the different types of quadrilaterals.

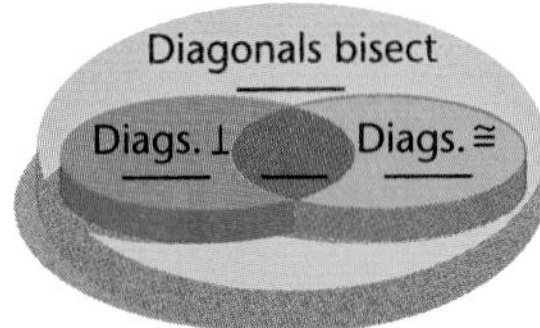

Exercises

CORE

P **Getting Started Classify quadrilateral *ABCD* using the given information.**

1. $\overline{AC}$ and $\overline{BD}$ bisect each other. Parallelogram
2. $\overline{AC}$ and $\overline{BD}$ bisect each other, and $\overline{AC} \cong \overline{BD}$. Rectangle
3. $\overline{AC}$ and $\overline{BD}$ bisect each other, and $\overline{AC} \perp \overline{BD}$. Rhombus
4. $\overline{AC}$ and $\overline{BD}$ bisect each other, $\overline{AC} \perp \overline{BD}$, and $\overline{AC} \cong \overline{BD}$. Square

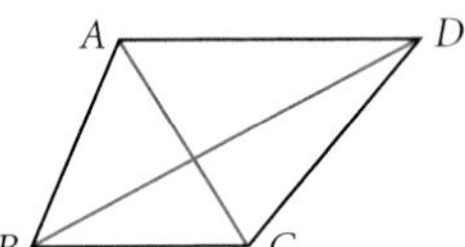

P **Copy the chart, and indicate with an X the quadrilaterals that have each property.**

	Property	Parallelogram	Rectangle	Rhombus	Square
5.	Opposite sides are parallel.				
6.	Opposite sides are congruent.				
7.	Opposite angles are congruent.				
8.	Diagonals bisect each other.				
9.	Diagonals are congruent.				
10.	Diagonals are perpendicular.				
11.	All angles are right angles.				
12.	All sides are congruent.				

Key

V Vocabulary
P Practice/Skills
R Review
MR Math Reasoning
PS Problem Solving
C Challenge

P **Find the values of x and/or y for each quadrilateral. Justify your answers.**

13.
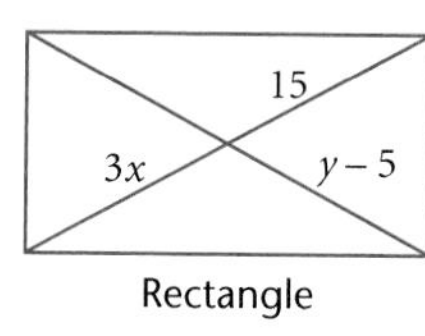

Rectangle

14.
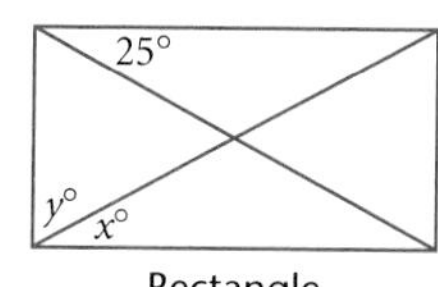

Rectangle

15.
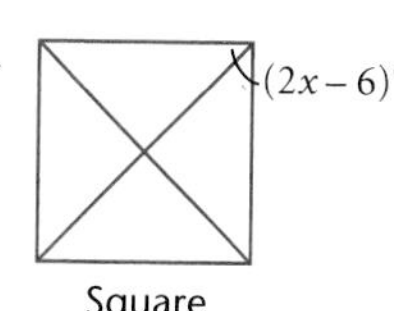

Square

P **Draw a parallelogram that satisfies each set of conditions or write *not possible.***

16. The diagonals are congruent, but the parallelogram has no right angles.

17. The diagonals are perpendicular but not congruent.

18. Two opposite angles are right angles, but the parallelogram is not a rectangle.

R **19.** Elm Street and Sixth Street are the diagonals of Quad City. They intersect at their midpoints. Assuming that Quad City is a parallelogram, determine its shape under each of the following conditions. Explain each of your answers.
a. Sixth Street is the same length as Elm Street, and they meet at a 45° angle.
b. Sixth Street is longer than Elm Street, and they meet at a right angle.
c. Sixth Street is the same length as Elm Street, and they meet at a right angle.

R **20. Support Your Case!** Nora is assembling a bookcase with diagonal supports. How can she use a tape measure to check that the sides are perpendicular to the shelves? Justify your answer.

R **21.** Suppose the diagonals of a quadrilateral are perpendicular, but they do not bisect each other. Sketch and describe a quadrilateral with these characteristics.

P **Sketch each figure and its line(s) of symmetry.**

22. a rectangle **23.** a rhombus **24.** a square

S **25.** Describe how to use reflections to generate a rhombus from a single right triangle.

R **26.** Prove the following theorem: If the diagonals of a parallelogram are congruent, then the parallelogram is a rectangle.

R **27.** Prove: If a parallelogram is a rhombus, then its diagonals are perpendicular.

Ongoing Assessment

Self-Assessment Exercises 1–19 odd, 23, 25, 27

Embedded Assessment Reflect 3; Exercises 4, 14, 20, 26

9. Rectangle, square

10. Rhombus, square

11. Rectangle, square

12. Rhombus, square

13. $3x = 15$ because diagonals bisect each other. So $x = 5$. $y - 5 = 15$ because diagonals are congruent and bisect each other. So $y = 20$.

14. Diagonals are congruent so $x = 25$ by the SSS Postulate and CPCTC. $x + y = 90$ because all angles are right angles. Solve for y when $x = 25$ to get $y = 65$.

15. $(2x - 6)° + (2x - 6)° = 90°$ because diagonals of squares bisect angles and angles of squares are right angles. Solve for x to get $(4x - 12)° = 90°$ or $x = 25.5$.

16. Not possible

17.
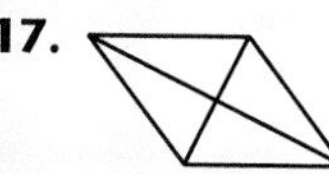

18. Not possible

19. a. Rectangle; Diagonals are congruent.

b. Rhombus; Diagonals are perpendicular but not congruent.

c. Square; Diagonals are perpendicular and congruent.

20. Check that the diagonals are congruent and bisect each other—then the bookcase is rectangular.

21. It is not a parallelogram, but may be a trapezoid or kite. Possible answer:

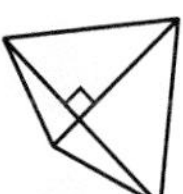

22.
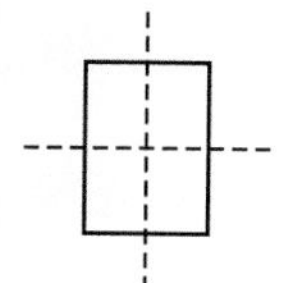

23.
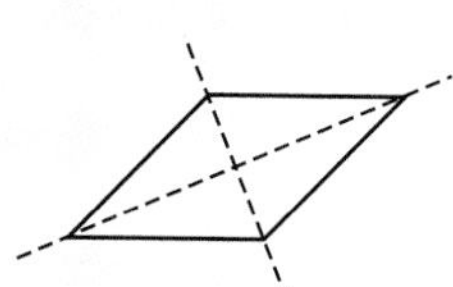

Deductive Proof with Quadrilaterals

24.

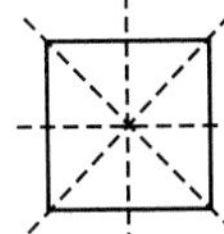

25. Reflect the triangle in one leg. Then reflect the result in the other leg. Reflect once more in the first leg. The four hypotenuses form a rhombus.

26. Possible answer:

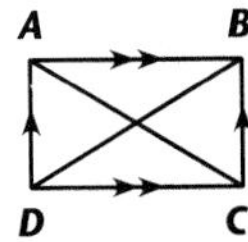

Given: $ABCD$ is a parallelogram. $\overline{AC} \cong \overline{BD}$.
Prove: $ABCD$ is a rectangle.

Proof: $ABCD$ is a parallelogram by the given information. $\overline{AB} \cong \overline{DC}$ because opposite sides of a parallelogram are congruent. $\overline{BC} \cong \overline{BC}$ and $\overline{AD} \cong \overline{AD}$ by the Reflexive Property. $\overline{AC} \cong \overline{BD}$ is given. $\triangle BDC \cong \triangle CAB$ and $\triangle ACD \cong \triangle DBA$ by the SSS Postulate. $\angle DAB \cong \angle ADC$ and $\angle DCB \cong \angle ABC$ by CPCTC. $m\angle DAB = m\angle ADC$ and $m\angle DCB = m\angle ABC$ by definition of *congruent.* $\overline{AB} \parallel \overline{DC}$ and $\overline{AD} \parallel \overline{BC}$ by definition of *parallelogram.* $m\angle DAB + m\angle ADC = 180°$ and $m\angle ABC + m\angle DCB = 180°$ because same-side interior angles of a parallel line cut by a transversal are supplementary. Therefore, $2(m\angle DAB) = 2(m\angle ADC) = 2(m\angle ABC) = 2(m\angle DCB) = 180°$ by substituting $m\angle DAB = m\angle ADC$ and $m\angle DCB = m\angle ABC$. Divide by 2 to get $m\angle DAB = m\angle ADC = m\angle ABC = m\angle DCB = 90°$, so $\angle DAB, \angle ADC, \angle ABC, \angle DCB$ are right angles by definition. $ABCD$ is a rectangle by definition.

27–42. See Additional Answers p. T190.

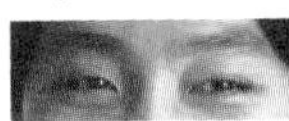

LOOK AHEAD

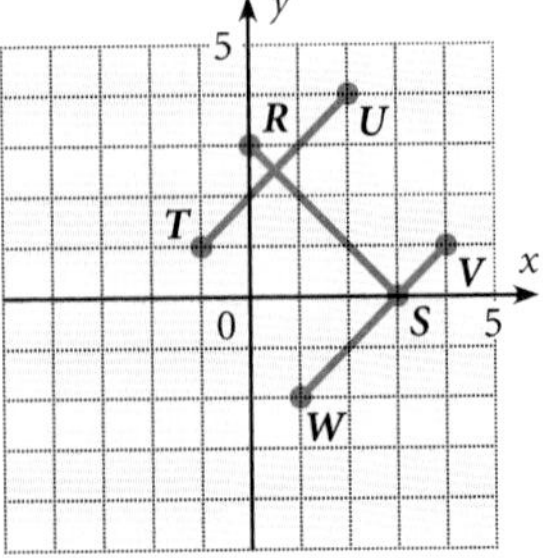

R **28.** Find the length of $\overline{TU}$.

R **29.** Find the slopes of $\overline{TU}$, $\overline{WV}$, and $\overline{RS}$.

R **30.** Are $\overline{TU}$ and $\overline{WV}$ parallel? Explain.

R **31.** Are $\overline{TU}$ and $\overline{RS}$ perpendicular? Explain.

R **32.** Is $TUVW$ a parallelogram? Explain.

MORE PRACTICE

P **What diagonal properties are true for quadrilateral *PQRS* if**

33. $PQRS$ is a rectangle?

34. $PQRS$ is a rhombus?

35. $PQRS$ is a square?

P **Find the values of *x* and *y* for each quadrilateral. Justify your answers.**

36.

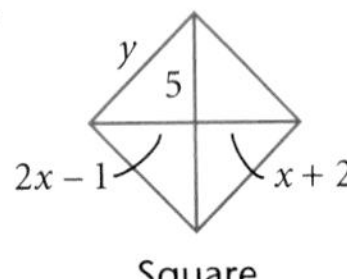

Square

37.

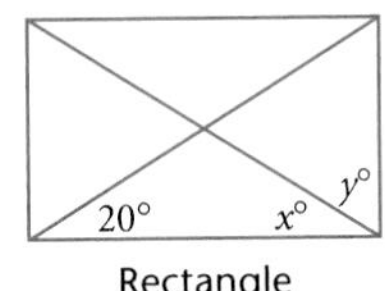

Rectangle

38.

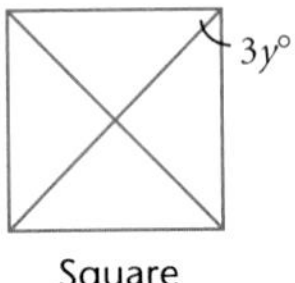

Square

MORE MATH REASONING

MR **39.** Prove: If the diagonals of a parallelogram are perpendicular and congruent, then the parallelogram is a square.

MR, C **40.** Prove: If a diagonal of a parallelogram bisects an angle of the parallelogram, then the parallelogram is a rhombus.

MR, C **41.** A kite is a quadrilateral with two distinct pairs of adjacent, congruent sides.

Prove: If exactly one diagonal of a quadrilateral bisects the other diagonal and the diagonals are perpendicular, then the quadrilateral is a kite.

PS **42. Contractor Corner** A contractor needs to mark the corners of the foundation of a new house. She has stakes to mark the corners, but the only other equipment she has are two long pieces of rope and a tape measure. Explain how she can mark the corners for a square foundation if she has no way to cut the rope or to measure angles.

Careers

Key

- V Vocabulary
- P Practice/Skills
- R Review
- MR Math Reasoning
- PS Problem Solving
- C Challenge

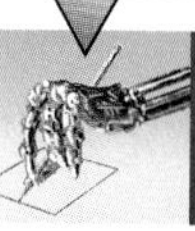

6-2 PART D Quadrilaterals and Coordinate Proof

← CONNECT → *You've already used the coordinate system to see the relationship between algebra and geometry. Now you will use algebra to help you in geometric proofs.*

Algebra and geometry do not lead separate lives. You've used algebra to find distances, midpoints, slopes of lines, and equations of lines and circles. When you assign coordinates to geometric figures, you are using *coordinate geometry.*

Many proofs can be made easier using coordinate geometry. To use this method, we first place the figure on a coordinate plane. Then we name the vertices and assign coordinates to them. An example is shown below for quadrilateral *WXYZ.*

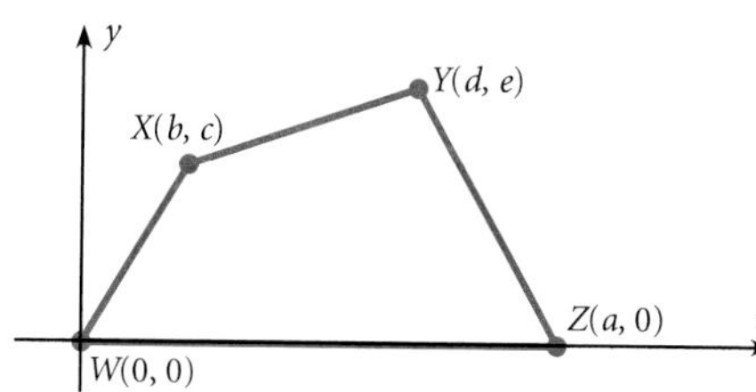

It's usually helpful to place the figure so that one vertex is at the origin and one side is on an axis. An easy problem can turn into a hard one if you don't choose a convenient placement.

TRY IT

ABCD is a square. For each figure, assign coordinates to the vertices, using as few variables as possible, and find the length of $\overline{AB}$.

a.

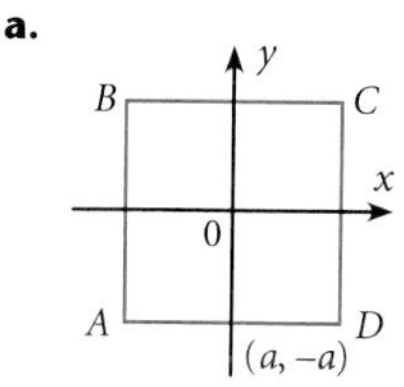

b.

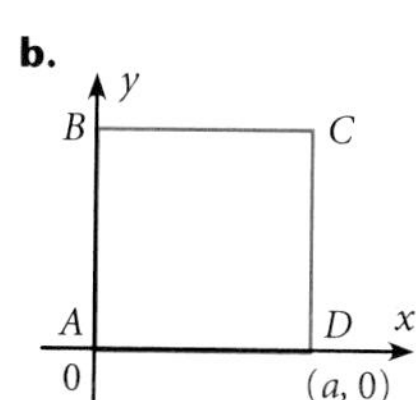

c.

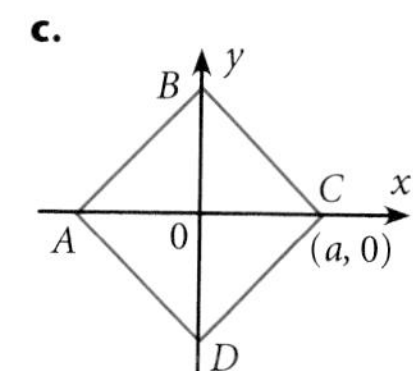

a. C(a, a), B(−a, a), A(−a, −a), AB = 2a
b. C(a, a), B(0, a), A(0, 0), AB = a
c. D(0, −a), B(0, a), A(−a, 0), AB = $a\sqrt{2}$

In the following, two students prove a theorem using different methods. (We have already proved this theorem using a flow proof on page 429.)

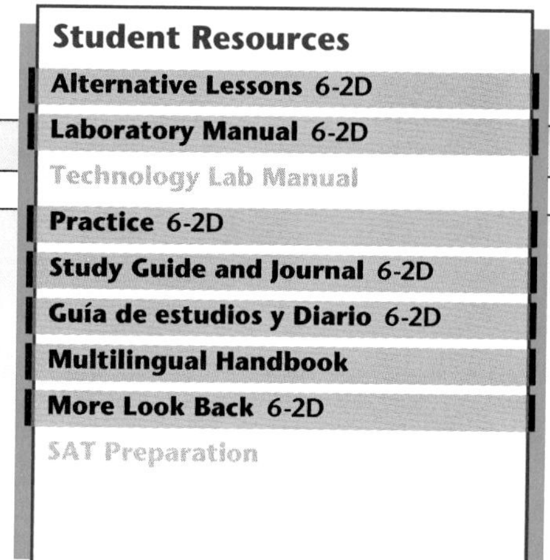

Student Resources
- **Alternative Lessons 6-2D**
- **Laboratory Manual 6-2D**
- Technology Lab Manual
- **Practice 6-2D**
- **Study Guide and Journal 6-2D**
- **Guía de estudios y Diario 6-2D**
- **Multilingual Handbook**
- **More Look Back 6-2D**
- SAT Preparation

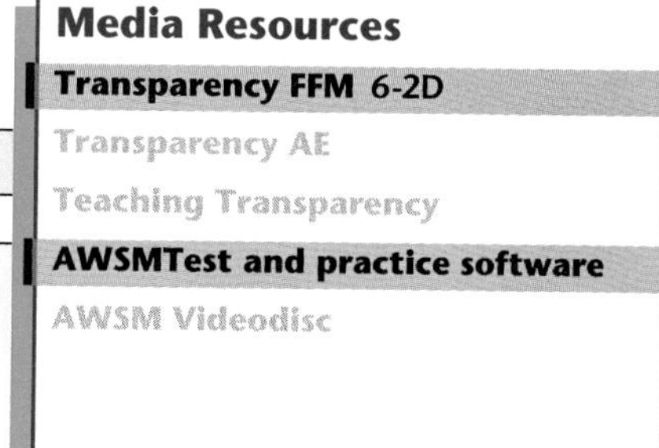

Media Resources
- **Transparency FFM 6-2D**
- Transparency AE
- Teaching Transparency
- **AWSMTest and practice software**
- AWSM Videodisc

PART D At a Glance

Objective
To use coordinate geometry in proofs about quadrilaterals.

Development
First, students see how to place a geometric figure on a coordinate plane. In **What Do You Think?** students see both a synthetic and a coordinate approach to a proof. Here, they begin to see the possible advantages of a coordinate proof.

After this introduction to coordinate proof, students use coordinate techniques in the **Explore** to show that the diagonals of a square are perpendicular.

Suggested Materials
Student Graph paper

Teacher Graph paper transparency

First Five Minutes
Transparency FFM 6-2D

Read the paragraphs above the **Try It** on page 433. Then do **Try It a–c.**

Motivate
Ask...
- How can you calculate the slope of a line on a coordinate plane? $\frac{\text{rise}}{\text{run}} = \frac{y_2 - y_1}{x_2 - x_1}$
- What is true about the slopes of perpendicular lines? parallel lines? Slopes of perpendicular lines are negative reciprocals; slopes of parallel lines are equal.

6-2

Deductive Proof with Quadrilaterals

WHAT DO YOU THINK?

In this situation, two students do the same proof using different methods. Henry's proof uses familiar techniques and formats, while Janice's is a coordinate proof.

Compares advantages and disadvantages of the proof methods in **What Do You Think?**

Possible Answer

1. Henry's approach does not require any algebraic manipulations, but the proof is long; there are several intermediate steps before we begin to look at the lengths of the diagonals. Janice's proof required more preliminary work—she had to set up the coordinates of the vertices—and required algebraic work. However, it was relatively short.

   Both proofs are correct.

EXPLORE

A Well-Coordinated Proof

Recommended group size: 4

The Point

To use coordinate techniques to show that the diagonals of a square are perpendicular.

Look and Listen...

- For students who have assigned specific numerical coordinates to the vertices of their square.
- For students whose vertex coordinates do not reflect the fact that the figure is a square.

Ask...

- (For students using numerical coordinates.) What is the length of a side of your square? Do all squares have the same side length?
- In choosing your coordinates, how did you show that all the sides had the same length?

WHAT DO YOU THINK?

Henry and Janice were assigned the following proof for homework.

Prove: If a parallelogram is a rectangle, then its diagonals are congruent.

Given: Parallelogram $DEFG$ is a rectangle with diagonals $\overline{DF}$ and $\overline{EG}$.

Prove: $\overline{DF} \cong \overline{EG}$

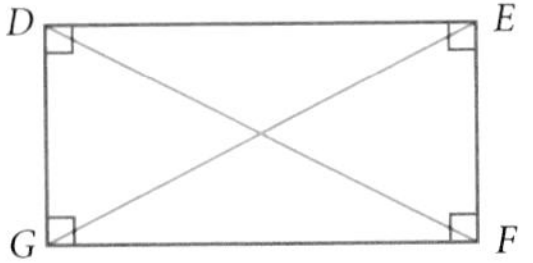

Henry thinks . . .

I'll see if I can prove that two of the triangles formed by the diagonals are congruent, and use CPCTC.

Proof: We are given that $DEFG$ is a rectangle, so $\angle DGF$ and $\angle EFG$ are right angles, by the definition of a rectangle. $\triangle DGF$ and $\triangle EFG$ are right triangles by definition. Both share $\overline{GF}$, which is congruent to itself by the Reflexive Property. Since a rectangle is a parallelogram, its opposite sides are congruent, so $\overline{DG} \cong \overline{EF}$. $\triangle DGF \cong \triangle EFG$ by the LL Theorem, and $\overline{DF} \cong \overline{EG}$ by CPCTC.

Janice thinks . . .

I'll put $DEFG$ on a coordinate plane and use the distance formula. If G is at (0, 0), I can have F on the x-axis at $(a, 0)$ and D above G at $(0, b)$. $\overline{GF}$ is a units long, and opposite sides of $DEFG$ are congruent, so E is a units across from D at (a, b).

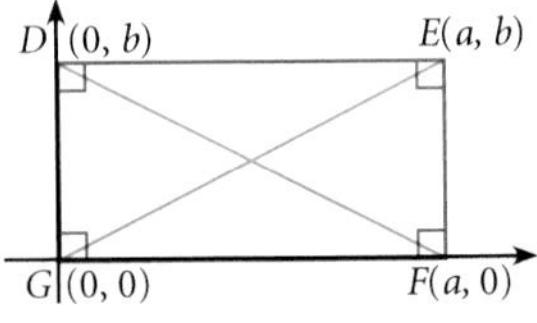

Proof: Using the distance formula, $EG = \sqrt{(a-0)^2 + (b-0)^2} = \sqrt{a^2 + b^2}$. Also, $DF = \sqrt{(0-a)^2 + (b-0)^2} = \sqrt{a^2 + b^2}$. Since their lengths are equal, the diagonals are congruent by the definition of congruent segments.

1. Explain the advantages and disadvantages of the methods Henry and Janice used. Are both methods correct?

Alert

Many students have difficulty seeing how to use the properties of a figure to simplify the coordinates of its vertices. You may want to stress that the fewer the variables used, the less complex the algebra will be. You may need to ask questions like, "What do you know about the sides of a parallelogram?"

Tips from Teachers

You may need to help students see the strengths of the coordinate approach. You might point out that the actual proof part of Janice's coordinate proof is shorter than Henry's proof.

In the following Explore, you will get some practice with coordinate proof.

EXPLORE: A WELL COORDINATED PROOF

MATERIALS

Graph paper

Prove that the diagonals of a square are perpendicular.

1. First, place square $ABCD$, with side length a, on a coordinate plane. Label the vertices, and give their coordinates. Explain how and why you chose this placement.
2. Use the slope formula to find the slopes of the diagonals $\overline{AC}$ and $\overline{BD}$.
3. Use your results from Step 2 to show that $\overline{AC}$ and $\overline{BD}$ are perpendicular. Explain your thinking.
4. Compare your results with those of your classmates. If you chose different placements for the square, discuss how your choices affected your proofs.

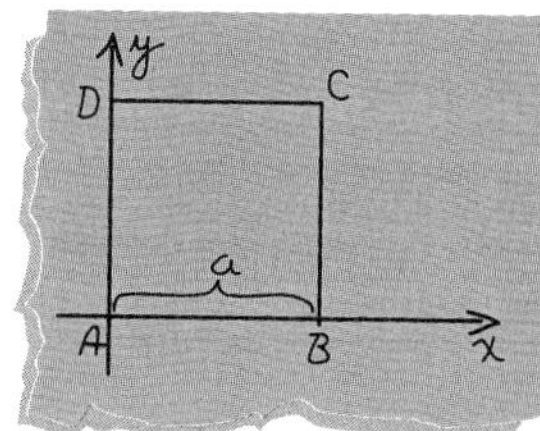

REFLECT

1. What properties can be used to show that lines are parallel or perpendicular when doing a coordinate proof?
2. Why is the use of coordinates a helpful strategy in some proofs?
3. In trapezoid $MNPQ$, you could give point P the coordinates (c, d). However, there is a better choice for them. Give coordinates for P, and explain why your choice is better than (c, d).

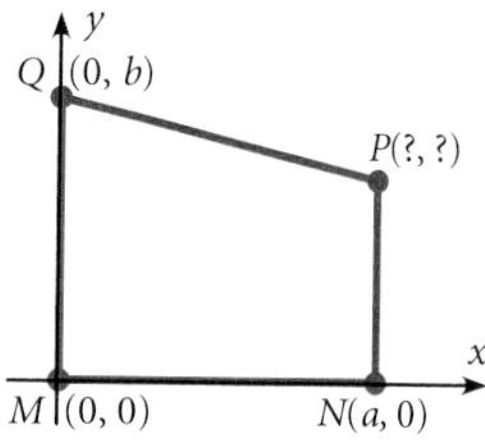

Exercises

CORE

1. **Getting Started** The figure shown at the right is an isosceles trapezoid. What are the coordinates of vertex C? (Hint: You will have to introduce one new variable. Remember that the bases are parallel.) What are the coordinates of vertex D? (c, b); $(c + a, 0)$

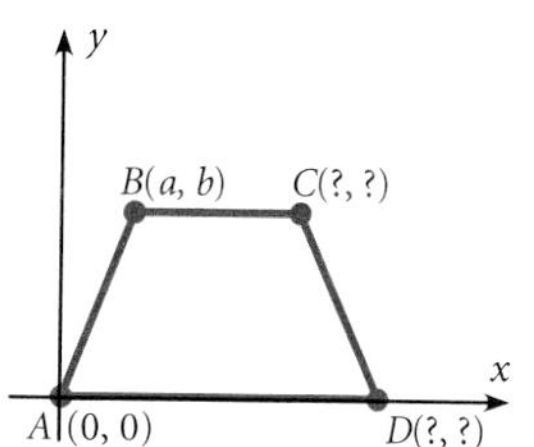

For Groups That Finish Early
Find a different position for your square on the coordinate plane, and prove the theorem again, using this new placement.

Follow Up
Ask students to describe the placement of their squares. If choices differ, you may want to discuss strengths and weaknesses of each. Then have one student or group present their proof.

Possible Answers

1. $A(0, 0)$, $B(a, 0)$, $C(a, a)$, $D(0, a)$ is one choice.
2. Using the coordinates above, the slope of $\overline{AC}$ is 1 and the slope of $\overline{BD}$ is -1.
3. Since the slopes of $\overline{AC}$ and $\overline{BD}$ are negative reciprocals, $\overline{AC} \perp \overline{BD}$.

Journal 

Consider question 1 and **Reflect** 1 and 2 are suitable for journal entries.

REFLECT

Possible Answers

1. Parallel lines: slopes are equal. Perpendicular lines: slopes are negative reciprocals.
2. Coordinates can be used to find lengths of segments and slopes of lines. We can use these techniques to show congruent segments, parallel lines, and perpendicular lines in ways that are impossible without using coordinates.
3. (a, c) is a better choice. With this choice, we need only three variables to describe the coordinates of the points instead of four.

Part D Exercises

Exercise Notes

Core

8. and 9. Students use coordinate techniques to write proofs.

Ongoing Assessment

Self-Assessment Exercises 1–9 odd

Embedded Assessment Reflect 2; Exercises 2, 6, 8

Vocabulary
Practice/Skills
Review
Math Reasoning
Problem Solving
Challenge

Deductive Proof with Quadrilaterals

More Math Reasoning

21. Students use coordinate techniques to prove that the midsegment of a trapezoid is parallel to its bases, and its length is the average of the base lengths.

23. Students analyze a "conversation" between a human and a computer program that simulates language. Students identify the statements made by the computer and make hypotheses about the rules it uses to simulate a conversation.

History Note: In 1950, English mathematician Alan Turing proposed a test for computer "intelligence." If a person asked questions (via a terminal) of another person and a computer, and, after 5 minutes, had no more than a 70% chance of identifying the computer, the computer could be said to be "intelligent."

Exercise Answers

Core

5. Slope of $\overline{HJ} = \frac{b}{a}$, slope of $\overline{GF} = \frac{b}{a}$, slope of $\overline{JF} = 0$, slope of $\overline{HG} = 0$. So $\overline{HJ} \parallel \overline{GF}$ and $\overline{JF} \parallel \overline{HG}$.

6. $JF = c$, $HG = c$, $HJ = \sqrt{a^2 + b^2}$, $GF = \sqrt{a^2 + b^2}$. So $\overline{JF} \cong \overline{HG}$ and $\overline{HJ} \cong \overline{GF}$.

7. a. Rectangle; Possible answer: The diagonals are congruent and the opposite sides are congruent.

b. Possible answer: The distance from (0, 0) to (200, 120) is $\sqrt{(200)^2 + (120)^2} = 40\sqrt{34}$. The distance from (0, 120) to (200, 0) is $\sqrt{(200)^2 + (-120)^2} = 40\sqrt{34}$. The distance from (0, 0) to (0, 120) is 120. The distance from (200, 0) to (200, 120) is 120. The distance from (0, 0) to (200, 0) is 200. The distance from (0, 120) to (200, 120) is 200.

P **For each figure in Exercises 2–4, assign coordinates to the vertices. Do not introduce any new variables.**

2. *ABCD* is a rectangle.

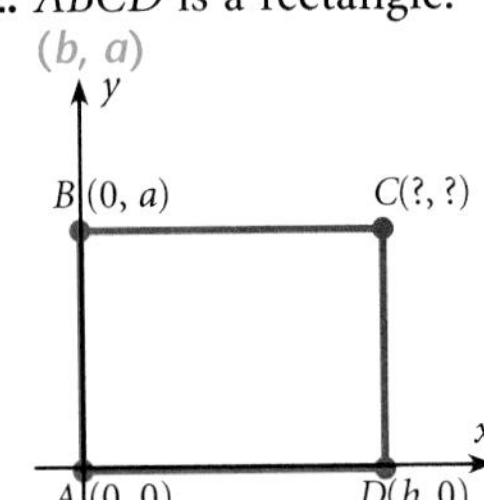

3. *DEFG* is a parallelogram.

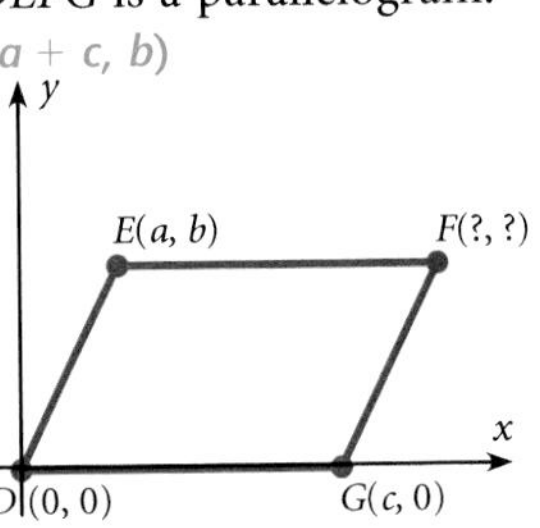

4. $\triangle HIJ$ is equilateral.

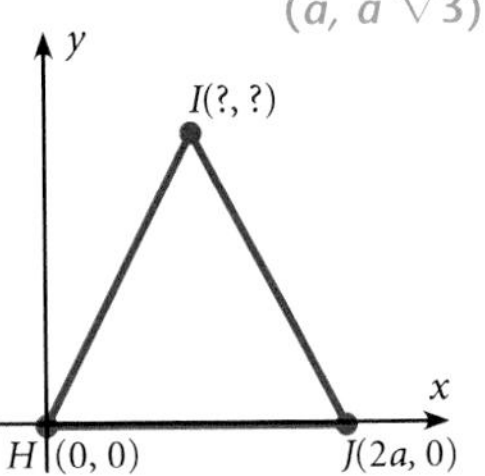

P **Use the figure at the right to verify each statement.**

5. The opposite sides of *FGHJ* are parallel.

6. The opposite sides of *FGHJ* are congruent.

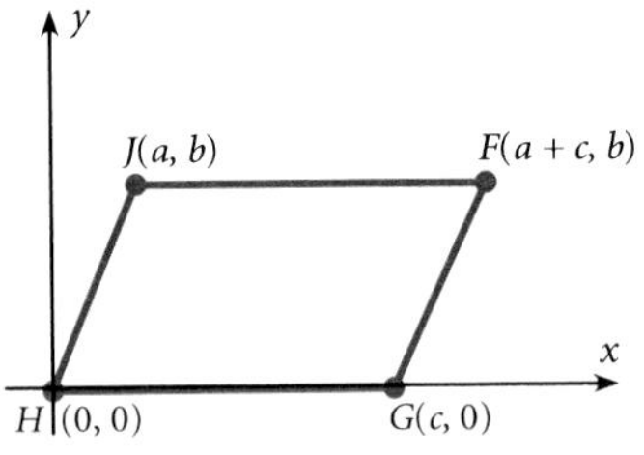

MR History

7. MariTime The ancient city-state of Mari, in what is now Syria, flourished around 2000 B.C. The main palace had 250 rooms. Suppose that archaeologists studying the palace set up a coordinate system to identify and record the location of artifacts. As shown below, (0, 0) is at the lower left corner of the palace, and each unit represents 20 meters.

a. What type of quadrilateral is the base of the palace? Explain how you know.

b. Prove that your answer in **7a** is correct.

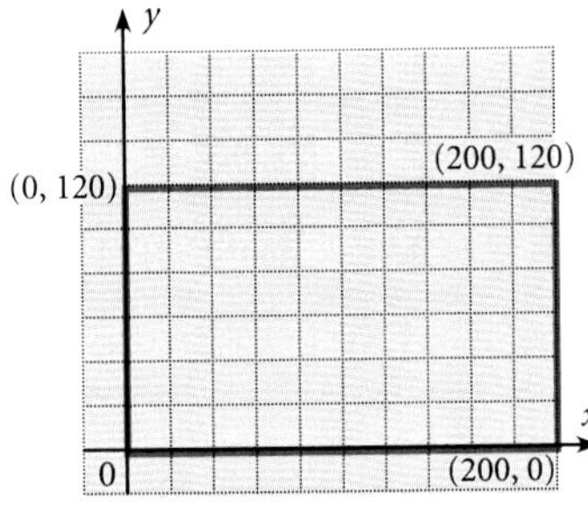

MR **8.** Use a coordinate proof to prove the following: If a quadrilateral is a square, then its diagonals are congruent.

MR **9.** Use a coordinate proof to prove the following: If a quadrilateral is a parallelogram, then its diagonals bisect each other. (Hint: Find the midpoints of the diagonals.)

Key

- **V** Vocabulary
- **P** Practice/Skills
- **R** Review
- **MR** Math Reasoning
- **PS** Problem Solving
- **C** Challenge

CR **10.** *Given:* *WXYZ* is a rhombus.
Prove: $\overline{WY} \perp \overline{XZ}$

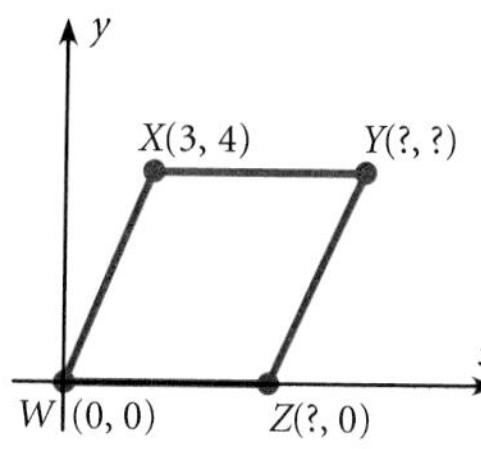

a. Find the coordinates of points *Y* and *Z*.
b. Find the slopes of $\overline{WY}$ and $\overline{XZ}$. If the segments are perpendicular, what should be true about their slopes?
c. Give a written proof in paragraph form.

LOOK BACK

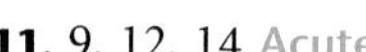

R **Given the following side lengths, classify each triangle as acute, obtuse, or right. [5-3]**

11. 9, 12, 14 Acute

12. 3, 3, $3\sqrt{2}$ Right

13. 12.3, 13.1, 24 Obtuse

14. 14, 48, 50 Right

R **15.** Draw a net for the polyhedron at the right. What figures form its faces? [1-1, 6-1]

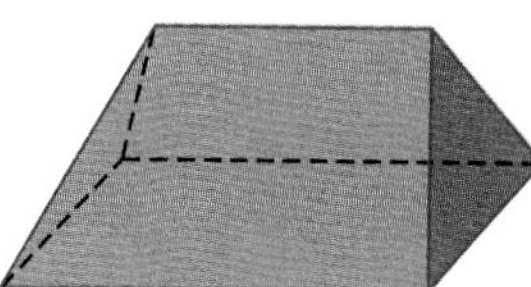

R **16.** Classify the polyhedron. [6-1] Pentahedron

R **17.** Verify that Euler's Formula holds for the polyhedron. [6-1]
$F = 5, V = 6, E = 9; 5 + 6 - 9 = 2.$

MORE PRACTICE

P **For each figure in Exercises 18–19, assign coordinates to the vertices. Do not introduce any new variables.**

18. *ABCD* is a square. *C*(*x*, *x*), *D*(*x*, 0)

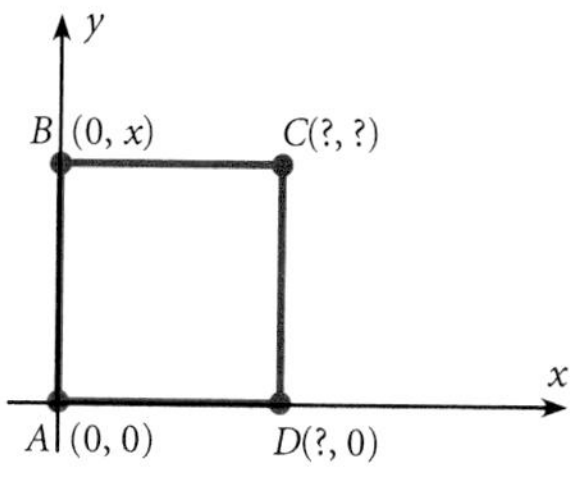

19. *DEFG* is a rectangle. *F*(2*a*, 2*b*)

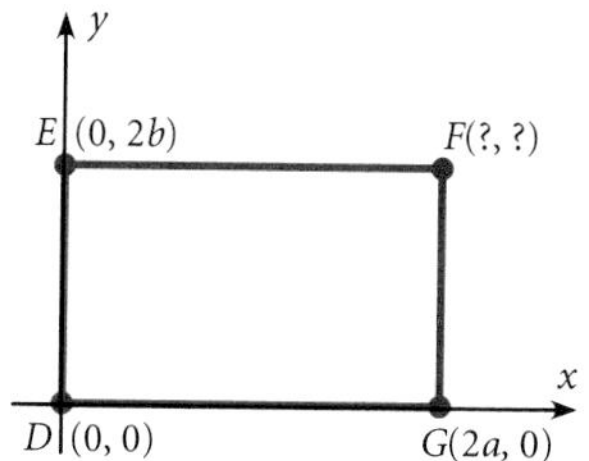

R **20.** Use the figure to prove that the diagonals of square *WXYZ* are perpendicular.
The slope of $\overline{YW} = \frac{(a-0)}{(a-0)} = 1$. The slope of $\overline{XZ} = \frac{(a-0)}{(0-a)} = -1$. The slopes are negative reciprocals of each other, so $\overline{YW} \perp \overline{XZ}$.

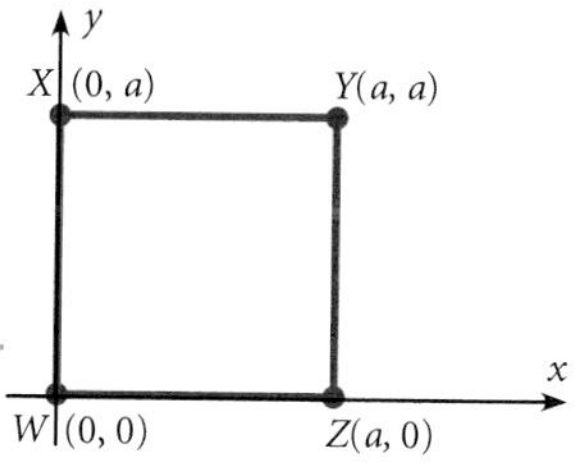

8. Possible answer:

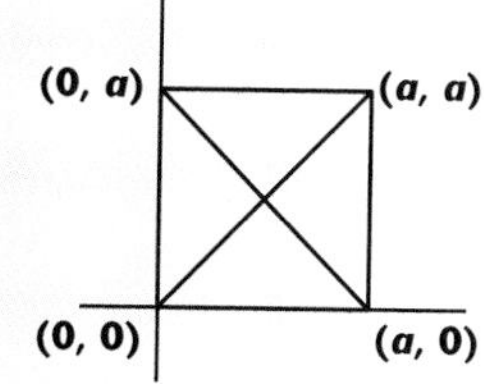

The distance from (0, 0) to (*a*, *a*) is $\sqrt{a^2 + a^2} = a\sqrt{2}$. The distance from (0, *a*) to (*a*, 0) is $\sqrt{a^2 + (-a)^2} = a\sqrt{2}$. The diagonals are congruent by definition.

9. Possible answer:

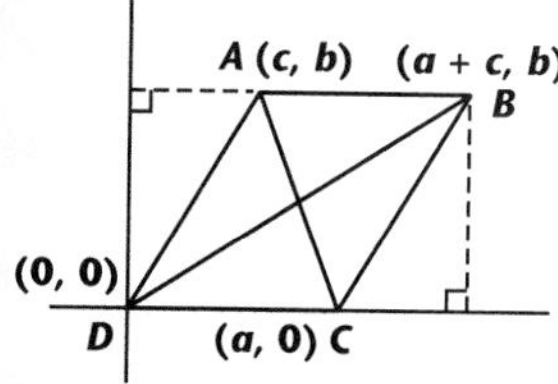

The midpoint of $\overline{DB}$ is
$\left(\frac{0 + (a + c)}{2}, \frac{0 + b}{2}\right) = \left(\frac{a + c}{2}, \frac{b}{2}\right)$.
The midpoint of $\overline{AC}$ is
$\left(\frac{a + c}{2}, \frac{0 + b}{2}\right) = \left(\frac{a + c}{2}, \frac{b}{2}\right)$.
The midpoints are identical, so $\overline{AC}$ bisects $\overline{DB}$ and $\overline{DB}$ bisects $\overline{AC}$ by definition of *bisect*.

10. a. *Y*(8, 4), *Z*(5, 0)

b. Slope of $\overline{WY} = 0.5$; Slope of $\overline{XZ} = -2$; The slopes are negative reciprocals of each other.

c. The slope of $\overline{WY}$ is 0.5. The slope of $\overline{XZ}$ is -2. The product of the slopes is -1, so $\overline{WY} \perp \overline{XZ}$.

Look Back

15. Possible answer: One rectangle, two trapezoids, and two triangles.

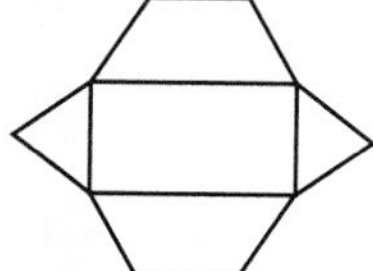

21–23.
See Additional Answers p. T440.

6-2

Deductive Proof with Quadrilaterals

PART E At a Glance

Objective

To discover and prove that the midpoints of the sides of a quadrilateral determine a parallelogram.

Development

In the **Explore,** students use inductive evidence to make a conjecture that the midpoints of the sides of any quadrilateral determine a parallelogram. Then they use a coordinate proof to prove their conjecture.

Suggested Materials

Student Ruler, protractor, geometry software

First Five Minutes

Transparency FFM 6-2E

In your own words, state as many of the properties of parallelograms, rectangles, rhombuses, and squares as you can.

EXPLORE

Midpoint Surprise

Recommended group size: 4

The Point

To discover and then prove, using coordinate methods, that the quadrilateral formed by joining the midpoints of the sides of any quadrilateral is a parallelogram.

Look and Listen...

- For students who do not remember the midpoint formula or do not understand how to apply it to variable coordinates.

Ask...

- How do you find the midpoint of (2, 4) and (6, 10)? Can you apply this method to the points on your figure?

Algebra | Functions | Discrete Math | Probability | Data/Statistics

MORE MATH REASONING

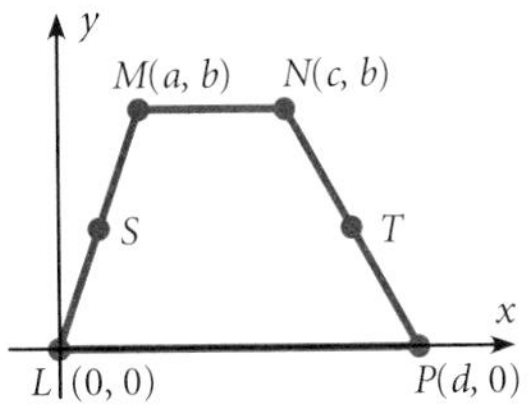

MR, C **21.** The **midsegment** of a trapezoid is the segment that joins the midpoints of its legs. Use a coordinate proof to prove the following: The midsegment of a trapezoid is parallel to the bases, and its length is the average of the lengths of the bases. (Hint: See the figure at the right.)

MR **22.** A kite is a quadrilateral with two distinct pairs of adjacent, congruent sides. Prove: If a quadrilateral is a kite, then its diagonals are perpendicular.

MR **23. Who's the Human?** The photo below shows humans interacting with a computer of the 1940s. The following excerpt of a "conversation" is from *Computer Power and Human Reason,* by Joseph Weizenbaum. It is an example of a communication between a human and a computer. (Some punctuation has been added.)

A: Do you think coming here will help you not to be unhappy?
B: I need some help, that much seems certain.
A: What would it mean to you if you got some help?
B: Perhaps I could learn to get along with my mother.
A: Tell me more about your family.
B: My mother takes care of me.
A: Who else in your family takes care of you?
B: My father.
A: Your father.
B: You are like my father in some ways.

a. Identify whether A or B is the computer. Explain.

b. What rules do you think the computer is following to model human conversation?

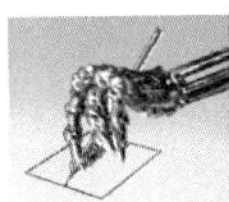

6-2 PART E Making Connections

← CONNECT →

You've investigated the properties of specific types of quadrilaterals. These properties are important in many professions, including carpentry and product design. You've also developed skills in writing and demonstrating a deductive proof.

In the following Explore, you will use what you know to investigate a property of quadrilaterals that may surprise you.

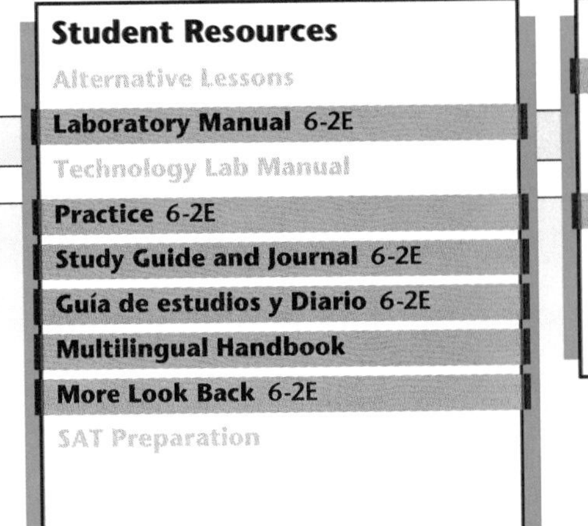

Student Resources

Alternative Lessons
Laboratory Manual 6-2E
Technology Lab Manual
Practice 6-2E
Study Guide and Journal 6-2E
Guía de estudios y Diario 6-2E
Multilingual Handbook
More Look Back 6-2E
SAT Preparation

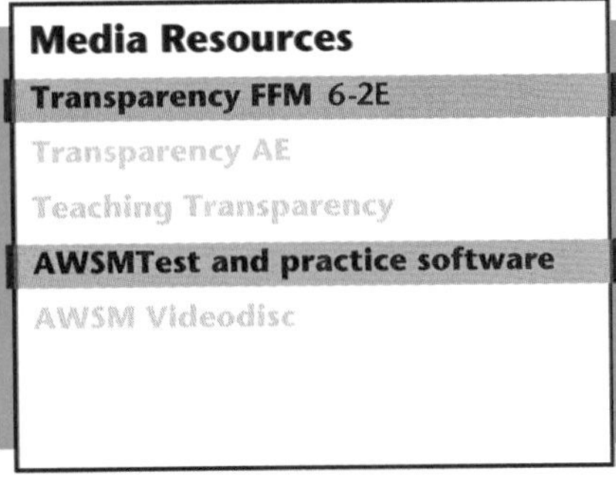

Media Resources

Transparency FFM 6-2E
Transparency AE
Teaching Transparency
AWSMTest and practice software
AWSM Videodisc

EXPLORE: MIDPOINT SURPRISE

MATERIALS

Ruler
Protractor
Geometry software (optional)

1. Use geometry software or a ruler to draw any quadrilateral, and mark the midpoint of each of its sides, as shown on the left below. Connect the midpoints of adjacent sides. What type of quadrilateral seems to result? Draw several quadrilaterals, and join their midpoints until you feel confident enough to make a conjecture.

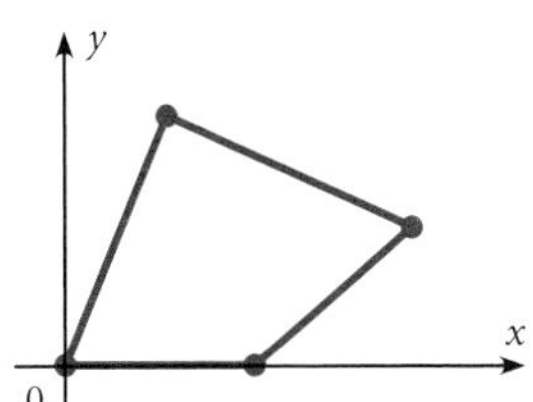

2. Now prove your conjecture with a coordinate proof. (Hint: Use the figure on the right above. When finding the coordinates of the vertices, remember that this quadrilateral is not necessarily a parallelogram. Once you have coordinates for the vertices, you can use the midpoint formula to find the coordinates of the midpoint of each side.)

REFLECT

1. Prepare a Venn diagram that shows how quadrilaterals are related. Explain how to read your diagram, and give all of the properties of each quadrilateral that you list.
2. Is coordinate proof an appropriate method for all proofs? Summarize the advantages and disadvantages of coordinate proofs, and give examples of things that might be difficult to prove with them.

Self-Assessment

Complete each statement with *always, sometimes,* or *never.* Explain each answer.

1. A rectangle ___ has perpendicular diagonals.
2. The diagonals of a rhombus ___ bisect each other.
3. The diagonals of a trapezoid ___ bisect each other.

Vocabulary
Practice/Skills
Review
Math Reasoning
Problem Solving
Challenge

For Groups That Finish Early
Repeat Steps 1 and 2, starting with a rectangle instead of a quadrilateral. What figure is formed by the midpoints of its sides? **A rhombus**

Follow Up
Ask students to share their conjectures and explain how they justified them.

Possible Answers

1. The quadrilateral formed by joining the midpoints of the sides of a quadrilateral is a parallelogram.
2. For easiest positioning, one vertex of the quadrilateral should be at the origin and one side should lie on an axis. Students should find the coordinates of the midpoint of each side, and then find the slopes of the segments joining the midpoints. Slopes of opposite sides will be parallel.

Portfolio

Have students select items from their work that demonstrate their understanding of the material in 6-2.

You may want to have students include their best noncoordinate and coordinate proofs from **Exercises** and an application problem where they used the properties of quadrilaterals.

REFLECT

Possible Answers

1.

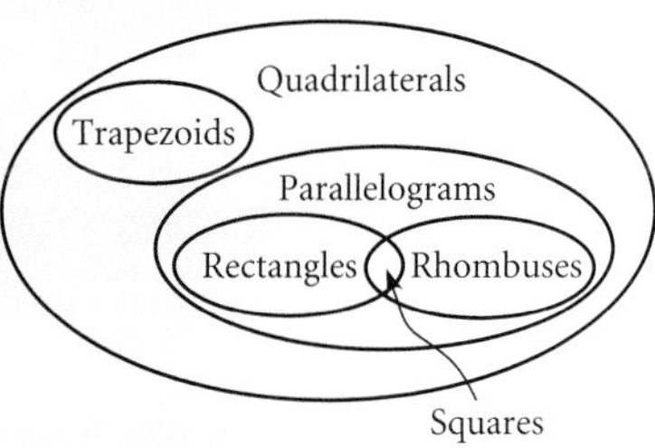

2. Coordinate proof is not appropriate for all proofs. It is sometimes convenient for proving segments congruent, perpendicular, or parallel, but the necessary algebra can be complicated. It would be difficult to prove conjectures involving angles with coordinate methods.

6-2

Deductive Proof with Quadrilaterals

Algebra | Logic/Reasoning

Self-Assessment

Exercise Notes

7. Similar to multiple-choice questions on standardized tests.

18. Students summarize advantages and disadvantages of synthetic and coordinate proofs.

Self-Assessment Answers

1. Sometimes; When the rectangle is a square.

2. Always; The diagonals of a parallelogram bisect each other and a rhombus is a parallelogram.

3. Never; When the diagonals bisect each other the figure is a parallelogram, and a trapezoid is never a parallelogram.

16. $\overline{AB}$ is always parallel to the ground and $\overline{DC}$ is always parallel to $\overline{AB}$. *ABCD* is a parallelogram since $AB = CD$ and $AD = BC$.

17.

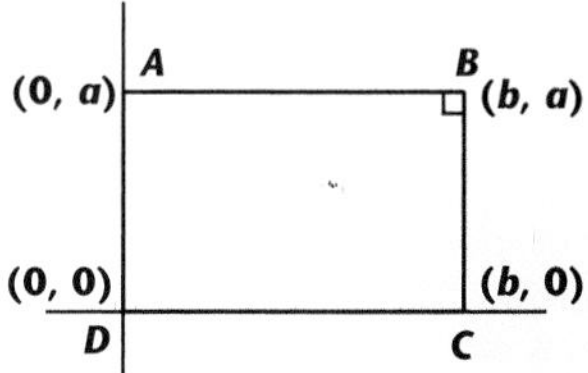

$\overline{DB} = \sqrt{a^2 + b^2}$. $\overline{AC} = \sqrt{(0 - b)^2 + a^2} = \sqrt{a^2 + b^2}$. Therefore, $\overline{AC} \cong \overline{DB}$ by definition of *congruent.*

18. Possible answer: The advantage of a coordinate proof is that you are able to do calculations using the coordinates. A disadvantage is that the coordinate method may involve complicated calculations. Segments can be shown to be parallel, perpendicular, or congruent using coordinate methods.

P **List the types of quadrilaterals that have each property.**

4. Diagonals are perpendicular and bisect each other. Rhombus

5. Diagonals are congruent and bisect each other. Rectangle, square

6. Diagonals are perpendicular, congruent, and bisect each other. Square

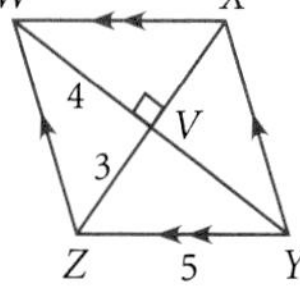

V **7.** In the figure at the right, *WXYZ* is a (c)

(a) rectangle (b) trapezoid (c) rhombus
(d) square (e) rhombus and square

P ***ABCD* is a parallelogram.**

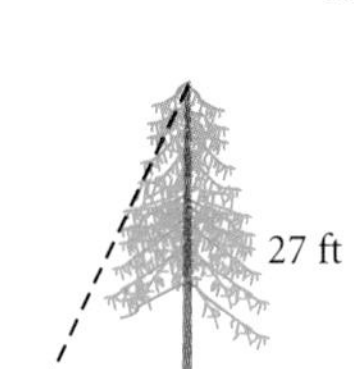

8. If $m\angle DAB = 65°$, find $m\angle ABC$. 115°

9. If $AC = 6$, find CE. 3

10. If $m\angle CAB = 28°$, find $m\angle DCA$. 28°

11. If $AD = 4y - 6$ and $BC = y + 6$, find AD. 10

R, PS **12.** A bird lays an egg in a nest at the top of a twenty-seven-foot tree. A conservation worker is trying to retrieve the eggs so that they can be safely hatched. If she places the base of the ladder thirteen feet from the tree, how long is the ladder? Round your answer to the nearest tenth of a foot. [5-3] 30.0 ft

27 ft

13 ft

R **Suppose the measures of all of the angles in each polygon are equal. Find the measure of one angle of each of the polygons. [6-1]**

13. a quadrilateral 90°

14. a hexagon 120°

15. a decagon 144°

MR **16. Geometry Glide** A children's glider swing hangs from a horizontal bar as shown below. The hangers are identical metal bars that are attached to the horizontal bar and to the swing so that they pivot freely at points *A*, *B*, *C*, and *D*. $AB = CD$. Explain why the swing is always parallel to the ground.

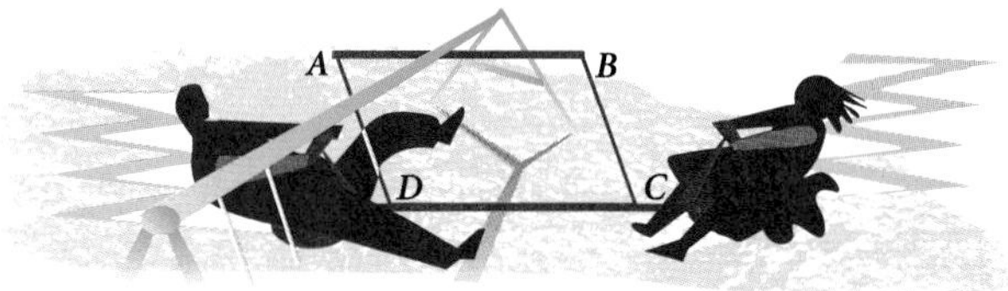

MR **17.** Use a coordinate proof to prove the following: If a quadrilateral is a rectangle, then its diagonals are congruent.

MR **18.** Summarize the advantages and disadvantages of using a coordinate proof instead of the proofs you worked with earlier (called *synthetic* proofs). Give examples of some of the relationships between segments that can be demonstrated using coordinate methods.

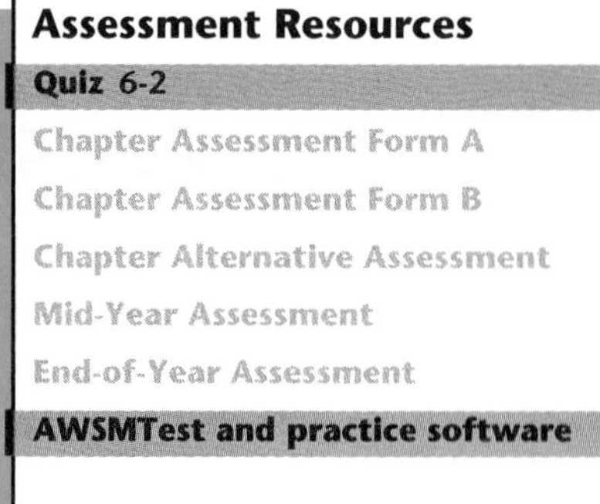

Assessment Resources
Quiz 6-2
Chapter Assessment Form A
Chapter Assessment Form B
Chapter Alternative Assessment
Mid-Year Assessment
End-of-Year Assessment
AWSMTest and practice software

Ongoing Assessment

Self-Assessment Self-Assessment Exercises

Embedded Assessment Explore Step 2; Reflect 1

ADDITIONAL ANSWERS

6-2 Part D Exercises

More Math Reasoning

21. Possible answer: S is the midpoint of $\overline{LM}$ so its coordinates are $\left(\frac{a}{2}, \frac{b}{2}\right)$. T is the midpoint of $\overline{PN}$ so its coordinates are $\left(\frac{c+d}{2}, \frac{b}{2}\right)$.

The slope of $\overline{ST}$ is $\dfrac{\frac{b}{2}-\frac{b}{2}}{\frac{c+d}{2}-\frac{a}{2}} = 0.$

The slope of $\overline{LP}$ is $\frac{0-0}{d-0} = 0$

and the slope of $\overline{MN}$ is $\frac{b-b}{c-a} = 0.$

Therefore, $\overline{ST} \parallel \overline{LP}$ and $\overline{ST} \parallel \overline{MN}$. $ST = \frac{c+d-a}{2}$. $MN = c - a$ and $LP = d$. The average of MN and LP is $\frac{MN + LP}{2} = \frac{c+d-a}{2}$.

Therefore $ST = \frac{MN + LP}{2}$.

22.

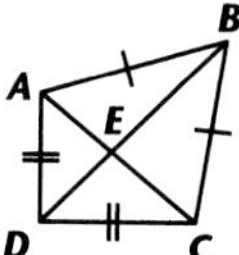

Given: $ABCD$ is a kite, with $\overline{AB} \cong \overline{BC}$ and $\overline{AD} \cong \overline{DC}$.
Prove: $\overline{AC} \perp \overline{DB}$
Proof: $\overline{AB} \cong \overline{BC}$ and $\overline{AD} \cong \overline{DC}$ by the given information. $\overline{DB} \cong \overline{DB}$ by the Reflexive Property. $\triangle DAB \cong \triangle DCB$ by the SSS Postulate. $\angle BDA \cong \angle BDC$ by CPCTC. $\triangle DAC$ is isosceles by definition. $\angle DAC \cong \angle DCA$ by the Isosceles-Triangle Theorem. $\triangle AED \cong \triangle CED$ by the ASA Postulate. $\angle AED \cong \angle CED$ by CPCTC. $m\angle AED = m\angle CED$, by the definition of *congruent*. $m\angle AED + m\angle CED = 180°$, by the Linear-Pair Postulate. By substitution and algebra, $m\angle AED = 90°$, so it is a right angle. $\overline{AC} \perp \overline{DB}$ by the definition of *perpendicular.*

23. a. A is the computer. It asks questions or makes restatements.

b. Possible answer: It asks questions using key words from the previous response.

6-3 Part C Reflect

1. Regular polygons are two-dimensional; regular polyhedrons are three-dimensional. Both have all sides/edges congruent. The faces of a regular polyhedron are regular polygons.

2. Regular tetrahedron: 4 equilateral triangular faces; regular hexahedron (cube): 6 square faces; regular octahedron: 8 equilateral triangular faces; regular dodecahedron: 12 regular pentagonal faces; regular icosahedron: 20 equilateral triangular faces.

3. Reflecting an equilateral triangle across a side 5 times creates a regular hexagon. Rotating it 60° around one vertex 5 times also creates a regular hexagon.

Chapter 6 Review

14. $h = 2\sqrt{21}$ cm; Area $= 34\sqrt{21} \approx 155.8$ cm^2

15. Possible answer: The sum of the interior angles of a convex polygon is given by the formula $(n-2)180°$ where n is the number of sides. The sum of the exterior angles is always 360°.

Chapter 6 Review

16.

The top is a square, with interior angles and diagonals undistorted.

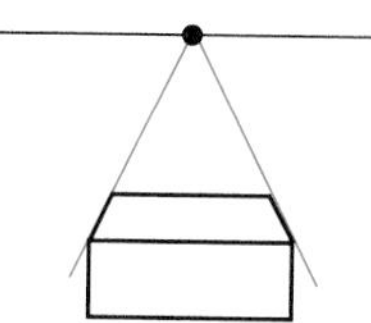

The top is a trapezoid. The diagonals are still congruent, but the front two interior angles are smaller and the back two are larger.

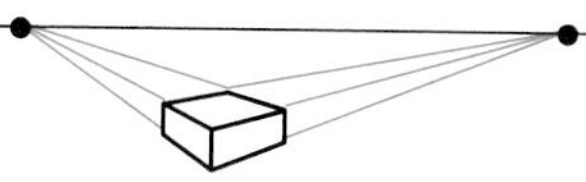

The top is an irregular quadrilateral. The diagonals are no longer congruent. The left and right angles now measure less than 90°, the middle two more. Note: These distortions depend on the positions of the box and the vanishing points.

Chapter 6 Assessment

12. Possible answer:
Proof: Draw line BD because two points determine a line. $\overline{AB} \parallel \overline{CD}$ is given. $\angle ABD \cong \angle CDB$ since alternate interior angles of parallel lines cut by a transversal are congruent. $\overline{BD} \cong \overline{BD}$ by the Reflexive Property. $\overline{AB} \cong \overline{CD}$ is given. $\triangle ABD \cong \triangle CDB$ by the SAS Postulate. Then $\angle ADB \cong \angle CBD$ by CPCTC. So $\overline{AD} \parallel \overline{BC}$ because if alternate interior angles of lines cut by a transversal are congruent, then the lines are parallel. $ABCD$ is a parallelogram by definition.

6-3

Regular Polygons and Polyhedrons

SUPERLESSON AT A GLANCE

Superlesson Goal

Students will investigate properties of regular polygons—including their areas and angle measures—and regular polyhedrons.

Management Guide

	Topic	Objectives	Key Terms	New Ideas	Materials
Part A	Regular Polygons	To discover and use the area formula for a regular polygon, and to find measures of one interior and one exterior angle of a regular polygon.	Regular polygon, center of a regular polygon, radius of a regular polygon, apothem	Regular polygons. Areas of regular polygons. Angle measures of regular polygons.	
Part B	Regular Polyhedrons	To become familiar with the Platonic solids.	Regular polyhedron, Platonic solid	Platonic solids.	**Student** Segments and connectors (e.g., toothpicks and gumdrops) **Teacher** Models of regular polyhedrons
Part C	Making Connections	To discover why regular hexagons are a good choice for the openings in beehive cells.	In Making Connections, students apply and synthesize key terms and new ideas.		**Student** Straightedge, paper, scissors

Pacing Chart (45-Minute Periods)

	Comprehensive Course	Core Course	Informal Course
Part A	1	1	1
Part B	1	1	1
Part C	1	1	1
TOTAL periods for Superlesson	3	3	3

NCTM Standards

Mathematics as Problem Solving

Mathematics as Communication

Mathematics as Reasoning

Mathematical Connections

Geometry from a Synthetic Perspective

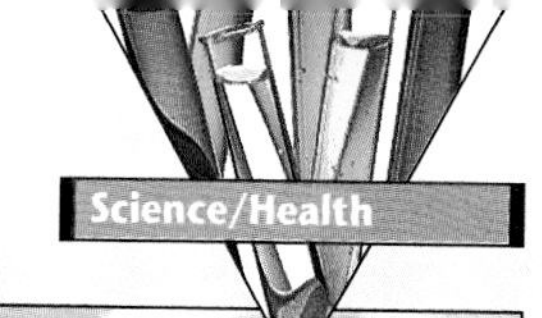

6-3 Regular Polygons and Polyhedrons

BEAUTY

AND THE BEES

The honeybee is one of nature's greatest architects. The home of the honeybee is called a comb. A comb is made up of hexagonal cells where the bees raise their young and store their food supply.

The comb itself is one of the marvels of animal architecture. It consists of a regular back-to-back pattern of hexagonal cells. There are two types of cells. The larger cells—worker cells—may be used for raising worker bees or for storing honey or pollen. The smaller cells—drone cells—are usually used for raising drone bees or for storing honey.

Hexagonal cells are common among cell-building insects, and there are good reasons for using this shape. Round, octagonal, or pentagonal cell arrangements leave empty spaces between cells, and triangles or squares have a greater perimeter than hexagons with the same area.

Unlike most other social insects, honeybees build their cells horizontally rather than hanging them vertically. However, the cells are angled up at about 13° from base to opening to prevent honey from running out.

1. Describe some advantages of using hexagonal cells instead of other shapes.

2. Why do you think it is important not to have empty spaces between cells?

More About Social Insects

Bees, ants, termites, and some wasps live in cooperative colonies. Ants have developed particularly intriguing social structures. Dairying ants live off secretions from aphids or plant lice. They protect their "cows" against predators, and some ants even "milk" these insects by stroking them with their antennae. Fungus-growing ants harvest fungi that they grow in their nests. When a new queen leaves on her mating flight, she carries a pellet of the fungus along with her so that she can begin a crop for her new colony.

Where Are We Now?

Students are familiar with classifications of polygons and polyhedrons, the angle measures of polygons, and relationships between vertices, edges, and faces of polyhedrons.

Where Are We Going?

In 6-3, students will explore regular polygons and polyhedrons. They discover the area formula for a regular polygon and explore convex regular polyhedrons (Platonic solids).

The area formula for a regular polygon is the foundation for the area formula for the circle developed in 8-1.

The study of three-dimensional figures continues in Chapter 9, when students discover surface area and volume formulas.

Possible Answers

1. Hexagons with congruent angles and sides tessellate, so they use available space efficiently. They also have a smaller ratio of perimeter to surface area than that of triangles or squares, so they use materials efficiently.
2. Hives with empty space between cells would require more material to house the same number of bees. The bees would therefore have to do more work to maintain the same population.

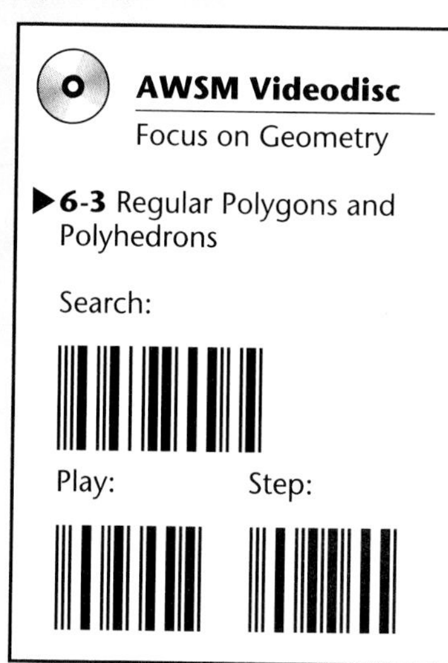

Regular Polygons and Polyhedrons

PART A At a Glance

Objective

To discover and use the area formula for a regular polygon, and to find measures of one interior and one exterior angle of a regular polygon.

Development

First, students see the definition of a regular polygon. In a **Consider** question, they discover how to calculate the measures of its interior and exterior angles.

In the **Explore,** students use triangle areas to derive the area formula for a regular polygon.

Key Terms

Regular polygon, center of a regular polygon, radius of a regular polygon, apothem

First Five Minutes

Transparency FFM 6-3A

Read the opening paragraph on page 442. Then do **Try It a–c.**

Motivate

Ask...

- What is the sum of the measures of the interior angles of a convex polygon? Is this result true for every convex polygon?
  $(n-2)180°$; yes

Shows how to find the measures of an interior and exterior angle of a regular polygon.

Possible Answer

1. Measure of an interior angle = 120°, since $(6-2)180° = 720°$ and $\frac{720}{6} = 120°$. Measure of an exterior angle $= \frac{360}{6} = 60°$.

6-3 PART A Regular Polygons

← CONNECT → ***You have learned some of the properties that hold true for all convex polygons. Now you will look at a special type of polygon—the regular polygon.***

Many natural objects and manufactured products are regular polygons. A **regular polygon** is both equilateral and equiangular. Some traffic signs are regular polygons, such as the Australian sign shown at the right.

TRY IT

Classify each polygon as equilateral, equiangular, and/or regular.

a.

b.

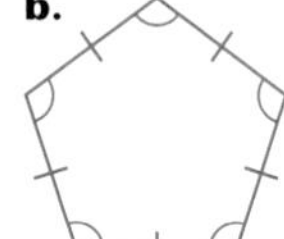

c.

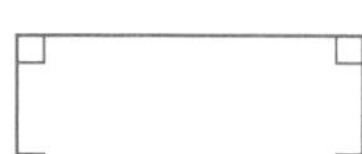

CONSIDER

1. **Using what you know about the sum of the measures of the interior and exterior angles of polygons, find the measure of each interior and exterior angle of a regular hexagon. Explain your method.**

The **center** of a regular polygon is the point of intersection of the perpendicular bisectors of the sides. The segment (or length of the segment) from a vertex to the center is the **radius.**

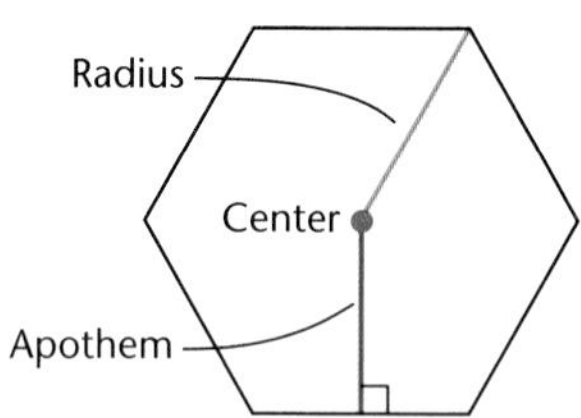

The perpendicular segment (or length of the segment) from the center to a side is an **apothem** (AP uh THEM).

Research Note

In the Cognitive Development and Achievement in Secondary School Geometry study...no significant differences were found between girls' and boys' abilities to write proofs in geometry. Yet...a disproportionate percentage of boys plan careers in the sciences. (William F. Burger and Barbara Culpepper, "Restructuring Geometry," *Research Ideas for the Classroom: High School Mathematics,* NCTM Research Interpretation Project, Patricia S. Wilson, ed., p. 151. © 1993 NCTM.)

All of the radii of a regular polygon are congruent. Any regular polygon can be divided into congruent isosceles triangles by drawing all of its radii.

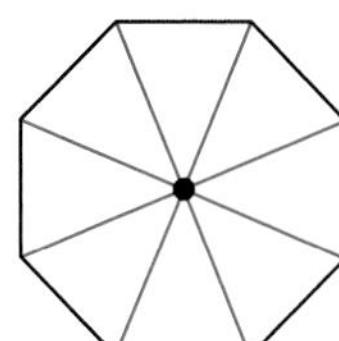

Regular octagon: eight congruent isosceles triangles

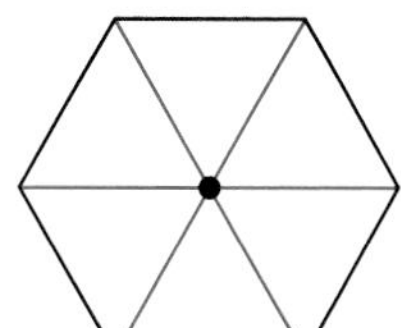

Regular hexagon: six congruent equilateral triangles

To find the area of a regular polygon, you could add the areas of all of these triangles. In the following Explore, you will investigate a faster way to find the area of a regular polygon.

EXPLORE: YOU'RE IN THE AREA

1. Answer the following questions for each regular polygon shown below.
   a. How many sides does the polygon have?
   b. Into how many triangles is it divided by the radii?
   c. What is the area of each of these triangles in terms of a and s?
   d. What is the area of the polygon in terms of a and s?

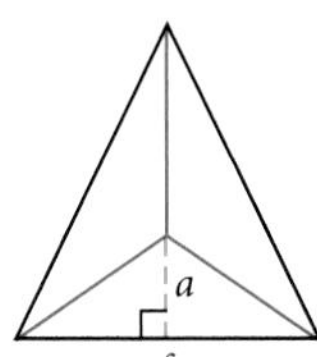

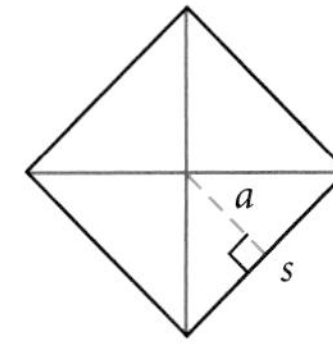

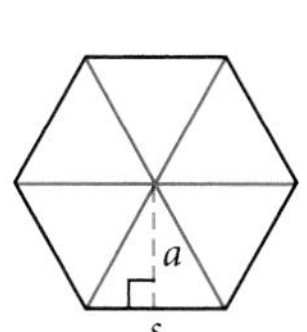

2. Write a formula for the area of a regular n-gon in terms of n, a, and s.
3. If a regular n-gon has apothem a and perimeter p, write a formula for its area in terms of a and p.

Problem-Solving Tip

See if your formula makes sense by testing it with specific three- and four-sided figures.

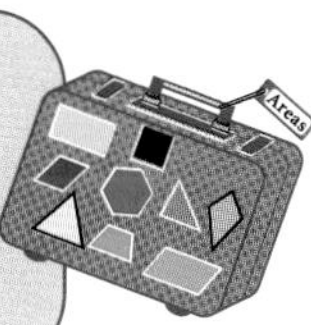

Student Resources
- Alternative Lessons 6-3A
- Laboratory Manual 6-3A
- Technology Lab Manual
- Practice 6-3A
- Study Guide and Journal 6-3A
- Guía de estudios y Diario 6-3A
- Multilingual Handbook
- More Look Back 6-3A
- SAT Preparation

Media Resources
- Transparency FFM 6-3A
- Transparency AE 6-3A
- Teaching Transparency
- AWSMTest and practice software
- AWSM Videodisc

EXPLORE

You're in the Area

Recommended group size: 4

The Point

To discover the formula for the area of a regular polygon.

Look and Listen...

- For students who do not see that ns is equal to the perimeter of the polygon.

Ask...

- How would you calculate the perimeter of a regular hexagon? Is the information you need to do this present in the area formula you found in Step 2?

For Groups That Finish Early

Your result from Step 3 should work for any regular polygon, including a square. But we already know an area formula for a square. Check to see whether the two formulas are equivalent. **For a square, $a = \frac{1}{2}s$ and $p = 4s$; Area $= \frac{1}{2}ap = \left(\frac{1}{2}\right)\left(\frac{1}{2}s\right)(4s) = s^2$**

Follow Up

Ask students to present their results to Step 3 and explain the process they used to find it.

Possible Answers

1. a. Triangle, 3; square, 4; hexagon, 6
   b. Triangle, 3; square, 4; hexagon, 6
   c. $\frac{1}{2}as$
   d. Triangle, $\frac{3}{2}as$; square, $2as$; hexagon, $3as$
2. $\frac{1}{2}nas$
3. $\frac{1}{2}ap$

Regular Polygons and Polyhedrons

ALTERNATE EXAMPLE

Find the area of the regular heptagon.

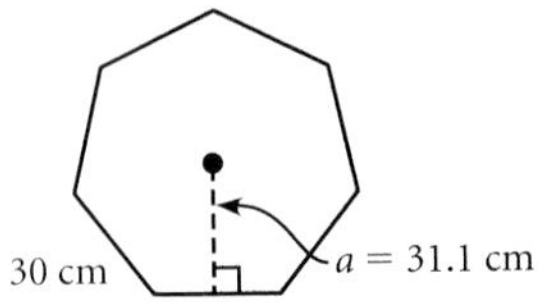

The perimeter of the regular heptagon is $7 \times 30 = 210$.

$$\text{Area} = \tfrac{1}{2}ap$$
$$= \tfrac{1}{2}(31.1)(210)$$
$$= 3265.5 \text{ cm}^2$$

Journal

Reflect 1 and 3 and **Exercise** 10 are suitable for journal entries.

REFLECT

Possible Answers

1. All of the radii are congruent, and the radii are two of the three sides of the triangles, so they are isosceles. Since all of the third sides (sides of the regular polygon) are congruent, the triangles are congruent by SSS.
2. There are six congruent angles around the center, so each of these measures $\frac{360}{6} = 60°$. If one angle of an isosceles triangle measures 60°, the other two must also, so the triangle is equilateral.
3. Construct perpendicular bisectors of two of the sides. The point of intersection is the center of the regular polygon. If the regular polygon has an even number of sides, you can draw two of the diagonals joining opposite vertices; their intersection point is the center.

EXAMPLE

Find the area of the regular pentagon.

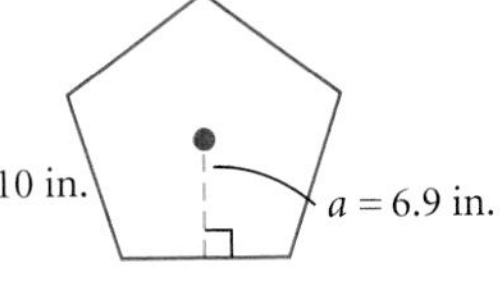

Since a regular pentagon has five congruent sides, the perimeter of this pentagon is $5 \times 10 = 50$.

$$\text{Area} = \tfrac{1}{2}ap = \tfrac{1}{2}(6.9)(50)$$
$$= 172.5 \text{ in.}^2$$

TRY IT

d. Find the area of the regular octagon.

1086 cm²

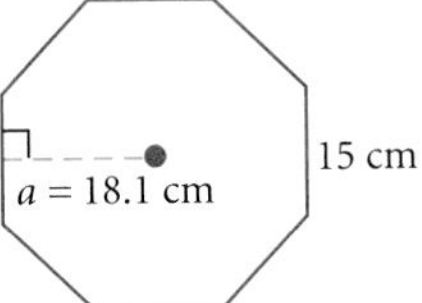

We can summarize the results about the area and angles of regular polygons as follows.

THEOREMS ABOUT REGULAR POLYGONS

The area of a regular polygon is one-half the product of its perimeter and its apothem. $A = \frac{1}{2}ap$

Each angle of a regular n-gon measures $\frac{(n-2)180°}{n}$.

Each exterior angle of a regular n-gon measures $\frac{360°}{n}$.

REFLECT

1. Explain why the radii of any regular polygon divide it into congruent isosceles triangles.
2. Why do the radii of a regular hexagon divide it into six congruent equilateral triangles?
3. Describe a method for constructing the center of a regular polygon with a compass and straightedge. Is there an easy method for finding the center of some regular polygons that doesn't work for others? Explain.

Alert

The properties of 30°-60°-90° and 45°-45°-90° triangles are important in *Exercises* 20–23 and 37–39. Since students often find these difficult, you may want to review special right triangles before they attempt these exercises.

Exercises

CORE

Getting Started Classify each polygon as equilateral, equiangular, and/or regular.

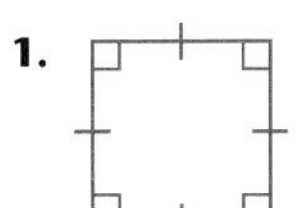

1. Regular
2. Equilateral
3. Equiangular

Find the measure of one interior angle and one exterior angle of each polygon.

4. regular heptagon
5. regular octagon
6. regular decagon
7. **The Measure of Angle Bee** Find the measure of one interior angle and one exterior angle for a regular hexagonal beehive cell.
8. One angle of a regular polygon measures 160°. How many sides does the polygon have?
9. Is it possible for a regular polygon to have an interior angle of 156°? Explain.
10. As the number of sides of a regular polygon increases, what happens to the size of each interior angle of the polygon? Explain.

Write the word or phrase that correctly completes each statement.

11. The perpendicular bisectors of the sides of a regular polygon meet at its ___. Center
12. The distance from the center of a regular polygon to one of its sides is the ___ of the polygon. Apothem
13. The distance from the center of a regular polygon to one of its vertices is the ___ of the polygon. Radius
14. An interior decorator is tiling a floor with the pattern of octagons and squares shown. Explain why this pattern tessellates a plane.

In Exercises 15–19, find the area of each regular polygon.

15. 1545 cm^2

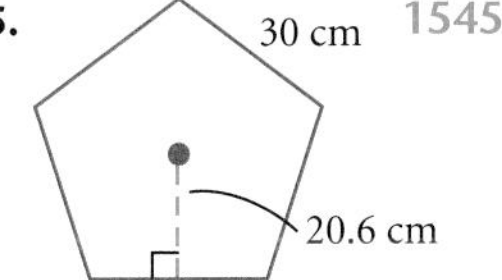

16. 19.2 $in.^2$

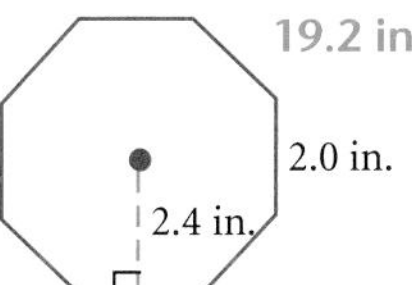

17. 64 m^2

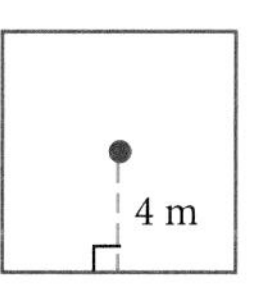

18. a regular decagon with apothem 6.8 m and side length 4.4 m 149.6 m^2
19. a regular octagon with apothem 14.5 in. and side length 12 in. 696 $in.^2$

Part A Exercises

Exercise Notes

Core

10. Students see that the measure of an interior angle of a regular polygon is a function of the number of sides of the polygon.

25. Students develop a technique for constructing a regular hexagon.

More Math Reasoning

40. Students compare the areas of an inscribed and circumscribed hexagon of a circle. This previews the inscribed and circumscribed polygons they will see in 8-1.

Exercise Answers

Core

4. Interior angle = 128.57°; Exterior angle = 51.43°

5. Interior angle = 135°; Exterior angle = 45°

6. Interior angle = 144°; Exterior angle = 36°

7. Interior angle = 120°; Exterior angle = 60°

8. 18 sides

9. Yes; If it is possible, then there is a positive integer n such that $\frac{n-2}{n}180° = 156°$. Solve for n to get $n = 15$.

10. The size of each interior angle increases. As n increases, $\frac{n-2}{n}180°$ increases.

14. At each vertex, there are two 135° angles from regular octagons and a 90° angle from the square. The 360° total completely surrounds the vertex.

Vocabulary
Practice/Skills
Review
Math Reasoning
Problem Solving
Challenge

Ongoing Assessment

Self-Assessment Exercises 1, 3, 5, 7, 11–23 odd

Embedded Assessment Try It d; Exercises 6, 9, 16, 24

Regular Polygons and Polyhedrons

20. $a = 6$; $r = 6\sqrt{2}$; Area $= 144$

21. $a = 6\sqrt{3}$; $r = 12$; Area $= 216\sqrt{3} \approx 374.1$

22. $a = 2\sqrt{3}$; $r = 4\sqrt{3}$; Area $= 36\sqrt{3} \approx 62.4$

23. $\frac{21\sqrt{3}}{2} \approx 18.2$ ft^2

24. a. Octagon **b.** 135°

c. Mark the intersection of the diagonals of the square.

d. 15 in. **e.** 744 in.^{2}

f. Measure 8.8 in. from each corner to make the cuts.

25. a–c.

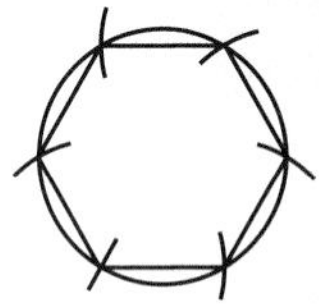

d. Regular hexagon; The distances between the marked points are equal to each other and to the radius.

Look Back

26. The diagonals are perpendicular and bisect each other.

27. The diagonals are perpendicular, congruent, and bisect each other.

28. The diagonals are congruent and bisect each other.

More Math Reasoning

40. The ratio of the area of the outer hexagon to the area of the inner hexagon is $\frac{4}{3}$.

Algebra	Functions	Discrete Math	Probability	Data/Statistics

P **Find the apothem and radius of each regular polygon. Then find its area.**

20.

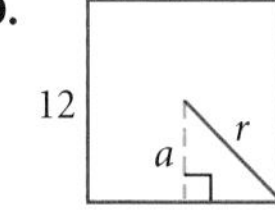

21.

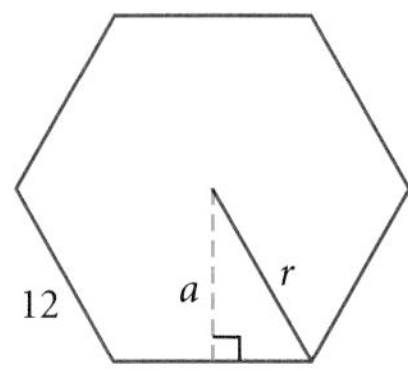

22.

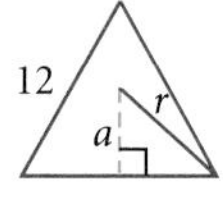

PS **23. Picnic Polygons** The top view of a hexagonal picnic table and bench is shown at the right. The table top has a radius of three feet, and the radius of the table top with the bench is four feet. How many square feet of seating are available on the bench?

PS **24. Stop Everything!** The stop sign at the right below was cut from a 30-in.-square piece of metal.

a. What type of regular polygon is the stop sign?
b. What is the measure of each interior angle of the sign?
c. How could you locate the center of the polygon?
d. Find the length of the apothem.
e. If the polygon's side length is 12.4 in., find the area of the stop sign.
f. Describe how to make this sign from a square piece of metal.

MR **25. a.** Use your compass to draw a circle. Mark a point on the circle.
b. Without changing the setting, move the tip of the compass to the point you marked on the circle. Draw an arc that intersects the circle as shown.
c. Move the tip of your compass to the intersection of the arc and the circle, and make another arc that intersects the circle. Repeat until you come back to the place you started. Draw segments that join the consecutive points on the circle.
d. What type of figure did you construct? Explain why this construction works. (Hint: Consider equilateral triangles.)

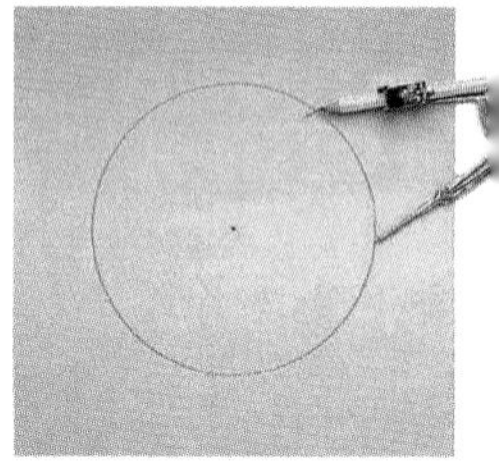

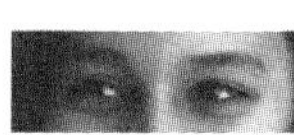

LOOK BACK

R **List all of the characteristics that you can for the diagonals of each figure. [6-2]**

26. rhombus **27.** square **28.** rectangle

R **Solve each quadratic equation. [5-1]**

29. $x^2 + 7x + 3 = 0$ $x = \frac{-7 \pm \sqrt{37}}{2} \approx -0.46$ or -6.54

30. $x^2 - 10x + 21 = 0$ $x = 3$ or $x = 7$

31. $3x^2 - 4x = 10$ $x = \frac{2 \pm \sqrt{34}}{3} \approx -1.28$ or 2.61

Key

V Vocabulary
P Practice/Skills
R Review
MR Math Reasoning
PS Problem Solving
C Challenge

MORE PRACTICE

Find the measure of one interior angle and one exterior angle of each polygon.

32. regular pentagon
Interior angle = 108°;
Exterior angle = 72°

33. regular 12-gon
Interior angle = 150°;
Exterior angle = 30°

34. regular 18-gon
Interior angle = 160°;
Exterior angle = 20°

Find the area of each regular polygon.

35. a regular pentagon with apothem 2.2 ft and side length 3.2 ft 17.6 ft^2

36. a regular octagon with apothem 12.1 cm and side length 10 cm 484 cm^2

Find the apothem and radius of each regular polygon. Then find its area.

37. 16
$a = 8$;
$r = 8\sqrt{2}$;
Area = 256

38.

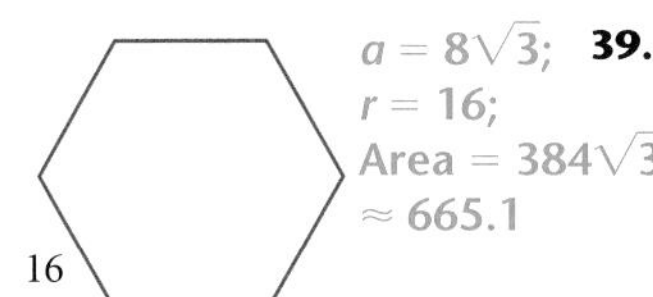

$a = 8\sqrt{3}$;
$r = 16$;
Area $= 384\sqrt{3}$
≈ 665.1

39.

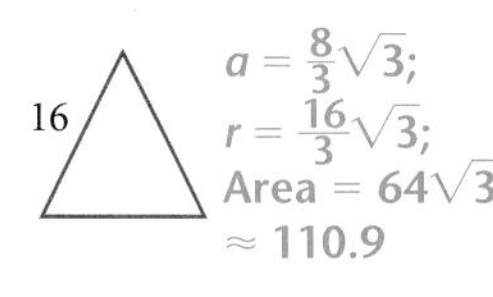

$a = \frac{8}{3}\sqrt{3}$;
$r = \frac{16}{3}\sqrt{3}$;
Area $= 64\sqrt{3}$
≈ 110.9

MORE MATH REASONING

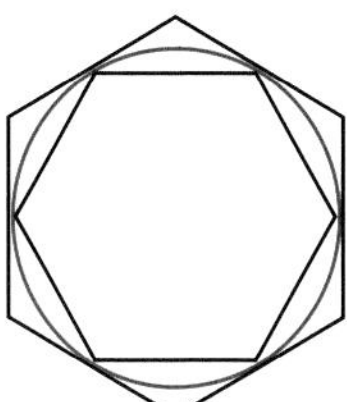

40. The circle in the figure at the right has a radius of 12 in. Find the ratio of the areas of the two regular hexagons.

41. Sign In, Please The diamond-shaped sign shown is a warning that you are coming to a stop sign. Most square warning signs are made with 30-in. sides. The actual stop sign is an octagon. It was cut from a 30-in. piece of metal, and each side of the octagon is 12.4 in. long.

a. What is the area of the octagon on the warning sign if its dimensions are one-half those of the actual stop sign? 186 in.^{2}

b. Excluding the octagon, how many square inches need to be painted on the front of the warning sign? 714 in.^{2}

c. How many times greater is the area of the actual stop sign than the area of the octagon on the warning sign? 4 times greater

Regular Polygons and Polyhedrons

PART B At a Glance

Objective

To become familiar with the Platonic solids.

Development

Students see the definitions of *regular polyhedron* and *Platonic solid,* and learn that there are only five Platonic solids.

In the **Explore,** students see characteristics of two of the solids. They discover the other three Platonic solids and explore their characteristics.

Suggested Materials

Student Segments and connectors (e.g., toothpicks and gumdrops)

Key Terms

Regular polyhedron, Platonic solid

First Five Minutes

Transparency FFM 6-3B

Find the area of a regular hexagon with side length 6.8 cm and apothem 5.9 cm. **120.36 cm²**

Motivate

Ask...

- Why do you think there are only a few possible Platonic solids? **The polygonal faces must fit together perfectly to form a solid figure with no gaps or overlaps.**

EXPLORE

Purely Platonic

Recommended group size: 2

The Point

To find three of the five Platonic solids.

6-3 PART B Regular Polyhedrons

← CONNECT → ***You've investigated some properties of polyhedrons. Now you will see how regular polygons can be used to form special polyhedrons.***

A regular polyhedron has:

- congruent edges and faces;
- faces that are regular polygons;
- an equal number of edges meeting at each vertex.

A *convex* regular polyhedron is one with no "dents."

Although there are an infinite number of convex regular *polygons* (just keep adding sides!), there are only five convex regular *polyhedrons.* These polyhedrons were discovered over two thousand years ago and are named the **Platonic solids,** in honor of the Greek philosopher Plato.

In the following Explore, you will look for some of the Platonic solids and investigate a few of their properties.

EXPLORE: PURELY PLATONIC

MATERIALS

Segments
Connectors
(for example, toothpicks and gumdrops)

Two of the Platonic solids are shown below.

Regular icosahedron
(20 triangular faces)

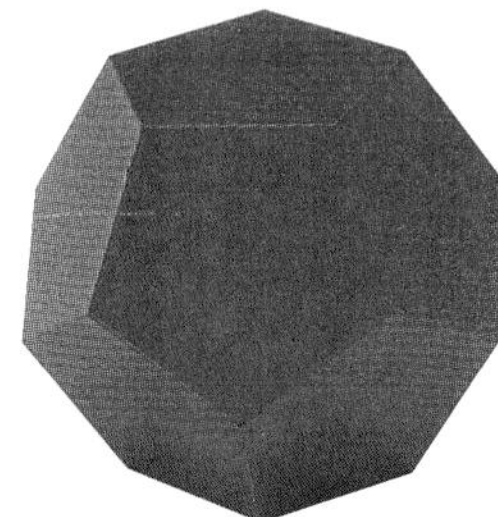

Regular dodecahedron
(12 pentagonal faces)

Use whatever segments and connectors you have available to find the rest of the Platonic solids. There are only three others, and they all have fewer faces than the two shown. Make a sketch of each, and complete the table on page 449. (If you need help remembering the names of polyhedrons, see page 410.)

Research Note

The best way to learn to visualize three dimensions is to make objects that demonstrate the spatial concepts. Students can observe and use many spatial relationships while they construct polyhedr[ons]. (Victoria Pohl, "Visualizing Three Dimensions by Constructing Polyhedra," *Learning and Teaching Geometry K–12, 1987 Yearbook,* Mary Montgomery Lindquist and Albert P. Shulte, eds., p. 144. © 1987 NCTM.)

Name	Type of Face	No. of Faces	No. of Vertices	No. of Edges
	Triangle			
	Square			
	Triangle			
Regular dodecahedron	Pentagon	12	20	30
Regular icosahedron	Triangle	20	12	30

TRY IT

Name the convex regular polyhedron that has the given set of characteristics.

a. five equilateral triangular faces meet at each vertex **Regular icosahedron**
b. square faces **Regular hexahedron (cube)**
c. three equilateral triangular faces meet at each vertex **Regular tetrahedron**

The Platonic solids occur in nature in many ways. Sodium sulphantimonate molecules are tetrahedrons, chrome alum molecules are octahedrons, and salt crystals are cubes (hexahedrons). The photograph at the right shows the hexahedral structure of salt crystals.

Although there are only five Platonic solids, there are other regular polyhedrons. Two were discovered in the sixteenth century and two more in the nineteenth century. These *concave* regular polyhedrons are shown below.

REFLECT

1. Give examples of Platonic solids in your classroom or in other everyday situations. Classify each by the number of faces.
2. What can you say about the faces of any Platonic solid? Explain.

Student Resources
- **Alternative Lessons** 6-3B
- **Laboratory Manual** 6-3B
- Technology Lab Manual
- **Practice** 6-3B
- **Study Guide and Journal** 6-3B
- **Guía de estudios y Diario** 6-3B
- **Multilingual Handbook**
- **More Look Ahead** 6-3B
- SAT Preparation

Media Resources
- **Transparency FFM** 6-3B
- Transparency AE
- Teaching Transparency
- **AWSMTest and practice software**
- AWSM Videodisc

Look and Listen...
- For students who do not remember that the polygonal faces must be congruent regular polygons.

Ask...
- Can you think of a familiar solid whose faces are congruent squares?
- The faces of two of the solids you are looking for must be regular triangles. What types of triangles should you use for these?

For Groups That Finish Early
Should Euler's Formula work for the Platonic solids? Check your answer by substituting the results from your table into Euler's Formula. **Euler's Formula holds for the Platonic solids.**

Follow Up
Ask students to display models of the three Platonic solids they identified. Have the class give the names of the solids. **Regular tetrahedron, regular hexahedron (cube), regular octahedron.**

Possible Answer
The remaining solids are the regular tetrahedron (with 4 triangular faces, 6 edges, 4 vertices), the regular hexahedron/cube (with 6 square faces, 12 edges, and 8 vertices), and the regular octahedron (with 8 triangular faces, 12 edges, and 6 vertices).

Journal

Reflect 2 and **Exercise** 17 are suitable for journal entries.

REFLECT
Possible Answers

1. Regular hexahedrons may be found in dice, some math puzzles, and some boxes. Others are harder to find.
2. By definition, the faces of a Platonic solid are congruent regular polygons.

Regular Polygons and Polyhedrons

Part B Exercises

Exercise Notes

Core

11. Students use visual thinking skills to imagine tessellations of three-dimensional space.

17. This version of the "spider and fly" problem asks students to visualize paths that follow several planes. Unfolding a net helps them realize that there is a two-dimensional way to solve this three-dimensional problem. Students may be surprised that the shortest path is a slanted one that crosses three of the room's faces, not one that involves its edges.

Look Ahead

These exercises review skills in working with ratio and proportion. These will be very important as students work with similar figures in Chapter 7.

More Math Reasoning

27. Students find that a regular tetrahedral die gives an equal probability of four different outcomes. Dice in the shapes of the Platonic solids are available in many game stores.

Exercise Answers

Core

8.

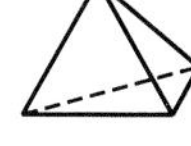

9.

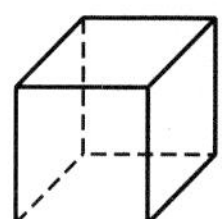

10.

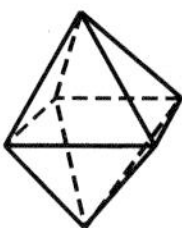

11. Regular hexahedron

Exercises

CORE

P **Getting Started Classify each regular polyhedron shown.**

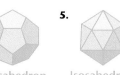

1.  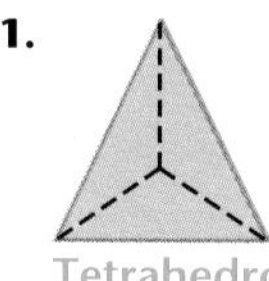 Tetrahedron

2. 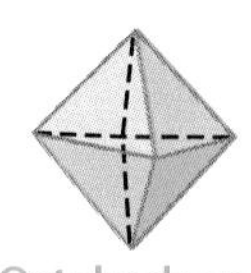 Octahedron

3. 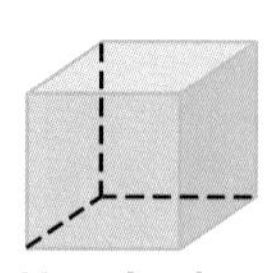 Hexahedron

4. **5.** 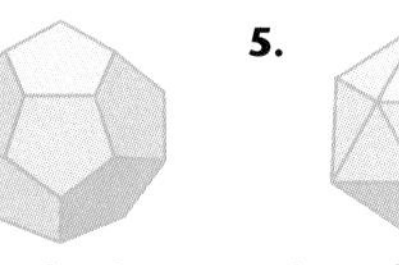 Dodecahedron Isosahedron

P **Name the convex regular polyhedron that has the given set of characteristics.**

6. Four equilateral triangular faces meet at each vertex. Regular octahedron

7. pentagonal faces Regular dodecahedron

P **Sketch each Platonic solid.**

8. a regular tetrahedron (4 faces)

9. a regular hexahedron (6 faces)

10. a regular octahedron (8 faces)

MR **11.** Name a Platonic solid that tessellates space.

P **12.** If a Platonic solid is randomly selected from the five possibilities, what is the probability that the solid will have

a. triangular faces? $\frac{3}{5}$

b. square faces? $\frac{1}{5}$

c. pentagonal faces? $\frac{1}{5}$

P **13.** As shown in the photo at the right, a sodium chloride (salt) crystal has a hexahedral shape. *Science*

a. What is another name for a convex regular hexahedron? Cube

b. Verify that Euler's Formula holds for a hexahedral salt crystal. $F = 6$, $V = 8$, $E = 12$; $6 + 8 - 12 = 2$

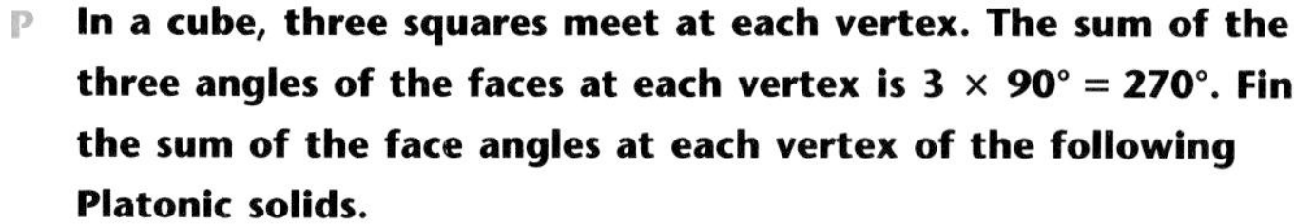

P **In a cube, three squares meet at each vertex. The sum of the three angles of the faces at each vertex is 3 × 90° = 270°. Find the sum of the face angles at each vertex of the following Platonic solids.**

14. a regular octahedron 240° **15.** a regular dodecahedron 324°

P **16.** In the regular hexahedron at the right, $\overrightarrow{AB} = \overrightarrow{DC}$. Find at least three additional pairs of equal vectors, using the vertices of the hexahedron.

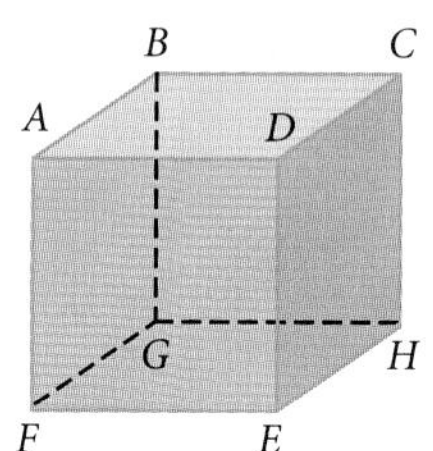

Key

V Vocabulary
P Practice/Skills
R Review
MR Math Reasoning
PS Problem Solving
C Challenge

History Connection

Plato was not the first to be fascinated by the "Platonic solids." The Pythagoreans associated these solids with the four elements of Greek antiquity: the tetrahedron represented fire; the cube, earth; the octahedron, air; and the icosahedron, water. The dodecahedron, probably the last discovered, symbolized the universe.

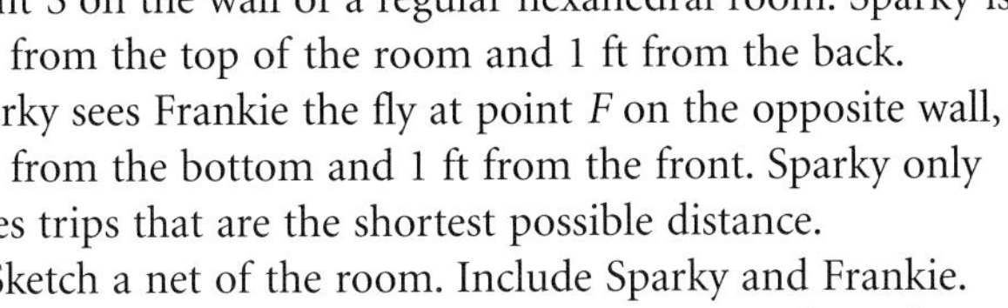

17. Crawling Out for Dinner Sparky the spider is located at point S on the wall of a regular hexahedral room. Sparky is 1 ft from the top of the room and 1 ft from the back. Sparky sees Frankie the fly at point F on the opposite wall, 1 ft from the bottom and 1 ft from the front. Sparky only takes trips that are the shortest possible distance.

a. Sketch a net of the room. Include Sparky and Frankie.

b. Draw the path Sparky takes on your net. Explain why you think this is the shortest path.

c. What is the shortest distance along the walls from Sparky to Frankie?

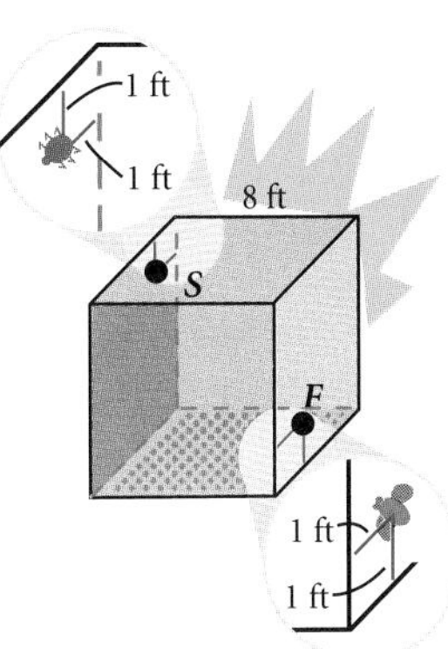

LOOK AHEAD

Solve each proportion.

18. $\frac{x}{12} = \frac{6}{9}$ $x = 8$ **19.** $\frac{3}{5} = \frac{8}{z}$ $x = \frac{40}{3}$ **20.** $\frac{AB}{8} = \frac{9}{12}$ $AB = 6$

In Exercises 21 and 22, a 90-m long rope is cut into two pieces.

21. One piece of rope has a length of 70 m. What is the ratio of the longer piece to the shorter piece? $\frac{7}{2}$

22. Suppose the two pieces have a length ratio of 13:5. How long is each piece? 25 m and 65 m

MORE PRACTICE

23. Which Platonic solids have the same number of vertices as faces? Regular tetrahedron

24. Which Platonic solids have the same number of vertices as edges? None

Find the sum of the face angles at each vertex of the following Platonic solids.

25. a regular tetrahedron 180° **26.** a regular icosahedron 300°

MORE MATH REASONING

27. On a Roll Suppose you create a game in which you want an equal chance of any of *four* numbers coming up on a roll of a die. Design a die for your game. Explain your design.

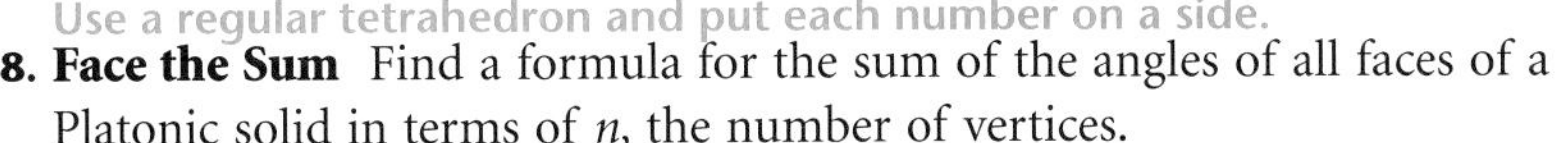
Use a regular tetrahedron and put each number on a side.

28. Face the Sum Find a formula for the sum of the angles of all faces of a Platonic solid in terms of n, the number of vertices.

Ongoing Assessment

Self-Assessment Exercises 1, 3, 5, 7, 11, 13, 15, 16

Embedded Assessment Try It a; Exercises 8, 12, 14, 17

16. Possible answers: $\overrightarrow{BC} = \overrightarrow{AD}$; $\overrightarrow{BH} = \overrightarrow{AE}$; $\overrightarrow{AC} = \overrightarrow{FH}$

17. a. Possible answer:

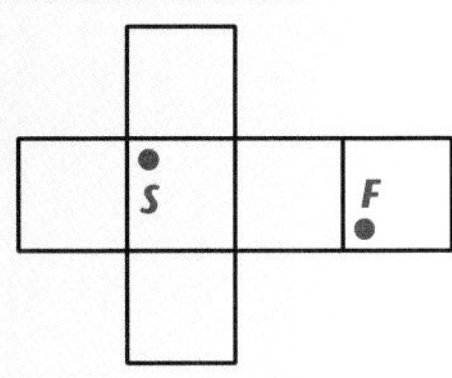

b. Possible answer: It is a straight line on the net.

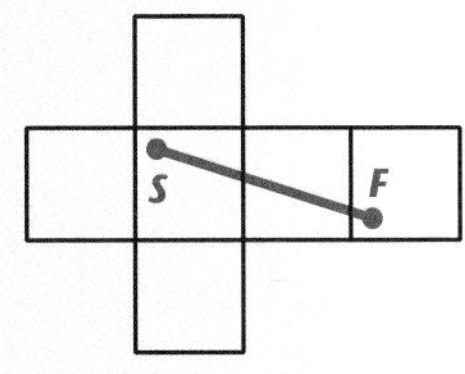

c. ≈ 17.1 ft

More Math Reasoning

28. $(n - 2)360°$

Regular Polygons and Polyhedrons

PART C At a Glance

Objective

To discover why regular hexagons are a good choice for the openings in beehive cells.

Development

In the **Explore,** students discover why regular hexagons are efficient for beehive cell openings.

Suggested Materials

Student Straightedge, paper, scissors

First Five Minutes

Transparency FFM 6-3C

In your own words, define *regular polygon, regular polyhedron,* and *Platonic solids.* List as many other properties of these figures as you can.

EXPLORE

Back to the Bees

Recommended group size: 4

The Point

To see why the regular hexagon is an efficient shape for the opening of a beehive cell.

Look and Listen...

- For students who do not see why a regular hexagon is more efficient than a square or an equilateral triangle.

Ask...

- Sketch a square, an equilateral triangle, and a regular hexagon that have the same perimeter. Which of these cells would you prefer to live in? Why?

For Groups That Finish Early

What must the sum of the angles at a tessellation vertex be? Using this fact, design some tessellations that use *two* kinds of congruent regular polygons. Octagon and square, hexagon and triangle, triangle and square, 12-gon and triangle, pentagon and 10-gon.

6-3 PART C Making Connections

← CONNECT → *Honeybees, gem cutters, and even Plato have found regular polygons and polyhedrons useful. You've investigated the properties of these figures.*

The photograph at the left shows honeybees at work in a hive. In the following Explore, you will become more familiar with the ingenuity of the honeybee and learn more about why it makes the architectural choices it does.

EXPLORE: BACK TO THE BEES

MATERIALS

Straightedge
Paper
Scissors

Is there a reason honeybees make hexagonal cells? Why not pentagons? octagons? 54-gons?

1. Make several copies of each figure. Check to see if they will tessellate a plane.

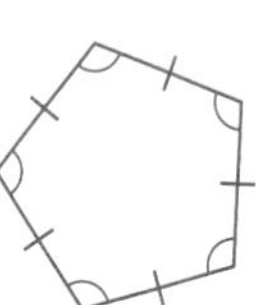

Regular pentagon

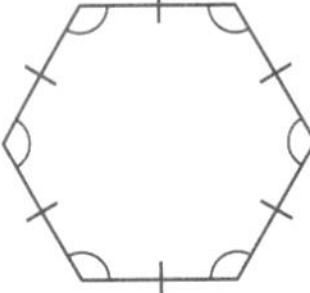

Regular hexagon

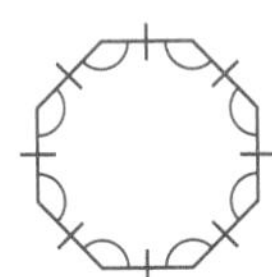

Regular octagon

2. Name three types of regular polygons that tessellate a plane, and explain why they tessellate. Are there other regular polygons that tessellate? Why or why not?
3. Explain why bees might want to have cell openings that tessellate.
4. Why do you think bees make hexagonal cells instead of using another regular polygon that tessellates? (We will investigate this in more detail in Chapter 11.)
5. Are beehive cells regular polyhedrons? Support your answer.

Student Resources

Alternative Lessons 6-3C
Laboratory Manual 6-3C
Technology Lab Manual
Practice 6-3C
Study Guide and Journal 6-3C
Guía de estudios y Diario 6-3C
Multilingual Handbook
More Look Back 6-3C
SAT Preparation

Media Resources

Transparency FFM 6-3C
Transparency AE
Teaching Transparency
AWSMTest and practice software
AWSM Videodisc

REFLECT

1. Write a short paragraph comparing and contrasting regular polygons and regular polyhedrons.
2. There are only five convex regular polyhedrons. List them and give the number and type of faces for each.
3. How can you make a regular hexagon by reflecting an equilateral triangle? Is there another way to use transformations to make a hexagon from an equilateral triangle? Explain your methods.

Self-Assessment

1. Explain the relationship between regular polygons and regular polyhedrons.
2. **Hive Society** As shown in the figure, there are approximately five worker-bee cells for each 25 mm in a comb.

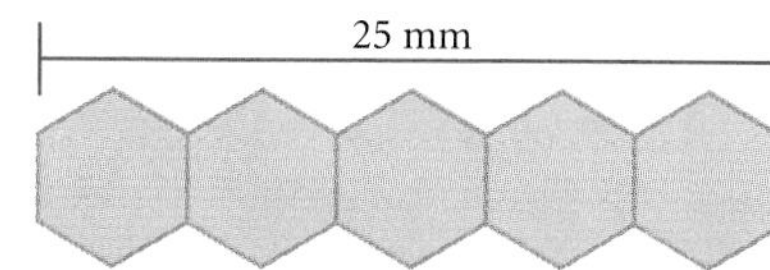

a. What is the measure of one interior angle of each cell? 120°
b. What is the measure of one exterior angle of each cell? 60°
c. Find the apothem, radius, and area of one of the cells. $a = \frac{5}{2}$ mm; $r = \frac{5}{3}\sqrt{3}$ mm; $A = \frac{25}{2}\sqrt{3} \approx 21.65$ mm^2
d. How many cells take up an area of 100 cm^2? ≈ 4.62 cells

3. The measure of an exterior angle of a regular n-gon is equal to (b)

(a) 360° (b) $\frac{360°}{n}$ (c) 180° (d) $\frac{(n-2)180°}{n}$ (e) $\frac{1}{2}ap$

In Exercises 4–6, sketch the following regular polygons, showing the lines of symmetry of each figure.

4. an equilateral triangle
5. a square
6. a regular hexagon
7. How many lines of symmetry are there in a regular n-gon? $2n$
8. Prove: If the diagonals of a parallelogram are perpendicular, then it is a rhombus. [6-2]
9. What quadrilateral is determined by the cross section of the cube containing A, B, G, and H? Why?

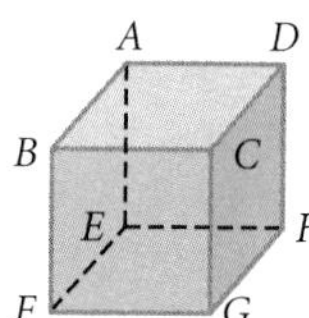

Key

Vocabulary
Practice/Skills
Review
Math Reasoning
Problem Solving
Challenge

Follow Up

Ask students to give a brief statement explaining why the regular hexagon is an excellent choice for the opening of a beehive cell.

Possible Answers

1. Of these three figures, only the regular hexagon tessellates.
2. Equilateral triangles, squares, and regular hexagons tessellate. Other regular polygons do not, since the measures of their interior angles do not divide evenly into 360°.
3. They can fill an area with no wasted space. Wasted space means inefficiently used building materials.
4. The hexagon gives the greatest area for a given perimeter.
5. No. All of the faces of a regular polyhedron are congruent.

Portfolio

Have students select items from their work that demonstrate their understanding of the material in 6-3.

You may wish to have students include their favorite application problem involving regular polygons, their best sketch of a regular polyhedron other than a cube, and an **Exercise** that they found interesting or challenging.

REFLECT

Possible Answers

See Additional Answers p. T440.

Self-Assessment

Exercise Notes

3. Similar to multiple-choice questions on standardized tests.
13. Students investigate the Archimedean solids.

Self-Assessment Answers

1. The faces of regular polyhedrons are regular polygons.

Regular Polygons and Polyhedrons

4.

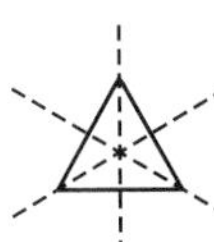

5.

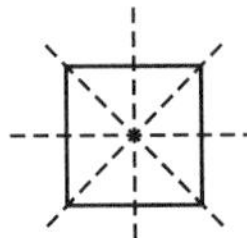

6.

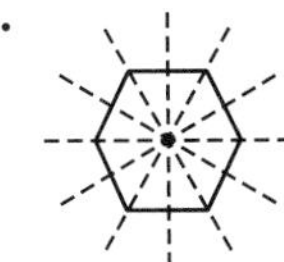

8. Possible Answer:

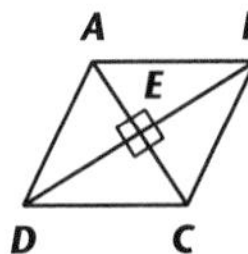

Given: $ABCD$ is a parallelogram, $\overline{AC} \perp \overline{DB}$.
Prove: $ABCD$ is a rhombus.
Proof: $\overline{BD}$ bisects $\overline{AC}$ because diagonals of a parallelogram bisect each other. $\overline{AE} \cong \overline{EC}$ by the definition of *bisect.* $\overline{EB} \cong \overline{EB}$ by the Reflexive Property. $\overline{AC} \perp \overline{DB}$ is given. $\angle AEB$ and $\angle CEB$ are right angles by definition of *perpendicular.* $\triangle AEB \cong \triangle CEB$ by LL. $\overline{AB} \cong \overline{BC}$ by CPCTC. $\overline{AB} \cong \overline{DC}$ and $\overline{AD} \cong \overline{BC}$ because opposite sides of a parallelogram are congruent. $\overline{AB} \cong \overline{DC} \cong \overline{BC} \cong \overline{AD}$ by the Transitive Property. $ABCD$ is a rhombus by definition.

9. Rectangle; $\overline{AH} \cong \overline{BG}$ and $\overline{AB} \cong \overline{HG}$ so it is a parallelogram. $AG = BH$ so it is a rectangle. It is not a square because $AB \neq AH$.

10. Let x be the width, then $x(x + 48) = 41{,}040$. So $x^2 + 48x - 41{,}040 = 0$. Solve for x to get $x = 180$ (or $x = -228$). 180 ft wide and 228 ft long.

12. Regular tetrahedron; Regular octahedron; Regular icosahedron

13. From left to right: Cut off vertices of a regular tetrahedron, hexahedron, octahedron, icosahedron, and dodecahedron.

14. Regular octahedron

R History **10. Mayan Palace** The floor plan of the Palacio (shown at the right), a building in the ancient Mayan city of Palenque, is 48 ft longer than it is wide. The area of the base of the Palacio is 41,040 ft^2. Find the length and the width of the Palacio to the nearest tenth of a foot. Explain your method. [5-1]

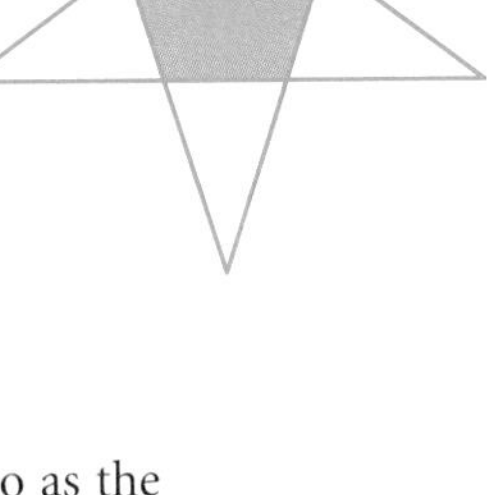

PS **11. Angle on the Stars** A star is formed by extending each side of a regular n-gon until it meets the extensions of the other sides. Find the angle measure at a point of the n-pointed star if the n-gon inside is

a. a pentagon 36°

b. a hexagon 60°

P **12.** A deltahedron is a convex polyhedron whose faces are all triangles. Which of the five Platonic solids are deltahedrons?

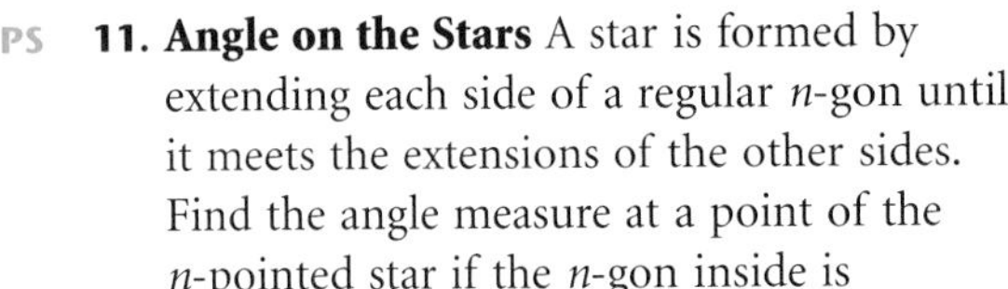

MR **13. Archimedean Solids** Another set of polyhedrons is referred to as the Archimedean solids. There are thirteen of these solids. Five of them are shown below.

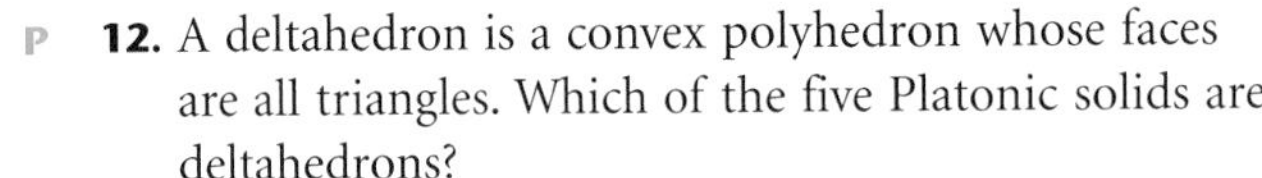

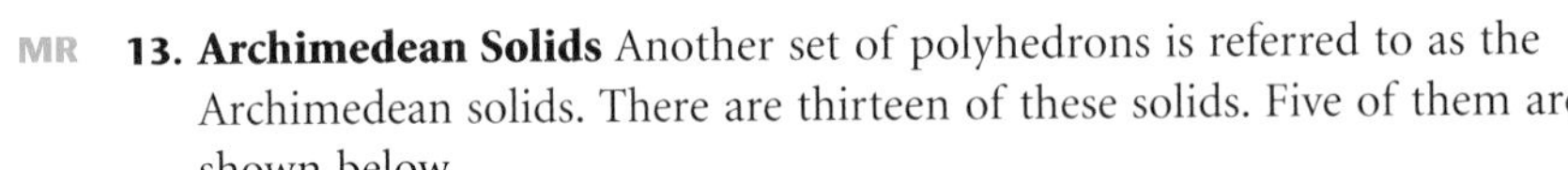

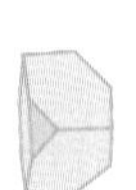

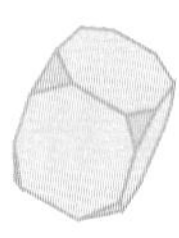

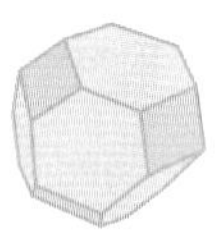

These five solids are truncated Platonic solids. This means that the vertices of a Platonic solid have been cut off to produce each solid. Describe how this was done to create the solids shown here.

PS History **14.** Grace Chisholm Young (1868–1944) was an English mathematician. The net shown at the right is adapted from a net in her *First Book of Geometry,* published in 1905. When folded, the triangle labeled 1a coincides with the triangle labeled 1, and so on. What regular polyhedron results from folding up this net?

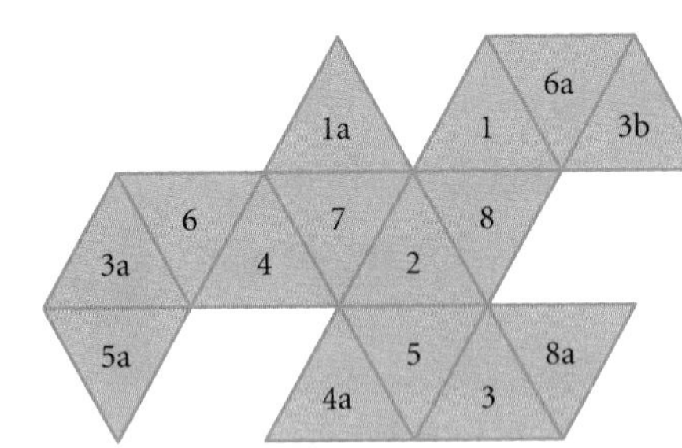

Assessment Resources

- **Quiz 6-3**
- Chapter Assessment Form A
- Chapter Assessment Form B
- Chapter Alternative Assessment
- Mid-Year Assessment
- End-of-Year Assessment
- **AWSMTest and practice software**

Ongoing Assessment

Self-Assessment Self-Assessment Exercises

Embedded Assessment Explore Step 4; Reflect 1,

Logic/Reasoning | Industry/Careers | Science/Health | Social Science/History | Fine Arts/Literature

Chapter 6 Review

In Chapter 6, you explored polygons and polyhedrons, including properties of quadrilaterals, applications of regular polygons, and connections to coordinate proof.

KEY TERMS

apothem [6-3]	diagonal [6-1]	radius of a regular polygon [6-3]
center of a regular polygon [6-3]	Platonic solids [6-3]	regular polygon [6-3]
concave polygon [6-1]	polyhedron [6-1]	regular polyhedron [6-3]
convex polygon [6-1]		

From each group of terms, choose the term that does not belong and explain why.

1. Convex, concave, regular, apothem
2. Center, altitude, radius, apothem

CONCEPTS AND APPLICATIONS

3. Find the sums of the measures of the interior angles and exterior angles (one at each vertex) for a pentagon. [6-1] Interior, 540°; Exterior 360°

Sketch each of the following, if possible. If it is not possible, say so.

4. a concave hexagon [6-1]
5. a regular polygon whose interior angles measure 135° each [6-3] Octagon
6. A polyhedron has twelve edges and six vertices. How many faces does the polyhedron have? Name the polyhedron by its number of faces. [6-1] 8; Octahedron

Determine whether each quadrilateral must be a parallelogram. Explain. [6-2]

7. 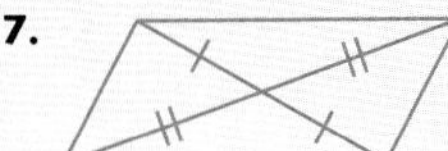

8. 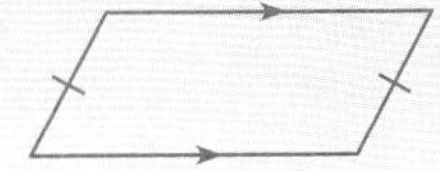

9. 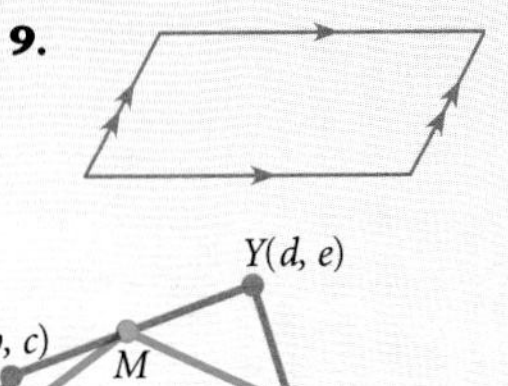

10. Points M, N, O, and P are the midpoints of the sides of quadrilateral $XYZW$. Prove that $MNOP$ is a parallelogram. [6-2]

Student Resources
Alternative Lessons
Laboratory Manual
Technology Lab Manual
Practice
Study Guide and Journal Ch 6
Guía de estudios y Diario Ch 6
Multilingual Handbook
More Look Ahead
SAT Preparation

Media Resources
Transparency FFM
Transparency AE
Teaching Transparency
AWSMTest and practice software
AWSM Videodisc

Chapter 6 Review

Journal

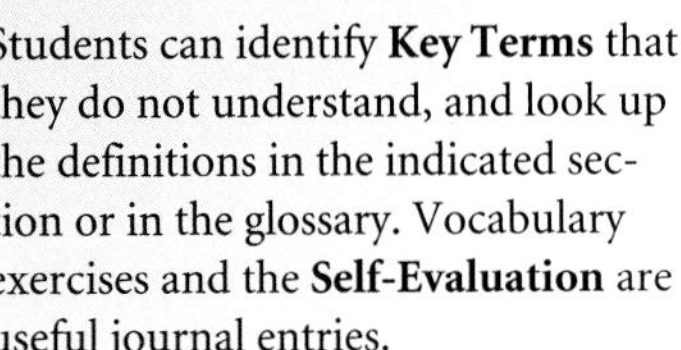

Students can identify **Key Terms** that they do not understand, and look up the definitions in the indicated section or in the glossary. Vocabulary exercises and the **Self-Evaluation** are useful journal entries.

Review Answers

1. Apothem; The other terms are all classifications of polygons and polyhedrons.
2. Center; The other terms all refer to distances/segments.
4. Possible answer: 
7. Parallelogram; The diagonals bisect each other.
8. May not be a parallelogram; The congruent sides may not be parallel.
9. Parallelogram; Both pairs of opposite sides are parallel.
10. M is at $\left(\frac{b+d}{2}, \frac{c+e}{2}\right)$. N is at $\left(\frac{a+d}{2}, \frac{e}{2}\right)$. O is at $\left(\frac{a}{2}, 0\right)$. P is at $\left(\frac{b}{2}, \frac{c}{2}\right)$. Slope of $\overline{MN}$ is $\dfrac{\frac{e}{2} - \frac{(c+e)}{2}}{\frac{(a+d)}{2} - \frac{(b+d)}{2}} = \dfrac{-\frac{c}{2}}{\frac{(a-b)}{2}} = \frac{c}{b-a}$. Slope of $\overline{NO}$ is $\dfrac{0 - \frac{e}{2}}{\frac{a}{2} - \frac{(a+d)}{2}} = \dfrac{-\frac{e}{2}}{-\frac{d}{2}} = \frac{e}{d}$. Slope of $\overline{OP}$ is $\dfrac{\frac{c}{2} - 0}{\frac{b}{2} - \frac{a}{2}} = \dfrac{\frac{c}{2}}{\frac{(b-a)}{2}} = \frac{c}{b-a}$. Slope of $\overline{PM}$ is $\dfrac{\frac{(c+e)}{2} - \frac{c}{2}}{\frac{(b+d)}{2} - \frac{b}{2}} = \dfrac{\frac{e}{2}}{\frac{d}{2}} = \frac{e}{d}$. So $\overline{MN} \parallel \overline{OP}$ and $\overline{NO} \parallel \overline{PM}$. Therefore, $MNOP$ is a parallelogram by definition.
12. Put 1, 2, 3, and 4 on two faces and 5 on four faces.
13. $a = \sqrt{3}$ in.; $r = 2\sqrt{3}$ in.; Area $= 9\sqrt{3} = 15.6$ in.^{2}
14–16. See Additional Answers p. T440.

Chapter 6 Assessment

Portfolio

Students may select items that represent their mathematical understanding of the ideas in Chapter 6 and that illustrate the effort they put into this chapter.

A rubric for assessing portfolios is included in the introduction to the Teacher's Edition.

Assessment Answers

1. Possible answer:

2. May not be a parallelogram; The diagonals might not bisect each other.

3. Parallelogram; Both pairs of opposite sides are congruent.

4. May not be a parallelogram; Opposite sides may not be parallel.

5. $a = \frac{5\sqrt{3}}{2}$ m; Area $= \frac{75\sqrt{3}}{2} \approx$ 64.95 m^2

6. The sum of the interior angles is given by $(n - 2)180°$. There are $n - 2$ triangles created by the $n - 3$ diagonals that can be drawn from any one vertex, and the sum of the interior angles of a triangle is 180°.

9. Possible answer: Use a cube. Put 1 on one face, 3 on two faces, and 2 on three faces.

10. a. $F = 6$, $V = 8$, $E = 12$; $6 + 8 - 12 = 2$

b. Trapezoid

11. Parallelogram—the diagonals must bisect each other; Rectangle—the diagonals must be congruent and bisect each other; Rhombus—the diagonals must be perpendicular and bisect each other.

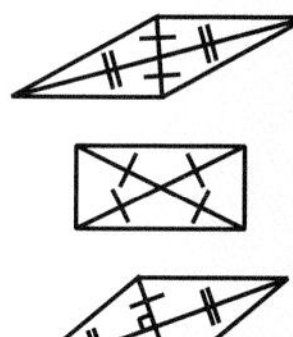

P **11.** What is the measure of each interior angle of a regular 10-gon? [6-3] 144°

PS **12.** A children's game uses a regular dodecahedron as a die. Explain how to assign the digits 1, 2, 3, 4, and 5 to the 12 pentagonal faces so that the probabilities of rolling 1, 2, 3, or 4 are the same and the probability of rolling a 5 is twice the probability of rolling a 1. [6-3]

P **13.** Find the apothem, radius, and area of an equilateral triangle with side length 6 in. [6-3]

R **14.** Find the altitude, h, and area of this trapezoid. [5-2, 5-3]

13 cm, 10 cm, h, 10 cm, 21 cm

MR **15.** Write a summary of formulas related to the angles of convex polygons.

CONCEPTS AND CONNECTIONS

MR **16.** **Technical Drawing** An isometric view of a square-topped box is shown at the right. Draw orthogonal views of the box, as well as one-point and two-point perspective drawings. Describe the polygon that is used to represent the square top in each drawing. For each polygon, describe how the interior angles and any diagonal relationships differ from those of the square.

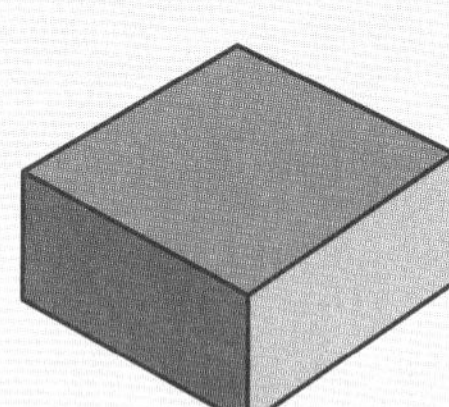

SELF-EVALUATION

Write a summary of the most important ideas in Chapter 6. Include in your summary the special properties of quadrilaterals, properties of regular polygons and polyhedrons, and important formulas. Mention concepts that gave you trouble.

Chapter 6 Assessment

TEST

P **1.** Sketch a concave quadrilateral, if possible. If it is not possible, say so.

Determine whether each quadrilateral must be a parallelogram. Justify your answers.

P **2.**

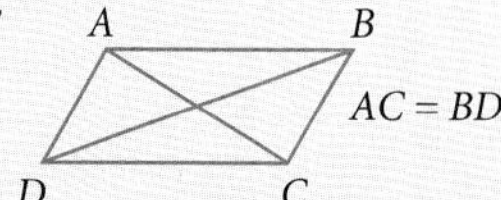

3.

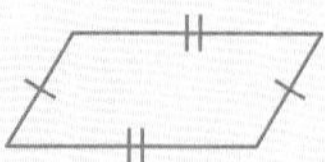

4.

Key

- V Vocabulary
- P Practice/Skills
- R Review
- MR Math Reasoning
- PS Problem Solving
- C Challenge

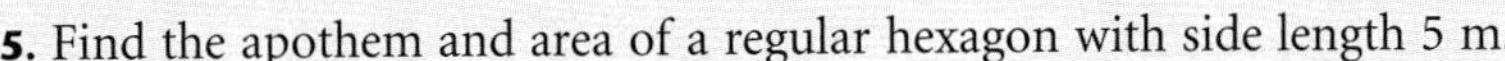

5. Find the apothem and area of a regular hexagon with side length 5 m.

6. An n-gon is partitioned into triangles by drawing all of the diagonals from one vertex as shown. Explain what property of the n-gon is given by the expression $(n - 2)180°$ and explain how it is derived from this partitioning.

7. What is the sum of the measures of the exterior angles (one at each vertex) of a regular pentagon? What is the measure of each of its interior angles? 360°; 108°

8. A triangle has sides of lengths 12, 17, and 27. Determine whether the triangle is acute, obtuse, or right. Explain. Obtuse; $(12)^2 + (17)^2 = 433 < 729 = (27)^2$

9. A designer of a board game has asked you to design a die. The probability of rolling a 3 must be twice the probability of rolling a 1; the probability of rolling a 2 must be three times the probability of rolling a 1. Choose one of the Platonic solids, and explain how to assign numbers to its faces to satisfy the designer's criteria.

10. Pyramids in many areas of the ancient world were actually *frustums* of pyramids, like the frustum of a square pyramid shown here.

a. Show that Euler's Formula holds for this frustum.

b. Describe a vertical cross section of the frustum that contains the center of its base.

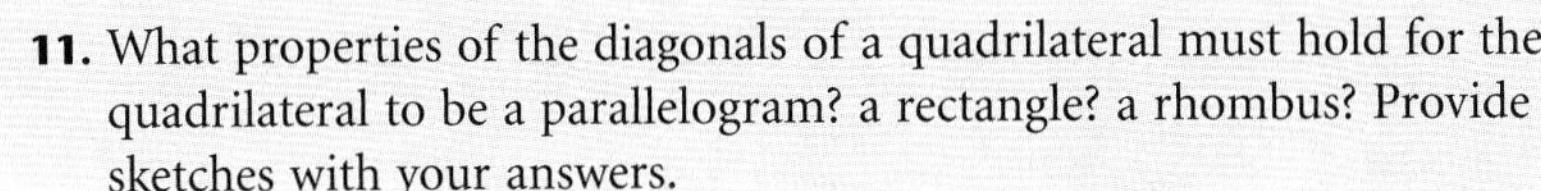

11. What properties of the diagonals of a quadrilateral must hold for the quadrilateral to be a parallelogram? a rectangle? a rhombus? Provide sketches with your answers.

12. Prove the following.

Given: $\overline{AB} \cong \overline{CD}, \overline{AB} \parallel \overline{CD}$

Prove: $ABCD$ is a parallelogram.

See Additional Answers p. T440.

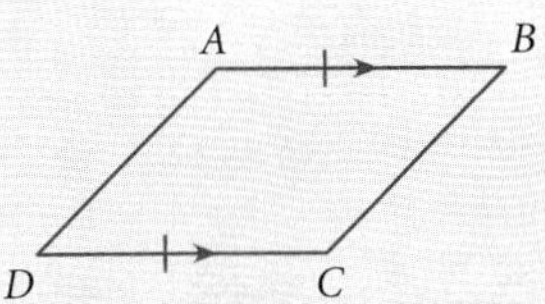

PERFORMANCE TASK

Carefully draw several right triangles and the median to the hypotenuse of each. Measure the median and hypotenuse in each triangle. Then state a conjecture relating the length of the hypotenuse and the length of the median to the hypotenuse.

Use the figure to help prove your conjecture. (Hint: Begin by locating a point P on $\overrightarrow{CM}$ so that $ACBP$ is a parallelogram. The other key step to the proof is showing that $ACBP$ is a rectangle.)

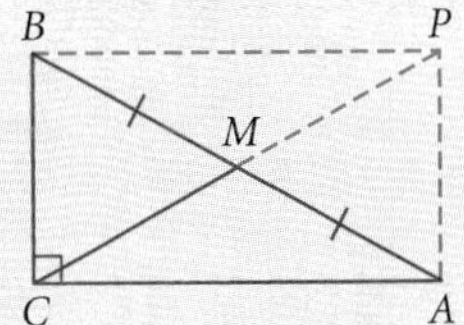

Assessment Resources

Quiz

Chapter 6 Assessment Form A

Chapter 6 Assessment Form B

Chapter 6 Alternative Assessment

Mid-Year Assessment

End-of-Year Assessment

AWSMTest Chapter 6

Ongoing Assessment

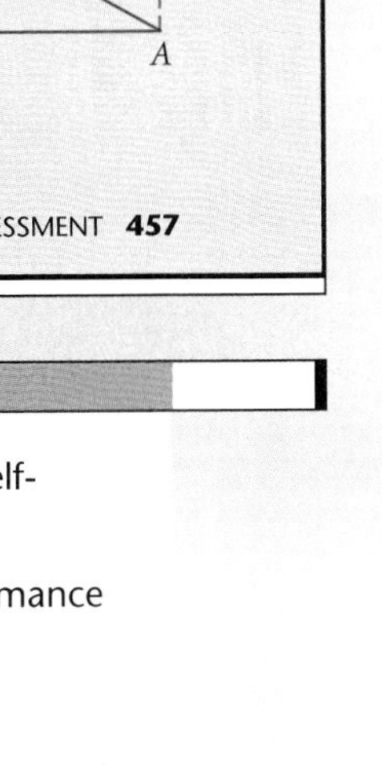

Self-Assessment Chapter 6 Review and Self-Evaluation

Embedded Assessment Chapter 6 Performance Task

Test Chapter 6 Test

Performance Task

Answer

The median is half the length of the hypotenuse. Plan for proof: Mark a point P on $\overrightarrow{CM}$ so $CM = MP$. Then $ACBP$ is a parallelogram since its diagonals bisect. Since consecutive angles are supplementary and $\angle BCA$ is a right angle, $ACBP$ is a rectangle, and $CP = AB$. This means $CM = \frac{1}{2}AB$.

Suggested Scoring Rubric

Level 4 Full Accomplishment

- Shows full understanding of the definitions of median, hypotenuse, and right triangle and of deductive proof.
- Makes correct conjecture that the median to the hypotenuse is half its length.
- Proof is complete and clear. Proof justifies the existence of the point that completes the parallelogram and uses the fact that diagonals of a rectangle are congruent and bisect each other.

Level 3 Substantial Accomplishment

- Shows essential grasp of the definitions of median, hypotenuse, and right triangle and of deductive proof.
- Makes correct conjecture that the median to the hypotenuse is half its length.
- Proof is essentially complete, but may fail to justify the existence of the point that completes the parallelogram.

Level 2 Partial Accomplishment

- Shows partial grasp of the definitions of median, hypotenuse, and right triangle and of deductive proof.
- Makes correct conjecture that the median to the hypotenuse is half its length.
- Proof is incomplete.

Level 1 Little Accomplishment

- Shows little or no grasp of the definitions of median, hypotenuse, and right triangle or of deductive proof.
- Conjecture is incorrect.

7

Chapter 7 Similarity

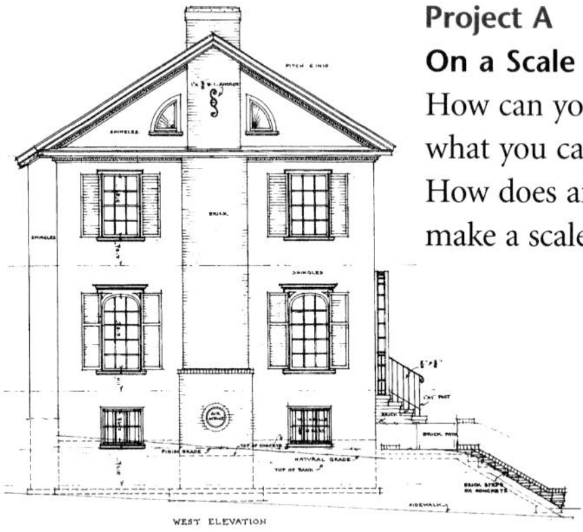

Project A
On a Scale of 1 to 10
How can you measure what you can't reach? How does an architect make a scale drawing?

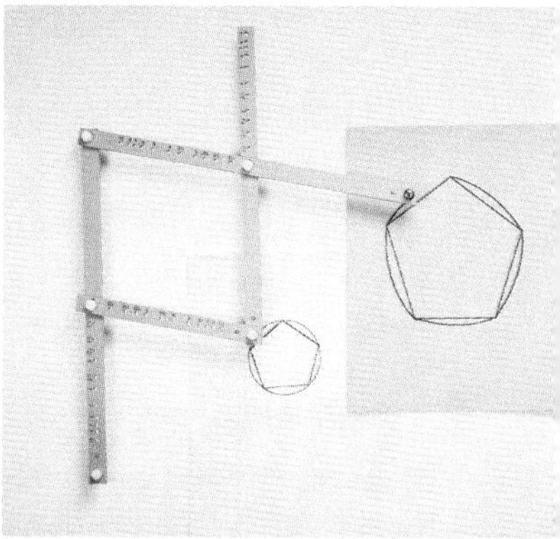

Project B
Do You Copy?
What is a pantograph? How were maps and drawings enlarged and reduced before photocopying was invented?

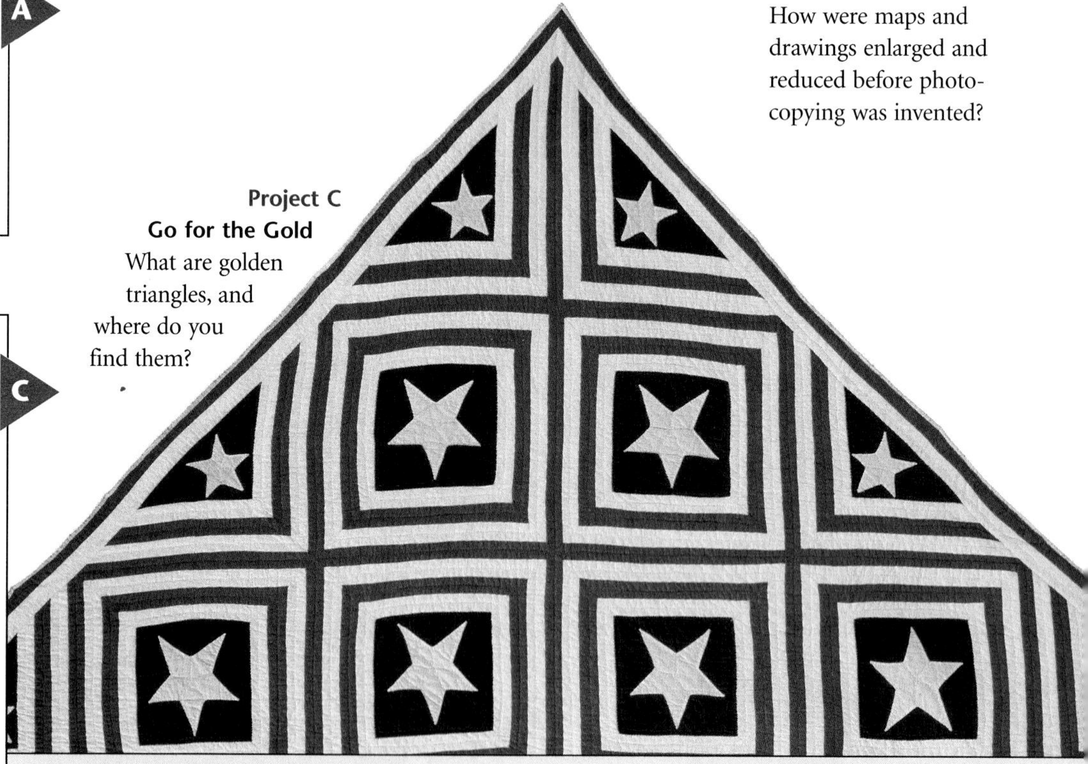

Project C
Go for the Gold
What are golden triangles, and where do you find them?

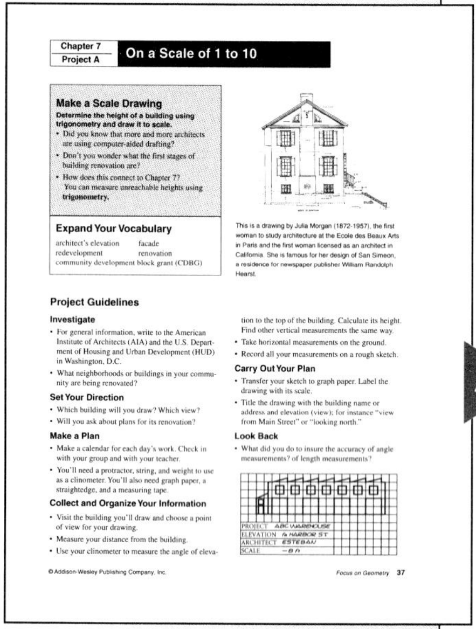

A

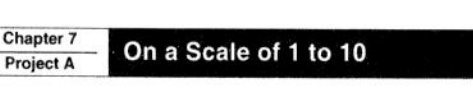

Chapter 7 | Project A — **On a Scale of 1 to 10**

Make a Scale Drawing
Determine the height of a building using trigonometry and draw it to scale.
- Did you know that more and more architects are using computer-aided drafting?
- Don't you wonder what the first stages of building renovation are?
- How does this connect to Chapter 7? You can measure unreachable heights using **trigonometry.**

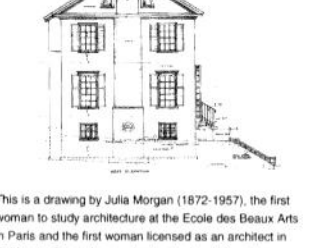

This is a drawing by Julia Morgan (1872-1957), the first woman to study architecture at the Ecole des Beaux Arts in Paris and the first woman licensed as an architect in California. She is famous for her design of San Simeon, a residence for newspaper publisher William Randolph Hearst.

Expand Your Vocabulary
architect's elevation, facade, redevelopment, renovation, community development block grant (CDBG)

Project Guidelines

Investigate
- For general information, write to the American Institute of Architects (AIA) and the U.S. Department of Housing and Urban Development (HUD) in Washington, D.C.
- What neighborhoods or buildings in your community are being renovated?

Set Your Direction
- Which building will you draw? Which view?
- Will you ask about plans for its renovation?

Make a Plan
- Make a calendar for each day's work. Check in with your group and with your teacher.
- You'll need a protractor, string, and weight to use as a clinometer. You'll also need graph paper, a straightedge, and a measuring tape.

Collect and Organize Your Information
- Visit the building you'll draw and choose a point of view for your drawing.
- Measure your distance from the building.
- Use your clinometer to measure the angle of elevation to the top of the building. Calculate its height. Find other vertical measurements the same way.
- Take horizontal measurements on the ground.
- Record all your measurements on a rough sketch.

Carry Out Your Plan
- Transfer your sketch to graph paper. Label the drawing with its scale.
- Title the drawing with the building name or address and elevation (view); for instance "view from Main Street" or "looking north."

Look Back
- What did you do to insure the accuracy of angle measurements? of length measurements?

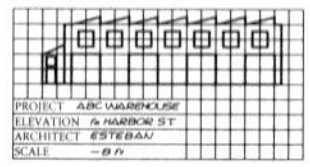

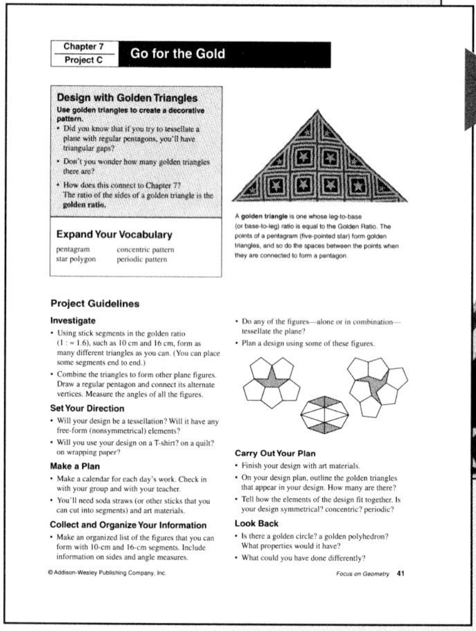

C

Chapter 7 | Project C — **Go for the Gold**

Design with Golden Triangles
Use golden triangles to create a decorative pattern.
- Did you know that if you try to tessellate a plane with regular pentagons, you'll have triangular gaps?
- Don't you wonder how many golden triangles there are?
- How does this connect to Chapter 7? The ratio of the sides of a golden triangle is the **golden ratio.**

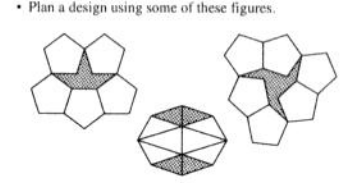

A **golden triangle** is one whose leg-to-base (or base-to-leg) ratio is equal to the Golden Ratio. The points of a pentagram (five-pointed star) form golden triangles, and so do the spaces between the points when they are connected to form a pentagon.

Expand Your Vocabulary
pentagram, concentric pattern, star polygon, periodic pattern

Project Guidelines

Investigate
- Using stick segments in the golden ratio (1 : ≈ 1.6), such as 10 cm and 16 cm, form as many different triangles as you can. (You can place some segments end to end.)
- Combine the triangles to form other plane figures. Draw a regular pentagon and connect its alternate vertices. Measure the angles of all the figures.
- Do any of the figures—alone or in combination—tessellate the plane?
- Plan a design using some of these figures.

Set Your Direction
- Will your design be a tessellation? Will it have any free-form (nonsymmetrical) elements?
- Will you use your design on a T-shirt? on a quilt? on wrapping paper?

Make a Plan
- Make a calendar for each day's work. Check in with your group and with your teacher.
- You'll need soda straws (or other sticks that you can cut into segments) and art materials.

Collect and Organize Your Information
- Make an organized list of the figures that you can form with 10-cm and 16-cm segments. Include information on sides and angle measures.

Carry Out Your Plan
- Finish your design with art materials.
- On your design plan, outline the golden triangles that appear in your design. How many are there?
- Tell how the elements of the design fit together. Is your design symmetrical? concentric? periodic?

Look Back
- Is there a golden circle? a golden polyhedron? What properties would it have?
- What could you have done differently?

Chapter 7
Project B

Do You Copy?

Make Your Own Pantograph

Construct a mechanical device for enlarging and reducing maps or drawings.

- Did you know that modern electrostatic photocopying was invented in 1938?
- Don't you wonder how maps and drawings were enlarged or reduced before photocopying was available?
- How does this connect to Chapter 7? Pantographs use **similar triangles** to enlarge or reduce designs.

Expand Your Vocabulary

pantograph	pivot	reprographics
tracer pointcalibrate		graduated scale
xerography	photostat	electrostatic

What other objects have you seen that work on the same mechanical idea—a set of hinged sticks or rods? What functions do they have? Are similar triangles involved?

Project Guidelines

Investigate

- Read about pantographs in a math dictionary.
- Read about photocopying in an encyclopedia.

Set Your Direction

- Choose a simple design to reduce or enlarge.

Make a Plan

- Make a calendar for each day's work. Check in with your group and with your teacher.
- You'll need:

2 small rubber bands		2 short pencils
4 1-ft strips of cardboard		3 paper fasteners
craft knife	push-pin	drawing paper

Collect and Organize Your Information

- Loosely fasten the "arms" at the intersections as shown. Pin the end of one arm to a safe surface (like a bulletin board laid flat) so that it pivots. Set pencils at two endpoints.
- Trace your design with one pencil, letting the other draw freely. Compare the sizes of the drawings.
- Diagram the arm positions in relation to the drawings at a few points. Look for relationships.
- Which pencil is the tracer point if you want to enlarge? If you want to reduce?

Carry Out Your Plan

- Refine your device by calibrating the arms for easy readjustment.
- Use your diagrams to explain how the pantograph relies on similar triangles.
- Tell how to make a drawing half the size and how to make one twice the size of the original.

Look Back

- How would you adjust your pantograph to reduce or enlarge a drawing by a factor of 3?
- What could you have done differently?

Focus on Geometry 39

SUSAN HELMAN-BRADFORD

I enjoyed algebra and trig in high school, but advanced math and physics were hard for me.

I was interested in art and engineering, and found both in architecture. I didn't realize the extent to which math is used in this field. I use math every day to calculate square footage, estimate structural loads, create detailed drawings for construction, and develop construction estimates. Math will always be a standard part of life, no matter what your work or lifestyle.

Susan Helman-Bradford
Designer and Computer Drafter
Helman/Bradford
Napa, CA

Biographical Note

Susan Helman-Bradford graduated from St. Helena High School in St. Helena, CA. She took Algebra I and II, Trigonometry, and Advanced Math.

Chapter 7

Overview

Similarity

7-1 Similar Figures

The use of similar figures is important in many careers, including engineering and the arts. You will develop a more precise definition of similarity and use this concept to solve problems.

7-2 Properties of Similar Figures

The special characteristics of similar figures are important in architecture and other professions. You will investigate ways to show that triangles are similar, and also investigate a new transformation—the dilation—and see how it is related to similarity.

7-3 Trigonometry

The relationships between the sides and angles of similar right triangles are useful in many fields, including astronomy, surveying, and engineering. These relationships are so important that the subject is given a special name–trigonometry. You will use trigonometry to find unknown side lengths and angle measures in right triangles.

CHAPTERS

Chapter 7 Planning Guide

The following ancillaries are recommended for each course level. The additional resources, *Technology Lab Manual, Study Guide and Journal, Multilingual Handbook,* and *Assessment,* are recommended for all levels.

	Comprehensive Course	Core Course	Informal Course
7-1 Part A	▲	▲	▲
Alternative Lessons			▲
Laboratory Manuals	▲	▲	▲
Practice			▲
More Look Ahead		▲	▲
7-1 Part B	▲	▲	▲
Alternative Lessons			▲
Laboratory Manuals	▲	▲	▲
Practice			▲
More Look Back		▲	▲
7-1 Part C	▲	▲	▲
Alternative Lessons			▲
Laboratory Manuals	▲	▲	▲
Practice			▲
More Look Ahead		▲	▲
7-1 Part D	▲	▲	▲
Alternative Lessons			▲
Laboratory Manuals	▲	▲	▲
Practice			▲
More Look Back		▲	▲
7-1 Part E	▲	▲	▲
More Look Back		▲	▲
Quiz 7-1	▲	▲	▲
7-2 Part A	▲	▲	▲
Alternative Lessons			▲
Laboratory Manuals	▲	▲	▲
Practice			▲
More Look Back		▲	▲
7-2 Part B	▲	▲	▲
Alternative Lessons			▲
Laboratory Manuals	▲	▲	▲
Practice			▲
More Look Ahead		▲	▲
7-2 Part C	▲	▲	▲
Alternative Lessons			▲
Laboratory Manuals	▲	▲	▲
Practice			▲
More Look Back		▲	▲
7-2 Part D	▲	▲	
Alternative Lessons			
Laboratory Manuals	▲	▲	
Practice			
More Look Ahead		▲	
7-2 Part E	▲	▲	▲
More Look Back		▲	▲
Quiz 7-2	▲	▲	▲
7-3 Part A	▲	▲	▲
Alternative Lessons			▲
Laboratory Manuals	▲	▲	▲
Practice			▲
More Look Back		▲	▲
7-3 Part B	▲	▲	▲
Alternative Lessons			▲
Laboratory Manuals	▲	▲	▲
Practice			▲
More Look Ahead		▲	▲
7-3 Part C	▲	▲	
Alternative Lessons			
Laboratory Manuals	▲	▲	
Practice			
More Look Back		▲	
7-3 Part D	▲	▲	▲
More Look Back		▲	▲
Quiz 7-3	▲	▲	▲

BIBLIOGRAPHY

Teacher Resources

Math Motivators! Investigations in Geometry, Alfred Posamentier and Gordon Sheridan. Addison-Wesley, 1982 (05583).

Mathematics Appreciation, Theoni Pappas. © 1986 by Theoni Pappas/Math Aids.

Videos

Similarity, Project Mathematics!—California Institute of Technology. Available through Dale Seymour Publications (NS22386).

7-1

Similar Figures

SUPERLESSON AT A GLANCE

Superlesson Goal

Students will explore scale factors and learn about similar figures and the ratios of their areas and perimeters.

Management Guide

	Topic	Objectives	Key Terms	New Ideas	Materials
Part A	Changing the Size of Figures	To explore scale factors and develop a formal definition of similar figures.	Enlargement, reduction, similar, scale factor, similarity ratio	Scale factor, similarity ratio. Similar polygons have congruent angles and proportional side lengths.	**Student** Graph paper **Teacher** Graph paper transparency
Part B	Similar Polygons	To use proportions to find side lengths of similar figures.		Similarity correspondence. Writing proportions involving sides of similar figures.	**Student** Ruler
Part C	Areas and Perimeters of Similar Polygons	To discover a relationship between area and perimeter ratios of similar figures and their similarity ratio.		The ratio of the perimeters of similar figures is equal to their similarity ratio. The ratio of the areas of similar figures is equal to the square of their similarity ratios.	**Student** Ruler
Part D	Golden Rectangles	To determine a numerical value for the golden ratio.	Golden rectangle, golden ratio	The golden ratio and its algebraic definition.	**Student** Ruler
Part E	Making Connections	To use similarity to investigate the models used in the making of *King Kong.*	In Making Connections, students apply and synthesize key terms and new ideas.		**Student** Tape measure

Pacing Chart (45-Minute Periods)

	Comprehensive Course	Core Course	Informal Course
Part A	1	1	1
Part B	1	1	2
Part C	1	1	2
Part D	1	1	2
Part E	1	1	1
TOTAL periods for Superlesson	5	5	8

NCTM Standards

Mathematics as Problem Solving

Mathematics as Communication

Mathematics as Reasoning

Mathematical Connections

Geometry from a Synthetic Perspective

7-1 Similar Figures
FROM SILVER SCREEN TO GOLDEN RATIO

Advertisements for the 1933 film *King Kong* claimed that the movie "out-thrilled the wildest thrills!" The film was one of the first in which small models were used to give the illusion of an enormous monster. Marcel Delgado, an animator who worked on the film, wrote about his work in *King Kong and Me.*

"I made the two full-body models used in *King Kong*. Both models were 18 inches high, which is $\frac{3}{4}$ inch to the foot ...The skeletons of the limbs were made in the studio machine shops and I covered them with muscles and fur. The full-sized arm and hand had to be large enough to hold Fay Wray..."

Actress Fay Wray, best known for struggling in King Kong's hand as he stood on top of the Empire State Building, described her experiences in *The New York Times.*

"Then I saw the figure of Kong. He was in a miniature jungle habitat, and was less than 2 feet tall! It was only the great furry paw, in which I would spend much of the next ten months, that was absolutely enormous...the hand and arm in which my close-up scenes were made was about 8 feet in length."

1. Name three other films in which small models might have been used to represent large creatures or objects.

2. What do you think Marcel Delgado meant when he described his model as $\frac{3}{4}$ inch to the foot?

3. Describe a situation for which you might need to make a model of something that is very large or very small. What advantages would the model have over the actual object?

461

Where Are We Now?

Students are probably familiar with ratio and proportion from earlier courses. In Chapter 4, they became familiar with triangle-congruence correspondences; in Chapter 5, they explored area and perimeter; and in Chapter 6, they investigated polygons. All of these concepts will be important in 7-1.

Where Are We Going?

In 7-1, students will see the definition of similarity and find side lengths, perimeters, and areas of similar figures. In 7-2, students will call on their understanding of similarity as they do proofs involving similarity and explore dilations.

Possible Answers

1. *Godzilla, Star Trek,* etc. (In recent films, computer simulation has become more important than the use of scale models.)
2. Every $\frac{3}{4}$ of an inch on the model represented one foot on the "actual" King Kong.
3. The model would be easier to manipulate; models of small objects enable you to see things without the help of a microscope; models of large objects enable you to see the entire object at once.

More About Using Models in Movies

The popular *Star Wars* movies used models in many of their special-effects scenes. Nearly 50 models were used in the making of *Star Wars.* To film the second *Star Wars* movie, *The Empire Strikes Back,* about 100 additional models were needed, and for the third, *The Return of the Jedi,* 160 more were required. To make a stationary model appear to move against a background, the camera filming the scene is moved past the model.

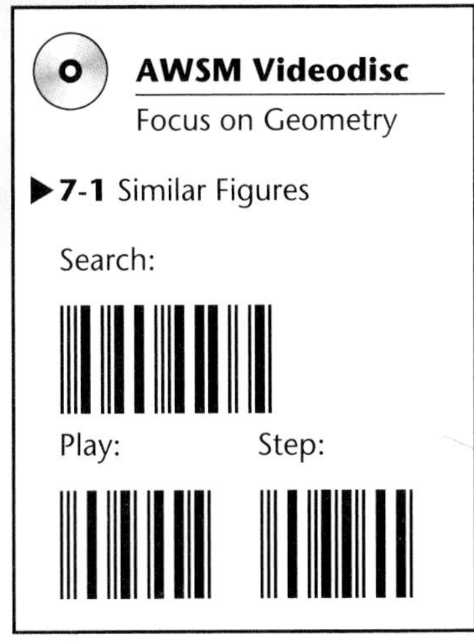

7-1

Similar Figures

Algebra	Functions	Discrete Math	Probability	Data/Statistics

PART A At a Glance

Objective
To explore scale factors and develop a formal definition of similar figures.

Development
First, students develop an intuitive feeling for similar figures and scale factor.

In the **Explore,** they call on this understanding to draw enlargements and reductions of figures. By measuring corresponding parts, they come to a formal definition of similar figures.

Suggested Materials
Student Graph paper

Teacher Graph paper transparency

Key Terms
Enlargement, reduction, similar, scale factor, similarity ratio

First Five Minutes
Transparency FFM 7-1A

Determine whether each pair of fractions is equal or unequal.

1. $\frac{2}{4}, \frac{31}{62}$ Equal
2. $\frac{12}{14}, \frac{16}{18}$ Unequal
3. $\frac{25}{30}, \frac{45}{54}$ Equal
4. $\frac{10}{8}, \frac{32}{40}$ Unequal

Motivate
Ask...

- List as many familiar objects as you can that use a length *scale* or *scale factor.* Maps, dollhouse/model railroad items, diagrams of automobiles, etc.

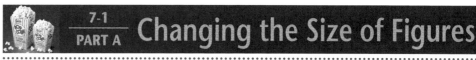

7-1 PART A Changing the Size of Figures

← CONNECT → ***You've seen maps as scaled-down models of cities and countries. Now you will see what happens to the sides and angles of figures when you enlarge or shrink them.***

In everyday conversation, we say two things are *similar* when we mean they are alike in some way. In mathematics, **similar** figures have the same shape but not necessarily the same size. Photographs, dollhouse furniture, and building plans are all mathematically similar versions of real objects.

These pairs of figures are similar. They have the same shape but not the same size.

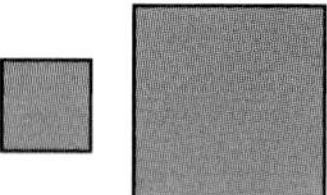 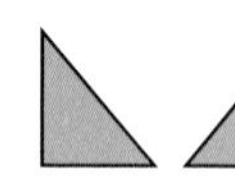 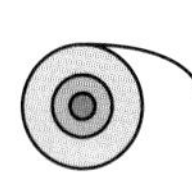 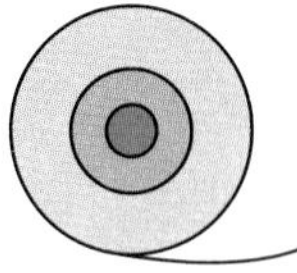

These pairs of figures are not similar. None of the paired figures have the same shape.

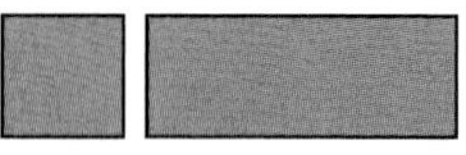 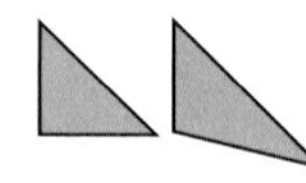 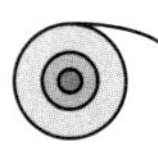 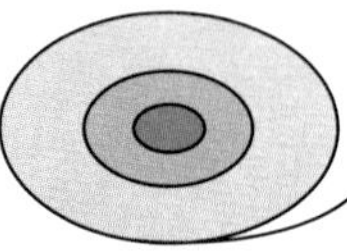

You may have noticed that similar figures are enlargements or reductions of each other. When two figures are similar, the amount of enlargement or reduction needed to get one figure from the other is called the **scale factor.** To find the dimensions of the enlarged or reduced figure, you multiply the dimensions of the original figure by the scale factor.

If the scale factor (s) is greater than 1, the similar figure is an **enlargement;** if the scale factor is less than 1, it is a **reduction.**

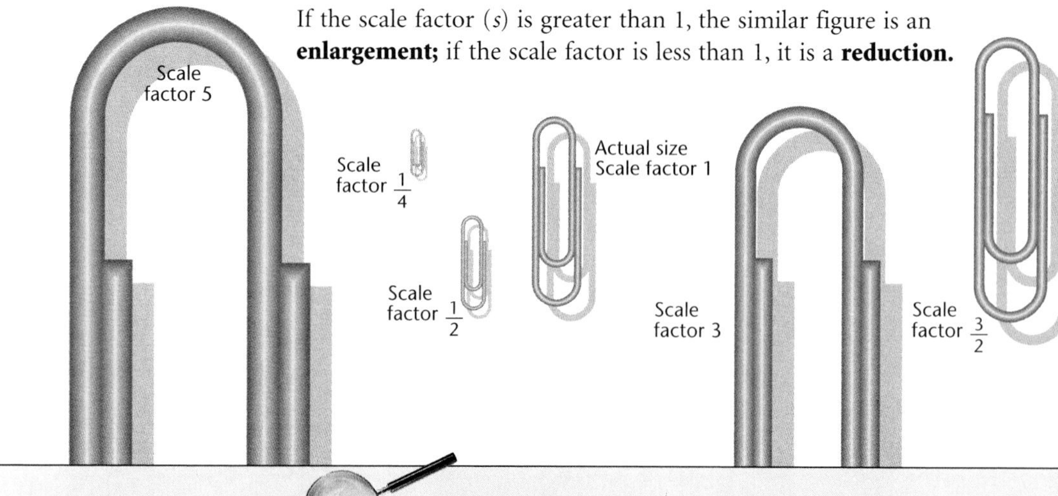

Research Note

Very few secondary students use typical textbook generalizations to solve proportion problems. Rather, they use less formal strategies that vary with the task.... (Linda C. Fisher, "Strategies Used by Secondary Mathematics Teachers to Solve Proportion Problems," *Journal for Research in Mathematics Education,* Sept. 1988, Vol. 19, No. 2, p. 157. © 1988 NCTM.)

EXPLORE: HUMAN PHOTOCOPY MACHINE

MATERIALS

Graph paper

Use graph paper to enlarge or reduce each figure to create a similar figure.

1. Enlarge side lengths by a factor of 3.
2. Reduce side lengths by a factor of $\frac{1}{2}$.

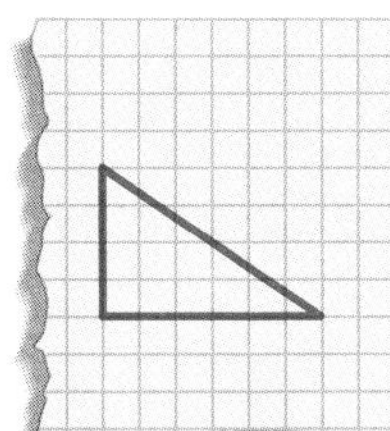

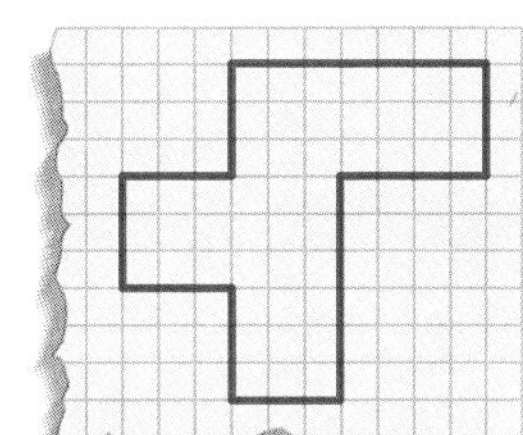

3. Choose a side in one of the original figures, and identify the corresponding side in your enlarged or reduced version. Find the ratio of the lengths of the sides. Is this ratio the same for any two corresponding sides of the figures?
4. Find pairs of corresponding angles and measure them. How do the corresponding angles compare?
5. Write a definition of similar figures based on your observations. Compare your definition with those of your classmates.

The ratio of the lengths of two corresponding sides of similar figures is the **similarity ratio.**

EXAMPLES

$\triangle ABC$ is similar to $\triangle XYZ$.

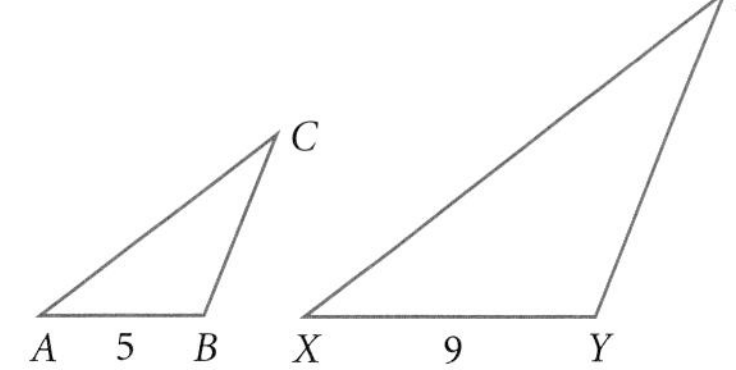

1. Find the similarity ratio of $\triangle ABC$ to $\triangle XYZ$.
   The similarity ratio of $\triangle ABC$ to $\triangle XYZ = \frac{AB}{XY} = \frac{5}{9}$.
2. Find the similarity ratio of $\triangle XYZ$ to $\triangle ABC$.
   The similarity ratio of $\triangle XYZ$ to $\triangle ABC = \frac{XY}{AB} = \frac{9}{5}$.

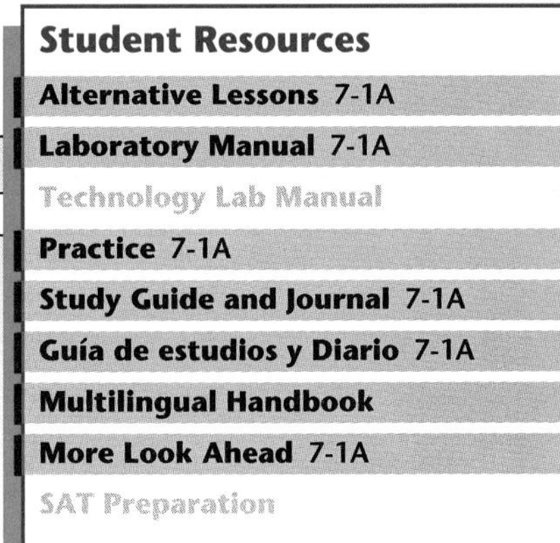

Student Resources
- Alternative Lessons 7-1A
- Laboratory Manual 7-1A
- Technology Lab Manual
- Practice 7-1A
- Study Guide and Journal 7-1A
- Guía de estudios y Diario 7-1A
- Multilingual Handbook
- More Look Ahead 7-1A
- SAT Preparation

Media Resources
- Transparency FFM 7-1A
- Transparency AE 7-1A
- Teaching Transparency
- AWSMTest and practice software
- AWSM Videodisc

EXPLORE

Human Photocopy Machine

Recommended group size: 4

The Point

To write a formal definition of similar figures.

Look and Listen...

- For students who do not see that the lengths of corresponding sides are proportional.

Ask...

- Have you reduced the side length ratios to lowest terms?

For Groups That Finish Early

Use your compass to draw a circle. How could you draw a second circle that is enlarged by a scale factor of 2? **Double the radius.**

Follow Up

Ask students to share their definitions of similar figures. Have the class come to a consensus on one definition before proceeding.

Possible Answers

3. The ratio is the same for any two corresponding sides.
4. Corresponding angles are congruent.
5. Similar figures have congruent corresponding angles and proportional corresponding side lengths.

Similar Figures

ALTERNATE EXAMPLES

$\triangle FGH$ is similar to $\triangle LMN$.

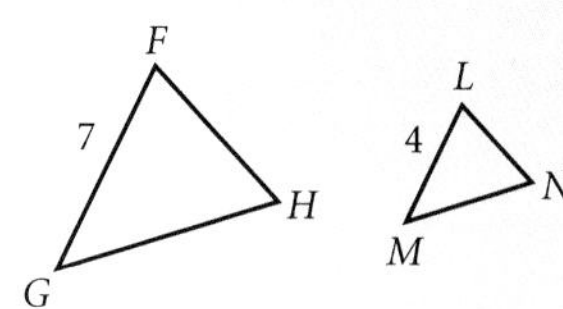

1. Find the similarity ratio of $\triangle FGH$ to $\triangle LMN$.

The similarity ratio of $\triangle FGH$ to $\triangle LMN = \frac{FG}{LM} = \frac{7}{4}$.

2. Find the similarity ratio of $\triangle LMN$ to $\triangle FGH$.

The similarity ratio of $\triangle LMN$ to $\triangle FGH = \frac{LM}{FG} = \frac{4}{7}$.

Shows that the scale factor and the similarity ratio for two similar figures are reciprocals.

Possible Answers

1. $\frac{1}{s}$

2. The similarity ratio is the ratio of the lengths of two corresponding sides. If the similarity ratio of Figure A to Figure B is 2 to 1, the side lengths in B are *half* those in A. The scale factor is the number you multiply the side lengths of one figure by to create a second similar figure. If the scale factor from Figure A to Figure B is 2, the side lengths in B are *twice* those in A.

TRY IT

State whether or not each pair of figures is similar. For each pair of similar figures, find the similarity ratio of the figure on the left to the figure on the right.

a. Similar; $\frac{1}{2}$

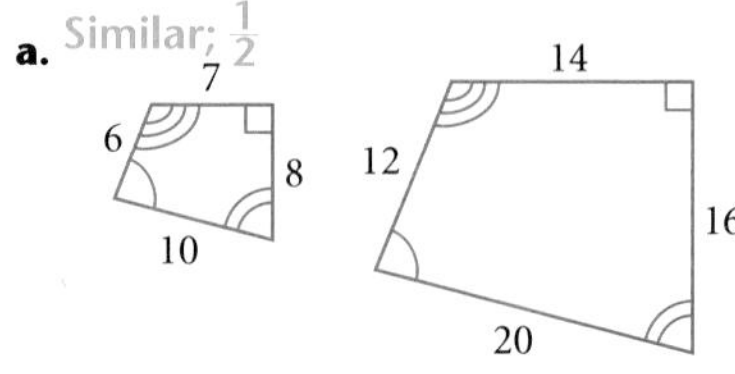

b. Similar; 3

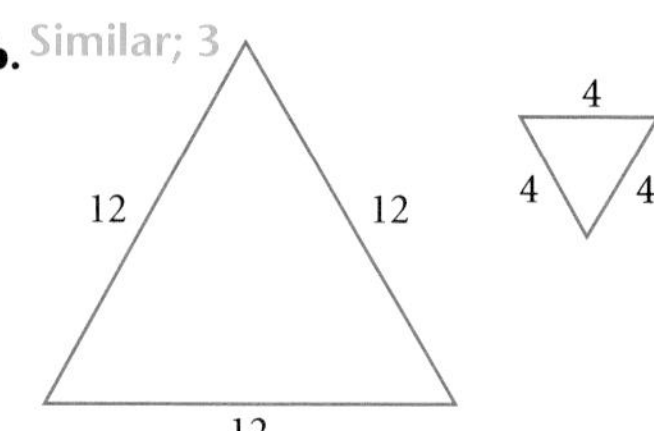

c. Not similar

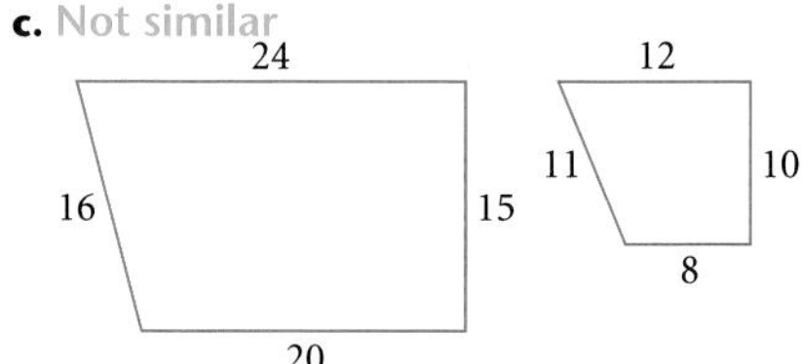

d. Similar; $\frac{1}{3}$

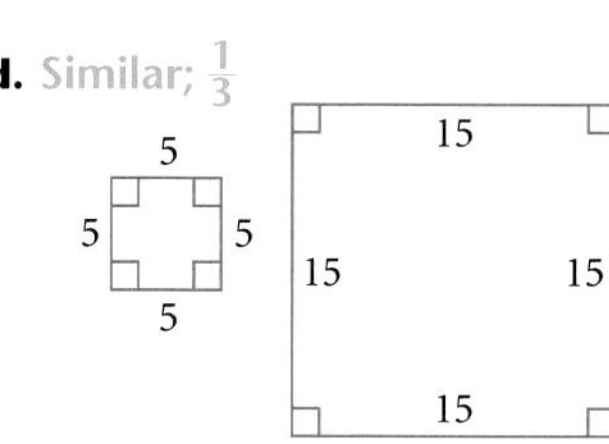

1. Suppose you enlarge Figure A by a scale factor of s to create Figure B. What is the similarity ratio of Figure A to Figure B?

2. Explain the difference between *similarity ratio* and *scale factor.*

The properties of similar figures that you've investigated are summarized in the following definition.

DEFINITION

Two polygons are **similar** if and only if (1) their corresponding angles are congruent and (2) their corresponding side lengths are proportional.

Diversity Issues

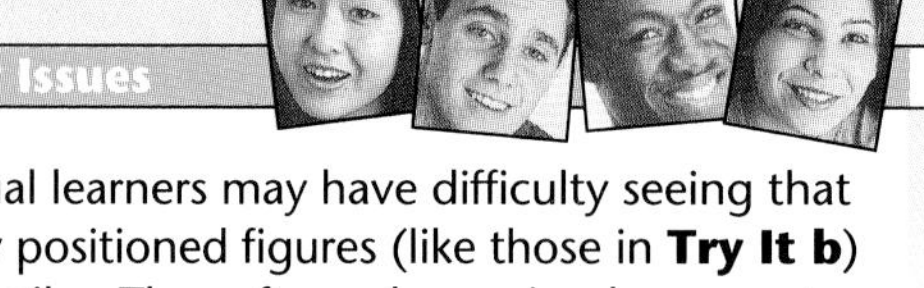

Some visual learners may have difficulty seeing that differently positioned figures (like those in **Try It b**) may be similar. They often rely on visual cues, not side proportionality, to determine similarity. You might have them trace and cut out the figures and then flip or rotate them until they can see the similarity.

REFLECT

1. Suppose you enlarge or reduce a figure to make a similar figure.
   a. What happens to the measure of each of the angles?
   b. What happens to the length of each line segment?
2. If Figure X is similar to Figure Y, how is the similarity ratio from X to Y related to the similarity ratio from Y to X?

Exercises

CORE

1. **Getting Started** Estimate the scale factor of the photograph on the left to the photograph on the right. 2

Sketch each figure on graph paper. Then draw a similar figure, using the given scale factor.

2. scale factor of 3

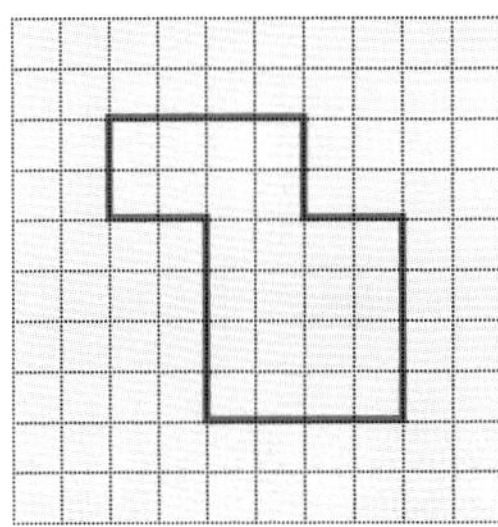

3. scale factor of $\frac{1}{2}$

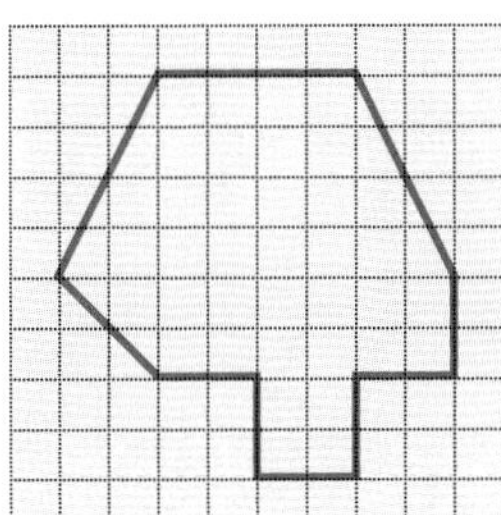

4. If you reduce a 15-cm × 20-cm rectangle by using a scale factor of $\frac{3}{5}$, what will the dimensions of the reduced rectangle be? 9 cm × 12 cm

5. If you enlarge a 9-in. × 12-in. drawing by using a scale factor of 2.5, what will its new dimensions be? 22.5 in. × 30 in.

Ongoing Assessment

Vocabulary
Practice/Skills
Review
Math Reasoning
Problem Solving
Challenge

Self-Assessment Exercises 1, 5–9 odd, 10, 13, 15

Embedded Assessment Try It d; Exercises 2, 4, 14, 16

Note: Students may need frequent reminders of the difference between *scale factor* and *similarity ratio.* It may help them to see that a scale factor is usually used to create a similar figure from a given figure, while a similarity ratio generally expresses a relationship between two existing figures.

Journal 

Explore 5, **Consider** 2, and **Reflect** 1 are suitable for journal entries.

REFLECT

Possible Answers

1. a. The angle measures stay the same.
   b. The side lengths are multiplied by the scale factor.
2. They are reciprocals of each other.

Part A Exercises

Exercise Notes

Core

10–11. The scale factor is seen in a real-world context. Exercise 11 asks students to do a composition of reductions; this previews compositions of transformations in Chapter 10.

17. Students must enlarge one object and reduce another so that the resulting figures are approximately the same size.

Look Ahead

These exercises review solving proportions. This is an important skill in 7-1 Parts B and C when students do calculations involving side lengths of similar figures.

Exercise Answers

Core

2.

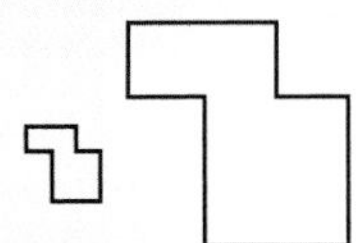

3.

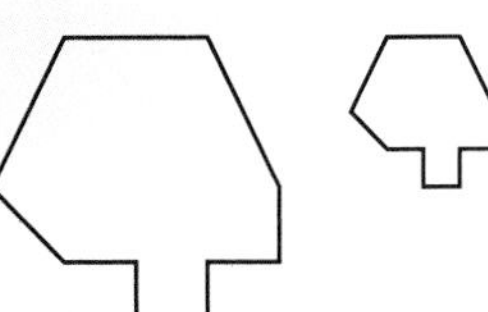

Similar Figures

6. T; All angles are 90° (therefore congruent) and all sides, being equal in length, are the same multiple of the original figure's sides.

7. F; The ratio of the lengths of the two rectangles may be different from the ratio of their widths.

8. F; The sides remain in proportion, but the angles can be changed.

9. T; All angles are 60° (therefore congruent) and all the sides, being equal in length, must be the same multiple of the original triangle's sides.

10. Smallest: 2.6 cm × 3.9 cm
Largest: 5.6 cm × 8.4 cm

11. Possible answer: Run the image through the photocopier 4 times on 67%.

17. Possible answer: The airport dimensions (in inches) must be reduced by a scale factor of 3168 and the amoeba dimensions must be increased by a scale factor of 666.67 so that each sketch fits in a 5 in. vertical space.

More Practice

23.

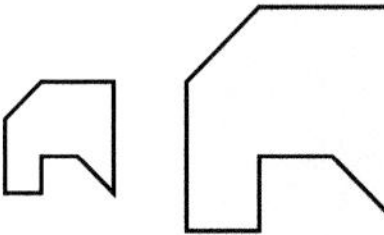

24.

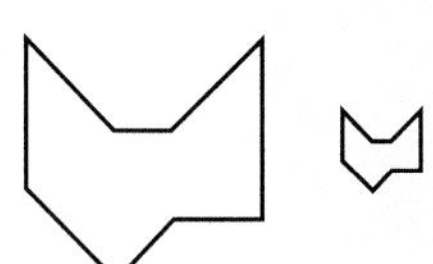

More Math Reasoning

28. $\triangle AFG$: 1, 1, $\sqrt{2}$
$\triangle AKC$: 2, 2, $2\sqrt{2}$
$\triangle ADP$: 3, 3, $3\sqrt{2}$
$\triangle AEU$: 4, 4, $4\sqrt{2}$
$\triangle AUM$: $2\sqrt{2}$, $2\sqrt{2}$, 4
$\triangle AIL$: $\sqrt{5}$, $\sqrt{5}$, $\sqrt{10}$
$\triangle AIW$: $\sqrt{10}$, $\sqrt{10}$, $2\sqrt{5}$

P **Determine whether each statement is true or false. Give reasons to support your answers.**

6. Any two squares are similar.

7. Any two rectangles are similar.

8. Any two rhombuses are similar.

9. Any two equilateral triangles are similar.

PS **Suppose a copy machine can make an image whose dimensions are 65% to 140% of the size of the original picture.**

10. If you have a 4-cm × 6-cm picture, what are the smallest and largest dimensions of a copy that you can make on one run through the machine?

11. How could you use this machine to create a reduction whose dimensions are approximately 20% of the original?

P **Each pair of figures is similar, and the lengths of corresponding sides are shown. Find the similarity ratio of Figure A to B and of Figure B to A.**

12.

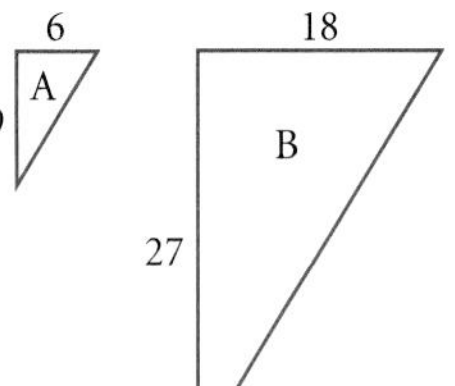

A to B = $\frac{1}{3}$; B to A = 3

13. A to B = $\frac{3}{2}$; B to A = $\frac{2}{3}$

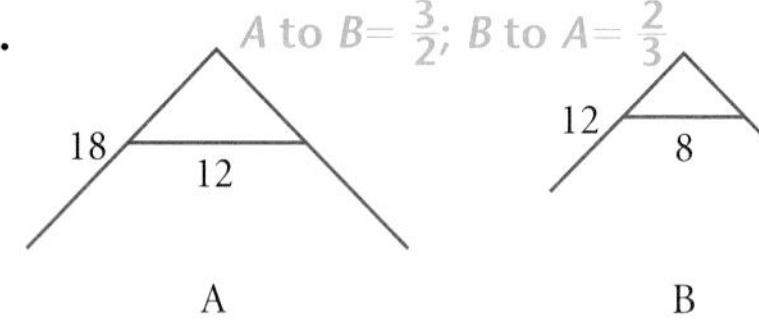

P **State whether or not each pair of figures is similar. If the figures are similar, find the similarity ratio of the figure on the left to the figure on the right. If the figures are not similar, explain why they are not similar.**

14.

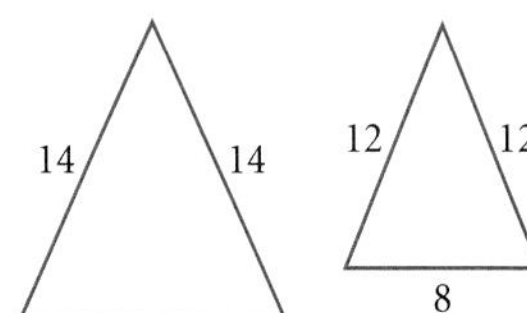

Not similar; Sets of corresponding sides do not have the same similarity ratio.

15.

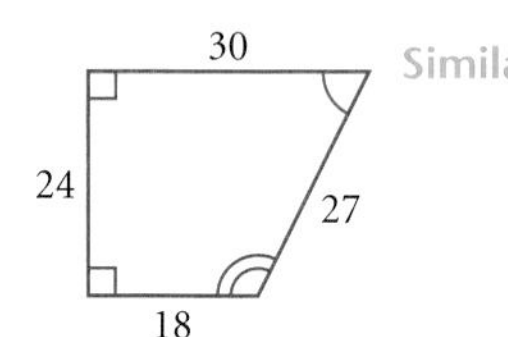

Similar;

P **16. Say Cheese** School pictures are offered in sizes of $2\frac{1}{2}$ in. × $3\frac{1}{2}$ in., $3\frac{1}{2}$ in. × 5 in., 4 in. × 6 in., 5 in. × 7 in., and 8 in. × 10 in. Which sizes are similar? Since the scale factor from $2\frac{1}{2}$ in. × $3\frac{1}{2}$ in. to 5 in. × 7 in. is 2, these picture sizes are similar.

Key

V Vocabulary
P Practice/Skills
R Review
MR Math Reasoning
PS Problem Solving
C Challenge

17. **Amoeba Attacks Airport!** Yvette is drawing scenes from a movie she is writing *(The Amoeba That Ate Altabula)*. She must show both an amoeba and the Altabula Airport on one $8\frac{1}{2}'' \times 11''$ sheet of paper. The actual airport is 2 mi wide and 3 mi long; an amoeba is 0.005 in. wide and 0.0075 in. long. What scale factors should she use for each so that sketches of both will fit on the paper and appear to have approximately the same size?

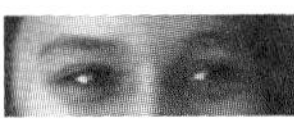

LOOK AHEAD

Solve each proportion.

18. $\frac{x}{8} = \frac{10}{16}$ 5

19. $\frac{8}{12} = \frac{6}{y}$ 9

20. $\frac{CD}{12} = \frac{7}{28}$ 3

21. $\frac{2}{EF} = \frac{5}{6}$ $2\frac{2}{5}$

22. A recipe that serves four people calls for two and one-half cups of flour. If you need to serve dinner to six people, how many cups of flour should you use in the adjusted recipe? $3\frac{3}{4}$ cups of flour

MORE PRACTICE

Sketch each figure on graph paper. Then draw a similar figure, using the given scale factor.

23. scale factor of 2

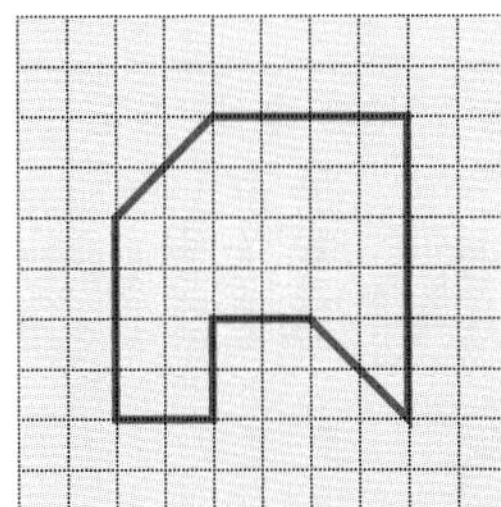

24. scale factor of $\frac{1}{3}$

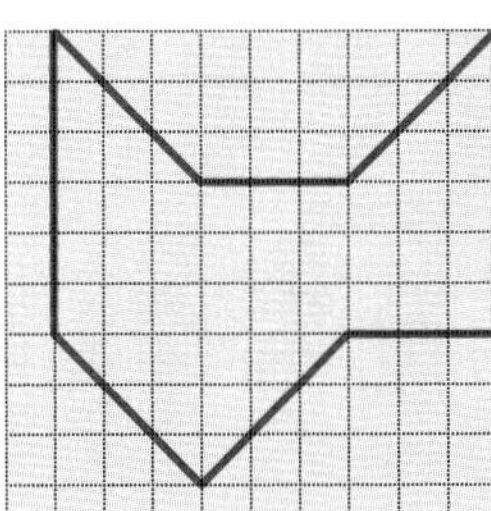

State whether or not each pair of figures is similar. If the figures are similar, find the similarity ratio of the figure on the left to the figure on the right. If the figures are not similar, explain why they are not similar.

25.

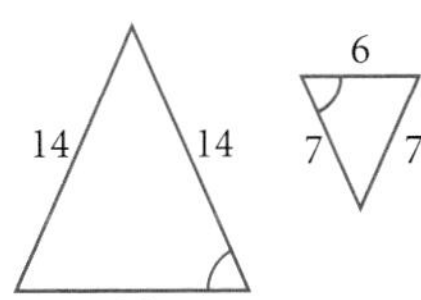

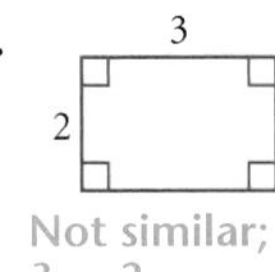

Similar; Similarity ratio = $\frac{2}{1}$

26.

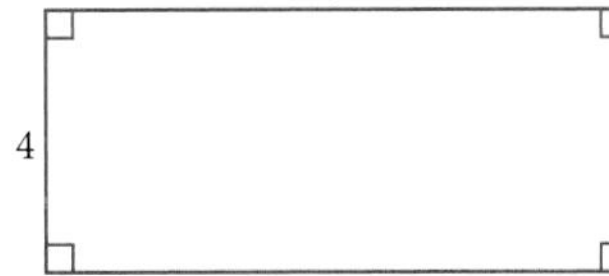

Not similar; $\frac{3}{9} \neq \frac{2}{4}$

27. A newspaper asked the P.T.A. to reduce its 12-cm × 18-cm advertisement by a scale factor of $\frac{2}{3}$. What are the dimensions of the reduced ad? 8 cm × 12 cm

PART B At a Glance

Objective

To use proportions to find side lengths of similar figures.

Development

In the **Explore,** students use a scale factor to find side lengths of actual structures similar to those shown on a map.

Then, in **What Do You Think?** students see how to use similarity statements to solve for missing side lengths of similar figures.

Suggested Materials

Student Ruler

First Five Minutes

Transparency FFM 7-1B

Read the material on page 468 through the **Example.** Then do **Try It a** and **b.**

Motivate

Ask...

- How does the congruence statement identify corresponding parts for two congruent triangles? **The order of the vertices shows the correspondence.**

ALTERNATE EXAMPLE

FGHK ~ *RSTV*. Name all pairs of congruent corresponding angles, and write proportions, using the pairs of corresponding sides.

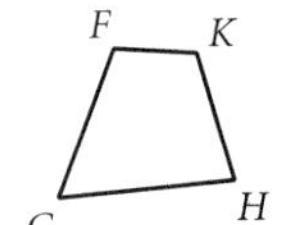

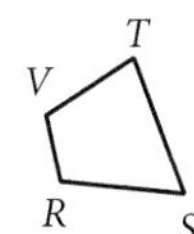

Angles: $\angle F \cong \angle R$, $\angle G \cong \angle S$, $\angle H \cong \angle T$, $\angle K \cong \angle V$

Side lengths: $\frac{FG}{RS} = \frac{GH}{ST} = \frac{HK}{TV} = \frac{KF}{VR}$

MORE MATH REASONING

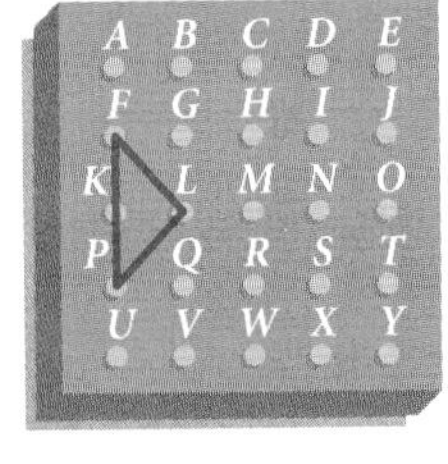

MR, C **28.** There are seven different sizes of triangles that are similar to $\triangle FPL$ with vertices at grid points, not including triangles congruent to $\triangle FPL$. For each size, name one triangle of that size, and give the lengths of its sides. (Use $AB = 1$ unit.)

PS **29. Reduce to Fit** An advertiser purchased a half-page ad (eleven inches by seventeen inches) in a school newspaper. They sent a fifteen-inch by twenty-inch poster and asked to have it reduced to fit the half-page. The newspaper ad must be similar to the poster. What are the dimensions of the ad that will take up the largest possible space on the half-page? 11 in. × 14.67 in.

7-1 PART B Similar Polygons

← CONNECT → ***You know how to work with proportions algebraically, and you've seen that the lengths of the corresponding sides of similar polygons are proportional. Now you will use proportions to work with similar polygons.***

If the makers of this souvenir had not used the concept of similarity, they would have had to place a snow-filled dome over the Guggenheim Museum in New York. Similarity and proportionality allow people to cut buildings and movie monsters down to size.

The symbol ~ means "is similar to." If pentagons *ABCDE* and *MNOPQ* are similar, we write *ABCDE* ~ *MNOPQ*. The order of the letters in the similarity correspondence indicates the corresponding parts.

EXAMPLE

ABCDE ~ *MNOPQ*. Name all pairs of congruent corresponding angles, and write proportions using the pairs of corresponding sides.

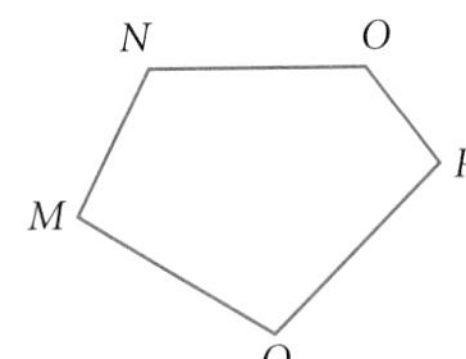

Angles: $\angle A \cong \angle M$, $\angle B \cong \angle N$, $\angle C \cong \angle O$, $\angle D \cong \angle P$, $\angle E \cong \angle Q$

Side lengths: $\frac{AB}{MN} = \frac{BC}{NO} = \frac{CD}{OP} = \frac{DE}{PQ} = \frac{EA}{QM}$

Key

- V Vocabulary
- P Practice/Skills
- R Review
- MR Math Reasoning
- PS Problem Solving
- C Challenge

Alert

Students may be confused by the notation "1 cm = 1500 km" in the *Explore* on page 469 since these quantities are obviously not equal. You may wish to explain to them that, in this context, this means that 1 cm on the map corresponds to 1500 km on the actual region it represents.

TRY IT

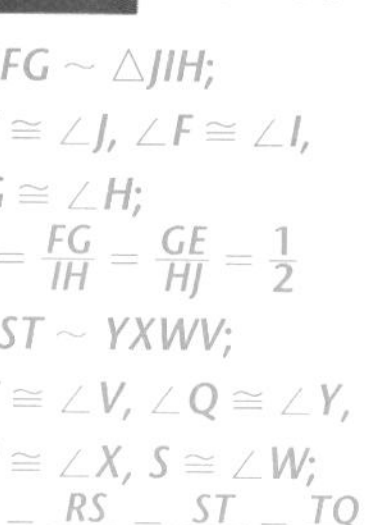

Write the similarity correspondence between each pair of figures. Name all pairs of congruent corresponding angles and write proportions using the pairs of corresponding sides.

a.

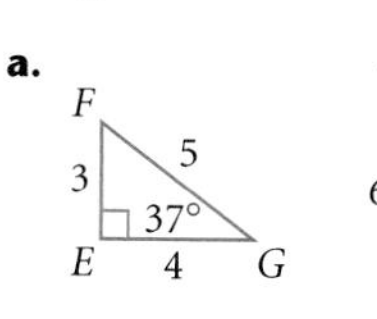

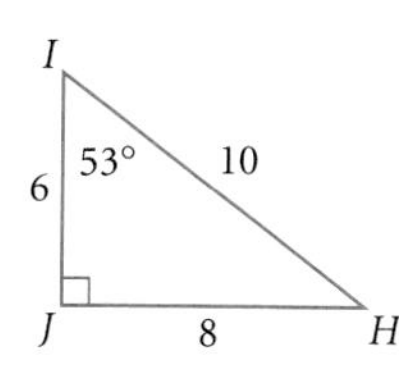

b.

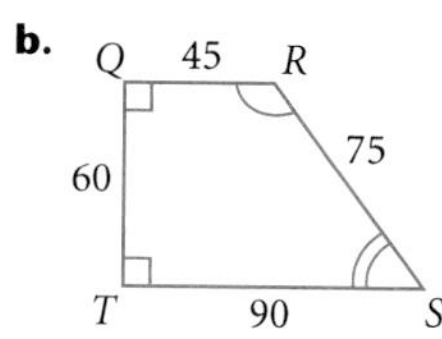

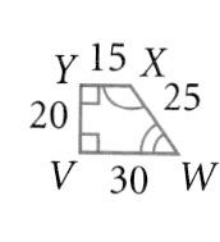

The scale on a map relates the size of an object on the map to its actual size. You can interpret the scale as a ratio and use algebra to find unknown lengths.

EXPLORE: MAPPING THE CAPITAL

MATERIALS

Ruler

This map shows the ruins of Angkor (the capital city) in Cambodia, built by the Khmer people from the 9th through the 12th centuries A.D.

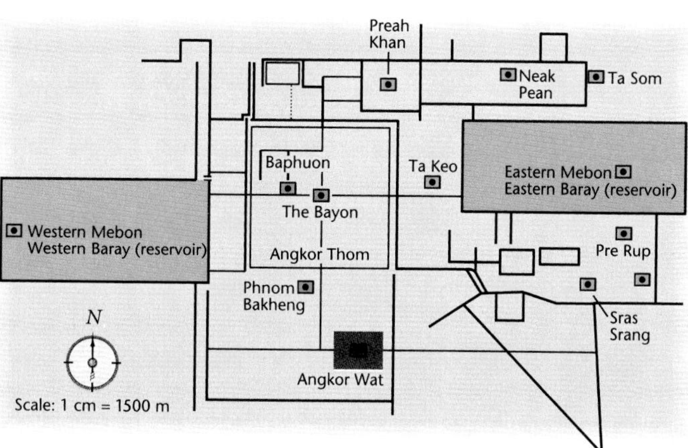

1. Measure the length and width of the Western Mebon Reservoir on the map. Then find the actual dimensions of the reservoir.
2. Find the shortest distance between Angkor Wat and Preah Kan.
3. Find the actual dimensions of Angkor Wat.
4. Explain how you can use scale drawings to find the actual dimensions of objects. Why does this method work?

Student Resources

- **Alternative Lessons 7-1B**
- **Laboratory Manual 7-1B**
- Technology Lab Manual
- **Practice 7-1B**
- **Study Guide and Journal 7-1B**
- **Guía de estudios y Diario 7-1B**
- **Multilingual Handbook**
- **More Look Back 7-1B**
- SAT Preparation

Media Resources

- **Transparency FFM 7-1B**
- **Transparency AE 7-1B**
- Teaching Transparency
- **AWSMTest and practice software**
- AWSM Videodisc

EXPLORE

Mapping the Capital

Recommended group size: 4

The Point

To explore how scale drawings can be used to find actual dimensions of objects.

Look and Listen...

- For students who are measuring in inches, not centimeters.
- For students who are setting up proportions incorrectly.

Ask...

- In your proportions, are the centimeter lengths in similar positions?
- Does your answer seem reasonable?

For Groups That Finish Early

Find the approximate areas of the Eastern and Western Mebon reservoirs. Which reservoir is larger? **Eastern: about 10.7 million m^2; Western: about 11.2 million m^2**

Follow Up

Have students compare the actual size of Angkor Wat to sizes of familiar buildings or fields. **A football field is about 100 m long and 50 m wide. Angkor Wat is more than 10 times as long and more than 16 times as wide as a football field.**

Possible Answers

1. Length ≈ 3.2 cm, width ≈ 1.5 cm; Actual length ≈ 4800 m, actual width ≈ 2250 m
2. About 6000 m (distance between centers)
3. About 1125 m by 825 m
4. Possible methods: (1) Set up and solve a proportion involving the scale factor. (2) Multiply the length on the map/model by the scale factor.

   These methods work because the figure on the map or model is similar to the actual object.

Similar Figures

WHAT DO YOU THINK?

The situation shows two different ways to calculate a missing side length for similar figures. Some students will find it easier to solve proportions for the missing length, others may prefer to use the similarity ratio. You may want to explain why the two methods are algebraically equivalent.

You can use the definition of similar polygons to find unknown angle measures and side lengths in similar polygons. Proportional reasoning is also helpful in finding unknown side lengths.

WHAT DO YOU THINK?

Anne and Roberto were given the following problem to solve.

Given: $FGHJ \sim WXYZ$.
Find YZ.

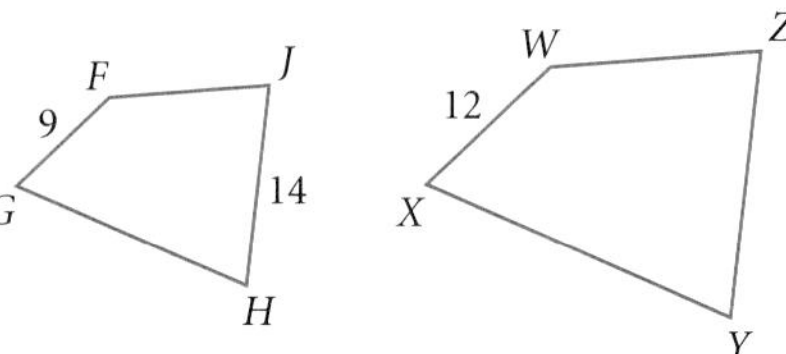

Anne thinks . . .

The similarity ratio is the ratio of the lengths of any two corresponding sides, so I can use $\frac{WX}{FG}$ to find it. The similarity ratio of $WXYZ$ to $FGHJ$ is $\frac{WX}{FG} = \frac{12}{9} = \frac{4}{3}$. YZ is HJ times the similarity ratio. $14 \times \frac{4}{3} = \frac{56}{3} = 18\frac{2}{3}$, so $YZ = 18\frac{2}{3}$.

Roberto thinks . . .

Since the lengths of the corresponding sides of similar figures are proportional, $\frac{FG}{WX} = \frac{HJ}{YZ}$.

Therefore, $\frac{9}{12} = \frac{14}{YZ}$.

$9 \times YZ = 14 \times 12$

$YZ = \frac{14 \times 12}{9}$

$YZ = 18\frac{2}{3}$

TRY IT

c. $m\angle E = 67°$, $m\angle G = 107°$, $m\angle N = 43°$
d. $x = 14$, $y = 15$, $z = 25$

$EFGH \sim KNML$.

c. Find the measures of $\angle E$, $\angle G$, and $\angle N$.
d. Find x, y, and z.
e. What is the similarity ratio of $KNML$ to $EFGH$? 2.5

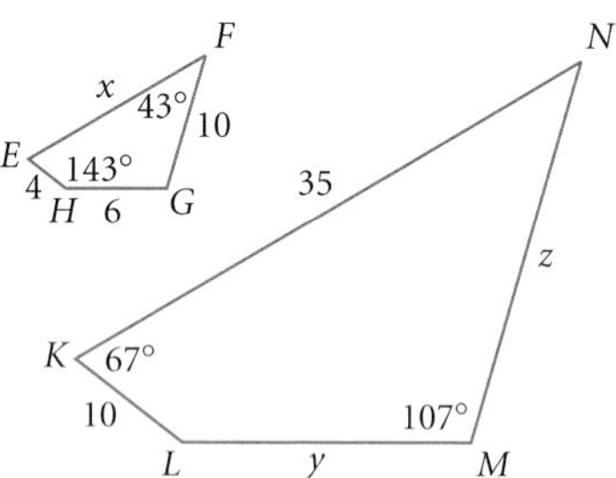

Social Science Connection

In U.S. courts, blueprints/maps and scale factors are not legally admissible evidence of the true dimensions of a building or lot.

History Connection

Angkor Wat is the largest temple ever constructed. The entire complex of 72 buildings, begun about 900 A.D., extends over a 75-square-mile area. According to the 1993 *Guinness Book of World Records,* its population was 80,000 before it was abandoned in 1432. (*The Guinness Book of World Records, 1993.* © 1993 Guinness Publishing Ltd.)

REFLECT

1. If you know all of the side lengths of one polygon, what other data do you need to solve for the side lengths of a similar polygon?
2. Write an explanation of how the scale of a map is related to the idea of a scale factor.

Exercises

CORE

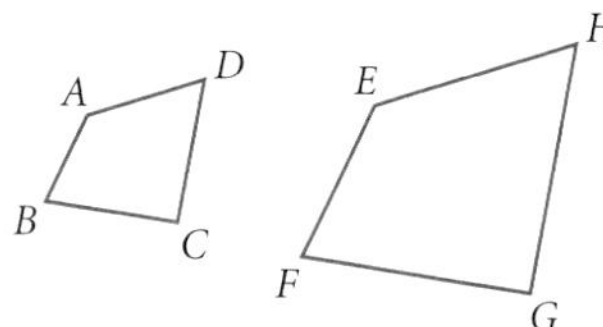

1. **Getting Started** $ABCD \sim EFGH$. Name all pairs of congruent corresponding angles and write proportions using the pairs of corresponding sides.

$IJKL \sim MNOP$. Find the following.

2. $m\angle N$ 106°
3. $m\angle L$ 49°
4. x 9
5. y 15
6. z 12
7. the similarity ratio of $IJKL$ to $MNOP$ $\frac{2}{3}$
8. the similarity ratio of $MNOP$ to $IJKL$ $\frac{3}{2}$

9. Ratios and proportions are important in many areas of mathematics. Describe how ratios and proportions are used in the following.
   a. identifying similar figures
   b. finding a probability
   c. calculating the slope of a line

10. **Working for the Government** In 1970, the population of the United States was about 203.3 million people, and 12.5 million people were employed by federal, state, and local governments. In 1990, the population had grown to 248.7 million.
   a. Estimate the number of people employed by federal, state, and local governments in 1990. Explain how you made your estimate.
   b. The actual number of government employees in 1990 was 18.3 million. Which grew at a faster rate from 1970 to 1990, the U.S. population or the number of government employees? Explain.

$\triangle ABC \sim \triangle DEF$. The similarity ratio of $\triangle ABC$ to $\triangle DEF$ is $\frac{7}{3}$.

11. If $AB = 27$, find DE. 11.57
12. If $EF = 14$, find BC. 32.67
13. Find $\frac{DF}{AC}$. $\frac{DF}{AC} = \frac{3}{7}$

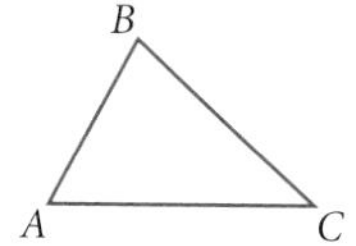

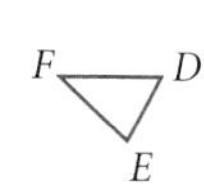

Ongoing Assessment

Vocabulary
Practice/Skills
Review
Math Reasoning
Problem Solving
Challenge

Self-Assessment Exercises 1, 3, 5, 7, 11, 13, 14, 15, 17

Embedded Assessment Explore Step 4; Exercises 4, 8, 12, 18

Journal

Reflect 2 and **Exercises** 9 and 10 are suitable for journal entries.

REFLECT

Possible Answers

1. The length of one side of the other polygon or the similarity ratio.
2. The scale of a map is the scale factor of a distance on the map to the actual distance it represents.

Part B Exercises

Exercise Notes

Core

10. Students use proportional thinking to make predictions about real-world trends, and then compare their predictions to actual data.

19. Extension: You may want to ask students whether a $\frac{1}{6}$ reduction in dimensions would correspond to a $\frac{1}{6}$ reduction in cost. **Due to fixed costs, the actual cost-reduction factor will probably be less than $\frac{1}{6}$.**

More Math Reasoning

34. Previews triangle-similarity postulates and theorems in 7-2.

Exercise Answers

Unless otherwise noted, lengths are rounded to the nearest hundredth.

Core

1. $\angle A \cong \angle E$, $\angle B \cong \angle F$, $\angle C \cong \angle G$, $\angle D \cong \angle H$

$\frac{AB}{EF} = \frac{BC}{FG} = \frac{CD}{GH} = \frac{DA}{HE}$

9. a. When the ratios of corresponding sides in each figure are constant, the figures may be similar.

b. Probability is defined as the number of "successful" outcomes divided by the total number of possible outcomes; i.e., a ratio between 0 and 1 inclusive.

c. Slope is the ratio of the change in y to the change in x.

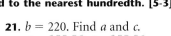

Algebra | Functions | Discrete Math | Probability | Data/Statistics

Similar Figures

10. a. Assuming the proportion of government employees is unchanged: $\frac{12.5}{203.3} = \frac{x}{248.7}$; $x \approx 15.3$ million.

b. $\frac{248.7}{203.3} \approx 1.22$ (a 22% increase from 1970). $\frac{18.3}{12.5} \approx 1.46$ (a 46% increase over 1970). The growth rate in government employment is greater.

19. $\left(\frac{5}{6}\right)(93.0) = 77.5$; $\left(\frac{5}{6}\right)(158.4) = 132$. New plan dimensions are 77.5 cm × 132 cm. $\frac{77.5}{x} = \frac{2.5}{1}$; $x = 31$ m; $\frac{132}{y} = \frac{2.5}{1}$; $y = 52.8$ m. Building will be 31 m × 52.8 m

More Practice

27. $\angle M \cong \angle P$, $\angle N \cong \angle Q$, $\angle O \cong \angle R$; $\frac{OM}{RP} = \frac{MN}{PQ} = \frac{NO}{QR}$

More Math Reasoning

34. Yes; Compare a right isosceles triangle and an equilateral triangle.

35. Let the polygons have perimeters A and B, and let each polygon have n sides. Since they are regular polygons, the sides are of length $\frac{A}{n}$ and $\frac{B}{n}$, respectively, and the ratio of the corresponding sides is always $\frac{\frac{A}{n}}{\frac{B}{n}} = \frac{A}{B}$.

Since the polygons are regular, the angles in each measure $\frac{(n-2)180°}{n}$, and are thus congruent. All corresponding sides are proportional and all corresponding angles are congruent. Therefore, the two regular n-sided polygons are similar.

P **The coordinates of rectangle *WXYZ* are *W*(1, 1), *X*(5, 1), *Y*(5, 4), and *Z*(1, 4). Rectangle *STUV* with lower left-hand vertex *S*(2, 7) is similar to *WXYZ*, and its sides are parallel to the corresponding sides of *WXYZ*. Find the coordinates of *T*, *U*, and *Z* for each similarity ratio.**

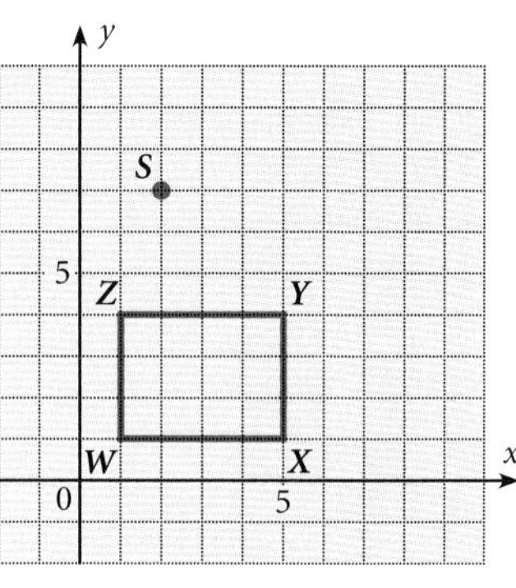

14. $\frac{ST}{WX} = 4$ T: (18, 7); U: (18, 19); V: (2, 19)

15. $\frac{ST}{WX} = 1$ T: (6, 7); U: (6, 10); V: (2, 10)

16. $\frac{ST}{WX} = \frac{1}{2}$ T: (4, 7); U: (4, 8.5); V: (2, 8.5)

P **The following questions refer to a map of the United States on which 1 in. equals 156 mi.**

17. If Boston and Houston are $10\frac{1}{4}$ in. apart on the map, what is the actual distance between the cities? 1,599 miles

18. If Los Angeles and New York are actually 2451 mi apart, how far apart are they on the map? 15.71 inches

PS **19. Scaling Down Your Expectations** The building plans for the new Washington High School gymnasium were drawn on a scale of 2.5 cm to the meter. The measurements on the original plans were 93.0 cm by 158.4 cm. However, due to budget cuts, the dimensions on the plans for the gym were reduced by $\frac{1}{6}$. What are the actual dimensions of the gym under the revised plan? Explain.

Problem-Solving Tip

Check to make sure that your answer makes sense.

LOOK BACK

R **Find the lengths of the unknown sides in each triangle. Express them as decimal approximations rounded to the nearest hundredth. [5-3]**

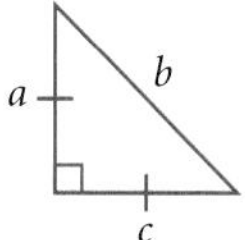

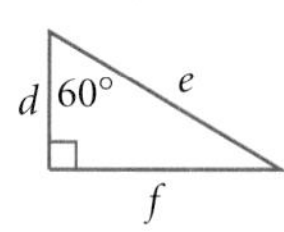

20. $a = 15$. Find b and c. $c = 15$; $b = 21.21$

21. $b = 220$. Find a and c. $a = 155.56$; $c = 155.56$

22. $e = 44$. Find d and f. $d = 22$; $f = 38.11$

23. $f = 5237$. Find d and e. $d = 3023.58$; $e = 6047.17$

R **Find the measure of one interior and one exterior angle of each polygon. [6-3]**

24. regular pentagon
Interior angle = 108°;
Exterior angle = 72°

25. regular nonagon
Interior angle = 140°;
Exterior angle = 40°

26. regular 14-gon
Interior angle = 154.29°;
Exterior angle = 25.71°

Key

V Vocabulary
P Practice/Skills
R Review
MR Math Reasoning
PS Problem Solving
C Challenge

MORE PRACTICE

27. $\triangle MNO \sim \triangle PQR$. Name all pairs of congruent corresponding angles and write proportions using the pairs of corresponding sides.

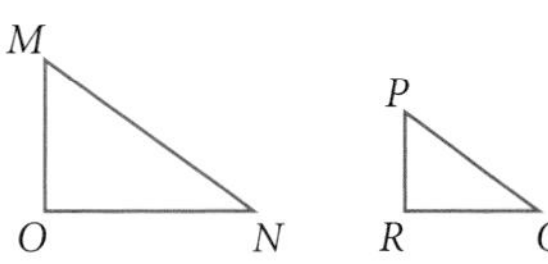

DEFGH **~** ***STUVW*. Find the following.**

28. $m\angle H$ 154° **29.** $m\angle U$ 100° **30.** FG $5\frac{1}{3}$ **31.** TU 12

32. the similarity ratio of $STUVW$ to $DEFGH$ $\frac{3}{4}$

33. the similarity ratio of $DEFGH$ to $STUVW$ $\frac{4}{3}$

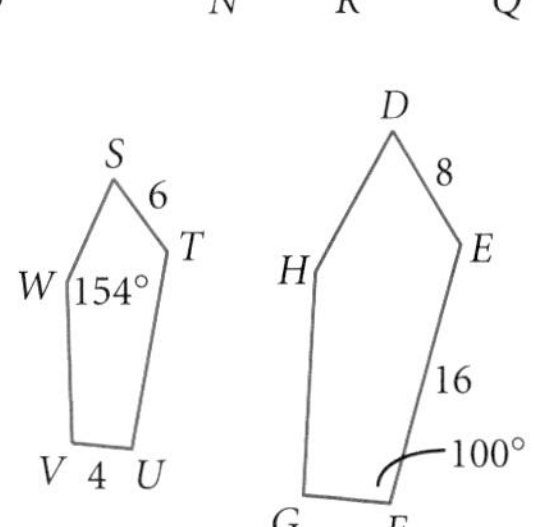

MORE MATH REASONING

34. Is it possible for two triangles that are not similar to have two pairs of sides whose lengths are proportional? If yes, give an example. If not, explain why not.

35. Prove: Any two regular polygons with the same number of sides are similar.

7-1 PART C Areas and Perimeters of Similar Polygons

← CONNECT → ***You've seen that the lengths of corresponding sides of similar figures are proportional. Now you will discover how the ratios of the areas and perimeters of similar figures are related to the similarity ratio.***

The photograph at the right shows a King Kong poster from the 1930s. Not surprisingly, the area and perimeter of this photograph are related to the area and perimeter of the actual poster.

If you enlarge a figure, the area and the perimeter of the enlargement must be greater than the area and perimeter of the original. But can you tell how much greater they will be? The following Explore will help you answer this.

Student Resources

- **Alternative Lessons 7-1C**
- **Laboratory Manual 7-1C**
- **Technology Lab Manual**
- **Practice 7-1C**
- **Study Guide and Journal 7-1C**
- **Guía de estudios y Diario 7-1C**
- **Multilingual Handbook**
- **More Look Ahead 7-1C**
- **SAT Preparation**

Media Resources

- **Transparency FFM 7-1C**
- **Transparency AE 7-1C**
- **Teaching Transparency**
- **AWSMTest and practice software**
- **AWSM Videodisc**

PART C At a Glance

Objective

To discover a relationship between area and perimeter ratios of similar figures and their similarity ratio.

Development

In the **Explore,** students discover relationships between the similarity ratio of two figures and the ratios of their perimeters and areas.

An **Example** shows calculations involving these relationships in a real-world setting.

Suggested Materials

Student Ruler

First Five Minutes

Transparency FFM 7-1C

Simplify each expression.

1. $\sqrt{64}$ 8

2. $\sqrt{\frac{81}{16}}$ $\frac{9}{4}$

3. $\left(\frac{3}{4}\right)^2$ $\frac{9}{16}$

4. $\left(\frac{10}{7}\right)^2$ $\frac{100}{49}$

Motivate

Ask...

- Do two congruent figures have the same area and perimeter? If two figures are similar, could they have the same area and perimeter? **Yes; yes, if the similarity ratio is 1.**

7-1

Algebra	Functions	Discrete Math	Probability	Data/Statistics

Similar Figures

EXPLORE

Similarity, Perimeter, and Area

Recommended group size: 4

The Point

To discover that the ratio of the perimeters of two similar figures is equal to their similarity ratio and the ratio of their areas is the square of their similarity ratio.

Look and Listen...

- For students whose rectangles are not similar.

Ask...

- How did you make sure that your second rectangle is similar to your first?

For Groups That Finish Early

Suppose you know that the ratio of the areas of two similar figures is $\frac{27}{8}$. Find the similarity ratio for the figures. Express your answer as a decimal rounded to the nearest hundredth. 1.84

Follow Up

Ask students to summarize their conjectures about similarity ratios and the areas and perimeters of similar figures.

Possible Answer

3. The ratio of the perimeters of two similar figures is equal to their similarity ratio, and the ratio of their areas is equal to the square of their similarity ratio.

EXPLORE: SIMILARITY, PERIMETER, AND AREA

MATERIALS

Ruler

1. Draw a rectangle and measure its dimensions. Label the rectangle A.
2. Draw Rectangle B that is similar to Rectangle A. What similarity ratio did you use?
3. Investigate the ratios of the perimeters and areas of the two rectangles. Draw and investigate more pairs of similar rectangles. How do the similarity ratios of the rectangles relate to the ratios of their areas and perimeters? Make any conjectures that you can, and compare your conjectures to those made by your classmates.

TRY IT

$ABCDE \sim GHIJK$. The similarity ratio of $ABCDE$ to $GHIJK$ is 2.

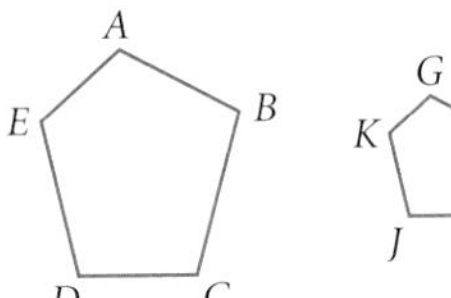

a. If the area of $ABCDE$ is 24 cm^2, what is the area of $GHIJK$? 6 cm^2

b. If the perimeter of $GHIJK$ is 10 cm, what is the perimeter of $ABCDE$? 20

You can use the similarity ratio to find the ratios of the areas of similar figures. It's also possible to use the area ratio to find the similarity ratio.

EXAMPLES

The children's entrance to a toy store is similar to the adults' (big kids') entrance, but its area is $\frac{4}{9}$ as large.

1. Find the similarity ratio of the children's entrance to the adults' entrance.
The similarity ratio is the square root of the ratio of the areas:
$\sqrt{\frac{4}{9}} = \frac{2}{3}$.

2. What is the ratio of the perimeter of the children's doorway to the perimeter of the adults' doorway?
The ratio of the perimeters is equal to the similarity ratio, so it is $\frac{2}{3}$.

Alert

Students may confuse simplification of radicals of fractions with simplification of the fractions themselves. For instance, they may simplify the ratio $\frac{4}{9}$ to $\frac{2}{3}$. You might need to remind them to check whether or not a radical is present before simplifying a fraction.

Music Connection

The Pythagoreans noticed that strings whose lengths are ratios of whole numbers produce pleasant harmonies. Strings whose lengths are in the ratio $\frac{1}{2}$ produce an octave, and those whose lengths are in the ratio $\frac{2}{3}$ produce a fifth.

3. If the adults' doorway is 210 cm tall and 120 cm wide, what are the dimensions of the children's doorway?
Height $= 210 \times \frac{2}{3} = 140$ cm; width $= 120 \times \frac{2}{3} = 80$ cm

The relationships between the similarity ratio and the ratios of the areas and perimeters of similar polygons are summarized below.

THEOREMS

The ratio of the perimeters of two similar polygons is equal to their similarity ratio.

The ratio of the areas of two similar polygons is equal to the square of their similarity ratio.

REFLECT

1. Use graph paper to help explain why doubling the length and width of a rectangle quadruples its area.
2. When a salesperson showed Glenn a rug, Glenn said, "I need one that's the same shape, but twice as big." The salesperson returned with two rugs and said, "I wasn't sure what you meant." How do you think the two rugs compared to the original? Explain why you need to be specific when you say one thing is "twice as big" as another.

Exercises

CORE

1. **Getting Started** The two figures shown are similar, and the lengths of a pair of corresponding sides are given.

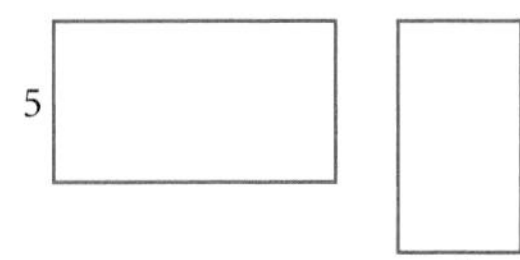

a. Find the similarity ratio of the figure on the left to the figure on the right. What is the ratio of the perimeter of the figure on the left to the perimeter of the figure on the right? $\frac{5}{4}$; $\frac{5}{4}$
b. The ratio of the areas of the figures is equal to the square of their similarity ratio. Find the ratio of the area of the figure on the left to the area of the figure on the right. $\left(\frac{5}{4}\right)^2 = \frac{25}{16}$

Ongoing Assessment

- Vocabulary
- Practice/Skills
- Review
- Math Reasoning
- Problem Solving
- Challenge

Self-Assessment Exercises 1, 3, 4, 5, 7, 8, 10

Embedded Assessment Exercises 2, 6, 9, 11, 12

ALTERNATE EXAMPLES

A reproduction of a painting has $\frac{4}{25}$ the area of the actual painting.

1. Find the similarity ratio of the reproduction to the actual painting.

   The similarity ratio is the square root of the ratio of the areas.
   $\sqrt{\frac{4}{25}} = \frac{2}{5}$
2. What is the ratio of the perimeters of the reproduction and the actual painting?

   The ratio of the perimeters is equal to the similarity ratio, so it is $\frac{2}{5}$.
3. If the actual painting is 24 in. tall and 20 in. wide, what are the dimensions of the reproduction?

   Height $= 24 \times \frac{2}{5} = \frac{48}{5} = 9.6$ in., width $= 20 \times \frac{2}{5} = 8$ in.

Journal

Reflect 2 and **Exercise** 12 are suitable for journal entries.

REFLECT

Possible Answers

1. Four times as many squares will be enclosed by the figure whose sides are twice as long.
2. One rug had twice the area and the other had dimensions twice as great as the original. There may be confusion about whether you mean the area is twice as large or the dimensions are twice as large.

Part C Exercises

Exercise Notes

Core

12. Students calculate areas of similar newspaper advertisements. They are also asked whether the usual cost of such advertisements is proportional to their area.

Look Ahead

These exercises look ahead to golden rectangles explored in 7-1 Part D.

More Math Reasoning

21. Students apply geometric probability to areas of similar figures.

Algebra | Functions | Discrete Math | Probability | Data/Statistics

Similar Figures

Exercise Answers

Core

10. Yes; $\frac{\text{Area}_1}{\text{Area}_2} = \text{ratio}^2$; ratio = 1 here, so that the sides are not only proportional, but congruent; Since the figures are similar, the corresponding angles are also congruent, so the figures are congruent.

11. Since the similarity ratio is 2, the ratio of the areas is 4. If the smaller pizza serves 2, the larger feeds $2(4) = 8$.

12. Price per square inch $= \frac{180}{12} =$ \$15. New ad is $\left(\frac{5}{3}\right)^2(12) = 33\frac{1}{3}$ square inches. Price of new ad is $15\left(33\frac{1}{3}\right) = \$500$. Possible answer: Larger ads probably cost a little less per square inch, so as to encourage people to buy large ads.

13. Maybe; If she meant the kitchen area is twice the bathroom area, then she was overcharged. If she meant the dimensions of the kitchen were twice those of the bathroom, then she was charged correctly.

Look Ahead

14. Check students' answers. Many of the objects typically have ratios around 1.6, the golden ratio.

15. Yes; Corresponding angles are congruent (here, 90° each); We are given $\frac{l_1}{w_1} = \frac{l_2}{w_2}$, but this can be rewritten as $\frac{l_1}{l_2} = \frac{w_1}{w_2}$; i.e., corresponding sides are in the same proportion.

More Math Reasoning

22. Students should use perpendicular line constructions and congruent segment constructions.

P **Find the ratio of the area of the figure on the left to the area of the figure on the right. Then find the ratio of the perimeter of the figure on the left to the perimeter of the figure on the right.**

2. Area ratio $= \frac{25}{16}$; Perimeter ratio $= \frac{5}{4}$

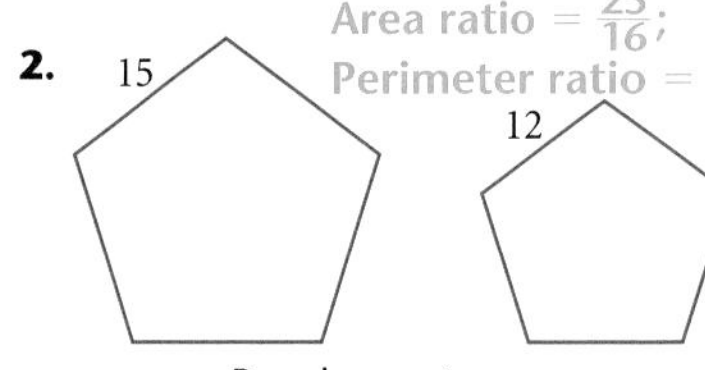

Regular pentagons

3. Area ratio $= \frac{64}{169}$; Perimeter ratio $= \frac{8}{13}$

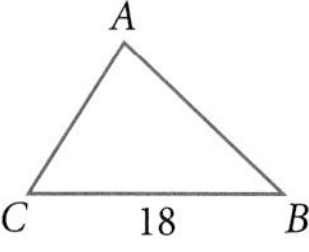

Equilateral triangles

P $\triangle ABC \sim \triangle DEF$. **Find each ratio.**

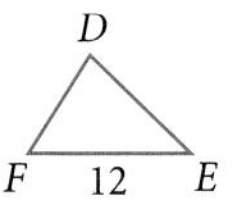

4. $\frac{AB}{DE}$ $\frac{3}{2}$

5. $\frac{\text{perimeter } \triangle ABC}{\text{perimeter } \triangle DEF}$ $\frac{3}{2}$

6. $\frac{\text{area } \triangle ABC}{\text{area } \triangle DEF}$ $\frac{9}{4}$

P **7.** The ratio of the areas of two similar quadrilaterals is $\frac{25}{16}$. What is the ratio of the lengths of a pair of corresponding sides? $\frac{5}{4}$

PS **8. Rooting in the Garden** A triangular garden has an area of 10 m^2. A similar garden has an area of 20 m^2. By what factor should you multiply the length of each side of the first garden to find the lengths of the sides of the second? Multiply by $\sqrt{2}$

MR **9.** Prove that changing the side length (s) of a square by a scale factor of k changes its area by a factor of k^2. $\text{Area}_1 = s \times s = s^2$; $\text{Area}_2 = (ks) \times (ks) = k^2s^2 = k^2\,\text{Area}_1$

MR **10.** If two similar polygons have the same area, must they be congruent? Explain your answer.

PS **11. Anchovy Area** Pauline's Proportional Pizza Parlor serves circular pizzas in two sizes. The small eight-inch-diameter pizza feeds two people. The large pizza has a sixteen-inch diameter. How many people do you think it serves? Explain your answer.

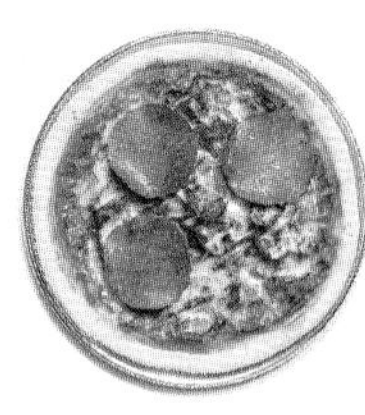

PS **12.** Joan wanted to run a 12-in.^{2} advertisement in a newspaper. The ad salesperson told her that a 12-in.^{2} ad costs \$180. The salesperson also told Joan that they had enough space available on the page to enlarge her ad by a scale factor of $\frac{5}{3}$. If the cost per square inch stays the same, how much does the larger ad cost? Do you think larger newspaper ads actually cost the same per square inch as smaller ones? Write a short paragraph explaining why or why not.

MR **13. Twice the Price?** Cecelia needed linoleum for the bathroom and kitchen in her house. Although she told the salesperson that the kitchen was twice the size of the bathroom, the linoleum for the kitchen cost her four times as much as the linoleum for the bathroom. Was Cecelia overcharged? Explain.

Key

V Vocabulary
P Practice/Skills
R Review
MR Math Reasoning
PS Problem Solving
C Challenge

LOOK AHEAD

14. Measure three rectangular objects from the following list: a playing card, a window, a postcard, a paperback book, a rectangular picture frame.
a. Calculate the ratio of length to width for each object. Are the ratios close?
b. Find the mean (average) of the ratios.

15. If two rectangles have the same length-to-width ratio, are they similar? Explain.

MORE PRACTICE

Each pair of figures shown is similar. Find the ratio of the area of the figure on the left to the area of the figure on the right. Then find the ratio of the perimeter of the figure on the left to the perimeter of the figure on the right.

16. Area Ratio = 9; Perimeter ratio = 3.

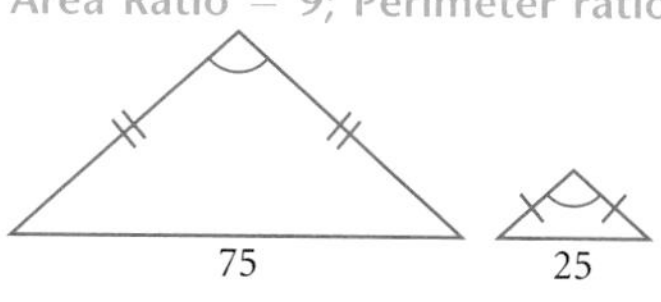

17. Area ratio = $\frac{9}{25}$; Perimeter ratio = $\frac{3}{5}$

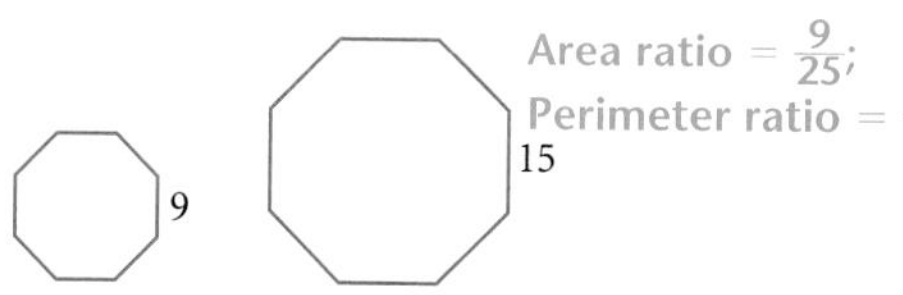

Both figures are regular octagons.

$\triangle MNO \sim \triangle JKL$. Find each ratio.

18. $\frac{MO}{JL}$ $\frac{4}{3}$

19. $\frac{\text{perimeter } \triangle MNO}{\text{perimeter } \triangle JKL}$ $\frac{4}{3}$

20. $\frac{\text{area } \triangle MNO}{\text{area } \triangle JKL}$ $\frac{16}{9}$

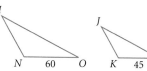

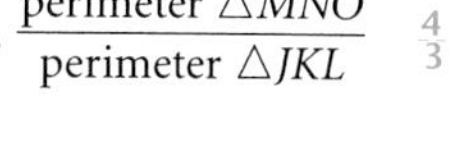

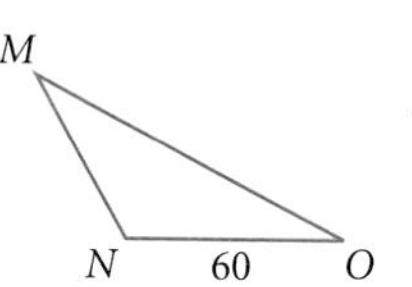

MORE MATH REASONING

21. Crop Circles Suppose a crop circle with a radius of $\frac{1}{4}$ mi is planted in a 1-mile-square field as shown.
a. To the nearest hundredth, what is the probability that a raindrop that falls on the field will land on the crops? (Recall that the area of a circle is given by $A = \pi r^2$.) 0.20
b. The farmer increases the radius of the crop circle by a scale factor of 2. What is the new probability that a raindrop will land on the crops? How does this probability relate to the one you found in **21a**? 0.80; 4 times part (a).

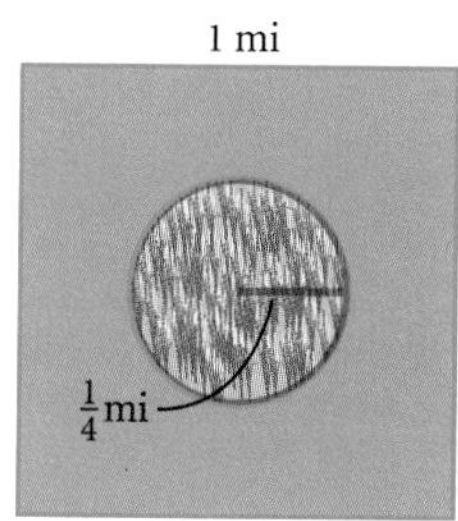

22. Carefully draw a rectangle. Then use a compass and straightedge to construct a rectangle similar to it whose area is four times as large. Explain how your construction works. Include sketches to illustrate your explanation.

PART D At a Glance

Objective

To determine a numerical value for the golden ratio.

Development

First, a **Consider** question asks students to choose a pleasing rectangle from a set of rectangles. This choice leads into a discussion of the golden rectangle.

In the **Explore,** students approximate the golden ratio by measuring several golden rectangles. Then they use algebra to find its exact value.

Suggested Materials

Student Ruler

Key Terms

Golden rectangle, golden ratio

First Five Minutes

Transparency FFM 7-1D

Read the first paragraph on page 478. Then answer the **Consider** question on that page.

Motivate

Ask...

- Do you think people have an "ideal" or "typical" mental model for other things besides rectangles? Think of a bird. What type of bird did you visualize? Did anyone think of a vulture? ostrich? penguin?

Introduces the idea that there is a "most pleasing" rectangle shape.

Possible Answer

1. Most students will probably choose rectangle 3 (the golden rectangle).

7-1 PART D Golden Rectangles

← CONNECT → ***You've seen many types of similar polygons. Now you will investigate a family of similar rectangles that has been important to many cultures for thousands of years.***

People throughout history have felt that a certain type of rectangle "looks right" and has the "right" proportions. This type of rectangle is called a **golden rectangle**.

CONSIDER

1. Which rectangle do you think is the best looking, or has the most pleasing shape?

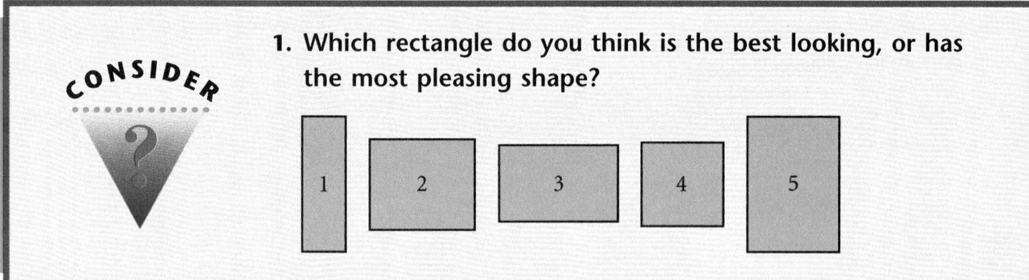

Rectangles similar to number 3 above have been preferred in art and architecture by the ancient Egyptians, Greeks, and Persians, and by many modern cultures. These golden rectangles are found in advertisements, movie screens, credit cards, windows, and buildings.

DEFINITION

Rectangle *ACDF* is a **golden rectangle** if and only if square *ABEF* with side lengths *w* makes rectangle *CDEB* similar to rectangle *ACDF.*

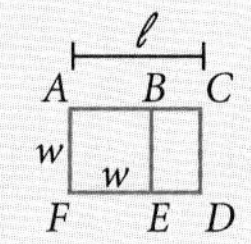

The definition above means that if you cut a golden rectangle into a square and a small rectangle, the small rectangle is also a golden rectangle. All golden rectangles are similar. The ratio of the length to the width is a constant called the **golden ratio.**

Mathematics Connection

A golden triangle is an isosceles triangle where the ratio of the length of a leg to the length of the base is the golden ratio. The triangle produced by two diagonals of a regular pentagon from one vertex to its "opposite" side is a golden triangle.

EXPLORE: SEARCHING FOR GOLD

MATERIALS

Ruler

1. Measure the length and width of the golden rectangles shown. Calculate the length-to-width ratio for each. How do the three ratios compare? Are the rectangles similar?

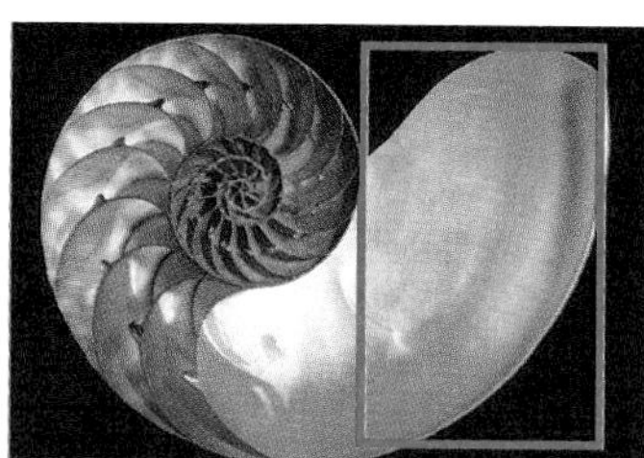

Seurat—*Invitation to the Sideshow (La Parade)*, The Metropolitan Museum of Art, Bequest of Stephen C. Clark, 1960 (61.101.17)

2. Discuss your findings with classmates and come up with an agreement on an approximate value for the golden ratio.
3. Now you can use the definition of a golden rectangle and some algebra to calculate the exact value of $\frac{\ell}{w}$, the golden ratio. (To simplify your work, use $w = 1$.)
   The definition of a golden rectangle tells you that $ACDF \sim CDEB$. Use the definition of similarity to complete the proportion $\frac{AC}{CD} = \frac{CD}{?}$. By substitution, this means $\frac{\ell}{1} = \frac{1}{?}$.

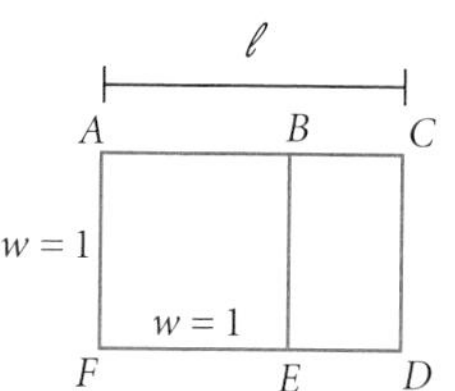

4. Use this proportion to write a quadratic equation for ℓ. Then use the quadratic formula to solve for ℓ. Give your answer in exact (square root) form.
5. Find a decimal approximation for your answer to the nearest thousandth. Is this close to the result you found in Step 2?

TRY IT

HIJK is a golden rectangle. Use an approximation for the golden ratio to find each length to the nearest tenth.

a. If $IJ = 25$, find JK. 40.5
b. If $HI = 10$, find HK. 6.2

H I K J

By using the definition of a golden rectangle, you calculated an exact value for the golden ratio. This is close to the length-to-width ratio for many rectangles seen in art, architecture, and everyday objects.

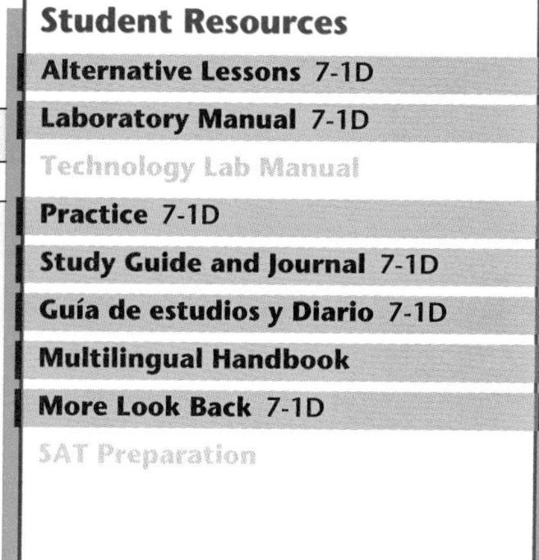

Student Resources

- Alternative Lessons 7-1D
- Laboratory Manual 7-1D
- Technology Lab Manual
- Practice 7-1D
- Study Guide and Journal 7-1D
- Guía de estudios y Diario 7-1D
- Multilingual Handbook
- More Look Back 7-1D
- SAT Preparation

Media Resources

- Transparency FFM 7-1D
- Transparency AE
- Teaching Transparency
- AWSMTest and practice software
- AWSM Videodisc

EXPLORE

Searching for Gold

Recommended group size: 4

The Point

To approximate the golden ratio from golden rectangles, and to use the quadratic formula to solve for its exact value.

Look and Listen...

- For students who do not complete the ratio in Step 3 with $\ell - 1$.
- For students who need help remembering the quadratic formula in Step 4.

Ask...

- What must one side of your quadratic equation be equal to before you use the quadratic formula?

For Groups That Finish Early

If the area of a golden rectangle is 20 square units, what are its approximate dimensions? Approximately 5.689 by 3.516.

Follow Up

Ask students for their approximate and exact values for the golden ratio. Have one student or group present Steps 3 and 4 at the board or overhead.

Possible Answers

1. All of the ratios are approximately 1.6; the rectangles are similar.
2. Values should be approximately 1.6.
3. DE; $\ell - 1$
4. $\ell^2 - \ell - 1$; $\frac{1 + \sqrt{5}}{2}$
5. $\frac{1 + \sqrt{5}}{2} \approx 1.618$; yes

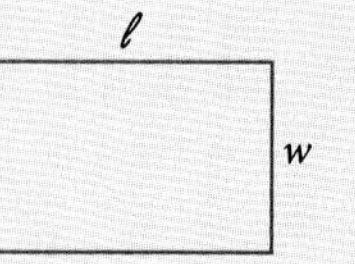

Algebra | Functions | Discrete Math | Probability | Data/Statistics

Similar Figures

Journal

Reflect 2 and **Exercise** 7 are suitable for journal entries.

REFLECT

Possible Answers

1. 3" × 5" cards, some windows, picture frames, driver's licenses, etc.

2. All golden rectangles are similar. Therefore, the ratio of the length to the width of any golden rectangle is the same.

Part D Exercises

Exercise Notes

Core

6. Students see that the golden ratio differs from its reciprocal by 1.

9. Shows the use of golden rectangles in art.

10. Students see a connection between the golden ratio and the Fibonacci sequence. This exercise also uses the idea of a limit.

Science Note: Fibonacci numbers appear frequently in nature. The number of petals in a blossom and the number of spirals on a pine cone are often Fibonacci numbers.

More Math Reasoning

22. Students *show* that the golden ratio differs from its reciprocal by 1.

Extension: Find a pair of reciprocals whose sum is 1. **There are no such real numbers.**

23. Shows another way to connect the golden ratio to Fibonacci numbers. The spiral that results is related to spirals in some shells.

Exercise Answers

Core

6. 0.618; 1.618 − 0.618 = 1

THE GOLDEN RATIO

In a golden rectangle, the ratio of the length, ℓ, to the width, w, is the golden ratio, $\frac{1+\sqrt{5}}{2}$ (≈ 1.618).

REFLECT

1. Identify some everyday objects that seem to be golden rectangles.

2. Explain why the value of the golden ratio does not depend on the size of the golden rectangle you are looking at.

Exercises

CORE

P **1. Getting Started** Identify the golden rectangle from the figures below. (b)

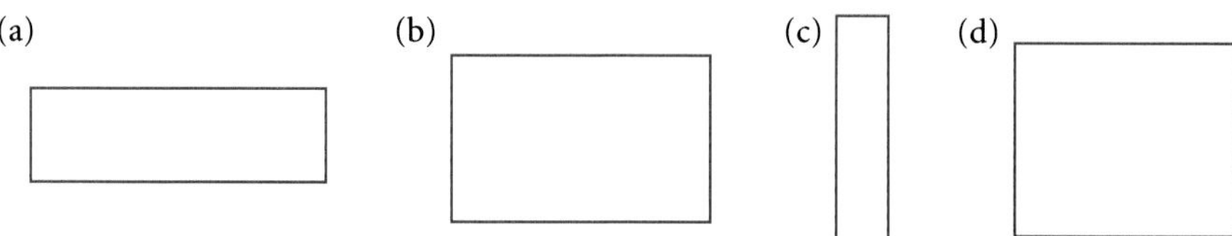

P ***GHIJ* is a golden rectangle. Find each ratio.**

2. $\frac{GH}{HI}$ 1.618 **3.** $\frac{GJ}{JI}$ 0.618

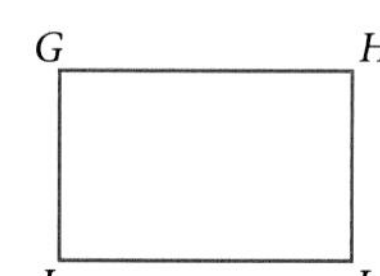

P **4.** If $GH = 25$, find HI to the nearest hundredth. 15.45

P **5.** If $GJ = 100$, find JI to the nearest hundredth. 161.80

P **6.** Find the reciprocal of the golden ratio. Round your answer to the nearest thousandth. Then subtract the reciprocal from the golden ratio itself. What do you find?

MR **7.** Find the area of a golden rectangle whose width is 20. Then find the length and width of a golden rectangle that has twice that area. Explain how you solved this problem.

V **8.** Write the phrases that correctly complete the following statement. If you divide the length of a ___ by its width, the number that you get is the ___.

Key

V Vocabulary
P Practice/Skills
R Review
MR Math Reasoning
PS Problem Solving
C Challenge

9. Yellow Gold, White Gold Copy the lines in the painting by Piet Mondrian shown at the right. Identify three different golden rectangles in the painting.

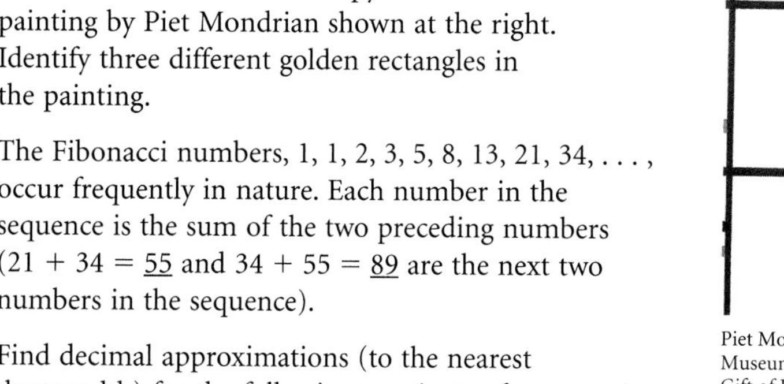

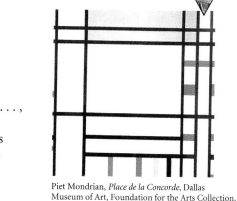

Piet Mondrian, *Place de la Concorde*, Dallas Museum of Art, Foundation for the Arts Collection, Gift of James H. and Lillian Clark Foundation

10. The Fibonacci numbers, 1, 1, 2, 3, 5, 8, 13, 21, 34, . . . , occur frequently in nature. Each number in the sequence is the sum of the two preceding numbers ($21 + 34 = \underline{55}$ and $34 + 55 = \underline{89}$ are the next two numbers in the sequence).

Find decimal approximations (to the nearest thousandth) for the following quotients of consecutive Fibonacci numbers.

a. $\frac{13}{8}$ 1.625 **b.** $\frac{21}{13}$ 1.615 **c.** $\frac{34}{21}$ 1.619 **d.** $\frac{89}{55}$ 1.618 **e.** $\frac{4181}{2584}$ 1.618

f. Make a conjecture about the ratio of two consecutive Fibonacci numbers as the Fibonacci numbers get larger. It approaches the golden ratio.

LOOK BACK

Find the area of each figure. [5-2, 5-3]

11.

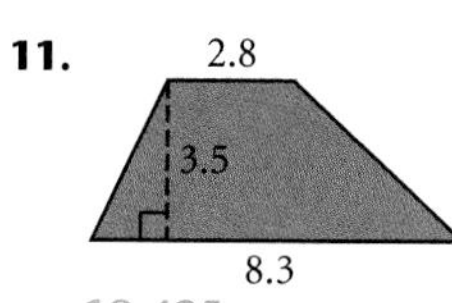

19.425

12.

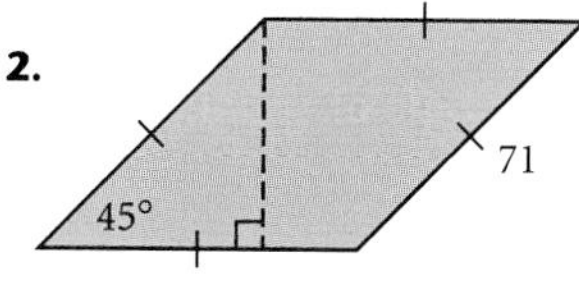

3,564.5

13.

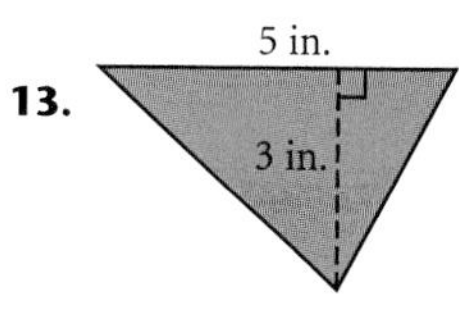

7.5

What values of x and y guarantee that each quadrilateral is a parallelogram? Justify your answers. [6-2]

14.

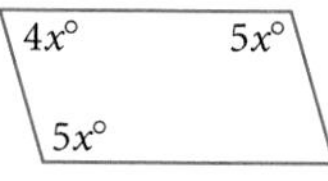

$x = 20$; Same side interior angles are supplementary.

15.

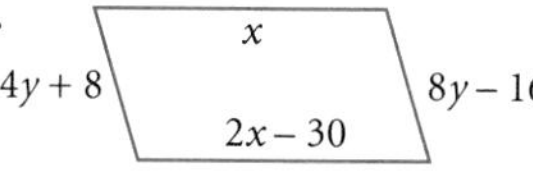

$x = 30$; $y = 6$; Opposite sides are congruent.

16.

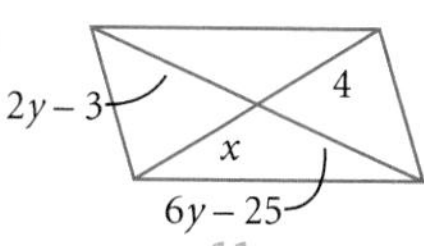

$x = 4$; $y = \frac{11}{2}$; Diagonals bisect each other.

MORE PRACTICE

***PQRS* is a golden rectangle. Find each ratio.**

17. $\frac{PQ}{QR}$ 1.618

18. $\frac{SP}{PQ}$ 0.618

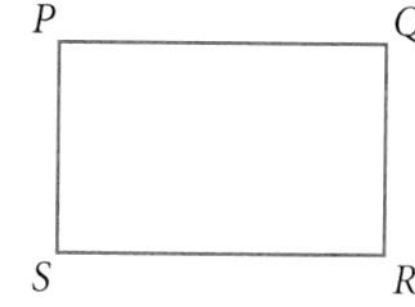

19. If $PQ = 30$, find PS to the nearest hundredth. 18.54

20. If $QR = 75$, find SR to the nearest hundredth. 121.35

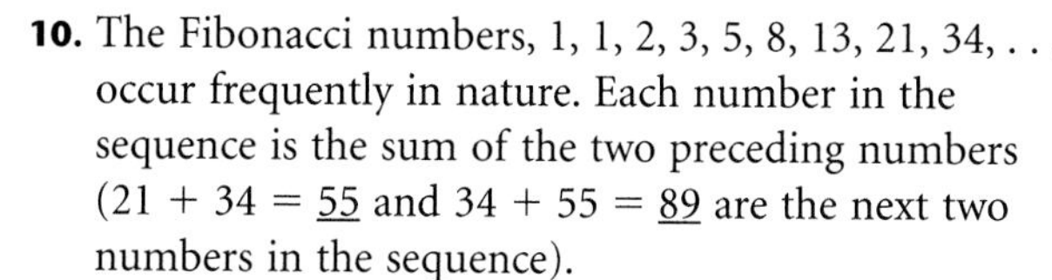

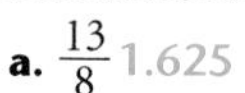

7. $\frac{l}{w} = 1.618$; $l = 1.618(20) = 32.36$; Area $= lw = 32.36(20) = 647.2$; $\frac{\text{Area}_2}{\text{Area}_1} = r^2$; $2 = r^2$; $r = \sqrt{2}$ so Length $= \sqrt{2}$(previous length) $= 45.76$, Width $= \sqrt{2}(20) = 28.28$

8. Golden rectangle; Golden ratio

9. Check students' answers.

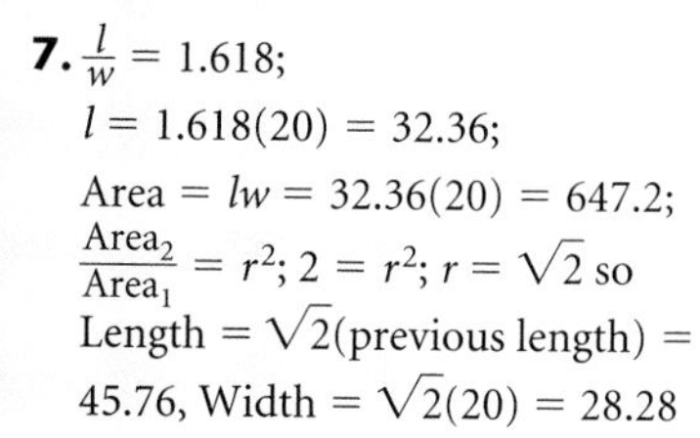

More Math Reasoning

21. Cut a strip $8.5 - 6.798 = 1.702$ in. wide (and 11 in. long) off along the 11 in. side.

22. Let $a - \frac{1}{a} = 1$, $a > 0$; $a^2 - 1 = a$; $a^2 - a - 1 = 0$; This quadratic equation gives $a = \frac{1 + \sqrt{5}}{2}$.

23.

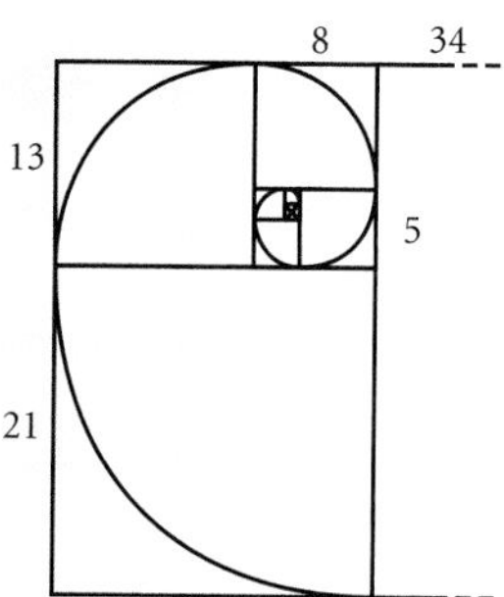

a. No; The numbers are a Fibonacci sequence, and $\frac{l}{w} = \frac{n\text{th sequence value}}{(n-1)\text{st sequence value}}$ which approaches the golden ratio as $n \to \infty$.

b. No; The limit is the golden ratio, but no member of the sequence of ratios will ever be exactly the value of the golden ratio.

c. Possible answer: Nautilus seashells.

Ongoing Assessment

Self-Assessment Exercises 1, 3, 5, 6, 8

Embedded Assessment Exercises 2, 4, 7, 10

PART E At a Glance

Objective

To use similarity to investigate the models used in the making of *King Kong.*

Development

In the **Explore,** students use similarity to compare models used in the making of *King Kong* to the "actual" King Kong.

Suggested Materials

Student Tape measure

First Five Minutes

Transparency FFM 7-1E

Suppose $ABCD \sim KLMN$. Name all pairs of congruent corresponding angles, and write proportions using the pairs of corresponding sides.

Angles: $\angle A \cong \angle K$, $\angle B \cong \angle L$, $\angle C \cong \angle M$, $\angle D \cong \angle N$

Sides: $\frac{AB}{KL} = \frac{BC}{LM} = \frac{CD}{MN} = \frac{DA}{NK}$

EXPLORE

Modeling for Movies

Recommended group size: 4

The Point

To use similarity to compare models used in the making of *King Kong* to the "actual" King Kong.

Look and Listen...

- For students who have difficulty working with the fraction when using the $\frac{3}{4}$-in. to 1-ft scale.
- For students who do not see how to use their arm length and height to predict the length of King Kong's arm.

Ask...

- What is the ratio of your arm length to your height? Can you use this ratio to set up a proportion involving King Kong's arm length and height?

MORE MATH REASONING

PS **21. Cutting a Golden Rectangle** From which side of an $8\frac{1}{2}$-in. × 11-in. sheet of paper should you cut a strip so that the remaining rectangle is a golden rectangle? How wide should the strip be?

C **22.** Show that if the difference between a positive number and its reciprocal is 1, then the number is the golden ratio.

MR **23.** Sketch the following on a piece of dot paper or graph paper.

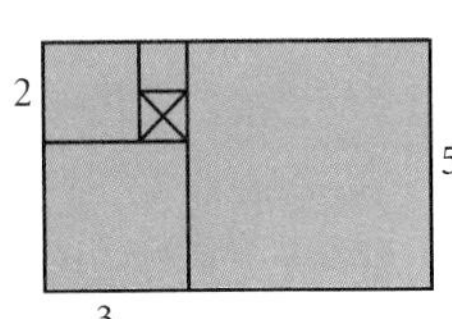

- Draw a square with sides 1 unit long. Mark an X inside the square.
- Attach a second 1-unit square to a side of the first as shown.
- Attach a 2-unit square.
- Attach a 3-unit square.
- Continue the pattern, attaching squares whose sides are 5, 8, 13, 21, and 34 units long.

a. Are the rectangles formed above golden rectangles? Why or why not?

b. Do you think that continuing this pattern will ever form a golden rectangle? Explain.

c. Beginning with the 1-unit square above the X, draw a quarter-circle in each square as shown. Can you think of anything in nature that has this type of spiral? If so, describe it.

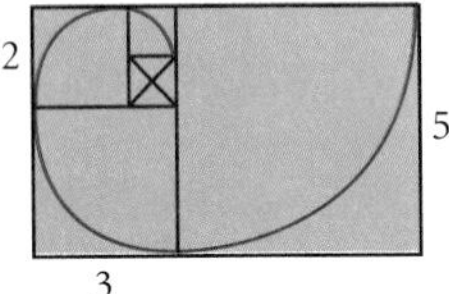

7-1 PART E Making Connections

← CONNECT → ***Models like the 18-in. version of King Kong are related to the mathematical idea of similarity. You've developed a precise definition of similarity and used this concept to solve problems.***

Movie directors often have designers build models of giant monsters, tall buildings, and futuristic spacecraft. Scale models are often used when the real object is too large, too expensive, or impossible to build.

In the following Explore, you will investigate the model used in the film *King Kong.*

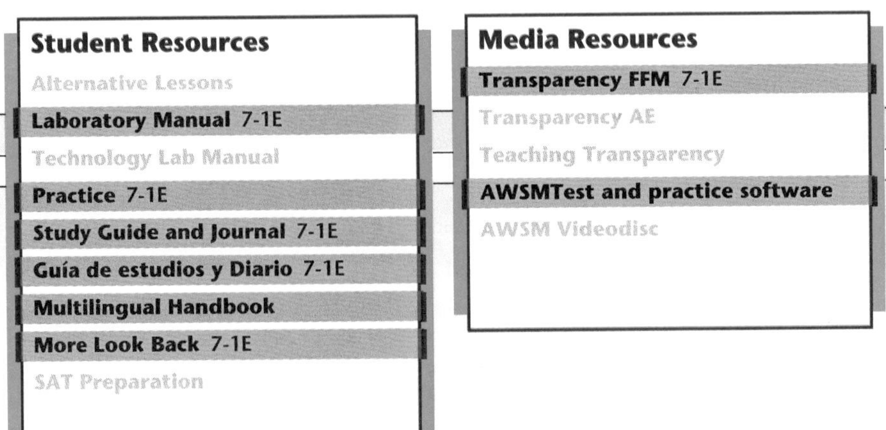

Logic/Reasoning | Industry/Careers | Science/Health | Social Science/History | Fine Arts/Literature

EXPLORE: MODELING FOR MOVIES

MATERIALS

Tape measure

Recall that the model of King Kong was built on the scale of $\frac{3}{4}$ inch to the foot.

1. If the King Kong model was 18 in. tall, how tall would King Kong have been?
2. With a partner, use a tape measure to find the length of your arm and your height. How long would your arm be if you were as tall as King Kong? Compare this result to your partner's.
3. Fay Wray said that the "full-sized" arm of King Kong was 8 ft long. Does the 8-ft arm make sense for King Kong according to your results from Step 2? If not, how long should King Kong's arm have been?
4. Are there any problems in using your proportions to estimate the length of King Kong's arm? Explain.

REFLECT

1. Write definitions of *similar polygons, similarity ratio,* and *scale factor* in your own words. Explain the relationship among the three terms.
2. Describe how the concept of similarity might be used in a career of your choice.

Self-Assessment

P **Determine whether each statement is *always, sometimes,* or *never* true. Explain your answers.**

1. Squares $ABCD$ and $EFGH$ are similar.
2. Isosceles triangles $\triangle PQR$ and $\triangle STU$ are similar.
3. An equilateral triangle, $\triangle GHJ$, and an equiangular triangle, $\triangle KLM$, are similar. Always true; Equal angles (60°) imply similar sides.

R **Find the measure of one interior and one exterior angle of each polygon. [6-3]**

4. regular hexagon Interior angle = 120°; Exterior angle 60°
5. regular 12-gon Interior angle = 150°; Exterior angle 30°
6. regular 16-gon Interior angle= 157.5°; Exterior angle 22.5°

ey

Vocabulary
Practice/Skills
Review
R Math Reasoning
S Problem Solving
Challenge

For Groups That Finish Early

Suppose you are making a movie in which you use a 6-in. doll as a model for a 6-ft human. Find the approximate arm length, head circumference, and foot length of the doll. Arm: 2.5 in., head: 2 in., foot: 0.9 in.

Follow Up

Ask students to explain whether an 8-ft arm makes sense for King Kong, and how they estimated the "actual" arm length.

Possible Answers

1. 24 ft
2. Typical answers are approximately 10 or 11 feet.
3. The 8-ft arm seems a bit short for the full-sized Kong.
4. Gorillas' arms are longer in proportion to their bodies than humans' arms.

Portfolio

Have students select items from their work that demonstrate their understanding of the material in 7-1.

You may wish to have students include an **Exercise** or **Explore** that asked them to use a scale factor, an **Exercise** where they calculated areas or perimeters of similar figures, and a **Reflect** question that they found challenging.

REFLECT

Possible Answers

1. *Similar polygons* have congruent corresponding angles and proportional corresponding side lengths. If Figure A is similar to Figure B, the *similarity ratio* of A to B is the ratio of the length of a side of A to the length of the corresponding side of B. But the *scale factor* of A to B is the ratio of a side length in B to a corresponding length in A. The scale factor and similarity ratios are reciprocals.
2. Students may describe a mapmaker using a scale factor, a photographer reducing or enlarging photos, a movie special-effects artist using models, etc.

7-1

Algebra | Logic/Reasoning

Similar Figures

Self-Assessment

Exercise Notes

10. Students find the size of an Empire State Building model on the same scale as the King Kong model used in the movie.

18. Similar to multiple-choice questions on standardized tests.

Self-Assessment Answers

1. Always true; All angles are 90° (therefore congruent) and all pairs of corresponding sides are proportional (since there is only one measurement for side length on each square).

2. Sometimes true; Need the third sides to have the same similarity ratio as the other pairs and need congruent corresponding angles for statement to be true.

PS **The scale for a drawing of a room is 1 to 50. Use this information in Exercises 7–9.**

7. The dimensions of the drawing are ten centimeters by eight centimeters. What are the dimensions of the room?
5 m by 4 m

8. A table in the room is 145 cm long and 55 cm wide. Find its dimensions in the drawing. 2.9 cm by 1.1 cm

9. A desk top in the drawing of the room is 1.5 cm by 2.0 cm. How long is the desk top? How wide is the desk top?
100 cm; 75 cm

PS **10. Gorilla in the Smog** In the final scene of the movie, King Kong climbs the Empire State Building. If the building is 1250 ft tall and the scale of the model is $\frac{3}{4}$ in. = 1 ft, how tall should a model of the building have been? 78.125 ft

P **$\triangle HJK \sim \triangle LMN$. Find the following.**

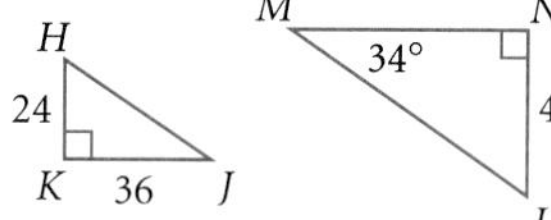

11. $m\angle N$ 90°   **12.** $m\angle H$ 56°   **13.** MN 60

P **14.** the similarity ratio of $\triangle HJK$ to $\triangle LMN$ $\frac{3}{5}$

P **15.** the similarity ratio of $\triangle LMN$ to $\triangle HJK$ $\frac{5}{3}$

P **Solve for *w*, *x*, *y*, and *z*.**

16. $RSTU \sim DEFG$ $x = 5$; $y = 4$; $z = 6$; $w = 65$ **17.** $\triangle JKL \sim \triangle JMN$ $x = 5.83$; $y = 5.14$; $z = 4.17$; $w = 55$

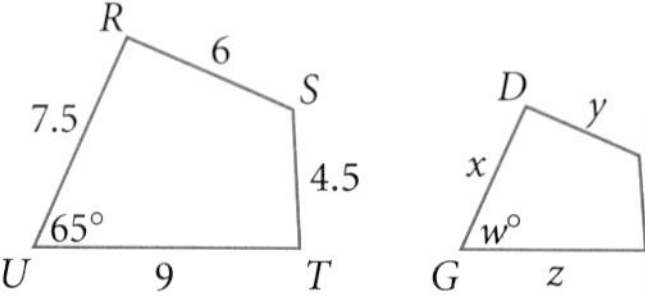

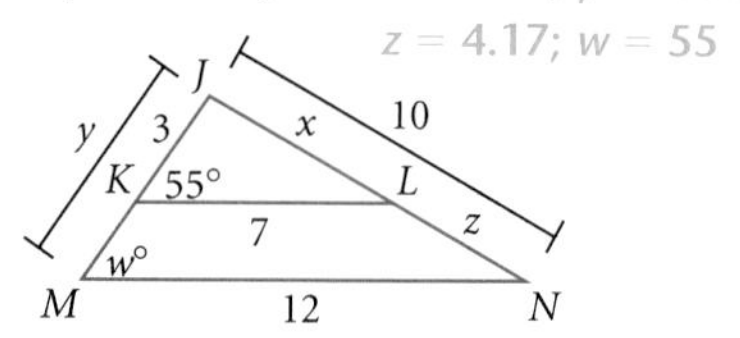

P **18.** The two triangles shown are similar, and the lengths of two corresponding sides are given. The ratio of the area of the larger triangle to the area of the smaller is (d)

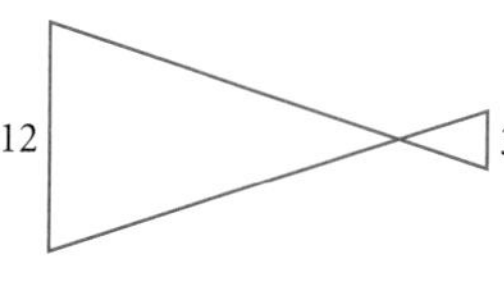

(a) $\frac{12}{3}$ (b) $\frac{4}{1}$ (c) $\frac{2}{1}$ (d) $\frac{16}{1}$

PS, MR **19. Golden Screen Awards** **a.** The owner of Comfy Cinema, a small movie theater, has a screen that is a golden rectangle. If it is eighteen feet long, how wide is it? 11.12 feet

b. The owner of Tremendo Theater also has a screen that is a golden rectangle. In her advertisements, she claims, "Our screens have four times the area of Comfy Cinema's!" If this is true, what are the dimensions of Tremendo Theater's screen? Explain how you found your answer.
$\frac{\text{Area of Tremendo}}{\text{Area of Comfy}} = 4 = 2^2$. Screen is 2(18) by 2(11.12), or 36 × 22.24 feet

Assessment Resources

- **Quiz 7-1**
- Chapter Assessment Form A
- Chapter Assessment Form B
- Chapter Alternative Assessment
- Mid-Year Assessment
- End-of-Year Assessment
- **AWSMTest and practice software**

Ongoing Assessment

Self-Assessment Self-Assessment Exercises

Embedded Assessment Explore Steps 2, 3; Refle 1, 2

ADDITIONAL ANSWERS

7-2 Part C Exercises

14.

Preserves...	Location	Size	Angle Measure	Orientation
Reflection	No	Yes	Yes	No
Rotation	No	Yes	Yes	Yes
Translation	No	Yes	Yes	Yes
Dilation	No	No	Yes	Yes

7-2

Properties of Similar Figures

SUPERLESSON AT A GLANCE

Superlesson Goal

Students will become familiar with postulates and theorems that can be used to prove triangles similar. They will also see connections between similarity and dilations.

Management Guide

	Topic	Objectives	Key Terms	New Ideas	Materials
Part A	Similar Triangles	To discover the AA similarity postulate and use it to solve a real-world problem.		The AA similarity postulate.	**Student** Protractor, ruler, geometry software
Part B	SAS Similarity	To discover the SAS similarity theorem and use it to solve a real-world problem.		The SAS similarity theorem.	**Student** Protractor, ruler, geometry software
Part C	Dilations	To explore dilations and their connection to similarity.	Dilation, center of dilation, scale factor of a dilation	Using dilations to enlarge or reduce a figure. Properties of dilations.	**Student** Protractor, ruler, geometry software
Part D	Triangle Midsegments	To investigate properties of midsegments of triangles.	Midsegment of a triangle	Midsegments and their properties.	**Student** Protractor, ruler, compass, geometry software
Part E	Making Connections	To make and use a tool that uses properties of similar triangles to measure distant objects.	In Making Connections, students apply and synthesize key terms and new ideas.		**Student** 3" × 5" card, scissors, ruler or meter stick, tape

Pacing Chart (45-Minute Periods)

	Comprehensive Course	Core Course	Informal Course
Part A	1	1	2
Part B	1	1	2
Part C	1	1	1
Part D	1	1	0
Part E	1	1	1
TOTAL periods for Superlesson	5	5	6

NCTM Standards

Mathematics as Problem Solving

Mathematics as Communication

Mathematics as Reasoning

Mathematical Connections

Geometry from a Synthetic Perspective

7-2 Properties of Similar Figures

San Francisco Chronicle

★★★★★ APRIL 14, 1993 50 CENTS

Building on Similarity

A story from the *San Francisco Chronicle* by Bill Workman on April 14, 1993, described plans for the construction of the world's tallest building in Tokyo, Japan. The following are excerpts from the article.

The Tokyo building will be 1,830 feet tall—or 376 feet taller than Chicago's Sears Tower, which is currently the world's tallest...The Shimizu office-retail skyscraper will have a daytime population of 50,000 and include two shopping malls and a major hotel in its upper floors, along with three stories of penthouse executive offices.

Seismic studies suggest that the Shimizu skyscraper's tapered, reinforced lightweight steel construction should be able to withstand a temblor of an unprecedented 8.4 magnitude and winds greater than 102 miles per hour...

Makato Watabe, senior managing director of the Shimizu Corporation, is one of many architects and structural engineers who have worked on the design of the project. To be able to design buildings of this size, people like Mr. Watabe coordinate aspects of perspective drawing, mathematics, structural engineering, and environmental control. As the project leader, he blends his technical knowledge with artistry and an understanding of the community's needs.

A model of the Shimizu skyscraper

1. Before any large building is constructed, a miniature model is made. How does the model help in the design of the building?

2. Describe how similarity might be used to construct the model.

3. What are some possible problems in using a model for a building of this size?

485

Where Are We Now?

Students have explored similar figures and applied their properties. In Chapter 6, they used triangle congruence postulates and theorems in deductive proofs.

Where Are We Going?

In 7-2, students will investigate ways to prove that triangles are similar and use similar triangles to solve real-world problems. They also explore dilation, a transformation that produces similar figures.

Similar triangles and their applications are important when students use trigonometry to work with similar right triangles in 7-3. The investigation of dilations completes their initial exploration of transformations. Compositions of transformations are explored in Chapter 10.

Possible Answers

1. It helps show the appearance of the building, so architects can get a sense of its proportions, relationship to other buildings in the area, etc. A model can be easily modified until a suitable design is found.

2. Scale factors can be used to determine lengths in the model.

3. The model will be made from different materials and with different construction techniques than the actual building. Therefore, many of its properties, including structural strength, earthquake resistance, etc., will be different from the properties of the actual building.

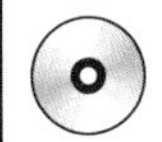

AWSM Videodisc

Focus on Geometry

▶ **7-2** Properties of Similar Figures

Search:

Play: Step:

More About Skyscrapers

The development of the skyscraper lagged behind the development of safe passenger elevators. The first such elevator was installed in New York City in 1857. The first "skyscraper," 130 feet tall, was the Equitable Life Assurance Society Building, also in New York, built in 1859. The Empire State Building, probably the most famous skyscraper, was completed in 1931. It reigned as the world's tallest until the early 1970s, when it was surpassed by both the Sears Towers in Chicago and the World Trade Center in New York.

Properties of Similar Figures

PART A At a Glance

Objective

To discover the AA similarity postulate and use it to solve a real-world problem.

Development

In the **Explore,** students discover the AA similarity postulate and then use it to solve a real-world problem.

Suggested Materials

Student Protractor, ruler, geometry software

First Five Minutes

Transparency FFM 7-2A

List all the ways that you know of to prove triangles congruent. **SSS, SAS, SAA, ASA, definition of congruent triangles; HL, HA, LL, LA**

Motivate

Ask...

- Is there an AAA congruence postulate? If not, show why there is no such postulate. **Two triangles can be drawn with equal angle measures but different side lengths.**

EXPLORE

Checking Up on the Architects

Recommended group size: 4

The Point

To discover the AA triangle similarity postulate and apply it to calculate a building's height.

Look and Listen...

- For students who do not remember that the angle of incidence is congruent to the angle of reflection.
- For students who do not realize that $\angle L$ is a right angle.

Ask...

- If Kyra stands straight up, what angle does she make with the ground?

7-2 PART A Similar Triangles

← CONNECT → ***Polygons are similar if their corresponding angles are congruent and the lengths of their corresponding sides are proportional. Now you will see whether you can conclude that triangles are similar with less information.***

Shortcuts like ASA and SSS let you prove triangles congruent without knowing about every pair of corresponding parts. You might wonder if there are any postulates or theorems like these for similarity.

In the following Explore, you will investigate whether two triangles are similar if two angles of one triangle are congruent to two angles of the other. In other words, is there an Angle-Angle (AA) similarity shortcut?

EXPLORE: CHECKING UP ON THE ARCHITECTS

MATERIALS

Ruler, Protractor
Geometry software (optional)

1. Draw two triangles of different sizes with two pairs of corresponding angles congruent on your paper or computer screen. Are the remaining angles congruent? Are the side lengths proportional? Write down any conjectures that you can about the triangles.
2. After the Shimizu skyscraper is completed, Kyra visits Tokyo. She wants to check whether the building is actually 1830 ft tall. She places a mirror at her feet and walks back so that she can see the top of the building in the mirror.
   Why is $\angle LMK \cong \angle SMT$? Does your conjecture from Step 1 apply to the triangles in the figure? Why or why not?
3. Kyra is 5′5″ tall, so she estimates that her eyes are 5 ft above the ground. The distance to the mirror, LM, is 1 ft. What other distance(s) does she need to measure before she can find TS, the height of the building?
4. Assume that the distance she needs to find in Step 3 is 366 ft. Is the building actually 1830 ft tall?

Technology Note

When using software to explore similarity, watch for students who use overly precise measurements. They may take longer to draw triangles (for instance, as they try to draw a 32.148° angle). Length inaccuracies evident at a high degree of precision may lead to unequal ratios and a misleading conclusion that triangles are not similar.

TRY IT

Give a similarity correspondence for each pair of triangles, and explain why the triangles are similar.

a.

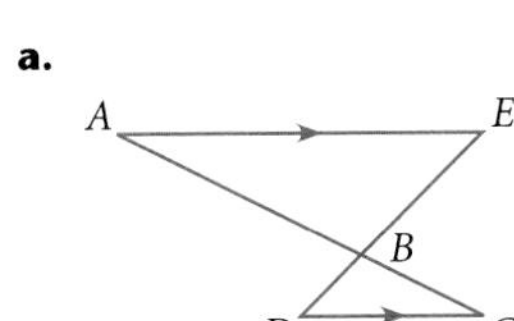

E ≅ ∠CBD since are vertical angles. ≅ ∠C because they alternate interior les ($\overline{AE}$ and $\overline{DC}$ are llel). By the two gruent angles ecture E ~ △CBD.

b.

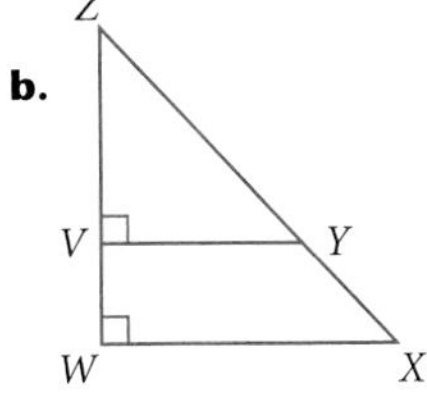

∠ZVY ≅ ∠W since both are right angles; ∠Z is used in both △VZY and △WZX; By the two congruent angles conjecture △ZVY ~ △ZWX.

EXAMPLE

Solve for x in the figure at the right.

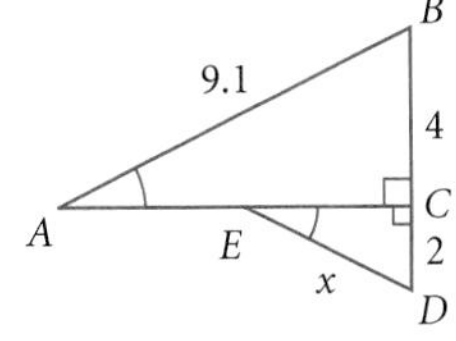

$\angle A \cong \angle DEC$, and $\angle DCE \cong \angle BCA$ because right angles are congruent. Therefore, $\triangle ACB \sim \triangle ECD$. Corresponding side lengths are proportional, so $\frac{x}{9.1} = \frac{2}{4}$.

Therefore, $4x = 18.2$, and $x = 4.55$.

You've seen a shortcut for showing that two triangles are similar—the AA Similarity Postulate.

AA SIMILARITY POSTULATE

If two angles of one triangle are congruent to two angles of another triangle, then the triangles are similar.

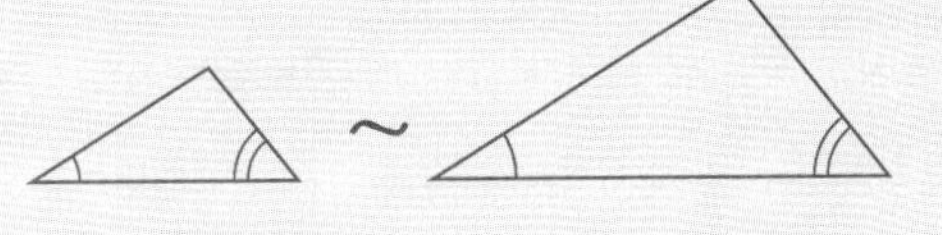

REFLECT

For a pair of triangles of each type, what additional information (if any) must be given about their angles for you to conclude that the triangles are similar?

1. right △s **2.** isosceles △s **3.** equilateral △s

4. Suppose you draw $\triangle ABC$. Describe a way to construct $\triangle DEF$ so that $\triangle ABC \sim \triangle DEF$, and the similarity ratio of $\triangle ABC$ to $\triangle DEF$ is $\frac{1}{2}$.

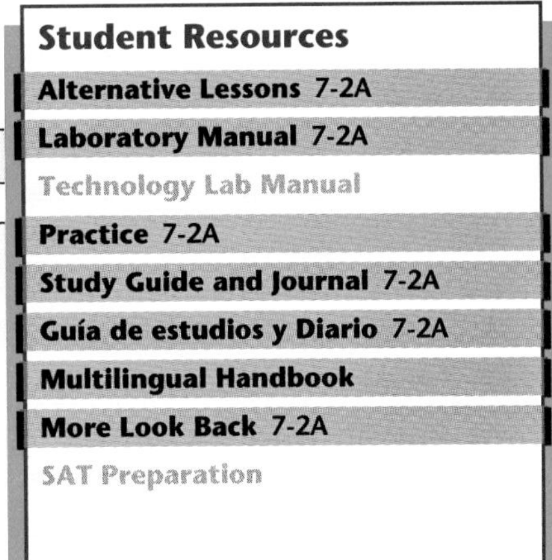

Student Resources
- Alternative Lessons 7-2A
- Laboratory Manual 7-2A
- Technology Lab Manual
- Practice 7-2A
- Study Guide and Journal 7-2A
- Guía de estudios y Diario 7-2A
- Multilingual Handbook
- More Look Back 7-2A
- SAT Preparation

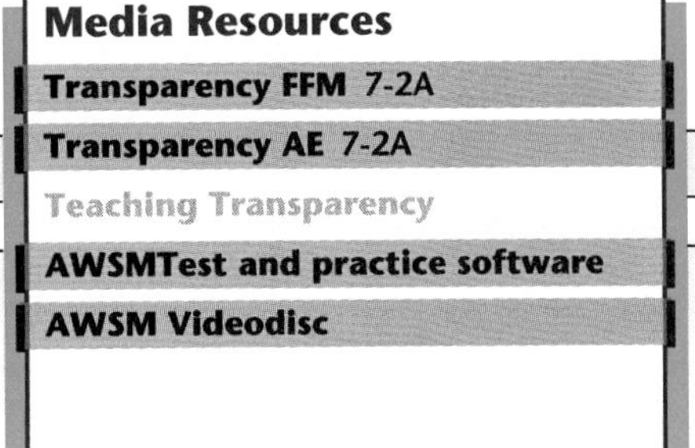

Media Resources
- Transparency FFM 7-2A
- Transparency AE 7-2A
- Teaching Transparency
- AWSMTest and practice software
- AWSM Videodisc

For Groups That Finish Early

If Kyra places the mirror 20 ft from the building, how far away from the reflection in the mirror must she stand to be able to see the top of the building? **0.055 feet (about $\frac{2}{3}$ of an inch)**

Follow Up

Ask students to share their conjectures from Step 1 and summarize this result in *if-then* form. Then ask whether the skyscraper is actually 1830 ft tall.

Possible Answers

1. Triangles with two pairs of congruent angles are similar.
2. $\angle L \cong \angle S$, because both are right angles. $\angle KML \cong \angle TMS$ because the angle of incidence is congruent to the angle of reflection. Thus, the triangles are similar from the conjecture in Step 1.
3. She needs to measure the distance from the mirror to the building.
4. Yes, the building is 1830 feet tall.

ALTERNATE EXAMPLE

Transparency AE 7-2A

Journal

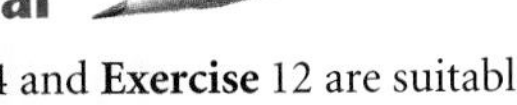

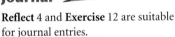

Reflect 4 and **Exercise** 12 are suitable for journal entries.

REFLECT

Possible Answers

1. One pair of acute angles is congruent.
2. One pair of vertex or base angles is congruent.
3. All equilateral triangles are similar.
4. Construct $\angle D \cong \angle A$. Using the congruent-segments construction, extend one side of $\angle D$ so that it is twice as long as $\overline{AB}$. Label the other endpoint of this segment E. Then construct an angle with vertex at E and one side $\overline{DE}$ so that $\angle E \cong \angle B$. Label the point where the unshared sides of $\angle D$ and $\angle E$ intersect with an F.

Properties of Similar Figures

Part A Exercises

Exercise Notes

Core

11. and 14. These are proofs that involve the AA postulate.

12. Students see that they must be careful before assuming that a real-world situation can be accurately modeled by similar triangles.

13. Students explore geometric means involving altitudes of right triangles.

More Math Reasoning

27. Students see how the principle of triangle similarity is used in cameras.

Exercise Answers

Core

4. $m\angle N = 70°$, so they are similar (AA).

5. Not similar; $m\angle N = 70°$, so there is no second pair of congruent angles.

6. $\angle ADE \cong \angle ABC$ and $\angle AED \cong \angle ACB$ because $DE \parallel BC$ (corresponding angles are congruent); Thus by AA, $\triangle ADE \sim \triangle ABC$; $x = 6\frac{2}{3}$; $y = 11\frac{2}{3}$

7. Given $\angle WXZ \cong \angle ZXY$ and $\angle WZX \cong \angle XYZ$, $\triangle XWZ \sim \triangle XZY$ by AA; $x = 7.5$; $y = 4.5$

8. $\angle FHG \cong \angle IHJ$ because they are vertical angles; $\angle F \cong \angle J$ is given; Thus by AA, $\triangle FHG \sim \triangle JHI$; $x = 5.67$; $y = 5.63$

10. Assume that both the meter stick and the tree are perpendicular to the ground; the sun's rays are parallel, so the angles the sun's rays make with the ground are congruent. Thus, by AA, the triangle formed by the sun's ray, the meter stick, and its shadow is similar to the triangle formed by the sun's ray, the tree, and its shadow. $\frac{t}{1} = \frac{10}{0.8}$; $t = 12.5$. The tree is 12.5 meters tall.

Exercises

CORE

P **Getting Started Find the measure of $\angle A$ that makes each pair of triangles similar.**

1. 30°

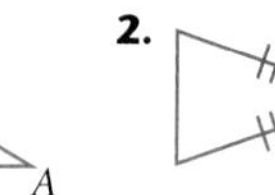

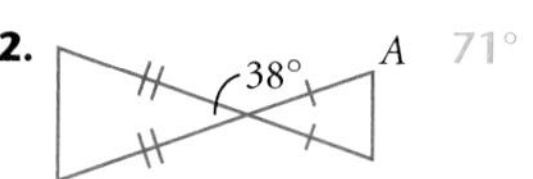

2. 71°

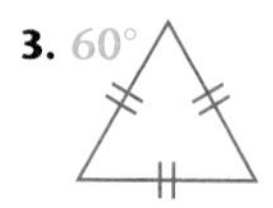

3. 60°

P **Determine whether each pair of triangles is similar. Explain your reasoning.**

4. $\triangle PQO$ and $\triangle NML$

5. $\triangle NML$ and $\triangle TSR$

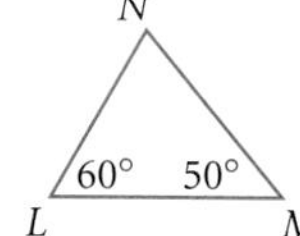

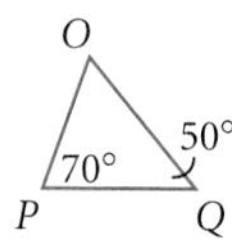

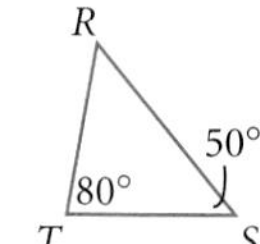

P **Give the similarity correspondence for each pair of triangles, and explain why the triangles are similar. Then solve for x and y.**

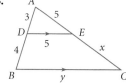

6. **7.**

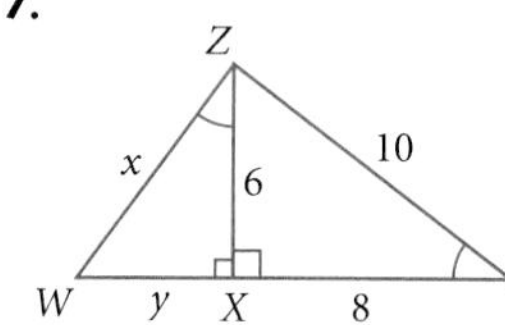

8.

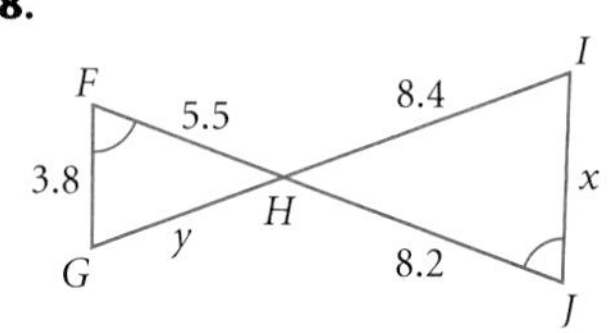

PS **9. Tall Buildings in a Single Calculation** From point A, a line segment includes the top of the head (E) of a person 6 ft tall and the top of a building (D). The distance AB is 8 ft, and the distance BC is 42 ft. What is the height of the building? 37.5 feet

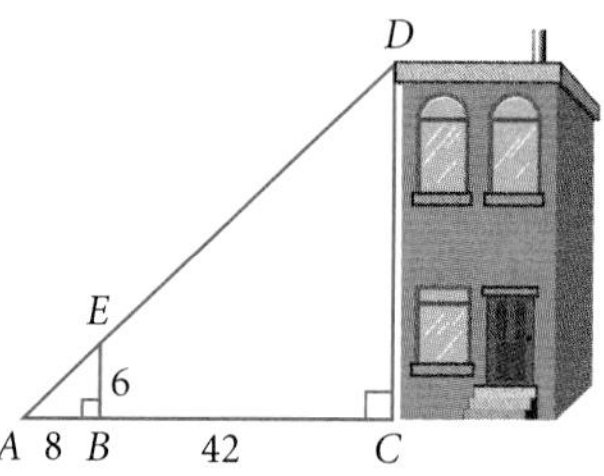

PS **10.** When an upright meter stick casts a shadow 0.8 m long, the shadow of a nearby tree is 10 m long. How tall is the tree? Explain your reasoning.

MR **11.** *Given:* $\overline{VW} \parallel \overline{YZ}$

Prove: $\frac{VW}{YZ} = \frac{WX}{XY}$

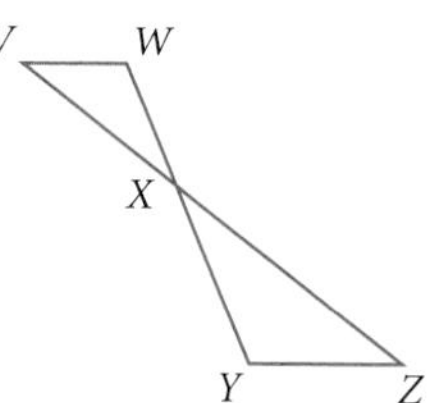

Key

V Vocabulary
P Practice/Skills
R Review
MR Math Reasoning
PS Problem Solving
C Challenge

12. Spike It! Marta hits a volleyball so that it strikes the ground fifteen feet away from her.

a. If her hand was nine feet off the ground when she hit the ball and the wall is fifty-four feet from where the ball hit the ground, use similar triangles to find how high up on the wall the ball will hit. Explain why the triangles you worked with are similar.

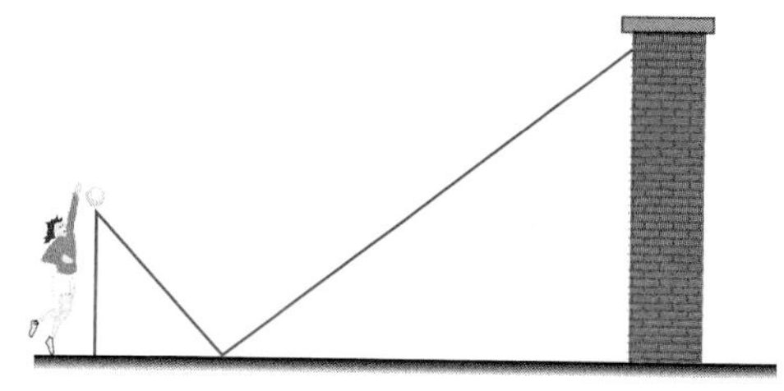

b. Do you think your answer in **12a** tells you exactly where the ball will hit, is a good approximation for where the ball will hit, or is a poor approximation for where the ball will hit? If it is an approximation, do you think it is an overestimate or an underestimate? Explain.

13. We say x is the **geometric mean** between a and b if $\frac{a}{x} = \frac{x}{b}$ and a, b, and x are positive. For example, 4 is the geometric mean between 2 and 8, since $\frac{2}{4} = \frac{4}{8}$. Use the figure to give examples of each of the following statements.

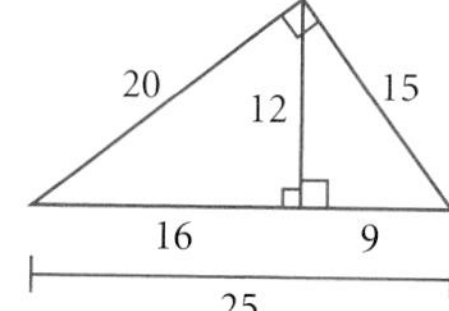

a. The length of the altitude to the hypotenuse of a right triangle is the geometric mean between the lengths of the two segments on the hypotenuse.

b. In a right triangle with an altitude to the hypotenuse, the length of each leg is the geometric mean between the length of the segment of the hypotenuse adjacent to the leg and the length of the whole hypotenuse.

14. *Given:* $\angle 1 \cong \angle 2$, $\overline{XY} \perp \overline{WZ}$

Prove: $\frac{WZ}{WY} = \frac{XZ}{YZ}$

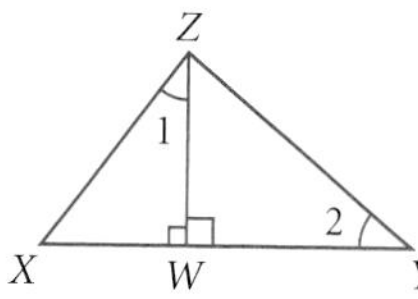

LOOK BACK

ABCD is a parallelogram. Complete each statement. [6-2]

15. If $AD = 16$, $BC =$ ____. 16

16. If $AE = 12$, $AC =$ ____. 24

17. If $m\angle ADC = 52°$, $m\angle BAD =$ ____. 128°

18. If $m\angle ADC = (2x + 24)°$ and $m\angle ABC = (5x - 57)°$, find $m\angle ABC$. 78°

Trapezoid *HJKL* ~ trapezoid *MNOP*. Find each ratio. [7-1]

19. $\frac{HJ}{MN}$ $\frac{2}{3}$ **20.** $\frac{\text{perimeter } HJKL}{\text{perimeter } MNOP}$ $\frac{2}{3}$ **21.** $\frac{\text{area } HJKL}{\text{area } MNOP}$ $\frac{4}{9}$

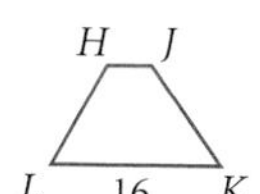

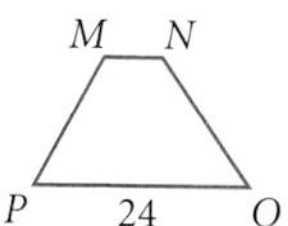

Ongoing Assessment

Self-Assessment Exercises 1–13 odd

Embedded Assessment Try It a and b; Exercises 8, 10, 14

11. $\angle VXW \cong \angle YXZ$ because they are vertical angles; $\angle W \cong \angle Y$ because they are alternate interior angles of two parallel lines; Thus, by AA, $\triangle VXW \sim \triangle ZXY$. Since the triangles are similar, the corresponding sides are proportional, so $\frac{VW}{YZ} = \frac{WX}{XY}$.

12. a. Assume that Marta and the wall are perpendicular to the ground. The angles formed where the ball hits the ground and where it continues toward the wall are congruent (angle of impact ≅ angle of rebound), so the triangles are similar by AA. $\frac{x}{9} = \frac{54}{15}$; $x = 32.4$ feet.

b. Possible answer: It is probably a poor approximation. In practice, the ball would be affected by gravity, so its path would be a curve, not a straight line. The 32.4 feet overestimates the real-world value.

13. a. $\frac{9}{12} = \frac{12}{16}$, so 12 is the geometric mean of 9 and 16.

b. $\frac{16}{20} = \frac{20}{25}$, so 20 is the geometric mean of 16 and 25. $\frac{9}{15} = \frac{15}{25}$, so 15 is the geometric mean of 9 and 25.

14. $\angle 1 \cong \angle 2$ (given). $\angle XWZ \cong \angle ZWY$ (right angles are congruent). $\triangle XWZ \sim \triangle ZWY$ by AA. Since they are similar, corresponding sides are proportional; i.e., $\frac{WZ}{WY} = \frac{XZ}{ZY}$.

Properties of Similar Figures

More Practice

22. $\angle T \cong \angle X$ (alternate interior angles), and $\angle TVU \cong \angle XVW$ (vertical angles are congruent). Therefore, by AA, $\triangle TUV \sim \triangle XWV$.

23. From the given information, $\angle T \cong \angle Q$. $\angle U \cong \angle R$ because right angles are congruent. By AA, $\triangle TUV \sim \triangle QRS$.

24. $\angle A \cong \angle E$ (given). $\angle ACB \cong \angle ECD$ (vertical angles). Therefore, by AA, $\triangle ACB \sim \triangle ECD$; $x = \frac{5}{2}$; $y = \frac{7}{2}$

25. Based on given information, $\triangle FHG \sim \triangle JHI$ by AA; $x = 4$; $y = 10$

26. The base angles of isosceles triangles are congruent, so by AA, $\triangle KLM \sim \triangle NPQ$; $x = 3$; $y = 38$

More Math Reasoning

27. a. Assume $\overline{XY} \parallel \overline{AB}$, so $\angle X \cong \angle B$ and $\angle Y \cong \angle A$ (alternate interior angles); By AA, the triangles are similar.

b. 3.5 m **c.** 2.5 m

28. Since both figures are rectangles, all (corresponding) angles are congruent (and are 90°). $\triangle AGF$ and $\triangle ADC$ share an angle and have one right angle, so by AA, the triangles are similar. Because the two figures of interest are rectangles, $BC = AD$, $BA = CD$, $AE = FG$, and $EF = AG$. Because the triangles are similar, $\frac{FG}{CD} = \frac{AG}{AD}$, and by substitution, $\frac{FG}{CD} = \frac{AG}{AD} = \frac{EF}{BC} = \frac{EA}{BA}$. Then, since corresponding sides are proportional and corresponding angles are congruent, the rectangles are similar.

MORE PRACTICE

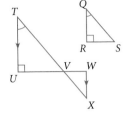

P **Determine whether each pair of triangles is similar. Explain your reasoning.**

22. $\triangle TUV$ and $\triangle XWV$

23. $\triangle TUV$ and $\triangle QRS$

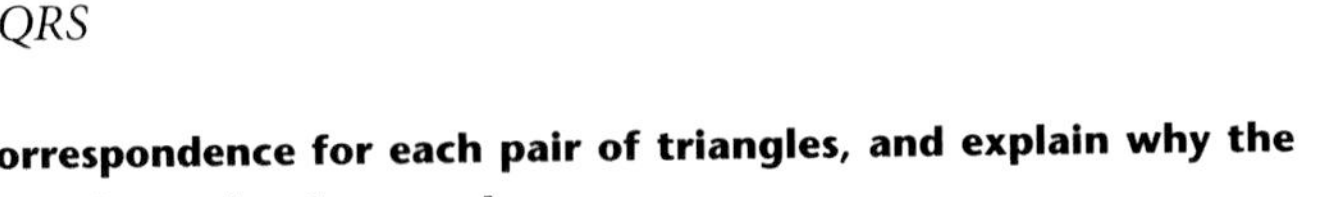

P **Give a similarity correspondence for each pair of triangles, and explain why the triangles are similar. Then solve for x and y.**

24.

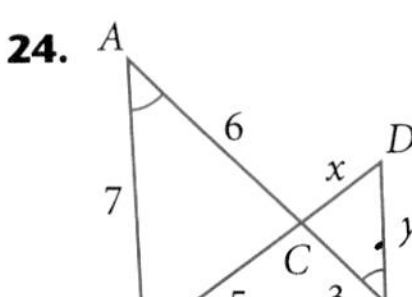

25.

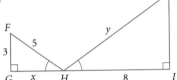

26.

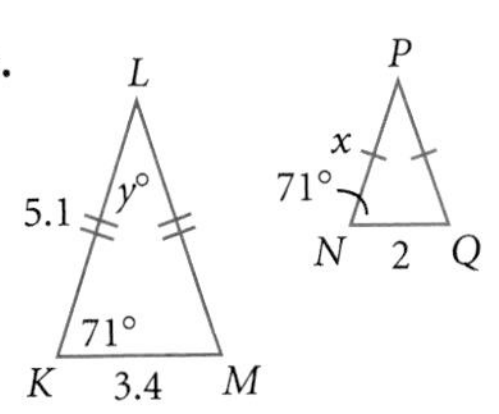

MORE MATH REASONING

PS Science **27. The Inside Scoop** The figure below shows a camera with a film width XY that is 35 mm and a focal length of 50 mm. The width of the scene is AB.

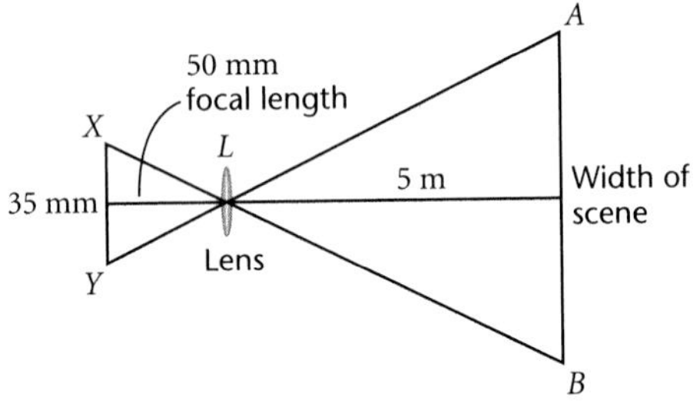

a. What assumptions could you make about this figure that allow you to conclude that $\triangle ALB \sim \triangle YLX$?

b. What is the width of the scene?

c. If the lens of the camera has a focal length of 70 mm, what is the width of the scene?

MR, C **28. The Diagonal Test** Rectangle $ABCD$ overlaps rectangle $AEFG$ so that $\overline{AE}$ lies on $\overline{AB}$ and $\overline{AG}$ lies on $\overline{AD}$. Show that the rectangles are similar if the diagonal from point A to point C passes through point F.

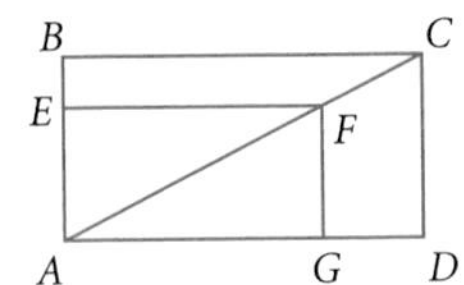

Key

V Vocabulary
P Practice/Skills
R Review
MR Math Reasoning
PS Problem Solving
C Challenge

7-2 PART B SAS Similarity

← CONNECT → ***You know one shortcut for showing that triangles are similar. Now you will investigate another way to prove triangle similarity.***

The congruence postulates and theorems for triangles all require that you have at least one pair of congruent sides. Of course, similar triangles have proportional side lengths. In the following Explore, you will see whether information about proportional side lengths can help you prove that two triangles are similar.

EXPLORE: USE SIMILAR REASONING

MATERIALS

Protractor, Ruler
Geometry software (optional)

1. An SAS similarity postulate or theorem would let you prove that two triangles are similar if two pairs of sides have proportional lengths and their included angles are congruent. Does SAS similarity work? To explore this, use geometry software or a protractor and ruler to draw two triangles with the SAS similarity characteristics. Are the triangles similar? Write a conjecture about SAS similarity.
2. Use similarity to make a plan for solving the following problem. Then create hypothetical values for any measurements you need, and solve the problem. Before making plans for a bridge from North Lake to Shore View, you need to know its approximate length. You can measure short distances using a tape measure and longer ones using the odometer on your truck. You can mark off straight lines, but you have no way to measure angles. How can you find the bridge's length?

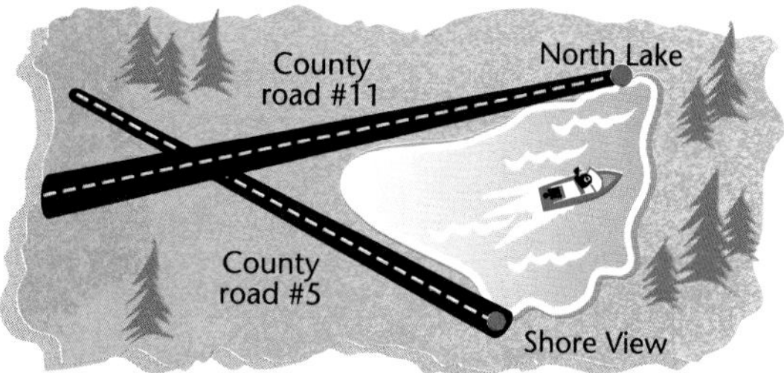

The following Example shows one way you can use SAS similarity.

Student Resources
- Alternative Lessons 7-2B
- Laboratory Manual 7-2B
- Technology Lab Manual
- Practice 7-2B
- Study Guide and Journal 7-2B
- Guía de estudios y Diario 7-2B
- Multilingual Handbook
- More Look Ahead 7-2B
- SAT Preparation

Media Resources
- Transparency FFM 7-2B
- Transparency AE 7-2B
- Teaching Transparency
- AWSMTest and practice software
- AWSM Videodisc

PART B At a Glance

Objective
To discover the SAS similarity theorem and use it to solve a real-world problem.

Development
In the **Explore,** students discover the SAS similarity theorem and use it in an applications setting.

Suggested Materials
Student Protractor, ruler, geometry software

First Five Minutes
Transparency FFM 7-2B

$\triangle ABC \sim \triangle EFG$. If $AB = 7$, $BC = 10$, and $FG = 12$, find EF. $EF = 8.4$

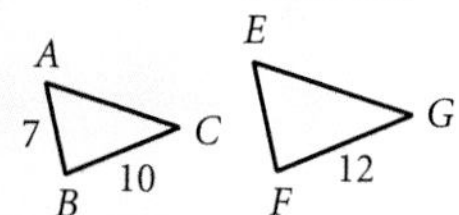

Motivate
Ask...
- If there were SAS or SSS similarity conjectures, what do you think you would have to know about the pairs of corresponding sides? That their lengths are proportional.

EXPLORE

Use Similar Reasoning
Recommended group size: 4

The Point
To discover the SAS similarity theorem and apply it to solve a real-world problem.

Look and Listen...
- For students who have difficulty devising a way to solve the application problem.

Ask...
- Which angles are congruent?
- Which segments would you need to work with to be able to use the conjecture you made in Step 1?

7-2

Properties of Similar Figures

For Groups That Finish Early

Suppose that you *can* measure angles. Is there another way to solve the problem in Step 2? **Measure an angle with its vertex at North Lake or Shore View. Use this angle measure to complete the smaller triangle, and then use AA similarity.**

Follow Up

Ask students to explain how they solved the problem in Step 2.

Possible Answers

1. If an angle in one triangle is congruent to an angle in another and the lengths of the sides that include the angles are proportional, then the triangles are similar.
2. Draw the segment joining North Lake and Shore View to complete one triangle. Use the truck odometer to measure the distances from North Lake and Shore View to the intersection of the roads (point X). Then use the tape measure to measure off distances along the roads so that the lengths of the shorter segments are in the same ratio as the lengths of the long segments. Complete the smaller triangle, and measure its third side. Use proportions to find the distance across the lake.

ALTERNATE EXAMPLE

Transparency AE 7-2B

Journal

Reflect 1 and 2 and **Exercise** 14 are suitable for journal entries.

REFLECT

Possible Answers

1. At least two pairs of sides are needed to set up a proportion.
2. To use congruent triangles, you must set up two triangles that are the same size. Using similar triangles is more convenient, because the second triangle can be made a convenient size.

EXAMPLE

Find a value of x that makes $\triangle ABC \sim \triangle EBD$.

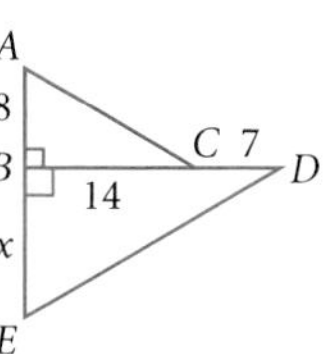

The right angles shown are congruent. Therefore, if $\frac{EB}{AB} = \frac{BD}{BC}$ or $\frac{x}{8} = \frac{21}{14}$, the triangles are similar.

$\frac{x}{8} = \frac{21}{14} = \frac{3}{2}$

$2x = 24$

Therefore, if $x = 12$, $\triangle ABC \sim \triangle EBD$.

TRY IT

Give a similarity correspondence for each pair of triangles, and explain why the triangles are similar. Then solve for x.

a.

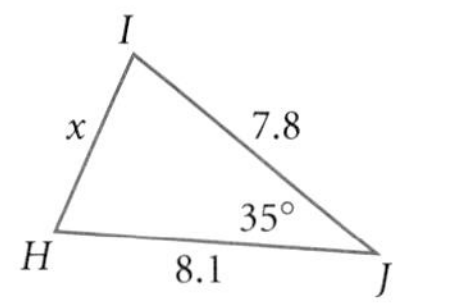

b.

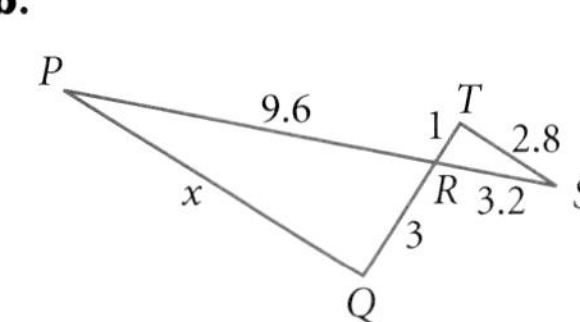

a. $\frac{7.8}{5.2} = \frac{8.1}{5.4} = 1.5$; Two pairs of corresponding sides are proportional, and the angles between them are given as congruent, so by SAS, $\triangle JHI \sim \triangle EDF$; $x = 4.8$

b. $\frac{TR}{RQ} = \frac{SR}{PR} = \frac{3.2}{9.6} = \frac{1}{3}$. The interior (to the triangles) angles formed by $\overline{TQ}$ intersecting $\overline{PS}$ are congruent because they are vertical angles. Thus, by SAS, $\triangle PRQ \sim \triangle SRT$; $x = 8.4$

SAS similarity can be proved from the AA Similarity Postulate, so this result is stated as a theorem.

SAS SIMILARITY THEOREM

If an angle of one triangle is congruent to an angle of another triangle and the lengths of the sides that include the angles are proportional, then the triangles are similar.

REFLECT

1. Explain why there is no SA Similarity Theorem.
2. Why do you think it is often more convenient to use similar triangles than congruent triangles to solve real-world problems?

Research Note

Computer graphics tools may positively affect spatial skills, with special benefits for girls. (Douglas H. Clements and Michael T. Battista, "Geometry and Spatial Reasoning," *Handbook of Research on Mathematics Teaching and Learning,* Douglas A. Grouws, ed., p. 452. © 1992 NCTM.)

Exercises

CORE

Getting Started For each of the following, write a similarity statement, and give a reason that the triangles are similar.

1.

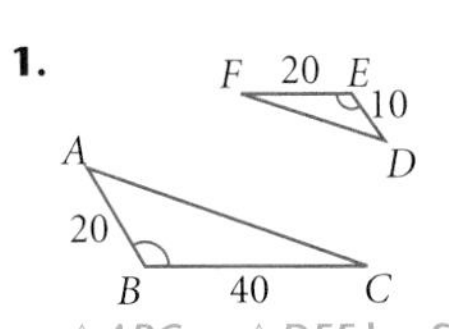

$\triangle ABC \sim \triangle DEF$ by SAS

2.

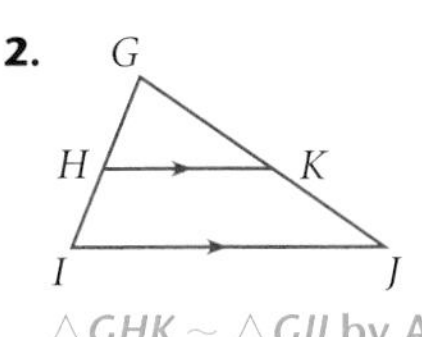

$\triangle GHK \sim \triangle GIJ$ by AA

3.

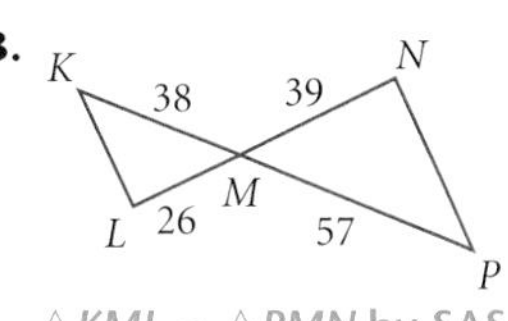

$\triangle KML \sim \triangle PMN$ by SAS

Give a similarity correspondence for each pair of triangles, and explain why the triangles are similar. Then solve for *x* and *y*. Give exact values for *x* and *y*.

4. $\triangle ACB \sim \triangle ECD$ by SAS; $x = 40.5$; $y = 98$

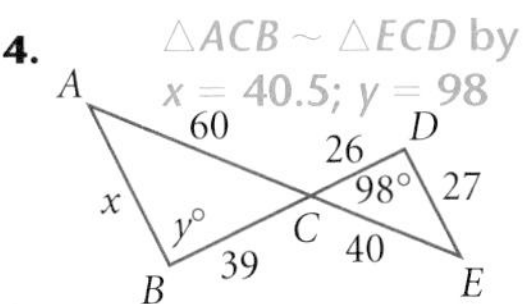

5. $\triangle FGH \sim \triangle JKH$ by SAS; $x = 124$; $y = 33$

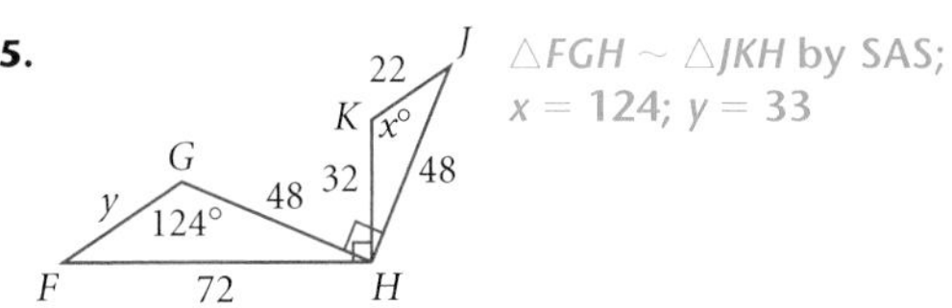

6. Off Course A golfer wanted to hit her ball 180 yd to the hole shown. She did hit the ball 180 yd, but, unfortunately, she sliced it in the wrong direction. She then put two 2-in. tees on the ground so that one lined up with her ball and one lined up with the hole. The ends of the tees were $\frac{1}{2}$ in. apart. How far is her ball from the hole? Explain your reasoning.

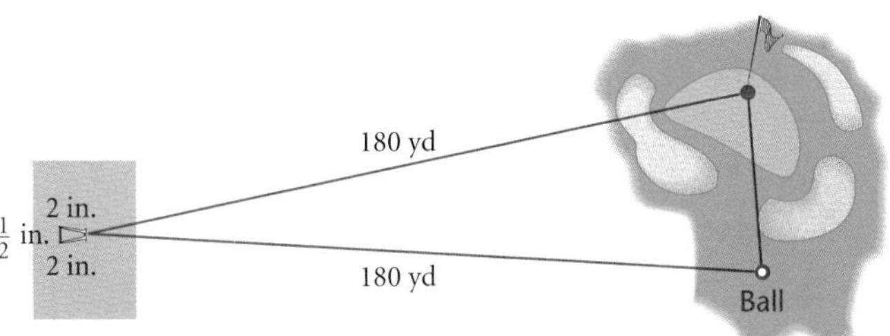

7. *Given:* $LN = 2NP$, $MN = 2NQ$

Prove: $\overline{LM} \parallel \overline{PQ}$

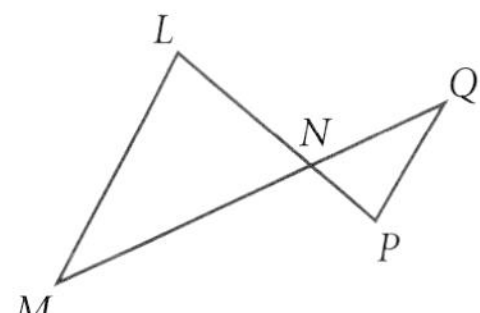

8. Do you think there is an SAS Similarity Theorem for parallelograms? Carefully draw several parallelograms to explore this possibility. Then state an SAS Similarity Theorem for parallelograms or provide a counterexample to show why it does not work.

Part B Exercises

Exercise Notes

Core

9–11. Students use the SSS and SAS similarity theorems.

15. When solving this exercise, students often overlook the fact that Thales had to take the distance from the middle of the pyramid to one of its sides into account.

Look Ahead

These exercises look ahead to 7-2 Part C, where students investigate dilations.

More Math Reasoning

23–24. Students prove that the lengths of corresponding medians and altitudes of similar triangles are in the same ratio as the lengths of a pair of corresponding sides.

Exercise Answers

Core

6. We have two isosceles triangles with congruent vertex angles. By SAS, they are similar. Then $\frac{x}{0.5 \text{ in}} = \frac{180 \text{ yd}}{2 \text{ in}}$; $x = 45$ yards.

7. $\triangle LMN \sim \triangle PQN$ by SAS: two sides are proportional and the angles between these two sides are congruent (vertical angles). Therefore, corresponding angles are congruent, for example, $\angle L$ and $\angle P$. $\angle L$ and $\angle P$ can be considered alternate interior angles, and when alternate interior angles are congruent, the lines cut by the transversal are parallel. Therefore, $\overline{LM} \parallel \overline{PQ}$.

8. If an angle of one parallelogram is congruent to an angle of another parallelogram and the lengths of the sides that include the angles are proportional, then the parallelograms are similar.

y

Vocabulary
Practice/Skills
Review
Math Reasoning
Problem Solving
Challenge

Ongoing Assessment

Self-Assessment Exercises 1, 2, 3, 5, 9, 11, 13

Embedded Assessment Try It b; Exercises 7, 10, 14, 15

Algebra | Functions | Discrete Math | Probability | Data/Statistics

Properties of Similar Figures

12. Possible answer: Measure the side lengths of the tower, and build a model whose sides are proportional to the corresponding parts of the tower; rely on SSS to get similarity.

13. If two triangles are equilateral, all angles measure 60° and are congruent. The triangles are similar by AA.

14. No. Since there is no SSA congruence, there cannot be SSA similarity.

15. Possible answer: Consider an imaginary line drawn through the top of the pyramid down to the ground perpendicular to the ground. The angle (90°) this line makes with the ground is congruent to the angle made by sticking the staff vertically in the ground. Rays of the sun are parallel, so the angle the light makes from the top of the pyramid to the ground is the same as the angle from the top of the staff to the ground; AA shows the triangles made by the staff and its shadow and by the pyramid and its shadow are similar. The heights of the staff and pyramid are in the same proportion as the length of the staff's shadow and the sum of the length of the pyramid's shadow and half the width of its shadow.

Look Ahead

16. Possible answer: The scale factor is the ratio of the length of a side in the enlarged/reduced figure to the corresponding side in the original.

17. Extend two line segments along $\overline{RS}$ and $\overline{RT}$. Place the compass point at S and mark segment $\overline{SV}$ such that $\overline{RS} \cong \overline{SV}$; Similarly use the compass to create $\overline{TW} \cong \overline{RT}$. $\frac{RV}{RS} = \frac{RW}{RT} = 2$. Both triangles share $\angle R$, so SAS assures similarity of $\triangle RST$ and $\triangle RVW$.

There is a third way to prove that triangles are similar. The SSS Similarity Theorem lets you conclude that two triangles are similar if all of the corresponding sides have proportional lengths.

SSS SIMILARITY THEOREM

If the lengths of three sides of one triangle are proportional to the lengths of three sides of another triangle, then the triangles are similar.

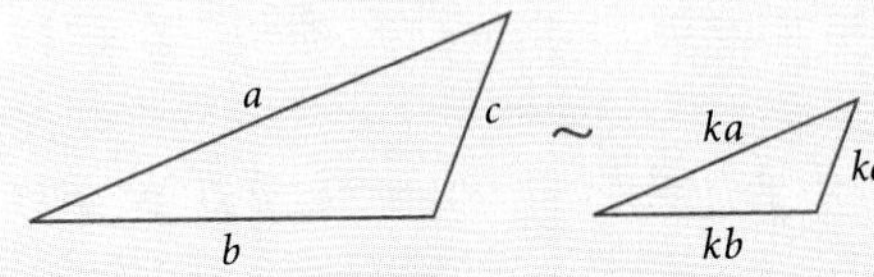

P **Find a value of *x* that makes each pair of triangles similar. State the theorem or postulate that justifies your answer.**

9. $x = 60$; SSS

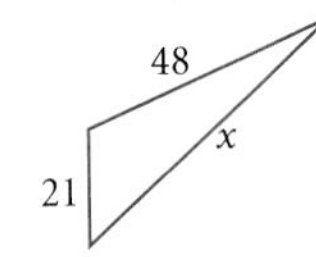

10.

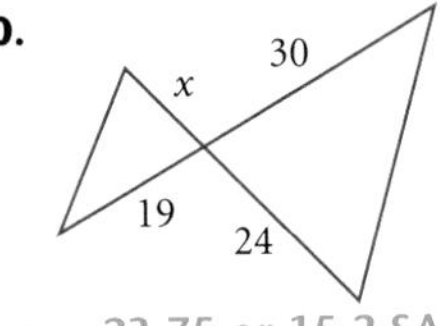

$x = 23.75$ or 15.2 SAS

11. $x = 6$; SAS

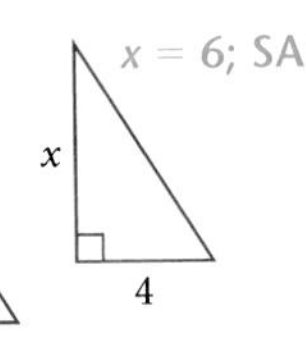

MR **12.** Could you make a scale model of the tower at the right without measuring any angles and be certain that it is similar to the actual tower? Write a short paragraph to explain your method.

MR **13.** Prove: If two triangles are equilateral, then they are similar.

MR **14.** Do you think there is an SSA similarity shortcut? Why or why not?

PS, C **15. A Shady Calculation** It is said that Thales, a teacher of Pythagoras, found the height of the Egyptian pyramids by using similar triangles. He began by placing his staff at the tip of a pyramid's shadow, as shown below. Explain how he found the height of the pyramid.

History

Key

- V Vocabulary
- P Practice/Skills
- R Review
- MR Math Reasoning
- PS Problem Solving
- C Challenge

LOOK AHEAD

V **16.** In your own words, define the scale factor of an enlargement or a reduction.

P **17.** Draw triangle *RST*. Then use a compass and straightedge to construct triangle *RVW* similar to $\triangle RST$ so that
- *R*, *S*, and *V* are collinear
- *R*, *T*, and *W* are collinear
- $\frac{RV}{RS} = 2$

Explain how you drew $\triangle RVW$. What similarity postulate or theorem ensures that the triangles are similar?

MORE PRACTICE

P **Give a similarity correspondence for each pair of triangles, and explain why the triangles are similar. Then solve for *x* and *y*. Give exact values for *x* and *y*.**

18.

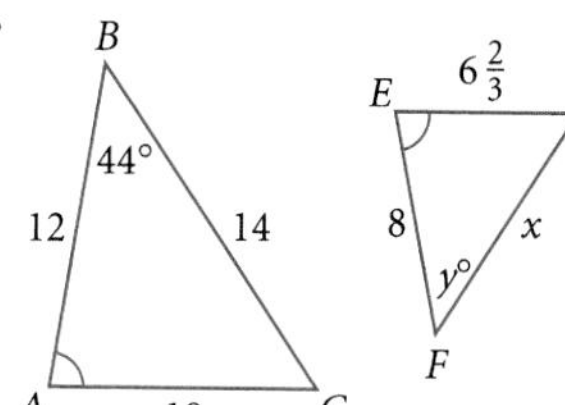

$\triangle ABC \sim \triangle EFD$ by SAS, $x = 9\frac{1}{3}$; $y = 44$

19.

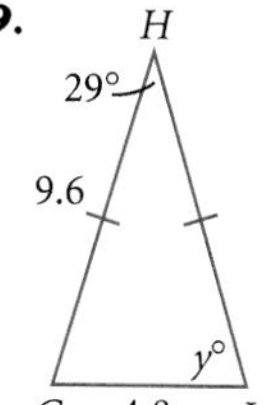

L x J, y°, 7.2, 29°, K

$\triangle GHI \sim \triangle LKJ$; Similarity by SAS; $x = 3.6$; $y = 75.5$

P **Find a value of *x* that makes each pair of triangles similar. State the theorem or postulate that justifies your answer.**

20.

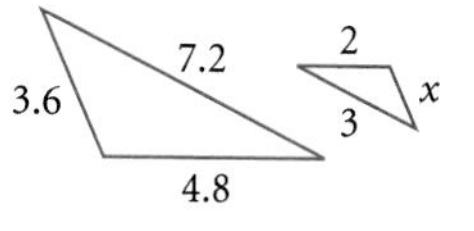

$x = 1.5$; SSS

21.

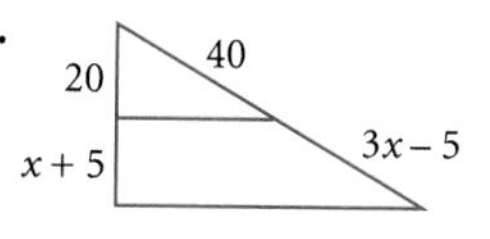

Possible answer: $x = 15$; SAS

22.

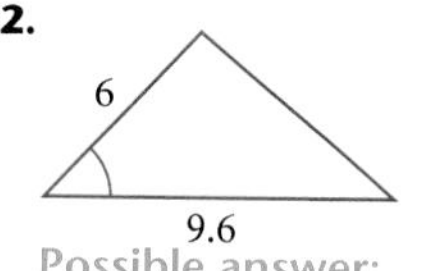

x, 7.2

Possible answer: $x = 4.5$ or 11.52; SAS

MORE MATH REASONING

R **Write a *plan* for each proof.**

23. Prove that the lengths of corresponding medians of two similar triangles are in the same ratio as the lengths of two corresponding sides.

24. Prove that the lengths of corresponding altitudes of two similar triangles are in the same ratio as the lengths of two corresponding sides.

More Math Reasoning

23.

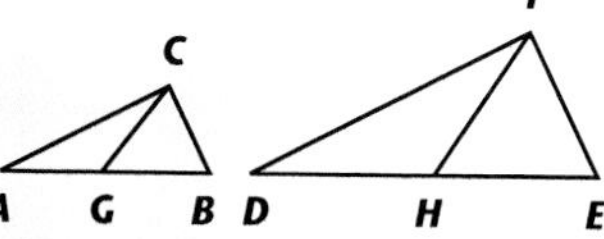

Possible answer: $\triangle ABC \sim \triangle DEF$ and $\overline{CG}$ and $\overline{FH}$ are medians. Show that $\triangle AGC \sim \triangle DHF$ by SAS. Therefore $\frac{AC}{DF} = \frac{GC}{HF}$.

24.

Possible answer: $\triangle ABC \sim \triangle EFG$. $\overline{BD}$ and $\overline{FH}$ are altitudes. Show that $\triangle BDC \sim \triangle FHG$ by AA. Therefore $\frac{BD}{FH} = \frac{BC}{FG}$.

Properties of Similar Figures

PART C At a Glance

Objective

To explore dilations and their connection to similarity.

Development

In the **Explore,** students see how to draw the dilation image of a figure, investigate properties of a figure that are and are not preserved by dilations, and discover the connection between dilation and similarity.

Then they see formal definitions of the terms and ideas they worked with in the **Explore.**

Suggested Materials

Student Protractor, ruler, geometry software

Key Terms

Dilation, center of dilation, scale factor of a dilation

First Five Minutes

Transparency FFM 7-1C

Sketch segment $\overline{AB}$. Then use a compass and straightedge to construct $\overline{CD}$ so that $CD = 3AB$.

Motivate

Ask...

- What transformations are you familiar with? Identify properties of a figure that are and are not preserved by each of these transformations. **Reflection, rotation, translation. Reflection reverses orientation; the others preserve it. All other properties of a figure (except for position) are preserved by these transformations.**

7-2 PART C Dilations

← CONNECT → *You've seen enlargements and reductions of everyday objects and geometric figures. Now you will use your knowledge of similarity to discover how a transformation can enlarge or reduce a figure.*

In the following Explore, we'll investigate a way to draw similar triangles. This method will introduce a new transformation—the **dilation.**

EXPLORE: A "DILATE-FUL" TRANSFORMATION

MATERIALS

Protractor, Ruler
Geometry software (optional)

1. Reproduce the steps shown at the bottom of this page on your paper or computer screen.
2. $\triangle A'B'C'$ is the **dilation image** of $\triangle ABC$. Make any measurements necessary to check whether $\triangle ABC \sim \triangle A'B'C'$. If you find that the triangles are similar, give your reason and the supporting data.
3. Draw another triangle and its dilation image. Make measurements, and give data to show whether or not the triangles are similar.
4. Use your data and any other measurements you need to identify the properties of the original triangles that are preserved by a dilation. Which properties are not preserved?
5. When you dilate a figure, is its image always similar to its pre-image? Explain.

CREATING A DILATION

A, P, B, C	P, A, B, C	P, A, A′, B, B′, C, C′
Draw any triangle, $\triangle ABC$. Draw a point P outside the triangle. P will be the **center of dilation.**	Draw $\overrightarrow{PA}$, $\overrightarrow{PB}$, and $\overrightarrow{PC}$. (Make the rays more than three times as long as $\overline{PA}$, $\overline{PB}$, and $\overline{PC}$.)	Draw points A', B', and C' so that $PA' = 3PA$, $PB' = 3PB$, and $PC' = 3PC$. Draw $\triangle A'B'C'$.

Technology Note

When using software to draw the image of point A on $\triangle ABC$, students will generally need to construct a point A' on $\overrightarrow{PA}$, then measure PA' and drag point A' until PA' is the desired length. Repeating this process for points B and C will locate the vertices of the image triangle.

Like reflections, rotations, and translations, dilations are transformations. Every dilation of a polygon produces a figure similar to the pre-image.

DEFINITION

A **dilation** with **center of dilation** C and **scale factor** $k > 0$ is a transformation of a plane that keeps point C where it is and maps every other point P to a point P' on $\overrightarrow{CP}$ so that $CP' = k(CP)$.

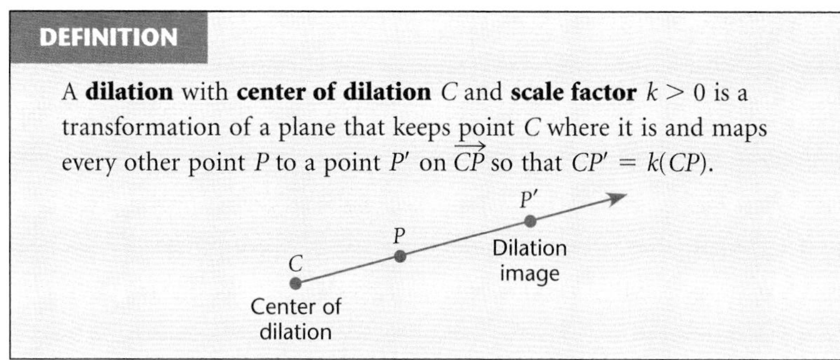

You use dilations of the coordinate plane when you use the *Zoom In* or *Zoom Out* features of a graphing utility.

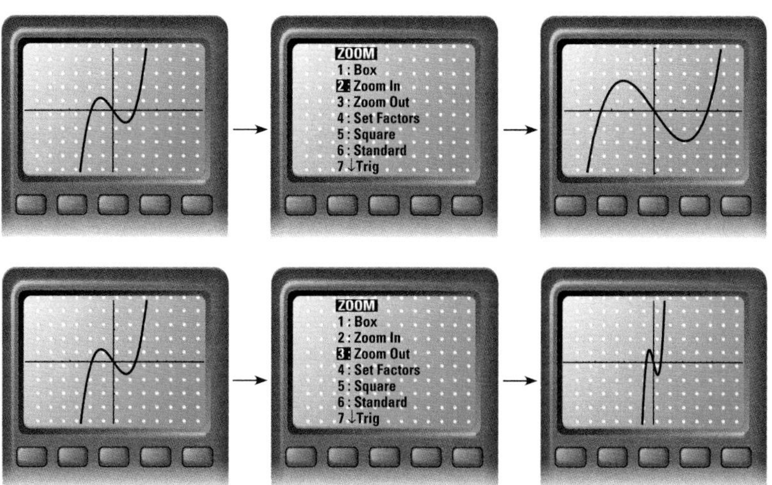

(The scale on the last window has been changed to make the graph visible.)

1. What point of the calculator screen appears to be the center of the dilation for the *Zoom In* and *Zoom Out* shown above?

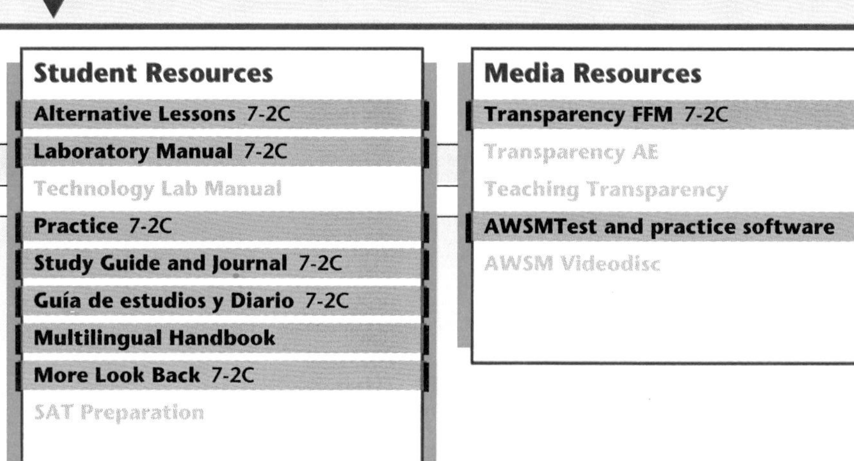

Student Resources

- Alternative Lessons 7-2C
- Laboratory Manual 7-2C
- Technology Lab Manual
- Practice 7-2C
- Study Guide and Journal 7-2C
- Guía de estudios y Diario 7-2C
- Multilingual Handbook
- More Look Back 7-2C
- SAT Preparation

Media Resources

- Transparency FFM 7-2C
- Transparency AE
- Teaching Transparency
- AWSMTest and practice software
- AWSM Videodisc

EXPLORE

A "Dilate-ful" Transformation

Recommended group size: 4

The Point

To explore dilations, identify the properties of a figure that are and are not preserved by a dilation, and discover the connection between dilation and similarity.

Look and Listen...

- For students who, because of inaccuracies in measurement, do not realize that the triangles are similar.

Ask...

- How confident are you that your measurements are exactly correct? Have you made allowances for this?

For Groups That Finish Early

Draw triangle $\triangle RST$. Then draw the dilation image of $\triangle RST$ with center R and scale factor $k = \frac{2}{3}$.

Follow Up

Ask students to make a list of the properties of a figure that are and are not preserved by dilations.

Possible Answers

2–3. The triangles are similar.

4. Dilation preserves orientation and angle measure. However, if $k \neq 1$, it does not preserve side length, perimeter, or area.

5. Since angle measures are preserved and the side lengths are changed by a constant scale factor, the image and pre-image must be similar.

Possible Answer

1. The center of the dilation appears to be the origin. (On some utilities, the center is off the origin when you zoom on the standard screen.)

Properties of Similar Figures

Journal

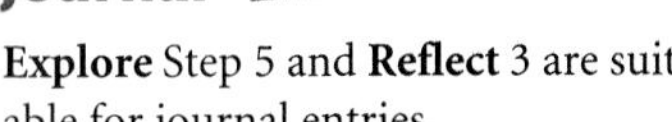

Explore Step 5 and **Reflect** 3 are suitable for journal entries.

REFLECT

Possible Answers

1. n^2
2. Measures of a figure's size (side lengths, area, and perimeter) are not preserved by dilation.
3. No, a triangle cannot always be mapped onto a similar triangle with just a dilation. Two similar triangles may have different orientations, and a dilation cannot change orientation.

Part C Exercises

Exercise Notes

Core

13. Students apply dilations to maps and explore the relationship between the area of a figure and the area of its dilation image.

More Math Reasoning

28. Students investigate dilations of lines on a coordinate plane.

Exercise Answers

7. Check students' art.
8. Reduction; $k = \frac{1}{2}$; Lower left corner of figure (this point remained fixed).
9. Enlargement; $k = 2$; Center of dilation is found by drawing lines through corresponding vertices and observing where lines intersect.

TRY IT

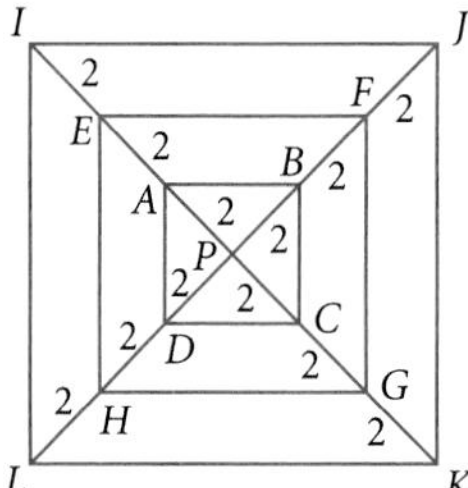

Answer each of the following for dilations with center P.

a. If $k = 3$, what is the image of $ABCD$? What is the pre-image of K? $IJKL$; C

b. If the image of F is J, find the scale factor k. $\frac{3}{2}$

c. If the image of $EFGH$ is $ABCD$, find k. $\frac{1}{2}$

The properties of a figure that are and are not preserved by a dilation are summarized below. Notice that these are consistent with the properties of similar polygons.

Dilations **change:**	Dilations **preserve:**
• the size of a figure (unless $k = 1$)	• the measures of the angles in a figure • the orientation of a figure • the shape of a figure

REFLECT

1. If the scale factor of a dilation is n, what is the ratio of the area of the image to the area of the pre-image?
2. What property of a figure that is preserved by translation, rotation, and reflection is not preserved by dilation?
3. If you dilate a triangle, then the dilation image is similar to the pre-image. Is the converse true? That is, given two similar triangles, is it always possible to map one onto the other with just a dilation? Why?

Exercises

CORE

P **1. Getting Started** A regular octagon with sides 2 cm long undergoes a dilation with a scale factor of 3.5.

a. How long is each side of the image? 7 cm

b. What is the measure of each angle of the image? 135°

Key

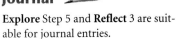

V Vocabulary
P Practice/Skills
R Review
MR Math Reasoning
PS Problem Solving
C Challenge

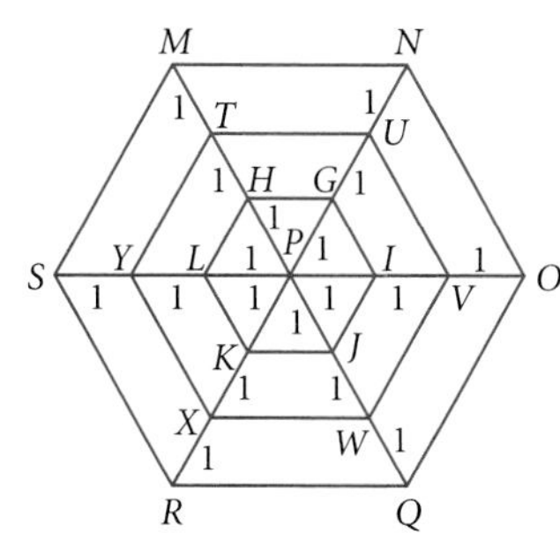

In Exercises 2–4, answer each of the following for dilations with center *P*.

2. If $k = 2$, what is the image of *HGIJKL*? What is the pre-image of *T*? *TUVWXY; H*

3. If the image of *Q* is *J*, find the scale factor *k*. $k = \frac{1}{3}$

4. If the image of *MNOQRS* is *TUVWXY*, find *k*. $k = \frac{2}{3}$

Write the word or phrase that correctly completes each statement.

5. The ratio of the length of a side of a dilation image to the length of the corresponding side in the pre-image is called the ___. Scale factor

6. A dilation image is always ___ to its pre-image. Similar

7. **Scale the Building** A sketch of a plan for a new office is shown at the right. Copy the figure and then sketch its dilation image, using center *R* and scale factor 2.5.

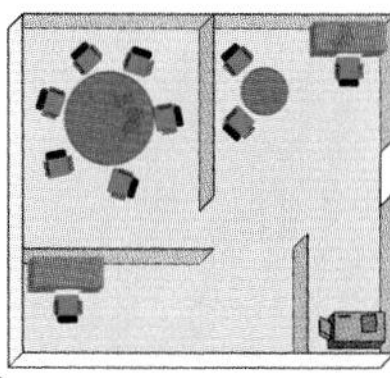

Copy each figure on graph paper. If the red figure is a dilation image of the black figure, is the dilation an enlargement or a reduction? Find the scale factor and the center of the dilation. Explain how you found the center of each dilation.

8.

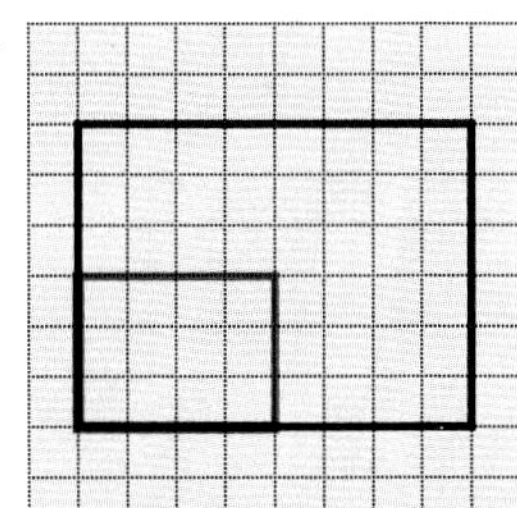

9.

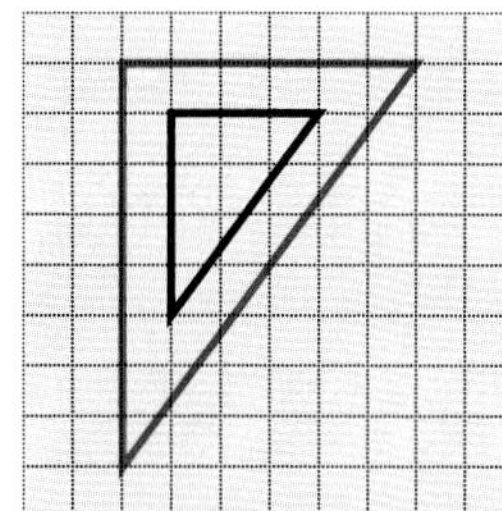

Find the coordinates of the images of points *A*, *B*, and *C* under a dilation with center *O* and the given scale factor.

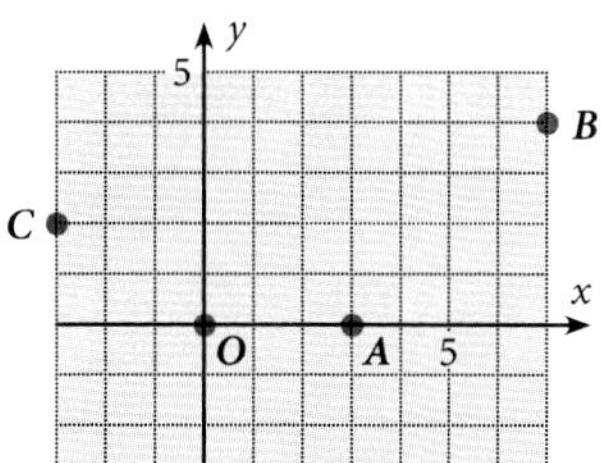

10. $k = 2$ $A' = (6, 0)$, $B' = (14, 8)$, $C' = (-6, 4)$

11. $k = \frac{1}{2}$ $A' = \left(\frac{3}{2}, 0\right)$, $B' = \left(\frac{7}{2}, 2\right)$, $C' = \left(-\frac{3}{2}, 1\right)$

12. $k = \frac{1}{3}$ $A' = (1, 0)$, $B' = \left(\frac{7}{3}, \frac{4}{3}\right)$, $C' = \left(-1, \frac{2}{3}\right)$

Ongoing Assessment

Self-Assessment Exercises 1, 3, 5, 6, 9, 11, 13

Embedded Assessment Exercises 4, 8, 12, 14

13. a. $\frac{1}{2}$ in. = 60 ft = 60(12) in. = 720 in., so $k = \frac{1}{2(720)} = \frac{1}{1440}$.

b. The courtyard is roughly rectangular, $\frac{1}{2}$ in. × $\frac{3}{8}$ in. in the plan. Using the scale, its actual dimensions are 60 ft × 45 ft, so its area is about 2700 ft^2.

c. Figures and their dilated images are similar, and the ratio of the areas of two similar polygons is (similarity ratio)^2, so $\frac{\text{Actual area}}{\text{Area in plan}} = (1440)^2$

14. See Additional Answers p. T484.

Look Back

15. They bisect each other.

16. They bisect each other and are perpendicular.

17. They bisect each other and are congruent.

18. They bisect each other, are congruent, and are perpendicular.

Properties of Similar Figures

More Practice

20. Reduction; $k = \frac{1}{4}$; Center is at intersection of lines joining corresponding vertices.

21. Enlargement; $k = 4$; Center of dilation is one unit to the left of the left leg (at the base) of the smaller "A".

22. $A' = (3, 3)$, $B' = (9, 6)$, $C' = \left(-\frac{3}{2}, -\frac{9}{2}\right)$

23. $A' = (6, 6)$, $B' = (18, 12)$, $C' = (-3, -9)$

24. $A' = \left(\frac{1}{2}, \frac{1}{2}\right)$, $B' = \left(\frac{3}{2}, 1\right)$, $C' = \left(-\frac{1}{4}, -\frac{3}{4}\right)$

25.

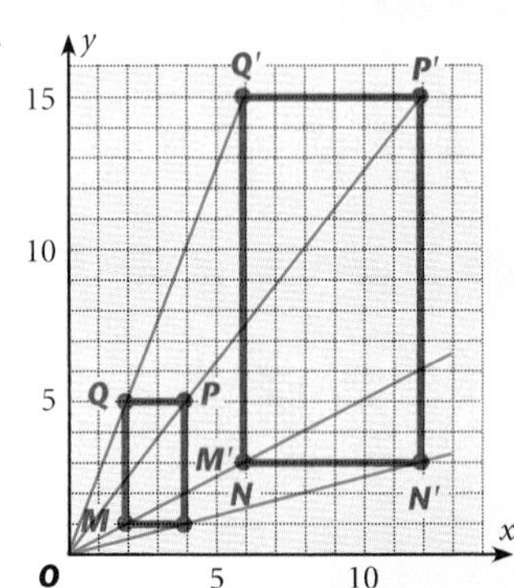

26.

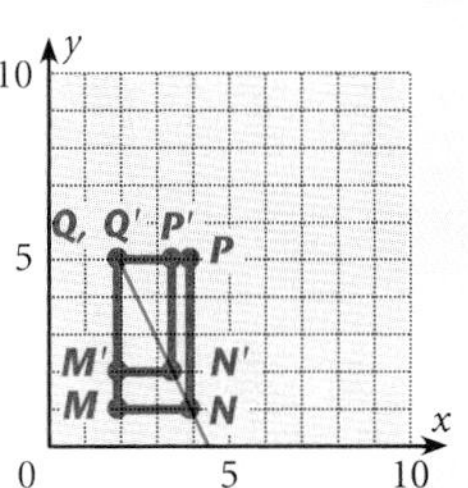

More Math Reasoning

27. Dilations preserve the measures of angles in a figure. Hence, a triangle will be similar to its image by AA.

28. a. $m_t = -\frac{3}{2}$; $m_{t'} = -\frac{3}{2}$; The slopes are the same.

b. All points lead to the same result. Consider the triangles formed (1) by the origin and any two points on the line and (2) by the origin and their dilation images. Because angle measures are preserved, corresponding angles are congruent, so the lines are parallel.

c. $y = mx$. p is its own image.

PS History **13. Palace Plans** The plan of the palace of the Deji of Akure (Nigeria) can be thought of as a dilation of the actual palace.

a. Find the scale factor of the dilation. How did you find this?

b. Find the approximate area of the actual courtyard K. Explain your method.

c. What is the ratio of the actual area of courtyard K to its area on the plan? Justify your answer.

Scale: $\frac{1}{2}$ in. = 60 ft

MR **14.** Make a chart to show the properties of a figure that are and are not preserved by the four transformations you've studied. These properties should include location, size, angle measure, and orientation.

LOOK BACK

R **Quadrilateral *ABCD* has diagonals $\overline{AC}$ and $\overline{BD}$. What is true about $\overline{AC}$ and $\overline{BD}$ if the following is true? [6-2]**

15. *ABCD* is a parallelogram. **16.** *ABCD* is a rhombus.

17. *ABCD* is a rectangle. **18.** *ABCD* is a square.

R, PS **19.** Carmen is drawing up blueprints for a new office building. On the blueprint, the reception area measures 5 in. by $3\frac{1}{2}$ in. If the scale used for the drawing is $\frac{1}{2}$ in. = 1 ft, what will the dimensions of the actual reception area be? [7-1] 10 ft × 7 ft

MORE PRACTICE

P **Copy each figure on graph paper. If the red figure is a dilation image of the black figure, is the dilation an enlargement or a reduction? Find the scale factor and the center of the dilation.**

20.

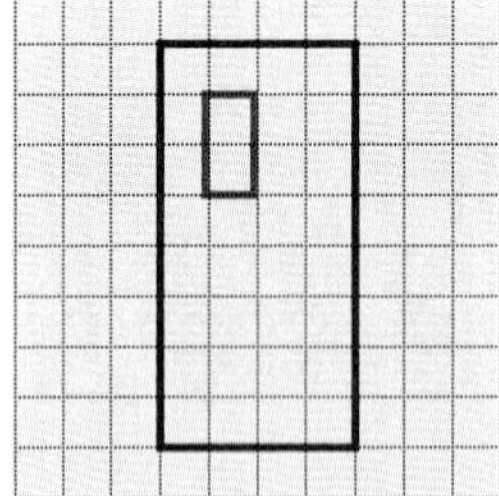

21.

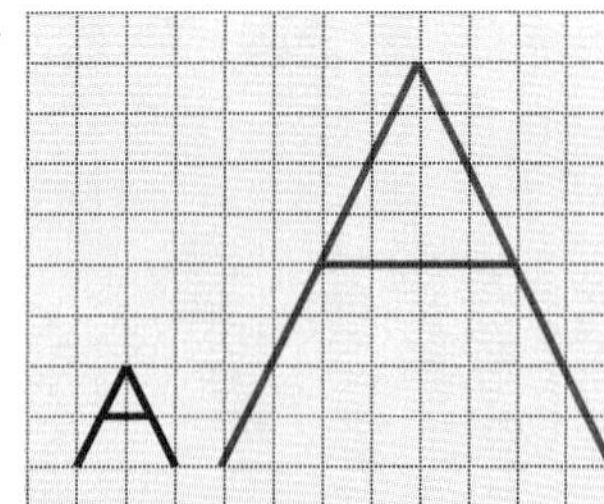

Key

V Vocabulary
P Practice/Skills
R Review
MR Math Reasoning
PS Problem Solving
C Challenge

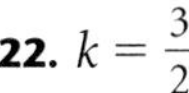

Find the coordinates of the images of points *A, B,* and *C* under a dilation with center *O* and the given scale factor.

22. $k = \frac{3}{2}$ **23.** $k = 3$ **24.** $k = 0.25$

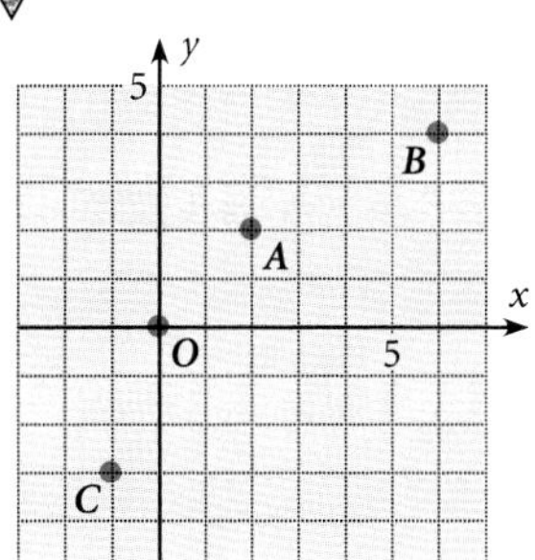

Copy rectangle *MNPQ* on graph paper. Then draw each dilation image, using the given scale factors and center.

25. scale factor 3, center O

26. scale factor 0.75, center Q

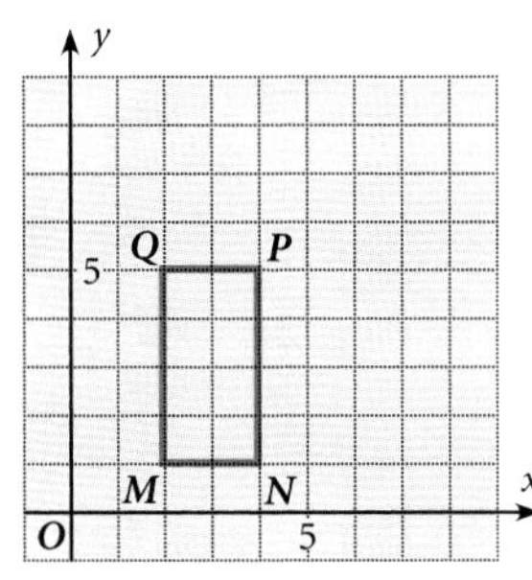

MORE MATH REASONING

27. Explain why a triangle is similar to its dilation image.

28. Line t contains the points (1, 5) and (3, 2). Line t' is the image of line t under a dilation with center (0, 0) and scale factor 2.

a. Calculate the slopes of t and t'. Do you notice a relationship between the slopes?

b. Do your slopes depend on the points of t chosen or do other points lead to the same result? Explain.

c. Suppose line p has the equation $y = mx$. What is the equation of the image of p under this dilation?

7-2 PART D Triangle Midsegments

← CONNECT → ***You've seen that parallel lines and transversals create special angle relationships. This knowledge will help you understand the connection between similarity and a special segment of a triangle.***

A segment whose endpoints are the midpoints of two of its sides is a **midsegment** of a triangle. You will investigate relationships involving a midsegment of a triangle, similar triangles, and parallel lines.

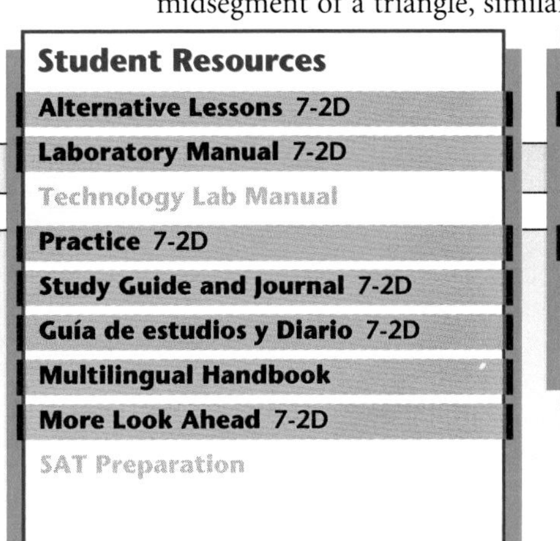

Student Resources

- Alternative Lessons 7-2D
- Laboratory Manual 7-2D
- Technology Lab Manual
- Practice 7-2D
- Study Guide and Journal 7-2D
- Guía de estudios y Diario 7-2D
- Multilingual Handbook
- More Look Ahead 7-2D
- SAT Preparation

Media Resources

- Transparency FFM 7-2D
- Transparency AE
- Teaching Transparency
- AWSMTest and practice software
- AWSM Videodisc

PART D At a Glance

Objective

To investigate properties of midsegments of triangles.

Development

Students see the definition of a midsegment of a triangle. In the **Explore,** they see that a midsegment is parallel to the nonintersected side and half its length.

In **What Do You Think?** students see two justifications for their midsegment conjectures. One approach uses similar triangles; the other uses dilations.

Suggested Materials

Student Protractor, ruler, compass, geometry software

Key Terms

Midsegment of a triangle

First Five Minutes

Transparency FFM 7-2D

Sketch two lines and a transversal. Then describe all of the ways that you can use angles to show that two coplanar lines cut by a transversal are parallel. **Corresponding/alternate interior/alternate exterior angles congruent, same-side interior angles supplementary.**

Motivate

Ask...

- Sketch a triangle. How can you add one segment to your drawing that creates two similar triangles? **Add a segment that intersects two sides and is parallel to the third.**

Properties of Similar Figures

EXPLORE

Measuring the Midsegments

Recommended group size: 2

The Point

To discover that a midsegment of a triangle is parallel to and half the length of the side it does not intersect.

Look and Listen...

- For students who do not see that the midsegment is parallel to the side it does not intersect.

Ask...

- Have you found any congruent angles? What do these angles tell you about some of the segments in your drawing?

For Groups That Finish Early

Sketch a triangle and draw a segment that intersects two of its sides $\frac{2}{3}$ of the way along the sides. Investigate the figure that results. **The segment is parallel to the nonintersected side, and its length is $\frac{2}{3}$ the length of that side.**

Follow Up

Ask students to summarize the properties of a midsegment of a triangle. Then ask if any of them can give an informal justification for these properties.

Possible Answer

3. The midsegment of a triangle is parallel to and half the length of the nonintersected side. Students may also see that it creates a smaller triangle similar to the original.

EXPLORE: MEASURING THE MIDSEGMENTS

MATERIALS

Protractor, Ruler
Compass (optional)
Geometry software (optional)

1. Use software or a straightedge to draw a large triangle. Measure the lengths of its sides.

2. Draw or construct the midpoints of two of the sides. Then add a midsegment of the triangle. Measure sides and angles.

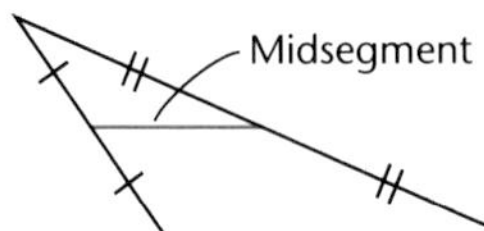

3. Repeat the process as needed to make as many conjectures as you can about the midsegment of a triangle.

TRY IT

Solve for x in each figure.

a. 8.5

17

x

b. 57

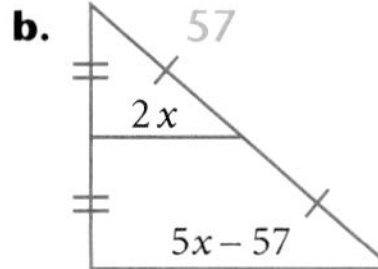

c.

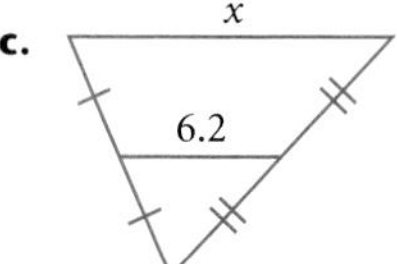

We can summarize the properties of triangle midsegments as follows.

MIDSEGMENT THEOREM FOR TRIANGLES

A segment whose endpoints are the midpoints of two sides of a triangle is parallel to the third side and half its length.

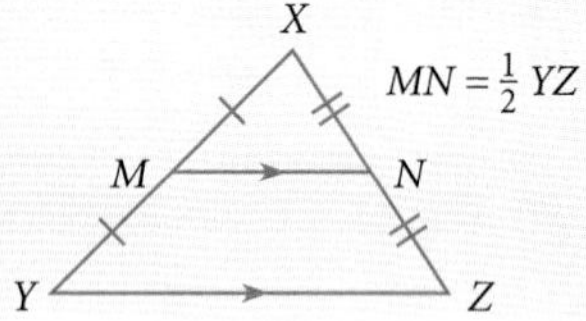

History Connection

Hypatia (370–415) was a famous author and teacher of mathematics at the University of Alexandria. Her teaching focused on Diophantine algebra, which included solutions of first- and second-degree equations. Hypatia's death in 415 at the hands of a mob is sometimes said to mark the end of ancient mathematics in the Western world.

WHAT DO YOU THINK?

Adam and Hulleah are planning justifications of the Midsegment Theorem to present to their geometry class.

Adam thinks . . .

I'll use similar triangles. Since B and C are midpoints, $\frac{AB}{AD} = \frac{1}{2}$, and $\frac{AC}{AE} = \frac{1}{2}$. $\triangle ABC$ and $\triangle ADE$ also share $\angle A$, so they are similar. Then $\frac{BC}{DE} = \frac{1}{2}$, so the midsegment is half the length of the third side. Since the triangles are similar, $\angle ABC \cong \angle ADE$. Therefore, $\overline{BC} \parallel \overline{DE}$, because $\angle ABC$ and $\angle ADE$ are congruent corresponding angles for $\overline{BC}$ and $\overline{DE}$.

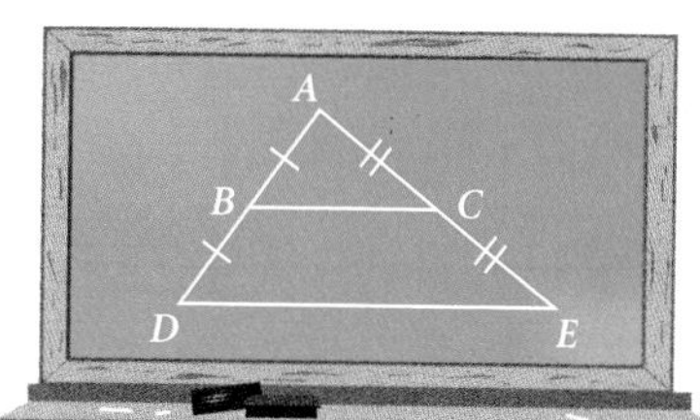

Hulleah thinks . . .

I'll sketch a figure to illustrate the theorem and show that the larger triangle is a dilation of the smaller one. If A is the center of a dilation with scale factor 2, $\triangle ADE$ is the image of $\triangle ABC$. Since the scale factor is 2, $\overline{BC}$ is half as long as $\overline{DE}$.

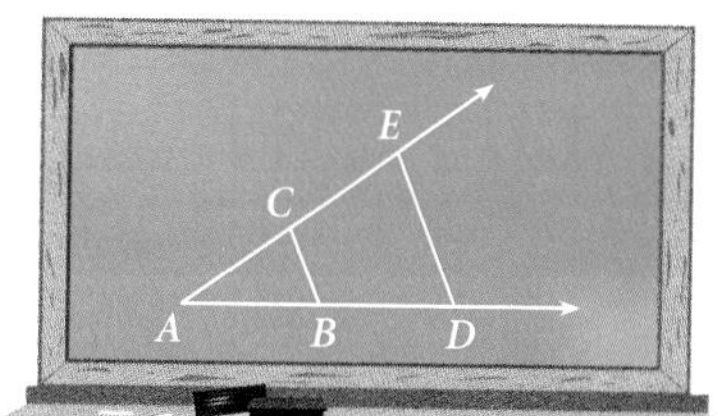

To show that $\overline{BC} \parallel \overline{DE}$, I can use corresponding angles. $\angle ACB$ and $\angle AED$ have to be congruent, so $\overline{BC} \parallel \overline{DE}$.

CONSIDER

1. How did Adam know that $\triangle ABC \sim \triangle ADE$?
2. How did Hulleah know that $\angle ACB \cong \angle AED$?

Triangle midsegments are useful in perspective drawings. You will see an example of this in Exercise 9.

Diversity Issues

At the International High School...the mathematics curriculum includes talking, sharing, and writing to lessen the effects of different language and ability levels in the classroom. (Felicita Santiago and George Spanos, "Meeting the NCTM Communication Standards for All Students," *Reaching All Students with Mathematics,* Gilbert Cuevas and Mark Driscoll, eds., p. 141. © 1993 NCTM.)

WHAT DO YOU THINK?

In the **What Do You Think?** students give two justifications for the Midsegment Theorem. One student uses a similarity argument to justify the theorem; the other uses dilations. You may want to emphasize that transformations are sometimes convenient to use when justifying a conjecture.

Asks students to supply reasons for some of the statements made in **What Do You Think?**

Possible Answers

1. The triangles are similar by the SAS similarity theorem.
2. The angles are congruent because dilations preserve angle measure.

7-2

Properties of Similar Figures

Journal

Explore Step 3, **Reflect** 2, and **Exercise** 8 are suitable for journal entries.

REFLECT

Possible Answers

1. $\overline{GH}$ is one unit long.
2. Divide 8 by 2 $(n - 1)$ times. $\left(\text{Length} = \frac{8}{2^{(n-1)}} = 2^{(4-n)}\right)$
3. They are all parallel.

Part D Exercises

Exercise Notes

Core

10. Students use a coordinate proof to prove the Midsegment Theorem. It might be helpful to discuss with students the choice of coordinates for this proof.

Look Ahead

These exercises look ahead to trigonometry. Students will investigate trigonometry in 7-3.

More Math Reasoning

19. Students complete a proof of the Side-Splitting Theorem. This theorem is a generalized converse of the Midsegment Theorem.

Exercise Answers

Core

3. $AC = 20$, $BC = 10$, $BE = 9$
4. $m\angle ADC = 41°$; $CD = 45.4$
5. $m\angle A = 54.5°$; $BE = 8.5$
6. Attach to midpoints of $\overline{YX}$, $\overline{XZ}$, $\overline{XW}$, and $\overline{VX}$; Since the supports have length $\frac{1}{2}YZ$, their length will fit exactly if they are used as midsegments and they will be parallel to the table top and floor, by the Midsegment Theorem for triangles.

REFLECT

In the figure, the second triangle's base is a midsegment of the first triangle, the third triangle's base is a midsegment of the second, and so on.

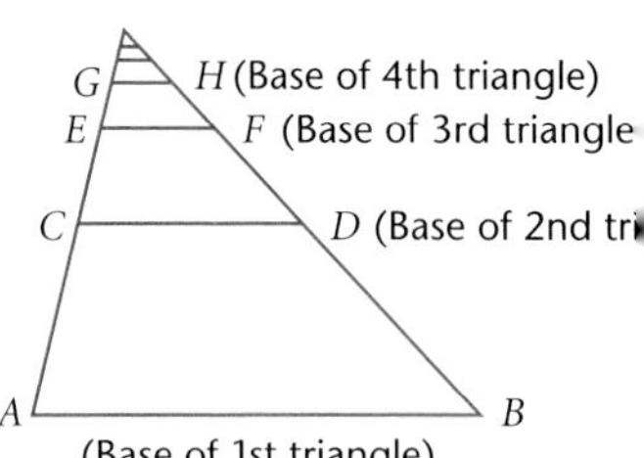

1. If the length of $\overline{AB}$ is 8, what is the length of $\overline{GH}$?
2. How could you find the length of the base of the nth triangle?
3. What is true about the bases of all of the triangles?

Exercises

CORE

P **Getting Started In the figure, *S*, *W*, and *U* are midpoints of the sides of $\triangle RTV$. $RT = 60$, $RV = 80$, and $TV = 100$.**

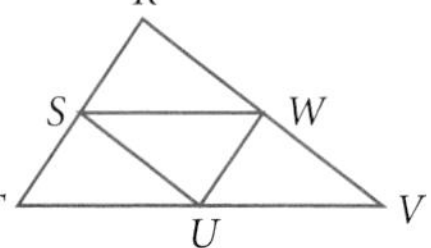

1. Find SW, WU, and US. $SW = 50$, $WU = 30$, $US = 40$
2. Name three pairs of parallel segments. $\overline{SW} \parallel \overline{TV}$, $\overline{UW} \parallel \overline{RT}$, $\overline{SU} \parallel \overline{RV}$

P ***B* is the midpoint of $\overline{AC}$ and *E* is the midpoint of $\overline{AD}$.**

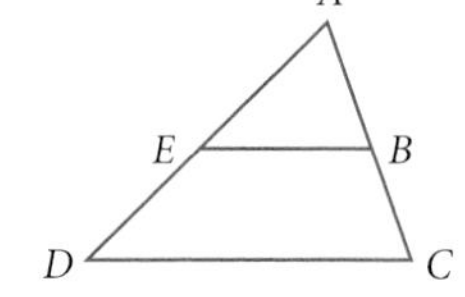

3. $AB = 10$, and $CD = 18$. Find AC, BC, and BE.
4. $m\angle AEB = 41°$, and $BE = 22.7$. Find $m\angle ADC$ and CD.
5. $DC = 17$, $CA = 17$, and $m\angle C = 71°$. Find $m\angle A$ and BE.

PS, MR

6. **Stable Table** A carpenter wants to add supports to the legs of the table as shown. The supports need to be parallel to the top of the table and the floor. The carpenter has made each support half the length of $\overline{YZ}$. The table is made so that $YX = ZX = WX = VX$. Write a short paragraph telling the carpenter how to find the places to attach the supports. Explain how you know your method works.

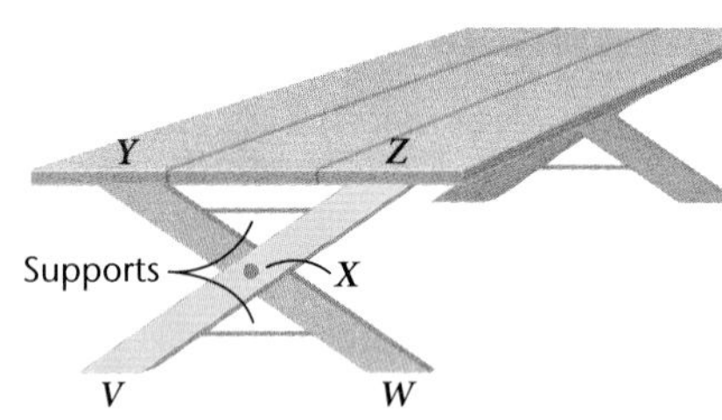

Key

- V Vocabulary
- P Practice/Skills
- R Review
- MR Math Reasoning
- PS Problem Solving
- C Challenge

7. Solve for x, y, and z in the figure at the right. $x = 3$, $z = 90$, $y = 12$

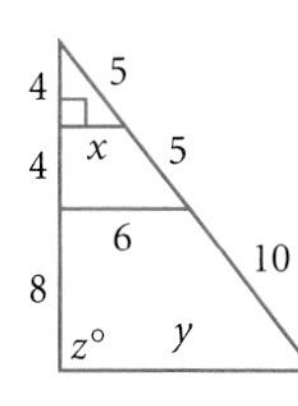

8. Draw a triangle, $\triangle JKL$. Use a compass and straightedge to construct the midsegment of $\triangle JKL$ that intersects $\overline{JK}$ and $\overline{JL}$. Explain your construction.

9. Art Training Kate is drawing a cartoon with railroad tracks disappearing into the distance as shown. To show perspective, she wants to add more ties (horizontal segments), with the first tie halfway to the horizon, the second tie half the remaining distance, and so on.

a. How long will the first tie be?

b. How long will the second tie be? Where should it be located?

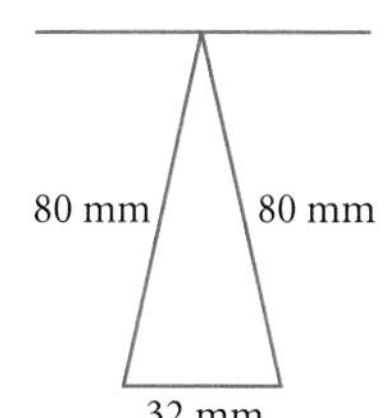

10. Prove the midsegment theorem using a coordinate proof.

Given: Y is the midpoint of $\overline{VW}$.
Z is the midpoint of $\overline{VX}$.

Prove: $\overline{YZ} \parallel \overline{WX}$
$YZ = \frac{1}{2}WX$

Before starting your proof, copy the figure at the right. Give the coordinates of Y and Z. (Hint: Use the Midpoint Formula.)

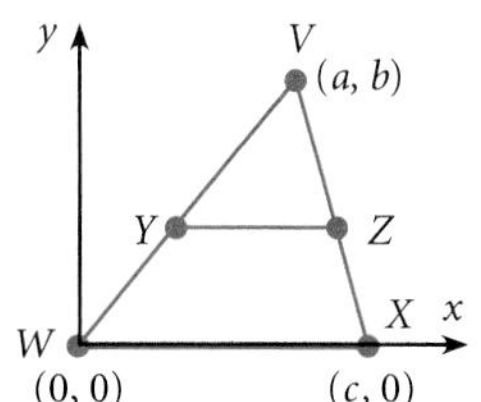

11. $\triangle ABC$ is isosceles, and $\overline{AD}$ is an altitude to base $\overline{BC}$. Does midsegment $\overline{EF}$ bisect $\overline{AD}$? Justify your answer.

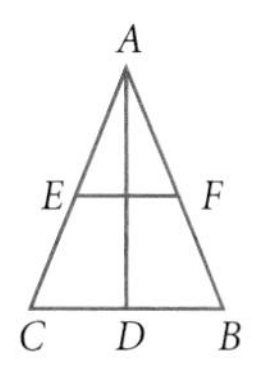

LOOK AHEAD

12. Are all 45°-45°-90° triangles similar? Explain. Yes; By AA

13. Are all 30°-60°-90° triangles similar? Explain. Yes; By AA

14. Find each ratio.

a. the ratio of the length of a leg in a 45°-45°-90° triangle to the length of the hypotenuse $\frac{\sqrt{2}}{2}$

b. the ratio of the length of the shorter leg in a 30°-60°-90° triangle to the length of the hypotenuse $\frac{1}{2}$

c. the ratio of the length of the longer leg in a 30°-60°-90° triangle to the length of the hypotenuse $\frac{\sqrt{3}}{2}$

d. Did any of your answers in **14a–c** depend on the size of the triangle? No

Ongoing Assessment

Self-Assessment Exercises 1, 3, 5, 9, 11

Embedded Assessment Explore Step 3; Exercises 4, 6, 7, 10

8.

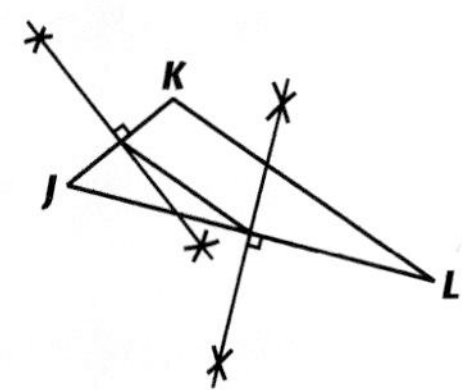

Construct the perpendicular bisectors of $\overline{JK}$, $\overline{JL}$ to locate the segments' midpoints; connect the midpoints.

9. a. 16 mm

b. 8 mm; 20 mm from the horizon measured along the tracks

10. $Y = \left(\frac{a+0}{2}, \frac{b+0}{2}\right) = \left(\frac{a}{2}, \frac{b}{2}\right)$

$Z = \left(\frac{a+c}{2}, \frac{b+0}{2}\right) = \left(\frac{a+c}{2}, \frac{b}{2}\right)$

$\overline{YZ} \parallel \overline{WX}$ because both have slope 0. $YZ = \frac{a+c}{2} - \frac{a}{2} = \frac{c}{2}$ and $WX = c$ so $YZ = \frac{1}{2}WX$.

11. Possible answer: $\overline{EF} \parallel \overline{CB}$ since a midsegment is parallel to the third side. Let G be the point where $\overline{AD}$ intersects $\overline{EF}$. $\angle AFE \cong \angle ABD$ because corresponding angles are congruent. $\angle DAB \cong \angle DAB$ by the Reflexive Property. $\triangle GAF \sim \triangle DAB$ by AA. $\frac{AF}{AB} = \frac{1}{2}$ because $\overline{EF}$ is the midsegment. $\frac{AG}{AD} = \frac{1}{2}$ by the definition of *similar*. $AG = \frac{1}{2}AD$, so $\overline{EF}$ bisects $\overline{AD}$.

Properties of Similar Figures

More Math Reasoning

19. 1. Given
2. Corresponding angles of two parallel lines are congruent.
3. AA
4. Corresponding sides of similar triangles are proportional.
5. Segment-Addition Postulate
6. Substitution (into Step 4).

MORE PRACTICE

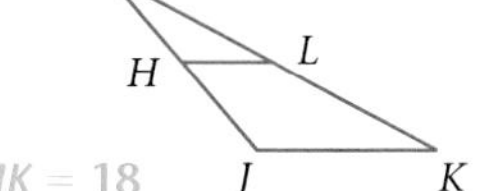

P ***H* is the midpoint of $\overline{GJ}$, and *L* is the midpoint of $\overline{GK}$.**

15. $GJ = 12$, and $HL = 9$. Find GH, HJ, and JK. $GH = 6$, $HJ = 6$, $JK = 18$

16. $m\angle GLH = 28°$, and $JK = 37.4$. Find $m\angle K$ and HL. $m\angle K = 28°$, $HL = 18.7$

17. $GH = 7$, $HL = 7$, and $m\angle G = 21°$. Find $m\angle J$ and JK. $JK = 14$, $m\angle J = 138°$

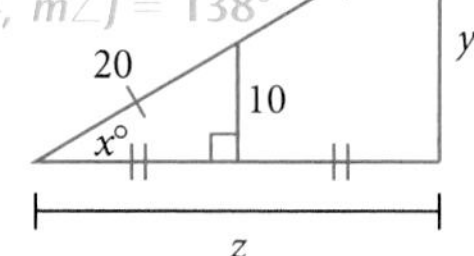

18. Solve for w, x, y, and z in the figure at the right.
$y = 20$; $z = 20\sqrt{3}$; $x = 30$; $w = 60$

MORE MATH REASONING

Parallel lines can divide the sides of a triangle in a special way.

SIDE-SPLITTING THEOREM

If a line parallel to a side of a triangle intersects the other two sides, then it divides those sides proportionally.

MR **19.** Fill in the reasons to complete the proof of the Side-Splitting Theorem.

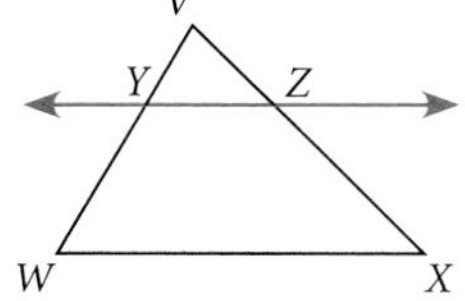

Given: $\overleftrightarrow{YZ} \parallel \overline{WX}$

Prove: $\frac{WY}{YV} = \frac{XZ}{ZV}$

Proof:

Statements	Reasons
1. $\overleftrightarrow{YZ} \parallel \overline{WX}$	**1.**
2. $\angle W \cong \angle VYZ$, and $\angle X \cong \angle VZY$.	**2.**
3. $\triangle WVX \sim \triangle YVZ$	**3.**
4. $\frac{WV}{YV} = \frac{XV}{ZV}$	**4.**
5. $WY + YV = WV$, and $XZ + ZV = XV$	**5.**
6. $\frac{WY + YV}{YV} = \frac{XZ + ZV}{ZV}$	**6.**
7. $\frac{WY}{YV} + \frac{YV}{YV} = \frac{XZ}{ZV} + \frac{ZV}{ZV}$	**7.** Algebra (Distributive Property)
8. $\frac{WY}{YV} = \frac{XZ}{ZV}$	**8.** Algebra (Addition Property of Equality)

Key

V Vocabulary
P Practice/Skills
R Review
MR Math Reasoning
PS Problem Solving
C Challenge

Tips from Teachers

You may want to prepare for the *Explore* on page 507 by finding the height of your classroom and of any other object you plan to have students measure. Also, if possible, have students go outside for their measurements in Step 3, so that they can actually measure the distance to the object.

C **Cross section $\triangle BCD$ of tetrahedron $AEFG$ is parallel to the base.**

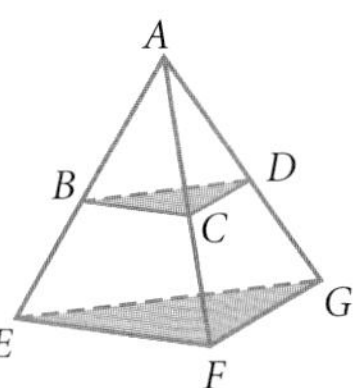

20. If $AB = 18$, $BE = 20$, and $AC = 15$, find AF. $31\frac{2}{3}$

21. If $AB = 10$, $BE = 14$, and $AG = 36$, find DG. 21

22. If $AB = 16$, $BE = 20$, and $BD = 22$, find EG. $49\frac{1}{2}$

23. Find the perimeter of $\triangle BCD$ if $AB = 14$, $AE = 35$, $EF = 27$, $FG = 21$, and $EG = 30$. $31\frac{1}{5}$

7-2 PART E Making Connections

← CONNECT → ***The characteristics of similar figures are important in architecture, computer-related design, and other industries. You've investigated ways to show that triangles are similar. You've also investigated dilations and seen how they are related to similarity.***

How can you find the height of a tall building like the Shimizu skyscraper described on page 485? In the following Explore, you will use similarity to measure some objects that are difficult to measure directly.

EXPLORE: THE HIP HYPSOMETER

MATERIALS
3 × 5 card, Scissors
Ruler or meter stick, Tape

To do this Explore, you will first need to construct a hypsometer. A hypsometer is used to measure an object or a distance by using similar triangles.

Take a 3 × 5 card, stand it on the 3-in. end, and cut a horizontal slit the width of a ruler from the bottom. Fold the card vertically as shown (the flap should make a right angle with the rest of the card). Use your ruler to mark off $\frac{1}{2}$-in. lengths along the edge of the fold (1-cm lengths if you are using a meter stick).

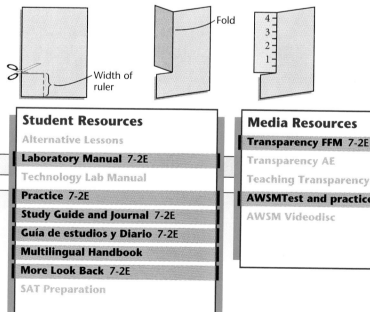

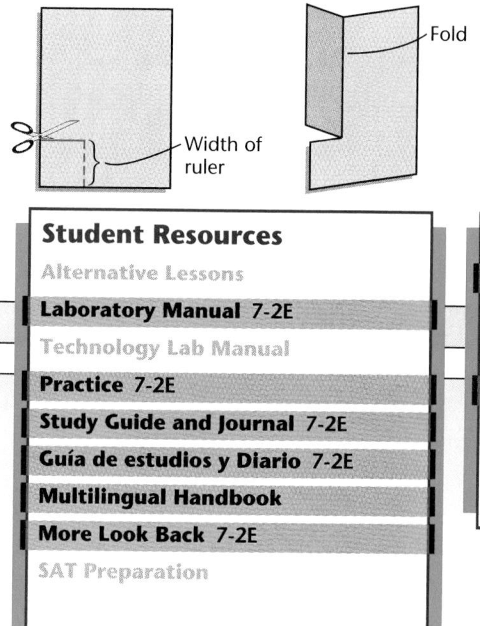

Student Resources
- Alternative Lessons
- Laboratory Manual 7-2E
- Technology Lab Manual
- Practice 7-2E
- Study Guide and Journal 7-2E
- Guía de estudios y Diario 7-2E
- Multilingual Handbook
- More Look Back 7-2E
- SAT Preparation

Media Resources
- Transparency FFM 7-2E
- Transparency AE
- Teaching Transparency
- AWSMTest and practice software
- AWSM Videodisc

PART E At a Glance

Objective
To make and use a tool that uses properties of similar triangles to measure distant objects.

Development
In the **Explore,** students build and use a measuring tool—the hypsometer. The use of the hypsometer is based on the properties of similar triangles.

Suggested Materials
Student 3" × 5" card, scissors, ruler or meter stick, tape

First Five Minutes
Transparency FFM 7-2E

Suppose that you want to measure the height of an object. Describe two methods to do this that use similar triangles. Draw sketches to illustrate each method, and list any necessary tools. **Use a mirror; position it so that you can see the top of the object. Use shadows; set up a stick and measure shadows cast by the stick and the object.**

EXPLORE

The Hip Hypsometer
Recommended group size: 2

The Point
To apply properties of similar triangles, using a simple measuring device.

Look and Listen...
- For students who are mixing units in their calculations.
- For students who do not take their own height into account when taking measurements.

Ask...
- Is your answer to Step 2 reasonable? If not, draw yourself into the sketch you made. Is there anything you haven't taken into account?

Properties of Similar Figures

For Groups That Finish Early

Can a hypsometer be used to measure the distance to an object? If so, what information would you need to know to be able to do this? **Yes. You need to know the height of the object.**

Follow Up

Ask students to use similar triangles to explain how a hypsometer works. Then have them share their measurements from Steps 2 and 3, and find the mean, median, and mode for these values. Discuss any reasons for possible discrepancies.

Possible Answers

1.

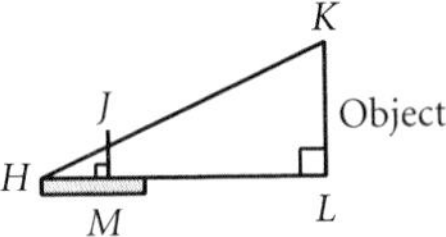

The hypsometer uses a triangle with vertices at the eye, a point on the top of the card, and the base of the card ($\triangle HJM$), and a triangle with vertices at the eye, the top of the object, and the point on the object across from the eye ($\triangle HKL$). $\triangle HJM \sim \triangle HKL$ by AA.

4. Inaccurate hypsometer construction, inaccurate length measurement, unsteady hands when using the hypsometer, etc.

Portfolio

Have students select items from their work that demonstrate their understanding of the material in 7-2.

You may wish to have students include their best proof that involves a triangle similarity postulate or theorem, a favorite solution to a real-world problem that uses similar triangles, and an **Exercise** in which they drew a dilation image of a figure.

Tape the 3×5 card to the ruler as shown so that the fold is exactly at the 6-in. mark (or 50-cm mark if you are using a meter stick).

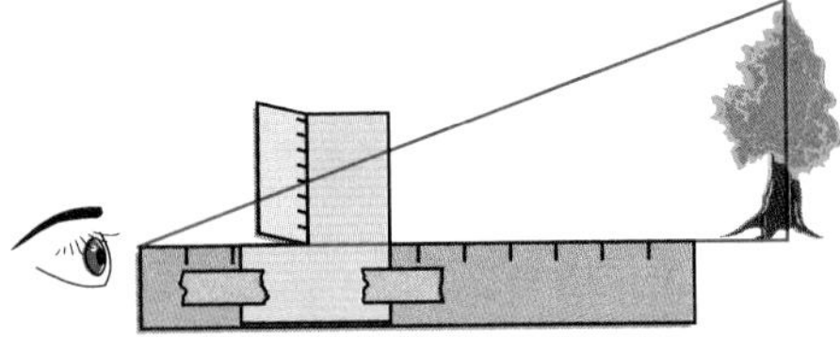

To use the hypsometer, hold it so that the bottom of the object is sighted along the ruler. Then read the length on the index card that corresponds to the top of the object. If you know the distance to the object, you can find its height and vice-versa.

1. Explain how the hypsometer works. What similar triangles does it use, and why are these triangles similar to each other?
2. Use the hypsometer to measure the height of your classroom. Record your readings, and sketch the similar triangles used to calculate the height. (Hint: Remember your own height when giving your final answer.)
3. If you can see a large object out of the window of your classroom, estimate how far you are from the object and calculate its height. You may need to break the object up into pieces, as shown. Record your readings, and sketch the similar triangles you used.
4. Compare your results with those of classmates. What might cause differences in your measurements?

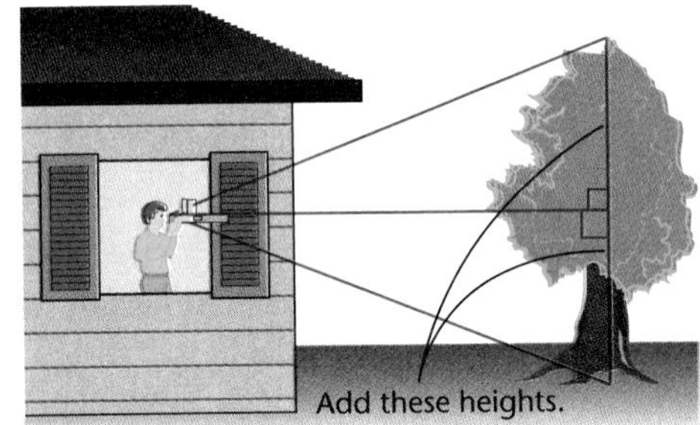

You will explore another device for indirect measurement in 7-3 Part D.

REFLECT

1. Using sketches, summarize the methods you know to show that two triangles are similar.
2. Explain how architects designing and building skyscrapers might use similarity concepts to help them in their planning.
3. What are the similarities and differences between dilations and the other transformations (reflections, rotations, and translations)?
4. Draw and label a figure to illustrate the Triangle Midsegment Theorem. Be sure to mark congruent angles and segments.

Self-Assessment

Find a value for x that makes the triangles similar. State the theorem or postulate that justifies your answer.

1. 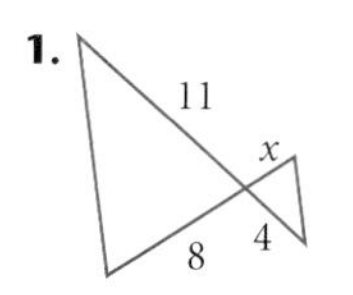

Possible answer: $x = 2\frac{10}{11}$ or 5.5; SAS

2. 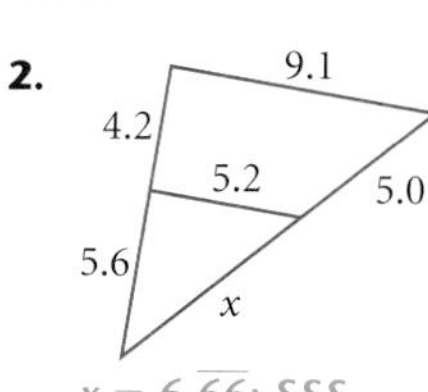

$x = 6.\overline{66}$; SSS

3. 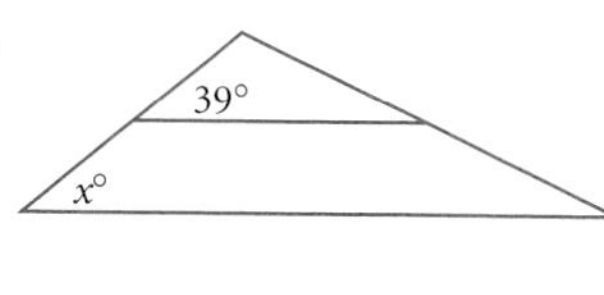

$x = 39$; AA

Give the similarity correspondence for each pair of triangles, and explain why the triangles are similar. Then solve for x and y.

4. 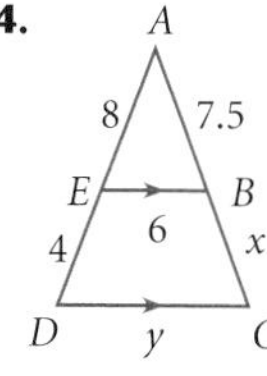

$\triangle AEB \sim \triangle ADC$; Similar by AA; $x = 3.75$; $y = 9$

5. 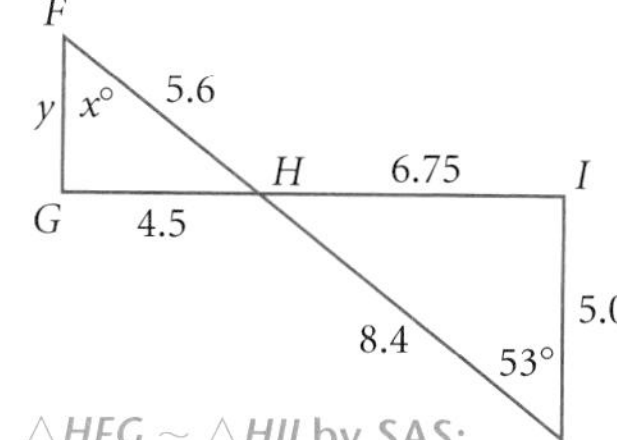

$\triangle HFG \sim \triangle HJI$ by SAS; $x = 53°$; $y = 3.\overline{33}$

6. 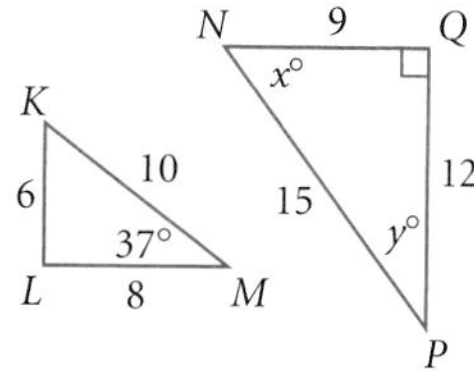

$\triangle LMK \sim \triangle QPN$ by SSS; $x = 53$; $y = 37$

7. **Thinking Deeply** A hiker at the base of the Grand Canyon is curious about the actual depth of the canyon. She places a mirror on the ground and walks back until she sees the top of the canyon in the mirror. The hiker is 5′10″ tall, so she estimates that her eyes are 5.5 ft above the ground. The distance to the mirror, IJ, is 1 ft. If the distance from J to K is 841.8 ft, how deep is this part of the Grand Canyon? 4,629.9 ft

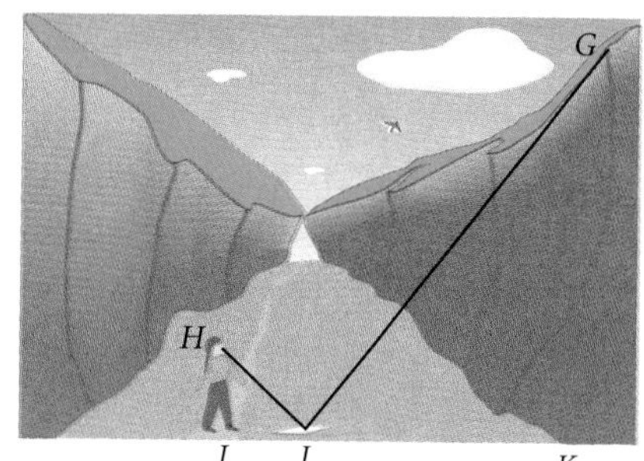

8. Use the figure at the right for the following.

Given: $\overline{TU}$ is a midsegment of $\triangle SVW$.

Prove: $\triangle STU \sim \triangle SVW$

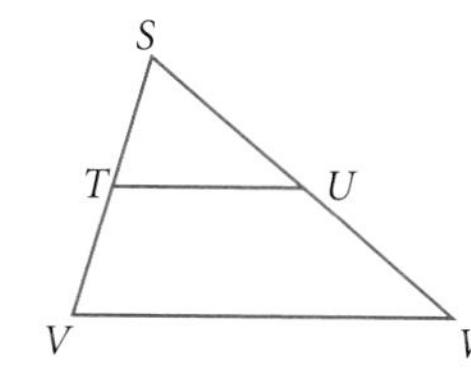

9. $\triangle XYZ$ is the image of $\triangle ABC$ under a dilation with scale factor 4. How is the area of $\triangle ABC$ related to the area of $\triangle XYZ$? Area $\triangle ABC = \frac{1}{16}$ area $\triangle XYZ$

Assessment Resources

- Quiz 7-2
- Chapter Assessment Form A
- Chapter Assessment Form B
- Chapter Alternative Assessment
- Mid-Year Assessment
- End-of-Year Assessment
- AWSMTest and practice software

Ongoing Assessment

Self-Assessment Self-Assessment Exercises

Embedded Assessment Explore Step 1; Reflect 1, 2, 3, 4

REFLECT

Possible Answers

1. AA

SAS $\left(\frac{a}{x} = \frac{b}{y}\right)$

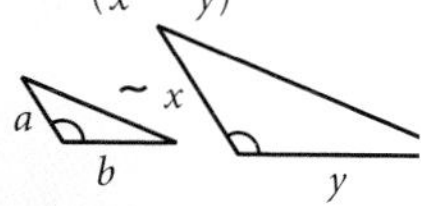

SSS $\left(\frac{a}{x} = \frac{b}{y} = \frac{c}{z}\right)$

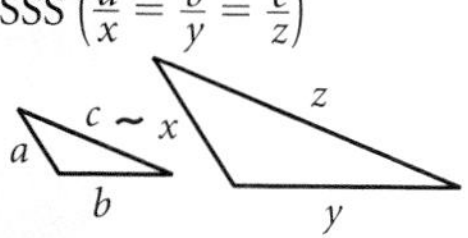

2. They use similarity to draw and build scale models of buildings before actually constructing them.

3. Dilation preserves angle measure, as do translations, rotations, and reflections. It preserves orientation, as do translations and rotations. It is the only one of the four that changes the size of a figure.

4. 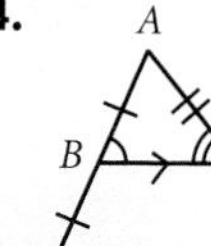

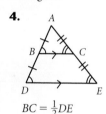

$BC = \frac{1}{2}DE$

Self-Assessment

Exercise Notes

7. Students use similar triangles to calculate the depth of the Grand Canyon.

19. Students use similarity concepts to design their own measurement tool.

Self-Assessment Answers

8. $ST = \frac{1}{2}SV$ and $SU = \frac{1}{2}SW$ since $\overline{TU}$ is the midsegment; So $\frac{ST}{SV} = \frac{SU}{SW} = \frac{1}{2}$. $\angle S \cong \angle S$ by the Reflexive Property. $\triangle STU \sim \triangle SVW$ by SAS.

Properties of Similar Figures

10. Diagonals bisect each other and are of the same length; $x = 9$, $y = -4$.

11. Diagonals bisect at right angles; $x = 132$, $y = 14$.

12. Opposite sides of a rectangle are congruent; $x = 5$, $y = 3$.

13. a. $\frac{b}{2}$ (half as much); Twice the acreage means twice the crop.

b. $\frac{A_1}{A_2} = \frac{2}{1} = \left(\sqrt{2}\right)^2$ where similarity ratio $= \sqrt{2}$. $\frac{P_1}{P_2} = \sqrt{2}$, $P_1 = \sqrt{2}P_2$. If cost per foot of fence is constant, it should cost $\sqrt{2}f$ dollars.

14.

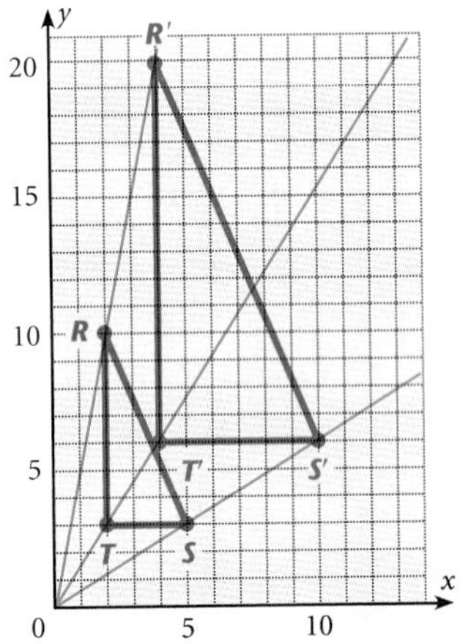

Perimeter ratio $= \frac{1}{2}$;
Area ratio $= \frac{1}{4}$

15.

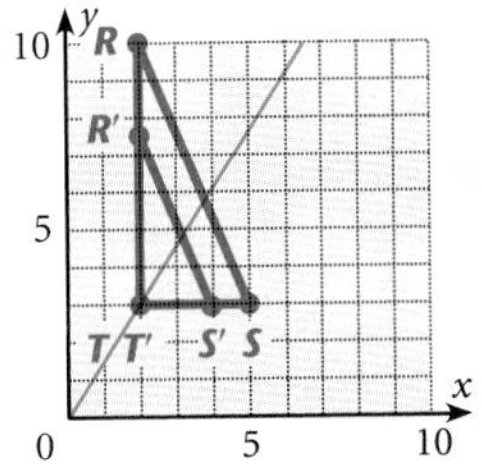

Perimeter ratio $= \frac{3}{2}$;
Area ratio $= \frac{9}{4}$

17. and 19.
See Additional Answers p. T510.

R **Find the values of x and y for each of the following quadrilaterals. Justify your answers. [6-2]**

10.

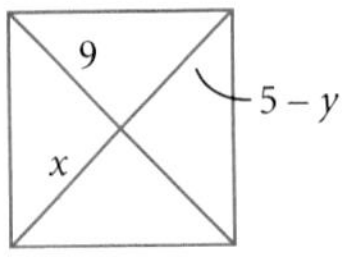

Square

11.

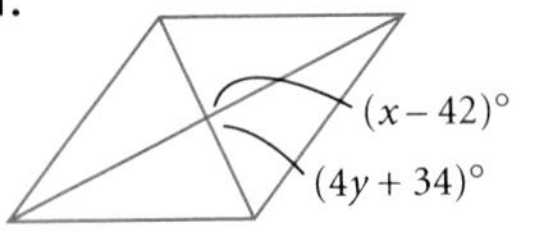

Rhombus

12.

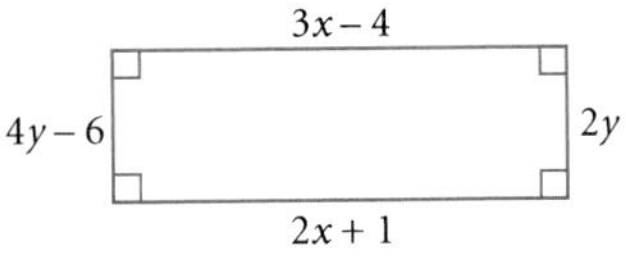

R, PS **13. A Corny Problem** Two cornfields have similar shapes, but the area of the larger one is twice the area of the smaller. [7-1]

a. Suppose the larger field produces b bushels of corn. How many bushels of corn would you expect the smaller one to produce? Explain your reasoning.

b. Suppose it costs f dollars to put a fence around the smaller cornfield. About how much would it cost to fence the larger one? Explain your reasoning.

P **Use the figure at the right for the following. Copy $\triangle RST$ on graph paper. Then draw each dilation image using the given scale factor and center. Also, give the ratios of the perimeters and the areas of the pre-images to the images.**

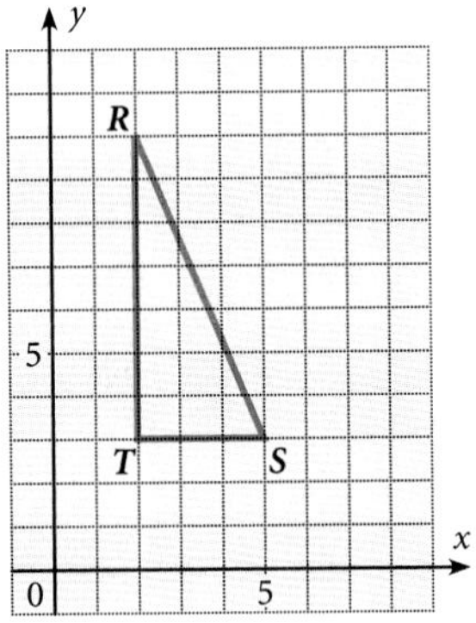

14. scale factor 2, center O

15. scale factor $\frac{2}{3}$, center T

V **16.** A figure undergoes a transformation. The pre-image is not congruent to the image. The transformation could have been a (a)

(a) dilation (b) reflection
(c) rotation (d) translation

MR **17.** Write a brief paragraph to explain in your own words how dilations and similarity are related.

MR **18.** What are the coordinates of the dilation image of any point (x, y) under a dilation with center (a, b) and scale factor k? $(k(x - a) + a, k(y - b) + b)$

PS, C **19.** Science You are designing tools for astronauts to use on a trip to an unexplored planet. Because of the planet's high atmospheric pressure, the space suits will need to be so rigid that the astronauts cannot bend over to measure small objects. You claim that you can design something that will allow them to do this using just two metal rods fastened at a pivot point and a ruler fastened to one of the handles. Draw a sketch of the tool, and give written instructions to the astronauts describing its use.

Key

V Vocabulary
P Practice/Skills
R Review
MR Math Reasoning
PS Problem Solving
C Challenge

ADDITIONAL ANSWERS

7-2 Part E Self-Assessment

17. Possible answer: Images under dilation are similar to the pre-image.

19. Possible answer: Create a scissors- or pliers-like device where the astronauts can close the handles to pick up/measure the object on the ground by using the distance between the handles to measure the size of the object via similar triangles.

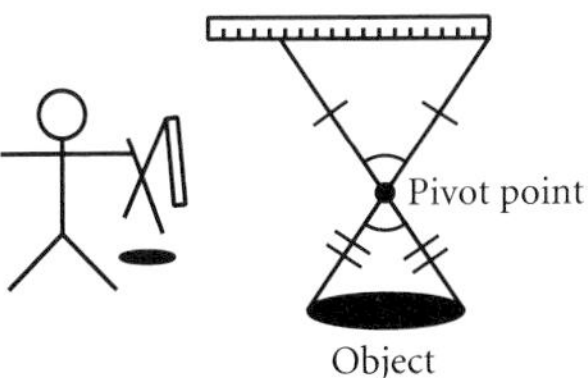

7-3 Part C Exercises

20. $\overrightarrow{JK} + \overrightarrow{KL} = \overrightarrow{JL}$

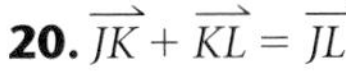

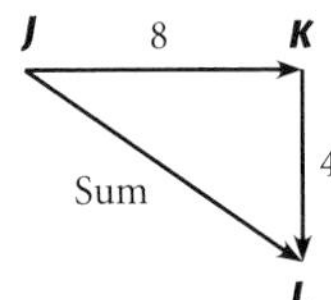

More Math Reasoning

21. $s = 354.40$ mph, $m\angle 1 = 74°$

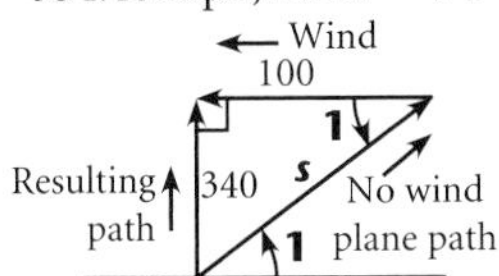

22. Possible answers: Sketch the situation accurately and take measurements. Or, to add two nonperpendicular vectors using trigonometry, use the sine and cosine functions to find the horizontal and vertical components of each vector. Then add corresponding components. The results are the horizontal and vertical components of the vector sum, and these can be used to find the length and direction.

7-3

Trigonometry

SUPERLESSON AT A GLANCE

Superlesson Goal

Students explore trigonometric ratios in right triangles and use trigonometry to solve real-world problems.

Management Guide

	Topic	Objectives	Key Terms	New Ideas	Materials
Part A	Trigonometric Ratios	To use trigonometry to solve for a side length in a right triangle.	Trigonometry, sine, cosine, tangent	Right-triangle similarity. Trigonometric ratios. Using trigonometry to find a side length.	**Teacher** Scientific calculator transparency
Part B	Angles of Elevation and Depression	To use angles of elevation and depression to solve real-world problems, and to use trigonometry to solve for an angle measure.	Angle of elevation, angle of depression	Angles of elevation and depression. Using trigonometry to find an angle measure.	**Teacher** Scientific calculator transparency
Part C	Vectors and Trigonometry	To use trigonometry to find the length and direction of a vector sum.		Using trigonometry to find a vector sum.	**Teacher** Graph paper transparency
Part D	Making Connections	To make and use a tool that uses trigonometry to measure distant objects.	In Making Connections, students apply and synthesize key terms and new ideas.		**Student** Protractor, string, tape, weight

Pacing Chart (45-Minute Periods)

	Comprehensive Course	Core Course	Informal Course
Part A	1	2	2
Part B	1	1	1
Part C	1	1	0
Part D	1	1	1
TOTAL periods for Superlesson	4	5	4

NCTM Standards

Mathematics as Problem Solving

Mathematics as Communication

Mathematics as Reasoning

Mathematical Connections

Functions

Geometry from a Synthetic Perspective

Trigonometry

Social Science/History

7-3 Trigonometry

From Stars to City Planning

In the early days of the United States, an African-American named Benjamin Banneker was a well known mathematician and astronomer. Banneker played an important part in planning Washington, D.C., in 1790–1791. As the astronomer for the surveying team, Banneker helped determine the borders of the District of Columbia. When the head of the planning committee suddenly resigned, taking the plans with him, it is said that Banneker reproduced the entire city plan from memory.

The Banneker U.S. Postal Service stamp.

The almanacs published by Banneker from 1792–1804 are his greatest scientific achievement. Using borrowed astronomy books and instruments, Banneker taught himself how to calculate the positions of the planets and predict the dates of lunar and solar eclipses. His almanacs gave the rising and setting times of the sun and moon and the positions of the planets for each day of the year. The almanacs were distributed internationally by the anti-slavery movement and Banneker's achievements were described as, "proof that the powers of the mind are disconnected with the colour of the skin."

1. **Banneker taught himself astronomy. Describe how you can learn about a subject on your own.**
2. **Some of the streets of Washington, D.C., go out from a center point like spokes of a wheel rather than running north-south or east-west. Why do you think the city planners did this? What do you think might be located at the major "hubs"?**

511

Where Are We Now?

Students are familiar with the properties of similar triangles and have used them to solve real-world problems.

Where Are We Going?

In 7-3, students will see that any right triangles with congruent acute angles are similar. This leads to the development of the trigonometric ratios. Students will use these ratios to solve a variety of problems, many with real-world settings.

Students will find trigonometry particularly useful in Chapter 12, where it is needed to calculate the circumference of the earth at different latitudes.

Possible Answers

1. Read books, magazines, and encyclopedias; use other media, including television, videos, and computer information services; talk to people familiar with the subject, etc.

2. The planners of Washington, D.C., set up central hubs to create points with magnificent views. These hubs are occupied by small parks or important buildings. Obviously designed before the introduction of the automobile, the traffic circles and radial streets have created traffic problems.

More About Benjamin Banneker

Benjamin Banneker was taught to read and write by his grandmother. One of his first achievements was the construction of a wooden striking clock. His only guide for its construction was a borrowed pocket watch. Banneker was over 50 when he was exposed to astronomy, surveying, and mathematics, which he mastered on his own. Thomas Jefferson supported hiring him as the astronomer for the Washington, D.C., surveying team. In Chapter 12, students calculate moonrise times similar to those seen in Banneker's almanacs.

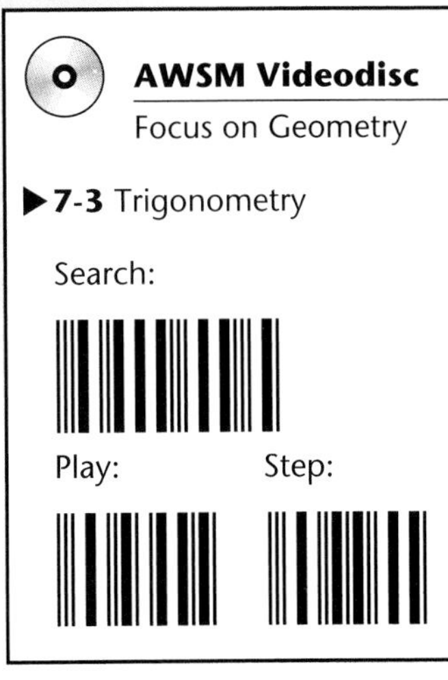

AWSM Videodisc
Focus on Geometry
▶7-3 Trigonometry
Search:
Play:
Step:

PART A At a Glance

Objective

To use trigonometry to solve for a side length in a right triangle.

Development

Students see that any two right triangles with a pair of corresponding acute angles congruent are similar. This leads to definitions of the sine, cosine, and tangent trigonometric ratios.

In the **Explore,** students apply trigonometry to find the range of safe heights for a ladder.

Suggested Materials

Teacher Scientific calculator transparency

Key Terms

Trigonometry, sine, cosine, tangent

First Five Minutes

Transparency FFM 7-3A

Carefully draw two right triangles with a 37° angle. For each, find the ratio of the side lengths of the side opposite the 37° angle to the hypotenuse of the triangle. **Both should be approximately 0.60.**

Motivate

Ask...

- Suppose that you know that an acute angle in one right triangle is congruent to an acute angle in another. Can you conclude that the triangles are similar? Explain. **The triangles must be similar by AA. (The given angles and right angles are congruent.)**

7-3 PART A Trigonometric Ratios

← CONNECT → ***You've seen that similar triangles have proportional side lengths. Now you will investigate these ratios in right triangles and see how to use them to find unknown side lengths.***

The study of the special relationships between the angle measures and side lengths of right triangles is **trigonometry** (Greek for "triangle measuring"). All of the similarity properties for triangles apply to right triangles. In fact, with right triangles you can shortcut the shortcuts.

The two triangles below are similar. Therefore, their side lengths are proportional; for example, $\frac{AB}{DE} = \frac{BC}{EF}$.

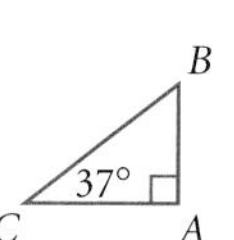

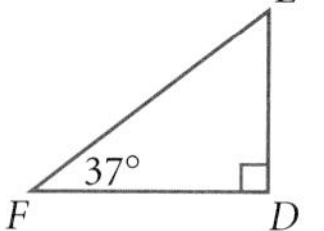

By applying algebra, we see that $\frac{AB}{BC} = \frac{DE}{EF}$; that is, the ratio of the length of the leg opposite the 37° angle to the length of the hypotenuse is the same in both triangles. No matter what size a right triangle with this acute angle measure is, the ratios of its side lengths are always the same. The trigonometry ratios you'll use are based on this fact.

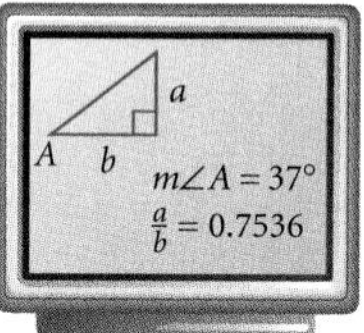

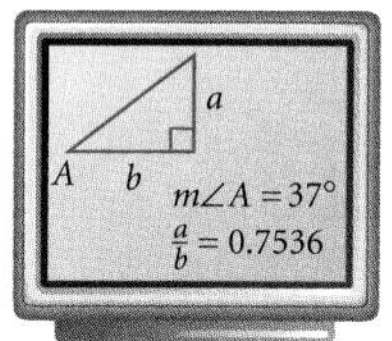

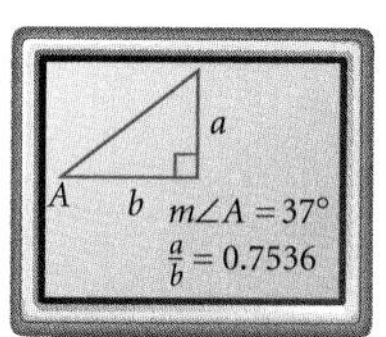

Trigonometric ratios are ratios of side lengths in right triangles. You've probably worked with the sine, cosine, and tangent ratios before.

Hypotenuse, Opposite leg for ∠A, Adjacent leg for ∠A (triangle ABC with sides a, b, c)

sine of $\angle A = \frac{\text{length of leg opposite } \angle A}{\text{length of hypotenuse}} = \frac{BC}{AB} = \frac{a}{c}$

cosine of $\angle A = \frac{\text{length of leg adjacent to } \angle A}{\text{length of hypotenuse}} = \frac{AC}{AB} = \frac{b}{c}$

tangent of $\angle A = \frac{\text{length of leg opposite } \angle A}{\text{length of leg adjacent to } \angle A} = \frac{BC}{AC} = \frac{a}{b}$

Research Note

[Two] projects determined that successful problem solvers tend to think at more than one level. They think about the problem at hand, but are also aware of their own thinking. (Merlyn J. Behr, Guershon Harel, Thomas Post, and Richard Lesh, "Rational Number, Ratio, and Proportion," *Handbook of Research on Mathematics Teaching and Learning,* Douglas A. Grouws, ed., pp. 330–331. © 1992 NCTM.)

The ratios and their definitions are often abbreviated as follows.

$$\sin A = \frac{\text{opposite}}{\text{hypotenuse}} = \frac{a}{c}$$

$$\cos A = \frac{\text{adjacent}}{\text{hypotenuse}} = \frac{b}{c}$$

$$\tan A = \frac{\text{opposite}}{\text{adjacent}} = \frac{a}{b}$$

TRY IT

Express each trigonometric ratio as a fraction.

a. $\sin L$ $\frac{5}{13}$ **b.** $\sin J$ $\frac{12}{13}$

c. $\cos L$ $\frac{12}{13}$ **d.** $\tan J$ $\frac{12}{5}$

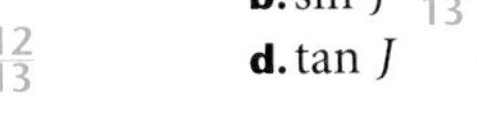

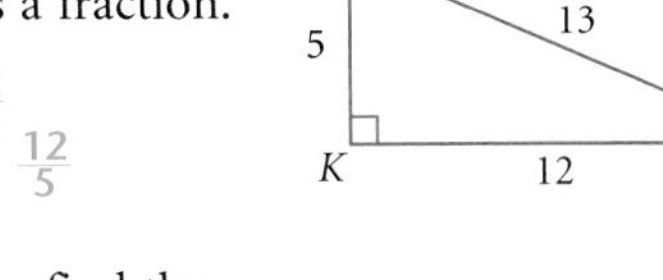

You can use a scientific calculator to find the value of a trigonometric ratio for an angle. To find the cosine of 58°, first make sure that the calculator is in "degree mode." Then enter the keystrokes shown.

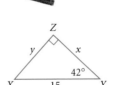

EXAMPLE

Find the values of x and y.

To find x, use the definition of *cosine.*

Cos $42° = \frac{x}{15}$; therefore, $x = 15 \cos 42°$.

Enter 15 [×] 42 [COS] [=] to get $11.14717238 \approx 11.15$.

To find y, use the definition of *sine.*

Sin $42° = \frac{y}{15}$, so $y = 15 \sin 42° \approx 10.04$.

(You can also find y using the Pythagorean Theorem, since you know the length of the hypotenuse and x.)

Trigonometric ratios are useful for solving problems involving side lengths of right triangles.

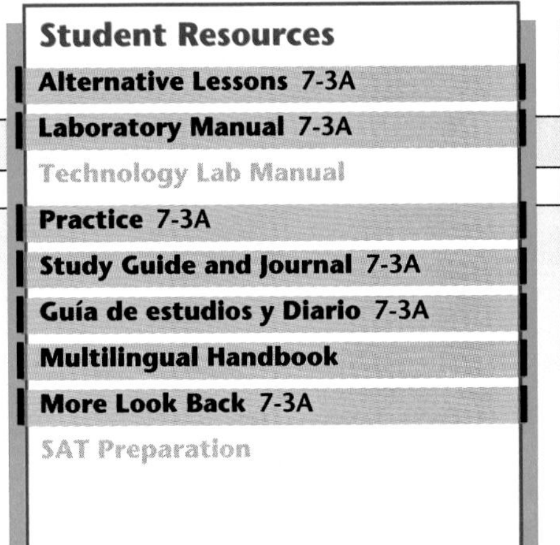

Student Resources
- Alternative Lessons 7-3A
- Laboratory Manual 7-3A
- Technology Lab Manual
- Practice 7-3A
- Study Guide and Journal 7-3A
- Guía de estudios y Diario 7-3A
- Multilingual Handbook
- More Look Back 7-3A
- SAT Preparation

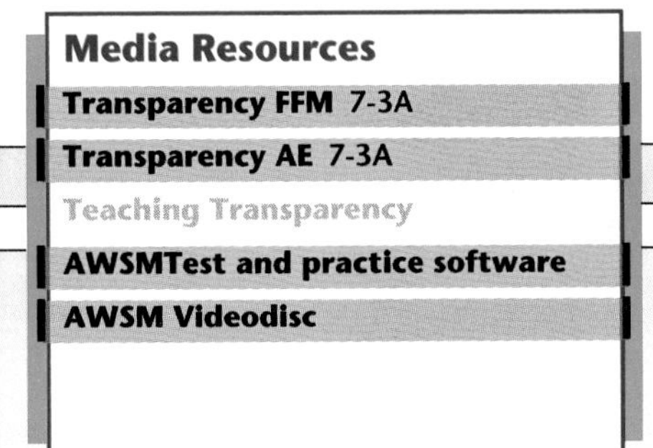

Media Resources
- Transparency FFM 7-3A
- Transparency AE 7-3A
- Teaching Transparency
- AWSMTest and practice software
- AWSM Videodisc

ALTERNATE EXAMPLE

Find the values of m and n.

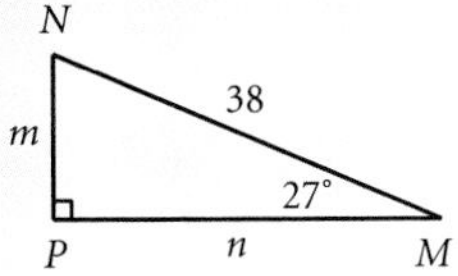

To find m, use the definition of *sine;* $\sin 27° = \frac{m}{38}$. Therefore, $m = 38 \times \sin 27°$. Enter 38 [×] 27 [SIN] [=] to get $17.25163899 \approx 17.25$.

To find n, use the definition of *cosine;* $\cos 27° = \frac{n}{38}$. Therefore, $n = 38 \times \cos 27°$. Enter 38 [×] 27 [COS] [=] to get $33.85824792 \approx 33.86$.

(You can also find n by using the Pythagorean Theorem.)

7-3

Trigonometry

Algebra | Functions | Discrete Math | Probability | Data/Statistics

EXPLORE

Climbing to New Heights

Recommended group size: 4

The Point

To use trigonometry to find the range of safe heights for a ladder.

Look and Listen...

- For students who do not see which angle they are changing.
- For students who do not see which trigonometric ratio to apply.

Ask...

- Have you drawn a sketch of the situation?
- Which angle measures between 50° and 75°?
- Which side length do you know? Which side length do you need? For the angle you're working with, are these sides the opposite and adjacent, opposite and hypotenuse, or adjacent and hypotenuse?

For Groups That Finish Early

Using your safe range of angles for the ladder, find the minimum and maximum distances the ladder can be from the building. **The minimum distance is 5.18 ft; the maximum distance is 12.86 ft.**

Follow Up

Ask students to give the heights of the lowest and highest windows you can safely reach with the ladder and explain how they found their results.

Possible Answer

The lowest point the ladder can safely reach is 15.32 ft high. The highest point it can safely reach is 19.32 ft high.

EXPLORE: CLIMBING TO NEW HEIGHTS

House painters know that if you lean a ladder against a wall so that the angle it makes with the ground is too small, you risk having the bottom of the ladder slide out from under you. If the angle of the ladder is too great, the ladder may tip over backwards.

Suppose that the safe range of angles for a ladder is between 50° and 75°. Find the heights of the lowest and highest windows you can safely reach with a 20-ft ladder.

REFLECT

1. Daniel said, "If I know the measure of one side and one acute angle in a right triangle, I can find the measures of every other side and angle." Is he right? If so, explain how this can be done. If not, explain why not.
2. Is there an angle whose sine and cosine are equal? If so, what is it, and why are these ratios equal?
3. Which of the three ratios, sin A, cos A, or tan A, is equal to the slope of line m? Explain your answer.

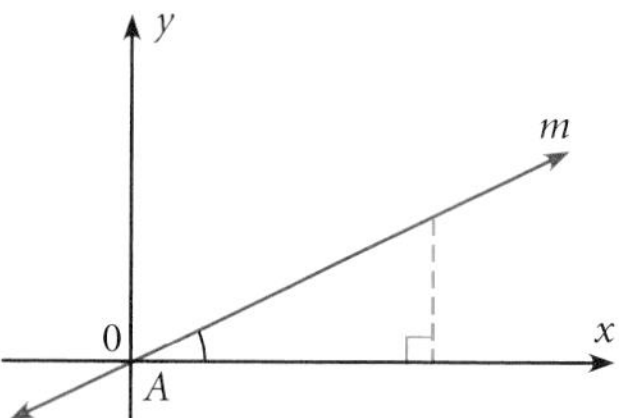

Exercises

CORE

P 1. **Getting Started** Follow these steps to solve for a in the right triangle.

a. Which acute angle measure do you know? $m\angle A = 34°$

b. Which trigonometric ratio should you use? (Hint: Which side length do you know? Which side length do you need?) $\tan A = \frac{a}{6}$

c. Use the definition of the trigonometric ratio you identified in **1b** to write an equation. $\tan 34° = \frac{a}{6}$; $6 \tan 34° = a$

d. Solve the equation for a. $a \approx 4.05$

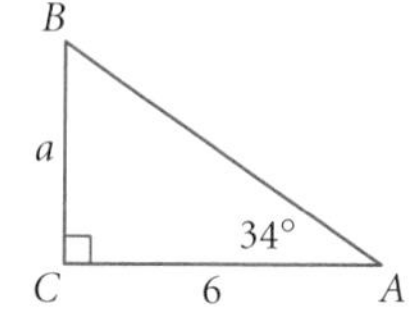

Key

V Vocabulary
P Practice/Skills
R Review
MR Math Reasoning
PS Problem Solving
C Challenge

Careers Connection

Dr. Alberto Vinicio Baez was born in Puebla, Mexico, in 1912. He earned his Ph.D. in physics from Stanford in 1950, and has taught and done research at several universities. Dr. Baez has done research in X-ray radiation, optics, and microscopy, and he shared the Gabor Award in 1991 for his research in X-ray imaging optics.

P **Express each trigonometric ratio as a fraction and as a decimal rounded to the hundredths place.**

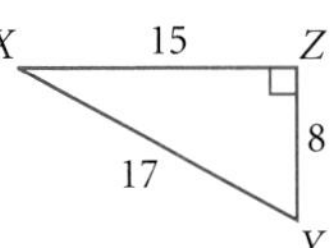

2. $\sin X$ $\frac{8}{17} = 0.47$ **3.** $\cos X$ $\frac{15}{17} = 0.88$ **4.** $\tan X$ $\frac{8}{15} = 0.53$

5. $\sin Y$ $\frac{15}{17} = 0.88$ **6.** $\cos Y$ $\frac{8}{17} = 0.47$ **7.** $\tan Y$ $\frac{15}{8} = 1.88$

V **Write the word or phrase that correctly completes each statement.**

8. The ____ of an angle is the ratio of the length of the adjacent leg to the length of the hypotenuse. Cosine

9. The ____ of an angle is the ratio of the length of the opposite leg to the length of the hypotenuse. Sine

P **Find the sine, cosine, and tangent of each angle. Round your answers to the nearest hundredth.**

10. 8° $\sin 8° = 0.14$, $\cos 8° = 0.99$, $\tan 8° = 0.14$ **11.** 72° $\sin 72° = 0.95$, $\cos 72° = 0.31$, $\tan 72° = 3.08$ **12.** 25° $\sin 25° = 0.42$, $\cos 25° = 0.91$, $\tan 25° = 0.47$

P **Find *x* and *y*.**

13. $x = 3.18$, $y = 6.24$

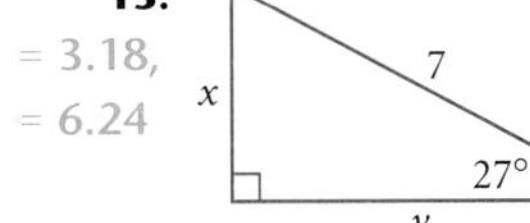

14. $x = 8.59$, $y = 13.96$

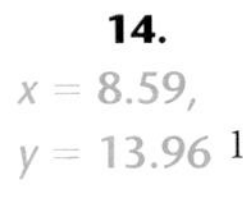

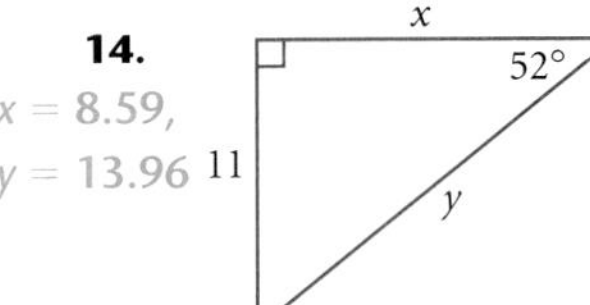

15. $x = 25.26$, $y = 28.88$

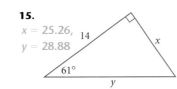

PS **16. Pet Trig** A firefighter is rescuing a cat in a tree. If the branch that the cat is on is fifteen feet above the ground and the ladder makes an angle of sixty-three degrees with the ground, how long is the ladder? Briefly describe the steps you used to solve this problem.

$\sin 63° = \frac{15}{h}$, $h = \frac{15}{\sin 63°} = 16.83$ feet

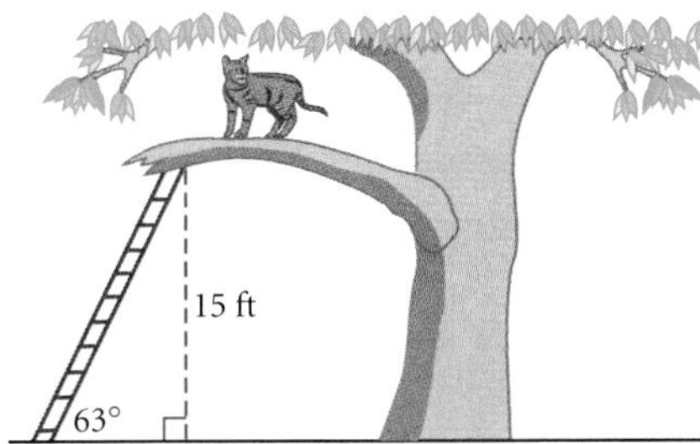

PS **17. Cable Television** A cable is used to support a 245-m television tower. If the angle the cable makes with the ground is 78°, how long is the cable? How far from the base of the tower is the cable anchored to the ground? 250.47 m; 52.08 m

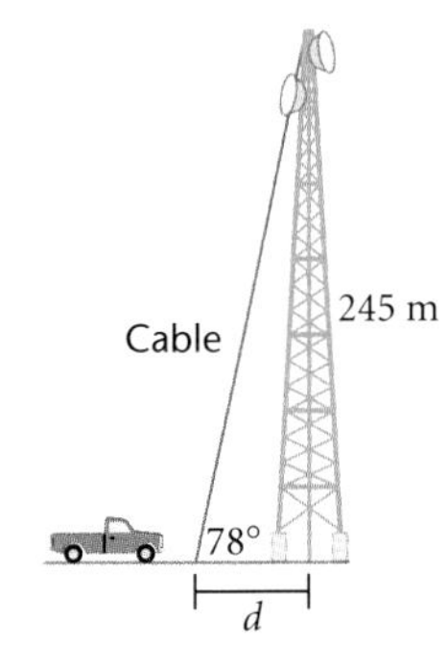

Journal

Reflect 1 and 3 and **Exercise** 21 are suitable for journal entries.

REFLECT

Possible Answers

1. Daniel is correct. The measure of the other acute angle can be found by subtracting the measure of the first from 90°. The length of the second side can be found by using a trigonometric ratio. The length of the third side can be found by using a trigonometric ratio or the Pythagorean Theorem.

2. A 45° angle has an equal sine and cosine. Because any right triangle with a 45° angle must be an isosceles right triangle, the adjacent and opposite sides for the 45° angle have equal length, so its sine and cosine are equal.

3. The tangent of *A* is equal to the slope of the line because $\frac{\text{rise}}{\text{run}} = \frac{\text{opposite}}{\text{adjacent}}$.

Part A Exercises

Exercise Notes

Core

19. Shows the accuracy of the measurements of Benjamin Banneker's surveying team.

21. Students find that the sine of an angle is equal to the cosine of its complement.

22. Illustrates a common student error. Students often forget that trigonometry only applies to right triangles.

Ongoing Assessment

Self-Assessment Exercises 1–17 odd, 20, 23

Embedded Assessment Reflect 1; Exercises 6, 12, 14, 18

Trigonometry

More Math Reasoning

37. Students discover the trigonometric identity that the square of the sine of an angle plus the square of its cosine always equals 1.

Extension: You may wish to justify this conjecture by writing the Pythagorean Theorem for a triangle with side lengths a, o, and h, and then dividing the resulting expression by h^2, as shown below.

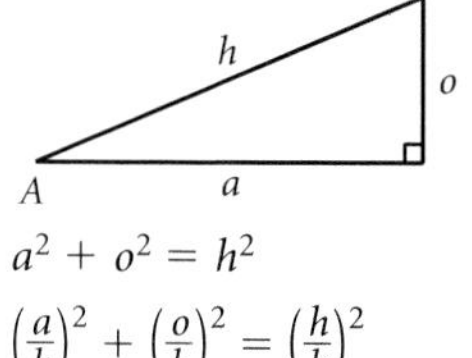

$a^2 + o^2 = h^2$

$\left(\frac{a}{h}\right)^2 + \left(\frac{o}{h}\right)^2 = \left(\frac{h}{h}\right)^2$

$\left(\frac{a}{h}\right)^2 + \left(\frac{o}{h}\right)^2 = 1$

$(\cos A)^2 + (\sin A)^2 = 1$

Exercise Answers

Unless otherwise noted, lengths are rounded to the nearest hundredth.

Core

21. $\sin 54° = 0.81$, $\cos 36° = 0.81$; $\sin 36° = 0.59$, $\cos 54° = 0.59$. Observe that the sine of an angle equals the cosine of the complement of the angle. Conjecture: $\sin A = \cos(90° - m\angle A)$. $\sin A = \frac{BC}{AB}$, $\cos(90° - m\angle A) = \cos B = \frac{BC}{AB}$. The trigonometric ratios are the same.

22. The opposite and adjacent sides should be the legs of a right triangle.

23. The tangent can be greater than 1. Both the sine and cosine are ratios of the length of one of the legs to the hypotenuse, but the hypotenuse is always longer than the legs, so the sine and cosine ratios are ≤ 1.

Look Back

24. Vertices: 4, edges: 6, faces: 4; Possible answer:

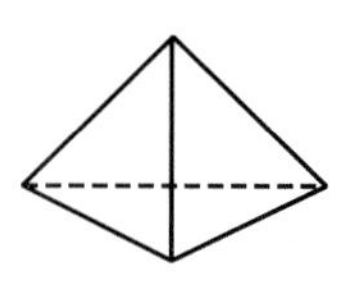

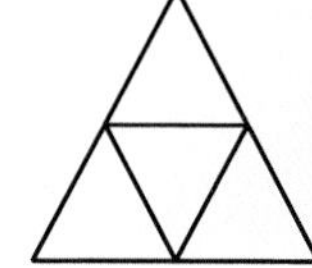

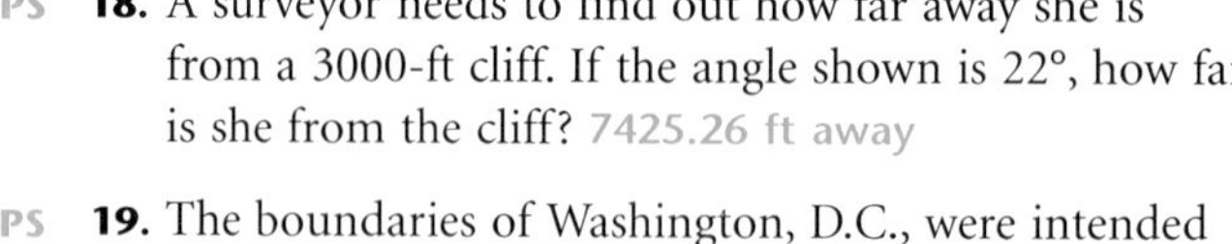

PS **18.** A surveyor needs to find out how far away she is from a 3000-ft cliff. If the angle shown is 22°, how far is she from the cliff? 7425.26 ft away

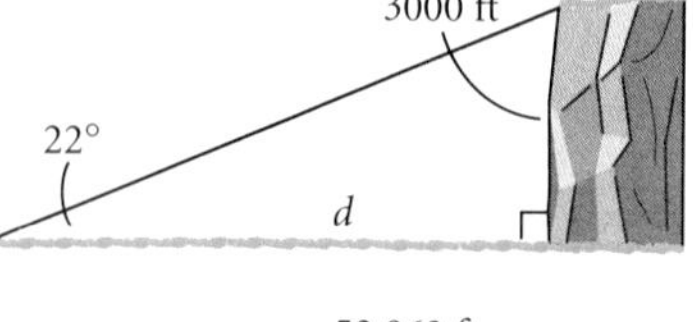

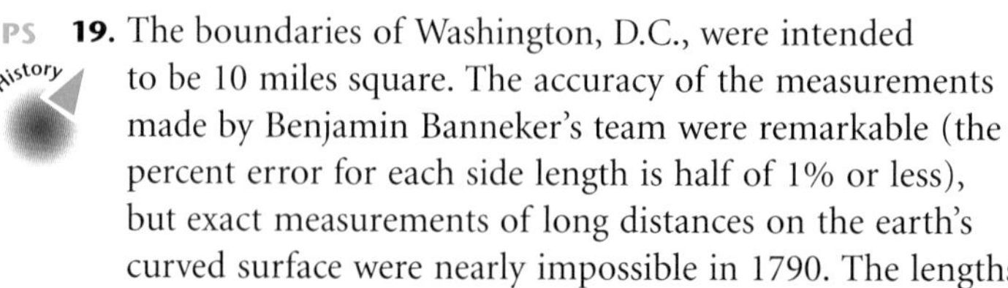

PS **19.** The boundaries of Washington, D.C., were intended to be 10 miles square. The accuracy of the measurements made by Benjamin Banneker's team were remarkable (the percent error for each side length is half of 1% or less), but exact measurements of long distances on the earth's curved surface were nearly impossible in 1790. The lengths of two of the sides of the "square" are shown.

History

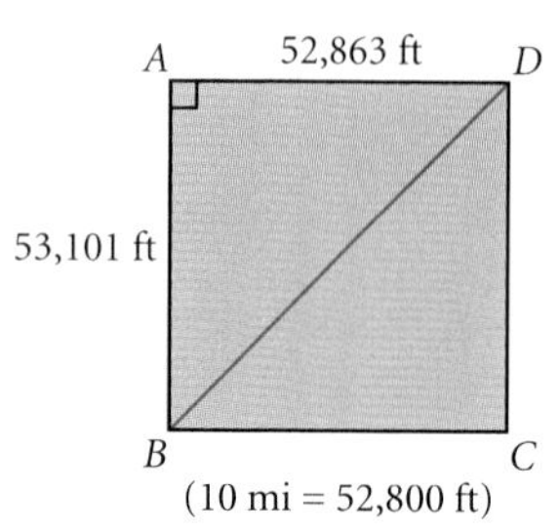

a. Assuming $\angle A$ is a right angle, what is the tangent of $\angle ABD$ to the nearest thousandth? 0.996

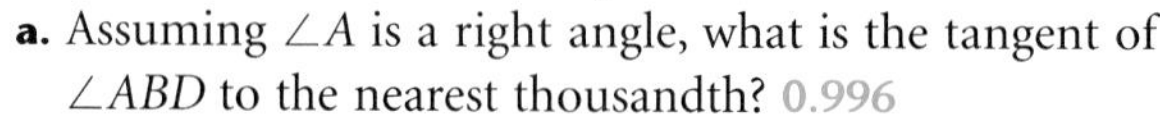

b. If Washington, D.C., were a perfect square, what would you expect the measure of $\angle ABD$ to be? What would you expect its tangent to be? 45°; 1.000

PS **20. Towering Tilt** The Leaning Tower of Pisa is 179 ft tall. It makes an angle of approximately 85° with the ground. About how far over does the tower lean? 15.6 feet

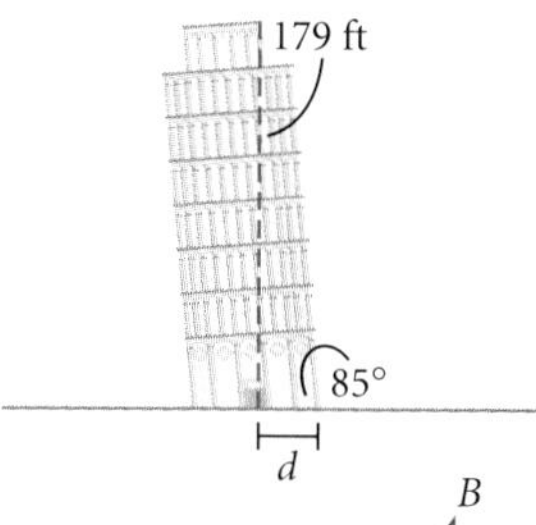

MR **21.** Use your calculator to find the sine of angle A and the cosine of the complement of the angle. Repeat, using angle B. What do you notice? Make a conjecture. Explain why your conjecture makes sense.

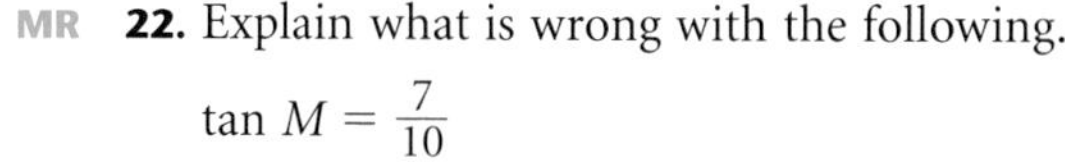

MR **22.** Explain what is wrong with the following.

$\tan M = \frac{7}{10}$

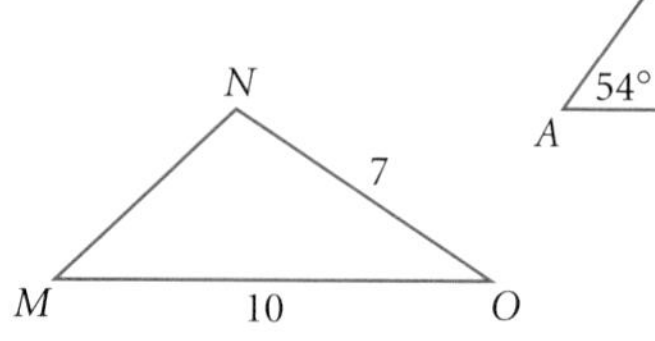

MR **23.** Only one of the three trigonometric ratios you have studied can have a value larger than 1. Identify the ratio, and explain why the values of the other two can never be greater than 1.

LOOK BACK

R **24.** Sketch a regular tetrahedron. Find the number of vertices, edges, and faces of the tetrahedron. Finally, sketch a net of the tetrahedron. [6-3]

R **25.** In the figure, $\overline{BC} \parallel \overline{DE}$. [7-2]

a. Explain why $\triangle ABC \sim \triangle ADE$.

b. Find the distance across the pond.

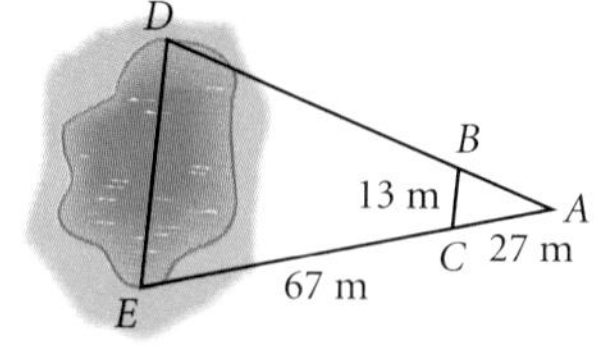

Key

V Vocabulary
P Practice/Skills
R Review
MR Math Reasoning
PS Problem Solving
C Challenge

MORE PRACTICE

Express each trigonometric ratio as a fraction and as a decimal rounded to the hundredths place.

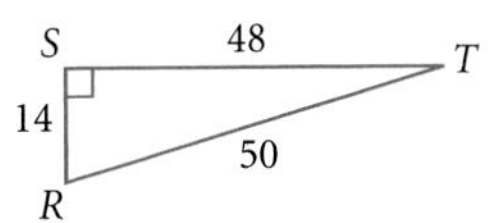

26. $\sin T$ $\frac{7}{25} = 0.28$ **27.** $\tan R$ $\frac{24}{7} \approx 3.43$ **28.** $\cos T$ $\frac{24}{25} = 0.96$

Find the sine, cosine, and tangent of each angle. Round your answers to the nearest hundredth.

29. 18° sin 18° = 0.31, cos 18° = 0.95, tan 18° = 0.32 **30.** 59° sin 59° = 0.86, cos 59° = 0.52, tan 59° = 1.66 **31.** 89° sin 89° = 1.00, cos 89° = 0.02, tan 89° = 57.29

Find x and y.

32. $y = 27.67$, $x = 9.46$

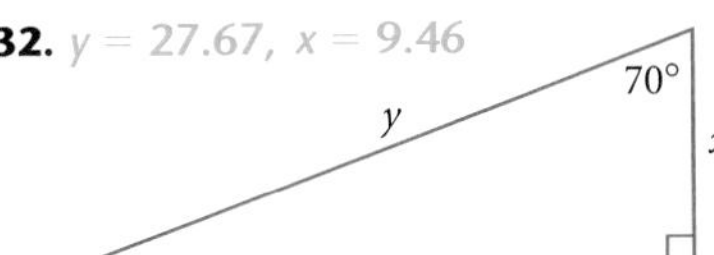

33. $x = 27.64$, $y = 26.14$

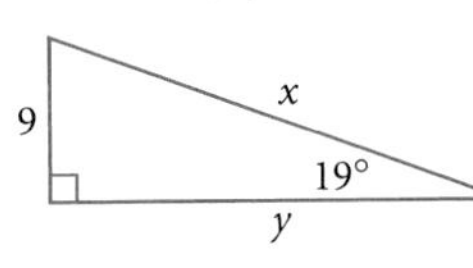

34. $x = 9.64$, $y = 11.49$

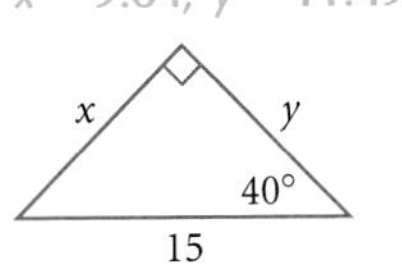

35. Kite Height A kite string is 100 m long. Find the height of the kite if the string makes an angle of 38° with the ground. (Assume the kite string does not sag.) 61.57 m

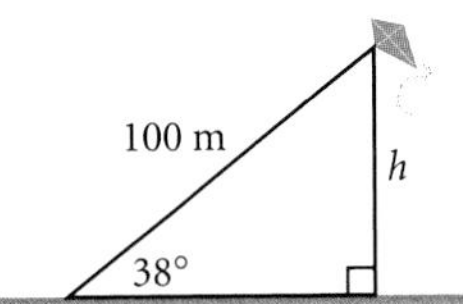

MORE MATH REASONING

36. It is often helpful to know the exact values of the trigonometric ratios for 30°, 45°, and 60° angles. Use what you know about the side lengths of special right triangles to prepare a table showing the sine, cosine, and tangent of 30°, 45°, and 60° angles. Express your results in simplified radical form.

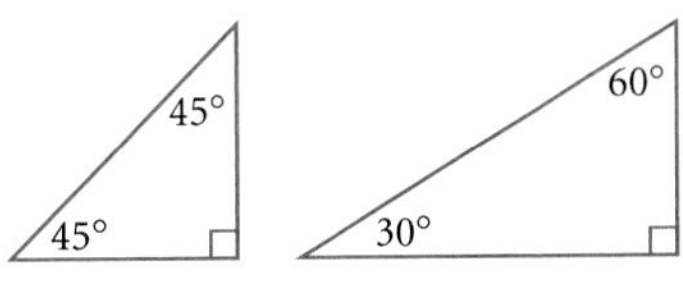

37. Find x in each of the following.

a. $x = (\sin 30°)^2 + (\cos 30°)^2$ $x = 1$

b. $x = (\sin 60°)^2 + (\cos 60°)^2$ $x = 1$

c. $x = (\sin 45°)^2 + (\cos 45°)^2$ $x = 1$

d. Make a conjecture about $(\sin A)^2 + (\cos A)^2$.
For any angle A, $(\sin A)^2 + (\cos A)^2 = 1$

38. Face Reality The area of a square base of an Egyptian pyramid is 52,900 m². The faces of the pyramid make an angle of about 52° with the base. What is the shortest distance you would have to climb up a face to reach the top? 186.79 meters

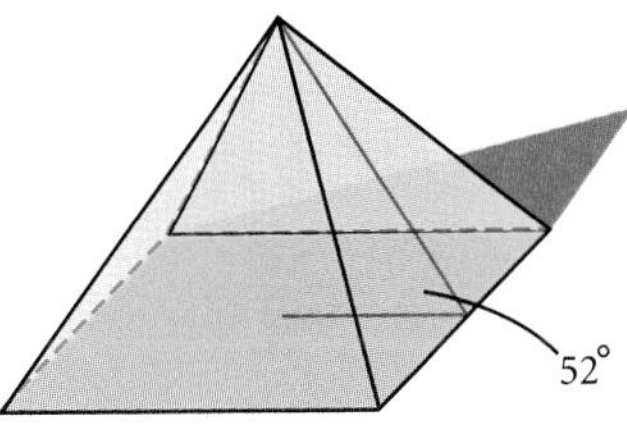

25. a. $\angle A \cong \angle A$ and $\angle D \cong \angle ABC$ (corresponding angles of parallel lines). $\triangle ABC \sim \triangle ADE$ by AA.

b. 45.26 m

More Math Reasoning

36.

	30°	**45°**	**60°**
sin	$\frac{1}{2}$	$\frac{\sqrt{2}}{2}$	$\frac{\sqrt{3}}{2}$
cos	$\frac{\sqrt{3}}{2}$	$\frac{\sqrt{2}}{2}$	$\frac{1}{2}$
tan	$\frac{\sqrt{3}}{3}$	1	$\sqrt{3}$

PART B At a Glance

Objective

To use angles of elevation and depression to solve real-world problems, and to use trigonometry to solve for an angle measure.

Development

Students see definitions of angles of elevation and depression.

In the **Explore,** students solve for an angle of elevation in a real-world context. They explore the capabilities of their calculators to solve for an angle measure.

Suggested Materials

Teacher Scientific calculator transparency

Key Terms

Angle of elevation, angle of depression

First Five Minutes

Transparency FFM 7-3B

Read the first paragraph on page 518. Then do **Try It a** and **b.**

Motivate

Ask...

- Suppose the length of the side opposite an acute angle in a right triangle is 4 and the length of the hypotenuse is 8. What is the measure of the acute angle? **The ratio of the side lengths is $\frac{1}{2}$, the triangle is a 30°-60°-90° triangle, and the angle is a 30° angle.**

Note: *Angle of elevation* and *angle of depression* are used to refer to the measure of an angle as well as the angle itself.

7-3 PART B Angles of Elevation and Depression

← CONNECT → *Now that you know how to use the trigonometric ratios to find side lengths in right triangles, you will use those ratios to find the measures of angles.*

We use special terminology to describe angles in some situations. As shown, an **angle of elevation** and an **angle of depression** are formed by the line of sight and a horizontal line. The vertex of such an angle is the eye of the person looking at the object.

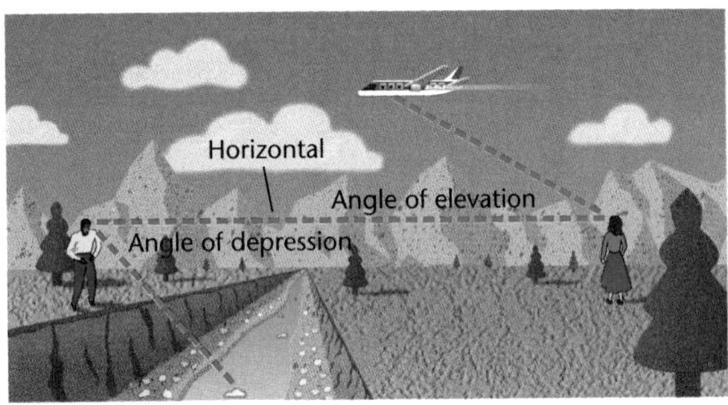

TRY IT

A person standing on a cliff looks up to see a hot air balloon and then looks down to see a sailboat.

a. Find the angle of elevation to the balloon. 34°

b. Find the angle of depression to the sailboat. 49°

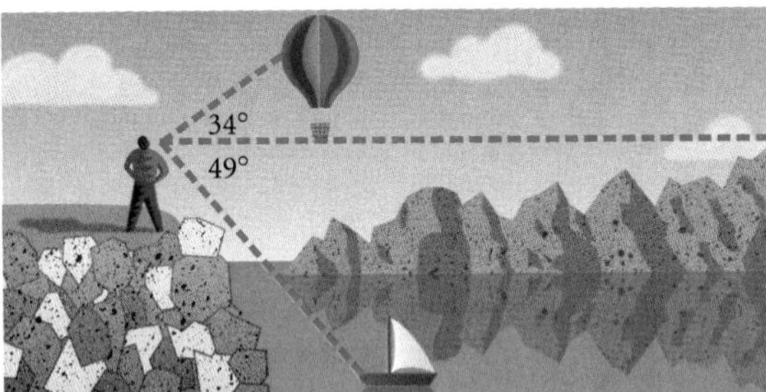

Sometimes you can use the angle of depression to find the angle of elevation or vice-versa.

Alert

Calculators vary greatly in the way they can be used to solve for angles. Some use the INV key, some use the 2nd function key, and some have trigonometric inverses (like SIN^{-1}) on their own keys. You may want to show two or three typical techniques to the class as a whole and answer questions about other calculators individually.

EXAMPLE

An observer in an airplane at a height of 500 m sees a car at an angle of depression of 31°. If the plane is over a barn, how far is the car from the barn?

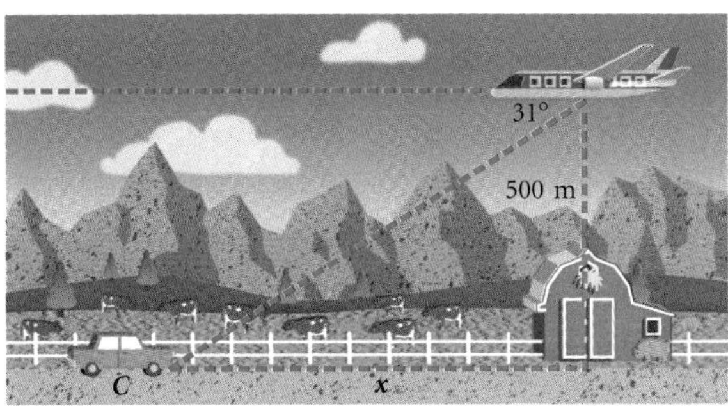

Alternate interior angles are congruent, so $m\angle C = 31°$. Therefore, $\tan 31° = \frac{500}{x}$, and $x = \frac{500}{\tan 31°} \approx 832.1$ m.

In the following Explore, you will find a way to use your calculator to solve for unknown angle measures.

EXPLORE: AN ANGLE IN THE SKY

A ground observer, 5 km from the space shuttle launch pad, watches the shuttle climb into the sky. The space shuttle's instruments report that it is 2 km above the ground. What is the shuttle's angle of elevation from the observer at that moment?

1. Draw a sketch of the problem. Write an equation in which one side length is the ratio of the two known distances and the other is a trigonometric ratio of the angle of elevation. Find the value of that ratio in decimal form.
2. Use your calculator to find the angle of elevation. (You may need to experiment with different keys on your calculator!) Write a brief explanation of how you used your calculator to solve for the angle. Compare results and methods with classmates.

Student Resources

- Alternative Lessons 7-3B
- Laboratory Manual 7-3B
- Technology Lab Manual
- Practice 7-3B
- Study Guide and Journal 7-3B
- Guía de estudios y Diario 7-3B
- Multilingual Handbook
- More Look Ahead 7-3B
- SAT Preparation

Media Resources

- Transparency FFM 7-3B
- Transparency AE 7-3B
- Teaching Transparency
- AWSMTest and practice software
- AWSM Videodisc

ALTERNATE EXAMPLE

Transparency AE 7-3B

EXPLORE

An Angle in the Sky

Recommended group size: 4

The Point

To discover how trigonometry and a calculator can be used to solve for an angle measure.

Look and Listen...

- For students who cannot find a way to use their calculator to solve for the measure of the angle of elevation.

Ask...

- Have you tried using guess-and-check? See if experimenting with the tangents of different angles helps you.
- (For students who have used guess-and-check.) Do you know what the 2nd or INV keys on your calculator are for? Explore these keys.

For Groups That Finish Early

Use two different methods to find the distance from the rocket to the observer. About 5.39 km

Follow Up

Ask students to give their answers and explain how they used their calculators to find the angle of elevation. You may want to demonstrate the use of the 2nd or INV keys to the class at this point.

Possible Answers

1.

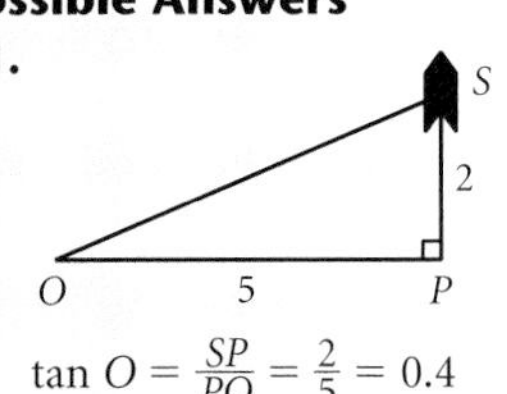

$\tan O = \frac{SP}{PO} = \frac{2}{5} = 0.4$

2. Angle of elevation ≈ 22°.

7-3

Trigonometry

Journal

Reflect 1 and 2 and **Exercise** 11 are suitable for journal entries.

REFLECT

Possible Answers

1. The angle of elevation decreases as you move farther from the base of the flagpole.
2. In the first equation, the ratio of two side lengths is known, and the equation can be solved for an angle measure. To do this, find INV SIN (or 2nd SIN, or SIN^{-1}) of 0.87.

   In the second equation, an angle measure and one side length are known. The other side length can be found by evaluating 10 × sin 87°.

Part B Exercises

Exercise Notes

Core

11–14. Students use trigonometry to solve problems in real-world contexts.

Look Ahead

These exercises review vectors, vector sums, and vector notation. In 7-3 Part C, students apply trigonometry to vector addition.

More Math Reasoning

24. Students use the height of Mt. Everest and an angle of depression to calculate the radius of the earth. In 12-1 Part B, Exercise 29, students will use trigonometry to calculate the distance a person can see from the top of Mt. Everest.

Exercise Answers

Unless otherwise noted, lengths are rounded to the nearest hundredth and angle measures to the nearest degree.

Core

11. a. About 4°

b. So that ramps are not too difficult to ascend.

12. $m\angle P \approx 49°$; $m\angle R \approx 41°$; 954 ft

TRY IT

c. Solve for $m\angle 1$ and $m\angle 2$ to the nearest degree. $m\angle 1 = 49°$, $m\angle 2 = 41°$

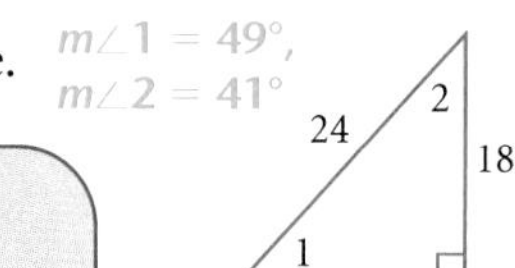

Problem-Solving Tip

Check to make sure that your answer makes sense.

REFLECT

1. What happens to the angle of elevation to the top of a flagpole as you move farther away from its base? Explain.
2. What is the difference between the two equations below? How can you use your calculator to solve each of them?

   $\sin A = \frac{87}{100}$ $\qquad$ $\sin 87° = \frac{x}{10}$

Exercises

CORE

P **1. Getting Started** From a scenic overlook, you can look up to see the top of a mountain and down to see a bridge on a river.

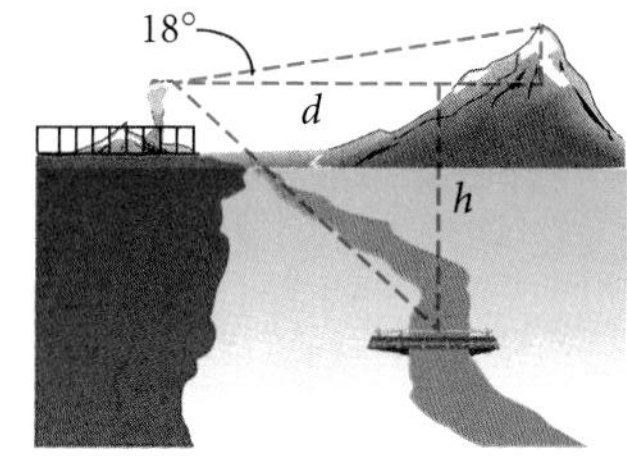

a. Find the angle of elevation to the top of the mountain. 18°

b. If you know the height of the overlook, h, as well as the horizontal distance d to the bridge, what trigonometric ratio can you use to find the angle of depression? $\tan A = \frac{h}{d}$

P **2.** What forms the two sides of any angle of elevation or depression? Where is the vertex of the angle? The line of sight and a horizontal line; At the eye of the person looking at the object

P **Find the measure of $\angle L$.**

3. $\sin L = 0.6691$ 42° **4.** $\cos L = 0.2588$ 75° **5.** $\tan L = 1.2799$ 52° **6.** $\tan L = 1$ 45°

P **Solve for each indicated angle measure.**

7. 28°

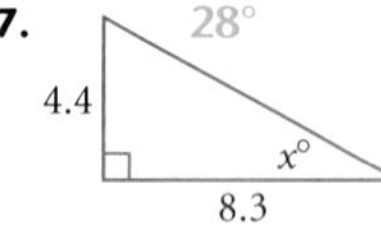

8. 57°

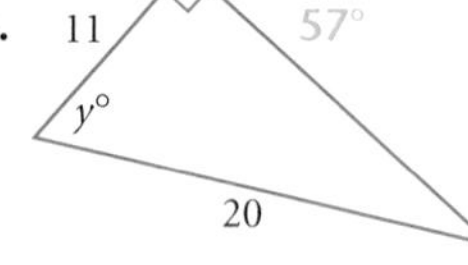

9. 61°

Key

V Vocabulary
P Practice/Skills
R Review
MR Math Reasoning
PS Problem Solving
C Challenge

Tips from Teachers

Some calculators will give values of angles in decimal form; others use degrees and minutes. You may want to ask students to round their answers to the nearest degree, and to give credit for answers within a degree of the actual angle measure to ease student anxiety about differences in calculators.

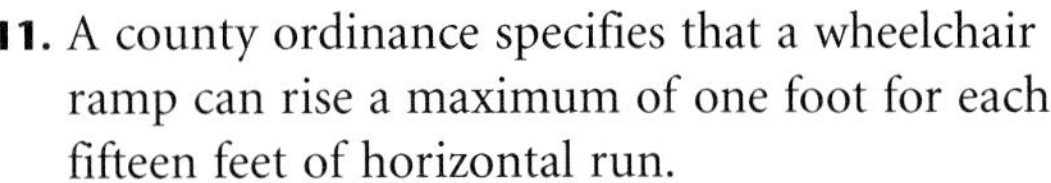

10. From a point 340 m from the base of Hoover Dam, the angle of elevation to the top of the dam is 33°. Find the height of the dam to the nearest meter. 221 m

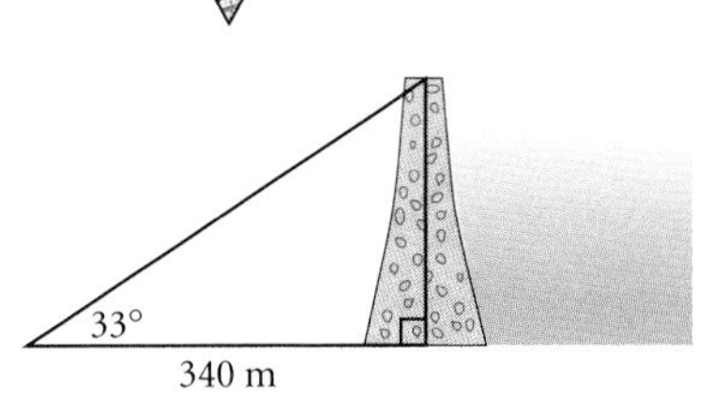

11. A county ordinance specifies that a wheelchair ramp can rise a maximum of one foot for each fifteen feet of horizontal run.

a. What is the maximum permissible angle of the ramp?

b. Write a short paragraph explaining why specifications like this are needed.

12. Surveying the Scene A surveyor stands at the intersection of two perpendicular roads. The distance to an underpass on Hwy 37 is 725 ft. The distance to an irrigation pumping station on County Road 15 is 620 ft. Find the measures of $\angle P$ and $\angle R$ and the distance from the underpass to the pumping station to the nearest foot.

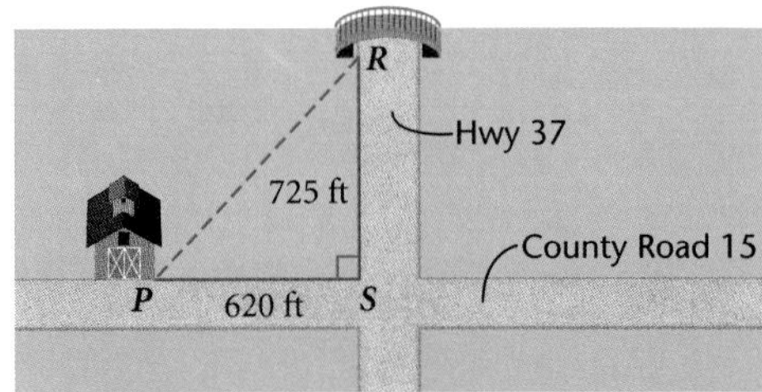

13. Solid as a Rock Some 13th-century buildings in Ethiopia were carved from solid mountain rock. First, a deep trench was dug, leaving a block of stone. Then the building was carved out of the remaining stone. The top of the Church of St. George (in Lalibela, Ethiopia) is at ground level, as shown in the photo.

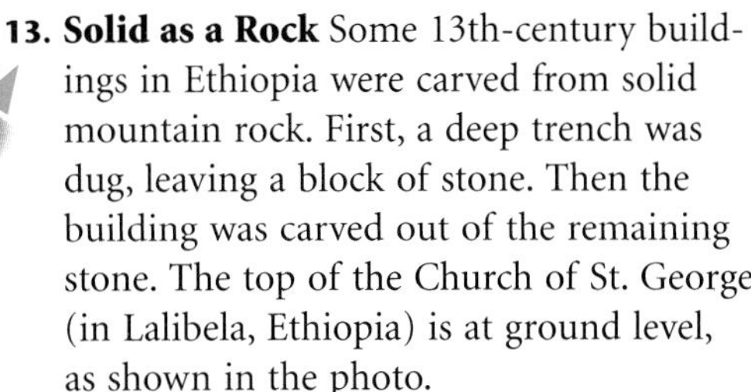

Suppose an observer is at ground level. His eyes are 5.5 ft above the ground, and his horizontal distance from the church is 25 ft. If the angle of depression to the base of the church is 61.2°, how tall is the church? 40 ft

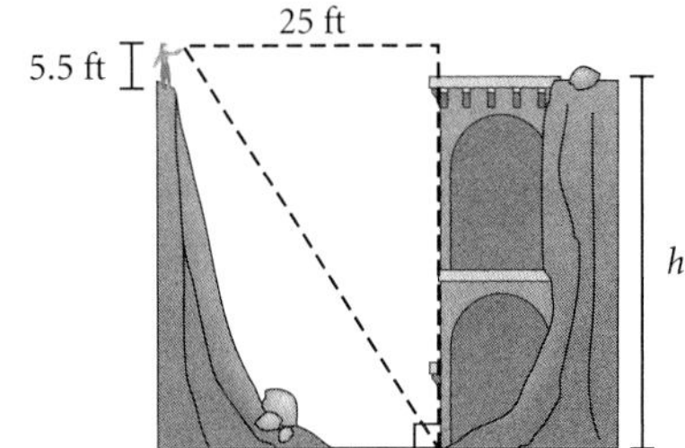

14. A helicopter pilot sights a life raft. The angle of depression is 28°, and the helicopter's altitude is 2.5 km.

a. Draw a figure to represent the situation.

b. What is the horizontal distance from the helicopter to the raft?

c. If the helicopter flies at a constant speed of 200 km/hr, how long will it be before it is directly above the raft? Assume that the altitude of the helicopter does not change.

14. a. Helicopter

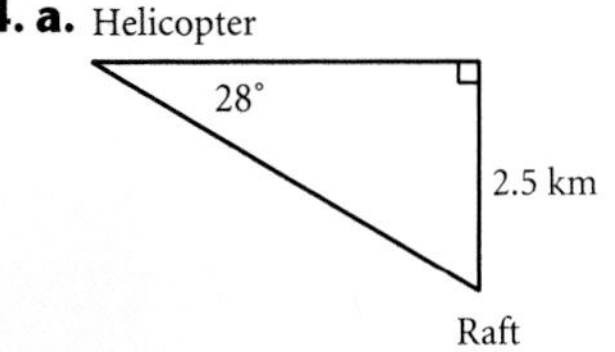

b. 4.70 km

c. 0.0235 hr = 1.41 min

Ongoing Assessment

Self-Assessment Exercises 1–9 odd, 12, 13

Embedded Assessment Try It c; Exercises 4, 10, 11, 14

Trigonometry

Look Ahead

16.

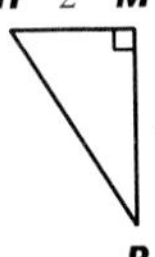

a. $\overrightarrow{HM} + \overrightarrow{MR} + \overrightarrow{RH}$

b. Use the Pythagorean Theorem; $2^2 + 3^2 = h^2 = 13$; $h = \sqrt{13} \approx 3.61$ km

More Math Reasoning

24. a. $\sin 87° = \frac{R}{R + 5.5}$; $R = \frac{5.5 \sin 87°}{1 - \sin 87°} \approx 4000$ mi

b. Possible answer: Since the denominator of the fraction which simplifies as R is $1 - \sin(90° -$ depression angle), a small error in the angle measure can produce a large error in the estimated R. Errors in the measured height of the mountain also affect the estimated R significantly.

LOOK AHEAD

P **15.** Write the names for the vectors shown below. Use a ruler and protractor to find their directions and lengths. $\overrightarrow{ST}$: 4 cm, 44°; $\overrightarrow{UV}$: 4.5 cm, 17°, $\overrightarrow{WX}$: 4.7 cm, 199°

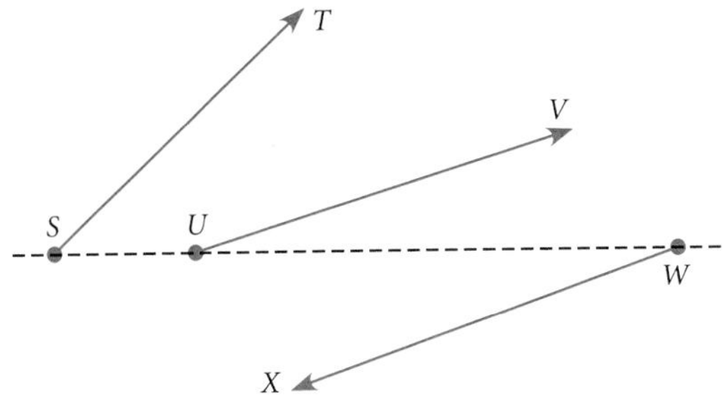

R **16.** Use a ruler and protractor to draw a vector model of the following situation. Use a scale of 3 cm to 1 km.

Rina bicycled from her house (H) two kilometers east to the shopping mall (M). After doing some shopping, she rode three kilometers south to a restaurant (R). She then bicycled home.

a. Write Rina's ride as a sum of vectors.

b. Find the length of $\overrightarrow{RH}$. Explain how you found this length.

MORE PRACTICE

P **Find the measure of ∠W.**

17. $\tan W = 0.0349$ 2°

18. $\sin W = \frac{1}{2}$ 30°

19. $\cos W = 0.4695$ 62°

P **Solve for each indicated angle measure.**

20. 48°

$x°$, 50, 56

21. 63°

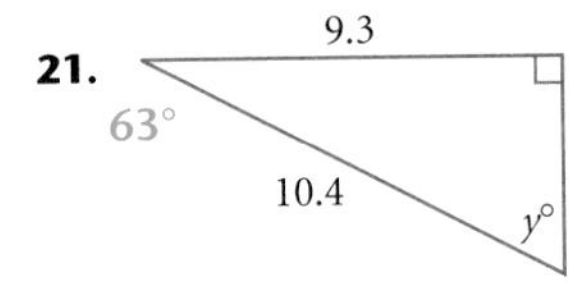

PS **22.** On a tour of Washington, D.C., Martha goes to the top of the 555-ft-tall Washington Monument. She spots her friend Chris 210 ft from the base of the monument. Find the angle of depression shown to the nearest degree. Then find the line-of-sight distance MC. 69°; MC = 593.40 ft

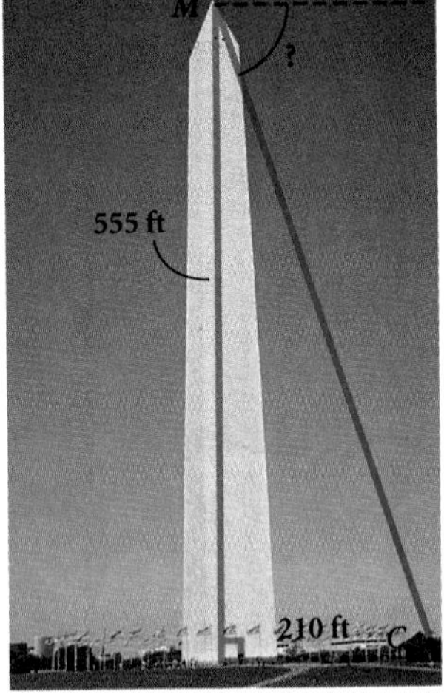

Key

V Vocabulary
P Practice/Skills
R Review
MR Math Reasoning
PS Problem Solving
C Challenge

MORE MATH REASONING

23. Speed Trap A car is passing by a police motorcyclist. At its closest point, it is 2500 ft from the motorcycle. Ten seconds later, the car is 2625 ft away.

a. What is the measure of $\angle M$? 18°

b. How far did the car travel along the highway during this time? about 800 ft

c. If the speed limit is 55 mi/hr, is the car speeding? No

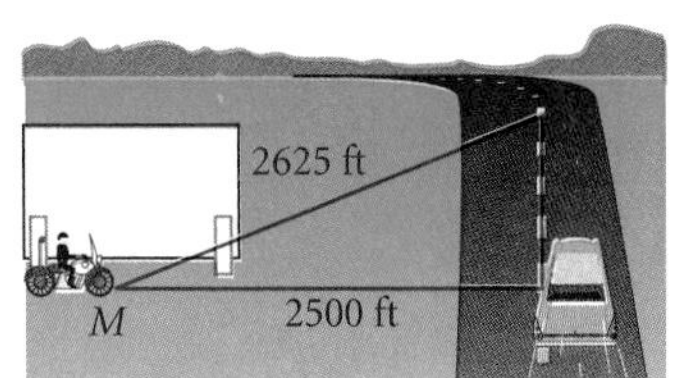

24. When the horizon is sighted from the top of the world's tallest mountain, Mt. Everest, the angle of depression is 3°. The height of Mt. Everest, to the nearest hundredth of a mile, is 5.50 mi.

a. How can you use this information to find the distance, R, from the center of the earth to the earth's surface? Find R.

b. Investigate how an error in measuring the angle of depression or the height of the mountain might affect the value of R. Explain your findings.

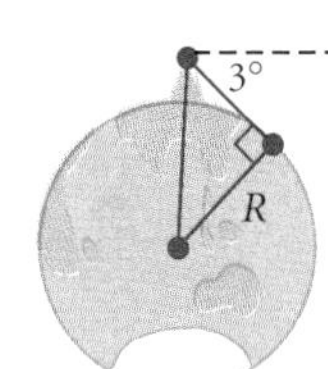

7-3 PART C Vectors and Trigonometry

← CONNECT → ***You are already familiar with vectors and vector addition. Now you will use trigonometric ratios to find the direction and length of the sum of two perpendicular vectors.***

Vectors have both a length and a direction. This makes them ideal for modeling forces and velocities. You need to know both the size and the direction of a force or velocity to completely understand what is happening—driving north at 30 mi/hr gets you to a very different place than driving south at the same speed!

1. Why do you think vectors are used to represent things like forces and velocities but not things like lengths and areas?

Student Resources

- Alternative Lessons 7-3C
- Laboratory Manual 7-3C
- Technology Lab Manual
- Practice 7-3C
- Study Guide and Journal 7-3C
- Guía de estudios y Diario 7-3C
- Multilingual Handbook
- More Look Back 7-3C
- SAT Preparation

Media Resources

- Transparency FFM 7-3C
- Transparency AE 7-3C
- Teaching Transparency
- AWSMTest and practice software
- AWSM Videodisc

PART C At a Glance

Objective

To use trigonometry to find the length and direction of a vector sum.

Development

First, students review vectors. In an **Example,** they see how to find the length and direction of the sum of two perpendicular vectors using trigonometry.

Then, in the **Explore,** students experiment with paper to see what happens when a plane travels in a wind perpendicular to its path. Once they have an intuition for what will happen, they use vectors to find the speed and direction of a plane traveling in a crosswind.

Suggested Materials

Teacher Graph paper transparency

First Five Minutes

Transparency FFM 7-3C

Read the first paragraph in Part C on page 523. Then answer the **Consider** question.

Motivate

Ask...

- Suppose you are walking on a moving walkway that travels 2 mi/hr, and your walking speed on solid ground is 3 mi/hr.

  If you are walking in the same direction as the walkway, how fast are you traveling? **5 mi/hr**

  If you are walking in the opposite direction, how fast are you going? **1 mi/hr**

Possible Answer

1. Lengths and areas measure sizes, but they do not have a direction. When describing forces and velocities, both direction and size are important.

ALTERNATE EXAMPLE

Find the direction and length of $\overline{RT}$.

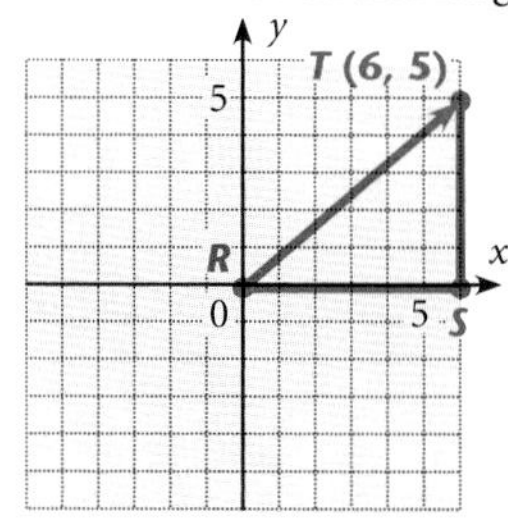

Length $= \sqrt{(6-0)^2 + (5-0)^2}$

$= \sqrt{61} \approx 7.81$

$\tan \angle SRT = \frac{5}{6} \approx 0.833.$

Using the inverse tangent key on a calculator, we find that $m\angle SRT \approx 40°$.

EXPLORE

Just Plane Vectors

Recommended group size: 4

The Point

To use trigonometry to find the sum of two perpendicular vectors.

Look and Listen...

- For students who do not understand the concept of headwind and tailwind.
- For students who have difficulty sketching the vectors in Step 3.
- For students who do not remember how to describe the direction of a vector.

Ask...

- If you think of your graph paper as a map, in what direction does the positive y-axis point? The positive x-axis?
- Can you show me the direction of the vector sum on your sketch?

For Groups That Finish Early

Suppose that the wind speed changes, so that the actual speed of the plane is 504 mi/hr. Find the new wind speed and direction of the plane to the nearest degree. 63.37 mi/hr; 7°

Follow Up

Ask one student or group to present their solutions to Steps 2 and 3 and explain their methods.

The velocity of a car traveling west at 50 mi/hr can be represented by a vector whose length is 50 and whose direction is 180°.

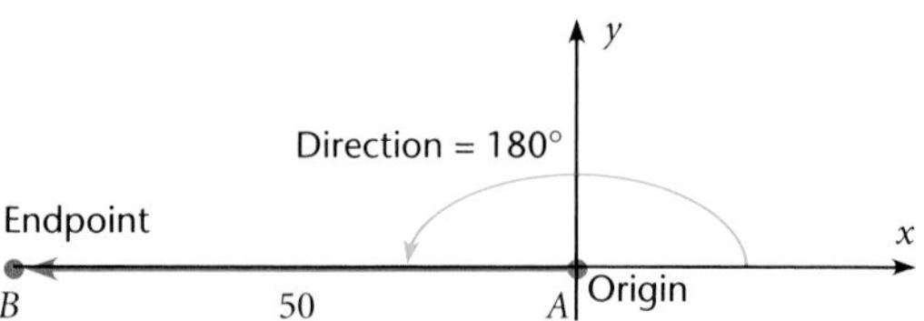

EXAMPLE

Find the direction and length of $\overrightarrow{MN}$.

Length $= \sqrt{(7-0)^2 + (3-0)^2} = \sqrt{58}$

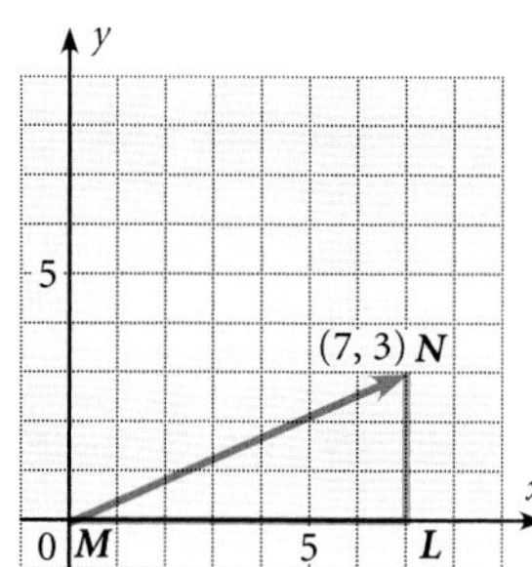

We can use trigonometry to find the direction of $\overrightarrow{MN}$. By drawing the triangle shown, $\tan \angle LMN = \frac{3}{7} \approx 0.4286$. To find the angle when we know the value of its tangent, use the inverse tangent keys on your calculator. This gives a result of 23.19. . . °. Therefore, $m\angle LMN \approx 23°$.

Recall that to find the sum of two vectors, you position the origin of the second vector at the endpoint of the first. In the figure, $\overrightarrow{XZ}$ is the vector sum of $\overrightarrow{XY}$ and $\overrightarrow{YZ}$.

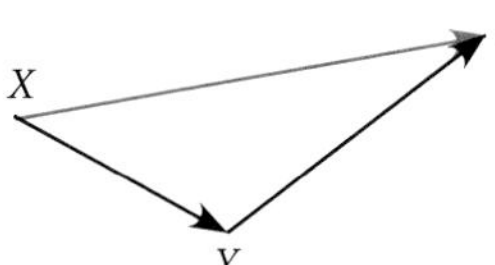

When a plane moves with or against a wind, its actual speed is just the sum or difference of the plane's speed and the wind's speed. However, this is only true when the velocities have the same or opposite directions.

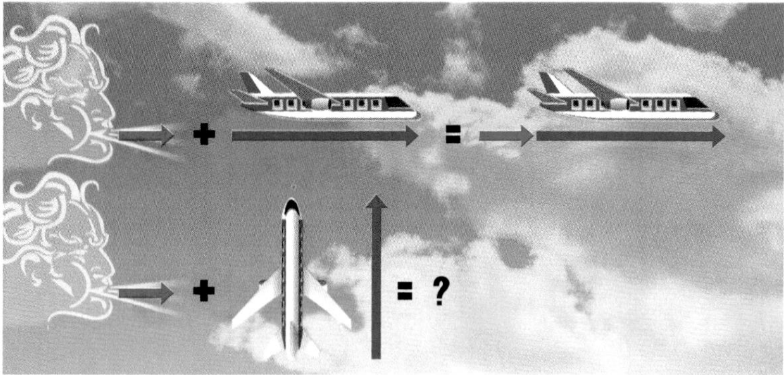

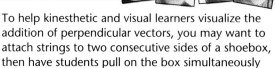

Diversity Issues

To help kinesthetic and visual learners visualize the addition of perpendicular vectors, you may want to attach strings to two consecutive sides of a shoebox, then have students pull on the box simultaneously from consecutive sides of a desk. The box will slide "between" the directions of the two forces.

With vectors and trigonometry, you can investigate what happens when velocities are perpendicular to one another. You will take a closer look at this in the following Explore.

EXPLORE: JUST PLANE VECTORS

1. Crumple up a small piece of paper. Roll it across your desk while blowing gently at a right angle to the path of the paper. Make a sketch to illustrate what happens to the paper. Vary the speed of the paper and the force with which you blow and see how this changes the paper's path.
2. A passenger jet is heading due east. Without wind, the speed of the jet is 500 mi/hr. A strong 80 mi/hr wind is blowing. What will the actual speed and direction of the jet be
   a. if the wind is a tailwind?
   b. if the wind is a headwind?
   Make a sketch using vectors to show what happens in each case.
3. Now, suppose the wind in Step 2 is blowing due north at 80 mi/hr.
   a. Guess the approximate direction and speed of the plane in this wind.
   b. Draw vectors that represent the velocities of the plane and the wind. (Be sure the origin of the second vector is at the endpoint of the first.) Then draw the vector that shows the actual velocity of the airplane.
   c. Find the speed of the plane in the wind. How does this compare to the speeds you found in **2a** and **2b**? Does this make sense? Explain.
   d. Use a trigonometric ratio to find the direction of the plane. Does this answer seem reasonable? Why?

REFLECT

1. If you add two vectors that are perpendicular, is the length of their vector sum always greater than the length of either vector? Explain why or why not.
2. Suppose a boat sailing due east at 10 mi/hr suddenly meets a 10 mi/hr current that is moving due north. Find the speed and direction of the actual path of the boat without using trigonometry. Explain your method.

Alert

In Step 1, students may have drawn both of their vectors beginning at (0, 0). If they complete this triangle, their plane will appear to be heading northwest instead of northeast. You may need to remind them that, when sketching the sum of two vectors, the origin of one vector is positioned at the endpoint of the other.

Possible Answers

1.

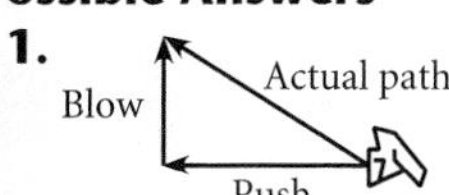

The faster you roll the paper, the more closely it follows its original direction. The harder you blow, the more it deviates from its original direction.

2. a. 580 mi/hr

b. 420 mi/hr

3. b.

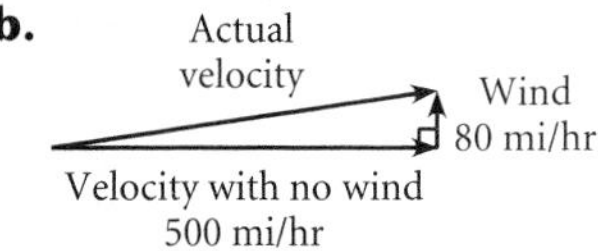

c. Speed ≈ 506.4 mi/hr. This is between the speed in a headwind and the speed with a tailwind. This makes sense, because a headwind gives the greatest resistance and the tailwind the greatest assistance.

d. The actual direction is about 9°. This is reasonable because the plane should travel slightly north of east.

Journal 

Consider question 1, **Reflect** 1, and **Exercise** 9 are suitable for journal entries.

REFLECT

Possible Answers

1. The length of their vector sum must be greater than the length of either vector. The diagram of the situation is a right triangle with the vector sum as the hypotenuse. Since the hypotenuse is the longest side, the sum has the greatest length.
2. The actual speed of the boat is $10\sqrt{2} \approx 14.14$ mi/hr, and its direction is 45°. The vectors and the vector sum make a 45°-45°-90° triangle, so the length of the hypotenuse is $\sqrt{2}$ times the length of either leg.

Part C Exercises

Exercise Notes

Core

11. Students may be interested to find that, in three of the four cases listed here, the wind makes the boat go faster.

Exercise Answers

Unless otherwise noted, lengths and speeds are rounded to the nearest hundredth and angle measures to the nearest degree.

Core

3. a–b.

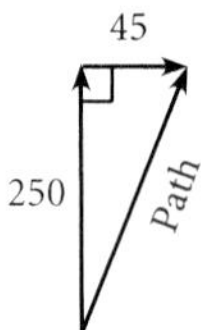

c. 254.02 mph

4. Length = 5.83; $m\angle 1 = 31°$

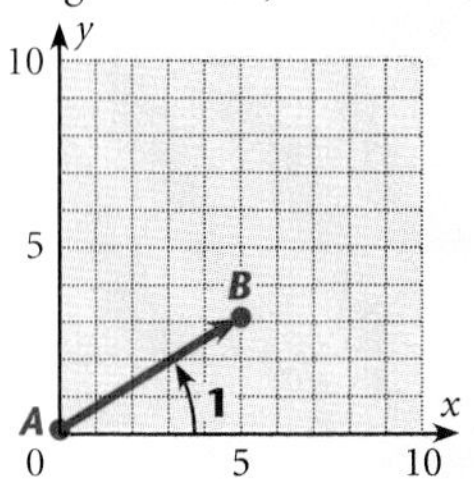

5. Length = 7.28; $m\angle 1 = 16°$

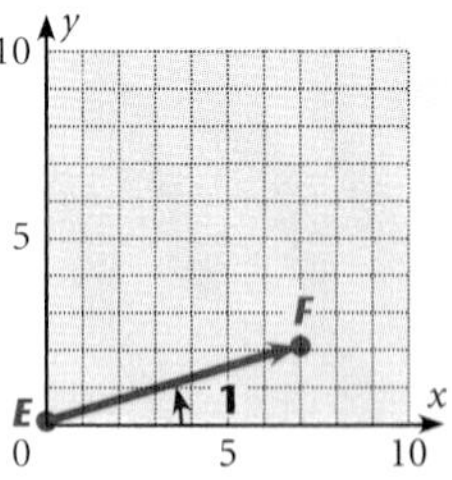

6. Length = 6.40; $m\angle 1 = 51°$

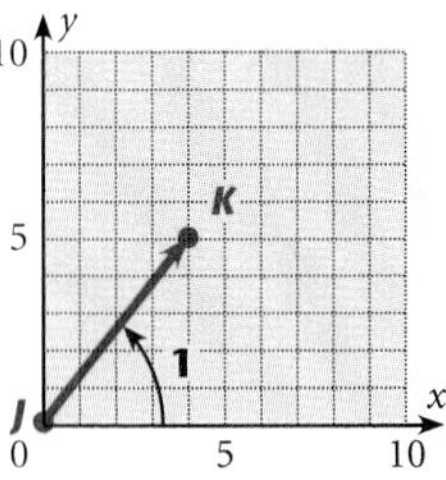

Exercises

CORE

P, PS **Getting Started In Exercises 1–3, an airplane is flying due north with a speed (in still air) of 250 mi/hr.**

250 mi/hr

1. Find the plane's actual speed and direction if there is a 45 mi/hr headwind. Due north at 205 mph

2. Find the plane's actual speed and direction if there is a 45 mi/hr tailwind. Due north at 295 mph

3. Suppose the wind blows due east at 45 mi/hr.

a. Sketch a vector to represent the plane's velocity. Starting at the endpoint of the plane's velocity vector, sketch a vector to represent the wind's velocity.

b. Sketch the vector sum that represents the actual path of the plane. The origin of this vector should be at the origin of the vector you drew in **3a**.

c. Use the Pythagorean Theorem to find the length of the actual velocity vector.

P **Draw each vector on graph paper. Find its length, and use trigonometry to find its direction.**

4. $\overrightarrow{AB}$ for $A(0, 0)$ and $B(5, 3)$ **5.** $\overrightarrow{EF}$ for $E(0, 0)$ and $F(7, 2)$

6. $\overrightarrow{JK}$ for $J(0, 0)$ and $K(4, 5)$

P **Sketch each pair of vectors on graph paper. Then sketch the vector sum of the two vectors. Write a vector equation that uses vector addition to describe your sketch.**

7. $\overrightarrow{LM}$ has length 5 and direction 0°; $\overrightarrow{MN}$ has length 8 and direction 90°.

8. $\overrightarrow{RS}$ has length 7 and direction 90°; $\overrightarrow{ST}$ has length 3 and direction 180°.

PS, MR **9. Off Course** Sean is paddling his kayak due east. In still water, his speed would be 15 km/hr. There is a 9 km/hr current going from north to south. Draw a sketch to illustrate this situation. Then find the actual speed of the kayak and the measure of the angle between its actual direction and its intended direction. Explain how you solved this problem.

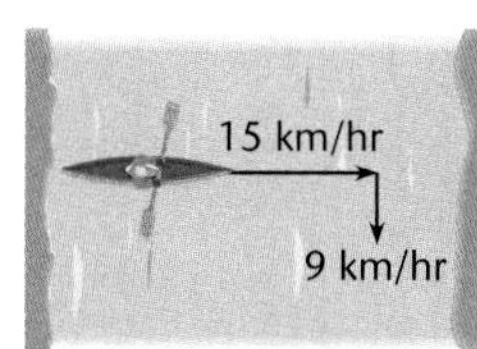

PS **10. Parrot Path** Ozzie the parrot is flying 20 mi/hr due east. There is an 11 mi/hr wind blowing due north. Find Ozzie's actual speed and the measure of the angle his actual path makes with his intended path. $s = 22.83$ mph, $m\angle A = 29°$

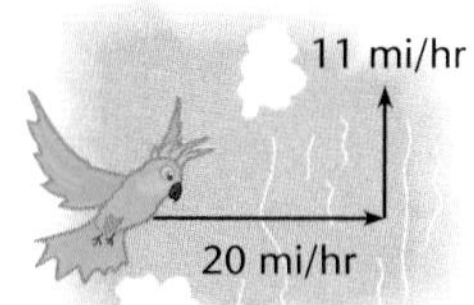

Key

V Vocabulary
P Practice/Skills
R Review
MR Math Reasoning
PS Problem Solving
C Challenge

11. A sailboat is sailing due west on a lake. Identify whether each of the following directions for the wind makes the boat go faster or slower.
a. due north Faster **b.** due east Slower **c.** due south Faster **d.** due west Faster

LOOK BACK

Find the area of each figure. Express your answer as a decimal rounded to the nearest hundredth. [6-3]

12. an equilateral triangle with radius 4.1 cm 21.84 cm^2

13. a regular hexagon with side length 8 in. 166.28 in.^{2}

***Z* is the midpoint of $\overline{VY}$, and *W* is the midpoint of $\overline{VX}$. [7-2]**

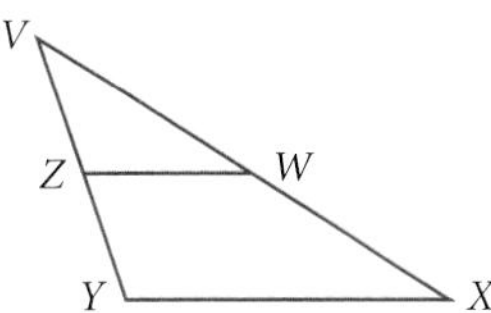

14. $VZ = 6$, and $XY = 13$. Find VY, WZ, and ZY.

15. $m\angle VWZ = 38°$, and $WZ = 34.4$. Find $m\angle VXY$ and XY.

16. $XY = 12$, $VX = 17$, and $m\angle Y = 84°$. Find $m\angle VZW$, VW, and WZ.

MORE PRACTICE

Draw each vector on graph paper. Find its length, and use trigonometry to find its direction.

17. $\overrightarrow{AB}$ for $A(0, 0)$ and $B(2, 6)$

18. $\overrightarrow{EF}$ for $E(0, 0)$ and $F(4, 7)$

Sketch each pair of vectors on graph paper. Then sketch the vector sum of the two vectors. Write a vector equation that uses vector addition to describe your sketch.

19. $\overrightarrow{GH}$ has length 6 and direction 180°; $\overrightarrow{HI}$ has length 7 and direction 90°.

20. $\overrightarrow{JK}$ has length 8 and direction 0°; $\overrightarrow{KL}$ has length 4 and direction 270°.

MORE MATH REASONING

21. A plane is flying in a strong wind. The wind is blowing due west at 100 mi/hr. The plane's actual speed is 340 mi/hr, and its actual direction is due north. Find the speed and direction it would be flying if there were no wind.

22. Do you think you can use trigonometry to find the sum of two vectors that are not perpendicular? If so, write an explanation of your method. If not, explain how you could find the length and direction of the sum of two such vectors.

7. $\overrightarrow{LM} + \overrightarrow{MN} = \overrightarrow{LN}$

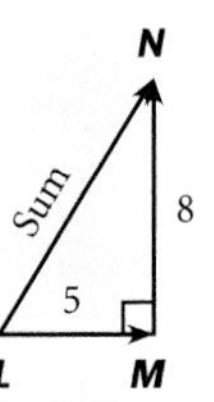

8. $\overrightarrow{RS} + \overrightarrow{ST} = \overrightarrow{RT}$

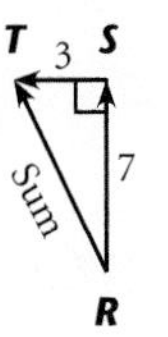

9. $(\text{speed})^2 = 15^2 + 9^2 = 306$;
$s = \sqrt{306} \approx 17.49$ km/hr;
$\tan A = \frac{9}{15} = 0.6$;
$m\angle A = 31°$

Look Back

14. $VY = 12$, $WZ = \frac{13}{2} = 6.5$, $ZY = 6$

15. $m\angle VXY = 38°$, $XY = 68.8$

16. $m\angle VZW = 84°$, $VW = \frac{17}{2} = 8.5$, $WZ = 6$

More Practice

17. Length = 6.32, $m\angle 1 = 72°$

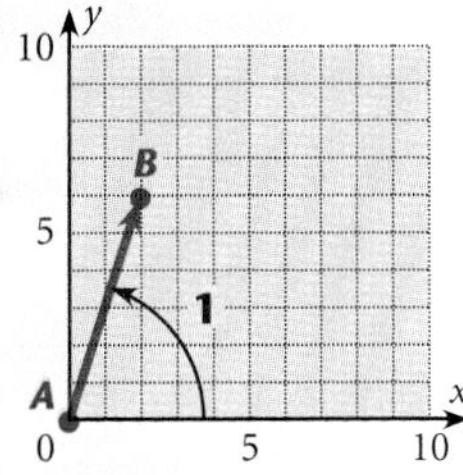

18. Length = 8.06, $m\angle 1 = 60°$

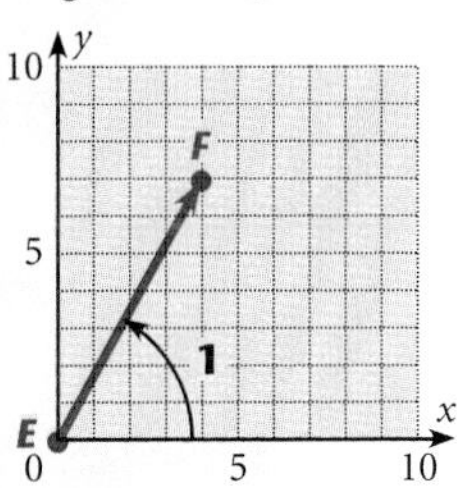

19. $\overrightarrow{GH} + \overrightarrow{HI} = \overrightarrow{GI}$

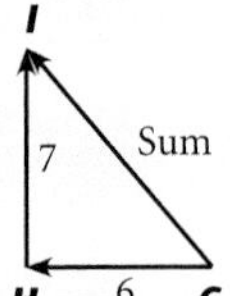

20–22. See Additional Answers p. T510.

Tips from Teachers

If at all possible, have students go outside for their measurements in the *Explore* on page 528, so that they can actually measure the distance to the object.

Ongoing Assessment

Self-Assessment Exercises 1, 3, 5, 7, 10, 11

Embedded Assessment Explore Step 3; Reflect 1; Exercises 6, 8, 9

PART D At a Glance

Objective

To make and use a tool that uses trigonometry to measure distant objects.

Development

In the **Explore,** students make a clinometer—a tool for measuring angles—and use it to find the height of a distant object.

Suggested Materials

Student Protractor, string, tape, weight

First Five Minutes

Transparency FFM 7-3D

Draw right triangle $\triangle ABC$ with right angle at C. Then list the ratios of side lengths in $\triangle ABC$ for sin A, cos A, and tan A.

EXPLORE

Angle Sighting

Recommended group size: 2

The Point

To make an angle-measuring device and use it to find the height of an object.

Look and Listen...

- For students who do not see that the angle of elevation is the complement of the angle measured by the weight.

Ask...

- Where is the angle measured by the weight? The angle you want to measure? How can you find the angle of elevation by reading the clinometer?

For Groups That Finish Early

Compare the clinometer to the hypsometer used in 7-2 Part E.

Follow Up

Have students give the height of one of the objects they measured and explain how they made their measurement.

7-3 PART D Making Connections

← CONNECT → ***The relationships between the sides and angles of similar right triangles are useful in many fields, including astronomy, surveying, and engineering. You've used trigonometry to solve for unknown side lengths and angle measures in right triangles.***

Benjamin Banneker was a self-taught surveyor who helped draw up the original plans for Washington, D.C. One of the jobs of a surveyor is to determine the heights of hills, trees, and other objects on a piece of property. You can use trigonometry to recreate some of the things Banneker's surveying team may have done.

EXPLORE: ANGLE SIGHTING

MATERIALS

Protractor, String Tape, Weight

For this Explore, you will need to turn your protractor into a *clinometer.*

Hold your protractor with the straight edge up. Securely tape a string at the origin of the protractor. Tie a weight (like a key or a small washer) to the other end of the string.

To use the clinometer to measure angles, hold it up to your eye and look along its edge to sight an object. A partner can then read the angle the string is resting on. Using this angle, you can find the measure of the angle of elevation or depression. To find the height of the object, the only other information you need is the distance to the object.

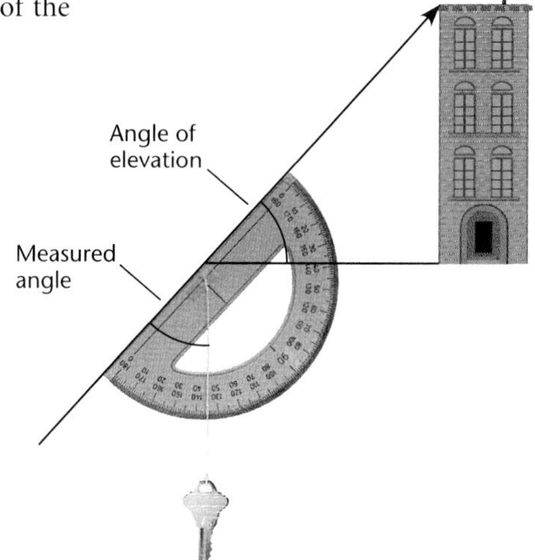

Explain how you can use the clinometer to find the height of a building or a tall tree. Choose an object that you know the distance to (or can find the distance to) and find its height. Record your readings and sketch the similar triangles you used.

Student Resources

- Alternative Lessons
- **Laboratory Manual** 7-3D
- Technology Lab Manual
- **Practice** 7-3D
- **Study Guide and Journal** 7-3D
- **Guía de estudios y Diario** 7-3D
- **Multilingual Handbook**
- **More Look Back** 7-3D
- SAT Preparation

Media Resources

- **Transparency FFM** 7-3D
- Transparency AE
- Teaching Transparency
- **AWSMTest and practice software**
- AWSM Videodisc

REFLECT

1. Assume that you know the length of one side of a right triangle and the measure of an acute angle. Which trigonometric ratio do you use to find an unknown side length in the triangle? Explain.
2. You want to find the height of a tall tree. Draw a sketch showing how you can use trigonometry to find its height. Draw another sketch showing how you can use similar triangles. What are the advantages of each method?
3. What can you find out about the sum of two perpendicular vectors without using trigonometry? When do you need to use trigonometry?

Self-Assessment

Express each trigonometric ratio as a fraction and as a decimal rounded to the hundredths place.

1. sin J $\frac{24}{25} = 0.96$
2. cos J $\frac{7}{25} = 0.28$
3. tan J $\frac{24}{7} \approx 3.43$
4. sin K $\frac{7}{25} = 0.28$
5. cos K $\frac{24}{25} = 0.96$
6. tan K $\frac{7}{24} \approx 0.29$

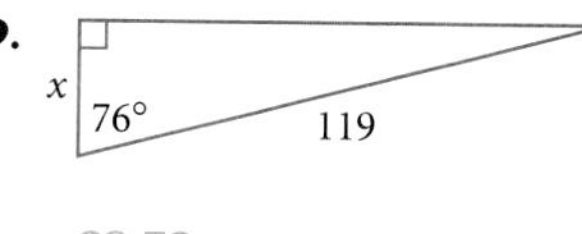

Find each indicated angle measure to the nearest degree or side length to the nearest hundredth.

7.
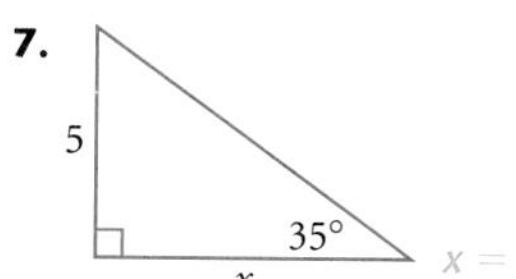

$x = 7.14$

8.
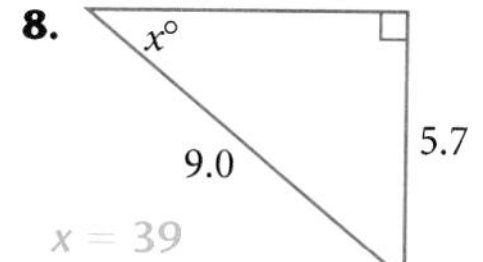

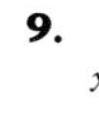
$x = 39$

9.

$x = 28.79$

10. **Angle Falls** From a spot 383 ft from the base of Kaloba Falls in Zaire, the angle of elevation to the top of the falls is approximately 71°. Find the height of the waterfall to the nearest foot. (Allow 5 ft for the height of the viewer's eyes above the ground.) 1,117 ft

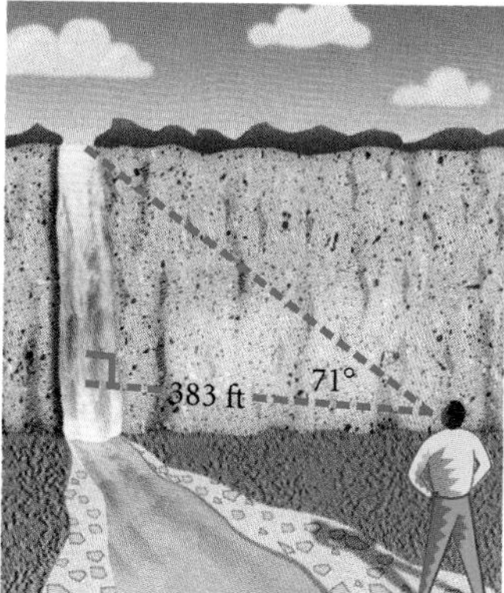

Find the area of each figure. Express your answer as a decimal rounded to the nearest hundredth. [6-3]

11. an equilateral triangle with radius 4 cm 20.78 cm²
12. a square with radius 4 cm 32 cm²
13. a regular hexagon with radius 4 cm 41.57 cm²

Vocabulary
Practice/Skills
Review
Math Reasoning
Problem Solving
Challenge

Possible Answer

To use the clinometer, find the angle of elevation to the top of an object and the distance to the object. The tangent of the angle of elevation is equal to the height of the object (above eye level) divided by the distance to the object. So, multiplying the distance to the object by the tangent of the angle of elevation gives the height of the object.

Portfolio

Have students select items from their work that demonstrate their understanding of the material in 7-3.

You may wish to have students include an applications problem where they used trigonometry to find a length or distance, one where they solved for an angle, and an **Exercise** that they found challenging.

REFLECT

Possible Answers

1. For the known angle, decide whether the side whose length you know and the side whose length you need are adjacent and opposite, adjacent and hypotenuse, or opposite and hypotenuse. Use the trigonometric ratio that involves these two sides.
2. Trigonometry: measure angle of elevation and distance to the tree; use the tangent ratio. Similarity: Use a mirror to sight the top of the tree; measure distance from you to the mirror, the mirror to the tree, and your eyes to the ground; use proportions. (Could also use shadows or a hypsometer.) Trigonometry advantages: one less measurement to take. Similarity advantages: you may be better able to measure distances than angles; you can solve a proportion without a calculator.
3. You can find the length of the vector sum by using the Pythagorean Theorem. Unless the triangle is a 30°-60°-90° or 45°-45°-90° right triangle, trigonometry must be used to solve for the direction of the vector sum.

Trigonometry

Self-Assessment

Exercise Notes

10. and 18–20. Students use trigonometry to solve problems in real-world contexts.

17. Similar to multiple-choice questions on standardized tests.

Self-Assessment Answers

Unless otherwise noted, lengths and speeds are rounded to the nearest hundredth and angle measures to the nearest tenth.

18. $\tan\angle 1 = \frac{622}{260} = 2.39$; $m\angle 1 = 67°$

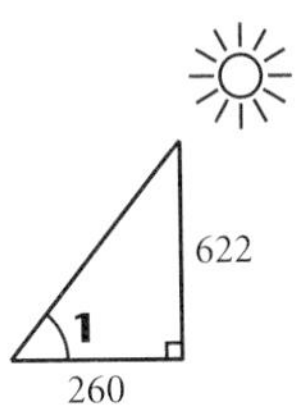

20. 156.6 mph; $m\angle 1 = 17°$

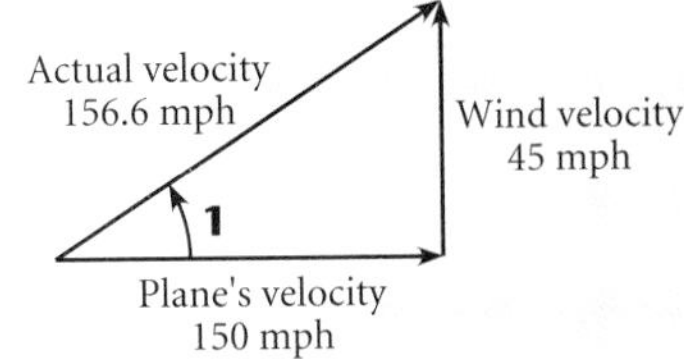

21. Sometimes; $\tan A = \frac{\text{opposite}}{\text{adjacent}}$; If opposite side is shorter than adjacent side, $\tan A < 1$; If opposite side is longer than adjacent side, then $\tan A > 1$.

22. Never; The closer you are, the greater the angle you must look up; As you near the flagpole, you must look nearly straight up; i.e., the angle approaches 90°.

23. Always; If the acute angle has the known side adjacent, use $\cos A = \frac{\text{known side}}{\text{hypotenuse}}$; If the known side is opposite, $\sin A = \frac{\text{known side}}{\text{hypotenuse}}$; Solve for hypotenuse.

R **Find the value for x that makes the triangles similar. State the theorem or postulate that justifies your answer. [7-2]**

14.

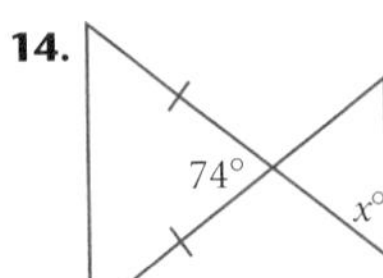

$x = 53$; AA

15. **16.**

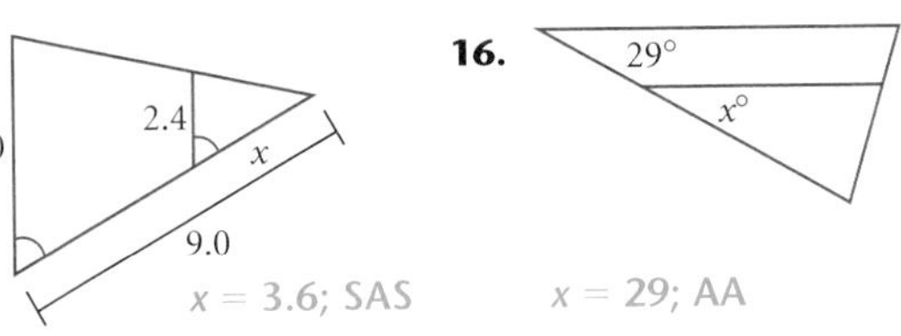

$x = 3.6$; SAS $x = 29$; AA

P **17.** Which trigonometric ratio could be used to solve directly for AC? (a)
(a) sin (b) cos (c) tan
(d) You cannot use trigonometry to solve for AC.

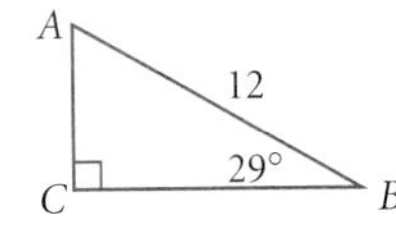

PS, MR **18.** If the 622-ft-tall Tower of the Americas in San Antonio casts a 260-ft shadow, what is the angle of elevation of the sun, to the nearest degree? Explain how you solved this problem. If you used a sketch to help you, include it with your solution.

PS **19.** **Both Boats** An observer at the top of a 50-m lighthouse (with its base at sea level) sees two boats approaching, one behind the other. The angles to the boats are 39° and 25°, as shown. Find the distance between the boats to the nearest meter. 17 m

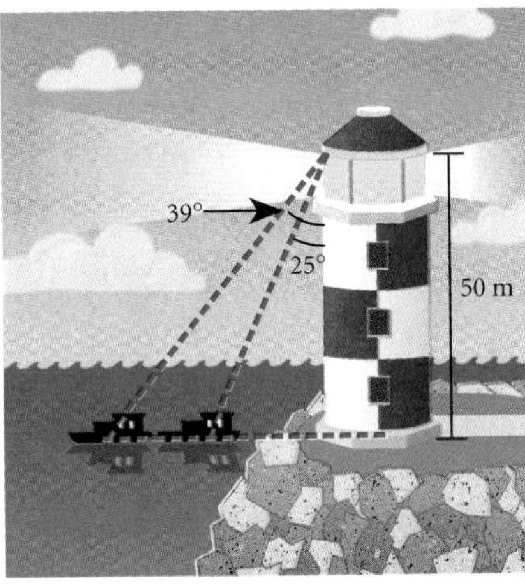

PS Science **20.** A plane is heading due east at 150 mi/hr, and the wind is blowing due north at 45 mi/hr. Sketch vectors to represent the plane's velocity in still air, the wind's velocity, and the actual velocity of the plane. Find the actual speed of the plane to the nearest tenth and the measure of the angle its actual path makes with due east to the nearest degree.

P **Complete each of the following statements with *always, sometimes,* or *never.* Explain each of your answers.**

21. The tangent of an angle is ___ less than 1.

22. The angle of elevation from your eye to the top of a twenty-foot flagpole ___ gets smaller as you walk towards the flagpole.

23. Given the measure of an acute angle in a right triangle and the length of one of the triangle's legs, you can ___ use trigonometry to find the length of the hypotenuse.

Assessment Resources

- **Quiz 7-3**
- Chapter Assessment Form A
- Chapter Assessment Form B
- Chapter Alternative Assessment
- Mid-Year Assessment
- End-of-Year Assessment
- **AWSMTest and practice software**

Ongoing Assessment

Self-Assessment Self-Assessment Exercises

Embedded Assessment Reflect 1, 2, 3

Chapter 7 Review

In Chapter 7, you looked at applications of similarity. These included enlargements and reductions, the golden rectangle, dilations, and trigonometry. You also explored various ways to show that two triangles are similar. All of these ideas are useful to artists, surveyors, and mapmakers.

KEY TERMS

angle of depression [7-3]	golden ratio [7-1]	similar [7-1]
angle of elevation [7-3]	golden rectangle [7-1]	similarity ratio [7-1]
center of dilation [7-2]	midsegment [7-2]	sine [7-3]
cosine [7-3]	reduction [7-1]	tangent [7-3]
dilation [7-2]	scale factor [7-1]	trigonometry [7-3]
enlargement [7-1]		

Write the word or phrase that correctly completes each statement.

1. An enlargement and a reduction are both examples of a ____. Dilation

2. A midsegment of a triangle is the segment joining ____. The midpoints of two sides

3. A pilot considering the angle formed by the horizontal and his line of sight to an airport below is estimating an angle of ____. Depression

4. The scale factor of an enlargement is ____ than 1. Greater than

CONCEPTS AND APPLICATIONS

Determine whether each statement is true or false. If it is true, explain why. If it is false, provide a counterexample. [7-1]

5. Any equilateral triangle is similar to any equiangular triangle.

6. All isosceles triangles are similar.

$\triangle MNO \sim \triangle RST$. Find the following. [7-1]

7. the similarity ratio of $\triangle MNO$ to $\triangle RST$ $\frac{6}{8} = \frac{3}{4}$

8. $m\angle N$ 34°

9. RS 10 cm

10. area of $\triangle MNO$ 12.6 cm^2

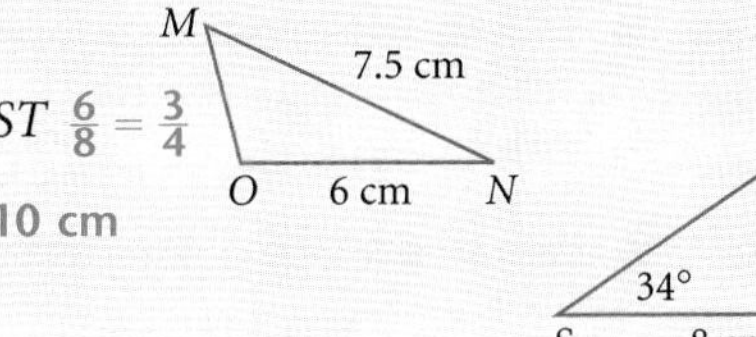

Student Resources
- Alternative Lessons
- Laboratory Manual
- Technology Lab Manual
- Practice
- Study Guide and Journal Ch 7
- Guía de estudios y Diario Ch 7
- Multilingual Handbook
- More Look Ahead
- SAT Preparation

Media Resources
- Transparency FFM
- Transparency AE
- Teaching Transparency
- AWSMTest and practice software
- AWSM Videodisc

Chapter 7 Review

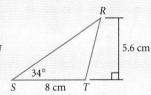

Journal

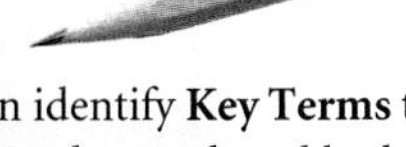

Students can identify **Key Terms** that they do not understand, and look up the definitions in the indicated section or in the glossary. Non-English-speaking students may want to use the *Multilingual Handbook.*

Vocabulary exercises and the **Self-Evaluation** are useful journal entries.

Review Answers

5. T; An equilateral triangle has all angle measures = 60° and so it is equiangular too; By AA, two such triangles are similar.

6. F; Similarity also requires that the third sides be in proportion, or that the angles between the equal sides be congruent.

13. Possible answer:

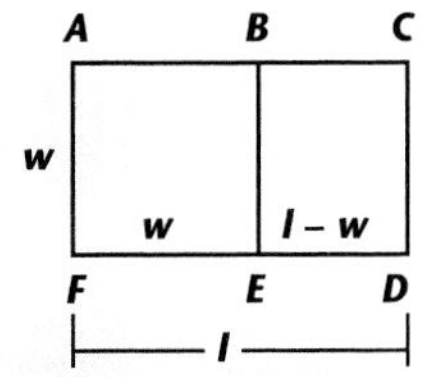

Rectangle $ACDF$ is a golden rectangle if square $ABEF$ with sides of length w makes rectangle $CDEB$ similar to rectangle $ACDF$. That is, if you divide a golden rectangle into a square and a smaller rectangle, the smaller rectangle is also a golden rectangle. All golden rectangles are similar. The ratio of length to width, $\frac{l}{w}$, is a constant called the golden ratio, and $\frac{l}{w} = \frac{1+\sqrt{5}}{2} \approx 1.618$.

14. $\frac{\text{area } \triangle RUV}{\text{area } \triangle RST} = \left(\frac{UV}{ST}\right)^2 = \left(\frac{1}{2}\right)^2 = \frac{1}{4}$ since triangles are similar by AA.

area $\triangle RUV = \left(\frac{1}{4}\right)$ area $\triangle RST =$ $\frac{1}{4}$(area $\triangle RUV$ + area $UVTS$) = $\frac{1}{4}$ area $\triangle RUV$ + $\frac{1}{4}$ area $UVTS$; $\frac{3}{4}$ area $\triangle RUV = \frac{1}{4}$ area $UVTS$;

$\frac{\text{area } \triangle RUV}{\text{area } UVTS} = \frac{\frac{1}{4}}{\frac{3}{4}} = \frac{1}{3}$

22. $P = 89.57$, $A = 249.42$

24.

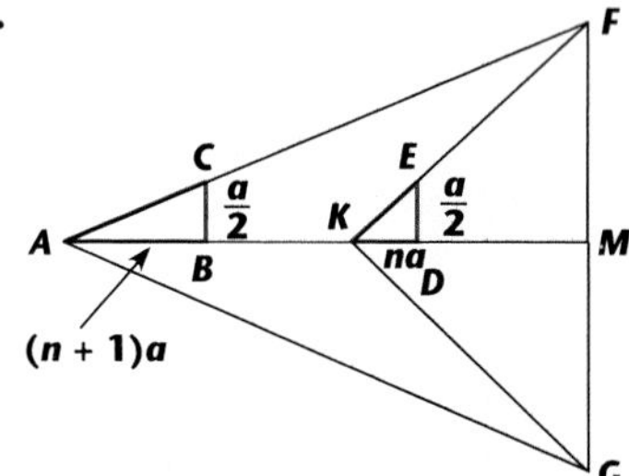

Due to right angles and parallel lines, $\triangle ABC \sim \triangle AMF$ and $\triangle KDE \sim \triangle KMF$.

So, $\frac{(n+1)a}{\frac{a}{2}} = \frac{AK + KM}{FM}$ and

$\frac{na}{\frac{a}{2}} = \frac{KM}{FM}$. Simplifying gives

$n + 1 = \frac{AK + KM}{2FM}$ and $n = \frac{KM}{2FM}$.

Substituting into the first equation for n shows that $\frac{KM}{2FM} + 1 = \frac{AK + KM}{2FM}$. Rewriting 1 as $\frac{2FM}{2FM}$ and multiplying through by $2FM$, we find that $KM + 2FM = AK + KM$, so $2FM = AK$. $2FM = FG$, so $FG = AK$.

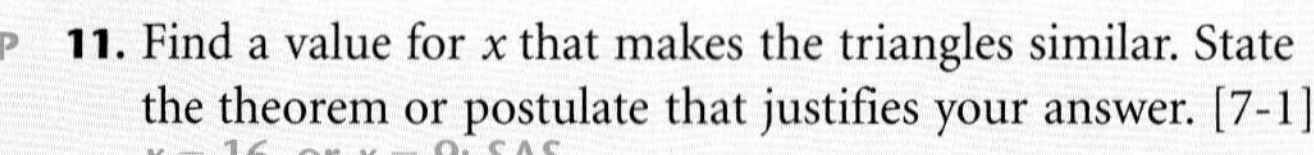

P **11.** Find a value for x that makes the triangles similar. State the theorem or postulate that justifies your answer. [7-1] $x = 16$, or $x = 9$; SAS

P, PS **12.** A 60-ft wall of an office building is represented on a scale drawing by a segment $2\frac{1}{2}$ in. long. [7-1]

a. On the drawing, what is the length of a 15-ft-long deck of the building? $\frac{5}{8}$ in.

b. If a planter box is a 1-in. × $1\frac{1}{4}$-in. rectangle on the drawing, what are its actual dimensions? 24 ft × 30 ft

MR **13.** Write a summary of facts about golden rectangles and the golden ratio. Include illustrations with your summary. [7-1]

P **14.** $\overline{UV}$ is a midsegment of $\triangle RST$ in the figure at the right. What is the ratio of the area of $\triangle RUV$ to the area of trapezoid $UVTS$? Explain how you know. [7-2]

P **15.** You are planning to draw a smaller version of this boat by using a dilation with the center at the origin and a scale factor of $\frac{1}{2}$. [7-2]

a. What will be the length of the image of the deck, $\overline{AB}$? 4.5

b. Give the coordinates of the image of point C, the top of the mast. $C' = (4, 6)$

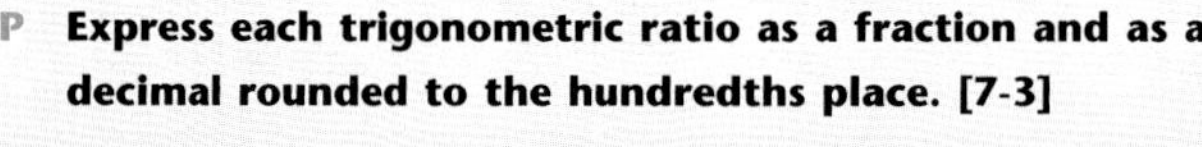

P **Express each trigonometric ratio as a fraction and as a decimal rounded to the hundredths place. [7-3]**

16. $\cos R$ $\frac{24}{25} = 0.96$

17. $\sin R$ $\frac{7}{25} = 0.28$

18. $\tan P$ $\frac{24}{7} \approx 3.43$

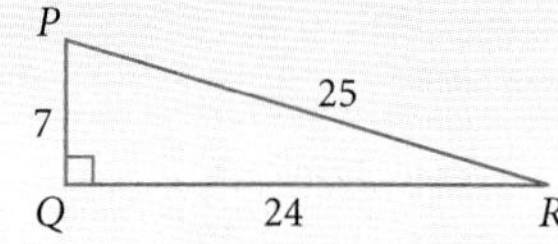

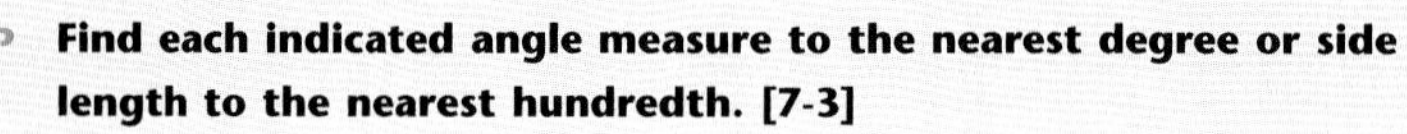

P **Find each indicated angle measure to the nearest degree or side length to the nearest hundredth. [7-3]**

19. $x = 23.66$

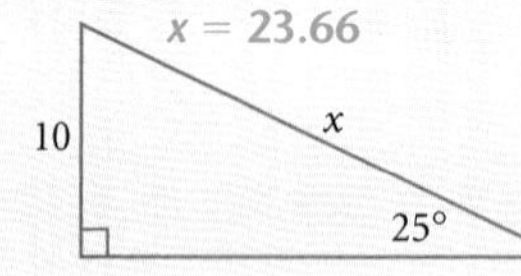

20. $x = 56$

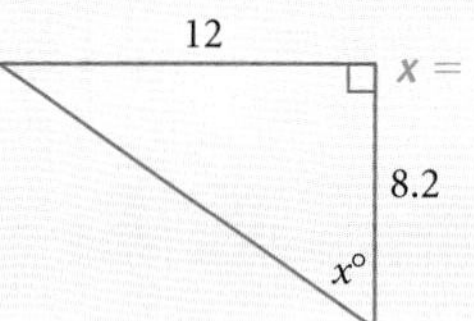

21. $x = 5.54$

R **22.** Find the perimeter and area of parallelogram $ABCE$. [5-2, 5-3]

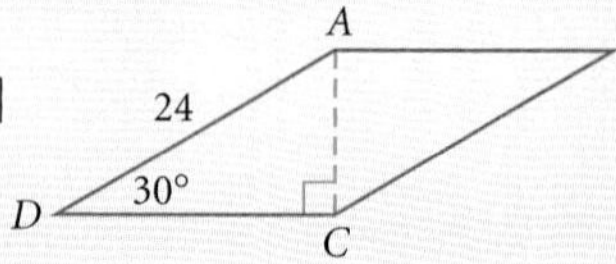

Key

- V Vocabulary
- P Practice/Skills
- R Review
- MR Math Reasoning
- PS Problem Solving
- C Challenge

23. The Pyramid of the Sun (ca. 150 A.D.) in the ancient Mexican city of Teotihuacán was unearthed from 1904–1910. From a point on the ground 300 ft from the center of its square base, the angle of elevation to its top would have been 31°. [7-3]

a. What was the height of the pyramid? 180.26 feet

b. If one story of a modern building is about 10 ft tall, about how many stories tall was this pyramid? 18

CONCEPTS AND CONNECTIONS

24. History In Oronce Fine's *De Re & Praxi Geometrica*, published in 1556, the method of measuring with a *baculum* is described. As shown in the lower figure at the right, the staff was marked off in intervals that were each as long as the crosspiece. First, the crosspiece was set at one of the interval marks. The user sighted along the staff to the approximate midpoint of the segment to be measured, $\overline{FG}$, standing at a distance chosen so that the crosspiece was parallel to the segment and barely covered its view. The crosspiece was then set one interval closer to the user and the process was repeated at a nearer position. The distance between the two observation positions, AK in the figure, equaled the desired length, FG. In terms of similar triangles, explain why this method worked.

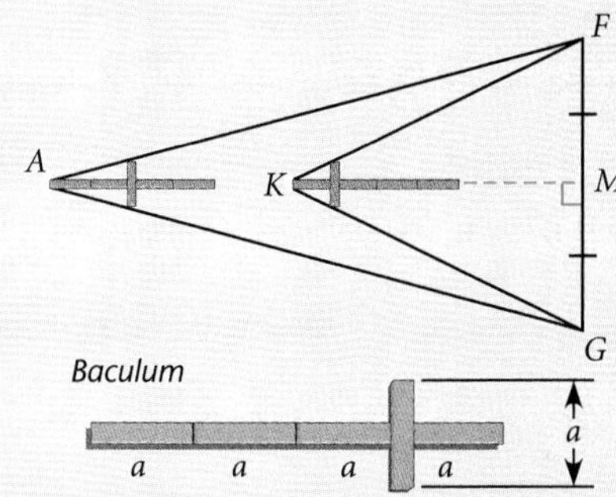

SELF-EVALUATION

Write a summary of what you know about similarity. Include as many methods as possible for concluding that two figures are similar. Also, include examples of how similarity can be applied to various careers. Be sure to discuss areas in which you had trouble, and describe your plans for studying these topics.

Assessment Resources

- Quiz
- Chapter 7 Assessment Form A
- Chapter 7 Assessment Form B
- Chapter 7 Alternative Assessment
- Mid-Year Assessment
- End-of-Year Assessment
- WSMTest Chapter 7

Ongoing Assessment

Self-Assessment Chapter 7 Review and Self-Evaluation

Embedded Assessment Chapter 7 Performance Task

Test Chapter 7 Test

Chapter 7 Assessment

Portfolio

Students may select items that represent their mathematical understanding of the ideas in Chapter 7 (especially the application of similarity and trigonometry to solve real-world problems), as well as illustrating the effort that they put into this chapter.

A rubric for assessing portfolios is included in the introduction to the Teacher's Edition.

Assessment Answers

13.

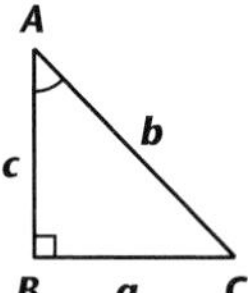

$\sin A = \frac{a}{b}$, $\cos A = \frac{c}{b}$, $\tan A = \frac{a}{c}$

15. Possible answer: Choose rectangle *BPJN*. $\triangle BDA \sim \triangle BJN$ by AA (shared angle at *B*, plus 90° angle) so $\frac{JN}{BN} = \frac{DA}{BA}$.

17. 11.54 feet

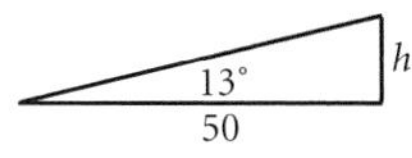

Chapter 7 Assessment

TEST

P **Give a similarity correspondence for each pair of triangles, and explain why the triangles are similar.**

1. $\triangle ADE \sim \triangle ACB$ by AA

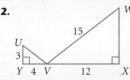

2. $\triangle UYV \sim \triangle WXV$ by SSS or SAS

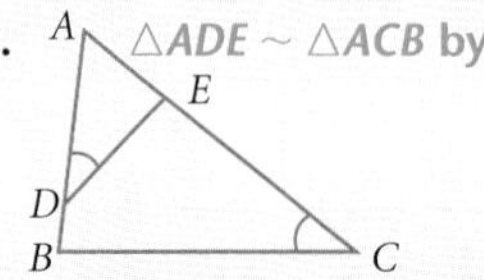

P **Use the figure at the right for items 3–5.**

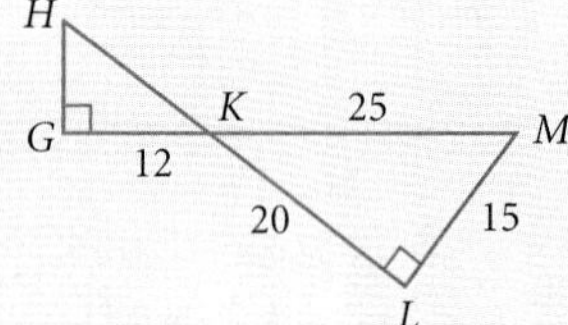

3. State a postulate or theorem that can be used to show $\triangle GHK \sim \triangle LMK$. AA

4. What is the similarity ratio of $\triangle GHK$ to $\triangle LMK$? $\frac{12}{20} = 0.6$

5. Find *HG* in the figure at the right. $HG = 9$

P, MR **6.** The similarity ratio between two polygons is $\frac{2}{5}$. The perimeter of the larger polygon is 85 m, and its area is 320 m^2. What are the perimeter and area of the smaller polygon? Explain your thinking. $P_S = 34$ m, $A_S = 51.2$ m^2

P **Find each indicated angle measure to the nearest degree or side length to the nearest hundredth.**

7. 55°

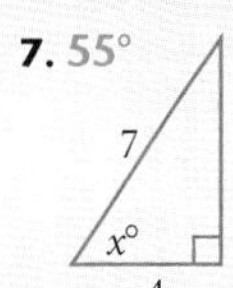

8. 74.62

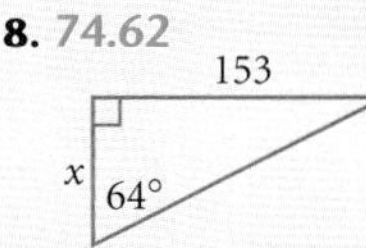

9. 10.65

x
62°
5

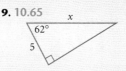

P **In $\triangle GHJ$, $GJ = 4$ and $\overline{KL}$ is a midsegment.**

10. Find *KL*. 4

11. Find the area of $\triangle JKL$. Area $\triangle JKL = 2\sqrt{3} \approx 3.46$

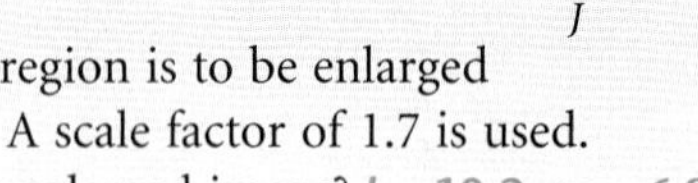

PS **12.** A sketch that fills a 4″ × 6″ rectangular region is to be enlarged to fit onto an $8\frac{1}{2}$″ × 11″ piece of paper. A scale factor of 1.7 is used.

a. What are the length and width of the enlarged image? $l = 10.2$, $w = 6.8$

b. The enlarging machine does not print within a $\frac{1}{4}$-in. margin around the edges of the paper. Can the entire image be printed? Yes

Key

- V Vocabulary
- P Practice/Skills
- R Review
- MR Math Reasoning
- PS Problem Solving
- C Challenge

P **13.** Sketch a right triangle, $\triangle ABC$, with a right angle at B. Label the hypotenuse and the legs adjacent and opposite to $\angle A$. Then write each of the three trigonometric ratios of $\angle A$ as a formula involving the lengths of its adjacent leg, its opposite leg, and the hypotenuse.

P **14.** Find the area of rhombus $WXYZ$ in the figure below. 124.71 mm²

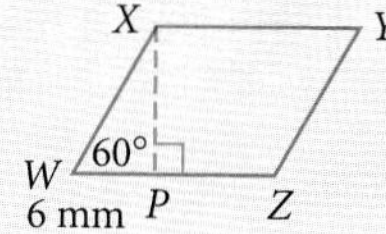

R **15.** Well-known artists, such as Leonardo da Vinci and the French impressionist George Seurat, used golden rectangles in their paintings. The canvas $ABCD$ is a golden rectangle. Each of the smaller rectangles is also a golden rectangle. Choose one of the smaller rectangles, and give a paragraph proof that it is a golden rectangle; that is, prove that its sides are in the same ratio as $\frac{AB}{BC}$.

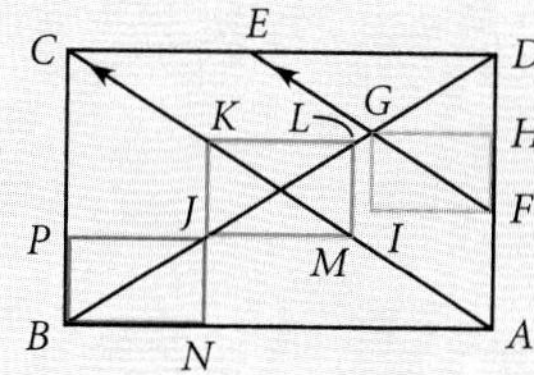

S **16.** A swimmer starts out due north across a lake at 40 m/min, but encounters a 22 m/min current running from east to west. Find the swimmer's actual speed in the water and the angle between the actual direction and the intended direction. $s = 45.65$ m/min; $m\angle A = 29°$

S **17.** At a point 50 ft in front of you, a helium balloon is released and floats straight upward. When the balloon's angle of elevation from the ground is 13°, how far above the ground is the balloon? Draw a sketch to illustrate your solution.

PERFORMANCE TASK

Carefully draw a right triangle and the altitude to its hypotenuse. You will notice that the altitude divides the triangle into two smaller triangles. Use a protractor to measure all of the angles in your figure. Record your data. Repeat the process for two more right triangles. On the basis of your observations, make a conjecture about the relationship among a right triangle and the two triangles created by the altitude to its hypotenuse. Then write a deductive argument to justify your conjecture.

Performance Task

Answer

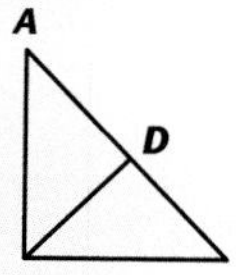

Conjecture: The two triangles are similar to the larger right triangle and to each other.

Given: $\triangle ABC$ is a right triangle with right $\angle B$, $\overline{BD}$ is an altitude.
Prove: $\triangle ABC \sim \triangle ADB \sim \triangle BDC$
Proof: $\triangle ABC \sim \triangle ADB$ by AA since $\angle ABC$ and $\angle ADB$ are congruent right angles and $\angle A \cong \angle A$. $\triangle ABC \sim \triangle BDC$ since $\angle ABC$ and $\angle BDC$ are congruent right angles and $\angle C \cong \angle C$. Because corresponding angles of similar triangles are congruent, $\angle DBC \cong \angle DAB$ and $\angle ABD \cong \angle BCD$, so $\triangle ADB \sim \triangle BDC$ by AA.

Suggested Scoring Rubric

Level 4 Full Accomplishment

- Makes the correct conjecture that the triangles produced are similar to each other and to the original triangle.
- Deductive justification is complete and clear, explaining why each pair of triangles is similar.

Level 3 Substantial Accomplishment

- Makes the correct conjecture that the triangles produced are similar to each other and to the original triangle.
- Deductive justification may not show that each pair of triangles is similar. Students may prove that the two smaller triangles are similar to the larger one, but not that they are similar to each other.

Level 2 Partial Accomplishment

- Makes the conjecture that the two triangles formed are similar to each other, but does not see that they are similar to the original triangle.
- Deductive justification is incomplete, unclear, or vague.

Level 1 Little Accomplishment

- Does not recognize that any of the triangles formed are similar.

Chapter 8

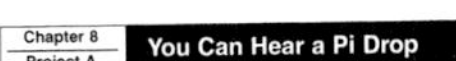

Chapter 8 — Project A

You Can Hear a Pi Drop

Approximate π Experimentally

Conduct an historic experiment with a needle on ruled paper. Calculate π from the data.

- Did you know that 18th century advances in the insurance business generated interest in probability?
- Don't you wonder how you can estimate π by dropping pins or needles?
- How does this connect to Chapter 8? The number π relates the diameter of a **circle** to its circumference and area.

Expand Your Vocabulary

axiomatic/statistical probability
conditional/unconditional probability
transcendental number   protocol

Project Guidelines

Investigate

- Read about the contributions to probability made by George Louis Buffon (1707-1788) with his famous "needle problem."
- Experiment with a line segment modeled by a pencil. What characteristics describe its position in the plane? (*Hint:* What characteristics define a line's equation algebraically?)

Set Your Direction

- From what height will you drop the needle?
- How many trials will you run?

Make a Plan

- Make a calendar for each day's work.
- You'll need a ruler and a needle (or a toothpick).

Collect and Organize Your Information

- Rule a sheet of paper with lines a distance apart, so that $a > l$, where l is the length of your needle.
- When you drop the needle, how many possibilities are there for the position of the center point of the needle with respect to the nearest line? Are they equally probable?

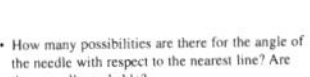

- How many possibilities are there for the angle of the needle with respect to the nearest line? Are they equally probable?
- Write a protocol for your experiment.

Carry Out Your Plan

- Conduct your experiment. Keep good records.
- Determine the probability (p) that the needle will intersect a line. (Divide the number of intersections by the number of trials.)
- The probability can be given by the formula

$$p = \frac{2l}{\pi d}$$

Using your values for p, l, and a, solve for π.

- Tell why l must be less than a for the experiment to work.

Look Back

- Instead of dropping one needle a hundred times, could you estimate π by dropping a hundred needles at once?
- What did you do to insure random needle drops?

A

Project A

You Can Hear a Pi Drop

What does a pin-drop have to do with π?

Project B

A Piece of the Pie

What is a market share? When is a circle graph the best visual display of data?

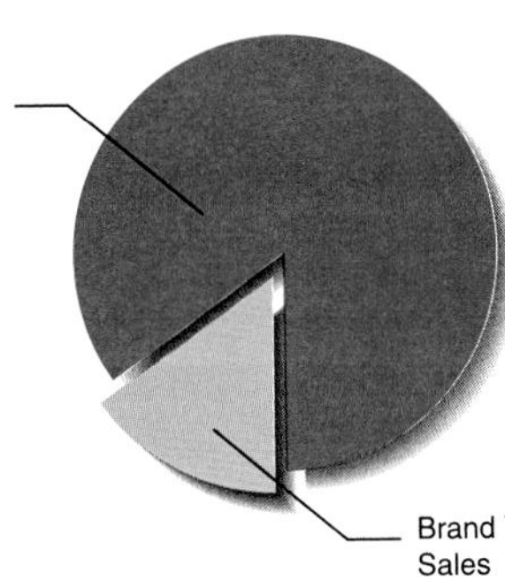

Chapter 8 — Project C

Round and Round

Make a Nature Scrapbook

Find examples of natural things and natural events in the form of circles. Make a scrapbook of your discoveries.

- Did you know that rainbows can sometimes be seen as complete circles?
- Don't you wonder why wild mushrooms grow in circular patterns?
- How does this connect to Chapter 8? **Circles** and **spheres** occur in natural things and as a result of natural processes.

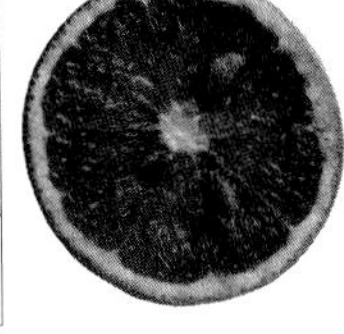

Expand Your Vocabulary

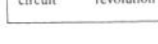
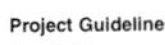

orb	globular	globule
halo	annular	spherule
circuit	revolution	phenomenon

Project Guidelines

Investigate

- Read about plant and animal forms in a high school biology book.
- Read about air, water, and light in a high school physics book.
- Interview a naturalist or science teacher. Ask how the geometry of a circle is related to growth, motion, food gathering, and other processes.

Set Your Direction

- Will you take photographs? Make sketches? Clip pictures from magazines?
- Will you limit your study to animal life? to plant life? Will you include air, water, and light effects?

Make a Plan

- Make a calendar for each day's work. Check in with your group and with your teacher.
- You'll need a camera (optional) and a scrapbook.

Collect and Organize Your Information

- Walk through a park or other natural setting. Notice plants and their flowers, leaves, and seeds.
- Watch animals and note their physical features and their movements.
- Watch the effects of rain and wind on the ground surface. Look at rocks pebbles, and the shapes in the overall landscape.
- Organize your samples using headings like *animal, vegetable, mineral,* or other categories.

Carry Out Your Plan

- Collect samples of natural things and events by sketching or by taking photographs.
- Supplement things you discovered in nature with photographs from magazines. Assemble them in your scrapbook. Label each entry.
- Write a paragraph for each section telling why a circular form occurs.

Look Back

- Are there invisible things that are circular or spherical?

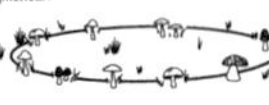

C

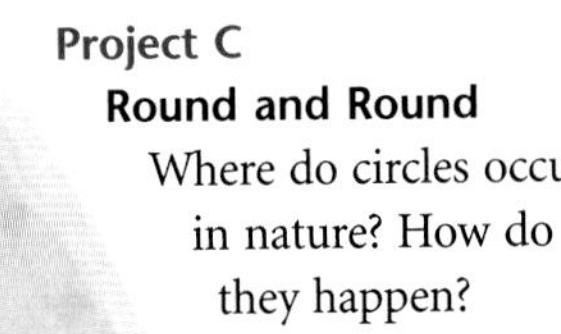

Project C

Round and Round

Where do circles occur in nature? How do they happen?

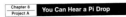

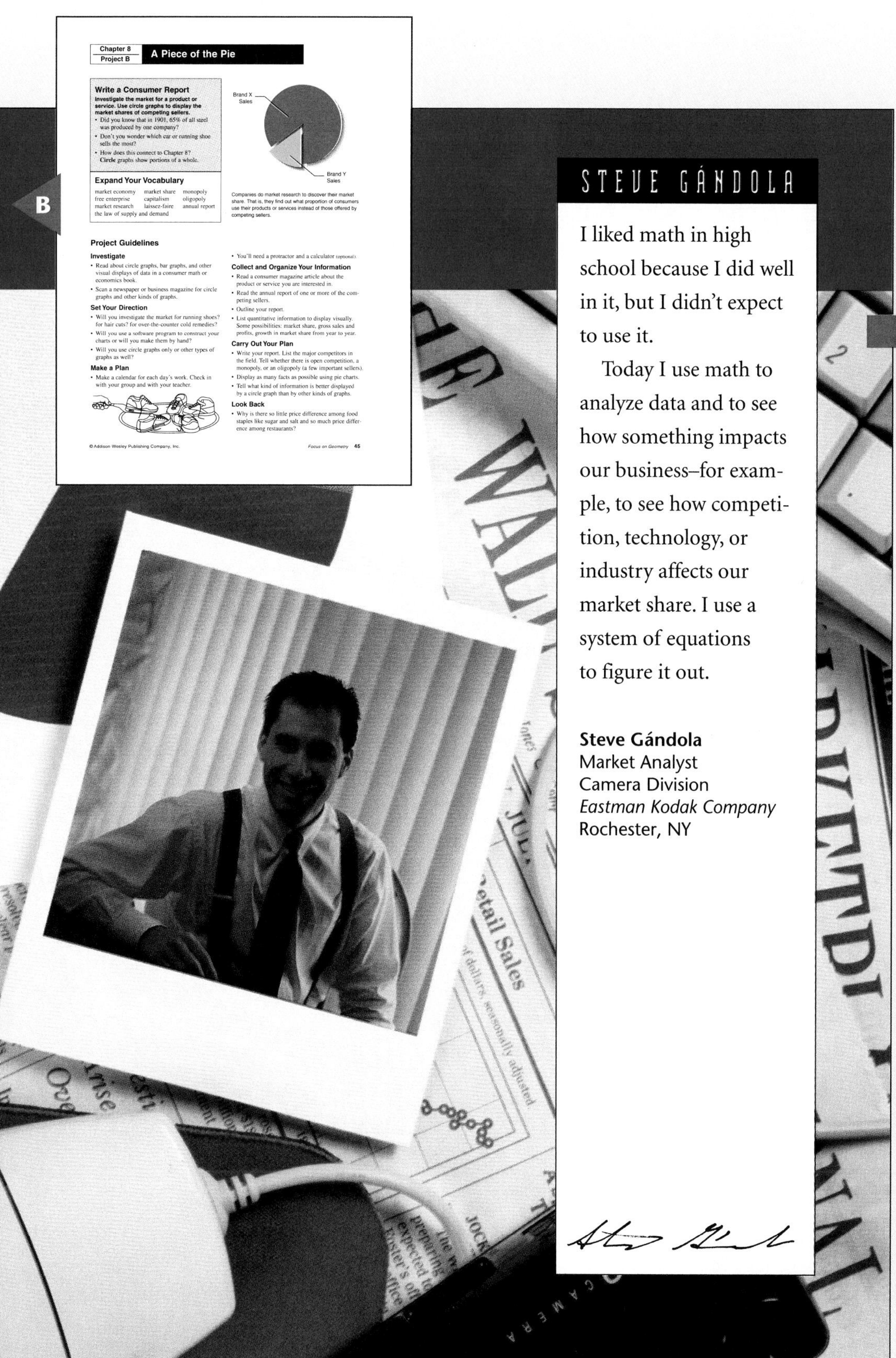

Chapter 8
Project B

A Piece of the Pie

Write a Consumer Report

Investigate the market for a product or service. Use circle graphs to display the market shares of competing sellers.

- Did you know that in 1901, 65% of all steel was produced by one company?
- Don't you wonder which car or running shoe sells the most?
- How does this connect to Chapter 8? **Circle** graphs show portions of a whole.

Companies do market research to discover their market share. That is, they find out what proportion of consumers use their products or services instead of those offered by competing sellers.

Expand Your Vocabulary

market economy	market share	monopoly
free enterprise	capitalism	oligopoly
market research	laissez-faire	annual report
the law of supply and demand		

Project Guidelines

Investigate

- Read about circle graphs, bar graphs, and other visual displays of data in a consumer math or economics book.
- Scan a newspaper or business magazine for circle graphs and other kinds of graphs.

Set Your Direction

- Will you investigate the market for running shoes? for hair cuts? for over-the-counter cold remedies?
- Will you use a software program to construct your charts or will you make them by hand?
- Will you use circle graphs only or other types of graphs as well?

Make a Plan

- Make a calendar for each day's work. Check in with your group and with your teacher.
- You'll need a protractor and a calculator (optional).

Collect and Organize Your Information

- Read a consumer magazine article about the product or service you are interested in.
- Read the annual report of one or more of the competing sellers.
- Outline your report.
- List quantitative information to display visually. Some possibilities: market share, gross sales and profits, growth in market share from year to year.

Carry Out Your Plan

- Write your report. List the major competitors in the field. Tell whether there is open competition, a monopoly, or an oligopoly (a few important sellers).
- Display as many facts as possible using pie charts.
- Tell what kind of information is better displayed by a circle graph than by other kinds of graphs.

Look Back

- Why is there so little price difference among food staples like sugar and salt and so much price difference among restaurants?

STEVE GÁNDOLA

I liked math in high school because I did well in it, but I didn't expect to use it.

Today I use math to analyze data and to see how something impacts our business–for example, to see how competition, technology, or industry affects our market share. I use a system of equations to figure it out.

Steve Gándola
Market Analyst
Camera Division
Eastman Kodak Company
Rochester, NY

Biographical Note

Steve Gándola graduated from Canoga Park High School in Los Angeles, CA. He took Algebra I and II, Geometry, Trigonometry, and Solid Geometry.

Chapter 8

Overview

Circles and Spheres

8-1 Circles, Circumference, and Area

Circles are the shape of choice for many everyday objects, such as utility hole covers and wheel rims. You will become familiar with some of the terms associated with circles, and see where the formulas for their circumference and area come from.

8-2 Angles, Arcs, and Chords

Central angles of circles, the regions they determine, and the arcs they intersect allow you to apply proportional thinking to circles, just as they enabled Eratosthenes to find the circumference of the earth. Now you will investigate angles, arcs, and chords.

8-3 The Inscribed Angle Theorem

Inscribed angles can tell you where a soccer player has the best chance of scoring a goal, and how light is reflected in a curved mirror. You will investigate inscribed angles and a few of the theorems that are based on their properties.

CHAPTERS

Chapter 8 Planning Guide

The following ancillaries are recommended for each course level. The additional resources, *Technology Lab Manual, Study Guide and Journal, Multilingual Handbook,* and *Assessment,* are recommended for all levels.

	Comprehensive Course	Core Course	Informal Course
8-1 Part A	▲	▲	▲
Alternative Lessons			▲
Laboratory Manuals	▲	▲	▲
Practice			▲
More Look Ahead		▲	▲
8-1 Part B	▲	▲	▲
Alternative Lessons			▲
Laboratory Manuals	▲	▲	▲
Practice			▲
More Look Back		▲	▲
8-1 Part C	▲	▲	▲
Alternative Lessons			▲
Laboratory Manuals	▲	▲	▲
Practice			▲
More Look Ahead		▲	▲
8-1 Part D	▲	▲	▲
Alternative Lessons			▲
Laboratory Manuals	▲	▲	▲
Practice			▲
More Look Back		▲	▲
8-1 Part E	▲	▲	▲
More Look Back		▲	▲
Quiz 8-1	▲	▲	▲
8-2 Part A	▲	▲	▲
Alternative Lessons			▲
Laboratory Manuals	▲	▲	▲
Practice			▲

	Comprehensive Course	Core Course	Informal Course
More Look Ahead		▲	▲
8-2 Part B	▲	▲	▲
Alternative Lessons			▲
Laboratory Manuals	▲	▲	▲
Practice			▲
More Look Back		▲	▲
8-2 Part C	▲	▲	▲
Alternative Lessons			▲
Laboratory Manuals	▲	▲	▲
Practice			▲
More Look Ahead		▲	▲
8-2 Part D	▲	▲	▲
More Look Back		▲	▲
Quiz 8-2	▲	▲	▲
8-3 Part A	▲	▲	
Alternative Lessons			
Laboratory Manuals	▲	▲	
Practice			
More Look Back		▲	
8-3 Part B	▲	▲	
Alternative Lessons			
Laboratory Manuals	▲	▲	
Practice			
More Look Ahead		▲	
8-3 Part C	▲	▲	
More Look Back		▲	
Quiz 8-3	▲	▲	

BIBLIOGRAPHY

Reading for Students

Women and Numbers, Teri Perl. © 1993 by Teri Perl. Published by Wide World Publishing/Tetra.

Teacher Resources

From Home Runs to Housing Costs: Data Resource for Teaching Statistics, Gail Burrill, ed. Dale Seymour Publications, 1994 (NS21225).

Videos

The Story of π, Project Mathematics!—California Institute of Technology. Available through Dale Seymour Publications (NS20079).

8-1

Circles, Circumference, and Area

SUPERLESSON AT A GLANCE

Superlesson Goal

Students will learn the formal definition of a circle and see how to calculate circumferences and areas of circles.

Management Guide

	Topic	Objectives	Key Terms	New Ideas	Materials
Part A	Inscribed and Circumscribed Figures	To investigate circles and inscribed and circumscribed figures.	Circle, center of a circle, radius, diameter, concentric circles, inscribed, circumscribed	Circle terminology. Inscribed and circumscribed figures. Constructing inscribed and circumscribed figures.	**Student** Compass, straightedge
Part B	Circles and Tangent Lines	To discover that a tangent line is perpendicular to the radius of a circle at the point of tangency and other theorems about tangent lines and segments.	Secant line, tangent line, point of tangency, tangent segment, sphere, radius and center of a sphere, tangent line and plane to a sphere, great circle	A tangent segment is perpendicular to the radius of a circle at the point of tangency. Tangent segments from the same exterior point are congruent.	**Student** Compass, ruler, protractor
Part C	The Circumference of a Circle	To discover that the ratio of the circumference of a circle to its diameter is constant and that this constant is π.	Circumference, pi (π)	The ratio of the circumference of a circle to its diameter is π. $C = \pi d$	**Student** Tape measure, three circular objects
Part D	The Area of a Circle	To develop and use a formula for the area of a circle.		$A = \pi r^2$	**Student** Compass, scissors
Part E	Making Connections	To use circumference and area to compare the sizes of records and compact disks.	In Making Connections, students apply and synthesize key terms and new ideas.		

Pacing Chart (45-Minute Periods)

	Comprehensive Course	Core Course	Informal Course
Part A	1	1	1
Part B	1	2	2
Part C	1	2	2
Part D	1	2	2
Part E	1	1	1
TOTAL periods for Superlesson	5	8	8

NCTM Standards

Mathematics as Problem Solving

Mathematics as Communication

Mathematics as Reasoning

Mathematical Connections

Conceptual Underpinnings of Calculus

8-1 Circles, Circumference, and Area

Years ago, phonograph records played at a speed of 78 rpm (revolutions per minute). As hi-fi (high-fidelity) recording processes improved, the speed of rotation of the record player slowed to $33\frac{1}{3}$ rpm. Both 78 rpm and $33\frac{1}{3}$ rpm records were recorded by an analog process that transferred sound vibrations to the grooves in the record.

The record is now almost extinct because of the advent of the compact disk (CD). The disk is 12.5 cm in diameter, but the track in which information is coded is thinner than a hair, and has a length of several miles! The CD rotates at a speed of 200 rpm.

A CD is recorded digitally. Digital recording preserves sound information electronically. It is more accurate than analog recording and it is free of the "hiss" that always enters the analog recording process. Although some people still keep their records, the cleaner sound of the CD is making the "LP" record an antique.

1. CDs are just one type of circular item. Name three other examples of circular objects, and give reasons why a circle is a suitable shape for each.
2. Why do you think circles, rather than other geometric figures, are used in manufacturing CDs?
3. How is a circle different from a regular polygon? How is it similar to a regular polygon?

539

More About Compact Disks

When music is recorded onto a compact disk master, each second of sound is broken down into 44,100 samples. These samples are encoded into the tight spiral on a disk as millions of microscopic pits. When a consumer plays a copy of the master disk on a CD player, the disk spins and a laser beam follows the spiral. The reflections of the laser light are translated electronically into sound. CDs were first sold in Japan in 1982 and in the U.S. in 1983. As they became less expensive, their advantages soon made the vinyl record obsolete.

Where Are We Now?

Students are familiar with several area and perimeter formulas, including those for regular polygons.

Where Are We Going?

In 8-1, students will investigate circles and lines that intersect them. They will find circumference and area formulas for a circle and see how to derive these from the formula for a regular polygon, using the concept of a limit.

The circumference and area formulas for a circle will be especially important when students investigate volumes and surface areas of cylinders and cones in Chapter 9.

Possible Answers

1. A wheel (rolls easily and so is convenient for carrying loads); a Frisbee (for aerodynamic reasons); a plate (easy to make on a spinning potter's wheel, highest area-to-perimeter ratio).
2. Information on a CD is recorded on a spiral track, so any other shape would include wasted space. Also, a circular disk spins smoothly.
3. A circle has a curved edge; the polygon has straight sides. A circle has no angles at its edge. Both enclose an area; both have a radius and a center; both are two-dimensional.

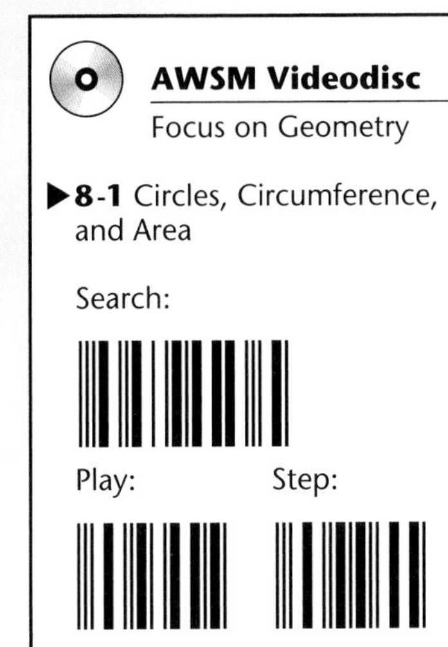

Circles, Circumference, and Area

PART A At a Glance

Objective

To investigate circles and inscribed and circumscribed figures.

Development

First, students see definitions of circles and circumscribed and inscribed figures.

In the **Explore,** they investigate ways to inscribe regular polygons in circles. Students discover that regular polygons with a greater number of sides more nearly approach a circle, an important fact in justifying circumference and area formulas.

Suggested Materials

Student Compass, straightedge

Key Terms

Circle, center of a circle, radius, diameter, concentric circles, inscribed, circumscribed

First Five Minutes

Transparency FFM 8-1A

Read page 540, and answer the **Consider** question.

Motivate

Ask...

- What is the radius of a regular polygon? How is it different from the radius of a circle? **Radius of regular polygon = distance from center to a vertex. Points on the polygon are not equidistant from its center.**

Possible Answer

1. The diameter of a circle is twice its radius.

8-1 PART A Inscribed and Circumscribed Figures

← CONNECT → ***You've already worked with circles. Now you will look at the mathematical definition of a circle and investigate some polygons that fit perfectly inside and outside circles.***

You may have drawn a circle by using a pencil tied to a piece of string. Tightly holding one point on the string and moving the pencil makes a circle.

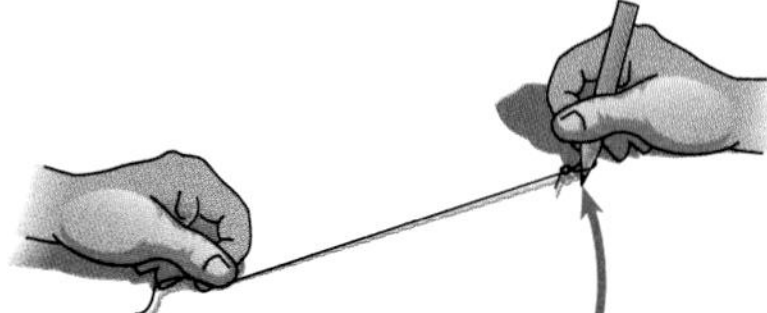

Although this may appear to be an informal way to construct a circle, it is based on the mathematical definition of a circle.

> **DEFINITION**
>
> A **circle** is the locus of points in a plane equidistant from a given point. That point is the **center** of the circle.

We name a circle by its center. The circle shown is ⊙*Q*. A **radius** of the circle is a segment from the center to any point on the circle. A **diameter** is a segment that contains the center of the circle and has endpoints on the circle. We also use the words *radius* and *diameter* to refer to the lengths of those segments. Point *E* is in the **exterior** of ⊙*Q* and point *I* is in the **interior.**

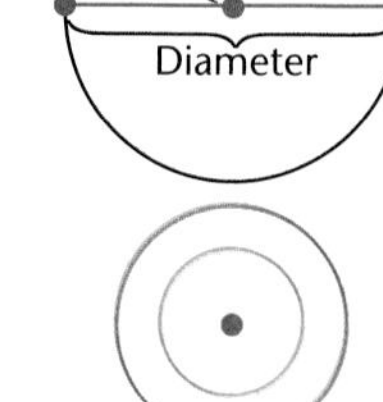

Two coplanar circles with the same center are **concentric** circles.

Concentric circles

1. What is the relationship between the diameter of a circle and its radius?

Tips from Teachers

Students may need to be reminded that a *locus* is a set of points that satisfy a given condition or set of conditions. For more review on locus, refer them to 4-3 Part C.

Logic/Reasoning | Industry/Careers | Science/Health | Social Science/History | Fine Arts/Literature

TRY IT

a. Name a radius of $\odot T$. Possible answer: $\overline{TS}$
b. Name a diameter of $\odot T$. $\overline{NM}$
c. Describe the locations of points X and Z.
d. If the diameter of $\odot T$ is 4 cm, what is the radius? 2 cm

c. X, interior; Z, exterior

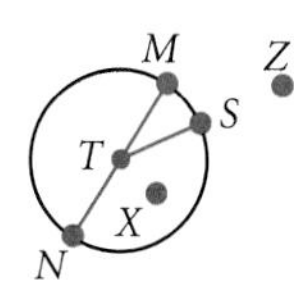

When you draw a polygon that fits perfectly inside a circle, it is **inscribed** in the circle. At the same time, the circle is **circumscribed** around the polygon.

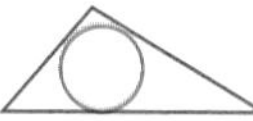

The triangle is circumscribed around the circle. Each of its sides touches the circle at exactly one point.

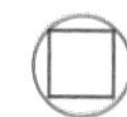

The square is inscribed in the circle. All of its vertices are on the circle.

In the following Explore, you will investigate ways to inscribe regular polygons inside a circle.

EXPLORE: POLYGONS INSIDE, CIRCLES OUTSIDE

MATERIALS

Compass
Straightedge

Use your compass to draw one circle on each of four sheets of paper. All four circles should have the same radius.

1. Inscribe a regular hexagon inside one of your circles, using a compass and straightedge. (Hint: Refer to Exercise 25 on page 446.)
2. Develop methods for inscribing an equilateral triangle, a square, and a regular 12-gon in your three remaining circles. Your figures do not have to be constructions; you may choose to use paper-folding or other techniques. Explain how each of your methods works, and compare your ideas with those of your classmates. (Hint: You may want to use the construction in Step 1 as a starting point for some of your work.)
3. Among your four figures, which polygon's area is closest to the area of the circle? Which polygon's perimeter is closest to the circumference (perimeter) of the circle?

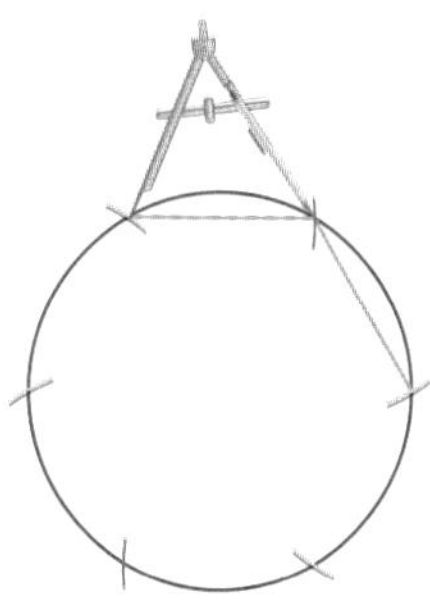

Student Resources

- Alternative Lessons 8-1A
- Laboratory Manual 8-1A
- Technology Lab Manual
- Practice 8-1A
- Study Guide and Journal 8-1A
- Guía de estudios y Diario 8-1A
- Multilingual Handbook
- More Look Ahead 8-1A
- SAT Preparation

Media Resources

- Transparency FFM 8-1A
- Transparency AE
- Teaching Transparency
- AWSMTest and practice software
- AWSM Videodisc

EXPLORE

Polygons Inside, Circles Outside

Recommended group size: 4

The Point

To see that the greater the number of sides, the more nearly a regular polygon approaches a circle.

Look and Listen...

- For students who do not see how diameters of the circle can help them draw the square.
- For students who do not see how the regular hexagon construction can help them inscribe the triangle or 12-gon.

Ask...

- (Square) What is true about the diagonals of a square? Would it help you to find a diameter of the circle?
- (Equilateral triangle) Could you use vertices of a regular hexagon to help draw an equilateral triangle?
- (12-gon) Suppose you use vertices of a regular hexagon for six of the vertices. Where would the others be?

For Groups That Finish Early

Find the $\frac{\text{apothem}}{\text{radius}}$ ratio for an equilateral triangle, square, and regular hexagon. Is this ratio increasing or decreasing as the number of sides of the polygon increases? Equilateral triangle: $\frac{1}{2}$; square, $\frac{\sqrt{2}}{2} \approx 0.71$; regular hexagon, $\frac{\sqrt{3}}{2} \approx 0.87$; increasing.

Follow Up

Ask students to explain their construction methods.

Possible Answers

See Additional Answers p. T562.

Circles, Circumference, and Area

Journal

Reflect 1 and 2 and **Exercise** 7 are suitable for journal entries.

REFLECT

Possible Answers

1. Use a straightedge to draw diagonals joining opposite vertices of the hexagon to identify its center. Measure the distance from the center to a vertex with the compass. Draw a circle with its center at the center of the polygon, using this radius.
2. The regular octagon has the greatest area and perimeter because its sides most nearly approach the sides of the circle.

Part A Exercises

Exercise Notes

Core

19. and 20. Students review the algebraic equation for a circle that they investigated in 5-3 Part C.

Look Ahead

This exercise previews a justification of the circumference formula for a circle seen in 8-1 Part C.

More Math Reasoning

26. Students write a deductive justification for the construction of the bisector of an angle.

27. Students derive the general form of the equation of a circle whose center is not necessarily (0, 0).

Exercise Answers

Core

6. The string is the radius. It keeps the center-to-locus distance (radius) constant, just as a compass with a fixed setting does.
7. Possible answer: Congruent circles have congruent radii.

REFLECT

1. Explain how you can use a compass and straightedge to circumscribe a circle around a given regular hexagon.
2. Suppose an equilateral triangle, a regular hexagon, and a regular octagon are inscribed in the same circle. Which of the polygons has the largest area? perimeter? Why?

Exercises

CORE

P **Getting Started** **Use the circle at the right for each of the following.**

1. Name the circle. $\odot S$
2. Name three radii of the circle. $\overline{SU}$, $\overline{SR}$, $\overline{ST}$
3. Name a diameter of the circle. $\overline{RT}$
4. If the radius of the circle is 3 cm, what is its diameter? 6 cm
5. If the diameter of the circle is 16.4 in., what is its radius? 8.2 in.

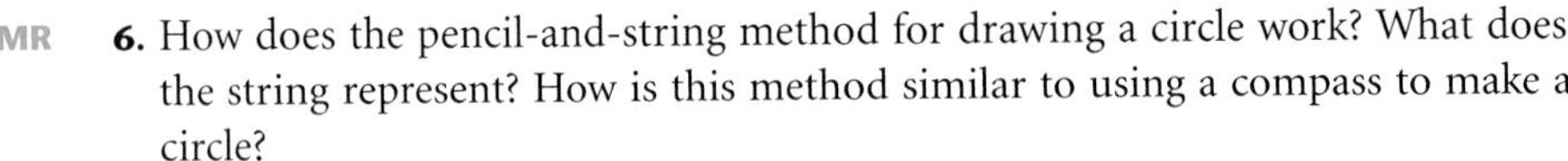

MR 6. How does the pencil-and-string method for drawing a circle work? What does the string represent? How is this method similar to using a compass to make a circle?

MR 7. What do you think is true about congruent circles? Write a definition of congruent circles.

P **Sketch each of the following.**

8. $\odot C$ with diameter $\overline{AB}$ and radii $\overline{CD}$ and $\overline{CE}$
9. a circle inscribed in a square
10. a circle circumscribed around a pentagon

V **Write the word or phrase that correctly completes each statement.**

11. If the vertices of a polygon are on a circle, then the polygon is ___ the circle. Inscribed in
12. The radius of a circle is always half of its ___. Diameter

PS 13. Trees add a ring to their cross sections for every year of their lives. If the trunk of a 20-year-old redwood tree has a diameter of 8 in., find the average width of each ring. 0.2 in.

Science

Key

- V Vocabulary
- P Practice/Skills
- R Review
- MR Math Reasoning
- PS Problem Solving
- C Challenge

14. A record album with a diameter of twelve inches has a label with a diameter of four inches. Find the width of the exposed vinyl on the record. 4 in.

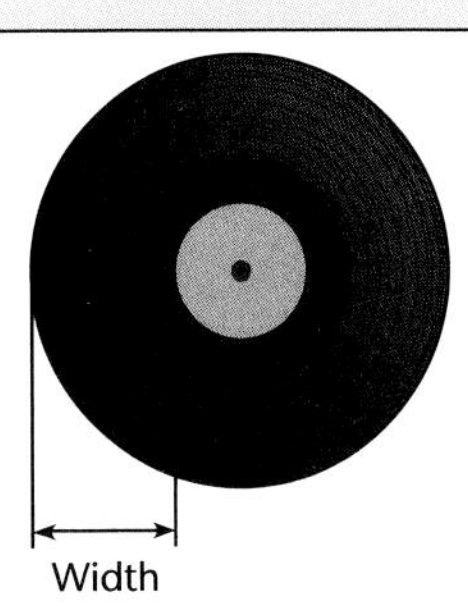

15. Using the regular-hexagon construction as a guide, construct 30°, 60°, and 120° angles, using only a compass and straightedge.

A regular hexagon is inscribed in ⊙*M* as shown. Find each of the following.

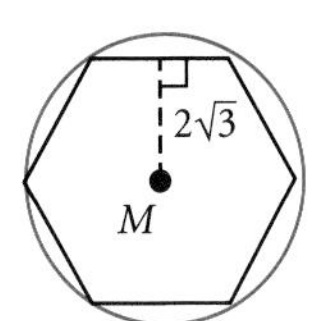

16. the radius of the circumscribed circle 4
17. the length of each side of the hexagon 4
18. the area of the hexagon to the nearest tenth 41.6

The circle shown has radius 3, and its center is at the origin. Recall that the equation for this circle is $x^2 + y^2 = 9$.

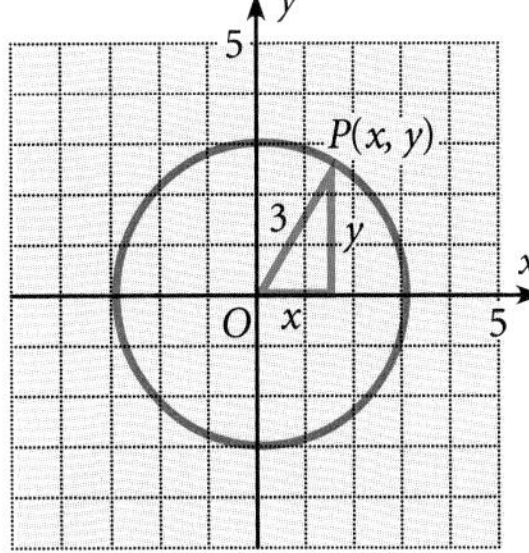

19. Give an equation for the circle with center at the origin and radius 4. $x^2 + y^2 = 16$

20. Give an equation for the circle with center at the origin and radius $\frac{7}{3}$. $x^2 + y^2 = \frac{49}{9}$

LOOK AHEAD

21. Follow the steps below to find the perimeter of a regular 20-gon with radius 0.5 in.
   a. Draw a radius and an apothem to make a right triangle. Find the measure of the angle shown. (Hint: There are two such angles for each of the 20 sides of the polygon.) 9°
   b. Use trigonometry to find the length of a half-side of the polygon. Use this result to find the perimeter of the 20-gon. ≈ 3.13

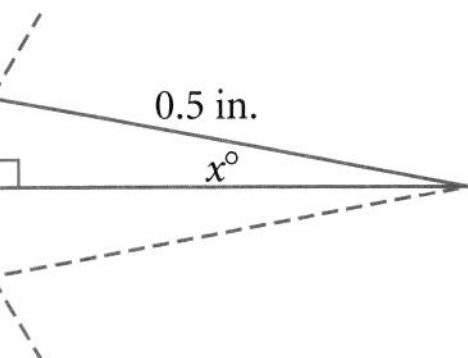

MORE PRACTICE

Sketch each of the following.

22. ⊙*L* with diameter $\overline{HJ}$ and radii $\overline{LK}$ and $\overline{LM}$
23. a square inscribed in a circle
24. a circle circumscribed around a triangle
25. One way to construct a hexagon is to rotate an equilateral triangle around one vertex five times. How many degrees are in each rotation? Why?

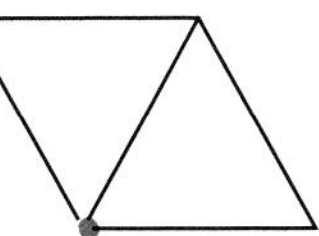

Ongoing Assessment

Self-Assessment Exercises 1, 3, 5, 9, 11, 12, 13, 16, 17, 19

Embedded Assessment Explore Step 3; Exercises 4, 6, 14, 18

8.
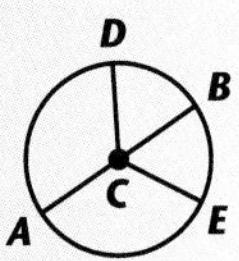

9.
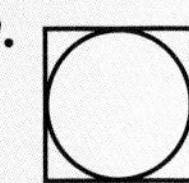

10.
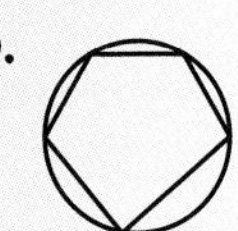

15. Possible answer: Construct the hexagon. Each angle measures 120°. Bisect one angle to make 60° angles. Bisect a 60° angle to make 30° angles.

More Practice

22.

23.
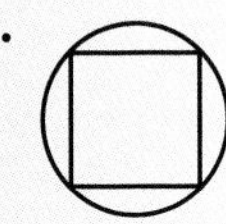

24.
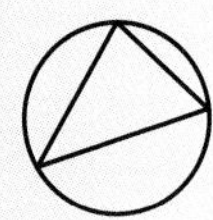

25. $\frac{360}{6} = 60°$; It takes six rotations to go around 360°.

More Math Reasoning

26.
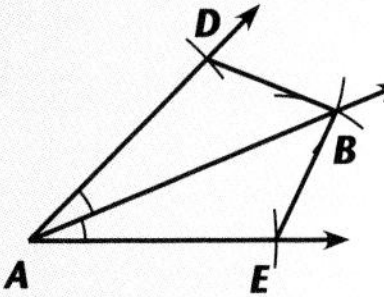

Let $AE = AD$. Draw circles at centers *E* and *D* with the same radii. Let *B* be the intersection. Therefore $BD = BE$. $\triangle ADB \cong \triangle AEB$ by SSS; Therefore $\angle DAB \cong \angle EAB$ by CPCTC.

27. a. $\sqrt{(x-1)^2 + (y-2)^2} = 3$
   b. $(x-1)^2 + (y-2)^2 = 9$; 9 is the square of the radius; 1 and 2 are the center's *x*- and *y*-coordinates.
   c. $(x-h)^2 + (y-k)^2 = r^2$

Circles, Circumference, and Area

PART B At a Glance

Objective

To discover that a tangent line is perpendicular to the radius of a circle at the point of tangency and other theorems about tangent lines and segments.

Development

Students see definitions of *secant line, tangent line,* and *point of tangency.*

In the **Explore,** they discover the following:

- A tangent to a circle is perpendicular to the radius at the point of tangency.
- A coplanar line perpendicular to a radius at a point on the circle is a tangent.
- Tangent segments from the same external point are congruent.

Suggested Materials

Student Compass, ruler, protractor

Key Terms

Secant line, tangent line, point of tangency, tangent segment, sphere, radius and center of a sphere, tangent line and plane to a sphere, great circle

First Five Minutes

Transparency FFM 8-1B

Read the opening paragraphs on page 544. Then answer the **Consider** question.

Motivate

Ask...

- What do you think is true about the distance from the center of a circle to a tangent line for the circle? The distance from the center to a secant line? **It is equal to the radius of the circle; it is less than the radius of the circle.**

MORE MATH REASONING

MR **26.** Sketch an angle, $\angle A$, and construct its angle bisector, $\overrightarrow{AB}$. Then justify this construction. (Hint: Add lines to form triangles in your construction, and use what you know about radii of a circle.)

MR, C **27.** Suppose a circle with radius 3 has its center at (1, 2) as shown at the right.

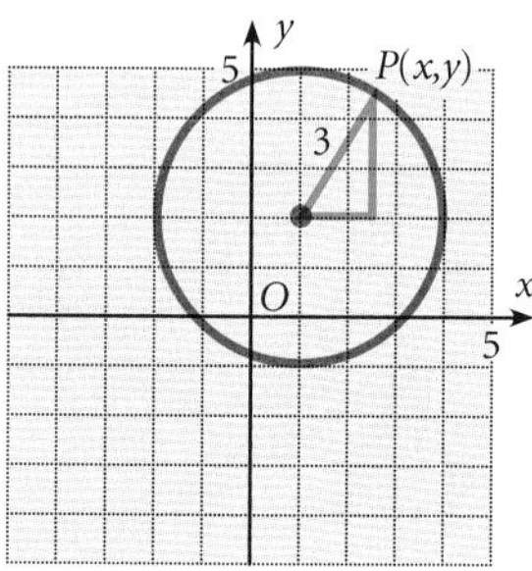

a. Use the distance formula to write an equation that says that the distance from (1, 2) to any point (x, y) on the circle is equal to 3.

b. Square both sides of the equation. This is the equation for your circle. Where does the radius of the circle appear in this equation? Where do the coordinates of the center appear?

c. Write the general equation for a circle whose radius is r and whose center is at (h, k).

8-1 PART B Circles and Tangent Lines

← CONNECT → ***Each of the sides of a polygon that is circumscribed around a circle touches the circle at exactly one point. Now you will discover some of the properties of lines that intersect circles in this way.***

A line in the plane of a circle can intersect the circle in no points, in two points, or in exactly one point. Lines that intersect circles have special names.

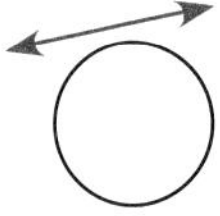

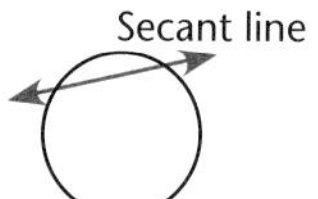

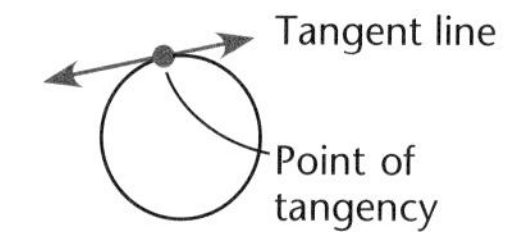

1. Is it possible for a line that is *not* in the plane of a circle to intersect the circle in two points? one point? Justify your answers.

Key

- V Vocabulary
- P Practice/Skills
- R Review
- MR Math Reasoning
- PS Problem Solving
- C Challenge

EXPLORE: OFF ON A TANGENT

MATERIALS

Compass
Ruler
Protractor

1. Carefully trace or copy the square and regular hexagon shown. Then use a compass to inscribe a circle inside each. How did you find the center of each polygon? How did you find the radius of the circle?

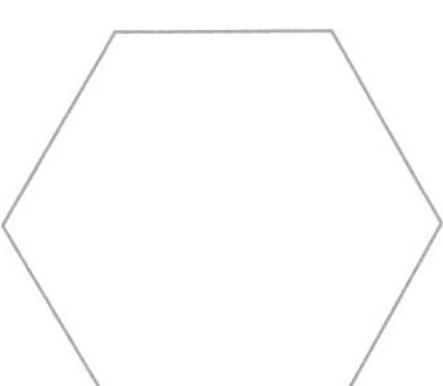

2. The sides of your regular polygons are tangent to the circle. Draw the radius of the circle to each point of tangency. Then measure each angle that the radius makes with the tangent. What conjecture can you make?
3. Investigate the converse of your conjecture. If your investigation leads to additional conjectures, be sure to record these.
4. Draw a circle, and add two tangent lines to your drawing. Extend the lines until they intersect. Then measure the lengths of the two **tangent segments** (from the point of tangency to the point of intersection). Repeat the process, and use your results to make a conjecture.

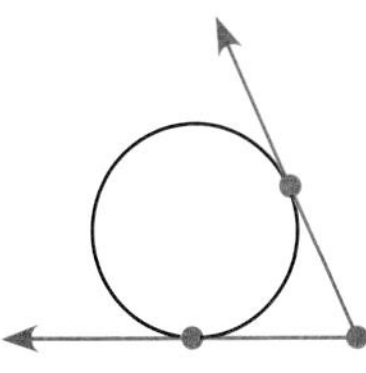

You will see that your conjectures from the Explore are useful in solving problems related to circles.

TRY IT

In the figure at the right, $\overleftrightarrow{AB}$ is tangent to $\odot C$ at B.

a. What is $m\angle CBA$? 90°

b. Find AC. $AC \approx 40.80$

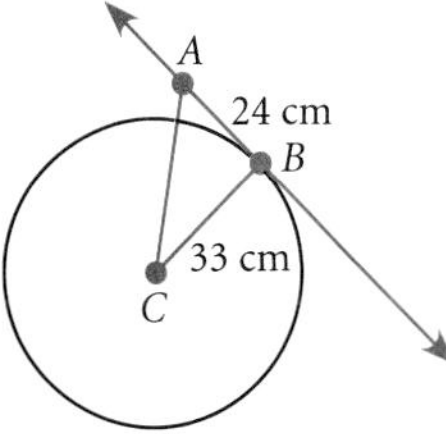

Student Resources
- Alternative Lessons 8-1B
- Laboratory Manual 8-1B
- Technology Lab Manual
- Practice 8-1B
- Study Guide and Journal 8-1B
- Guía de estudios y Diario 8-1B
- Multilingual Handbook
- More Look Back 8-1B
- SAT Preparation

Media Resources
- Transparency FFM 8-1B
- Transparency AE
- Teaching Transparency
- AWSMTest and practice software
- AWSM Videodisc

Possible Answer

1. A noncoplanar line cannot intersect a circle in two points; since two such points would lie in the plane of the circle, the line would also be in that plane. A noncoplanar line can intersect a circle in one or zero points.

EXPLORE

Off on a Tangent

Recommended group size: 4

The Point

To investigate relationships between tangent lines, tangent segments, and radii.

Look and Listen...

- For students who do not see how to draw the inscribed polygons in Step 1.
- For students who have trouble finding the converse they are to investigate in Step 3.

Ask...

- Would drawing diagonals of the square and hexagon help you find their centers?
- In Step 2, you started with tangents and made a conjecture about angles. When you investigate the converse of this statement, what will you start with?

For Groups That Finish Early

Give a deductive argument to explain why tangent segments from the same external point are congruent. **The triangles determined by the center of the circle, the external point, and the points of tangency are congruent by HL, and the segments are congruent by CPCTC.**

Follow Up

Ask students to summarize their results for Steps 2, 3, and 4.

Circles, Circumference, and Area

Possible Answers

1. Find the centers of the polygons by drawing diagonals; find the radii of the circles by trial and error, using the compass.
2. The tangents are perpendicular to the radii at the points of tangency.
3. If a coplanar line is perpendicular to a radius of a circle at a point on the circle, then the line is tangent to the circle.
4. Tangent segments to a circle from the same exterior point are congruent.

Journal

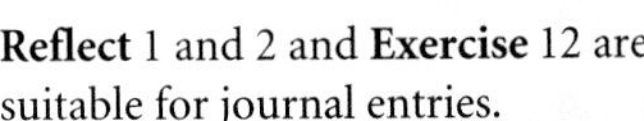

Reflect 1 and 2 and **Exercise** 12 are suitable for journal entries.

REFLECT

Possible Answers

1. If the words *in a plane* are left out of the circle definition, it becomes the definition for a sphere.
2. Yes. All circles have the same shape. (The ratio of their radii is the similarity ratio.)

Much of the terminology that we apply to circles in two dimensions is also used to describe spheres in three dimensions.

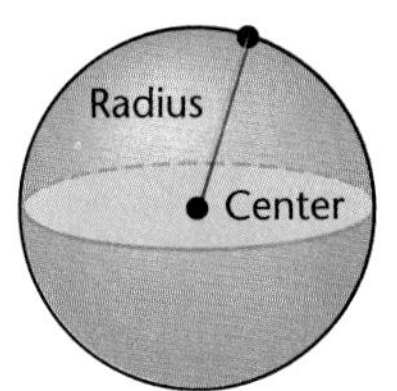

A **sphere** is the locus of points in space a given distance from a point called the **center** of the sphere. The **radius** of the sphere is a segment from the center to a point on the sphere; the *distance* from the center to any point on the sphere is also called the radius.

Like tangents to circles, tangents to spheres touch the sphere at exactly one point. A **tangent line** or **tangent plane** contains exactly one point of the sphere. A **great circle** is a circle on the sphere whose center is also the center of the sphere.

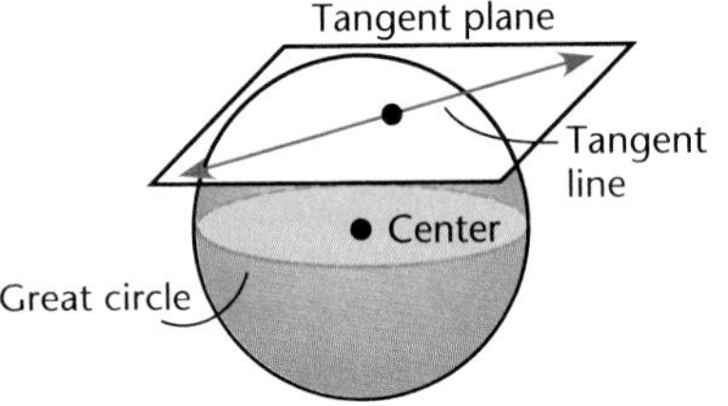

Some of the properties of tangents that you've investigated are summarized below.

THEOREMS ABOUT TANGENTS TO A CIRCLE

If a line is tangent to a circle, then it is perpendicular to a radius at the point of tangency.

If a line coplanar to a circle is perpendicular to a radius of a circle at a point on the circle, then the line is tangent to the circle.

Two tangent segments to a circle from the same exterior point are congruent.

REFLECT

1. Why does the definition of a circle include the words *in a plane*? If these words are left out, what figure does the definition describe?
2. Are any two circles similar? Explain.

History Connection

The first African-American to earn a Ph.D. in mathematics was Elbert Francis Cox (1896–1962). He received his doctorate from Cornell in 1925. Dr. Cox was the head of the mathematics department at Howard University for 32 years.

Exercises

CORE

Getting Started Use the figure at the right to name each of the following.

1. a diameter of ⊙O $\overline{AB}$
2. three radii of ⊙O $\overline{AO}$, $\overline{OB}$, $\overline{OE}$
3. a tangent line and its point of tangency $\overleftrightarrow{FG}$; E
4. a secant line $\overleftrightarrow{CD}$
5. Sketch and label ⊙R with radius $\overline{RP}$ and tangent n with its point of tangency at P.

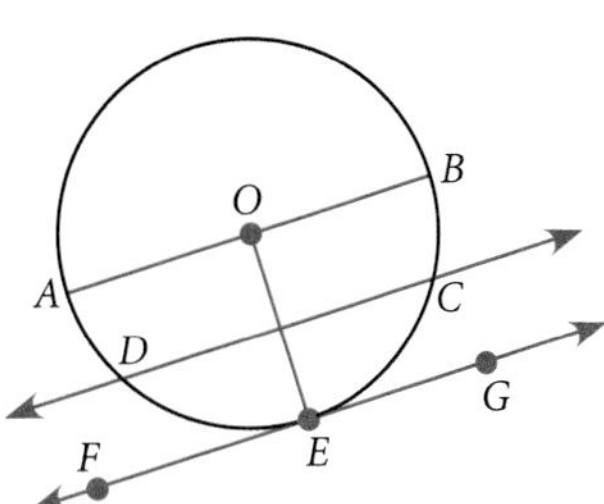

Write the word or phrase that correctly completes each statement.

6. A circle on a sphere whose center is also the center of the sphere is a ___ of the sphere. Great circle
7. If a line intersects a circle in two points, then it is a ___ of the circle. Secant

In the figure, $\overleftrightarrow{XY}$ is tangent to ⊙Z at Y.

8. What is $m\angle XYZ$? 90°
9. If $XY = 12$ and $YZ = 16$, find XZ. 20
10. If $XZ = 3.2$ and $XY = 1.4$, find YZ. 2.88
11. If $YZ = 7.4$ and $XZ = 9.7$, find XY. 6.27
12. The radius of a circle is 7 cm, and the length of a tangent segment from an exterior point A is 12 cm. How far is A from the center of the circle? Explain.

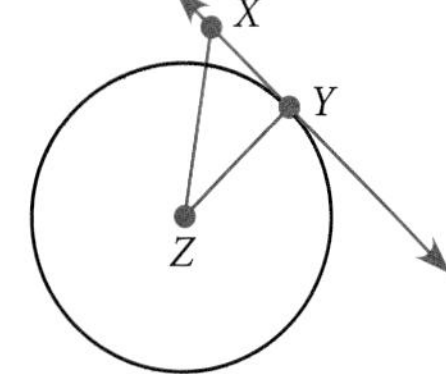

⊙T is inscribed in △QRS.

13. Solve for x. 2.8
14. Solve for y. 3.2
15. Solve for z. 3.7
16. Find the perimeter of △QRS. 19.4
17. Prove the following: Two tangent segments to a circle from the same exterior point are congruent.

    Given: $\overline{QS}$ and $\overline{QT}$ are tangent segments to ⊙R.

    Prove: $\overline{QS} \cong \overline{QT}$

    (Hint: Draw $\overline{QR}$, $\overline{RS}$, and $\overline{RT}$.)

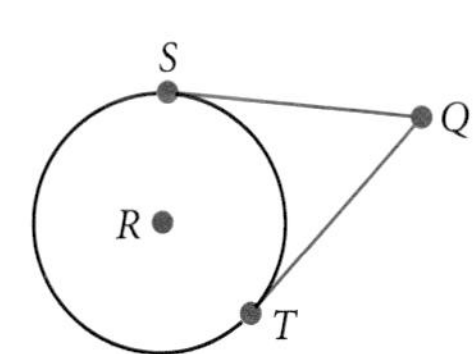

Part B Exercises

Exercise Notes

Core

19. Students see that the path of an object leaving a spinning disk is tangent to the disk.

Science Note: This exercise is related to an important principle in physics. A moving object travels in a straight-line path unless acted on by an external force (such as the gravitational pull of a planet).

More Math Reasoning

37. Students use tangents to explore total solar eclipses.

Exercise Answers

Core

5.

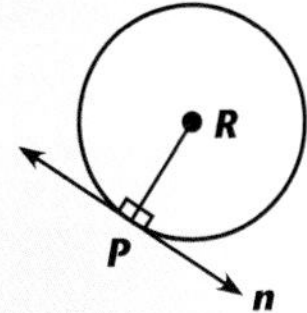

12. 13.9 cm; The distance is the hypotenuse of a triangle with legs of 7 and 12 cm.

17. $\overline{RS} \cong \overline{RT}$; Definition of *circle*. $\angle S$ and $\angle T$ are right angles; Radii are perpendicular to tangents at points of tangency. $\overline{RQ} \cong \overline{RQ}$; Reflexive Property. $\triangle SRQ \cong \triangle TRQ$; HL theorem. $\overline{QS} \cong \overline{QT}$; CPCTC.

18. Possible answer: Draw a circle and its diameter, which represent a pair of radii. Using the midpoint of each radius as a new center, draw two smaller semicircles whose diameters equal the radius of the larger circle. Draw two small circles equidistant from the large circle's center. Shade as appropriate.

19. It will take a path tangent to the circular path it was traveling before it broke loose.

Key

Vocabulary
Practice/Skills
Review
R Math Reasoning
S Problem Solving
Challenge

Ongoing Assessment

Self-Assessment Exercises 1–15 odd, 20, 21, 23

Embedded Assessment Try It b; Exercises 8, 10, 16, 18

Circles, Circumference, and Area

More Practice

35. Possible answer: Draw segments $\overline{RB}$, $\overline{RC}$, and $\overline{BC}$. Since $RB = RC$, $\triangle RBC$ is isosceles and $\angle RBC \cong \angle RCB$. Since $\angle RBA$ and $\angle RCA$ are right angles, $\angle ABC$ is complementary to $\angle RBC$ and $\angle ACB$ is complementary to $\angle RCB$. Complements of congruent angles are congruent, so $\angle ABC \cong \angle ACB$.

More Math Reasoning

36. 26.9 ft

37. $LM \approx 1100$ mi; $\triangle ERS \sim \triangle ELM$ by AA, so $\frac{LM}{RS} = \frac{EM}{ES}$. Solve for LM.

Algebra	Functions	Discrete Math	Probability	Data/Statistics

MR **18. Yin Yang** In Chinese philosophy, two principles, yin and yang, are often symbolized by a figure like the one shown below. Yin is the feminine principle, and yang is the masculine principle. It is said that the two combine to produce harmony in nature.

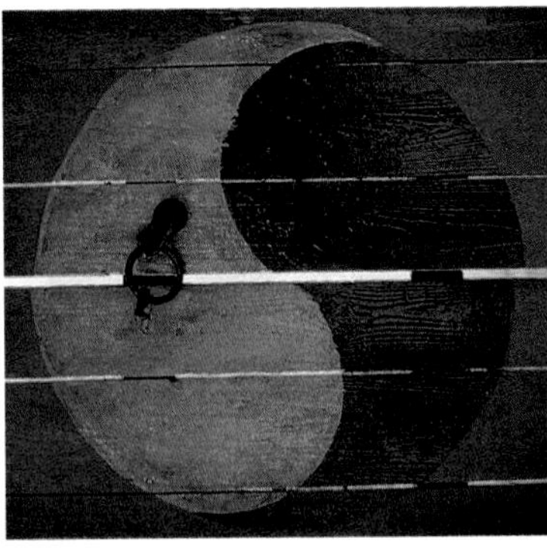

Social Science

A yin-yang symbol can be constructed with a compass and straightedge. Analyze the yin-yang symbol, and describe how it can be made. Use terms like *radius, midpoint, tangent,* and *concentric circles* in your explanation. Then construct your own yin-yang symbol.

MR **19.** Suppose a speck of dust on a compact disk flies off the disk while it is spinning. Illustrate the path you think the speck takes. Explain your answer using circle terminology.

Science

P **Use the figure at the right to name each of the following.**

20. the point of tangency for the tangent plane to sphere O E

21. a secant line for sphere O $\overleftrightarrow{AB}$

22. a radius of sphere O $\overline{OE}$

23. a line that is tangent to sphere O $\overleftrightarrow{DC}$

LOOK BACK

R **Find the measure of one interior and one exterior angle of each polygon. [6-3]**

24. regular hexagon Interior: 120°; Exterior: 60°

25. regular octagon Interior: 135°; Exterior: 45°

26. regular decagon Interior: 144°; Exterior: 36°

R **27.** Square $HJKL$ undergoes a dilation with scale factor 3 and center H. Give the coordinates of H', J', K', and L', which are the dilation images of H, J, K, and L. [7-2]
$H'(2, 3)$, $L'(2, 9)$, $J'(8, 3)$, $K'(8, 9)$

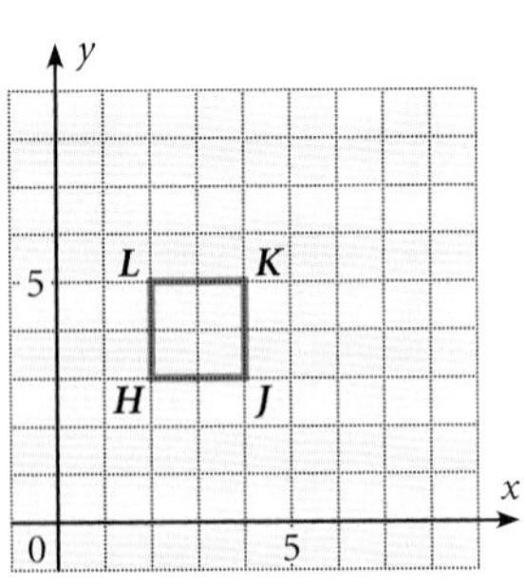

Key

V Vocabulary
P Practice/Skills
R Review
MR Math Reasoning
PS Problem Solving
C Challenge

MORE PRACTICE

In the figure, $\overleftrightarrow{HG}$ is tangent to $\odot F$ at H.

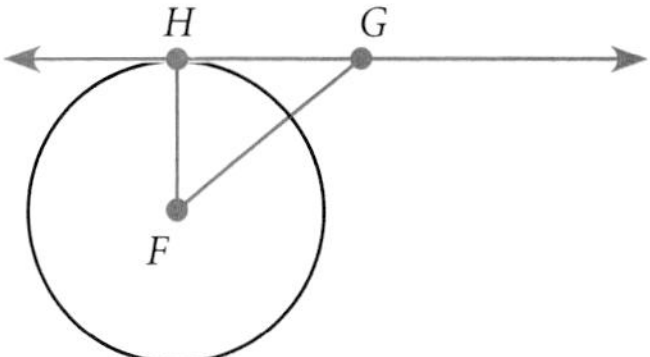

28. If $GH = 12$ and $FH = 5$, find FG. 13

29. If $FG = 35.3$ and $GH = 26.5$, find FH. 23.32

30. If $m\angle F = 60°$ and the radius of $\odot F$ is 3, find exact values for GH and FG. $GH = 3\sqrt{3}$; $FG = 6$

$\odot T$ is inscribed in *MNOP*.

31. Solve for a. $a = 18$

32. Solve for b. $b = 7$

33. Solve for c. $c = 13$

34. Find the perimeter of $MNOP$. 88

35. *Given:* $\overline{AB}$ and $\overline{AC}$ are tangent to $\odot R$ at B and C.

Prove: $\angle ABC \cong \angle ACB$

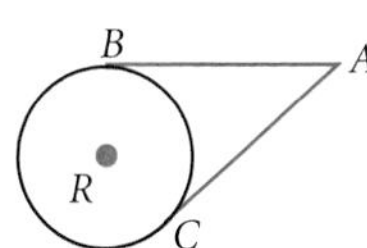

MORE MATH REASONING

36. A large drum of crude oil rolled off a truck and came to rest at edge of a wall. Emergency services officials need to know the diameter of the drum in order to send the proper equipment to reload it. Calculate the diameter of the drum to the nearest tenth of a foot. Assume that $WX = 19$ ft and $\overline{XY} \perp \overline{WY}$.

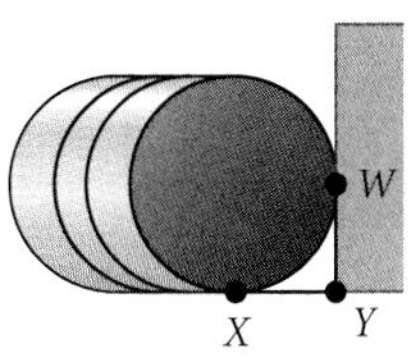

37. Sun Block During a total eclipse of the sun, the disk of the moon almost exactly covers the disk of the sun at certain locations on the earth (E). The average distance from the earth to the moon (EM) is approximately 237,000 mi. The average distance to the sun (ES) is approximately 93,000,000 mi, and the sun's radius (SR) is about 433,000 mi. Find the approximate radius of the moon, and explain your method.

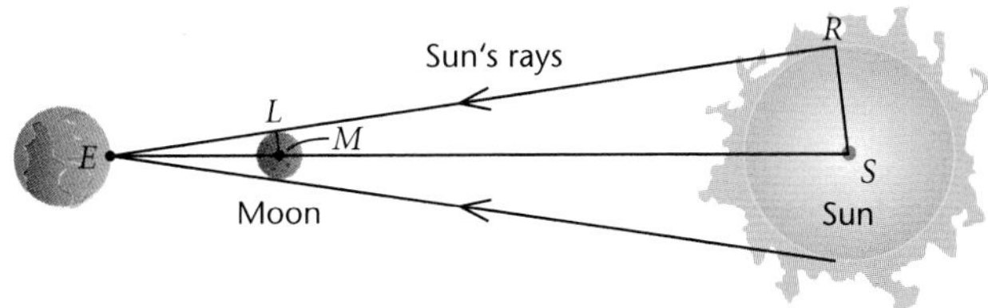

38. Find the equation for the line tangent to the circle $x^2 + y^2 = 25$ at the point (3, 4). $y = -\frac{3}{4}x + 6\frac{1}{4}$

PART C At a Glance

Objective

To discover that the ratio of the circumference of a circle to its diameter is constant and that this constant is π.

Development

First, students see the definition of *circumference.* Next, in the **Explore,** they find that a circle's circumference-to-diameter ratio is always the same.

Then, students see more evidence for this fact that uses the idea of a limit. The definition of π leads to formulas for the circumference of a circle.

Suggested Materials

Student Tape measure, three circular objects

Key Terms

Circumference, pi (π)

First Five Minutes

Transparency FFM 8-1C

If the radius of an equilateral triangle is 12 cm, what is its perimeter? Round your answer to the nearest tenth.
62.4 cm

Motivate

Ask...

- What is the ratio of the perimeter of a regular hexagon to the length of a diagonal that joins opposite vertices? **3**

EXPLORE

Easy as...

Recommended group size: 2

The Point
To discover that the ratio of the circumference of a circle to its diameter is a constant.

8-1 PART C The Circumference of a Circle

← CONNECT → ***You've calculated the perimeter of many different figures. Now you will discover a formula for the perimeter of a circle.***

As you know, the distance around a polygon is its perimeter. The distance around a circle is its **circumference.** Early in the history of mathematics, people discovered an important fact about the ratio of the circumference to the diameter of any circle.

EXPLORE: EASY AS . . .

MATERIALS

Tape measure
Three circular objects

Use a tape measure to measure the circumference and the diameter of three circular objects. For each object, calculate the ratio of the circumference to the diameter to the nearest tenth. Make a table to organize your results. What pattern do you see? What number do you think is equal to the circumference-to-diameter ratio for any circle?

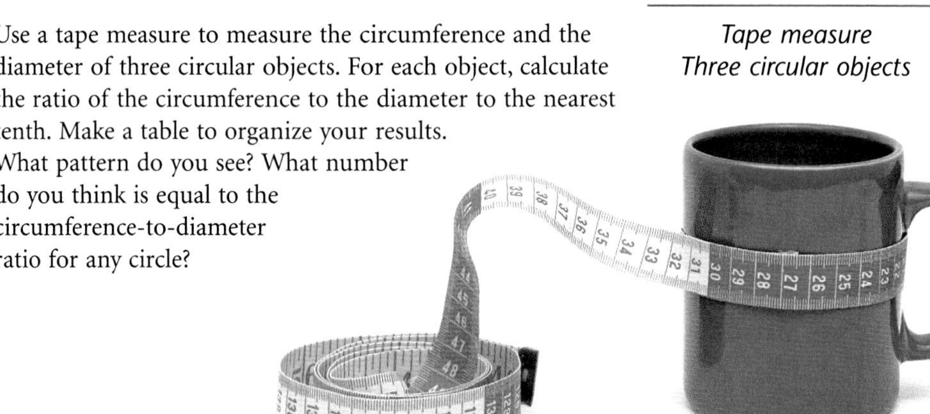

Now we will look at another way to find the circumference-to-diameter ratio of a circle.

Although it is not always possible to construct inscribed regular n-gons accurately by hand, computers can generate and measure such figures easily.

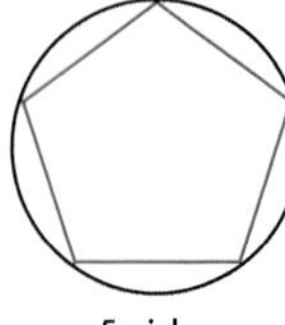
5 sides

8 sides

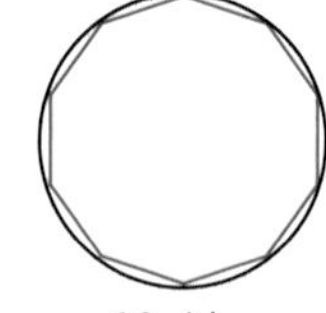
10 sides

History Connection

Bhaskara (whose proof of the Pythagorean Theorem appears in Chapter 5) gave $\frac{3927}{1250} = 3.1416$ as the "near value" for π around the year 1150. In 1220, Fibonacci gave a value of $\frac{864}{275} = 3.141818$.

1. As the number of sides of the inscribed regular polygon increases, how does the perimeter of the polygon compare to the circumference of the circle?

The table shows what happens as the number of sides of the inscribed regular polygon increases.

Regular Polygons Inscribed in a Circle of Diameter 1						
Number of sides	5	8	10	25	50	100
$\frac{\text{Perimeter}}{\text{Diameter}}$	2.939	3.061	3.090	3.133	3.140	3.141

Notice that the $\frac{\text{perimeter}}{\text{diameter}}$ ratio seems to approach a particular value as the sides of the inscribed polygons get closer to the circle. This "limiting" value, the ratio of the circumference of a circle to its diameter, is the number π **(pi).**

DEFINITION

The number π is the ratio of the circumference of any circle to its diameter. $\pi = \frac{c}{d}$

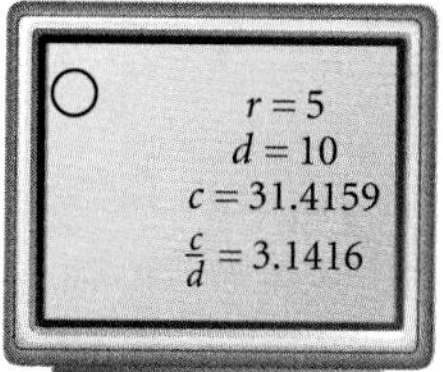

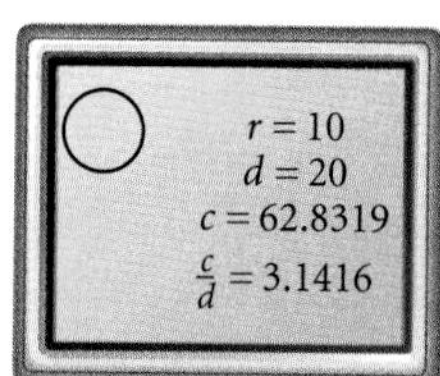

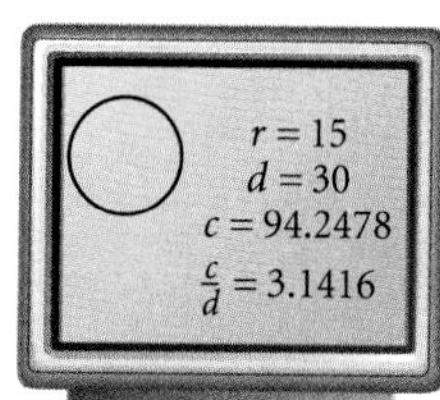

The definition of π leads immediately to two formulas for the circumference of a circle. These formulas are summarized as theorems at the top of page 552.

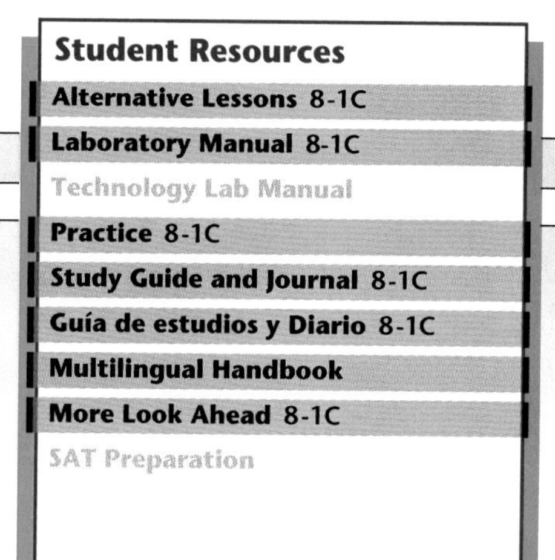
Student Resources

Alternative Lessons 8-1C
Laboratory Manual 8-1C
Technology Lab Manual
Practice 8-1C
Study Guide and Journal 8-1C
Guía de estudios y Diario 8-1C
Multilingual Handbook
More Look Ahead 8-1C
SAT Preparation

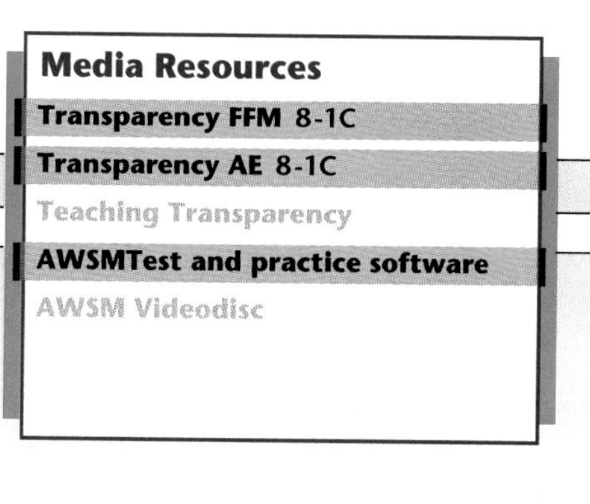
Media Resources

Transparency FFM 8-1C
Transparency AE 8-1C
Teaching Transparency
AWSMTest and practice software
AWSM Videodisc

Look and Listen...

- For students who are not wrapping their tape measure tightly around the objects or are measuring at a slant.
- For students who are having difficulty using a tape measure correctly.

Ask...

- Are you measuring the *shortest* path around the objects?

For Groups That Finish Early

Draw a circle with your compass. Measure its diameter, and then calculate the circumference of the circle. **The circumference is approximately 3.1 times the measured diameter.**

Follow Up

Ask students whether the ratio of the circumference to the diameter of any circle is the same, and, if so, what its approximate value is. If time permits, ask students whether this is true of any regular polygon as well. **It is.**

Possible Answer

The ratio of the circumference to the diameter of all of the objects is the same. This ratio is approximately 3.1. (Exact value is $\pi \approx 3.14159$.)

Shows that the perimeter of an inscribed regular polygon approaches the circumference of a circle as the number of sides increases.

Possible Answer

1. As the number of sides increases, the perimeter of the inscribed polygon gets closer and closer to the circumference of the circle.

Circles, Circumference, and Area

ALTERNATE EXAMPLE

If the diameter of $\odot M$ is 15 in., what is its circumference to the nearest hundredth of an inch?

$C = \pi d$

$C = \pi(15) \approx 47.12$ in.

Journal

Reflect 1 and 3 are suitable for journal entries.

REFLECT

Possible Answers

1. No. The ratio is a constant, π.
2. The ratio of the circumference of a circle to its diameter is π.
3. As the number of sides of these regular polygons increases, their perimeter-to-"diameter" ratio gets closer and closer to π.

THEOREMS

The circumference of a circle is the product of π and its diameter, d.

$C = \pi d$

The circumference of a circle is twice the product of π and its radius, r.

$C = 2\pi r$

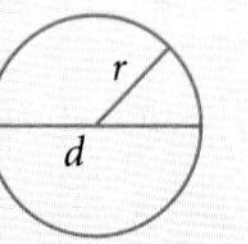

The number π is irrational—it cannot be written as an exact decimal. The first forty-five decimal places of π follow:

$\pi \approx 3.141592653589793238462643383279502884197169399$

Of course, you don't usually need this degree of accuracy. When working with problems involving π that call for an exact answer, leave π in the calculations and the answer. If you need an answer in decimal form, use the π key on your calculator and round your answer as necessary.

EXAMPLE

If the radius of $\odot C$ is 4 cm, what is its circumference to the nearest tenth of a centimeter?

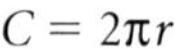

$C = 2\pi r$

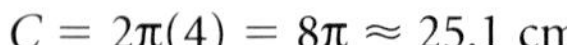

$C = 2\pi(4) = 8\pi \approx 25.1$ cm

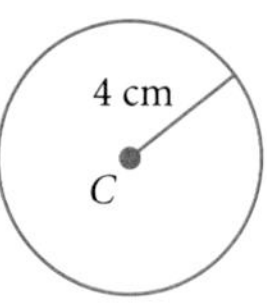

TRY IT

Round answers to the nearest tenth.

a. What is the circumference of the pan? 25.1 in.

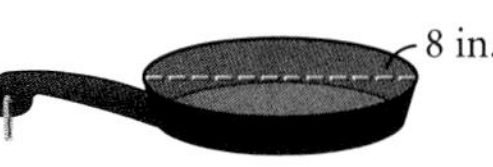

b. The circumference of a trash-can lid is 22π in. What is its diameter? 22.0 in.

REFLECT

1. Does the ratio of the circumference to the diameter of a circle get larger if the radius of the circle is increased? Explain.
2. In your own words, explain what π is.
3. Suppose you find the perimeter-to-"diameter" ratio for a square, then a regular hexagon, octagon, decagon, 12-gon, etc. What does it mean to say that π is the limiting value for the perimeter-to-diameter ratio of these polygons?

Alert

Students who have used approximations for π in previous work may believe that π is *equal* to $\frac{22}{7}$ or 3.14. You may want to emphasize that π is an irrational number, and that these are only approximations to its value. Students who do not realize this may not understand how to give an exact answer for an exercise involving π.

Exercises

CORE

1. **Getting Started** Find the diameter and circumference of a circle whose radius is 3 in. Give your answers in exact form. 6 in.; 6π in.

Find the circumference of each circle. Give your answers in exact form and as decimals rounded to the nearest hundredth.

2. a circle with diameter 42 ft 42π ft; 131.95 ft
3. a circle with radius 5.7 mm 11.4π mm; 35.81 mm

Find the radius of the circle with each circumference.

4. 24π cm 12 cm
5. 1.07 in. 0.17 in.
6. A rubber belt connects the two flywheels shown. Find the total length of the belt. 29.42 in.

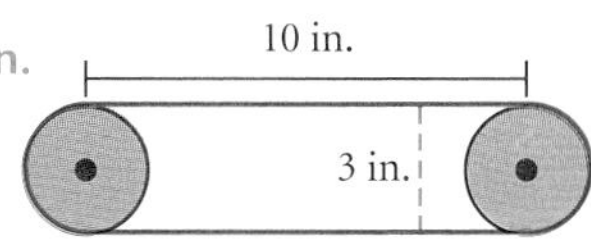

Find the perimeter of each figure.

7. 54.85
8. 21.42

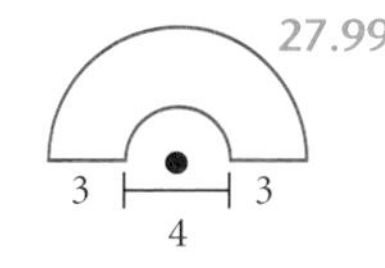

9. 27.99

10. If a sphere has radius 22 cm, find the circumference of one of its great circles. $44\pi \approx 138.23$ cm
11. Max stores his collection of CDs in a trunk. Unfortunately, he never put wheels on the trunk, and he can only move it with rollers. If each roller is 42 cm in diameter, how far does the trunk move in one complete revolution of the rollers? 131.95 cm

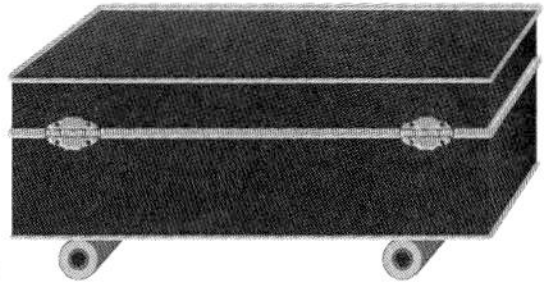

12. **Fogg Around the World** In *Around the World in Eighty Days* by Jules Verne, Phileas Fogg boasts that he can travel around the world in 80 days or less. (Since he was traveling in the late 1800s, he couldn't take an airplane!) What average speed is needed to go around the earth at the equator in 80 days? Use 3960 mi for the radius of the earth, and assume you travel 12 hr each day. 25.92 mi/hr
13. Ch'ang Höng (78–139 A.D.), a Chinese astrologer and government minister, used $\sqrt{10}$ as a value for π in his writings.
    a. Find the difference between $\sqrt{10}$ and the actual value of π. Round your answer to the nearest thousandth. 0.021
    b. Tsu Ch'ung-Chih (430–501 A.D.) gave $\frac{355}{113}$ as the "accurate value" for π. Is this approximation closer to the actual value for π than $\sqrt{10}$? Explain. Yes; It differs from π by only about 0.00000027

Part C Exercises

Exercise Notes

Core

13. Students investigate ancient Chinese approximations for π.

Look Ahead

15–17. Review calculations involving squares and square roots. Such calculations will be important when students find circle areas in 8-1 Part D.

18. Students review a rearrangement technique that justifies the parallelogram area formula. They will use a similar technique in the **Explore** in 8-1 Part D.

19. Reviews the area formula for a regular polygon. In 8-1 Part D, this formula is used to justify the area formula for a circle.

More Math Reasoning

27. This "ribbon around the earth" problem is a famous one. Students are often surprised to find how small the difference is between the lengths of the ribbons.

Extension: Ask students to find the difference in such a pair of ribbons for a one-foot sphere. (The difference is exactly the same.)

y

Vocabulary
Practice/Skills
Review
Math Reasoning
Problem Solving
Challenge

Ongoing Assessment

Self-Assessment Exercises 1–13 odd

Embedded Assessment Reflect 2; Exercises 2, 4, 12, 14

8-1

Algebra | Functions | Discrete Math | Probability | Data/Statistics

Circles, Circumference, and Area

Exercise Answers

Look Ahead

18. a. Cut a right triangle off one side and add it to the other side.

b. The area of the parallelogram is equal to the area of a rectangle with base = length an height = width, that is, bh.

More Math Reasoning

27. a. Check students' answers.

b. 20,926,436.2 ft

c. Circumference of bottom ribbon ≈ 131,484,670.2 ft, circumference of top ribbon ≈ 131,484,676.5 ft. There is a 6.3 ft difference. (Top longer by 2π ft. Let r be the radius of the earth in feet. The length of the lower ribbon is $2\pi r$ while the top one is $2\pi(r + 1)$. The difference is 2π.)

d. Check students' answers.

28. a. All sides are straight lines; For an n-gon with many sides, the shape approximates a circle.

b. $r \approx 0.48$ ft; $\frac{\text{Perimeter}}{2\pi}$ gives the radius.

PS **14. The Inside Track** The track shown has semicircular turns. In a race on the track, Manuela got to the inside lane, and Beth was forced to run 1 yd outside of Manuela. In one lap around the track, how much farther does Beth run than Manuela? Why do runners prefer to run on the inside of a track?
$2\pi \approx 6.28$ yd; The outside runner has farther to run.

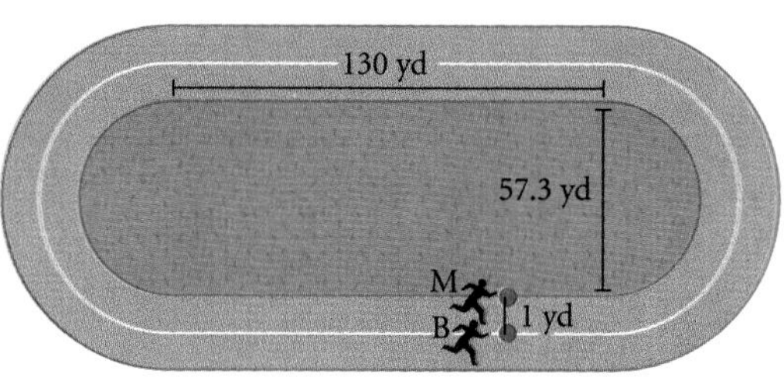

LOOK AHEAD

R **Evaluate each expression. Round answers to the nearest hundredth.**

15. $3x^2$ for $x = 4$ 48

16. $5.24y^2$ for $y = 2.23$ 26.06

17. $\sqrt{\frac{z}{4.32}}$ for $z = 72.31$ 4.09

MR **18.** Draw a parallelogram.

a. Describe how you can make one cut and move one piece of the parallelogram to form a rectangle.

b. Explain how this rearrangement can be used to justify the area formula for a parallelogram.

R **19.** State the area formula for a regular polygon. Then find the area of a regular hexagon with a radius of five centimeters. $\frac{1}{2}ap$; 64.95 cm^2

MORE PRACTICE

P **Find the circumference of each circle. Give your answers in exact form and as decimals rounded to the nearest hundredth.**

20. a circle with diameter 31 m
31π m; 97.39 m

21. a circle with radius 13.8 in.
27.6π in.; 86.71 in.

P **Find the radius of a circle with each circumference.**

22. 15π mm $r = 7.5$ mm

23. 77.1 yd $r = 12.27$ yd

P **Find the perimeter of each shaded figure.**

24. 7.6, 3
25.54

25. 6.0, 3.0
$9\pi \approx 28.27$

26.

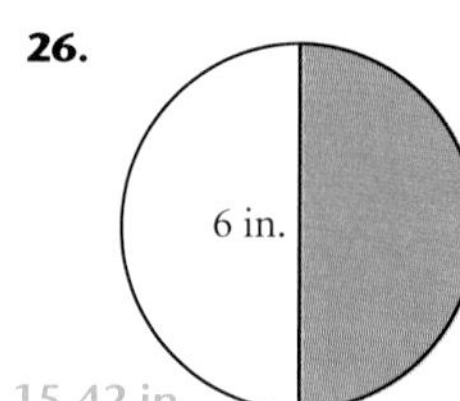

15.42 in.

Key

V Vocabulary
P Practice/Skills
R Review
MR Math Reasoning
PS Problem Solving
C Challenge

MORE MATH REASONING

27. Suppose you tightly wrap a ribbon around the earth's equator and then add a second ribbon, supported by one-foot posts, above the first. The ribbons are concentric circles. (Assume that the earth is spherical and that each ribbon forms a circle.)

a. Guess how much longer you think the top ribbon is than the lower ribbon.

b. The radius of the earth at its equator is 20,926,435.2 ft. Find the radius of the top ribbon to the nearest tenth of a foot.

c. Find the circumferences of the top and bottom ribbons. What is the difference?

d. Compare your answer in **27c** to your guess in **27a**. Are you surprised?

28. In *Flatland,* Edwin Abbott describes a two-dimensional world inhabited by polygons. The highest class in the society is the Circular Class.

"[I]t is known that no Circle is really a Circle, but only a Polygon with a very large number of very small sides. . . . It is always assumed, by courtesy, that the Chief Circle . . . has ten thousand sides."

a. Explain why "no Circle is really a Circle" in Flatland. Why do the inhabitants refer to them as "circles" at all?

b. The perimeter of a Flatland polygon is three feet. Find the approximate radius of the Chief Circle. Explain how you found your answer.

8-1 PART D The Area of a Circle

← CONNECT → ***You know how to calculate the circumference of a circle. Now you will investigate and use the formula for the area of a circle.***

In order to know how much glass is needed for a circular stained-glass window, the artist must calculate the area of a circle. The area formula for a circle may be familiar to you. In the following Explore, you will discover this formula for yourself.

Student Resources

- **Alternative Lessons** 8-1D
- **Laboratory Manual** 8-1D
- Technology Lab Manual
- **Practice** 8-1D
- **Study Guide and Journal** 8-1D
- **Guía de estudios y Diario** 8-1D
- **Multilingual Handbook**
- **More Look Back** 8-1D
- SAT Preparation

Media Resources

- **Transparency FFM** 8-1D
- **Transparency AE** 8-1D
- Teaching Transparency
- **AWSMTest and practice software**
- AWSM Videodisc

PART D At a Glance

Objective

To develop and use a formula for the area of a circle.

Development

In the **Explore,** students find a formula for the area of a circle by rearranging pieces of a circle into a "parallelogram." Then they see a deductive justification for the formula that uses the area of an inscribed polygon as the number of its sides increases.

Suggested Materials

Student Compass, scissors

First Five Minutes

Transparency FFM 8-1D

Find the following.

1. The area of a parallelogram whose height is 4 cm and base length is 9 cm. **36 cm²**

2. The area of a regular hexagon whose side length is 2.4 in. and apothem is 2.1 in. ≈ **15.1 in.²**

3. The circumference of a circle whose radius is 3 in. ≈ **18.8 in.**

Motivate

Ask...

- Explain how you can use the area formula for a rectangle to justify the area result for a parallelogram. **Cut off a right triangle from one end of the parallelogram; move it to the other end to make a rectangle.**

8-1

Circles, Circumference, and Area

EXPLORE

Cutting a Mean Circle

Recommended group size: 2

The Point

To discover the area formula for a circle.

Look and Listen...

- For students who do not see how the radius of the circle is related to the height and base length of the parallelogram.

Ask...

- What is the circumference of the circle in terms of r? How many slices did you divide it into?
- How many of these slices make up a "base" of the parallelogram?
- Sketch a height for your parallelogram. Is this height related to a measurement in the original circle?

For Groups That Finish Early

Would your "parallelogram" look more like an actual parallelogram if you had divided the circle into 32 parts? **The new figure would be closer to a true parallelogram; the smaller arcs would approximate a segment more closely.**

Follow Up

Ask students to share their answers to Step 3 and explain their reasoning.

Possible Answer

3. Area of "parallelogram" = Area of circle = πr^2. (Base length = πr, height = r.)

EXPLORE: CUTTING A MEAN CIRCLE

MATERIALS

Compass
Scissors

1. Use your compass to construct a circle with a radius of approximately 3 in. Cut out the circular region. Fold the region in half. Then fold your paper in half three more times.

2. Unfold your circular region, and cut it along the folds to create sixteen wedges. Place the wedges in a row as shown in the lower figure, so that they resemble a parallelogram.

3. What is the area of the "parallelogram" you created? (Hint: Label the base and height of the "parallelogram." The radius of the original circle is r, and the circumference is $2\pi r$. Use this information to find the base and height of the "parallelogram," and then find its area.) How is this related to the area of the circle?

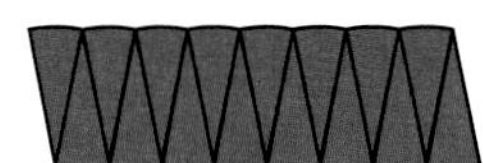

Problem-Solving Tip

See if you can use familiar facts in a new setting.

Now, let's see why the formula for the area of a circle works. Consider a series of inscribed regular polygons.

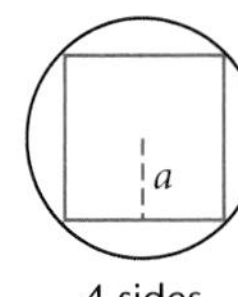

4 sides

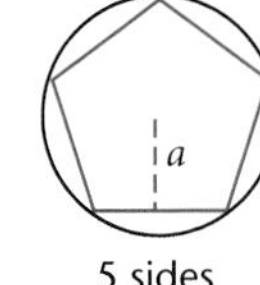

5 sides

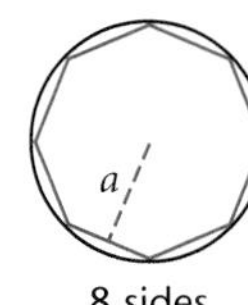

8 sides

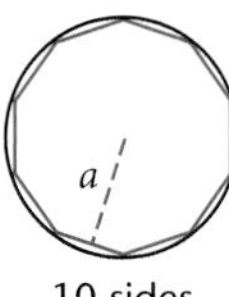

10 sides

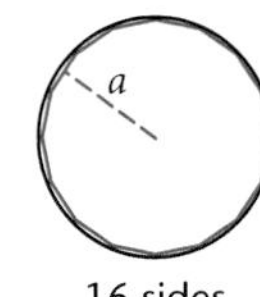

16 sides

Recall that the formula for the area of a regular polygon is $A = \frac{1}{2}ap$, where a is the length of the apothem, and p is the perimeter of the polygon. As you can see, the greater the number of sides in the regular polygon, the more closely it resembles a circle.

The following calculation shows how we can derive the area formula for a circle.

Diversity Issues

Students may be familiar with the circle area formula. However, the manipulative support for this theorem in the **Explore** and the visual "limit" justification in the text give students different ways to see why the formula is true. Multiple representations of the same concept can help all learners grasp it more completely.

By substituting the limiting values into the area formula for a regular polygon, you can justify a familiar result.

Area of a polygon $= \frac{1}{2}ap$

Area of a circle $= \frac{1}{2}rC$ — Substitute the radius for the apothem and the circumference for the perimeter.

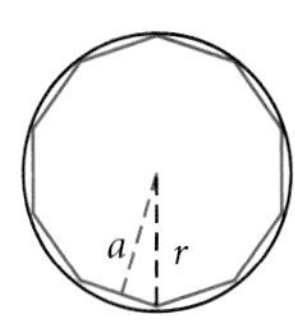

Area of a circle $= \frac{1}{2}r(2\pi r)$ — Substitute $2\pi r$ for C.

Area of a circle $= \pi r^2$

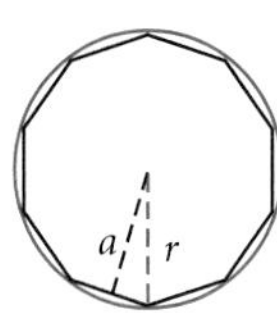

EXAMPLES

Leave answers in exact form.

1. If the radius of $\odot C$ is 3 cm, what is its area?
   $A = \pi r^2 = 9\pi \text{ cm}^2$
2. If the area of $\odot C$ is $49\pi \text{ ft}^2$, what is its diameter?
   If $A = \pi r^2 = 49\pi$, $r^2 = 49$. Since the radius must be a positive number, $r = 7$ ft and $d = 14$ ft.

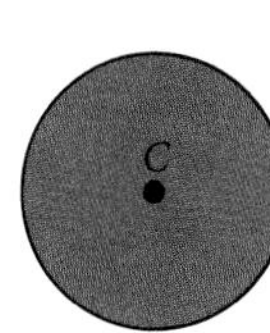

TRY IT

a. The diameter of the Aztec calendar stone shown at the right is 12 feet. This stone, which weighs over 24 tons, may have enabled the Aztecs to calculate the motions of the planets. Find the area and circumference of the face of the calendar stone.
   $A = 36\pi \approx 113.10 \text{ ft}^2$;
   $C = 12\pi \approx 37.70$ ft

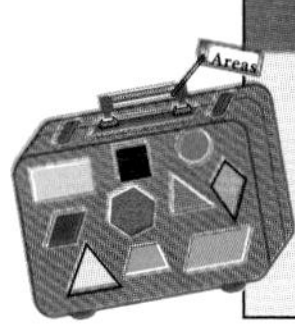

THEOREM

The area of a circle is the product of π and the square of its radius, r.

$A = \pi r^2$

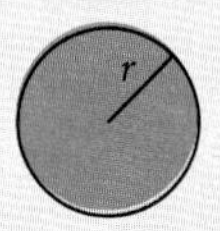

ALTERNATE EXAMPLES

Leave answers in exact form.

1. If the radius of a circle is 5 cm, what is its area?
   $A = \pi r^2 = 25\pi \text{ cm}^2$
2. If the area of a circle is $144\pi \text{ in.}^2$, what is its diameter?
   If $A = \pi r^2 = 144\pi$, $r^2 = 144$. Since the radius must be a positive number, $r = 12$ in., and $d = 24$ in.

Research Note

There is clear and compelling evidence that small-group instructional models can facilitate student achievement (most notably in basic skills) as well as more favorable attitudes toward peers and subject matter. (Thomas L. Good, Catherine Mulryan, and Mary McCaslin, "Grouping for Instruction in Mathematics: A Call for Programmatic Research in Small-Group Processes," *Handbook of Research on Mathematics Teaching and Learning,* Douglas A. Grouws, ed., p. 167. © 1992 NCTM.)

Circles, Circumference, and Area

Journal

Explore Step 3 and **Reflect** 1 and 2 are suitable for journal entries.

REFLECT

Possible Answers

1. The curved edges of the pieces of the circle only approximate the straight bases of the parallelogram. If the circle is divided into more pieces, its rearranged slices will be closer to a true parallelogram.
2. No. Its perimeter will be very close to the circle's circumference, but they will not be exactly equal, since each side of the polygon joining consecutive vertices must be shorter than the arc of the circle containing them.

Part D Exercises

Exercise Notes

Core

7. Art Note: The use of the circle as a symbol of wholeness and continuity has been common through history and across cultures.

11. Shows that the formulas for the area and circumference of a circle can be thought of as quadratic and linear functions.

13. Explores the idea of maximization of area subject to restrictions on perimeter. This idea is explored in depth in Chapter 11.

More Math Reasoning

21. Students explore a type of calculus developed in Japan. The idea of inscribed rectangles used in this exercise recalls the work on area under a curve in 5-2 Part C.

REFLECT

1. Why does rearranging segments of a circle as shown in the preceding Explore give only an *approximate* parallelogram? How can you use this method to get a figure that is closer to a true parallelogram?
2. Do you think a regular polygon with 1000 sides has a perimeter equal to the circumference of its circumscribed circle? Explain.

Exercises

CORE

P **1. Getting Started** Find the diameter, circumference, and area of a circle whose radius is 5 cm. Give your answers in exact form. $d = 10$ cm; $C = 10\pi$ cm; $A = 25\pi$ cm^2

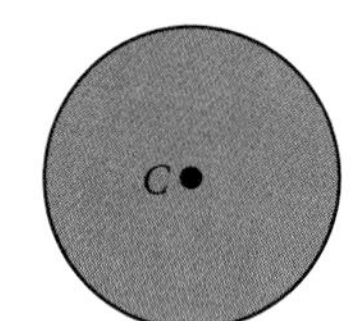

P **Find each of the following for $\odot C$. Give your answers in exact form and as decimals rounded to the nearest hundredth.**

2. If its radius is 4 in., find its area. 16π in.^{2}; 50.27 in.^{2}
3. If its area is 25π cm^2, find its diameter. 10 cm
4. If its diameter is 12.6 mm, find its area. 39.69π mm^2; 124.69 mm^2
5. If its circumference is 6π ft, find its area. 9π ft^2; 28.27 ft^2
6. If its area is 1.75 in.^{2}, find its circumference. $2\sqrt{1.75\pi}$ in.^{2}; 4.69 in.^{2}

PS Fine Arts **7.** Sara Bates, a Cherokee artist, makes circular works of art from natural materials like feathers, berries, and pine cones. Her art uses patterns, repetition, and symbols that recall Cherokee traditions, but her work is a new way of expressing these forms.

Bates's works are usually from seven to eleven feet in diameter. Find the minimum and maximum areas of these pieces. 38.48 ft^2; 94.03 ft^2

PS **8.** The radius of the signal of a radio station extends 78 km from the base of the tower. What is the area of the region that the signal can reach? 19,113.45 km^2

PS **9.** Suppose a square with an area of 100 in.^{2} is inscribed in a circle. Find the circumference and the area of the circle. $C = 10\pi\sqrt{2} \approx 44.43$ in.; $A = 50\pi \approx 157.08$ in.^{2}

MR **10.** If the radius of a circle is tripled, what effect does this have on the area of the circle? Explain why your result makes sense. Area is 9 times larger; $\pi(3r)^2 = 9\pi r^2$

Key

- V Vocabulary
- P Practice/Skills
- R Review
- MR Math Reasoning
- PS Problem Solving
- C Challenge

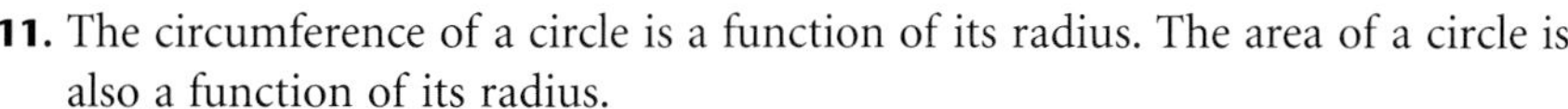

11. The circumference of a circle is a function of its radius. The area of a circle is also a function of its radius.

a. Graph the function $C = 2\pi r$ on a coordinate plane for r-values from 0 to 4.

b. On the same plane, graph the function $A = \pi r^2$ for r-values from 0 to 4.

c. Compare the shapes of your two graphs. Why does each graph have the shape it does?

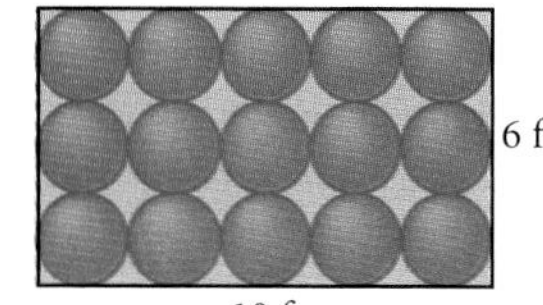

12. Circles of equal radii are packed in a rectangle as shown. If you throw a dart and hit the target, what is the probability that your dart will land inside one of the circles? 78.5%

13. Suppose you have 240 yd of fencing and want to enclose the greatest possible area with it.

a. Find the area of the largest equilateral triangle, square, and regular hexagon that you can enclose with this amount of fencing.

b. Find the area of the largest circle that you can enclose.

c. Of the four, which figure gives the greatest area for a given perimeter? Do you think this is the best possible figure?

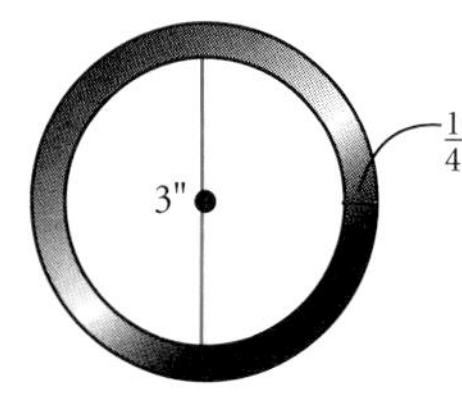

14. The figure at the right represents the cross section of a pipe $\frac{1}{4}$ in. thick, with an inside diameter of 3 in. Find the area of the shaded region. 2.55 in.^{2}

LOOK BACK

15. Prove: If a quadrilateral is a parallelogram, then a diagonal divides it into two congruent triangles. [6-2]

16. Asoka (273-232 B.C.), an emperor of the Maruya Empire in India, had sandstone pillars set up throughout the empire. The shadow cast by one of these pillars when the sun's angle of elevation is 61° is 6 m long. How tall is the pillar? [7-3] 10.82 m

MORE PRACTICE

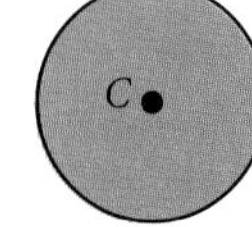

Find each of the following for ⊙C. Give your answers in exact form and as decimals rounded to the nearest hundredth.

17. If its radius is 5 ft, find its area. 25π ft^2; 78.54 ft^2

18. If its area is 36π in.^{2}, find its radius. 6 in.

19. If its area is 563 cm^2, find its circumference. $2\sqrt{563\pi}$ cm; 84.11 cm

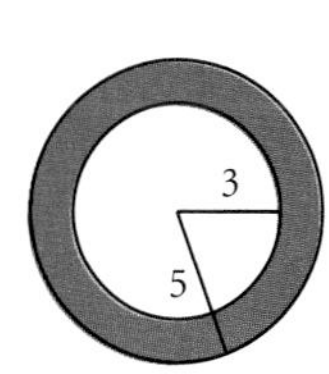

20. Find the area of the *annulus* (the shaded region) shown at the right. 16π; 50.27

Ongoing Assessment

Self-Assessment Exercises 1–9 odd, 13, 14

Embedded Assessment Try It a; Exercises 6, 8, 11, 12

Exercise Answers

Core

11. a–b.

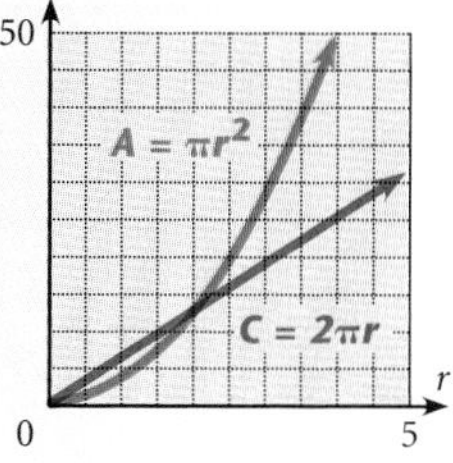

c. $C = 2\pi r$ is linear, so its graph is a line. $A = \pi r^2$ is quadratic, so its graph is a parabola.

13. a. Triangle: 2771.28 yd^2; Square: 3600 yd^2; Hexagon: 4156.92 yd^2

b. 4583.66 yd^2

c. The circle. This is the best possible figure.

Look Back

15.

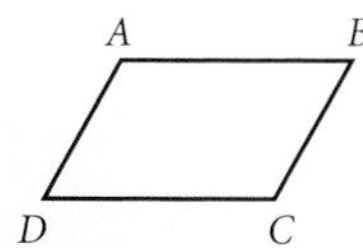

Draw $\overline{AC}$: two points determine a line.
$\overline{AB} \cong \overline{DC}$: Opposite sides are congruent.
$\overline{AD} \cong \overline{BC}$: Opposite sides are congruent.
$\overline{AC} \cong \overline{AC}$: Reflexive Property
$\triangle CAB \cong \triangle ACD$: SSS

More Math Reasoning

21. a–c. Check students' drawings.

d. About 290 cm^2

e. 314.16 cm^2

f. Make narrower rectangles

8-1

Algebra	Functions	Discrete Math	Probability	Data/Statistics

Circles, Circumference, and Area

PART E At a Glance

Objective

To use circumference and area to compare the sizes of records and compact disks.

Development

In the **Explore,** students calculate areas of records and compact disks. Then they connect the ideas of circumference and rotation by calculating the distance covered in a given time by a point on the edge of each type of recording.

First Five Minutes

Transparency FFM 8-1E

Sketch a circle and an inscribed square. If the radius of the circle is $5\sqrt{2}$ cm, find the area and circumference of the circle and the area and perimeter of the square. Give answers in exact form. **Circle: area 50π cm^2; circumference $10\pi\sqrt{2}$ cm. Square: area 100 cm^2; perimeter 40 cm.**

EXPLORE

Sound Calculations

Recommended group size: 4

The Point

To calculate areas and circumferences of circles in a real-world context.

Look and Listen...

- For students who do not understand how to use the rotation speeds to find the distances covered by the dust speck in Step 2.
- For students who do not convert the CD's radius to inches. (Note: 1 cm $\approx$ 0.3937 in.)

Ask...

- How far will the dust speck travel in one revolution? If a record turns at 78 rpm, how many revolutions does it make in two minutes?
- What fraction of a minute is 26 seconds? How can you use this to find the number of revolutions the recording makes in 26 sec?

MORE MATH REASONING

MR, C

21. The Yenri Method Seki Kowa, born in 1642 in Edo (now Tokyo), Japan, is credited with developing a calculus native to seventeenth-century Japan. This early form of calculus is known as the *yenri* (circle principle). *Yenri* was a method of finding the area of a circle. Follow the steps to get an idea of how the method works.

a. Open your compass to 10 cm, and draw a circle on a sheet of paper.

b. Draw a horizontal diameter in your circle. Mark off 1-cm lengths from the center of the circle as shown.

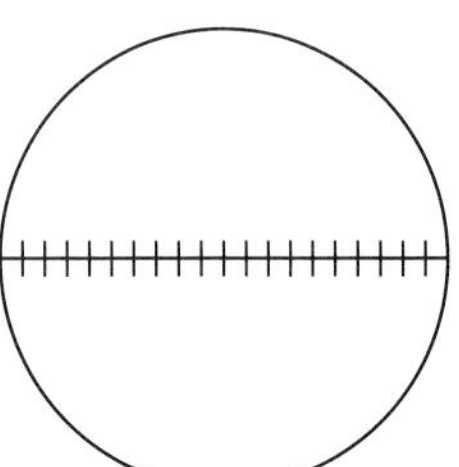

c. Draw vertical segments through each of the points marked off in **21b.** Then draw horizontal segments to form rectangles as shown.

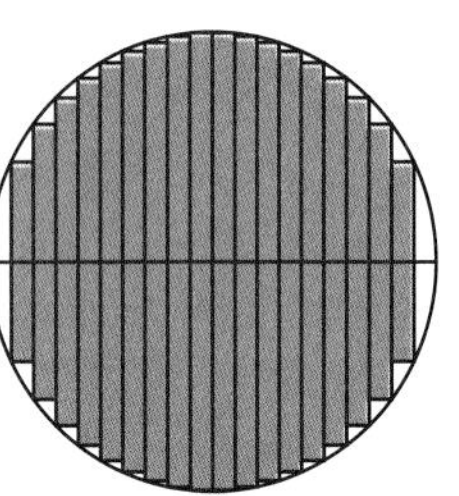

d. Each rectangle has a width of 1 cm. Measure the height of each rectangle. Then find the area of each rectangle, and add all the areas to find the approximate area of the circle.

e. Your result should be a reasonable estimate for the area of the circle. Use the formula $A = \pi r^2$ to calculate the actual area of the circle. Compare the two results.

f. How could you modify this method to get a better estimate of the area of the circle?

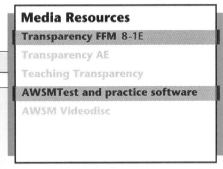

8-1 PART E Making Connections

← CONNECT → *Circles are the "shape of choice" for many real-world objects, like utility-hole covers and wheel rims. You've become familiar with some of the terms associated with circles and investigated the formulas for their circumference and area.*

Now that you've learned some of the terminology and formulas associated with circles, you can compare some characteristics of $33\frac{1}{3}$, 45, and 78 rpm (revolutions per minute) records and compact disks.

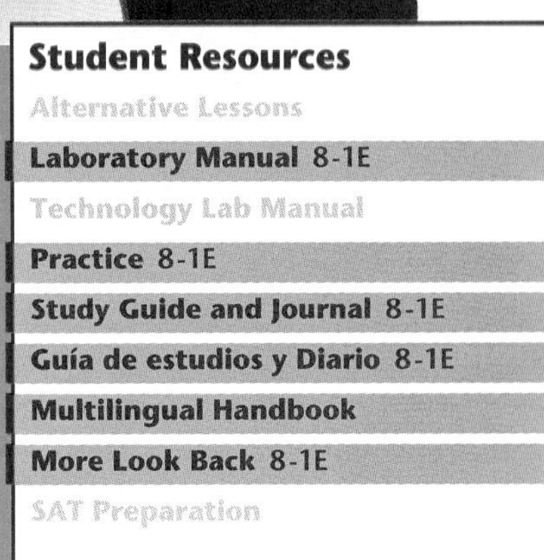

Student Resources

- Alternative Lessons
- Laboratory Manual 8-1E
- Technology Lab Manual
- Practice 8-1E
- Study Guide and Journal 8-1E
- Guía de estudios y Diario 8-1E
- Multilingual Handbook
- More Look Back 8-1E
- SAT Preparation

Media Resources

- Transparency FFM 8-1E
- Transparency AE
- Teaching Transparency
- AWSMTest and practice software
- AWSM Videodisc

EXPLORE: SOUND CALCULATIONS

The table lists some characteristics of CDs and records.

	78 rpm Record	45 rpm Single	$33\frac{1}{3}$ rpm LP	CD
Diameter	10 in.	7 in.	12 in.	12.5 cm
Speed of Rotation	78 rpm	45 rpm	$33\frac{1}{3}$ rpm	200 rpm

1. Convert the diameter of the compact disk to inches. Then calculate the area of each type of recording. Give your answers in square inches to the nearest hundredth.
2. Aretha Franklin's recording of *Respect* plays for 2 min, 26 sec. How far does a speck of dust on the edge of each type of recording travel during that time? Give answers in inches to the nearest inch. On which type of recording does the speck travel the farthest?

REFLECT

1. The diameters and circumferences of two circles may be very different. Which property of the circles is always the same? Explain.
2. Create an illustrated summary of terms associated with circles.

Self-Assessment

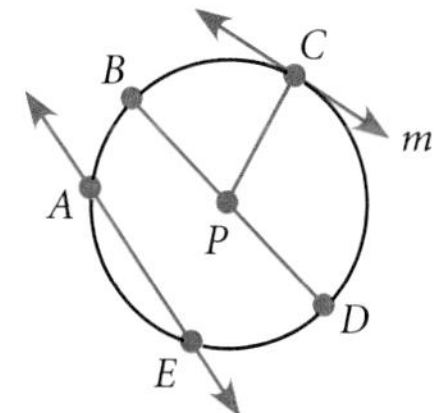

1. Name the circle at the right. ⊙P
2. Name three radii of the circle. $\overline{BP}$, $\overline{PD}$, $\overline{PC}$
3. Name a diameter of the circle. $\overline{BD}$
4. Name a secant line. $\overleftrightarrow{AE}$
5. Name a tangent to the circle, and identify the point of tangency. *m*; *C*

Vocabulary
Practice/Skills
Review
Math Reasoning
Problem Solving
Challenge

For Groups That Finish Early

A $33\frac{1}{3}$ rpm record could hold 6 times as much music as a 78 rpm. Compare their areas. If the area of the $33\frac{1}{3}$ was not 6 times as great, explain how this might be possible. **The spiral groove in the $33\frac{1}{3}$ record was tighter than that in the 78 rpm record.**

Follow Up

Ask students to share their answers for areas. Then have one student or group explain how they calculated the distances traveled by the dust speck and give their answers.

Possible Answers

1. Diameter of CD ≈ 4.92 in.

   78 rpm: ≈ 78.54 in.^{2}

   45 rpm: ≈ 38.48 in.^{2}

   $33\frac{1}{3}$ rpm: ≈ 113.10 in.^{2}

   CD: ≈ 19.01 in.^{2}

2. 78 rpm: ≈ 5963 in.

   45 rpm: ≈ 2408 in.

   $33\frac{1}{3}$ rpm: ≈ 3057 in.

   CD: ≈ 7522 in.

   The speck travels farthest on the CD.

Portfolio

Have students select items from their work that demonstrate their understanding of the material in 8-1.

You may wish to have students include an **Exercise** that involves an inscribed or circumscribed figure, a real-world problem that requires the calculation of an area or circumference, and a **Reflect** question that they found interesting.

REFLECT

Possible Answers

1. The ratio of the circumference to the diameter (or radius) of any circle is the same.
2. Terms may include *circle, center of a circle, radius, diameter, interior and exterior of a circle, concentric circles, inscribed, circumscribed, secant line, tangent line, point of tangency, tangent segment, circumference,* and π.

Algebra | Probability | Logic/Reasoning | Science/Health | Social Science/History

Circles, Circumference, and Area

Self-Assessment

Exercise Notes

13. Students calculate geometric probabilities, using inscribed and circumscribed polygons.

14. Similar to multiple-choice questions on standardized tests.

Self-Assessment Answers

13. a.

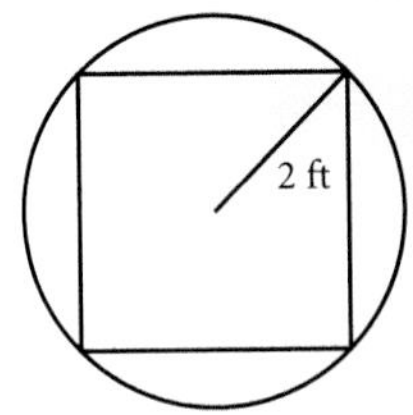

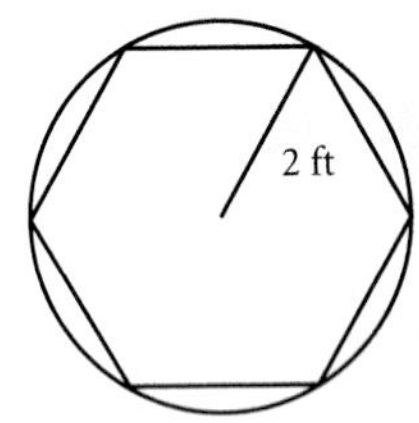

b. Square: 63.66%;
Hexagon: 82.70%

16. $\angle ABD \cong \angle BDC$: Given
$\overline{AB} \cong \overline{CD}$: Given
$\overline{DB} \cong \overline{DB}$: Reflexive Property
$\triangle ABD \cong \triangle CDB$: SAS
$\angle ADB \cong \angle CBD$: CPCTC
$\overline{AD} \parallel \overline{BC}$: Lines parallel if alternate interior angles are congruent
$\overline{AB} \parallel \overline{CD}$: Lines parallel if alternate interior angles are congruent
$ABCD$ is a parallelogram: Definition of *parallelogram*

P **In the figure at the right, $\overleftrightarrow{HF}$ is tangent to $\odot G$ at F.**

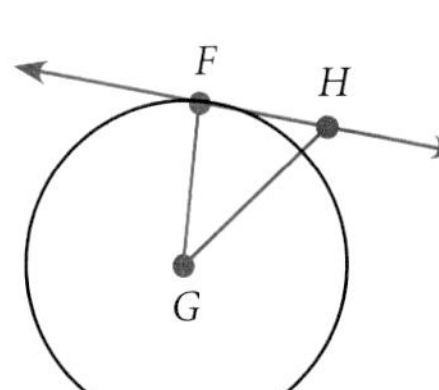

6. What is $m\angle HFG$? 90°

7. If $FG = 4$ and $HG = 5$, find HF. 3

8. If $HF = 3.7$ and $FG = 5.6$, find HG. 6.71

9. If $HF = 14.3$ and $HG = 22.6$, find FG. 17.50

10. If the radius of $\odot M$ is 57 in., find its area. $3249\pi \approx 10{,}207.03$ in.^{2}

11. If its area is 22.45 cm^2, find its radius. $r = 2.67$ cm

12. If its area is 121 m^2, find its circumference. 38.99 m

PS **13.** A square and a regular hexagon are inscribed in separate circles, each 4 ft in diameter.
a. Make an accurate sketch of each of the figures.
b. Find the probability that a randomly selected point within each circle will be inside the inscribed polygon.

PS **14.** Two semicircles are drawn inside a square as shown. What is the probability that a randomly selected point inside the square will lie in a shaded region? (a)

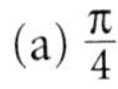
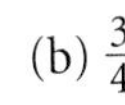

(a) $\frac{\pi}{4}$ (b) $\frac{3}{4}$ (c) $\frac{\pi}{6}$ (d) $\frac{4}{5}$ (e) $\frac{\pi}{2}$

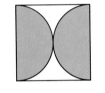

R, PS **15.** A scientist is observing a Cape Mountain zebra, an endangered species, running across a field as shown. At its closest approach, the zebra is 300 ft from the scientist. Fifteen seconds later, it is 930 ft from the scientist.
a. Find the distance CZ and the speed of the zebra in feet per second. [5-3] 880.28 ft; 58.69 ft/sec
b. Find the measure of the angle $\angle CSZ$. [7-3] 71°

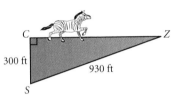

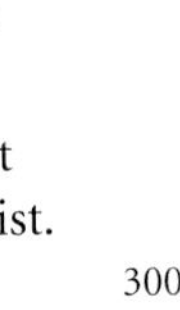
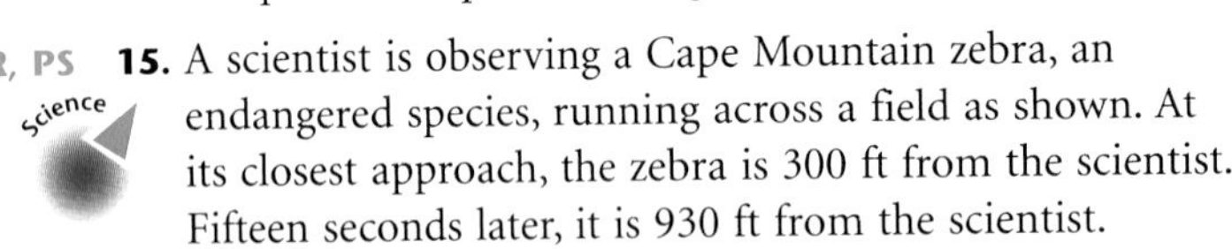

R, MR **16.** *Given:* $\angle ABD \cong \angle BDC$, and $\overline{AB} \cong \overline{CD}$.
Prove: $ABCD$ is a parallelogram. [6-2]

PS **17.** The ivory bracelet shown comes from Ardra, in what is now Benin, and probably dates from the early 1600s. Its diameter is approximately $3\frac{1}{8}$ in. Find the circumference of the bracelet. 9.82 in.

PS **18.** The diameter of a circular bike gear with center P is eighteen centimeters.
a. Find the circumference of the gear. $18\pi \approx 56.55$ cm
b. If the length of chain $\overline{MN}$ is forty-four centimeters, find the distance PN. 44.91 cm

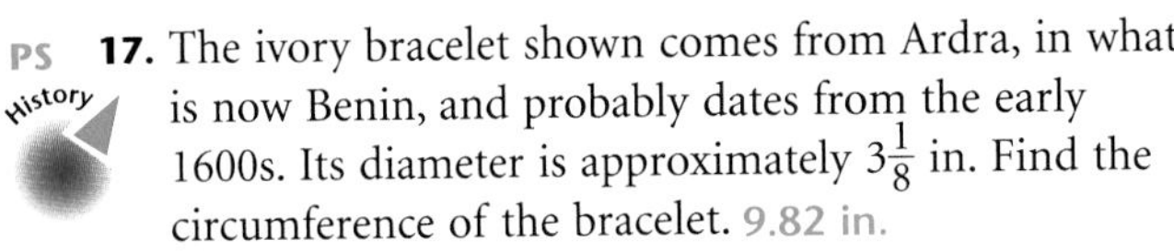
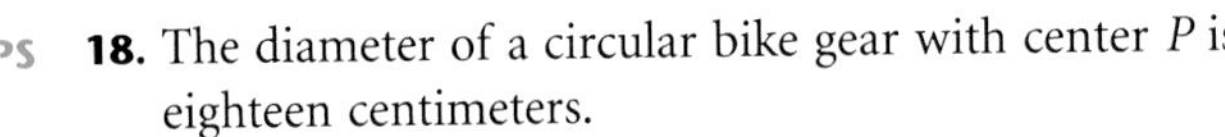
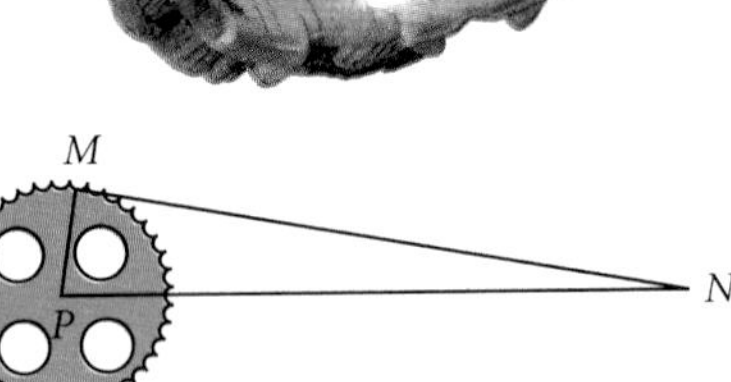

Assessment Resources
Quiz 8-1
Chapter Assessment Form A
Chapter Assessment Form B
Chapter Alternative Assessment
Mid-Year Assessment
End-of-Year Assessment
AWSMTest and practice software

Ongoing Assessment

Self-Assessment Self-Assessment Exercises

Embedded Assessment Explore Steps 1, 2; Refle
1, 2

8-1 Part A Explore

1. See method in **Exercise** 25, page 446.

2. Equilateral triangle: Construct the vertices for a regular hexagon; connect every other vertex. Square: Use paper-folding to make a diameter of the circle; fold again to find a second diameter perpendicular to the first. The intersections of the folds and the circle determine a square. 12-gon: Construct the vertices for a regular hexagon; fold consecutive vertices onto each other three times to find the other six vertices.

3. The regular 12-gon's area and perimeter are closest to those of the circle.

8-2

Angles, Arcs, and Chords

SUPERLESSON AT A GLANCE

Superlesson Goal

Students will investigate arcs and chords of circles and use proportional thinking to find areas of sectors and arc lengths.

Management Guide

	Topic	Objectives	Key Terms	New Ideas	Materials
Part A	Arcs and Central Angles	To explore central angles and measures of major and minor arcs.	Central angle, minor arc, major arc, semi-circle, arc measure, congruent arcs	Central angles of circles. Arcs and arc measure.	**Student** Compass, straightedge, protractor **Teacher** Angle-maker transparency, protractor transparency
Part B	Arc Length and Sectors	To use proportional thinking to find areas of sectors and lengths of arcs.	Sector	Sectors of a circle. Arc length. Using proportions to find sector area and arc length.	**Student** Protractor **Teacher** Globe, world map transparency, angle-maker transparency, protractor transparency
Part C	Radius-Chord Conjectures	To explore relationships between chords and radii.	Chord	The perpendicular bisector of a chord contains the circle's center. If a radius bisects a chord that is not a diameter, it is perpendicular to the chord; if it is perpendicular, it bisects the chord.	**Student** Compass, ruler, scissors, protractor
Part D	Making Connections	To use proportional thinking and arc measures to duplicate Eratosthenes' measurement of the earth's circumference.	In Making Connections, students apply and synthesize key terms and new ideas.		

Pacing Chart (45-Minute Periods)

	Comprehensive Course	Core Course	Informal Course
Part A	1	1	1
Part B	1	1	2
Part C	1	1	2
Part D	1	1	1
TOTAL periods for Superlesson	4	4	6

NCTM Standards

Mathematics as Problem Solving

Mathematics as Communication

Mathematics as Reasoning

Mathematical Connections

Geometry from a Synthetic Perspective

Statistics

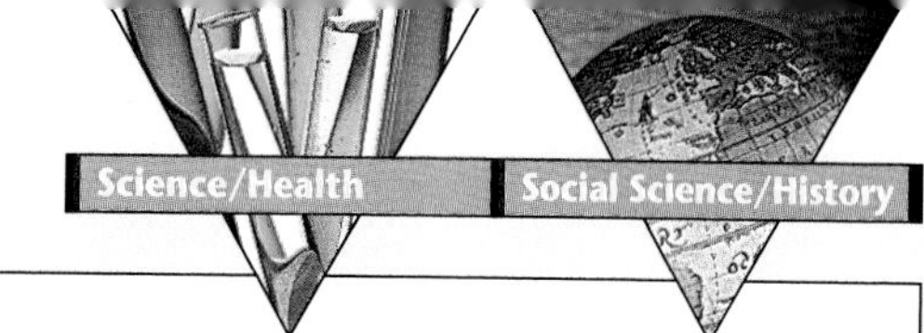

8-2 Angles, Arcs, and Chords

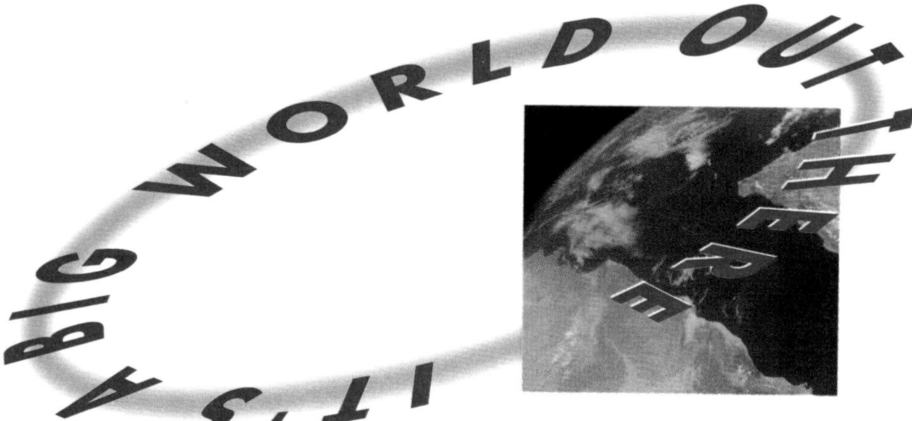

IT'S A BIG WORLD OUT THERE

How do we know how large the earth really is? If calculating the size of the earth seems difficult now, imagine how impossible it must have seemed before anyone had been around the world—or even across the Atlantic Ocean.

Eratosthenes, an ancient geometer, mathematician, geographer, and poet, made one of the earliest calculations of the circumference of the earth. His calculations differ from the present measurement by less than one percent!

Eratosthenes was born in Cyrene (in what is now Libya) around 274 B.C. His nickname, "Beta"(the second letter of the Greek alphabet), may have shown that Eratosthenes was considered the second great thinker of ancient times, after Plato.

In mathematics, Eratosthenes is best known for his prime number "sieve." He started by writing a list of several consecutive whole numbers greater than 1. Next, he went through the list and crossed off all numbers greater than 2 that were multiples of 2:

2, 3, ~~4,~~ 5, ~~6,~~ 7, ~~8,~~ 9, ~~10,~~ 11, ~~12,~~ 13, ~~14,~~ 15, ~~16~~....

Then he found the next number that was not crossed off—in this case, 3—and crossed off all its multiples greater than itself:

2, 3, ~~4,~~ 5, ~~6,~~ 7, ~~8,~~ ~~9,~~ ~~10,~~ 11, ~~12,~~ 13, ~~14,~~ ~~15~~....

The process continued in this way. When it was finished, the numbers that were not crossed off were prime numbers.

1. **After crossing off all the multiples of 3 on the list, which multiples would Eratosthenes have crossed off next? Why?**

2. **Explain why the sieve of Eratosthenes works.**

3. **Eratosthenes calculated the circumference of the earth by *indirect measurement*. Explain what you think is meant by this term.**

More About the Size of the Earth

The problem of finding the distance around the earth, which students explore in 8-2 Part D, is equivalent to finding the length of a 1° arc of a great circle of the earth. The actual value for this measurement is approximately 69 miles. Eratosthenes, using his remarkably accurate measurement of the earth's circumference, arrived at a value of $694\frac{4}{9}$ stadia (about 69.4 miles) to the degree. Around 150 B.C., Ptolemy arrived at a value of only 500 stadia to a degree.

Where Are We Now?

In 8-1, students learned terminology related to circles and calculated circle areas and circumferences. In Chapter 7, they worked with ratios and proportions when investigating similarity.

Where Are We Going?

In 8-2, students will explore central angles and arcs of circles. They will use proportional thinking to calculate areas of sectors and lengths of arcs. Students will also investigate relationships between radii and chords of circles.

Proportional thinking is important throughout this course. Arc measures will be of particular importance in Chapter 12, when students calculate distances to planets and stars.

Possible Answers

1. He would have crossed off multiples of 5. (It is not necessary to check for multiples of 4, since all of them must be multiples of 2.)
2. Any number that has factors other than 1 and itself is crossed off, leaving only the prime numbers.
3. An indirect measurement is a measurement that is not done directly with a measuring tool, but is a result of calculations based on other measurements.

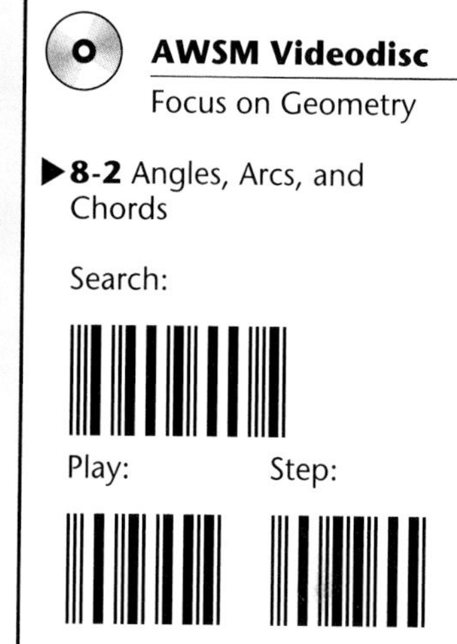

AWSM Videodisc
Focus on Geometry
▶8-2 Angles, Arcs, and Chords
Search:
Play:
Step:

PART A At a Glance

Objective

To explore central angles and measures of major and minor arcs.

Development

In the **Explore,** students make a circle graph. This graph uses the concept of a central angle and the fact that the sum of the measures of the central angles add to 360°.

Then, the formal definition of *central angle* is presented. Students see how arcs of circles are defined and measured.

Suggested Materials

Student Compass, straightedge, protractor

Teacher Angle-maker transparency, protractor transparency

Key Terms

Central angle, minor arc, major arc, semicircle, arc measure, congruent arcs

First Five Minutes

Transparency FFM 8-2A

Study the circle graph on p. 564, and give a written estimate of the percentage of the total land area each continent takes up. **Asia: 30%; Africa 20%; North America 16%; South America 12%; Antarctica 10%; Europe 7%; Australia/Oceania 6% (numbers do not add to 100% due to rounding).**

Motivate

Ask...

- How is a circle graph used to display data?

EXPLORE

A Slice of Data

Recommended group size: 4

The Point

To create a circle graph. Students use the concept of central angles intuitively in making the graph.

8-2 PART A Arcs and Central Angles

← CONNECT → *You already know a great deal about angles in polygons. Now you will work with angles and arcs in circles.*

The circle graph shows the land areas of the continents.

Land Area of Continents

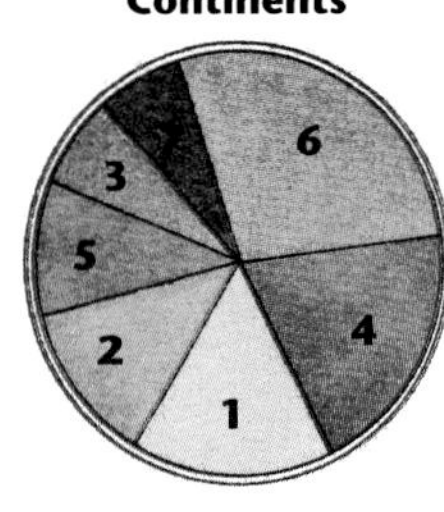

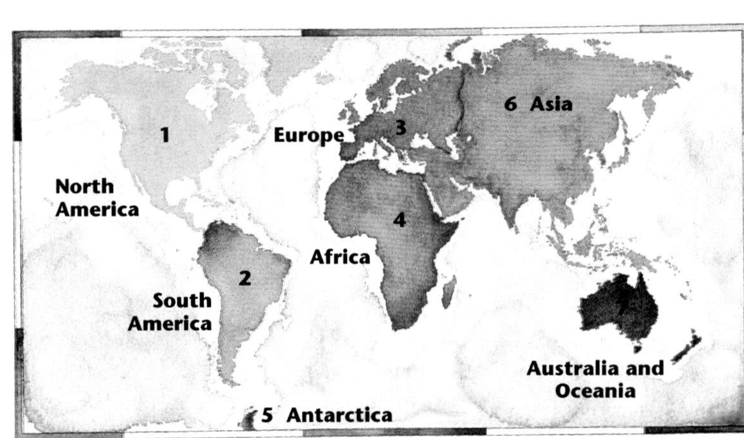

EXPLORE: A SLICE OF DATA

MATERIALS

Compass
Straightedge
Protractor

1. Choose a topic on which to collect data. Use a question from the following list, or use one suggested by your teacher.
   - How many pens and pencils do you have with you right now?
   - How many brothers and sisters do you have?
   - How many hours do you sleep per night?
2. Take a survey. Have each person answer the question, and tally the responses as shown.
3. To make your circle graph, you'll have to find the angle measure of the "pie piece" that represents each response. Calculate and record the angle measure of the pie piece for each response. How did you calculate the angle measures?
4. Make a circle graph showing the frequency of each response. Where did you locate the vertices of the angles in your graph?

Tips from Teachers

If you have students working in groups of four, you may want to have each student obtain data from the students in one or two other groups, and then have all four students work together to make the graph.

The angles in a circle graph and the **arcs** (parts of a circle) they cut off have special names.

When you make a circle graph, the vertices of all of the angles are at the center of the circle. These angles are called **central angles.** Any central angle divides a circle into two arcs.

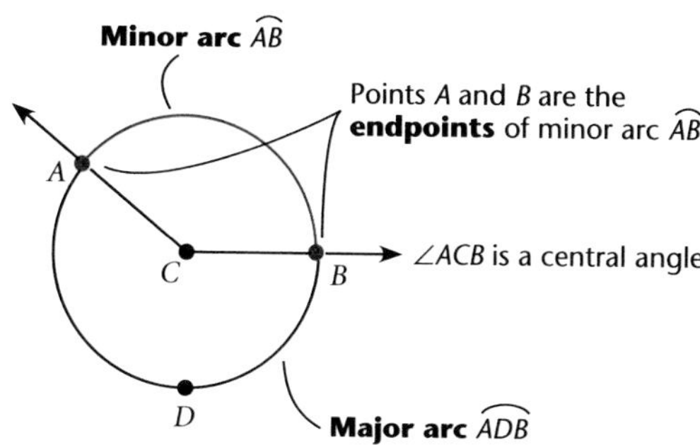

We name a minor arc by its endpoints. Notice that we need to use *three* points to name a major arc. If the endpoints of an arc lie on the diameter of a circle, then the arc is a **semicircle.** Like major arcs, semicircles are named with three letters.

You know that a complete circle has 360°. The measures of the arcs of a circle are based on this idea.

The **measure of a minor arc** is equal to the measure of its central angle. Central angle $\angle WYX$ intercepts minor arc $\overset{\frown}{WX}$, so $m\overset{\frown}{WX} = m\angle WYX = 80°$.

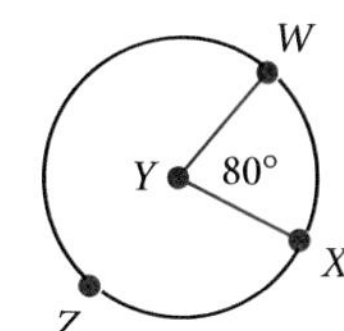

The **measure of a major arc** is 360° minus the measure of its minor arc. $m\overset{\frown}{XZW} = 360° - m\overset{\frown}{WX} = 280°$.

The **measure of any semicircle** is 180°.

TRY IT

Find each arc measure in $\odot L$.

a. $m\overset{\frown}{MN}$ 54°

b. $m\overset{\frown}{MPN}$ 306°

c. $m\overset{\frown}{PQN}$ 180°

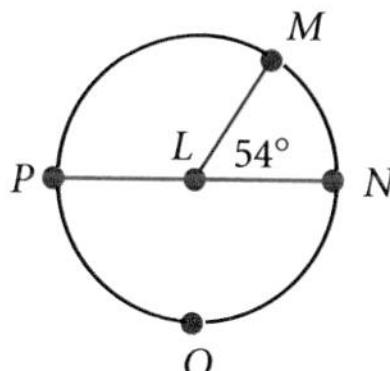

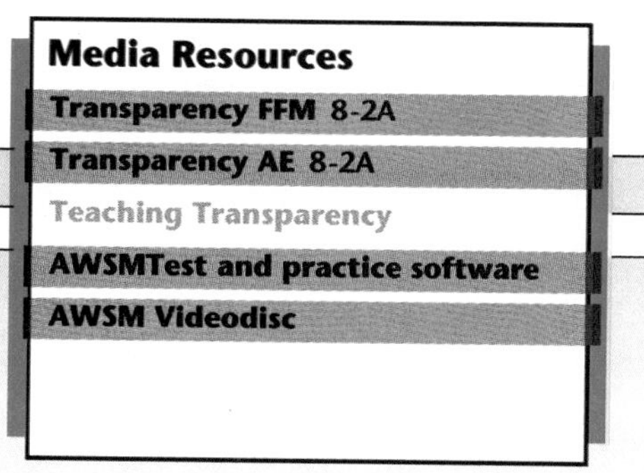

Student Resources

- Alternative Lessons 8-2A
- Laboratory Manual 8-2A
- Technology Lab Manual
- Practice 8-2A
- Study Guide and Journal 8-2A
- Guía de estudios y Diario 8-2A
- Multilingual Handbook
- More Look Ahead 8-2A
- SAT Preparation

Media Resources

- Transparency FFM 8-2A
- Transparency AE 8-2A
- Teaching Transparency
- AWSMTest and practice software
- AWSM Videodisc

Look and Listen...

- For students who do not understand how to find the central angle measures for their graph.

Ask...

- What is the sum of the measures of the angles in the circle graph? How can you figure out how much of this total should be given to each measure?
- Can you write a proportion that will help you?

For Groups That Finish Early

Make a bar graph to display the information shown in your circle graph.

Follow Up

Ask each student or group to display their graph. Have one of them explain how they calculated their angle measures.

Possible Answers

3. Angle measures can be found by solving the proportion

$$\frac{\text{no. with this response}}{\text{total number}} = \frac{\text{angle measure}}{360°},$$

or by calculating the fraction of students with the given response in decimal form and multiplying by 360°.

4. Vertices of the angles should be at the center of the circle.

Angles, Arcs, and Chords

ALTERNATE EXAMPLES

Find each arc measure.

1. $m\widehat{XY}$

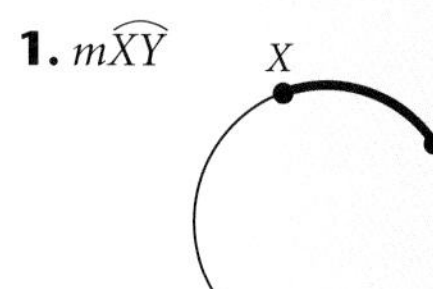

$m\widehat{XY} = 360° - 286° = 74°$

2. $m\widehat{AB}$

A
B
81°

$m\widehat{AB} = 180° - 81° = 99°$

3. $m\widehat{JKL}$

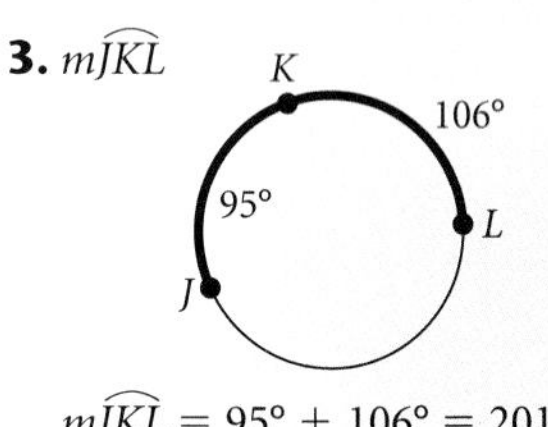

$m\widehat{JKL} = 95° + 106° = 201°$

Journal

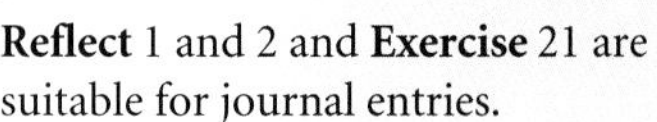

Reflect 1 and 2 and **Exercise** 21 are suitable for journal entries.

When two arcs are adjacent, you can find the measure of the larger arc they determine simply by adding their measures.

ARC-ADDITION THEOREM

The measure of two adjacent, nonoverlapping arcs is the sum of the measures of the two arcs. That is, if C is on arc $\widehat{AB}$, then $m\widehat{AB} = m\widehat{AC} + m\widehat{CB}$.

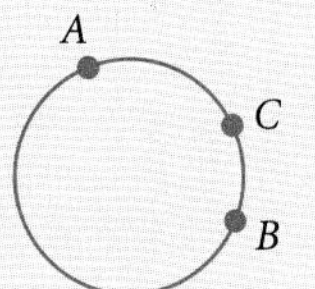

EXAMPLES

Find each arc measure.

1. $m\widehat{RST}$

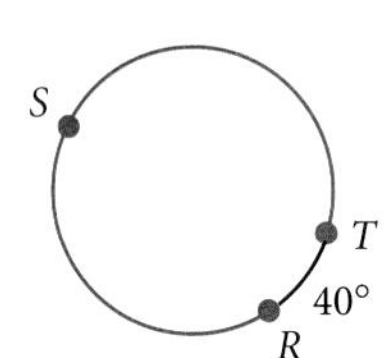

$m\widehat{RST} = 360° - 40°$
$= 320°$

2. $m\widehat{DE}$

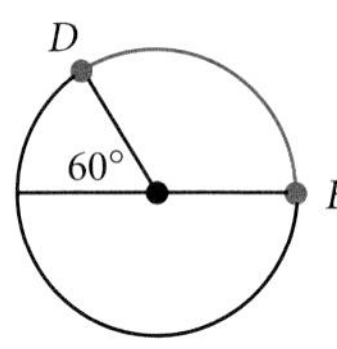

$m\widehat{DE} = 180° - 60°$
$= 120°$

3. $m\widehat{HGF}$

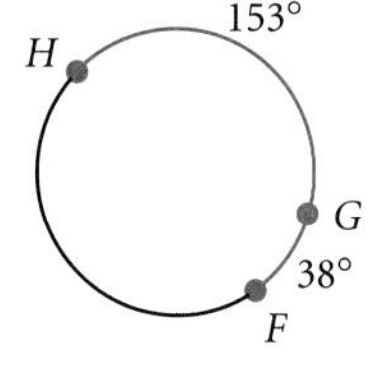

$m\widehat{HGF} = 153° + 38°$
$= 191°$

Like other geometric figures, arcs of circles can be congruent. Consider the following definition.

DEFINITION

Congruent arcs are arcs in the same circle (or congruent circles) that have the same measure.

REFLECT

1. Explain why the words "in the same circle (or congruent circles)" are needed in the definition of congruent arcs.
2. Explain why the measure of a major arc is equal to 360° minus the measure of its minor arc. Why is the measure of a semicircle 180°?
3. What is the range of possible measures for a minor arc? a major arc? Explain.

Research Note

Research suggests that carefully planned activities and efforts to involve students lead to understanding.... Since individual learners have different ways of making sense out of ideas, it is not sufficient for a learner to listen to and practice the teacher's ideas. Each student must be actively involved in the learning process. (Patricia S. Wilson, *Research Ideas for the Classroom: High School Mathematics,* NCTM Research Interpretation Project, Patricia S. Wilson, ed., p. xi. © 1993 NCTM.)

Exercises

CORE

Getting Started **Use ⊙D for each of the following.**

1. Name two central angles. Possible answer: $\angle ADB$, $\angle BDC$

2. Name two minor arcs. $\widehat{AB}$, $\widehat{BC}$

3. Name two major arcs. $\widehat{BAC}$, $\widehat{ACB}$

4. Name a semicircle. $\widehat{ABC}$

5. Find $m\widehat{AB}$. 45°

6. Find $m\widehat{ACB}$. 315°

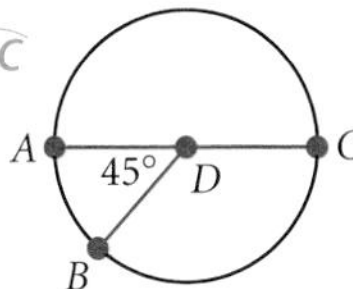

Find each arc measure.

7. $m\widehat{GFH}$ 217°

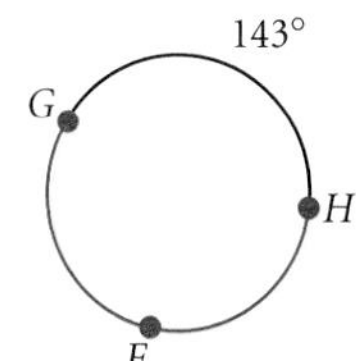

8. $m\widehat{JK}$ 128°

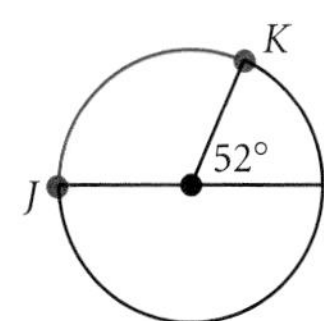

9. $m\widehat{LMN}$ 195°

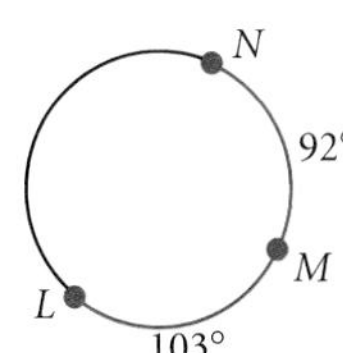

Find each arc measure.

10. $m\widehat{HI}$ 30°

11. $m\widehat{KJ}$ 90°

12. $m\widehat{HGI}$ 330°

13. $m\widehat{KJI}$ 180°

14. $m\widehat{GI}$ 105°

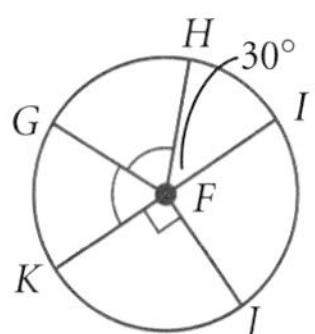

What fractional part of a circle is each of the following arc measures?

15. 90° $\frac{1}{4}$

16. 270° $\frac{3}{4}$

17. 120° $\frac{1}{3}$

What is the arc measure of each of the following fractional parts of a circle?

18. $\frac{1}{6}$ 60°

19. $\frac{7}{12}$ 210°

20. $\frac{15}{36}$ 150°

21. Draw a spinner for a game that has the correct probability for each of the following outcomes. Explain why your spinner works.

- Ahead 1 space 35%
- Pick a card 20%
- Ahead 2 spaces 20%
- Back 1 space 15%
- Lose a turn 10%

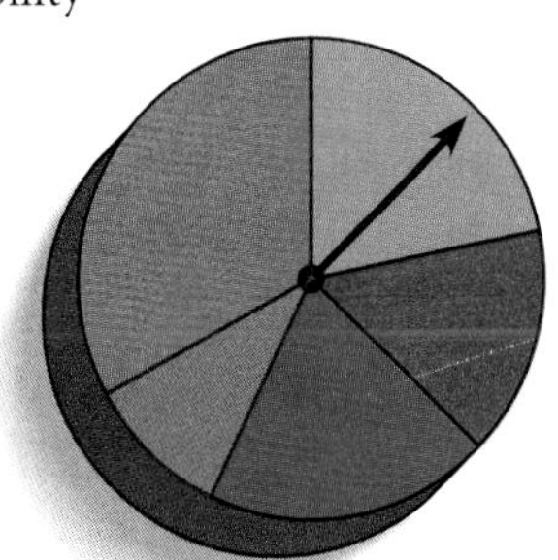

REFLECT

Possible Answers

1. Arcs with the same measure in different-sized circles have different sizes.

2. The sum of the central angles of a circle is 360°, so the sum of the measures of a major arc and its minor arc must be 360°. Therefore, the measure of the major arc is 360° minus the measure of its minor arc. The measure of a semicircle is half of 360°, or 180°.

3. Minor arc: $0° < x < 180°$. Major arc: $180° < x < 360°$. The minor arc's measure must be in this range because it is equal to an angle measure. The major arc is in the specified range because it is the difference between 360° and the measure of a minor arc.

Part A Exercises

Exercise Notes

Core

23. Students make a circle graph, using real-world data.

Look Ahead

These exercises look ahead to calculations of arc length and sector area in 8-2 Part B.

More Math Reasoning

39. Students explain why the perpendicular bisector construction works.

40–42. Deal with *angular velocity*, an important concept in physics.

Exercise Answers

Core

21. Possible answer:

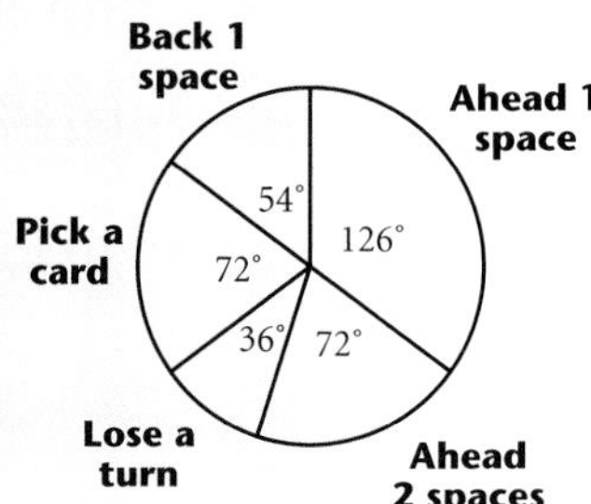

The area of each wedge is proportional to the measure of the corresponding central angle.

Key

Vocabulary
Practice/Skills
Review
Math Reasoning
Problem Solving
Challenge

Ongoing Assessment

Self-Assessment Exercises 1–19 odd, 22, 24

Embedded Assessment Reflect 2; Exercises 8, 12, 20, 23

Angles, Arcs, and Chords

22. $\triangle PQR$ is isosceles, so $\angle PQR \cong \angle PRQ$; $m\angle QPR = 100°$; Sum of $\angle$'s in $\triangle PQR = 180° = 100° + 2x$; $m\angle PQR = m\angle PRQ = 40°$

23.

Social Security	321	80.1°
Defense	307	76.6°
Medicare	213	53.1°
Interest	200	49.9°
Income security	196	48.9°
Commerce	55	13.7°
Other	151	37.7°
Total	1443	360.0°

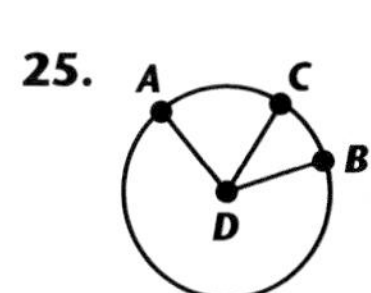

25.

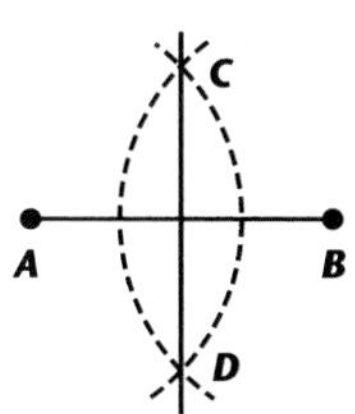

Given: C is on $\widehat{AB}$.
Prove: $m\widehat{AB} = m\widehat{AC} + m\widehat{CB}$
$m\angle ADB = m\angle ADC + m\angle CDB$, by the Angle Addition Postulate. By the definition of *measure of a minor arc*, $m\angle ADB = m\widehat{AB}$, $m\angle ADC = m\widehat{AC}$, and $m\angle CDB = m\widehat{CB}$. By substitution, $m\widehat{AB} = m\widehat{AC} + m\widehat{CB}$.

More Math Reasoning

39. Possible answer:

C
A B
D

Construction works since the radii of the two arcs are equal. The intersection points and *A* and *B* form a rhombus, where the diagonals are perpendicular bisectors of each other.

MR **22.** Find $m\angle PQR$ and $m\angle PRQ$ in the figure at the right. Explain your reasoning.

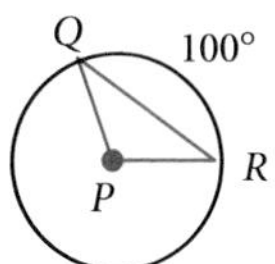

P **23.** Draw a circle graph for the given data in the following table. Below your graph, list the measure of the central angle for each data category. (Source: *The 1993 Information Please Almanac.*)

Expenditures of the United States Federal Government in 1992 (in billions of dollars)	
• Social Security and veterans' benefits	321
• Defense	307
• Medicare and health	213
• Interest (on national debt, etc.)	200
• Income security (unemployment, etc.)	196
• Commerce and housing	55
• Other (education, transportation, cost of government, etc.)	151

P **24.** Solve for x in the figure at the right. $x = 44$

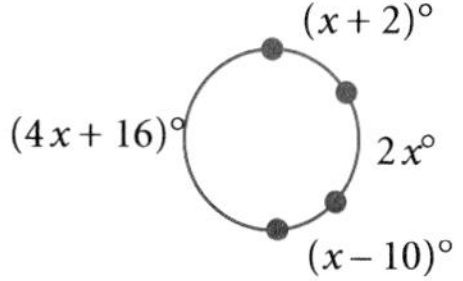

MR **25.** Prove the Arc-Addition Theorem. (Hint: Use the Angle-Addition Postulate.)

LOOK AHEAD

PS **26.** A phone company worker is wrapping telephone cable around a 5-ft-diameter storage spool. To the nearest hundredth of a foot, what is the length of cable needed to go halfway around the spool? 7.85 ft

PS **27. Pi or Pie?** An apple pie was baked in a tin with a nine-inch diameter.

a. What is the area of the pie? 63.62 in.^{2}

b. If the pie is cut into four equal wedge-shaped pieces, what is the area of each? 15.90 in.^{2}

c. If the pie is cut into six equal wedges, what is the area of each? 10.60 in.^{2}

d. Describe how you calculated your answers to **27b** and **27c.** $\frac{1}{4}$ or $\frac{1}{6}$ of the pie means $\frac{1}{4}$ or $\frac{1}{6}$ of the area.

Key

V Vocabulary
P Practice/Skills
R Review
MR Math Reasoning
PS Problem Solving
C Challenge

MORE PRACTICE

Find each arc measure.

28. $m\widehat{VW}$ 70°

29. $m\widehat{UV}$ 65°

30. $m\widehat{TYW}$ 180°

31. $m\widehat{VWT}$ 250°

32. $m\widehat{UW}$ 135°

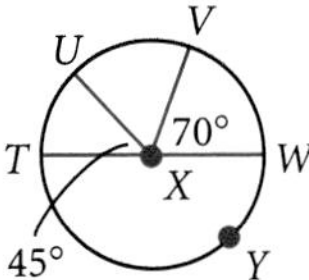

Find each arc measure.

33. $m\widehat{DF}$ 176°

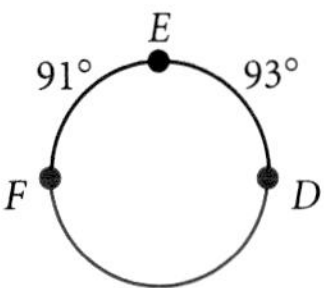

34. $m\widehat{GHI}$ 260°

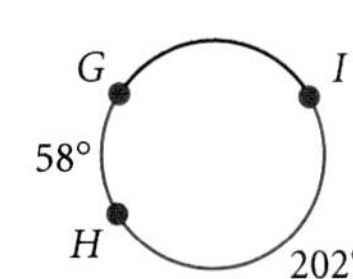

35. $m\widehat{JK}$ 78°

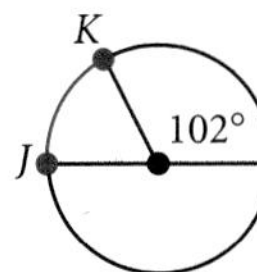

MORE MATH REASONING

Find the measure of the arc of a circle cut off by one side of each regular inscribed polygon.

36. 90°

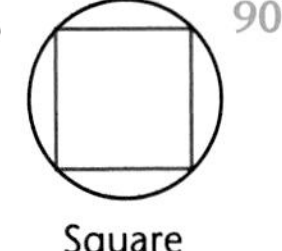

Square

37. 60°

Hexagon

38. 45°

Octagon

39. Sketch a segment $\overline{AB}$, and construct its perpendicular bisector $\overleftrightarrow{CD}$. Then use your knowledge of circles to explain why this construction works.

The *angular velocity* of a rotating object is the measure of the arc it turns through in a given amount of time. Find the angular velocity, in degrees per second, of each object.

40. the second hand on a clock 6°/sec

41. a speck of dust on the outside of a record rotating at 45 rpm 270°/sec

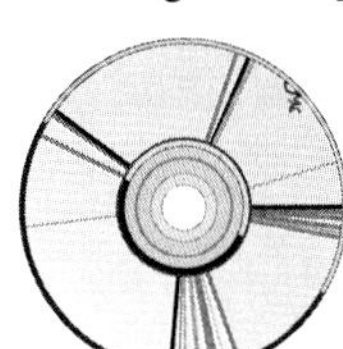

42. a person on the earth's surface 0.004167°/sec

PART B At a Glance

Objective

To use proportional thinking to find areas of sectors and lengths of arcs.

Development

First, students see the definition of a sector of a circle. Then, an **Example** shows how to use proportions to find the area of a sector and the length of an arc.

In the **Explore,** students use proportions to calculate arc lengths on the earth's surface.

Suggested Materials

Student Protractor

Teacher Globe, world map transparency, angle-maker transparency, protractor transparency

Key Terms

Sector

First Five Minutes

Transparency FFM 8-2B

Solve each proportion. Where necessary, round answers to the nearest tenth.

1. $\frac{90}{360} = \frac{x}{24}$ 6
2. $\frac{24}{360} = \frac{x}{35}$ 2.3
3. $\frac{7}{12} = \frac{18}{x}$ 30.9

Motivate

Ask...

- Suppose you know the radius of a circle graph and the measure of each central angle. How could you find the area of each "piece" of the graph? **Find the total area. Use central angles to find the fraction each piece represents. Use proportions to find the area it covers.**

ALTERNATE EXAMPLES

Transparency AE 8-2B

8-2 PART B Arc Length and Sectors

← CONNECT → ***You know how to find the circumference and area of an entire circle. Now you will use proportional thinking to find arc lengths and areas of portions of circles.***

Central angles cut the circumference of a circle into arcs. They also cut the interior of the circle into wedge-shaped regions. You can use proportions to find the **arc lengths** and the areas of these regions.

DEFINITION

A **sector** of a circle is a region formed by two radii and an arc of a circle. ABC is a sector of $\odot B$.

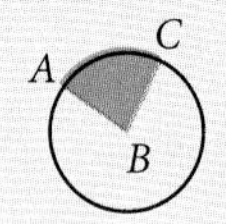

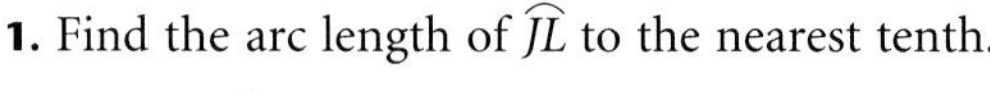

EXAMPLES

In the figure at the right, $\angle JKL$ is a central angle of $\odot K$.

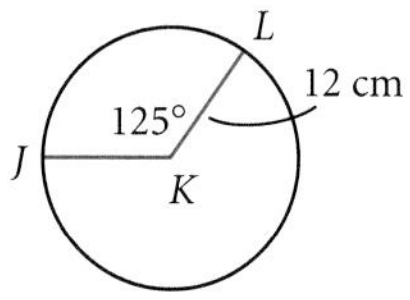

(Figure: circle K with points J, L; central angle 125°; radius 12 cm)

1. Find the arc length of $\overset{\frown}{JL}$ to the nearest tenth.

The arc $\overset{\frown}{JL}$ covers 125° of the total 360° in $\odot K$. Thus, 125 is to 360 as the length of $\overset{\frown}{JL}$ is to the circumference (total arc length) of the circle.

$$\frac{125}{360} = \frac{\text{length } \overset{\frown}{JL}}{\text{circumference } \odot K} = \frac{\text{length } \overset{\frown}{JL}}{75.4}$$

The circumference of $\odot K$ is $2(12)\pi \approx 75.4$.

$$360 \times \text{length } \overset{\frown}{JL} = 75.4 \times 125 = 9425.0$$

$$\text{length } \overset{\frown}{JL} = \frac{9425}{360} \approx 26.2 \text{ cm}$$

2. Find the area of sector JKL to the nearest tenth.

The ratio of the area of sector JKL to the area of $\odot K$ is equal to the ratio of $m\angle JKL$ to 360°.

$$\frac{\text{area sector } JKL}{\text{area } \odot K} = \frac{\text{area sector } JKL}{452.4} = \frac{125}{360}$$

The area of $\odot K$ is $\pi r^2 = \pi(12)^2 \approx 452.4$.

$$360 \times \text{area sector } JKL = 56{,}550$$

$$\text{area sector } JKL \approx 157.1 \text{ cm}^2$$

History Connection

According to V. Frederick Rickey, Columbus, in planning his first voyage, did not use Eratosthenes' value for the circumference of the earth, but the smaller estimate given by Ptolemy. This and other errors led him to estimate a distance of only 2400 nautical miles to Asia. The actual value is 10,600 nautical miles. (V. Frederick Rickey, "How Columbus Encountered America," *Mathematics Magazine,* Vol. 65, No. 4, October 1992, p. 219–225.)

1. What is the difference between the length of an arc and the degree measure of an arc?

In the following Explore, you will use proportions to find arc lengths on the earth's surface.

EXPLORE: A TRIP THROUGH AFRICA

MATERIALS

Protractor

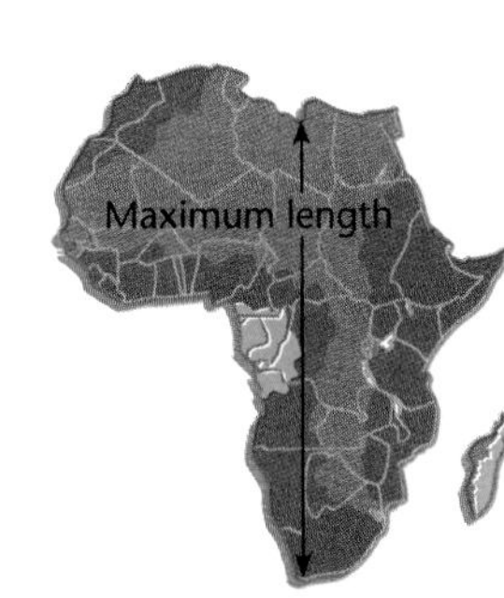

Suppose you want to find the maximum north-south length of the African continent, as shown on the map. The lower figure on the right shows a scale drawing of the earth, including North America, South America, and part of Africa. Point C is the center of the disk representing the earth.

1. The rays on the map go from the center of the circle through the northernmost and southernmost points of Africa on the circumference of the circle. Use a protractor to measure the angle formed.
2. The circumference of the earth is close to 40,000 km. Use this value to find the maximum north-south length of Africa in kilometers.
3. What must be true about the position of Africa in the figure in order to make the calculation work?

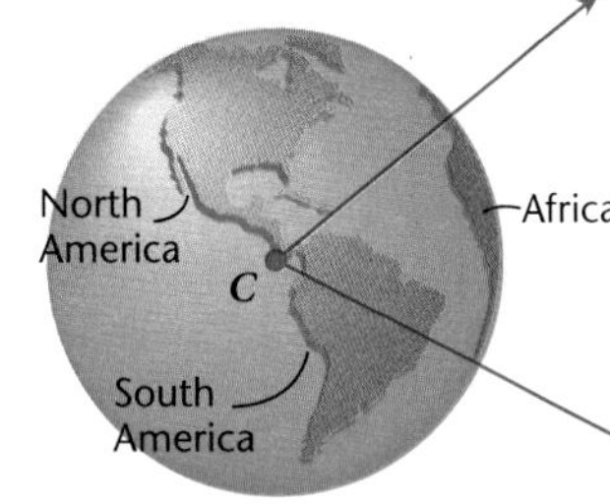

TRY IT

In $\odot C$, $m\widehat{AB} = 103°$, and $AC = 20$ in.

a. Find the area of sector ACB to the nearest tenth.
b. Find the length of arc $\widehat{AB}$ to the nearest tenth.
c. If the circumference of a circle is 21π, what is the length of a 30° arc?

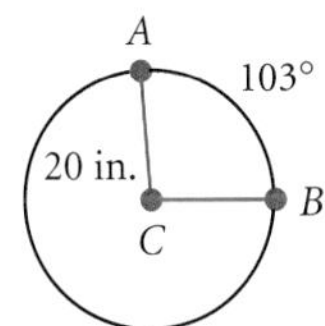

a. 359.5 in.^{2}
b. 36.0 in.
c. $\frac{21}{12}\pi = \frac{7}{4}\pi$

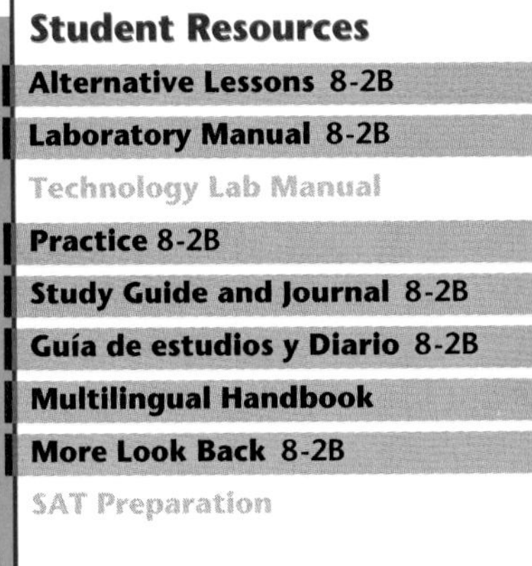

Student Resources
- Alternative Lessons 8-2B
- Laboratory Manual 8-2B
- Technology Lab Manual
- Practice 8-2B
- Study Guide and Journal 8-2B
- Guía de estudios y Diario 8-2B
- Multilingual Handbook
- More Look Back 8-2B
- SAT Preparation

Media Resources
- Transparency FFM 8-2B
- Transparency AE 8-2B
- Teaching Transparency
- AWSMTest and practice software
- AWSM Videodisc

Possible Answer

1. The length of an arc is the distance along the circle between its endpoints. Arc length is measured in linear units. The measure of an arc is given in degrees. It represents the portion of the 360° that the arc covers.

EXPLORE

A Trip Through Africa

Recommended group size: 4

The Point

To use proportional thinking to calculate lengths of an arc on the earth's surface.

Look and Listen...

- For students who do not realize that they are looking for an arc length.
- For students who have set up their proportion incorrectly.

Ask...

- If you think of the edge of the earth as a circle, what does the length of Africa represent?
- Is your answer reasonable?

For Groups That Finish Early

The maximum north-south distance of Argentina is approximately 3600 km. What is the measure of this arc on a great circle of the earth? About 32.4°

Follow Up

Ask students to share their answers to Step 2. Have them calculate the average answer and the range of answers, and ask them what may have caused the variation in the answers.

Possible Answers

1. Approximately 65°
2. About 7220 km
3. The part of Africa with the maximum north-south length must be on the circle itself.

Angles, Arcs, and Chords

Journal 

Reflect 1 and 2 and **Exercise** 9 are suitable for journal entries.

REFLECT

Possible Answers

1. A central angle determines both a sector of a circle and a minor arc on the circle. The ratio of the measure of the central angle to the total of 360° is equal to both the ratio of the area of the sector to the total area and the ratio of the length of the arc to the total circumference.
2. A right angle cuts off $\frac{1}{4}$ of the circle, so the length of the minor arc should be $\frac{1}{4}$ of 20π, or 5π, not 4π.

Part B Exercises

Exercise Notes

Core

9. Students calculate areas of *segments* of circles.

12. Students need to realize that when the cord of the mower becomes blocked by a corner of the house, the radius of the sector the mower can reach changes.

More Math Reasoning

21. Students may be surprised to find that circular sprinklers cannot water a square field without leaving some areas unwatered or "double-watered."

Exercise Answers

Core

1. a. $A = 25\pi \approx 78.54$ in.^{2}; $C = 10\pi \approx 31.42$ in.

b.

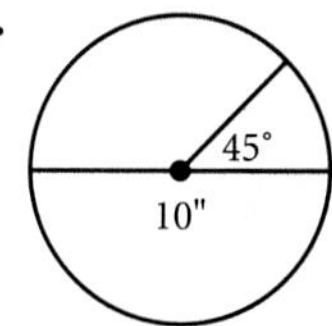

c. 9.8 in.^{2} **d.** 3.9 in.

CIRCLE PROPORTIONS

In $\odot Y$, with central angle $\angle XYZ$, all of the following ratios are equal.

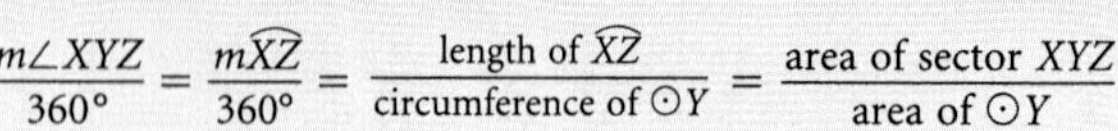

$$\frac{m\angle XYZ}{360°} = \frac{m\widehat{XZ}}{360°} = \frac{\text{length of } \widehat{XZ}}{\text{circumference of } \odot Y} = \frac{\text{area of sector } XYZ}{\text{area of } \odot Y}$$

REFLECT

1. Explain why all of the circle ratios shown above are equal.
2. Give a convincing argument explaining why the information shown in the figure at the right cannot be correct.

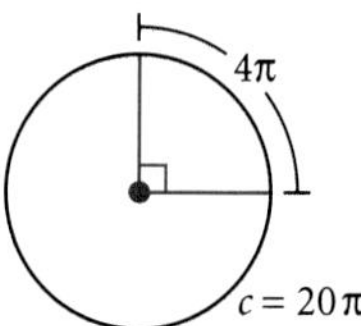

Exercises

CORE

P **1. Getting Started** Suppose a pie has a 10-in. diameter.

a. Draw a sketch of the pie. Calculate its area and circumference.

b. Suppose you cut a slice of the pie with a 45° central angle. Modify your sketch to show the sector.

c. To find the area of the sector represented by this slice, set up a proportion involving 45°, 360°, the area of the sector, and the area of the pie you found in **1a.** Solve the proportion to find the area of the sector. Round your answer to the nearest tenth.

d. The rim of the sector of pie represents a minor arc of the circle. Set up and solve a proportion to find the length of this 45° arc. Round your answer to the nearest tenth.

P **Find the length of $\widehat{AB}$ and the area of sector *ACB* for each measure of central angle $\angle ACB$ and radius of $\odot C$. Give answers in exact form.**

2. $m\angle ACB = 90°$, radius = 10 cm
$L = 5\pi$ cm; $A = 25\pi$ cm^2

3. $m\angle ACB = 72°$, radius = 15 in.
$L = 6\pi$ in.; $A = 45\pi$ in.^{2}

4. $m\angle ACB = 55°$, radius = 2.5 ft
$L = 2.4$ ft; $A = 3$ ft^2

5. $m\angle ACB = 55°$, radius = 5 ft
$L = 4.8$ ft; $A = 12$ ft^2

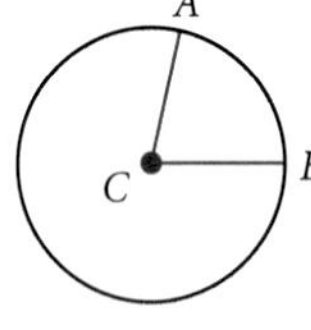

Key

- V Vocabulary
- P Practice/Skills
- R Review
- MR Math Reasoning
- PS Problem Solving
- C Challenge

Alert

Students often confuse arc measure and arc length. You may need to remind them that length is measured in units like inches, centimeters, etc., while an arc measure, like an angle measure, is given in degrees. It may also be helpful to show a 90° arc on two circles with different radii.

Find the length of each arc in the circle at the right.

6. a 30° arc $0.7\pi \approx 2.20$ **7.** a 144° arc $3.36\pi \approx 10.56$ **8.** a semicircle $4.2\pi \approx 13.19$

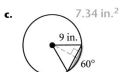

9. A **segment** of a circle is the region formed by an arc of the circle and the segment joining its endpoints. Find the area of each shaded segment. (Hint: Can you subtract areas to find the area of the segment?)

a. 18.27 cm^2

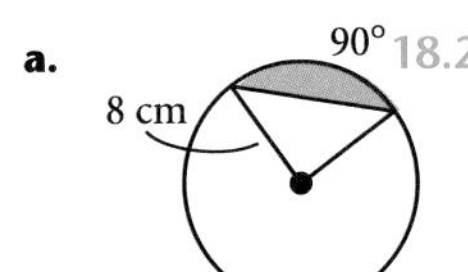

b. 43.84 in.^{2}

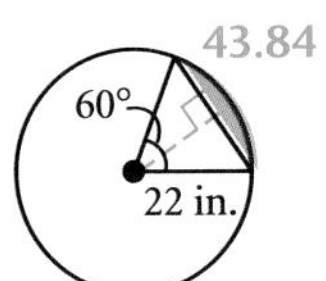

c. 7.34 in.^{2}

d. Write a brief explanation of your method for finding the area of a segment.
Find the area of the sector and subtract the area of the triangle.

Suppose that contestants on a game show spin a wheel with a radius of 6 ft. It is evenly divided into 24 different sectors.

10. Find the area and arc length of one sector of the wheel.
$A = 1.5\pi \approx 4.71$ ft^2; $L = 0.5\pi \approx 1.57$ ft

11. Three of the sectors read "Spin Again."

a. What is the total area of the sectors that read "Spin Again"? $4.5\pi \approx 14.14$ ft^2

b. What is the probability that a contestant will land on "Spin Again" on any one spin of the wheel? 12.5%

12. An electric lawn mower with a twenty-meter cord is plugged into an outlet at the corner of the house shown. (Assume the fence is perpendicular to the wall of the house.)

a. What is the total area that can be mowed from this outlet? 647.95 m^2

b. If the fence was not in the way, what area could be mowed from this outlet? 1040.65 m^2

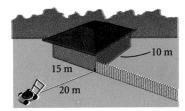

LOOK BACK

13. *Given:* $\triangle ABC$ and $\triangle DEC$ are right triangles.

Prove: $\frac{AC}{DC} = \frac{BC}{EC}$ [7-2]

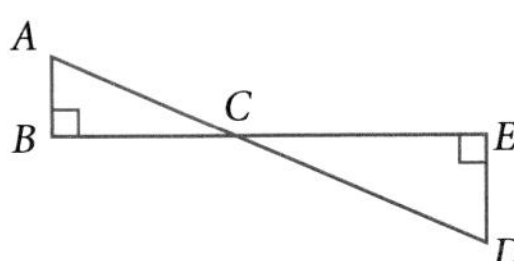

Find the area and the circumference for a circle with each of the given dimensions. Give your answers in exact form and as decimals rounded to the nearest hundredth. [8-1]

14. radius = 3 cm **15.** diameter = 16 in. **16.** radius = 8.32 ft

Look Back

13. $\angle ACB \cong \angle ECD$: Vertical angles are congruent.
$\angle B \cong \angle E$: Right angles are congruent.
$\triangle ACB \sim \triangle DCE$: AA
$\frac{AC}{DC} = \frac{BC}{EC}$: Definition of *similar*

14. $A = 9\pi$ cm^2; 28.27 cm^2; $C = 6\pi$ cm; 18.85 cm

15. $A = 64\pi$ in.^{2}; 201.06 in.^{2}; $C = 16\pi$ in.; 50.27 in.

16. $A = 69.2224\pi$ ft^2; 217.47 ft^2; $C = 16.64\pi$ ft ; 52.28 ft

More Math Reasoning

21. a.

b. 5707.96 m^2

c. No; One cannot tile a square region with circular sectors without either gaps or overlap.

Ongoing Assessment

Self-Assessment Exercises 1, 3, 5, 7, 10, 11

Embedded Assessment Explore Step 2; Try It a; Exercises 4, 8, 12

PART C At a Glance

Objective

To explore relationships between chords and radii.

Development

Students see the definition of a chord of a circle.

In the **Explore,** they investigate relationships between chords and radii, including the fact that a chord's perpendicular bisector contains the center of the circle.

Suggested Materials

Student Compass, ruler, scissors, protractor

Key Terms

Chord

First Five Minutes

Transparency FFM 8-2C

$\triangle ABC$ is a right triangle with right angle A. Find each side length. Where necessary, round lengths to the nearest tenth.

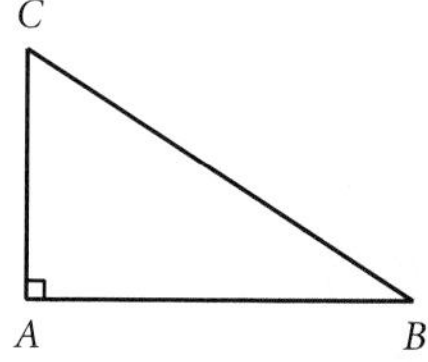

1. $AB = 9$, $AC = 12$. Find BC. 15

2. $AB = 12$, $BC = 13$. Find AC. 5

3. $AC = 16$, $BC = 19$. Find AB. 10.2

Motivate

Ask...

- Suppose n chords of a circle share an endpoint A. Into how many regions do these chords divide the circle? $n + 1$

MORE PRACTICE

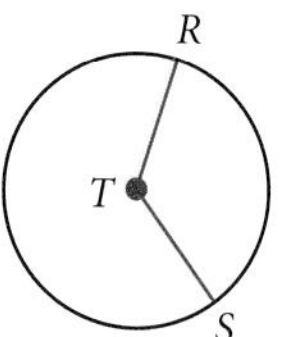

P **Find the length of $\widehat{RS}$ and the area of sector RTS for each measure of central angle $\angle RTS$ and radius of $\odot T$.**

17. $m\angle RTS = 36°$, radius = 8 in.
$L = 1.6\pi \approx 5.03$ in.; $A = 6.4\pi \approx 20.11$ in.^{2}

18. $m\angle RTS = 45°$, radius = 4.8 m
$L = 1.2\pi \approx 3.77$ m; $A = 2.88\pi \approx 9.05$ m^2

19. $m\angle RTS = 108°$, radius = 9.1 ft
$L = 5.46\pi \approx 17.15$ ft; $A = 24.843\pi \approx 78.05$ ft^2

P **20.** Find the area of the shaded segment in the figure at the right. 7.72 mm^2

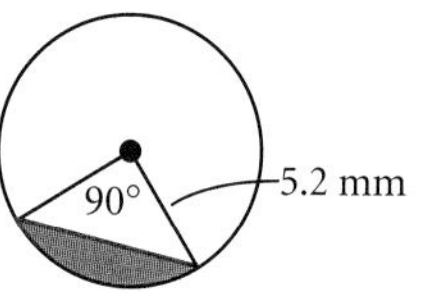

MORE MATH REASONING

C, MR **21.** A 100-m square field is watered by sprinklers at the midpoints of each of its sides. Each sprinkler sprays water in a 50-m radius and covers an 180° arc so that all of its water lands on the field.

a. Draw a sketch to represent this situation.

b. Find the area of the field that is watered by more than one sprinkler.

c. Suppose the watering radius of each of the sprinklers can be adjusted to any radius less than or equal to 50 m. Can you find a way to set these sprinklers so that every location in the field is watered by only one sprinkler? If so, explain your plan. If not, explain why not.

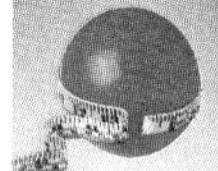

8-2 PART C Radius-Chord Conjectures

← CONNECT → ***You've seen some relationships between radii and tangents. Now you will make conjectures about the relationships between radii and chords.***

As you've seen, secant lines intersect a circle in two points. The photograph at the left shows how the strings of a guitar are similar to secant lines. The segment determined by the points where a secant line intersects a circle has a special name. This is described in the following definition.

Key

V Vocabulary
P Practice/Skills
R Review
MR Math Reasoning
PS Problem Solving
C Challenge

DEFINITION

A **chord** is a line segment that joins two points on a circle.

In the figure, $\overline{AB}$ is a chord of $\odot D$.

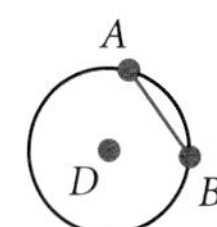

EXPLORE: STRIKING A CHORD

MATERIALS

Compass
Ruler
Scissors
Protractor

1. Use your compass to draw a large circle on a sheet of paper. Mark the center of the circle, and cut the circle out.
2. As shown in the figure, draw two chords anywhere on the circle that do not contain the center. By folding your paper, construct the perpendicular bisector of each chord. Where do the bisectors meet?
3. Add a third chord and its perpendicular bisector to confirm your results from Step 2. Make a conjecture about the perpendicular bisector of a chord.
4. The following two statements are closely related to your conjecture. One of them is true as written, but the other needs some modification. Investigate each statement to see which one needs to be changed. Then rewrite the statement that needs to be changed.
   - If a radius of a circle bisects a chord of the circle, then it is perpendicular to the chord.
   - If a radius of a circle is perpendicular to a chord of the circle, then it bisects the chord.

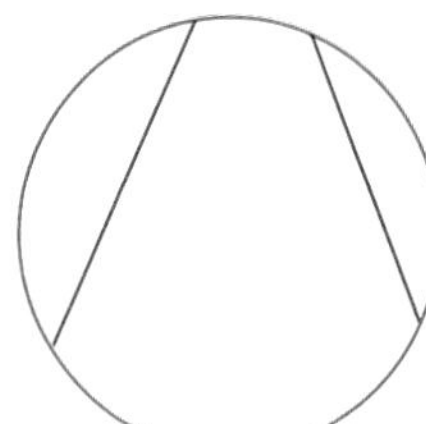

Problem-Solving Tip

Remember to consider special cases.

CONSIDER

1. **Is there a maximum length for chords in a given circle? Is there a minimum length? Explain.**

Student Resources
- Alternative Lessons 8-2C
- Laboratory Manual 8-2C
- Technology Lab Manual
- Practice 8-2C
- Study Guide and Journal 8-2C
- Guía de estudios y Diario 8-2C
- Multilingual Handbook
- More Look Ahead 8-2C
- SAT Preparation

Media Resources
- Transparency FFM 8-2C
- Transparency AE 8-2C
- Teaching Transparency
- AWSMTest and practice software
- AWSM Videodisc

EXPLORE

Striking a Chord

Recommended group size: 4

The Point

To discover relationships between radii and chords.

Look and Listen...

- For students who do not realize that a diameter is a chord.

Ask...

- (In Step 4) Is it possible for a chord to pass through the center of a circle? If so, does this cause a problem for one or both of the statements?

For Groups That Finish Early

Suppose a chord is perpendicular to and intersects a radius of a circle at the midpoint of the radius. What type of quadrilateral is formed if you join their endpoints? Why is this the case? **A rhombus; the diagonals are perpendicular bisectors of each other.**

Follow Up

Ask students to share their conjectures from Step 3 and their answers to Step 4.

Possible Answers

2. At the center of the circle.
3. The perpendicular bisector of a chord contains the center of the circle.
4. The first statement needs to be changed to, "If a radius of a circle bisects a chord of the circle *that is not a diameter,* then it is perpendicular to the chord."

CONSIDER

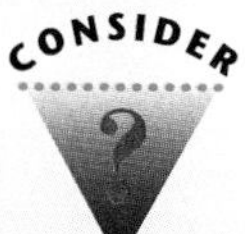

Possible Answer

1. Yes. The maximum length is the diameter. The length must be greater than zero.

Angles, Arcs, and Chords

ALTERNATE EXAMPLE

The radius of circle W is 25 cm. The length of chord $\overline{YZ}$ is 48 cm. Find the distance from chord $\overline{YZ}$ to the center of the circle W.

Draw $\overline{WX} \perp \overline{YZ}$. Label the point of intersection T. Draw radius $\overline{WZ}$ to complete a right triangle.

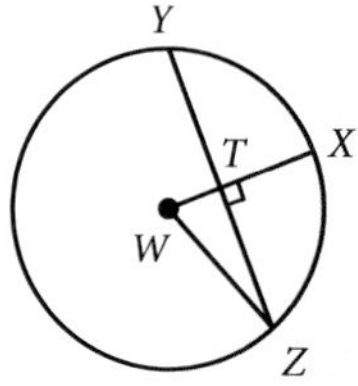

Since a radius perpendicular to a chord bisects the chord, $ZT = \frac{1}{2}YZ = \frac{1}{2}(48) = 24$.

Using the Pythagorean Theorem, $WT^2 + 24^2 = 25^2$.

Therefore, $WT = 7$ cm.

Journal

Reflect 1 and 2 and **Exercise** 9 are suitable for journal entries.

REFLECT

Possible Answers

1. Natasha is correct. The sides of the polygon are chords of the circle. The perpendicular bisectors of the sides (chords) meet at the center of the circle. Since the bisectors contain the apothems, this intersection point must also be the center of the polygon.

2. The apothem of a regular polygon always bisects the side. The side is a chord of the circle, and the radius that contains the apothem, since it is perpendicular to the chord, bisects it.

EXAMPLE

The radius of circle O is 13 mm. The length of chord $\overline{PQ}$ is 10 mm. Find the distance from chord $\overline{PQ}$ to the center of the circle O.

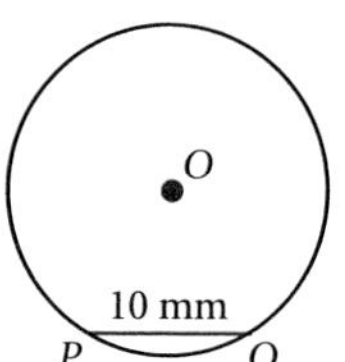

Draw $\overline{OR} \perp \overline{PQ}$. Draw radius $\overline{OP}$ to complete a right triangle.

Since a radius perpendicular to a chord bisects the chord, $PR = \frac{1}{2}PQ = \frac{1}{2}(10) = 5$.

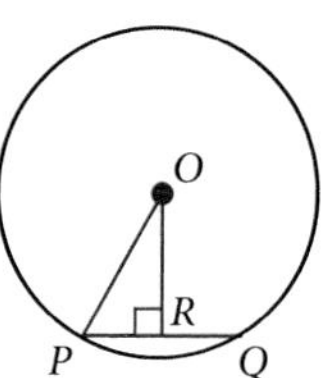

Using the Pythagorean Theorem, $OR^2 + 5^2 = 13^2$.

Therefore, $OR = 12$ mm.

TRY IT

State a conclusion that can be drawn from each figure.

a.

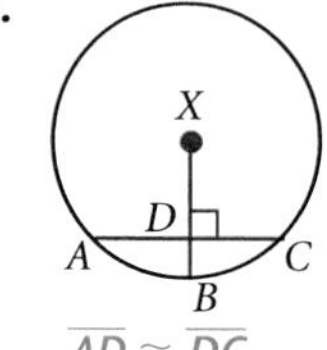

$\overline{AD} \cong \overline{DC}$

b.

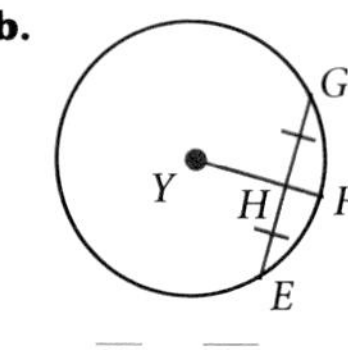

$\overline{YF} \perp \overline{EG}$

c.

m contains Z

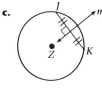

You have investigated the following theorems about chords, their perpendicular bisectors, and radii.

> **THEOREMS**
>
> The perpendicular bisector of a chord contains the center of the circle.
>
> If a radius of a circle bisects a chord of the circle that is not a diameter, then it is perpendicular to the chord.
>
> If a radius of a circle is perpendicular to a chord of the circle, then it bisects the chord.

REFLECT

1. Natasha said that the center of any regular polygon must be the same as the center of its circumscribed circle. Is she right? If she is, give a justification; if not, give a counterexample.

Diversity Issues

The consequences of the different participation rates of males and females in mathematics and physical science subjects are far-reaching. Mathematical qualifications are commonly used as a critical entry barrier to [college] courses, further training, and apprenticeships... (Hansen, 1981; Sells, 1973). (Gilah C. Leder, "Mathematics and Gender: Changing Perspectives," *Handbook of Research on Mathematics Teaching and Learning,* Douglas A. Grouws, ed. p. 607. © 1992 NCTM.)

2. Draw a regular hexagon inscribed in a circle. Use your drawing to help you decide whether an apothem of a regular polygon always bisects the side of the polygon it intersects. Explain your conclusion.

Exercises

CORE

P **Getting Started** **Refer to ⊙*T* for Exercises 1–3.**

1. If $QS = 14$, what is QP? 7

2. What is $m\angle TPQ$? 90°

3. What is the relationship between $\overline{TR}$ and $\overline{QS}$? $\overline{TR}$ is a perpendicular bisector of $\overline{QS}$.

P 4. $AD = 15$; $AC = 17$. Find the length of chord $\overline{AE}$. 30

P 5. $AE = 12$; $AC = 10$. Find the distance of chord $\overline{AE}$ from the center of the circle C. 8

P 6. $AE = 24$; $CD = 9$. Find the radius of $\odot C$. 15

V 7. From the four terms below, choose the one term that does not belong and explain why. Secant; It alone extends beyond the boundary of a circle.

chord, radius, secant, diameter

PS 8. A 48-in. chord is 8 in. closer to the center of a circle than a 40-in. chord. Find the radius of the circle. 25 in.

MR 9. **Getting Centered** An archaeologist finds a piece of the rim of an ancient wheel. She wants to figure out how big the wheel was. She begins by drawing two chords as shown. Explain what she should do next to find the radius of the wheel.

P 10. In $\odot G$, $\overline{GH}$ bisects $\overline{JK}$. If $GH = 16$ and $JK = 9$, find the distance of $\overline{JK}$ from G. 15.35

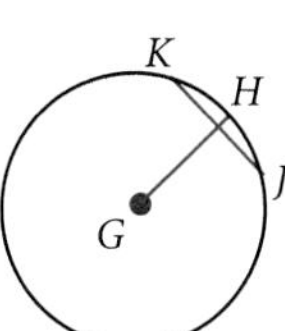

There is a special relationship between congruent chords and congruent arcs. You will prove this relationship in Exercise 11.

THEOREM

In a circle (or in congruent circles), minor arcs are congruent if and only if they have congruent chords.

Part C Exercises

Exercise Notes

Core

17. Students use inductive reasoning to make conjectures about the number of arcs and chords determined by n points on a circle.

Look Ahead

These exercises look ahead to the measures of inscribed angles seen in 8-3 Part A.

Exercise Answers

Core

9. Draw the perpendicular bisectors of the chords. They will meet at the center of the circle.

Key

V Vocabulary
P Practice/Skills
R Review
MR Math Reasoning
PS Problem Solving
C Challenge

Ongoing Assessment

Self-Assessment Exercises 1, 3, 5, 7, 10, 11, 12, 13, 15

Embedded Assessment Try It c; Exercises 4, 8, 14, 16

Angles, Arcs, and Chords

11.

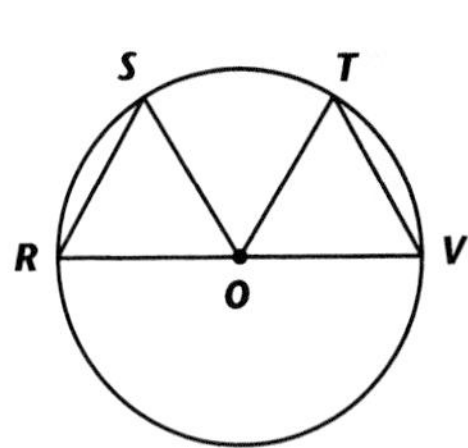

$\widehat{RS} \cong \widehat{TV}$: Given
$m\widehat{RS} = m\widehat{TV}$: Definition of *congruent arcs*
$m\widehat{RS} = m\angle ROS$; $m\widehat{TV} = m\angle TOV$: Definition of *measure of a minor arc*
$m\angle ROS = m\angle TOV$: Substitution
$\angle ROS \cong \angle TOV$: Definition of *congruent angles*
$\overline{OS} \cong \overline{OR} \cong \overline{OT} \cong \overline{OV}$: Definition of *circle*
$\triangle OSR \cong \triangle OTV$: SAS
$\overline{RS} \cong \overline{TV}$: CPCTC

17.

Points	2	3	4	5	n
Chords	1	3	6	10	$\frac{n(n-1)}{2}$
Arcs	2	6	12	20	$n(n-1)$

Chords: Each point can be connected to $(n - 1)$ others, divide by two to avoid double-counting. Arcs: Each point is an endpoint for $(n - 1)$ arcs.

More Math Reasoning

27. Draw $\overline{XV}$, $\overline{VY}$, $\overline{ZV}$, and $\overline{VW}$. $\triangle XVY \cong \triangle ZVW$ by SSS, and $\angle XVY \cong \angle WVZ$ by CPCTC. Since their central angles are congruent, $\widehat{XY} \cong \widehat{WZ}$.

28. Infinitely many; Yes; Possible answer:

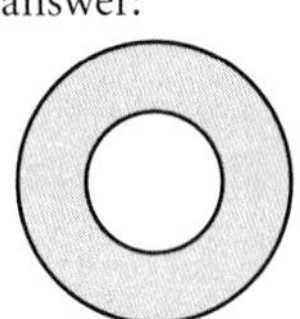

29. $YZ = 9.75$; For a point A on $\odot Z$, $\triangle AYZ$ is a right triangle. Then, use the Pythagorean Theorem with $AZ = 7$ and $AY = 12$ to find YZ.

MR **11.** Prove: In a circle, if two minor arcs are congruent, then their chords are congruent.

Given: Circle O with $\widehat{RS} \cong \widehat{TV}$

Prove: $\overline{RS} \cong \overline{TV}$

(Hint: Draw radii $\overline{OR}$, $\overline{OS}$, $\overline{OT}$, and $\overline{OV}$.)

P **In the figure, $m\widehat{AB} = m\widehat{CD} = 92°$, $\overline{AB} \perp \overline{EH}$, $\overline{DC} \perp \overline{EI}$, $AE = 25$, and $AH = 7$. Find each of the following.**

12. AB 14 **13.** DC 14 **14.** EH 24 **15.** EI 24

PS **16.** In the figure at the right, two flywheels are connected with a rubber belt. Line t is tangent to both circles. Line t is a **common external tangent** because it does not cross the line segment joining the centers of $\odot C$ and $\odot D$. Find the length of $\overline{AB}$ if $AC = 10$, $BD = 5$, and $CD = 23$. (Hint: Draw $\overline{CA}$, $\overline{DB}$, and $\overline{CD}$. Then draw a rectangle $ABDX$, where X is a point on $\overline{AC}$. Use the Pythagorean Theorem to find DX.) $AB = 22.45$

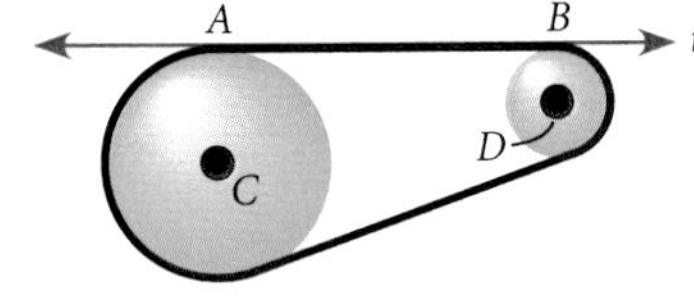

MR, C **17.** Complete the table below to develop formulas for the numbers of chords and arcs determined by n points on a circle. Explain how you developed your formulas.

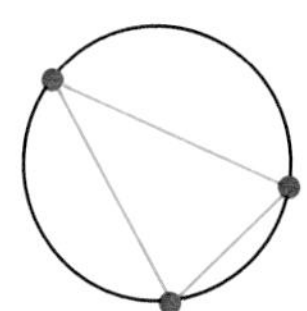

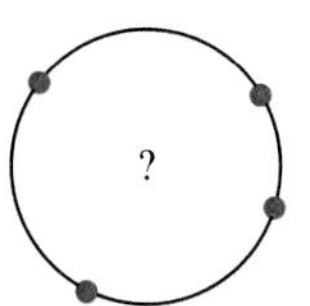

No. of Points	2	3	4	5	...	n
No. of Chords	1	3			...	
No. of Arcs	2	6			...	

LOOK AHEAD

MR **18.** Explain the relationship between the measure of a central angle and its intercepted arc.
Measure of the central angle is equal to the measure of the arc.

P **19.** $\angle ABC$ and central angle $\angle AOC$ intercept the same arc. Which angle appears to have a greater measure? $\angle AOC$

Key

V Vocabulary
P Practice/Skills
R Review
MR Math Reasoning
PS Problem Solving
C Challenge

MORE PRACTICE

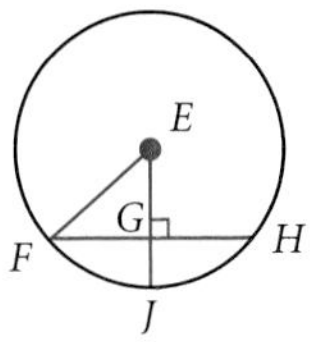

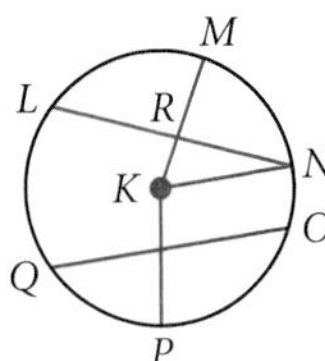

20. $EG = 24$, and $EF = 25$. Find the length of chord $\overline{FH}$. 14

21. $EG = 15$, and $FH = 20$. Find the radius of $\odot E$. 18.03

22. $EF = 2.7$, and $FH = 3.2$. Find the distance of chord $\overline{FH}$ from the center of $\odot E$. 2.17

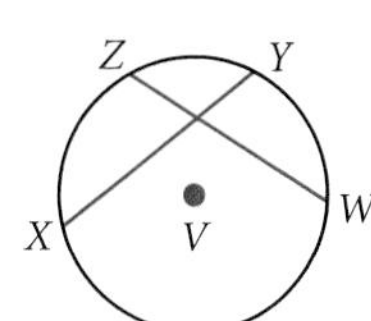

In the figure, $m\widehat{LN} = m\widehat{OQ} = 135°$, $\overline{KM} \perp \overline{LN}$, $\overline{KP} \perp \overline{OQ}$, $KN = 13$, and $NL = 20$. Find each of the following.

23. KM 13

24. LR 10

25. RM 4.69

26. OQ 20

MORE MATH REASONING

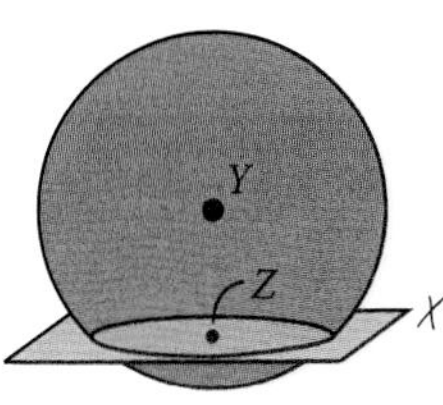

27. Prove: In a circle, congruent chords cut off congruent minor arcs.

Given: Circle V with $\overline{XY} \cong \overline{WZ}$

Prove: $\widehat{XY} \cong \widehat{WZ}$

28. How many lines of symmetry does a circle have? Does any other two-dimensional figure have this property? If so, give an example; if not, explain why the circle is unique in this way.

29. Plane X passes through a sphere with center Y as shown, and it cuts off $\odot Z$. If the radius of the sphere is 12 and the radius of the circle is 7, how far is Z from Y? Explain your answer.

30. The photo at the right shows a utility hole cover. The diameter of the cover is four feet. Suppose the cover is slid over the hole so that the center of the cover rests on the edge of the hole. Find the area of the hole that is exposed. 7.65

Angles, Arcs, and Chords

PART D At a Glance

Objective

To use proportional thinking and arc measures to duplicate Eratosthenes' measurement of the earth's circumference.

Development

In the **Explore,** students use proportional thinking and the concepts of arc measure and arc length to reproduce Eratosthenes' measurement of the earth's circumference.

First Five Minutes

Transparency FFM 8-2D

Using sketches and your own words, define *minor arc, major arc,* and *semicircle.* Then explain how to find the measure of each.

EXPLORE

Around the Earth with Eratosthenes

Recommended group size: 4

The Point

To use arc measure and arc length to find the circumference of the earth.

Look and Listen...

- For students who do not see that they need to use trigonometry to solve for the measure of $\angle 1$.

Ask...

- What angle does the pole make with the ground? What type of triangle is formed by the base of the pole, the tip of the pole, and the tip of the shadow?
- If one stadium is $\frac{1}{10}$ of a mile long, should you get a larger or smaller number when you convert stadia to miles?

8-2 PART D Making Connections

← CONNECT → ***Central angles of circles, the regions they determine, and the arcs they intersect allow you to apply proportional thinking to circles. They enabled Eratosthenes to find the circumference of the earth.***

In the following Explore, you will see how Eratosthenes used proportions to calculate the circumference of the earth.

EXPLORE: AROUND THE EARTH WITH ERATOSTHENES

Eratosthenes knew that the sun cast no shadows in Syene, Africa, at noon on June 21. The sun did cast shadows at that time in Alexandria, which is due north of Syene.

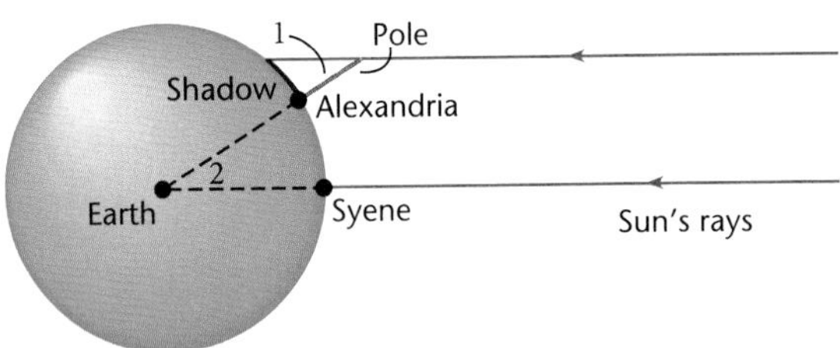

1. Eratosthenes may have used the height of a pole in Alexandria and the length of its shadow at noon on June 21 to calculate $m\angle 1$. Assume that the pole was 16 ft tall and the shadow it cast was 2.02 ft long. Use these measurements to find $m\angle 1$ to the nearest tenth of a degree. Explain your method.
2. Because the sun is so far from the earth, its rays are virtually parallel. What can you conclude about $\angle 1$ and $\angle 2$? Why?
3. When Eratosthenes did his calculations, the main unit used to measure long distances was the *stadium* (plural, *stadia*). Eratosthenes used 5000 stadia for the distance from Syene to Alexandria, an arc on the surface of the earth. Calculate the circumference of the earth in stadia.
4. It is thought that 1 stadium was about $\frac{1}{10}$ of a mile long. Convert your measurement of the circumference of the earth to miles.
5. The actual average value for the circumference of the earth is about 24,874 mi. How close was Eratosthenes's measurement?

Student Resources

- Alternative Lessons
- **Laboratory Manual 8-2D**
- Technology Lab Manual
- **Practice 8-2D**
- **Study Guide and Journal 8-2D**
- **Guía de estudios y Diario 8-2D**
- **Multilingual Handbook**
- **More Look Back 8-2D**
- SAT Preparation

Media Resources

- **Transparency FFM 8-2D**
- Transparency AE
- Teaching Transparency
- **AWSMTest and practice software**
- AWSM Videodisc

REFLECT

1. Sketch a circle and a central angle. Then write three equal ratios involving the measure of a central angle, the length of the minor arc it cuts off, and the area of the sector it determines.
2. In your own words, briefly describe the relationships between chords and radii of a circle.

Self-Assessment

P **Find each measure.**

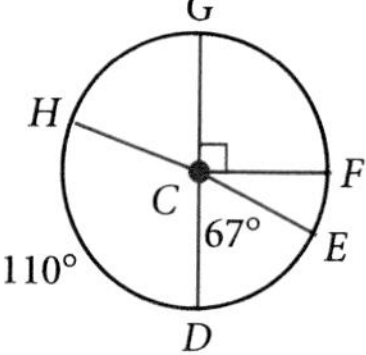

1. $m\widehat{DE}$ 67°
2. $m\widehat{EF}$ 23°
3. $m\angle HCG$ 70°
4. $m\widehat{HDG}$ 290°

P 5. **Tennis Anyone?** The women's championship at the Wimbledon tennis tournament had the following winners over a twelve-year period. Make a circle graph to illustrate these results.

1981: Chris Evert-Lloyd	1987: Martina Navratilova
1982: Martina Navratilova	1988: Steffi Graf
1983: Martina Navratilova	1989: Steffi Graf
1984: Martina Navratilova	1990: Martina Navratilova
1985: Martina Navratilova	1991: Steffi Graf
1986: Martina Navratilova	1992: Steffi Graf

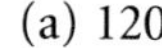
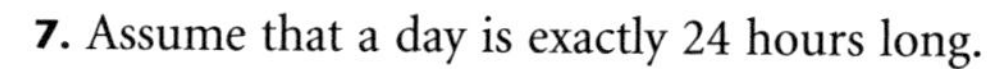

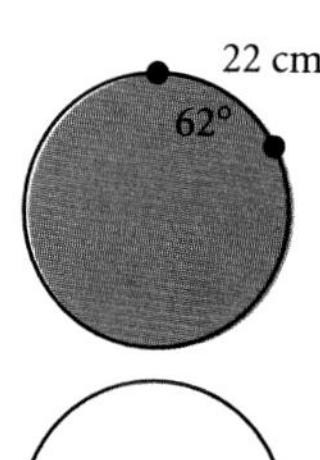

P 6. In the figure, points A, B, C, D, E, and F divide the circle into six equal arcs. If $AD = 9$, which of the following is the length of $\widehat{AC}$? (d)

(a) 120 (b) 9π (c) $\frac{1}{3}$ (d) 3π (e) $\frac{2}{3}\pi$

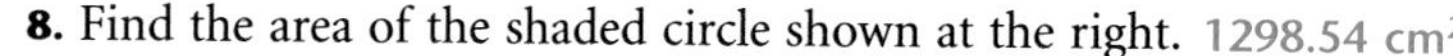

S 7. Assume that a day is exactly 24 hours long.

a. What is the measure of the arc through which the earth turns in one hour? 15°

b. The circumference of the earth at the equator is about 25,000 mi. Find the distance a point on the earth's equator travels in an hour. 1041.67 mi

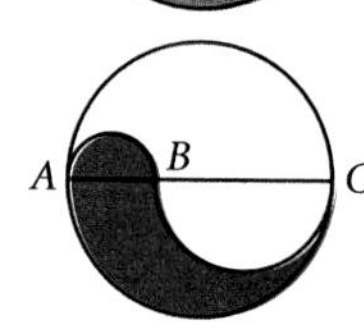

S 8. Find the area of the shaded circle shown at the right. 1298.54 cm²

C 9. If $BC = 2AB$, what fraction of the circle is shaded? If the area of the circle is 121π mm², what is the area of the shaded portion? $\frac{1}{3}$; 126.71 mm²

A B C

Key

Vocabulary
Practice/Skills
Review
R Math Reasoning
Problem Solving
Challenge

For Groups That Finish Early

Give two different ways to express the size of the error in your result for Step 4. Which method is a better measure of the relative size of the error? **Subtracting their value from the actual value; finding the percent error, etc. Percent error expresses the relative size of the error better.**

Follow Up

Ask students to share their results to Step 4.

Possible Answers

1. 7.2°
2. $\angle 1 \cong \angle 2$ because alternate interior angles of parallel lines are congruent.
3. 250,000 stadia
4. 25,000 miles
5. Eratosthenes' measurement was 126 miles off. The percent error is about 0.5 percent.

Portfolio

Have students select items from their work that demonstrate their understanding of the material in 8-2.

You may wish to have students include a circle graph that they drew in 8-2, their favorite **Exercise** where they used proportions to find an arc length or a sector area, and an **Exercise** that they found challenging.

REFLECT

Possible Answers

See Additional Answers p. T582.

Self-Assessment

Exercise Notes

6. Similar to multiple-choice questions on standardized tests.
13. Students prove that chords equidistant from the center of a circle are congruent.

Algebra | Logic/Reasoning | Science/Health

Angles, Arcs, and Chords

Self-Assessment Answers

5.

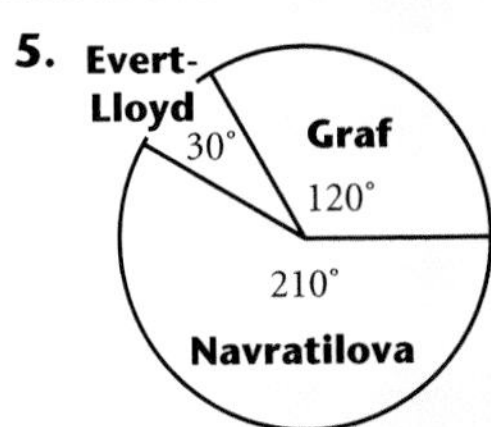

10. $\triangle ACB \sim \triangle ECD$. Since $\frac{6.0}{4.0} = \frac{7.5}{5.0} = 1.5$, the triangles are similar by SAS. $x = \frac{5.6}{1.5} \approx 3.73$.

11. a. $C = 1.766 \times 10^{15}$ km

b. $r = 2.81 \times 10^{14}$ km

c. $A = 2.48 \times 10^{29}$ km^2

12. 69.81 cm^2; The total area of the circle is 100π cm^2. Since $m\angle FKJ = 80°$, the sector FKJ fills $\frac{80}{360}$ of the total area.

13. Show that $\triangle ZWY \cong \triangle ZTV$ by HL. Then $\overline{WY} \cong \overline{VT}$ by CPCTC. Use $WY = \frac{1}{2}WX$ and $VT = \frac{1}{2}ST$ to show that $\overline{WX} \cong \overline{ST}$.

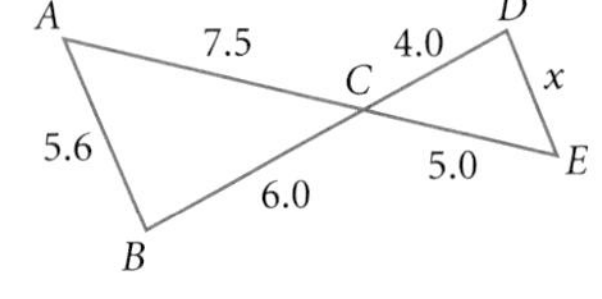

R **10.** Write a similarity statement for the triangles in the figure at the right, and explain how you know they are similar. Then solve for x. [7-2]

R Science **11. That's Astronomical!** The sun orbits the center of the Milky Way galaxy at a speed of about 8.83×10^9 km/yr. Its orbit is roughly circular, and it takes the sun about 200,000 years to make a complete orbit. [8-1]

a. What is the circumference of the sun's orbit? Express your answer in scientific notation.

b. How far is the sun from the center of the Milky Way galaxy?

c. What is the area of the circular region determined by the sun's orbit?

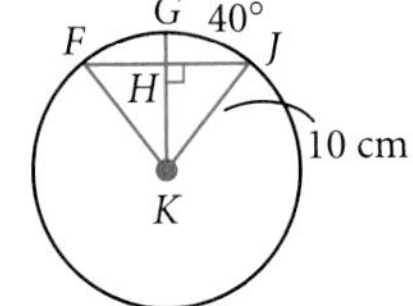

MR **12.** Find the area of sector FJK. Write a short paragraph explaining how you solved this problem.

If you know the radius of a circle and the length of a chord, you can calculate the distance from the center of the circle to the chord. Therefore, if two chords of a circle have equal lengths, they should be the same distance from the center.

THEOREM

Two chords of a circle are congruent if and only if they are equidistant from the center.

MR **13.** Write a *plan* for proving the following half of the preceding theorem.

Prove: If two chords are equidistant from the center of a circle, then they are congruent.

Given: $ZV = ZY$

Prove: $\overline{WX} \cong \overline{ST}$

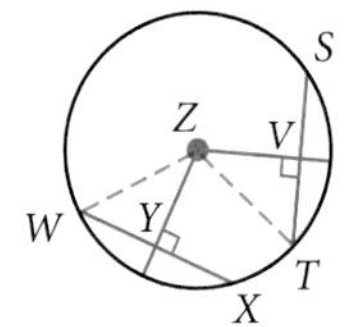

PS **14. The Grass Is Greener . . .** An automatic sprinkler is set so that it turns through an angle of 220° before returning to its original setting. If the sprinkler sprays water a distance of up to 20 m, find the total area watered by the sprinkler. 767.94 m^2

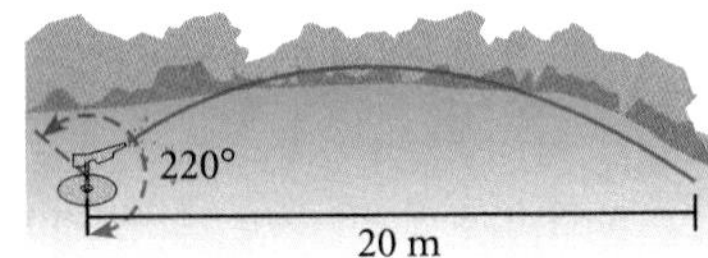

Assessment Resources

Quiz 8-2

Chapter Assessment Form A

Chapter Assessment Form B

Chapter Alternative Assessment

Mid-Year Assessment

End-of-Year Assessment

AWSMTest and practice software

Ongoing Assessment

Self-Assessment Self-Assessment Exercises

Embedded Assessment Explore Steps 3, 4; Refl
1, 2

8-2 Part D Reflect

1. $\frac{\text{measure of central angle}}{360} = \frac{\text{arc length}}{\text{circumference}} = \frac{\text{area of sector}}{\text{circle area}}$
2. The perpendicular bisector of a chord contains the center of the circle, so it contains a radius of the circle. If a radius bisects a chord that is not a diameter, then it is perpendicular to the chord. If a radius is perpendicular to a chord, then it bisects the chord.

8-3

The Inscribed-Angle Theorem

SUPERLESSON AT A GLANCE

Superlesson Goal

Students will investigate the relationships between the measure of inscribed, tangent-tangent, and tangent-secant angles and the arcs they intercept.

Management Guide

	Topic	Objectives	Key Terms	New Ideas	Materials
Part A	Inscribed Angles	To discover that the measure of an inscribed angle is one-half the measure of its intercepted arc.	Inscribed angle	Inscribed angles. The measure of an inscribed angle is one-half the measure of its intercepted arc.	**Student** Compass, straightedge, protractor, geometry software
Part B	Angles Formed by Secants and Tangents	To explore relationships between the measures of secant-tangent and tangent-tangent angles and the arcs they determine.	Tangent-secant angle, tangent-tangent angle	Tangent-secant and tangent-tangent angles. The measure of one of these angles is one-half the difference of the measures of the arcs in its interior.	**Student** Compass, straightedge, protractor, geometry software
Part C	Making Connections	To use inscribed angles to find the best region for a shot in a soccer match.	In Making Connections, students apply and synthesize key terms and new ideas.		**Student** Straightedge, scissors, protractor

Pacing Chart (45-Minute Periods)

	Comprehensive Course	Core Course	Informal Course
Part A	1	1	0
Part B	1	1	0
Part C	1	1	0
TOTAL periods for Superlesson	3	3	0

NCTM Standards

Mathematics as Problem Solving

Mathematics as Communication

Mathematics as Reasoning

Mathematical Connections

Geometry from a Synthetic Perspective

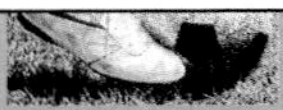

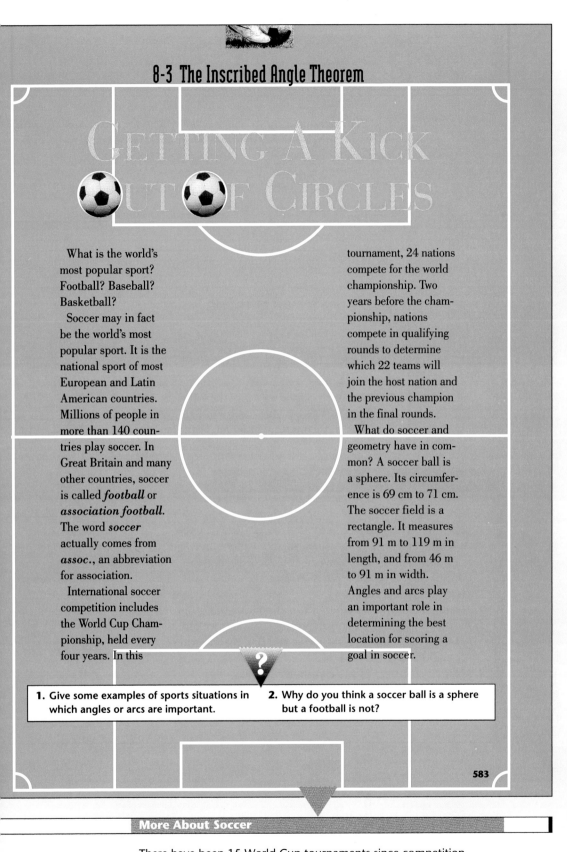

8-3 The Inscribed Angle Theorem

Getting a Kick out of Circles

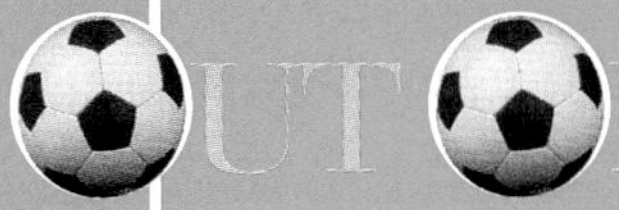

What is the world's most popular sport? Football? Baseball? Basketball?

Soccer may in fact be the world's most popular sport. It is the national sport of most European and Latin American countries. Millions of people in more than 140 countries play soccer. In Great Britain and many other countries, soccer is called *football* or *association football.* The word *soccer* actually comes from *assoc.*, an abbreviation for association.

International soccer competition includes the World Cup Championship, held every four years. In this tournament, 24 nations compete for the world championship. Two years before the championship, nations compete in qualifying rounds to determine which 22 teams will join the host nation and the previous champion in the final rounds.

What do soccer and geometry have in common? A soccer ball is a sphere. Its circumference is 69 cm to 71 cm. The soccer field is a rectangle. It measures from 91 m to 119 m in length, and from 46 m to 91 m in width. Angles and arcs play an important role in determining the best location for scoring a goal in soccer.

1. **Give some examples of sports situations in which angles or arcs are important.**

2. **Why do you think a soccer ball is a sphere but a football is not?**

583

More About Soccer

There have been 15 World Cup tournaments since competition began in 1930. Only six different nations have been World Cup champions. Brazil has won the Cup four times, West Germany and Italy were champions on three occasions, Argentina and Uruguay twice, and England won the Cup once. The most goals scored by a player in a World Cup game is five, scored by Oleg Salenko for Russia against Cameroon on June 28, 1994. The legendary Brazilian player Pelé is the only player to have been on three championship teams.

Where Are We Now?

Students are familiar with the relationship between the measure of a central angle and the measure of its intercepted arc, and they know how to find the measures of major arcs and semicircles.

Where Are We Going?

In 8-3, students will become familiar with other relationships between arc measures and angle measures. They will discover that the measure of an inscribed angle is one-half the measure of its intercepted arc and see some consequences of this fact.

Possible Answers

1. In hockey and indoor soccer, players angle passes off the boards. In basketball, shots with a higher arc have a better chance of going in. In slow-pitch softball, there is a minimum arc for legal pitches.
2. A soccer ball is kicked in the air and along the ground, so it needs to roll in a predictable way. The round soccer ball rolls in a straight path, whereas a football takes peculiar bounces. A football is thrown and carried. The pointed ends of a football make it more aerodynamic and easier to throw for distance. It is also easier to carry.

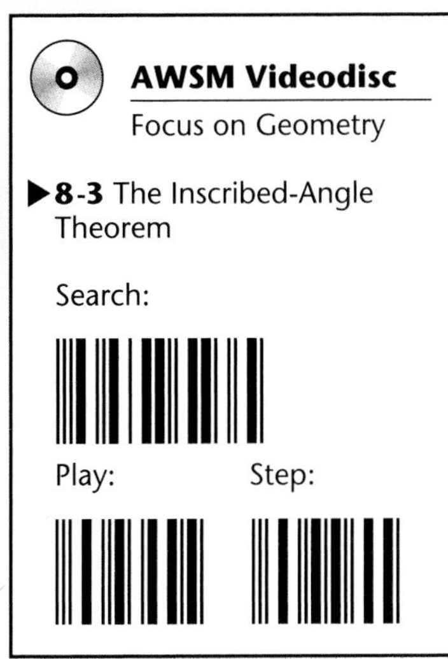

8-3

The Inscribed-Angle Theorem

PART A At a Glance

Objective

To discover that the measure of an inscribed angle is one-half the measure of its intercepted arc.

Development

Students see the definition of an inscribed angle. In the **Explore,** they find that the measure of an inscribed angle is one-half the measure of its intercepted arc.

Suggested Materials

Student Compass, straightedge, protractor, geometry software

Key Terms

Inscribed angle

First Five Minutes

Transparency FFM 8-3A

Find the measure of each arc.

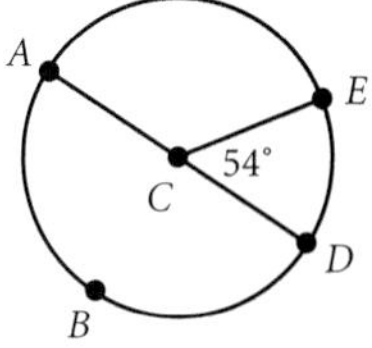

1. $m\widehat{DE}$ 54° **2.** $m\widehat{AED}$ 180°

3. $m\widehat{EBD}$ 306°

Motivate

Ask...

- What does it mean to say that a polygon is inscribed in a circle? **It has its vertices on the circle.**

EXPLORE

Sizing Up Inscribed Angles

Recommended group size: 4

The Point
To discover that the measure of an inscribed angle is one-half the measure of its intercepted arc and that inscribed angles intercepting the same arc are congruent.

8-3 PART A Inscribed Angles

← CONNECT → ***The vertex of a central angle is the center of a circle. Now you will investigate angle-arc relationships when the vertex of an angle is on the circle.***

A polygon that is inscribed in a circle has its vertices on the circle. In the same way, an inscribed angle also has its vertex on a circle.

DEFINITION

An **inscribed angle** is an angle with its vertex on a circle and sides that contain chords of the circle.

In the figure at the right, $\angle BAC$ is an inscribed angle.

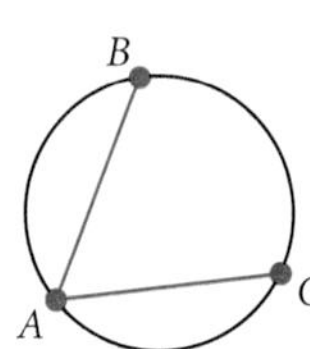

You know that the measure of a minor arc is equal to the measure of its central angle. In the following Explore, you'll investigate how the measure of an inscribed angle is related to the measure of its intercepted arc.

EXPLORE: SIZING UP INSCRIBED ANGLES

MATERIALS

Compass
Straightedge
Protractor
Geometry software (optional)

1. Use geometry software or a compass to construct a circle. As shown below, mark its center, C, and two points, A and B, on the circle. Draw central angle $\angle ACB$. Then place a point D on $\odot C$ so that $\widehat{ADB}$ is a major arc, and draw inscribed angle $\angle ADB$.
2. Measure $\angle ACB$. What other information does this give you?
3. Measure $\angle ADB$. What do you notice? Choose three other locations for point D on the circle, and find the measures of $\angle ADB$ and $\widehat{AB}$ in each case.
4. Make any conjectures you can about the following.
   - The relationship between the measure of an inscribed angle and its intercepted arc.
   - Inscribed angles that intercept the same arc.

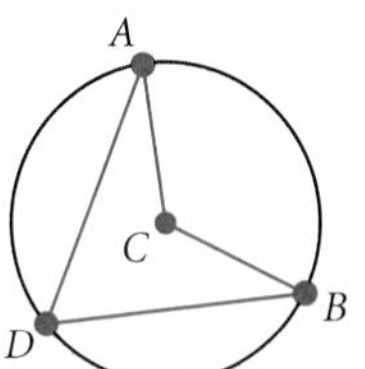

Technology Note

As an extension to this **Explore,** you may want to have students drag an inscribed angle's vertex around a circle and observe the angle measure. When the vertex is on the major arc, the (acute) angle measure stays constant. When it is on the minor arc, the measure is the supplement of this acute angle measure.

TRY IT

Find the measure of each angle or arc indicated by a variable in the following figures.

a.

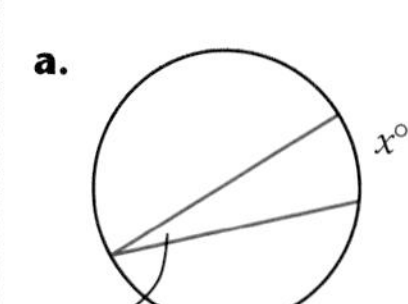

48°

b.

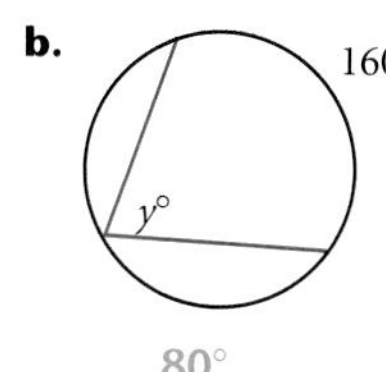

80°

c.

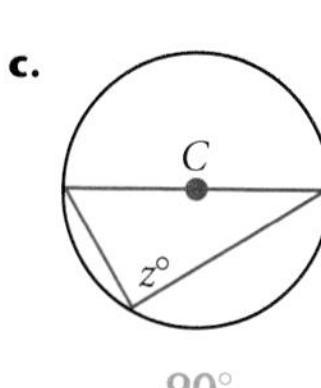

90°

1. What type of inscribed angle intercepts a semicircle? How do you know?

You have investigated three important theorems about inscribed angles and arcs. These include the Inscribed-Angle Theorem and the two related results that are summarized below.

INSCRIBED-ANGLE THEOREM

The measure of an inscribed angle is half the measure of its intercepted arc.

THEOREMS

If two inscribed angles intercept the same arc, then they are congruent.

An inscribed angle that intercepts a semicircle is a right angle.

REFLECT

1. What type of inscribed angle intercepts a minor arc? a major arc? Explain.
2. Suppose you are given a drawing of a circle and its center. How can you make an accurate drawing of a right angle using only a straightedge?

Student Resources

- Alternative Lessons 8-3A
- Laboratory Manual 8-3A
- Technology Lab Manual
- Practice 8-3A
- Study Guide and Journal 8-3A
- Guía de estudios y Diario 8-3A
- Multilingual Handbook
- More Look Back 8-3A
- SAT Preparation

Media Resources

- Transparency FFM 8-3A
- Transparency AE
- Teaching Transparency
- AWSMTest and practice software
- AWSM Videodisc

Look and Listen...

- For students who are drawing central angles, not inscribed angles.
- For students who change the locations of points A and B in Step 3.

Ask...

- Should you move points A and B each time you choose a new location for D?

For Groups That Finish Early

Is there a maximum measure for an inscribed angle? If so, what is it, and how did you find it? **The measure of an inscribed angle is less than 180°. It is one-half the measure of the intercepted arc, and an arc's measure is less than 360°.**

Follow Up

Ask students to summarize the conjectures they made in Step 4.

Possible Answers

2. This is equal to $m\widehat{AB}$.

3. Students may notice that $m\angle ADB = \frac{1}{2}m\widehat{AB}$.

4. The measure of an inscribed angle is one-half the measure of its intercepted arc.

If two inscribed angles intercept the same arc, then they are congruent.

Possible Answer

1. A right angle intercepts a semicircle. Since a semicircle measures 180°, the inscribed angle measures half of 180°.

Journal

Reflect 1 and 2 and **Exercise** 17 are suitable for journal entries.

The Inscribed-Angle Theorem

REFLECT

Possible Answers

1. An acute inscribed angle intercepts a minor arc; an obtuse inscribed angle intercepts a major arc.

$0° < \text{measure minor arc} < 180°$

$\frac{0}{2} < \text{measure inscr. angle} < \frac{180}{2}$

$180° < \text{measure major arc} < 360°$

$\frac{180}{2} < \text{measure inscr. angle} < \frac{360°}{2}$

2. Draw a diameter. Then draw an angle whose vertex is on the circle and each of whose sides contains an endpoint of the diameter. Since this inscribed angle intercepts a semicircle, it must be a right angle.

Part A Exercises

Exercise Notes

Core

19. Students see that the position of the vertex of an inscribed angle has no effect on its measure or the measure of its inscribed arc.

More Math Reasoning

39. Students explore reflections of parallel light rays in a spherical mirror.

Science Note: These reflections will not all meet at exactly the same point. The fact that spherical mirrors do not reflect parallel rays to a common point is referred to as *spherical aberration.* Parabolic mirrors do reflect parallel rays to a common point.

Exercise Answers

Core

17. Measure the inscribed angle from the ends of the straight side. The angle should be 90° if the opening is a semicircle.

Exercises

CORE

P **Getting Started** **Find the measure of each angle or arc indicated by a variable.**

1. 136°

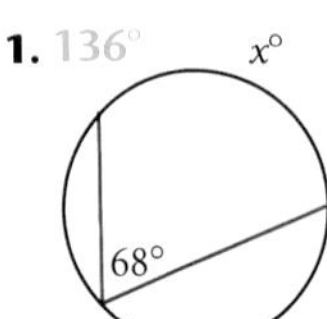

2. 46°

92°
y°

3. 90°

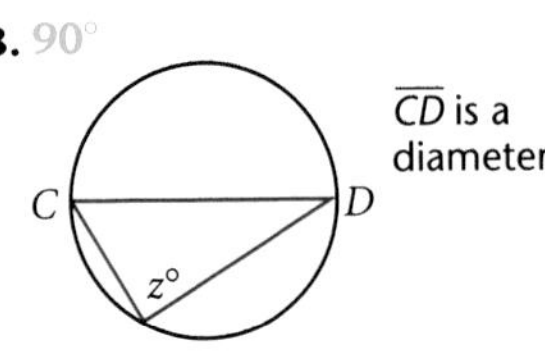

4. a = 50; b = 40; c = 80

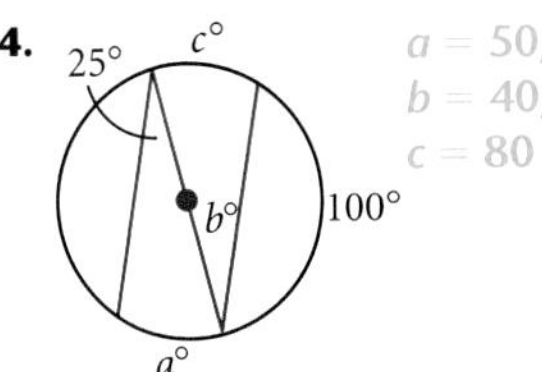

5. d = 80; e = 140

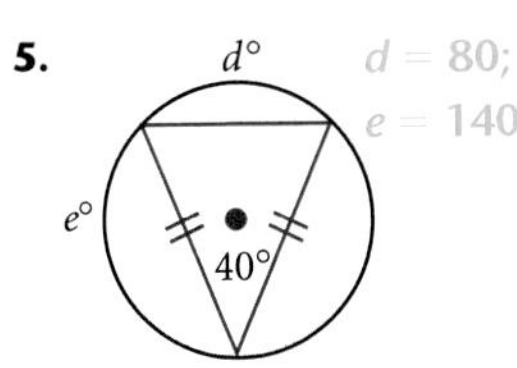

6. 148°

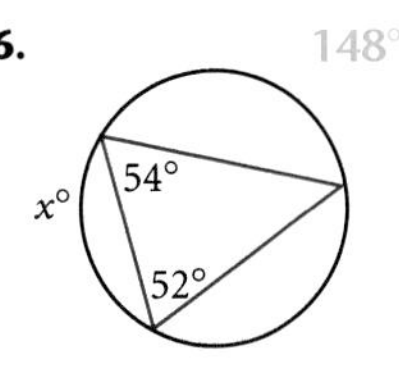

PS **7. Under the Sea** A cylindrical underwater tank for viewing marine animals has a window that covers one-fourth of the circumference of its circular cross-section. Find the measure of the viewing angle of a person at the wall of the tank opposite the window. Compare this to the viewing angle of a person at the center of the tank. 90° at center; 45° at wall

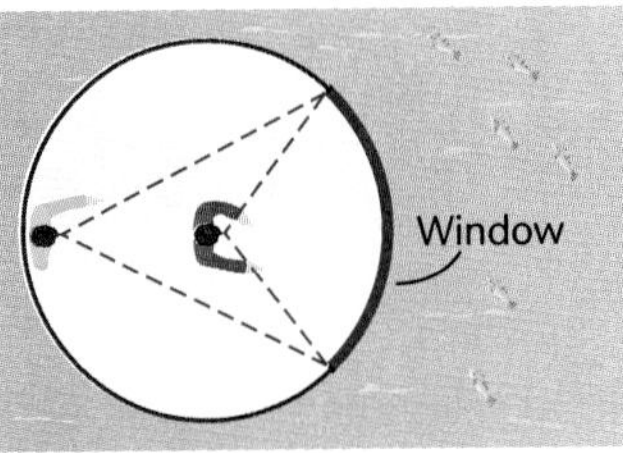

P **Find each angle or arc measure.**

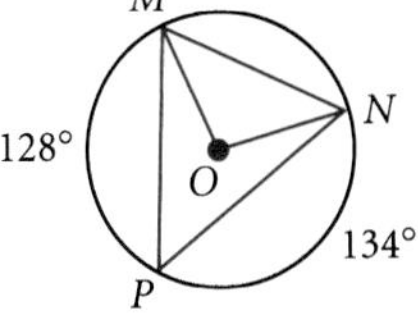

8. $m\widehat{MN}$ 98°

9. $m\angle NOM$ 98°

10. $m\angle MPN$ 49°

11. $m\angle MNP$ 64°

12. $m\angle NMP$ 67°

P $\overrightarrow{AB}$ **bisects** $\angle CAD$, $m\widehat{BD} = 95°$, **and** $m\widehat{AD} = 74°$. **Find each measure.**

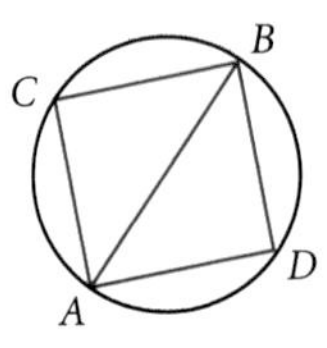

13. $m\angle CAD$ 95°

14. $m\angle BCA$ 84.5°

15. $m\angle CAB$ 47.5°

16. $m\angle CBD$ 85°

Key

V Vocabulary
P Practice/Skills
R Review
MR Math Reasoning
PS Problem Solving
C Challenge

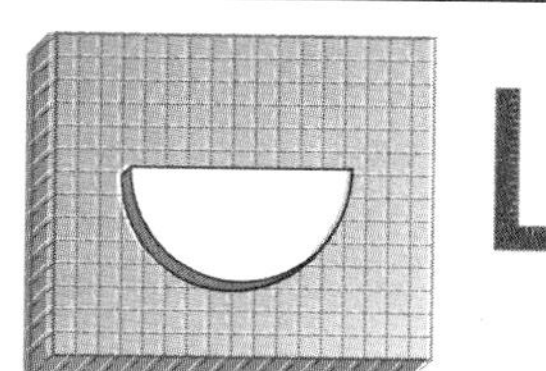

17. Odette cut what she thinks is a semicircular opening for her new sink. How can she use a carpenter's square to test whether she has really cut a semicircle?

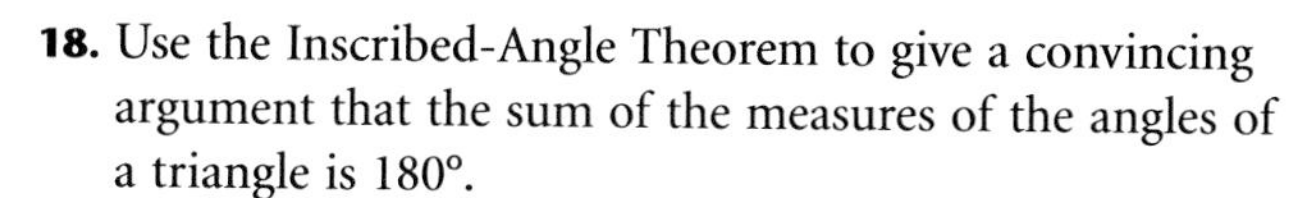

18. Use the Inscribed-Angle Theorem to give a convincing argument that the sum of the measures of the angles of a triangle is 180°.

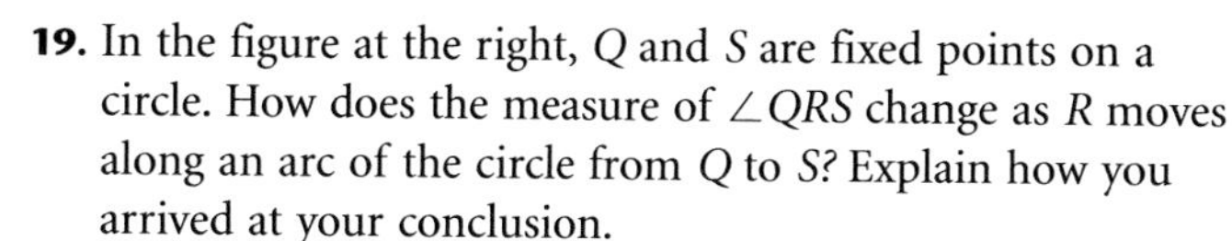

19. In the figure at the right, Q and S are fixed points on a circle. How does the measure of $\angle QRS$ change as R moves along an arc of the circle from Q to S? Explain how you arrived at your conclusion.

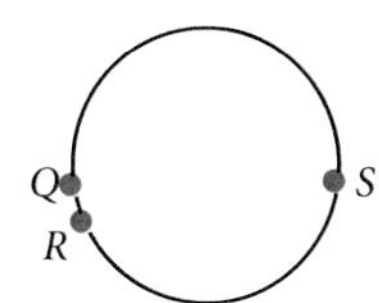

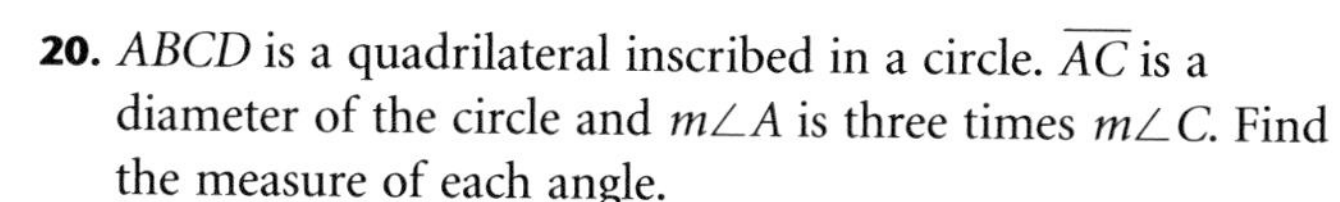

20. $ABCD$ is a quadrilateral inscribed in a circle. $\overline{AC}$ is a diameter of the circle and $m\angle A$ is three times $m\angle C$. Find the measure of each angle.

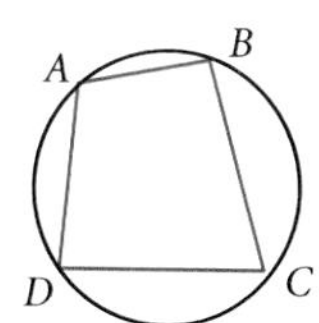

21. Prove: If an angle is inscribed in a semicircle, then it is a right angle.

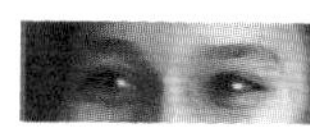

LOOK BACK

Draw a sketch to illustrate each situation. [8-1]

22. Line m is tangent to $\odot C$ at P, and line n is tangent to $\odot C$ at Q. Lines m and n intersect at R.

23. Line s is tangent to $\odot Z$ at A. $\overleftrightarrow{BC}$ is a secant line that intersects $\odot Z$ at B and C. Line s and $\overleftrightarrow{BC}$ intersect at D.

Find each arc measure. [8-2]

24. $m\overset{\frown}{UV}$ 47°

25. $m\overset{\frown}{YV}$ 94°

26. $m\overset{\frown}{UYV}$ 313°

27. $m\overset{\frown}{XYU}$ 180°

28. $m\overset{\frown}{VW}$ 86°

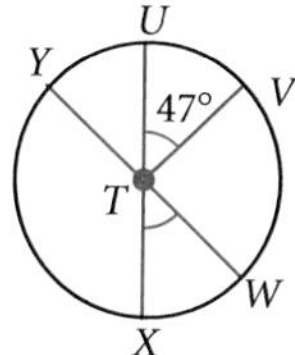

MORE PRACTICE

Find each angle or arc measure.

29. $m\overset{\frown}{BC}$ 118°

30. $m\angle ADB$ 31°

31. $m\angle BDC$ 59°

32. $m\angle ADC$ 90°

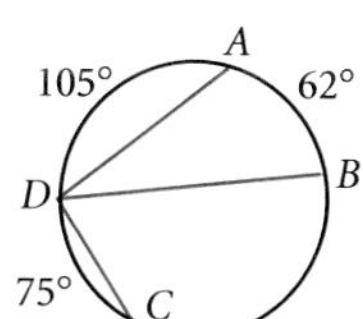

33. $m\overset{\frown}{RS}$ 40°

34. $m\overset{\frown}{RU}$ 100°

35. $m\angle R$ 110°

36. $m\angle S$ 130°

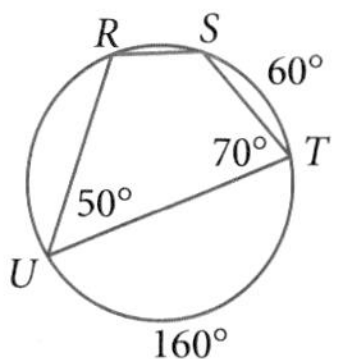

Ongoing Assessment

Self-Assessment Exercises 1–15 odd, 19, 20, 21

Embedded Assessment Reflect 1; Exercises 6, 12, 16, 18

18. $m\overset{\frown}{AB} + m\overset{\frown}{BC} + m\overset{\frown}{AC} = 360°$; $m\angle A = \frac{1}{2}m\overset{\frown}{BC}$, $m\angle B = \frac{1}{2}m\overset{\frown}{AC}$, $m\angle C = \frac{1}{2}m\overset{\frown}{AB}$; Therefore, $m\angle A + m\angle B + m\angle C = 180°$

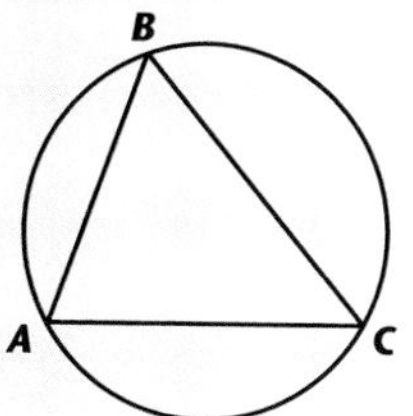

19. Angle remains same since intercepted arc doesn't change.

20. $m\angle A = 135°$; $m\angle B = m\angle D = 90°$; $m\angle C = 45°$

21. The measure of an inscribed angle is half the measure of its intercepted arc. For a semicircle the arc measures 180°, so the angle measures 90°.

Look Back

22.

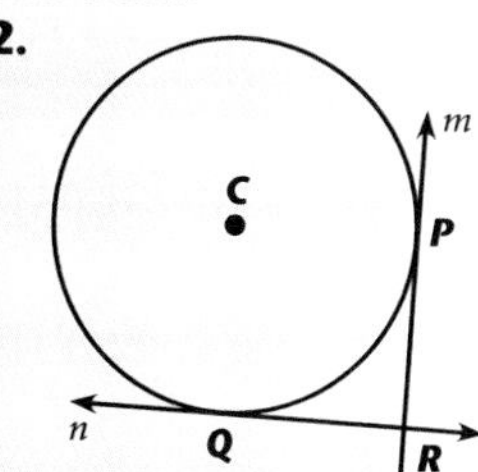

23.

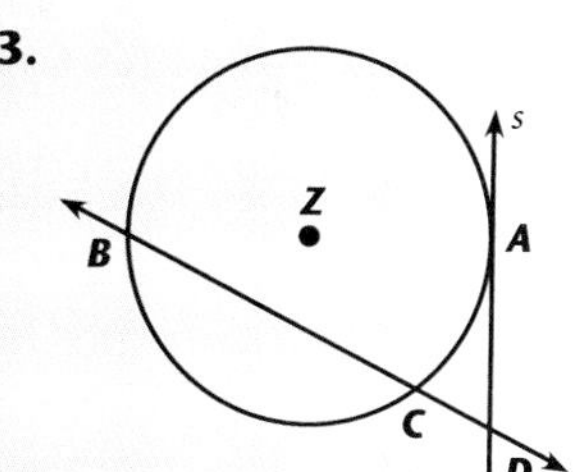

More Math Reasoning

37. Draw $\overline{WX}$ and $\overline{WY}$. Since $\overline{XY}$ is a diameter, $\angle XWY$ intercepts a semicircle and so is a right angle. Then $\triangle XWY$ is a right triangle with hypotenuse $\overline{XY}$. $WX^2 + WY^2 = XY^2$ by the Pythagorean Theorem.

39.

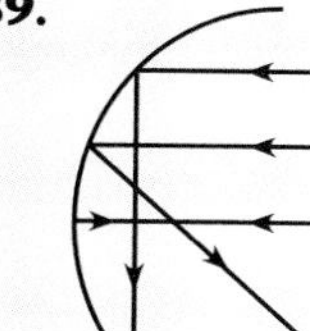

Note: The reflections of the rays are not concurrent.

8-3

The Inscribed-Angle Theorem

PART B At a Glance

Objective

To explore relationships between the measures of secant-tangent and tangent-tangent angles and the arcs they determine.

Development

In the **Explore,** students learn what tangent-secant and tangent-tangent angles are. They discover that the measure of an angle of either type is one-half the difference of the measures of its intercepted arcs.

Suggested Materials

Student Compass, straightedge, protractor, geometry software

Key Terms

Tangent-secant angle, tangent-tangent angle

First Five Minutes

Transparency FFM 8-3B

In your own words, write definitions of *secant, tangent,* and *chord.* Draw one figure that shows an example of each.

Motivate

Ask...

- Draw a circle. Then add a secant and tangent line from the same external point. How many arcs on the circle are determined by these lines? 3

Algebra	Functions	Discrete Math	Probability	Data/Statistics

MORE MATH REASONING

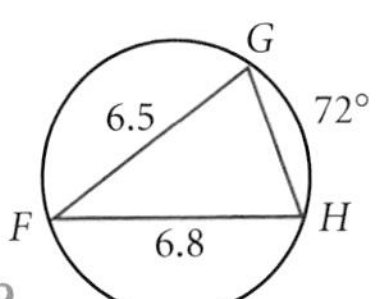

MR **37.** $\overline{XY}$ is a diameter of $\odot Z$. Prove that for any point W on $\odot Z$, $WX^2 + WY^2 = XY^2$.

PS **38.** $\triangle FGH$ is inscribed in a circle as shown. Find the area of $\triangle FGH$. 12.99

C **39. Mirror Image** The cross-section of a spherical mirror is shown in Figure A. When a light ray strikes the mirror, it is reflected so that the angle of incidence is congruent to the angle of reflection, as shown in Figure B. Use a compass and straightedge to make an enlargement of Figure A. Show the incoming light rays x, y, and z. By carefully constructing tangents and measuring angles, find the paths of the rays as they are reflected in the mirror.

Science

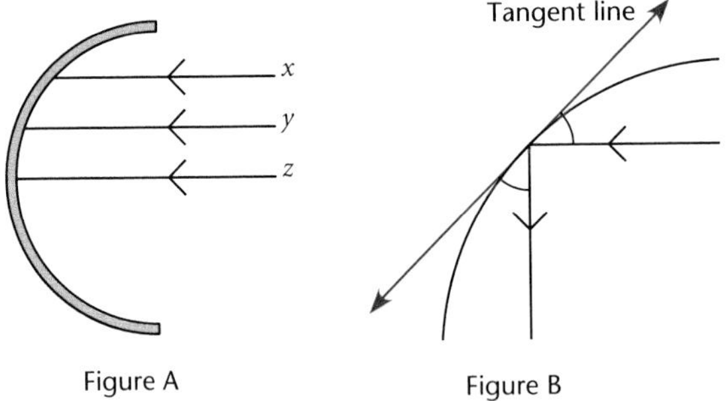

Figure A

Figure B

8-3 PART B Angles Formed by Secants and Tangents

← CONNECT → ***You've investigated some properties of angles that have their vertices on a circle. Now you will discover some relationships between arcs of a circle and angles that have their vertices outside the circle.***

The Inscribed-Angle Theorem can be used to discover several other theorems. These theorems include results about tangent-secant angles, which are often seen in the wheels of railroad trains.

You will investigate two theorems related to the Inscribed-Angle Theorem in the following Explore.

Key

- V Vocabulary
- P Practice/Skills
- R Review
- MR Math Reasoning
- PS Problem Solving
- C Challenge

Technology Note

In the **Explore** on page 589, students will have to draw tangent lines to circles. To do this with software, they will probably need to draw the circle, add a radius, and then construct the line perpendicular to the radius at its endpoint on the circle.

EXPLORE: MOVING OUT

MATERIALS

Compass
Straightedge
Protractor
Geometry software (optional)

1. Use geometry software or a compass and straightedge to construct a figure like the one shown below. $\angle AED$ is a **tangent-secant** angle.

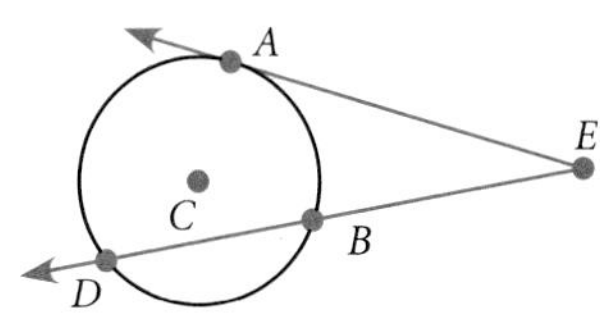

2. Find the measures of the two intercepted arcs. Explain how you did this. Then find the measure of the tangent-secant angle.
3. Repeat Steps 1 and 2 until you think you have found a relationship between the measures of the two intercepted arcs and the measure of the tangent-secant angle. Make a conjecture, and compare your conjecture with your classmates' results.

Problem-Solving Tip
Record your results in a table.

4. Now construct a figure like the one at the right. $\angle FJH$ is a **tangent-tangent** angle.
5. As above, identify a relationship between the measure of a tangent-tangent angle and the measures of the arcs it intercepts. Make a conjecture.

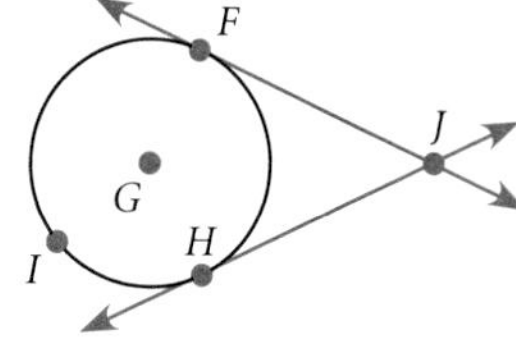

EXAMPLES

1. Find $m\angle VWY$.

The measure of $\angle VWY$ is equal to half the difference of the measures of the arcs it intercepts.

$m\angle VWY = \frac{1}{2}(m\widehat{VY} - m\widehat{VX})$

$m\angle VWY = \frac{1}{2}(146° - 98°) = \frac{1}{2}(48°) = 24°$

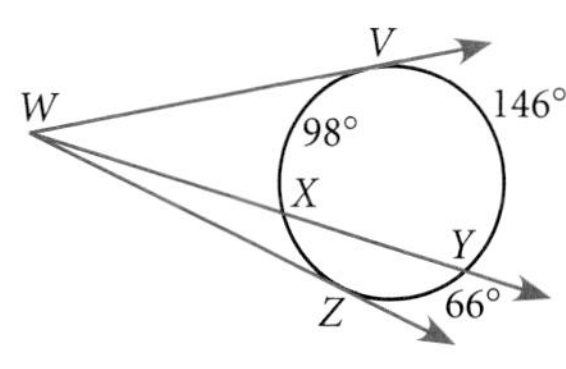

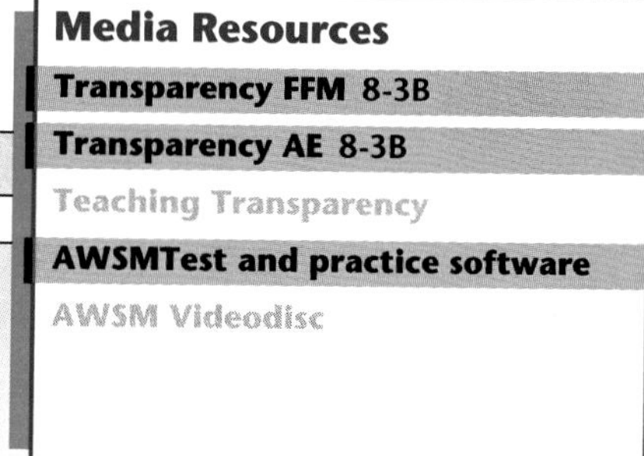

Student Resources
- Alternative Lessons 8-3B
- Laboratory Manual 8-3B
- Technology Lab Manual
- Practice 8-3B
- Study Guide and Journal 8-3B
- Guía de estudios y Diario 8-3B
- Multilingual Handbook
- More Look Ahead 8-3B
- SAT Preparation

Media Resources
- Transparency FFM 8-3B
- Transparency AE 8-3B
- Teaching Transparency
- AWSMTest and practice software
- AWSM Videodisc

EXPLORE

Moving Out

Recommended group size: 4

The Point
To see definitions of tangent-secant and tangent-tangent angles, and to discover that the measure of an angle of either type is one-half the difference of the measures of its intercepted arcs.

Look and Listen...
- For students who do not see how to find the measures of the arcs.
- For students who do not think to look at the difference of the measures of the intercepted arcs.

Ask...
- What type of angle will help you measure an arc?
- Have you tried adding or subtracting the measures of the intercepted arcs?

For Groups That Finish Early
You cannot inscribe a circle inside every parallelogram. Experiment with circles inscribed in parallelograms until you feel confident enough to make a conjecture about which parallelograms can have a circle inscribed in them. **If a circle can be inscribed in a parallelogram, then the parallelogram is a rhombus.**

Follow Up
Ask students to share the conjectures they made in Steps 3 and 5 and to explain how they arrived at those conjectures.

Possible Answers
2. Students who do not use software will need to find the measures of central angles to find the measures of the arcs.
3. The measure of a tangent-secant angle is one-half the difference of the measures of its intercepted arcs.
5. The measure of a tangent-tangent angle is one-half the difference of the measures of its intercepted arcs.

The Inscribed-Angle Theorem

ALTERNATE EXAMPLES

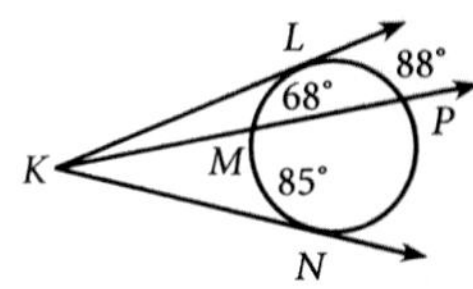

1. Find $m\angle LKP$.

$m\angle LKP = \frac{1}{2}(m\widehat{LP} - m\widehat{LM})$

$m\angle LKP = \frac{1}{2}(88° - 68°)$

$m\angle LKP = \frac{1}{2}(20°) = 10°$

2. Find $m\widehat{LPN}$.

$m\widehat{LPN} = 360° - (68° + 85°)$

$m\widehat{LPN} = 207°$

3. Find $m\angle LKN$.

$m\angle LKN = \frac{1}{2}(207° - 153°) = 27°$

2. Find $m\widehat{XZ}$.

Since a circle has 360°, we can find $m\widehat{XZ}$ by subtraction.

$m\widehat{XZ} = 360° - 66° - 146° - 98° = 50°$

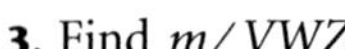

3. Find $m\angle VWZ$.

$m\angle VWZ$ is equal to half the difference of the measures of the arcs it intercepts.

$m\angle VWZ = \frac{1}{2}(m\widehat{VYZ} - m\widehat{VZ})$

$m\angle VWZ = \frac{1}{2}(212° - 148°) = \frac{1}{2}(64°) = 32°$

TRY IT

Find the measure of each angle or arc indicated by a variable.

a. $a = 86$

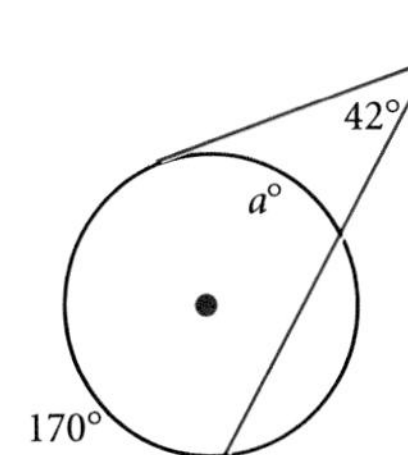

b. $b = 60$

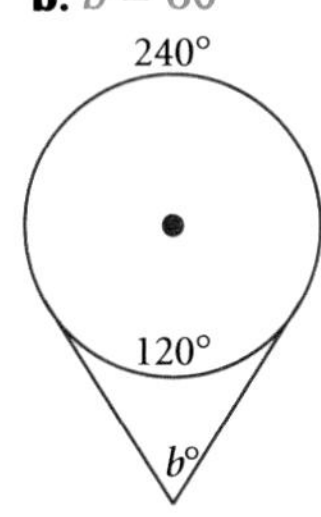

c. $c = 40$

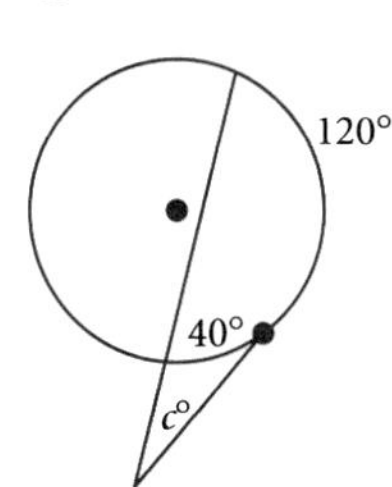

The theorems you've explored are stated below.

TANGENT-SECANT ANGLE THEOREM

The measure of a tangent-secant angle is one-half the difference of the measures of its two intercepted arcs.

$m\angle ADC = \frac{1}{2}(m\widehat{AC} - m\widehat{BC})$

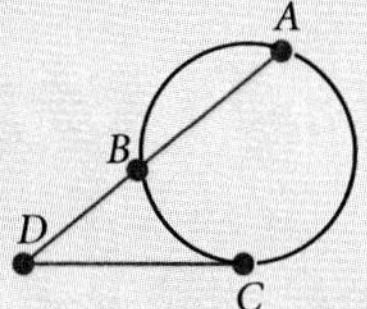

TANGENT-TANGENT ANGLE THEOREM

The measure of a tangent-tangent angle is one-half the difference of the measures of its two intercepted arcs.

$m\angle QTS = \frac{1}{2}(m\widehat{QRS} - m\widehat{QS})$

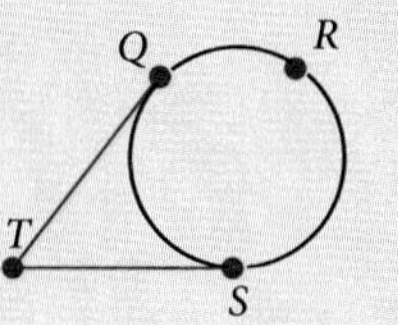

REFLECT

1. Sketch a *secant-secant* angle. How do you think the measure of this angle is related to the measures of the arcs it intercepts?
2. Write one theorem about angle and arc measures that begins, "If an angle intercepts two arcs of a circle and its vertex lies outside the circle . . . "

Exercises

CORE

1. **Getting Started** Follow the steps below to find $m\angle A$.
   a. What is $m\widehat{BDC}$? 240°
   b. What is the difference of $m\widehat{BDC}$ and $m\widehat{BC}$? 120°
   c. Take half of the difference you found in **1b.** This is $m\angle A$. 60°

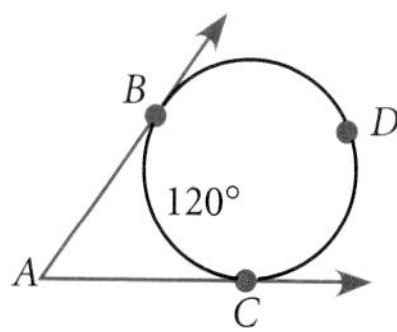

Find the measure of each numbered angle.

2. 51°

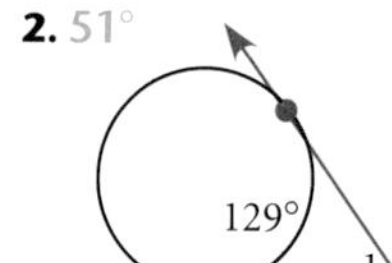

3. 47.5°

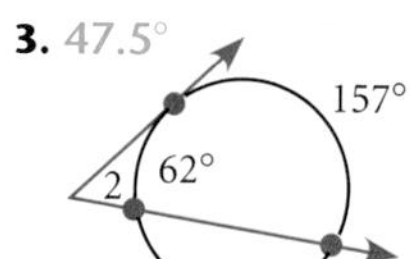

4. 54°

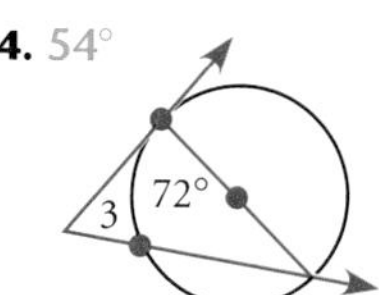

5. 148°

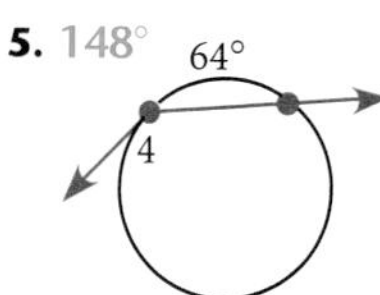

6. **Eye See!** In a farsighted person, light from nearby objects is focused beyond the retina of the eye, so these objects appear blurred. Assume that the eyeball shown is perfectly round. If $m\angle J = 8°$ and $m\widehat{MN} = 25°$, find $m\widehat{KL}$. 9°

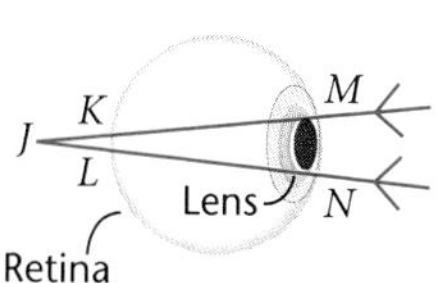

Write the word or phrase that correctly completes each statement.

7. A tangent-tangent angle intersects a circle in ___ points. Two
8. The measure of a tangent-secant angle is ___ the difference of the measures of its intercepted arcs. Half

Find the measure of each angle or arc.

9. If $m\widehat{AC} = 152°$, find $m\angle ABC$. 28°
10. If $m\widehat{ADC} = 248°$, find $m\angle ABC$. 68°
11. If $m\angle ABC = 44°$, find $m\widehat{AC}$ and $m\widehat{ADC}$. $m\widehat{ADC} = 224°$; $m\widehat{AC} = 136°$
12. If $m\widehat{AC} = x$, find $m\angle ABC$ in terms of x. $(180 - x)°$

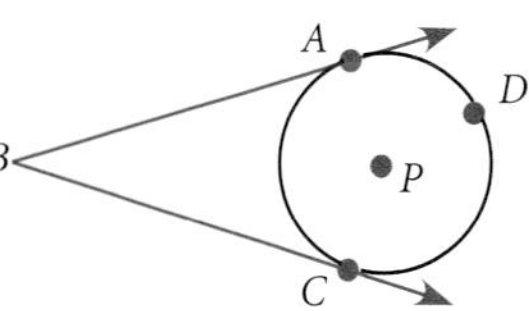

Ongoing Assessment

Vocabulary
Practice/Skills
Review
Math Reasoning
Problem Solving
Challenge

Self-Assessment Exercises 1–19 odd

Embedded Assessment Reflect 1; Exercises 4, 10, 12, 14, 18

Journal

Reflect 1 and 2 are suitable for journal entries.

REFLECT

Possible Answers

1. The measure of a secant-secant angle is one-half the difference of the measures of its intercepted arcs.

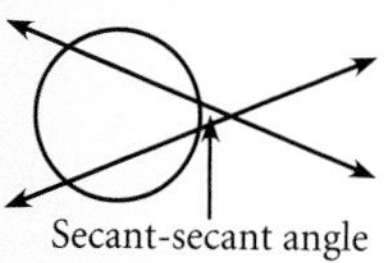

Secant-secant angle

2. If an angle intercepts two arcs of a circle and its vertex lies outside the circle, then its measure is one-half the difference of the measures of its intercepted arcs.

Part B Exercises

Exercise Notes

Core

14. Students apply knowledge of angles and arcs to investigate the region served by a navigational satellite.

15. Students complete the proof of a secant-secant angle theorem.

Look Ahead

These exercises review skills in computing areas. These skills will be important throughout Chapter 9 as students find volumes and surface areas of solids.

More Math Reasoning

32. Students use angles and arcs to calculate the distance from the earth to Mars.

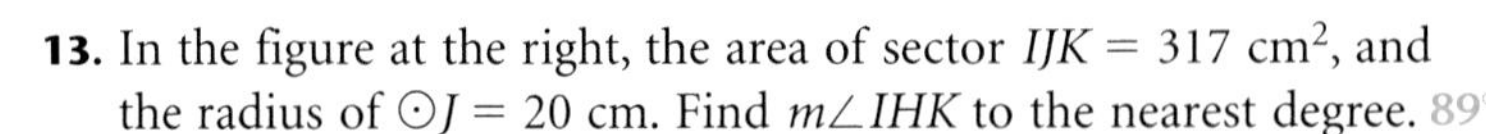

The Inscribed-Angle Theorem

Exercise Answers

Core

14. a. 152°

b. $m\angle LEM = m\widehat{LM} = 152°$; $m\angle N = 180° - m\angle LEM = 28°$

15. 1. Exterior Angle Theorem
2. Algebra; Addition Property of Equality
3. Inscribed-Angle Theorem
4. Substitution

More Math Reasoning

32. a. $m\widehat{LK} = m\angle KEL = 179.9910°$; The central angle is equal to the measure of the arc it intercepts.

b. $\overline{EK}$ is perpendicular to $\overline{KM}$ since $\overline{KM}$ is a tangent.

c. $m\angle KEM = 89.9955°$; $\triangle KEL \cong \triangle LEM$ by HL.

d. About 50,463,000 mi

e. $EM = \frac{KE}{\cos(m\angle KEM)}$, which is highly sensitive to small variations in $m\angle KEM$ near 90°.

PS **13.** In the figure at the right, the area of sector $IJK = 317 \text{ cm}^2$, and the radius of $\odot J = 20$ cm. Find $m\angle IHK$ to the nearest degree. 89°

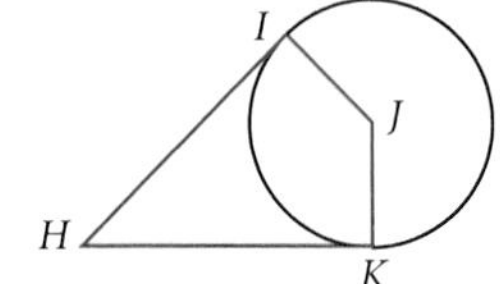

PS Industry **14.** According to Harry Garland of Canon Research Center America, NAVSTAR navigational satellites send radio signals that ships at sea can use to find their exact locations. These signals travel in straight lines. The area of the earth that the signal covers is related to the measure of central angle $\angle LEM$.

a. If the length of $\widehat{LM} = 16{,}900$ km and the radius of the earth is approximately 6370 km, find $m\widehat{LM}$.

b. Use your answer to **14a** to find $m\angle N$ and $m\angle LEM$. Explain how you found each angle measure.

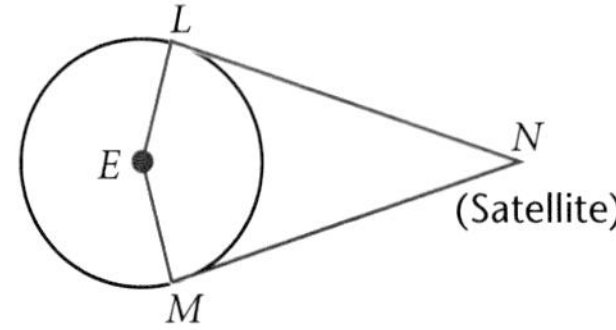

There is a theorem for secant-secant angles that follows the same pattern as those for secant-tangent angles and tangent-tangent angles.

SECANT-SECANT ANGLE THEOREM

The measure of a secant-secant angle is one-half the difference of the measures of its two intercepted arcs.

$m\angle CAD = \frac{1}{2}(m\widehat{CD} - m\widehat{BE})$

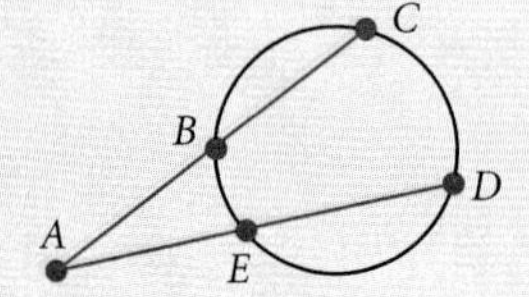

MR **15.** Complete the following proof of the Secant-Secant Angle Theorem.

Given: Figure as shown.

Prove: $m\angle CAD = \frac{1}{2}(m\widehat{CD} - m\widehat{BE})$

Proof:

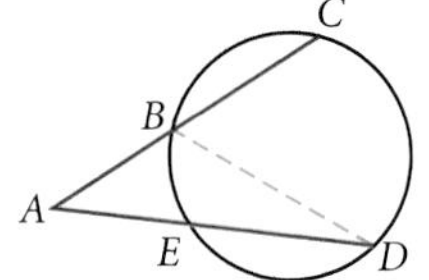

Statements	Reasons
1. $m\angle CBD = m\angle CAD + m\angle BDA$	**1.**
2. $m\angle CBD - m\angle BDA = m\angle CAD$	**2.**
3. $m\angle CBD = \frac{1}{2}m\widehat{CD}$, $m\angle BDA = \frac{1}{2}m\widehat{BE}$	**3.**
4. $\frac{1}{2}m\widehat{CD} - \frac{1}{2}m\widehat{BE} = m\angle CAD$	**4.**
5. $m\angle CAD = \frac{1}{2}(m\widehat{CD} - m\widehat{BE})$	**5.** Algebra; Symmetric Property of Equality, Distributive Property

Key

V Vocabulary
P Practice/Skills
R Review
MR Math Reasoning
PS Problem Solving
C Challenge

P **Find the measure of each angle or arc.**

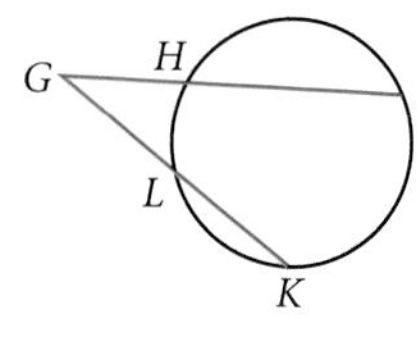

16. If $m\widehat{JK} = 105°$ and $m\widehat{HL} = 41°$, find $m\angle G$. 32°

17. If $m\widehat{JK} = 145°$ and $m\angle G = 38°$, find $m\widehat{HL}$. 69°

18. If $m\angle G = 53°$ and $m\widehat{HL} = 62°$, find $m\widehat{JK}$. 168°

19. If $m\widehat{JK} = (3x - 22)°$ and $m\widehat{HL} = (x - 16)°$, find $m\angle G$ in terms of x. $(x - 3)°$

LOOK AHEAD

R **Find the area of each figure. Round answers to the nearest tenth.**

20. 18.9

21. 51.3

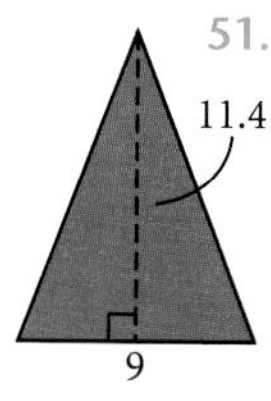

22. 1661.9

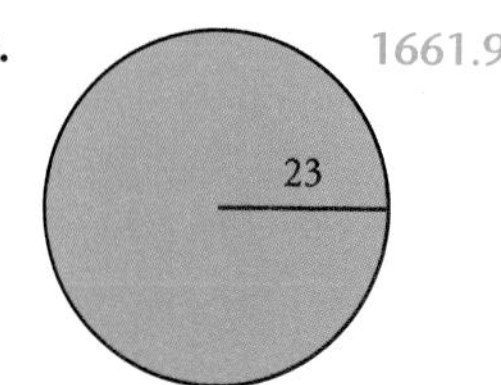

MORE PRACTICE

P **Find the measure of each numbered angle.**

23. 90°

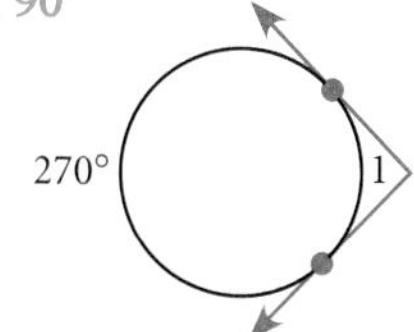

24. 8°

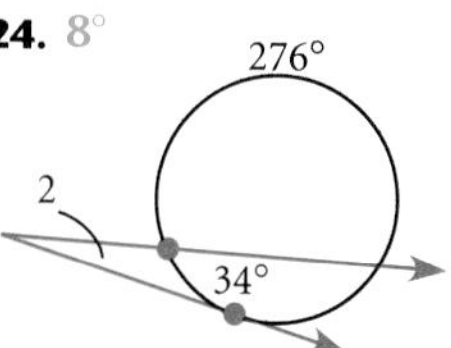

25. 111°

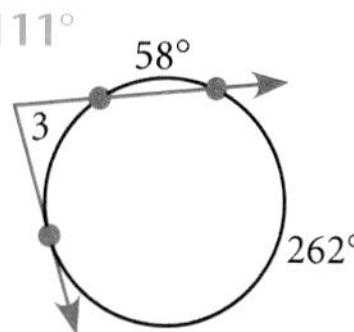

26. 101°

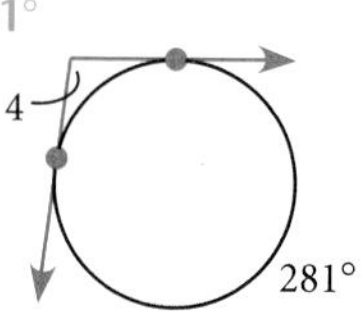

27. 42°

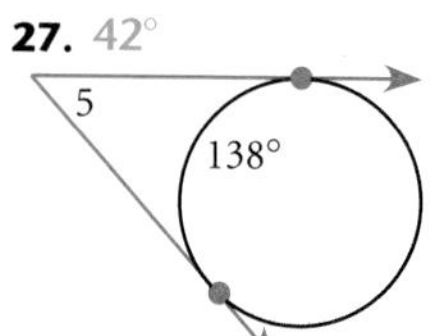

28. 99°

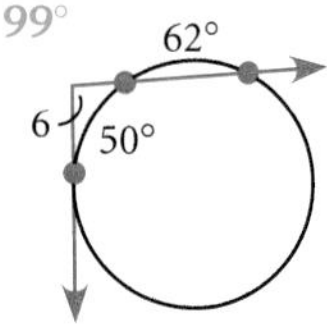

P **Find the measure of each angle or arc.**

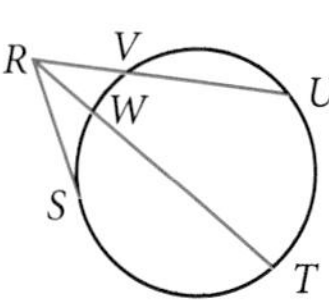

29. If $m\widehat{UT} = 32°$ and $m\widehat{VW} = 27°$, find $m\angle URT$. 2.5°

30. If $m\angle URS = 77°$ and $m\widehat{VS} = 95°$, find $m\widehat{UTS}$. 249°

31. If $m\angle URS = 68°$, $m\angle TRS = 30°$, $m\widehat{WS} = 41°$, and $m\widehat{UTS} = 255°$, find $m\widehat{VW}$. 18°

The Inscribed-Angle Theorem

PART C At a Glance

Objective

To use inscribed angles to find the best region for a good shot in a soccer match.

Development

In the **Explore,** students see how to use inscribed angles to describe the best area for scoring goals in a soccer match.

Suggested Materials

Student Straightedge, scissors, protractor

First Five Minutes

Transparency FFM 8-3C

Give a brief written and illustrated summary of inscribed angles, tangent-secant angles, and tangent-tangent angles. Explain how the measures of these angles are related to the measures of their intercepted arcs.

EXPLORE

Going for the Goal

Recommended group size: 4

The Point

To see how measures of inscribed angles are related to the chance of scoring a goal in a soccer match. Students discover that the "danger area" described is a circular region.

Look and Listen...

- For students whose angle cutout is too small.
- For students who do not understand how to use their angle cutout to find points in the danger area.

Ask...

- Position the 40° angle on the field so that its sides just touch both of the goal posts. What does this tell you about the vertex of the angle?

MORE MATH REASONING

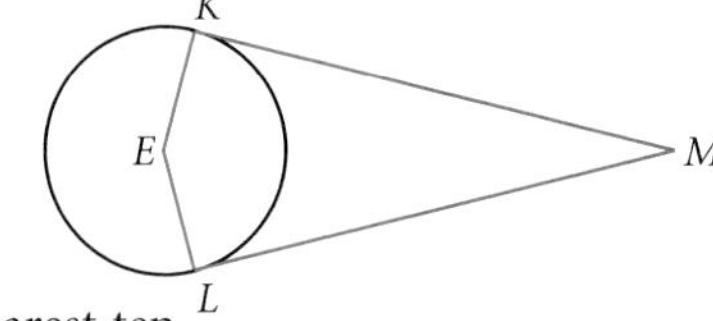

MR, C Science **32.** Suppose that Mars, M, is rising in your city K at the same time it is setting in city L. The radius of the great circle of the earth shown is 3963.34 miles. The distance from city L to city K is 12,450.58 miles.

a. Find the measure of $\widehat{LK}$. Record your answer to the nearest ten-thousandth. What is $m\angle KEL$? Explain how you found this value.

b. What is true about $\overline{EK}$ and $\overline{KM}$? How do you know this?

c. Draw $\overline{EM}$. What do you think $m\angle KEM$ is? Justify your answer.

d. Use trigonometry to find EM.

e. Why do you think such accuracy was needed in **32a**? (Hint: See what happens if you round your answers in **32a** to the nearest degree.)

PS **33.** Soccer goalies know that a player directly in front of the goal is more dangerous than one off to one side, even when the player is the same distance from the goal.

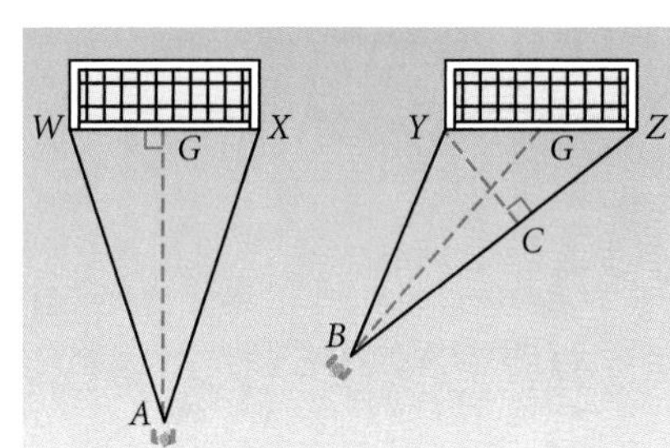

a. Player A is 18 yd from G, the center of the 8-yd-wide goal, so $AG = 18$ yd, and $WX = 8$ yd. Find the measure of the "shooting angle," $\angle WAX$. 25°

b. Player B is also 18 yd from the center of the goal, so $BG = 18$ yd and $YZ = 8$ yd. In this position, $BY = 15$ yd and $YC = 4.22$ yd. Find the measure of shooting angle $\angle YBZ$. 16°

8-3 PART C Making Connections

← CONNECT → ***Inscribed angles can tell you where a soccer player has the best chance of scoring a goal and how light is reflected in a curved mirror. You've investigated inscribed angles and a few of the theorems that are based on their properties.***

When you're trying to score a goal in soccer, you want to have the largest possible angle to shoot for. This is one reason why it's easier to score a goal from the center of the field than from the sidelines. In the following Explore, you will see how inscribed angles affect your chances of scoring a goal in a soccer game.

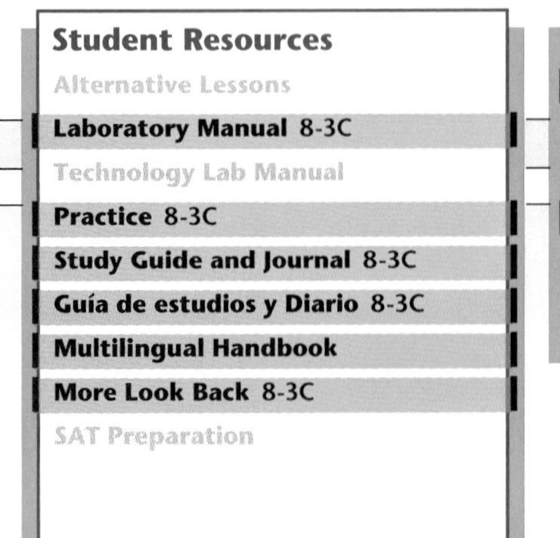

Student Resources

Alternative Lessons
Laboratory Manual 8-3C
Technology Lab Manual
Practice 8-3C
Study Guide and Journal 8-3C
Guía de estudios y Diario 8-3C
Multilingual Handbook
More Look Back 8-3C
SAT Preparation

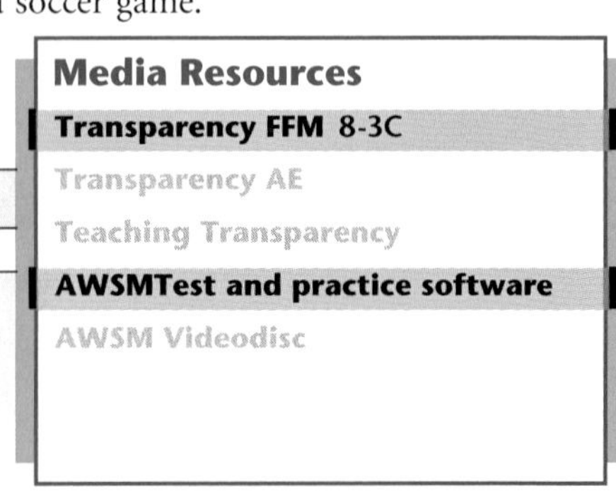

Media Resources

Transparency FFM 8-3C
Transparency AE
Teaching Transparency
AWSMTest and practice software
AWSM Videodisc

EXPLORE: GOING FOR THE GOAL

MATERIALS

Straightedge
Scissors
Protractor

As the coach of a soccer team, you know that your next opponent has one very dangerous player. Whenever she gets the ball positioned so that the angle formed by one goal post (A), her position (at the vertex, P) and the other goal post (B) measures 40° or more, she always scores a goal.

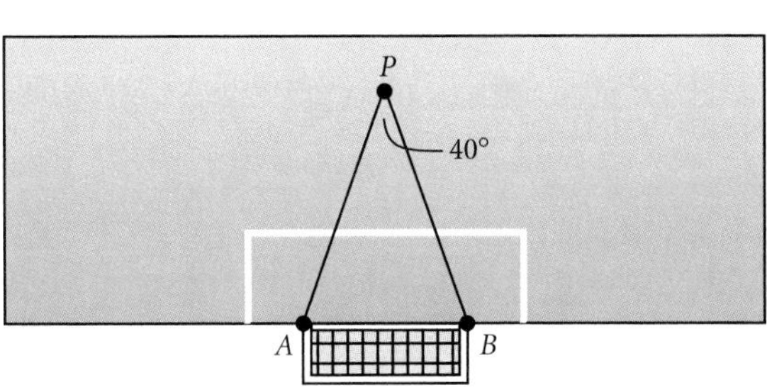

You tell your players never to let this player get the ball to where this angle is 40° or more. They reply that they need a better description of where this "danger area" is.

1. Make a sketch of the part of a soccer field nearest the goal, as shown above.
2. Cut out a large 40° angle. Place it on your sketch as shown. Move it around and mark the locus of points for which the goal posts exactly determine a 40° angle. Describe these points.
3. Use your answer from Step 2 to help identify all the points where the goal posts determine an angle of 40° or more. Shade this area on your drawing. What does it look like?
4. Suppose the length of $\widehat{AB}$ is 8 yd. Find the radius of the circle. Then prepare an illustration and written description of the "danger area" for your team. Give specific measurements wherever you can.

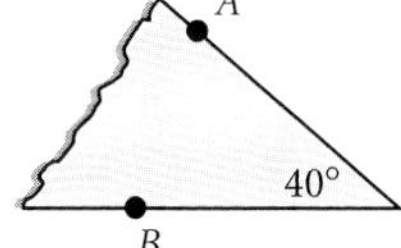

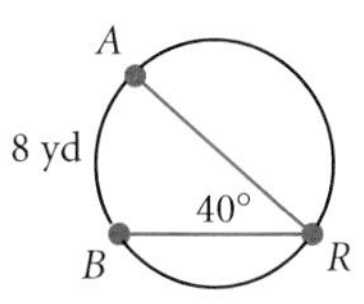

REFLECT

1. Give a short written summary of the relationships between the measures of angles and their intercepted arcs.
2. In your own words, explain why an inscribed angle that intercepts a semicircle must measure 90°.

ssessment Resources

uiz 8-3
hapter Assessment Form A
hapter Assessment Form B
hapter Alternative Assessment
lid-Year Assessment
nd-of-Year Assessment
WSMTest and practice software

Ongoing Assessment

Self-Assessment Self-Assessment Exercises

Embedded Assessment Explore Steps 2, 3, 4; Reflect 1, 2

For Groups That Finish Early

Find the radius of the danger area if the danger angle is 20° instead of 40°. **11.5 yd**

Follow Up

Ask students to come to the board and sketch the danger area. Have them describe this area as accurately as they can.

Possible Answers

2. The points form a major arc of a circle. (Its minor arc is the arc inside the goal.)
3. The danger area is a circle and its interior, except for the region of the circle that lies inside the goal.
4. The radius of the circle is approximately 5.7 yd.

   The danger area is the region outside the goal that is on or inside a circle with two points on the goal posts and a 5.7-yd radius. The goal posts cut off an arc of length 8 yd and measure 80°, and the center of the circle is about 4.4 yd from the segment containing the goal posts.

Portfolio

Have students select items from their work that demonstrate their understanding of the material in 8-3.

You may want to have students include their favorite applications problems involving at least two of the following: inscribed angles, tangent-secant angles, and tangent-tangent angles.

REFLECT

Possible Answers

1. The measure of a minor arc equals the measure of its central angle. The measure of a major arc is 360° minus the measure of its minor arc. The measure of a tangent-secant or tangent-tangent angle is one-half the difference of the measures of its intercepted arcs. The measure of an inscribed angle is half the measure of its intercepted arc.
2. Since the semicircle measures 180°, and the measure of an inscribed angle is half the measure of its intercepted arc, the inscribed angle measures 90°.

The Inscribed-Angle Theorem

Self-Assessment

Exercise Notes

5. Similar to multiple-choice questions on standardized tests.

11. Students use inscribed angles to investigate a "danger circle" used to help ships avoid shallow waters.

Self-Assessment Answers

11. The danger angle is always $180° - \frac{m\widehat{XY}}{2}$.

12. a. 7.51 cm

b. Using trigonometry, $m\angle UVW = 84°$; $m\widehat{UW} = 180° - 84° = 96°$; $m\widehat{USW} = 360° - 96° = 264°$.

c. 10 cm

Self-Assessment

P **Find the measure of each angle or arc.**

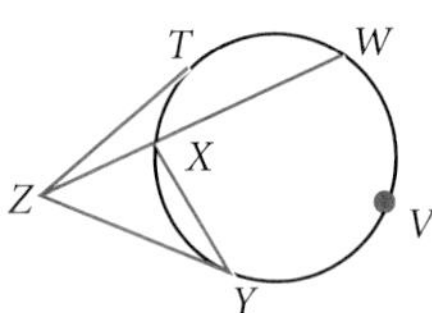

1. If $m\widehat{WVY} = 184°$, find $m\angle WXY$. 92°

2. If $m\angle WXY = 68°$, find $m\widehat{WVY}$. 136°

3. If $m\widehat{TY} = 116°$, find $m\angle TZY$. 64°

4. If $m\widehat{TX} = 32°$ and $m\widehat{XY} = 84°$, find $m\angle TZY$. 64°

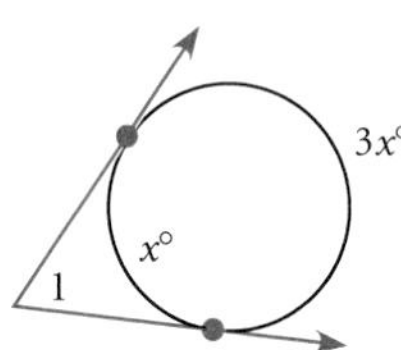

P **5.** In the figure, $m\angle 1 =$ (c)
(a) 45° (b) 60° (c) 90°
(d) 120° (e) 150°

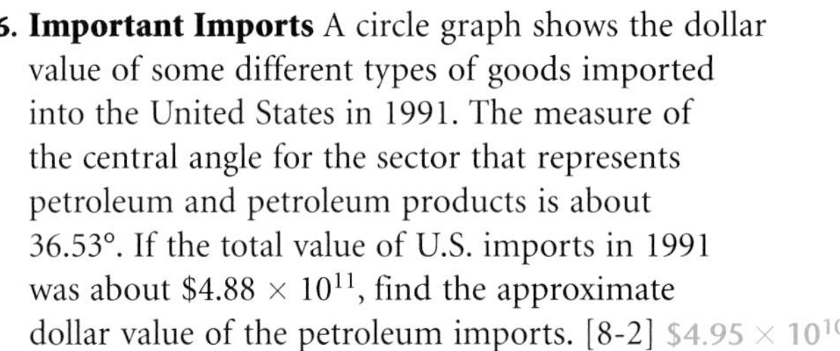

PS Social Science **6. Important Imports** A circle graph shows the dollar value of some different types of goods imported into the United States in 1991. The measure of the central angle for the sector that represents petroleum and petroleum products is about 36.53°. If the total value of U.S. imports in 1991 was about $\$4.88 \times 10^{11}$, find the approximate dollar value of the petroleum imports. [8-2] $\$4.95 \times 10^{10}$

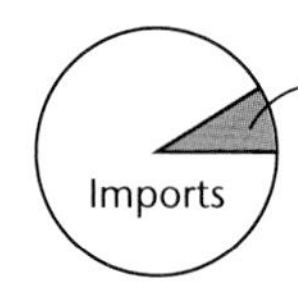

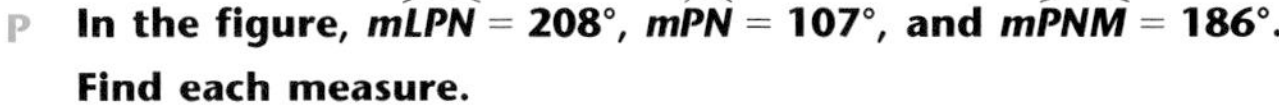

P **In the figure, $m\widehat{LPN} = 208°$, $m\widehat{PN} = 107°$, and $m\widehat{PNM} = 186°$. Find each measure.**

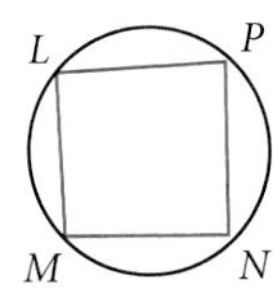

7. $m\angle L$ 93°

8. $m\angle M$ 104°

9. $m\angle N$ 87°

10. $m\angle P$ 76°

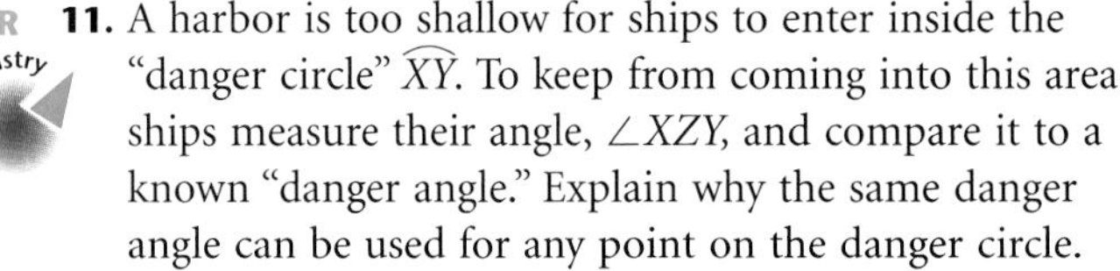

MR Industry **11.** A harbor is too shallow for ships to enter inside the "danger circle" $\widehat{XY}$. To keep from coming into this area, ships measure their angle, $\angle XZY$, and compare it to a known "danger angle." Explain why the same danger angle can be used for any point on the danger circle.

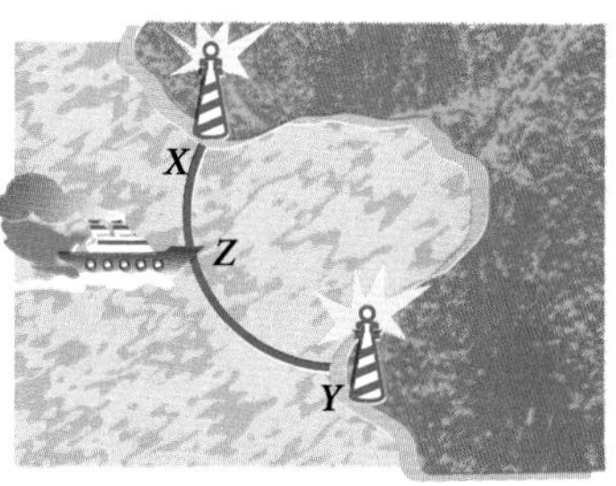

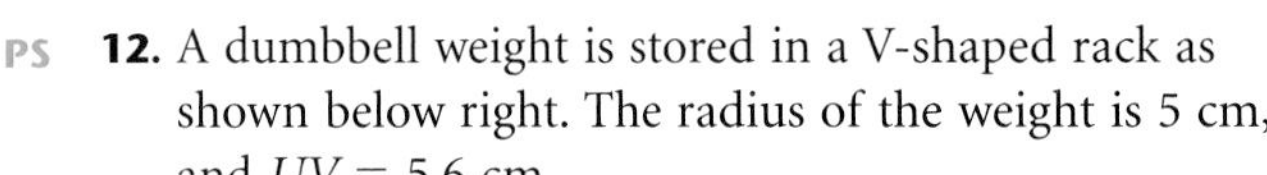

PS **12.** A dumbbell weight is stored in a V-shaped rack as shown below right. The radius of the weight is 5 cm, and $UV = 5.6$ cm.

a. Find the distance VT from the tip of the V to the center of the weight.

b. Find $m\angle UVW$, $m\widehat{USW}$, and $m\widehat{UW}$. Explain how you found each of these.

c. If $m\angle UVW$ were 60°, what would VT be?

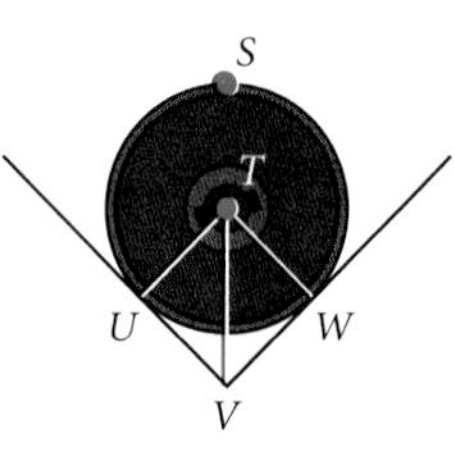

Key

V Vocabulary
P Practice/Skills
R Review
MR Math Reasoning
PS Problem Solving
C Challenge

gic/Reasoning | Industry/Careers | Science/Health | Social Science/History | Fine Arts/Literature

Chapter 8 Review

In Chapter 8, you learned several properties of circles and spheres. You also explored the lines, angles, and regions associated with these figures.

KEY TERMS

arc [8-2]	concentric [8-1]	pi (π) [8-1]
center of a circle [8-1]	diameter [8-1]	radius [8-1]
central angle [8-2]	great circle [8-1]	secant line [8-1]
chord [8-2]	inscribed [8-1]	sector [8-2]
circle [8-1]	inscribed angle [8-3]	semicircle [8-2]
circumference [8-1]	major arc [8-2]	sphere [8-1]
circumscribed [8-1]	minor arc [8-2]	tangent line [8-1]

Determine whether each statement is true or false. If the statement is false, change the underlined word or phrase to make it true.

1. Pi is the ratio of the circumference of a circle to its <u>diameter.</u> T
2. The center of a circle is the vertex of <u>an inscribed angle</u> of the circle. F; A central angle
3. A polygon is <u>circumscribed about</u> a circle if each of its vertices lies on the circle. F; Inscribed in

CONCEPTS AND APPLICATIONS

4. Find the radius and area of a circle with a circumference of 14π. [8-1] 7; $49\pi \approx 153.94$

In the figure, $\overleftrightarrow{QZ}$ is tangent to $\odot O$ at Z, $m\widehat{YZ} = 82°$, and $m\widehat{XY} = 70°$. Give an example of each of the following. [8-1, 8-2, 8-3]

5. an inscribed angle $\angle YWZ$
6. a secant line Possible answer: $\overleftrightarrow{XY}$
7. a minor arc Possible answer: $\widehat{XY}$

Find each of the following. [8-2, 8-3]

8. $m\angle YWZ$ 41°
9. $m\angle YOZ$ 82°
10. $m\widehat{XWZ}$ 208°
11. $m\angle OZQ$ 90°
12. $m\angle Q$ 63°
13. A square with a side length of twenty centimeters is inscribed in a circle. What are the circumference and area of the circle? [8-1] $20\pi\sqrt{2} \approx 88.86$ cm; $200\pi \approx 628.32$ cm^2

y

Vocabulary
Practice/Skills
Review
R Math Reasoning
Problem Solving
Challenge

Chapter 8 Review

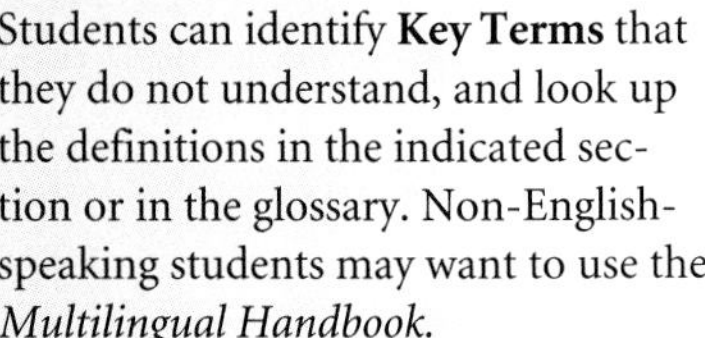

Journal

Students can identify **Key Terms** that they do not understand, and look up the definitions in the indicated section or in the glossary. Non-English-speaking students may want to use the *Multilingual Handbook.*

Vocabulary exercises and the **Self-Evaluation** are useful journal entries.

Review Answers

14. Since the perpendicular from the center to a chord bisects it, $WY = \frac{1}{2}WX = \frac{1}{2}TS = TV$, so $\overline{WY} \cong \overline{TV}$. $\overline{WZ} \cong \overline{TZ}$ because radii are congruent. Then $\triangle WZY \cong \triangle TZV$ by HL for right triangles, and $\overline{ZY} \cong \overline{ZV}$ by CPCTC. Therefore, $ZY = ZV$ by definition of *congruent segments.*

17. a.

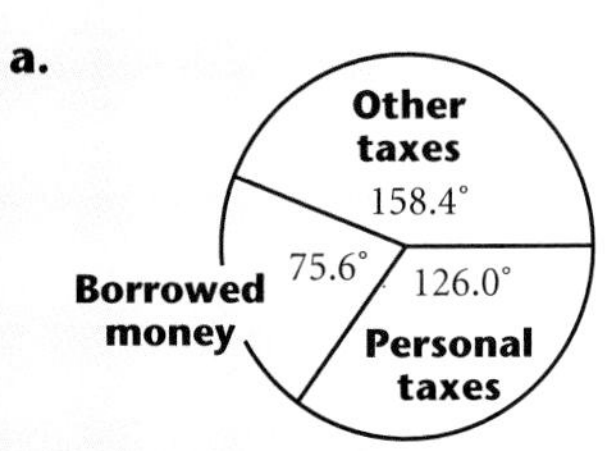

b. 0.16 in.^{2} **c.** 75.6°; 0.7 in.

18. a. Possible answer:

r	R	d	D	D−d
10	11	31.42	34.56	3.14
100	101	314.2	317.3	3.14

b. $\pi(R - r) = D - d$

Chapter 8 Assessment

Portfolio

Students may select items that represent their mathematical understanding of the ideas in Chapter 8 and that illustrate the effort that they put into this chapter.

A rubric for assessing portfolios is included in the introduction to the Teacher's Edition.

Assessment Answers

12. If a radius bisects a chord, then they are perpendicular. If a radius is perpendicular to a chord, then it bisects the chord. The perpendicular bisector of a chord contains the center of the circle.

14. a. 36°

b. $8800\pi \approx 27{,}646.02$ mi; About 28 times as fast

MR **14.** Prove: If two chords of a circle (that are not diameters) are congruent, then they are equidistant from its center. [8-2]

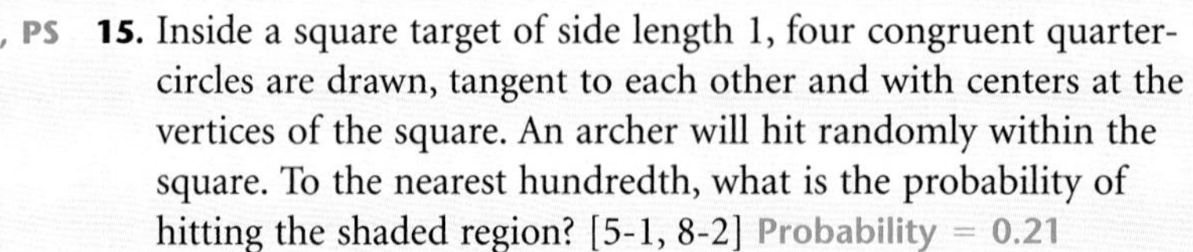

Given: $\overline{WX} \cong \overline{ST}$, $\overline{ZY} \perp \overline{WX}$, $\overline{ZV} \perp \overline{ST}$

Prove: $\overline{ZY} \cong \overline{ZV}$

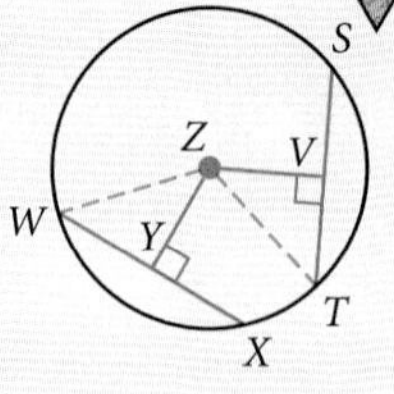

R, PS **15.** Inside a square target of side length 1, four congruent quarter-circles are drawn, tangent to each other and with centers at the vertices of the square. An archer will hit randomly within the square. To the nearest hundredth, what is the probability of hitting the shaded region? [5-1, 8-2] Probability = 0.21

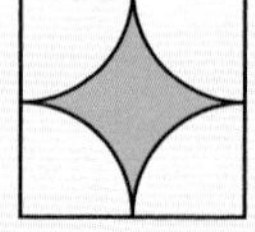

P **16.** What are the center and radius of the circle with equation $x^2 + y^2 = 13$? [8-1]
Center: (0, 0); Radius: $\sqrt{13}$

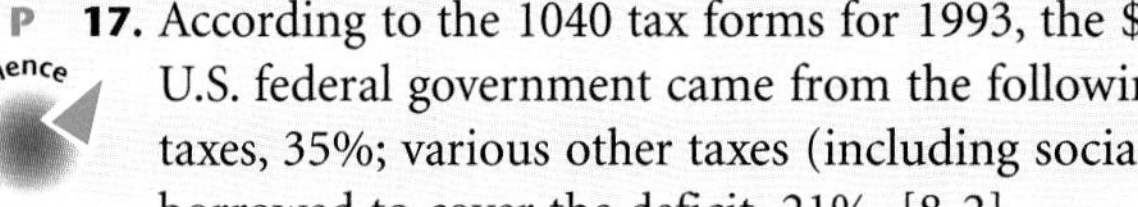

P **17.** According to the 1040 tax forms for 1993, the $1381-billion budget of the U.S. federal government came from the following sources: personal income taxes, 35%; various other taxes (including social security, etc.), 44%; money borrowed to cover the deficit, 21%. [8-2]

Social Science

a. Make a circle graph of radius $\frac{1}{2}$ in. to represent these income sources.

b. What is the area of the sector representing borrowed money?

c. To the nearest tenth, give the degree measure and the length of the arc intercepted by the central angle of the sector representing borrowed money.

CONCEPTS AND CONNECTIONS

PS, C **18. Sports** In races on an oval track, the leader usually takes the inside lane when going around curves. The oval tracks are actually semicircles connected by straightaways as shown.

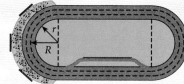

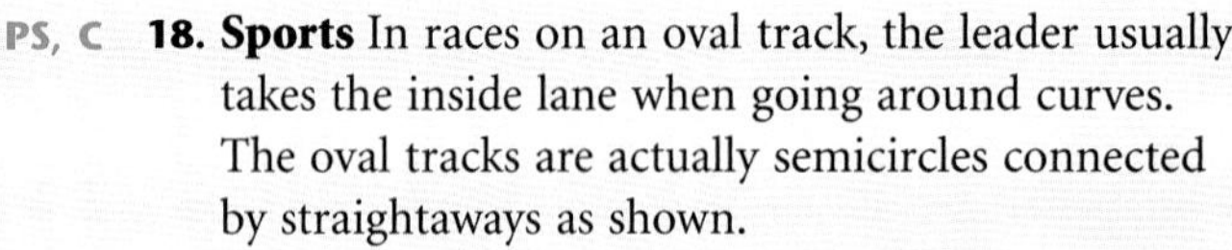

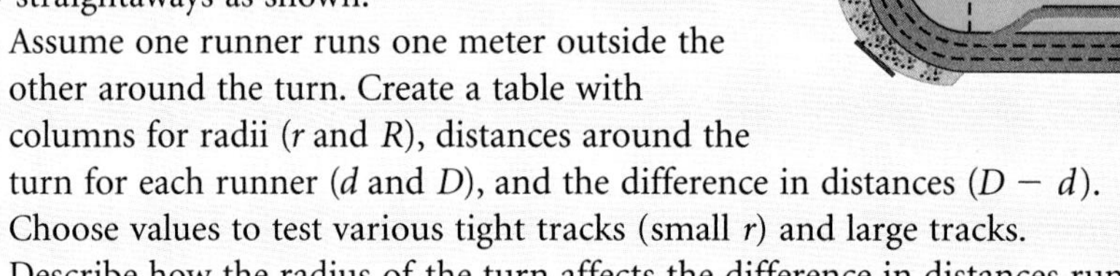

a. Assume one runner runs one meter outside the other around the turn. Create a table with columns for radii (r and R), distances around the turn for each runner (d and D), and the difference in distances ($D - d$). Choose values to test various tight tracks (small r) and large tracks. Describe how the radius of the turn affects the difference in distances run.

b. Now develop a general formula for the difference in distances around one turn in terms of r and R.

SELF-EVALUATION

Write a summary of the most important facts from Chapter 8. Include properties and formulas related to angle and arc measurement, length, and area. Provide sketches to communicate your ideas more completely.

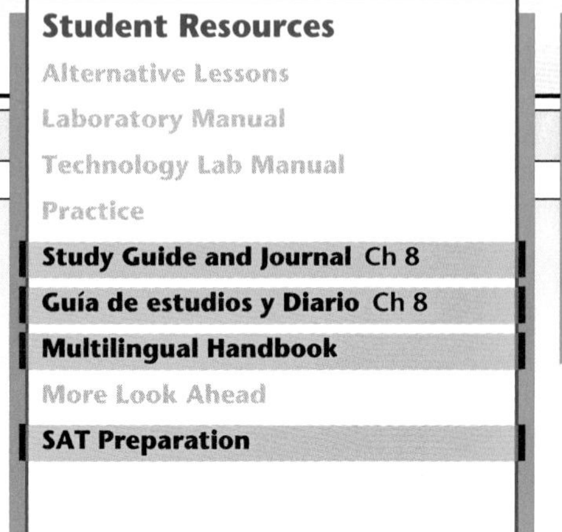

Student Resources

Alternative Lessons
Laboratory Manual
Technology Lab Manual
Practice
Study Guide and Journal Ch 8
Guía de estudios y Diario Ch 8
Multilingual Handbook
More Look Ahead
SAT Preparation

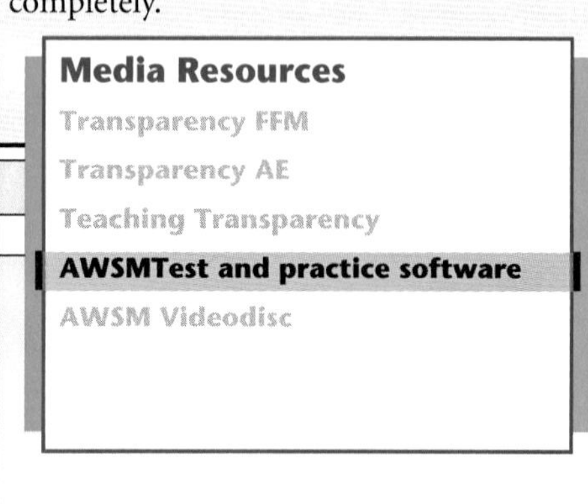

Media Resources

Transparency FFM
Transparency AE
Teaching Transparency
AWSMTest and practice software
AWSM Videodisc

gic/Reasoning | Industry/Careers | Science/Health | Social Science/History | Fine Arts/Literature

Chapter 8 Assessment

TEST

1. The diameter of a circle is 12 m. Find its circumference and area.
 $C = 12\pi \approx 37.70$ m; $A = 36\pi \approx 113.10$ m^2

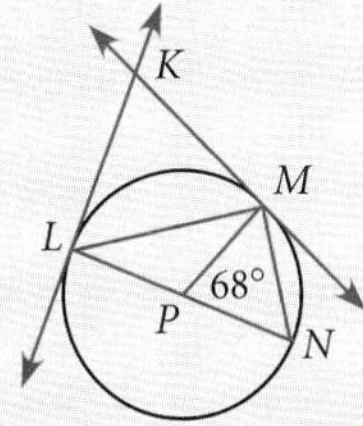

In the figure, $\overleftrightarrow{KM}$ and $\overleftrightarrow{KL}$ are tangent to ⊙P, whose radius is 20 mm. Give an example of each of the following.

2. a chord
 Possible answer: $\overline{LM}$

3. a point of tangency
 Possible answer: L

4. a radius
 Possible answer: $\overline{PN}$

Find each of the following.

5. $m\widehat{MN}$ 68°

6. $m\angle NML$ 90°

7. $m\angle MNL$ 56°

8. $m\angle MKL$ 68°

9. length of $\widehat{MN}$ 23.74 mm

10. Give an equation for a circle with its center at the origin and radius 8. $x^2 + y^2 = 64$

11. A chord of a circle has length 4.2 cm and is 8 cm from the center of the circle. What is the radius of the circle to the nearest hundredth? 8.27 cm

12. Write a brief summary of the relationships among a chord, its perpendicular bisector, and the radii of a circle. Include illustrations with your summary.

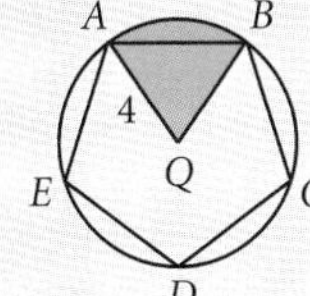

13. Regular pentagon *ABCDE* is inscribed in ⊙Q with radius 4.
 a. Find the area of sector *AQB* to the nearest hundredth. 10.05
 b. Use an auxiliary line and trigonometry to find *AB*. 4.70

14. The equatorial radius of Jupiter is 44,000 miles—about 11 times that of the earth. However, Jupiter's "day"—the time it takes to rotate once on its axis—is only 10 hr!
 a. What is the measure of the arc through which Jupiter turns in 1 hr?
 b. Find the distance that a point on Jupiter's equator travels in 1 hr. How does this compare with the earth's rotational speed of about 1000 mi/hr?

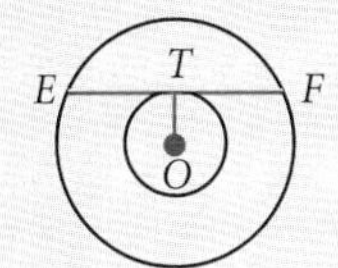

15. The radius of the smaller of two concentric circles is 1.2 m. $\overline{EF}$ is tangent to the smaller circle at *T* and is a chord of the larger circle. If $EF = 3.2$, what is the radius of the larger circle? 2 m

PERFORMANCE TASK

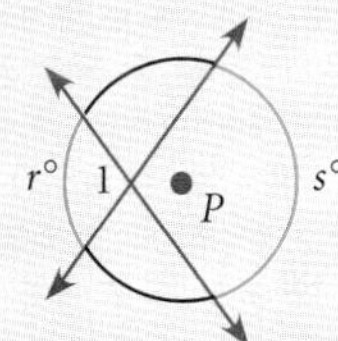

Draw several circles with intersecting secant lines as shown. For each, measure arcs and angles. Then state a conjecture about the relationship between the measure of an angle formed by secants intersecting inside a circle and the measures of the intercepted arcs.

Assessment Resources

uiz
hapter 8 Assessment Form A
hapter 8 Assessment Form B
hapter 8 Alternative Assessment
Mid-Year Assessment
nd-of-Year Assessment
WSMTest Chapter 8

Ongoing Assessment

Self-Assessment Chapter 8 Review and Self-Evaluation

Embedded Assessment Chapter 8 Performance Task

Test Chapter 8 Test

Performance Task

Answer

$m\angle 1 = \frac{s + r}{2}$

Suggested Scoring Rubric

Level 4 Full Accomplishment

- Students make the correct conjecture that the measure of the angle is one-half the sum of the measures of the intercepted arcs.
- Drawings and data show evidence that the conjecture is based on the results of more than one trial. (If students try more than four or five cases, you may want to remind them that since there are an infinite number of points inside the circle, they can never *prove* their conjecture this way.)

Level 3 Substantial Accomplishment

- Students make the correct conjecture that the measure of the angle is one-half the sum of the measures of the intercepted arcs.
- Drawings and data show evidence that the conjecture is only based on one trial.

Level 2 Partial Accomplishment

- Students make a reasonable but incorrect conjecture that makes sense for some of their collected data.
- Drawings and tables show evidence that students have collected data.

Level 1 Little Accomplishment

- No conjecture is made, or the conjecture is incompatible with the collected data.
- There is no evidence of data collection.

Chapter 9 Surface Area and Volume

Project A

Play Ball!

Did you know that the circumference of the first softball was five inches more than today's standard softball?

Project B

For Here or To Go?

What did take-out restaurants do before the invention of styrofoam?

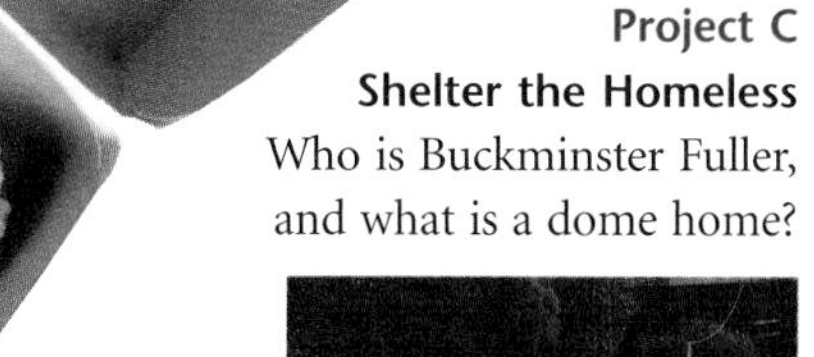

Project C

Shelter the Homeless

Who is Buckminster Fuller, and what is a dome home?

600

A

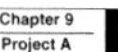

Chapter 9 Project A

Play Ball!

Sew Your Own Ball Pattern

Discover the two-dimensional net of a basketball or softball. Sew the pieces together.

- Did you know that the circumference of the first softball was 5 in. more than today's standard softball?
- Don't you wonder how flat material is formed into a sphere?
- How does this connect to Chapter 9? Balls with different **surface area** patterns can have the same form and **volume.**

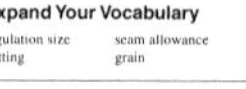

Expand Your Vocabulary

regulation size, seam allowance, batting, grain

Project Guidelines

Investigate

- Read about the standard sizes of sport balls in an encyclopedia or in a sporting goods catalog.
- Measure the diameters of several balls. Calculate their surface areas and volumes.

Set Your Direction

- Will you make a pattern for a softball? a basketball? a soccer ball?
- What kind of fabric will you use? What will you stuff it with? (If you want to give the ball to a child, be sure to use clean material.)

Make a Plan

- Make a calendar for each day's work. Check in with your group and with your teacher.
- Gather materials. You'll need:
  a real sport ball to copy; fabric; pattern paper (newspaper or tissue); stuffing material (rags, foam pellets, or batting); scissors, needle, thread, and chalk

Collect and Organize Your Information

- Rub chalk on the seams of the ball. Methodically roll the ball on tissue paper to discover the flat pattern of the ball.
- Fit the pattern on the ball and make adjustments. Mark some intersections where the pieces go together. Keep a tracing of the pattern.

Carry Out Your Plan

- Lay the pattern on the ball fabric and cut out the pieces, transferring intersection markings and leaving an allowance for seams.
- Stitch the fabric together, leaving a slot open for stuffing.

- Stuff the ball and stitch the slot closed.
- Tell whether you cut the ball fabric economically.
- If your ball is not round or is not as big as the one you used as a model, explain what might account for the difference.

Look Back

- How could you estimate the volume of a football?

B

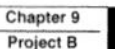

Chapter 9 Project B

For Here or To Go?

Design a Take-Out Container

Choose a food menu item and design an efficient container for it.

- Did you know that more than 50% of the packages used in the U.S. are for foods and beverages?
- Don't you wonder how restaurants packaged foods before the invention of Styrofoam™?
- How does this connect to Chapter 9? Packaging involves both **surface area** and **volume.**

Expand Your Vocabulary

barrier	laminate	Dixie Cup™	prototype
pulp	cellulose	vacuum-formed	polystyrene
gusset	toxicity	thermo-formed	permeable

Project Guidelines

Investigate

- Find about the roles of the Food and Drug Administration (FDA) and the Consumer Product Safety Commission in food packaging.
- Study the construction of a few take-out containers. Compare their surface areas and volumes.
- Talk to a restaurant manager about package costs, food preservation, and consumer satisfaction.

Set Your Direction

- What kind of food will your container hold?
- Will you try molding paper material? Folding it?

Make a Plan

- Make a calendar for each day's work.
- For a molded package you'll need papier-maché (or paper egg cartons soaked in water and mixed in a blender). For a folded package you'll need stiff paper or foil, craft knife or scissors.

Collect and Organize Your Information

- What properties should your package have? Consider temperature, pressure, and moisture.
- What economic factors should you consider?
- Will it be recyclable?
- Estimate the volume of your container, its surface area, and the area of its net, including flaps.

Carry Out Your Plan

- Construct a prototype of your container. Label it with weight or volume, and with a logo or commercial message.
- Tell why your design is economical and convenient for the retailer and for the consumer.

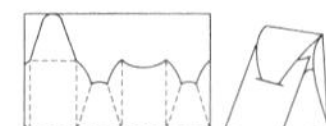

Look Back

- How can packaging waste be minimized?
- What should you have done differently?

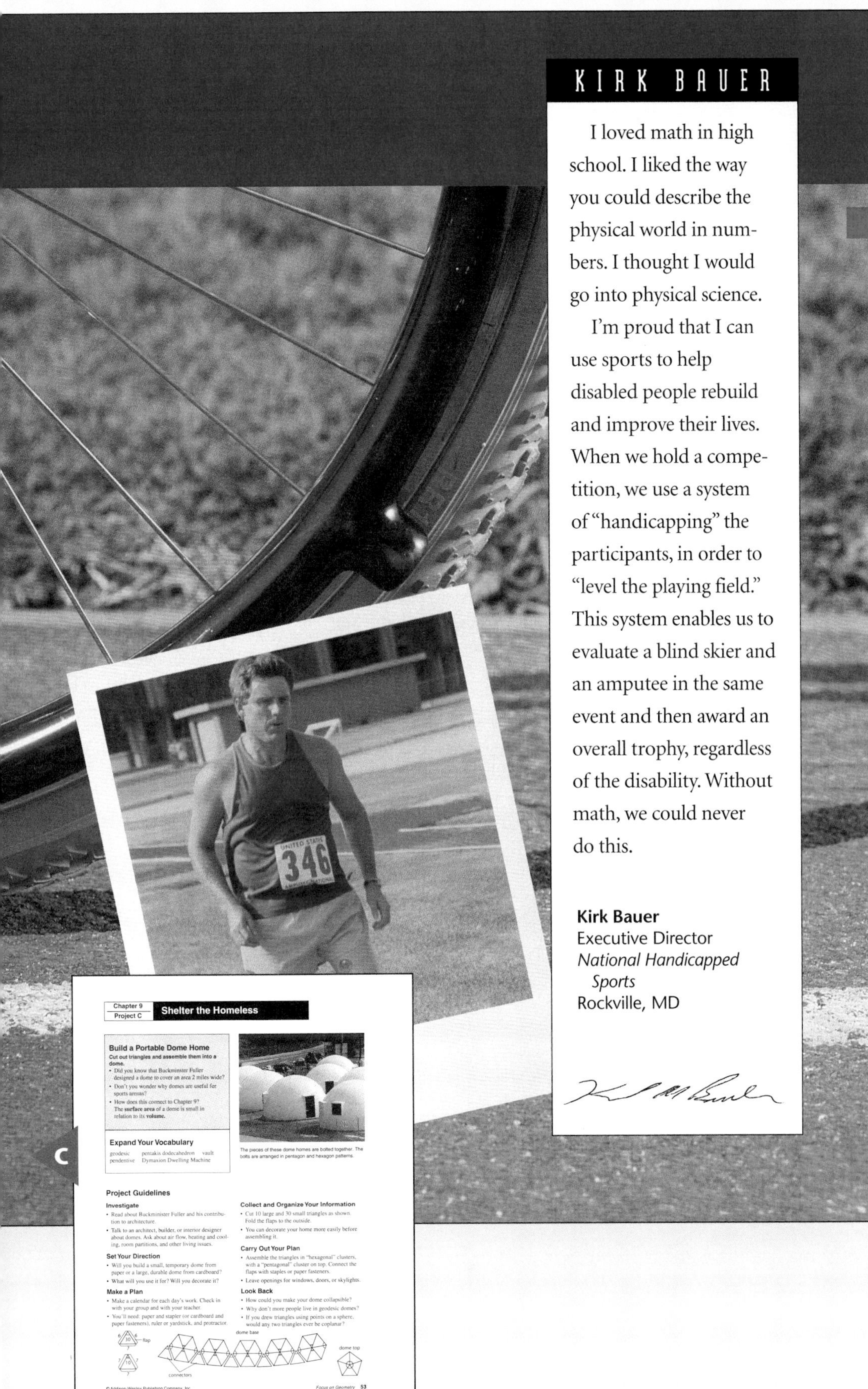

Chapter 9
Project C

Shelter the Homeless

Build a Portable Dome Home

Cut out triangles and assemble them into a dome.

- Did you know that Buckminster Fuller designed a dome to cover an area 2 miles wide?
- Don't you wonder why domes are useful for sports arenas?
- How does this connect to Chapter 9? The **surface area** of a dome is small in relation to its **volume.**

Expand Your Vocabulary

geodesic pentakis dodecahedron vault
pendentive Dymaxion Dwelling Machine

The pieces of these dome homes are bolted together. The bolts are arranged in pentagon and hexagon patterns.

Project Guidelines

Investigate

- Read about Buckminister Fuller and his contribution to architecture.
- Talk to an architect, builder, or interior designer about domes. Ask about air flow, heating and cooling, room partitions, and other living issues.

Set Your Direction

- Will you build a small, temporary dome from paper or a large, durable dome from cardboard?
- What will you use it for? Will you decorate it?

Make a Plan

- Make a calendar for each day's work. Check in with your group and with your teacher.
- You'll need: paper and stapler (or cardboard and paper fasteners), ruler or yardstick, and protractor.

Collect and Organize Your Information

- Cut 10 large and 30 small triangles as shown. Fold the flaps to the outside.
- You can decorate your home more easily before assembling it.

Carry Out Your Plan

- Assemble the triangles in "hexagonal" clusters, with a "pentagonal" cluster on top. Connect the flaps with staples or paper fasteners.
- Leave openings for windows, doors, or skylights.

Look Back

- How could you make your dome collapsible?
- Why don't more people live in geodesic domes?
- If you drew triangles using points on a sphere, would any two triangles ever be coplanar?

© Addison-Wesley Publishing Company, Inc.

Focus on Geometry 53

KIRK BAUER

I loved math in high school. I liked the way you could describe the physical world in numbers. I thought I would go into physical science.

I'm proud that I can use sports to help disabled people rebuild and improve their lives. When we hold a competition, we use a system of "handicapping" the participants, in order to "level the playing field." This system enables us to evaluate a blind skier and an amputee in the same event and then award an overall trophy, regardless of the disability. Without math, we could never do this.

Kirk Bauer
Executive Director
National Handicapped Sports
Rockville, MD

Biographical Note

Kirk Bauer graduated from Castlemont High School in Oakland, CA. He took Algebra I and II, Geometry, Trigonometry, and Calculus. He lost a leg in the Vietnam War in 1969 and was introduced to skiing by other disabled veterans.

Chapter 9

Overview

Surface Area and Volume

9-1 Surface Area

Businesspeople need to know about the surface area of product packaging. Carpenters, map makers, architects, and machinists also work with surface area measurements. You will learn how to calculate the surface area of many three-dimensional objects.

9-2 Volume

When you're deciding which product is the best buy in a grocery store or which cooler to take on a picnic, you're using the idea of volume. You will investigate volume, and see how to measure the volume of familiar solids.

9-3 Similar Solids

The surface area and volume of an animal affect its appearance. You will investigate the surface area and volume of similar solids, and explore how similarity can help you understand the way animals look.

CHAPTERS

602

Chapter 9 Planning Guide

The following ancillaries are recommended for each course level. The additional resources, *Technology Lab Manual, Study Guide and Journal, Multilingual Handbook,* and *Assessment,* are recommended for all levels.

	Comprehensive Course	Core Course	Informal Course
9-1 Part A	▲	▲	▲
Alternative Lessons			▲
Laboratory Manuals	▲	▲	▲
Practice			▲
More Look Ahead		▲	▲
9-1 Part B	▲	▲	▲
Alternative Lessons			▲
Laboratory Manuals	▲	▲	▲
Practice			▲
More Look Back		▲	▲
9-1 Part C	▲	▲	▲
Alternative Lessons			▲
Laboratory Manuals	▲	▲	▲
Practice			▲
More Look Ahead		▲	▲
9-1 Part D	▲	▲	▲
More Look Back		▲	▲
Quiz 9-1	▲	▲	▲
9-2 Part A	▲	▲	▲
Alternative Lessons			▲
Laboratory Manuals	▲	▲	▲
Practice			▲
More Look Back		▲	▲
9-2 Part B	▲	▲	▲
Alternative Lessons			▲
Laboratory Manuals	▲	▲	▲
Practice			▲
More Look Ahead		▲	▲
9-2 Part C	▲	▲	▲
Alternative Lessons			▲
Laboratory Manuals	▲	▲	▲
Practice			▲
More Look Back		▲	▲
9-2 Part D	▲	▲	▲
Alternative Lessons			▲
Laboratory Manuals	▲	▲	▲
Practice			▲
More Look Ahead		▲	▲
9-2 Part E	▲	▲	▲
More Look Back		▲	▲
Quiz 9-2	▲	▲	▲
9-3 Part A	▲	▲	▲
Alternative Lessons			▲
Laboratory Manuals	▲	▲	▲
Practice			▲
More Look Back		▲	▲
9-3 Part B	▲	▲	▲
Alternative Lessons			▲
Laboratory Manuals	▲	▲	▲
Practice			▲
More Look Ahead		▲	▲
9-3 Part C	▲	▲	▲
More Look Back		▲	▲
Quiz 9-3	▲	▲	▲

BIBLIOGRAPHY

Teacher Resources

How to Enrich Geometry Using String Designs, Victoria Pohl. NCTM, 1986.

Packaging and the Environment: Real-World Mathematics Through Science, Christine V. Johnson. Addison-Wesley, 1994 (86124).

Classic Math: History Topics for the Classroom, Art Johnson. Dale Seymour Publications, 1994 (NS21301).

9-1

Surface Area

SUPERLESSON AT A GLANCE

Superlesson Goal

Students will discover and apply formulas for the lateral and surface areas of prisms, pyramids, cylinders, and cones.

Management Guide

	Topic	Objectives	Key Terms	New Ideas	Materials
Part A	Surface Area of Prisms	To discover and use formulas for lateral and surface areas of right prisms.	Prism, right prism, oblique prism, base, lateral face, lateral edge, altitude, height, lateral area, surface area	Lateral area, surface area. For a right prism, $LA = ph$ and $SA = ph + 2B$.	**Teacher** Models of prisms
Part B	Surface Area of Pyramids	To discover and use formulas for lateral and surface areas of regular pyramids.	Pyramid, regular pyramid, vertex, slant height	For a regular pyramid, $LA = \frac{1}{2}ps$ and $SA = \frac{1}{2}ps + B$.	**Teacher** Models of pyramids
Part C	Surface Area of Cylinders and Cones	To discover and use formulas for lateral and surface areas for right cylinders and cones.	Cylinder, right cylinder, axis, cone, right cone	For a right cylinder, $LA = 2\pi rh$ and $SA = 2\pi rh + 2\pi r^2$. For a right cone, $LA = \pi rs$ and $SA = \pi rs + \pi r^2$.	**Student** Can with label, scissors **Teacher** Models of cylinders and cones
Part D	Making Connections	To design packages for a consumer product, and to calculate their surface areas.	In Making Connections, students apply and synthesize key terms and new ideas.		**Student** Construction paper, colored pens or pencils

Pacing Chart (45-Minute Periods)

	Comprehensive Course	Core Course	Informal Course
Part A	1	1	1
Part B	1	1	1
Part C	1	1	1
Part D	1	1	1
TOTAL periods for Superlesson	4	4	4

NCTM Standards

Mathematics as Problem Solving

Mathematics as Communication

Mathematics as Reasoning

Mathematical Connections

Geometry from a Synthetic Perspective

9-1 Surface Area

When it's time for breakfast, you probably don't ask yourself, "Should I have the cereal in the rectangular prism or in the cylinder?" But deciding how to package a product requires a great deal of time, creativity, and money. Package designers make trade-offs between how much a package costs, how well it protects its contents, and whether or not the product can be stacked and displayed easily and safely.

Package Engineering, Inc., of Phoenix, Arizona, recently developed corrugated plastic containers. These containers look like cardboard and are as strong as wood, but they are 75% lighter than wood. A small box can support 200 pounds. The containers are recyclable, reusable, and moisture-resistant.

Chesapeake Display & Packaging Co. of North Carolina designed a display for gallon jugs of antifreeze. The display shown below used corrugated trays and partitions that are 35% recycled paper. Using recycled paper saved 475 tons of paperboard in one year. In addition, the materials went through humidity-chamber, compression, impact, and vibration tests that are probably far more severe than actual shipping and warehouse conditions.

1. Products are often packaged in a bag, box, bottle, or can. Name one type of product for which each of these packages is best. Then choose a material (paper, glass, plastic, metal, etc.) for each product's package. Justify your choices.
2. What factors (besides cost, safety, and "stackability") might influence the design of a product's package?

More About Packaging

The growth in popularity of warehouse shopping clubs has led to new demands on the packaging industry. Items in these stores are often sold in multiple-item packs that are not seen in typical retail stores. Technology for enclosing several items in a film-wrapped pack is becoming extremely important. Problems involved with shrink-wrapping include designing the material for the wrap, deciding how the products are to be held together before the wrap is applied, and determining how to apply the wrap.

Where Are We Now?

Students are familiar with area formulas for many figures, including circles, squares, rectangles, parallelograms, and regular polygons.

Where Are We Going?

In 9-1, students will explore surface areas and lateral areas of three-dimensional figures. Many of the area formulas they have already worked with will be important for finding the areas of bases and lateral faces of solids.

In 9-2, students will explore the volumes of these three-dimensional figures.

Possible Answers

1. Bag: dog food. Heavy paper—strong enough to resist tearing but light and flexible enough to carry easily. Box: cereal. Cardboard boxes—inexpensive and easy to pack. Bottle: water. Glass or plastic—moisture-proof. Can: soup. Aluminum—sturdy and preserves freshness.
2. The appeal of a package to the consumer may influence package design. Consumers may be attracted to packages that have convenient features (pour spouts, resealable bags), ones that biodegrade or can be recycled, and/or ones that are visually appealing.

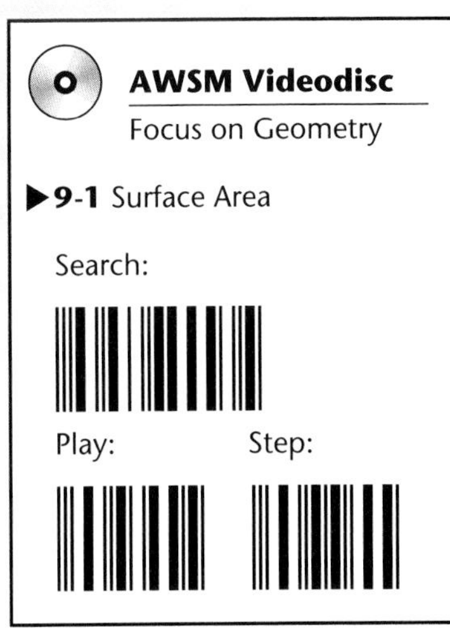

AWSM Videodisc
Focus on Geometry
▶9-1 Surface Area
Search:
Play:
Step:

Algebra	Functions	Discrete Math	Probability	Data/Statistics

Surface Area

PART A At a Glance

Objective

To discover and use formulas for lateral and surface areas of right prisms.

Development

First, students learn important terminology related to prisms. Then they see definitions of *lateral area* and *surface area.*

In the **Explore,** students find a formula for the surface area of a right prism by sketching a net and applying familiar area formulas.

Suggested Materials

Teacher Models of prisms

Key Terms

Prism, right prism, oblique prism, base, lateral face, lateral edge, altitude, height, lateral area, surface area

First Five Minutes

Transparency FFM 9-1A

Read page 604, and do the **Try It** at the top of page 605.

Motivate

Ask...

- How would you measure the amount of paper you needed to wrap a package? **Find the sum of the areas of its "sides" (lateral faces and bases).**

9-1 PART A Surface Area of Prisms

← CONNECT → ***You've studied the areas and perimeters of two-dimensional figures. Now you will use nets to help calculate the surface areas of prisms.***

Although we often refer to packages as *boxes,* the mathematically aware shopper knows that they're formally known as *rectangular prisms.*

A **prism** is a polyhedron with two identical polygonal faces, called **bases,** that lie in parallel planes. The other parallelogram-shaped faces are **lateral faces.**

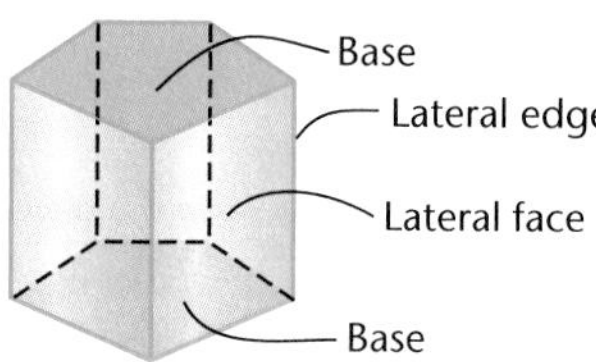

An **altitude** of a prism is a segment perpendicular to both bases whose endpoints are in the planes of the bases. The length of an altitude is the **height** of the prism.

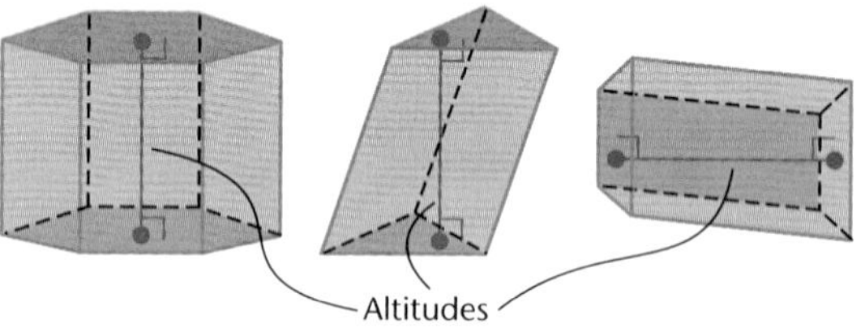

Prisms are classified by their bases. For example, a prism with triangular bases is classified as a triangular prism. If the lateral edges of a prism are perpendicular to its bases, the prism is a **right prism;** if not, it is an **oblique prism.** Unless told otherwise, you may assume that all prisms in this text are right prisms.

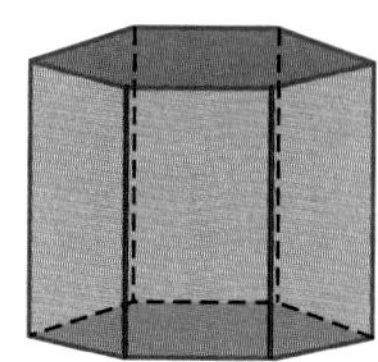
Right hexagonal prism

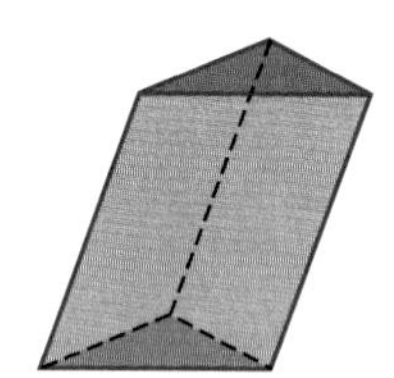
Oblique triangular prism

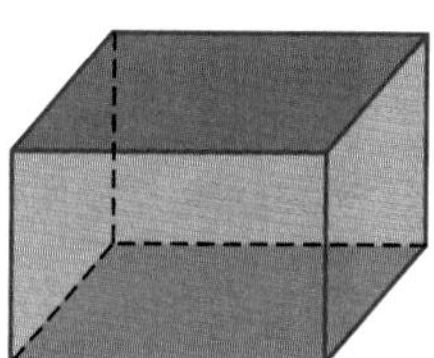
Right rectangular prism

Research Note

Students' beliefs, attitudes, and emotions are important factors in mathematics teaching and learning. If we help students develop positive beliefs and attitudes toward mathematics, their performance should improve. (Douglas B. McLeod and Michele Ortega, "Affective Issues in Mathematics Education," *Research Ideas for the Classroom: High School Mathematics,* NCTM Research Interpretation Project, Patricia S. Wilson, ed., p. 33. © 1993 NCTM.)

TRY IT

Classify each prism.

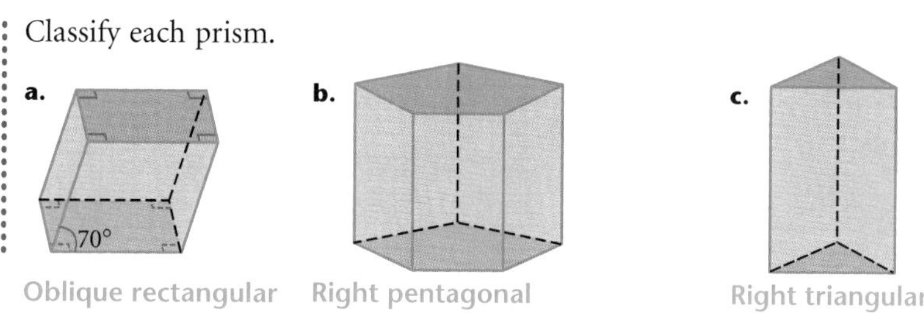

Oblique rectangular   Right pentagonal   Right triangular

The sum of the areas of the lateral faces of a prism is its **lateral area.** The **surface area** of the prism is the total area of all of its faces, including the bases.

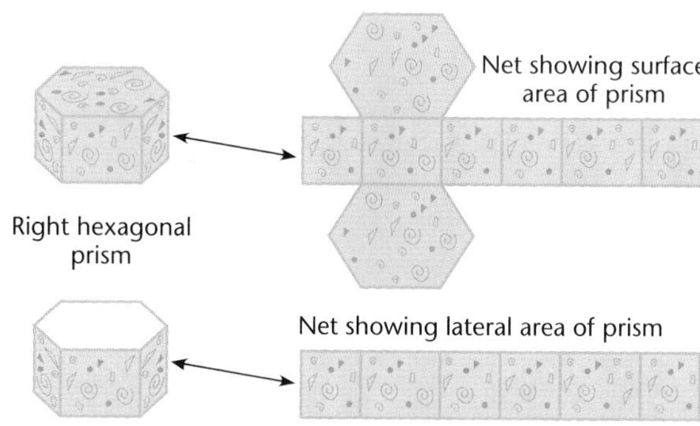

In the following Explore, you will use nets to help discover how to calculate the surface area of a right prism.

EXPLORE: PRISMANIA

1. The photograph shows light refracted through a right triangular prism. Make a sketch of a right triangular prism. Sketch a net for the prism, and describe all of the figures in the net.
2. Suppose you know the height of your prism, h, and the perimeter of its base, p. Use your net to help explain how you can find the lateral area of the prism.
3. Now write a formula for the surface area of any right prism that uses p, the perimeter of the base, h, the height of the prism, and B, the area of one of the bases.

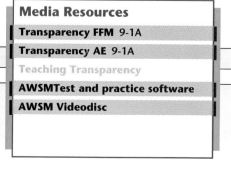

Student Resources

- Alternative Lessons 9-1A
- Laboratory Manual 9-1A
- Technology Lab Manual
- Practice 9-1A
- Study Guide and Journal 9-1A
- Guía de estudios y Diario 9-1A
- Multilingual Handbook
- More Look Ahead 9-1A
- SAT Preparation

Media Resources

- Transparency FFM 9-1A
- Transparency AE 9-1A
- Teaching Transparency
- AWSMTest and practice software
- AWSM Videodisc

EXPLORE

Prismania

Recommended group size: 4

The Point
To use a net to find the lateral area of a right triangular prism, and to derive a formula for the surface area of any right prism.

Look and Listen...
- For students who do not recognize the lateral faces of the prism.
- For students who do not see how the perimeter of the base of the prism can help them find its lateral area.

Ask...
- How is the perimeter of the prism's base related to the lengths of the rectangular lateral faces?

For Groups That Finish Early
Apply the formula you developed in Step 3 to find the surface area of a cube with side length s. Does your answer make sense? $SA = 6s^2$.

Follow Up
Have students share their results for Steps 2 and 3 with the class. Come to a class consensus on lateral area and surface area formulas for a right prism before proceeding.

Possible Answers
1. The net contains two triangles and three rectangles.
2. If the base lengths of the rectangles are a, b, and c, the sum of the areas is $ah + bh + ch = (a + b + c)h$. Since $a + b + c$ is the perimeter of the base, the lateral area is equal to ph.
3. $SA = ph + 2B$.

Algebra | Functions | Discrete Math | Probability | Data/Statistics

Surface Area

ALTERNATE EXAMPLES

1. Find the lateral area of the right rectangular prism shown.

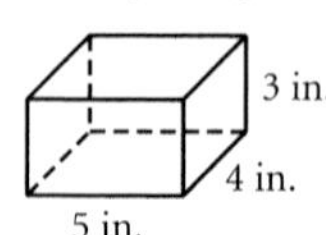

If the rectangles at the top and bottom of the prism are used as the bases, $p = 2\ell + 2w = 2(5) + 2(4) = 18$ in., so $LA = ph = 18(3) = 54$ in.^{2}.

2. Find the surface area of the prism.

$SA = ph + 2B$.
$B = \ell w = 5 \times 4 = 20$ in.^{2}, so
$SA = 54 + 2(20) = 94$ in.^{2}.

Journal

Reflect 2 and 3 are suitable for journal entries.

REFLECT

Possible Answers

1. $SA = 6s^2$

2. The total surface area of the two prisms is greater than that of the original prism because two new surfaces are formed.

3. Square meters, square inches, etc. are appropriate for measuring surface area because area is measured in square units.

Part A Exercises

Exercise Notes

Core

21. Students express a surface area in terms of a variable. In Exercise 21b they solve a quadratic equation to find a side length.

Look Ahead

Students practice finding side lengths of triangles. This will be important in 8-1 Part B when they find the areas of the triangular lateral faces of a pyramid.

More Math Reasoning

38. Students may disagree with each other's answers, depending on whether they feel that a part of the cube on the ground or the underside of the chameleocube's body is "exposed" or not.

EXAMPLES

1. Find the lateral area of the right prism with right triangular bases shown.

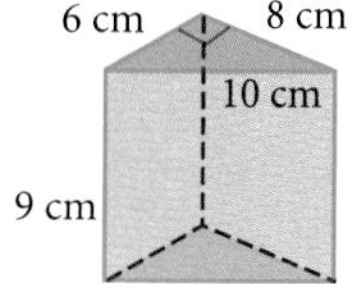

$LA = ph$
$LA = (6 + 8 + 10)(9) = 24(9) = 216 \text{ cm}^2$

2. Find the surface area of the prism.

$SA = LA + 2B = 216 + 2(\frac{1}{2})(8)(6) = 216 + 48 = 264 \text{ cm}^2$

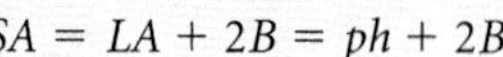

THEOREMS

The lateral area of a right prism is the product of the perimeter of its base and the height of the prism.

$LA = ph$

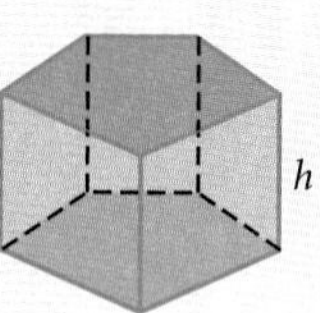

The surface area of a right prism is the sum of its lateral area and the areas of its bases.

$SA = LA + 2B = ph + 2B$

REFLECT

1. Give a formula for the surface area of a cube in terms of its side length, *s*.

2. If a solid prism is cut in half to form two smaller prisms, is the total surface area of the two prisms greater than, less than, or equal to the surface area of the original prism? Why?

3. Give some examples of units that are appropriate for measuring surface area. Explain your choices.

Exercises

CORE

Where necessary, approximate answers are given in the margin notes.

P **Getting Started** **Classify each prism.**

1.

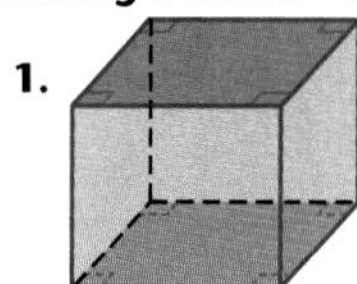

2.

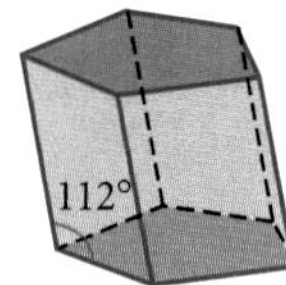

3.

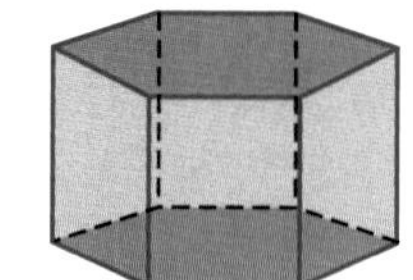

4.

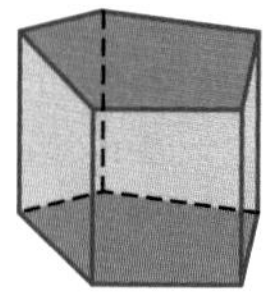

Key

V Vocabulary
P Practice/Skills
R Review
MR Math Reasoning
PS Problem Solving
C Challenge

Tips from Teachers

Students may feel overwhelmed by the number of formulas they see in 9-1 and 9-2. You may want to emphasize frequently the general principles involved and the relationships between the solids, so that the formulas make sense and the connections between them are clear.

Sketch a net for each prism.

5.

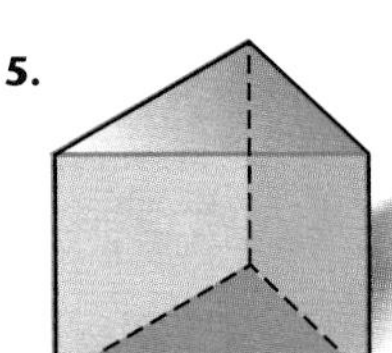

6.

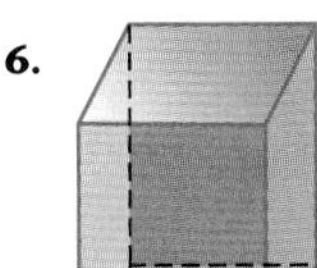

7.

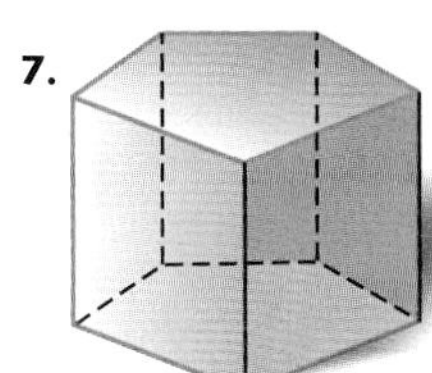

8.

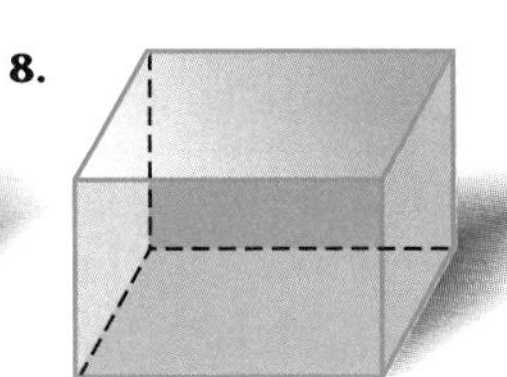

Find the lateral area and surface area of each prism.

9.

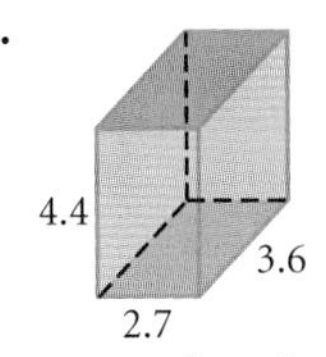
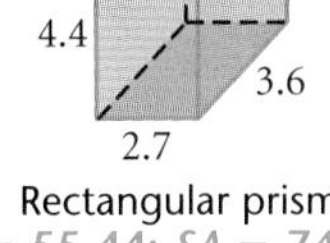

Rectangular prism
LA = 55.44; SA = 74.88

10.

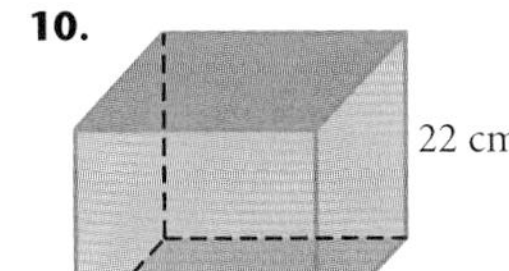

Cube LA = 1936 cm²; SA = 2904 cm²

11.

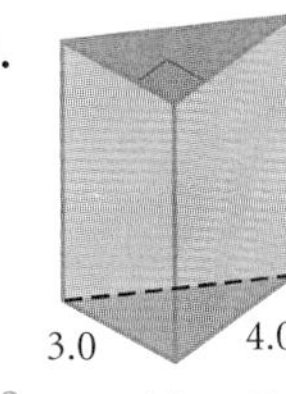

LA = 97.2; SA = 109.2

12.

4 in.

3 in.

Regular hexagonal prism
LA = 72 in.²; SA = 155.14 in.²

Write the word or phrase that correctly completes each statement.

13. A ___ of a prism is a segment whose endpoints are vertices of opposite bases. Lateral edge

14. The length of the altitude of a prism is the ___ of the prism. Height

15. If the lateral edges of a prism are perpendicular to its bases, then the prism is a ___. Right prism

16. Little Red Shed The outside of the shed at the right (including its roof) needs paint. Each gallon of paint costs $8.99, and a gallon of paint covers 300 ft². Assuming that there is no sales tax, how much will it cost to paint the shed? (You must buy the paint in whole gallons.) $17.98

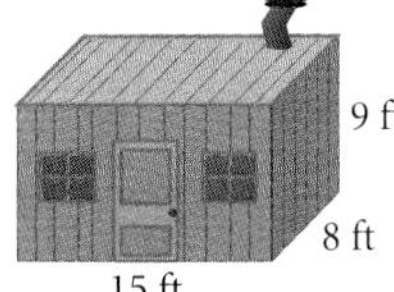

17. What is the difference between the lateral faces of a right prism and the lateral faces of an oblique prism?

18. The box for a videotape is 19 cm tall, 10.5 cm long, and 2.5 cm wide. It is open on one of the long sides, so that the tape can slide in. What is the surface area of the box? 499 cm²

19. In *Gulliver's Travels,* Jonathan Swift describes the land of Lilliput, where people are "not quite six inches high."

The walls of the outer court of the Lilliputian palace are rectangular solids forty feet long, two feet tall, and four inches thick. Find the surface area of one of the walls. (In making your calculations, you may ignore any overlap between the walls and you should include the face in contact with the ground.) 188 ft²

Exercise Answers

Core

1. Right rectangular

2. Oblique pentagonal

3. Right hexagonal

4. Right pentagonal

5.

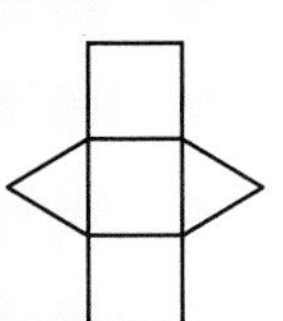

6.

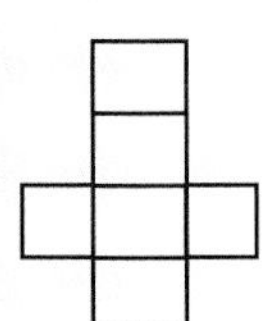

7.

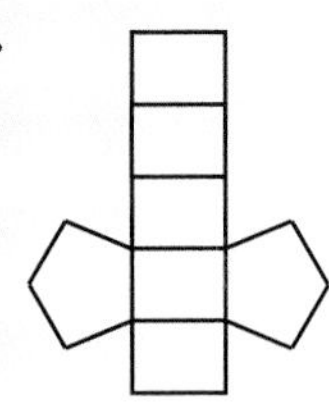

8.

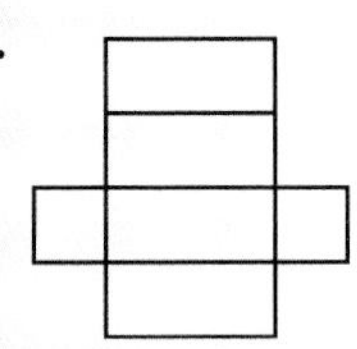

17. In the right prism the faces are rectangles. In the oblique prism the faces are parallelograms.

Ongoing Assessment

Self-Assessment Exercises 1–23 odd

Embedded Assessment Exercises 10, 12, 16, 20, 22

Surface Area

23. Possible answer: Move one of the top blocks on the left away from the block it is touching to expose two new faces.

24. Possible answer: Slide the top block on the right leftward until it touches the other block. Two more faces will be covered up.

Look Ahead

27. $x = 6\sqrt{3} \approx 10.4$

28. $x = 8\sqrt{2} \approx 11.3$

More Practice

29.

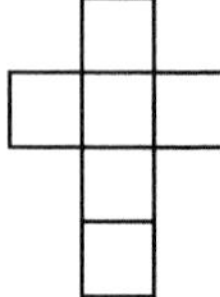

30.

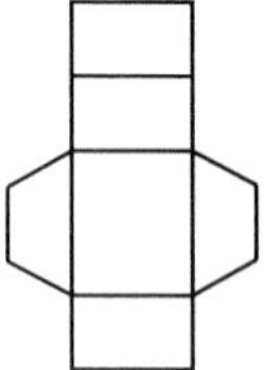

31.

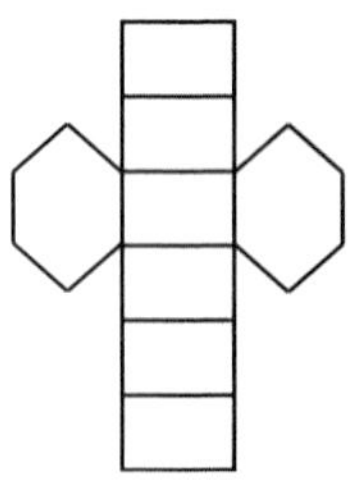

More Math Reasoning

38. a. Possible answer:

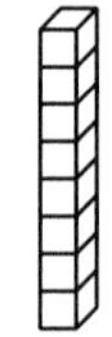

b. A cube:

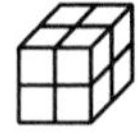

This way as many faces as possible are in contact with other faces.

41.

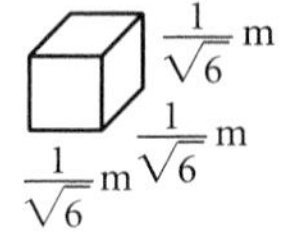

Algebra | Functions | Discrete Math | Probability | Data/Statistics

P **20.** The surface area of a cube is a function of one of its side lengths.

a. Express the surface area of a cube in terms of the length of a side. $SA = 6s^2$

b. Is your answer to **20a** a linear, quadratic, or cubic function? Explain. Quadratic, since the highest power is 2.

PS **21.** In a rectangular prism, $h = x$; $w = x - 2$; and $\ell = 2x$.

a. Find the surface area of the prism in terms of x. $SA = 10x^2 - 12x$

b. Suppose the surface area of the prism is 112 ft^2. Solve for x. $x = 4$ ft

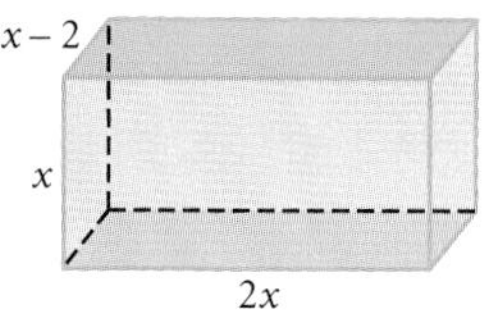

P **The solid at the right is made of twelve cubes.**

22. The edge of each cube measures 1 cm. What is the surface area of the solid? 40 cm^2

23. How can you move one block so that the surface area of the solid increases by 2 cm^2?

24. How can you move one block so the surface area decreases by 2 cm^2?

LOOK AHEAD

R **Solve for x in each triangle.**

25.

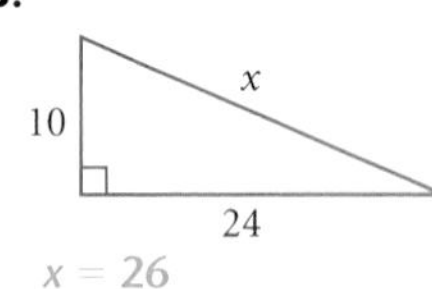

$x = 26$

26.

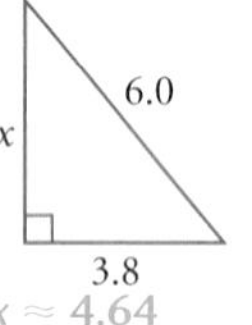

$x \approx 4.64$

27.

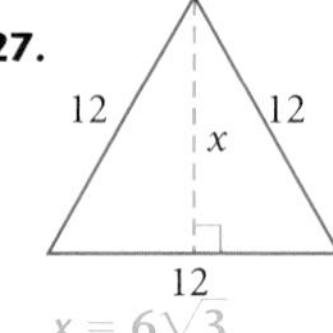

$x = 6\sqrt{3}$

28.

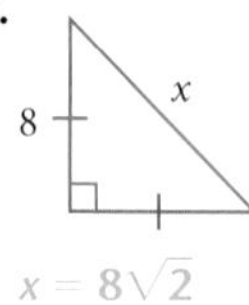

$x = 8\sqrt{2}$

MORE PRACTICE

P **Sketch a net for each prism.**

29.

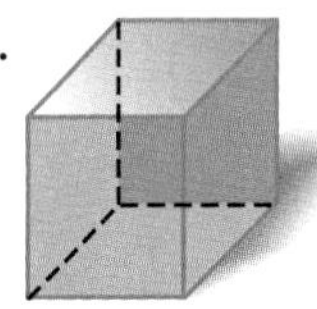

30.

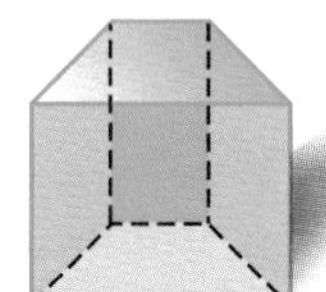

31.

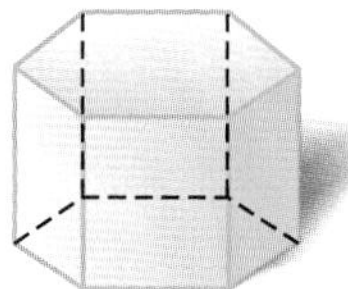

P **Find the lateral area and surface area of each prism.**

32. 54.72 mm^2; 66.24 mm^2

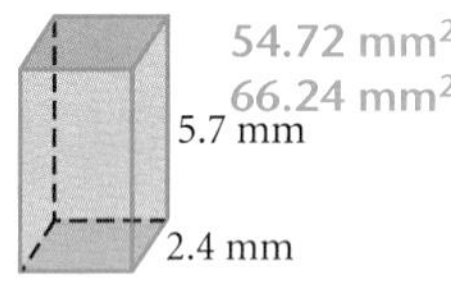
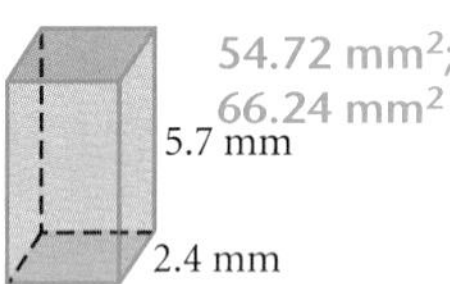

Square prism

33. 163.88; 179.88

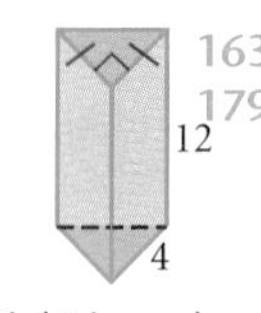

Right isosceles triangular prism

34. 2352 in.^{2}; 3370.4 in.^{2}

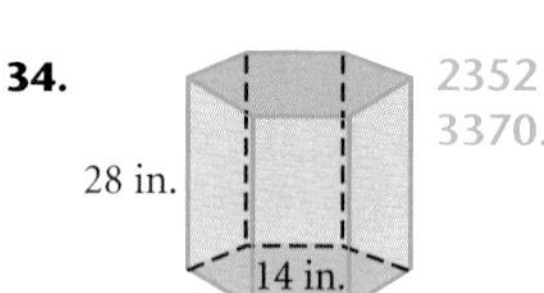

Regular hexagonal prism

Key

V Vocabulary
P Practice/Skills
R Review
MR Math Reasoning
PS Problem Solving
C Challenge

The edges of the cubes in each figure measure 1 in. Find the surface area of each solid.

35.

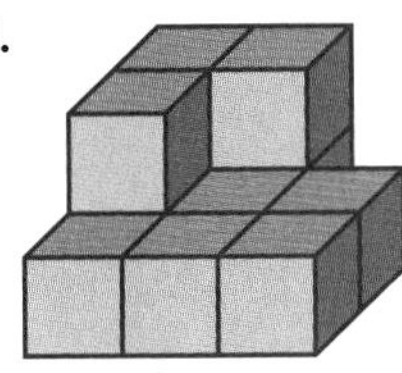

36 in.^{2}

36.

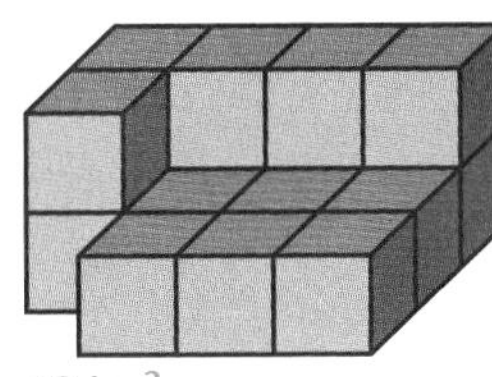

48 in.^{2}

37.

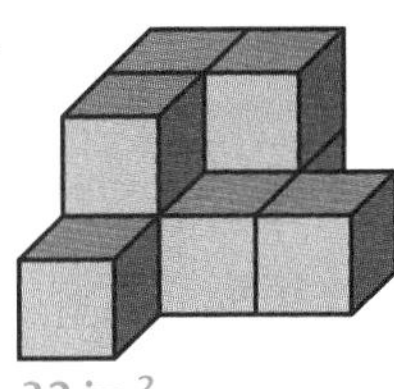

32 in.^{2}

MORE MATH REASONING

38. Chameleocube Crossing The chameleocube is an imaginary animal made up of eight cubes. It can rearrange its cubes any way it wants to as long as at least one face of each cube completely overlaps a face of another cube. One arrangement of the chameleocube is shown at the right.

a. While warming itself in the sun, the chameleocube wants to expose the greatest surface area possible. Describe and sketch a shape for the chameleocube that has the greatest possible surface area. (Hint: There is more than one correct solution!)

b. When frightened, the chameleocube rearranges itself so that the least possible surface area is exposed. Describe and sketch a shape that has the least possible surface area. Explain why this shape is the best.

39. Is the surface area of an oblique prism greater than, equal to, or less than the surface area of a right prism with the same base and the same height? Explain. Greater; The lateral area is larger.

Problem-Solving Tip

Make a set of drawings.

40. Not Very Shelf-ish Cruncheteria Cereal (The Cafeteria in a Bowl!) has made a terrible mistake in its packaging! Their boxes—2 in. wide, 6 in. long, and 16 in. tall—are too tall to fit on most people's shelves. Their new marketing director proposes that the width and length of these boxes be increased by 40% while keeping the surface area of the boxes the same. She claims that the new box will fit on a 12-in.-tall shelf. Is she right? Yes

41. Sketch a right rectangular prism that has a surface area of one square meter. Include dimensions in your sketch.

Algebra	Functions	Discrete Math	Probability	Data/Statistics

Surface Area

PART B At a Glance

Objective

To discover and use formulas for lateral and surface areas of regular pyramids.

Development

Students see definitions of terms related to pyramids.

Then, in the **Explore,** students use nets and sketches to find formulas for the lateral and surface areas of pyramids.

Suggested Materials

Teacher Models of pyramids

Key Terms

Pyramid, regular pyramid, vertex, slant height

First Five Minutes

Transparency FFM 9-1B

Read the definitions at the top of page 610, and answer the **Consider** question at the bottom of the page.

Motivate

Ask...

- Which of the Platonic solids is a pyramid? Is it a regular pyramid? How would it be classified by its base? **The tetrahedron; yes; equilateral triangular pyramid.**

Students see that the lateral faces of all pyramids are triangular. This is important for the derivation of a lateral area formula.

Possible Answer

1. They are triangular.

9-1 PART B Surface Area of Pyramids

← CONNECT → *You've seen how to find the surface area of a right prism. Now you will discover how to calculate the surface area of a pyramid.*

The photograph at the left shows the pyramid of Cheops in Giza, Egypt. A **pyramid** is a polyhedron. The vertices of its polygonal **base** are connected to one other point called the **vertex** of the pyramid. The **height** of the pyramid is the length of its altitude.

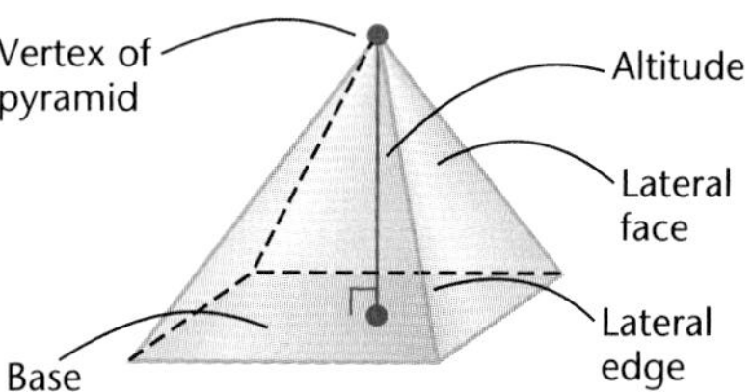

The base of a **regular pyramid** is a regular polygon. All of the lateral edges of a regular pyramid are congruent. Unless told otherwise, you may assume that all pyramids in this text are regular pyramids. The **slant height** of a regular pyramid is the height of any of its lateral faces. Like prisms, pyramids are classified by their bases.

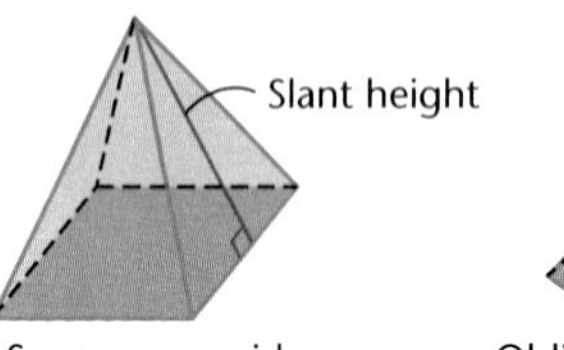

Square pyramid

Oblique hexagonal pyramid

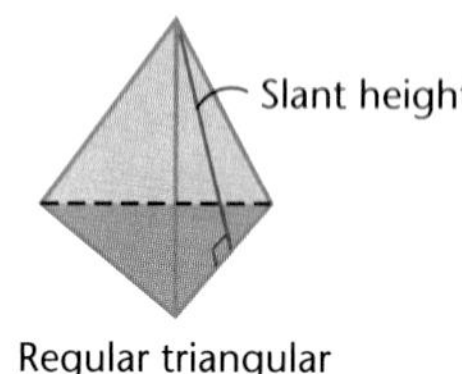

Regular triangular pyramid

1. What do all lateral faces of pyramids have in common?

Diversity Issues

Some students may have difficulty visualizing three-dimensional figures from their two-dimensional projections. You could have them make three-dimensional models of some of these solids out of paper. Then have them mark or color appropriate features (bases, slant heights, etc.).

EXPLORE: NETTING THE WILD PYRAMID

Find formulas for the lateral area and surface area of a regular pyramid with base area B, base perimeter p, and slant height s. Use sketches and nets of pyramids to help you. Compare your results with the formulas your classmates find. When you are confident of your results, explain why your formulas work.

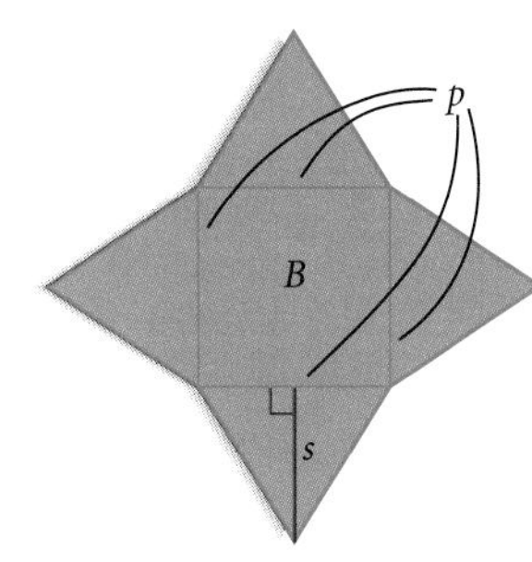

EXAMPLES

1. Find the lateral area of the regular hexagonal pyramid shown.

   $LA = \frac{1}{2}ps = \frac{1}{2}(24)(10) = 120 \text{ cm}^2$

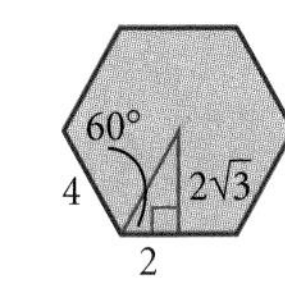

2. Find the surface area of the pyramid.

   To find the surface area, first find the area of the regular hexagonal base.

   Using 30°-60°-90° triangle side-length ratios, the apothem of the hexagon is $2\sqrt{3}$ cm.

   60° 4 $2\sqrt{3}$ 2

   $$SA = LA + B$$
   $$= 120 \text{ cm}^2 + \frac{1}{2}ap = 120 \text{ cm}^2 + \frac{1}{2}(2\sqrt{3})(24)$$
   $$= 120 \text{ cm}^2 + 24\sqrt{3} \text{ cm}^2 \approx 161.6 \text{ cm}^2$$

The results for the lateral area and surface area of a regular pyramid are stated as theorems below.

THEOREMS

The lateral area of a regular pyramid is one-half the product of the perimeter of its base and the slant height of the pyramid. $LA = \frac{1}{2}ps$

The surface area of a regular pyramid is the sum of its lateral area and the area of its base. $SA = LA + B = \frac{1}{2}ps + B$

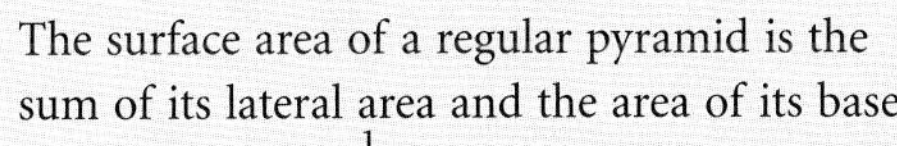

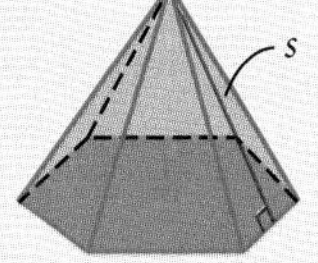

Student Resources

- Alternative Lessons 9-1B
- Laboratory Manual 9-1B
- Technology Lab Manual
- Practice 9-1B
- Study Guide and Journal 9-1B
- Guía de estudios y Diario 9-1B
- Multilingual Handbook
- More Look Back 9-1B
- SAT Preparation

Media Resources

- Transparency FFM 9-1B
- Transparency AE 9-1B
- Teaching Transparency
- AWSMTest and practice software
- AWSM Videodisc

EXPLORE

Netting the Wild Pyramid

Recommended group size: 4

The Point

To use nets and sketches to discover formulas for the lateral area and surface area of a regular prism.

Look and Listen...

- For students who do not understand that the slant height of the regular pyramid is the height of the triangular lateral faces.
- For students who do not see how the perimeter can be used in the formula.

Ask...

- The perimeter of the base of this regular pyramid is p. What is the length of the base of *one* of the triangles? $\frac{1}{4}p$

  What is the area of one of the triangles? $\frac{1}{8}ps$

  What is the lateral area of the pyramid if there are four such triangles? $\frac{1}{2}ps$

For Groups That Finish Early

Are the lateral faces of a regular pyramid congruent? If so, why? If not, why not? **Yes, by SSS.**

Follow Up

Have one student or group of students present their formulas to the class and explain the reasoning they used to derive them.

Possible Answers

$LA = \frac{1}{2}ps$; $SA = LA + B = \frac{1}{2}ps + B$

ALTERNATE EXAMPLES

Transparency AE 9-1B

Surface Area

Journal

Reflect 1 and 2 are suitable for journal entries.

REFLECT

Possible Answers

1. The altitude of the pyramid does not lie on the lateral faces. The slant height is the height of each triangular lateral face.
2. Any face of a rectangular prism can be considered a base of the prism, because (1) there is an identical polygon opposite it in a parallel plane, and (2) the other faces are always rectangles. Only one face of a rectangular pyramid—the rectangle—can be considered its base. The rectangle cannot be a lateral face, because lateral faces of pyramids are triangular.

Part B Exercises

Exercise Notes

Core

15. Students find the lateral area of the Great Pyramid.

More Math Reasoning

26. Students explore issues involved in product packaging.

Exercise Answers

Core

2.

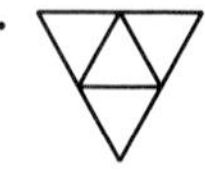

3.

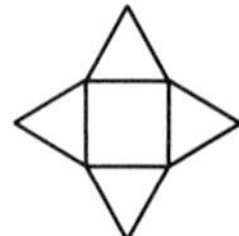

4.

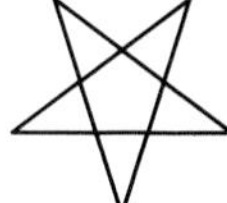

5.

Algebra | Functions | Discrete Math | Probability | Data/Statistics

REFLECT

1. Why does the formula for the surface area of a pyramid involve its slant height, rather than the length of its altitude?
2. Can any face of a rectangular prism be considered a base of the prism? Explain. Can any face of a rectangular pyramid be considered its base? Why or why not?

Exercises

CORE

Where necessary, approximate answers are given in the margin notes.

P **1. Getting Started** Follow the steps to find the surface area of the square pyramid. (25 cm; 20 cm)

a. How many lateral faces does the pyramid have? What is the shape of each face? 4; Triangle

b. What is the lateral area of the pyramid? 1000 cm^2

c. What figure is the base of the pyramid? What is the area of the base? Square; 400 cm^2

d. What is the surface area of the pyramid? 1400 cm^2

P **Sketch a net for each pyramid.**

2.

3.

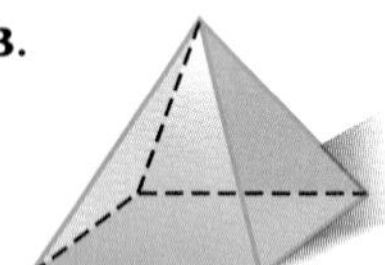

4.

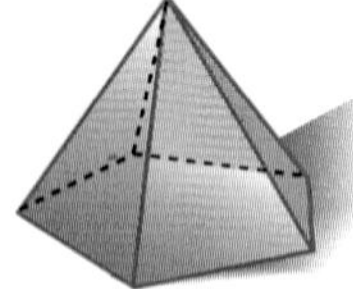

5.

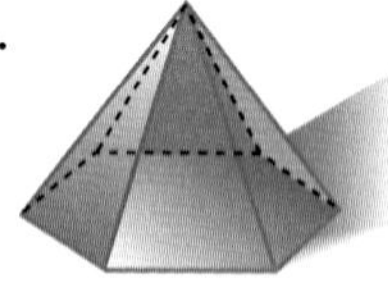

P **Find the lateral area and surface area of each pyramid.**

6.

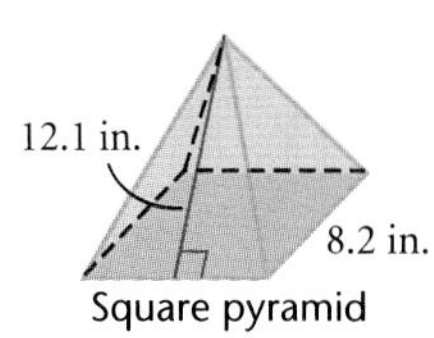

Square pyramid

198.44 $in.^2$; 265.68 $in.^2$

7.

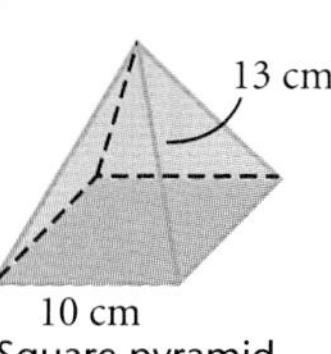

Square pyramid

240 cm^2; 340 cm^2

8.

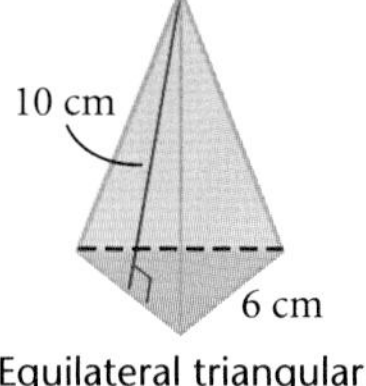

Equilateral triangular pyramid

90 cm^2; 105.59 cm^2

9. (8.9 cm; 5.4 cm)

Regular hexagonal pyramid

144.18 cm^2; 219.94 cm^2

P **10.** Find the surface area of the square pyramid shown. 39.00 $in.^2$ (4.2 in.; 3.2 in.)

PS **11.** A square pyramid has height h and base side length ℓ. Find expressions for its slant height and the length of one of its lateral edges in terms of h and ℓ.

Key

- V Vocabulary
- P Practice/Skills
- R Review
- MR Math Reasoning
- PS Problem Solving
- C Challenge

8 ft

30 ft

10 ft

12. **Time to Find the Area** A clock tower in a civic center consists of a square-based prism topped by a square pyramid. Find the lateral area of the clock tower so it can be painted. 1360 ft^2

Write the word or phrase that correctly completes each statement.

13. The lateral edges of a pyramid connect the ___ of the pyramid to all of the vertices of the base. Vertex

14. The ___ of a pyramid is the distance from the vertex to a side of its base. Slant height

15. **Goodbye, Mr. Cheops** The largest Egyptian pyramid, the Great Pyramid of Cheops (or Khufu), had an original height of about 482 ft. The sides of its square base are 755 ft long. What was its original lateral area? $924{,}473.1\text{ ft}^2$

16. Recall that the regular tetrahedron is one of the five Platonic solids. Find the surface area of a regular tetrahedron with edges six centimeters long. (Hint: What are the measures of the angles of the faces?) 62.36 cm^2

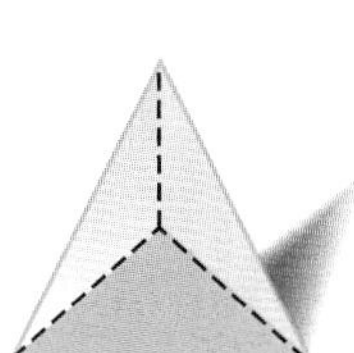

LOOK BACK

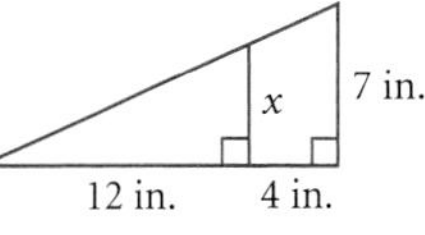

17. Solve for x in the figure at the right. Explain your method. [7-2]

18. Suppose that the packaging for a frozen dinner includes a plate with a 12-in. diameter divided into three sections. [8-2]

a. Find the area of each sector.

b. Find the length of the arc of the plate that each sector determines.

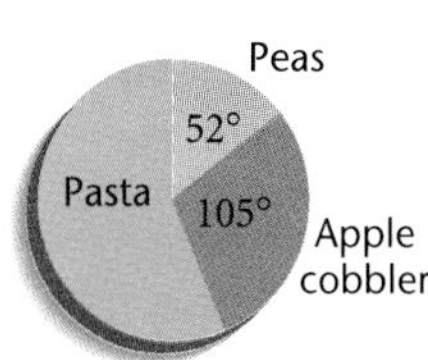

MORE PRACTICE

Sketch a net for each pyramid.

19.

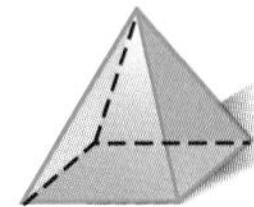

20.

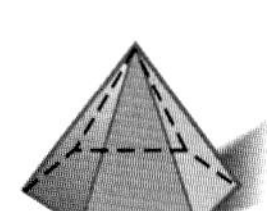

21.

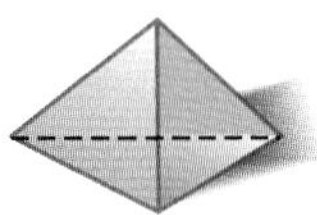

Find the lateral area and surface area of each pyramid.

22.

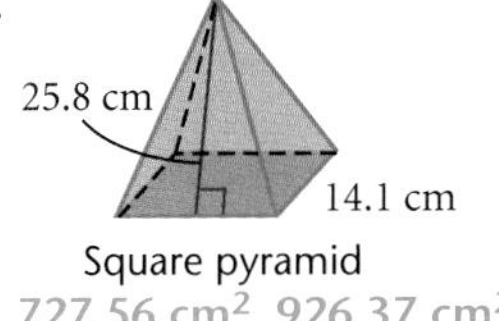

Square pyramid
727.56 cm^2, 926.37 cm^2

23.

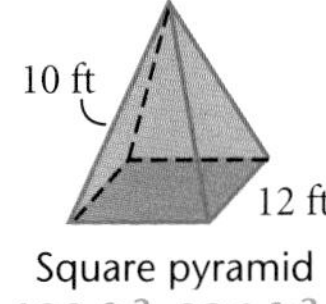

Square pyramid
192 ft^2, 336 ft^2

24.

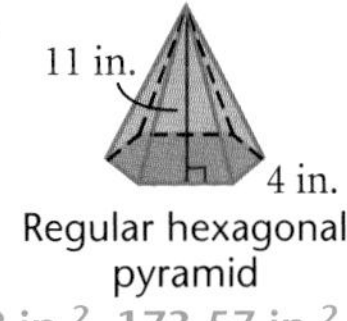

Regular hexagonal pyramid
132 in.^2, 173.57 in.^2

Ongoing Assessment

Self-Assessment Exercises 1–15 odd

Embedded Assessment Reflect 1; Exercises 6, 8, 12, 16

11. $s = \sqrt{\frac{l^2}{4} + h^2}$; Lateral edge $= L = \sqrt{\frac{l^2}{2} + h^2}$

Look Back

17. $x = 5.25$ in.; Use similar triangles

18. a. $5.2\pi \approx 16.3\text{ in.}^2$, $10.5\pi \approx 33.0\text{ in.}^2$, $20.3\pi \approx 63.8\text{ in.}^2$

b. 5.4 in., 11.0 in., 21.3 in.

More Practice

19.

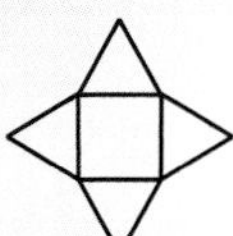

20.

21.

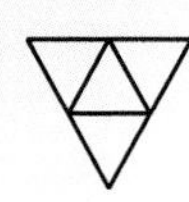

PART C At a Glance

Objective

To discover and use formulas for lateral and surface areas for right cylinders and cones.

Development

Students see definitions of terms associated with cylinders.

In the **Explore,** students discover formulas for the lateral area and surface area of a right cylinder by seeing that its lateral surface is actually a rectangle.

Then, students learn terminology associated with cones and see formulas for the lateral area and surface area of a cone.

Suggested Materials

Student Can with label, scissors

Teacher Models of cylinders and cones

Key Terms

Cylinder, right cylinder, axis, cone, right cone

First Five Minutes

Transparency FFM 9-1C

In your own words, define *lateral area* and *surface area.*

Motivate

Ask...

- Give some examples of everyday situations where it might be important to find the surface area of a cylinder. Finding the amount of material needed to manufacture a can, amount of paint needed to cover a silo, etc.

MORE MATH REASONING

PS, C **25.** A square pyramid is inscribed in a cube with 4-cm sides so that they share a base. Find the surface area of the pyramid and the ratio of its surface area to that of the cube. 51.78 cm^2; 0.54

PS, MR **26. Sell Those Beans!** You work for the Micro Bean Corporation, the world's largest manufacturer of tiny jellybeans. You've decided to try packaging them in regular tetrahedral containers with a small opening at the vertex.

a. If the total surface area of the cardboard used for the container can be no more than 100 in.^{2}, what are the longest possible edge lengths for your container? 7.6 in.

b. What are some advantages and disadvantages of a tetrahedral container? Possible answer: It is a strong design, but the packages will not fit into larger containers efficiently.

9-1 PART C Surface Area of Cylinders and Cones

← CONNECT → *You've investigated the surface areas of solids with polygonal bases. Now you will explore the surface areas of solids whose bases are circles.*

Andy Warhol, *CAMPBELL'S SOUP CAN, 1964,* ©1994 The Andy Warhol Foundation for the Visual Arts, Inc.

As shown in the Andy Warhol painting at the left, soup is often packaged in a cylindrical container.

A **cylinder** has two congruent circular bases in parallel planes. The **axis** of a cylinder is the segment that joins the centers of the bases. If the axis is perpendicular to the base, the figure is a **right cylinder.** (Again, assume all cylinders in this text are right cylinders unless otherwise noted.) An **altitude** of a cylinder is a segment that joins the planes of the bases and is perpendicular to them. The **height** of a cylinder is the length of an altitude.

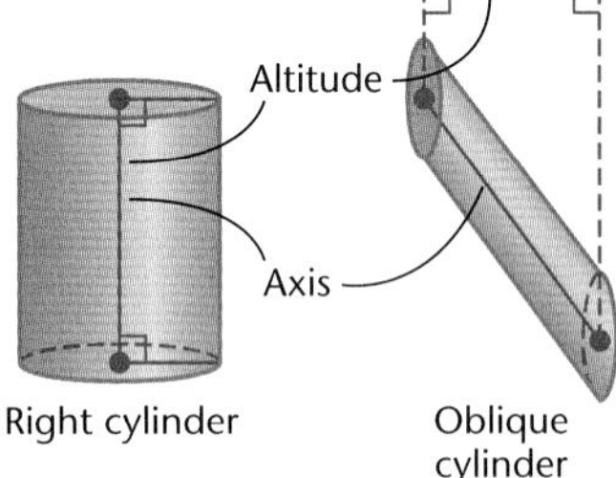

Key

V Vocabulary
P Practice/Skills
R Review
MR Math Reasoning
PS Problem Solving
C Challenge

EXPLORE: CYLINDER CUTS

MATERIALS

Can, Scissors

1. Make a single, straight cut, so that you can unroll the label of a can as shown in the photo. What does the lateral surface of a cylinder look like when it is flattened out? How do you calculate the area of this figure?
2. You know the height of the figure you unrolled is equal to the height of the cylinder. How can you determine the length of the figure?
3. Using your result from Step 2, find a formula for the lateral area of a right cylinder. Explain how you found this formula.
4. Suppose that the height of a right cylinder is h, and its bases have radius r. What is the area of each base of the cylinder? Find a formula for the surface area of a right cylinder.

TRY IT

a. $LA = 201.1$ in.^{2}; $SA = 603.2$ in.^{2}
b. $LA = 791.7$ cm^2; $SA = 1300.6$ cm^2

Find the lateral area and surface area of a right cylinder for each set of dimensions. Round answers to the nearest tenth.

a. Radius = 8 in., height = 4 in.
b. Circumference = 18π cm, height = 14 cm

Like prisms, pyramids have a polygonal base, but instead of having a second base, they come to a point. Cones are related to cylinders in the same way.

A **cone** has a vertex and a circular base. The **axis** of a cone is the segment from the vertex to the center of the base. If the axis is perpendicular to the base, the cone is a **right cone.** All cones in this text are right cones unless otherwise indicated.

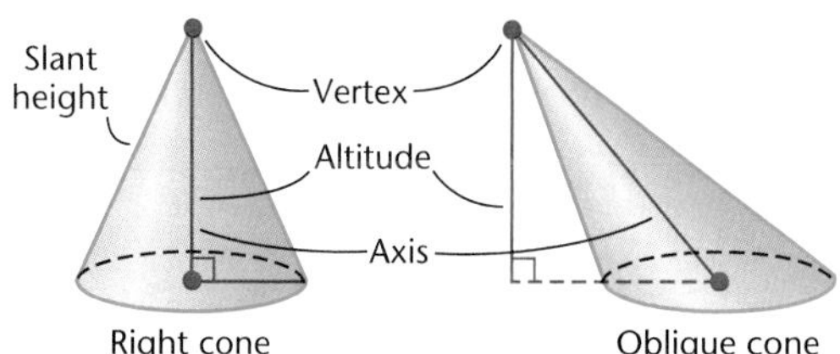

Student Resources
- Alternative Lessons 9-1C
- Laboratory Manual 9-1C
- Technology Lab Manual
- Practice 9-1C
- Study Guide and Journal 9-1C
- Guía de estudios y Diario 9-1C
- Multilingual Handbook
- More Look Ahead 9-1C
- SAT Preparation

Media Resources
- Transparency FFM 9-1C
- Transparency AE 9-1C
- Teaching Transparency
- AWSMTest and practice software
- AWSM Videodisc

EXPLORE

Cylinder Cuts

Recommended group size: 4

The Point

To discover that the lateral surface of a right cylinder is a rectangle/parallelogram, and use this knowledge to write formulas for the lateral and surface areas.

Look and Listen...

- For students who do not make a straight cut when removing the label.
- For students who do not see that the base length of the unrolled label is equal to the circumference of the base of the cylinder.

Ask...

- Wrap the label around the can again. Where does the bottom of the label go? How is its length related to a measurement of the circular base?

For Groups That Finish Early

Do you think that the formulas you discovered also work for an oblique cylinder? If not, why not? **They do not apply; the height of the oblique cylinder is different than the "height" of its lateral surface.**

Follow Up

Have students compare their answers. Be sure that their answers are consistent with the theorems on page 616 before proceeding.

Possible Answers

1. The lateral surface is a rectangle if a straight cut is made down the label and a parallelogram if the cut is made at a slant. Rectangle area = length × width; parallelogram area = base length × height.
2. The length of the figure is equal to the circumference of a base.
3. $LA = 2\pi rh$; $2\pi r$ is the circumference of the base = length of the label; h = the height of the label.
4. Area of each base = πr^2. $SA = LA + 2B = 2\pi rh + 2\pi r^2$.

9-1 Surface Area

Shows the relationship between the surface-area formulas for a right prism and a right cylinder.

Possible Answer

1. Both formulas are equal to the lateral area plus twice the base area. Both lateral areas are equal to the distance around the base times the height of the solid. Because the cylinder has circular bases, we use $2\pi r$ for the base circumference (instead of perimeter) and πr^2 for the base area in these formulas.

ALTERNATE EXAMPLES

1. Find the lateral area of a right cone whose base radius is 8 cm and slant height is 15 cm.

$$LA = \pi rs = \pi(8)(15) = 120\pi \text{ cm}^2 \approx 377.0 \text{ cm}^2$$

2. Find the surface area of the cone in Alternate Example 1.

$$SA = LA + B = LA + \pi r^2 = 120\pi + \pi(8)^2 = 184\pi \text{ cm}^2 \approx 578.1 \text{ cm}^2$$

Additional terminology for cones is similar to that for pyramids and is shown in the figure on page 615.

The results for the lateral area and surface area of a right cylinder are presented below as theorems, along with the corresponding formulas for a right cone.

THEOREMS ABOUT CYLINDERS

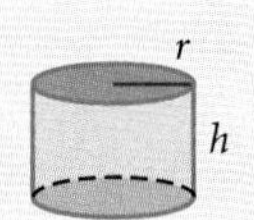

The lateral area of a right cylinder is the product of the circumference of its base and the height of the cylinder.
$LA = 2\pi rh$

The surface area of a right cylinder is the sum of its lateral area and the areas of its bases. $SA = LA + 2B = 2\pi rh + 2\pi r^2$

THEOREMS ABOUT CONES

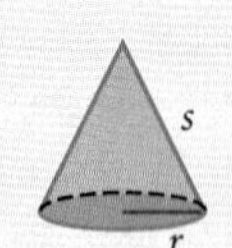

The lateral area of a right cone is one-half the product of the circumference of its base and the slant height of the cone. $LA = \frac{1}{2} \cdot 2\pi rs = \pi rs$

The surface area of a right cone is the sum of its lateral area and the area of its base. $SA = LA + B = \pi rs + \pi r^2$

1. Compare the formulas for the surface areas of a right prism and a right cylinder. Explain the similarities and differences between the two.

EXAMPLES

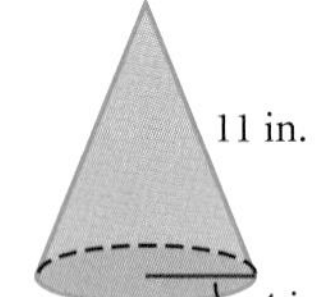

1. Find the lateral area of a right cone whose base radius is 4 in. and slant height is 11 in.

   $LA = \pi rs = \pi(4)(11) = 44\pi \text{ in.}^2 \approx 138.2 \text{ in.}^2$

2. Find the surface area of the cone.

   $SA = LA + B = LA + \pi r^2 = 44\pi + \pi(4)^2 = 60\pi \text{ in.}^2 \approx 188.5 \text{ in.}^2$

REFLECT

1. Name some products that are packaged in cylindrical containers.
2. Compare the formulas for the surface areas of a regular pyramid and a right cone. Explain the similarities and differences between the two.
3. Sketch a net for a right cylinder. Use the net to justify the formulas for the lateral area and the surface area of a cylinder.

Exercises

CORE

Where necessary, approximate answers are given in the margin notes.

1. **Getting Started** Follow the steps to find the surface area of the cylinder.
   a. What is the shape of the lateral surface of the cylinder? Rectangle
   b. You are given the height of the lateral surface of the cylinder. To find its width, use the radius of a base to find the circumference of a base. What is the lateral area of the cylinder? 60π cm^2
   c. What is the area of one of the circular bases? What is the total area of the bases? 25π cm^2; 50π cm^2
   d. What is the surface area of the cylinder? 110π cm^2

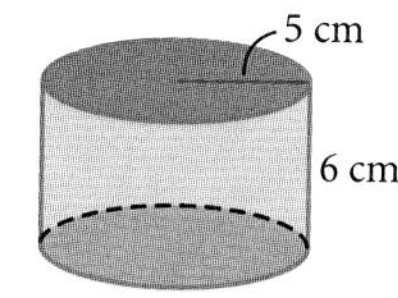

Find the lateral area and surface area of a right cylinder, given each set of dimensions.

2. Radius = 6 cm, height = 10 cm 120π cm^2; 192π cm^2
3. Base circumference = 8π in., height = 9 in. 72π in.^{2}; 104π in.^{2}
4. Radius = 5.5 m, height = 11.4 m 125.4π m^2; 185.9π m^2

Find the lateral area and surface area of a right cone, given each set of dimensions.

5. Base radius = 3 in., slant height = 8 in. 24π in.^{2}; 33π in.^{2}
6. Base circumference = 3π cm, slant height = 5 cm 7.5π cm^2; 9.75π cm^2
7. Base radius = 2.4 ft, height = 6.3 ft 50.8 ft^2; 68.9 ft^2
8. Base circumference = 22.3 mm, slant height = 8.5 mm 94.8 mm^2; 134.3 mm^2

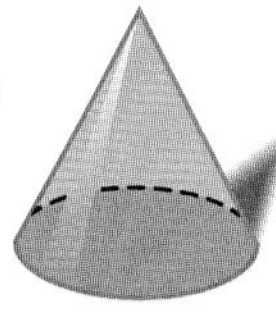

Determine whether each statement is true or false. If the statement is false, change the underlined word or phrase to make it true.

9. The bases of a cylinder are two <u>congruent</u> circles. T
10. The <u>height</u> of a right cone is the length of a segment along the surface of the cone from vertex to base. F; Slant height

Journal

Explore Step 3 and **Reflect** 1 and 2 are suitable for journal entries.

REFLECT

Possible Answers

1. Oatmeal, canned drinks, posters, etc.
2. Both formulas are equal to the lateral area plus the base area. Both lateral areas are equal to one-half the product of the distance around the base times the slant height of the solid. Because the cone has a circular base, we use $2\pi r$ for the base circumference (instead of perimeter) and πr^2 for the base area in these formulas.
3. The net consists of a rectangle or parallelogram with two congruent circles tangent to two of its opposite sides.

Part C Exercises

Exercise Notes

Core

14. Students see that two cylinders with the same lateral area may not have the same surface area.

Look Ahead

16. Looks ahead to the concept of volume, the central idea of 9-2.

17. Reminds students of the reasoning behind the formula for the area of a rectangle. Parallel reasoning will be used to present the formula for the volume of a rectangular solid.

More Math Reasoning

26. An applications problem. Students see that there are many issues involved in the efficient use of packaging materials.

Ongoing Assessment

Vocabulary
Practice/Skills
Review
Math Reasoning
Problem Solving
Challenge

Self-Assessment Exercises 1–15 odd

Embedded Assessment Try It a, b; Exercises 6, 12, 14

9-1

Surface Area

Exercise Answers

Core

1. a. Rectangle/parallelogram

b. $60\pi \approx 188.5$ cm^2

c. 25π cm^2; $50\pi \approx 157.1$ cm^2

d. $110\pi \approx 345.6$ cm^2

2. $120\pi \approx 377.0$ cm^2; $192\pi \approx 603.2$ cm^2

3. $72\pi \approx 226.2$ in.^{2}; $104\pi \approx 326.7$ in.^{2}

4. $125.4\pi \approx 394.0$ m^2; $185.9\pi \approx 584.0$ m^2

5. $24\pi \approx 75.4$ in.^{2}; $33\pi \approx 103.7$ in.^{2}

6. $7.5\pi \approx 23.6$ cm^2; $9.75\pi \approx 30.6$ cm^2

7. 50.8 ft^2; 68.9 ft^2

8. 94.8 mm^2; 134.3 mm^2

9. T

10. F; Slant height **11.** 304.52 cm^2

12. a. 3.95 **b.** 196

13. $52\pi \approx 163.4$ in.^{2} more

14. $r_1 \approx 1.75$ in.; $h_1 = 8.5$ in.; $r_2 \approx 1.35$ in.; $h_2 = 11$ in.; LA of both $= 93.5$ in.^{2}; The first cylinder has the greater surface area.

15. ≈ 877.8 ft^2

Look Ahead

16. Yes; Equal surface areas do not necessarily enclose equal amounts of space.

17. Possible answer: If you divide the rectangle into squares it has l rows of w squares each.

PS **11. In Hot Water** You can make coffee by putting coffee grounds into a conical filter, then putting the filter into a funnel and pouring hot water through the grounds. If the funnel's height is 15 cm and its base radius is 6 cm, what is the surface area of the filter? 304.52 cm^2

P **12.** Suppose that a cylinder has a radius of r units, and that the height of the cylinder is also r units. The lateral area of the cylinder is 98 square units.

a. Find the radius of the cylinder. 3.95

b. Find the surface area of the cylinder. 196

PS **13. Eat Your Oatmeal!** Suppose that a cylindrical, regular-size box of oatmeal is 9 in. tall and has a radius of 3.5 in. The large box has a height of 11 in. and a radius of 4.5 in. If the boxes are made of cardboard, how much more cardboard does the large box use? $52\pi \approx 163.4$ in.^{2} more

PS **14.** An $8\frac{1}{2}'' \times 11''$ sheet of paper can be curled into an open right cylinder in two different ways. Find the height, radius, and lateral area of the two cylinders. If the cylinders are given bases, which has a greater surface area?

PS History **15.** A walled, sixteenth-century fortress in Zimbabwe, constructed for the Rozvi monarchs, features a 34-ft-tall conical tower, seen in the center of this photograph. The base of the tower is about 16 ft in diameter. What would the lateral area of the tower be if it were exactly conical? ≈ 877.8 ft^2

LOOK AHEAD

MR **16.** Do you think it is possible for two drink containers with equal surface areas to be completely filled with different amounts of liquid? Explain why or why not.

MR **17.** Explain why the area of a rectangle is the product of its length and its width.

Key

- V Vocabulary
- P Practice/Skills
- R Review
- MR Math Reasoning
- PS Problem Solving
- C Challenge

MORE PRACTICE

Find the lateral area and surface area of a right cylinder, given each set of dimensions.

18. Radius = 3.7 m, height = 9.2 m 213.9 m^2; 299.2 m^2

19. Base circumference = 10π ft, height = 15 ft 150π ft^2; 200π ft^2

20. Base circumference = 2.9 ft, height = 7.3 ft 21.2 ft^2; 22.5 ft^2

Find the lateral area and surface area of a right cone, given each set of dimensions.

21. Base radius = 6 in., height = 8 in. 60π in.^{2}; 96π in.^{2}

22. Base circumference = 8.2 mm, slant height = 15 mm 61.5 mm^2; 66.85 mm^2

23. Base radius = 7.2 ft, height = 8.9 ft 258.94 ft^2; 421.80 ft^2

24. Base circumference = 4π cm, slant height = 8 cm 16π cm^2; 20π cm^2

MORE MATH REASONING

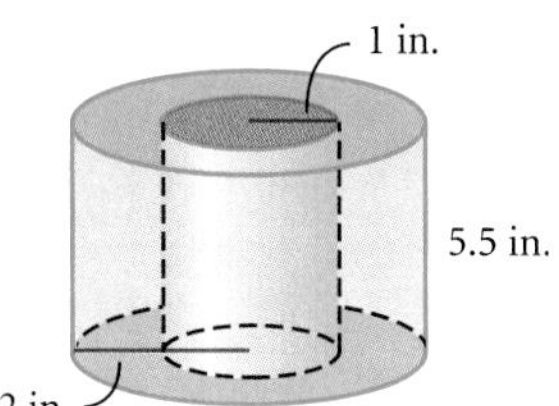

25. One of the blocks in a child's building set is a hollow cylinder, as shown. Find its surface area. 39π in.^{2}

26. Tea for Two A cylindrical aluminum iced tea can is 12.3 cm tall and has a radius of approximately 3.1 cm. A square prism (box) with the same height that holds almost exactly the same amount of liquid has base side lengths of 5.5 cm.

a. Find the total surface area for 24 containers of each type. Identify the container that uses more aluminum, and tell how much more aluminum it uses per 24-container case.

b. Suppose these containers are shipped in cardboard cartons in a 4×6 arrangement. Which uses more cardboard, a carton for cans or a carton for boxes? How much more?

c. Name some other advantages and disadvantages of drink cans and drink boxes. Which container do you think is better for packaging drinks? Why?

More Practice

18. 213.9 m^2; 299.9 m^2

19. $150\pi \approx 471.2$ ft^2; $200\pi \approx 628.3$ ft^2

20. 21.2 ft^2; 22.5 ft^2

21. $60\pi \approx 188.5$ in.^{2}; $96\pi \approx 301.6$ in.^{2}

22. 61.5 mm^2; 66.9 mm^2

23. 258.9 ft^2; 421.8 ft^2

24. $16\pi \approx 50.3$ cm^2; $20\pi \approx 62.8$ cm^2

More Math Reasoning

25. $39\pi \approx 122.5$ in.^{2}

26. a. Total for cylinders $\approx$ 6474.4 cm^2; total for prisms = 7946.4 cm^2. Prisms use $\approx$ 1472 cm^2 more aluminum.

b. The carton for the cylinders uses more cardboard by 565.3 cm^2.

c. Check students' answers.

9-1

Surface Area

Part D At a Glance

Objective

To design packages for a consumer product, and to calculate their surface areas.

Development

In the **Explore,** students design two different packages for a consumer product and calculate the surface area of each package.

Suggested Materials

Student Construction paper, colored pens or pencils

First Five Minutes

Transparency FFM 9-1D

Sketch a right prism, a regular pyramid, a right cylinder, and a right cone. Give the formulas for the lateral and surface areas of each type of solid.

EXPLORE

Packaging Sells!

Recommended group size: 2

The Point

To design two different packages for a product, find the surface area of each package, and list the advantages and disadvantages of each design.

Look and Listen...

- For students who do not take the dimensions of the product into account when designing their packages.
- For students whose packages are not one of the solids studied in 9-1.

Ask...

- If your package is not a prism, pyramid, cylinder, or cone, do you know some ways to find or approximate the areas of its faces?

For Groups That Finish Early

Suppose that you must convince a committee to choose your package design. Develop a sales presentation for your design.

9-1 PART D Making Connections

← CONNECT → ***Businesspeople need to know about the surface area of product packaging. Carpenters, map makers, architects, and machinists also work with surface-area measurements. You've discovered how to calculate the surface areas of many three-dimensional objects.***

In the following Explore, you will use your knowledge of surface area to design a new package.

EXPLORE: PACKAGING SELLS!

MATERIALS

Construction paper (optional)
Colored pens or pencils (optional)

You've been selected to design the package for a consumer product.

1. Choose a product that you want to work with. (Possibilities include food, drinks, musical instruments, compact disks, or other products). What are some of the things you will want to take into consideration when packaging this product?
2. The manufacturer has asked for two different designs to choose from. Draw and describe two different package designs for your product. Include the dimensions of your packages, and be sure that the dimensions are reasonable for the product you've chosen.
3. Find the surface area of each of your package designs. Sketch nets of the packages if this helps you in your calculations.
4. What will your packages be made of? Explain why you decided to use these materials.
5. Make sketches of your final designs, showing how the packages will be decorated and displayed. Describe the advantages of each design.

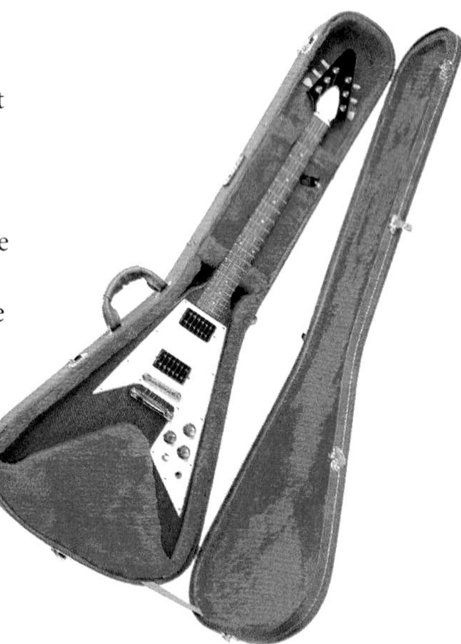

Student Resources

Alternative Lessons
Laboratory Manual 9-1D
Technology Lab Manual
Practice 9-1D
Study Guide and Journal 9-1D
Guía de estudios y Diario 9-1D
Multilingual Handbook
More Look Back 9-1D
SAT Preparation

Media Resources

Transparency FFM 9-1D
Transparency AE
Teaching Transparency
AWSMTest and practice software
AWSM Videodisc

REFLECT

1. Make a table of the lateral area and surface area formulas for right prisms, regular pyramids, right cylinders, and right cones. Summarize and explain the similarities and differences in these formulas as simply as you can.
2. Explain why the pyramid surface area formula you've worked with applies only to regular pyramids, rather than to all pyramids.

Self-Assessment

Where necessary, approximate answers are given in the margin notes.

Find the lateral area and surface area of each of the following.

1.

5.2 7.3 4.1

Rectangular prism

118.56; 178.42

2.

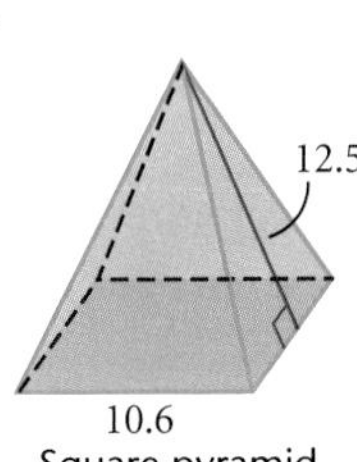

Square pyramid

265; 377.36

3.

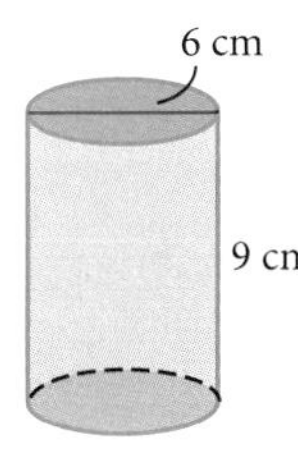

54π cm^2; 72π cm^2

4.

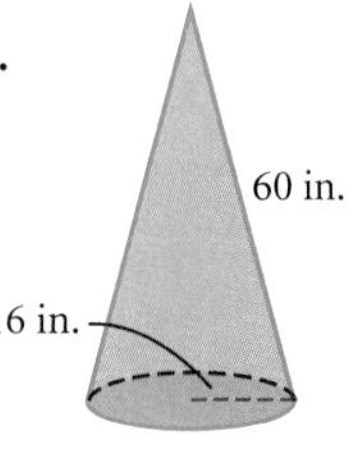

960π in.^{2}; 1216π in.^{2}

5. Sketch a net for a regular pyramid. Then use your net to justify the formula for the surface area of a regular pyramid.

6. Light-sensitive cell structures, called *cones,* in the retina of the eye enable people to see colors. If a cone has a radius of 0.01 mm and a slant height of 0.05 mm, find the surface area of the cone. $(6 \times 10^{-4})\pi \approx 1.9 \times 10^{-3}$ mm^2

7. Suppose a cylinder has a radius of x units and a height of $2x + 12$ units. Write an expression for the surface area of the cylinder. $6\pi x^2 + 24\pi x$

8. A regular pyramid is inscribed in a right hexagonal prism, as shown at the right. Find the surface area of each solid. 12,404.6 cm^2; 6643.0 cm^2

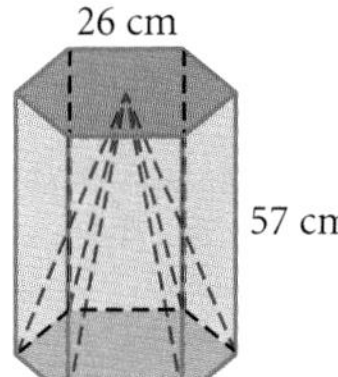

9. Suppose cylinder A has twice the radius but half the height of cylinder B. What is true about their lateral areas? (c)
(a) The lateral area of A is twice as large.
(b) The lateral area of B is twice as large.
(c) They are equal.
(d) The lateral area of A is four times as large.
(e) Not enough information is given to solve this problem.

Vocabulary
Practice/Skills
Review
Math Reasoning
Problem Solving
Challenge

Follow Up

Have students present their designs to the class. You might want to have students vote on the most creative or attractive design.

Possible Answers

Answers depend on the product chosen and packages designed.

Portfolio

Have students select items from their work that demonstrate their understanding of the material in 9-1.

You may want to have students include their best sketch of a net for one of the solids, an **Exercise** that involved the use of one of the solids in a package design, and a **Reflect** or **Consider** question where they compared and contrasted formulas for different solids.

REFLECT

Possible Answers

1. See Additional Answers p. T622.

2. In a regular pyramid, all of the triangles have the same slant height. If this is not true, the formula is not valid, and the area of each triangular face must be calculated individually.

Self-Assessment

Exercise Notes

9. Similar to multiple-choice questions on standardized tests.

14. Students compare the surface areas of several different designs for a drink container. Then they must choose the best design and defend that choice.

When discussing student solutions to this problem, you may want to note that minimizing surface area is *not* the only concern in choosing the best design. For instance, if the container is to be made of metal, the corners of the prism and the pyramid could be dangerous.

Surface Area

Self-Assessment Answers

3. $54\pi \approx 169.6$ cm²; $72\pi \approx 226.2$ cm²

4. $960\pi \approx 3015.9$ in.²; $1216\pi \approx 3820.2$ in.²

5.

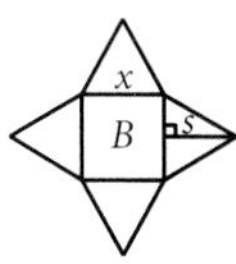

The surface area is the area of the base (B) plus the areas of the triangles.
For a base with n sides, the total area of the triangles would be $n\left(\frac{1}{2}xs\right)$. The perimeter is nx, so the total area of the pyramid is $\frac{1}{2}ps + B$.

6. $(6 \times 10^{-4})\pi \approx 1.9 \times 10^{-3}$ mm²

10. a. 4

b. Possible answer: $\triangle AGK$, $\sqrt{3}$; $\triangle ACL$, 2; $\triangle AHP$, $\sqrt{7}$; $\triangle ADQ$, 3.

c. They all are equilateral, like $\triangle FBA$.

11. a. $440\pi \approx 1382.3$ cm²

b. $33\frac{1}{3}\pi \approx 104.7$ cm²

c. 120°

14. Cylinder: 296.9 cm²; Square prism: 324.9 cm²; Square pyramid: 353.7 cm²; Cone: 324.3 cm². Possible answer: The cylinder, because it uses the least aluminum.

15. A segment perpendicular to a plane is perpendicular to every line in the plane that contains the point of intersection of the segment and the plane.

Algebra | Functions | Discrete Math | Logic/Reasoning | Industry/Careers

MR **10. a.** How many different sizes of triangles similar to $\triangle FBA$ with vertices at grid points are there on the grid at the right? (Do not include triangles on the grid that are congruent to $\triangle FBA$.) [7-2]

b. For each size, name one triangle of that size, and give the similarity ratio of that triangle to $\triangle FBA$.

c. Explain how you know that the triangles you named in **10b** are similar to $\triangle FBA$.

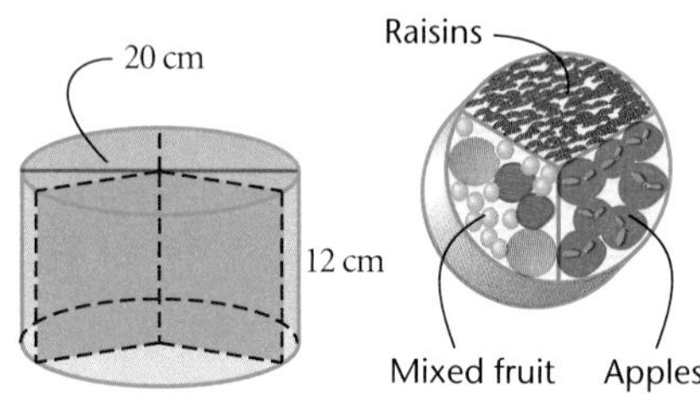

PS **11.** A cylindrical package for dried fruit is divided into three equal sectors, as shown.

a. Find the surface area of the cylindrical container. 440π cm²

b. Find the area of each sector of the circular base of the container. [8-2] $33\frac{1}{3}\pi$ cm²

c. Find the measure of each arc of the circular base of the container. [8-2] 120°

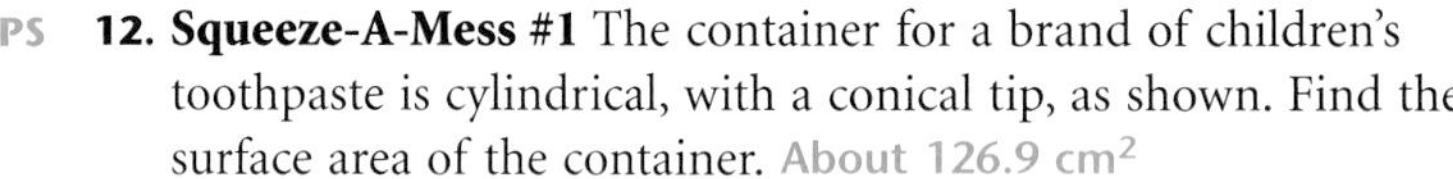

PS **12. Squeeze-A-Mess #1** The container for a brand of children's toothpaste is cylindrical, with a conical tip, as shown. Find the surface area of the container. About 126.9 cm²

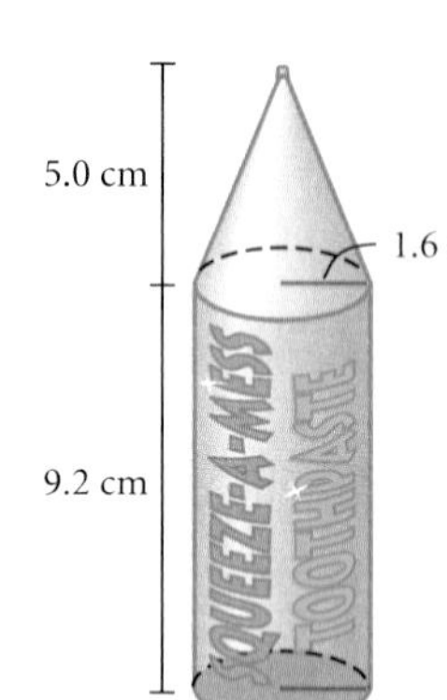

PS **13.** A square pyramid has a slant height equal to the length of a side of its base, ℓ. Write an equation that expresses the surface area of the pyramid as a function of ℓ. $SA = 3\ell^2$

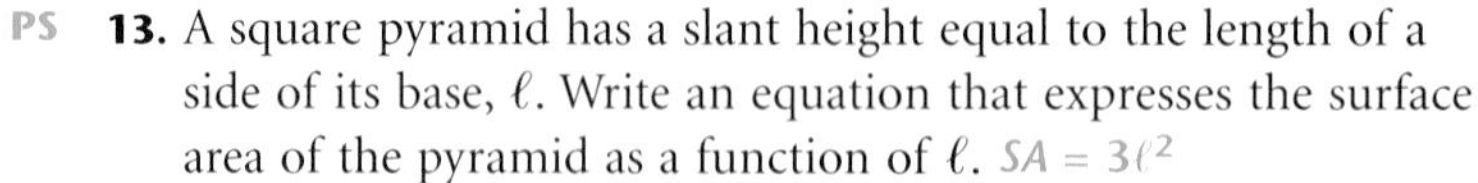

MR, C **14. A Fluid Design** The containers in the following chart all hold approximately the same amount of juice. Find the surface area of each. Then decide which you feel is the best choice for a juice container. Explain how you made your choice, and justify your answer.

Industry

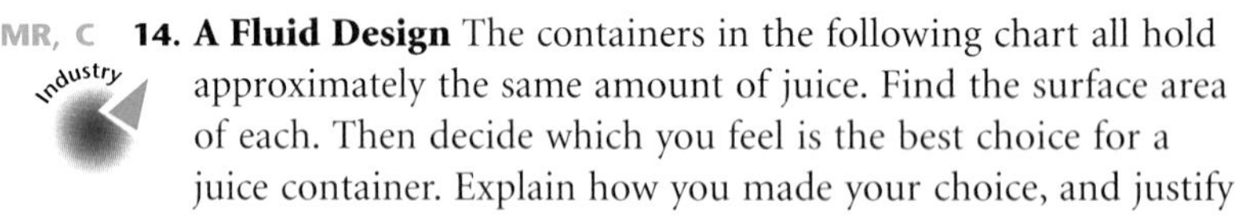

Container	Dimensions
Cylinder	$h = 10$ cm, $r = 3.5$ cm
Square prism	$\ell = 6.2$ cm, $w = 6.2$ cm, $h = 10$ cm
Square pyramid	sides of base = 8.5 cm, $h = 16$ cm
Cone	$h = 16$ cm, $r = 4.8$ cm

MR **15.** The definition of the altitude of a prism uses the idea of a segment that is perpendicular to a plane. Give a definition of *segment perpendicular to a plane,* and explain why your definition makes sense.

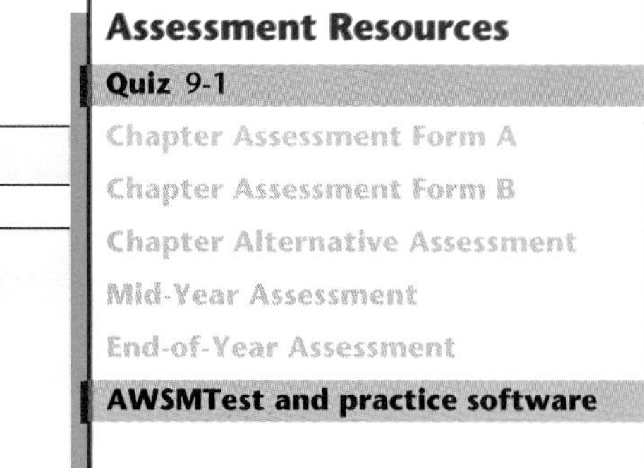

Assessment Resources

Quiz 9-1
Chapter Assessment Form A
Chapter Assessment Form B
Chapter Alternative Assessment
Mid-Year Assessment
End-of-Year Assessment
AWSMTest and practice software

Ongoing Assessment

Self-Assessment Self-Assessment Exercises

Embedded Assessment Explore Steps 3, 5; Ref 1, 2

9-1 Part D Reflect

1.

	Lateral area	**Surface area**
Right prism	ph	$ph+2B$
Regular pyramid	$\frac{1}{2}ps$	$\frac{1}{2}ps+B$
Right cylinder	$2\pi rh$	$2\pi rh+2\pi r^2$
Right cone	πrs	$\pi rs+\pi r^2$

The lateral areas of the prism and the cylinder are the distance around the base times the height; the surface-area formula of each is the sum of the lateral area and the areas of the two bases.

The pyramid is related to the prism in the same way that the cone is related to the cylinder. The lateral-area formulas for the pyramid/cone are similar to those for the prism/cylinder, but they have a factor of $\frac{1}{2}$ and use the slant height instead of the height. The surface-area formulas for the pyramid/cone add the area of the (one) base to the lateral area.

9-2

Volume

SUPERLESSON AT A GLANCE

Superlesson Goal

Students will discover and apply formulas for the volumes of prisms, pyramids, cylinders, and cones, and they will see and use formulas for the surface area and volume of a sphere.

Management Guide

	Topic	Objectives	Key Terms	New Ideas	Materials
Part A	Volume of Prisms	To explore the concept of volume, and to discover and use a formula for the volume of a prism.	Volume	Volume, units for volume. Cavalieri's Principle. For a right rectangular prism, $V = \ell wh$; for any prism, $V = Bh$.	**Student** Cubes **Teacher** Models of prisms
Part B	Volume of Pyramids	To discover and use a formula for the volume of a pyramid.		For a pyramid, $V = \frac{1}{3}Bh$.	**Student** Cardboard, tape, scissors, filler material **Teacher** Models of pyramids
Part C	Volume of Cylinders and Cones	To discover and use formulas for the volumes of cylinders and cones.		For a cylinder, $V = \pi r^2 h$. For a cone, $V = \frac{1}{3}\pi r^2 h$.	**Student** Pennies **Teacher** Models of cylinders and cones
Part D	Surface Area and Volume of Spheres	To see and use formulas for the surface area and the volume of a sphere.		For a sphere, $SA = 4\pi r^2$ and $V = \frac{4}{3}\pi r^3$.	**Teacher** Tennis-ball can, tennis balls
Part E	Making Connections	To calculate the volume of Mount St. Helens, a conical volcano.	In Making Connections, students apply and synthesize key terms and new ideas.		

Pacing Chart (45-Minute Periods)

	Comprehensive Course	Core Course	Informal Course
Part A	1	1	1
Part B	1	1	1
Part C	1	1	1
Part D	1	2	2
Part E	1	1	1
TOTAL periods for Superlesson	5	6	6

NCTM Standards

Mathematics as Problem Solving

Mathematics as Communication

Mathematics as Reasoning

Mathematical Connections

Geometry from a Synthetic Perspective

9-2 Volume

A VOLCANO BLOWS ITS TOP

The above photo shows Mount St. Helens, located 95 miles south of Seattle, Washington.

Although a volcano may be inactive for hundreds of years, it can suddenly reawaken. In *The Eruption and Healing of Mount St. Helens*, Patricia Lauber describes a volcano unleashing its enormous power…

For many years the volcano slept. It was silent and still, big and beautiful. Then the volcano, which was named Mount St. Helens, began to stir. On March 20, 1980, it was shaken by a strong earthquake. The quake was a sign of movement inside St. Helens. It was a sign of a waking volcano that might soon erupt again.

On May 18, 1980, Mount St. Helens erupted. The force of the eruption equaled that of the largest hydrogen bomb ever detonated. Huge trees were uprooted and tossed around like toothpicks. The morning sky turned as black as night. Ash, deadly gas, flying rocks, and heat from the eruption killed about 65 people. Millions of deer, elk, birds, and other wildlife also perished.

When the mountain finally quieted, the eruption had ripped away 1200 ft of mountaintop. The destruction took only minutes. But the process of renewal will take many years.

1. **A volcano is an example of a naturally occurring cone. Give examples of other three-dimensional figures in nature.**
2. **Do you think the surface area of a solid is a good measure of the amount of material it can hold? Explain.**

More About Volcanoes

There are four types of volcanoes. *Cinder cones,* like Paricutín in Mexico, are created by a single vent and tend to be relatively small. *Shield volcanoes* are made almost entirely from lava and have gently sloping sides. Mauna Loa in Hawaii is a shield volcano. Lassen Peak in California is a *lava dome,* created mainly by expansion from within the volcano. The most spectacular volcanoes, including Mount Fuji in Japan and Mount St. Helens, are *composite* volcanoes. They are formed by several volcanic materials and tend to be conical and steep.

Where Are We Now?

Students have discovered and applied formulas for the lateral and surface areas of prisms, pyramids, cylinders, and cones.

Where Are We Going?

In 9-2, students will investigate the concept of volume and explore volumes for the solids listed above, as well as the surface area and volume of a sphere.

Students will explore volumes and surface areas of similar solids in 9-3.

Possible Answers

1. Sphere: planets, stars; cylinder: tree trunk; prism: salt crystal.
2. Surface area is not a good measure of the amount a solid can hold. It measures the areas of the faces of a solid, not the amount of space in its interior.

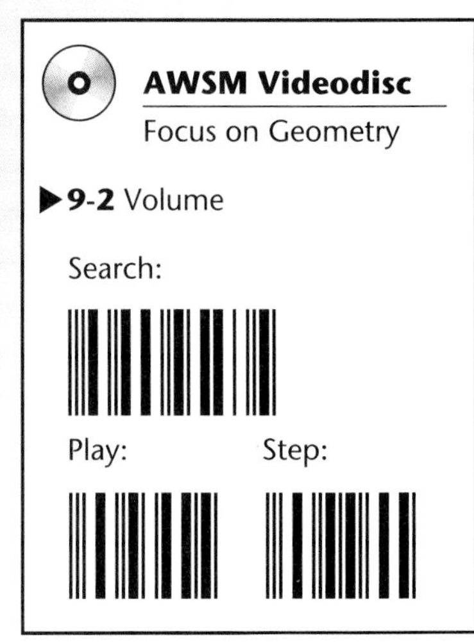

PART A At a Glance

Objective

To explore the concept of volume, and to discover and use a formula for the volume of a prism.

Development

Students see the concept of volume and comparisons of different units for volume.

In the **Explore,** students count cubes to find the volume of a right rectangular prism and then generalize their result so that it applies to all right prisms.

Next, students see Cavalieri's Principle and see why this result applies to *all* prisms.

Suggested Materials

Student Cubes

Teacher Models of prisms

Key Terms

Volume

First Five Minutes

Transparency FFM 9-2A

Read the material on page 624 and the top of page 625. Then answer the **Consider** question on page 625.

Motivate

Ask...

- What characteristics of a box affect the amount of material it can hold?

WHAT DO YOU THINK?

Students see two different but equivalent ways to convert units. Some students prefer to do the conversion in one step; others feel more confident if they do each multiplication individually.

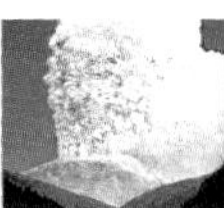

9-2 PART A Volume of Prisms

← CONNECT → *You know how to find the surface area of a prism. Now you will discover how to calculate its volume.*

The **volume** of a solid is the number of cubic units contained in the solid. Volume measures how much a solid can "hold."

A teaspoon holds $\frac{1}{6}$ of a fluid ounce of water. That's about 4930 cubic millimeters (mm^3).

A small glass holds about 8 fluid ounces of water, or 236.6 cubic centimeters (cm^3). It takes 48 teaspoons to fill an 8-ounce glass.

One cubic millimeter

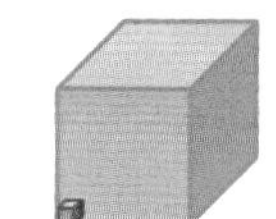

One cubic centimeter has 1000 times the volume of a cubic millimeter.

The volume of a typical refrigerator is about 1.1 cubic meters (m^3). That's 1,100,000 cm^3, the volume of about 4650 8-ounce glasses of water.

Lake Mead (shown on the left), on the Nevada-Arizona border, has a capacity of 35,154,000 m^3. It would take about 148,600,000,000 glasses of water to fill Lake Mead.

The oceans of the world have a total capacity of 317,000,000 cubic miles. That's about 1.32×10^{18} m^3. It would take 37,560,000,000 Lake Meads to fill the world's oceans! Over 97% of the earth's water is contained in its oceans.

WHAT DO YOU THINK?

Maria and Janice needed to convert 2457 cm^3 to m^3. They were asked to explain their reasoning to the class.

Maria thinks . . .

There are 100 cm in 1 m, so there are 100^3 cm^3 in 1 m^3.

Therefore, I need to divide 2457 by 100^3 (or 1,000,000) to see how many cubic meters there are.

$$\frac{2457}{1{,}000{,}000} = 0.002457 \text{ m}^3 \text{ or } 2.457 \times 10^{-3} \text{ m}^3$$

Tips from Teachers

As in 9-1, students may feel that they have to memorize several formulas in 9-2. Again, you may want to stress general principles: The volume of a solid determined by congruent bases in parallel planes (prism and cylinder) is *Bh*, and the volumes of their "partners" that come to a point (pyramid and cone) are $\frac{1}{3}$ times as great.

Janice thinks . . .

There are 100 cm in every meter. So, I have to multiply 2457 cm^3 by $\frac{1}{100}$ three times to convert it to cubic meters.

$2457 \times \frac{1}{100} \times \frac{1}{100} \times \frac{1}{100} = 0.002457 \text{ m}^3$ or $2.457 \times 10^{-3} \text{ m}^3$

CONSIDER

1. If you convert 2457 cm^3 to mm^3, will the resulting value be greater than or less than 2457? Why?

EXPLORE: COUNT UP THE VOLUME

MATERIALS

Cubes (optional)

The photograph below illustrates the volume of a right rectangular prism. One way to find its volume is to count the cubes it holds.

1. Find the volume of the right rectangular prism shown. (Assume the edges of the cubes measure 1 cm.) Explain your method. Then write a formula for finding the volume of a right rectangular prism.

Problem-Solving Tip

You may want to make a model to help in your investigation.

2. The area of the rectangular base of the prism, *B*, is its length times its width. Using this idea, is there another way to write your volume formula?
3. Does your result apply to the prism at the right? Does it apply to any right prism? Explore this possibility, and then write your conclusion. See if your results agree with those of your classmates.

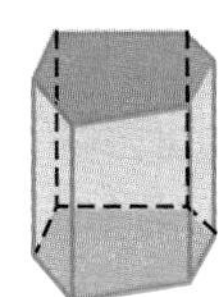

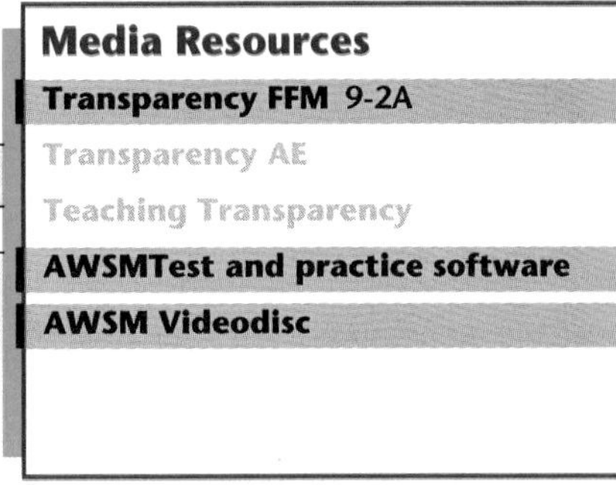

Student Resources

- Alternative Lessons 9-2A
- Laboratory Manual 9-2A
- Technology Lab Manual
- Practice 9-2A
- Study Guide and Journal 9-2A
- Guía de estudios y Diario 9-2A
- Multilingual Handbook
- More Look Back 9-2A
- SAT Preparation

Media Resources

- Transparency FFM 9-2A
- Transparency AE
- Teaching Transparency
- AWSMTest and practice software
- AWSM Videodisc

CONSIDER

Possible Answer

1. The resulting value will be greater than 2457, since you must *multiply* by 10 to convert centimeters to millimeters.

EXPLORE

Count Up the Volume

Recommended group size: 2

The Point

To discover a formula for the volume of a right rectangular prism, and, by generalizing the formula, to find a volume formula that applies to all right prisms.

Look and Listen...

- For students who do not see why their result for a right rectangular prism can be extended to all right prisms.

Ask...

- Suppose that the base of a right prism has an area of *B* units and a height of 1 unit. What do you think its volume is? If you stack *h* of these on top of one another to form a right prism, what is its total volume?

For Groups That Finish Early

Find the volume and surface area of a cube with an edge length of 2 cm. Then give the dimensions of a rectangular solid with the same volume but a different surface area. **$V = 8$ cm^3, $SA = 24$ cm^2; possible dimensions of other solid: $1 \times 1 \times 8$.**

Follow Up

Ask students to present their results to Step 3. To preview Cavalieri's Principle, ask them whether they think their result also applies to an oblique prism.

Possible Answers

1. Volume of prism shown = 42 cm^3; Volume of a right rectangular prism = ℓwh
2. $V = Bh$
3. The result applies to the prism at the right and to any right prism.

Algebra	Functions	Discrete Math	Probability	Data/Statistics

Volume

TRY IT

Find the volume of each right prism.

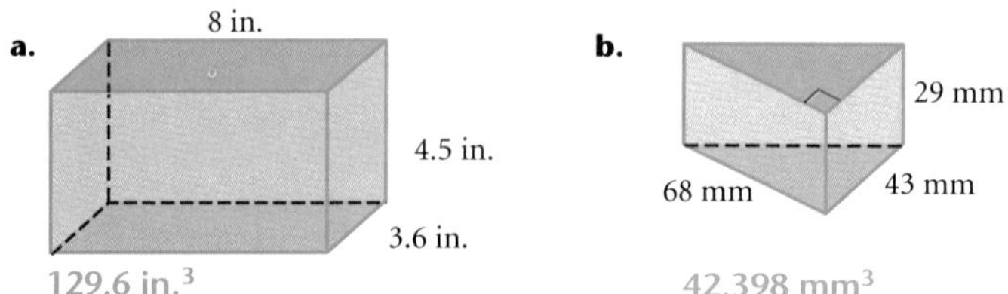

129.6 in.^{3} 42,398 mm^3

When you found surface areas of prisms, you had to be careful—the formula applied only to right prisms. Let's see whether this is the case for volume as well.

Suppose you have some neatly stacked concert programs several inches high. The stack is a right prism. If you accidentally nudge the stack of programs so that it forms an oblique prism, does the amount of space it takes up change?

No! Unless you add or take away programs, the volume of the stack must stay the same. The area of the base and the height of the stack are also the same as they were before. It seems that the volume of *any* prism is equal to the area of its base times its height.

The sliding stack of programs illustrates a postulate that is useful in deriving volume formulas.

POSTULATE: CAVALIERI'S PRINCIPLE

Suppose M and N are two solids. If every plane that intersects both M and N at the same height cuts off equal cross-sectional areas on each, then the solids have the same volume.

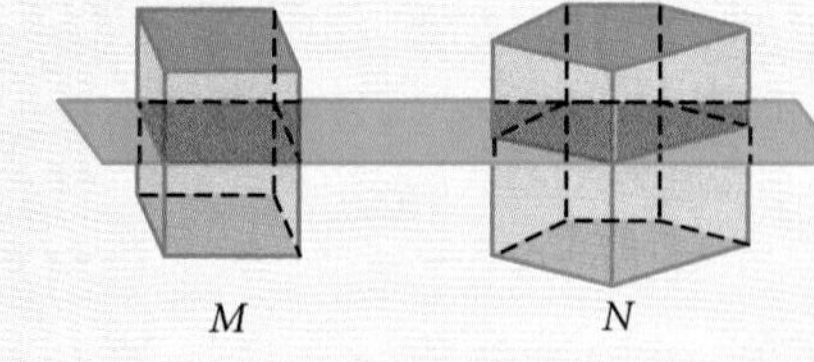

If the cross-sectional areas cut off are always equal, M and N have the same volume.

Research Note

All these perspectives [on teaching and learning] accept the premise that students are not passive absorbers of information, but rather have an active part in the acquisition of knowledge and strategies. (Mary Schatz Koehler and Douglas A. Grouws, "Mathematics Teaching Practices and Their Effects," *Handbook of Research on Mathematics Teaching and Learning,* Douglas A. Grouws, ed., p. 123. © 1992 NCTM.)

Cavalieri's principle ensures that if two prisms have the same base area and the same height, then they have the same volume. This is illustrated in the following figures.

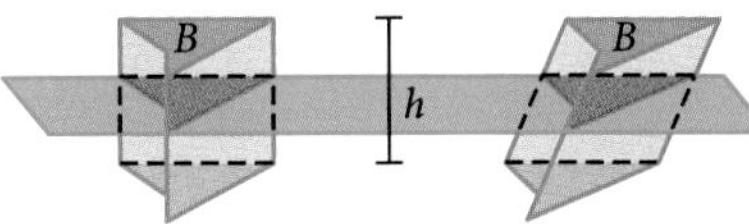

These prisms have congruent bases and equal heights. Their volumes are equal.

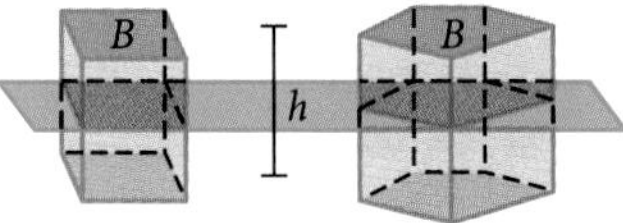

These prisms have bases with the same area and equal heights. Their volumes are also equal.

We can now state as a theorem the specific formula for the volume of a right rectangular prism, as well as a more general formula that applies to any prism.

THEOREMS

The volume of a right rectangular prism is the product of its length, width, and height. $V = \ell wh$

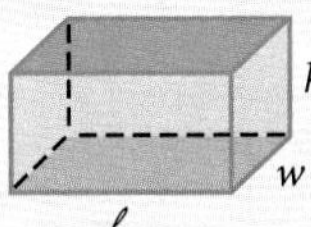

The volume of any prism is the product of the area of its base and its height. $V = Bh$

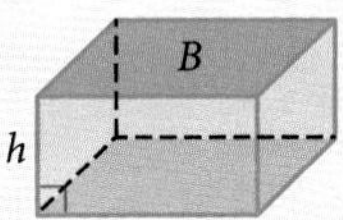

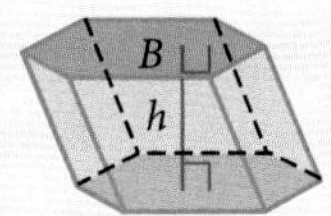

REFLECT

1. If the dimensions of a solid are measured in centimeters, what dimensions are used for its volume? What dimensions are used for its surface area?
2. If you manufacture flour that is packaged in boxes, does the cost of the material for the box depend on its surface area or its volume? Does the cost of the flour itself depend on surface area or volume? Justify your answers.

Careers Connection

Margarita Colmenares was born in Sacramento, California, in 1957, and she received her degree in civil engineering from Stanford University in 1981. Colmenares has worked for Chevron in many capacities, including that of air quality specialist. She was chosen national president of the Society of Hispanic Professional Engineers in 1989.

Journal

Consider 1 and **Reflect** 2 are suitable for journal entries.

REFLECT

Possible Answers

1. Cubic centimeters are used to measure volume; square centimeters are used to measure surface area.
2. The cost of the materials for the box depends primarily on the surface area. The cost of the flour depends on the volume.

Algebra	Functions	Discrete Math	Probability	Data/Statistics

Volume

Part A Exercises

Exercise Notes

Core

7. Students draw a visual comparison of cubic feet and cubic yards. Many students need visual confirmation of the fact that, even though 1 yd = 3 ft, 1 $yd^3 \neq 3$ ft^3.

19. Reminds students that surface area and volume are different quantities, even when the numbers associated with them are equal.

More Math Reasoning

31. Students use the measurements of an inscribed regular octagonal prism to find the volume of a rectangular solid. They need to use their knowledge of angles in a regular polygon and 45°-45°-90° triangles.

Exercise Answers

Core

7. 27 ft^3

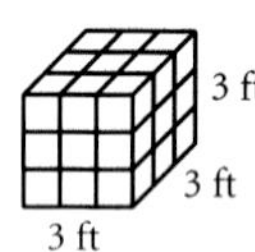

8. 162 ft^3

9. 2.24×10^{-2} m^3

10. 1 ft^3

11. 72,000 cm^3 **12.** 402.192 $in.^3$

13. $1075.2\sqrt{3} \approx 1862.3$ m^3

14. 550 cm^3

15. \$0.59 **16.** 84 ft^3

17. $3\sqrt{3} \approx 5.2$ cm

18. $2.125\sqrt{3} \approx 3.7$ $in.^3$

19. No; They have the same numerical value but are not equal since one is in cm^2 and the other is in cm^3.

Look Back

20. 4,181 ft **21.** 944 cm^2

22. 2105.1 cm^2

23. $210\pi \approx 659.7$ cm^2

Exercises

CORE

Where necessary, approximate answers are given in the margin notes.

P **Getting Started** **A meter is equivalent to 100 centimeters and to 1000 millimeters. Convert each quantity to the indicated units.**

1. 1 cm^2 to m^2 10^{-4} m^2 **2.** 1 m^2 to mm^2 10^6 mm^2 **3.** 25 cm^2 to mm^2 2500 mm^2

P **Complete each statement with the most appropriate unit (m^3, cm^3, or mm^3).**

4. The volume of a schoolroom is about 250 ____. m^3

5. The volume of a can of iced tea is 355 ____. cm^3

6. The volume of an allergy capsule is about 784 ____. mm^3

7. One yard is equal to three feet. How many cubic feet are equal to one cubic yard? Draw a three-dimensional sketch to illustrate your answer.

P **Convert each quantity to the indicated unit. Explain how you did each conversion.**

8. 6 yd^3 to ft^3 **9.** 22,400 cm^3 to m^3 **10.** 1728 $in.^3$ to ft^3

P **Find the volume of each right prism.**

11.

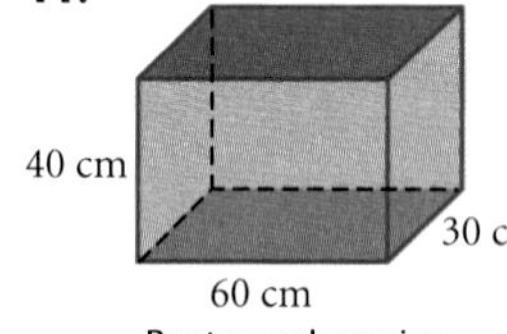

Rectangular prism
72,000 cm^3

12. 15.2 in. 8.4 in. 6.3 in.

Right triangular prism
402.192 $in.^3$

13. 11.2 m 8.0 m

Regular hexagonal prism
$1075.2\sqrt{3}$ m^3

14. 11 cm

Base area = 50 cm^2
550 cm^3

PS **15.** Marcia's garden needs watering equivalent to one-third of an inch of rainfall each day. If the garden has the dimensions shown and water costs 1.261¢ per cubic foot, how much will watering the garden in June cost her? \$0.59

10 ft, 8 ft, 6 ft, 4 ft, 2 ft

PS **16.** **Hog Heaven** A trough with trapezoidal cross sections has the dimensions shown. How much food will it hold? 84 ft^3

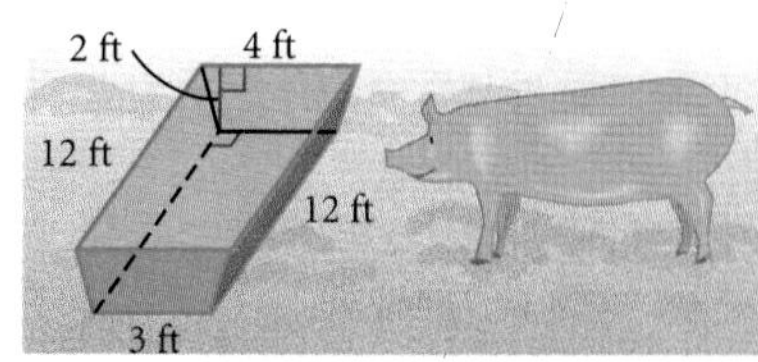

628 9-2 • VOLUME

Key

V Vocabulary
P Practice/Skills
R Review
MR Math Reasoning
PS Problem Solving
C Challenge

17. A cube has a volume of 27 cm^3. What is the length of one of its diagonals? $3\sqrt{3}$ cm

Diagonal

18. Quadrilateral Crackers Mr. Perry L. O'Graham, a high school math teacher, makes geometry cookies around the holidays. The base of his parallelogram cookie cutter is shown at the right. The cookies rise to a thickness of $\frac{1}{2}$ in. What is the volume of one cookie? $2.125\sqrt{3} \approx 3.7$ in.^{3}

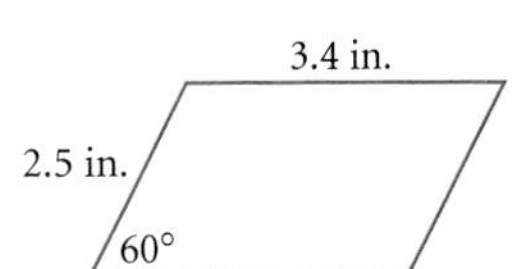

19. A cube has edges of length 6 cm. Are its surface area and volume equal? Justify your answer.

LOOK BACK

20. One of the most famous volcanic eruptions in history, the eruption of Mt. Vesuvius in 79 A.D., destroyed the Roman cities of Pompeii and Herculaneum. From 5 mi (26,400 ft) away in the Adriatic Sea, the angle of elevation to the top of Mt. Vesuvius is about 9°. Find the approximate height of Mt. Vesuvius. [7-3] 4,181 ft

Find the surface area of each figure. [9-1]

21.

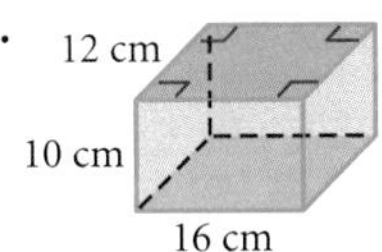

944 cm^2

22.

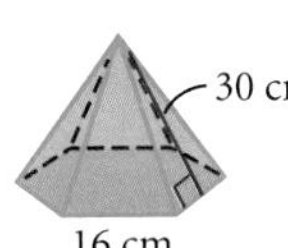

Regular hexagonal pyramid

2105.1 cm^2

23.

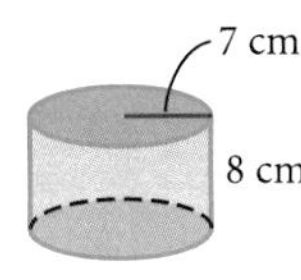

210π cm^2

MORE PRACTICE

Convert each quantity to the indicated unit. Explain how you did each conversion.

24. 54 ft^3 to yd^3

25. 700 mm^3 to cm^3

26. 12,000 cm^3 to m^3

Find the volume of each right prism.

27.

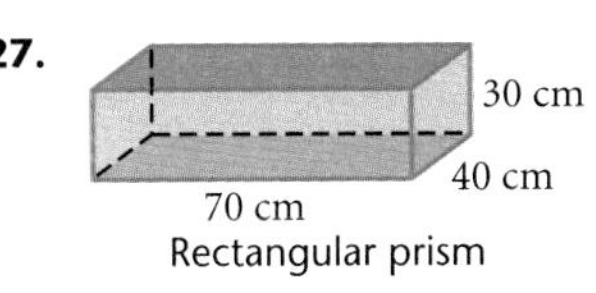

Rectangular prism

84,000 cm^3

28.

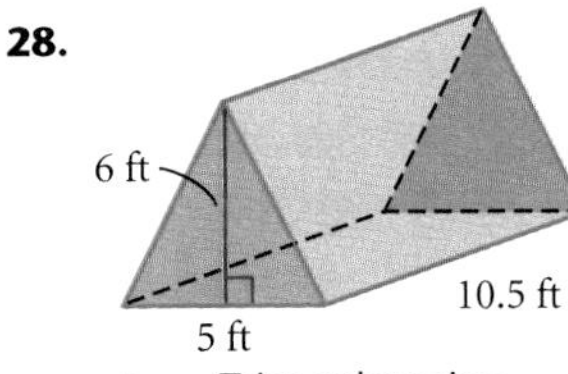
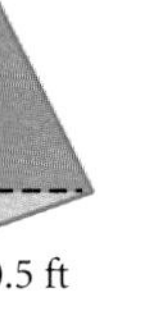

Triangular prism

157.5 ft^3

29.

5.1 in.

12.2 in.

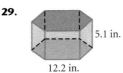

Regular hexagonal prism

$1{,}138.626\sqrt{3} \approx 1972.2$ in.^{3}

More Practice

24. 2 yd^3

25. 0.7 cm^3

26. 1.2×10^{-2} m^3

27. 84,000 cm^3 **28.** 157.5 ft^3

29. $1{,}138.626\sqrt{3} \approx 1972.2$ in.^{3}

More Math Reasoning

30. Length of side $\approx$ 6.3 cm; Height $\approx$ 12.6 cm

Ongoing Assessment

Self-Assessment Exercises 1–17 odd

Embedded Assessment Reflect 1; Exercises 10, 12, 16, 19

PART B At a Glance

Objective

To discover and use a formula for the volume of a pyramid.

Development

In the **Explore,** students make a prism and a pyramid with equal heights and congruent bases. Using filler material, they find that the pyramid's volume is one-third of the prism's volume.

Suggested Materials

Student Cardboard, tape, scissors, filler material

Teacher Models of pyramids

First Five Minutes

Transparency FFM 9-2B

Read the introductory paragraph on page 630. Then answer the **Consider** question.

Motivate

Ask...

- Can the height of a pyramid ever be greater than its slant height? Justify your answer. **No. A right triangle can be drawn that includes the altitude as a leg and the slant height as its hypotenuse.**

Compares a pyramid's volume to that of a prism with a congruent base and the same height.

Possible Answer

1. The prism has a larger volume. Except for the bases, the area of every cross section of the pyramid at a given height is smaller that the corresponding area in the prism.

Algebra | Functions | Discrete Math | Probability | Data/Statistics

MORE MATH REASONING

MR, PS **30.** A regular hexagonal prism has a volume of 1300 cm^3. Its height is twice the length of a side of its base. Find the height and the length of a side of the base of the prism.

MR, C **31.** A regular octagonal prism with base side length 6 in. and height 9 in. is inscribed in a rectangular solid as shown at the right. Find the volume of the rectangular solid. 1888.41 in.^{3}

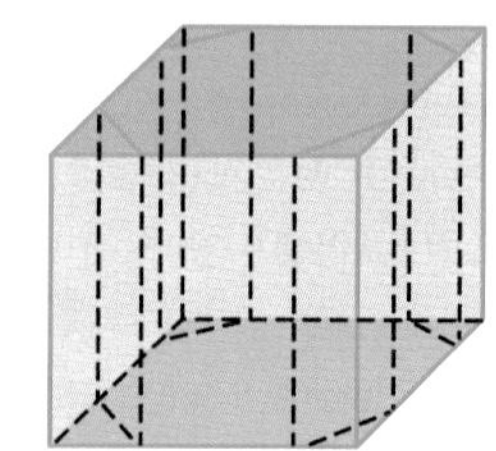

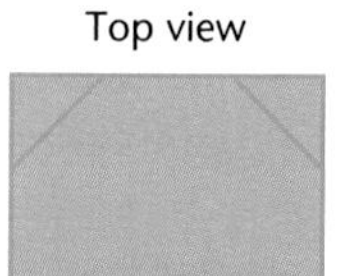

← CONNECT → ***You've seen that prisms and pyramids are alike in some ways. Now you will investigate a connection between the formulas for their volumes.***

A pyramid and a prism both have polygonal bases. However, the prism has the same cross-sectional area all along its height, while the pyramid tapers to a point.

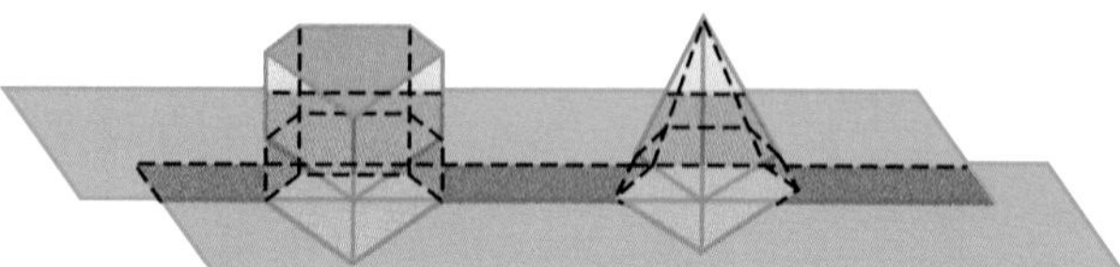

1. If a pyramid and a prism have congruent bases and equal heights, which has a larger volume? Why?

In the following Explore, you will investigate the relationship between the volume of a prism and the volume of a pyramid.

Key

- V Vocabulary
- P Practice/Skills
- R Review
- MR Math Reasoning
- PS Problem Solving
- C Challenge

Tips from Teachers

Using very small material in the *Explore* on page 631 increases both the accuracy of the results and the mess produced in obtaining them. If you use birdseed or sand, you may want to do this *Explore* outside or provide boxes to catch any spills.

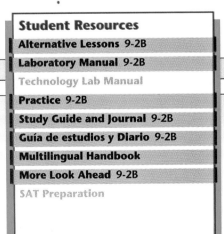

EXPLORE: "IMPRISMING" THE PYRAMID

MATERIALS

Cardboard
Tape
Scissors
Filler material

1. Carefully draw this net for an open prism on cardboard. Cut out the net, and tape it tightly together to form an open prism.

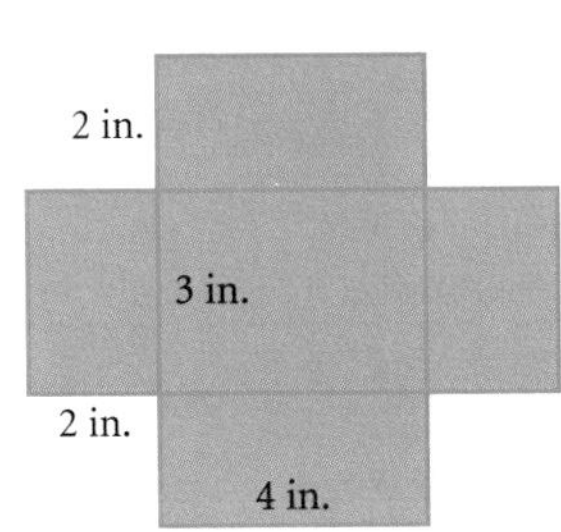

2. Use the dimensions shown to draw two sets of these triangles on cardboard. Then tape them together to form an open pyramid. (When taping the triangles, the two triangles with 4-in. bases should not be taped together.)

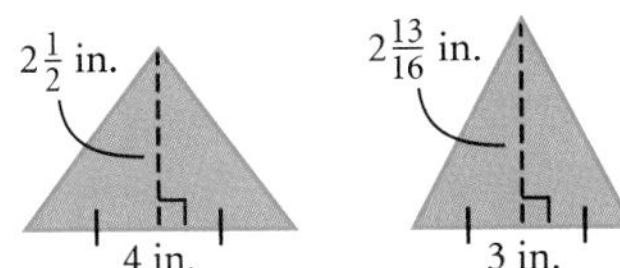

3. Use rice or other material to fill the pyramid. Then pour the contents of the pyramid into the prism. How many times can you fill the prism with the contents of the pyramid? Based on your results, write a formula for the volume of a pyramid with base area B and height h.

TRY IT

Find the volume of each pyramid.

a. 480 cm^3

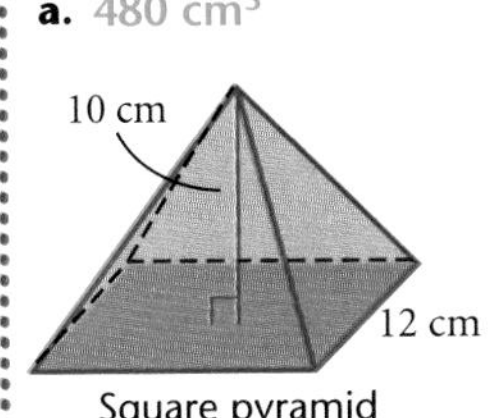

Square pyramid

b. 80 in.^{3}

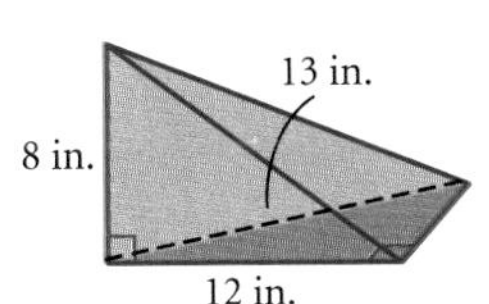

c. $180\sqrt{3}$ mm^3

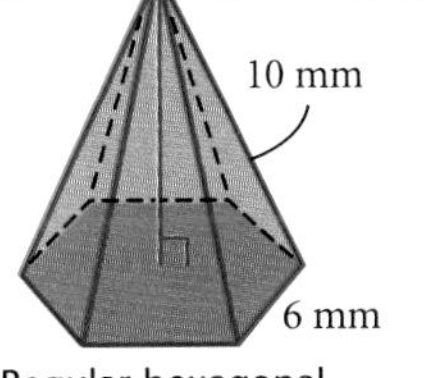

Regular hexagonal pyramid

Student Resources
- Alternative Lessons 9-2B
- Laboratory Manual 9-2B
- Technology Lab Manual
- Practice 9-2B
- Study Guide and Journal 9-2B
- Guía de estudios y Diario 9-2B
- Multilingual Handbook
- More Look Ahead 9-2B
- SAT Preparation

Media Resources
- Transparency FFM 9-2B
- Transparency AE
- Teaching Transparency
- AWSMTest and practice software
- AWSM Videodisc

EXPLORE

Imprising the Pyramid

Recommended group size: 4

The Point
To discover the volume formula for a pyramid by seeing how many full scoops of material from the pyramid it takes to fill a prism with a congruent base and the same height.

Look and Listen...
- For students who do not draw the nets or construct the solids accurately.
- For students who are trying to generate too precise a result for the materials used.

Ask...
- Do you think you can guarantee a precise answer with this method and these materials?

For Groups That Finish Early
Do you think your results for this **Explore** would have been as accurate if you had used larger, more irregularly shaped filler material? Explain your answer. **The results probably would have been less accurate, because the volume in the solids would not have been filled as efficiently.**

Follow Up
Ask students to share their results for Step 3. Also, ask them whether they think their results apply to any pyramid.

Possible Answer
3. $V = \frac{1}{3}Bh$

9-2

Volume

Journal

Reflect 2 and **Exercises** 12 and 14 are suitable for journal entries.

REFLECT

Possible Answers

1. $V = \frac{1}{3}\ell wh$

2. To find the volume of the frustum, find the volume of the complete pyramid, and subtract the volume of the missing top section.

Part B Exercises

Exercise Notes

Core

11. Students investigate pyramidal numbers.

14. Asks students to write a volume problem that has a given answer, and then write a solution for their problem.

Look Ahead

These exercises review cylinders and cones. In 9-2 Part C, students discover the volume formulas for these figures.

More Math Reasoning

24. A challenging exercise that uses similarity concepts. Students may use trial and error to find an approximate solution or, if they are familiar with cube roots, find an exact solution.

Exercise Answers

Core

11. a. The numbers 1, 4, 10,...,etc. are the number of balls needed to form a triangular pyramid stacked 1, 2, 3,..., etc. balls high.

b. 20, 35

12. Volume of cube $= s \cdot s \cdot s = s^3$; Volume of pyramid $= \frac{1}{3} \cdot s \cdot s \cdot s = \frac{1}{3}s^3$; Therefore, the volume of the pyramid is one-third the volume of the cube.

13. Possible answer:

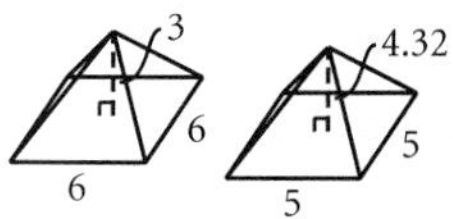

Algebra | Functions | Discrete Math | Probability | Data/Statistics

THEOREM

The volume of a pyramid is one-third the product of its base area and its height. $V = \frac{1}{3}Bh$

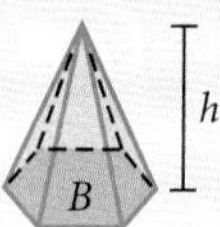

REFLECT

1. Write a volume formula for a rectangular pyramid with base dimensions ℓ and w and height h.

2. The photo at the right shows a structure in Meroe, Sudan, that is a *frustum* of a pyramid. A frustum of a pyramid is created when a pyramid is sliced by a plane parallel to its base. If you know the height and base area of the original pyramid and the height of the frustum and the area of its top base, describe how you can find the volume of the frustum.

Exercises

CORE

Where necessary, approximate answers are given in the margin notes.

P **1. Getting Started** Use the square pyramid shown for each of the following.

a. What is the height of the pyramid? 3 in.

b. What is the area of the base of the pyramid? 16 in.^{2}

c. What is the volume of the pyramid? 16 in.^{3}

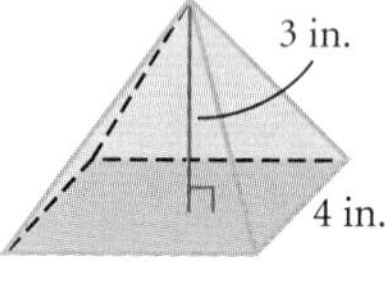

P **Find the volume of each pyramid.**

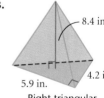

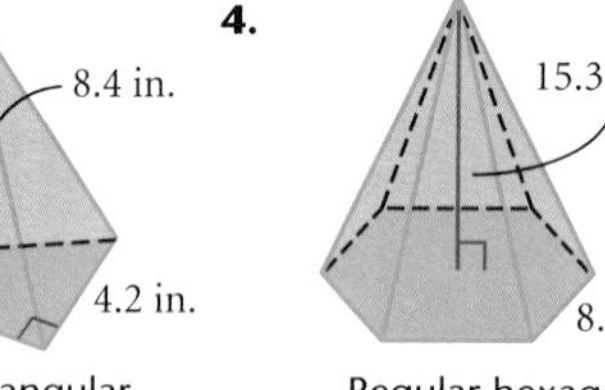

2. 10 cm; 4 cm. Square pyramid. $53\frac{1}{3}$ cm^3

3. 8.4 in.; 4.2 in.; 5.9 in. Right triangular pyramid. 34.7 in.^{3}

4. 15.3 mm; 8.2 mm. Regular hexagonal pyramid. $514.386\sqrt{3} \approx 890.9$ mm^3

5. 8 ft; 10 ft. Square pyramid. 384 ft^3

Key

V Vocabulary
P Practice/Skills
R Review
MR Math Reasoning
PS Problem Solving
C Challenge

6. A square prism has a length and width of 10 ft and a height of 15 ft. What is the height of a square pyramid with the same base dimensions and same volume as the prism? 45 ft

7. **Table Manors** A set of salt and pepper shakers looks like the towers of a castle. The base of each shaker is a square prism with base edges 3.5 cm long and a height of 8 cm. The top is a square pyramid with a height of 1.8 cm. What is the greatest volume of salt that one of the shakers can hold? 105.35 cm^3

8. A square pyramid is inscribed in the square prism shown. Find the pyramid's volume. 1296 cm^3

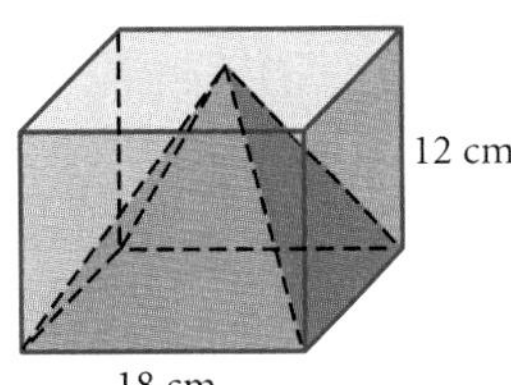

9. The volume of a square pyramid with height s and base side length s is 9 cubic units. Find s. 3 units

10. **Pyramid Pencil** A mechanical pencil is in the shape of a regular hexagonal prism topped by a pyramid. Find the volume of the pencil. $6.84\sqrt{3} \approx 11.8$ cm^3

11. The numbers 1, 4, 10, ... and so on are called *pyramidal numbers.*
   a. Use the figures below to explain why these numbers are called pyramidal numbers.
   b. Find the next two pyramidal numbers.

Top view

Side view

12. A square pyramid is inscribed in a cube, as shown at the right. Prove that the volume of the pyramid is one-third of the volume of the cube.

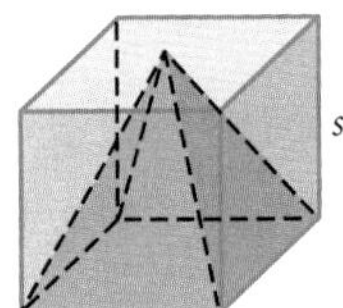

13. Sketch two different square pyramids that each have a volume of 36 in^3. Include dimensions in your sketches.

14. Write a volume problem about pyramids that has an answer of 100 m^3. Include a complete solution with your problem.

14. Possible answer: Find the volume of a square pyramid with base side length 6 m and height $8\frac{1}{3}$ m. Solution: $\frac{1}{3} \times 6 \times 6 \times 8\frac{1}{3} =$ 100 m^3.

Ongoing Assessment

Self-Assessment Exercises 1, 2, 3, 5, 7, 9, 13

Embedded Assessment Try It c; Exercises 4, 10, 11, 14

Algebra	Functions	Discrete Math	Probability	Data/Statistics

Volume

Look Ahead

15. 10 in.

16. $8\sqrt{10} \approx 25.3$ mm

17. Each cross-section is a circle. The cylinder has the larger cross-sectional areas since its side does not taper.

More Practice

18. 54.684 in.^{3} **19.** 39.975 mm^3

20. $21\sqrt{3} \approx 36.4$ cm^3

21. $96\sqrt{91} \approx 915.8$ cm^3

22. a. 24 in. **b.** 3,200 in.^{3}

LOOK AHEAD

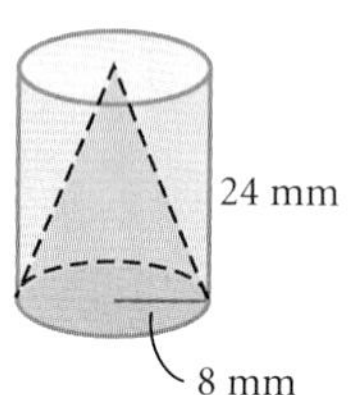

P **15.** The height of a right cone is 24 in., and its slant height is 26 in. Find its radius. 10 in.

P **16.** A cone is inscribed in a cylinder, as shown at the right. Find its slant height. $8\sqrt{10}$ mm

MR **17.** A cone and a cylinder have bases in the same plane. They have congruent bases, the same height, and they are cut by a plane parallel to their bases, as shown. What does the cross section of each look like? Which figure has larger cross-sectional areas? Explain.

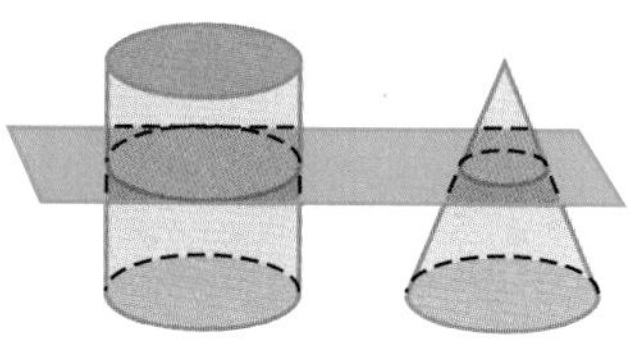

MORE PRACTICE

P **Find the volume of each pyramid.**

18. 54.684 in.^{3}

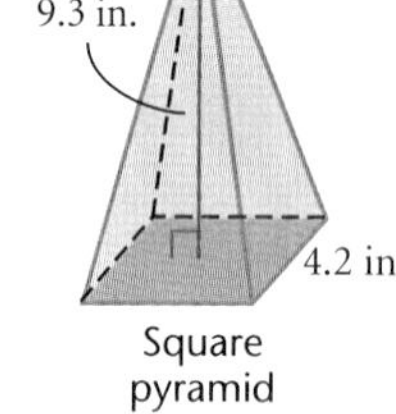

Square pyramid

19. 39.975 mm^3

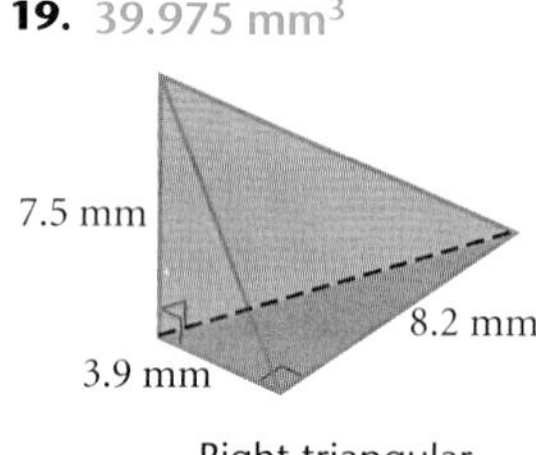

Right triangular pyramid

20. $21\sqrt{3}$ cm^3

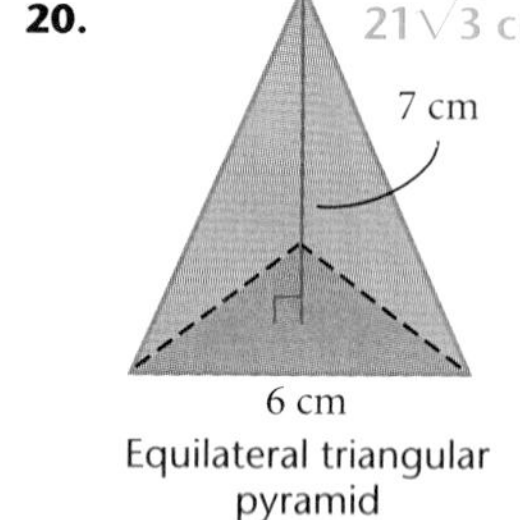

Equilateral triangular pyramid

PS **21.** A regular pyramid with a square base 12 cm on a side has a slant height of 20 cm. Find its volume. $96\sqrt{91} \approx 915.8$ cm^3

PS **22.** A regular pyramid with a square base 20 in. on a side has a slant height of 26 in.

a. Find the height of the pyramid. 24 in.

b. Find the volume of the pyramid. 3,200 in.^{3}

MORE MATH REASONING

$\frac{1000\sqrt{2}}{3} \approx 471.4$ cm^3

PS, C **23.** Find the volume of a regular octahedron whose edges are 10 cm long.

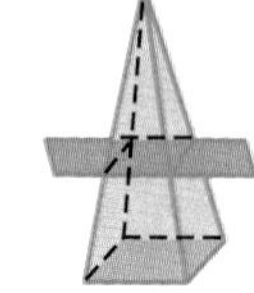

MR, PS **24.** A square pyramid has height 30 and base side length 10. A plane parallel to the base cuts the pyramid so that exactly half of its volume is above the plane and half below it. Where does the plane intersect the altitude of the pyramid? The plane intersects the pyramid about 6.19 units up from the base.

Key

- V Vocabulary
- P Practice/Skills
- R Review
- MR Math Reasoning
- PS Problem Solving
- C Challenge

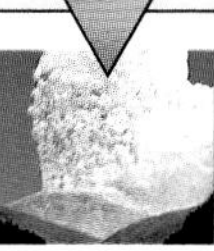

9-2 PART C Volume of Cylinders and Cones

← CONNECT → *You've already investigated the volumes of prisms and pyramids. Now you will turn your attention to solids with circular bases—cylinders and cones.*

You've seen some similarities and differences among prisms, pyramids, cylinders, and cones.

CONSIDER

Write the word that correctly completes each statement. Explain your answers.

1. *Pyramid* is to *prism* as ___ is to *cylinder.*
2. *Prism* is to *cylinder* as *pyramid* is to ___.

In the following Explore, your knowledge about prisms and pyramids will help you investigate the volumes of cylinders and cones.

EXPLORE: FORMULAS THAT MAKE CENTS

MATERIALS

Pennies

1. Take some pennies, and stack them into a cylindrical pile. Call the radius of a penny *r*. What is the formula for the area of the base of the cylinder?
2. If your stack of pennies has height *h*, what is the volume of the cylindrical stack? Explain your answer. If you used an idea that you've seen before, include it in your answer. Does this formula work for any cylinder, whether or not it is a right cylinder?
3. What do you think is the formula for the volume of a cone with the same base radius and height as your cylinder? Why? Compare your results with those of your classmates.

Student Resources

- Alternative Lessons 9-2C
- Laboratory Manual 9-2C
- Technology Lab Manual
- Practice 9-2C
- Study Guide and Journal 9-2C
- Guía de estudios y Diario 9-2C
- Multilingual Handbook
- More Look Back 9-2C
- SAT Preparation

Media Resources

- Transparency FFM 9-2C
- Transparency AE 9-2C
- Teaching Transparency
- AWSMTest and practice software
- AWSM Videodisc

PART C At a Glance

Objective

To discover and use formulas for the volumes of cylinders and cones.

Development

Consider questions review analogies involving solids.

In the **Explore,** students use a stack of pennies to discover the volume formula for a cylinder, and use the analogies from the **Consider** to predict the volume formula for a cone.

Suggested Materials

Student Pennies

Teacher Models of cylinders and cones

First Five Minutes

Transparency FFM 9-2C

A right cone has base radius 9 m and height 12 m.

1. Find the slant height of the cone. 15 m
2. If a plane parallel to the base cuts the cone 4 m from its vertex, what is the area of the circle it cuts off? $9\pi \approx 28.3$ m^2

Motivate

Ask...

- How are a prism and a cylinder similar? different?

Possible Answers

1. Cone
2. Cone

EXPLORE

Formulas That Make Cents

Recommended group size: 2

The Point

To discover volume formulas for a cylinder and a cone.

Volume

Look and Listen...

- For students who do not see how to use the volume result for a pyramid to predict the formula for a cone.

Ask...

- What is the volume formula for a prism? the formula for a pyramid?

For Groups That Finish Early

How can you use your stack of pennies and Cavalieri's Principle to demonstrate that your result in Step 2 applies to all cylinders? **Slanting the stack of pennies illustrates an oblique cylinder. The cross-sectional areas are still the same as for the right cylinder, so, by Cavalieri's Principle, the volumes are equal.**

Follow Up

Ask one student or group to present results for Steps 2 and 3. Have the class come to an agreement on these results before going on.

Possible Answers

1. $A = \pi r^2$
2. $V = \pi r^2 h$. The volume of a solid with equal cross-sectional areas (like a prism) is equal to the base area times the height. This result applies to all cylinders.
3. $V = \frac{1}{3}Bh = \frac{1}{3}\pi r^2 h$. The volume relationship between a cone and a cylinder is the same as that between a pyramid and a prism.

ALTERNATE EXAMPLE

Transparency AE 9-2C

Journal 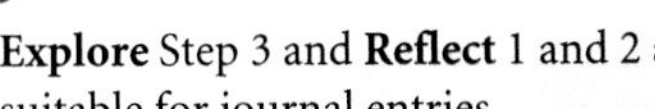

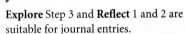

Explore Step 3 and **Reflect** 1 and 2 are suitable for journal entries.

REFLECT

Possible Answers

1. Fumiko can calculate the difference in the volumes of the water alone and the water with the rock.
2. Find the area of the complete cone; then subtract the area of the missing top.

EXAMPLE

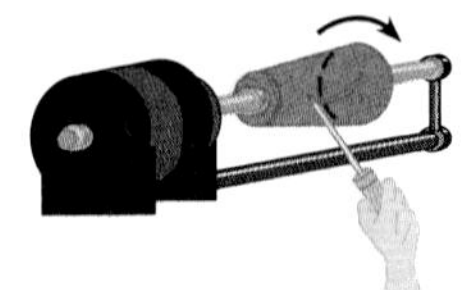

As part of a science project, Jocelyn used a lathe to help carve a model of a cone-shaped volcano from a wooden cylinder. If the base of the cylinder had a radius of 20 in. and its height was 12 in., find the volume of wood that Jocelyn cut away from the cylinder to make the volcano.

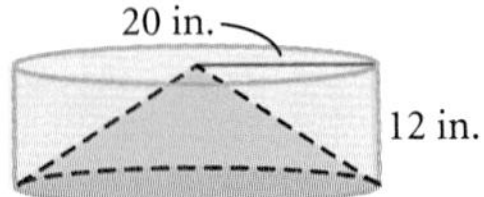

The volume of the wood that is cut away is the difference between the volume of the original cylinder and the volume of the volcano.

$$\begin{aligned} V_{\text{cut away}} &= V_{\text{cylinder}} - V_{\text{volcano}} \\ &= \pi r^2 h - \tfrac{1}{3}\pi r^2 h \\ &= \pi(20)^2(12) - \tfrac{1}{3}\pi(20)^2(12) \\ &= 3200\pi \text{ in.}^3 \approx 10{,}053.1 \text{ in.}^3 \end{aligned}$$

Jocelyn cut away about 10,053.1 in.^{3} of wood.

The volume formulas you've discovered for cylinders and cones parallel those for prisms and pyramids.

THEOREMS

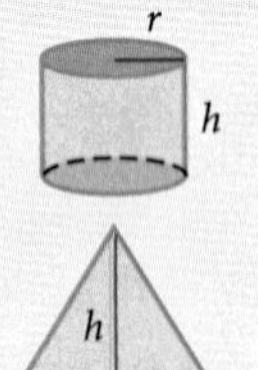

The volume of a cylinder is the product of its base area and its height. $V = Bh = \pi r^2 h$

The volume of a cone is one-third the product of its base area and its height. $V = \frac{1}{3}Bh = \frac{1}{3}\pi r^2 h$

REFLECT

1. Fumiko has a ruler, a cylindrical glass partially full of water, and an irregularly shaped rock. Describe how she can determine the volume of the rock.
2. Describe a method for finding the volume of a frustum of a cone.

Exercises

CORE

Where necessary, approximate answers are given in the margin notes.

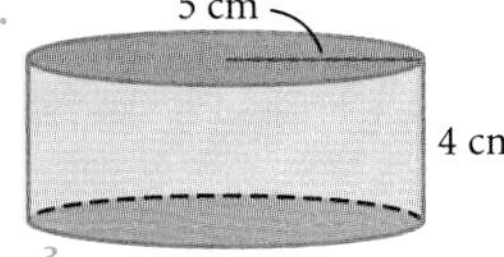

1. **Getting Started** Use the cylinder shown for each of the following.
   a. What is the height of the cylinder? 4 cm
   b. What is the area of a base of the cylinder to the nearest tenth? 78.5 cm^2
   c. What is the volume of the cylinder to the nearest tenth? 314.2 cm^3

Find the volume of each cylinder and cone.

2. 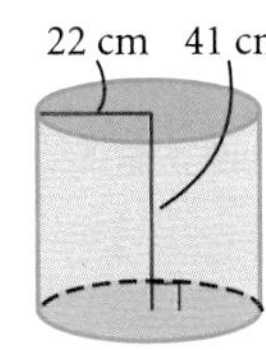

$19{,}844\pi$ cm^3

3. 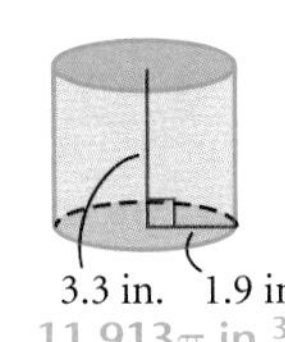

11.913π $in.^3$

4. 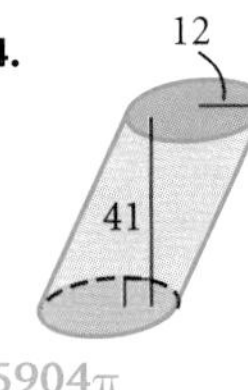

5904π

5. 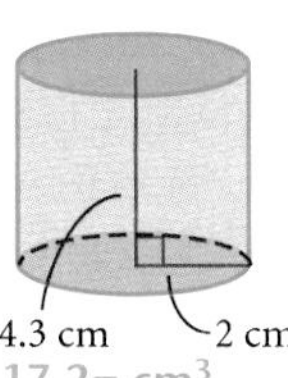

17.2π cm^3

6. 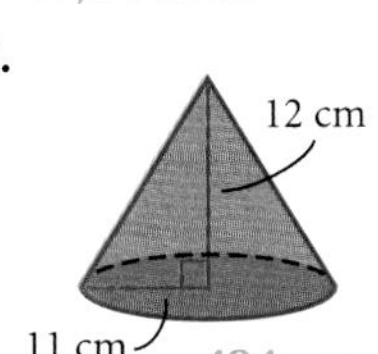

484π cm^3

7. 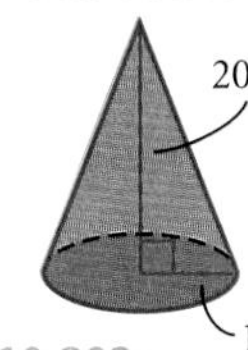

710.803π

8. 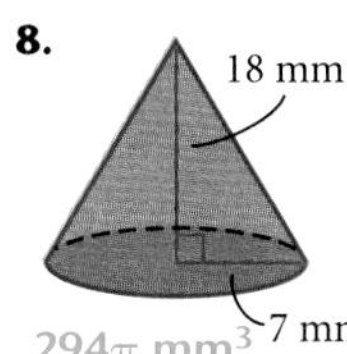

294π mm^3

9. 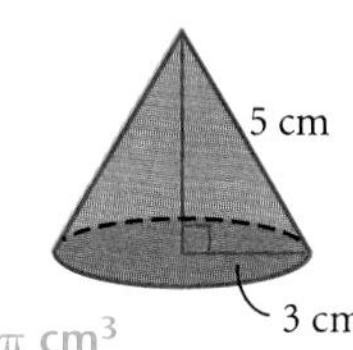

12π cm^3

10. **Martian Mountain** The tallest known mountain in the solar system is Olympus Mons on Mars. This extinct volcano is 15 mi high, 336 mi in diameter at the base, and is approximately conical. Find the volume of Olympus Mons. About 443,000 mi^3

11. The Bonaventure Hotel in Los Angeles consists of five cylindrical towers. The center tower has 36 floors, and the four surrounding towers all have 24 floors. Each floor is 10 ft in height. The center tower is 110 ft in diameter, and the outer towers are 85 ft in diameter.
    a. What is the volume of the center tower? $1{,}089{,}000\pi \approx 3{,}420{,}000$ ft^3
    b. What is the volume of each outer tower? $433{,}500\pi \approx 1{,}360{,}000$ ft^3
    c. What is the volume of the entire five-tower structure? $2{,}823{,}000\pi \approx 8{,}870{,}000$ ft^3

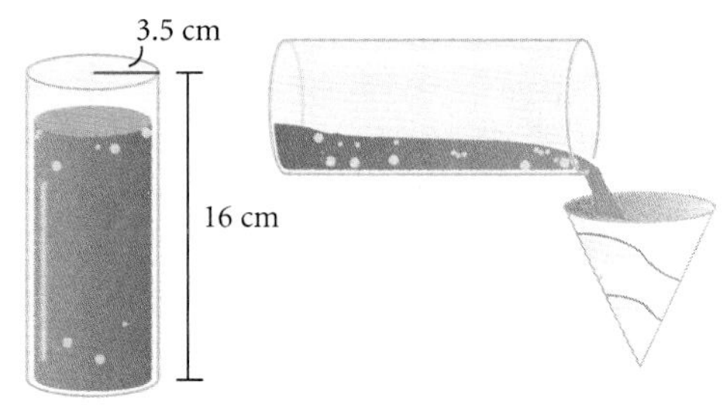

12. a. If the glass at the right is half-full of water, what is the volume of water in the glass? 98π cm^3
    b. Suppose you pour the water into a conical container with the same height and radius. To completely fill the cone, what is the minimum height of water needed in the glass? $\frac{16}{3}$ cm

Part C Exercises

Exercise Notes

Core

10. Students calculate the approximate volume of the largest known mountain in the solar system.

More Math Reasoning

31. In Part b of this exercise, students find the speed of water going through a hose.

32. Students describe a method for finding the volume of an irregularly shaped object.

Exercise Answers

Core

1. a. 4 cm **b.** 78.5 cm^2
c. 314.2 cm^3

2. $19{,}844\pi \approx 62{,}341.8$ cm^3

3. $11.913\pi \approx 37.4$ $in.^3$

4. $5904\pi \approx 18{,}548.0$

5. $17.2\pi \approx 54.0$ cm^3

6. $484\pi \approx 1520.5$ cm^3

7. $710.803\pi \approx 2233.1$

8. $294\pi \approx 923.6$ mm^3

9. $12\pi \approx 37.7$ cm^3

10. About 443,000 mi^3

11. a. $1{,}089{,}000\pi \approx 3{,}420{,}000$ ft^3
b. $433{,}500\pi \approx 1{,}360{,}000$ ft^3
c. $2{,}823{,}000\pi \approx 8{,}870{,}000$ ft^3

12. a. $98\pi \approx 307.9$ cm^3
b. $\frac{16}{3}$ cm

Ongoing Assessment

Vocabulary
Practice/Skills
Review
Math Reasoning
Problem Solving
Challenge

Self-Assessment Exercises 1–13 odd

Embedded Assessment Exercises 4, 8, 10, 12, 15

Algebra | Functions | Discrete Math | Probability | Data/Statistics

Volume

13. $7.5\pi \approx 23.6$ ft^3

14. a. Volume of cylinder 11 in. tall ≈ 63.2 in.^{3} Volume of cylinder 8.5 in. tall ≈ 81.8 in.^{3}

b. The lateral area of the two cylinders is the same.

15. The change in surface area is $2\pi rh - 2\pi r^2$. Therefore, the surface area increases if $h > r$. The volume always decreases by $\pi r^2 h$.

Look Back

16. Possible answer: A sphere is the locus of the points in space equidistant from a given point.

17. $64\pi \approx 201.1$ cm^2; $16\pi \approx 50.3$ cm

18. 4.5 in.; $20.25\pi \approx 63.6$ in.^{2}

19. 7 m; $14\pi \approx 44.0$ m

20. 9 m

21. $2042.5\pi \approx 6416.7$ cm^2

22. 3731.0 cm^2

23. $55.2\pi \approx 173.4$ in.^{2}

24. $94.5\pi \approx 296.9$ cm^2

25. About 167,000 ft^2

More Practice

26. $550\pi \approx 1727.9$ in.^{3}

27. $813.12\pi \approx 2554.5$ cm^3

28. $168.021\pi \approx 527.9$ mm^3

29. $392\pi \approx 1231.5$ cm^3

30. $2.025\pi \approx 6.4$ cm^3

More Math Reasoning

31. a. About 884 in.^{3}; About 389 in.^{3}

b. 117 ft/min

PS Fine Arts **13.** The pipes of a pipe organ are metal cylinders. Air forced through the cylinders produces musical notes. The larger the pipe, the lower the note it produces. The largest pipe on one pipe organ has a base diameter of one foot and is thirty feet long. Find the volume of the air inside the pipe. $7.5\pi \approx 23.6$ ft^3

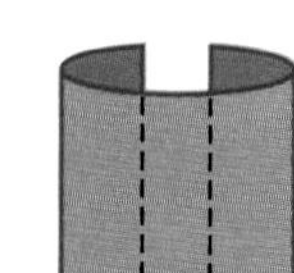

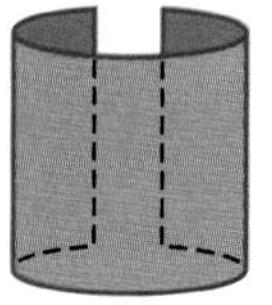

PS **14. Paper Cylinders** Any rectangular sheet of paper can be rolled into a right circular cylinder, as shown.

a. You can use an $8\frac{1}{2}'' \times 11''$ sheet of paper to make a right cylinder in two different ways. Use a sheet of paper to model these cylinders. Compare the volumes of the two cylinders.

b. What property of the two cylinders is the same?

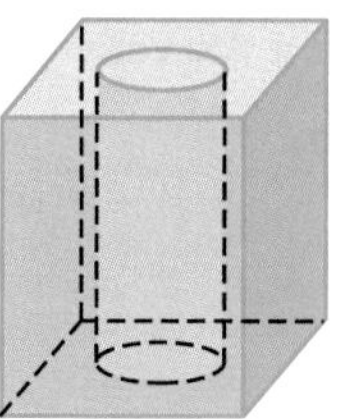

MR **15.** If you drill a hole through the prism at the right, as shown, does its surface area increase or decrease? What happens to its volume? Are these results the same for any solid, or do they depend on the solid and the size of the hole? Write a brief justification of each of your answers.

LOOK BACK

R **16.** In your own words, define *sphere.* [8-1]

R **17.** Find the area and circumference of a circle with radius 8 cm. [8-1] 64π cm^3; 16π cm

R **18.** Find the radius and area of a circle with circumference 9π in. [8-1] 4.5 in.; 20.25π in.^{2}

R **19.** Find the radius and circumference of a circle with area 49π m^2. [8-1] 7 m; 14π m

R **20.** Find the radius of a sphere if the area of one great circle of the sphere is 81π m^2. [8-1] 9 m

R **Find the surface area of each figure. [9-1]**

21.

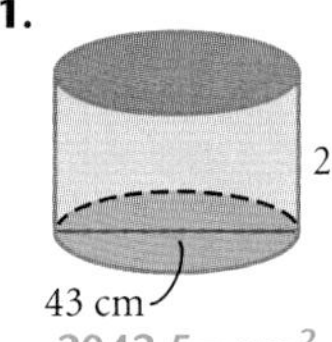

2042.5π cm^2

22.

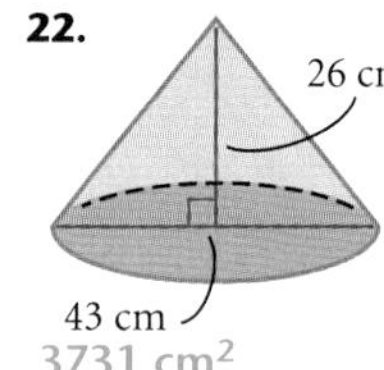

3731 cm^2

23.

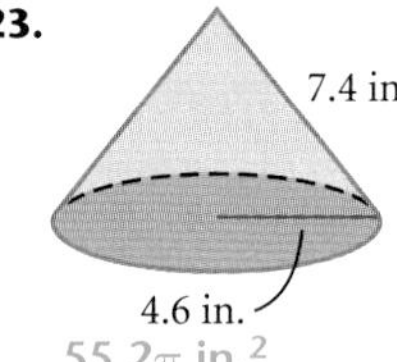

55.2π in.^{2}

24.

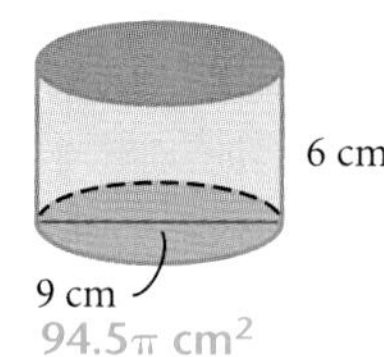

94.5π cm^2

PS, R Science **25.** In 1943, the first evidence of a volcano appeared in Mexico about 150 mi west of Mexico City. Within a week, the volcano, named Paricutín, was 140 feet tall, and its base had a circumference of $\frac{1}{4}$ mi (1320 ft). Find the surface area of Paricutín one week after its birth. (Paricutín was 7450 ft tall by 1993.) [9-1] About 167,000 ft^2

Key

V Vocabulary
P Practice/Skills
R Review
MR Math Reasoning
PS Problem Solving
C Challenge

MORE PRACTICE

Find the volume of each cylinder and cone.

26. **27.** **28.** **29.**

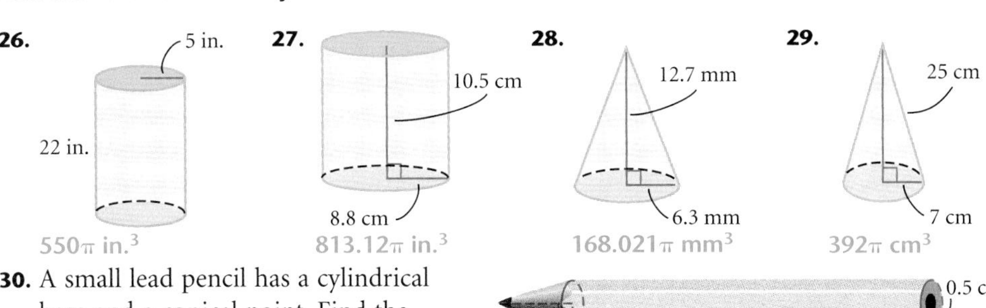

550π in.^{3} 813.12π in.^{3} 168.021π mm^3 392π cm^3

30. A small lead pencil has a cylindrical base and a conical point. Find the volume of the pencil. $2.025\pi \approx 6.4$ cm^3

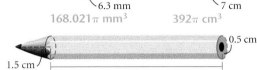

MORE MATH REASONING

31. a. A rubber hose 60 ft long has a $1\frac{1}{2}$-in. outer diameter and a $1\frac{1}{4}$-in. inner diameter. What is the volume of the water the hose can hold? What is the volume of the rubber in the hose?

b. Suppose the hose can fill a 1-ft^3 bucket in 1 min. What is the speed of the water through the hose?

32. The sculpture shown at the right is located in downtown Manhattan. Describe a method for finding the approximate volume of the sculpture. Subtract the volume of the cylindrical hole from the volume of the cube.

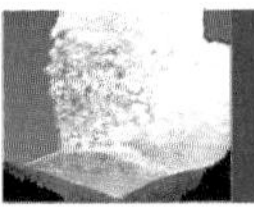

9-2 PART D Surface Area and Volume of Spheres

← CONNECT → ***You've investigated the surface areas and volumes of prisms, pyramids, cylinders, and cones. Now you will look at the surface area and volume of spheres.***

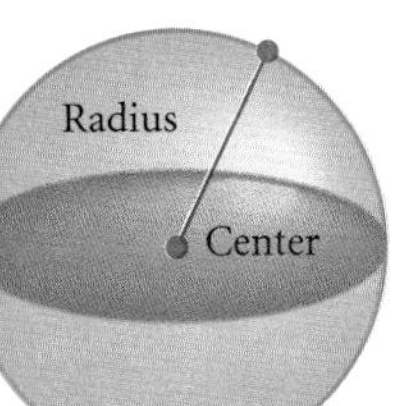

Prisms, pyramids, cylinders, and cones have at least one base. One solid that you've worked with before—the sphere—does not have a base.

You only need to know one measurement to describe a sphere—its radius. Therefore, it shouldn't be too surprising to discover that the surface area and volume of a sphere depend only on its radius.

Student Resources

- **Alternative Lessons 9-2D**
- **Laboratory Manual 9-2D**
- Technology Lab Manual
- **Practice 9-2D**
- **Study Guide and Journal 9-2D**
- **Guía de estudios y Diario 9-2D**
- **Multilingual Handbook**
- **More Look Ahead 9-2D**
- SAT Preparation

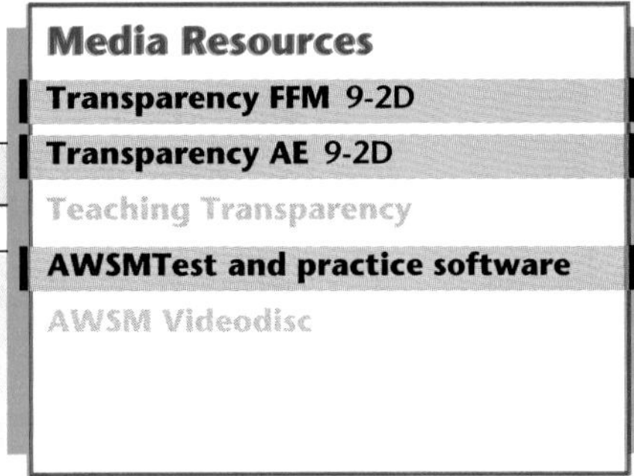

Media Resources

- **Transparency FFM 9-2D**
- **Transparency AE 9-2D**
- Teaching Transparency
- **AWSMTest and practice software**
- AWSM Videodisc

PART D At a Glance

Objective

To see and use formulas for the surface area and the volume of a sphere.

Development

First, students see the formulas for the surface area and volume of a sphere.

In the **Explore,** they use calculations of the volume of a sphere as they investigate whether a box or a can is a more efficient container for tennis balls.

Suggested Materials

Teacher Tennis-ball can, tennis balls

First Five Minutes

Transparency FFM 9-2D

Read the paragraphs at the bottom of page 639 and the formulas for the surface area and volume of a sphere on page 640. Then answer **Try It a** and **b** on page 640.

Motivate

Ask...

- Why do you think the surface area of a sphere depends on the square of its radius, while the volume depends on the cube of the radius? **Because surface area is measured in square units, and volume is measured in cubic units.**

Volume

ALTERNATE EXAMPLE

Find the volume of a sphere whose surface area is 100π cm^3.

$SA = 4\pi r^2 = 100\pi$

$r^2 = 25$; $r = 5$ cm

$V = \frac{4}{3}\pi r^3 = \frac{4}{3}\pi(5)^3 = \frac{500}{3}\pi$ cm^3
≈ 523.60 cm^3

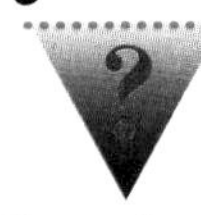

Shows that there is no lateral area for a sphere.

Possible Answer

1. A sphere has no base; therefore, it does not make sense to talk about the lateral area of a sphere.

EXPLORE

Tennis, Anyone?

Recommended group size: 4

The Point

To calculate the volume of a tennis ball and compare two containers for holding a stack of three tennis balls.

Look and Listen...

- For students who do not see that the heights of the cylinder and the prism must be six times the radius of a tennis ball.

Ask...

- Sketch a stack of three tennis balls. How is the radius of one of them related to the height of the stack?

THEOREM

The surface area of a sphere is 4π times the square of its radius. $SA = 4\pi r^2$

The volume of a sphere is four-thirds the product of π and the cube of its radius. $V = \frac{4}{3}\pi r^3$

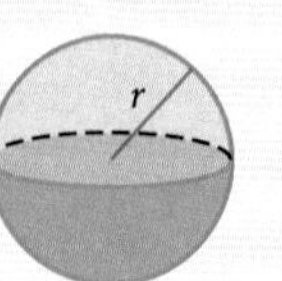

TRY IT

Find the volume and surface area of each sphere.

a. Radius = 5 cm $V = 166\frac{2}{3}\pi$ 523.6 cm^3; $SA = 100\pi$ 314.2 cm^2

b. The area of one of its great circles is 4π in.^{2} $V = 10\frac{2}{3}\pi$ 33.5 in.^{3}; $SA = 16\pi$ 50.3 in.^{2}

In the following Example, you will see how to work back and forth between the surface area and volume formulas.

EXAMPLE

Find the volume of a sphere whose surface area is 36π m^2.

First, find the radius of the sphere.

$SA = 4\pi r^2 = 36\pi$

$r^2 = 9$

$r = 3$ m

Now that we know the radius of the sphere, it can be used to find the volume.

$V = \frac{4}{3}\pi r^3 = \frac{4}{3}\pi(3)^3 = 36\pi \text{ m}^3 \approx 113.1 \text{ m}^3$

1. Does it make sense to talk about the lateral area of a sphere? If so, what is the formula for the lateral area? If not, why not?

In the following Explore, you will apply the formula for the volume of a sphere to see whether a can is the most efficient container for tennis balls.

Alert

The formulas for the surface area and volume of a sphere look quite similar, and students often confuse them. You may want to emphasize that the volume formula must have the radius cubed because volume is measured in cubic units, and point out that the 3 in the $\frac{4}{3}$ matches the 3 in the exponent.

EXPLORE: TENNIS, ANYONE?

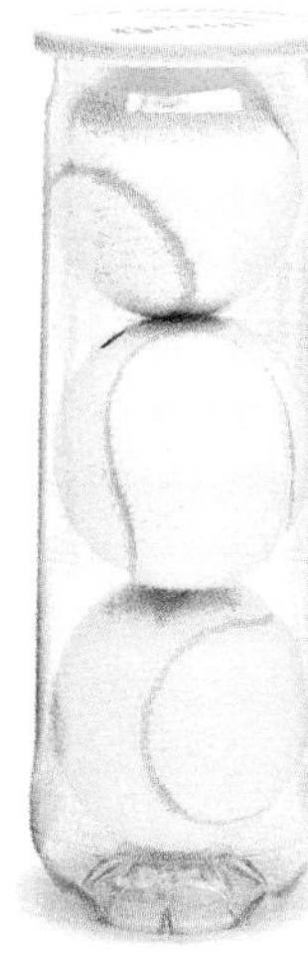

A cylindrical can of tennis "spheres" contains three balls, as shown. The radius of each ball is about 3.25 cm. Assume they fit snugly in the can.

1. Guess the percentage of empty space (volume) in the can.
2. Find the dimensions of the can. Then calculate the total volume of the three tennis balls and the volume of the can. What percentage of the space in the can is empty? How close is this to your guess?
3. Determine the dimensions of the right rectangular prism (box) that fits the tennis balls best.
4. Calculate the volume of this container and the percentage of wasted space. Compare your results to those from Step 2. Then calculate the surface areas of the prism and the cylinder to determine which container uses more material.
5. What three-dimensional figure do you think is the best for holding three tennis balls stacked on top of one another? Justify your answer.

REFLECT

1. A sphere has radius r. How many circles of radius r have the same total area as the surface area of the sphere?
2. Find formulas for the surface area and the volume of a hemisphere.

Exercises

CORE

Where necessary, approximate answers are given in the margin notes.

1. **Getting Started** Find the surface area and the volume of a sphere whose radius is 2 in. $V = 10\frac{2}{3}\pi$ in.^{3}; $SA = 16\pi$ in.^{2}

Use the given information to find each missing value for the sphere.

2. Radius = 5 cm Surface area = 100π cm^2 Volume = $166\frac{2}{3}\pi$ cm^3
3. Diameter = 8.4 in. Surface area = 70.56π in.^{2} Volume = 98.784π in.^{3}
4. Radius = $8\sqrt{2}$ in. Surface area = 512π in.^{2} Volume = $1365\frac{1}{3}\pi\sqrt{2}$ in.^{3}
5. Surface area = 8π m^2 Radius = $\sqrt{2}$ m Volume = $\frac{8\sqrt{2}}{3}\pi$ m^3
6. Volume = 288π mm^3 Radius = 6 mm Surface area = 144π mm^2

For Groups That Finish Early
Find the total surface area of the three tennis balls. Is their total area greater or less than the surface area of the cylindrical can? **398.19 cm^2; less**

Follow Up
Have a class discussion to decide which container is preferable. During the discussion, prompt students to give their answers for the percentage of wasted space and the surface area of each container.

Possible Answers

2. Can height = 19.5 cm; radius = 3.25 cm.
   Volume of the tennis balls = $3(\frac{4}{3}\pi r^3) \approx 431.38$ cm^3.
   Volume of the can = $\pi r^2 h = \pi(3.25)^2(19.5) \approx 647.07$ cm^3.
   Percentage of wasted space ≈ 33%.
3. The box that fits best is 19.5 cm tall, 6.5 cm long, and 6.5 cm wide.
4. Volume of the box = $19.5 \times 6.5 \times 6.5 \approx 823.88$ cm^3.
   Percentage of wasted space ≈ 48%.
   Surface area of the can ≈ 464.56 cm^2.
   Surface area of the box = 591.50 cm^2. The box uses more material.
5. The cylindrical can seems better because it wastes less space and uses less material.

Journal 
Explore Step 5 and **Exercises** 8 and 10 are suitable for journal entries.

REFLECT

Possible Answers

1. Four
2. For a hemisphere:
   $SA = \frac{1}{2}(4\pi r^2) = 2\pi r^2$
   $V = \frac{1}{2}(\frac{4}{3}\pi r^3) = \frac{2}{3}\pi r^3$

Ongoing Assessment

Vocabulary
Practice/Skills
Review
Math Reasoning
Problem Solving
Challenge

Self-Assessment Exercises 1–13 odd

Embedded Assessment Try It a, b; Exercises 6, 8, 10

Part D Exercises

Exercise Notes

Core

7. Students calculate the volumes of the sun and planets. Chapter 12 focuses on astronomy, and students will find many more measurements involving planets and stars.

Look Ahead

These exercises review similarity ratios, cubes, and cube roots. These concepts and skills will be important when students investigate surface areas and volumes of similar solids in 9-3.

More Math Reasoning

23. Students find the equation for a sphere in a three-dimensional coordinate system. The x-y-z coordinate system was also explored in 2-3 Part C, Exercise 33 on page 145.

24. Students see a justification for the area formula for a sphere that uses the concept of a limit.

Exercise Answers

Core

1. $V = 10\frac{2}{3}\pi \approx 33.5$ in.^{3}; $SA = 16\pi \approx 50.3$ in.^{2}

2. $100\pi \approx 314.2$ cm^2; $166\frac{2}{3}\pi \approx 523.6$ cm^3

3. $70.56\pi \approx 221.7$ in.^{2}; $98.784\pi \approx 310.3$ in.^{3}

4. $512\pi \approx 1608.5$ in.^{2}; $1365\frac{1}{3}\pi\sqrt{2} \approx 6066.0$ in.^{3}

5. $\sqrt{2} \approx 1.4$ m; $\frac{8\sqrt{2}}{3}\pi \approx 11.8$ m^3

6. 6 mm; $144\pi \approx 452.4$ mm^2

7. 99.82%

8. a. About 30.1 in.^{2}

b. There is more ice cream inside than outside because volume outside of cone = $\frac{1}{2} \cdot \frac{4}{3} \cdot \pi(1.25 \text{ in.})^3 \approx 4.09$ in.^{3} and volume inside of cone = $\frac{1}{3}\pi(1.25 \text{ in.})^2(5 \text{ in.}) \approx 8.18$ in.^{3}

9. a. $V_{cube} = 1000$ cm^3 $V_{sphere} = 166\frac{2}{3}\pi \approx 523.6$ cm^3

b. 52.36%

PS Science **7.** The radii of the sun and the planets in the solar system are given below. Assuming all of them are roughly spherical, what percentage of the total volume of the bodies in the solar system is the sun's volume? (We are ignoring the volumes of moons and asteroids.) 99.82%

Object	Sun	Mercury	Venus	Earth	Mars
Radius	696,000 km	2440 km	6050 km	6370 km	3400 km
Object	Jupiter	Saturn	Uranus	Neptune	Pluto
Radius	71,400 km	60,300 km	25,900 km	24,800 km	1150 km

PS, MR **8. Cool Problem #1** An ice cream cone with a height of 5 in. has a radius of 1.25 in. When the cone is filled, a hemisphere of ice cream shows over the top of the cone.

a. What is the total surface area of the cone plus the hemisphere of ice cream?

b. Is more of the ice cream inside the cone or outside it? Explain your answer.

PS **9.** A sphere with a radius of five centimeters is inscribed in a cube, as shown at the right.

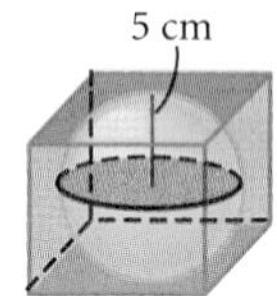

a. Find the volume of the sphere and the volume of the cube.

b. What is the probability that a randomly selected point inside the cube will also be inside the sphere?

MR **10.** Are the formulas for the surface area and volume of a sphere functions? For each formula that is a function, determine whether it is a linear, quadratic, or cubic function, and explain your choice.

PS, MR Science **11. Don't Bug Me!** A wood louse (commonly known as a *pill bug*) has a hard shell on the top side of its body. When frightened, it rolls up into a ball, so that only its shell is exposed. If the length of the top of a wood louse's shell is about 1 cm, what are the approximate surface area and volume of the shell? (Hint: What is the relationship between the length of the louse and a great circle of the sphere it rolls into?)

PS **12.** It takes 221.7 in.^{2} of black paint to cover a bowling ball. What is the radius of the bowling ball? 4.2 in

PS Science **13. The Sky Is Falling!** The average radius of the earth is about 3960 mi. The earth's total land area is about 58,430,000 mi^2. If a satellite falls out of orbit and randomly lands on the earth, what is the probability that it will fall on land? 29.65%

Key

V Vocabulary
P Practice/Skills
R Review
MR Math Reasoning
PS Problem Solving
C Challenge

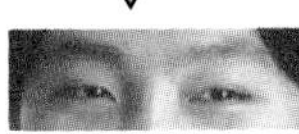

LOOK AHEAD

14. The similarity ratio of one figure to another is $\frac{3}{2}$. What is the ratio of their perimeters? their areas? $\frac{3}{2}$; $\frac{9}{4}$

Evaluate each expression.

15. $\left(\frac{2}{3}\right)^3$ $\frac{8}{27}$ **16.** $\left(\frac{4}{3}\right)^3$ $\frac{64}{27}$ **17.** $\sqrt[3]{64}$ 4 **18.** $\sqrt[3]{\frac{27}{125}}$ $\frac{3}{5}$

MORE PRACTICE

Use the given information to find each missing value for the sphere.

19. Radius = 5 in. Surface area = 100π cm^2 Volume = $166\frac{2}{3}\pi$ cm^3

20. Diameter = 0.76 cm Surface area = 1.81 cm^2 Volume = 0.23 cm^3

21. Surface area = 64π ft^2 Radius = 4 ft Volume = $85\frac{1}{3}\pi$ ft^3

22. Volume = 36π mm^3 Radius = 3 mm Surface area = 36π mm^2

MORE MATH REASONING

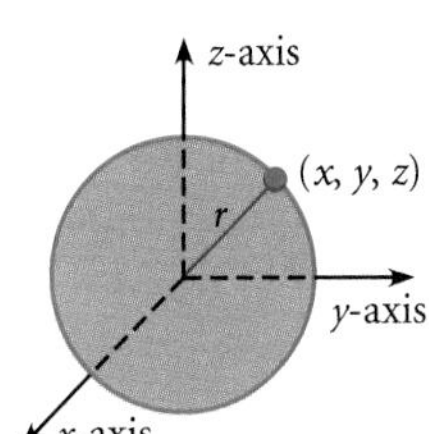

23. A sphere of radius r has its center at the origin of a three-dimensional coordinate system, as shown. A point on the sphere has coordinates (x, y, z). What do you think the equation for the sphere is? Explain why your answer makes sense.

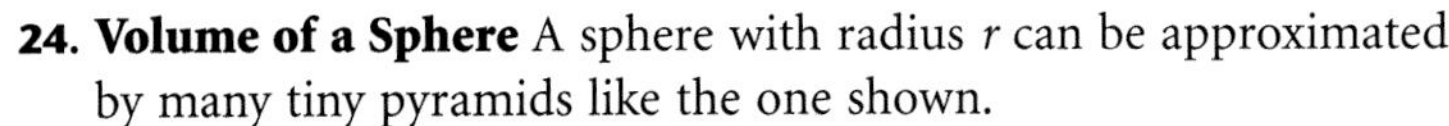

24. Volume of a Sphere A sphere with radius r can be approximated by many tiny pyramids like the one shown.

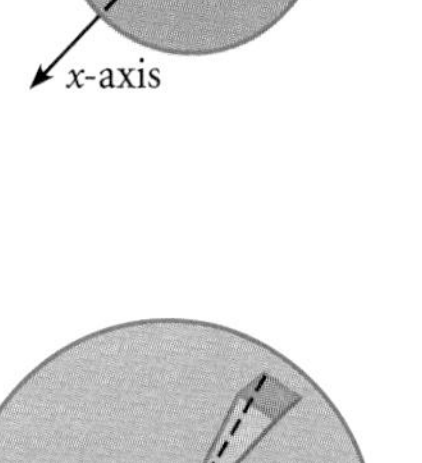

a. What is the formula for the volume of a pyramid?
The volume of the sphere is approximately the sum of the volumes of the pyramids. If we factor the $\frac{1}{3}h$ out of each individual volume formula, we have the following.

$V_{sphere} = \frac{1}{3}h \times$ (sum of the pyramid base areas)

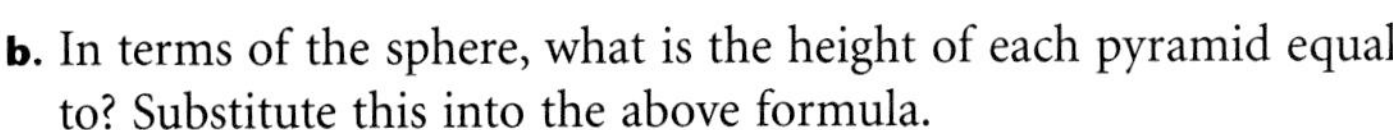

b. In terms of the sphere, what is the height of each pyramid equal to? Substitute this into the above formula.

c. In terms of the sphere, what is the sum of the areas of the bases of the pyramids approximately equal to? What is the formula for this surface area? Replace the sum of the pyramid base areas with this formula.

d. Simplify. What do you find?

10. Yes; Volume = $\frac{4}{3}\pi r^3$ is a cubic function of the radius and surface area = $4\pi r^2$ is a quadratic function of the radius.

11. About 0.32 cm^2; About 0.017 cm^3

More Practice

19. $100\pi \approx 314.2$ in.^{2}; $166\frac{2}{3}\pi \approx 523.6$ in.^{3}

20. ≈ 1.81 cm^2; ≈ 0.23 cm^3

21. 4 ft, $85\frac{1}{3}\pi \approx 268.1$ ft^3

22. 3 mm, $36\pi \approx 113.1$mm^2

More Math Reasoning

23. $x^2 + y^2 + z^2 = r^2$. This is the square of the distance formula for a point that is r units away from the origin.

24. a. $V_{pyr} = \frac{1}{3}Bh$

b. $h = r$; $V_{sphere} = \frac{1}{3}r \times$ (sum of the pyramid base areas)

c. Sum of the pyramid base areas = $4\pi r^2$; $V_{sphere} = \frac{1}{3}r \times (4\pi r^2)$

d. $V_{sphere} = \frac{4}{3}\pi r^3$

PART E At a Glance

Objective

To calculate the volume of Mount St. Helens, a conical volcano.

Development

In the **Explore,** students calculate the approximate volume of Mount St. Helens. Then they find how long it would take a truck to haul this volume of earth away.

First Five Minutes

Transparency FFM 9-2E

A rectangular solid is 4 m long, 3 m wide, and 5 m tall. Find the volume of the solid in cubic meters and cubic centimeters. 60 m^3, 60,000,000 cm^3

EXPLORE

Mount St. Helens and the Caterpillar

Recommended group size: 2

The Point

To calculate the volume of Mount St. Helens and find how long it would take a dump truck to haul away that volume of earth.

Look and Listen...

- For students who do not see that they must convert ft^3 to yd^3 to find the answer to Step 3, or who have difficulty converting the units.

Ask...

- What are your units for the volume of the volcano? for the capacity of the dump truck?
- How many feet are in a yard? If you convert from ft^3 to yd^3, will the number associated with the measurement increase or decrease?

For Groups That Finish Early

How long would it take the dump truck to haul away the part of Mount St. Helens that was destroyed by the eruption? About 6.38 years.

9-2 PART E Making Connections

← CONNECT → ***The volume of a three-dimensional figure measures its capacity. When you're deciding which product is the best buy in a grocery store or which cooler to take on a picnic, you're using the idea of volume. You've investigated volume and how to measure it for familiar solids.***

The photographs below show Mount St. Helens before and after its 1980 eruption. You will take a closer look at the volume of this volcano in the Explore.

EXPLORE: MOUNT ST. HELENS AND THE CATERPILLAR

1. Mount St. Helens is approximately conical. Its height on May 17, 1980, the day before its eruption, was 9677 ft. Mount St. Helens is about 30,000 ft in diameter. Find the approximate volume of Mount St. Helens the day before the eruption. Why might your result differ from its actual volume on that day?
2. According to the Caterpillar Tractor Company, the maximum load that their largest dump truck can carry is 240 yd^3. Guess how long it would take this dump truck, carrying a load every five minutes, to haul away the pre-eruption Mount St. Helens.
3. Calculate the answer to Step 2. (Hint: Watch units!) Your answer may seem surprising, considering that the eruption ripped away the top 1200 ft of Mount St. Helens in a matter of minutes!

REFLECT

1. Define *volume* in your own words. What are some similarities and differences between volume and surface area? In your answer, be sure to explain the appropriate units for measuring each.
2. Make a table of the volume formulas for prisms, pyramids, cylinders, cones, and spheres. Summarize these formulas as simply as you can.

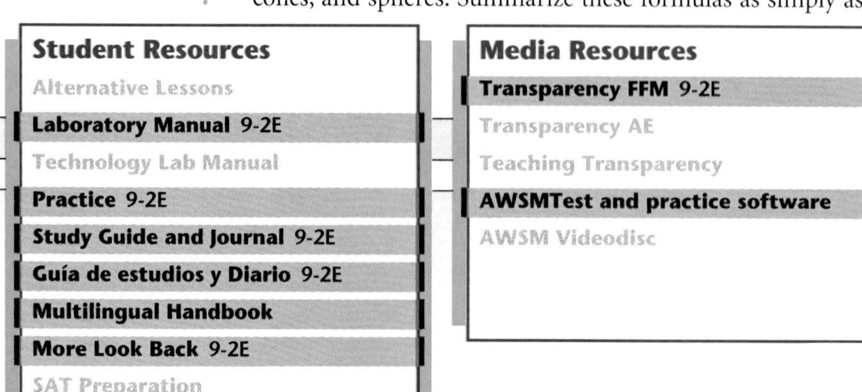

Student Resources

Alternative Lessons
Laboratory Manual 9-2E
Technology Lab Manual
Practice 9-2E
Study Guide and Journal 9-2E
Guía de estudios y Diario 9-2E
Multilingual Handbook
More Look Back 9-2E
SAT Preparation

Media Resources

Transparency FFM 9-2E
Transparency AE
Teaching Transparency
AWSMTest and practice software
AWSM Videodisc

Logic/Reasoning | Industry/Careers | Science/Health | Social Science/History | Fine Arts/Literature

Self-Assessment

Where necessary, approximate answers are given in the margin notes.

Find the volume of each of the following.

1. 1536 mm^3

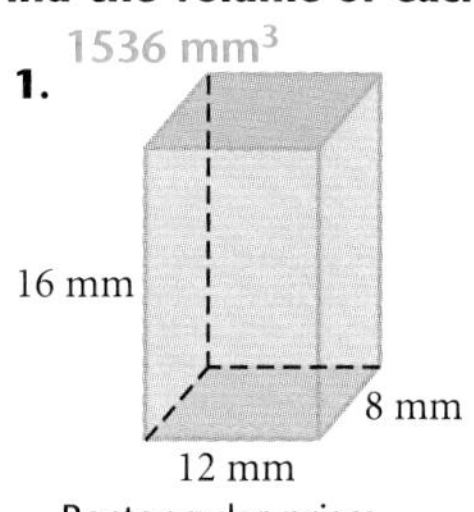

Rectangular prism

2. 129.73 cm^3

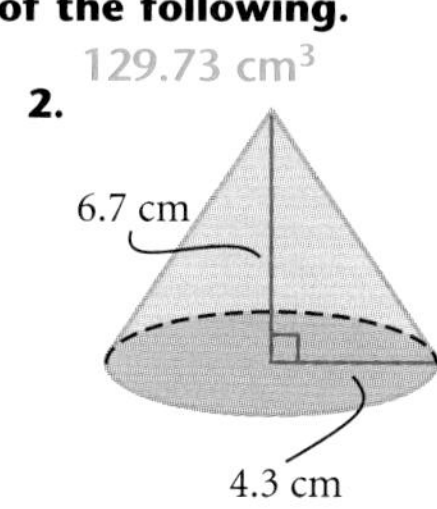

3. $3343.509\pi \approx 10{,}503.9$ ft^3

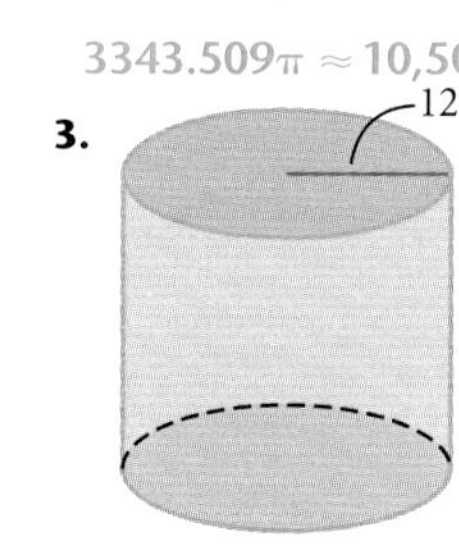

4. $112.5\sqrt{3} \approx 194.9$

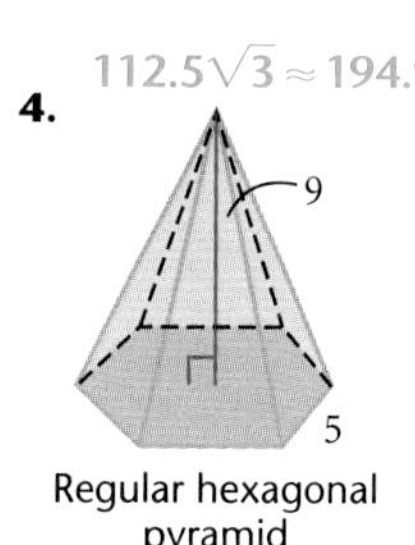

Regular hexagonal pyramid

5. The radius of the earth is approximately 6370 km. The radius of the moon is approximately 1740 km.

a. Find the volume of the earth. 1.08×10^{12} km^3

b. Find the volume of the moon. 2.21×10^{10} km^3

c. What percentage of the earth's volume is the moon's volume? $\approx 2.04\%$

6. Before an air filtration system for the building shown can be installed, engineers need to know the volume of the air in the building. Find the building's volume. 367,200 ft^3

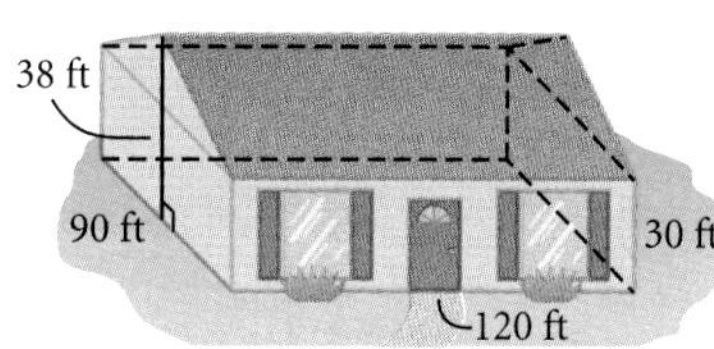

7. The area of the crater of Mauna Loa, a volcano on Hawaii, is 3.7 mi^2. Assuming the crater is perfectly circular, what is its radius? [8-1] 1.09 mi

Find the surface area of each figure. [9-1]

8.

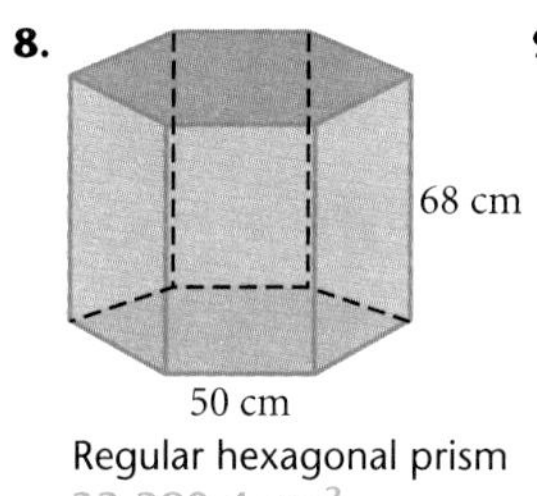

Regular hexagonal prism

33,390.4 cm^2

9.

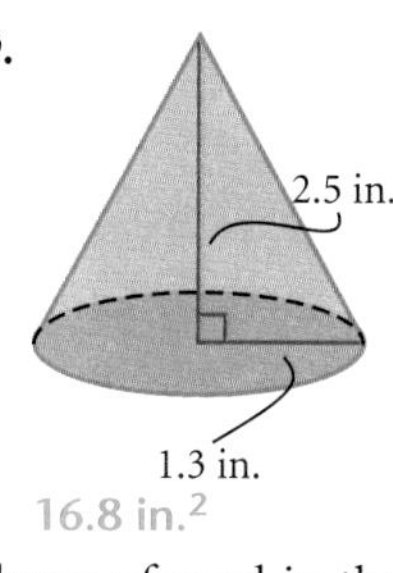

16.8 $in.^2$

10.

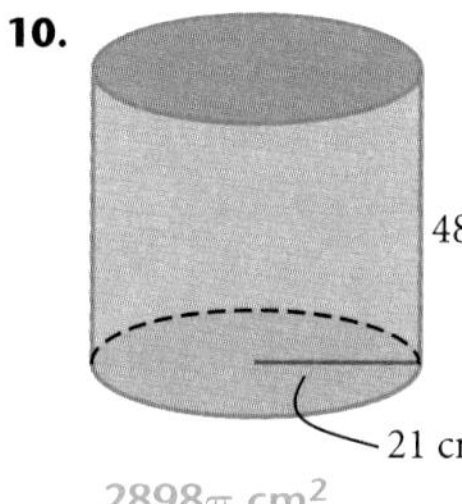

2898π cm^2

11.

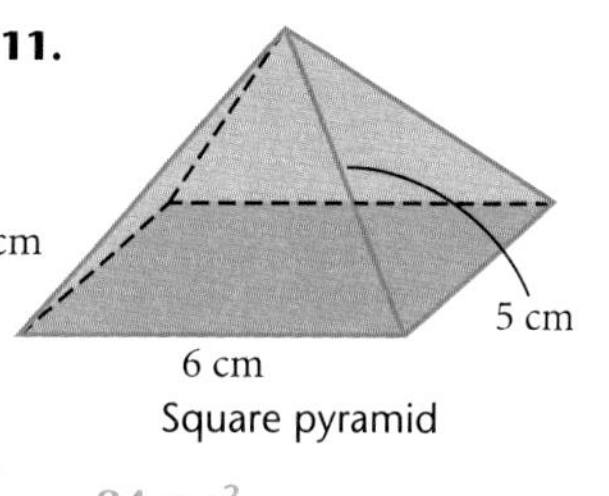

Square pyramid

84 cm^2

12. Find the ratio of the volume of sand in the hourglass to the volume of the cylinder holding the hourglass. (a)

(a) $\frac{1}{6}$ (b) $\frac{1}{4}$ (c) $\frac{1}{3}$ (d) $\frac{1}{2}$ (e) $\frac{2}{3}$

Vocabulary
Practice/Skills
Review
Math Reasoning
Problem Solving
Challenge

Follow Up

Ask students to share the guesses they made for Step 2 with the class. Have one student or group present their calculations and solution to Step 1, and another present theirs for Step 3.

Possible Answers

1. About 2,280,000,000,000 ft^3. This may differ from the actual volume, because the volcano was not a perfect cone.

3. About 3350 years.

Portfolio

Have students select items from their work that demonstrate their understanding of the material in 9-2.

You may want to have students include their favorite self-written definition, best sketch illustrating a postulate, and an **Exercise** that they found interesting or challenging.

REFLECT

Possible Answers

1. Volume and surface area are both measurements of three-dimensional figures. Surface area measures the area of material used to form the outer shell of a solid; volume measures the amount of space it occupies. Surface area is measured in square units; volume in cubic units.

2.

	Volume
Prism	Bh
Pyramid	$\frac{1}{3}Bh$
Cylinder	$\pi r^2 h$
Cone	$\frac{1}{3}\pi r^2 h$
Sphere	$\frac{4}{3}\pi r^3$

The volume of a prism or a cylinder, each of which has two parallel, congruent bases, is the product of its base area and its height. The formulas for the volumes of pyramids and cones are similar to those for prisms and cylinders, respectively, but each has a factor of one-third.

Volume

Self-Assessment

Exercise Notes

12. Similar to multiple-choice questions on standardized tests.

16. Students see one reason for the dent in the bottom of some packages—the container appears to hold more than it actually does.

Self-Assessment Answers

10. $2898\pi \approx 9104.4 \text{ cm}^2$

16. 78.8 cm^3; 8.6 cm^3 is lost; Possible answer: They have indentations to save money on product.

PS **13.** A cone is inscribed in a square prism with the dimensions shown.

a. Find the volume of each solid. $V_{prism} = 277.83 \text{ m}^3$; $V_{cone} \approx 72.74 \text{ m}^3$

b. Find the probability that a randomly selected point inside the prism will also be inside the cone. 26.18%

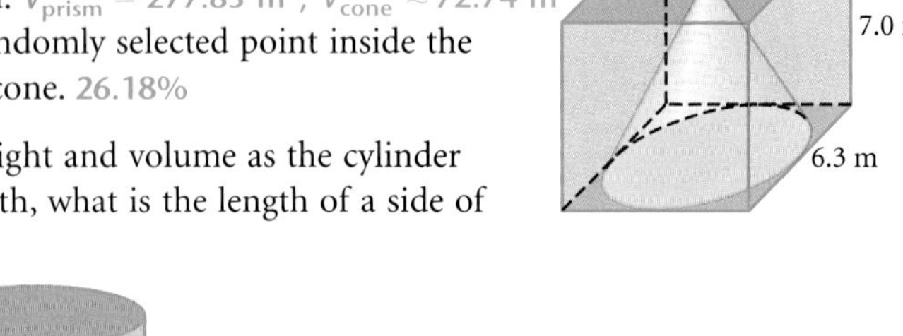

PS **14.** A square prism has the same height and volume as the cylinder shown below. To the nearest tenth, what is the length of a side of the prism's base? 5.0 in.

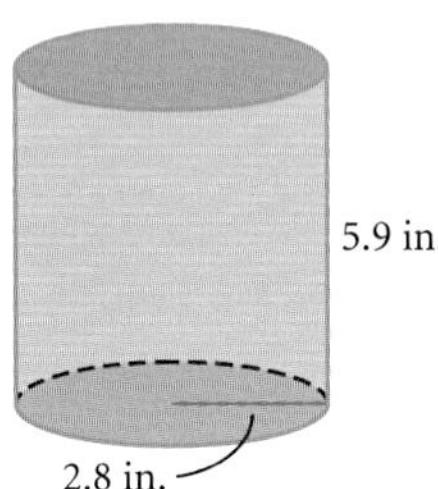

PS **15. A Cool Problem #2** To get some publicity for her new ice cream store, Natalie decided to serve ice cream in square pyramids instead of cones. Her "ice cream pyramids" have the same height and volume as a cone with a radius of 1.25 in. and a height of 5 in.

a. What is the volume of the ice cream pyramid? (Do not include the volume of the ice cream.) 8.18 in.^3

b. What are the base dimensions of the pyramid? 2.216 in. × 2.216 in.

c. What is the difference between the lateral area of the pyramid and that of a 1.25-in.-radius cone? 2.45 in.^2

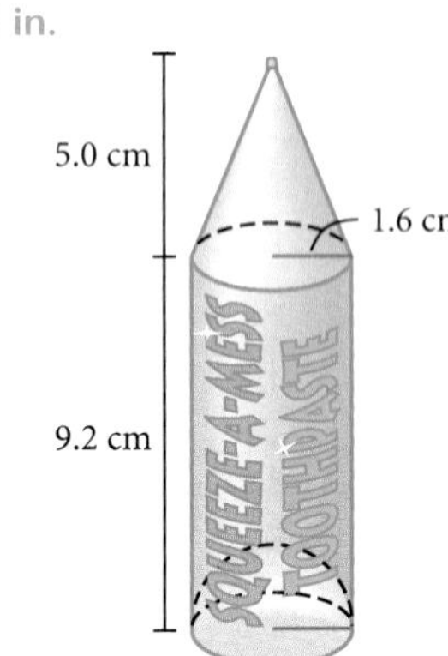

PS, MR **16. Squeeze-A-Mess #2** Suppose that the container for a brand of children's toothpaste is cylindrical, with a conical tip and a hemispherical dent in the bottom, as shown. What is the volume of the container? How much volume is lost because the bottom is not flat? Why do you think some containers have indentations like this?

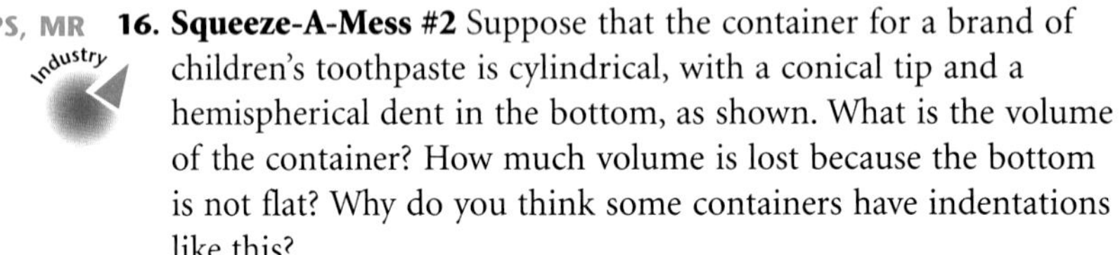

PS **17.** A storage tank is a cylinder with a hemisphere on either end. It takes Mike twenty-five minutes to paint one of the hemispheres. How long will it take him to paint the rest of the tank? 150 min.

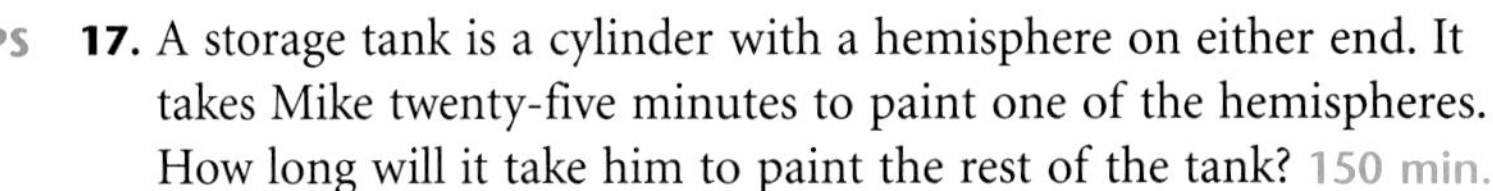

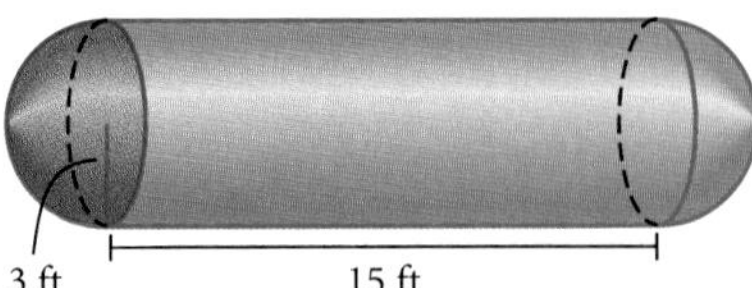

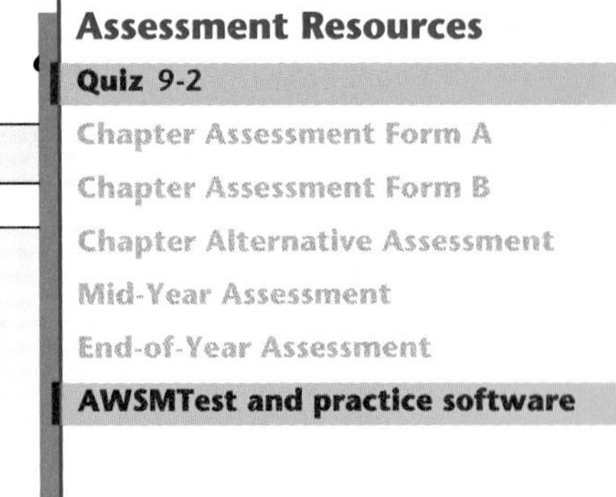

Assessment Resources

- **Quiz 9-2**
- Chapter Assessment Form A
- Chapter Assessment Form B
- Chapter Alternative Assessment
- Mid-Year Assessment
- End-of-Year Assessment
- **AWSMTest and practice software**

Ongoing Assessment

Self-Assessment Self-Assessment Exercises

Embedded Assessment Explore Step 1; Reflect 1, 2

ADDITIONAL ANSWERS

9-3 Part B Exercises

24. a. 97,200 g

b. 540 cm^2; 36 kg

c. i. $h = 1.2$ cm; $w = 0.2$ cm; $l = 0.12$ cm

ii. 0.0288 g

iii. 0.024 cm^2

iv. 0.0016 kg

d. 22,500 ants; 648 g. From this it appears the ant is more efficient.

e. The ratio of the cross-sectional area of their limbs to their weight is greater.

Chapter 9 Review

9.

	Surface area	Volume
Regular triangular prism	$3sh + \frac{s^2}{2}\sqrt{3}$	$\frac{s^2h}{4}\sqrt{3}$
Square prism	$4sh + 2s^2$	s^2h
Regular hexagonal prism	$6sh + 3s^2\sqrt{3}$	$\frac{3s^2h}{2}\sqrt{3}$

13. a–b.

Height	Radius	Area of base	Intensity of light
2 in.	1 in.	π in.^{2}	$\frac{L}{\pi}$
4 in.	2 in.	4π in.^{2}	$\frac{L}{4\pi}$
8 in.	4 in.	16π in.^{2}	$\frac{L}{16\pi}$

9-3

Similar Solids

SUPERLESSON AT A GLANCE

Superlesson Goal

Students will explore surface areas and volumes of similar solids, and the relationship between the ratios of these quantities for similar solids and the similarity ratio.

Management Guide

	Topic	Objectives	Key Terms	New Ideas	Materials
Part A	Surface Area of Similar Solids	To discover that the ratio of the surface areas of two similar solids is the square of their similarity ratio.	Similar solids, similarity ratio for similar solids	The ratio of the surface areas of two similar solids is the square of their similarity ratio.	
Part B	Volume of Similar Solids	To discover that the ratio of the volumes of two similar solids is the cube of their similarity ratio.		The ratio of the volumes of two similar solids is the cube of their similarity ratio.	
Part C	Making Connections	To use surface areas and volumes of similar solids to explain why large animals tend to have thick legs.	In Making Connections, students apply and synthesize key terms and new ideas.		

Pacing Chart (45-Minute Periods)

	Comprehensive Course	Core Course	Informal Course
Part A	1	1	2
Part B	1	1	2
Part C	1	1	1
TOTAL periods for Superlesson	3	3	5

NCTM Standards

Mathematics as Problem Solving

Mathematics as Communication

Mathematics as Reasoning

Mathematical Connections

Geometry from a Synthetic Perspective

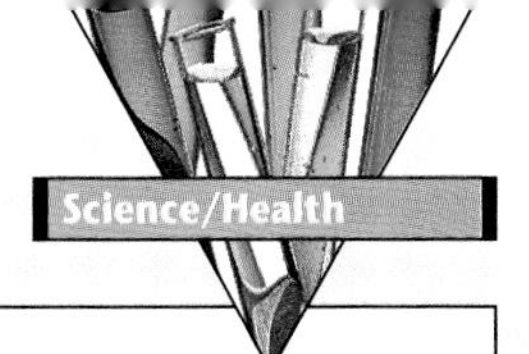

Science/Health

9-3 Similar Solids

why don't

Elephants

have skinny

Legs?

Why don't animals that weigh several hundred pounds ever look like insects? Although there is a great deal of variation in the way animals look, their appearance and behavior typically relate to their size.

For example, heavy land animals (like the rhinoceros, elephant, or hippopotamus) tend to have stumpy, thick legs. Insects and spiders usually have very long, thin legs in proportion to their bodies.

Although horror movies sometimes show gigantic insects devouring cities, you would probably be just as surprised (and a little frightened) to find an insect the size of a cat. Are there limitations on how large insects can grow? If so, why?

1. **What are some of the problems very large animals face in trying to survive? What difficulties do very small animals face?**

2. **Which animal do you think is more likely to break a leg while running: a rabbit or a racehorse? Why? (Don't base your answer on how fast they run—surprisingly, the domestic rabbit reach speeds of 35 mi/hr!)**

Where Are We Now?

Students explored similar solids in Chapter 7. In 9-1 and 9-2, they investigated surface areas and volumes of solids.

Where Are We Going?

In 9-3, students will explore surface areas and volumes of similar figures, and discover how these quantities are related to their similarity ratio. They will also connect these concepts to leg strength and weight in animals, and see why large animals tend to have thick, stubby legs.

Possible Answers

1. Very large animals must have enormous quantities of food and water to survive, and they find it hard to elude predators (though their sheer size tends to protect them.) Ironically, very small animals also have difficulty finding enough food; because of their high metabolism, they must spend much of their time eating. They must find ways to elude larger predators.
2. A racehorse is more likely to break a leg while running; its thin legs are placed under great stress by the weight of its large body.

More About Large Animals

Huge animals are not necessarily slow—the grizzly bear can maintain a speed of 30 mi/hr over several hundred yards. In recent years, paleontologists have debated whether *Tyrannosaurus rex* was a slow-moving creature or a speedy runner. Part of this debate centers around variance in estimates of its weight, which range from four to eight tons. A four-ton tyrannosaur would have been relatively speedy, perhaps able to run at 25 mi/hr. The eight-ton version would probably have been a plodder and, therefore, primarily a scavenger.

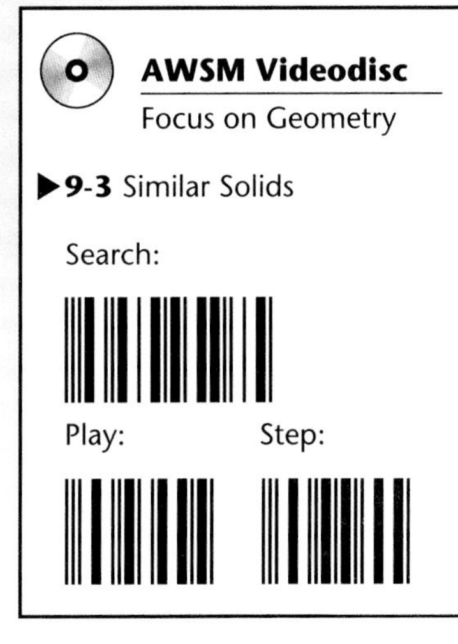

Similar Solids

PART A At a Glance

Objective

To discover that the ratio of the surface areas of two similar solids is the square of their similarity ratio.

Development

First, students see the definition of *similar solids.*

Then, in the **Explore,** students discover that the ratio of the surface areas of two similar solids is the square of their similarity ratio. They also learn that the strength of a given material is proportional to its cross-sectional area.

Key Terms

Similar solids, similarity ratio for similar solids

First Five Minutes

Transparency FFM 9-3A

Read the opening paragraphs on page 648. Then answer the **Consider** question at the bottom of the page.

Motivate

Ask...

- What is true about the ratio of the areas of two similar figures? **It is equal to the square of their similarity ratio.**

Reviews similarity ratio.

Possible Answer

1. The solids are congruent.

EXPLORE

A Leg to Stand On

Recommended group size: 4

The Point

To discover that the ratio of the surface areas of similar solids is the square of their similarity ratio, and to explore a connection between cross-sectional area and strength.

9-3 PART A Surface Area of Similar Solids

← CONNECT → ***You've investigated similarity and surface area as separate topics. Now you will apply the concept of similarity to the surface areas of solids.***

Similar two-dimensional figures have the same shape but not necessarily the same size. If two figures are similar, we know that the lengths of their corresponding sides are proportional, and their corresponding angles are congruent. These properties also apply to similar solids.

The **similarity ratio** of two similar solids is the ratio of the lengths of any two corresponding edges. The radii, heights, and slant heights of the solids are also proportional in the same way.

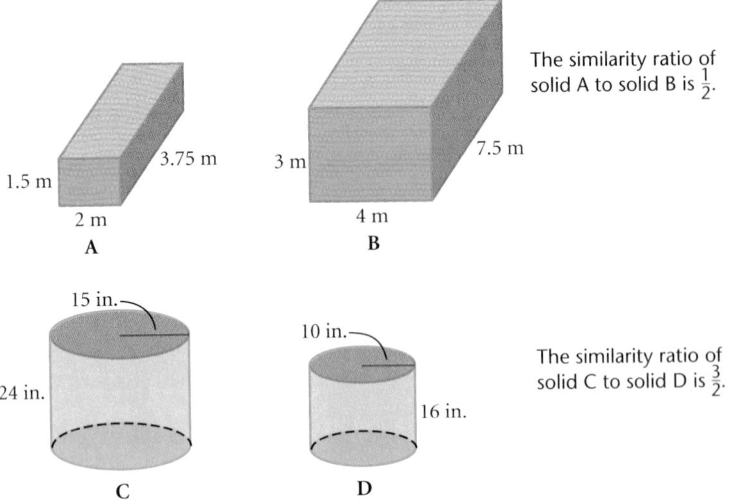

1. What does it mean for two solids to have a similarity ratio of 1?

In the following Explore, you will look for relationships in the surface areas of similar solids. You will also investigate the connection between the cross-sectional area of a solid and its strength.

Research Note

Perhaps the greatest boost a teacher can offer students toward developing…awareness [of their thought processes when solving problems] is a classroom environment where they are encouraged to *verbalize* their problem-solving experiences. (Mark Driscoll, *Research Within Reach: Secondary School Mathematics: A Research-Guided Response to the Concerns of Educators,* p. 75. 1982.)

EXPLORE: A LEG TO STAND ON

1. Sketch a rectangular solid and provide dimensions. Then sketch a second solid similar to the first. What similarity ratio did you use?
2. Find the surface areas of the two solids. (Sketch nets of the solids if this is helpful to you.) What is the ratio of the surface areas of the solids? How is this related to their similarity ratio?
3. In general, the strength of a given material is proportional to its cross-sectional area. This is one reason why thick cylindrical cables, rather than thin wires, are used to support bridges.

   Suppose one animal is 4 times as large as another. (Their similarity ratio is $\frac{4}{1}$.) How many times stronger are the larger animal's legs?

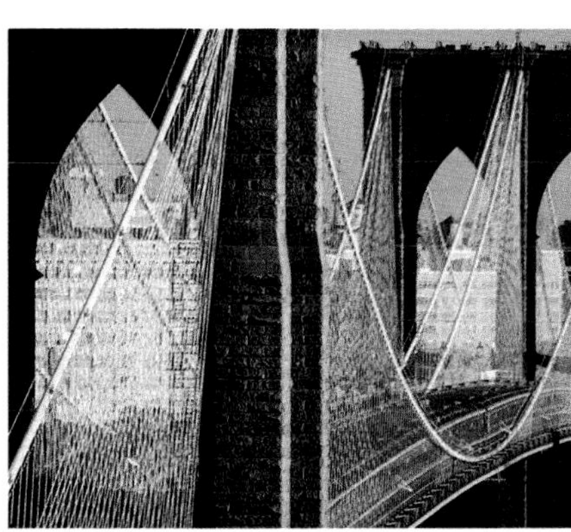

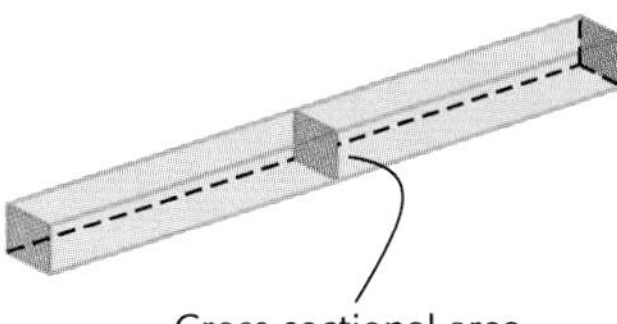

Problem-Solving Tip

You may want to make a mathematical model by choosing a geometric shape and dimensions for the legs of the animals.

In the following Example, you will see another application of similar solids.

EXAMPLE

The surface area of the earth is roughly 13.4 times that of the moon. How many times larger is the earth's radius than the moon's?

The ratio of the surface areas of similar solids is the square of their similarity ratios. Therefore, the similarity ratio is the square root of the surface-area ratio.

Similarity ratio $= \sqrt{13.4} \approx 3.66$

The radius of the earth is about 3.66 times that of the moon.

Student Resources

- Alternative Lessons 9-3A
- Laboratory Manual 9-3A
- Technology Lab Manual
- Practice 9-3A
- Study Guide and Journal 9-3A
- Guía de estudios y Diario 9-3A
- Multilingual Handbook
- More Look Back 9-3A
- SAT Preparation

Media Resources

- Transparency FFM 9-3A
- Transparency AE 9-3A
- Teaching Transparency
- AWSMTest and practice software
- AWSM Videodisc

Look and Listen...

- For students whose second solid is not similar to the first.
- For students who are not calculating the surface areas of their solids correctly.

Ask...

- What is the similarity ratio for your solids? Have you used this ratio to find the length, width, and height of your second solid?

For Groups That Finish Early

Explain why your result in Step 2 makes sense. **The ratio of the areas of similar two-dimensional figures is the square of their similarity ratio. The surface area of a solid is just the total of all its areas.**

Follow Up

Ask students to summarize their results for Step 2. Then have a class discussion about how this result applies to the leg strength of two similar animals. During this discussion, have students give their answers to Step 3.

Possible Answers

2. The ratio of the surface areas of the similar solids is the square of their similarity ratio.
3. The larger animal's legs are 16 times stronger.

ALTERNATE EXAMPLE

The surface area of a bowling ball is approximately 10.8 times larger than that of a tennis ball. How many times larger is the bowling ball's radius than the tennis ball's?

The ratio of the surface areas of similar solids is the square of their similarity ratio, so the similarity ratio is the square root of the surface area ratio. Similarity ratio $= \sqrt{10.8} \approx 3.29$. The radius of the bowling ball is about 3.29 times that of the tennis ball.

9-3

Similar Solids

Journal

Reflect 2, 4, and 5 are suitable for journal entries.

REFLECT

Possible Answers

1. False; a cone with $h = 4$ and $r = 2$ is not similar to one with $h = 4$ and $r = 4$.
2. True. Since all edges of a cube are congruent, if an edge in a second cube is k times as long as one in the first, all other pairs of edges are in this ratio.
3. False; a rectangular solid $2 \times 2 \times 5$ is not similar to one $3 \times 5 \times 6$.
4. True. The radius of a sphere is the only measure needed to define the size of the sphere, so if the radius of one is k times that of another, the spheres are similar.
5. The ratio of the lateral areas is also the square of the similarity ratio. We know the area ratio for two-dimensional figures is equal to the square of their similarity ratio, and the lateral surfaces of pyramids, prisms, cylinders, and cones are (or can be unrolled into) two-dimensional shapes.

Part A Exercises

Exercise Notes

Core

9. Students use real-world data to compare the leg strength of an elephant to that of a mouse.

12. Students express the surface area of similar solids as a function of their similarity ratio.

More Math Reasoning

26. Students estimate the similarity ratio of the earth to a globe. You may want to have a class discussion about the different methods students used to make their estimates.

Algebra | Functions | Discrete Math | Probability | Data/Statistics

TRY IT

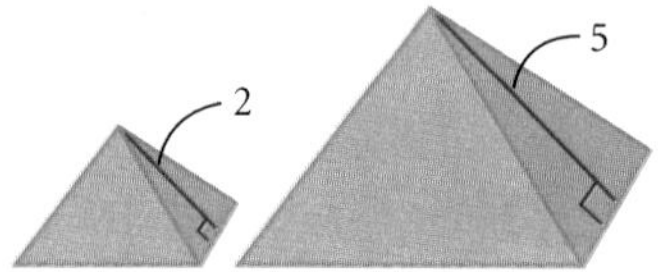

a. The pyramids shown are similar. Find the similarity ratio of the pyramid on the left to the pyramid on the right. Then find the ratio of their surface areas. $\frac{2}{5}$; $\frac{4}{25}$

b. A support beam for a ceiling is 6 in. wide and 6 in. high. If you need a second beam with a similar cross section that is 9 times as strong, what should its dimensions be? 18 in. $\times$ 18 in.

The property you explored about the surface areas of similar solids is stated below.

> **THEOREM**
>
> The ratio of the surface areas of two similar solids is the square of their similarity ratio.

REFLECT

Explain why each statement is true, or give a counterexample to show that it is false.

1. Any two cones are similar.
2. Any two cubes are similar.
3. Any two rectangular prisms are similar.
4. Any two spheres are similar.
5. Do you think that the ratio of the lateral areas of two similar solids is also the square of their similarity ratio? Explain why or why not.

Exercises

CORE

P **Getting Started** **State whether or not the figures in each pair appear to be similar.**

1.

Not similar

2.

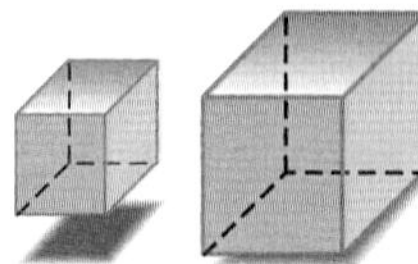

Similar

3.

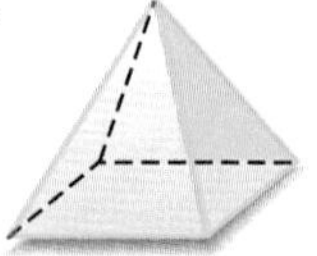

Not similar

Key

V Vocabulary
P Practice/Skills
R Review
MR Math Reasoning
PS Problem Solving
C Challenge

The cones shown at the right are similar.

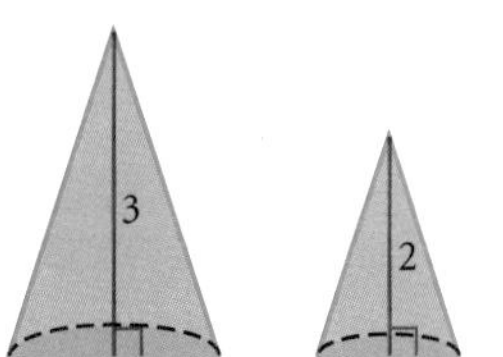

4. Find the similarity ratio of the cone on the left to the cone on the right. $\frac{3}{2}$

5. Find the ratio of their radii. $\frac{3}{2}$

6. Find the ratio of their surface areas. $\frac{9}{4}$

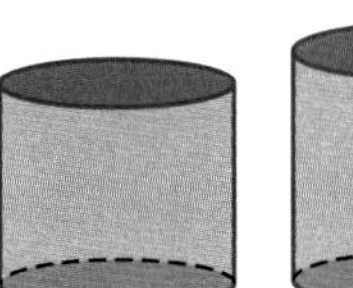

7. The surface areas of the similar cylinders shown have a ratio of $\frac{49}{64}$. What is the similarity ratio of the cylinders? $\frac{7}{8}$

8. A two-by-four is a board $3\frac{5}{8}$ in. wide and $1\frac{5}{8}$ in. thick. How many times stronger than a two-by-four is a board that is twice as wide and three times as thick? 6 times as strong

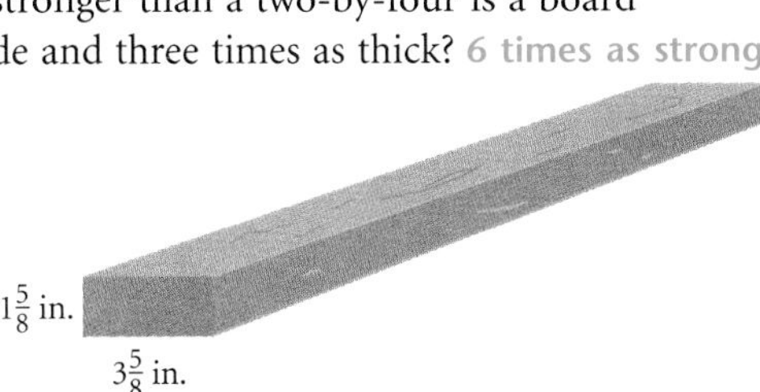

9. According to Lynn Barkley, Collections Manager of the Los Angeles Natural History Museum, the diameter of the tibia (leg bone) of an adult male Asiatic elephant is 75.4 mm. The diameter of the tibia of a California mouse is 1.45 mm. How many times stronger are the elephant's legs? 2704 times as strong

10. Udder Destruction Tara Fye is writing a script for a horror movie. In the movie, a mad scientist enlarges a cow to 100 times its normal size. How much stronger would its legs be than those of a normal cow? 10,000 times as strong

11. Prove: If the radius of sphere A is x and the radius of sphere B is $3x$, then the ratio of the surface area of A to the surface area of B is $\frac{1}{9}$.

12. The ratio of the surface areas of two similar solids is a function of the similarity ratio, k, of the solids. Express the surface-area ratio as a function of k. k^2

LOOK BACK

Two tangent segments intersect a circle as shown. Find each of the following. [8-3]

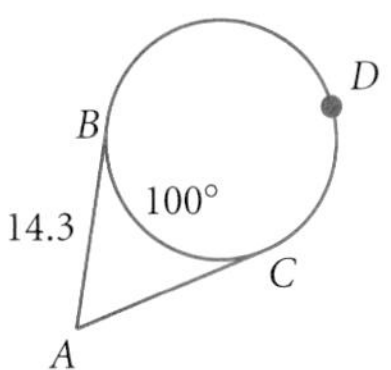

13. $m\widehat{BDC}$ 260°

14. AC 14.3

15. $m\angle BAC$ 80°

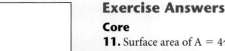

Exercise Answers

Core

11. Surface area of A $= 4\pi x^2$; Surface area of B $= 4\pi(3x)^2 = 36\pi x^2$; The ratio of the surface area of A to the surface area of B is $\frac{4\pi x^2}{36\pi x^2} = \frac{1}{9}$.

Ongoing Assessment

Self-Assessment Exercises 1, 3, 5, 7, 10

Embedded Assessment Try It a, b; Exercises 8, 9, 11

Algebra | Functions | Discrete Math | Probability | Data/Statistics

Similar Solids

Look Back

16. $7{,}776\pi \approx 24{,}429.0$ in.^{3}

18. $46.546\pi \approx 146.2$ m^3

More Math Reasoning

24. The smaller size is more effective. Eight small spheres per cm^3 have twice as much surface area as one big sphere.

R **Find the volume of each of the following. [9-2]**

16. $7{,}776\pi$ in.^{3}

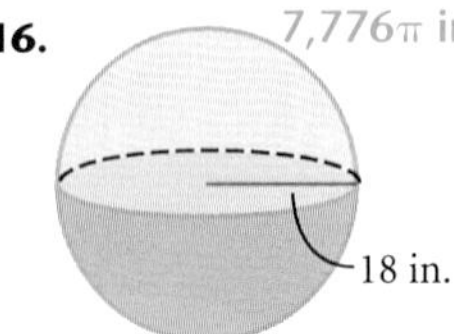

17. $58\frac{1}{3}$ cm^3

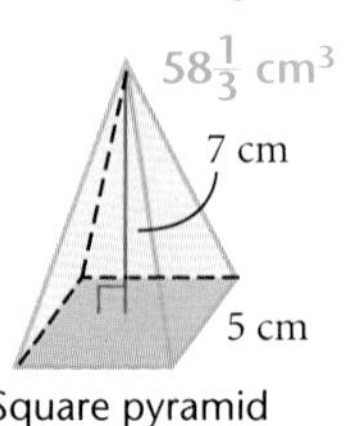

18. 46.546π m^3

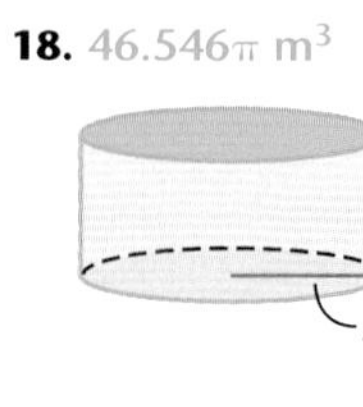

19. 28 mm^3

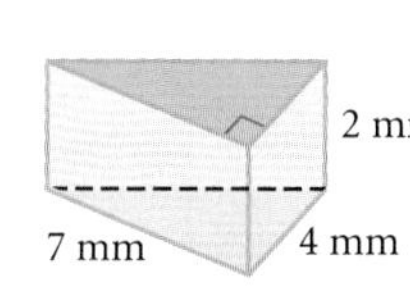

MORE PRACTICE

P **The cylinders shown at the right are similar. Use these cylinders for Exercises 20–22.**

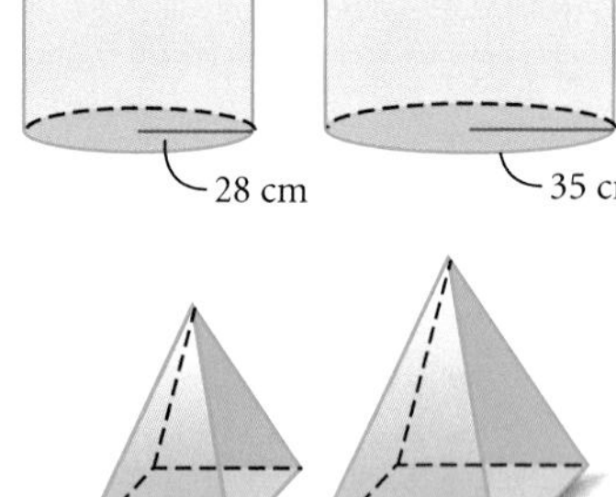

20. Find the similarity ratio of the cylinder on the left to the cylinder on the right. $\frac{4}{5}$

21. Find the ratio of their heights. $\frac{4}{5}$

22. Find the ratio of their surface areas. $\frac{16}{25}$

23. The surface areas of the similar pyramids shown at the right have a ratio of $\frac{25}{36}$. What is the similarity ratio of the pyramids? $\frac{5}{6}$

MORE MATH REASONING

PS **24.** Some filters contain spherical particles that absorb materials from liquids passed through the filters. The effectiveness of such a filter is proportional to the surface area of the particles. The particles come in two sizes—1 cm in diameter (or 1 particle per cm^3 of filter) and 0.5 cm in diameter (or 8 particles per cm^3). Which size is more effective? How do you know?

Industry

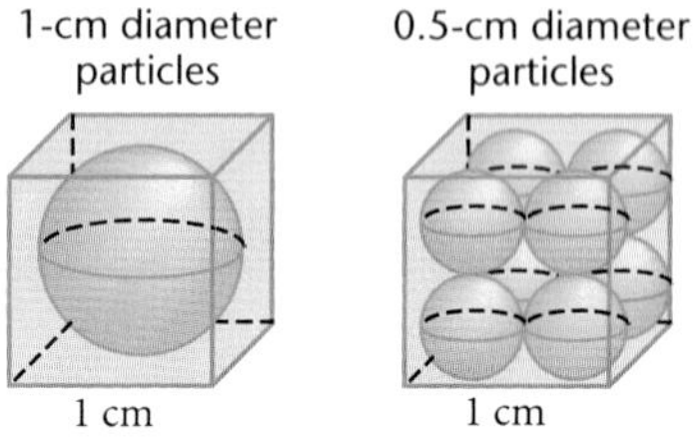

1-cm diameter particles — 1 cm

0.5-cm diameter particles — 1 cm

PS **25.** Suppose that the cross section of the arm of a person who can curl (lift) a 50-lb dumbbell has a circumference of 13.5 in. Assuming that the strength of an arm is proportional to its cross-sectional area, find the circumference of the arm of someone who can curl a 100-lb dumbbell. $13.5\sqrt{2} \approx 19.1$ in.

MR **26.** Estimate the similarity ratio of the earth to a globe that has a diameter of one foot. Write a brief paragraph explaining how you arrived at your estimate. Possible answer: The diameter of the earth $\approx 4.1773 \times 10^7$ ft, so the similarity ratio is about 4.18×10^7.

652 9-3 • SIMILAR SOLIDS

Key

- V Vocabulary
- P Practice/Skills
- R Review
- MR Math Reasoning
- PS Problem Solving
- C Challenge

9-3 PART B Volume of Similar Solids

← CONNECT → ***You know how the surface areas of similar solids are related to their similarity ratio. Now you will investigate the relationship between the similarity ratio of two similar solids and the volumes of those solids.***

A scale model of an apartment building made out of concrete, brick, and steel would be hard to make and inconvenient to pass around during presentations. But it would be difficult to convince people to move into a real building made out of cardboard and balsa wood! Though the model is similar to the actual building, its weight and strength are quite different from those of the building.

In the following Explore, you will investigate how the volumes of similar solids are related.

EXPLORE: SIMILAR CYLINDERS, SIMILAR ANIMALS

1. Suppose one cylindrical drum has radius r and height h, and another has radius $3r$ and height $3h$. Are the drums similar? Explain why or why not.
2. Find the volume of each drum. What is the ratio of their volumes?
3. Repeat Steps 1 and 2 for spheres of radius r and $2r$. How does the ratio of the volumes of two similar solids relate to their similarity ratio?
4. The weight of an object of a given density is proportional to its volume. Suppose the measurements of one animal are four times the measurements of another, and the two animals are geometrically similar. How many times greater is the weight of the larger animal than the weight of the smaller?

Student Resources
- Alternative Lessons 9-3B
- Laboratory Manual 9-3B
- Technology Lab Manual
- Practice 9-3B
- Study Guide and Journal 9-3B
- Guía de estudios y Diario 9-3B
- Multilingual Handbook
- More Look Ahead 9-3B
- SAT Preparation

Media Resources
- Transparency FFM 9-3B
- Transparency AE 9-3B
- Teaching Transparency
- AWSMTest and practice software
- AWSM Videodisc

PART B At a Glance

Objective
To discover that the ratio of the volumes of two similar solids is the cube of their similarity ratio.

Development
In the **Explore,** students first find the ratios of the volumes of similar figures, and discover that these ratios are the cubes of the similarity ratios. Then they see that the weight of an object is proportional to its volume, and calculate the ratio of the weights of two similar animals.

First Five Minutes
Transparency FFM 9-3B

Find the volume of each solid. Round your answers to the nearest tenth.

1. A cylinder of height 12 cm and radius 5 cm. **942.5 cm^3**
2. A sphere of radius 7.5 in. **1767.1 in.^{3}**

Motivate
Ask...
- Explain why there are 27 ft^3 in a cubic yard. **Each dimension of a cubic yard is equal to 3 ft. Therefore, the factor of 3 is multiplied three times in the conversion.**

EXPLORE

Similar Cylinders, Similar Animals
Recommended group size: 4

The Point
To discover that the ratio of the volumes of two similar solids is the cube of their similarity ratio, and to learn that the weight of an object is proportional to its volume.

Algebra | Functions | Discrete Math | Probability | Data/Statistics

Similar Solids

Look and Listen...

- For students who are having difficulty substituting terms like $3r$ into a formula and simplifying the result.

Ask...

- What is $(3r)^2$? If you multiply this result by π and then by $3h$, what do you get?

For Groups That Finish Early

Estimate the volume and surface area of one of your arms. Explain how you made your estimate.

Follow Up

Ask students to share their results to Steps 3 and 4. Then have the class explain why the result to Step 3 makes sense.

Possible Answers

1. The cylinders are similar because the corresponding lengths are proportional.
2. The ratio of the volume of the larger to the smaller is $\frac{27}{1}$.
3. The ratio of the volumes of the spheres is $\frac{8}{1}$. The ratio of the volumes of similar figures is the cube of their similarity ratio.
4. The weight of the larger animal is 64 times greater.

ALTERNATE EXAMPLE

Jo-Jo's cat has a kitten. The cat and the kitten are approximately similar. If the kitten weighs 0.75 lb and the cat is 2.5 times as long as the kitten, about how much does the cat weigh?

The similarity ratio is $\frac{2.5}{1}$. Therefore, the ratio of the volumes is $\frac{2.5^3}{1} \approx 15.6$.

Weight is proportional to volume, so the cat weighs about $0.75 \times 15.6 = 11.7$ lb.

EXAMPLE

Two years ago, José bought a puppy that weighed 2 lb. Since then, it has tripled in length. About how much does the dog weigh now?

The similarity ratio is $\frac{3}{1}$. Therefore, the ratio of the volumes is $\left(\frac{3}{1}\right)^3 = 27$.

Weight is proportional to volume, so the dog now weighs approximately $2 \times 27 = 54$ lb.

TRY IT

a. What is the ratio of the volumes of the two cubes shown? $\frac{1}{8}$

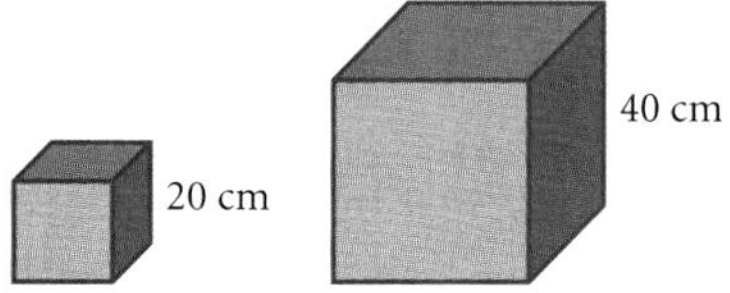

b. The ratio of the volumes of two similar cylinders is $\frac{125}{27}$. What is the ratio of their radii? $\frac{5}{3}$

c. Suppose that two similar animals have a similarity ratio of $\frac{3}{2}$. The smaller one weighs 100 lb. What does the larger one weigh? 337.5 lb

The property you've discovered about the volumes of similar solids is stated below.

> **THEOREM**
>
> The ratio of the volumes of two similar solids is the cube of their similarity ratio.

REFLECT

1. In your own words, explain why the ratio of the volumes of two spheres is the cube of their similarity ratio.
2. Suppose that a small scale model of a car is built out of exactly the same materials as the actual car. Name some properties that will be the same for the model and the actual car and some that will be different. Justify each of your answers.

Diversity Issues

According to Slavin...cooperative learning strategies have been shown to influence positively both student self-esteem and race relations. Cooperative learning activities can also help overcome barriers to friendship and interaction when handicapped students are mainstreamed....(Mary Kim Prichard and Sue Bingaman, "Instructional Activities and Decisions," *Research Ideas for the Classroom: High School Mathematics,* NCTM Research Interpretation Project, Patricia S. Wilson, ed., p. 222. © 1993 NCTM.)

Exercises

CORE

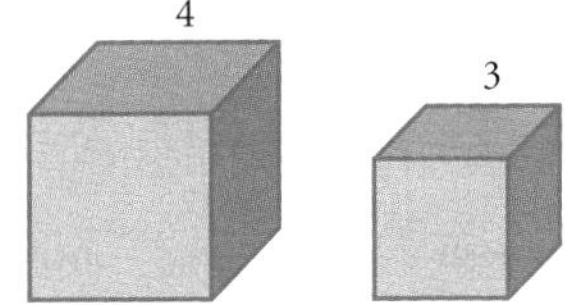

1. **Getting Started** Use the cubes at the right for the following.
   a. Find the similarity ratio of the cube on the left to the cube on the right. $\frac{4}{3}$
   b. Find the ratio of their surface areas. $\frac{16}{9}$
   c. Find the ratio of their volumes. $\frac{64}{27}$

The cylinders shown at the right are similar.

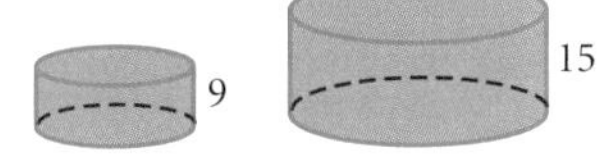

2. Find the similarity ratio of the cylinder on the left to the cylinder on the right. $\frac{3}{5}$
3. Find the ratio of their radii. $\frac{3}{5}$
4. Find the ratio of their surface areas. $\frac{9}{25}$
5. Find the ratio of their volumes. $\frac{27}{125}$

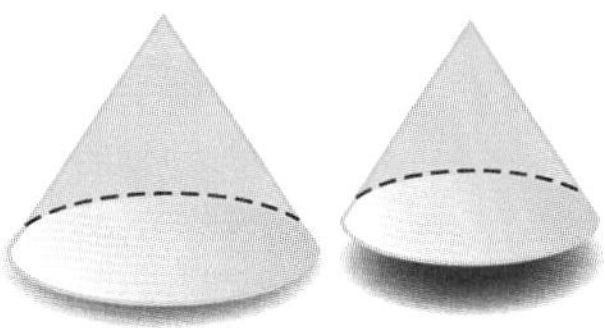

6. The volumes of the cones shown have a ratio of $\frac{125}{64}$. What is the similarity ratio of the cones? What is the ratio of their surface areas? $\frac{5}{4}$; $\frac{25}{16}$
7. The surface areas of two spheres are 36π and 324π. What is the ratio of their volumes? $\frac{1}{27}$

Write the word or phrase that correctly completes each statement.

8. The weight of an object is proportional to its ____. Volume
9. The strength of a beam is proportional to its cross-sectional ____. Area
10. A 16-in.-long crescent wrench is similar to an 8-in. wrench. How many times heavier is the 16-in. wrench than the 8-in. wrench? 8 times as heavy
11. **Dairy Disaster** You may recall that Tara Fye's script for *The Cow That Conquered Chicago* features a cow enlarged to 100 times its normal size. How many times more would this cow weigh than a normal cow? 10^6 times as heavy

12. **He Looks So Similar to His Father!** Baby Benjamin is 20 in. long and weighs 8 lb. His father, Keith, is 5 ft 8 in. tall. If Benjamin and Keith are geometrically similar, how much does his father weigh? Does this answer seem reasonable? Explain why your answer may not accurately predict Keith's weight. His father weighs 314.432 lbs. The answer does not seem reasonable. Babies and adults are not geometrically similar.

Journal 

Reflect 1 and 2, and **Exercise** 12 are suitable for journal entries.

REFLECT

Possible Answers

1. The volume of a sphere depends on the cube of its radius. If the radius of one sphere is k times the radius of another, the factor of k is cubed in the volume formula, and all other factors stay the same, so the ratio of the volumes is k^3.
2. The weight of the real car is larger, because its volume is larger. The surface area is larger, because the dimensions are larger. The ratio of two lengths in the model is the same as the ratio of the corresponding lengths in the real car. Each dimension is reduced by the same factor, so the ratio stays the same.

Part B Exercises

Exercise Notes

Core

12. Students find that an assumption of similarity can lead to inaccurate results. You may want to have students discuss why babies are not truly geometrically similar to adults.

Look Ahead

These exercises review transformations that students have worked with in earlier chapters. In Chapter 10, they will investigate compositions of transformations.

More Math Reasoning

23. and 24. Explore what similarity tells us about animal physiology. In Exercise 23, students see that the heartbeat of a small animal is much faster than that of a large one. In Exercise 24, they see why insects can lift many times their own weight.

y

Vocabulary
Practice/Skills
Review
Math Reasoning
Problem Solving
Challenge

Ongoing Assessment

Self-Assessment Exercises 1–13 odd

Embedded Assessment Try It a, b; Exercises 4, 6, 12

Similar Solids

Exercise Answers

Look Ahead

14. $A'(3, 1)$; $B'(7, -1)$

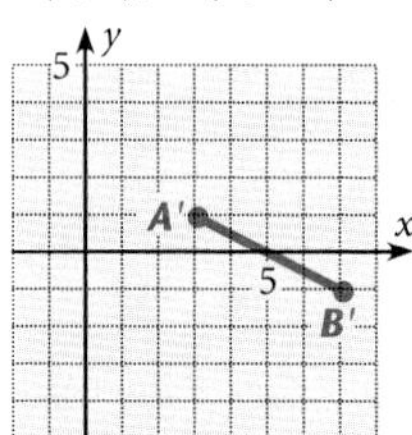

15. $A'(4, -2)$; $B'(2, -6)$

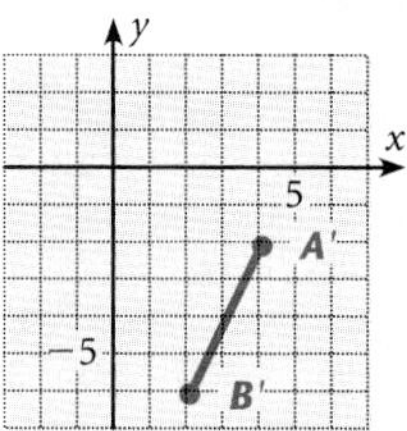

16. $A'(2, -4)$; $B'(6, -2)$

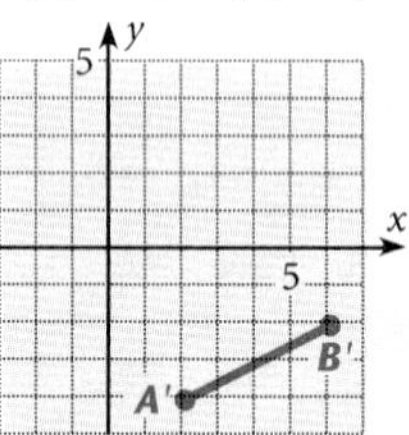

17. $A'(4, 8)$; $B'(12, 4)$

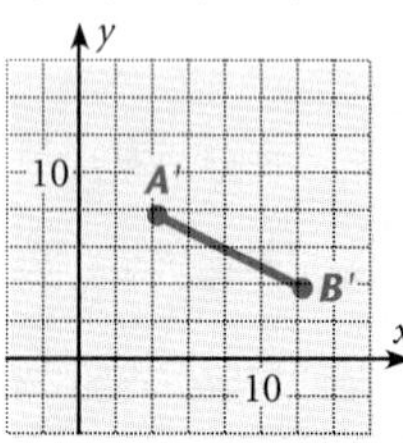

More Math Reasoning

23. ≈ 754 beats/min.; Possible answer: Assuming that surface area is proportional to height squared and blood volume is proportional to height cubed, then heart rate is proportional to $\frac{1}{\text{height}}$. Therefore, the ratio of a robin's heartbeat to a human's heartbeat is the same as the ratio of a human's height to a robin's height. So a robin's heartbeat = (human's heartbeat) × $\left(\frac{\text{human's height}}{\text{robin's height}}\right)$ = (70 beats/min)$\left(\frac{70 \text{ in.}}{6.5 \text{ in.}}\right)$ ≈ 754 beats/min.

24. See Additional Answers p. T646.

PS **13.** A globe is a scale model of the earth. Suppose that 1 in. on the globe represents 1200 mi on the earth. The circumference of the earth is about 24,900 mi. Find the radius, surface area, and volume of the globe. 3.30 in.; 137.05 in.^{2}; 150.87 in.^{3}

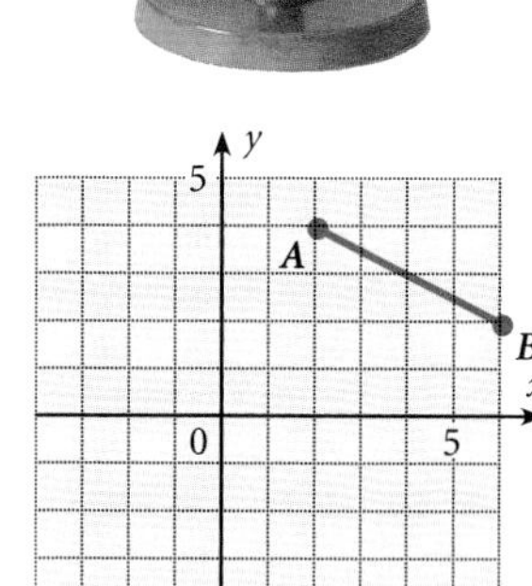

LOOK AHEAD

R **Sketch the image of $\overline{AB}$ for each transformation. Give the coordinates of points A' and B'.**

14. a translation with translation vector $<1, -3>$

15. a clockwise rotation of 90° around the origin

16. a reflection across the x-axis

17. a dilation with center (0, 0) and scale factor 2

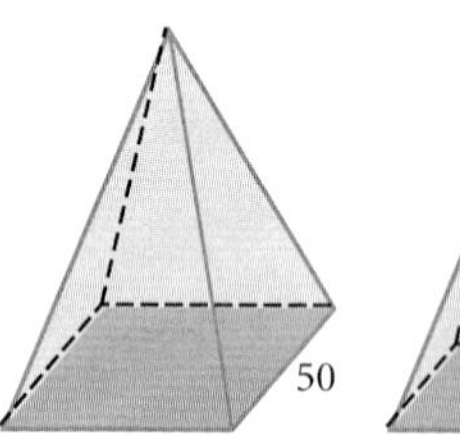

MORE PRACTICE

P **The square pyramids shown at the right are similar.**

18. Find the similarity ratio of the pyramid on the left to the pyramid on the right. $\frac{25}{16}$

19. Find the ratio of their slant heights. $\frac{25}{16}$

20. Find the ratio of their surface areas. $\frac{625}{256}$

21. Find the ratio of their volumes. $\frac{15625}{4096}$

22. The ratio of the surface areas of two similar cylinders is $\frac{81}{25}$. What is the similarity ratio of the cylinders? What is the ratio of their volumes? $\frac{9}{5}$; $\frac{729}{125}$

50

32

MORE MATH REASONING

PS, MR science **23.** Your heart rate is proportional to the ratio of your surface area (from which body heat escapes) to your blood volume (which keeps your body warm). This is also true for other animals. If a robin is 6.5 in. long and a human's heart beats an average of 70 times per minute, how fast do you think a robin's heart beats? Explain the process you used to find your answer. (Hint: Assume a human is 70 in. long.)

Key

V Vocabulary
P Practice/Skills
R Review
MR Math Reasoning
PS Problem Solving
C Challenge

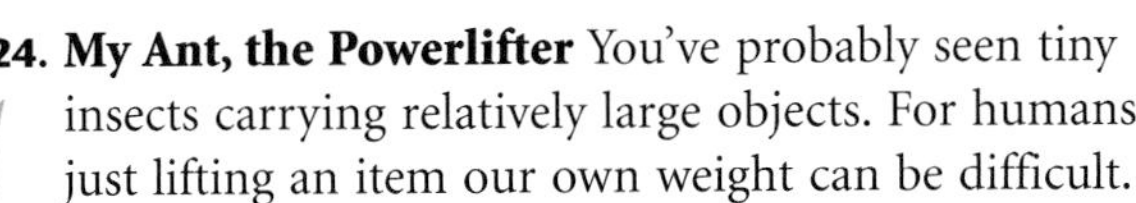

24. My Ant, the Powerlifter You've probably seen tiny insects carrying relatively large objects. For humans, just lifting an item our own weight can be difficult.

a. Model a human by a rectangular solid with a height of 180 cm, a width of 30 cm, and a length of 18 cm. Suppose the density of a human is approximately 1 gram per cubic centimeter (the density of water). What is the weight of this human in grams?

b. Find the length-width cross-sectional area of the rectangular human. If he or she can carry $\frac{1}{15}$ kg for every 1 cm^2 of cross-sectional area, how much should this person be able to carry?

c. Suppose that the similarity ratio of a human to an ant is approximately 150 to 1. Find the following.

i. the dimensions of the ant **ii.** its weight, if its density is 1 g/cm^3

iii. its cross-sectional area

iv. the weight it can carry at $\frac{1}{15}$ kg per cm^2 of cross-sectional area

d. How many ants does it take to carry the same amount a human can carry? What is their combined weight? Which species is more efficient?

e. Explain why small animals can lift and carry more in relation to their size than large animals.

PART C At a Glance

Objective

To use surface areas and volumes of similar solids to explain why large animals tend to have thick legs.

Development

In the **Explore,** students use similarity to investigate a grasshopper that has been enlarged to 600 times its normal proportions. They see that its legs would probably collapse under its own weight. Then they explain why heavy animals tend to have thick legs.

First Five Minutes

Transparency FFM 9-3C

Suppose the side lengths of one wooden cube are three times as long as those of another. How many times stronger is the cross-section of the larger cube? How many times heavier is the larger cube? 9 times; 27 times

9-3 PART C Making Connections

← CONNECT → *You've investigated the surface areas and volumes of similar solids, and you've seen how you can use similarity to help you understand the way animals look.*

The photograph at the right shows an Australian mantis, one of the world's largest insects. In the following Explore, you will see how the volumes and surface areas of similar solids limit the size of insects.

Student Resources

- Alternative Lessons
- **Laboratory Manual** 9-3C
- Technology Lab Manual
- **Practice** 9-3C
- **Study Guide and Journal** 9-3C
- **Guía de estudios y Diario** 9-3C
- **Multilingual Handbook**
- **More Look Back** 9-3C
- SAT Preparation

Media Resources

- **Transparency FFM** 9-3C
- Transparency AE
- Teaching Transparency
- **AWSMTest and practice software**
- AWSM Videodisc

Similar Solids

EXPLORE

Big Bug!

Recommended group size: 4

The Point

To use a similarity argument to show that movie monsters cannot exist, and to explain why large animals tend to have thick legs.

Look and Listen...

- For students who do not remember that the weight of the grasshopper is proportional to its volume.

Ask...

- Does the weight of a grasshopper depend on its volume or its surface area?

For Groups That Finish Early

Suppose the dimensions of the body of one animal are 4 times those of another. How many times greater would the radius of the larger animal's leg need to be to provide the same weight/leg-strength ratio as the smaller animal's legs? (To simplify the situation, assume that the legs weigh nothing.) **Leg radius would need to be 8 times greater.**

Follow Up

Ask students to explain why giant grasshoppers cannot exist.

Possible Answers

1. 1200 in. = 100 ft long.
2. $600^2 = 360{,}000$ times greater. The strength of the leg should also be 360,000 times greater.
3. $600^3 = 216{,}000{,}000$ times greater. The increase in the leg strength is many times less than this, so the giant grasshopper's legs would probably snap.
4. Heavy animals have thick legs because weight increases more rapidly than leg strength as dimensions increase.

EXPLORE: BIG BUG!

You've just seen a horror movie starring a grasshopper that has been enlarged to 600 times its normal measurements. You're pretty sure that this was done with models and trick photography, but just to make certain, you decide to check things out mathematically.

1. If a "normal" grasshopper is 2 in. long, how long is the enlarged grasshopper in the movie?
2. How many times greater is the cross-sectional area of one leg of the giant grasshopper than the cross-sectional area of one leg of the normal grasshopper? What does this tell you about the strength of the legs of the giant grasshopper?
3. How many times greater is the weight of the giant grasshopper than the weight of the normal grasshopper? Do you think the legs of the giant grasshopper could support its weight? Explain why or why not.
4. Why do many large animals have thick legs? (Hint: Suppose the measurements of the body of one animal are twice as large as the measurements of another. How many times greater is the weight of the larger animal? If the leg measurements of the larger animal were in the same proportion, how many times greater would the strength of the larger animal's legs be than that of the smaller?)

REFLECT

1. Compare the properties of similarity for solids and for plane figures. Describe similarities and differences.
2. Summarize the relationship among the similarity ratio of two solids, the ratio of their surface areas, and the ratio of their volumes.

Science Connection

Weight and *mass* are different quantities. Mass measures the amount of matter an object contains, and is constant unless the object adds or loses material. Weight measures the amount of gravitational force on an object. The weight of the object changes if it moves toward or away from the source of the gravitational pull.

Self-Assessment

Use the similar cones shown at the right for Exercises 1–4.

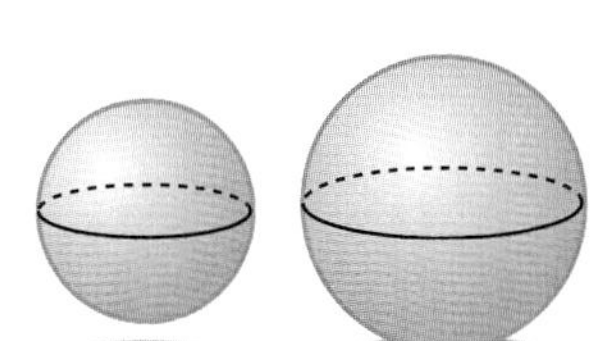

1. Find the similarity ratio of the cone on the left to the cone on the right. $\frac{3}{2}$
2. Find the ratio of their radii. $\frac{3}{2}$
3. Find the ratio of their surface areas. $\frac{9}{4}$
4. Find the ratio of their volumes. $\frac{27}{8}$
5. The volumes of the spheres shown have a ratio of $\frac{27}{64}$. What is the similarity ratio of the spheres? What is the ratio of their surface areas? $\frac{3}{4}$; $\frac{9}{16}$
6. Suppose that the corresponding sides of two similar solids have lengths 4 and 9. The ratio of the volume of the smaller solid to the larger is (d)

   (a) $\frac{2}{3}$ (b) $\frac{4}{9}$ (c) $\frac{16}{81}$ (d) $\frac{64}{729}$ (e) not here
7. Flakeos come in the two similar box sizes shown. The boxes are filled with equal densities of cereal. If the small box costs \$2.59 and the large box costs \$3.59, which one is a better buy? The larger box

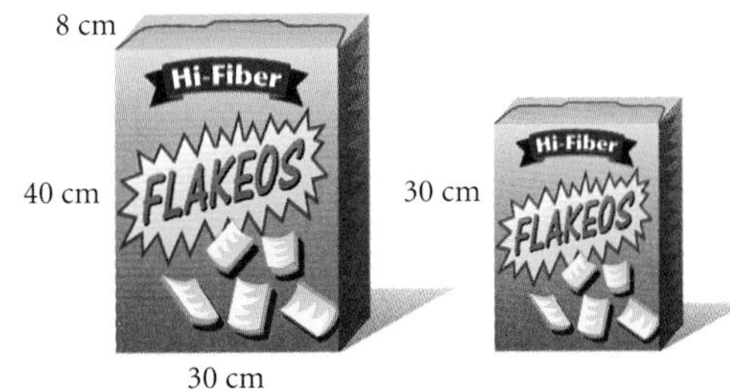

Find the measure of each angle or arc. [8-3]

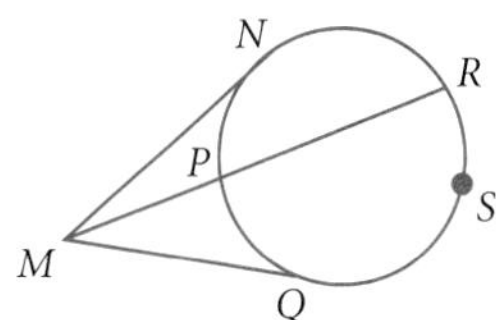

8. If $m\widehat{NSQ} = 286°$, find $m\angle NMQ$. 106°
9. If $m\angle NMQ = 68°$, find $m\widehat{NQ}$. 112°
10. If $m\widehat{QP} = 47°$ and $m\widehat{RQ} = 119°$, find $m\angle PMQ$. 36°
11. In many parts of Africa, homes are built with cylindrical bases and conical roofs. Suppose that the diameter of the base of a home is 15 ft, and its height is 6 ft. The conical roof is 25 ft in diameter, and its height is 4 ft. Find the volume enclosed by the home. [9-2] $545\frac{5}{6}\pi \approx 1714.8$ ft^3

ey

Vocabulary
Practice/Skills
Review
MR Math Reasoning
PS Problem Solving
Challenge

Portfolio

Have students select items from their work that demonstrate their understanding of the material in 9-3.

You may want to have students include their best answer to a **Reflect** question, an **Exercise** where they applied similarity to compare the leg strength or weight of two real or hypothetical animals, and an **Exercise** or **Reflect** question that they found challenging.

REFLECT

Possible Answers

1. In both cases, similar figures have the same shape, and have congruent corresponding angles and proportional corresponding side lengths. Similar solids have a volume ratio equal to the cube of their similarity ratio; similar plane figures do not have volumes.
2. The ratio of the surface areas of similar three-dimensional figures is the square of their similarity ratio; the ratio of their volumes is the cube of the similarity ratio.

Self-Assessment

Exercise Notes

6. Similar to multiple-choice questions on standardized tests.

12. Students make a scatter plot of real-world data to compare the leg diameters of animals to their weights, analyze the trend in the data, and make predictions. For this data, a curve is a better fit than a straight line.

    Technology Note: You may want to have students enter this data on a graphing utility and use the utility to find the equation of the best-fit line.

Similar Solids

Self-Assessment Answers

12. a–b.

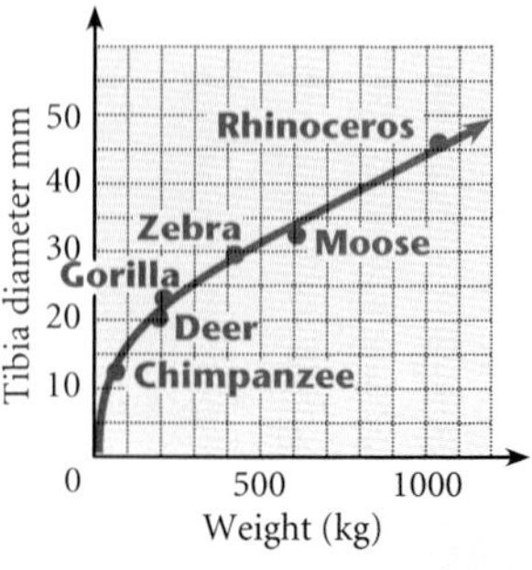

c. ≈ 3 mm for a dog; ≈ 13.5 mm for a human

d. Possible answer: Differences between dogs and humans and other animals, including number of legs.

13. Possible answer: Because of the relation between the mass and the strength of building components, light, cheap materials which would not be suitable for the actual buildings can be used in models.

14. a. 5 **b.** 50,000 lb

c. Each leg would be 25 times as strong.

d. Possible answer: No; It is unlikely that its legs would be able to carry the increased weight.

15. Height ≈ 9.6 cm; Radius ≈ 2.5 cm; The new volume is $\frac{1}{4}$ the old, so multiply old dimensions by $\frac{1}{\sqrt[3]{4}}$.

16. $\frac{1}{64}$; The answer is the ratio of the volumes of the two cubes, which is the cube of their similarity ratio.

PS, MR **12. How Big Should A Leg Be? a.** Mammals come in many different shapes and sizes. Make a scatter plot of the measurements given.

Science

Mammal	Weight	Diameter of Tibia (leg bone)
North American moose	600 kg	32.90 mm
Hartman zebra	425 kg	29.70 mm
Black rhinoceros	1035 kg	45.70 mm
Deer	170 kg	20.50 mm
Chimpanzee	60 kg	12.95 mm
Gorilla	200 kg	23.25 mm

Data courtesy of: Kent Yamaguchi, Curator of Education, Santa Ana Zoo, Santa Ana, CA; and Lynn Barkley, Collections Manager of the Los Angeles Natural History Museum.

b. Describe your scatter plot. Does a line seem to fit the points best, or does a smooth curve do a better job? Draw the line or curve that seems to fit your data best.

c. Use your scatter plot to predict the diameters of the tibia of a dog weighing 15 kg and a human weighing 70 kg.

d. What might be some of the sources of inaccuracy in your predictions in **12c**?

MR **13.** Why do you think small models of buildings are built of lighter materials than are used in the actual buildings?

PS, MR **14.** King Kong was supposed to have been 24 ft tall. Some real gorillas are about 5 ft tall and weigh about 400 pounds.

a. Find the similarity ratio of King Kong to a real gorilla. Round your answer to the nearest whole number.

b. Use your result in **14a** to help find King Kong's weight.

c. How many times stronger would one of King Kong's legs be than the leg of a real gorilla?

d. Do you think a gorilla the size of King Kong could actually exist? Why or why not?

PS **15.** A juice company sells a cylindrical 24-oz can of juice that is 15.2 cm tall and 8.0 cm in diameter. They've decided to sell 6-oz cans of juice in cylindrical cans similar to the 24-oz cans. Find the height and radius of the 6-oz can. Explain how you found these values. (Hint: Remember that ounces are a measure of volume.)

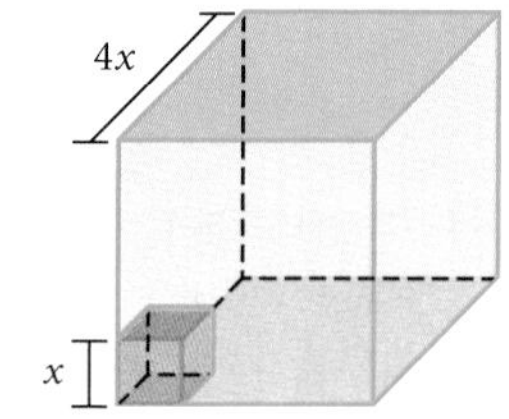

PS, MR **16.** What is the probability that a randomly selected point inside the large cube will also be inside the small cube? Explain how your answer is related to the similarity ratio of the two cubes.

Assessment Resources

- **Quiz** 9-3
- Chapter Assessment Form A
- Chapter Assessment Form B
- Chapter Alternative Assessment
- Mid-Year Assessment
- End-of-Year Assessment
- **AWSMTest and practice software**

Ongoing Assessment

Self-Assessment Self-Assessment Exercises

Embedded Assessment Explore Steps 2, 3, 4; Reflect 1, 2

Chapter 9 Review

In Chapter 9, you have learned about the properties of volume and surface area for some of the most common solids. By investigating similar solids, you gained insight into the reasons that living things are shaped as they are.

KEY TERMS

altitude [9-1]	lateral face [9-1]	right cylinder [9-1]
base [9-1]	oblique [9-1]	right prism [9-1]
cone [9-1]	prism [9-1]	slant height [9-1]
cylinder [9-1]	pyramid [9-1]	surface area [9-1]
lateral area [9-1]	regular pyramid [9-1]	volume [9-2]
lateral edge [9-1]	right cone [9-1]	

V **Write the letter of the second pair that best matches the first pair.**

1. Pyramid: cone as (a) oblique: right, (b) prism: cylinder, (c) sphere: great circle, (d) cylinder: sphere (b)
2. Oblique: right as (a) vertical: slanted, (b) lateral: regular, (c) cone: cylinder, (d) tilted: upright (d)

CONCEPTS AND APPLICATIONS

P **Find the surface area and volume of each solid to the nearest tenth. [9-1, 9-2]**

3.
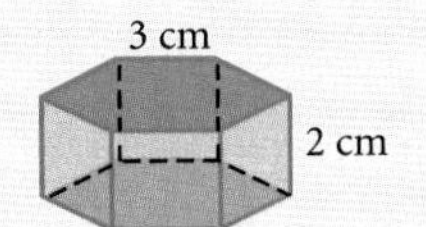

Regular hexagonal prism

4.
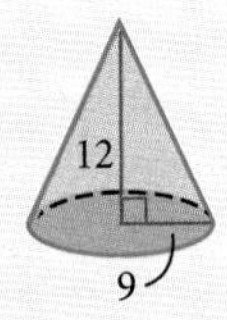

5.
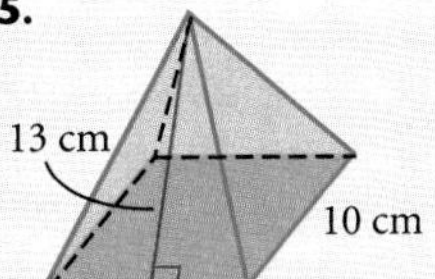

6.
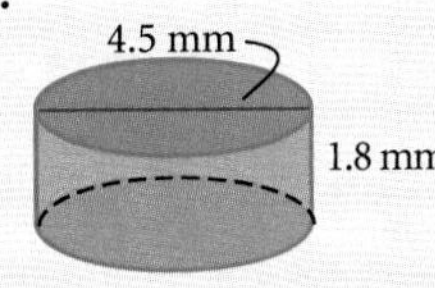

P 7. The diameter of a ball is $4\frac{1}{2}$ in. Find its surface area and volume. [9-2]
$20.25\pi \approx 63.6$ in.^{2}; $15.1875\pi \approx 47.7$ in.^{3}

R 8. The two prisms at the right have the same height. Do they have the same volume? Explain. [9-2]
Yes; They also have the same size base.

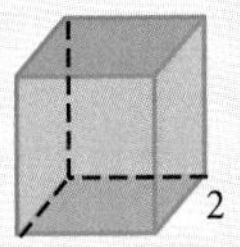

Right square prism

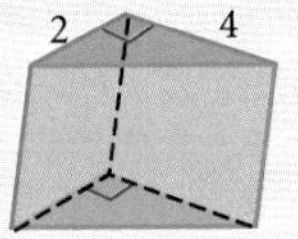

Oblique triangular prism

R 9. Create a table of formulas for the surface area and volume of a regular triangular prism, a square prism, and a regular hexagonal prism, each with base sides of length s and height h. [9-1, 9-2]

ey

Vocabulary
Practice/Skills
Review
IR Math Reasoning
S Problem Solving
Challenge

Chapter 9 Review

Journal

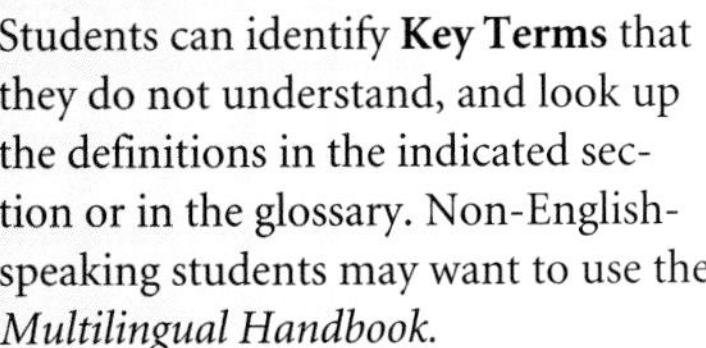

Students can identify **Key Terms** that they do not understand, and look up the definitions in the indicated section or in the glossary. Non-English-speaking students may want to use the *Multilingual Handbook.*

Vocabulary exercises and the **Self-Evaluation** are useful journal entries. Students may also want to write a brief explanation of the connection between similarity and animal shapes and sizes.

Review Answers

3. 82.8 cm^2; 46.8 cm^3

4. $SA = 678.6$; $V = 1017.9$

5. 360 cm^2; 400 cm^3

6. 57.3 mm^2; 28.6 mm^3

9. See Additional Answers p. T646.

10. $\frac{4}{3}\pi r^3$; This is the volume of a sphere of radius r.

11. a. 2.75 **b.** 6.5

c. The strips of fish will cook more quickly; The single slab of fish will hold its heat better. The ratio of surface area to volume makes the difference.

12. It will hold 27 times as much petroleum.

13. a–b. See Additional Answers, p. T646.

c. Each time the height is doubled the intensity is multiplied by $\frac{1}{4}$.

Algebra	Functions	Discrete Math	Probability	Data/Statistics

Chapter 9 Assessment

Portfolio

Students may select items that represent their mathematical understanding of the ideas in Chapter 9, as well as illustrating the effort that they put forth on this chapter.

A rubric for assessing portfolios is included in the introduction to the Teacher's Edition.

Assessment Answers

5. $166\frac{2}{3}\pi \approx 523.6$

6.

	Ratio
Length	k
Surface area	k^2
Volume	k^3

MR **10.** The diameter and height of a cylinder are equal. A cone of the same radius and height is inscribed in the cylinder. What is the volume of the cylinder that is not occupied by the cone? This volume is that of another familiar solid. Describe the solid and give its dimensions. [9-2]

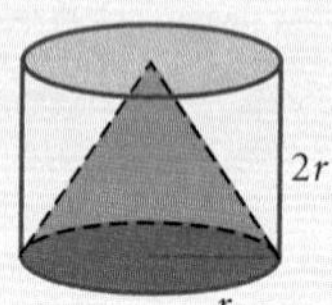

PS, MR **11.** In general, the greater an object's surface area in comparison to its volume, the faster it will heat up or cool down. [9-1, 9-2]

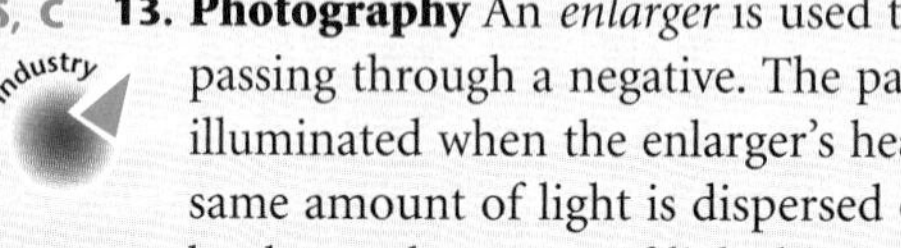

a. Imagine a slice of fish as a rectangular prism. Calculate the surface area and volume of a single slab of fish with the dimensions shown. Find the ratio of surface area to volume.

b. Repeat these calculations for the same slab cut into strips of the size shown.

c. When cooked at the same temperature, which form of the fish will cook more quickly? Which form will hold its heat better during a long meal?

P **12.** A cylindrical petroleum tank has diameter 40 m and height 30 m. How many times more petroleum can a similar tank hold if it is three times as tall? [9-3]

CONCEPTS AND CONNECTIONS

PS, C **13. Photography** An *enlarger* is used to expose paper to light passing through a negative. The paper is more brightly illuminated when the enlarger's head is lowered because the same amount of light is dispersed over a smaller area. Let L be the total amount of light hitting the paper. Then the intensity of the light is the amount of light per square inch, or $I = \frac{L}{\text{Area of base}}$.

Industry

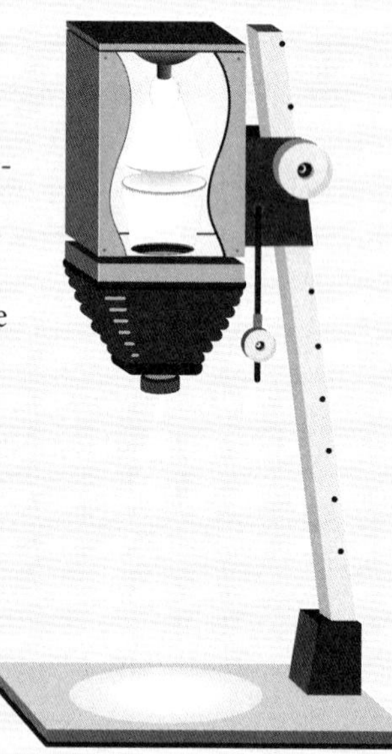

a. Make a table with columns for the height and radius of the cone, the area of the cone's base, and the intensity of light. When the enlarger is 2 in. above the paper, the radius of the cone is 1 in. Fill in a row of the table using this information, leaving entries in terms of L and π.

b. Use similarity to help complete table rows for cone heights of 4 in. and 8 in.

c. Describe how intensity is affected by doubling the height.

SELF-EVALUATION

Write a summary of the most important facts about surface area and volume that you learned from Chapter 9. Describe at least one technique you can use to help learn a concept you found difficult.

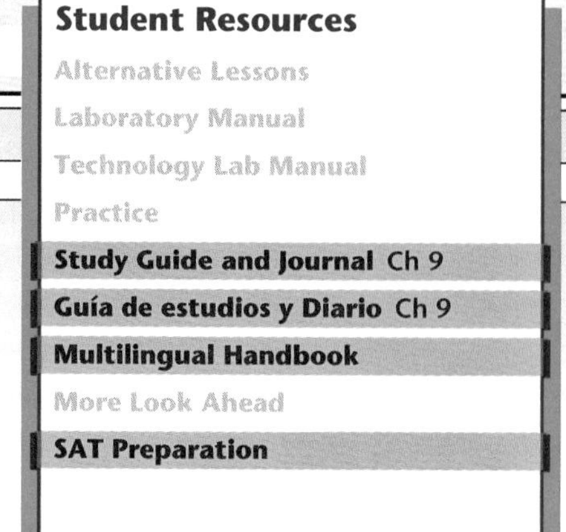

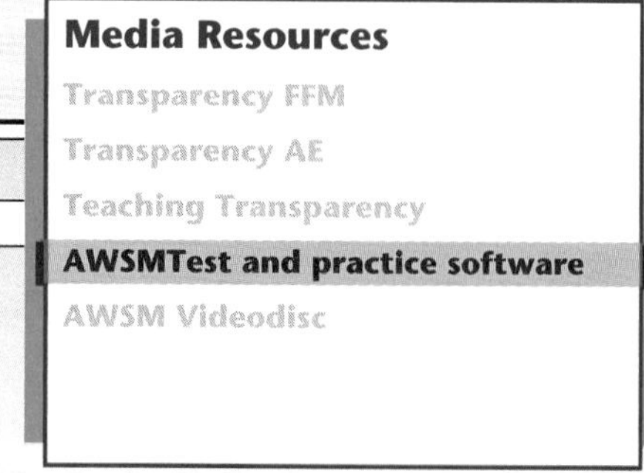

Chapter 9 Assessment

TEST

Find the surface area and volume of each solid to the nearest tenth.

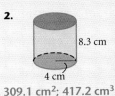

1. 7.2; 3.0; 4.0
SA 98.4; V 43.2

2. 8.3 cm; 4 cm
309.1 cm²; 417.2 cm³

3. 12; 5
SA 282.7; V 314.2

4. 26; 20; Square pyramid
SA 1440; V 3200

5. The surface area of a sphere is 100π. Find its volume. $166\frac{2}{3}\pi$

6. The similarity ratio between two similar solids is k. Write a summary of the ratios between different pairs of corresponding measures of the solids. Include measures of length, surface area, and volume.

7. If the uniform rainfall over a 2-mi.-square town is 2 in., what is the total volume of rainfall in cubic feet? If all of the rain drains into a small circular lake with a diameter of 0.5 mi, how many feet will the level of the lake rise?
1.86×10^7 ft³; $h \approx 3.4$ ft

8. The Transamerica Pyramid in San Francisco is approximately a square pyramid. Its base has sides 145 ft long, and the pyramid is 786 ft tall. A 3-ft-tall scale model is built.

a. To the nearest hundredth, what is the side length of the model's base? 0.55 ft long

b. To the nearest tenth, what is the model's lateral surface area? 6.6 ft²

9. In the figure at the right, a sphere is inscribed in a cylinder.

a. Find the ratio of the volume of the cylinder to that of the sphere. $\frac{3}{2}$

b. Find the ratio of the surface area of the cylinder to that of the sphere. $\frac{3}{2}$

c. Describe what is special about these ratios.
These ratios are equal.

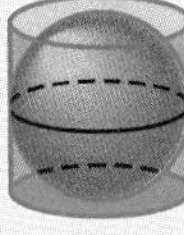

PERFORMANCE TASK

Before it erupted, Mount St. Helens had the approximate shape of a cone with a diameter of 30,000 ft and a height of 9700 ft. After the May 1980 eruption, the volcano lost its top—a cone 1200 ft in height.

One of the World Trade Center towers in New York is a 1350-ft-tall square prism with bases 210 ft on a side. Guess how many World Trade Center towers would make up the same volume as the destroyed top of Mount St. Helens. Then apply properties of similarity to find the approximate volume of the removed volcano top. Also find the volume of the tower and the number of towers that would fit in the volcano top. How good was your guess?

Assessment Resources

Quiz
Chapter 9 Assessment Form A
Chapter 9 Assessment Form B
Chapter 9 Alternative Assessment
Mid-Year Assessment
End-of-Year Assessment
AWSMTest Chapter 9

Ongoing Assessment

Self-Assessment Chapter 9 Review and Self-Evaluation

Embedded Assessment Chapter 9 Performance Task

Test Chapter 9 Test

Performance Task

Answer

Volume of top of Mount St. Helens: $\approx 4.3 \times 10^9$ ft³

Volume of World Trade Center: $\approx 5.9 \times 10^7$ ft³

Number of towers that would fit in the volcano top: ≈ 73

Suggested Scoring Rubric

Level 4 Full Accomplishment

- Shows full understanding of the concepts of similar figures and volume.
- Students find correct volumes of the top of Mount St. Helens and the World Trade Center, and the correct number of World Trade Centers to fit into the top of the volcano.

Level 3 Substantial Accomplishment

- Shows essential grasp of the concepts of similar figures and volume.
- Two of the three calculations—the volume of the top of Mount St. Helens, the volume of the World Trade Center, and the number of World Trade Centers (given student volume results)—are correct.

Level 2 Partial Accomplishment

- Shows partial grasp of the concepts of similar figures and volume.
- One calculation—the volume of the top of Mount St. Helens or the World Trade Center, or the number of World Trade Centers (given student volume results)—is correct.

Level 1 Little Accomplishment

- Shows little or no grasp of the concepts of similar figures and volume.
- All three calculations are incorrect.

10

Chapter 10

Transformations and Patterns

Chapter 10
Project A

We're Here to Stay

Design a Logo

Create a logo that conveys the right impression for a real or imaginary business.

- Did you know that the design of trademarks and logos has become a specialty in the communication arts?
- Don't you wonder how corporate identity can be conveyed visually?
- How does this connect to Chapter 10? **Transformation** of design elements in a logo can create a sense of progress, stability, or harmony.

Expand Your Vocabulary

copyright	corporate culture	camera-ready
trademark	corporate identity	letterhead

This logo is universally recognized as the "recycle" logo. How does the design itself remind people to recycle?

Project Guidelines

Investigate

- Read about logos and trademarks in a book about graphic design.
- Talk to business people about the image of the companies they own or work for. Does their logo reflect these qualities?

Set Your Direction

- What kind of business will you design a logo for? Will it be pictorial or strictly geometric? Will you do it freehand or on the computer?
- Would your logo likely be reproduced on a shirt or a jacket? on a neon sign?

Make a Plan

- Make a calendar for each day's work. Check in with your group and with your teacher.
- You'll need art materials, a protractor, and a ruler.

Collect and Organize Your Information

- Collect business cards from different firms, or sketch logos from clothing, packaging, or commercial signs.
- List the qualities you think each firm wants to project to the public. What features of their corporate logos convey this impression?
- Sketch several possible designs using repetitions and transformations of the same shapes. Ask several people what kind of company each logo suggests, and what the company's product, service, or reputation might be.

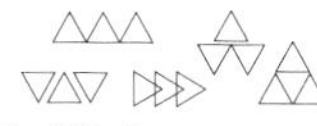

Carry Out Your Plan

- Refine your logo so that it is "camera ready."
- Present a series of sketches showing the logo on products, uniforms, vehicles, or signs, as it might be used commercially.

Look Back

- Will your logo be easy to recognize? easy to reproduce?
- What could you have done differently?

A

Project A

We're Here to Stay

How does a corporate logo give the impression that a company is reliable and stable?

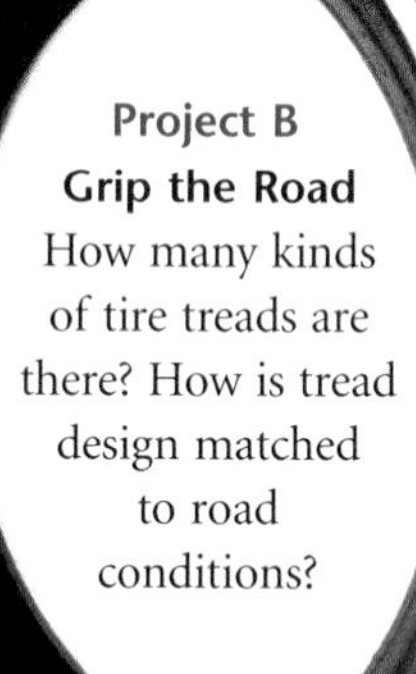

Project B

Grip the Road

How many kinds of tire treads are there? How is tread design matched to road conditions?

Chapter 10
Project B

Grip the Road

Make a Poster of Tread Types

Using photos, rubbings or sketches, create a visual display explaining tread types.

- Did you know studded snow tires are outlawed in some states?
- Don't you wonder why road traction is better when more tread is in contact with the road?
- How does this connect to Chapter 10? Tire tread patterns are **transformations.**

Expand Your Vocabulary

traction	steel belted	vulcanize	bias
pneumatic	bias belted	groove	studs
squirm	low profile	retread	skid
footprint	radial ply	side wall	sipe

Project Guidelines

Investigate

- Visit a tire dealer. Ask about tread pattern types and their uses. Ask about traction and skidding.
- Read about tire manufacture in a sales brochure or in an encyclopedia.
- Talk to drivers of several different vehicle types. Ask why they use the tires they have.

Set Your Direction

- Will you investigate automobile tires only or truck, wheel chair, and bicycle tires as well?
- Will your poster inform consumers? Explain scientific principles?

Make a Plan

- Make a calendar for each day's work. Check in with your group and with your teacher.
- You'll need posterboard and art materials.

Collect and Organize Your Information

- Take rubbings or make sketches of several tread patterns.
- Classify them by design and by their intended use.
- Find out which features of tread design help when the road is wet, icy, steep, gravelly, or smooth.
- Sketch a rough design for your poster. Plan where to place pictures and labels. Write a draft of each label, telling how each tread feature improves traction.

Carry Out Your Plan

- Complete your poster according to your sketch.
- Tell why the deepest tire grooves run along the circumference of the tire and not across its width.
- Tell why a zigzag pattern is used in so many tread designs.

Look Back

- What *road* features improve tire traction? Do they form transformation patterns?
- How is the action of other rolling tools (rolling pin, paint roller, film sprockets, lawn mower) like tire traction? How is it different? Is a transformation pattern formed?
- Do you think the average driver knows enough about tires on their vehicle? Why or why not?

B

Project C

Deck the Walls

How is wallpaper designed? How do interior designers combine motifs on the same wall for unity and variety?

F. TANI HASEGAWA

I never really thought about liking or disliking math in high school. I always liked numbers, and I still find myself counting in my mind as I do things.

Math is a language to me. It can be used to gain an understanding of the world around us, and to show us underlying connections and a certain sense of order. Things like form, pattern, sequence, and rhythm can be expressed mathematically, and are things we live with, create, and find in nature every day. I find beauty in this, and use this in my work to help people visually express ideas and organize information.

F. tani Hasegawa
Designer
OPEN MOUTH
San Francisco, CA

F. tani Hasegawa

Chapter 10 | Project C — **Deck the Walls**

Design Your Own Wallpaper

Use repeated transformations of a design to create a wallpaper pattern.

- Did you know that wallpaper with a small pattern is more economical to install than paper with a large pattern?
- Don't you wonder how interior designers combine motifs?
- How does this connect to Chapter 10? Wallpaper **patterns** are made up of **transformations** of figures.

When the motif of a wallpaper pattern is small, the adjacent panel of paper needs only slight shifting to match the pattern along the seam.

Expand Your Vocabulary

motif	plumb line	feature strip
template	figure-ground	wainscot

Project Guidelines

Investigate

- Visit a home decorating outlet. Look at wallpaper samples. Find where the pattern repeats.
- Talk to an interior decorator or to a wallpaper hanger. Ask about their client's tastes and about the ease or difficulty of matching patterns during installation.

Set Your Direction

- Will your design be abstract or pictorial? geometric or floral? Will it have other kinds of symmetry?
- Do you envision it in a kitchen? in a baby's room? in an office?

Make a Plan

- Make a calendar for each day's work. Check in with your group and with your teacher.
- You'll need a protractor, art materials, large paper, and a ruler.

Collect and Organize Your Information

- Sketch a design. Make a template from cardboard to help you trace the figure repeatedly.
- Create a grid of polygons that tessellate the plane.
- Make tracings or photocopies of your grid. Then combine the copies to see where the grid should go in relation to the paper edge (seam).

Carry Out Your Plan

- Transfer the grid to your large paper.
- Translate the design template to each intersection of the grid. Trace the template to repeat the figure.
- Use art materials to add color and interest.

Look Back

- Is your design economical to install? Is it easy to match at the seams?

© Addison-Wesley Publishing Company, Inc. *Focus on Geometry* 59

Biographical Note

F. tani Hasegawa graduated from Niles East High School in Skokie, IL. She took Algebra I and II, Geometry, and Precalculus.

Chapter 10

Overview

Transformations and Patterns

10-1 Putting Transformations Together

You've looked at four different transformations separately. Now you will look at the transformations together. These combinations can help you understand many different things, from the graphs of algebraic equations to the mechanisms in a car.

10-2 Classifying Patterns

Studying patterns on ancient artifacts helps archaeologists identify and classify the artifacts. These patterns are also present in modern design and architecture. You will apply your knowledge of transformational geometry and symmetry to two types of patterns—frieze and wallpaper patterns.

CHAPTERS

Chapter 10 Planning Guide

The following ancillaries are recommended for each course level. The additional resources, *Technology Lab Manual, Study Guide and Journal, Multilingual Handbook,* and *Assessment,* are recommended for all levels.

	Comprehensive Course	Core Course	Informal Course
10-1 Part A	▲	▲	
Alternative Lessons			
Laboratory Manuals	▲	▲	
Practice			
More Look Ahead		▲	
10-1 Part B	▲	▲	
Alternative Lessons			
Laboratory Manuals	▲	▲	
Practice			
More Look Back		▲	
10-1 Part C	▲	▲	
Alternative Lessons			
Laboratory Manuals	▲	▲	
Practice			
More Look Ahead		▲	

	Comprehensive Course	Core Course	Informal Course
10-1 Part D	▲	▲	
More Look Back		▲	
Quiz 10-1	▲	▲	
10-2 Part A	▲	▲	
Alternative Lessons			
Laboratory Manuals	▲	▲	
Practice			
More Look Back		▲	
10-2 Part B	▲	▲	
Alternative Lessons			
Laboratory Manuals	▲	▲	
Practice			
More Look Ahead		▲	
10-2 Part C	▲	▲	
More Look Back		▲	
Quiz 10-2	▲	▲	

BIBLIOGRAPHY

Teacher Resources

Introduction to Tessellations, Dale Seymour and Jill Britton. Dale Seymour Publications, 1989 (NS07901).

Tessellation Teaching Masters, Dale Seymour. Dale Seymour Publications, 1989 (NS07900).

Tessellations Using Logo, Margaret J. Kenney and Stanley J. Bezuszka. Dale Seymour Publications, 1987 (NS07701).

SPACES: Solving Problems of Access to Careers in Engineering and Science, Sherry Fraser, project director. © 1982 by the Regents of the University of California. Available through Dale Seymour Publications (NS07401).

10-1

Putting Transformations Together

SUPERLESSON AT A GLANCE

Superlesson Goal

Students will identify isometries, investigate compositions of transformations, and discover how differences in related algebraic equations can be seen in transformations of their graphs.

Management Guide

	Topic	Objectives	Key Terms	New Ideas	Materials
Part A	Isometries	To determine which of the transformations studied so far are isometries.	Isometry	Isometries as transformations that preserve distance. Translation, rotation, and reflection are isometries.	**Student** Protractor, ruler, geometry software
Part B	Compositions of Transformations	To explore compositions of transformations and identify single transformations equivalent to compositions.	Composition	Compositions of transformations. Reflections over parallel lines are equivalent to one translation, etc.	**Student** Compass, ruler
Part C	Transformations of Algebraic Functions	To use transformations to interpret the effects of constants on the graphs of equations.	Parent equation	Seeing how differences in equations are reflected in translations and reflections of their graphs	**Student** Graph paper, graphing utility **Teacher** Graph paper transparency
Part D	Making Connections	To show how transformations and their compositions are important in automobile mechanisms.	In Making Connections, students apply and synthesize key terms and new ideas.		

Pacing Chart (45-Minute Periods)

	Comprehensive Course	Core Course	Informal Course
Part A	1	1	0
Part B	1	1	0
Part C	1	1	0
Part D	1	1	0
TOTAL periods for Superlesson	4	4	0

NCTM Standards

Mathematics as Problem Solving

Mathematics as Communication

Mathematics as Reasoning

Mathematical Connections

Algebra

Functions

Geometry from a Synthetic Perspective

Geometry from an Algebraic Perspective

10-1 Putting Transformations Together

Pushing Paper

Mark Thomas is now an engineer for General Motors, but he didn't know much about engineering when his high school guidance counselors suggested it as a career. Now he helps high school students learn all about engineering. Thomas's "paper car" program earned him two national awards including 1993 Black Engineer of the Year for Community Service from *US Black Engineer* magazine.

Thomas developed a 12-week program where students design and build cars made entirely of paper. The cars are 5 ft tall, can be steered, and are designed to run on "push-power" (since real engines give off sparks).

The idea for the program came to Thomas and two colleagues (Vincent and Elliott Lyons) in 1990 while they were getting their master's degrees in mechanical engineering at Stanford University. The three were also teaching engineering at a high school in the San Francisco Bay Area.

Six Detroit area high schools now feature the program. Students attend class twice during the week, and most attend three-hour Saturday sessions. General Motors and two paper companies pay for equipment and supplies, and GM engineers act as instructors.

1. How do you think most students decide on a career to pursue?

2. Describe how you might find out more about engineering as a career.

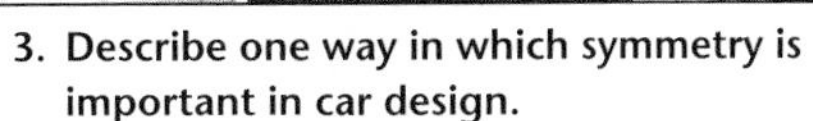

3. Describe one way in which symmetry is important in car design.

Where Are We Now?

Students are familiar with reflections, rotations, translations, and dilations.

Where Are We Going?

In 10-1, students determine which of these transformations are isometries. They'll see how the transformations work together and how they are related to graphs of functions.

Possible Answers

1. Students often become interested in a career that uses skills that they enjoy and/or are good at. They may learn more about the career from talking to adults or reading books.
2. Talking to career counselors, talking to adults in engineering, and reading books. Programs may be available where students spend a day at work with an engineer.
3. When viewed from the front or back, most cars have vertical line symmetry. A balanced design is important for stability, aerodynamics, and steering alignment.

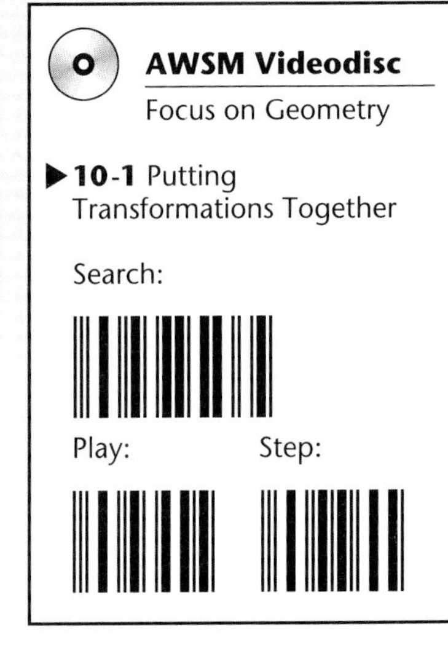

More About Automobiles

Though gasoline-powered engines rule the road today, this was not always so. Around 1900, about 40% of U.S. cars were powered by steam, 38% by electricity, and 22% by gasoline. The first self-propelled vehicle, powered by steam, was invented in 1769. Early steam vehicles managed about $2\frac{1}{4}$ mi/hr. The gasoline engine was invented in 1885, and electric cars followed in 1891. (The first car to exceed 60 miles per hour, in 1899, was electric.) Each system has drawbacks. Gasoline engines generate pollution and use natural resources. Steam engines small enough and powerful enough to use in a car are expensive, and batteries in electric cars need frequent recharging.

10-1

Putting Transformations Together

PART A At a Glance

Objective

To determine which of the transformations studied so far are isometries.

Development

First, students review four familiar transformations. Then they see the definition of an isometry.

Next, in the **Explore,** students determine which of the four transformations are isometries.

Suggested Materials

Student Protractor, ruler, geometry software

Key Terms

Isometry

First Five Minutes

Transparency FFM 10-1A

Read the first paragraphs on page 668. Then do **Try It a–c.**

Motivate

Ask...

- List some of the properties of figures that transformations may or may not preserve. **Congruence, distance, angle measure, shape, size, orientation, etc.**

Provides a connection between isometries and congruence.

Possible Answer

1. Isometries are sometimes called *congruence transformations* because pre-images and images are congruent.

10-1 PART A Isometries

← CONNECT → *You've already studied four transformations: reflections, rotations, translations, and dilations. Now you will review your knowledge of each of these transformations, learn what an isometry is, and see which of the transformations you've studied are isometries.*

A general term for change is *transformation:* for example, from seed to plant, or from caterpillar to butterfly. In geometry, transformations include the reflections, translations, rotations, and dilations that you investigated earlier.

TRY IT

Assume that each image shown in the figures below is created by a single transformation. Determine whether the transformation shown is a reflection, rotation, translation, or dilation. If the transformation is a reflection, identify the line of reflection. If it is a rotation, identify the center and angle of the rotation. If it is a translation, give the translation vector. If it is a dilation, identify the center and scale factor.

a. Translation, vector <3, −4>
b. Rotation, center (0, 0), 90° clockwise
c. Dilation, center (0, 0), scale factor 2

a.

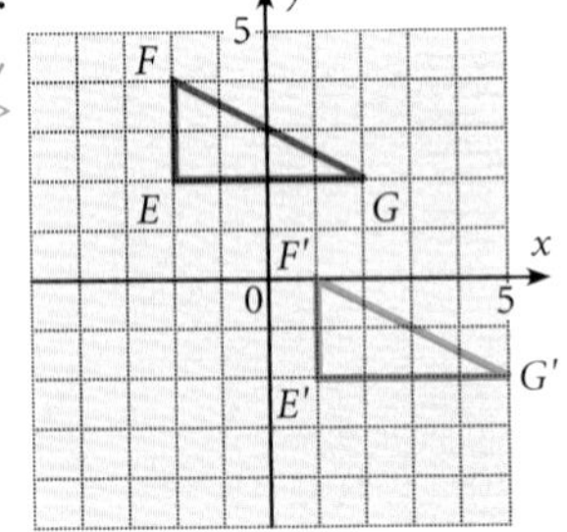

b.

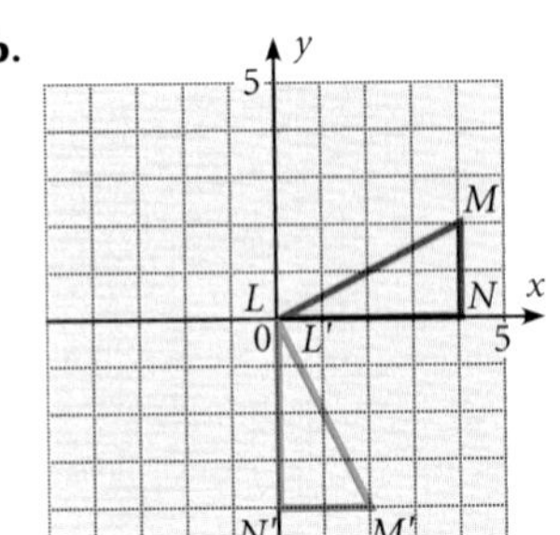

c.

For some transformations, the distance between any two points on the pre-image and the distance between the corresponding points on the image is always the same. (For any points A and B and their images A' and B', $AB = A'B'$.) Transformations that preserve distance have a special name.

DEFINITION

An **isometry** is a transformation that preserves distance.

Technology Note

In some software, it is best to select all sides and vertices of a figure before transforming it. Selecting many objects at once is usually done by holding down the shift key while selecting. When doing a dilation or rotation, the center of the transformation may need to be the last point selected while holding down the shift key.

1. Isometries can be called *congruence transformations.* Explain why this makes sense.

In the following Explore, you will review the properties of the four transformations you've studied and discover which of these transformations are isometries.

EXPLORE: ISOMETRY GEOMETRY

MATERIALS

Protractor, Ruler
Geometry software (optional)

1. Use geometry software or a protractor and ruler to investigate the properties of the four transformations. Which preserve distance? angle measure? shape? size? orientation? congruence? (Hint: Start with a simple figure, such as $\triangle ABC$. Then carry out each of the four transformations on the figure.) Prepare a table to show your results.
2. Which of the four transformations are isometries? Explain how you identified the isometries.

THEOREM

Translations, reflections, and rotations are isometries.

REFLECT

1. Suppose you take a paper car, push it 10 ft forward, and then turn it on its top. Is this transformation of the original paper car an isometry? Why or why not?
2. If you take a rubber band and stretch it taut, is this transformation of the original rubber band an isometry? Why or why not?

Student Resources
- Alternative Lessons 10-1A
- Laboratory Manual 10-1A
- Technology Lab Manual
- Practice 10-1A
- Study Guide and Journal 10-1A
- Guía de estudios y Diario 10-1A
- Multilingual Handbook
- More Look Ahead 10-1A
- SAT Preparation

Media Resources
- Transparency FFM 10-1A
- Transparency AE
- Teaching Transparency
- AWSMTest and practice software
- AWSM Videodisc

EXPLORE

Isometry Geometry

Recommended group size: 4

The Point
To review properties of translations, reflections, rotations, and dilations, and to identify which of these are isometries.

Look and Listen...
- For students who do not remember how to draw the image of a figure under one or more of the transformations.

Ask...
- Where is your center of rotation/center of dilation/line of reflection? How far away from that point/line is A? How can you determine where A' is?

For Groups That Finish Early
Sketch a triangle and translate it. Then reflect the translation image over a line. Is the final triangle congruent to the original? If so, explain why this makes sense. **Yes; the translation image is congruent to the original triangle; the reflection image is congruent to the translation image, so the original is congruent to the reflection image.**

Follow Up
Have one student or group present the table from Step 1. Then have the class decide which of the transformations are isometries.

Possible Answers
1. Translation and rotation preserve all six properties. Reflection preserves all of the properties except orientation. Dilation preserves orientation, shape, and angle measure.
2. Translation, reflection, and rotation are isometries—they preserve distance.

Journal 

Reflect 1 and 2 and **Exercise** 12 are suitable for journal entries.

Putting Transformations Together

REFLECT

Possible Answers

1. This transformation is an isometry; since all of the individual transformations involved preserve distance, their combination must also preserve distance.
2. No. Points on the stretched rubber band are a different distance from each other than they were when the band was relaxed.

Part A Exercises

Exercise Notes

Core

13. and 15. Students see how reflection helps determine the shortest path from a point to a line to a second point.

Look Ahead

16–19. Review graphing skills and terminology needed in 10-1 Part C.

20. Previews compositions of reflections seen in 10-1 Part B.

More Math Reasoning

27. Students see why one method for creating a flat earth map does not preserve distance.

Geography Note: The Mercator Projection is based on the technique described in this exercise.

28. Shows patterns in the Braille alphabet.

Exercise Answers

Core

12. a.

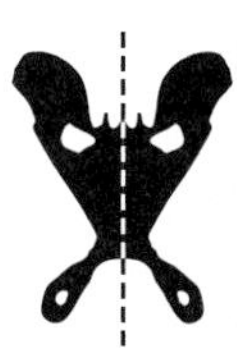

b. Check students' answers.

Exercises

CORE

P **Getting Started For each pair of figures, identify a single transformation that maps one figure onto the other. State whether the transformation is an isometry.**

1.

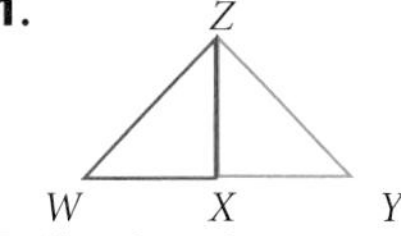

Reflection; Isometry

2.

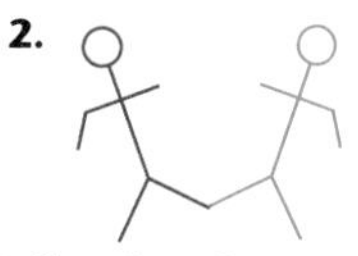

Reflection; Isometry

3.

Dilation; Not an isometry

4.

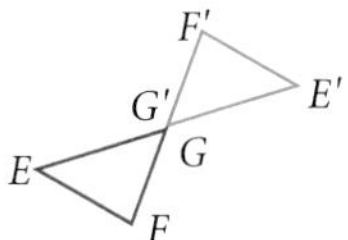

Rotation; Isometry

P **Using the tessellation shown, identify each transformation.**

D E F G H
M L K J I
N O P Q R

5. Segment $\overline{DE}$ is the image of $\overline{FG}$. Translation
6. Angle $\angle LKP$ is the image of $\angle JKF$. Rotation
7. Segment $\overline{ML}$ is the image of $\overline{KL}$. Rotation or reflection
8. From the four terms below, choose the term that does not belong, and explain why.

   rotation, reflection, dilation, translation Dilation; It it not an isometry.

P **Determine whether the transformation shown in each figure below is a reflection, rotation, translation, or dilation. If the transformation is a reflection, identify the line of reflection. If it is a rotation, identify the center and angle of the rotation. If it is a translation, give the translation vector. If it is a dilation, identify the center and scale factor.**

9.

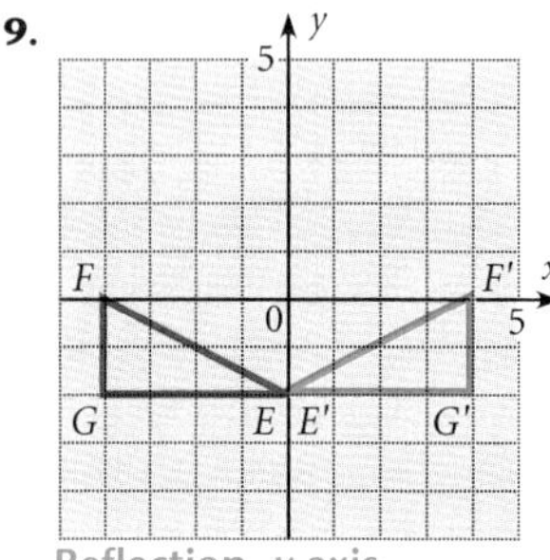

Reflection, y-axis

10.

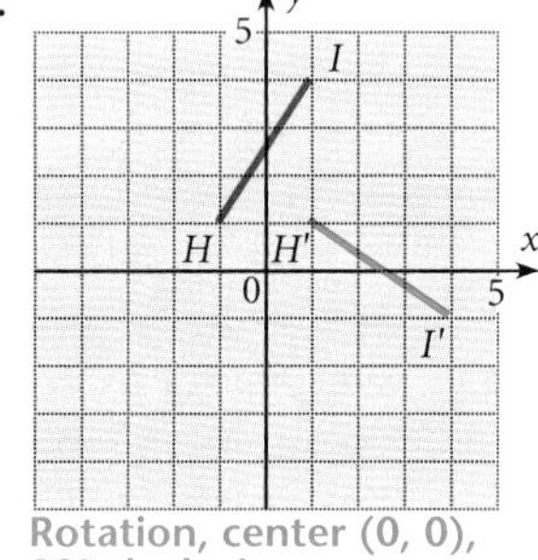

Rotation, center (0, 0), 90° clockwise

11.

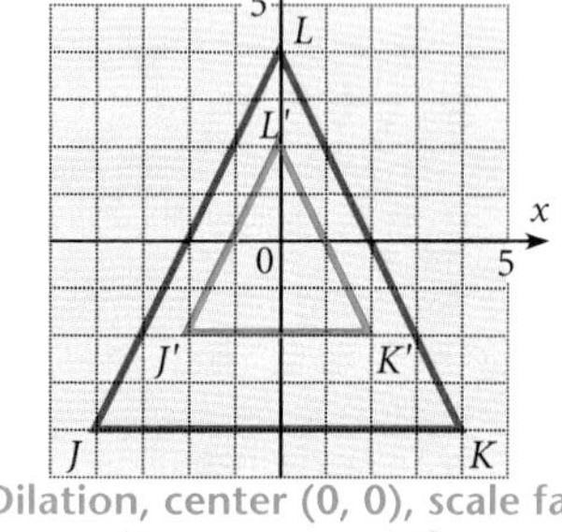

Dilation, center (0, 0), scale fac

MR Social Science **12.** A famous psychological test developed by Hermann Rorschach involves looking at an inkblot and describing what you see.

a. Sketch a rough copy of the inkblot shown. Show the line of symmetry for the blot.

b. What do you see in this inkblot?

Key

V Vocabulary
P Practice/Skills
R Review
MR Math Reasoning
PS Problem Solving
C Challenge

13. Camping Crisis Jonah's tent is on fire! He needs to get water from the river and get back to his tent as quickly as he can, so he must find the shortest possible route from his position, J, to the river and then to his tent, T.

You can find the shortest route from a point to a line to another point by using a reflection. Copy the figure at the right. Reflect T over the line created by the river. Call the image T'. Draw $\overline{JT'}$, and label as P the point where $\overline{JT'}$ intersects the river. The path from J to P to T is the shortest possible path. Why?

14. A dilation is not an isometry. However, one type of dilation does preserve distance. What is the scale factor of a dilation that preserves distance? 1

15. Shoreline Shortcut In a swimming race, contestants begin at A, swim to any point on the shoreline, and finish at B. Copy the figure. Then use a reflection to show where the contestant should touch the shoreline in order to swim the shortest possible route.

LOOK AHEAD

Graph each equation on a coordinate plane.

16. $y = x + 4$ **17.** $y = x^2 - 2$ **18.** $y = (x - 1)^2$

19. What is the graph of a quadratic equation called? A parabola

20. A single reflection reverses orientation. What happens to the orientation of a figure after it is reflected over two lines? Draw a sketch to illustrate your answer.

MORE PRACTICE

For each pair of figures, identify a single transformation that maps one figure onto the other. State whether the transformation is or is not an isometry.

21.

Reflection; Isometry

22.

Translation; Isometry

23.

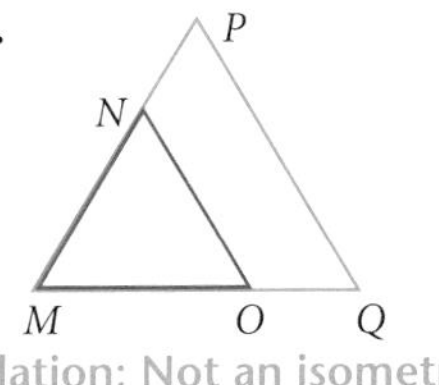

Dilation; Not an isometry

13.

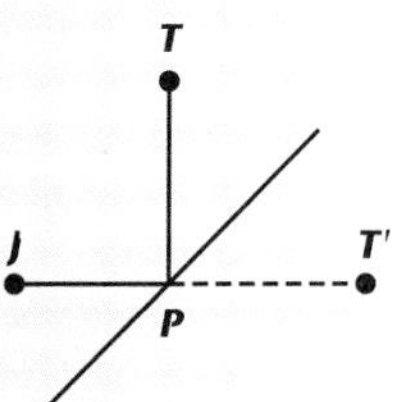

It is the shortest path possible because J to T' is a straight line (the shortest distance between two points).

15.

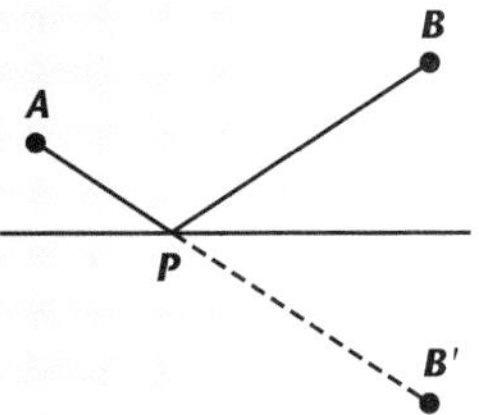

Look Ahead

16.

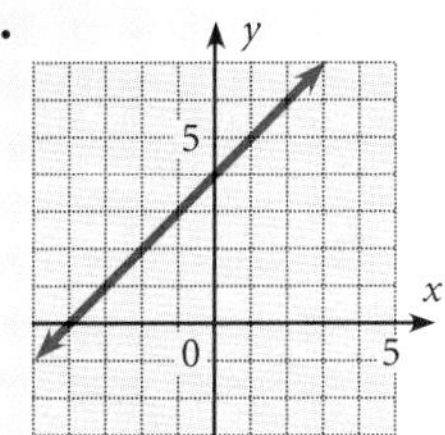

17.

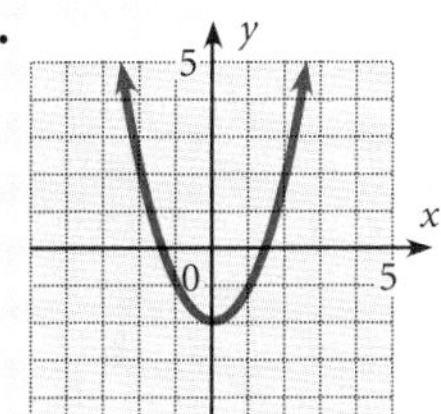

18.

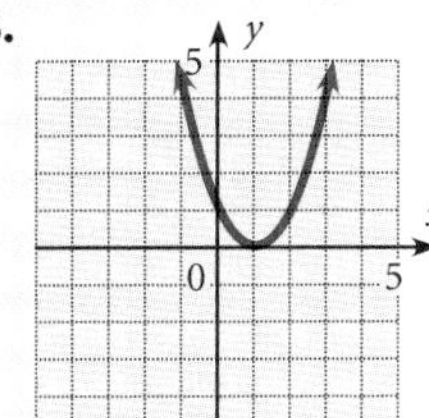

20. It is back to the original orientation. Possible answer:

Ongoing Assessment

Self-Assessment Exercises 1–11 odd, 14

Embedded Assessment Explore Step 2; Exercises 4, 6, 10, 15

Putting Transformations Together

More Math Reasoning

27. a. The equator is its own image.

b. They are the same size.

c. Yes; The north and south poles

d. Distances near the equator are distorted less. The projection is a dilation whose scale factor increases as points are further away from the equator.

28. a. d | f e | i r | w h | j v n m p z u

b.

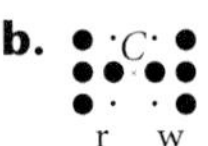

c. A blind person could not distinguish a translation.

d. Possible answer: Letters a through j have no dots on the bottom, letters k through t have only one, while u through z (except for w) have two.

P **Determine whether the transformation shown in each figure below is a reflection, rotation, translation, or dilation. If the transformation is a reflection, identify the line of reflection. If it is a rotation, identify the center and angle of the rotation. If it is a translation, give the translation vector. If it is a dilation, identify the center and scale factor.**

24.

Rotation, (0, 0), 180°

25.

Dilation, center (−4, −1), scale factor $1\frac{1}{2}$

26.

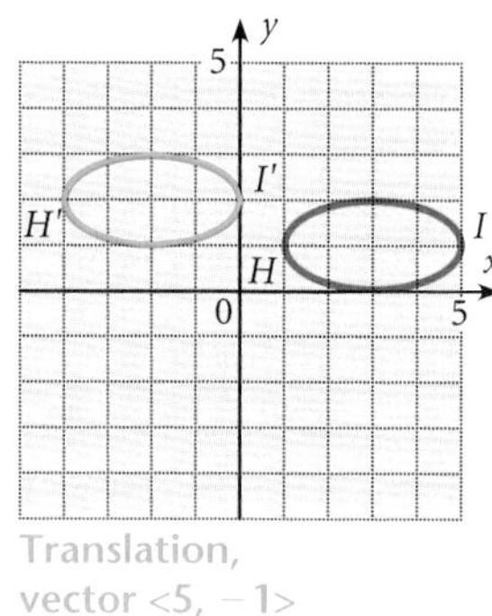

Translation, vector <5, −1>

MORE MATH REASONING

MR **27. Mapping the Globe** One way to make a flat map of the world is based on wrapping a piece of paper around the equator of a globe to form a cylinder, as shown. C is the center of the earth. Every point P on the globe's surface is projected along ray $\overrightarrow{CP}$ to a point P' on the cylinder.

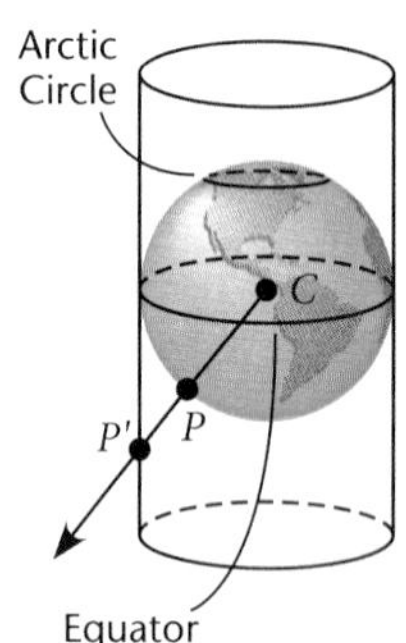

a. Describe the image of the globe's equator.

b. Compare the size of the image of the Arctic Circle to that of the image of the equator.

c. Are there points that have no image? If so, describe them.

d. When the globe is projected onto the cylinder, are distances near the equator distorted more or less than those near the North Pole? Explain.

MR History **28. Transformations in Braille** In the early 1800s, a fifteen-year-old blind student, Louis Braille, devised an alphabet that used raised dots to represent numbers and letters. Books printed in Braille are read with the fingers.

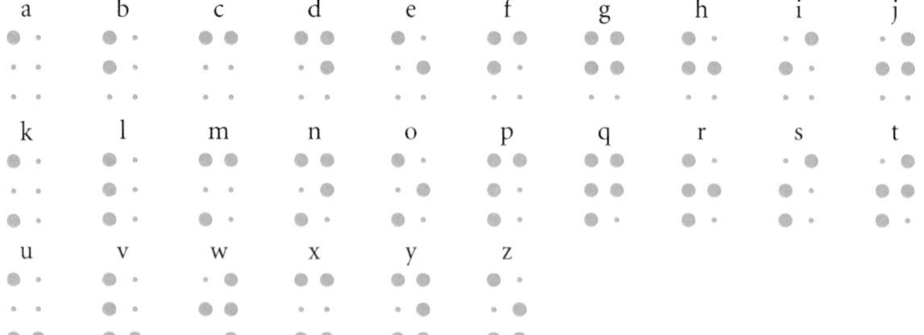

Key

V Vocabulary
P Practice/Skills
R Review
MR Math Reasoning
PS Problem Solving
C Challenge

Refer to the Braille alphabet on page 672 for the following.

a. Some pairs of letters in the Braille alphabet are reflections of each other. Sketch each pair, and show the line of reflection.

b. Some pairs of letters are rotations of each other. Sketch each pair, and indicate the center of rotation.

c. No pairs of letters are translations of each other. Why?

d. Describe any other patterns that Braille may have used in this alphabet.

10-1 PART B Compositions of Transformations

← CONNECT → ***You've transformed geometric figures, but you have mainly done one transformation at a time. Now you will investigate what happens when a figure undergoes more than one transformation.***

You may be familiar with the idea of a composite photograph—one made by superimposing one or more photographs. Because a computer can make a composite photo look like an actual one, photographs are no longer considered good evidence in court. A popular special effect in movies is called *morphing*. This effect changes one image into another. The photos below show a morphing sequence from the movie *Willow*.

The idea of changing one figure into another using a series of transformations is also important in geometry.

DEFINITION

When two or more transformations are performed on a figure, one after another, the result is the **composition** of the transformations.

Student Resources

- **Alternative Lessons** 10-1B
- **Laboratory Manual** 10-1B
- Technology Lab Manual
- **Practice** 10-1B
- **Study Guide and Journal** 10-1B
- **Guía de estudios y Diario** 10-1B
- **Multilingual Handbook**
- **More Look Back** 10-1B
- SAT Preparation

Media Resources

- **Transparency FFM** 10-1B
- Transparency AE
- Teaching Transparency
- **AWSMTest and practice software**
- AWSM Videodisc

PART B At a Glance

Objective

To explore compositions of transformations and identify single transformations equivalent to compositions.

Development

First, students see the definition of the composition of transformations and real-world illustrations of compositions.

In the **Explore,** students find single transformations equivalent to two reflections over intersecting and nonintersecting lines.

Suggested Materials

Student Compass, ruler

Key Terms

Composition

First Five Minutes

Transparency FFM 10-1B

Use a ruler to draw $\overline{FG}$. Then sketch a line. Use a ruler and protractor to draw $\overline{F'G'}$, the reflection image of $\overline{FG}$ over the line.

Motivate

Ask...

- Suppose you walk two blocks due east, turn right, then walk one block due south. How would you use transformations to describe this trip? **A translation of two blocks east, then a 90° clockwise rotation, then a translation of one block south.**

10-1

Algebra	Functions	Discrete Math	Probability	Data/Statistics

Putting Transformations Together

EXPLORE

Reflecting on Compositions

Recommended group size: 4

The Point

To discover that the composition of two reflections over parallel lines is equivalent to a single translation, and that the composition of two reflections over intersecting lines is equivalent to a single rotation.

Look and Listen...

- For students who do not understand the hint.

Ask...

- Have you tried reflecting a triangle over two parallel/intersecting lines?

For Groups That Finish Early

Make a conjecture about the distance of a point from its pre-image after reflection over two parallel lines. **The distance is twice the distance between the lines.**

Follow Up

Ask students to share their conjectures about transformations equivalent to the compositions of two reflections.

Possible Answers

A composition of two reflections over intersecting lines is equivalent to a single rotation. A composition of two reflections over parallel lines is equivalent to a single translation.

COMPOSITIONS OF TRANSFORMATIONS

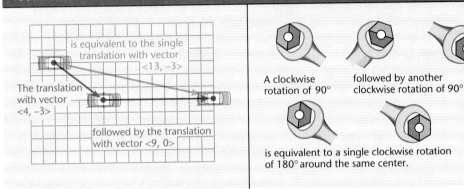

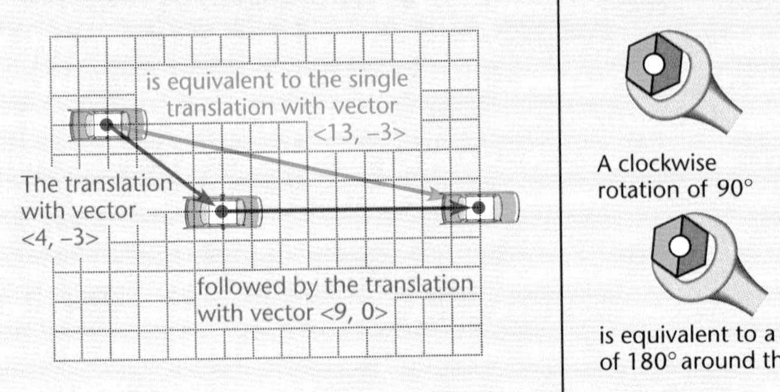

In analyzing a composition of transformations, the original figure is considered the pre-image for the composition, and the final figure is the image.

TRY IT

Find a single transformation equivalent to the composition of each pair of transformations.

a. a 75° counterclockwise rotation with center (2, 1) followed by a 38° counterclockwise rotation with center (2, 1)

b. a translation with vector <−2, 7> followed by a translation with vector <9, 3>

a. 113° counterclockwise rotation with center (2, 1)
b. Translation with vector <7, 10>

We have looked at the compositions of two translations and of two rotations. In the following Explore, you will investigate the composition of two reflections.

EXPLORE: REFLECTING ON COMPOSITIONS

MATERIALS

Compass, Ruler

Find a single transformation that is equivalent to the composition of two reflections. In other words, what happens when you reflect a figure over one line, then reflect the image over a second line? Explain how the position of the lines of reflection affects your results. (Hint: Does it matter whether the two lines of reflection intersect?)

Research Note

Journal writing allows students to reflect on what they are learning, extend ideas, discuss solutions and strategies, and, most important, create meaning for themselves. (Felicita Santiago and George Spanos, "Meeting the NCTM Communication Standards for All Students," *Reaching All Students with Mathematics,* Gilbert Cuevas and Mark Driscoll, eds., p. 138. © 1993 NCTM.)

Some compositions of transformations are equivalent to a single transformation. The ones that you have seen are summarized below.

EQUIVALENT TRANSFORMATIONS

These transformations...	are equivalent to...
Two translations	One translation
Two rotations (same center)	One rotation
Reflections over two parallel lines	One translation
Reflections over two intersecting lines	One rotation

REFLECT

1. Is the composition of two rotations around the same center always equivalent to a single rotation? If so, describe the rotation.
2. Suppose a figure is dilated twice. If the center of the dilations is the same, is their composition equivalent to one of the four basic transformations? If so, which one is it? If not, why not?
3. Reflecting a figure over two intersecting lines is equivalent to a rotation of the figure. Describe the center of the rotation.

Journal 

Reflect 1 and 2 are suitable for journal entries.

REFLECT

Possible Answers

1. Yes. It is equivalent to a rotation around the same center. The angle of rotation is the sum of the two angles if they are both in the same direction and the difference of the angles if they are in opposite directions.
2. The two dilations are equivalent to a single dilation with the same center. The scale factor of the composition is the product of the two scale factors.
3. The center of the rotation is the point of intersection of the lines.

History Connection

In 1914, Garrett Morgan, an African-American inventor, patented a gas mask to protect firefighters. This mask was the basis for the one used by the U.S. Army in World War I. In 1923, after witnessing a horse-automobile collision at an intersection, Morgan invented and patented the first automatic traffic signal.

10-1

Algebra | Functions | Discrete Math | Probability | Data/Statistics

Putting Transformations Together

Part B Exercises

Exercise Notes

Core

17–19. Students work with inverse transformations. Inverses of operations and functions are important concepts in future mathematics courses.

More Math Reasoning

28. Illustrates a connection between vector addition and the composition of translations.

29. Students see whether transformations are or are not commutative.

Exercise Answers

Core

5. 117° clockwise rotation with center at (4, −2)

6. Translation with vector <−2, −4>

7. Translation with vector <8, 0>

8. Sometimes; If the reflections are over parallel lines, then the composition is a translation.

9. Always; The distance is preserved by each isometry, hence the composition is an isometry.

10. Never; The orientation is preserved after each rotation, hence the composition is never a reflection.

11. Isometry; The composition of two isometries is always an isometry.

12. Not an isometry; The dilation alters distances.

13. Isometry; The composition of two isometries is always an isometry.

14. Possible answer: 60° clockwise rotation with center C followed by a dilation with center C and scale factor $\frac{1}{4}$ maps one triangle onto the other. For the vertices to match in the given order, also reflect over the altitude from A to $\overline{BC}$.

Exercises

CORE

V **Getting Started Complete each statement.**

1. Two translations are equivalent to a single ____. Translation

2. Two rotations around the same center are equivalent to a single ____. Rotation

3. Two reflections over intersecting lines are equivalent to a single ____. Rotation

4. Two reflections over parallel lines are equivalent to a single ____. Translation

P **Find a single transformation that is equivalent to the composition of each pair of transformations. If this transformation is a reflection, identify the line of reflection. If it is a rotation, identify the center and angle of the rotation. If it is a translation, give the translation vector. If it is a dilation, identify the center and scale factor.**

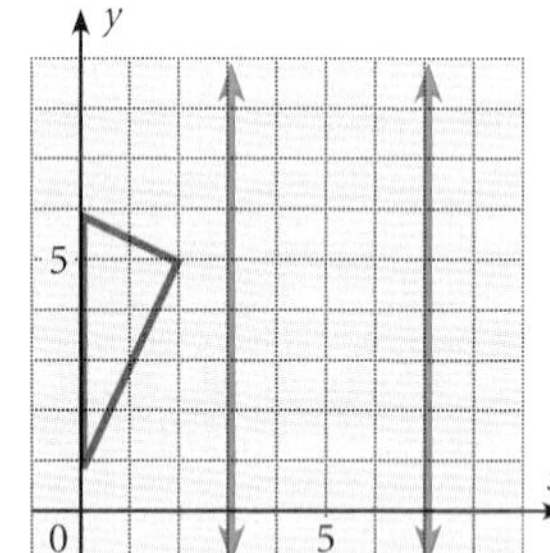

5. a 46° clockwise rotation with center (4, −2) followed by a 71° clockwise rotation with center (4, −2)

6. translation <−4, 3> followed by translation <2, −7>

7. a reflection over the line $x = 3$ followed by a reflection over the line $x = 7$ (Use the figure to help you.)

V **Complete each statement with *always, sometimes,* or *never.* Explain your answers.**

8. The composition of two reflections is ____ equivalent to a translation.

9. The composition of two isometries is ____ an isometry.

10. The composition of two rotations is ____ equivalent to a reflection.

P **Which of the following compositions of transformations are isometries? Explain your answers.**

11. two translations

12. a translation and a dilation

13. two reflections

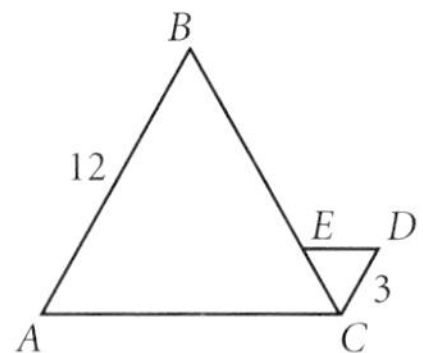

MR **14.** $\triangle BCA$ and $\triangle CDE$ are equilateral. Describe a composition of two or more transformations that maps $\triangle BCA$ onto $\triangle CDE$.

Key

V Vocabulary
P Practice/Skills
R Review
MR Math Reasoning
PS Problem Solving
C Challenge

15. **Sloppy Copy** A malfunctioning copy machine randomly gives copies that are either enlarged by a scale factor of 2 or reduced by a scale factor of $\frac{1}{2}$. If a copy is made, and then a copy is made of that copy, what is the probability that the final copy will be congruent to the original? $\frac{1}{2}$

16. Using the tessellation at the right, describe a transformation or composition of transformations that can be used for the following mappings.
    a. figure 1 onto figure 2
    b. figure 1 onto figure 3
    c. figure 2 onto figure 3

Inverse transformations **are transformations that undo each other. For example, the translation <2, −5> and the translation <−2, 5> are inverse transformations. Find an inverse transformation for each of the following transformations.**

17. translation <−3, 4> Translation <3, −4>

18. a clockwise rotation of 30° around (2, 4)

19. a dilation with scale factor $\frac{3}{2}$ and center at the origin

20. The two triangles at the right are similar.
    a. Describe a composition of transformations that maps the figure on the left onto the figure on the right.
    b. Do you think *any* figure can be mapped onto a similar figure by a series of transformations? Write a brief justification of your answer.
    c. A composition of an isometry and a dilation is called a **similarity transformation.** Explain why this term makes sense.

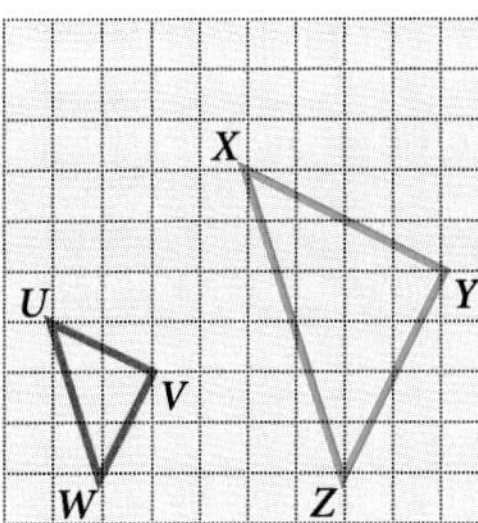

LOOK BACK

21. $AC = 22$ and $DC = 14$. Find the distance of chord $\overline{AC}$ from the center of the circle, D. [8-2] $5\sqrt{3} \approx 8.7$

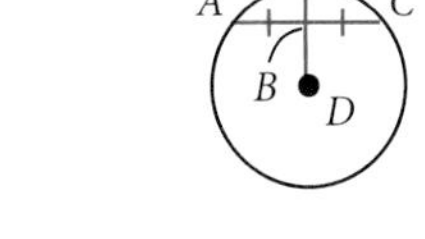

22. **Box Car** A rough design for the body of a car is shown. The design uses two right rectangular prisms.
    a. Find the volume of the car body. [9-2]
    b. Do you think this design is a good one? If so, explain why. If not, describe some changes you would make, and explain why you would make those changes.

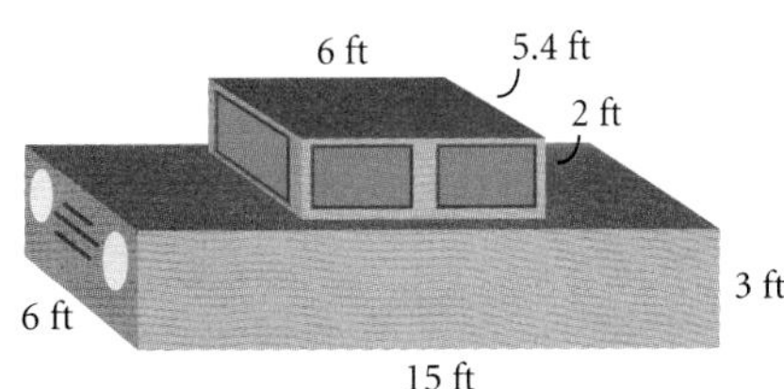

16. a. Translation

b. Possible answer: Translation followed by reflection

c. Possible answer: Translation followed by reflection

18. A counterclockwise rotation of 30° around (2, 4)

19. A dilation with scale factor $\frac{2}{3}$ and center at the origin

20. a. Possible answer: Translation <5, 0> followed by dilation with scale factor 2 and center Z.

b. Yes; Possible answer: A dilation can make the figures the same size, a reflection can give them the same orientation (if necessary), and translation and rotation can slide and twist the figures until they overlap.

c. It makes sense because the image is similar to the original figure.

Look Back

22. a. 334.8 ft^3

b. Possible answer: No, there would be too much wind resistance. Rounding the corners will make the car more aerodynamic.

Ongoing Assessment

Self-Assessment Exercises 1–19 odd

Embedded Assessment Try It a; Exercises 6, 12, 16, 18

Putting Transformations Together

More Practice

25. Isometry; The composition of two isometries is always an isometry.

26. Isometry; The composition of two isometries is always an isometry.

27. Not an isometry; The dilation does not preserve distance.

More Math Reasoning

28. a. $\overrightarrow{EF} + \overrightarrow{FG} = \overrightarrow{EG}$

b. Yes. The vector describing the composition of two translations is given by the sum of the translation vectors.

29. No. Possible answer: Consider reflections over two parallel lines.

MORE PRACTICE

P **Find a single transformation that is equivalent to the composition of each pair of transformations. If this transformation is a reflection, identify the line of reflection. If it is a rotation, identify the center and angle of the rotation. If it is a translation, give the translation vector. If it is a dilation, identify the center and scale factor.**

23. translation <3, −6> followed by translation <0, 5> Translation <3, −1>

24. a 102° counterclockwise rotation with center (2, −3) followed by a 219° clockwise rotation with center (2, −3) 117° clockwise rotation with center (2, −3)

P **Which of the following compositions of transformations are isometries? Explain your answers.**

25. two rotations

26. a translation and a rotation

27. a dilation and a reflection

MORE MATH REASONING

R, MR **28. a.** The figure at the right shows three vectors. Write a vector-sum equation based on the figure.

b. Are there any similarities between the composition of transformations and vector addition? If so, explain the connection.

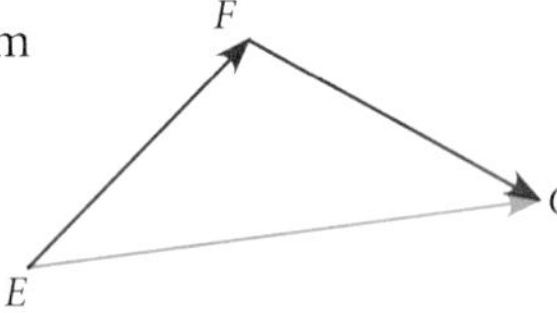

C, MR **29.** Are transformations commutative? In other words, if you perform any two transformations on a figure, do you get the same result regardless of the order of the transformations? Write a brief explanation of the method you used to solve this problem.

PS **30.** A line is an axis of symmetry of a cube if a rotation (of less than 360°) of the cube about the line maps the cube to itself. For example, line n is one line of symmetry for the cube shown. How many different lines of symmetry does a cube have? 13

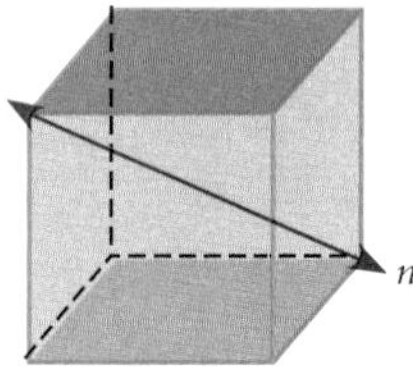

Key

V Vocabulary
P Practice/Skills
R Review
MR Math Reasoning
PS Problem Solving
C Challenge

Technology Note

If students use a graphing utility in the **Explore** on page 679, they should graph only two or three equations at a time, so they can see clearly what is happening.

10-1 PART C Transformations of Algebraic Functions

← CONNECT → *You've already studied functions in algebra. Now you will examine transformations of functions. You will investigate how a change in an equation affects the graph of the equation.*

Although you have usually performed transformations on geometric figures, transformations can also give you insights into the graphs of algebraic functions.

Graphs of whole families of functions are transformations of the graph of a **parent equation.** For example, the graph of any linear equation can be thought of as a transformation or composition of transformations of the parent equation $y = x$.

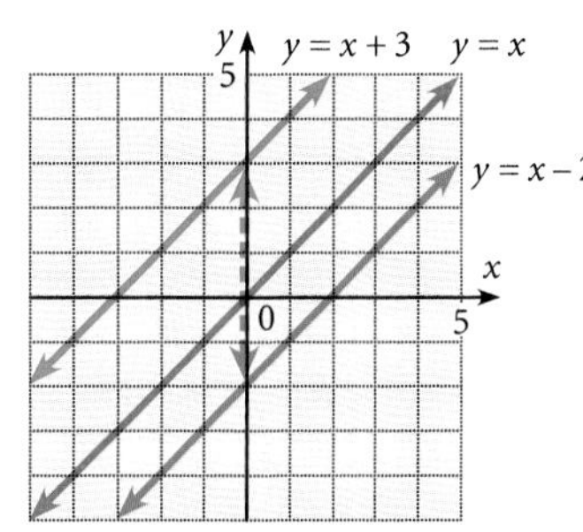

EXPLORE: PARABOLA MOVING CO.

MATERIALS

Graph paper
Graphing utility (optional)

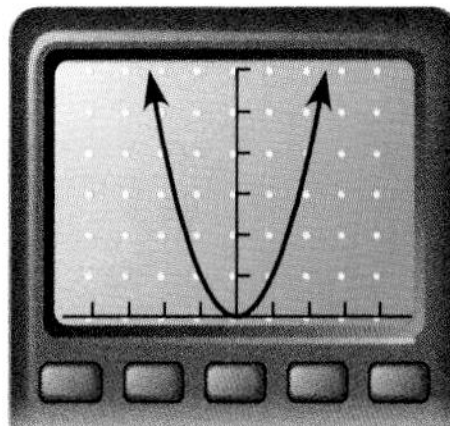

1. On a graphing utility or graph paper, draw an accurate graph of the parent equation $y = x^2$. Then describe the characteristics of the graph. Where is its vertex (turning point)? Does the curve turn upwards (∪) or turn downwards (∩)? Are there any symmetry lines?
2. On the same screen or sheet of paper, graph some other equations of the form $y = x^2 + k$ (where $k \neq 0$), such as $y = x^2 + 2$ and $y = x^2 - 3$. Notice where the vertex of each graph is. Use transformations to compare the graph of $y = x^2 + k$ to the graph of the parent equation $y = x^2$.
3. On a new screen or sheet of paper, graph $y = x^2$ and $y = -x^2$. Use transformations to describe the difference between the graphs. If you need more evidence, graph other pairs of equations, like $y = x^3$ and $y = -x^3$.
4. The graph of the function $y = -x^2 + k$ can be described as a composition of two transformations of the parent equation $y = x^2$. Identify the two transformations. Which one is associated with the negative sign? Which one is associated with the k term?

Student Resources

- Alternative Lessons 10-1C
- Laboratory Manual 10-1C
- Technology Lab Manual
- Practice 10-1C
- Study Guide and Journal 10-1C
- Guía de estudios y Diario 10-1C
- Multilingual Handbook
- More Look Ahead 10-1C
- SAT Preparation

Media Resources

- Transparency FFM 10-1C
- Transparency AE 10-1C
- Teaching Transparency
- AWSMTest and practice software
- AWSM Videodisc

PART C At a Glance

Objective

To use transformations to interpret the effects of constants on the graphs of equations.

Development

In the **Explore,** students see that graphs of families of functions are transformations of each other and how transformations are related to differences in their equations.

In an **Example,** students see how to apply their observations to graphs of general functions.

Suggested Materials

Student Graph paper, graphing utility

Teacher Graph paper transparency

Key Terms

Parent equation

First Five Minutes

Transparency FFM 10-1C

Evaluate each expression for $x = -2$.

1. x^2 4 **2.** $x^2 - 5$ −1

3. $-x^2 + 10$ 6 **4.** $(x - 7)^2$ 81

Motivate

Ask...

- Use two different transformations to describe the relationship between the graphs of the lines $x = 4$ and $x = 10$. **$x = 10$ is: translation of $x = 4$ six units right; reflection of $x = 4$ over $x = 7$**

EXPLORE

Parabola Moving Co.

Recommended group size: 4

The Point

To discover that the graph of $y = x^2 + k$ is a translation of the graph of $y = x^2$, that $y = -x^2$ is a reflection of $y = x^2$, and that other related graphs can be described by compositions of transformations.

10-1

Putting Transformations Together

Look and Listen...

- For students who are not drawing the graphs accurately.
- For students who are having difficulty describing the changes in the graphs.

Ask...

- (For Step 2) What is the distance between the vertices of these graphs? Compare this to the distance between two other corresponding points.

For Groups That Finish Early

Graph equations like $y = (x + 2)^2$ and $y = (x - 4)^2$. Compare these graphs to that of the parent equation, using transformations. **The graph of $y = (x - h)^2$ is translated h units to the right.**

Follow Up

Have students come to the board and graph equations of the form $y = \pm x^2 \pm k$. Have them explain how they drew their graphs.

Possible Answers

1. The vertex is at (0, 0), and the graph turns upwards.
2. The graph of $y = x^2 + k$ is translated k units vertically.
3. The graph of $y = -x^2$ is reflected over the x-axis.
4. The graph of $y = -x^2 + k$ is a reflection of $y = x^2$ over the x-axis (associated with the negative sign), followed by a translation of k units vertically (associated with the k term).

ALTERNATE EXAMPLE

Transparency AE 10-1C

Journal

Explore 4, **Reflect** 1, and **Exercise** 9 are suitable for journal entries.

REFLECT

Possible Answers

See Additional Answers p. T686.

TRY IT

Sketch the graph of $y = x^2$. Starting with this graph as a guide, use transformations to help you sketch the graph of each of the following on the same set of axes.

a. $y = x^2 + 1$ **b.** $y = -x^2 + 1$ **c.** $y = -x^2 - 3$

EXAMPLE

The graph of a parent equation, $y = \lozenge$, is shown at the right. With this graph as a guide, sketch graphs of the equations $y = -\lozenge$ and $y = -\lozenge - 1$.

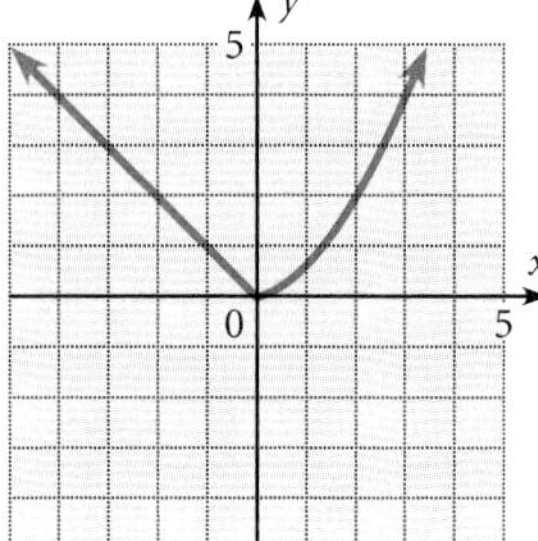

The negative sign in front of the $\lozenge$ in $y = -\lozenge$ tells us that its graph is a reflection of the parent equation over the x-axis. The -1 in the equation $y = -\lozenge - 1$ tells us that the reflected graph is then translated down 1 unit.

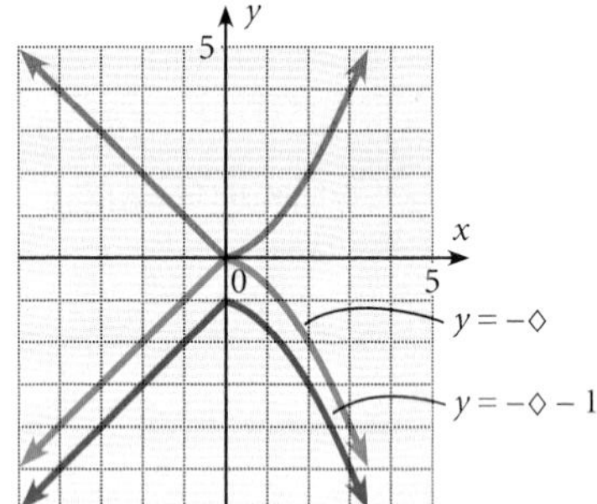

REFLECT

1. What is the vertex of $y = x^2 + k$? How can you tell whether the graph of this equation turns upwards or downwards?
2. Suppose that the point (0, 1) is on the graph of the parent equation $y = \mu$. Give the coordinates of a point on the graph of the equation $y = \mu + 4$.
3. Suppose you are given the graph of $y = \psi$ and need to sketch the graph of $y = -\psi + 2$. Do you get different graphs if you begin by reflecting the graph of $y = \psi$ and then translating the result than if you begin by translating the graph of $y = \psi$ and then reflecting the result? Explain.

Alert

Students may need a reminder of what a *function* is. You can refer them to the *Glossary* to review this term, or give them a more informal definition, like "A function has only one y-value for each x-value."

Exercises

CORE

1. Getting Started Sketch the graph of $y = x$. With this graph as a guide, use transformations to help you sketch the graph of each of the following on the same set of axes. Label each graph.

a. $y = x + 2$ **b.** $y = x - 3$ **c.** $y = -x + 1$

2. Sketch the graph of $y = x^2$. With this graph as a guide, use transformations to help you sketch the graph of each of the following on the same set of axes. Label each graph.

a. $y = x^2 + 4$ **b.** $y = -x^2 - 2$ **c.** $y = x^2 - 3$

3. The graph of the parent equation for absolute value functions, $y = |x|$, is shown at the right. Using this graph as a guide, sketch graphs of the following on the same set of axes. Label each graph.

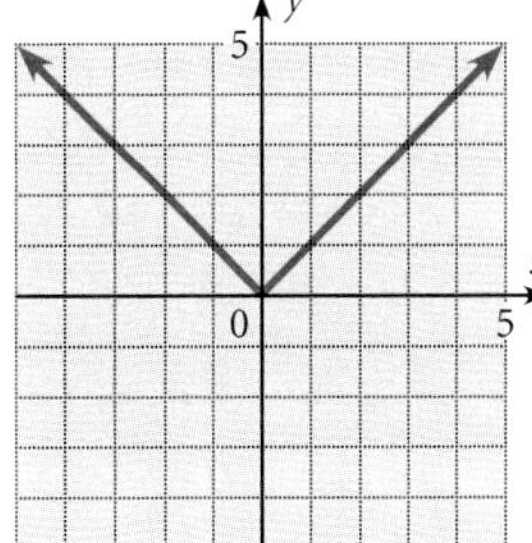

a. $y = |x| + 3$ **b.** $y = -|x|$

c. $y = -|x| - 2$

d. Explain how you used the parent equation to help make your sketches.

Write the word or phrase that correctly completes each statement.

4. The graph of $y = x^2 + 2$ is a ___ of the graph of $y = x^2$. Translation

5. The graph of $y = -x^2$ is a ___ of the graph of $y = x^2$. Reflection

6. Many Happy Returns Two students have started their own birthday-card business. They need $40 for supplies to get started, and they charge $2 for each hand-drawn card.

a. Write an equation that expresses their profit, P, in terms of the number of cards they sell, n. Sketch the graph of this equation.

b. They find that the supplies they need are on sale for 40% off. Write a new equation for their profit.

c. Sketch the graph of this equation on the same axes. Use transformations to describe the difference between the graphs, and explain why this makes sense.

7. a. Draw a graph of each of the following three equations on the same set of axes. Label each graph.

i. $y = x^2$ **ii.** $y = (x + 2)^2$ **iii.** $y = (x - 3)^2$

b. Compare the graph of $y = (x + h)^2$ to the graph of $y = x^2$.

c. Using transformations, make a quick sketch of the graph of each of the following equations on the same set of axes. Label each graph.

i. $y = (x + 3)^2$ **ii.** $y = (x - 2)^2$ **iii.** $y = (x - 2)^2 + 3$

Ongoing Assessment

Vocabulary
Practice/Skills
Review
Math Reasoning
Problem Solving
Challenge

Self-Assessment Exercises 1, 3, 4, 5, 6

Embedded Assessment Exercises 2, 7, 8, 9

TRY IT

Answers

a–c.

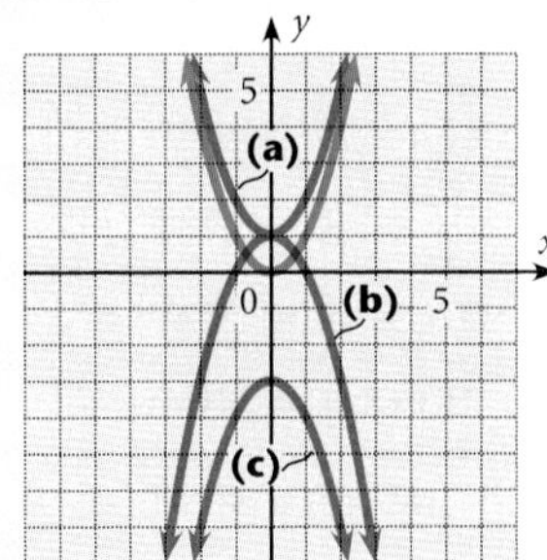

Part C Exercises

Exercise Notes

Core

6. and 9. Show equations in business contexts. Students will see that an additive constant in equations modeling profit or cost often represents a fixed cost.

7. Students discover the effect of h on the graph of $y = (x + h)^2$.

Look Ahead

These exercises review rotational and line symmetry. Students will examine frieze and wallpaper patterns for these and other symmetries in 10-2.

More Math Reasoning

17. Students discover the effect of a on the graph of the equation $y = a(x + h)^2 + k$.

Exercise Answers

Core

1. a–c.

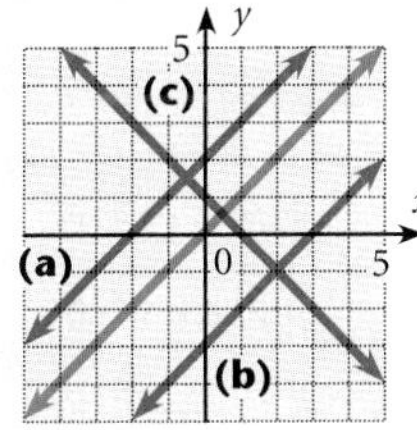

2. a–c.

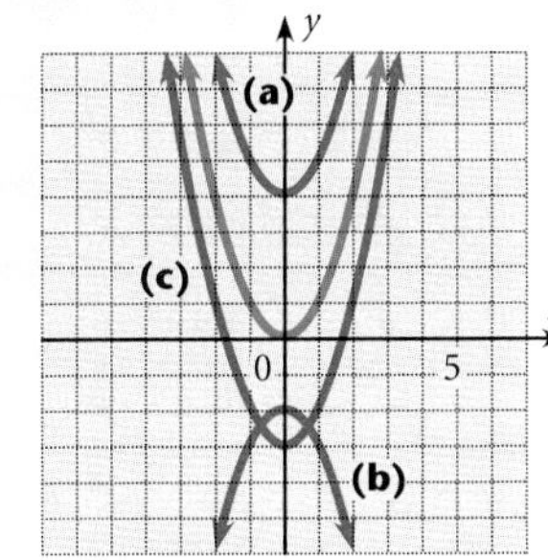

10-1

Putting Transformations Together

3. a–c.

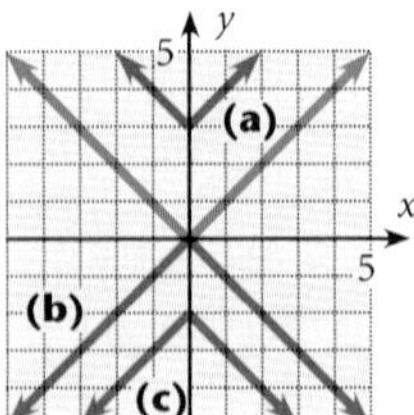

d. Possible answer: The graph of (a) is the graph of $y = |x|$ translated by <0, 3>. The graph of (b) is a reflection of the graph of $y = |x|$ across the x-axis. The graph of (c) is a reflection of the graph of $y = |x|$ across the x-axis followed by the translation <0, −2>.

6. a–c.

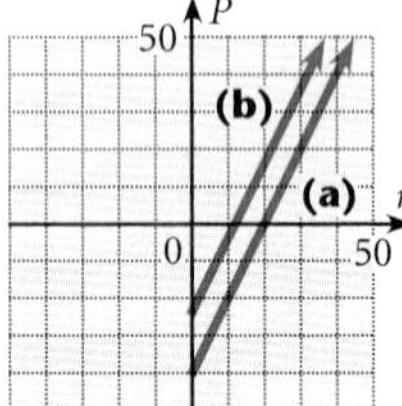

a. $P = 2n - 40$

b. $P = 2n - 24$

c. Translate original graph by <0, 16>, so the y-intercept is at −24. Makes sense because \$24 is 60% of \$40.

7. a.

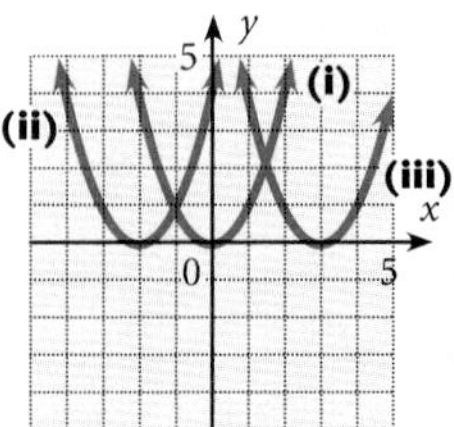

b. The graph of $y = (x + h)^2$ is a translation of the graph of $y = x^2$ by <−h, 0>.

c.

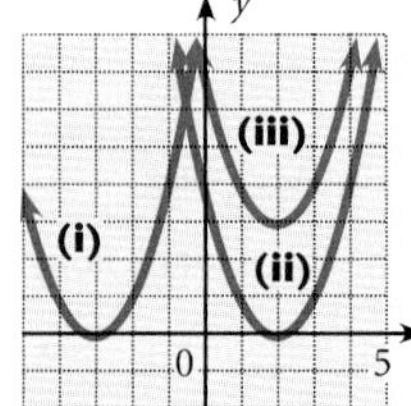

8, 9, 14–18.
See Additional Answers p. T686.

P **8.** The graph of a parent equation, y = ¤, is shown at the right. Using this graph as a guide, sketch graphs of the following on the same set of axes. Label each graph.

a. y = ¤ − 3
b. y = −¤ + 3
c. y = −¤ + 1

PS, MR *Industry* **9.** Suppose that a company manufacturing an item discovers that the cost, c, in hundreds of dollars, of producing n items is approximated by the equation $c = \sqrt{n} + 20$.

a. Sketch a graph of this equation.
b. Find the average cost to produce one item for each of the following production levels.
i. $n = 1$ **ii.** $n = 25$ **iii.** $n = 160$
c. Under this model, does the average cost to produce the item increase, decrease, or stay the same as production levels increase? Do you think this is usually true for manufacturing companies?
d. What do you think the number 20 represents in the cost equation $c = \sqrt{n} + 20$?

LOOK AHEAD

R **Match each letter on the left with the type(s) of symmetry it exhibits on the right.**

10. H a, b, c (a) rotational symmetry
11. A b (b) vertical line symmetry
12. S a (c) horizontal line symmetry
13. K c

MORE PRACTICE

P, MR **14.** The graph of the parent equation for square-root functions, $y = \sqrt{x}$, is shown at the right. Using this equation as a guide, sketch graphs of the following on the same set of axes. Label each graph.

a. $y = \sqrt{x} + 2$ **b.** $y = -\sqrt{x}$
c. $y = -\sqrt{x} - 4$
d. Explain how you used the parent equation to help make your sketches.

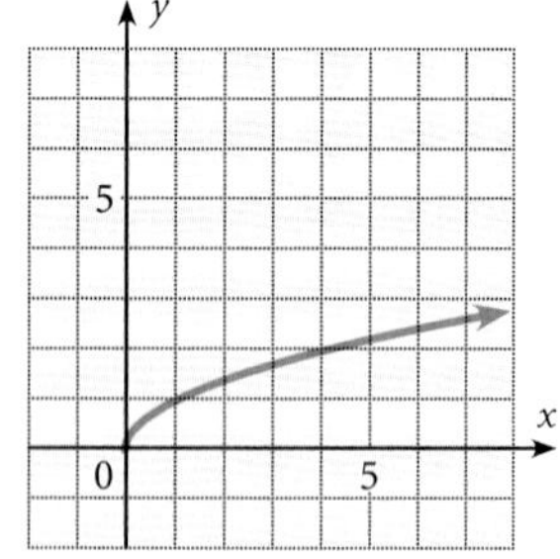

Key

V Vocabulary
P Practice/Skills
R Review
MR Math Reasoning
PS Problem Solving
C Challenge

15. Sketch the graph of $y = x^2$. With this graph as a guide, use transformations to help you sketch the graph of each of the following on the same set of axes. Label each graph.

a. $y = x^2 + 3$ **b.** $y = x^2 - 2$ **c.** $y = -x^2 - 4$

16. Make a sketch of the graph of each of the following equations on the same set of axes. Label each graph.

a. $y = (x + 1)^2$ **b.** $y = (x - 3)^2$ **c.** $y = (x - 1)^2 + 2$

MORE MATH REASONING

17. a. Sketch graphs of each of the following three equations on the same set of axes. Label each graph.

i. $y = x^2$ **ii.** $y = 3x^2$ **iii.** $y = \frac{1}{2}x^2$

b. In your own words, compare the graph of $y = ax^2$ to the graph of $y = x^2$.

c. Make a sketch of the graph of each of the following equations on the same set of axes. Label each graph.

i. $y = 2x^2$ **ii.** $y = 2x^2 + 3$ **iii.** $y = -2x^2 + 3$

d. Describe how the graph of any equation of the form $y = a(x + h)^2 + k$ is related to the graph of $y = x^2$.

18. Parabolic Profit Suppose the profit, P, that a small company makes when it manufactures n items is given by $P = -(n - 600)^2 + 250{,}000$. Find the number of items that the company should manufacture so that it makes the maximum possible profit. What is this maximum profit? Describe how you solved the problem.

10-1 PART D Making Connections

← CONNECT → ***You've looked at combinations of the four basic transformations. These combinations can help you understand many things, from the graphs of algebraic equations to the mechanisms in a car.***

When Mark Thomas's students build their paper cars, they use the same rack-and-pinion steering mechanism found in real automobiles, so that the cars can be steered. The following chart provides an overview of the rack-and-pinion steering system.

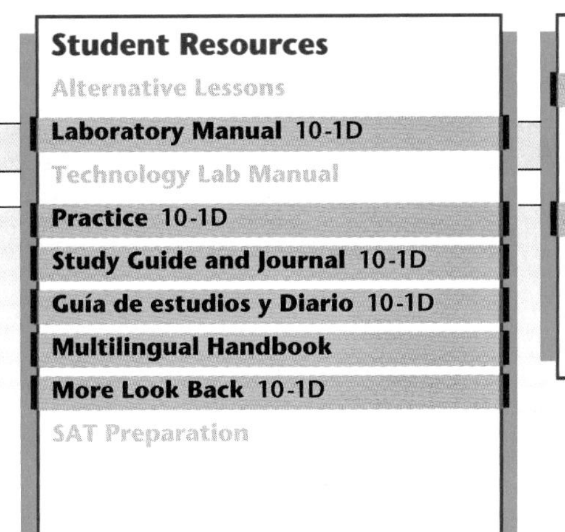
Student Resources

Alternative Lessons
Laboratory Manual 10-1D
Technology Lab Manual
Practice 10-1D
Study Guide and Journal 10-1D
Guía de estudios y Diario 10-1D
Multilingual Handbook
More Look Back 10-1D
SAT Preparation

Media Resources

Transparency FFM 10-1D
Transparency AE
Teaching Transparency
AWSMTest and practice software
AWSM Videodisc

PART D At a Glance

Objective

To show how transformations and their compositions are important in automobile mechanisms.

Development

In the **Explore,** students use transformations to describe the steering mechanism in a car.

First Five Minutes

Transparency FFM 10-1D

Describe a single transformation equivalent to the composition of each pair of transformations. Be as specific as you can.

1. Two translations. **One translation.**

2. Two clockwise rotations with the same center. **One clockwise rotation with that center. The measure of the angle of rotation is the sum of the individual angle measures.**

3. Two reflections over intersecting lines. **One rotation with its center at the point of intersection.**

4. Two reflections over parallel lines. **One translation.**

EXPLORE

Turning the Wheel Turns the Wheels

Recommended group size: 4

The Point

To use transformations to describe a rack-and-pinion steering mechanism and other automobile movements and mechanisms.

10-1

Algebra | Functions | Discrete Math | Probability | Data/Statistics

Putting Transformations Together

Look and Listen...

- For students who do not see how the parts of the mechanism interact.
- For students who confuse rotations of the wheels that move the car with rotations of the wheels that make the car turn left or right.

Ask...

- Why do the teeth in the pinion move the rack to the left or right?
- Does a car wheel rotate in only one way? Can you give me an example of two different rotations of a wheel?

For Groups That Finish Early

Use transformations to describe the movements or mechanisms of a bicycle. The pedals rotate a gear that translates the chain. The chain rotates a gear that is attached to a wheel. As the wheel rotates, the bicycle is translated.

Follow Up

Ask one student or group to present a description of the rack-and-pinion system.

Possible Answers

1. Rotating the steering wheel rotates the steering column and pinion. Rotation of the pinion translates the rack (a counterclockwise rotation pushes it to the right). The track rods push the steering arms, which rotate. (When the track rods move to the right, the steering arms pivot counterclockwise—to the left.) These are attached to the wheels, which rotate in the same direction.
2. Possible answers range from "The car translates when it moves" to explaining how translations of the pistons rotate a shaft that (eventually) causes a rotation of the wheels.

RACK-AND-PINION STEERING

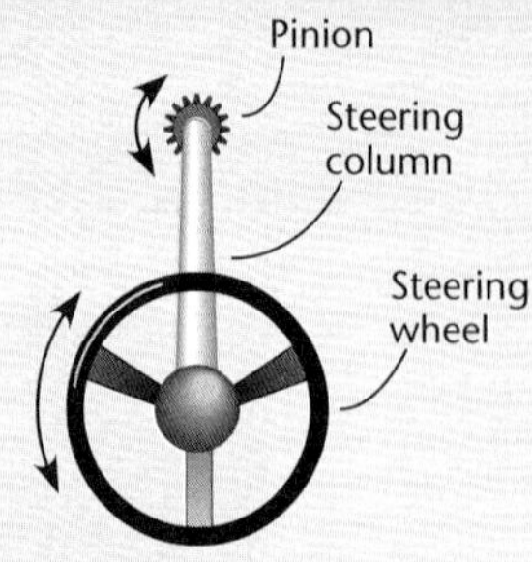

When you turn the steering wheel in a car, the steering column attached to the wheel also turns. The steering column turns a pinion (a small gear), as shown.

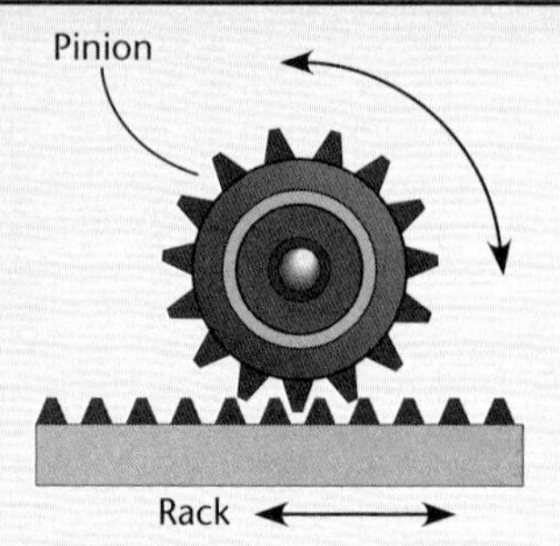

The teeth of the pinion are meshed in the teeth of a rack, as shown at the right. When the pinion turns, it shifts the rack to the left or right.

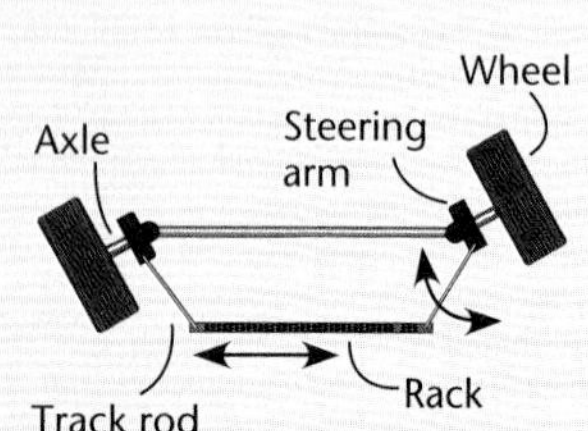

The rack is linked to a track rod, which, in turn, is connected to a steering arm that turns the axles of the front wheels. When the rack moves, the wheels pivot.

In the following Explore, you will see how transformations can be used to understand and describe the rack-and-pinion steering mechanism of a car.

EXPLORE: TURNING THE WHEEL TURNS THE WHEELS

The complete rack-and-pinion steering system is shown at the right.

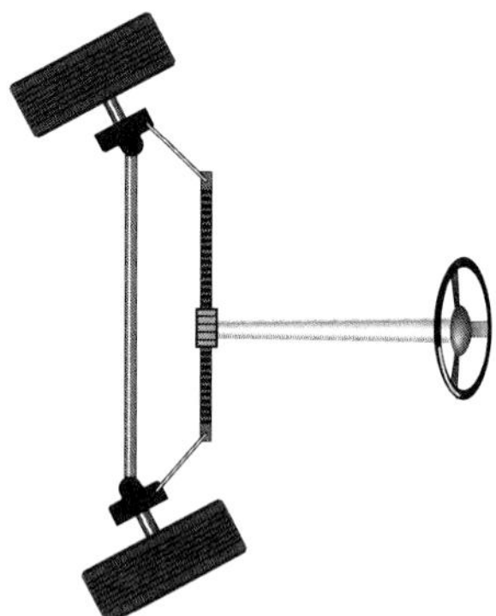

1. Describe all the transformations that occur when a rack-and-pinion steering mechanism is at work. To impress your teacher, explain why turning the steering wheel to the left (counterclockwise) makes the car turn to the left.
2. Describe any of the other movements or mechanisms of a car using the language of transformations. (For example, sliding the front seat backward is a translation.) A mechanically inclined member of your class may be able to explain how movements in the engine make the car go forward.

REFLECT

1. The person at the right is using a pulley to lift a box. Use transformations and the concept of compositions of transformations to explain how a pulley works.
2. Give as many examples as you can of compositions of two transformations that are equivalent to a single transformation.
3. Summarize how changes in equations result in transformations of their graphs. Give examples to illustrate your summary.

Self-Assessment

Find a single transformation equivalent to the composition of each pair of transformations described. Be as specific as you can.

1. a clockwise rotation of $x°$ followed by a clockwise rotation of $y°$ around the same center Clockwise rotation of $(x + y)°$ around the same center.
2. translation <*a*, *b*> followed by translation <*c*, *d*> Translation <*a* + *c*, *b* + *d*>
3. a reflection over line *m* followed by a reflection over line *n*, which is perpendicular to line *m* A 180° rotation around the intersection point of the two lines

Which of the following compositions of transformations are isometries? Explain.

4. a translation and a reflection
5. a rotation and a dilation
6. two rotations
7. **More Power to You** Acme Rentals and Begone Cleaners have office buildings located as shown. The power company needs to locate a transformer on a main power line, ℓ, to serve both Acme and Begone. Copy the figure, and show where the power company should locate the transformer to minimize the amount of wire needed. Explain how you found this point.

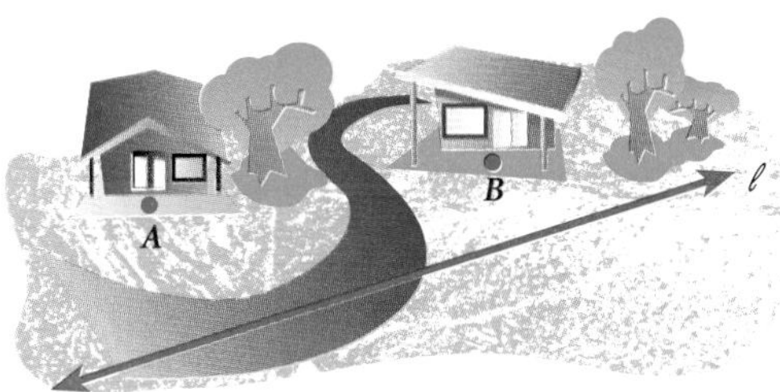

ey

- Vocabulary
- Practice/Skills
- Review
- R Math Reasoning
- S Problem Solving
- Challenge

Portfolio

Have students select items from their work that demonstrate their understanding of the material in 10-1.

You may want to have students include their favorite real-world application of transformations, an **Exercise** where they found a single transformation equivalent to a composition of transformations, and an **Exercise** where they used transformations to sketch the graph of an equation.

REFLECT

Possible Answers

1. The person pulls the rope, translating it downward. Translation of the rope rotates the wheel. This translates the rope on the other side of the pulley upward, lifting the box.
2. See chart, page 675.
3. If the parent equation is $y = \phi$: $y = -\phi$ is a reflection of the graph of the parent equation over the x-axis.

   $y = \phi + k$ is a translation of the graph of the parent equation k units up or down. When k is positive, the translation is up.

   Also, if a constant is added to the x-value directly, the effect is a translation to the left or right. When k is positive, the translation is to the left.

Self-Assessment

Exercise Notes

17. Shows a connection between transformations and functions.
18. Students see a contrived transformation. Repeated application of this transformation moves points closer and closer to the point (1, 1). This movement gives students more insight into the concept of a limit.

10-1

Putting Transformations Together

Self-Assessment Answers

4. Isometry; The composition of two isometries is always an isometry.

5. Not an isometry; Dilation does not preserve distance.

6. Isometry; The composition of two isometries is always an isometry.

7.

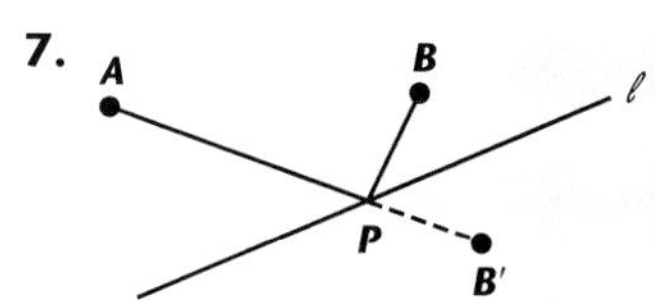

Find B' by reflecting B over ℓ. Locate transformer at P, point of intersection of $\overline{AB'}$ and ℓ.

8–10.

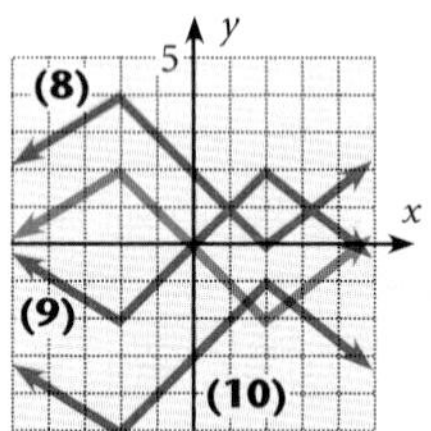

11. The graph of (8) was a translation <0, 2>. The graph of (9) was a reflection across the x-axis. The graph of (10) was a reflection across the x-axis followed by a translation <0, −3>.

17. All are functions because every point on the pre-image maps onto only one point on the image.

18. a. Points with negative coordinates; Square roots of negative numbers are not defined for real numbers.

b. $(81, 16) \rightarrow (9, 4) \rightarrow (3, 2) \rightarrow (1.7, 1.4)$; The point seems to be going to (1, 1). No. As you continue to rootate, the coordinates will approach 1, but never reach it.

c. No, distance is not preserved.

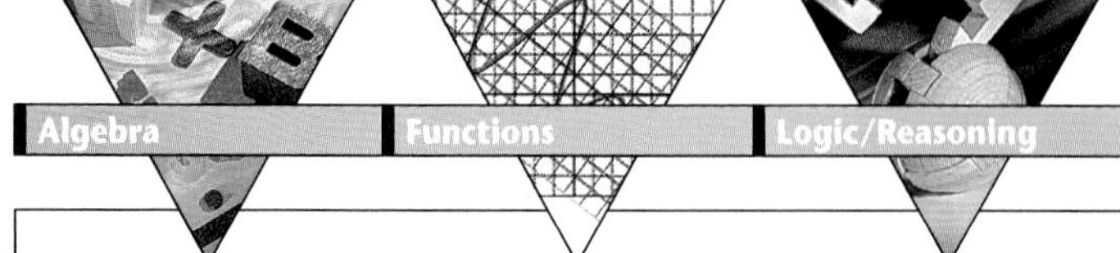

P **The graph of a function $y = p$ is shown at the right. Using this graph as a guide, make a sketch of the graph of each of the following equations on the same set of axes. Label each graph.**

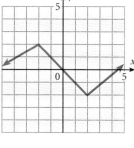

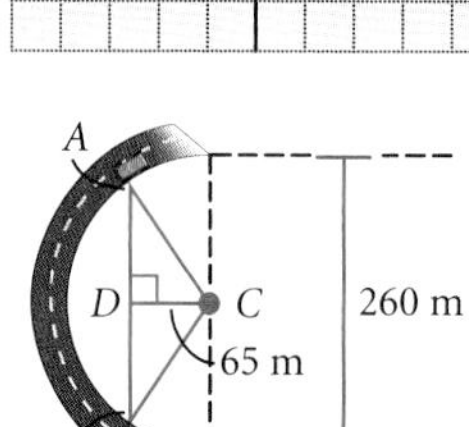

8. $y = p + 2$ **9.** $y = -p$ **10.** $y = -p - 3$

MR **11.** Explain how you used transformations to sketch each of your graphs in Exercises 8–10.

R, PS **12.** A car is being tested on a track with semicircular turns. The car is at point A on the turn with center C. How much longer is arc $\widehat{AB}$ than chord $\overline{AB}$? (Hint: Use your knowledge of right triangles to find AB and $m\angle ACB$. Then use proportional thinking to find the length of $\widehat{AB}$.) [8-2]
≈ 47.1 m

A
D
C
65 m
260 m
B

R **Find the surface area and volume of each figure. Round answers to the nearest tenth. [9-1, 9-2]**

13.

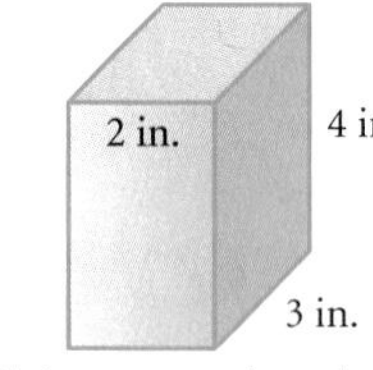

Right rectangular prism
52 in.²; 24 in.³

14.

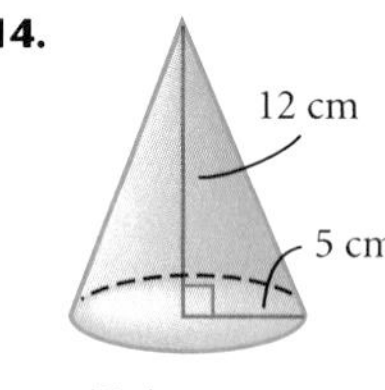

Right cone
282.7 cm²; 314.2 cm³

15.

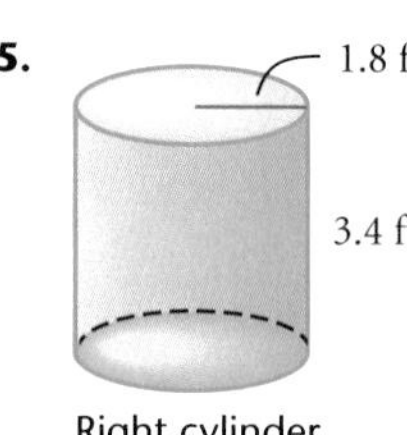

Right cylinder
58.8 ft²; 34.6 ft³

16.

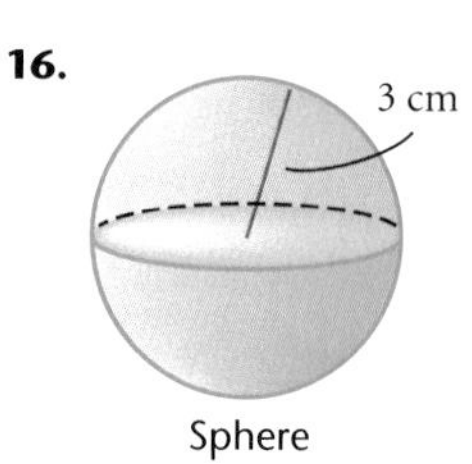

Sphere
113.1 cm²; 113.1 cm³

MR **17.** An equation represents a function if every value you substitute for one of the variables (called the *independent variable*) gives only one value for the other variable (the *dependent variable*).

Are the transformations you've studied functions? In other words, does every point on the pre-image always map onto just one point on the image, or are there times when a pre-image point corresponds to two or more image points? If you think reflections, rotations, translations, and dilations are functions, explain why. If not, explain why not.

MR, C **18. Rooting for Transformations** Suppose you invent a new transformation, called *rootation.* The image of any point (x, y) is the point $(\sqrt{x}, \sqrt{y})$.

a. Are there any points that cannot be rootated? If so, describe them, and tell why they cannot be rootated.

b. Investigate what happens when you perform an infinite number of rootations on a point. Start with the point (81, 16) and rootate it several times. Describe what happens as you continue rootating. Where does the point seem to be going? Will it ever get there? Why or why not?

c. Is rootation an isometry? Explain.

Assessment Resources

Quiz 10-1
Chapter Assessment Form A
Chapter Assessment Form B
Chapter Alternative Assessment
Mid-Year Assessment
End-of-Year Assessment
AWSMTest and practice software

Ongoing Assessment

Self-Assessment Self-Assessment Exercises

Embedded Assessment Explore Steps 1, 2; Refle
1, 2, 3

ADDITIONAL ANSWERS

10-1 Part C Reflect

1. The vertex is at $(0, k)$, and the graph turns upwards because the coefficient of x^2 is positive.

2. (0, 5)

3. You get the same graph. (If translation is done first, the line of reflection must be translated to $y = 2$.)

10-1 Part C Exercises

8. a–c.

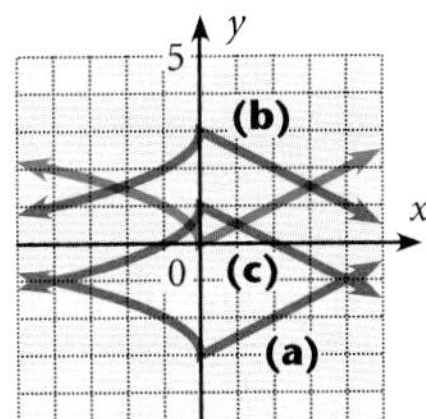

9. a.

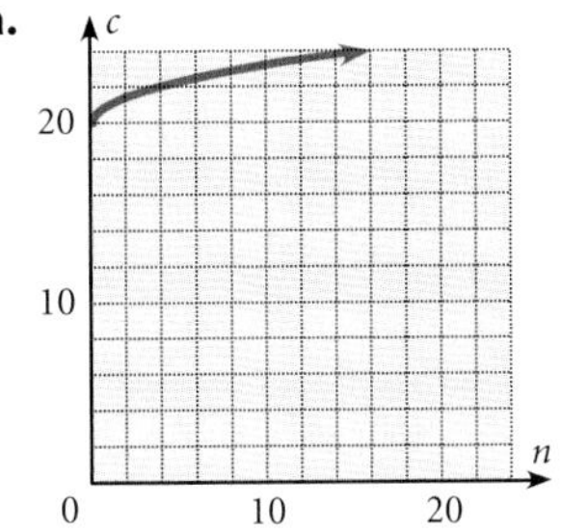

b. i. \$2100

ii. \$100

iii. \$20.41

c. Decrease; Yes

d. Possible answer: The cost of starting up production.

10-1 Part C Exercises

More Practice

14. a–c.

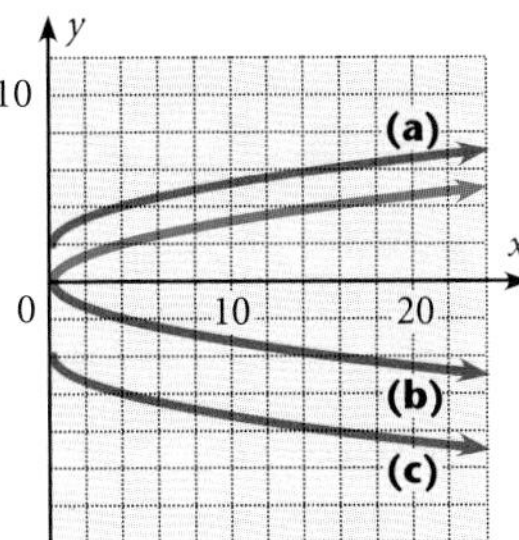

d. Graph (a) is translated 2 units up, graph (b) is reflected, graph (c) is reflected and translated 4 units down.

15. a–c.

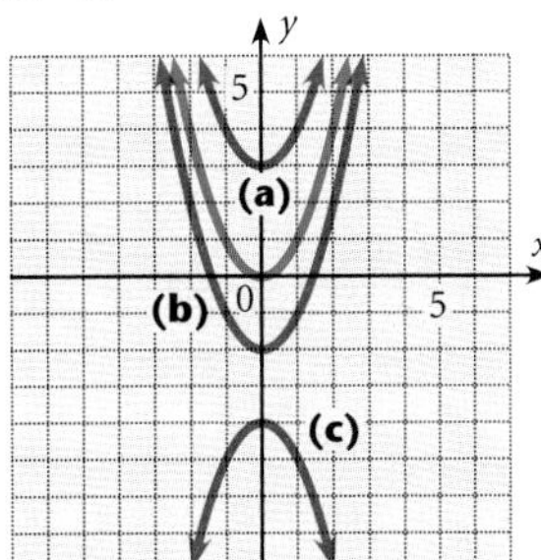

16. a–c.

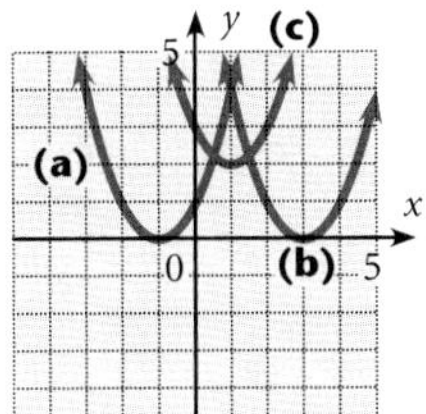

10-1 Part C Exercises

More Math Reasoning

17. a.

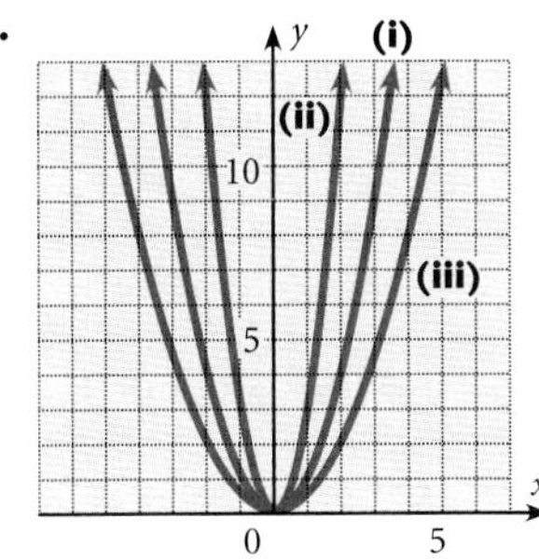

b. $y = ax^2$ has the same vertex as $y = x^2$. Its width is inversely related to $|a|$.

c.

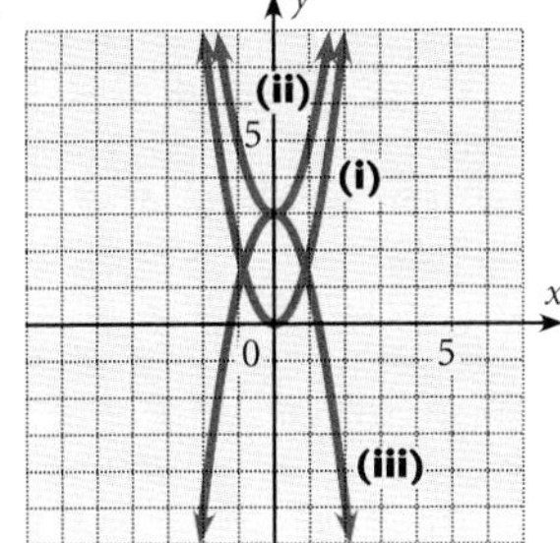

d. h translates the graph by $<-h, 0>$ and k translates by $<0, k>$, so the total translation is $<-h, k>$. a affects the width of the parabola. If a is negative, it is a reflection of $y = x^2$ across the x-axis.

18. Possible answer: $n = 600$, $P = 250{,}000$. The graph of the profit function is a translation of the graph $P = -n^2$ by $<600, 250{,}000>$. Therefore, the vertex is (600, 250,000) and is the maximum because the graph opens downward.

10-2

Classifying Patterns

SUPERLESSON AT A GLANCE

Superlesson Goal

Students will investigate different types of symmetry in frieze patterns and wallpaper patterns.

Management Guide

	Topic	Objectives	Key Terms	New Ideas	Materials
Part A	Frieze Patterns	To explore frieze patterns, identify types of symmetry that they exhibit, and to discover that all frieze patterns fall into seven symmetry classifications.	Frieze pattern, glide-reflection symmetry, translation symmetry	Frieze patterns. Translation and glide-reflection symmetries; identifying symmetries in frieze patterns. There are seven different types of frieze patterns.	
Part B	Wallpaper Patterns	To explore wallpaper patterns and identify types of symmetry that they exhibit.	Wallpaper pattern	Wallpaper patterns. Identifying symmetries in wallpaper patterns.	**Student** Protractor, straightedge
Part C	Making Connections	To classify frieze patterns found on pottery.	In Making Connections, students apply and synthesize key terms and new ideas.		

Pacing Chart (45-Minute Periods)

	Comprehensive Course	Core Course	Informal Course
Part A	1	1	0
Part B	1	1	0
Part C	1	1	0
TOTAL periods for Superlesson	3	3	0

NCTM Standards

Mathematics as Problem Solving

Mathematics as Communication

Mathematics as Reasoning

Mathematical Connections

10-2 Classifying Patterns

decoration detectives

Do you like solving mysteries? If so, maybe archaeology is the field for you. Archaeologists look at old buildings, tools, and other artifacts to recreate past human behavior. In a way, they are detectives.

As a high school student, Elain-Maryse Solari loved mysteries—not just reading them, but also playing the detective's role. Her love of solving mysteries drew her to archaeology. She majored in anthropology at the University of Arizona in Tucson and received her master's degree in cultural resource management at Sonoma State University in California. She has done archaeological work in Arizona, California, Italy, Wales, and on the Isle of Man.

In Wales, her team explored the remains of a fort from the Iron Age (about 1000 B.C. to 100 A.D.). Unfortunately, acids in the soil had eaten up all the buildings and most of the other archaeological evidence. However, rain falling off the roofs of the ancient structures left rings in the soil. If one ring was below another, the lower ring had to be older. With little evidence other than these rings, the archaeologists were able to determine where structures had been, their size, and the order in which they were built!

1. Explain how deductive reasoning plays a role in archaeology.
2. Why do you think the archaeologists in Wales concluded that the lower a ring was, the older it was?

Where Are We Now?

Students are familiar with transformations and their compositions. They have also investigated line symmetry (in Chapter 1) and rotational symmetry (in Chapter 3).

Where Are We Going?

In 10-2, students will investigate frieze patterns and wallpaper patterns. These repeating patterns can be generated by transformations and may feature many different types of symmetry.

Possible Answers

1. Archaeologists examine clues from the past and use them to make deductions about different cultures and time periods.
2. More recent rain fell from roofs onto the soil in which older rings existed and created new rings.

More About Pottery

There are four main methods of producing pottery. A pot may be made by rolling out and coiling a piece of clay. Moist clay can be poured into molds and baked. When making objects with flat sides, slabs of clay can be joined together. Finally, a lump of clay can be molded on a potter's wheel. Most Native American pottery was produced by the coil method. The Anasazi, ancestors of the Pueblo, began coating baskets with clay about 70 A.D. By 700, the Anasazi were making clay pots with elaborate black-and-white geometric designs.

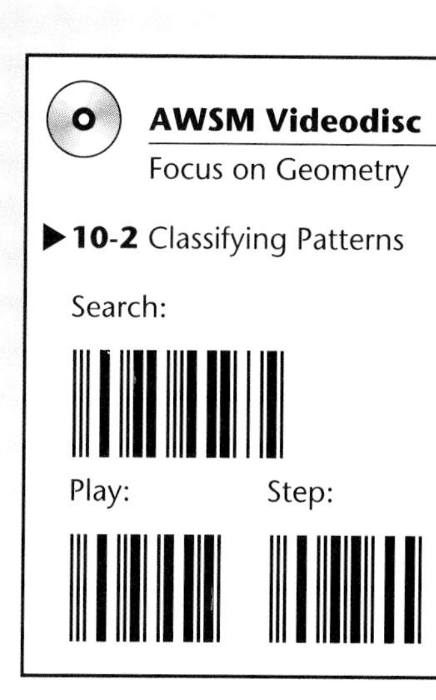

Classifying Patterns

PART A At a Glance

Objective

To explore frieze patterns, identify types of symmetry that they exhibit, and discover that all frieze patterns fall into seven symmetry classifications.

Development

First, students see examples of frieze patterns and definitions of *glide-reflection* and *translation symmetry.*

In the **Explore,** students create frieze patterns and identify the different types of symmetry they have. They discover that there are only seven different symmetry classifications for frieze patterns.

Key Terms

Frieze pattern, glide-reflection symmetry, translation symmetry

First Five Minutes

Transparency FFM 10-2A

Read the material on page 688. Then answer the **Consider** question at the top of page 689.

Motivate

Ask...

- Do you see any examples of frieze patterns in the classroom? (Hint: These patterns are often seen on clothing.)

10-2 PART A Frieze Patterns

← CONNECT → *You know about several different transformations and various types of symmetry. Now you will use symmetry and transformations to analyze and create frieze patterns.*

A frieze pattern is a strip design that repeats itself. You can find many everyday examples of frieze patterns in decorative borders on clothing, in the tracks made by tire treads, and in ancient Greek urns.

DEFINITION

A **frieze pattern** is created by repeated translations of a pattern along a line.

All of the frieze patterns that you will work with repeat horizontally. Also, you may assume that all patterns in this chapter continue indefinitely.

Many of these designs have interesting geometric properties, like line symmetry and rotational symmetry. For example, the pattern . . . ΣΣΣΣΣΣ . . . , shown above, has horizontal line symmetry.

Frieze patterns may also feature **glide-reflection symmetry,** which we touched on earlier. The frieze pattern below exhibits glide-reflection symmetry. A pattern has glide-reflection symmetry if it coincides with itself after undergoing a translation and a reflection.

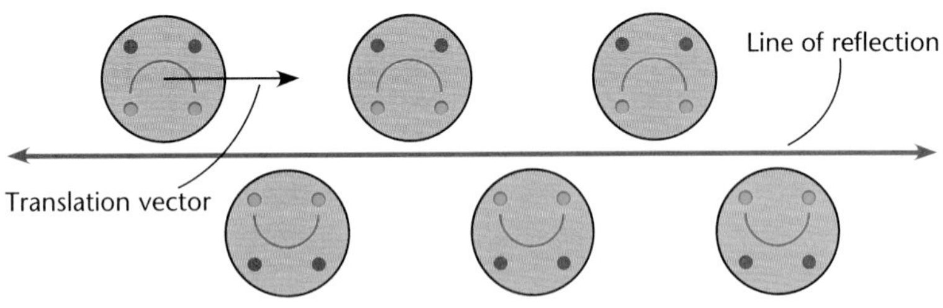

Research Note

One of the "modern" themes and approaches to geometry is transformation geometry....We shall illustrate the value of this alternative approach to geometry by means of recent developments in archaeology....If, as often happens, [pottery] motifs are arranged in repeated patterns,...then the whole pattern can be analyzed according to its symmetries. (Donald W. Crowe and Thomas M. Thompson, "Some Modern Uses of Geometry," *Learning and Teaching Geometry, K–12, 1987 Yearbook,* Mary Montgomery Lindquist and Albert P. Shulte, eds., p. 106. © 1987 NCTM.)

1. How is glide-reflection symmetry related to the idea of a composition of transformations?

EXAMPLE

Does the pattern at the right have glide-reflection symmetry? Why or why not?

The pattern does have glide-reflection symmetry. The translation vector and the line of reflection are shown.

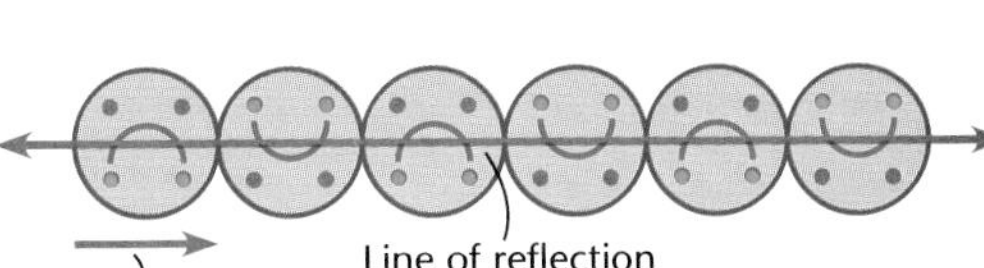

The wave pattern from the border of a second-century B.C. Roman mosaic coincides with itself when translated a certain distance to the right or to the left. When a pattern has this property, we say that it has **translation symmetry.** All frieze patterns exhibit translation symmetry.

TRY IT

Name all of the types of symmetry in each frieze pattern.

a. **b.** **c.**

Translation, glide reflection, horizontal line, vertical line
Translation, vertical line
Translation

Because frieze patterns repeat themselves horizontally, there are only a few types of symmetry they can have. In the following Explore, you will sketch examples of different frieze patterns.

Student Resources
- Alternative Lessons 10-2A
- Laboratory Manual 10-2A
- Technology Lab Manual
- Practice 10-2A
- Study Guide and Journal 10-2A
- Guía de estudios y Diario 10-2A
- Multilingual Handbook
- More Look Back 10-2A
- SAT Preparation

Media Resources
- Transparency FFM 10-2A
- Transparency AE 10-2A
- Teaching Transparency
- AWSMTest and practice software
- AWSM Videodisc

Shows the relationship of the idea of glide-reflection symmetry to composition of transformations.

Possible Answer

1. The figures in the pattern coincide after undergoing a composition of a reflection and a translation.

ALTERNATE EXAMPLE

Does the pattern shown have glide-reflection symmetry? Why or why not?

The pattern shown does have glide-reflection symmetry. The translation vector and the line of reflection are shown.

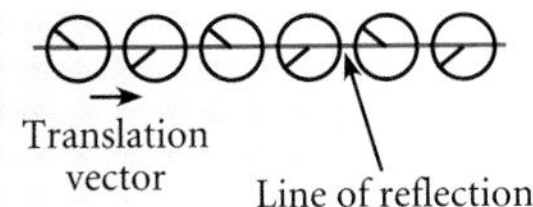

Classifying Patterns

EXPLORE

Symmetry Search

Recommended group size: 2

The Point
To create frieze patterns, identify symmetries in the patterns, and discover that there are only seven different symmetry classifications for frieze patterns.

Look and Listen...

- For students who do not see the difference between glide-reflection symmetry and point symmetry.

Ask...

- If you rotate the pattern 180°, do you get the same pattern? If so, what type of symmetry is this? Does it coincide with itself if you reflect it over a horizontal line and then slide it forward? If so, what type of symmetry does it have?

For Groups That Finish Early
Ask students to see how many of the seven types can be made using the ten numerals. Four: ...777..., ...333..., ...9696..., ...000...

Follow Up
List all of the different types of frieze patterns students found on the overhead or chalkboard. See if they can identify and eliminate patterns that are actually of the same type, until only the seven fundamental types remain.

Possible Answer

2. There are seven different types of symmetry classifications for frieze patterns. (See the chart at the bottom of page 690.)

EXPLORE: SYMMETRY SEARCH

As you can see in the photo at the right, frieze patterns are important in textile designs. Two frieze patterns are classified as different types if they have different symmetries.

1. Using capital letters, sketch examples of as many different types of frieze patterns as you can. Identify all of the types of symmetry each of your patterns has.
2. Compare your frieze patterns with the ones your classmates designed. While sharing your frieze patterns, list the different types of frieze patterns that you see. How many different types can you identify?

Frieze patterns may have glide-reflection symmetry, half-turn rotational symmetry (point symmetry), and/or line symmetry over vertical or horizontal lines. Due to these limitations, there are essentially only seven different types of frieze patterns! These are summarized in the chart. (Note that redundant symmetries are not listed.)

CLASSIFICATION OF FRIEZE PATTERNS

Type of symmetry (Translation symmetry plus...)	Example
No other symmetry	
Horizontal line symmetry	
Point symmetry	
Glide-reflection symmetry	
Vertical line symmetry	
Vertical line symmetry and glide-reflection symmetry	
Vertical line symmetry and horizontal line symmetry	

Alert

It is important for students to realize that redundant symmetries are not listed in the chart. For instance, the last type of pattern (vertical and horizontal line symmetry) also must have point symmetry, but this is not listed. In *Exercises,* however, when asked to identify symmetries, students should list all that they find.

REFLECT

1. Briefly explain the difference between translation symmetry and glide-reflection symmetry.
2. Describe some common frieze patterns seen in everyday life.
3. If a frieze pattern is flipped upside down, does its classification change? That is, does it still have the same types of symmetry?

Exercises

CORE

P 1. **Getting Started** Refer to the frieze pattern at the right for the following.

a. Does the pattern have horizontal line symmetry? No
b. Does the pattern have vertical line symmetry? No
c. Does the pattern have glide-reflection symmetry? No
d. Does the pattern have point symmetry? No

Although any part of a frieze pattern is repeated an infinite number of times, you can always find a minimal piece that can be translated to create the whole pattern. For instance, in . . . TTTTTTTTTT . . . , the piece TTT repeats itself, but a minimal piece that you could translate to make the pattern is a single T.

P **For each frieze pattern shown, sketch a minimal piece that can be translated to create the pattern.**

2. 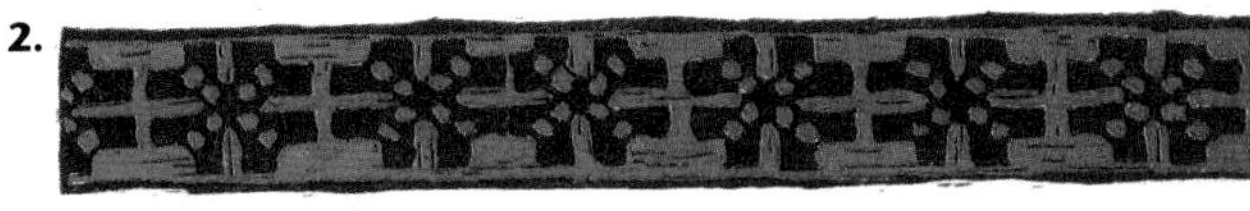

3. 

4. 

V 5. Determine whether the following statement is true or false. If the statement is false, change the underlined phrase to make it true. F; Translation and a reflection

A pattern has glide-reflection symmetry if it coincides with itself after a <u>rotation and a reflection</u>.

Key

V Vocabulary
P Practice/Skills
R Review
MR Math Reasoning
PS Problem Solving
C Challenge

Ongoing Assessment

Self-Assessment Exercises 1–15 odd, 18

Embedded Assessment Reflect 1; Exercises 4, 8, 12, 16, 19

Journal

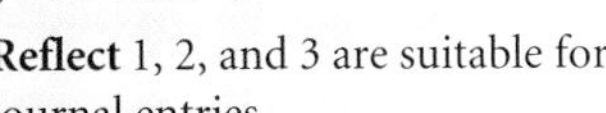

Reflect 1, 2, and 3 are suitable for journal entries.

REFLECT

Possible Answers

1. Any pattern that coincides with itself after a translation has translation symmetry. A pattern with glide-reflection symmetry coincides with itself after a translation *and a reflection.*
2. Molding on older buildings, trim on clothing, etc.
3. The classification of a frieze pattern does not change if it is flipped. Flipping a pattern does not change the types of symmetry it has.

Part A Exercises

Exercise Notes

Core

9. Shows a connection between the idea of a frieze pattern and the chemical structure of a polymer.

12, 13, and 19. Students identify frieze patterns in clothing designs from different cultures.

More Math Reasoning

32. Students see that any pattern with vertical line symmetry and point symmetry falls under one of the other classifications shown in the chart.

Exercise Answers

Core

2. Possible answer:

3. Possible answer:

4. Possible answer:

Algebra | Functions | Discrete Math | Probability | Data/Statistics

Classifying Patterns

9. Possible answer:

$$CH_2-\underset{}{\overset{CH_3}{\overset{|}{C}}}=CH-CH_2$$

10. Translation, vertical line

11. Translation, point

12. Translation, vertical line, horizontal line, glide-reflection, point

13. Translation, vertical line, horizontal line, glide-reflection, point

14. Possible answer:

15. Possible answer:

16. Possible answer:

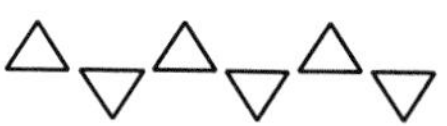

17. Check students' art.

19.  Translation, point, vertical line, glide-reflection (if color is not considered)

Translation, point, horizontal line, vertical line, glide-reflection

Translation, vertical line

P **Determine whether each pattern has glide-reflection symmetry.**

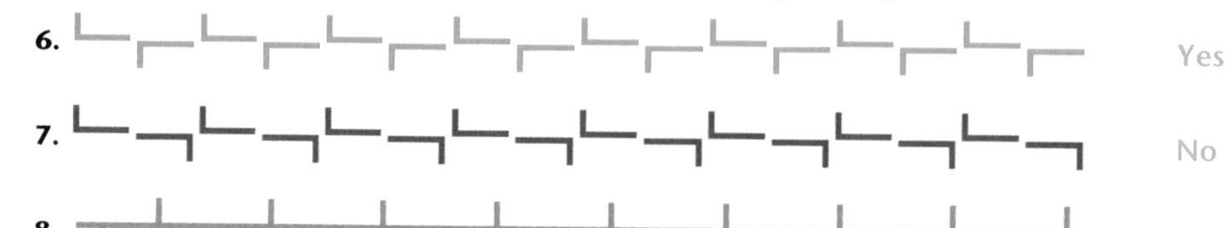

6. Yes

7. No

8.  Yes

PS **9. Rubber Band Strand** A *polymer* is a large molecule formed by the repeated bonding of smaller molecules. The figure shown below illustrates a natural rubber polymer strand. Identify and copy a minimal piece for this polymer.

Science

$$\ldots CH_2-\overset{CH_3}{\overset{|}{C}}=CH-CH_2-CH_2-\overset{CH_3}{\overset{|}{C}}=CH-CH_2-CH_2-\overset{CH_3}{\overset{|}{C}}=CH-CH_2-CH_2-\overset{CH_3}{\overset{|}{C}}=CH-CH_2\ldots$$

P **Name all of the types of symmetry in each frieze pattern. The patterns in Exercises 12 and 13 are found on cloth from Mali.**

Social Science

10. 

11. 

12. 

13. 

P **For each of the following, sketch a frieze pattern that has translation symmetry as well as the other type(s) of symmetry listed.**

14. Vertical line symmetry

15. Point symmetry

16. Vertical line symmetry and glide-reflection symmetry

MR **17.** Sketch and describe a frieze pattern that you've seen in architecture. Describe where you found the pattern.

P **18.** Suppose you choose a frieze pattern at random from the seven different classifications. What is the probability that the pattern will have vertical line symmetry? $\frac{3}{7}$

P **19.** This border design is from a pair of leggings of the Menominee Indians of Michigan. Sketch each of the different frieze patterns that you see in this design. Then name all of the types of symmetry in each frieze pattern.

Social Science

Key

V Vocabulary
P Practice/Skills
R Review
MR Math Reasoning
PS Problem Solving
C Challenge

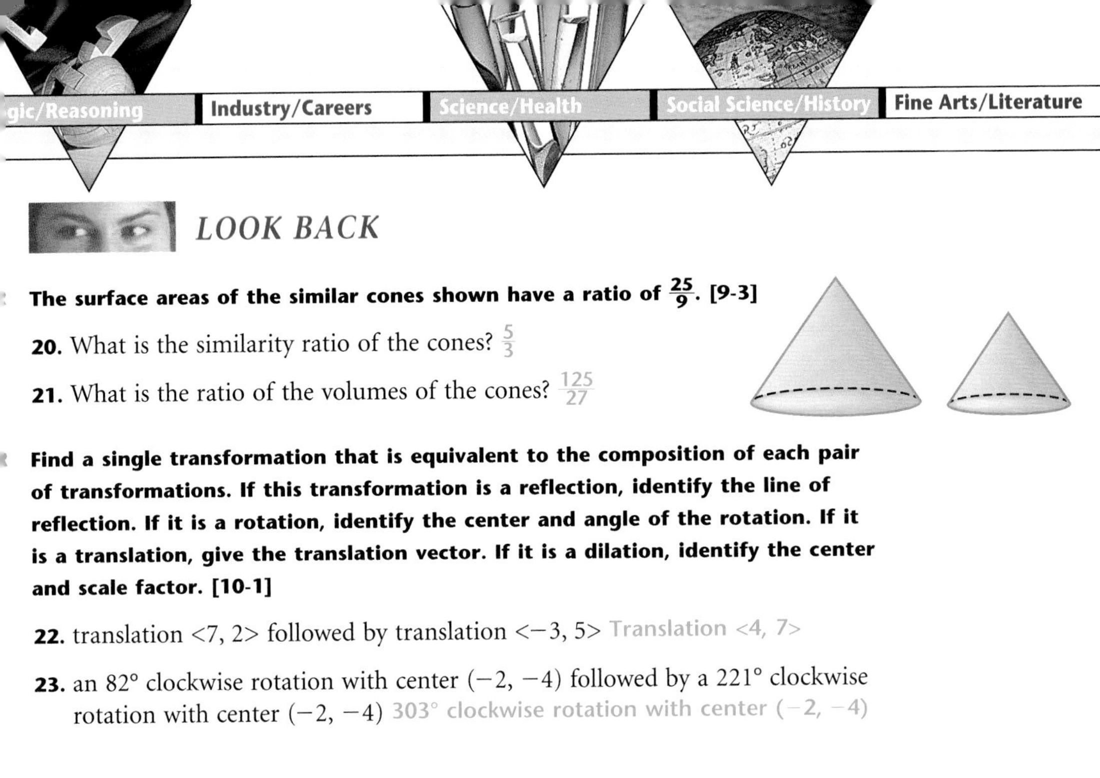

LOOK BACK

The surface areas of the similar cones shown have a ratio of $\frac{25}{9}$. [9-3]

20. What is the similarity ratio of the cones? $\frac{5}{3}$

21. What is the ratio of the volumes of the cones? $\frac{125}{27}$

Find a single transformation that is equivalent to the composition of each pair of transformations. If this transformation is a reflection, identify the line of reflection. If it is a rotation, identify the center and angle of the rotation. If it is a translation, give the translation vector. If it is a dilation, identify the center and scale factor. [10-1]

22. translation <7, 2> followed by translation <−3, 5> Translation <4, 7>

23. an 82° clockwise rotation with center (−2, −4) followed by a 221° clockwise rotation with center (−2, −4) 303° clockwise rotation with center (−2, −4)

MORE PRACTICE

For each frieze pattern, sketch a minimal piece that can be translated to create the pattern.

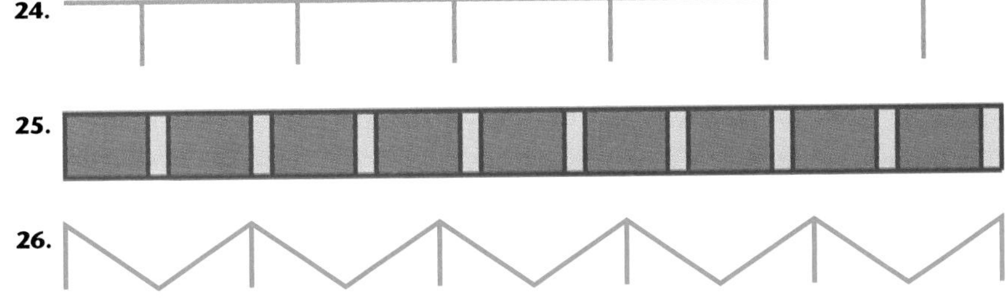

Name all of the types of symmetry in each frieze pattern.

27. AAAAAAAAAA

28. XXXXXXXXXXX

29.

30.

31. Name all the types of symmetry in the dancette (zigzag) mosaic pattern seen in Islamic architecture (shown at the right). Translation, vertical line

More Practice

24. Possible answer:

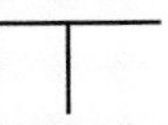

25. Possible answer:

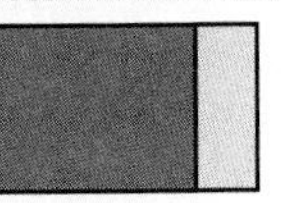

26. Possible answer:

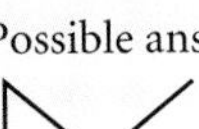

27. Translation, vertical line

28. Translation, vertical line, horizontal line, point, glide-reflection

29. Translation, vertical line, horizontal line, point, glide-reflection

30. Translation, vertical line, point, glide-reflection

More Math Reasoning

32. Such a pattern can always be classified as having either vertical line and horizontal line symmetry or vertical line and glide-reflection symmetry.

33. Possible answer: The tool could be a "wheel" with raised TM frieze pattern for its tread.

PART B At a Glance

Objective

To explore wallpaper patterns and identify types of symmetry that they exhibit.

Development

Students see the definition of a wallpaper pattern. **Examples** show students how to look for symmetries in these patterns.

In the **Explore,** students examine wallpaper patterns for different types of symmetry. Then they draw wallpaper patterns of their own.

Suggested Materials

Student Protractor, straightedge

Key Terms

Wallpaper pattern

First Five Minutes

Transparency FFM 10-2B

Sketch an equilateral triangle. What clockwise angles of rotation between 0° and 360° make the triangle rotate onto itself? 120°, 240°

Motivate

Ask...

- What is rotational symmetry? How is it related to point symmetry? **A figure with rotational symmetry coincides with itself after a rotation of less than 360°. A figure with point symmetry has 180° rotational symmetry.**

MORE MATH REASONING

MR **32.** Why isn't there a listing in the classification chart for frieze patterns that have both vertical line symmetry and point symmetry?

MR **33. Mass-Produced Pottery** The photo at the right shows pottery from the Acoma Pueblo in New Mexico. Suppose you plan to produce thousands of differently sized pottery bowls and pitchers with your trademark frieze pattern (shown below) on each one. The design goes completely around each piece of pottery.

TMTMTMTMTMTMTMTMTMTM

You need to design a tool to press this design into the clay. Describe a tool that could be used to do this.

10-2 PART B Wallpaper Patterns

← CONNECT → ***You've already created some frieze patterns and examined their symmetries. Now you will investigate patterns that repeat in more than one direction.***

Frieze patterns repeat forever, but only in a straight line. They're often used for decoration where a wall meets a ceiling. However, to decorate an entire wall, you need more than a pattern that extends horizontally. **Wallpaper patterns** are repeating patterns that cover a plane.

The design at the right is generated by overlapping translations of a regular hexagon. Notice that any row of this design is a frieze pattern. However, the basic pattern repeats itself in several different directions, not just in a horizontal line.

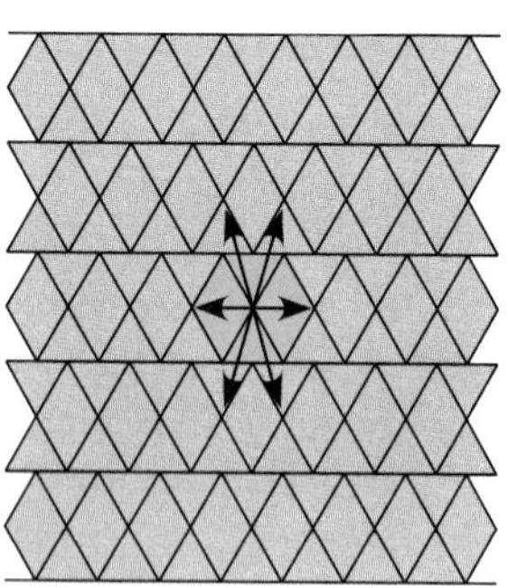

Key

V Vocabulary
P Practice/Skills
R Review
MR Math Reasoning
PS Problem Solving
C Challenge

Alert

Some students may have a hard time identifying rotational symmetries. You may want to suggest that they copy the patterns onto tracing paper as accurately as they can, and then physically rotate their copy on top of the original art to check for these symmetries.

DEFINITION

A **wallpaper pattern** is a plane pattern with translation symmetry along more than one line.

You may assume that all of the wallpaper patterns in this book extend indefinitely.

EXAMPLES

Name all of the types of symmetry in each wallpaper pattern.

1.

translation symmetry
rotational symmetry: 180°
line symmetry: vertical lines and horizontal lines
glide-reflection symmetry

2.

translation symmetry
rotational symmetry: 90°, 180°, and 270°
line symmetry: vertical lines, horizontal lines, lines at 45° and 135° to the horizontal
glide-reflection symmetry

Notice that there are an infinite number of lines of symmetry—we've only shown one of each type. For example, in the design in Example 1, all horizontal lines through the centers of the symbols are lines of symmetry, as are all horizontal lines halfway between the rows of symbols.

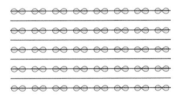

ALTERNATE EXAMPLES

Name all of the types of symmetry in each wallpaper pattern.

1.

Translation symmetry

Rotational symmetry: 180°

No other symmetry

2.

Translation symmetry

Rotational symmetry: 60°, 120°, 180°, 240°, 300°

Horizontal and vertical line symmetry; Lines at 30°, 60°, 120°, and 150° to the horizontal

Glide-reflection symmetry

Student Resources
- Alternative Lessons 10-2B
- Laboratory Manual 10-2B
- Technology Lab Manual
- Practice 10-2B
- Study Guide and Journal 10-2B
- Guía de estudios y Diario 10-2B
- Multilingual Handbook
- More Look Ahead 10-2B
- SAT Preparation

Media Resources
- Transparency FFM 10-2B
- Transparency AE 10-2B
- Teaching Transparency
- AWSMTest and practice software
- AWSM Videodisc

10-2

Algebra | Functions | Discrete Math | Probability | Data/Statistics

Classifying Patterns

EXPLORE

On the Wall

Recommended group size: 4

The Point
To examine two wallpaper patterns for different types of symmetry, and to draw a wallpaper pattern and list its types of symmetry.

Look and Listen...

- For students who do not realize that a center of rotation does not need to be on one of the designs in the pattern.

Ask...

- Have you tried rotating the pattern around different points?

For Groups That Finish Early
Draw a wallpaper pattern that has translation symmetry and vertical line symmetry, but does not have horizontal line symmetry.

Follow Up
Have students share their answers to Step 1 for patterns **A** and **B.** Resolve any differences of opinion on the symmetries these patterns have. Then have students display their wallpaper patterns for the class. You may want to make a place in the classroom to post their patterns.

Possible Answers

1. Pattern **A** has glide-reflection, rotation (180°), reflection (vertical line, horizontal line), and translation symmetry. Pattern **B** has the same symmetries.

Journal 

Reflect 1 and 2 are suitable for journal entries.

EXPLORE: ON THE WALL

MATERIALS
Protractor
Straightedge

1. Examine each of these African fabric patterns for symmetry by following the steps below.

A

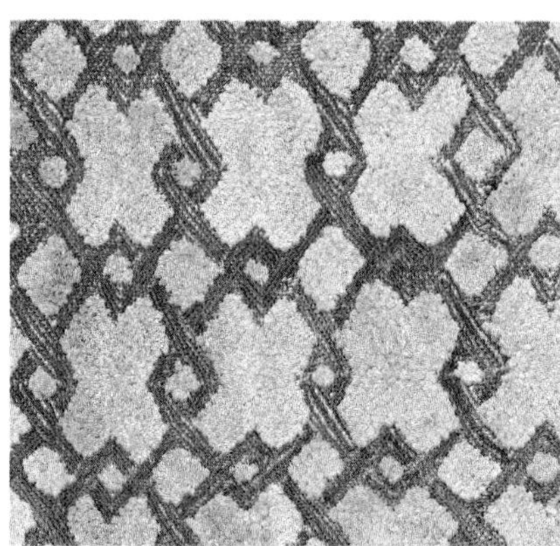

B

a. Determine whether the pattern has glide-reflection symmetry.
b. Examine the design for line symmetry. You may wish to sketch a copy of the design, so that you can test it for line symmetry by folding. Describe all of the different lines of symmetry that you identify.
c. See whether the design has rotational symmetry. Identify one of the centers of rotation, and list the degree measures of all of the clockwise rotations less than 360° that map the design onto itself.

2. Sketch a wallpaper pattern of your own. Describe all of the symmetries of your design. Compare your design to those of your classmates.

It may seem that there should be an infinite number of combinations for the symmetries of wallpaper patterns. However, the fact that they must have translation symmetry limits the possibilities. In fact, there are only seventeen different classifications for wallpaper patterns!

REFLECT

1. Why do you think there are more classifications for wallpaper patterns than there are for frieze patterns?
2. What is the relationship between wallpaper patterns and tessellations of a plane?

Diversity Issues

While visually oriented students may find it relatively easy to analyze frieze and wallpaper patterns, students whose strengths lie elsewhere may feel overwhelmed. It may help such students if you suggest that they use a system to search for symmetries; for instance, always search for line symmetry first, then glide-reflection symmetry, then rotational symmetry.

Exercises

CORE

1. **Getting Started** Refer to the wallpaper pattern at the right for the following.
   a. Does the wallpaper pattern have glide-reflection symmetry?
   b. Does the wallpaper pattern have line-reflection symmetry? If so, describe the different symmetry lines you identified.
   c. Does the wallpaper pattern have rotational symmetry? If so, list the degree measures of all clockwise rotations less than 360° that map the pattern onto itself.

Name all of the types of symmetry for each wallpaper pattern shown below. All of these patterns are typical *adire* cloth designs made by the Yoruba people of Nigeria.

2. 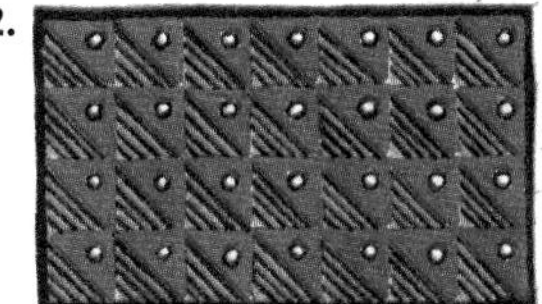

3. 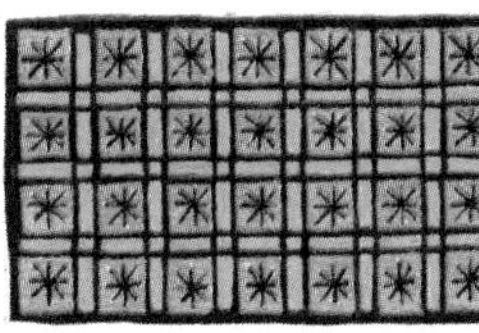

4. 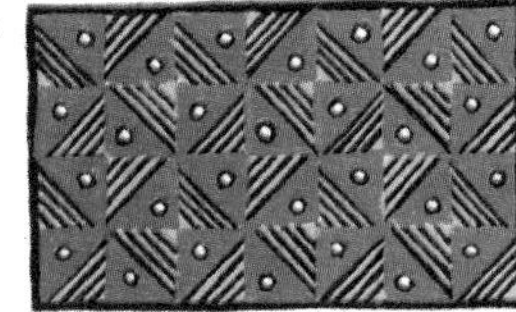

5. Write the letter of the second pair that best matches the first pair. (c)

   Frieze: line as (a) plain: decorated, (b) horizontal: vertical, (c) wallpaper: plane, (d) angle: vertex

Determine whether each statement is true or false. If the statement is false, change the underlined word or phrase to make it true.

6. A wallpaper pattern must have <u>rotational</u> symmetry. F; Translation
7. A wallpaper pattern is <u>sometimes</u> a tessellation. T
8. **Papering the Walls** Suppose you want to wallpaper the interior of the room shown at the right. How many square feet of wallpaper do you need for the job? (Do not include wallpaper for the floor, the door, or the ceiling.) 459 ft^2

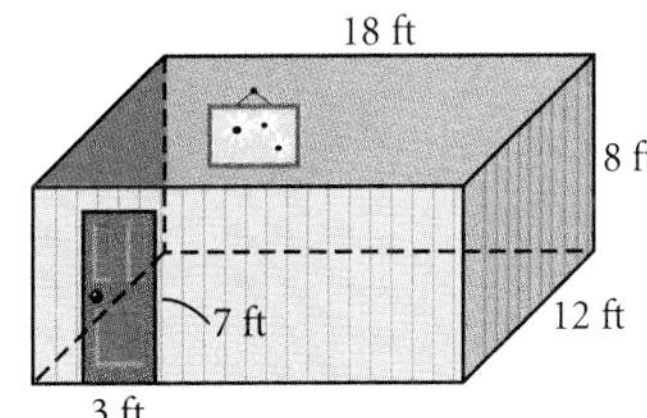

ey

Vocabulary
Practice/Skills
Review
Math Reasoning
Problem Solving
Challenge

Ongoing Assessment

Self-Assessment Exercises 1, 3, 5, 6, 7, 8

Embedded Assessment Explore Steps 1, 2; Exercises 4, 10, 12

REFLECT

Possible Answers

1. Frieze patterns extend in only one direction; therefore, they cannot have rotational symmetries for any angle other than 180°. Since wallpaper patterns cover a plane, they can have other rotational symmetries, so there are more possible types of patterns.
2. All tessellations are wallpaper patterns, but not every wallpaper pattern is a tessellation. In a tessellation, the plane surface is covered by repeating figures. In a wallpaper pattern, there may be space between the figures.

Part B Exercises

Exercise Notes

Core

2–4. Students identify symmetries in patterns found on Nigerian cloth.

Look Ahead

13–16. Review skills in solving inequalities. Students work with inequalities in geometric figures in 11-1.

17. Students find the rectangle of maximum area that can be enclosed in a given perimeter. In 11-2, students investigate optimization problems like this one.

More Math Reasoning

23. Students create a tessellation that is based on translations of a rectangle or parallelogram.

Exercise Answers

Core

1. a. Yes

b. Yes; Horizontal, vertical, and 45° and 135° to the horizontal

c. Yes; 90°, 180°, 270°

2. Translation; Line symmetry for lines at 45° to the horizontal; Glide-reflection (45° to the horizontal)

3. Translation; Horizontal line, vertical line, lines at 45° and 135° to the horizontal; Rotational: 90°, 180°, 270°; Glide-reflection

10-2

Classifying Patterns

4. Translation; Line symmetry for lines at 45° and 135° to the horizontal; Rotational: 180°; Glide-reflection (45° to the horizontal)

9. Possible answer:

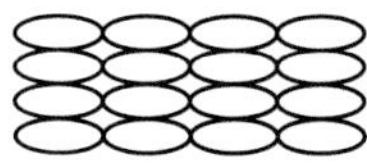

10. Possible answer:

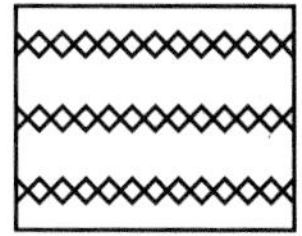

11. Possible answer:

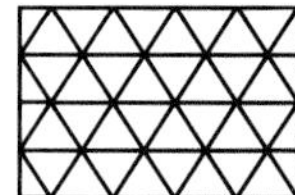

Look Ahead

17. a. 1 km × 3 km and 2 km × 2 km

b. 2 km × 2 km gives 4 km², which is the greatest possible area. The fenced region is a square.

More Practice

18. Translation; Rotational: 60°, 120°, 180°, 240°, 300°; Line: vertical, horizontal, lines at 30°, 60°, 120°, and 150° to the horizontal; Glide-reflection

19. Translation; Rotational: 90°, 180°, 270°; Line: vertical, horizontal, lines at 45° and 135° to the horizontal; Glide-reflection

20. Translation; Rotational: 90°, 180°, 270°; Line: vertical, horizontal, lines at 45° and 135° to the horizontal; Glide-reflection

Algebra | Functions | Discrete Math | Probability | Data/Statistics

P **For each of the following, sketch a wallpaper pattern that has translation symmetry as well as the other type(s) of symmetry listed.**

9. vertical line symmetry **10.** point symmetry

11. rotational symmetry for a 60° clockwise rotation

MR **12.** How many different directions are there for translations that map this wallpaper design onto itself? Infinitely many

Problem-Solving Tip

Be sure that you've covered all of the possibilities.

LOOK AHEAD

R **Find the solution set for each inequality.**

13. $x - 6 \geq 10$ $x \geq 16$ **14.** $3(y + 12) < 30$ $y < -2$ **15.** $7z - 13 \geq 2(z + 8)$ $z \geq \frac{29}{5}$

16. If $a + 7 = b$, is $a > b$ or is $b > a$? Explain. $b > a$ since 7 must be added to a to equal b

PS **17. Barb's Wire Fence** Barb has 8 km of wire fencing, and she wants to enclose a rectangular region of farmland.

a. Assuming each side length must be a whole number, list all of the possible dimensions for the fenced land.

b. Identify the dimensions that give the greatest possible area for the fenced region. What shape is the fenced region with the greatest area?

MORE PRACTICE

P **Name all of the types of symmetry for each wallpaper pattern.**

18.

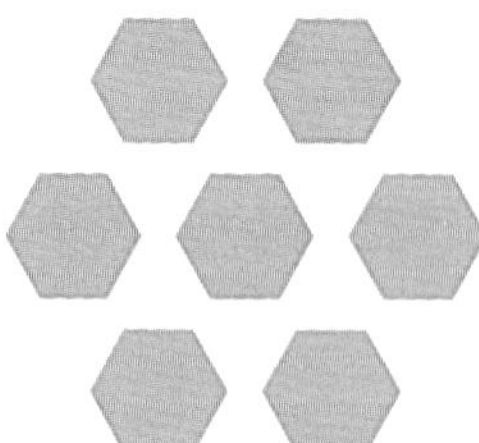

19.

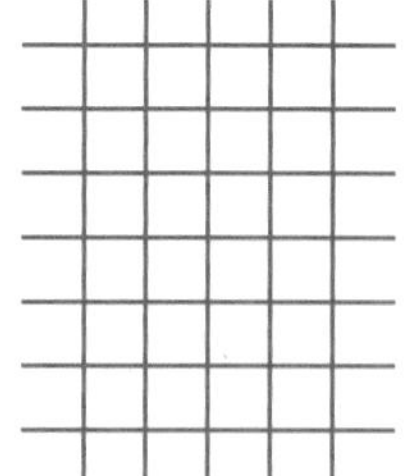

20.

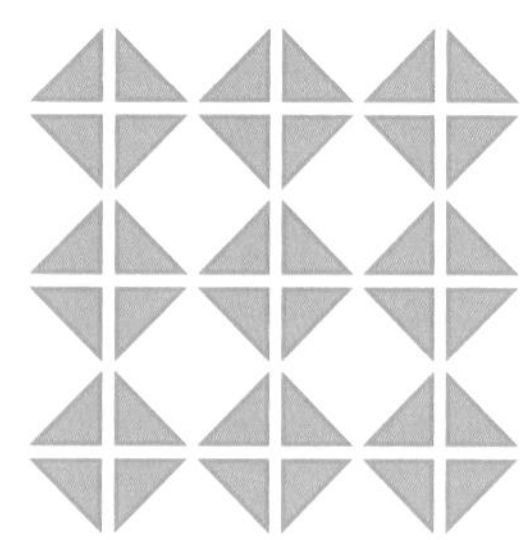

Key

V Vocabulary
P Practice/Skills
R Review
MR Math Reasoning
PS Problem Solving
C Challenge

For each of the following, sketch a wallpaper pattern that has translation symmetry as well as the other type of symmetry listed.

21. glide-reflection symmetry

22. horizontal line symmetry

MORE MATH REASONING

23. Wallpaper by Slide Tessellations are wallpaper patterns. By following these steps, you can make your own translation-based tessellation.

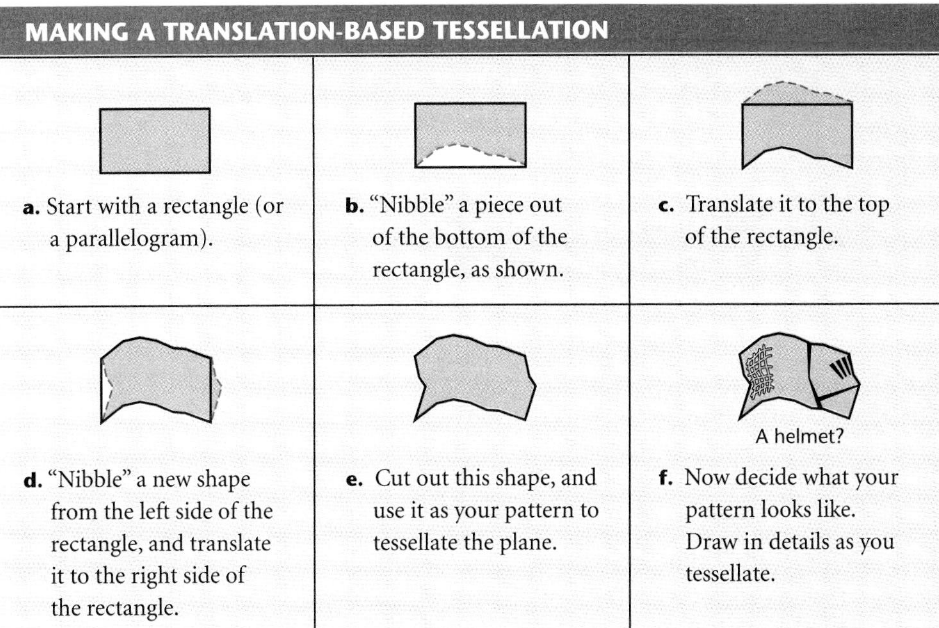

MAKING A TRANSLATION-BASED TESSELLATION
a. Start with a rectangle (or a parallelogram).
b. "Nibble" a piece out of the bottom of the rectangle, as shown.
c. Translate it to the top of the rectangle.
d. "Nibble" a new shape from the left side of the rectangle, and translate it to the right side of the rectangle.
e. Cut out this shape, and use it as your pattern to tessellate the plane.
A helmet?
f. Now decide what your pattern looks like. Draw in details as you tessellate.

24. A glide reflection can be described as a composition of a translation and a reflection. However, there is another composition of transformations—one that doesn't use a translation—that produces a glide reflection. Describe this other composition of transformations. Make a sketch to illustrate your answer.

Problem-Solving Tip

Eliminate unreasonable possibilities, and then use guess-and-check.

21. Possible answer:

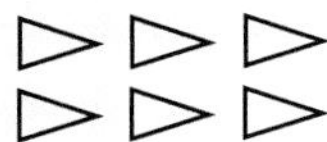

22. Possible answer:

▷ ▷ ▷
▷ ▷ ▷

More Math Reasoning

23. Check students' work.

24. A reflection and a rotation. Reflection over m followed by 180° rotation around P produces a glide reflection.

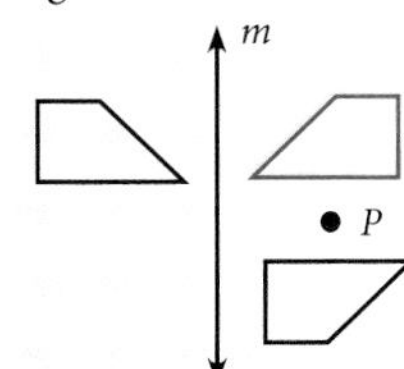

PART C At a Glance

Objective

To classify frieze patterns found on pottery.

Development

In the **Explore,** students classify frieze patterns similar to those found on Pueblo pottery by their symmetries.

First Five Minutes

Transparency FFM 10-2C

Sketch a frieze pattern that has glide-reflection symmetry and horizontal line symmetry.

EXPLORE

Classification Class

Recommended group size: 2

The Point

To classify frieze patterns similar to those on pottery at San Ildefonso Pueblo.

Look and Listen...

- For students who are confused when they find more symmetries than those listed in the chart on page 690.

Ask...

- Does the chart on page 690 list *all* the symmetries for each type of pattern?

For Groups That Finish Early

If a frieze pattern has horizontal line symmetry, must it have glide-reflection symmetry? Is the converse true? **Yes; no.**

Follow Up

Ask students to list the symmetries they found in each type of pattern.

10-2 PART C Making Connections

← CONNECT → *Studying patterns helps archaeologists to identify and classify ancient artifacts. These patterns are also present in modern design and architecture. You've applied your knowledge of transformational geometry and symmetry to two types of patterns—frieze patterns and wallpaper patterns.*

Archaeologists must be able to identify patterns that are typical of different cultures and time periods. The photograph at the left shows a piece of pottery from San Ildefonso Pueblo in New Mexico. The pottery typically found in this pueblo shows all seven different frieze-pattern classifications. The patterns you will work with in the following Explore are similar to some found on that pottery.

EXPLORE: CLASSIFICATION CLASS

Classify each frieze pattern using the appropriate line, point, and glide-reflection symmetries. If necessary, use the chart on page 690 to remind you of the different types of frieze patterns and their symmetries.

1.

2.

3.

4.

5.

6.

7. 

By now you've probably noticed that classification is an important idea in mathematics. In addition to frieze patterns and wallpaper patterns, you've seen how to classify angles, triangles, quadrilaterals, polygons, and transformations.

Student Resources

- Alternative Lessons
- Laboratory Manual 10-2C
- Technology Lab Manual
- Practice 10-2C
- Study Guide and Journal 10-2C
- Guía de estudios y Diario 10-2C
- Multilingual Handbook
- More Look Back 10-2C
- SAT Preparation

Media Resources

- Transparency FFM 10-2C
- Transparency AE
- Teaching Transparency
- AWSMTest and practice software
- AWSM Videodisc

REFLECT

1. Why do you think frieze patterns and wallpaper patterns are used so often in decorations?
2. Draw the simplest example you can for each of the seven types of frieze patterns. Write a brief explanation of the different types of frieze patterns.
3. Write a short paragraph explaining the similarities and differences between frieze patterns and wallpaper patterns.

Self-Assessment

Name all of the types of symmetry for each frieze pattern or wallpaper pattern.

1. EEEEEEEEEEEEEEE Translation; horizontal line; glide reflection
2. an embroidery border design from Afghanistan Translation; vertical and horizontal line; point; glide reflection

3.  Translation

4. 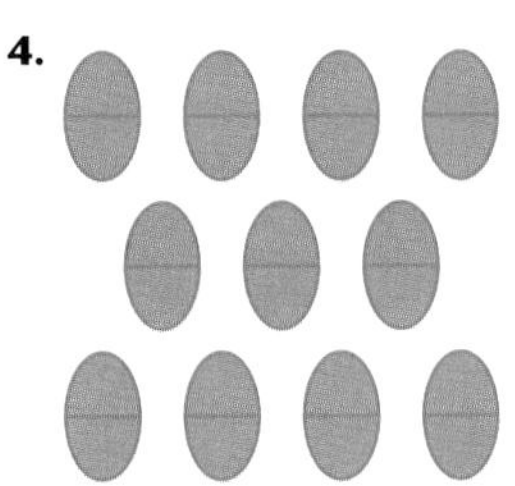

5. 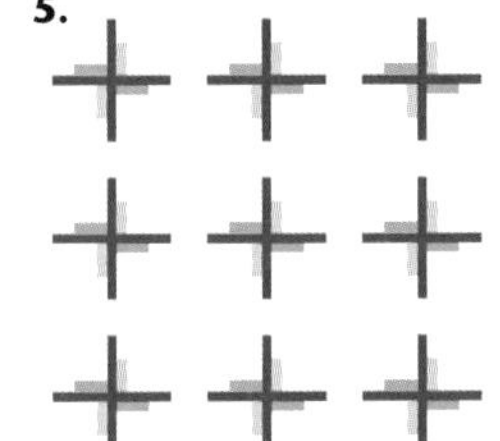

6. 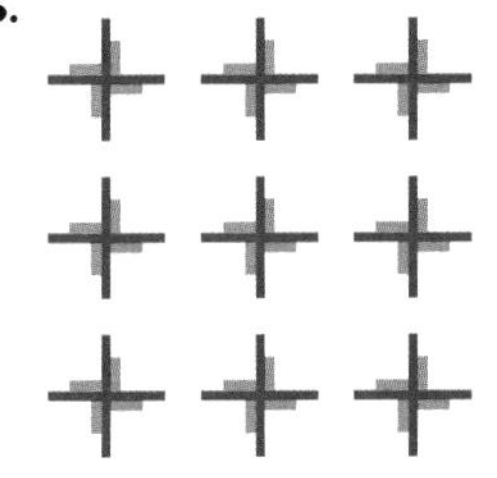

7. **Dig This!** An archaeologist unearths two hemispherical pots. The larger pot has twice the radius of the smaller. [9-3]
   a. What is the ratio of the surface area of the larger pot to the surface area of the smaller pot? 4
   b. What is the ratio of the volume of the larger pot to the volume of the smaller pot? 8

Vocabulary
Practice/Skills
Review
Math Reasoning
Problem Solving
Challenge

Possible Answers

Note: All patterns have translation symmetry. All other symmetries are listed below.

1. Point symmetry
2. Point symmetry, glide-reflection symmetry, vertical line symmetry
3. Glide-reflection symmetry, horizontal line symmetry
4. Vertical line symmetry
5. Glide-reflection symmetry, point symmetry, horizontal line symmetry, vertical line symmetry
6. Glide-reflection symmetry
7. No other symmetry

Portfolio

Have students select items from their work that demonstrate their understanding of the material in 10-2.

You may wish to have students include a frieze pattern and a wallpaper pattern that they drew, and an **Exercise** where they identified the symmetries in a pattern taken from a real-world object.

REFLECT

Possible Answers

1. The repeating patterns are easy to mass-produce.
2. See chart, page 690.
3. Frieze patterns repeat themselves in one direction; wallpaper patterns extend over a plane. Both repeat indefinitely, and both can be classified according to their symmetries. There are a finite number of classifications for both types of patterns.

Self-Assessment

Exercise Notes

9. Students "play archaeologist" and decide which piece of pottery might have been made by a particular civilization.

14. Students determine whether a wave pattern is or is not a wallpaper pattern.

Classifying Patterns

Self-Assessment Answers

4. Translation; Rotational: 180°; Line: vertical, horizontal; Glide-reflection

5. Translation; Rotational: 180°

6. Translation; Rotational: 90°, 180°, 270°

8. The graph of $y = -x^2 + 4$ is the graph of $y = x^2$ reflected across the x-axis and translated by <0, 4>.

10. Possible answer:

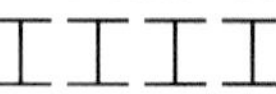

11. Possible answer:

12. Possible answer:

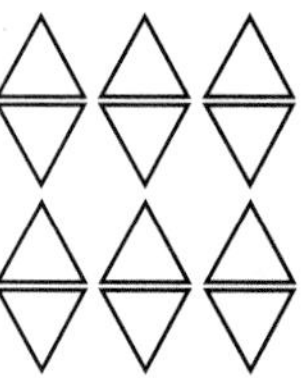

13. Possible answer:

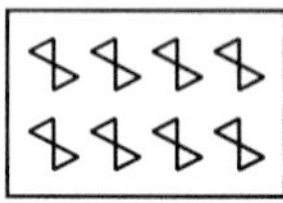

14. No. The pattern approximates a wallpaper pattern, but the waves are not identical.

R **8.** Compare the graph of $y = x^2$ to the graph of $y = -x^2 + 4$. Use the language of transformations to describe the relationships between the graphs. [10-1]

PS Careers **9.** Cristina is an archaeologist. She discovers that all of the pottery of an ancient civilization has the same symmetries as the fragment shown at the right.

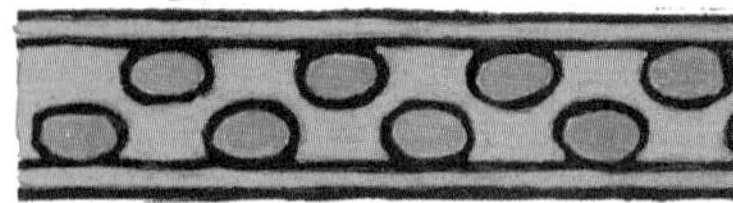

At a different site, Cristina finds four more fragments of pottery. Which one might have been made by this civilization? (c)

(a) 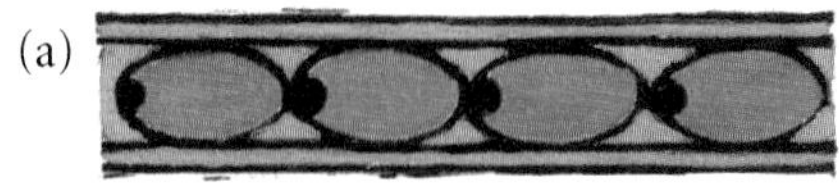

(b) 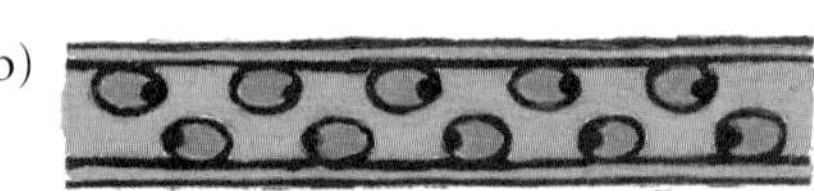

(c) 

(d) 

P **For each of the following, sketch a frieze pattern that has translation symmetry as well as the other type(s) of symmetry listed.**

10. vertical line symmetry and horizontal line symmetry

11. glide-reflection symmetry

P **For each of the following, sketch a wallpaper pattern that has translation symmetry as well as the other type of symmetry listed.**

12. vertical line symmetry

13. point symmetry

MR **14. Wave for the Camera!** The waves in the photograph were generated by an oscillating wavemaker. Does this wave pattern, as seen in two dimensions, appear to be a wallpaper pattern? If so, identify at least two types of symmetry in the pattern. If not, explain why you feel it is not a wallpaper pattern.

R **15.** Choose the equation that is represented by the graph at the right. [10-1] (c)

(a) $y = x^2 + 4$
(b) $y = -x^2 + 4$
(c) $y = x^2 - 4$
(d) $y = -x^2 - 4$

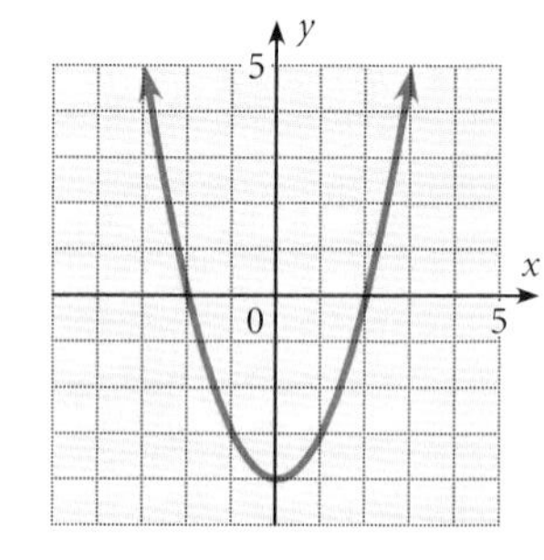

Assessment Resources

- **Quiz 10-2**
- Chapter Assessment Form A
- Chapter Assessment Form B
- Chapter Alternative Assessment
- Mid-Year Assessment
- End-of-Year Assessment
- **AWSMTest and practice software**

Ongoing Assessment

Self-Assessment Self-Assessment Exercises

Embedded Assessment Reflect 1, 2, 3

Chapter 10 Review

In Chapter 10, you have looked at applications of transformations. These included their classification and composition. You also learned about the connections of transformations to applications as diverse as algebra, automobiles, and art from all over the world.

KEY TERMS

composition [10-1]	isometry [10-1]	translation symmetry [10-2]
frieze pattern [10-2]	parent equation [10-1]	wallpaper pattern [10-2]
glide-reflection symmetry [10-2]		

Write the word or phrase that correctly completes each statement.

1. All frieze patterns have ___ symmetry. Translation
2. A pattern has glide-reflection symmetry if it coincides with itself after undergoing a ___ and a ___. Translation, reflection (or reflection, rotation)
3. An isometry that changes the orientation of a figure is a ___. Reflection
4. Translating a figure and then rotating its image is an example of a ___ of transformations. Composition

CONCEPTS AND APPLICATIONS

Describe a single transformation that is equivalent to the composition of each pair of transformations. Be as specific as you can. [10-1]

5. translation <2, −10> followed by translation <10, −2> Translation <12, −12>
6. a reflection over line p followed by a reflection over line q, which is parallel to line p Translation
7. Which of the following transformations are not isometries? [10-1] (d)
   (a) translation (b) reflection
   (c) rotation (d) dilation
8. A sphere is inscribed in a cube so that each face of the cube is tangent to the sphere. If each edge of the cube is 3 cm long, what is the ratio of the surface area of the sphere to that of the cube? [9-1, 9-2] $\frac{\pi}{6}$

Vocabulary
Practice/Skills
Review
Math Reasoning
Problem Solving
Challenge

Chapter 10 Review

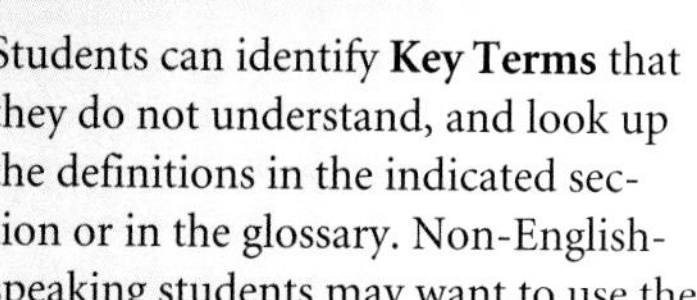

Journal

Students can identify **Key Terms** that they do not understand, and look up the definitions in the indicated section or in the glossary. Non-English-speaking students may want to use the *Multilingual Handbook.*

Vocabulary exercises and the **Self-Evaluation** are useful journal entries.

Review Answers

9–10.

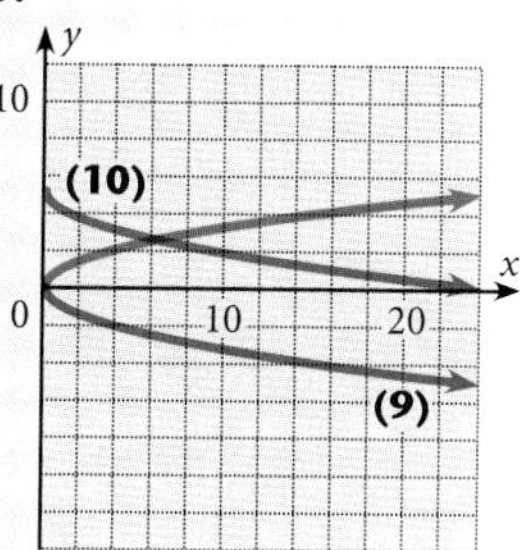

11. Possible answer:

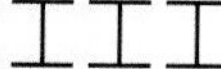

12. Translation; translation, horizontal line; translation, vertical line; translation, horizontal and vertical line; translation, point; translation, vertical line, and glide-reflection; translation, glide-reflection

13. Translation, vertical line

14. Translation, vertical line, horizontal line, glide-reflection, point

16. Check students' answers.

Chapter 10 Assessment

Portfolio

Students may select items that represent their mathematical understanding of the ideas in Chapter 10, and that illustrate the effort that they put into this chapter. At least one of these items should be a frieze or wallpaper pattern of their own design.

A rubric for assessing portfolios is included in the introduction to the Teacher's Edition.

Assessment Answers

1.

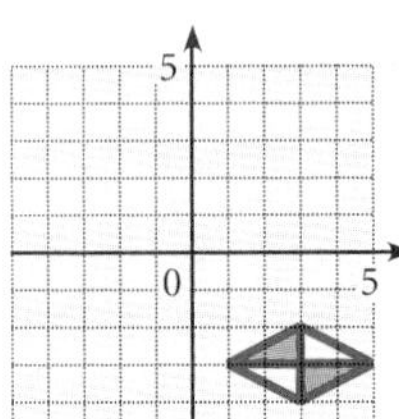

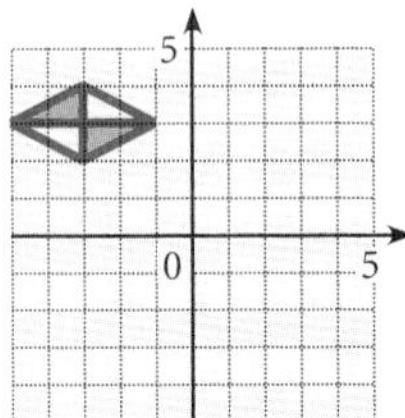

A 90° counterclockwise rotation centered at the origin.

2.

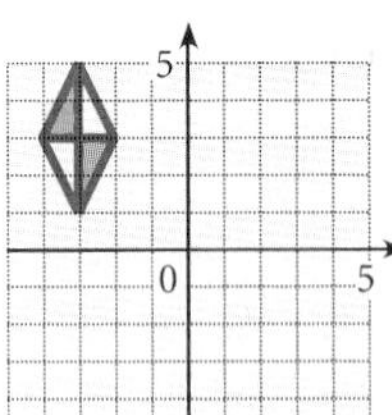

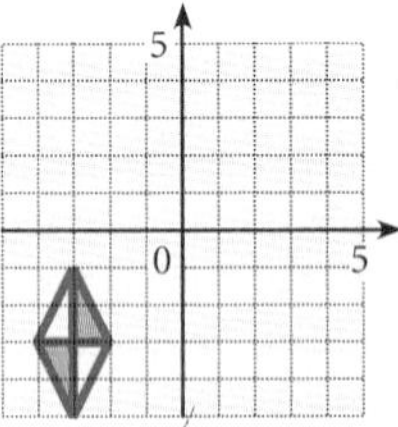

A 180° rotation centered at the the origin.

7. Possible answer:

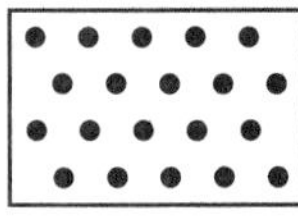

8. a. Translation, vertical line

b. Translation, vertical line, point, glide-reflection

9. The graph of $y = x^2 + k$ is a translation <0, k>. The graph of $y = -x^2$ is a reflection across the x-axis. The graph of $y = -x^2 + k$ is a reflection across the x-axis followed by a translation <0, k>.

P **The parent equation $y = \sqrt{x}$ is graphed at the right. Copy the graph, and then sketch the graph of each function on the same set of axes. Describe how each graph is related to the parent equation. [10-1]**

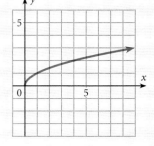

9. $y = -\sqrt{x}$

10. $y = -\sqrt{x} + 5$

P **11.** Draw a frieze pattern with horizontal and vertical line symmetry. [10-2]

P **12.** Write a summary of the seven combinations of symmetry possible in a frieze pattern. [10-2]

P **The patterns shown are used on clothing of the Menominee people of the Great Lakes region. Describe the different types of symmetry in each pattern. [10-2]**

Social Science

13.

14.

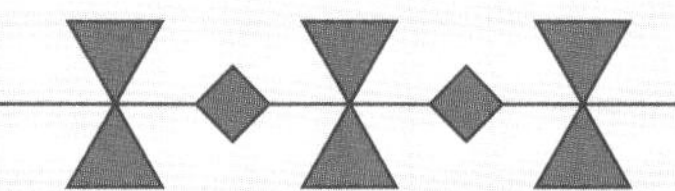

P **15.** List the degree measures of all clockwise rotations less than 360° that map this wallpaper pattern onto itself. [10-2]
90°, 180°, 270°

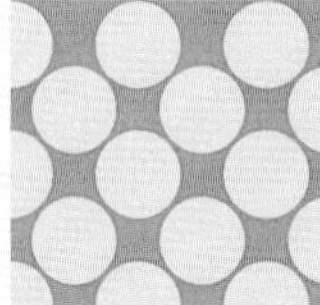

CONCEPTS AND CONNECTIONS

MR **16. Art** John T. Biggers' *Third Ward Housing* (1985) shows African-American women in front of rows of "shotgun" houses, common in the south. They were so named because a shotgun could be fired through such a house from front to back without hitting anything. Describe how aspects of the painting are similar to wallpaper and frieze patterns. Explain what Biggers may be trying to communicate by these patterns.

Fine Arts

SELF-EVALUATION

Write a summary of what you have learned about transformations in Chapter 10. Include concepts that relate to isometries, algebraic functions, frieze patterns, and wallpaper patterns. Describe the concepts that you found the most difficult, and discuss your plans to study them.

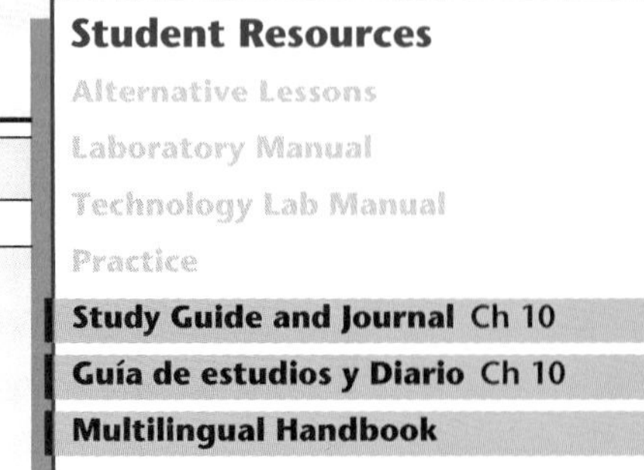

Student Resources
- Alternative Lessons
- Laboratory Manual
- Technology Lab Manual
- Practice
- **Study Guide and Journal** Ch 10
- **Guía de estudios y Diario** Ch 10
- **Multilingual Handbook**
- More Look Ahead
- **SAT Preparation**

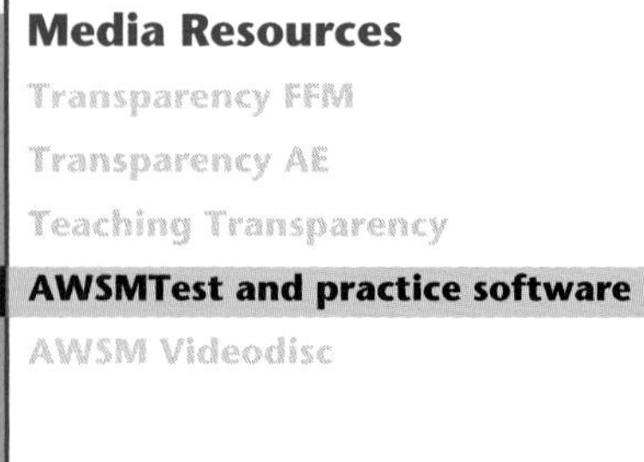

Media Resources
- Transparency FFM
- Transparency AE
- Teaching Transparency
- **AWSMTest and practice software**
- AWSM Videodisc

Chapter 10 Assessment

TEST

Sketch the image of each transformation of the figure shown. Then describe a single transformation that has the same image as the composition of transformations.

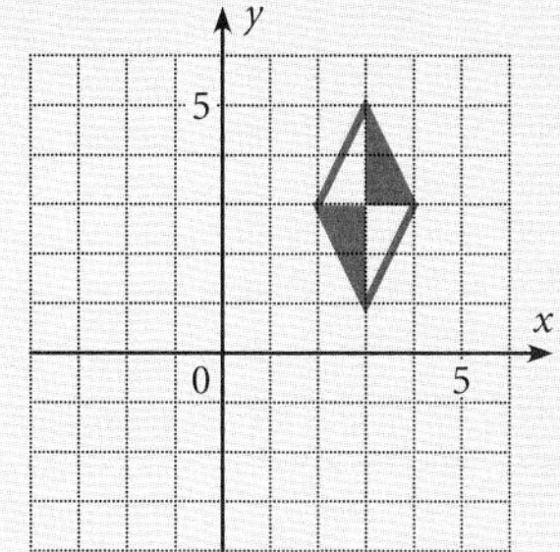

1. a 90° clockwise rotation centered at the origin followed by a 180° counterclockwise rotation centered at the origin

2. a reflection across the y-axis followed by one across the x-axis

3. A poster advertising a concert is reduced to appear on each ticket for the concert. Is this an example of a transformation? an isometry? Explain. Yes, addition; No; Distance is not preserved.

4. What transformation may be applied to the graph of $y = x^2$ to produce the graph of $y = x^2 - 6$. Be as specific as you can. A translation <0, −6>

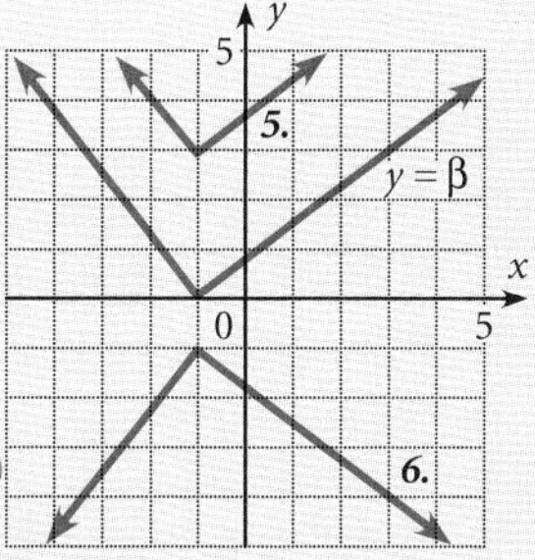

The graph of a parent equation, $y = \beta$, is shown. For each of the other graphs shown in the figure, give the letter of its equation.

5. (a) $y = -\beta - 3$ (b) $y = -\beta + 3$ (c) $y = \beta + 3$ (d) $y = \beta - 3$ (c)

6. (a) $y = -\beta + 1$ (b) $y = -\beta - 1$ (c) $y = \beta - 1$ (d) $y = -\beta$ (b)

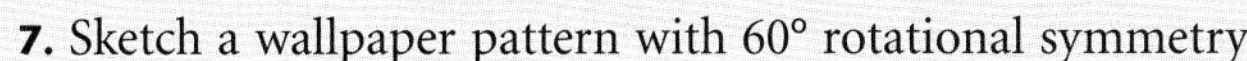

7. Sketch a wallpaper pattern with 60° rotational symmetry.

8. Geometric designs are common in Islamic architecture. An example of an Islamic frieze pattern is shown at the right.

a. If the colors are considered part of the pattern, what types of symmetry are present in this frieze pattern?

b. Disregarding colors, what types of symmetry are present?

9. Use the language of transformations to write a brief summary of how the graphs of $y = x^2 + k$, $y = -x^2$, and $y = -x^2 + k$ are related to the graph of the parent equation $y = x^2$.

PERFORMANCE TASK

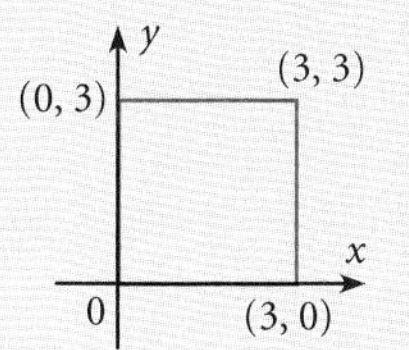

Copy the square. On the same axes, transform the square by mapping each point (x, y) to the point $(x + y, y)$. Repeat the transformation, using some figures of your own. Describe the general effect of such a transformation. Is it an isometry? Does it seem to preserve area? Explain.

ssessment Resources

uiz

apter 10 Assessment Form A

apter 10 Assessment Form B

apter 10 Alternative Assessment

id-Year Assessment

d-of-Year Assessment

WSMTest Chapter 10

Ongoing Assessment

Self-Assessment Chapter 10 Review and Self-Evaluation

Embedded Assessment Chapter 10 Performance Task

Test Chapter 10 Test

Performance Task

Answer

The transformation is not an isometry but does preserve area.

Suggested Scoring Rubric

Level 4 Full Accomplishment

- Shows full understanding of transformations and isometries.
- Shows evidence of experiments with different figures. A variety of figures are investigated; for instance, circles, polygons with more than four sides, etc.
- Correct conclusions are drawn as to whether or not the transformation is an isometry and preserves area.

Level 3 Substantial Accomplishment

- Shows essential grasp of the transformations and isometries.
- Shows evidence of experiments with several different figures, but experiments are on simple figures (squares, rectangles, etc.).
- Correct conclusions are drawn as to whether or not the transformation is an isometry and preserves area.

Level 2 Partial Accomplishment

- Shows partial grasp of transformations and isometries.
- Shows evidence of experimentation with only a few other figures.
- Students realize that the transformation is not an isometry, but draw incorrect conclusions about its other effects and properties.

Level 1 Little Accomplishment

- Shows little or no grasp of the concepts of transformations and isometries.
- No evidence of experimentation with other figures is given.
- Students fail to realize that the transformation is not an isometry.

Chapter 11 Geometric Inequalities and Optimization

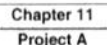

Chapter 11 | Project A

Sew What?

Compare Cutting Layouts

For a given size and style of garment, find the optimum fabric width and pattern layout.

- Did you know that 45 in. is the standard width for most shirt fabrics? That most suit fabrics are 60 in. wide?
- Don't you wonder whether a wider or narrower fabric width would result in less waste?
- How does this connect to Chapter 11? The **optimum** width varies with the size and style of garment.

Expand Your Vocabulary

selvage bias seam allowance dart
grain bolt yardage nap facing

Project Guidelines

Investigate

- Examine an article of your own clothing. If you took it apart at the seams, what flat shapes would you have?
- How would you estimate the amount of material in a shirt or blouse?
- Read about fabric and pattern layouts in a how-to-sew book.

Set Your Direction

- Will you actually take apart an old garment? Make a new one?
- Will you compare cutting layouts on commercial patterns for several sizes of the same style?

Make a Plan

- Make a calendar for each day's work. Check in with your group and with your teacher.
- You'll need a measuring tape, a tissue paper pattern, sewing pins, and fabric or newspapers.

Collect and Organize Your Information

- Visit a fabric store. Learn how to choose patterns for size, style, and economy. Check fabric widths.
- Ask someone who sews clothing or craft items about fabric economy and waste.
- Choose a size and style of garment pattern or make a tissue pattern from an article of your own clothing. Include seam allowances, darts, gathers, and facings.
- Calculate the total area of the pattern pieces.

Carry Out Your Plan

- Use actual fabric or cut and tape newspapers to simulate fabrics of different widths.
- Use the layout instructions included in the pattern (or your own judgment) to position the pattern pieces. Align the vertical direction of garment parts with the fabric grain. Place the center back or center front on a fold to avoid a seam.
- Measure lengthwise (along the selvage) the yardage needed for the garment. Calculate the minimum fabric area including waste.
- Explain which layout and fabric width is optimum.

Look Back

- Would the optimization of pattern and fabric be different if you cut several of the same garments?

 Focus on Geometry 61

A

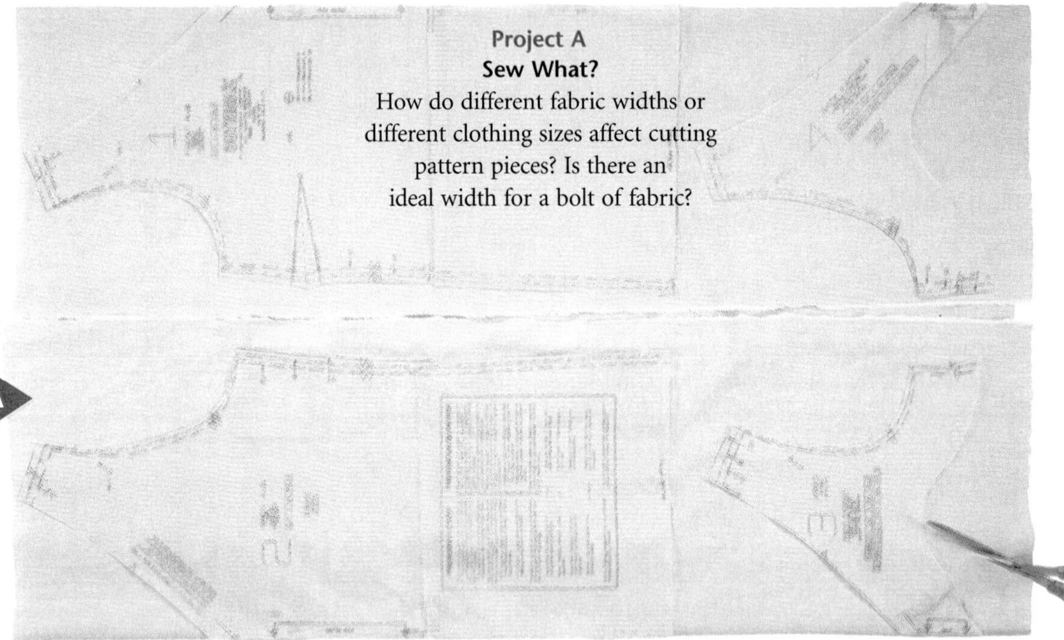

Project A

Sew What?

How do different fabric widths or different clothing sizes affect cutting pattern pieces? Is there an ideal width for a bolt of fabric?

Chapter 11 | Project B

Have a Great Flight

Plan a Flight Between Two Cities

Show that the shortest route between two cities at the same latitude is a great circle.

- Did you know that a great circle is formed on the surface of a sphere by a plane passing through the sphere's center?
- Don't you wonder why planes fly on great circle routes from city to city?
- How does this connect to Chapter 11? A great circle is the **shortest path** between two cities.

A great circle route from Los Angeles to Zurich passes over Greenland. Prove it to yourself by stretching a piece of string between the cities on a globe.

Expand Your Vocabulary

parallel (latitude) Prime Meridian
graticule projection International Date Line

Project Guidelines

Investigate

- Use string on a globe to find the shortest path between pairs of cities at the same latitude.
- Draw circles of different sizes that intersect in two points. Which arc between the points is shorter?
- Get flight routes from an airline or travel agent. Trace the routes on a globe and on a flat map.

Set Your Direction

- Will you show algebraically as well as geometrically that a great circle is the shortest path?

Make a Plan

- Make a calendar for each day's work. Check in with your group and with your teacher.
- Gather tools. You'll need:

  Mercator world map globe string
  compass protractor straightedge

Collect and Organize Your Information

- Find two cities at the same latitude (such as St. Paul, MN and Milan, Italy). Draw their latitude circle (parallel) and the triangle they make with its center.
- Find the great circle through the two cities and the triangle they make with the earth's center.

Carry Out Your Plan

- Use what you have learned about arcs and their central angles to show that the great circle route is shorter. Tell how you might prove that the great circle route is the *shortest* path.
- Draw the great circle path of your "flight" on a Mercator projection map. Tell why it isn't straight.

Look Back

- How could you adapt your procedure to show that the great circle between two points of *different* latitudes is still the shortest route?

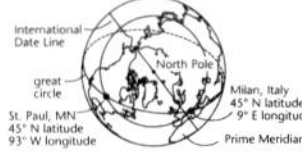

 Focus on Geometry 63

B

Project B

Have a Great Flight

Why should you fly over Greenland to get from Los Angeles to Zurich?

KEEP OFF THE GRASS

Project C

Keep Off the Grass

Why cut corners when the sidewalk goes around the block?

AZZAM BAKKAR

I loved math in high school, although I hated algebra at first. My father wanted me to go into engineering design. My plan was to get into a cockpit.

I've flown military and civilian transports. Math helped me to understand how an airplane functions. I calculate my own fuel economy, too. Math is close to reality.

Azzam Bakkar
Pilot
Continental Airlines
Houston, TX

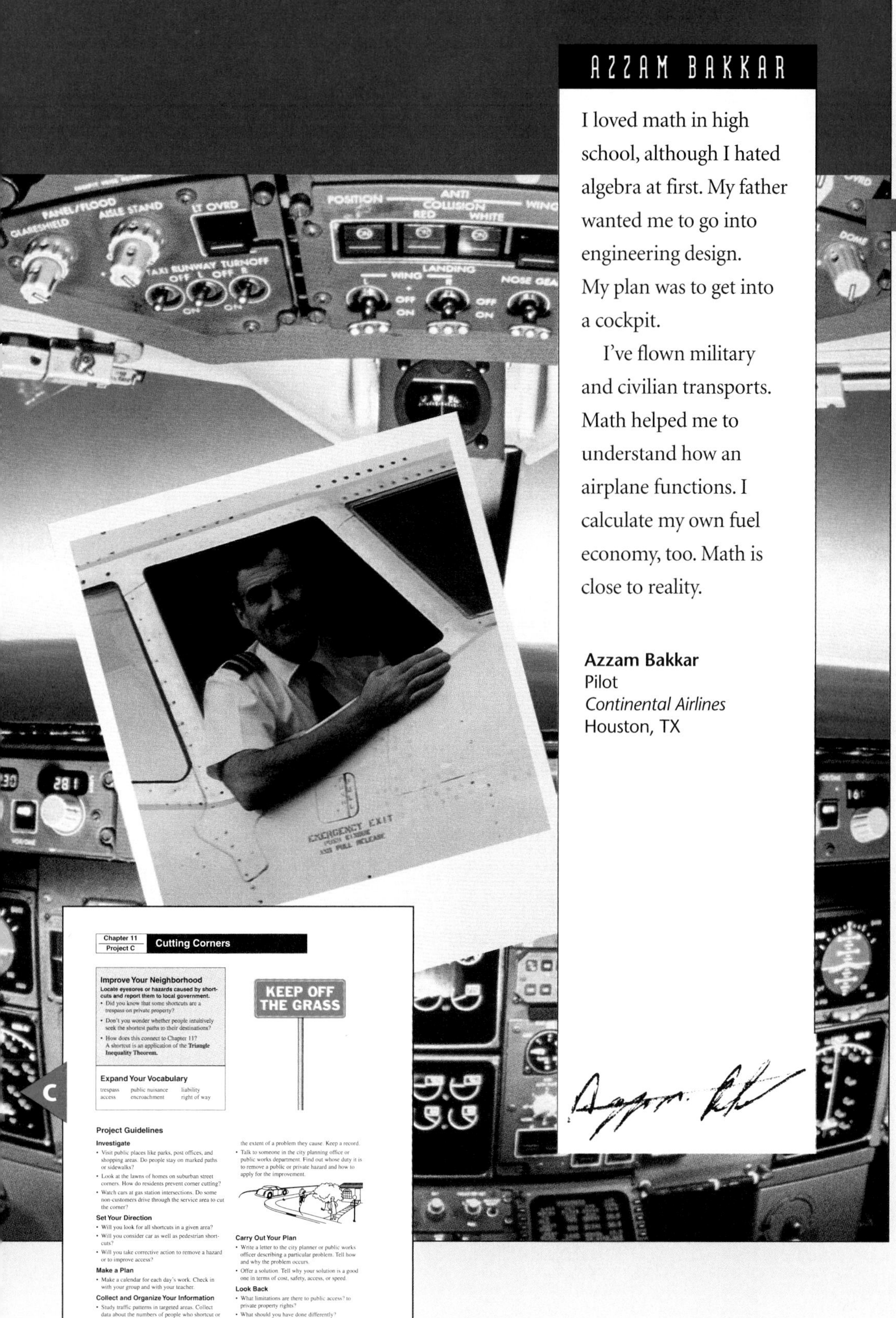

Chapter 11
Project C

Cutting Corners

Improve Your Neighborhood

Locate eyesores or hazards caused by short-cuts and report them to local government.

- Did you know that some shortcuts are a trespass on private property?
- Don't you wonder whether people intuitively seek the shortest paths to their destinations?
- How does this connect to Chapter 11? A shortcut is an application of the **Triangle Inequality Theorem.**

Expand Your Vocabulary

trespass	public nuisance	liability
access	encroachment	right of way

Project Guidelines

Investigate

- Visit public places like parks, post offices, and shopping areas. Do people stay on marked paths or sidewalks?
- Look at the lawns of homes on suburban street corners. How do residents prevent corner cutting?
- Watch cars at gas station intersections. Do some non-customers drive through the service area to cut the corner?

Set Your Direction

- Will you look for all shortcuts in a given area?
- Will you consider car as well as pedestrian short-cuts?
- Will you take corrective action to remove a hazard or to improve access?

Make a Plan

- Make a calendar for each day's work. Check in with your group and with your teacher.

Collect and Organize Your Information

- Study traffic patterns in targeted areas. Collect data about the numbers of people who shortcut or the extent of a problem they cause. Keep a record.
- Talk to someone in the city planning office or public works department. Find out whose duty it is to remove a public or private hazard and how to apply for the improvement.

Carry Out Your Plan

- Write a letter to the city planner or public works officer describing a particular problem. Tell how and why the problem occurs.
- Offer a solution. Tell why your solution is a good one in terms of cost, safety, access, or speed.

Look Back

- What limitations are there to public access? to private property rights?
- What should you have done differently?

Focus on Geometry 65

Biographical Note

Azzam Bakkar graduated from Abdulahmeed Ziharawi School in Homs, Syria. He took Calculus I and II.

Chapter 11

Overview

Geometric Inequalities and Optimization

11-1 Indirect Reasoning and Inequalities

Industries that connect many locations with wires or cables need to find the shortest paths that join these locations. You will investigate shortest paths, explore their connections to inequalities in triangles, and look at another strategy for proofs.

11-2 Optimization

Optimization is important in many fields. A package designer is often concerned with using the least amount of material to enclose a given volume. Now you will study ways to maximize and minimize geometric and real-world quantities under given conditions.

CHAPTERS

Chapter 11 Planning Guide

The following ancillaries are recommended for each course level. The additional resources, *Technology Lab Manual, Study Guide and Journal, Multilingual Handbook,* and *Assessment,* are recommended for all levels.

	Comprehensive Course	Core Course	Informal Course
11-1 Part A	▲	▲	▲
Alternative Lessons			▲
Laboratory Manuals	▲	▲	▲
Practice			▲
More Look Back		▲	▲
11-1 Part B	▲	▲	▲
Alternative Lessons			▲
Laboratory Manuals	▲	▲	▲
Practice			▲
More Look Ahead		▲	▲
11-1 Part C	▲	▲	▲
Alternative Lessons			▲
Laboratory Manuals	▲	▲	▲
Practice			▲
More Look Ahead		▲	▲

	Comprehensive Course	Core Course	Informal Course
11-1 Part D	▲	▲	▲
More Look Back		▲	▲
Quiz 11-1	▲	▲	▲
11-2 Part A	▲	▲	
Alternative Lessons			
Laboratory Manuals	▲	▲	
Practice			
More Look Ahead		▲	
11-2 Part B	▲	▲	
Alternative Lessons			
Laboratory Manuals	▲	▲	
Practice			
More Look Back		▲	
11-2 Part C	▲	▲	
More Look Back		▲	
Quiz 11-2	▲	▲	

BIBLIOGRAPHY

Reading for Teachers

Calculators in Mathematics Education, James T. Fey, ed. NCTM, 1992.

Teacher Resources

Building Toothpick Bridges, Jeanne Pollard. Dale Seymour Publications, 1985 (NS01510).

Making Connections with Mathematics, John Egsgard, Gary Flewelling, Craig Newell, Wendy Warburton. Janson Publications, 1988.

Algebra Experiments: Exploring Nonlinear Functions, Ronald J. Carlson and Mary Jean Winter. Addison-Wesley, 1993 (81525).

11-1

Indirect Reasoning and Inequalities

SUPERLESSON AT A GLANCE

Superlesson Goal

Students will explore inequalities of side lengths and angle measures in triangles and use indirect reasoning to verify conjectures.

Management Guide

	Topic	Objectives	Key Terms	New Ideas	Materials
Part A	Indirect Reasoning	To investigate indirect reasoning.	Indirect reasoning, negation	Forming the negation of a statement. Indirect reasoning and indirect proof.	
Part B	Inequalities in a Triangle	To discover that the longest side of a triangle is opposite the largest angle, and vice versa.		The longest side of a triangle is opposite the largest angle, and vice versa.	**Student** Ruler, protractor, geometry software
Part C	The Triangle Inequality Theorem	To discover and apply the Triangle Inequality Theorem.		The sum of the lengths of two sides of a triangle must be greater than the length of the third side. A line segment is the shortest path between two points.	**Student** Scissors, ruler, paper
Part D	Making Connections	To use triangle inequalities to find the shortest path on an orienteering map.	In Making Connections, students apply and synthesize key terms and new ideas.		

Pacing Chart (45-Minute Periods)

	Comprehensive Course	Core Course	Informal Course
Part A	1	1	1*
Part B	1	1	2
Part C	1	1	1
Part D	1	1	1
TOTAL periods for Superlesson	4	4	5

*Material on proof in this part may be omitted or downplayed in an Informal Course.

NCTM Standards

Mathematics as Problem Solving

Mathematics as Communication

Mathematics as Reasoning

Mathematical Connections

Geometry from a Synthetic Perspective

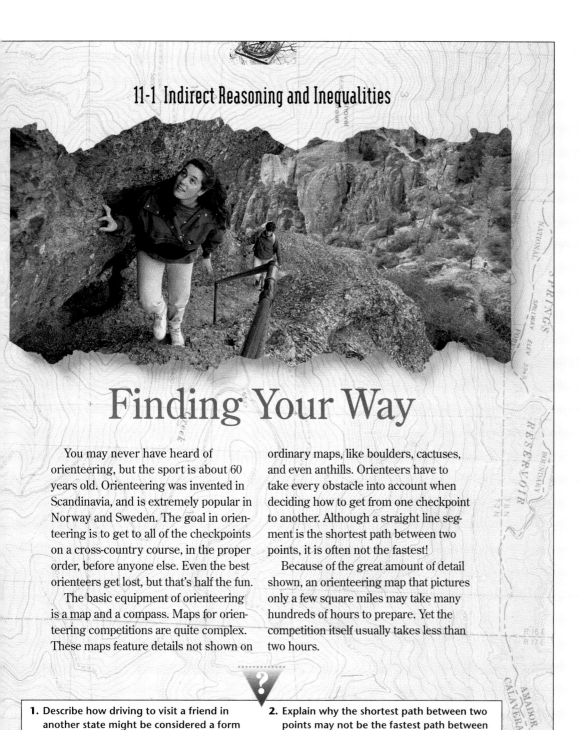

11-1 Indirect Reasoning and Inequalities

Finding Your Way

You may never have heard of orienteering, but the sport is about 60 years old. Orienteering was invented in Scandinavia, and is extremely popular in Norway and Sweden. The goal in orienteering is to get to all of the checkpoints on a cross-country course, in the proper order, before anyone else. Even the best orienteers get lost, but that's half the fun.

The basic equipment of orienteering is a map and a compass. Maps for orienteering competitions are quite complex. These maps feature details not shown on ordinary maps, like boulders, cactuses, and even anthills. Orienteers have to take every obstacle into account when deciding how to get from one checkpoint to another. Although a straight line segment is the shortest path between two points, it is often not the fastest!

Because of the great amount of detail shown, an orienteering map that pictures only a few square miles may take many hundreds of hours to prepare. Yet the competition itself usually takes less than two hours.

?

1. Describe how driving to visit a friend in another state might be considered a form of orienteering.

2. Explain why the shortest path between two points may not be the fastest path between these points.

709

More About Orienteering

According to *The Guinness Book of World Records,* world orienteering championships were first held in 1966. Sweden has won the most women's relay titles with nine, and Norway has captured the men's championship a record seven times. The greatest number of competitors at a one-day orienteering contest was 38,000 at an event in Romania in 1982. The five-day O-Ring competition in Sweden had 120,000 participants in 1983. (*The Guinness Book of World Records,* © 1993, Guinness Publishing Ltd.)

Where Are We Now?

Students have used direct reasoning to justify conjectures, and they know that angles of a triangle that are opposite congruent sides must also be congruent.

Where Are We Going?

In 11-1, students will become familiar with a new strategy for proof—indirect proof. Then they discover triangle inequalities involving side lengths and angle measures, including the Triangle Inequality Theorem and the relationship between the side lengths and opposite angle measures. The justifications of many geometric inequalities rely on indirect reasoning.

Possible Answers

1. In traveling to visit a friend, you must read maps. You try to find the fastest route by looking for a relatively direct path that can be traveled quickly.
2. It may be difficult or impossible to travel the shortest path. For instance, a person would travel some extra distance to find a bridge across a wide river rather than try to swim across the river itself.

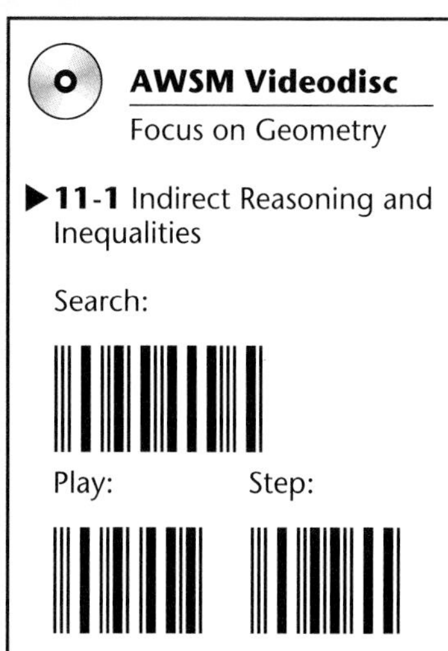

AWSM Videodisc
Focus on Geometry
▶11-1 Indirect Reasoning and Inequalities
Search:
Play:
Step:

Algebra | Functions | Discrete Math | Probability | Data/Statistics

Indirect Reasoning and Inequalities

PART A At a Glance

Objective

To investigate indirect reasoning.

Development

Students are introduced to indirect reasoning and given an **Example** of its use in a proof.

In the **Explore,** students use indirect reasoning to prove a familiar property: that the shortest segment from a point to a line is the perpendicular segment.

Key Terms

Indirect reasoning, negation

First Five Minutes

Transparency FFM 11-1A

Read the material on page 710. Then answer the Consider question at the bottom of the page.

Motivate

Ask...

- How might a doctor use indirect reasoning to determine what was causing a patient's symptoms? **The doctor might use tests or information from the patient to determine things that were *not* causing the symptoms.**

Shows how to begin an indirect proof of a conditional statement.

Possible Answers

1. For any conditional, assume (1) the hypothesis is true and (2) the conclusion is false (the *negation* of the conclusion).

ALTERNATE EXAMPLE

Transparency AE 11-1A

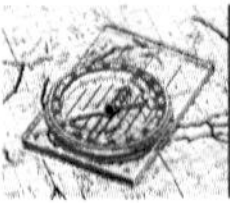

11-1 PART A Indirect Reasoning

← CONNECT → ***The proofs that you've done so far have been direct proofs. In a direct proof, you assume that the hypothesis of a conjecture is true and show that the conclusion must also be true. Now you will investigate another strategy for proof.***

The Ellery Queen mystery series is comprised of about 33 books written from 1929 to 1971.

When using **indirect reasoning,** you show that a statement is true by proving that it cannot be false. In the following passage from *The Greek Coffin Mystery* (1932), detective Ellery Queen uses indirect reasoning to show that a suspect is innocent of murder.

Now, if Mr. Knox had been the murderer, why hadn't he removed the [$1000] bill, as I said a moment ago? . . . You see, his action was so wholly at variance with what he would have done had he been the murderer or the accomplice, that I was compelled to say at that time: "Well, no matter where the guilt lies, it certainly isn't in the direction of James Knox."

To prove that James Knox was *not* guilty, Ellery Queen first assumed that he *was* guilty! He showed that this assumption led to a contradiction.

There are three key steps in an indirect proof.

- Assume that the statement you are trying to prove is false. (If the statement is a conditional, you assume its hypothesis and **negate** its conclusion.)
- Show that this assumption leads to a contradiction of something you know is true.
- Conclude that your assumption was incorrect, so that the statement you originally wanted to prove must be true.

The word *not* is often important when writing the negation of a statement.

Statement	Negation
It is raining.	It is not raining.
The lines are not coplanar.	The lines are coplanar.

1. Give a conditional statement in if-then form. What would you assume in order to begin an indirect proof of your statement?

710 11-1 • INDIRECT REASONING AND INEQUALITIES

Research Note

Informational feedback is more useful to children than grades....[It] tells children specifically what behavior shows achievement or what action will lead to attaining goals, and it conveys the idea that learning results from effort and leads to feelings of self-worth. (Emma E. Holmes, "Motivation: An Essential Component of Instruction," *Teaching and Learning Mathematics in the 1990s, 1990 Yearbook,* Thomas J. Cooney and Christian R. Hirsch, eds., p. 106. © 1990 NCTM.)

TRY IT

a. It rains and I do not wash my car.
b. $m\angle R = 20°$, and $\overline{ST} \not\cong \overline{XY}$

What would you assume in order to begin an indirect proof of each of the following?

a. If it rains, then I will wash my car. **b.** If $m\angle R = 20°$, then $\overline{ST} \cong \overline{XY}$.

The following Example shows a complete indirect proof.

EXAMPLE

Use an indirect proof to prove the following.

If two lines intersect, then they intersect in only one point.

First, we assume the hypothesis and negate the conclusion of the statement we are trying to prove.

Two lines intersect and they do not intersect in only one point. (That is, they intersect in more than one point.)

In the following proof, we show that this leads to a contradiction.

Proof: Assume that two lines, m and n, both contain D and E. This contradicts the Straight-Line Postulate: "Two points are contained in one and only one line." Therefore, the original statement cannot be false, so the statement "If two lines intersect, then they intersect in only one point" must be true.

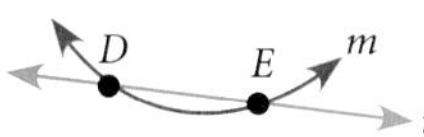

EXPLORE: NOT FALSE = ?

Use an indirect proof to prove the following.

If a perpendicular segment is drawn from a point not on a line to the line, then it is the shortest such segment.

1. Write the negation of the conclusion of the statement.
2. Assume that this statement is true. In that case, there must be another segment from the point to the line that is shorter than the perpendicular segment. Draw and label a figure showing the line, the point not on the line, the perpendicular segment, and the "shorter" segment.
3. Use the Pythagorean Theorem to show that your assumption leads to a contradiction. What is the contradiction?
4. What do you conclude? Explain how you can justify this conclusion.

Student Resources

- Alternative Lessons 11-1A
- Laboratory Manual 11-1A
- Technology Lab Manual
- Practice 11-1A
- Study Guide and Journal 11-1A
- Guía de estudios y Diario 11-1A
- Multilingual Handbook
- More Look Back 11-1A
- SAT Preparation

Media Resources

- Transparency FFM 11-1A
- Transparency AE 11-1A
- Teaching Transparency
- AWSMTest and practice software
- AWSM Videodisc

EXPLORE

Not False = ?

Recommended group size: 4

The Point
To use indirect reasoning to prove that the shortest segment from a point to a line is the perpendicular segment.

Look and Listen...

- For students who do not understand how to draw a "shorter" segment in Step 2.
- For groups who do not see how the Pythagorean Theorem leads to a contradiction.

Ask...

- Is the situation that you're sketching actually possible? Why might your figure look unusual?
- If one number is equal to the sum of two other positive numbers, which of them is the largest?

For Groups That Finish Early
Explain why the altitude to a side of a triangle cannot be longer than the other two sides of the triangle. **The altitude is the perpendicular segment to the line containing that side, so it must be the shortest segment.**

Follow Up
Ask a different student or group of students to present their answer to each step.

Possible Answers

1. It is not the shortest such segment.

2.

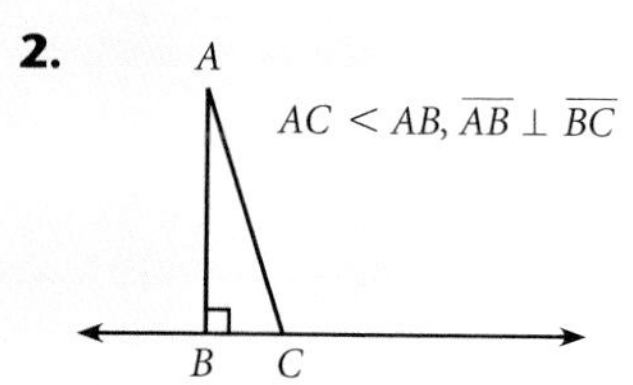

3–4. See Additional Answers p. T726.

Journal

Reflect 1 and 3 and **Exercise** 13 are suitable for journal entries.

Indirect Reasoning and Inequalities

REFLECT

Possible Answers

1. In indirect reasoning, you prove that a statement is true by first assuming it is false and then showing that your assumption contradicts a known fact, thus proving that your original statement must be true. It is called *indirect* because it involves proving that the original statement is not false instead of directly showing that it is true.

2. In each strategy, you prove that a conjecture is true in all cases by using undefined terms, definitions, theorems, and postulates. In both, you assume the hypothesis of the conjecture is true. However, in direct proof, you show that the conclusion must also be true. In indirect reasoning, you assume that the conclusion is false and then show that this assumption leads to a contradiction.

3. In indirect proof, the sequence of steps is not as straightforward as in a direct proof, so it is more difficult to write out in a two-column or flow-proof format.

Part A Exercises

Exercise Notes

Core

9–11. Students negate statements made by Cicero, Queen Victoria, and Mark Twain.

14. Guides students through an indirect proof.

More Math Reasoning

33. In 33a, students solve a familiar problem: to find the average speed for a trip, given the distance and time. Students sometimes think that the "rate" that they solve for in a time-rate-distance problem must be the speed maintained for the entire trip. However, in 33b, they see that they should not make this assumption.

Indirect reasoning is an important tool in logic. It is used by mechanics working on automobiles and by physicians in diagnosing diseases. They study the ailments of the engine or patient and list the causes that might produce these ailments. Eliminating possibilities that contradict a known fact can lead them to the actual cause of the problem.

REFLECT

1. Write a short description of indirect reasoning. Why do you think indirect reasoning is called *indirect*?

2. Briefly explain the similarities and differences between direct proof and indirect proof.

3. Paragraph proof is the format most often used to demonstrate an indirect proof. Why do you think this is the case?

Exercises

CORE

P **Getting Started It's important to be able to recognize contradictions when doing indirect proofs. For each set of statements, identify the two that form a contradiction.**

1. (a) $ABCD$ is a rectangle. (a), (b)
(b) $ABCD$ is a trapezoid.
(c) $ABCD$ is a quadrilateral.

2. (a) $\overleftrightarrow{AB} \nparallel \overleftrightarrow{CD}$ (b), (c)
(b) $\overleftrightarrow{AB}$ and $\overleftrightarrow{CD}$ are skew lines.
(c) $\overleftrightarrow{AB} \perp \overleftrightarrow{CD}$

P **Write the negation of the conclusion of each statement.**

3. If it is Monday, then tomorrow is Tuesday.

4. If $3x < 24$, then $x < 8$.

5. If I catch a fish, then I won't throw it back.

6. If $a = b$, then $a + c = b + c$.

7. If $AB = DE$, then $\triangle ABC \cong \triangle DEF$.

8. If $\triangle ABC$ is scalene, then $\angle A \ncong \angle B$.

P **In Exercises 9–11, write the negation of each statement from a famous author or statesperson.**

9. The good of the people is the most important law. [Cicero (106–43 B.C.)]

10. We are not amused. [Queen Victoria (1819–1901)]

11. The report of my death was an exaggeration. [Mark Twain (1835–1910)]

R **12.** If the probability that an event will occur is p, what is the probability that it will not occur?

Key

V Vocabulary
P Practice/Skills
R Review
MR Math Reasoning
PS Problem Solving
C Challenge

Alert

Some students find indirect reasoning difficult—working with an assumption that cannot be true can be confusing. You may want to emphasize the fact that they are looking for a *contradiction*, and suggest that they look for it in theorems and postulates that relate to the statement to be proved.

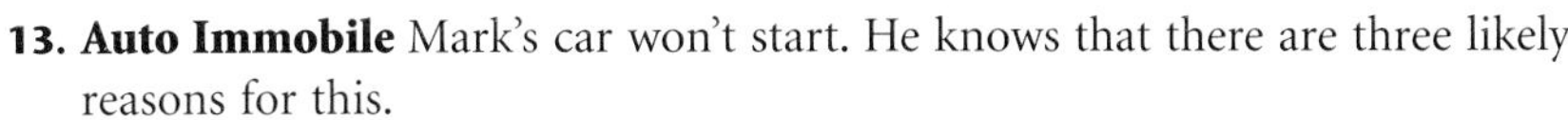

13. Auto Immobile Mark's car won't start. He knows that there are three likely reasons for this.
(1) His battery is dead. (2) His starter doesn't work. (3) He is out of gas.

When a car's starter needs to be replaced, the car is silent when you try to start it. If the battery is dead, the engine "turns over" slowly, if at all. When Mark tries to start his car, it sounds normal. What do you think is wrong with his car? Explain your reasoning. In your explanation, be sure to discuss any indirect reasoning you may have used.

14. Follow the given steps to prove the following.

If a point is not on a line, then there is no more than one perpendicular from the point to the line.

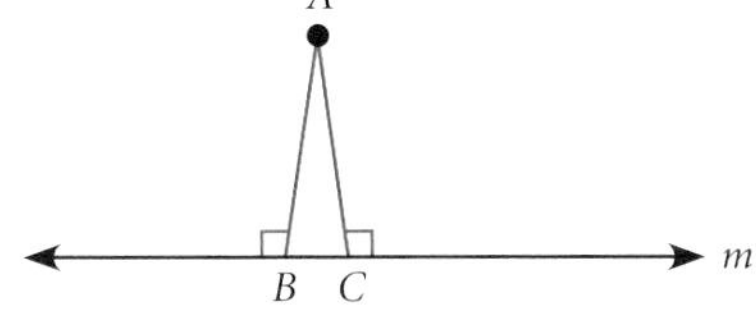

a. Write the negation of the conclusion of the statement you are trying to prove.
b. Explain how the figure at the right illustrates this.
c. Explain how assuming that this negation is true leads to a contradiction of a known fact or theorem.

Use an indirect proof to prove each of the following.

15. A right triangle has only one right angle.

16. If $\triangle ABC$ is scalene, then $\angle A \ncong \angle C$.

17. *Given:* Quadrilateral $PQRS$, $\overline{PQ} \cong \overline{QR}$, and $\overline{PS} \ncong \overline{RS}$.

Prove: $\overline{QS}$ does not bisect $\angle PQR$.

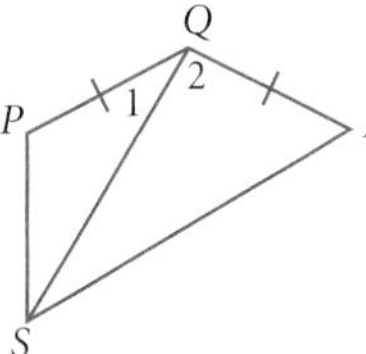

18. Describe a method for finding the minimum distance between two parallel lines. Explain why your method works.

LOOK BACK

Find the sum of the measures of the interior and exterior angles (one at each vertex) for each polygon. Then give the measure of each interior and exterior angle of the polygon. [6-1, 6-3]

19. regular octagon **20.** regular 12-gon **21.** regular 20-gon

$\triangle ABC \sim \triangle EDF$. Find each of the following. [7-2]

22. $m\angle B$ 61° **23.** BC 54 **24.** $m\angle E$ 79°

25. $m\angle C$ 40° **26.** $m\angle F$ 40° **27.** EF 32

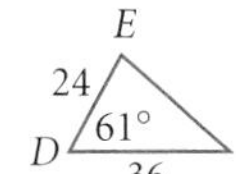

28. Sketch a wallpaper pattern that has translation symmetry and point symmetry. [10-2]

Ongoing Assessment

Self-Assessment Exercises 1, 3, 5, 7, 8, 9, 11, 12, 15

Embedded Assessment Explore Step 4; Exercises 4, 6, 10, 16

Exercise Answers

Core

3. Tomorrow is not Tuesday.

4. $x \geq 8$.

5. I will throw it back.

6. $a + c \neq b + c$

7. $\triangle ABC \ncong \triangle DEF$

8. $\angle A \cong \angle B$

9. The good of the people is not the most important law.

10. We are amused.

11. The report of my death wasn't an exaggeration.

12. $1 - p$

13. He is out of gas; A normal sound contradicts the symptoms associated with the other causes.

14. a. There is more than one line perpendicular to a given line from a point not on the line.

b. It shows two perpendicular segments from point A to line m.

c. Possible answer: If $\overline{AB}$ and $\overline{AC}$ are two distinct line segments, then $m\angle A > 0$, and A, B, C form a triangle. $\angle ABC$ and $\angle ACB$ must each be 90° since they are supplementary angles to right angles. This implies that the sum of the angle measures in $\triangle ABC$ is greater than 180°, which contradicts the Triangle Angle-Sum Theorem.

15. Possible answer: Suppose there are two right angles. Then the sum of the measures of the angles in the triangle is greater than 180°, which contradicts the Triangle Angle-Sum Theorem.

16. Assume $\triangle ABC$ is scalene, and suppose $\angle A \cong \angle C$. Then $\overline{AB} \cong \overline{CB}$ by the converse of the Isosceles Triangle Theorem, which contradicts the definition of a scalene triangle. Therefore, $\angle A \ncong \angle C$.

17–21., 28–33.
See Additional Answers p. T726.

Indirect Reasoning and Inequalities

PART B At a Glance

Objective

To discover that the longest side of a triangle is opposite the largest angle and vice versa.

Development

First, students see algebraic Properties of Inequality that they will use as they explore triangle inequalities.

Then, in the **Explore,** students discover that the longer the side of a triangle, the larger its opposite angle.

Suggested Materials

Student Ruler, protractor, geometry software

First Five Minutes

Transparency FFM 11-1B

Read the paragraphs at the bottom of page 714 and the Properties of Inequality at the top of page 715. Then name the Property of Inequality illustrated by each of the following.

1. $2 < 4$ and $4 < 6$, so $2 < 6$.
Transitive Property

2. If $x = y + 2$, then $x > y$.
Comparison Property

3. If $AB < CD$, then $AB + BC < CD + BC$. Addition Property

Motivate

Ask...

- Suppose you know that two sides of a triangle have equal lengths. Can you draw any conclusions about the angles in the triangle? The angles opposite those sides are congruent.

MORE PRACTICE

P **Write the negation of the conclusion of each statement.**

29. If $\overline{PQ} \not\perp \ell$, then $\angle 1$ is not a right angle.

30. If two planes intersect, then they intersect in no more than one line.

31. If ℓ is not parallel to m, then $\angle 1 \not\cong \angle 2$.

MORE MATH REASONING

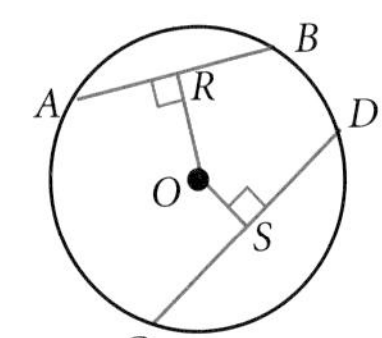

MR, C **32.** Prove: In circle O, if $\overline{AB} \not\cong \overline{CD}$, then $\overline{OR} \not\cong \overline{OS}$.

MR **33. An Indirect Route** David rode his motorcycle from Lincoln to Omaha, a 55-mi trip on Interstate 80.

a. If the trip took David 45 minutes, prove that he went faster than the 65 mi/hr speed limit for at least part of the trip.

b. David's friend, Iona, rode with him for the first half of the trip. She claims that David did not go faster than 65 mi/hr while the two rode together. Is Iona telling the truth? Explain.

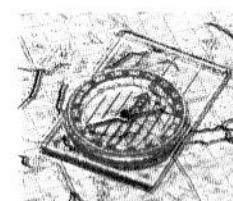

11-1 PART B Inequalities in a Triangle

← CONNECT → ***You've already explored congruent sides and congruent angles in triangles. Now you will investigate parts of a triangle that are not congruent.***

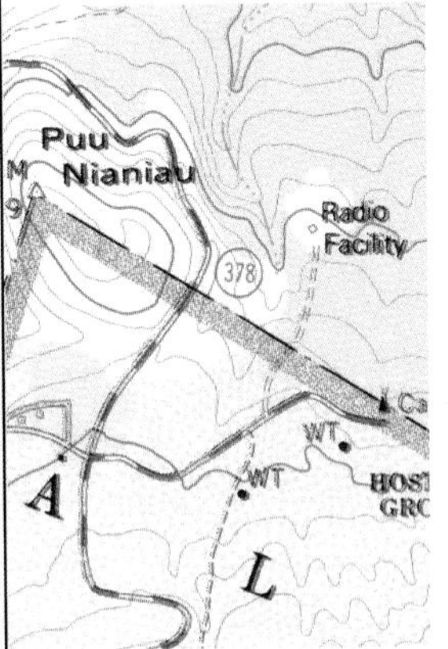

Orienteers can look at a map like the one at the left and visualize their approach to every checkpoint. You can also apply these skills to geometry. If you look at an accurate figure, you may be able to make a good guess at which sides and angles are the largest or smallest. In mathematics, however, you need to make sure that your visual intuition is correct and provide a justification for your ideas.

You will be showing that parts of triangles have unequal measures. To do this, you will need the help of some properties of inequality, which are reviewed on page 715.

Key

V Vocabulary
P Practice/Skills
R Review
MR Math Reasoning
PS Problem Solving
C Challenge

PROPERTIES OF INEQUALITY

The following are true for all real numbers a, b, and c.

Trichotomy Law	Exactly one of the following is true: $a < b$, $a = b$, or $a > b$.
Transitive Property	If $a < b$ and $b < c$, then $a < c$.
Addition Property	If $a < b$, then $a + c < b + c$.
Comparison Property	$a > b$ if and only if there is a $c > 0$ such that $a = b + c$.

1. How can you use the Comparison Property to show that the measure of an exterior angle of a triangle is greater than the measure of either of its remote interior angles? (In other words, prove that $m\angle YXZ > m\angle YWX$, and $m\angle YXZ > m\angle WYX$.)

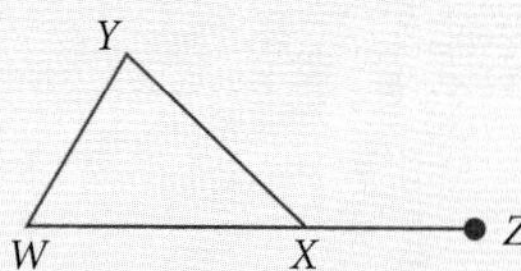

In the following Explore, you will investigate a relationship between the lengths of the sides of a triangle and the measures of its angles.

EXPLORE: THE LITTLEST ANGLE

MATERIALS

Ruler, Protractor
Geometry software (optional)

Draw several scalene triangles. Measure the sides and angles of one of the triangles. Make as many conjectures as you can that involve the longest and shortest sides and the largest and smallest angles. Use your other triangles to check your conjectures. Then discuss your conjectures with classmates.

Student Resources
- Alternative Lessons 11-1B
- Laboratory Manual 11-1B
- Technology Lab Manual
- Practice 11-1B
- Study Guide and Journal 11-1B
- Guía de estudios y Diario 11-1B
- Multilingual Handbook
- More Look Ahead 11-1B
- SAT Preparation

Media Resources
- Transparency FFM 11-1B
- Transparency AE
- Teaching Transparency
- AWSMTest and practice software
- AWSM Videodisc

Possible Answer

1. $\angle YWX$ and $\angle WYX$ are remote interior angles for $\angle YXZ$. Thus, $m\angle YXZ = m\angle YWX + m\angle WYX$. By the Comparison Property, $m\angle YXZ > m\angle YWX$ and $m\angle YXZ > m\angle WYX$.

EXPLORE

The Littlest Angle

Recommended group size: 2

The Point

To discover the relationship between opposite side lengths and angle measures in triangles.

Look and Listen...

- For students who are not seeing the connection between side lengths and angle measures.

Ask...

- Which side of a right triangle is the longest? Which angle is the largest? Is there a connection between the two?

For Groups That Finish Early

Suppose right triangle $\triangle ABC$ with hypotenuse $\overline{BC}$ shares $\overline{BC}$ with equilateral triangle $\triangle BCD$. Write an inequality involving AB and CD. Explain your reasoning. $AB < CD$. $\overline{BC}$ is the longest side in $\triangle ABC$, and $CD = BC$.

Follow Up

Ask students to summarize their conjectures. Then ask them to make a conjecture about the longest side in an obtuse triangle.

Possible Answers

If two sides of a triangle have unequal lengths, the angle opposite the longer side is larger than the angle opposite the shorter side.

If two angles of a triangle have unequal measures, the side opposite the larger angle is longer than the side opposite the smaller angle.

11-1

Indirect Reasoning and Inequalities

Journal

Reflect 1 and 3 and **Exercise** 16 are suitable for journal entries.

REFLECT

Possible Answers

1. We know that the right angle must be the largest angle; therefore, from the second theorem above, the side opposite it (the hypotenuse) must be the longest side. The Pythagorean Theorem can also be used to justify this fact.
2. They are converses of each other.
3. No. The concept of "opposite side" does not apply in a polygon with more than three sides.

TRY IT

a. Largest: $\angle C$; Smallest: $\angle B$
b. Largest: $\angle E$; Smallest: $\angle D$
c. Largest: $\angle R$; Smallest: $\angle RSP$
d. Longest: $\overline{AC}$; Shortest: $\overline{AB}$
e. Longest: $\overline{QT}$ or $\overline{QR}$; Shortest: $\overline{TS}$
f. Longest: $\overline{VX}$; Shortest: $\overline{WV}$

Name the largest and smallest angles in the triangles in each figure.

a.

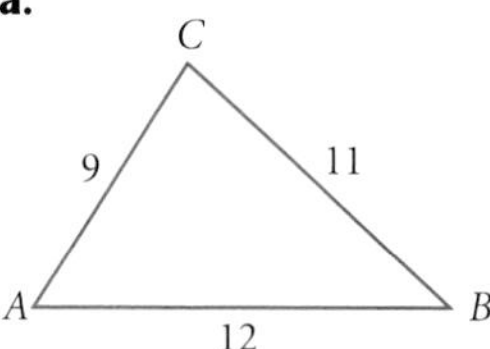

b.

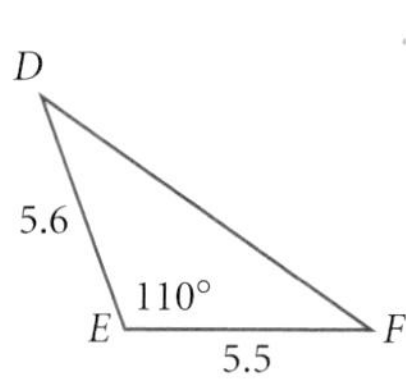

c.

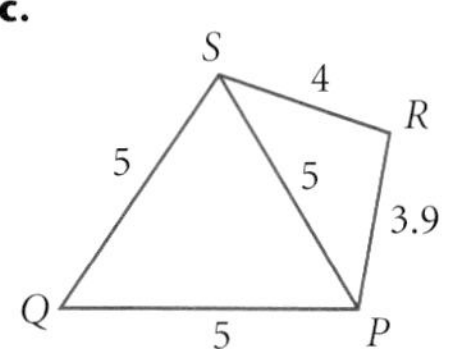

Name the longest and shortest segments in each figure.

d.
A 30°
130°
20°
B
C

e.

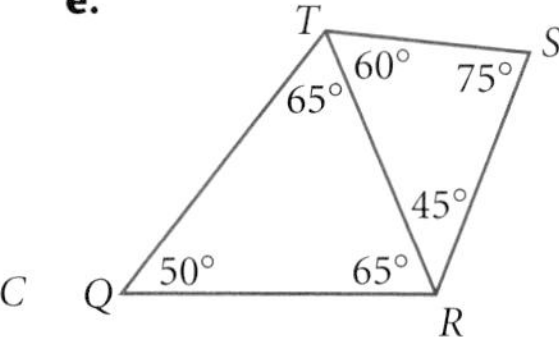

f.

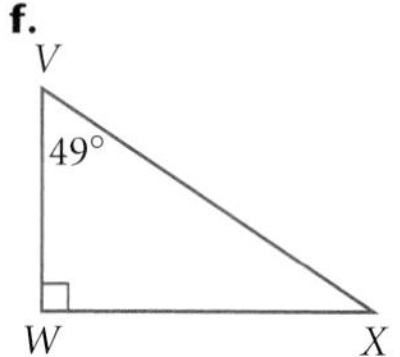

The relationships you've discovered among triangle side lengths and angle measures are summarized below. In Exercise 22, you will use indirect proof to justify one of these theorems.

> **THEOREMS**
>
> If two sides of a triangle have unequal lengths, then the measure of the angle opposite the longer side is greater than the measure of the angle opposite the shorter side.
>
> If two angles of a triangle have unequal measures, then the side opposite the larger angle is longer than the side opposite the smaller angle.

REFLECT

1. Use one of the above theorems to explain why the hypotenuse is the longest side of a right triangle. Then describe another way to justify this fact.
2. How are the two theorems about unequal side lengths and angle measures in triangles related to each other?
3. Is the shortest side of any convex polygon opposite its smallest angle? Explain.

Diversity Issues

[I]t may be that emphasizing [mathematics'] value as a tool for future career possibilities will keep the girls in the courses long enough to begin to see its beauty. When girls...become aware that mathematics may be the key to their future,... the number of girls participating in mathematics-related courses may increase. (Dianne Tobin and Lynn H. Fox, "Career Interests and Career Education: A Key to Change," *Women and the Mathematical Mystique,* Lynn H. Fox, Linda Brody, and Dianne Tobin, eds., p. 189. © 1980 The Johns Hopkins University Press.)

Exercises

CORE

Getting Started **Name the largest and smallest angles in each figure.**

1. Largest: ∠B; Smallest: ∠C

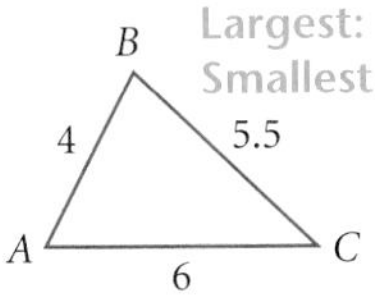

2. Largest: ∠D; Smallest: ∠E

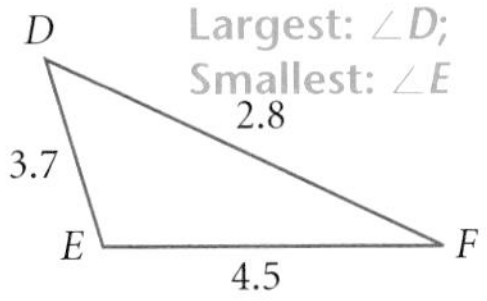

3. Largest: ∠H; Smallest: ∠G

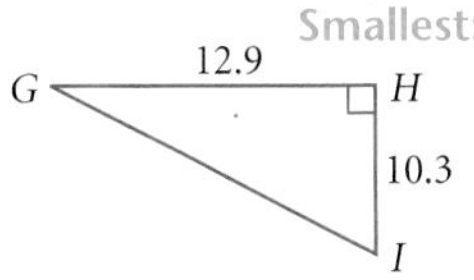

4. Which side of $\triangle QPR$ is the longest? Why?

5. Which side of $\triangle QRS$ is the longest? Why?

6. Which side of $\triangle QPR$ is the shortest?

7. Which side of $\triangle QRS$ is the shortest?

8. Which side of quadrilateral $PQSR$ is the longest? $\overline{PQ}$

9. Which side of quadrilateral $PQSR$ is the shortest? $\overline{QS}$

10. List the segments in the figure from shortest to longest. $\overline{QS}$, $\overline{SR}$, $\overline{QR}$, $\overline{PR}$, $\overline{PQ}$

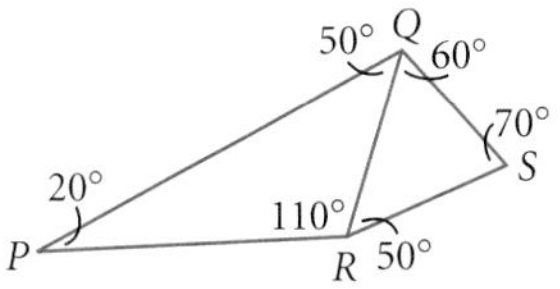

Name the longest and shortest segments in each figure.

11. Longest: $\overline{RT}$; Shortest: $\overline{RS}$

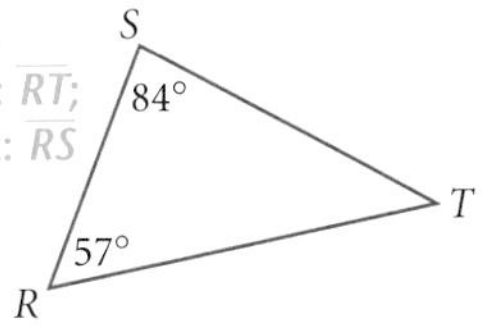

12. Longest: $\overline{BC}$; Shortest: $\overline{DC}$

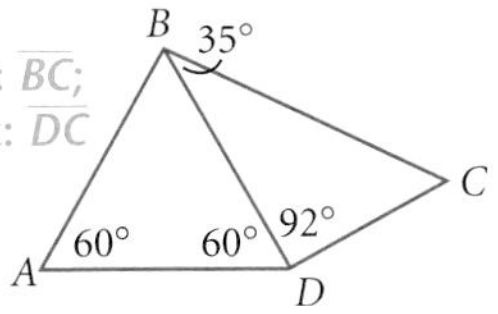

13. Longest: $\overline{EF}$; Shortest: $\overline{DE}$

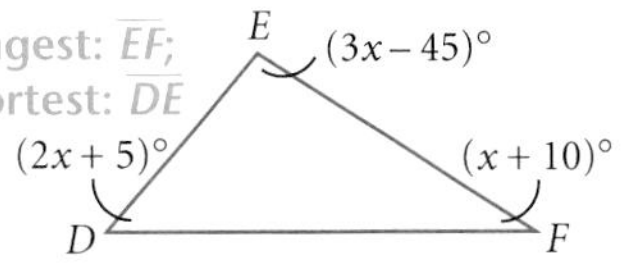

14. The coordinates of the vertices of $\triangle ABC$ are $A(-1, 1)$, $B(2, 2)$, and $C(0, 5)$. List the angles of $\triangle ABC$ from smallest to largest. ∠C, ∠A, ∠B

15. Ohio Angle On a map, the approximate distance from Akron to Youngstown is 40 miles, the distance from Youngstown to Steubenville is 50 miles, and the distance from Steubenville to Akron is 75 miles. Identify the largest angle of the triangle formed by these three cities, and explain your answer. If you used a sketch to help you, include it with your explanation.

Part B Exercises

Exercise Notes

Core

14. Students use the distance formula to find side lengths of a triangle and then list the angles from smallest to largest.

22. This is an indirect proof of one of the theorems from this part.

Look Ahead

These exercises prepare students to work with the Triangle Inequality Theorem in 11-1 Part C.

More Math Reasoning

40. Students solve an algebraic inequality.

Exercise Answers

Core

4. $\overline{PQ}$; $\overline{PQ}$ is opposite the largest angle in $\triangle QPR$.

5. $\overline{QR}$; $\overline{QR}$ is opposite the largest angle in $\triangle QRS$.

6. $\overline{QR}$; $\overline{QR}$ is opposite the smallest angle in $\triangle QPR$.

7. $\overline{QS}$; $\overline{QS}$ is opposite the smallest angle in $\triangle QRS$.

15.

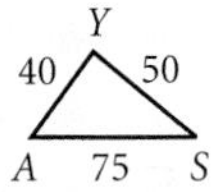

The angle at Youngstown, which is opposite the longest side.

Key

Vocabulary

Practice/Skills

Review

MR Math Reasoning

PS Problem Solving

Challenge

Ongoing Assessment

Self-Assessment Exercises 1–13 odd, 17, 19, 21

Embedded Assessment Try It b; Exercises 6, 12, 15, 22

Indirect Reasoning and Inequalities

16. a. Barika

b. Barika is closer to the checkpoint than she is to Alicia. The measure of the angle at the checkpoint is 60°. Therefore the side opposite $\angle A$ is shorter than the side opposite the angle at the checkpoint.

21. Possible answer: Suppose $\overline{JK}$ is the shortest side of $\triangle JKL$, and $\angle L$ is obtuse. Then $m\angle L > 90°$, and since the angle measures must sum to 180°, $m\angle L > m\angle K$ and $m\angle L > m\angle J$. Thus $JK > JL$ and $JK > KL$; $\overline{JK}$ is the longest side, which contradicts the given fact that $\overline{JK}$ is the shortest side.

22. a. If $BC = AB$, then $\triangle ABC$ is an isosceles triangle and $m\angle A = m\angle C$ by the Isosceles-Triangle Theorem, which contradicts the given information.

b. If $BC < AB$, then $m\angle A < m\angle C$, which contradicts the given information.

c. The negation of $BC > AB$ is $BC \leq AB$, which is equivalent to $BC < AB$ or $BC = AB$. Both possibilities must be addressed.

PS **16. Who's Closer?** Two participants in an orienteering competition, Alicia and Barika, know each other's location. Alicia, at point A, finds that $m\angle A = 55°$. Barika finds that $m\angle B = 65°$.

a. Who is closer to the checkpoint?

b. Is one participant closer to the checkpoint than to her competitor? If so, which one? How do you know?

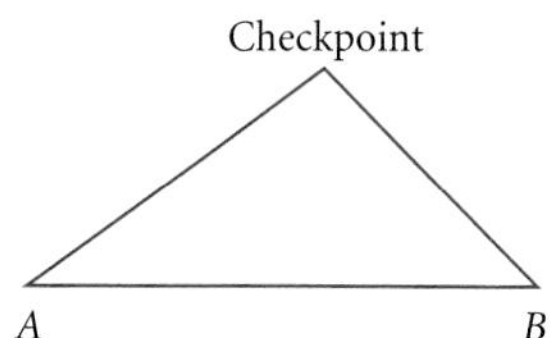

P **In $\triangle RST$, $RS = 3$, and $RT = 4$. The length of $\overline{ST}$ is chosen randomly from the numbers 2, 3, 4, 5, and 6. Find each of the following.**

17. The probability that $\angle R$ is the largest angle in $\triangle RST$ $\frac{2}{5}$

18. The probability that $\angle T$ is the smallest angle in $\triangle RST$ $\frac{3}{5}$

19. The probability that $\triangle RST$ is isosceles $\frac{2}{5}$

20. The probability that $\triangle RST$ is a right triangle $\frac{1}{5}$

MR **21.** Use an indirect proof to prove the following.

If $\overline{JK}$ is the shortest side of $\triangle JKL$, then $\angle L$ is not an obtuse angle.

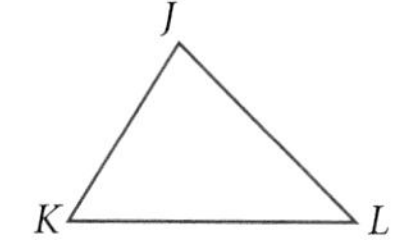

MR **22.** Use an indirect proof to prove the following theorem.

If two angles of a triangle have unequal measures, then the side opposite the larger angle is longer than the side opposite the smaller angle.

Given: $m\angle A > m\angle C$

Prove: $BC > AB$

a. Part 1: Assume $BC = AB$.

b. Part 2: Assume $BC < AB$.

c. Why must this proof be done in two parts?

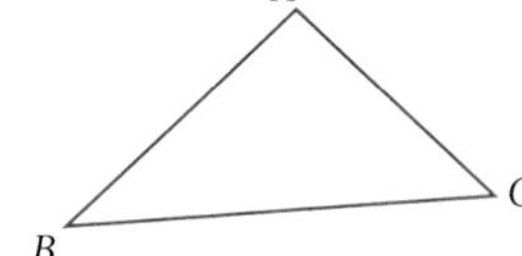

LOOK AHEAD

P **23.** Write a single inequality that combines the two statements $x < y$ and $y < z$. $x < y < z$

P **In the table, the sum of any two numbers in a row must be greater than the third number. Write an inequality that expresses the range of possible values for *c*.**

	a	b	c	
24.	3.0	5.0		$2 < c < 8$
25.	10.0	15.0		$5 < c < 25$
26.	1.7	3.3		$1.6 < c < 5$

Key

V Vocabulary
P Practice/Skills
R Review
MR Math Reasoning
PS Problem Solving
C Challenge

MORE PRACTICE

27. Which side of $\triangle WXZ$ is the longest? Why?

28. Which side of $\triangle XYZ$ is the longest? Why?

29. Which side of $\triangle WXZ$ is the shortest?

30. Which side of $\triangle XYZ$ is the shortest?

31. Which side of quadrilateral $WXYZ$ is the longest? $\overline{XY}$

32. Which side of quadrilateral $WXYZ$ is the shortest? $\overline{WX}$

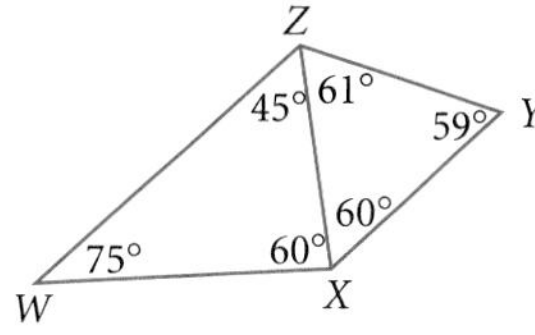

Name the largest and smallest angles in the triangles in each figure.

33. Largest: $\angle Y$; Smallest: $\angle X$

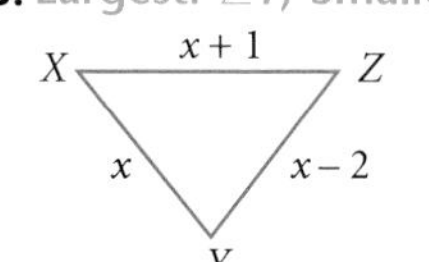

34. Largest: $\angle M$; Smallest: $\angle N$

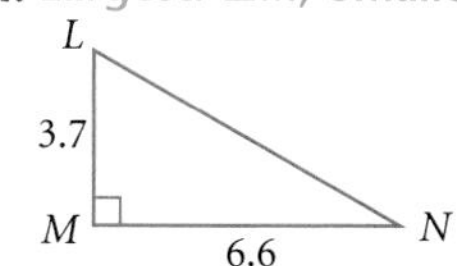

35. Largest: $\angle DAC$ and $\angle ACB$; Smallest: $\angle CAB$ and $\angle ACD$

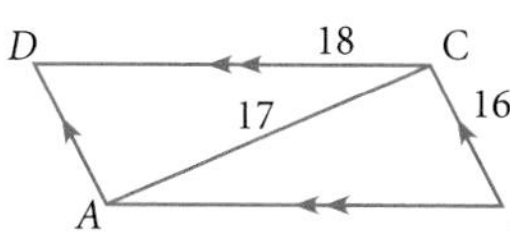

Name the longest and shortest sides in each figure.

36.

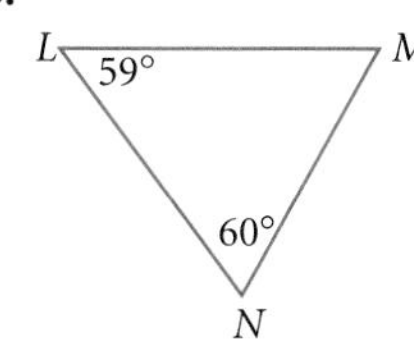

Longest: $\overline{LN}$; Shortest: $\overline{MN}$

37.

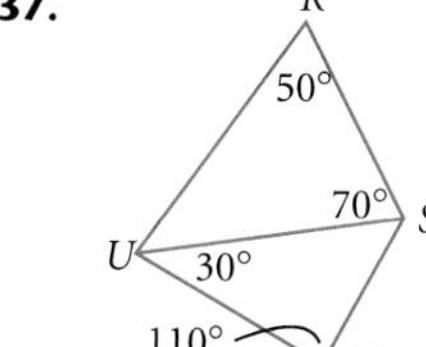

Longest: $\overline{UR}$; Shortest: $\overline{ST}$

38.

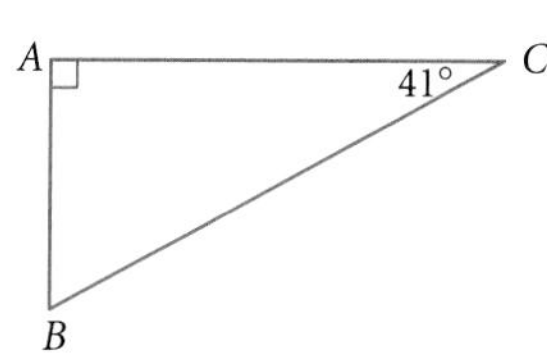

Longest: $\overline{BC}$; Shortest: $\overline{AB}$

39. The coordinates of the vertices of $\triangle DEF$ are $D(-1, 4)$, $E(2, 0)$, and $F(-3, -1)$. List the angles of $\triangle DEF$ from smallest to largest. $\angle F$, $\angle D$, $\angle E$

MORE MATH REASONING

40. Refer to the figure at the right. If $m\angle 1 = 70°$, $m\angle 2 = (2x - 10)°$, and $m\angle 3 = (3x - 40)°$, write an inequality that expresses the range of possible values for x.

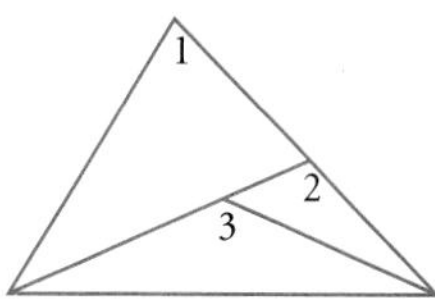

41. *Given:* $\triangle ABC$ is isosceles, with legs $\overline{AB}$ and $\overline{AC}$, and R is any point on $\overleftrightarrow{BC}$ that is not on $\overline{BC}$.

Prove: $RA > AB$

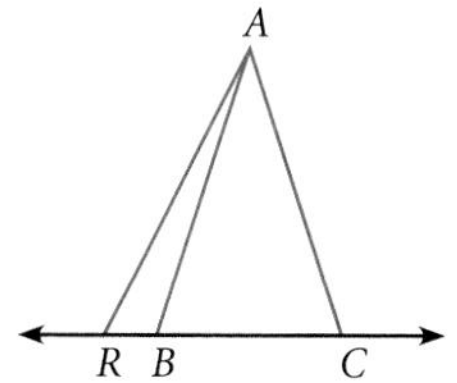

More Practice

27. $\overline{ZX}$; $\overline{ZX}$ is opposite the largest angle in $\triangle WXZ$.

28. $\overline{XY}$; $\overline{XY}$ is opposite the largest angle in $\triangle XYZ$.

29. $\overline{WX}$; $\overline{WX}$ is opposite the smallest angle in $\triangle WXZ$.

30. $\overline{ZX}$; $\overline{ZX}$ is opposite the smallest angle in $\triangle XYZ$.

More Math Reasoning

40. $70 < 2x - 10 < 3x - 40 < 180$, so $40 < x < 73\frac{1}{3}$

41. Possible answer: $\triangle ABC$ is isosceles from the given information. $\angle ABC \cong \angle ACB$ by the Isosceles-Triangle Theorem, so $m\angle ABC = m\angle ACB$. $m\angle ABC > m\angle ARB$ by the Exterior Angle Inequality Theorem. By substitution, $m\angle ACB > m\angle ARB$. Therefore, $RA > AB$ because it is opposite the larger angle in $\triangle ARC$.

Indirect Reasoning and Inequalities

PART C At a Glance

Objective

To discover and apply the Triangle Inequality Theorem.

Development

In the **Explore,** students cut strips of paper to given lengths. They see which combinations of these strips make triangles and in doing so, they discover the Triangle Inequality Theorem.

Suggested Materials

Student Scissors, ruler, paper

First Five Minutes

Transparency FFM 11-1C

Write an inequality to represent each statement.

1. x is less than or equal to 3. $x \leq 3$
2. y is between 4 and 7. $4 < y < 7$
3. k can have any value between 2 and 10, including 2 and 10. $2 \leq k \leq 10$

Motivate

Ask...

- City A is 10 mi from City B, and City B is 8 mi from City C. What can you say about the distance from City A to City C? **It is at least 2 mi but no more than 18 mi.**

EXPLORE

Is It a Triangle?

Recommended group size: 4

The Point

To discover that the sum of the lengths of two sides of a triangle must be greater than the length of the third (the Triangle Inequality Theorem).

11-1 PART C The Triangle Inequality Theorem

← CONNECT → ***You've looked at inequalities that involve the sides and angles of a triangle. Now you will investigate a triangle inequality that involves just side lengths. This inequality will help you understand why a straight line segment is the shortest path between two points.***

Other things being equal, orienteers travel in a straight line from one checkpoint to the next. Why? In the following Explore, you will discover a relationship that governs side lengths in a triangle. This relationship helps you identify the shortest path between two points.

EXPLORE: IS IT A TRIANGLE?

MATERIALS

Scissors
Ruler
Paper

1. Cut out strips of paper 1 cm wide with lengths of 2 cm, 3 cm, 4 cm, 5 cm, 8 cm, and 11 cm. Draw a line segment down the center of each strip, and write down its length, as shown.

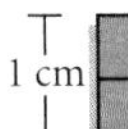

2. Choose three strips at random. See if you can use them to form a triangle like the one shown at the right. Make a table to record the lengths of the three strips and whether or not they form a triangle.

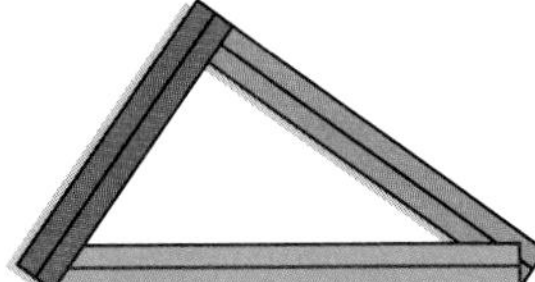

3. Repeat Step 2 until you have several combinations of side lengths that do and do not form triangles. Then write an inequality to describe the relationship among the side lengths of any triangle.

TRY IT

Determine whether each set of numbers could represent the lengths of the sides of a triangle.

a. 4, 7, 10 Yes **b.** 3, 5, 8 No **c.** 3, 5, 7.9 Yes

History Connection

Emmy Noether (1882–1935) was a major force in the development of abstract algebra. She received her doctorate from the University of Erlangen, Germany, in 1907 and became a professor at the University of Göttingen in 1922. Noether made important contributions to a mathematical formulation of the general theory of relativity.

EXAMPLE

Two sides of a triangle measure 6 cm and 9 cm. Write an inequality that represents the range of values for the possible lengths of the third side.

Let x represent the length of the unknown side. The sum of the lengths of two sides of a triangle must be greater than the length of the third side.

Therefore: $x + 6 > 9$ and $6 + 9 > x$

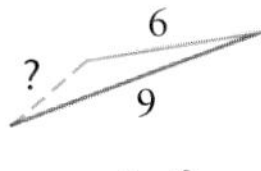

$x > 3$ and $15 > x$

Putting these two inequalities together, we find that $3 < x < 15$. The length of the third side must be greater than 3 cm but less than 15 cm.

The observation you've made about triangle side lengths is stated below.

TRIANGLE INEQUALITY THEOREM

The sum of the lengths of any two sides of a triangle is greater than the length of the third side.

The Triangle Inequality Theorem helps you see why a line segment is the shortest path between two points.

REFLECT

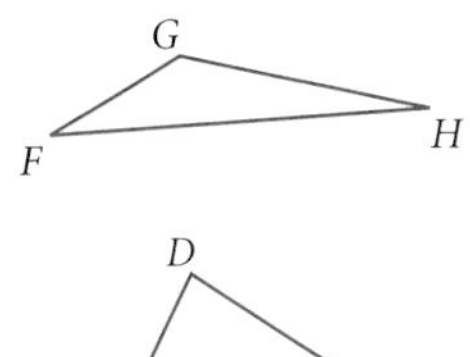

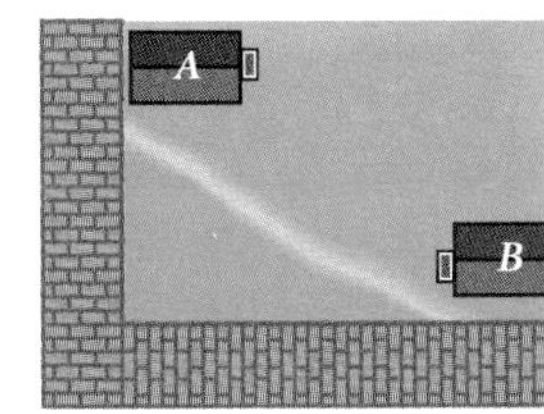

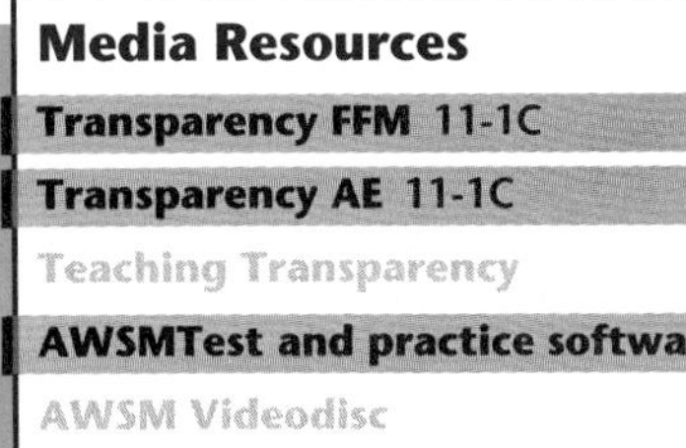

1. Other things being equal, why does an orienteer prefer to travel in a straight line from point F to point H rather than going from F to G to H?
2. Write all the side-length relationships you can for scalene triangle $\triangle CDE$, using the Triangle Inequality Theorem.
3. The two brick sidewalks shown at the right connect buildings A and B. However, people have walked through the grass between the buildings so often that they have worn a path in the grass. Use the Triangle Inequality Theorem to explain why this path is there.

Student Resources
- Alternative Lessons 11-1C
- Laboratory Manual 11-1C
- Technology Lab Manual
- Practice 11-1C
- Study Guide and Journal 11-1C
- Guía de estudios y Diario 11-1C
- Multilingual Handbook
- More Look Ahead 11-1C
- SAT Preparation

Media Resources
- Transparency FFM 11-1C
- Transparency AE 11-1C
- Teaching Transparency
- AWSMTest and practice software
- AWSM Videodisc

Look and Listen...

- For students who are not considering sums of side lengths.

Ask...

- Take the 3-cm and 5-cm strips. Identify the lengths that will not work for the third side. What is true about the side lengths that are too long to make a triangle? too short?

For Groups That Finish Early

If x and y are the lengths of two sides of a triangle, and $x > y$, write an inequality that gives the range of values for the length of the third side, z. $x - y < z < x + y$

Follow Up

Ask students to share their results to Step 3. Then have them use their strips of paper to explain why this relationship makes sense.

Possible Answers

2. The following combinations make a triangle: 2, 3, 4; 2, 4, 5; 3, 4, 5; 4, 5, 8; 4, 8, 11; 5, 8, 11.

3. The sum of the lengths of any two sides of a triangle is greater than the length of the third side.

ALTERNATE EXAMPLE

Transparency AE 11-1C

Journal

Reflect 1 and 3 and **Exercise** 13 are suitable for journal entries.

REFLECT

Possible Answers

1. Because the shortest path between two points on a flat surface is a straight line segment.
2. $CD + DE > CE$

   $CD + CE > DE$

   $CE + DE > CD$
3. According to the Triangle Inequality Theorem, the sum of the lengths of two sides of a triangle is greater than the length of the third. Therefore, walking through the grass is shorter than walking around the corner to get from one building to the other.

Indirect Reasoning and Inequalities

Part C Exercises

Exercise Notes

Core

9–11. Students use the Triangle Inequality Theorem to find ranges of distances between cities.

13. Applies the Triangle Inequality Theorem to kitchen design.

14. Students see and apply the Hinge Theorem, which involves inequalities in two triangles.

Look Ahead

These exercises review algebraic skills that are important in 11-2.

More Math Reasoning

31. Students use the Triangle Inequality Theorem to help justify the optimal placement for a well.

Exercise Answers

Core

7. The shortest route is M to N to Q to X and the length of the shortest route is between 10 and 18. There are two possible routes. The route M to N to P to X has length $4 + 8 + 6 = 18$. The route M to N to Q to X has length $4 + 6 + QX = 10 + QX$. By the Triangle Inequality Theorem, $PQ < QN + PN$, so $6 + QX < 8 + 6$ or $QX < 8$. Therefore, $10 + QX < 18$.

8. Let y be the length of the third side. Then $y + 4 > 7$ and $4 + 7 > y$, or $3 < y < 11$. Since y is an integer, the possible values of y are 4, 5, 6, 7, 8, 9, and 10.

9. Between 701 and 1411

10. Between 1229 and 1939

11. Between 566 and 2602

12. Assume $AB + BC = AC$ and suppose A, B, C are not collinear. Then A, B, C form a triangle, and $AB + BC > AC$. This contradicts the given information that $AB + BC = AC$. Therefore, $A, B,$ and C are collinear.

Algebra | Functions | Discrete Math | Probability | Data/Statistics

Exercises

CORE

P **Getting Started Determine whether each set of numbers could represent the lengths of the sides of a triangle.**

1. 3, 4, 6 Yes **2.** 10, 12, 22 No **3.** 3.2, 5.5, 8.8 No

P **The lengths of two sides of a triangle are given. Write an inequality that represents the range of values for the possible lengths of the third side.**

4. 3, 5 $2 < x < 8$ **5.** $13\frac{1}{2}, 24\frac{4}{5}$ $11\frac{3}{10} < x < 38\frac{3}{10}$ **6.** $n, 3n$ $2n < x < 4n$

PS, MR **7.** Find the shortest route from M to X along the segments shown. (The figure may not be drawn to scale.) Give a value or range of values for the length of this route. Explain how you found the shortest route.

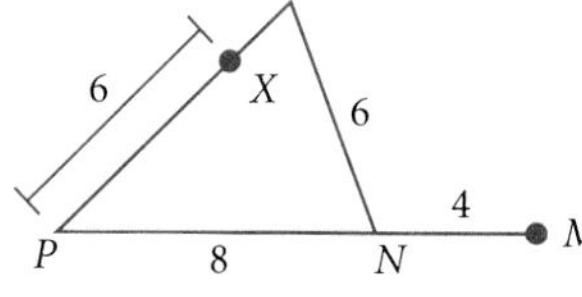

PS **8.** Suppose you know that the lengths of all three sides of a triangle are integers and that the lengths of two of its sides are 4 and 7. Give all of the possible lengths for the third side. Explain how you found your answer.

PS **The map shows air travel distances from Minneapolis to four other cities. Use the Triangle Inequality Theorem to find the range of possible distances between the following pairs of cities.**

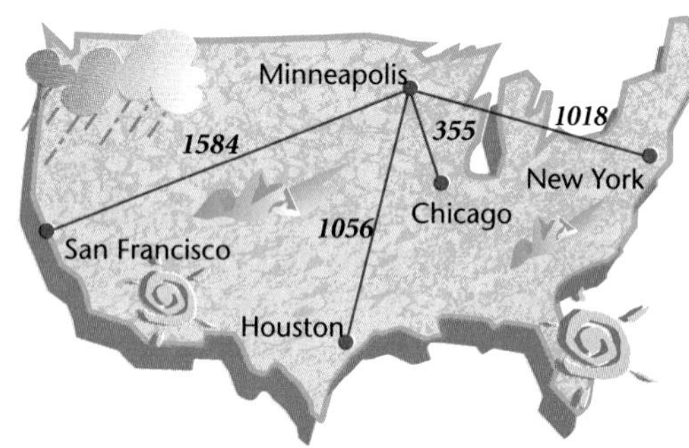

9. Chicago and Houston

10. San Francisco and Chicago

11. New York and San Francisco

MR **12.** Use an indirect proof to prove the following.

If $AB + BC = AC$, then A, B, and C are collinear.

A B C

PS **13. Cooking with Geometry** When installing a kitchen, it is recommended that the sum of the distances between the sink, stove, and refrigerator should be less than 26 ft and more than 12 ft. Also, no leg of this "kitchen triangle" should be less than 4 ft long or more than 9 ft long.

a. Why do you think these distance recommendations exist?

b. In a kitchen, the sink is 4 ft from the stove, and the stove is 4 ft from the refrigerator. Find the minimum and maximum possible distances from the sink to the refrigerator that meet the preceding recommendations.

Key

V Vocabulary
P Practice/Skills
R Review
MR Math Reasoning
PS Problem Solving
C Challenge

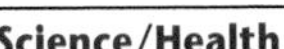

Logic/Reasoning | Industry/Careers | Science/Health | Social Science/History | Fine Arts/Literature

14. The Hinge Theorem **a.** Using a ruler, draw $\triangle EFG$ as shown. Measure EF and FG, and then use your protractor to find $m\angle F$.

b. Now draw $\angle K$ so that $m\angle K > m\angle F$. Locate points J and L on the sides of $\angle K$ so that $\overline{KJ} \cong \overline{FE}$ and $\overline{KL} \cong \overline{FG}$. Draw $\overline{JL}$ to complete $\triangle JKL$.

c. Measure $\overline{EG}$ and $\overline{JL}$. Which is longer? How does this relate to the relationship between $m\angle F$ and $m\angle K$?

d. The Hinge Theorem begins, "If two sides of one triangle are congruent to two sides of a second triangle and the measure of the included angle of the first triangle is greater than the measure of the included angle of the second triangle, then . . ." Complete the Hinge Theorem.

e. Why do you think this theorem is called the Hinge Theorem?

f. What conclusion can you draw from the figure at the right, using the Hinge Theorem? Justify your conclusion.

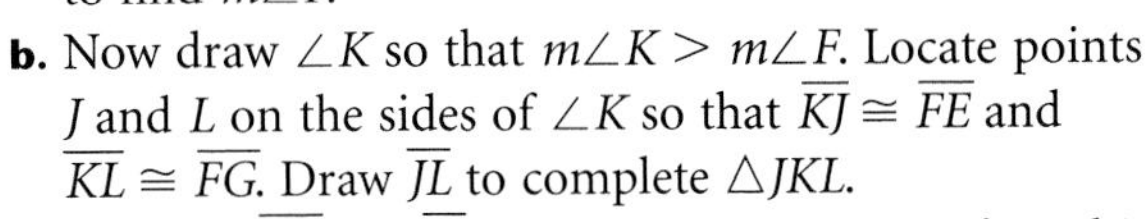
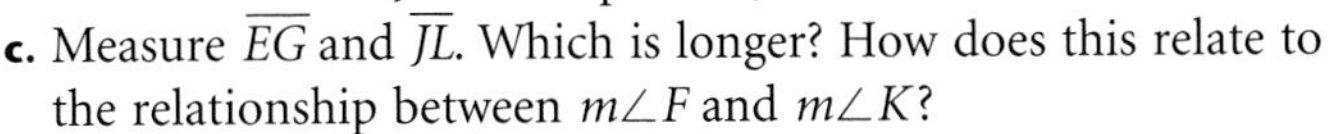
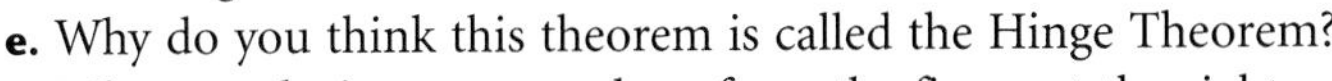
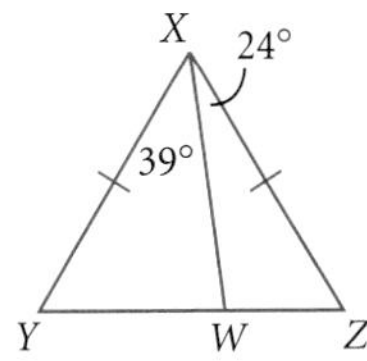

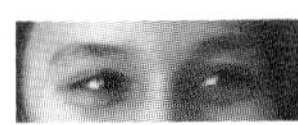

LOOK AHEAD

Solve each formula for the specified variable.

15. $A = \frac{1}{2}bh$, for h $h = 2\frac{A}{b}$

16. $P = 2\ell + 2w$, for w $w = \frac{P - 2\ell}{2}$

17. $A = 4\pi r^2$, for r $r = \pm\frac{1}{2}\sqrt{\frac{A}{\pi}}$

Rewrite the second equation in each pair so that y is in terms of x only. (Hint: Use substitution.)

18. $z = 2x$
$y = 3x + 2z$ $y = 7x$

19. $z = \frac{4}{x}$
$y = 2x^2 + 12xz$ $y = 2x^2 + 48$

20. $3z + 12x = 6$
$y = 7x^3 + 2z$ $y = 7x^3 + 4 - 8x$

MORE PRACTICE

Determine whether each set of numbers could represent the lengths of the sides of a triangle.

21. 2, 7, 8 Yes

22. 9, 14, 20 Yes

23. $2\frac{1}{2}, 4\frac{1}{3}, 6\frac{2}{3}$ Yes

24. 1.5, 9.2, 7.7 No

25. $\frac{1}{3}, \frac{2}{5}, \frac{1}{4}$ Yes

26. 18.5, 5.3, 13.8 Yes

The lengths of two sides of a triangle are given. Write an inequality that represents the range of values for the possible lengths of the third side.

27. 10, 15 $5 < y < 25$

28. 14, 22 $8 < y < 36$

29. n, $2n$ $n < y < 3n$

Ongoing Assessment

Self-Assessment Exercises 1–11 odd

Embedded Assessment Exercises 4, 6, 8, 10, 12, 13

13. a. Possible answer: The maximum distance recommendation could exist to insure convenience for the kitchen user. The minimum distance recommendation could exist to insure safety for the kitchen user.

b. Less than 8 ft and more than 4 ft

14. a.

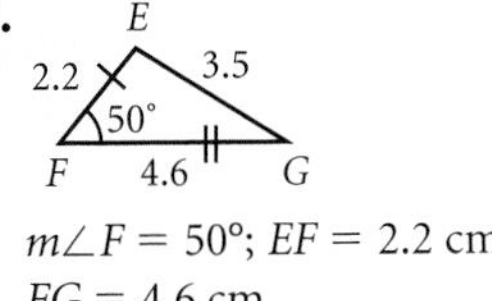

$m\angle F = 50°$; $EF = 2.2$ cm; $FG = 4.6$ cm

b. Possible answer:

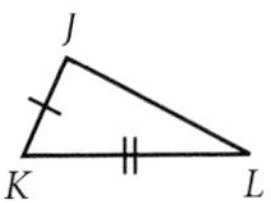

c. $\overline{JL}$ is longer, corresponding to $m\angle K$ being larger than $m\angle F$.

d. The length of the side opposite the included angle of the first triangle is greater than the length of the side opposite the included angle of the second triangle.

e. Possible answer: When two hinged sides are opened wider, the distance between the far ends of the sides increases.

f. Since $\overline{XY} \cong \overline{XZ}$, $\overline{XW} \cong \overline{XW}$ by the Reflexive Property, and $m\angle YXW > m\angle WXZ$, we know $YW > WZ$ by the Hinge Theorem.

More Math Reasoning

30. a. $6 < t < 276$; $64 < v < 346$; $109 < w < 301$; $39 < x < 231$

b. Triangle Inequality Theorem

c. Each traveled a distance $d = t + v + w + x$; Because of upper limits from part a, $d < 1154$. From the Triangle Inequality Theorem, $x + w > 340$ and $v + t > 340$, so $d > 680$. So the claims of A and B are impossible, and C's is possible only if C did unnecessary driving.

31. See Additional Answers p. T726.

Algebra | Functions | Discrete Math | Probability | Data/Statistics

Indirect Reasoning and Inequalities

PART D At a Glance

Objective

To use triangle inequalities to find the shortest path on an orienteering map.

Development

In the **Explore,** students use triangle inequalities to find the shortest path through an orienteering course.

First Five Minutes

Transparency FFM 11-1D

Explain why the straight-line distance from City A to City B is always shorter than the sum of the straight-line distances from City A to City C to City B. The Triangle Inequality Theorem guarantees that the length of one side of a triangle is shorter than the sum of the lengths of the other sides.

EXPLORE

Path Finder

Recommended group size: 2

The Point

To use triangle inequalities to find the shortest path through an orienteering course.

Look and Listen...

- For students who are not justifying their choices.

Ask...

- How do you *know* that the segment/path you chose is shorter than the alternative?

For Groups That Finish Early

Design your own orienteering course similar to the one on page 725. Give just enough information for a person to be able to find the shortest route.

Follow Up

Ask the winning group to share their solution with the class and to justify the decisions they made.

MORE MATH REASONING

PS Social Science

30. The map at the right shows distances between several cities.

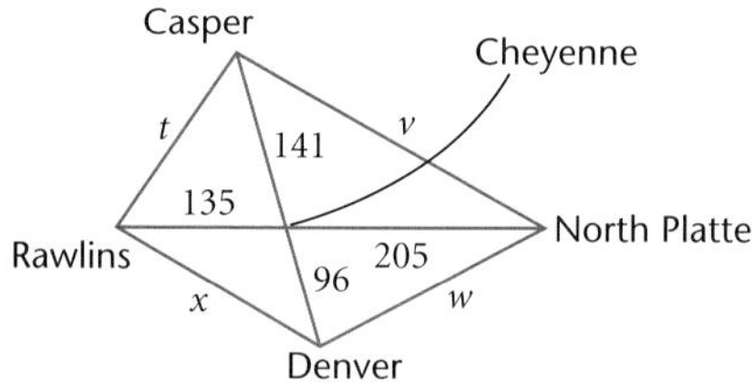

a. What is the possible range of distances for t? v? w? x?

b. What theorem did you use in **30a**?

c. Each of three travelers drove through all of the cities shown (except Cheyenne) and ended up where they started. Traveler A claimed to have traveled 600 mi, Traveler B 900 mi, and Traveler C 1325 mi. Explain why each of these mileages is possible or impossible.

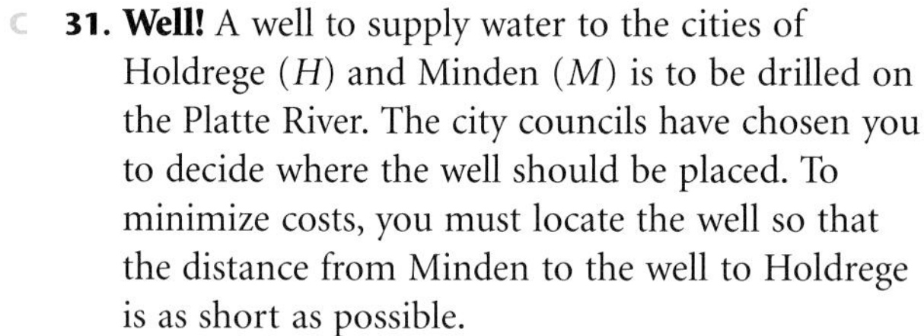

MR, C

31. Well! A well to supply water to the cities of Holdrege (H) and Minden (M) is to be drilled on the Platte River. The city councils have chosen you to decide where the well should be placed. To minimize costs, you must locate the well so that the distance from Minden to the well to Holdrege is as short as possible.

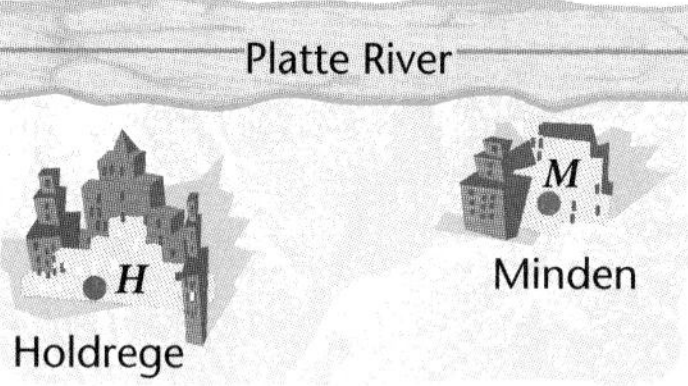

a. Copy the figure, and find the best location for the well. (Hint: Use a technique from Chapter 10.)

b. Use the Triangle Inequality Theorem and your knowledge of transformations to convince the city councils that you've found the best site. (Hint: Draw any other point, X, on the river, and show that the distance from H to your point to M must be shorter than the distance from H to X to M.)

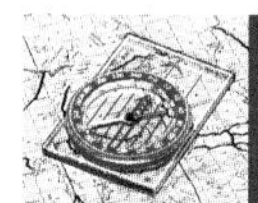

11-1 PART D Making Connections

← CONNECT → ***Industries that connect locations with wires or cables—like telephone, power, and cable television companies—need to find the shortest paths that join these points. You've investigated shortest paths, explored their connections to inequalities in triangles, and looked at another strategy for proof.***

In the following Explore, you will use geometry to find the shortest path that links two points. As shown on the map at the left, this skill can be important in planning long trips, as well as in orienteering.

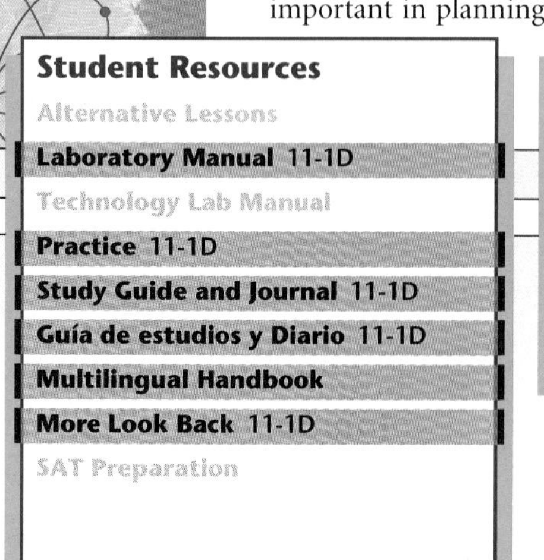

Student Resources

- Alternative Lessons
- **Laboratory Manual 11-1D**
- Technology Lab Manual
- **Practice 11-1D**
- **Study Guide and Journal 11-1D**
- **Guía de estudios y Diario 11-1D**
- **Multilingual Handbook**
- **More Look Back 11-1D**
- SAT Preparation

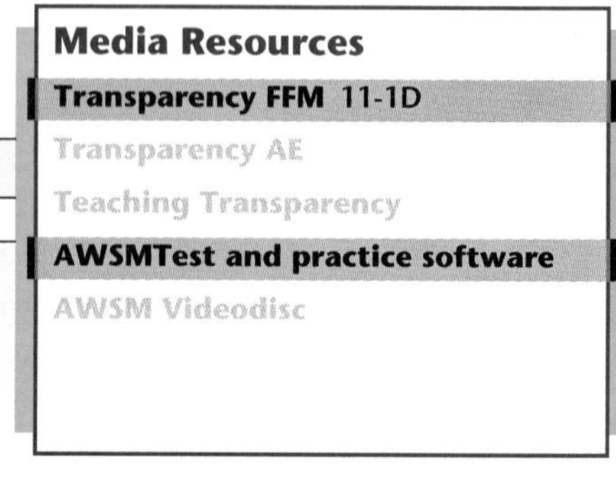

Media Resources

- **Transparency FFM 11-1D**
- Transparency AE
- Teaching Transparency
- **AWSMTest and practice software**
- AWSM Videodisc

Logic/Reasoning | Industry/Careers | Science/Health | Social Science/History | Fine Arts/Literature

EXPLORE: PATH FINDER

Your "geometeering" team is in a competition to find the shortest path from point *A* to point *I*. You may only travel along the segments shown in the figure. Beware—the figure is not necessarily drawn accurately!

To win, you must find the shortest path from *A* to *I* and justify each decision you make along the way. The first team with the correct path and valid explanations for all of its choices wins the competition. On your mark . . . get set . . . go!

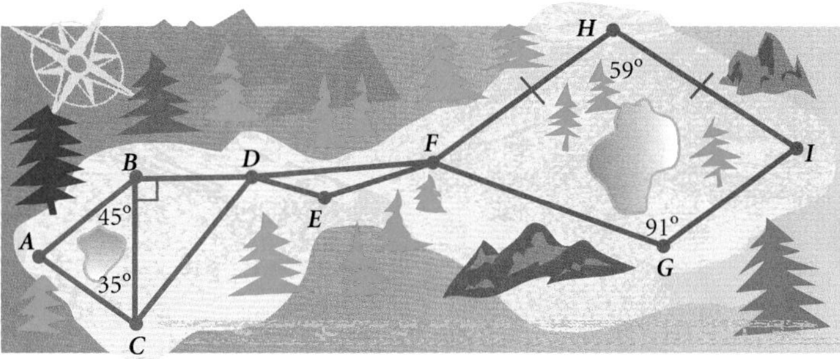

Possible Answer

The path from *A* to *B* to *D* to *F* to *G* to *I* is the shortest.

$AB < AC$ because $\overline{AB}$ is opposite a smaller angle, and $BD < CD$ because $\overline{CD}$ is the hypotenuse of the right triangle. Thus, $AB + BD$ is less than $AC + CD$.

The Triangle-Inequality Theorem guarantees that it is shorter to go directly from *D* to *F* than from *D* to *E* to *F*.

$\overline{FI}$ (not drawn) is the longest side in $\triangle FGI$ because it is opposite the largest angle. The base angles of isosceles $\triangle FHI$ each measure 60.5°, so $\overline{FI}$ is its shortest side. This means that $FH > FI > FG$ and $HI > FI > GI$, so the path from *F* to *G* to *I* is shorter than the one from *F* to *H* to *I*.

Portfolio

Have students select items from their work that demonstrate their understanding of the material in 11-1.

You may wish to have students include an indirect proof, an **Exercise** where they used a triangle inequality to solve a real-world problem, and a **Reflect** question that they found interesting or challenging.

REFLECT

1. In your own words, describe the process of indirect proof.
2. Write a summary of all the inequalities you know relating to triangles. Include drawings with your summary.
3. Is the base of an isosceles triangle always its shortest side? Explain.

REFLECT

Possible Answers

See Additional Answers p. T726.

Self-Assessment

P **Write the negation of the conclusion of each statement.**

1. If an animal is a horse, then it does not have toes. The animal does have toes.
2. If $\angle A \cong \angle B$, then $\angle B \cong \angle A$. $\angle B \not\cong \angle A$
3. If I try out for softball, then I might make the team. I cannot make the team.

P 4. List the segments in the figure at the right from shortest to longest. $\overline{XY}, \overline{YZ}, \overline{XZ}, \overline{WZ}, \overline{XW}$

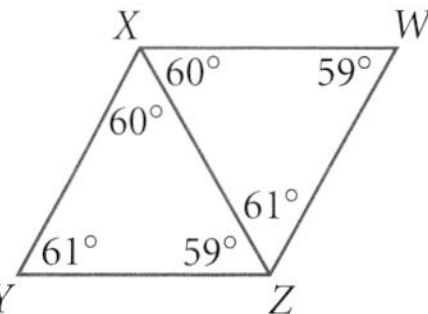

Self-Assessment

Exercise Notes

12–13. Similar to multiple-choice questions on standardized tests.

15. Students see that the shortest path between two points is not always the fastest.

16. Applies the Triangle Inequality Theorem in a probability setting.

ey

Vocabulary
Practice/Skills
Review
R Math Reasoning
S Problem Solving
Challenge

11-1

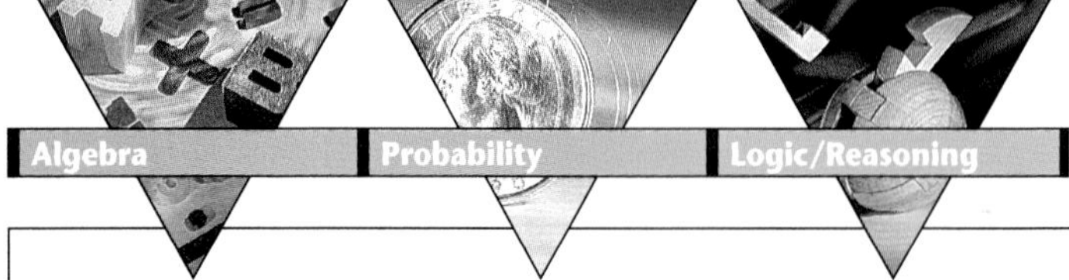

Indirect Reasoning and Inequalities

Self-Assessment Answers

6. Possible answer:

8. Interior: 120°; Sum: 720°
Exterior: 60°; Sum: 360°

9. Interior: 144°; Sum: 1440°
Exterior: 36°; Sum: 360°

10. Interior: 156°; Sum: 2340°
Exterior: 24°; Sum: 360°

11. The two triangles are similar because vertical angles and alternate interior angles of parallel lines are congruent; Let x be the distance across the swamp, so $\frac{62}{120} = \frac{54}{x}$, $x = \frac{54(120)}{62}$; Therefore, $x \approx 104.5$ m.

14. Possible answer: Assume $\triangle ABD$ is scalene, $\overline{AC}$ is a median, and suppose $\overline{AC} \perp \overline{BD}$. $\overline{BC} \cong \overline{DC}$ by definition of *median*. $\angle ACB$ and $\angle ACD$ are right angles by definition of perpendicular. $\triangle ACB$ and $\triangle ACD$ are right triangles by definition. $\overline{AC} \cong \overline{AC}$ by the Reflexive Property. $\triangle ACB \cong \triangle ACD$ by the LL Theorem. $\overline{AB} \cong \overline{AD}$ by CPCTC, which contradicts the assumption that $\triangle ABD$ is scalene. Therefore, $AC \not\perp BD$.

15. a. Possible answer: Marvin should travel by way of point X since that route has to be less than twice as long as the other (X to 9 is less than 750 m).

b. By the Triangle Inequality Theorem, $d + 250 \text{ m} > 500 \text{ m}$, so $d > 250$ m. Therefore, $\angle 3$ is the smallest because it is opposite the shortest side. It cannot be determined which is the largest since d may be greater or less than 500 m.

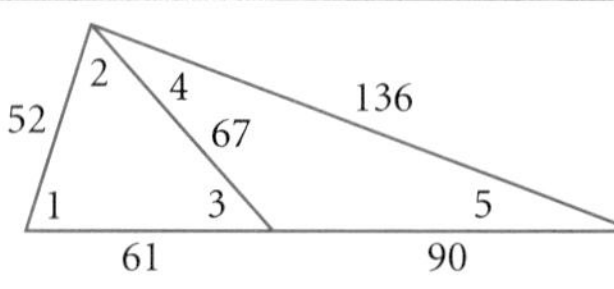

P **5.** List the numbered angles in the figure at the right from smallest to largest. $\angle 5$, $\angle 4$, $\angle 3$, $\angle 2$, $\angle 1$

R **6.** Sketch a frieze pattern that has translation symmetry, vertical line symmetry, and glide-reflection symmetry. [10-2]

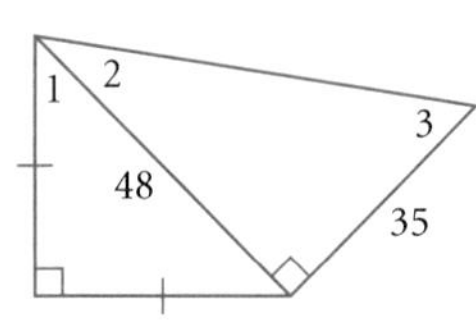

P **7.** List the numbered angles in the figure at the right from smallest to largest. $\angle 2$, $\angle 1$, $\angle 3$

R **Find the sum of the measures of the interior and exterior angles (one at each vertex) for each polygon. Then give the measure of each interior and exterior angle. [6-1, 6-3]**

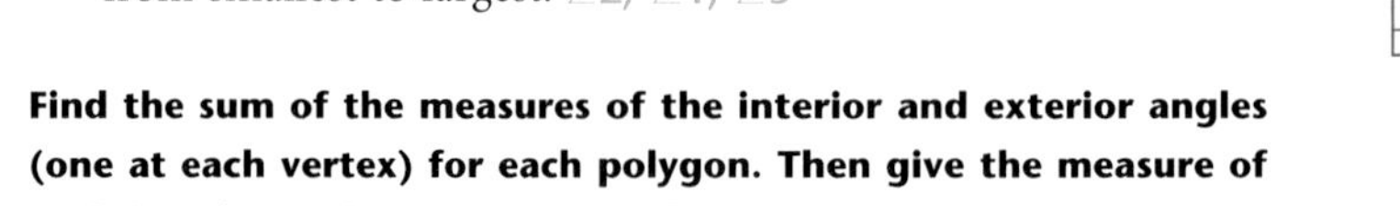

8. regular hexagon **9.** regular decagon **10.** regular 15-gon

R **11. Bogged Down** In an orienteering competition, Helena needs to know how far it is across the swamp. Find the distance, and explain how you found it. [7-2]

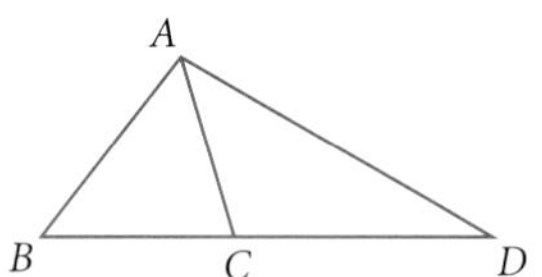

P **The lengths of two sides of $\triangle EFG$ are given. Choose the number that could represent the length of the third side.**

12. $EF = 3$, and $FG = 8$. EG could be (c)
(a) 4 (b) 5 (c) 6 (d) 12

13. $EF = 2x$, and $FG = 4x$. EG could be (a)
(a) $5x$ (b) $6x$ (c) $7x$ (d) $8x$

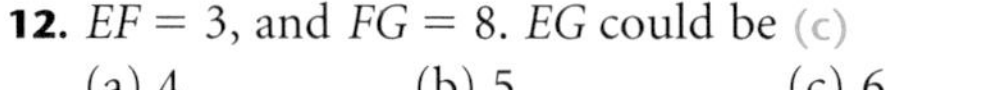

MR **14.** Use an indirect proof to prove the following.
If $\triangle ABD$ is scalene and $\overline{AC}$ is a median, then $\overline{AC} \not\perp \overline{BD}$.

A
B C D

PS, MR **15.** Marvin is in an orienteering competition, and he has reached Checkpoint 8. There are two ways to reach Checkpoint 9.

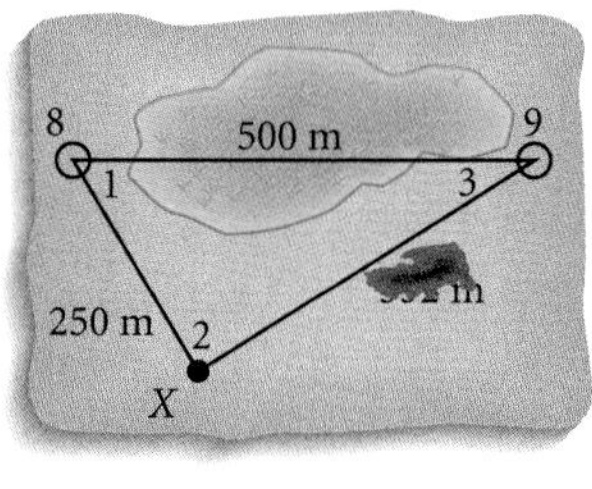

He can go directly from Checkpoint 8 to Checkpoint 9, but this route takes him through some swampy ground. He can go at twice the speed if he goes along a dirt path from Checkpoint 8 to point X and then to Checkpoint 9. (The distance from X to Checkpoint 9 is unreadable due to a smudge on the map.)

a. Which route should Marvin take? How do you know that this is the faster way for him to get to Checkpoint 9?

b. Which of the numbered angles in the figure is the smallest? Do you know which one is the largest? Explain.

PS **16.** Three sticks are chosen randomly from a set of sticks measuring 3, 5, 7, 9, and 11 cm. What is the probability that the three sticks will form a triangle? $\frac{7}{10}$

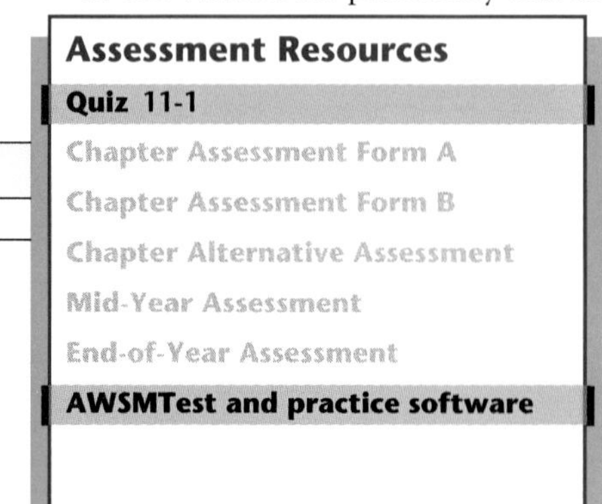

Assessment Resources
Quiz 11-1
Chapter Assessment Form A
Chapter Assessment Form B
Chapter Alternative Assessment
Mid-Year Assessment
End-of-Year Assessment
AWSMTest and practice software

Ongoing Assessment

Self-Assessment Self-Assessment Exercises

Embedded Assessment Reflect 1, 2, 3

ADDITIONAL ANSWERS

11-1 Part A Explore

3. Since $\triangle ABC$ is a right triangle with hypotenuse $\overline{AC}$, $AC^2 = AB^2 + BC^2$. All side lengths (and their squares) must be positive numbers. Thus, AC^2 must be greater than AB^2. Since the larger a positive number is, the larger its square root is, $AC > AB$. This contradicts the statement that $\overline{AC}$ is the shortest segment.

4. Conclude that the statement "If a perpendicular segment is drawn from a point not on a line to the line, then it is the shortest such segment" is true. It must be true because we have shown that it cannot be false.

11-1 Part A Exercises

17. Suppose $\overline{QS}$ bisects $\angle PQR$. Then $\angle 1 \cong \angle 2$ by the definition of *bisect*. $\overline{QS} \cong \overline{QS}$ by the Reflexive Property. $\overline{PQ} \cong \overline{RQ}$ is given. $\triangle PQS \cong \triangle RQS$ by the SAS Postulate. Therefore, $\overline{PS} \cong \overline{RS}$ by CPCTC, which contradicts the given information. Therefore, $\overline{QS}$ does not bisect $\angle PQR$.

18. Possible answer: Choose a point on one line and construct the perpendicular segment from it to the other line. The length of the perpendicular segment is the minimum distance between the parallel lines since the perpendicular segment from a point to the line is the shortest.

11-1 Part A Exercises

Look Back

19. Interior: 135°; Sum: 1080°
Exterior: 45°; Sum: 360°

20. Interior: 150°; Sum: 1800°;
Exterior: 30°; Sum: 360°

21. Interior: 162°; Sum = 3240°;
Exterior: 18°; Sum = 360°

28. Possible answer:

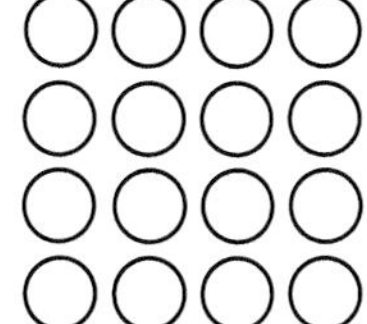

More Practice

29. $\angle 1$ is a right angle.

30. They intersect in more than one line.

31. $\angle 1 \cong \angle 2$

More Math Reasoning

32. Suppose $\overline{OR} \cong \overline{OS}$. Draw $\overline{OB}$ and $\overline{OD}$ to form right triangles $\triangle RBO$ and $\triangle SDO$. By the definition of *circle*, $\overline{OB} \cong \overline{OD}$, so $\triangle RBO \cong \triangle SDO$ by HL. By CPCTC, $\overline{RB} \cong \overline{SD}$, so $RB = SD$. A radius perpendicular to a chord bisects the chord, so R and S are the midpoints of $\overline{AB}$ and $\overline{CD}$. Thus, $AR = RB$ and $CS = SD$. By the Segment-Addition Postulate, $AB = AR + RB$ and $SC = CS + SD$. By substitution and algebra, $AB = 2RB$ and $CD = 2SD$. Using substitution and transitivity, $AB = CD$. This contradicts the given information. Our assumption must be incorrect, so $\overline{OR}$ is not congruent to $\overline{OS}$.

33. a. Suppose he went at most 65 mph. Then his trip took at least $\frac{55}{65}$ hours or $50\frac{10}{13}$ minutes, which contradicts the given information.

b. Iona may be telling the truth, since David could have driven at 65 or less while Iona was with him and driven faster for the rest of the trip.

11-1 Part C Exercises

31. a.

Platte River X W M′ M H Minden Holdrege

M' is the reflection of M across the river. Locate W where $\overleftrightarrow{HM'}$ intersects the river.

b. Let X be any other point on the river. $WM = WM'$ and $XM = XM'$ because reflections preserve distance. Therefore, $HW + WM = HW + WM' = HM'$. $HM' < HX + XM'$ by the Triangle Inequality Theorem and $HX + XM' = HX + XM$. So $HM + WM < HX + XM$.

11-1 Part D Reflect

1. In an indirect proof, assume that the statement you want to prove is false. (For a conditional statement, this means assuming that the hypothesis is true and the conclusion is false.) Then show that this assumption leads to a contradiction, proving that the original statement must be true.

2. The sum of the lengths of any two sides of a triangle is greater than the length of the third side.

If two sides of a triangle have unequal lengths, then the measure of the angle opposite the longer side is greater than the measure of the angle opposite the shorter side.

If two angles of a triangle have unequal measures, then the side opposite the larger angle is longer than the side opposite the smaller angle.

3. The base of an isosceles triangle is not always its shortest side. If the measures of the base angles are less than 60°, the vertex angle is the largest angle and the base the longest side.

11-2

Optimization

SUPERLESSON AT A GLANCE

Superlesson Goal

Students will investigate optimization problems and see how to use tables of values and graphs to find approximate solutions to these problems.

Management Guide

	Topic	Objectives	Key Terms	New Ideas	Materials
Part A	Optimizing Areas and Perimeters	To use different methods to solve optimization problems involving perimeters and areas.	Optimal solution	Optimization problems. Using graphing and tabular techniques to find optimal solutions.	**Student** Graphing utility, spreadsheet software **Teacher** Graph paper transparency, graphing calculator transparency
Part B	Optimizing Volumes and Surface Areas	To use different methods to solve optimization problems involving surface areas and volumes.		Using graphing and tabular techniques to optimize three-dimensional figures.	**Student** 9-in. by 12-in. paper, scissors, ruler, graphing utility, spreadsheet software **Teacher** Graph paper transparency, graphing calculator transparency
Part C	Making Connections	To design a cylindrical can that uses the least possible amount of aluminum.	In Making Connections, students apply and synthesize key terms and new ideas.		**Student** Graphing utility, spreadsheet software **Teacher** Graph paper transparency, graphing calculator transparency, soft-drink can

Pacing Chart (45-Minute Periods)

	Comprehensive Course	Core Course	Informal Course
Part A	1	1	0
Part B	1	1	0
Part C	1	1	0
TOTAL periods for Superlesson	3	3	0

NCTM Standards

Mathematics as Problem Solving

Mathematics as Communication

Mathematics as Reasoning

Mathematical Connections

Algebra

Functions

Geometry from an Algebraic Perspective

Conceptual Underpinnings of Calculus

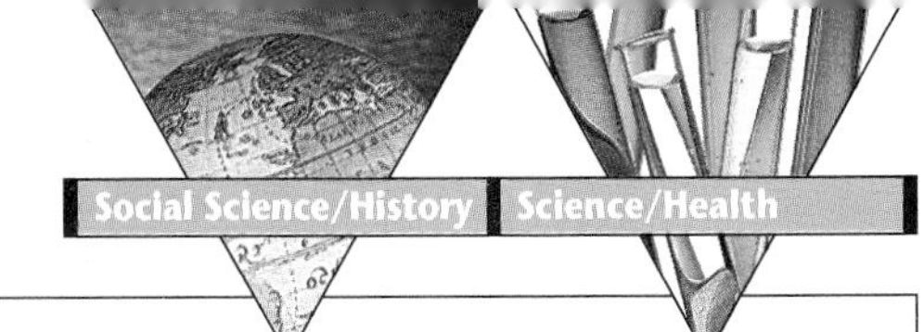

11-2 Optimization

a little better all the time

The following passage from *50 Simple Things You Can Do to Save the Earth* shows just how many aluminum cans we use, and dispose of, every year.

Aluminum is the most abundant metal on earth, but it was only discovered in the 1820s. At that time it was worth $1,200 a kilogram, more than gold. According to Worldwatch Institute: "Since its first use as a toy rattle for Napoleon's son, aluminum's use has escalated. The first all-aluminum beverage can appeared in 1963, and today accounts for the largest single use of aluminum.... In 1985 more than 70 billion beverage cans were used, of which almost 66 billion—or 94%—were aluminum."

Aluminum cans, cardboard cartons, and other packaging materials are a major part of the waste disposal problem in the United States. Recycling helps us minimize the amount of trash we generate. However, making containers that use the least possible amount of materials (that is, optimizing the use of the materials) also helps reduce waste and conserve natural resources.

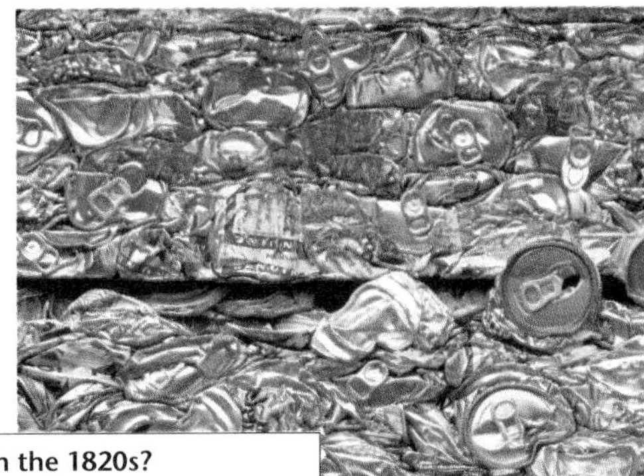

1. Why do you think aluminum was so expensive in the 1820s?
2. Is the best package always the one that makes the most efficient use of materials? Explain.
3. Do you think other countries have as significant a problem with waste disposal as the United States does? Why or why not?

More About Package Optimization

When CDs began to enter the market, music stores were filled with record albums—and the large bins used to display them. The small CD box itself was not visible in these bins, so the box was inserted in a long cardboard package. This long-box package was also believed to discourage theft. However, environmentally conscious consumers protested the waste of materials involved in the production of the long box. On February 27, 1992, the Recording Industry Association of America announced the end of long-box CD packaging.

Where Are We Now?

Students are familiar with calculations of perimeters, areas, surface areas, and volumes of two- and three-dimensional figures. In 11-1, students used triangle inequalities to find the shortest path between two points.

Where Are We Going?

In 11-2, students continue to find the "best" solutions to problems. They will find approximate solutions to optimization problems involving perimeters, areas, surface areas, and volumes, using tables and graphs.

Possible Answers

1. Aluminum is abundant, but it is not found in pure form. A method for processing aluminum cheaply was not discovered until the late 1800s.
2. No. Other factors, such as convenience, may be more important. A spherical package makes more efficient use of materials than a rectangular prism, but a supermarket filled with spherical packages would be a dangerous place!
3. The United States produces a great deal of garbage per person. However, U.S. waste-processing and recycling technology is relatively advanced. In general, industrial nations with high population densities will generate much more garbage than agricultural ones with low population densities.

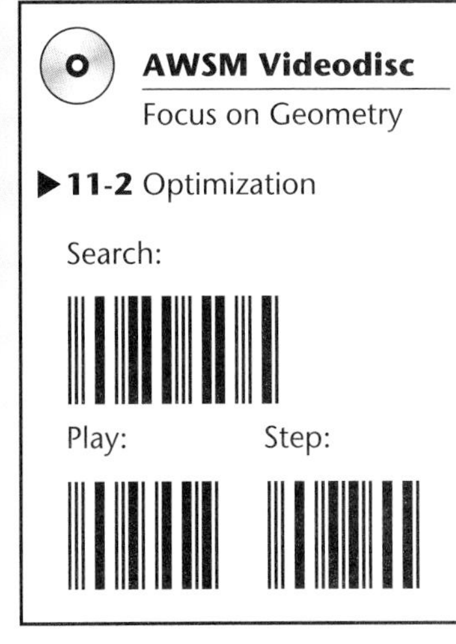

AWSM Videodisc
Focus on Geometry
▶11-2 Optimization
Search:
Play:
Step:

11-2

Optimization

PART A At a Glance

Objective

To use different methods to solve optimization problems involving perimeters and areas.

Development

Students see the meaning of an optimal solution. **What Do You Think?** shows two ways to find an approximate solution to an optimization problem.

In the **Explore,** students use the solution method of their choice to find the dimensions of a three-sided corral that encloses the greatest possible area for a given amount of fence.

Suggested Materials

Student Graphing utility, spreadsheet software

Teacher Graph paper transparency, graphing calculator transparency

Key Terms

Optimal solution

First Five Minutes

Transparency FFM 11-2A

Solve each equation for w.

1. $\ell w = 18$ $w = \frac{18}{\ell}$
2. $P = 2w + 8$ $w = \frac{P-8}{2} = \frac{P}{2} - 4$

Motivate

Ask...

- If you had a certain amount of fencing and you were asked to fence off a children's playground on a vacant lot, what shape would you make the playground? Explain your choice.

WHAT DO YOU THINK?

Demonstrates two different ways to find a solution to an optimization problem. Some of the features of graphing-utility technology are shown.

11-2 PART A Optimizing Areas and Perimeters

← CONNECT → ***You've already calculated the perimeters and areas of geometric figures. Now you will find figures that have the greatest area or least perimeter under certain conditions.***

Some problems have only one solution; others have many solutions. For example, there is an infinite number of ways to make a rectangle whose perimeter is 12. When you want to find the best possible solution to a problem, like finding the rectangle of perimeter 12 with the greatest possible area, you are looking for an **optimal solution.**

WHAT DO YOU THINK?

Kimiko and Adam needed to find the dimensions of the rectangle with an area of 1 square unit that has the minimum perimeter.

Kimiko thinks . . .

If I graph the relationship between the side length and the perimeter, I can look for the point that gives the minimum perimeter. Then I can use the coordinates of that point to help find the dimensions of the optimum rectangle.

Length

Area = 1

Width

To make a graph, I need to express the value I want to optimize—in this case, the perimeter—as a function of only one other variable. I'll let w represent the width of the rectangle and let ℓ represent its length. The area of the rectangle is 1, so $\ell w = 1$. Solving for w gives $w = \frac{1}{\ell}$.

The perimeter of a rectangle is $P = 2\ell + 2w$. Substituting $\frac{1}{\ell}$ for w, I have:

$$P = 2\ell + \frac{2}{\ell}$$

$$= 2(\ell + \tfrac{1}{\ell})$$

I can graph this function on a graphing utility. I'll enter the equation to be graphed, using Y and X to represent P and ℓ, respectively.

Y = 2(X + 1/X)

Technology Note

If you have spreadsheet software, you may want to demonstrate its use before beginning the **Explore** on page 730. Students will need to know how to enter a formula into a cell, including the use of the symbols ^ for exponents and / for division. Students will also need to be able to copy a cell containing a formula and paste it into other cells.

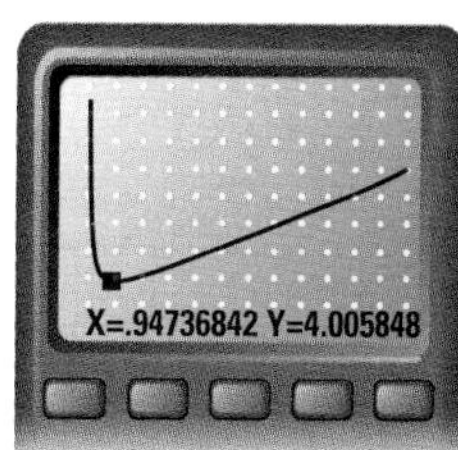

Using an appropriate range gives the graph at the right. I can TRACE to find the point with the least Y-value (perimeter). Reading the X-value for this point tells me that a length of about 0.95 gives a perimeter of about 4.01. If the length is 0.95, the width is $\frac{1}{0.95} \approx 1.05$.

Since I want a more precise answer, I'll ZOOM IN and TRACE again. This gives a perimeter of about 4.00 for a length of about 1.00. If the length is 1, the width is also 1.

Adam thinks . . .

I can make a table of values and look for the dimensions that give the least perimeter. I'll start by choosing a length for the rectangle. Using this length, I can use the area equation $\ell w = 1$ to find the value for the rectangle's width. Using this length and width, I can use $P = 2\ell + 2w$ to calculate the perimeter of the rectangle.

I'll use spreadsheet software to make a table of values. Using the table, I conclude that the 1-square-unit rectangle with the least perimeter is 1 unit long and 1 unit wide.

	A	B	C	D
1	Length	Width	Area	Perimeter
2	10	0.1	1	20.2
3	8	0.125	1	16.25
4	4	0.25	1	8.5
5	2	0.5	1	5
6	1	1	1	4
7	0.5	2	1	5
8	0.3	3.333	1	7.267

1. In the above, what type of rectangle resulted in the minimum perimeter? Why does this answer make sense?

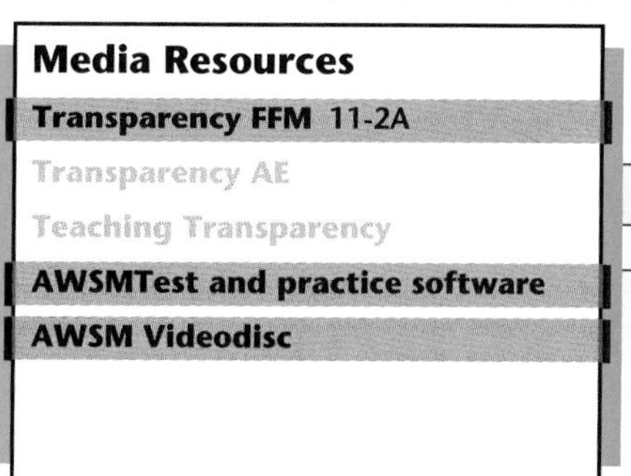

Student Resources

Alternative Lessons 11-2A
Laboratory Manual 11-2A
Technology Lab Manual
Practice 11-2A
Study Guide and Journal 11-2A
Guía de estudios y Diario 11-2A
Multilingual Handbook
More Look Ahead 11-2A
SAT Preparation

Media Resources

Transparency FFM 11-2A
Transparency AE
Teaching Transparency
AWSMTest and practice software
AWSM Videodisc

Note: Use of spreadsheet software and graphing utilities will make these solution methods less time-consuming.

Identifies the solution to **What Do You Think?** as a square, and asks why it makes sense that this is the rectangle with the smallest perimeter for a given area.

Possible Answer

1. A square gave the smallest perimeter for a given area. The perimeter of a long, thin rectangle is large compared to its area. To enclose a larger area with the same perimeter, we can "even out" the length and width. When the length and width are exactly equal, we have a square.

Optimization

EXPLORE

How Optimal Can You Get?

Recommended group size: 4

The Point
To find the dimensions for a three-sided corral of maximum area that uses 400 yd of fence.

Look and Listen...

- For students who do not see how to use algebra to write the dimensions of the corral.
- For students who do not see what should be graphed or evaluated in the table.

Ask...

- Suppose a side of the corral that meets the old fence has length *x*. What must the length of the opposite side be? How much of the 400-yd fence is left over for the third side?
- What are you trying to maximize? Can you graph this? Can you calculate its values for different dimensions of the fence?

For Groups That Finish Early
How much smaller would the area of the corral be if there were no existing fence? **10,000 yd^2 smaller; the best corral would be square, 100 yd by 100 yd.**

Follow Up
Ask a student or group to present their optimal solution and demonstrate their technique. Then have a student or group that used a different method do the same.

Possible Answer
100 yd by 200 yd. The 200-yd side is opposite the old fence. (The area of the corral is 20,000 yd^2.)

Journal

Reflect 1, 2, and 3 are suitable for journal entries.

In the following Explore, you will maximize the area of a rectangle that has some limitations on its perimeter.

EXPLORE: HOW OPTIMAL CAN YOU GET?

MATERIALS

Graphing utility (optional)
Spreadsheet software (optional)

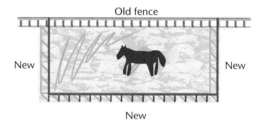

You have 400 yd of new fencing with which to enclose a rectangular corral that uses one side of an existing fence. You'd like to build the corral that has the greatest possible area.

Find the approximate dimensions of the largest corral you can build with 400 yd of fencing. You may use one of the methods shown earlier or come up with one of your own. Give an explanation of your method and your solution.

When you use tables or graphing to solve an optimization problem, you can't be sure that your answer is the best one possible, because a table cannot list all possible values, and a graph has limited accuracy. Many of the methods for finding exact solutions for these problems are topics in calculus.

REFLECT

1. What type of rectangle has the least perimeter for a given area? Is this the same as the rectangle that has the greatest area for a given perimeter? Explain.
2. Suppose we don't restrict ourselves to rectangles. What two-dimensional geometric figure has the greatest area for a given perimeter? Why?
3. Describe some careers or industries in which optimization is important. Give an example of an optimization problem that might occur in each.

Alert

In this *Explore* and the one in 11-2B, you may want to be especially active in checking on student progress. Students who use incorrect algebraic expressions may spend a great deal of time obtaining meaningless results.

Tips from Teachers

It may be helpful to have students choose a value for the length of one side of the corral in the *Explore* and calculate the other side lengths on the basis of that value. This may help them write correct algebraic expressions.

Exercises

CORE

1. **Getting Started** Suppose you want to find the approximate dimensions of the rectangle with the smallest perimeter whose area is 12. Use the table to find the approximate dimensions of this rectangle. 3.50 × 3.43

Length	Width	Perimeter	Area
3.00	4.00	14.00	12
3.25	3.69	13.88	12
3.50	3.43	13.86	12
3.75	3.20	13.90	12
4.00	3.00	14.00	12

2. Suppose you want to find the dimensions of the rectangle with the greatest area whose perimeter is 20.
   a. Make a conjecture about the shape and dimensions of this rectangle. The rectangle is a 5 × 5 square.
   b. Complete the table, and find the dimensions of the rectangle with the maximum area. Does this support your conjecture in **2a**?

Length	Width	Perimeter	Area
1	9	20	
2	8	20	
3	7	20	
4	6	20	
5	5	20	
6	4	20	
7	3	20	
8	2	20	
9	1	20	

   c. Does this table show all of the possibilities for the length and width of the rectangle? Why or why not? No; It shows integer values only.

Ongoing Assessment

Vocabulary
Practice/Skills
Review
Math Reasoning
Problem Solving
Challenge

Self-Assessment Exercises 1, 3, 5, 9, 10

Embedded Assessment Exercises 2, 4, 6, 7, 8

REFLECT

Possible Answers

1. The rectangle that has the least perimeter for a given area is a square. A square also has the greatest area for a given perimeter. These questions both ask for the most "efficient" rectangle; the difference between them is the known information.

2. A circle has the greatest area for a given perimeter. The more even the figure, the more efficiently it uses its perimeter.

3. Any industry that uses materials to package or manufacture goods will find it important to try to optimize those resources. Designers and engineers try to make product designs as efficient as possible; industrial engineers try to optimize production schedules and processes.

Part A Exercises

Exercise Notes

Core

6. and 11. Students optimize the area enclosed by a fence.

9. Students find the optimal annual production level for a product.

Business Note: Manufacturing companies use mathematics, especially statistics, to model and predict demand. They use these predictions to help set production levels and keep their inventory at an efficient level.

Look Ahead

These exercises review surface-area and volume formulas that will be important in 11-2 Part B.

More Math Reasoning

18. Students show why a hexagonal opening is an efficient choice for a beehive cell. They first explored this question in 6-3.

19. Requires the use of trigonometry.

20. Extension: Ask students how the wire should be cut so that the area of the squares is a maximum. **It should not be cut at all—the optimal solution is to devote all of the wire to one square!**

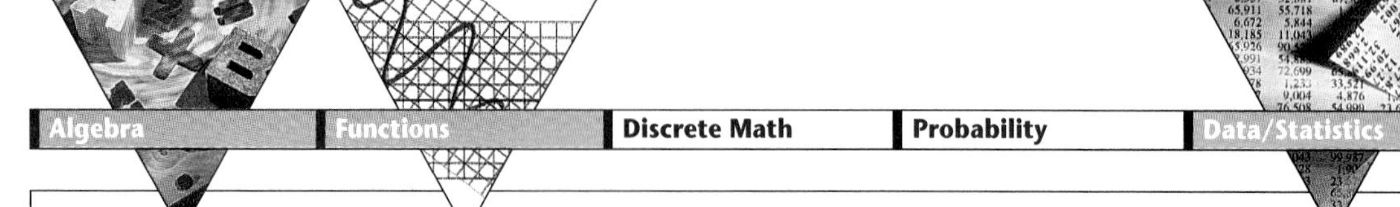

Optimization

Exercise Answers

Core

2. b. Yes. Areas: $1 \times 9 = 9 \times 1 = 9$, $2 \times 8 = 8 \times 2 = 16$, $3 \times 7 = 7 \times 3 = 21$, $4 \times 6 = 6 \times 4 = 24$, $5 \times 5 = 25$

7. a. Possible answer: The a and b that minimize the fence perimeter for the triangle also minimize the fence perimeter for a rectangle of size $a \times b$ with area 8. Thus we need $a = b = \sqrt{8}$, a square. The fence endpoints should be $\sqrt{8} \approx 2.83$ km from the intersection.

b. Possible answer: A square field is easier to manage.

8. The triangle is a right triangle; Yes; Conjecture: for a triangle with two fixed side lengths, the maximum area occurs when the angle between the sides measures 90°.

P **For each graph, estimate the coordinates of the point that has the minimum y-value.**

3. (4, 3)

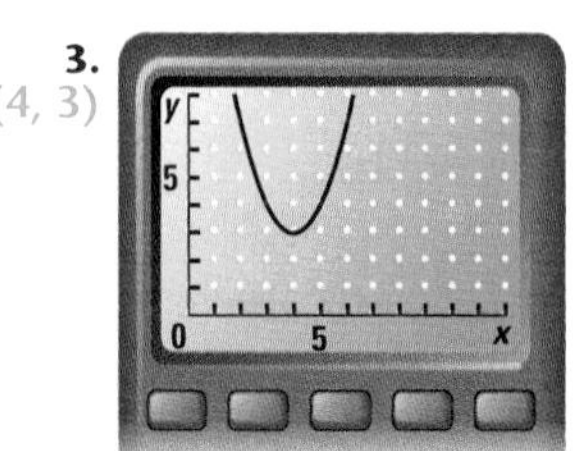

4. (1, 4)

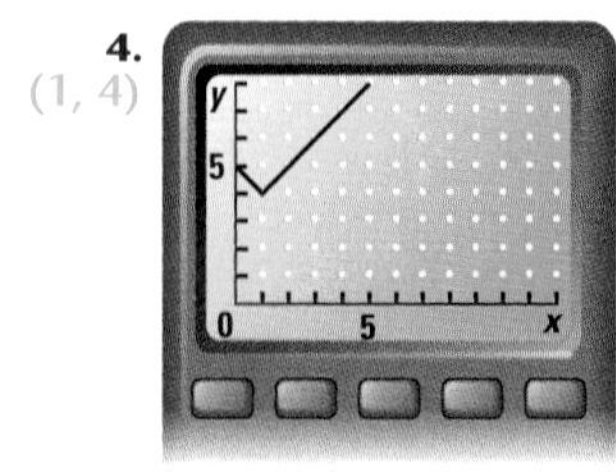

5. (1, 2)

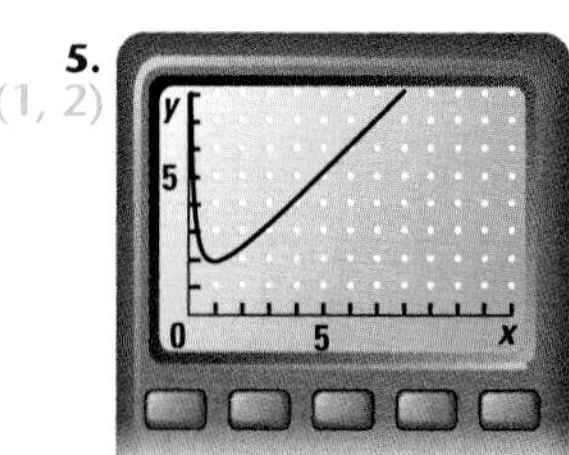

PS **6. Picket Problem** Consuela has one hundred meters of picket fencing to enclose a rectangular yard. She needs to leave an eight-meter gap in the fence for a driveway. What are the approximate dimensions for the fence that encloses the greatest possible area? (Hint: Make a table.) 27 m × 27 m

8 m

PS, MR **7. Use the Hypotenuse** A farmer decides to use a diagonal fence to fence off a field at the perpendicular intersection of two county roads. The field must have an area of 4 km^2, and the farmer wants to use the least possible amount of fencing.

a. Describe where the endpoints of the fence should be. Explain how you found your answer.

b. You won't see many triangular fields on actual farms. Why?

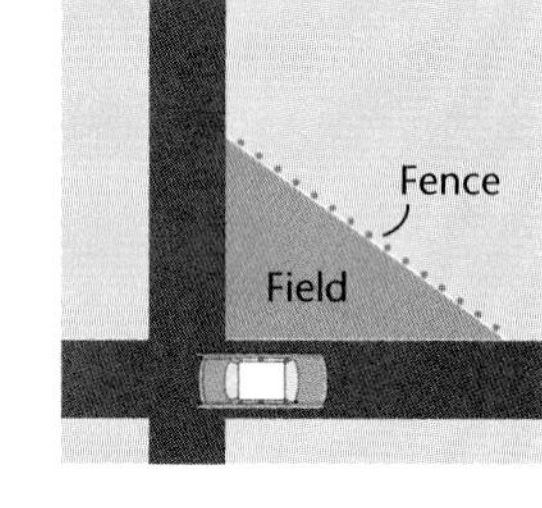

MR **8.** What does the data at the right suggest about the triangle with the side lengths shown that has the maximum possible area? Do you think this is true for any values of AB and AC? If so, write a conjecture that summarizes this idea. If not, explain why not.

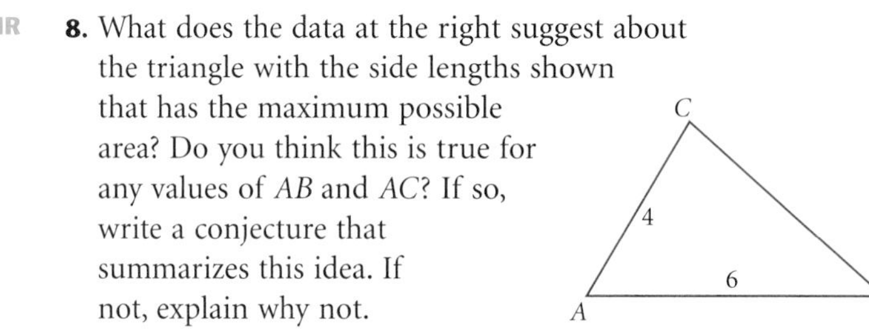

$m\angle A$	Area
20°	4.1
40°	7.7
60°	10.4
90°	12.0
120°	10.4
140°	7.7

PS Industry **9. Parabolic Profit** An auto parts company makes a slow-selling, custom-made item. They make all of their year's supply of the item at one time. Suppose that the profit (in dollars) for this item, P, as a function of the number produced, n, is given by $P = -3n^2 + 67n + 700$.

Find the maximum possible profit for this item and the number of items that the company should produce to achieve this profit. $1074; 11 items.

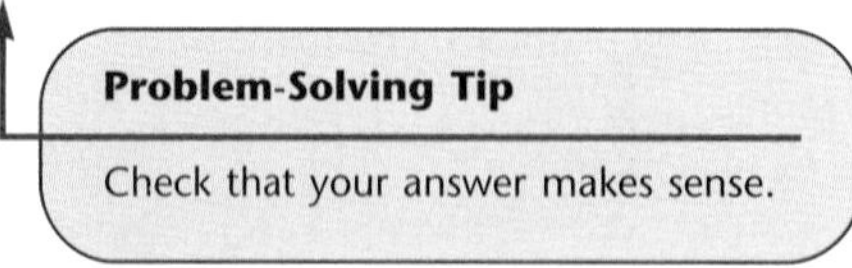

Problem-Solving Tip
Check that your answer makes sense.

Key

- V Vocabulary
- P Practice/Skills
- R Review
- MR Math Reasoning
- PS Problem Solving
- C Challenge

Diversity Issues

The graphical and tabular methods presented for solving optimization problems may appeal to different learning styles. However, both techniques require skills in translating geometric conditions into algebraic expressions and manipulating those expressions. Students weak in these areas may benefit from working with others who have strong algebraic skills.

10. Use your knowledge of rectangles to find the dimensions of the rectangle whose area is 36 in.^{2} and whose perimeter is a minimum. A square of side 6 in.

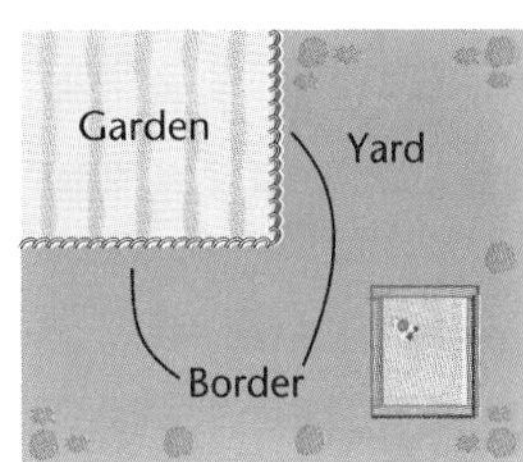

11. Dave's yard is surrounded by a fence. He wants to make a small rectangular garden in a corner of the yard, using a thirty-foot plastic border. Find the dimensions of the largest garden he can make. Explain how you found your answer.

LOOK AHEAD

Find the surface area and the volume of each rectangular prism.

12. length = 4 cm, width = 8 cm, height = 7 cm $SA = 232\text{ cm}^2$; $V = 224\text{ cm}^3$

13. length = x, width = x, height = h $SA = 2x^2 + 4xh$; $V = x^2h$

14. length = $2x$, width = x, height = $3x$ $SA = 22x^2$; $V = 6x^3$

MORE PRACTICE

For each graph, estimate the coordinates of the point that has the maximum *y*-value.

15. (5, 7)

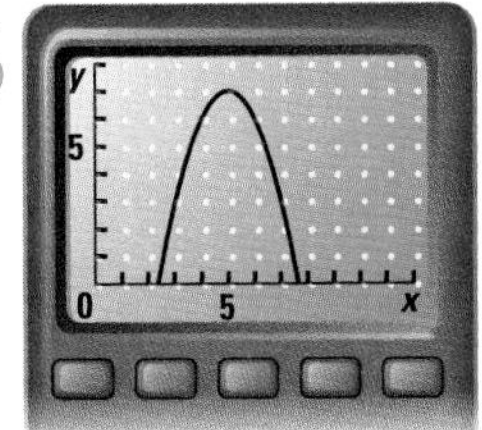

16. (5, 4)

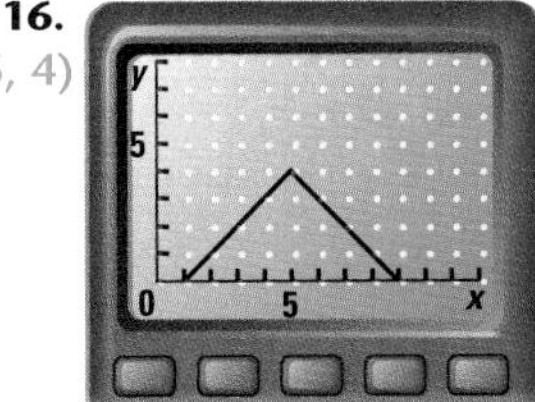

17. (1.5, 7)

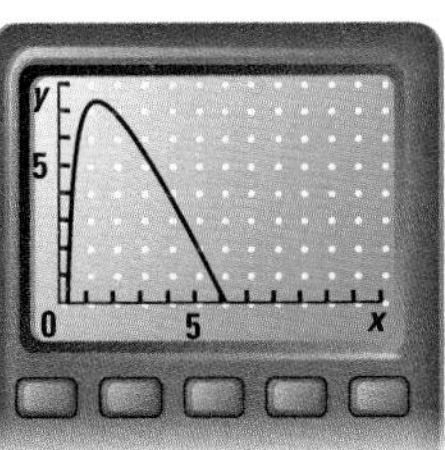

MORE MATH REASONING

18. Bee Optimal! The cells in a beehive have regular hexagonal openings.

a. A regular hexagon tessellates a plane. Why is it efficient for bees to use a cell shape that tessellates?

b. An equilateral triangle and a square also tessellate a plane. Of these three shapes, show that the regular hexagon has the maximum area for a given perimeter. Explain the method you used to solve this problem. (Hint: Begin by choosing a convenient value for the perimeter.)

c. Why might bees want to have the largest possible cell area for a given perimeter?

11. Possible answer: For maximum area, he needs a square garden. Each side of the square should be $\frac{30}{2} = 15$ ft.

More Math Reasoning

18. a. Possible answers: Bees can build cells in any direction, it uses all the space in the plane.

b. Suppose the perimeter of each shape is 12 units. The length of a side of the equilateral triangle is 4 units. The area of the triangle is $\frac{1}{2}(4)(2\sqrt{3}) = 4\sqrt{3}$ square units. The length of a side of the square is 3 units. The area of the square is $(3)^2 = 9$ square units. The length of a side of the hexagon is 2 units. The area of the hexagon is $\frac{6}{2}(2)(\sqrt{3}) = 6\sqrt{3}$ square units. Therefore, for equal perimeters, the hexagon has the maximum area.

c. Possible answer: To get the maximum storage for a given amount of building material.

19. $m\angle Z = 90°$; The height of the parallelogram is $3\sin(m\angle Z)$, so the area is $12\sin(m\angle Z)$. Since the maximum of the sine is when the angle is 90°, $m\angle Z = 90°$.

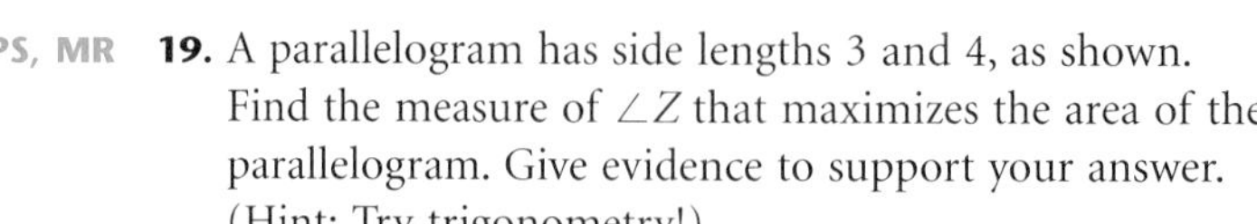

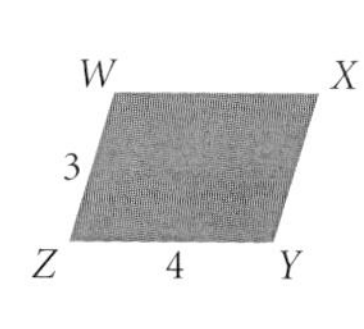

PART B At a Glance

Objective

To use different methods to solve optimization problems involving surface areas and volumes.

Development

Students see an **Example** where the surface area of a box with a given volume is minimized.

Then, in the **Explore,** students make open boxes by cutting corners out of sheets of paper and folding up the sides. Then they use techniques similar to those in the **Example** to find the dimensions of the box with the greatest volume that can be made in this way.

Suggested Materials

Student 9-in. by 12-in. paper, scissors, ruler, graphing utility, spreadsheet software

Teacher Graph paper transparency, graphing calculator transparency

First Five Minutes

Transparency FFM 11-2B

1. Find the surface area and the volume of the rectangular solid shown.

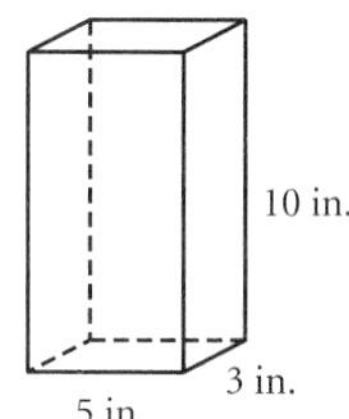

$SA = 190$ in.^{2}; $V = 150$ in.^{3}

2. How would your answers change if the solid were open on top?
$SA = 175$ in.^{2}; the volume stays the same.

Motivate

Ask...

- Give examples of industries where optimizing a three-dimensional figure might be important.
Food and drink packaging, construction, etc.

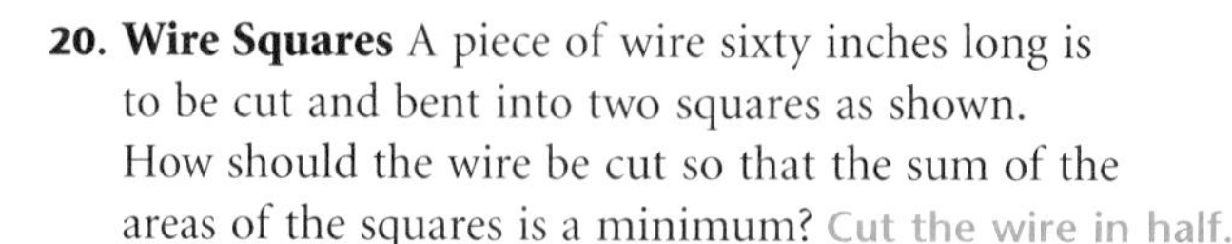

PS, MR **19.** A parallelogram has side lengths 3 and 4, as shown. Find the measure of $\angle Z$ that maximizes the area of the parallelogram. Give evidence to support your answer. (Hint: Try trigonometry!)

C **20. Wire Squares** A piece of wire sixty inches long is to be cut and bent into two squares as shown. How should the wire be cut so that the sum of the areas of the squares is a minimum? Cut the wire in half.

11-2 PART B Optimizing Volumes and Surface Areas

← CONNECT → ***You've looked at maximum areas and minimum perimeters of two-dimensional figures. Now you will apply optimization techniques to three-dimensional figures.***

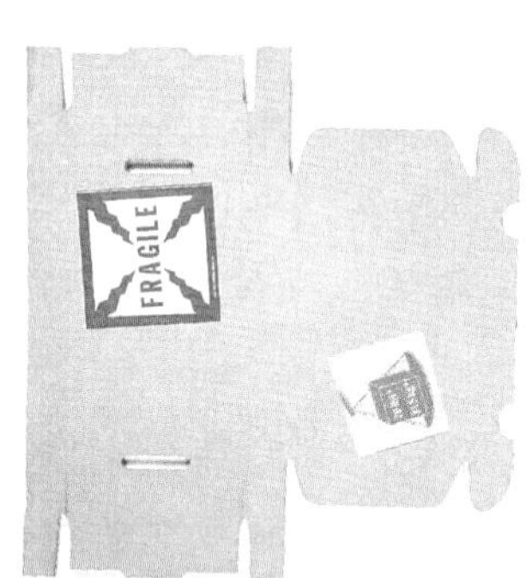

When you maximize volumes or minimize surface areas, you are working in three dimensions. However, the techniques you will use and the ideas behind them are the same as those for two-dimensional figures.

EXAMPLE

The Peerless Packaging Company wants to manufacture a box whose length is twice its width. The volume of the box must be 9 ft^3. Find the dimensions of the box with the least possible surface area that satisfies these requirements.

Let h represent the height of the box, and let x represent the width of the box. Then the length of the box is $2x$. Since the volume of the rectangular prism is 9, we have $V = \ell wh$, or $9 = 2x(x)(h) = 2x^2h$.

We want to minimize the surface area. For a rectangular solid, the surface area is $2B + ph$. In this case, $SA = 2(2x^2) + 6xh = 4x^2 + 6xh$.

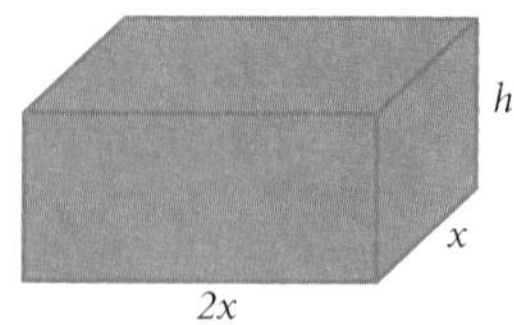

Key

V Vocabulary
P Practice/Skills
R Review
MR Math Reasoning
PS Problem Solving
C Challenge

Technology Note

When using a graphing utility in the **Explore** on page 736, students need to experiment with different range values for the viewing window. (An x-range from 0 to 4.5 and a y-range from 0 to 90 work well for this function.) This provides an opportunity to discuss how the nature of this real-world problem limits the allowable range of x-values.

We need to express the surface area in terms of x alone. To do this, we first solve the volume equation, $9 = 2x^2h$, for h. This gives $\frac{9}{2x^2} = h$. Substituting this result into the surface-area equation gives the following:

$$SA = 4x^2 + 6x\left(\frac{9}{2x^2}\right) = 4x^2 + \frac{27}{x}$$

Using a table of values, a spreadsheet (below), or a graphing utility (right), the dimensions we find for the "best" box are 1.5 ft by 3 ft by 2 ft. Notice how we "zoomed in" on our answer in the spreadsheet.

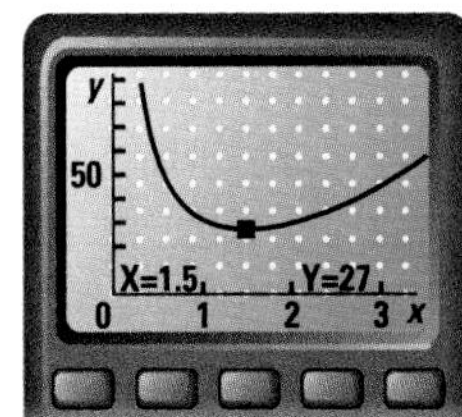

	A	B	C	D
1	x	h	Vol.	$SA = 4x^2 + \frac{27}{x}$
2	1	4.5	9	31.0
3	2	1.125	9	29.5
4	3	0.5	9	45.0
5	4	0.281	9	70.75
6	1.2	3.125	9	28.26
7	1.4	2.296	9	27.12571429
8	1.6	1.758	9	27.115
9	1.8	1.389	9	27.96
10	1.5	2.0	9	27.0

1. Describe the advantages and disadvantages of using a spreadsheet to solve an optimization problem like the one in the preceding example.
2. Describe the advantages and disadvantages of using a graphing utility to solve an optimization problem like the one in the preceding example.

ALTERNATE EXAMPLE

Transparency AE 11-2B

Students discuss advantages and disadvantages of the methods used in the **Example.**

Possible Answers

1. Advantages: Once the formulas are plugged in, there are no calculations to do by hand. Any value can be substituted into the formula easily. Disadvantages: It may take a long time to zoom in on the optimal solution.
2. Advantages: When an appropriate window is chosen, the maximum and minimum values can be seen. Zooming in enables you to close in on the answer quickly. Disadvantages: It may take time to find range values that display the graph effectively. Only one of the dimensions of the box can be displayed on the graph; other methods will have to be used to find the other dimension(s).

Student Resources
- **Alternative Lessons 11-2B**
- **Laboratory Manual 11-2B**
- Technology Lab Manual
- **Practice 11-2B**
- **Study Guide and Journal 11-2B**
- **Guía de estudios y Diario 11-2B**
- **Multilingual Handbook**
- **More Look Back 11-2B**
- SAT Preparation

Media Resources
- **Transparency FFM 11-2B**
- **Transparency AE 11-2B**
- Teaching Transparency
- **AWSMTest and practice software**
- AWSM Videodisc

Optimization

EXPLORE

The Champion Boxer

Recommended group size: 4

The Point
To find the dimensions of the open box with the largest volume that can be made by cutting squares from the corners of a 9-in. by 12-in. sheet of paper.

Look and Listen...

- For students who are having difficulty finding expressions for the length and the width of the box.

Ask...

- Look at the figure on page 736. If the length of the paper is 12 in. and the side length of a square is x, what is the length of the box? Can you find a similar expression for the width of the box?

For Groups That Finish Early
Find the percentage error in the volume of the best box found in Step 1 compared to the value found in Step 4.

Follow Up
Ask students to give the dimensions of their boxes in Step 1 and identify the box with the largest volume. Then have them share their results from Step 4 and compare the two results. If time permits, have them explain their methods.

Possible Answers

1. See answer to Step 4 for dimensions of the optimal box.

2. Height $= x$, length $= 12 - 2x$, and width $= 9 - 2x$.

3. $V = (12 - 2x)(9 - 2x)x$

4. The optimal box is made by a cutout square about 1.697 in. on a side. The height of the box is then 1.697 in., the length of the box is about 8.606 in., and its width is about 5.606 in. Its volume is about 81.87 in.^{3}

Journal

Reflect 1 and 2 and **Exercise** 7 are suitable for journal entries.

In the following Explore, you will find the approximate dimensions of the largest box you can make by folding up a sheet of paper.

EXPLORE: THE CHAMPION BOXER

MATERIALS

9-in. × 12-in. paper
Scissors, Ruler
Spreadsheet software (optional)
Graphing utility (optional)

1. Cut out small congruent squares from each corner of a 9-in. × 12-in. piece of paper, as shown. Fold up the sides and ends, as shown by the dashed lines in the figure. Measure the dimensions of your box, and compute its volume. Compare the volume of your box with those made by your classmates. Which dimensions gave the greatest volume?

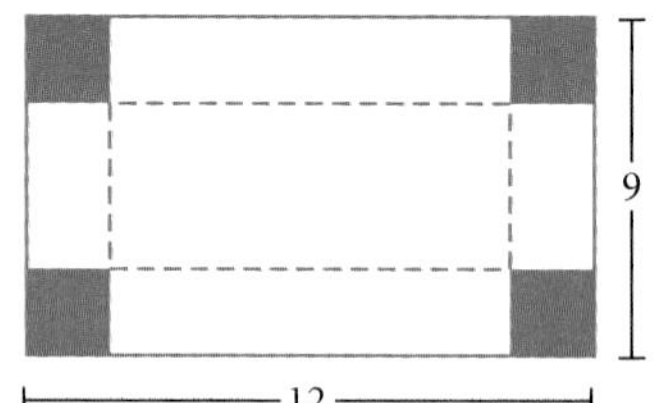

Now use algebra and geometry to confirm or improve your experimental results.

2. Let x represent the side length of the cut-out squares. Express the height, length, and width of the box in terms of x.

3. Write an equation for the volume of the box in terms of x.

4. Find the approximate value of x that maximizes the volume of the box. Give the dimensions and the volume of this optimal box. Compare this box to the one with maximum volume you found in Step 1.

REFLECT

1. Suppose you want to maximize the volume of a solid. You've written an equation for the volume in terms of x and started a table of values, as shown. Can you conclude that the maximum volume of the solid is 20.4? Explain.

2. What are some advantages and disadvantages of finding optimal values by making a table of values? by graphing?

x	Volume
1	15.2
2	20.4
3	8.8
4	3.6
5	2.0

Research Note

[Calculus] students have very little trouble applying calculus to finding the maximum of a function of one variable. Their real difficulties lie in finding the function!... [S]tudents could benefit greatly from practice on precalculus problems that focus on the geometric strategies typically needed in the[se] exercises. (Richard H. Balomenos, Joan Ferrini-Mundy, and Thomas Dick, "Geometry for Calculus Readiness," *Learning and Teaching Geometry K–12, 1987 Yearbook,* Mary Montgomery Lindquist and Albert P. Shulte, eds., p. 198. © 1987 NCTM.)

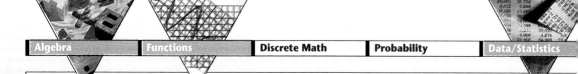

Exercises

CORE

1. **Getting Started** Suppose you want to find the approximate dimensions of the box with the smallest surface area whose height is half its length and whose volume is 32. Use the table to find the approximate dimensions of this box.
4.50 × 3.16 × 2.25

Length	Width	Height	Surface Area	Volume
4.00	4.00	2.00	64.00	32
4.50	3.16	2.25	62.92	32
5.00	2.56	2.50	63.40	32
5.50	2.12	2.75	65.16	32

2. Suppose you want to find the dimensions of the box with the greatest volume for which the sum of the length, width, and height is 6.
   a. Make a conjecture about the shape and dimensions of this box.
   b. Complete the table, and find the dimensions of the box with the maximum volume. Does this support your conjecture in **2a**?

Length	Width	Height	Volume
1	1	4	
1	2	3	
1	3	2	
1	4	1	
2	1	3	
2	2	2	
2	3	1	
3	1	2	
3	2	1	
4	1	1	

   c. Explain how the numbers above for length, width, and height were selected. Could some possibilities have been left out without losing any data? Explain.
   d. Does this table show all of the possibilities for the length, width, and height of the box? Why or why not?

y

Vocabulary
Practice/Skills
Review
R Math Reasoning
Problem Solving
Challenge

Ongoing Assessment

Self-Assessment Exercises 1, 3, 5, 8

Embedded Assessment Explore Step 4; Exercises 2, 4, 6, 7

REFLECT

Possible Answers

1. You cannot conclude that the maximum value of the solid is 20.4. A table cannot display all possible values for dimensions, volumes, etc.

2. When doing these methods by hand, there is little difference, since you will probably make a table of values to draw the graph. When using technology, the graph gives you a better picture of the equation and allows you to zoom in quickly; the table (spreadsheet) enables you to do calculations of all values instantly and to plug in any value you wish.

Part B Exercises

Exercise Notes

Core

7. This is another open-box problem similar to the one in the **Explore.**

More Math Reasoning

16. Students find the dimensions of the largest open box cut from a 12-cm by 18-cm sheet that can hold itself together with tabs and slots.

17. Students find that an "optimal" yogurt cone is very shallow. This cone would be difficult to hold and eat from.

Exercise Answers

Core

2. a. The box is a $2 \times 2 \times 2$ cube.

b. Yes. Volumes: $1 \times 1 \times 4 = 1 \times 4 \times 1 = 4 \times 1 \times 1 = 4$, $1 \times 2 \times 3 = 1 \times 3 \times 2 = 2 \times 1 \times 3 = 2 \times 3 \times 1 = 3 \times 1 \times 2 = 3 \times 2 \times 1 = 6$, $2 \times 2 \times 2 = 8$

c. The numbers are all positive integers whose sum is 6. Permutations of the same set of numbers could be left out because their product will always be the same.

d. No; Dimensions need not be integer-valued.

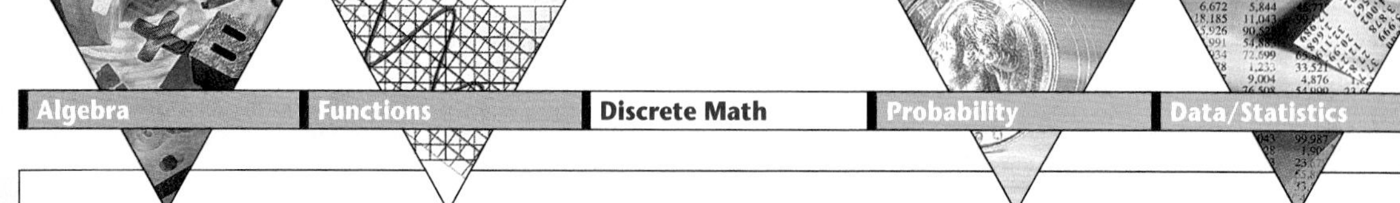

Optimization

6. Conjecture: The box is a $4 \times 4 \times 4$ cube.

l	w	h	V	SA
1	1	64	64	258
2	2	16	64	136
3	3	7.11	64	103.32
4	4	4	64	96
5	5	2.56	64	101.2
6	6	1.78	64	114.67

7. Possible answer: 13.3 cm $\times$ 7.3 cm $\times$ 2.35 cm; The volume of the box is $(18 - 2x)(12 - 2x)x = 216x - 60x^2 + 4x^3$. The possible values of x are values between 0 and 6. Use a graphing utility to estimate the x-value for the maximum volume; $x \approx 2.35$.

Look Back

10. Ralph is allergic to house dust. The facts rule out pet hair and ragweed pollen.

More Practice

15. The box is a $2 \times 2 \times 2$ cube.

l	w	h	V	SA
0.5	0.5	32	8	64.5
1	1	8	8	34
1.5	1.5	3.56	8	25.86
2	2	2	8	24
2.5	2.5	1.28	8	25.3
2.75	2.75	1.06	8	26.79

More Math Reasoning

16. a.

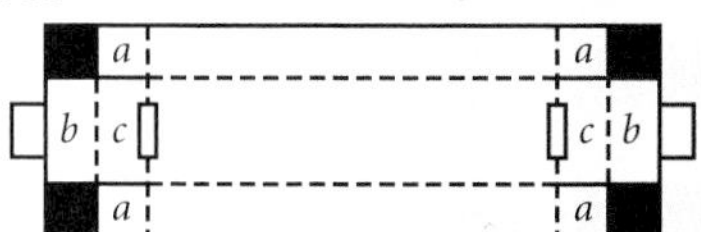

Fold the long sides up, turn flap a 90° toward slot, fold b to the inside over c covering a, and tuck tab in slot.

b. $x \approx 3.4$

17.

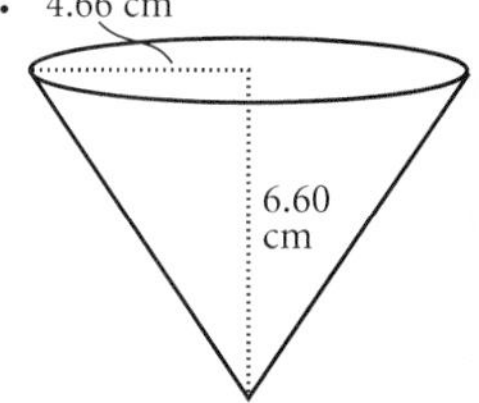

P **For each situation, decide which quantity is to be optimized and whether it should be maximized or minimized.**

3. A cardboard carton must have a volume of four cubic feet. You want to use the least possible amount of cardboard to make the carton. Minimize surface area of carton

4. You have 144 in.^{2} of wood with which to make a storage box. You want the box to hold as many pennies as possible. Maximize volume of box

5. You are curling a sheet of metal into a tube with a volume of 2 m^3. You want to use as little metal as possible. Minimize surface area of tube

6. A box has a square base and a volume of 64. Make a conjecture about the box with the minimum surface area. Then confirm your conjecture by making a table of values for the length, width, height, volume, and surface area of the box.

PS **7.** Suppose you make a box by cutting congruent squares of side length x from each corner of a sheet of paper and then folding up the sides. Find the approximate dimensions of the box with the greatest volume that you can make from a 12-cm $\times$ 18-cm piece of paper. Write a brief explanation of the method you used to solve the problem.

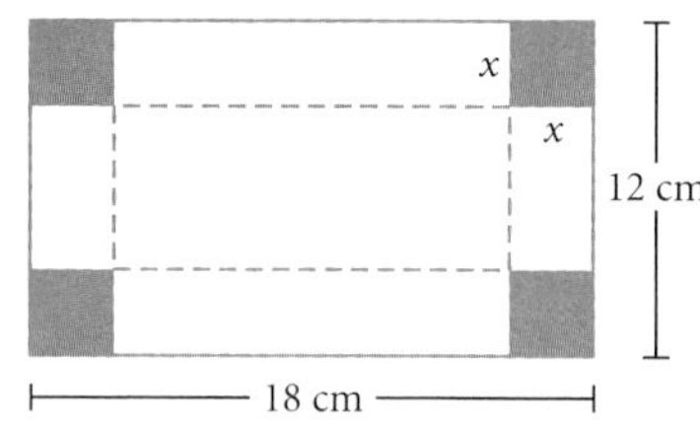

PS **8.** You have been asked to design an open box whose length is twice its width and whose volume is 36 in^3. You want to design the box so that it uses the least possible amount of cardboard. Find the approximate dimensions of the box with the least surface area that satisfies these conditions. 6 in. $\times$ 3 in. $\times$ 2 in.

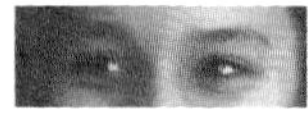

LOOK BACK

R **9.** Find the probability that a point inside the regular hexagon will also be inside the inscribed circle. Express your answer as a decimal rounded to the nearest hundredth. [5-1, 6-3, 8-1] 0.91

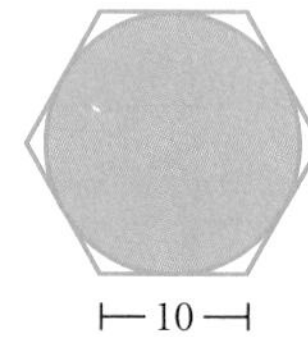

R Health **10. Watery-Eyed and Sneezing** Ralph has had allergic symptoms for almost a year. His allergist, Dr. Rodriguez, believes that he is allergic either to pet hair, house dust, or ragweed pollen (which is at its highest levels in the fall). By talking to Ralph, Dr. Rodriguez discovers the following.

- Ralph does not own any pets.
- Ralph's symptoms have not changed with the seasons.

What do you think Dr. Rodriguez will conclude? Why? If you used indirect reasoning, explain how. [11-1]

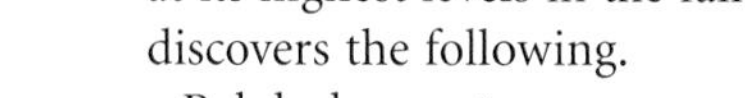

Key

V Vocabulary
P Practice/Skills
R Review
MR Math Reasoning
PS Problem Solving
C Challenge

MORE PRACTICE

P **For each situation in Exercises 11–13, decide which quantity is to be optimized and whether it should be maximized or minimized.**

11. You have 120 ft^2 of material with which to build a breeding cage for birds. You want the birds to have the greatest amount of space possible. Maximize volume of cage

12. A juice can must hold forty-six fluid ounces. You want the can to use the least possible amount of aluminum. Minimize surface area of can

13. You have to design a cardboard carton to hold twelve of the juice cans from Exercise 12. Minimize surface area of carton

PS **14.** Find the dimensions of the box with the greatest volume for which the sum of the length, width, and height is 9. $3 \times 3 \times 3$

PS **15.** A box has a square base and a volume of 8 cubic units. Make a conjecture about the box with the minimum surface area. Then confirm your conjecture by making a table of values for the length, width, height, volume, and surface area of the box.

MORE MATH REASONING

PS **16. Boxed In** With the addition of some tabs and slots, the box shown at the right can hold itself together. (Dashed lines indicate folds; solid lines show cuts.)

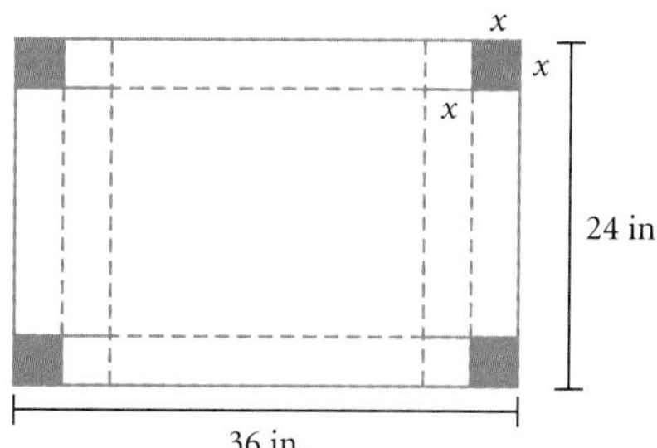

a. Copy the figure, and add small tabs and slots to the design so that the box can hold itself together.

b. If congruent squares are cut from each corner of a 24-in. × 36-in. piece of cardboard and the sides are folded up to make a box as shown in the figure, find the value of x that gives the box a maximum volume.

C **17. Yogurt to Go** You've been asked by a frozen yogurt company to design a cone for frozen yogurt that uses the least possible amount of material. The interior of the cone should hold 150 cm^3 of frozen yogurt. Find the approximate dimensions for the cone. (Hint: Use the Pythagorean Theorem to express the slant height of the cone in terms of the radius and the height.) Do you think the dimensions you calculated should actually be used for the cone? Explain why or why not. $r \approx 4.66$ cm, $h \approx 6.60$ cm; No, the radius is too big for its height so the cone is hard to hold. (See figure)

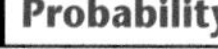

Optimization

PART C At a Glance

Objective

To design a cylindrical can that uses the least possible amount of aluminum.

Development

In the **Explore,** students find the dimensions of the cylindrical can that uses the least surface area to hold a given volume of iced tea.

Suggested Materials

Student Graphing utility, spreadsheet software

Teacher Graph paper transparency, graphing calculator transparency, soft-drink can

First Five Minutes

Transparency FFM 11-2C

Name each of the following.

1. The rectangle that encloses the greatest area for a given perimeter. A square.
2. The plane figure that has the shortest border to enclose a given area. A circle.
3. The rectangular prism that requires the least surface area to enclose a given volume. A cube.

EXPLORE

Can You Optimize It?

Recommended group size: 4

The Point

To design a 12-oz can that uses the least possible amount of aluminum.

Look and Listen...

- For students who are having a difficult time with the algebra: solving for h in Step 1, or substituting in Step 2.

Ask...

- (Step 1) How can you isolate h? (Step 2) What expression can you substitute for h? Can you simplify the new equation?

11-2 PART C Making Connections

← CONNECT → ***Optimization is important in many fields. A package designer is often concerned with using the least amount of material to enclose a given volume. You've studied ways to maximize and minimize geometric and real-world quantities under given conditions.***

Most of the cylindrical aluminum drink cans that you see have the same dimensions. Do these dimensions use the least possible amount of aluminum? In the following Explore, you will look for the dimensions of the 12-oz can that uses the minimum amount of material.

EXPLORE: CAN YOU OPTIMIZE IT?

MATERIALS

Graphing utility (optional)
Spreadsheet software (optional)

You've been hired by a drink company to design a 12-fluid-ounce can that uses the least possible amount of aluminum. The can is to be a right cylinder. (Note: 12 fluid oz $\approx$ 21.66 in^3.)

1. Write the formula for the volume of the can in terms of its radius, r, and its height, h. Set this equal to the volume that you know the can must have. Then solve this equation for h.
2. Write the formula for the surface area of the can in terms of r and h. Then eliminate h from this equation by substitution, using your result from Step 1.
3. Use a table of values, spreadsheet software, or a graphing utility to find, to the nearest tenth of an inch, the radius and height of the can that uses the least amount of aluminum. (Hint: The best value for r is between 1 in. and 3 in.)
4. Compare the dimensions of a typical 12-oz can to those you found in Step 3. Are the dimensions of your ideal can different from those of a real can? If so, what reasons might there be for the difference?

Student Resources

Alternative Lessons
Laboratory Manual 11-2C
Technology Lab Manual
Practice 11-2C
Study Guide and Journal 11-2C
Guía de estudios y Diario 11-2C
Multilingual Handbook
More Look Back 11-2C
SAT Preparation

Media Resources

Transparency FFM 11-2C
Transparency AE
Teaching Transparency
AWSMTest and practice software
AWSM Videodisc

REFLECT

1. If both methods are available to you, how might you decide whether to solve an optimization problem by using a table or by graphing?
2. Name some containers for which maximizing the container's volume or minimizing its surface area could be a consideration.
3. Some cans have very different dimensions from those of drink cans. Name some of these types of cans. Why might they be designed differently?

Self-Assessment

P **For each situation, decide which quantity is to be optimized and whether it should be maximized or minimized.**

1. You have eighty feet of fencing with which to enclose a yard. You want the yard to be as large as possible. Maximize the area of the yard.
2. An air tank must hold 22.4 L of compressed air. The tank should be built from the least possible amount of steel. Minimize the surface area of the tank.

P **For each graph, estimate the coordinates of the point that has the minimum *y*-value.**

3. (6, 2)

4. $\left(\frac{2}{3}, 1\right)$

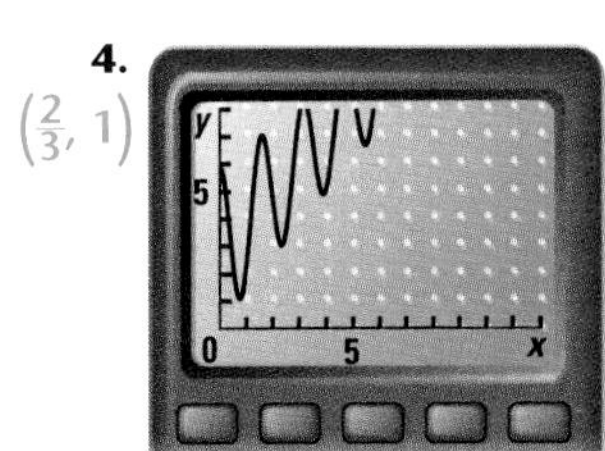

5. (1.4, 1)

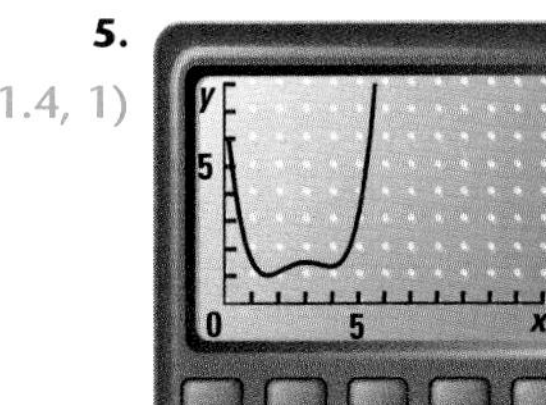

P 6. Which of the following figures has the greatest area for a given perimeter? (e)
(a) equilateral triangle (b) square (c) regular hexagon
(d) regular decagon (e) regular 2000-gon

PS 7. **Fence Me In** The Green Acre Animal Clinic has 500 ft of fence to build an exercise area for small animals. The fence is shown by diagonal lines. What should *x* and *y* be to make the area of the rectangular yard as large as possible? $x = 136.25$ ft; $y = 136.25$ ft

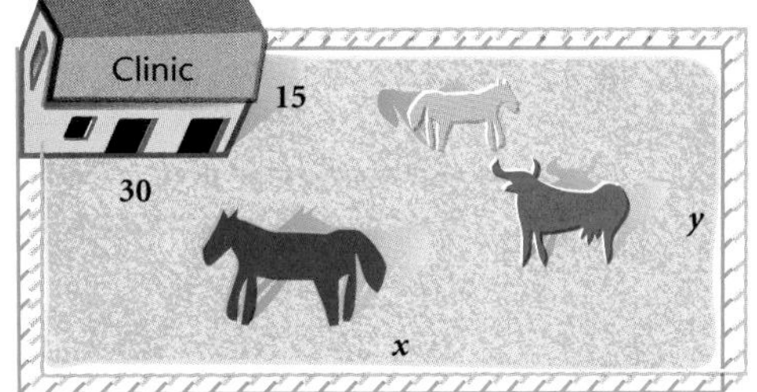

For Groups That Finish Early

Calculate the surface area of a typical soft-drink can. What percentage of this value is the surface area of your can? **About 95%; *SA*, typical ≈ 45.2 in.²; *SA*, optimal ≈ 43.0 in.²**

Follow Up

Have students share their answers to Step 3. Come to an agreement on the dimensions. Discuss whether the can would be a good one for iced tea.

Possible Answers

1. $V = \pi r^2 h = 21.66$; $h = \frac{21.66}{\pi r^2}$
2. $SA = 2\pi rh + 2\pi r^2$; $SA = \frac{43.32}{r} + 2\pi r^2$
3. $r \approx 1.5$ in.; $h \approx 3.0$ in.
4. Typical dimensions for a drink can: $r \approx 1.2$ in.; $h \approx 4.8$ in. It is a taller, slimmer can that fits more comfortably in the hand.

Portfolio

Have students select items that demonstrate their understanding of the material in 11-2.

You may want to have students include the favorite definition they wrote, best sketch illustrating a postulate, and an **Exercise** that they found challenging.

REFLECT

Possible Answers

1. If you do not know the approximate value of the optimal solution, a graph may be better, since you can see its location. A table of values is useful when you need to check specific values or to find several dimensions for the object.
2. Maximizing volumes: pet cages, moving boxes. Minimizing surface area: food containers, coolers.
3. A tuna or pet food can tends to be wide and shallow. This shape may have been chosen because it makes it easier to scoop out food.

Key

V Vocabulary
P Practice/Skills
R Review
MR Math Reasoning
PS Problem Solving
C Challenge

Packaging Connection

Because of seams needed to hold together the can, the true "best" dimensions of a can are not the same as those found in the **Explore**.

Optimization

Self-Assessment

Exercise Notes

6. Similar to multiple-choice questions on standardized tests.

16. Students explain why a cube is the rectangular solid that has the greatest volume for a given surface area.

Self-Assessment Answers

8. Approximate dimensions are $3 \times 6 \times 4.22$; Yes; Possible answer: Check decimal width values between 2 and 4.

10. No; Possible answer: Suppose $\overline{AB} \parallel \overline{CD}$, then $\angle BAC \cong \angle DCA$ because they are alternate interior angles of parallel lines. $\overline{AC} \cong \overline{AC}$ and $\overline{AB} \cong \overline{CD}$, so $\triangle BAC \cong \triangle DCA$ by the SAS Postulate. Therefore, $\overline{AD} \cong \overline{BC}$ by CPCTC, which contradicts $AD = 4$ and $BC = 10$. Therefore, $\overline{AB} \nparallel \overline{CD}$.

16. A cube; Possible answer: It is the most compact form; just as areas of quadrilaterals in two dimensions are maximized by figures approximating a square, in three dimensions, a rectangular solid's volume is maximized by its approximating a cube.

PS **8. Table Talk** Use the table to find the approximate dimensions of the box with the greatest volume whose surface area is 112 and whose length is twice its width. Could there be a better answer than the one you identified from the table? If so, explain what you would do next to search for it.

Width	Length	Height	Surface Area	Volume
1	2	18	112	36
2	4	8	112	64
3	6	4.22	112	76
4	8	2	112	64
5	10	0.4	112	20

R **9.** The square shown has a side length of eight units. Find the probability that a point inside the larger circle will also be inside the smaller circle. Express your answer as a decimal rounded to the nearest hundredth. [5-1, 5-3, 8-1] 0.50

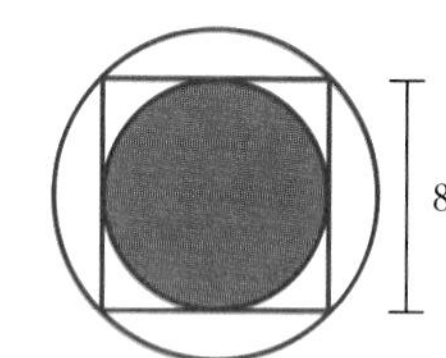

R **10.** Is $\overline{AB} \parallel \overline{CD}$ in the figure at the right? If so, explain why; if not, explain why not. [3-4, 11-1]

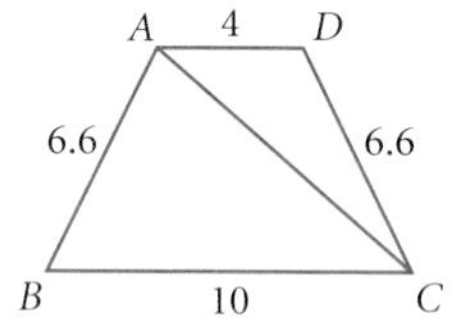

R **Determine whether each set of numbers could represent the lengths of the sides of a triangle. [11-1]**

11. 2, 3, 5 No **12.** 84, 32, 101 Yes **13.** 7, 5.2, 2.9 Yes

PS **14.** You are to design a box whose length is three times its width and whose volume is thirty cubic inches. Find the approximate dimensions of the box with the least surface area that satisfies these conditions. 1.88 in. × 5.65 in. × 2.82 in.

PS **15.** Suppose you make a box by cutting congruent squares of side length x from each corner of a sheet of paper and then folding up the sides. Find the approximate dimensions of the box with the greatest volume that you can make from a 10-in. × 12-in. piece of paper. 8.38 in. × 6.38 in. × 1.81 in.

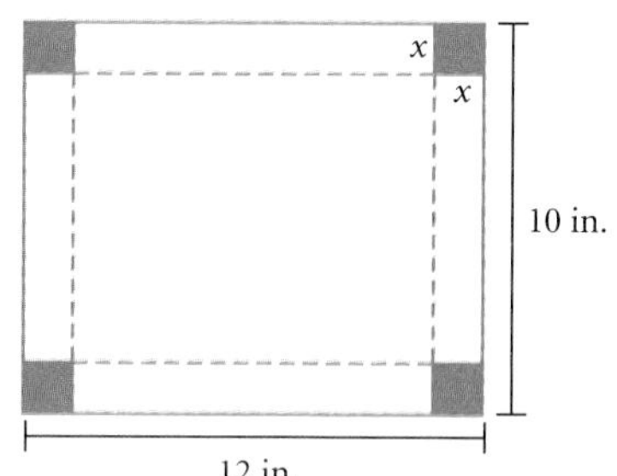

MR **16.** If there are no restrictions on its length, width, and height, what type of rectangular solid provides the greatest volume for a given surface area? Write a brief paragraph explaining your answer, and include sketches if they help support your reasoning. (Note: At this point in your mathematical studies, you probably will not be able to *prove* that you are correct.)

Assessment Resources

- **Quiz 11-2**
- Chapter Assessment Form A
- Chapter Assessment Form B
- Chapter Alternative Assessment
- Mid-Year Assessment
- End-of-Year Assessment
- **AWSMTest and practice software**

Ongoing Assessment

Self-Assessment Self-Assessment Exercises

Embedded Assessment Explore Step 3; Reflect 1, 2, 3

Chapter 11 Review

In Chapter 11 you explored indirect reasoning and applied triangle inequalities. You also looked at the solution of optimization problems.

KEY TERMS

indirect reasoning [11-1] negate [11-1] optimal solution [11-2]

Determine whether each statement is true or false. If the statement is false, change the underlined word or phrase to make it true.

1. Indirect reasoning involves making an assumption that leads to a contradiction. T
2. The Triangle Inequality Theorem states that the sum of the measures of any two angles of a triangle must be greater than the measure of the third. F; Sides
3. "If he was at the scene of the crime, then he is a witness" is the negation of "If he is not a witness, then he was not at the scene of the crime." F; Contrapositive

CONCEPTS AND APPLICATIONS

Write the negation of the conclusion of each statement. [11-1]

4. If humans were meant to fly, they would have wings. Humans do not have wings.
5. If $\angle A$ and $\angle B$ are base angles of an isosceles triangle, then $\angle A \not\cong \angle B$. $\angle A \cong \angle B$
6. Consider the statement "The defendant was found guilty." [11-1]
   a. Write the negation of the statement.
   b. Assume there was a trial and the negation is true. Explain why the negation does not mean that the defendant was found "not guilty." Describe a situation in which the negation is true, but a "not guilty" verdict is not delivered.
7. A circle is circumscribed around a square of side length s. Another circle is inscribed in the square. What is the ratio of the area of the smaller circle to the area of the larger circle? [5-3, 8-1] $\frac{1}{2}$

Quadrilateral *RSTU* is a trapezoid. [11-1]

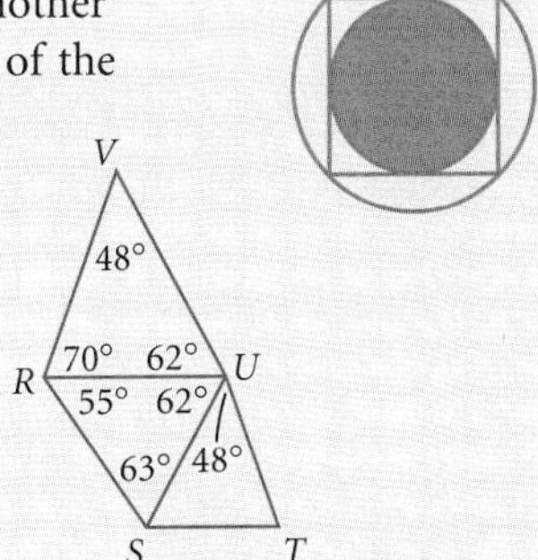

8. Which segment of the figure is the shortest? Why?
9. Which segment of the figure is the longest? Why?
10. Two sides of a triangle have lengths 5 cm and 11.2 cm. What are the possible lengths for the third side? [11-1] Between 6.2 cm and 16.2 cm.

Chapter 11 Review

Journal 

Students can identify **Key Terms** that they do not understand, and look up the definitions in the indicated section or in the glossary. Non-English-speaking students may want to use the *Multilingual Handbook.*

Vocabulary exercises and the **Self-Evaluation** are useful journal entries.

Review Answers

6. a. The defendant was not found guilty.

b. The negation implies that the verdict was not "guilty." Possible answer: There was a hung jury, so the case had to be retried.

8. Use the angle measures of the triangles and the theorem of opposite sides. In $\triangle RUV$, $RU < RV < VU$. In $\triangle RSU$, $SU < RS < RU$. In $\triangle STU$, $ST < TU < SU$. Therefore, the shortest side is $\overline{ST}$.

9. The longest side is $\overline{VU}$. See Exercise 8.

10. Between 6.2 cm and 16.2 cm.

14. Possible answer: Suppose the portrait is in the gold casket. Then the inscriptions on both the gold and silver caskets are true, which contradicts Portia's assertion. Suppose the portrait is in the silver casket. Then only the inscription on the lead casket is true and there is no contradiction. Suppose the portrait is in the lead casket. Then the inscriptions on both the silver and lead caskets are true, which contradicts Portia's assertion. Therefore the portrait must be in the silver casket.

ey

Vocabulary
Practice/Skills
Review
R Math Reasoning
Problem Solving
Challenge

Algebra	Functions	Discrete Math	Probability	Data/Statistics

Chapter 11 Assessment

Portfolio

Students may select items that represent their mathematical understanding of the ideas in Chapter 11 and that illustrate the effort that they put into this chapter.

A rubric for assessing portfolios is included in the introduction to the Teacher's Edition.

Assessment Answers

7. Possible answer: $\angle 5, \angle 3, \angle 1, \angle 2, \angle 4$; In $\triangle WXY$, $m\angle 1 < m\angle 2$ because $YW < XW$. In $\triangle WYZ$, $m\angle 5 < m\angle 3$ because $YW < ZW$. $m\angle 1 = m\angle YWX$ by the Isosceles Triangle Theorem, and $m\angle YWX = m\angle 3 + m\angle 5$ by the Exterior Angle Theorem. So $m\angle 1 = m\angle 3 + m\angle 5$ and $m\angle 3 < m\angle 1$. $m\angle 4 = m\angle 1 + m\angle 2$ by the Exterior Angle Theorem, so $m\angle 2 < m\angle 4$. By the Transitive Property, $m\angle 5 < m\angle 3 < m\angle 1 < m\angle 2 < m\angle 4$.

8. Possible answer: For a given perimeter, the maximum area is contained in a square. Divide the perimeter by 4 to find the length of a side.

P **This graph represents a manufacturer's profit per bicycle as a function of the number of bicycles manufactured. [11-2]**

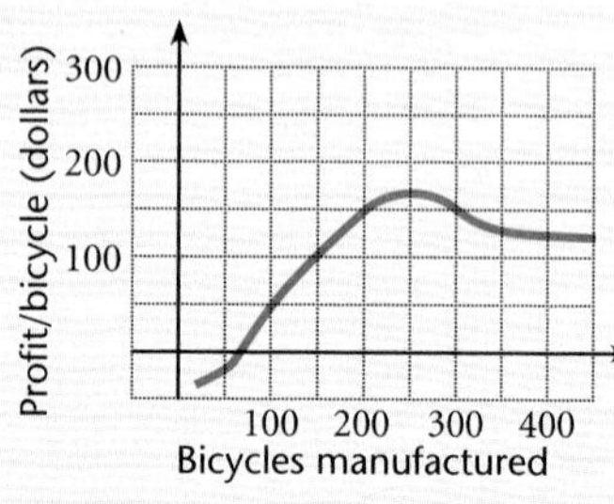

11. What is the maximum profit per bicycle, to the nearest ten dollars? $170

12. To the nearest ten bicycles, how many bicycles should be manufactured to maximize the profit per bicycle? 250

PS **13.** An open-top cylindrical cup is to have a volume of 100 in^3. Find the radius and height of the cup that minimizes the surface area of the cup. Round answers to the nearest tenth. [11-2]
$r = h \approx 3.2$ in.

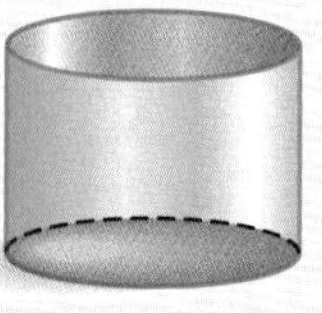

CONCEPTS AND CONNECTIONS

MR, C **14. Literature** In his book *What Is the Name of This Book?* logician Raymond Smullyan adapts a scene from Shakespeare's *Merchant of Venice,* in which Portia presents her suitor with three small caskets. He will have her hand if he guesses the one containing her portrait. Smullyan adds a twist, giving the gold casket the inscription "The portrait is in this casket," the silver casket "The portrait is not in this casket," and the lead casket "The portrait is not in the gold casket." Portia explains that at most one inscription is true. Use indirect reasoning to determine the suitor's correct choice. Write a convincing argument that your choice is the only possible correct choice.

SELF-EVALUATION

Write a summary of the most important concepts from Chapter 11. Include properties of triangles, techniques of indirect reasoning, and methods of finding optimal solutions. Include areas in which you had difficulty, and describe your plans for reviewing these topics.

Chapter 11 Assessment

TEST

P **Write the negation of the conclusion of each statement.**

1. If an animal is a fish, then it has scales.
A fish does not have scales.

2. If $a < b$, then $a + c < b + c$.
$a + c \geq b + c$

Student Resources
- Alternative Lessons
- Laboratory Manual
- Technology Lab Manual
- Practice
- **Study Guide and Journal** Ch 11
- **Guía de estudios y Diario** Ch 11
- **Multilingual Handbook**
- More Look Ahead
- **SAT Preparation**

Media Resources
- Transparency FFM
- Transparency AE
- Teaching Transparency
- **AWSMTest and practice software**
- AWSM Videodisc

R **3.** You are attempting to prove the Exterior-Angle Inequality Theorem by first proving that $m\angle 4 > m\angle 2$. A friend suggests doing an indirect proof by first assuming $m\angle 4 < m\angle 2$. Is your friend's suggestion correct? Why or why not? No; Assume that $m\angle 4 \leq m\angle 2$

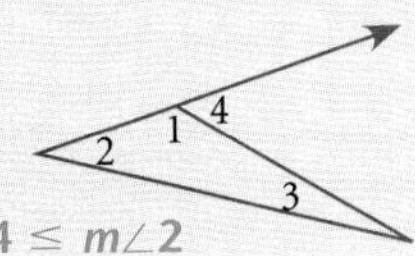

P **Determine whether each set of numbers could represent the lengths of the sides of a triangle.**

4. 10, 13, 23 No **5.** 21, 5, 24 Yes **6.** 2, $\sqrt{3}$, 4 No

P **7.** In the figure, $\overline{XY} \cong \overline{WY}$. List the numbered angles from smallest to largest. Explain your reasoning.

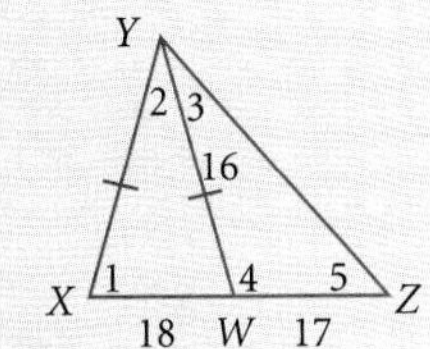

R **8.** Suppose you need to maximize the area of a rectangle with a given perimeter. Describe a step-by-step process you could use to find the side lengths of this rectangle.

S **9.** A garden is bounded on one side by an irrigation ditch and partially bounded on another side by a 10-ft walkway. A 220-ft fence will be used to complete its boundary. Find the length, ℓ, and width, w, that will provide the maximum area for the rectangular garden. $w \approx 57.5$ ft; $l \approx 115$ ft

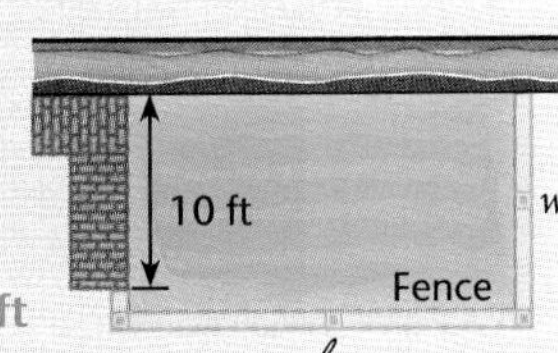

S **10.** An equilateral triangle is inscribed in a circle with a radius of eight meters. What is the area of the triangle? ≈ 55.43 m^2

S **11.** To make a gift box from a 14-in. × 20-in. piece of cardboard, you could make four slits, each of length x, as shown. Then fold up the sides and glue each shaded square to the adjoining side. Find the value of x, to the nearest tenth of an inch, that produces the box with the largest volume. $x = 2.7$ in.

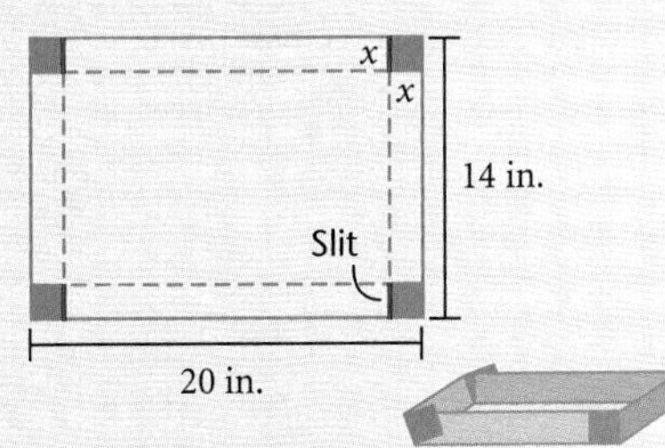

PERFORMANCE TASK

An orienteer must decide whether to travel distance c over the hill shown or take the longer route of distance $a + b$. Make a table with columns for c, r (the speed in mi/hr over the hill), and t (the time over the hill from Checkpoint 1 to Checkpoint 2). Also include columns for a, b, $a + b$, and R (the speed using the longer route). For each row of the table, make up distances for a, b, and c, and choose a speed r (normally between 3 and 5 mi/hr). Calculate t. Then calculate the minimum value for R that makes the longer route the faster route. Vary your choices for a, b, c, and r to complete several rows of the table. Then develop a formula that expresses R in terms of a, b, c, and r.

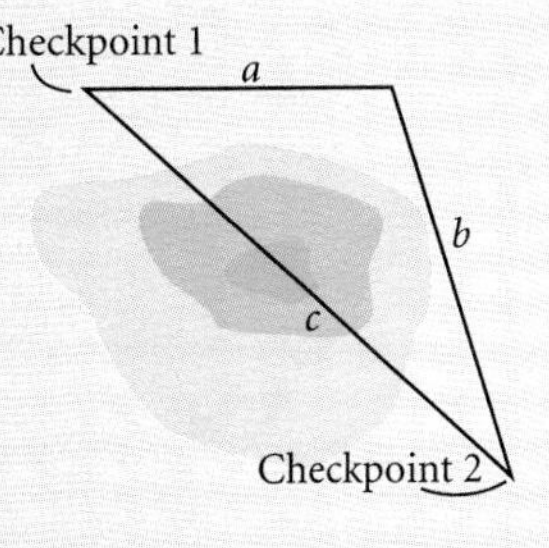

Assessment Resources

Quiz
Chapter 11 Assessment Form A
Chapter 11 Assessment Form B
Chapter 11 Alternative Assessment
Mid-Year Assessment
End-of-Year Assessment
AWSMTest Chapter 11

Ongoing Assessment

Self-Assessment Chapter 11 Review and Self-Evaluation

Embedded Assessment Chapter 11 Performance Task

Test Chapter 11 Test

Performance Task

Answer

$\frac{r(a+b)}{c} = R$. This is the R value that makes the two times equal; any value greater than this makes the longer route faster.

Suggested Scoring Rubric

Level 4 Full Accomplishment

- Shows full understanding of the Triangle Inequality Theorem and the relationships among distance, rate, and time.
- Table shows evidence of experimentation, calculated values are correct, and all a, b, and c values represent possible triangles.
- Correct formula for R is given.

Level 3 Substantial Accomplishment

- Shows essential grasp of the Triangle Inequality Theorem and the relationships among distance, rate, and time.
- Table shows evidence of experimentation, most calculated values are correct, and all a, b, and c values represent possible triangles.
- Correct formula for R is given. This formula may express R in terms of a, b, and t, instead of the variables requested in the task.

Level 2 Partial Accomplishment

- Shows partial grasp of the Triangle Inequality Theorem and the relationships among distance, rate, and time.
- Table shows some evidence of experimentation, but some calculated values are incorrect and some a, b, and c values do not represent possible triangles.
- An incorrect formula for R is given.

Level 1 Little Accomplishment

- Shows little or no grasp of the Triangle Inequality Theorem and the relationships among distance, rate, and time.
- Table is missing or extremely short. Not enough evidence or reasoning is shown to support any formula presented.

Chapter 12 Astronomy and Geometric Models

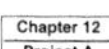

Chapter 12 / Project A

Thirty Days Has September

Explain the Gregorian Calendar

Make a poster that tells the basis of our time measurement system and compares it to other calendars.

- Did you know that a century year is a leap year only if it is divisible by 400??
- Don't you wonder if this year is a leap year?
- How does this connect to Chapter 11? Calendars are based on the **astronomy** of the sun and moon.

Expand Your Vocabulary

Gregorian calendar	solar day	solar year
perpetual calendar	sidereal day	sidereal year
intercalation	lunar month	lunar year
B.C./A.D. B.C.E./C.E.	leap year	leap second

25 26 27 28 29

A perpetual calendar shows that September 1st falls on Wednesday in 1999, 2004, and 2012.

Project Guidelines

Investigate

- Read about calendars in an encyclopedia or in an astronomy book.
- Study a current calendar. Is this a leap year?
- Learn the origins of words we use for the days of the week and the months of the year.

Set Your Direction

- Will you compare the Gregorian calendar to the Hebrew calendar? to the Chinese calendar? to an ancient calendar?

Make a Plan

- Make a calendar (Gregorian!) for each day's work. Check in with your group and with your teacher.
- You'll need posterboard and art materials.

Collect and Organize Your Information

- Investigate several calendars. For each calendar, find out whether the system is based on a solar or lunar year and how its starting year was chosen. Find out how many months it has and whether it has leap years. Record your findings in a chart.
- Choose a certain date and year (your birthday?) and find the equivalent date on another calendar.
- Sketch out your poster plan. Include a chart comparing at least two calendars. Include a formula or steps that tell how to find equivalent dates.
- Decide whether to illustrate your poster with a solar system model or with other pictures.

Carry Out Your Plan

- Transfer your sketch to posterboard.
- Complete your poster with art materials.

Look Back

- Can your classmates determine their birthdates in another calendar system by using your poster?

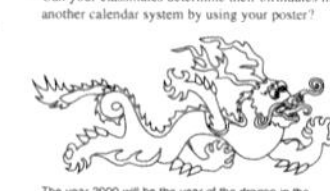

The year 2000 will be the year of the dragon in the Chinese calendar.

A

27 28 29 30 31

Project A

Thirty Days Has September

Is this a leap year? What is the Gregorian calendar, and how did it get started?

Chapter 12 / Project B

When the Earth Was Flat

Compare Cosmic Visions

Study the conceptions of the earth and sun developed by different cultures. Write an illustrated story using a myth.

- Did you know that early peoples invented myths to explain natural phenomena?
- Don't you wonder how people explained sunrise before they knew that the earth turns?
- How does this connect to Chapter 12? We study the physical universe through **astronomical observation**.

Expand Your Vocabulary

cosmos	cosmology	allegory	myth
canopy	personification	celestial	mythology
primal	aborigines	mandala	

Project Guidelines

Investigate

- Read about ancient conceptions of the sun and earth in a book about mythology.
- Read about the early history of astronomy in an encyclopedia or in an astronomy book.
- Recall your own childhood conceptions of the universe. Ask a very young child why it is sometimes light and sometimes dark. Ask him or her to draw a picture showing how it happens.

Set Your Direction

- Do you want to concentrate on the ideas of a particular culture?

Make a Plan

- Make a calendar for each day's work. Check in with your group and with your teacher.
- You'll need art materials to illustrate your report, or you can photocopy illustrations that you find.

Collect and Organize Your Information

- Find as many different names and depictions for the earth and sun as you can.
- Make an organized list of major cultures and their cosmologies. Be sure to look up information from several world cultures, such as Aztec, Greek, Egyptian, and Australian aborigine.

Carry Out Your Plan

- Imagine that you are explaining a natural phenomenon like the sunrise to a child of a particular culture. Tell the story in your own words, using your research as the basis of your explanation.
- Draw or show a picture that might have been used as part of the explanation.
- Tell why you think the story might have been believed at that time and in that culture.

Look Back

- Why do people invent explanations for things they don't understand?
- How do the discoveries of science and space travel compare to the invented harmonies of ancient myths about the universe?
- Why are circles and squares so often used in ancient cosmologies?
- How does a knowledge of math influence beliefs about the physical world?

B

Project B

When the Earth Was Flat

How were sunrise and sunset explained before people knew that the earth revolves around the sun?

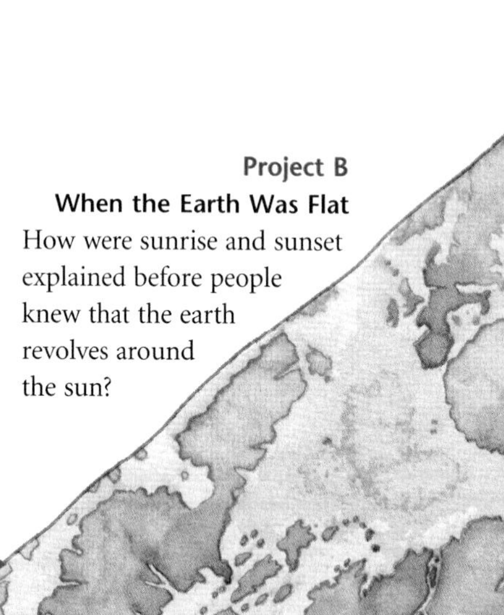

Project C

Watch It Happen

How far would you travel to see a total eclipse of the sun? How are people affected by events such as eclipses or passing comets?

HECTOR DELGADO

I liked math in high school because it was challenging. And I knew I was going to be an engineer. I didn't know what kind of engineer I would be, but I was going to be one.

As an engineer, I use math every day to solve problems related to the space shuttle at the Kennedy Space Center.

Math is a very important tool in our goal to reach for the stars and beyond.

Hector Delgado
Space Shuttle Engineer
National Aeronautics and Space Administration (NASA)
Kennedy Space Center, FL

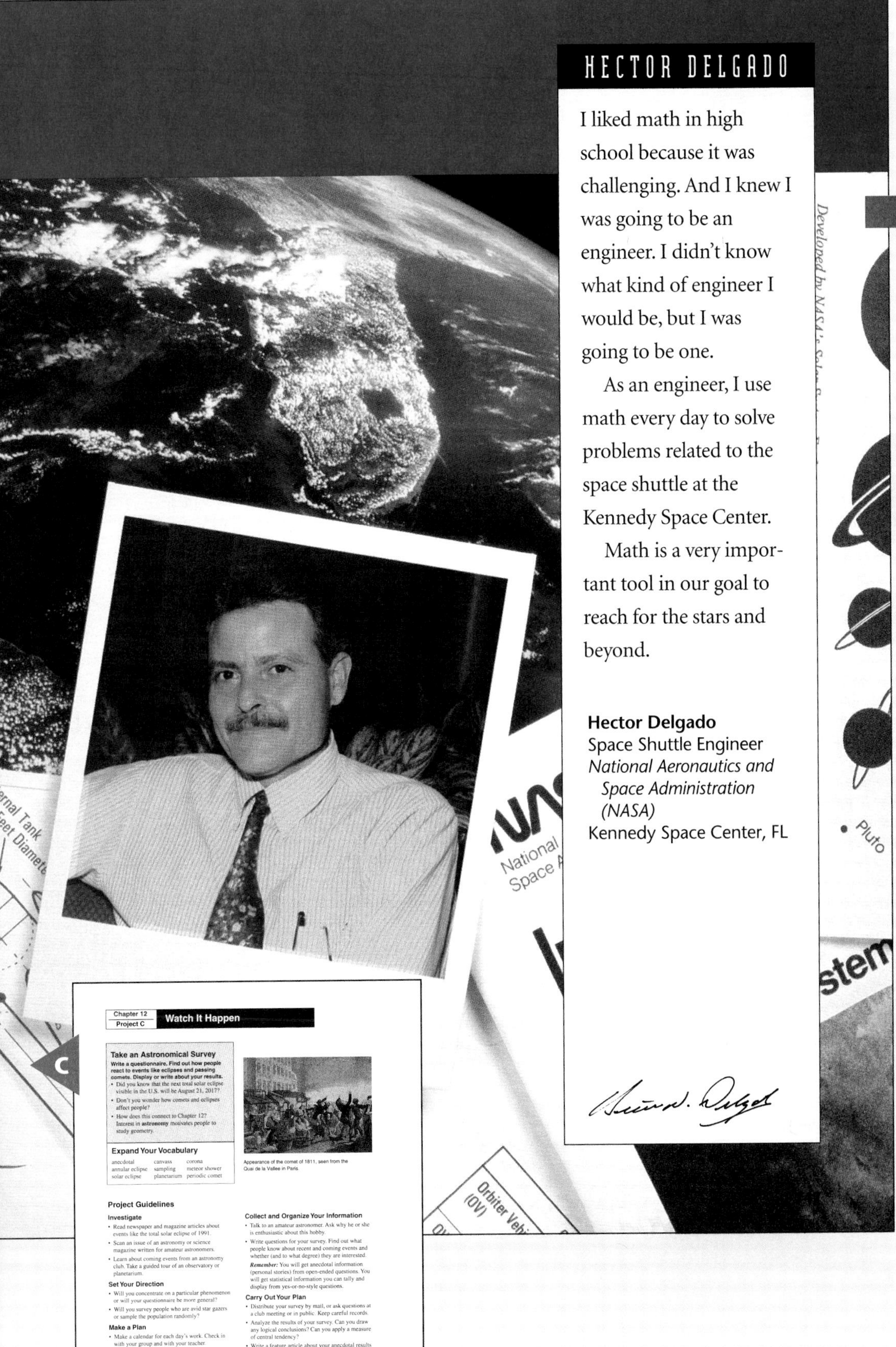

Chapter 12
Project C
Watch It Happen

Take an Astronomical Survey

Write a questionnaire. Find out how people react to events like eclipses and passing comets. Display or write about your results.

- Did you know that the next total solar eclipse visible in the U.S. will be August 21, 2017?
- Don't you wonder how comets and eclipses affect people?
- How does this connect to Chapter 12? Interest in **astronomy** motivates people to study geometry.

Expand Your Vocabulary

anecdotal	canvass	corona
annular eclipse	sampling	meteor shower
solar eclipse	planetarium	periodic comet

Appearance of the comet of 1811, seen from the Quai de la Vallee in Paris.

Project Guidelines

Investigate

- Read newspaper and magazine articles about events like the total solar eclipse of 1991.
- Scan an issue of an astronomy or science magazine written for amateur astronomers.
- Learn about coming events from an astronomy club. Take a guided tour of an observatory or planetarium.

Set Your Direction

- Will you concentrate on a particular phenomenon or will your questionnaire be more general?
- Will you survey people who are avid star gazers or sample the population randomly?

Make a Plan

- Make a calendar for each day's work. Check in with your group and with your teacher.
- Do you expect particular results from your survey? Can you form a hypothesis?
- Will there be a way to quantify the results of your survey? For instance, how far a person would travel, how much they would spend to witness an eclipse?

Collect and Organize Your Information

- Talk to an amateur astronomer. Ask why he or she is enthusiastic about this hobby.
- Write questions for your survey. Find out what people know about recent and coming events and whether (and to what degree) they are interested.

Remember: You will get anecdotal information (personal stories) from open-ended questions. You will get statistical information you can tally and display from yes-or-no-style questions.

Carry Out Your Plan

- Distribute your survey by mail, or ask questions at a club meeting or in public. Keep careful records.
- Analyze the results of your survey. Can you draw any logical conclusions? Can you apply a measure of central tendency?
- Write a feature article about your anecdotal results or display your statistical data in a chart or graph.

Look Back

- What kinds of governmental decisions are made based on public interest in astronomy? What kinds of commercial decisions are made?

Focus on Geometry 71

Biographical Note

Hector Delgado graduated from Miami Senior High School in Miami, FL. He took Algebra I and II, Geometry, Trigonometry, and Analytic Geometry.

Overview

Chapter 12

Astronomy and Geometric Models

12-1 Using Geometry to Model the Earth
Geometry has helped people understand the earth for thousands of years. With familiar tools like proportions and new tools like fractals, you will investigate some ways to measure and model the earth, our solar system, and our galaxy.

12-2 Euclidean and Non-Euclidean Geometries
Changing just one of Euclid's postulates—the Parallel Postulate—has allowed mathematicians to develop completely different systems of geometry. You will review some of Euclid's assumptions, and see how a change in the Parallel Postulate affects the properties of some geometric figures.

CHAPTERS

Chapter 12 Planning Guide

The following ancillaries are recommended for each course level. The additional resources, *Technology Lab Manual, Study Guide and Journal, Multilingual Handbook,* and *Assessment,* are recommended for all levels.

	Comprehensive Course	Core Course	Informal Course
12-1 Part A	▲	▲	
Alternative Lessons			
Laboratory Manuals	▲	▲	
Practice			
More Look Ahead		▲	
12-1 Part B	▲	▲	
Alternative Lessons			
Laboratory Manuals	▲	▲	
Practice			
More Look Back		▲	
12-1 Part C	▲	▲	
Alternative Lessons			
Laboratory Manuals	▲	▲	
Practice			
More Look Ahead		▲	

	Comprehensive Course	Core Course	Informal Course
12-1 Part D	▲	▲	
More Look Back		▲	
Quiz 12-1	▲	▲	
12-2 Part A	▲	▲	
Alternative Lessons			
Laboratory Manuals	▲	▲	
Practice			
More Look Ahead		▲	
12-2 Part B	▲	▲	
Alternative Lessons			
Laboratory Manuals	▲	▲	
Practice			
More Look Back		▲	
12-2 Part C	▲	▲	
More Look Back		▲	
Quiz 12-2	▲	▲	

BIBLIOGRAPHY

Reading for Students

Powers of Ten, Philip and Phylis Morrison. Scientific American Books, 1982.

Teacher Resources

Space Mathematics: A Resource for Secondary School Teachers, Bernice Kastner. NASA, 1985.

Fractals for the Classroom: Strategic Activities, Volumes 1 and 2, Heinz-Otto Peitgen, et al. © 1992 Springer-Verlag New York, Inc. Published in cooperation with the National Council of Teachers of Mathematics (NCTM).

Reading for Teachers

Fractal Music, Hypercards, and More,... Martin Gardner, W. H. Freeman and Company, 1992.

12-1

Using Geometry to Model the Earth

SUPERLESSON AT A GLANCE

Superlesson Goal

In this Superlesson, students will again focus on the idea of mathematical modeling. They will find that fractals are a useful model for many of the earth's features, that latitudes and longitudes can describe locations on the earth, and that geometry can be used to find distances from the earth to other astronomical objects.

Management Guide

	Topic	Objectives	Key Terms	New Ideas	Materials
Part A	Fractals	To investigate fractal patterns.	Fractal, self-similar	Self-similarity. Creating fractal patterns through repeated application of rules.	**Student** Ruler
Part B	Longitude and Latitude	To become familiar with latitude and longitude.	Equator, prime meridian, latitude, longitude	The latitude-longitude system for locating points on the surface of the earth.	**Teacher** Globe, world map transparency
Part C	Measurement in Astronomy	To use geometry to measure distances to and sizes of moons, planets, and stars.	Astronomical unit, light-year, parallax	Units of measure for large distances. Using parallax and arc measures to find astronomical measurements.	
Part D	Making Connections	To use latitudes and longitudes to find moonrise times in different cities.	In Making Connections, students apply and synthesize key terms and new ideas.		**Teacher** Globe, world map transparency, United States map

Pacing Chart (45-Minute Periods)

	Comprehensive Course	Core Course	Informal Course
Part A	1	1	0
Part B	1	1	0
Part C	1	1	0
Part D	1	1	0
TOTAL periods for Superlesson	4	4	0

NCTM Standards

Mathematics as Problem Solving
Mathematics as Communication
Mathematics as Reasoning
Mathematical Connections
Geometry from a Synthetic Perspective
Trigonometry
Discrete Mathematics

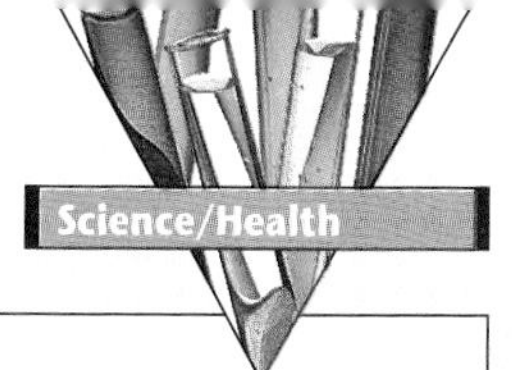

Science/Health

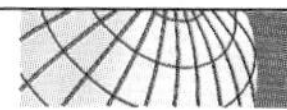

12-1 Using Geometry to Model the Earth

The Earth and Beyond

Let's take a trip into space. The pictures we'll see on this journey are from Powers of Ten, published by Scientific American. This book shows pictures of the same area taken from various distances, each ten times farther away than the last.

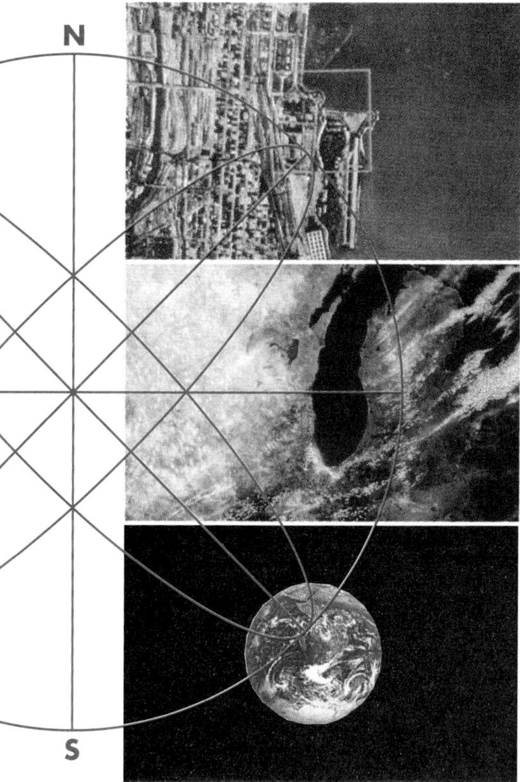

This is downtown Chicago, shown from an altitude of 10 kilometers—about 6 miles. We're a little higher than Mt. Everest, the world's tallest mountain. Over a million people live or work in this region. Soldier Field, the home of the Chicago Bears, and Meigs Field lie inside the square.

Now we're 100 times higher, at an altitude of 1000 kilometers—3 to 4 times higher than the orbit of a space shuttle. We can see all of Lake Michigan and parts of the four states that surround it. Although millions of people live in this area, from this distance we see little evidence of human life.

Now we've zoomed out to an altitude of 100,000 kilometers. This is about one-fourth of the distance from the earth to the moon. The earth and its billions of inhabitants seem isolated in space as they race around the sun at 67,000 mi/hr.

?

1. **Suppose you are given photographs of an unfamiliar coastline taken from two different altitudes. Can you tell which was taken from the higher altitude? If so, how?**
2. **How can you describe Chicago's exact location on the earth's surface?**
3. **Is it important to know the exact size of the earth? Why? Would this knowledge have been as important thousands of years ago? Why or why not?**

More About Astronomical Distances

Light reaching us from stars and planets originated in the past, so seeing these objects is like looking back in time—we see the sun as it was about 8 minutes ago. *Quasars,* which may be the cores of exploding galaxies, are the objects with the greatest actual brightness in the universe and therefore can be seen at the greatest distances. When we observe a quasar, we may see it as it was about 9 billion years ago.

Where Are We Now?

Students have explored a wide range of topics in geometry and developed many skills. Their abilities to work with arc measures and trigonometry are of particular importance in 12-1.

Where Are We Going?

In 12-1, students will explore different ways to use geometry to model the earth and other astronomical objects. They will learn about fractals, which can be used to model landscapes, and latitude and longitude lines, which describe locations. They will also see how to use geometry to measure sizes of and distances to far-off objects.

The study of longitude and latitude in 12-1 prepares students for their exploration of Riemannian geometry in 12-2.

Possible Answers

1. You may be able to compare sizes of objects in the pictures to decide which was taken from a higher altitude. However, the general appearance of the outline of the coast will not change much with altitude.

2. By using latitude and longitude.

3. In today's world, there is a great deal of intercontinental travel on planes and boats, and knowing the size of the earth is important for these trips. Thousands of years ago, most trips were shorter, so measurements of local distances were much more important than knowledge of the overall size of the earth.

AWSM Videodisc

Focus on Geometry

▶ **12-1** Using Geometry to Model the Earth

Search:

Play: Step:

Using Geometry to Model the Earth

PART A At a Glance

Objective

To investigate fractal patterns.

Development

Students see a definition of self-similarity and learn what a fractal pattern is.

In the **Explore,** students create a fractal pattern known as the Koch Snowflake.

Suggested Materials

Student Ruler

Key Terms

Fractal, self-similar

First Five Minutes

Transparency FFM 12-1A

Read the introductory material on page 750 and the **Example** on pages 750–751. Then answer the **Consider** question on page 751.

Motivate

Ask...

- Give some examples of real-world objects that show self-similarity. Explain how each is self-similar.

ALTERNATE EXAMPLE

Transparency AE 12-1A

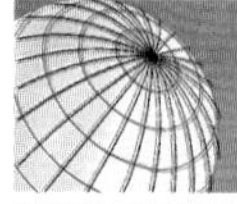

12-1 PART A Fractals

← CONNECT → *You know how to identify and draw similar figures. Now you will investigate figures whose parts are similar to the whole figure. Some of these figures can be used to model the earth in fascinating ways.*

Some real-world shapes, like coastlines, mountains, and leaves, may seem too complex to model mathematically. However, in 1982, Benoit Mandelbrot gained worldwide attention by connecting mathematics and nature through **fractal geometry.**

A baseball card of Mike Perez that shows him holding his baseball card suggests a fractal. If you think about this situation, you realize that the card Perez is holding also has a picture of him holding the card. That card also has a picture of Perez, and he's holding a card with his picture, and so on.

A fractal has some of the same characteristics as the "infinite" baseball card. Fractals are patterns that are **self-similar.** When magnified, small parts of a self-similar figure cannot be distinguished from the whole figure. The figure below shows self-similarity.

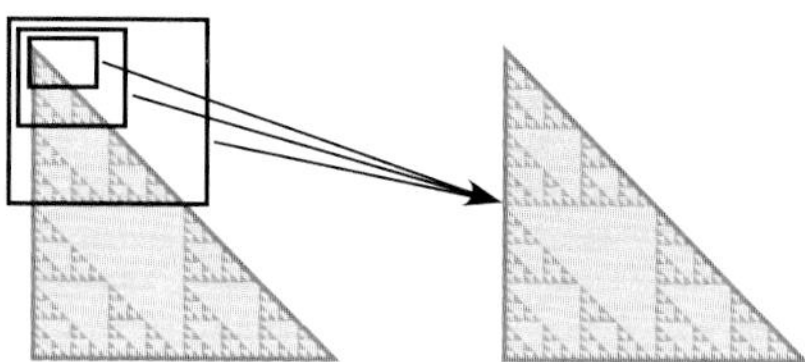

In the following example, we apply a rule that divides a triangle into smaller and smaller triangles. The figure that results is a fractal.

EXAMPLE

Start with a shaded equilateral triangle. Use the following rule.

For each shaded triangle:

a. Connect the midpoints of the sides with line segments.
b. Remove the middle triangle of the four triangles formed.

We can begin to draw this fractal as shown in the series of figures at the top of page 751.

Mathematics Connection

Benoit Mandelbrot, "the father of fractals," was born in 1924 in Warsaw and moved to the United States in 1958. Dr. Mandelbrot is a mathematics professor and researcher who made many important discoveries in this field during the 1970s and 1980s. The Mandelbrot set, an extremely complex fractal, was named after Dr. Mandelbrot.

Technology Note

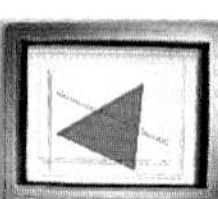

Several software packages, including many geometry packages, have installed procedures for drawing fractals. You may want to set up a display monitor and show students a Sierpinski Gasket, Koch Snowflake, or other pattern such as a Julia set.

These are the first four stages of the self-similarity pattern.

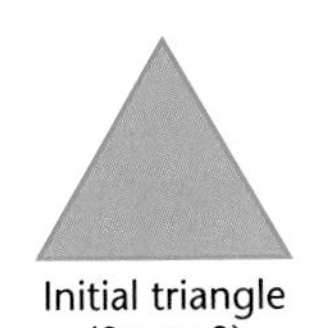
Initial triangle (Stage 0)

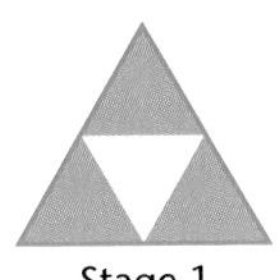
Stage 1

Stage 2

Stage 3

Stage 4

The figure created by carrying out this rule an infinite number of times is called a Sierpinski Gasket, after its inventor, mathematician Waclaw Sierpinski.

1. At Step b in creating each stage of the Sierpinski Gasket, what fraction of the remaining area is removed?

In the following Explore, you will investigate several stages of a fractal pattern.

EXPLORE: FRACTAL FIGURES

MATERIALS

Ruler

1. Use the following rule to sketch the first three stages of a fractal pattern. (Hint: Draw with a pencil, so that you can erase.) Start with a large equilateral triangle. Remove the center third of each segment, and replace it with two congruent segments that form an equilateral "bump." Repeat this rule until you have completed three stages of the design. (The figure at the right shows the first two stages of one side of the triangle.)
2. Does this rule eventually form a Sierpinski Gasket? If not, describe your completed pattern.

Initial side (top of triangle)

Stage 1

Stage 2

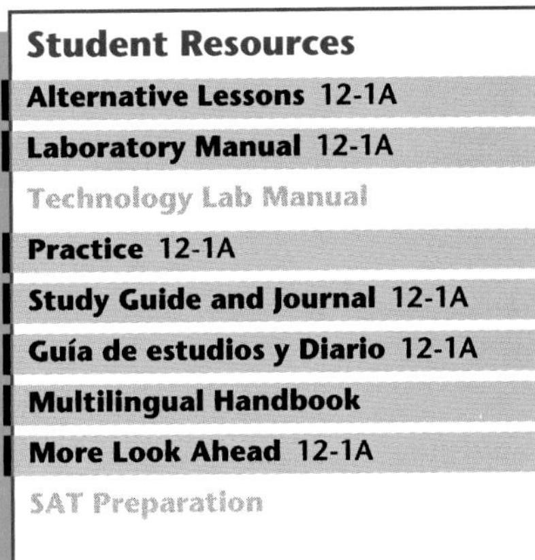

Student Resources
- **Alternative Lessons** 12-1A
- **Laboratory Manual** 12-1A
- Technology Lab Manual
- **Practice** 12-1A
- **Study Guide and Journal** 12-1A
- **Guía de estudios y Diario** 12-1A
- **Multilingual Handbook**
- **More Look Ahead** 12-1A
- SAT Preparation

Media Resources
- **Transparency FFM** 12-1A
- **Transparency AE** 12-1A
- Teaching Transparency
- **AWSMTest and practice software**
- **AWSM Videodisc**

Investigates areas in the Sierpinski Gasket.

Possible Answer

1. At each stage, $\frac{1}{4}$ of the remaining area is removed.

EXPLORE

Fractal Figures

Recommended group size: 2

The Point

To sketch a fractal pattern known as the Koch Snowflake.

Look and Listen...

- For students who are not making their "bumps" equilateral.
- For students who are not erasing the center third of each segment.

Ask...

- Are the sides of the "bump" you're adding the same length as the gap?

For Groups That Finish Early

Draw an equilateral triangle inscribed in a circle, and sketch several stages of the Snowflake pattern. Do you think the fractal will ever go outside the boundary of this circle? Why or why not? **No. The peaks of the bumps constructed at Stage 1 touch the circle; all other new points are in the interior of the circle.**

Follow Up

Ask students to display their fractal sketches. Tell them that this figure is called the Koch Snowflake, and ask why they think it might have this name. (Some students may remember this figure from **Exercise** 14 in 5-2 Part C, on page 360.)

Possible Answers

1. The first three stages of the pattern are shown on page 755.

2. The rule does not form a Sierpinski Gasket. The fractal pattern looks like a star or snowflake with "spikes" that get smaller and smaller at each stage.

12-1

Using Geometry to Model the Earth

Journal

Reflect 1 and 2 and **Exercise** 10 are suitable for journal entries.

REFLECT

Possible Answers

1. Both involve the concept of similarity; figures that look alike but are not (necessarily) the same size. However, self-similarity is a characteristic of one figure, whereas similarity refers to two or more figures.

2. A mathematical fractal has an infinite number of stages. A fractal in nature is limited by the minimum sizes of its parts—a branch of a tree cannot be infinitesimally small.

3. The tiny piece of the fractal would look like a corresponding piece of the whole figure.

Part A Exercises

Exercise Notes

Core

7. Illustrates fractal patterns in Pascal's Triangle.

10. Shows that a linear graph has self-similarity.

Look Ahead

11–13. Review the radius-circumference relationship for a circle. Students will use this relationship in finding measurements in 12-1 Parts B and C.

14–16. Review circle arc calculations. Students will use central angles to calculate distances in 12-1 Parts B and C.

17–19. Review trigonometry. Trigonometry is required to calculate the distance around the earth at different latitudes in 12-1 Part B.

More Math Reasoning

24. and 25. Students investigate the area and perimeter of the Koch Snowflake.

Computers can be programmed to generate fractals that are much more complex than the ones you have explored. The image at the right is a computer-generated fractal that models a mountain.

REFLECT

1. How is self-similarity related to similarity? How is it different?
2. What is the difference between a fractal found in nature and the mathematical idea of a fractal?
3. Lilia programmed her computer to draw 1000 stages of a pattern for a fractal. If she were to zoom in on a tiny part of this picture, what could she expect to see?

Exercises

CORE

P **1. Getting Started** Follow the steps to create a pattern similar to a fractal.

a. Draw a square. This initial square is Stage 0 of the pattern.

b. Mark the midpoint of each side of the square. Then connect the midpoints to form a new square. This is Stage 1 of the pattern.

c. Mark the midpoint of each side of the new square. Connect the midpoints to make Stage 2.

d. Repeat **1c** two more times to create Stages 3 and 4 of the pattern.

P **Sketch the next stage of each pattern and describe the rule for the pattern.**

2.

Initial square (Stage 0) | Stage 1 | Stage 2

3.

Initial grid (Stage 0)

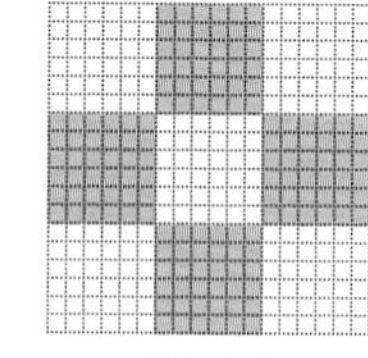

Stage 1

Key

V Vocabulary
P Practice/Skills
R Review
MR Math Reasoning
PS Problem Solving
C Challenge

Literature Connection

Your students might enjoy this poetic portrayal of self-similarity:

Great fleas have little fleas upon their backs to
bite 'em,
And little fleas have lesser fleas, and so *ad infinitum.*

Augustus de Morgan, *A Budget of Paradoxes,* 1872.

In Exercises 4 and 5, sketch the second stage of each fractal.

4. Start with an equilateral triangle. Use the following rule.
  a. Divide the sides of each unshaded triangle into three congruent segments.
  b. Connect the dividing points as shown.
  c. Shade the inverted triangles.

Stage 1

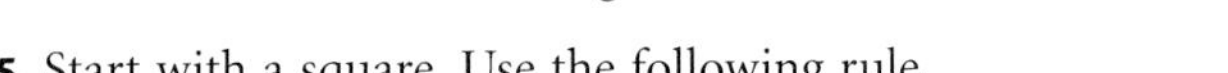

5. Start with a square. Use the following rule.
  a. Divide the sides of each unshaded square into three congruent segments.
  b. Connect the dividing points as shown.
  c. Shade the inner square.

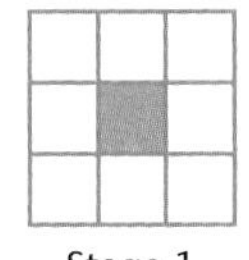

Stage 1

6. The first four stages of the Sierpinski Gasket are shown. Use these figures to investigate number patterns that emerge from stage to stage.

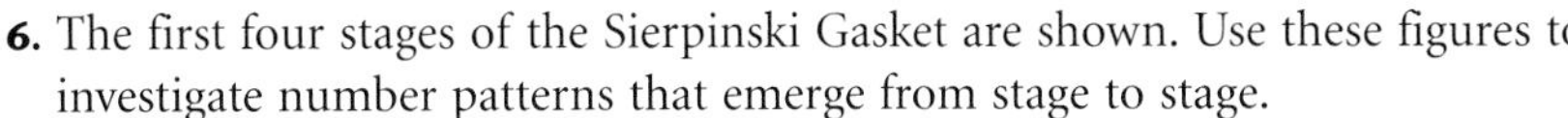

Initial triangle (Stage 0)

Stage 1

Stage 2

Stage 3

Stage 4

  a. Make a table to record the number of shaded triangles for Stages 0–4.
  b. Predict the number of shaded triangles for Stage 5.
  c. Suppose there are t shaded triangles at one stage of the pattern. How many will there be at the next stage?
  d. Write an equation for the number of shaded triangles at Stage n.
  e. Suppose the area of the triangle in Stage 0 is 1. Make a table to record the total shaded area for Stages 0–4. Then predict the total shaded area for Stage 5.
  f. Suppose the shaded area at one stage of the pattern is $\frac{a}{b}$. What will the area be at the next stage?
  g. What happens to the shaded area when you repeat the pattern n times?

7. Fractals in Pascal's Triangle The figure at the right shows the beginning of Pascal's Triangle. The number in each hexagon is the sum of the numbers in the two hexagons immediately above it.
  a. On dot paper, sketch hexagons, and fill in the numbers for Rows 0–7 of Pascal's Triangle.
  b. Shade any hexagons in the first eight rows of Pascal's Triangle that contain an odd number. Look at Rows 0–3 of Pascal's Triangle after shading the odd numbers. How do they compare to Stage 1 of the Sierpinski Gasket?
  c. Now consider Rows 0–7 of Pascal's Triangle after shading the odd numbers. How do they compare to Stage 2 of the Sierpinski Gasket?

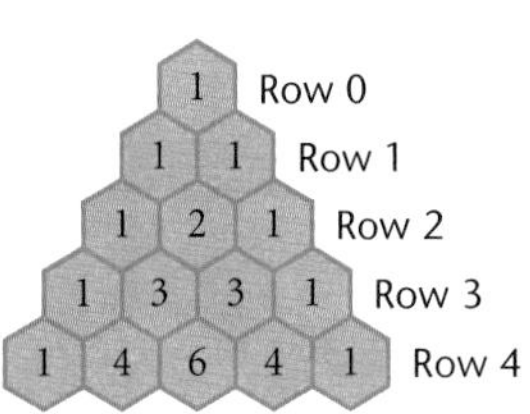

8. Create a rule for a fractal design of your own. Sketch the first three stages of the design.

Exercise Answers

Core

1. a.

Stage 0

b.

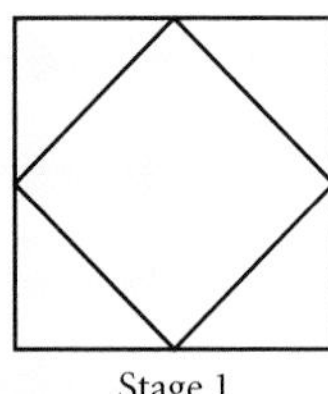

Stage 1

c.

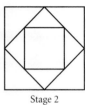

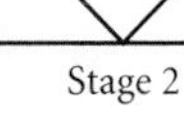

Stage 2

d.

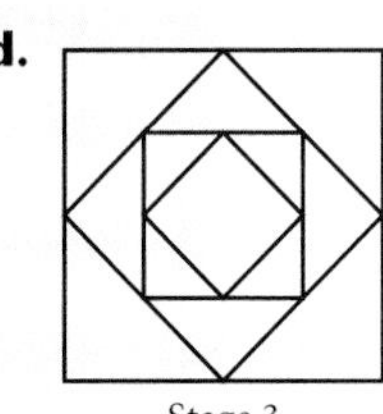

Stage 3

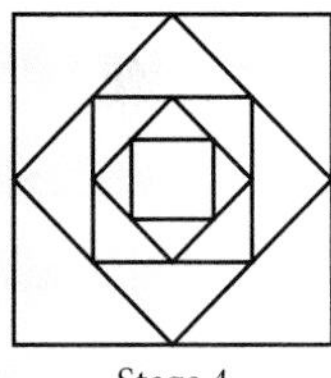

Stage 4

2.

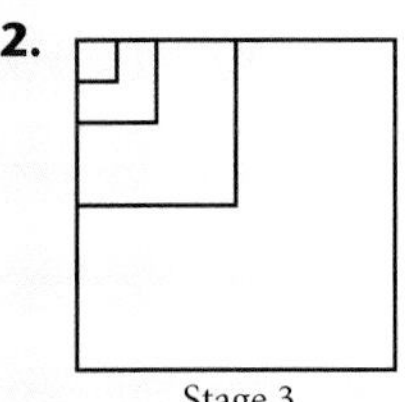

Stage 3

Draw a square in the upper left corner whose side length is half that of the previous square.

Ongoing Assessment

Self-Assessment Exercises 2, 3, 5, 7, 9

Embedded Assessment Reflect 3; Exercises 2, 4, 6, 8

Using Geometry to Model the Earth

3. 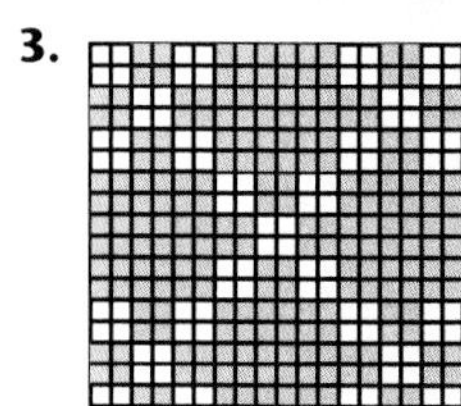

Stage 2

Divide each unshaded square into nine congruent smaller squares and shade the middle squares along the sides of each square just divided.

4. 

Stage 2

5. 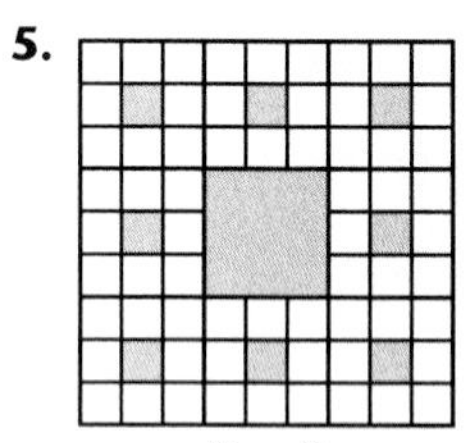

Stage 2

6. a.

Stage	Shaded triangles
0	1
1	3
2	9
3	27
4	81

b. 243 c. $3t$

d. $N = 3^n$

e.

Stage	Area of shaded triangles
0	1
1	$\frac{3}{4}$
2	$\frac{9}{16}$
3	$\frac{27}{64}$
4	$\frac{81}{256}$
5	$\frac{243}{1024}$

f. $\left(\frac{3}{4}\right)\left(\frac{a}{b}\right)$

g. The shaded area changes by a factor of $\left(\frac{3}{4}\right)^n$.

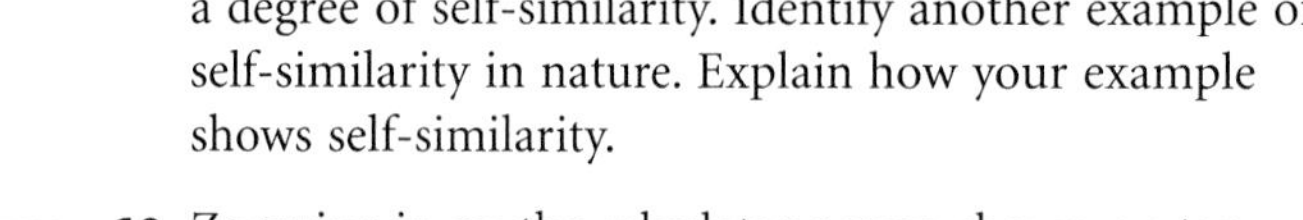

MR 9. Coastlines, mountains, oak trees, and broccoli all have a degree of self-similarity. Identify another example of self-similarity in nature. Explain how your example shows self-similarity.

MR 10. Zooming in on the calculator screen shown on top at the right produces the screen shown below it.

a. If you continue to zoom in on this graph, will it always have the same shape? Explain why or why not.

b. Do you think this graph shows self-similarity? If so, do all types of graphs have self-similarity? Explain.

LOOK AHEAD

R **Find the radius or circumference for each circle described. Round answers to the nearest tenth.**

11. $r = 12.4$ in., $C =$ 77.9 in. 12. $C = 29.6$ cm, $r =$ 4.7 cm 13. $r = 3960$ mi, $C =$ 24,881.4 m

R **Find each missing value. Round answers to the nearest tenth.**

14. $r = 20$, $s = 10$, $m\angle A =$ 28.6° 15. $r = 20$, $m\angle A = 60°$, $s =$ 20.9

16. $s = 150$, $m\angle A = 10°$, $r =$ 859.4

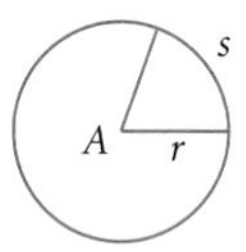

R **Use trigonometry to find *k* for each $m\angle k$ given. Round answers to the nearest tenth.**

17. $m\angle K = 35°$ 3441.5 km 18. $m\angle K = 42°$ 4014.8 km 19. $m\angle K = 71°$ 5673.1 km

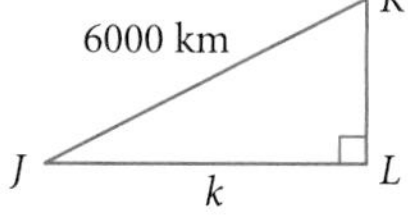

MORE PRACTICE

P **Sketch the next stage of each pattern, and describe the rule for the pattern.**

20. 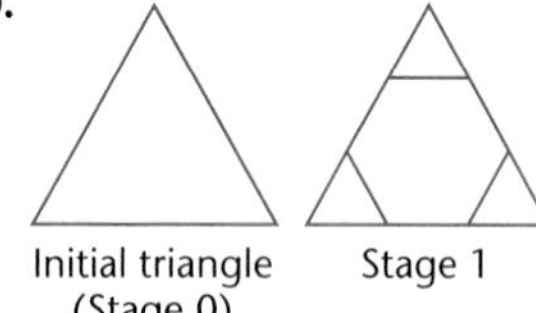

Initial triangle (Stage 0) Stage 1

21. 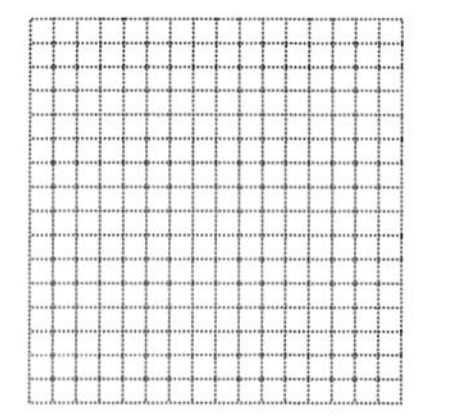 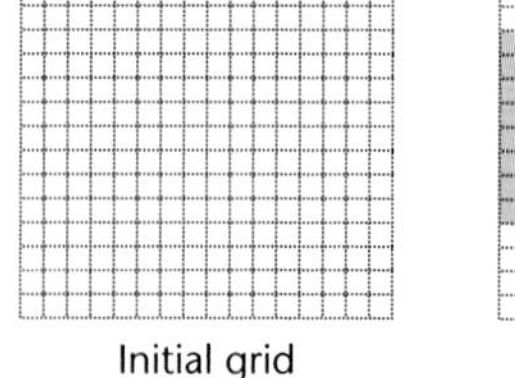

Initial grid (Stage 0) Stage 1

Key

V Vocabulary
P Practice/Skills
R Review
MR Math Reasoning
PS Problem Solving
C Challenge

In Exercises 22 and 23, sketch the second stage of each fractal.

22. Start with an isosceles right triangle. Use the following rule.

a. Find the midpoint of the hypotenuse of each triangle.

b. Make a square in each triangle by drawing perpendicular segments from the midpoint to the legs. Shade the square.

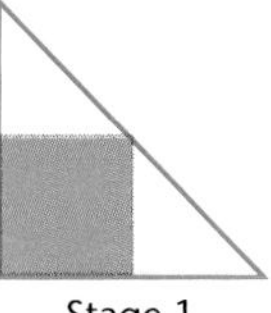

Stage 1

23. Start with a square. Use the following rule.

a. Divide the sides of each unshaded square into three equal parts.

b. Connect the dividing points, as shown at the right.

c. Shade the middle square on each side of these squares, as shown.

Stage 1

MORE MATH REASONING

The Koch Snowflake is formed by starting with an equilateral triangle and adding an equilateral "bump" to each segment at every stage. Stages 0–3 are shown.

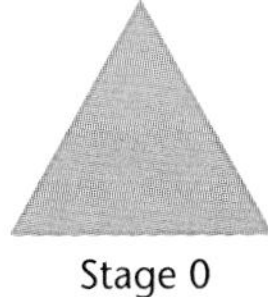

Stage 0

Stage 1

Stage 2

Stage 3

24. Measuring Snowflakes Investigate what happens to the perimeter of the Koch Snowflake as the number of sides increases.

Stage	Number of Segments	Length of Each Segment	Perimeter
0	3	1	$3 \cdot 1 = 3$
1			

a. Complete the table for stages 0–3.

b. Predict the number of segments at Stage 4. Then find the ratio of the number of segments at one stage to the number at the preceding stage. 768; 4:1

c. Write an equation in terms of n for the number of segments at Stage n. 3×4^n

d. Assume the length of a side of the original triangle is 1. Predict the length of each segment at Stage 4. Then find the ratio of the length of each segment at one stage to the length of each segment at the preceding stage. $\frac{1}{81}$; 1:3

e. Write an equation in terms of n for the length of each segment at Stage n. $\ell = \left(\frac{1}{3}\right)^n$

f. Predict the perimeter at Stage 4. Then describe the ratio of the perimeters at two consecutive stages. $\frac{256}{27}$; 4:3

g. Is the perimeter increasing or decreasing? What will happen to the perimeter of the Koch Snowflake if you repeat the pattern an infinite number of times? Increasing; It will become an infinite length.

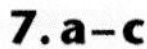

7. a–c.

b. Similar **c.** Similar

8. Possible answer: Start with a square.

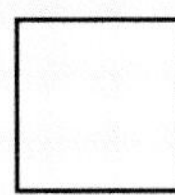

Stage 0

Find the midpoint of each side of the unshaded squares. Connect opposite midpoints with a line in each square. Shade in the upper right and lower left boxes.

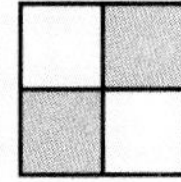

Stage 1

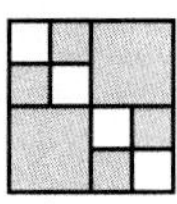

Stage 2

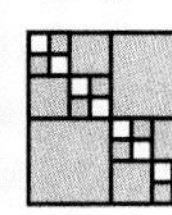

Stage 3

9. Possible answer: A fern. Each branch is similar in shape and structure to the original plant.

10. a. Yes. If you zoom in on any segment of a straight line, it will have the same slope as the line.

b. Yes; No; Only graphs of straight lines have self-similarity.

More Practice

20.

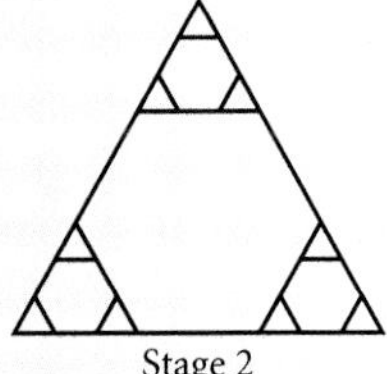

Stage 2

Divide sides of the new triangles into thirds. Connect the dividing points to form new triangles.

21–23, 24a, and 25a.

See Additional Answers p. T770.

Using Geometry to Model the Earth

PART B At a Glance

Objective

To become familiar with latitude and longitude.

Development

Students see a description of the latitude-longitude system and an **Example** of its use.

In the **Explore,** students use latitudes and longitudes to help calculate the widths of continents.

Suggested Materials

Teacher Globe, world map transparency

Key Terms

Equator, prime meridian, latitude, longitude

First Five Minutes

Transparency FFM 12-1B

A central angle of 80° cuts off an arc on a circle. Find the length of the arc for the circle of each radius. Round answers to the nearest tenth.

1. 10 cm 14.0 cm

2. 44 ft 61.4 ft

3. 3960 mi 5529.2 mi

Motivate

Ask...

- How are the x-y coordinate system and the longitude-latitude system different?

MR, C **25.** Investigate what happens to the area of the Koch Snowflake (described on page 755) as the number of sides increases.

a. Complete the table.

Stage Number	Number of Segments	Number of Triangles Added	Additional Area	Total Area
0	3	0	0	1
1				
2				
3				

b. Predict the number of triangles added at Stage 4. Then find the ratio of the number of new triangles at one stage to the number of new triangles at the preceding stage. 192; 4:1

c. Write an equation in terms of n for the number of new triangles at Stage n. $N = 3 \times 4^{n-1}$

d. Assume the area of the original triangle is 1. Predict the additional area at Stage 4. Then find the ratio of the additional areas at two consecutive stages. $\frac{64}{2187}$; $\frac{4}{9}$

e. Write an equation in terms of n for the additional area at Stage n. $A = \frac{1}{3}\left(\frac{4}{9}\right)^{n-1}$

f. Predict the total area at Stage 4. Is it increasing or decreasing as n increases? $1\frac{1261}{2187}$; Increa

g. Does the area of the Koch Snowflake become infinitely large, or does there seem to be a limit on its area? Explain. There seems to be a limit; The additional area at each stage is $\frac{4}{9}$ smaller than the area added at the preceding stage.

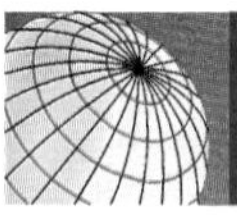

12-1 PART B Longitude and Latitude

← CONNECT → *You've used maps to model the earth, and you've learned about the properties of spheres. Now you will use a sphere to model the earth and learn how to use latitude and longitude lines.*

When you see mountains or canyons, you may wonder how spherical the earth is. Nevertheless, a model of the earth 8 ft in diameter would be smoother than a polished bowling ball. The highest mountain would be represented by a bump rising only 0.067 in. above the surface, and the difference between the polar and equatorial diameters would not be noticeable. A sphere is, therefore, a good model of the earth.

You know how to use coordinates to locate points on a plane. We also use a coordinate system to locate a point on a sphere. This system is based on two reference lines (like the x- and y-axes).

Key

V Vocabulary

P Practice/Skills

R Review

MR Math Reasoning

PS Problem Solving

C Challenge

Alert

Students may have difficulty remembering the difference between latitude and longitude. You may want to use a globe to show them that some latitude lines are shorter than others, while *longitude* lines are all very long.

One of these lines is the **equator.** The equator and the lines parallel to it are called lines of **latitude.** The equator is at 0° latitude, the North Pole is at 90° north latitude (90° N), and the South Pole at 90° S.

The other reference line is the **prime meridian.** This north-south line runs through England, continental Europe, and West Africa. The prime meridian marks 0° **longitude.** Other longitude lines range from 0° to 180°, east or west.

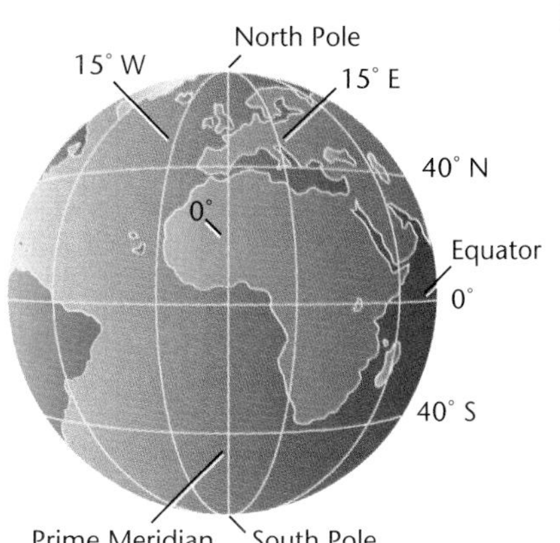

ALTERNATE EXAMPLE

Using the map on page 757, give the approximate latitude and longitude of Los Angeles and of Nairobi, Kenya.

Los Angeles has latitude 34° N and longitude 118° W.

Nairobi has latitude 1° S and longitude 37° E.

EXAMPLE

Give the approximate latitude and longitude of New York City and Buenos Aires, Argentina.

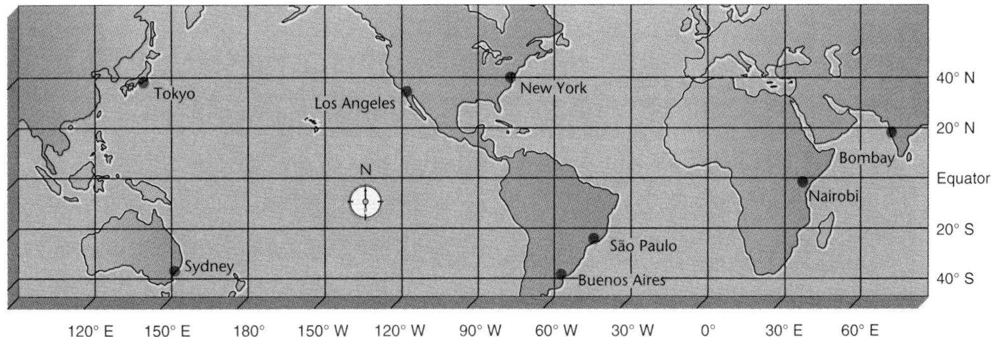

New York City has latitude 41° N and longitude 74° W.

Buenos Aires has latitude 35° S and longitude 58° W.

TRY IT

Give the approximate latitude and longitude of each city.

a. Bombay, India 18° N, 73° E **b.** Tokyo, Japan 35° N, 140° E **c.** São Paulo, Brazil 22° S, 45° W

The average radius of the earth is about 3960 mi, and its average circumference is approximately 24,900 mi. In the following Explore, you will use that information, some proportional thinking, and longitudes and latitudes to measure distances.

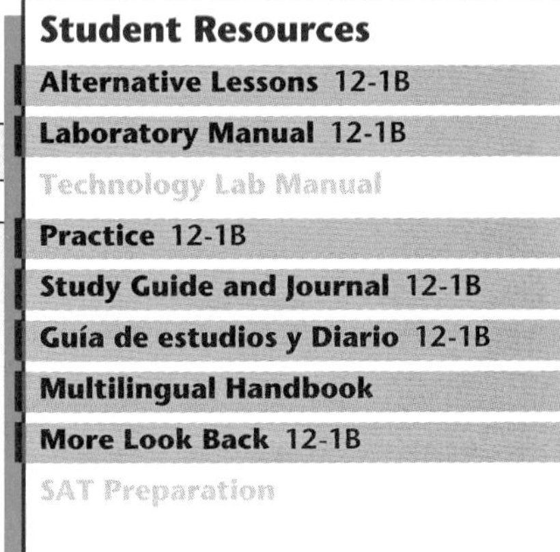

Student Resources

Alternative Lessons 12-1B
Laboratory Manual 12-1B
Technology Lab Manual
Practice 12-1B
Study Guide and Journal 12-1B
Guía de estudios y Diario 12-1B
Multilingual Handbook
More Look Back 12-1B
SAT Preparation

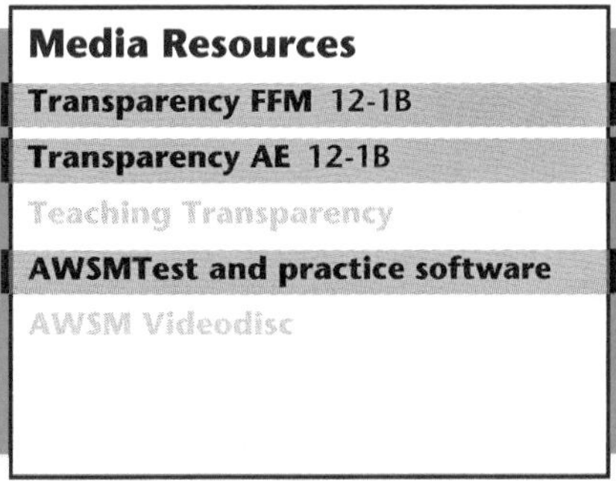

Media Resources

Transparency FFM 12-1B
Transparency AE 12-1B
Teaching Transparency
AWSMTest and practice software
AWSM Videodisc

Using Geometry to Model the Earth

EXPLORE

Crossing the Continents

Recommended group size: 4

The Point

To use longitudes and arc lengths to measure widths of continents.

Look and Listen...

- For students who do not see that they need to use trigonometry in Step 2.
- For students who do not see how to use r to find d.

Ask...

- Do you see a triangle in the figure on page 758? Do you know any of its angle measures and sides? How can you solve for a missing side length in a right triangle?
- How does knowing the radius of the 40° latitude line help you find its length?

For Groups That Finish Early

Find the distance around the earth at your school's latitude. (The map on page 757 may help you approximate the latitude.)

Follow Up

Ask students to share answers for Steps 1–3. Have one student or group explain why it is important to know the latitude before doing calculations like these.

Possible Answers

1. Width of South America ≈ 2075 mi; width of Africa ≈ 2283 mi. The equator is the only latitude line that is a great circle of the earth, so it is the only one whose circumference is equal to the earth's circumference.
2. $\frac{r}{R} = \sin 50°$, so $r = R \sin 50° \approx 3960 \times 0.766$; $r \approx 3034$ mi. Circumference $= 2\pi r = 2\pi(3034) \approx 19060$ mi.
3. Width of Asia at 40° N ≈ 5400 mi.

EXPLORE: CROSSING THE CONTINENTS

1. The equator passes through South America and Africa. The longitudes of the easternmost and westernmost locations where it touches these continents are given below. Find the width of each continent at the equator. Explain why it is important to use the equator in this situation instead of a different line of latitude.

Continent	Easternmost Longitude	Westernmost Longitude
South America	50° W	80° W
Africa	42° E	9° E

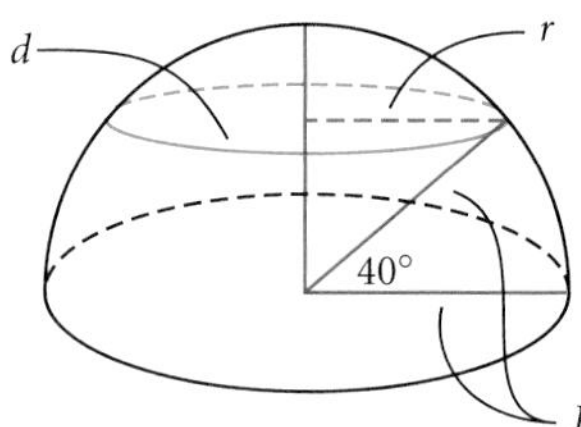

2. To find the widths of continents at other latitudes, we first need to find the length of the latitude line. Calculate the distance, d, around the earth at 40° N latitude. Give a detailed explanation of your calculation.
3. At 40° N latitude, Asia extends from 26° E longitude to 128° E longitude. Find the width of Asia at 40° N.

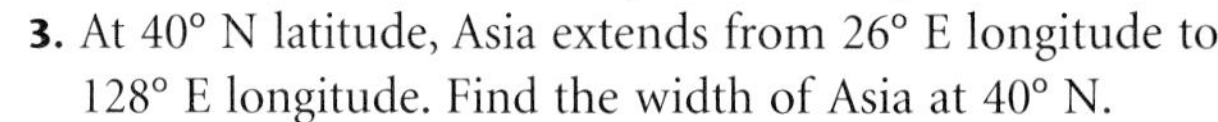

Time zones are based on lines of longitude. If you were looking down at the North Pole, you would see the earth complete one counterclockwise rotation of 360° every 24 hours. Therefore, each 1-hour time zone should correspond to $\frac{360°}{24} = 15°$ of longitude.

1. If the earth rotates 15° in one hour, how long does it take to rotate 1°?

REFLECT

1. Are latitude lines all the same length? are longitude lines? Illustrate your answer.
2. The earth is a three-dimensional object. Why are just two coordinates (longitude and latitude) enough to describe any point on the surface of the earth?

Alert

Students may need to be reminded that latitude and longitude "lines" are circles.

History Connection

For many years, mapmakers chose any 0° meridian convenient for their map—perhaps one containing a capital or landmark. In 1766, an influential navigational almanac used a 0° meridian through Greenwich, England, the home of an important observatory. In 1884, the International Meridian Conference adopted this line as the Prime Meridian.

Exercises

CORE

In the Exercises, use 3960 mi for the radius of the earth and 24,900 mi for the circumference of the earth.

Getting Started In Exercises 1–3, use the map at the right to give the approximate latitude and longitude of each city.

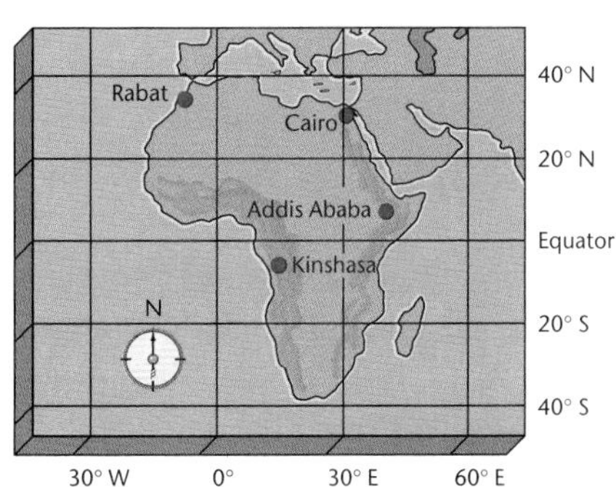

1. Cairo, Egypt 30° N, 31° E

2. Kinshasa, Zaire 4° S, 15° E

3. Addis Ababa, Ethiopia 7° N, 40° E

4. The equator passes through the island of Borneo, in Indonesia. The easternmost location where it touches Borneo is at 117° E longitude, and the westernmost location is at 109° E longitude. Find the width of Borneo at the equator. About 553 mi

The pairs of cities in the following table have approximately the same longitude. Find the distance between each pair of cities.

	Name	Latitude	Name	Latitude	
5.	Seattle, WA	47.62° N	Oakland, CA	37.80° N	≈ 679 mi
6.	Santa Fe, NM	35.68° N	Moose Jaw, Saskatchewan	50.62° N	≈ 1033 mi
7.	Irkutsk, Russia	52.50° N	Singapore, Singapore	1.23° N	≈ 3546 mi
8.	Beijing, China	39.92° N	Perth, Australia	31.95° S	

9. Tundra Trek An expedition led by Robert Peary was the first to reach the North Pole (90° N latitude) in 1909. They traveled by sledge from Ellesmere Island (approximately 83° N latitude) to the pole. The journey from Ellesmere to the North Pole took just over one month. Approximately how far did they travel by sledge? 484 mi

10. Write the letter of the second pair that best matches the first pair. (c)

Longitude: latitude as (a) circle: sphere, (b) parallel: perpendicular, (c) *x*-coordinate: *y*-coordinate, (d) *y*-coordinate: *x*-coordinate

CONSIDER ?

Finds the time needed for the earth to rotate 1°. This information previews the **Explore** in 12-1 Part D.

Possible Answer

1. $\frac{60 \text{ min}}{15} = 4$ minutes to rotate 1°.

Journal

Reflect 1 and 2 and **Exercises** 12 and 14 are suitable for journal entries.

REFLECT

Possible Answers

1. Longitude lines are all great circles of the earth, so they are all the same length (assuming the earth is a perfect sphere). The only latitude line that is a great circle is the equator; others are shorter.

2. Because we know that we are describing points on the sphere's surface. (If we also had to specify the depth of the position, three coordinates would be needed.)

Part B Exercises

Exercise Notes

Core

9. Students approximate the distance traveled by Robert Peary, Matthew Henson, and Smith Sound Eskimos Ootah, Egingwah, Seegloo, and Ooqueah when they reached the North Pole.

More Math Reasoning

29. Students calculate how far a person can see from the top of Mount Everest.

ey

Vocabulary
Practice/Skills
Review
R Math Reasoning
S Problem Solving
Challenge

Ongoing Assessment

Self-Assessment Exercises 1–13 odd

Embedded Assessment Try It a; Explore Step 3; Exercises 4, 8, 12

12-1

Using Geometry to Model the Earth

Exercise Answers

Core

13. a. 15°. The earth makes a full rotation every 24 hours, so there should be 24 time zones. Therefore, $\frac{360°}{24} = 15°$ per time zone.

b. 5–6 time zones

14. Knowing the city's latitude is more helpful since latitude tells how close to the equator you are. Possible answer: The city's altitude.

Look Back

15. Statement 1: $\overline{AB} \parallel \overline{FE}$, $\overline{AB} \cong \overline{FE}$, $\overline{AC} \cong \overline{ED}$
Reason 1: Given
Statement 2: $\angle A \cong \angle E$
Reason 2: Alternate interior angles of parallel lines cut by a transversal are congruent.
Statement 3: $\triangle ABC \cong \triangle EFD$
Reason 3: SAS Postulate

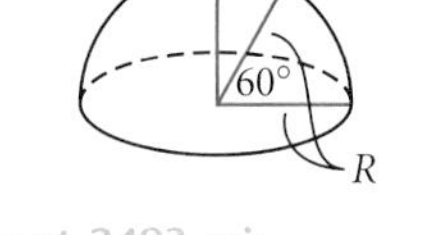

PS **11.** Calculate the distance, *d*, around the earth at 60° N latitude. (Hint: First find the radius, *r*, of the 60° latitude line.) How does the radius of the 60° latitude line compare to the radius of the earth? About 12,441 mi; Half the earth's radius

PS **12.** At 35° N latitude, the United States extends from 121° W longitude to 77° W longitude. Find the width of the United States at 35° N. Give a brief explanation of the method you used to solve this problem. About 2493 mi; $\frac{121 - 77}{360} \times 24{,}900 \cos 3$

MR **13. a.** How far apart in longitude should the world's time-zone divisions be? Explain.

b. Europe's westernmost point is at 10° W longitude, and its easternmost point is at 65° E longitude. Predict the number of time zones spanned by Europe.

MR **14. What to Pack?** Alberta is traveling to an unfamiliar city, and she needs to know something about its climate. Will it help her more to know the city's longitude or its latitude? Explain how knowing the longitude or latitude of a city can help her predict its climate. What other information about the city might help Alberta?

LOOK BACK

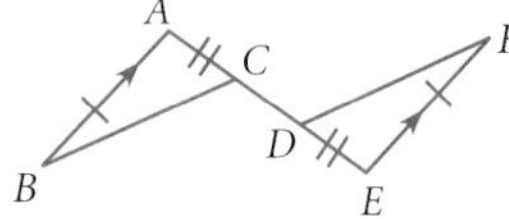

R **15.** *Given:* $\overline{AB} \parallel \overline{FE}$, $\overline{AB} \cong \overline{FE}$, and $\overline{AC} \cong \overline{ED}$.

Prove: $\triangle ABC \cong \triangle EFD$ [4-2]

R **For each graph, estimate the coordinates of the point that has the maximum *y*-value. [11-2]**

16. (4, 7)

17. (1, 6)

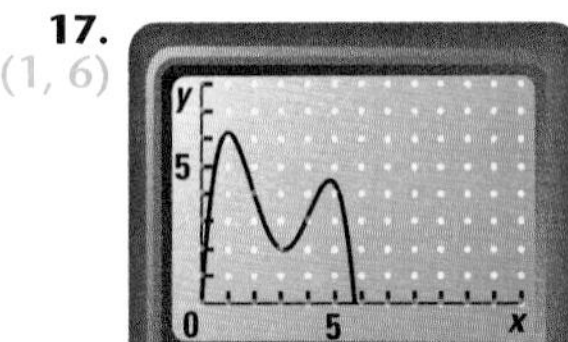

18. (5, 5)

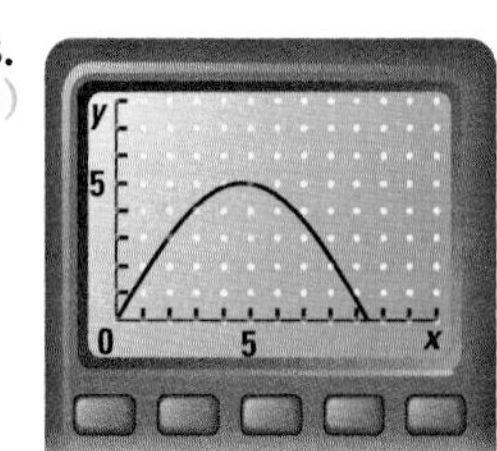

MORE PRACTICE

P **Give the approximate latitude and longitude of each city.**

19. Caracas, Venezuela 10° N, 67° W

20. Bogotá, Colombia 5° N, 74° W

21. Quito, Ecuador 1° S, 78° W

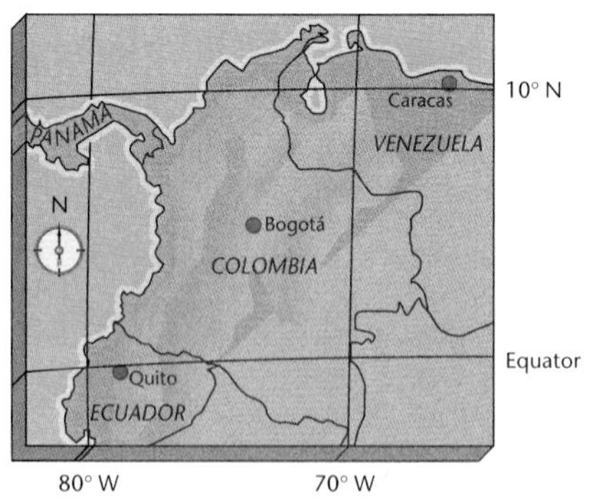

Key

V Vocabulary
P Practice/Skills
R Review
MR Math Reasoning
PS Problem Solving
C Challenge

The pairs of cities in the following table have approximately the same longitude. Find the distance between each pair of cities.

	Name	Latitude	Name	Latitude	
22.	Cleveland, OH	41.47° N	Columbia, SC	34.00° N	≈ 517 mi
23.	Providence, RI	41.83° N	Quebec, Quebec	46.82° N	≈ 345 mi
24.	Athens, Greece	37.97° N	Hammerfest, Norway	70.63° N	≈ 2259 mi
25.	Tokyo, Japan	35.67° N	Adelaide, Australia	34.92° S	≈ 4882 mi

26. Calculate the distance, d, around the earth at 45° N latitude. (Hint: First find the radius, r, of the 45° latitude line.) How does the radius of the 45° latitude line compare to the radius of the earth? ≈ 17,594 mi; It is $\frac{\sqrt{2}}{2}$ times the radius of the earth

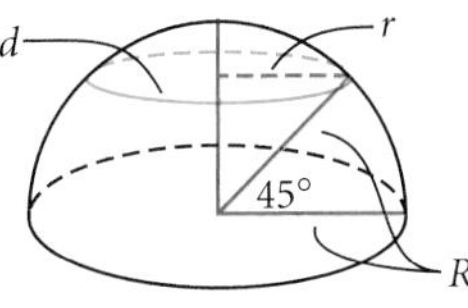

MORE MATH REASONING

27. Suppose Ze-Yuan knows the longitudes of two cities on the equator. Explain how she can use proportions to find the distance between these two cities.

28. Lost at Sea Suppose you're lost at sea and need to find your position. You know that the sun is directly overhead at noon at the equator. At noon, a 30-cm ruler on your boat casts a 24-cm shadow. What is your latitude? Write an explanation of the method you used to solve this problem. If you used a diagram to help solve the problem, include it with your solution, and explain how you used it.

29. Distant Horizons How far can a person see on the earth? Suppose Manuela is at an altitude of h kilometers and is looking at the horizon. The length of the tangent segment t approximates the length of the arc on the earth's surface that she can see.

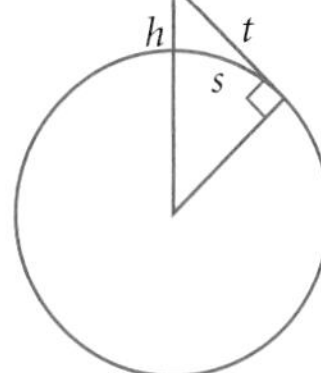

a. Assume the radius of the earth is 6370 km. Derive a formula for t in terms of h. $t = \sqrt{h^2 + 12{,}740h}$

b. Mt. Everest is approximately 8.85 km tall. Find t for a person standing at the peak of Mt. Everest. $t \approx 335.9$ km

c. Find s, the actual length of the arc on the earth's surface that a person can see from the peak of Mt. Everest. Is t a good approximation for s? $s \approx 335.6$ km; Yes

30. The earth makes one complete rotation around its axis each day. Because the distance around the earth at the equator is greater than the distance around the earth at other latitudes, a point on the equator travels farther during one day than points elsewhere on the earth. What does this tell you about the speed at which points on the earth travel? A point on the equator travels faster than points elsewhere on the earth.

More Math Reasoning

27. Use the following proportion:

$$\frac{\text{difference in longitudes}}{360} = \frac{\text{distance}}{24{,}900}$$

28.

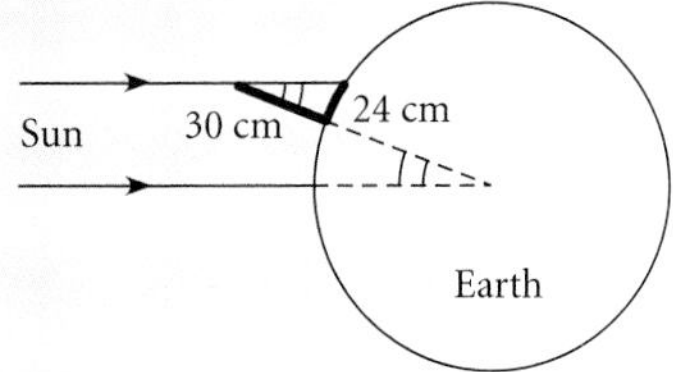

Latitude $= \tan^{-1}\left(\frac{24}{30}\right) \approx 39°$

Note: This method only works on the vernal and autumnal equinoxes.

12-1

Using Geometry to Model the Earth

PART C At a Glance

Objective

To use geometry to measure distances to and sizes of moons, planets, and stars.

Development

First, an **Example** shows how arc measures can be used to find the diameter of the moon. Students then see definitions of units appropriate for measuring large distances and become familiar with the idea of *parallax.*

In the **Explore,** students use arcs and parallax to calculate the distance to the sun's nearest star neighbor, Alpha Centauri.

Key Terms

Astronomical unit (A.U.), light-year, parallax

First Five Minutes

Transparency FFM 12-1C

On a circle, a central angle of 2° cuts off an arc of length 14 cm. Find the radius of the circle. **Radius ≈ 401 cm**

Motivate

Ask...

- Give two reasons why measuring distances to planets and stars might be important. **To give a clearer picture of the nature of the universe; to aid in determining the feasibility of space travel.**

ALTERNATE EXAMPLES

1. It would take a radar signal about 66.7 sec to make a round trip from Saturn to one of its moons, Phoebe. If radar travels at the speed of light (300,000 km/sec), how far from Saturn is Phoebe?
The round-trip distance is:
66.7 sec × 300,000 ≈ 20,000,000 km.
The one-way distance is half of this: 10,000,000 km.

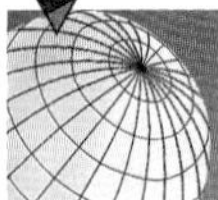

12-1 PART C Measurement in Astronomy

← CONNECT → ***You've used geometry to measure a variety of objects, including the earth. Now you will apply your knowledge of several concepts to calculate distances and sizes associated with the moon, the planets, and the stars.***

If you need to measure an unknown distance on the earth, you can use a ruler, a tape measure, or the odometer on a car. But how did we know how far away or how large the moon was before anyone had traveled there?

Earthbound humans have been interested in measuring astronomical distances for hundreds of years. You can use your knowledge of geometry to make some of these measurements yourself.

EXAMPLES

1. It takes a radar signal 2.56 sec to make a round trip from the earth to the moon. If radar travels at the speed of light (300,000 km/sec), how far away is the moon?

The round-trip distance is 2.56 sec × 300,000 km/sec = 768,000 km.

The one-way distance is half of this: 384,000 km.

2. The diameter of the moon covers an arc of about 0.52° in the sky. What is the diameter of the moon?

We can use our knowledge of circles to set up a proportion. The ratio of 0.52° to 360° is approximately equal to the ratio of the moon's diameter to the circumference of its orbit. In Example 1, we found that the radius of the moon's orbit is about 384,000 km. We can use this value to find C, the circumference of the moon's orbit.

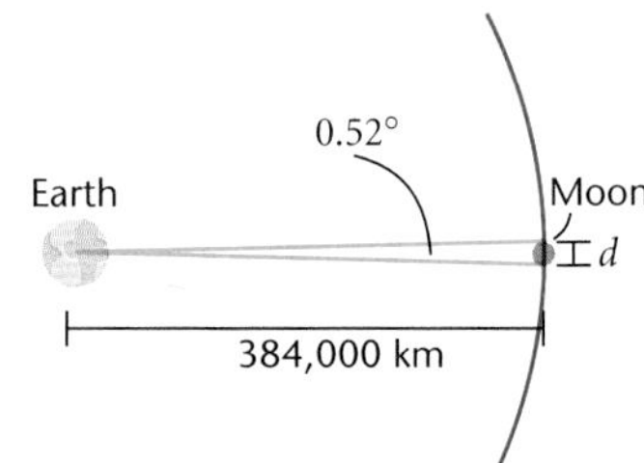

$C = 2\pi(384{,}000 \text{ km}) \approx 2{,}410{,}000 \text{ km}$

$\frac{0.52}{360} = \frac{d}{2{,}410{,}000}$

Solving this proportion shows that d, the diameter of the moon, is approximately 3480 km.

Alert

Some students may have little background in astronomy. You may want to give them a brief introduction to (1) the solar system and the orbits of the planets, (2) our Milky Way galaxy, consisting of about 100 billion stars, and (3) the fact that our galaxy is only one of billions of star systems.

Science Connection

Many natural phenomena exhibit self-similarity. In addition to familiar shapes like clouds and trees, fractals have been used to model galactic clusters, earthquake faults, vegetation distribution, the effects of acid rain, and the behavior of protein molecules.

TRY IT

The speed of light is approximately 300,000 km/sec. Find the amount of time it takes light to travel between the following bodies. Give your answers in appropriate units.

a. the earth and Venus (distance at their closest approach: 41,800,000 km) $139\frac{1}{3}$ sec

b. the sun and Jupiter (average distance: 778,300,000 km) 43 min, $14\frac{1}{3}$ sec

Because distances in space are so large, we need to use some units that measure large distances conveniently.

An **astronomical unit** (A.U.) is the average distance from the earth to the sun—about 150,000,000 km (≈ 93,000,000 mi). This unit is particularly useful for measuring distances within the solar system.

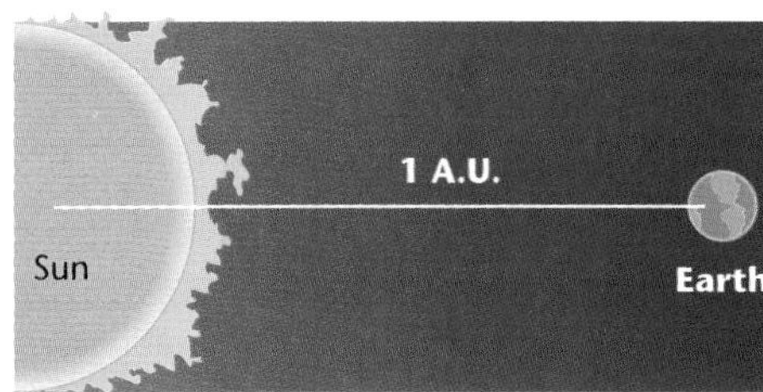

When measuring distances between stars, however, the astronomical unit is still too small to be convenient. Alpha Centauri, the star nearest the sun, is about 270,000 A.U. away! The **light-year** is a more appropriate unit to describe distances between stars and across galaxies. One light-year is the distance light travels (in a vacuum) in one year. Since light travels at a speed of nearly 300,000 km/sec, a light-year is a very large unit, approximately 9.5 trillion kilometers.

1. Mars is farther from the sun than the earth is. Is the distance from Mars to the sun less than or greater than 1 A.U.? How do you know?

2. Does a light-year measure time or distance? Explain.

Although all stars (except the sun) are many light-years away, some stars are closer than others. As the earth orbits the sun, we look at the stars from different positions. As this happens, nearer stars appear to shift slightly against a background of more distant stars. This shift is called **parallax.** You can do a simple experiment that illustrates parallax.

2. The polar diameter of Saturn would cover an arc of about 0.63° in the sky as seen from Phoebe. What is the polar diameter of Saturn?

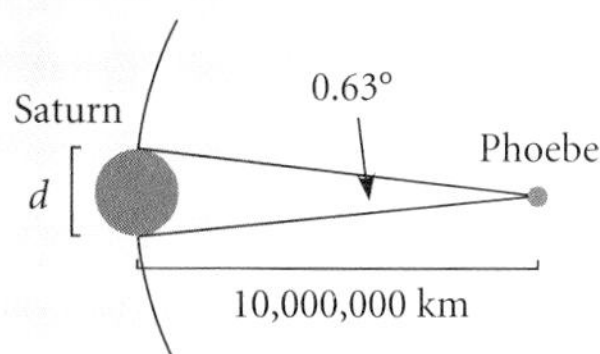

From the **Example** above, the distance from Phoebe to Saturn is about 10,000,000 km. So the circumference of the circle shown is $C = 2\pi(10,000,000 \text{ km}) \approx 62,800,000$ km.

The fraction that 0.63° is of 360° is approximately equal to the fraction that Saturn's diameter is of the circumference of the circle shown. Therefore, $\frac{0.63}{360} = \frac{d}{62,800,000}$.

Solving this equation gives d, the polar diameter of Saturn, to be approximately 110,000 km.

Possible Answers

1. Greater than one A.U.; an A.U. is the distance from the earth to the sun, and Mars is farther from the sun than the earth is.

2. A light-year measures distance. It is the distance light travels in one year.

Student Resources

- Alternative Lessons 12-1C
- Laboratory Manual 12-1C
- Technology Lab Manual
- Practice 12-1C
- Study Guide and Journal 12-1C
- Guía de estudios y Diario 12-1C
- Multilingual Handbook
- More Look Ahead 12-1C
- SAT Preparation

Media Resources

- Transparency FFM 12-1C
- Transparency AE 12-1C
- Teaching Transparency
- AWSMTest and practice software
- AWSM Videodisc

12-1

Using Geometry to Model the Earth

EXPLORE

How Far to the Nearest Star?

Recommended group size: 2

The Point
To use proportional thinking and facts about parallel lines and circles to calculate the distance to Alpha Centauri in astronomical units and in light-years.

Look and Listen...

- For students who do not see how to set up the proportion in Step 2.
- For students who have only the radius (r), and not the circumference ($2\pi r$), in their proportion.

Ask...

- Where is the circumference of the circle in your proportion? What is a formula for the circumference that involves r?

For Groups That Finish Early
Estimate, then calculate, the distance to Alpha Centauri in miles. If a jet flies at the speed of sound, about 740 mi/hr (and if it were able to fly in space!), how long would it take to reach Alpha Centauri?
Distance ≈ 2.56 10^{13} mi
Time ≈ 3.46 × 10^{10} hr ≈ 3.9 million years

Follow Up
Ask students to share their proportions from Step 2 and their answers from Steps 3 and 4.

Possible Answers

1. When lines are parallel, alternate interior angles are congruent.
2. $\frac{m\angle XAY}{360} = \frac{SY}{2\pi r}$. The ratio of the measure of the central angle to 360° is equal to the ratio of the arc it cuts to the circumference of the circle.
3. $r \approx 275{,}000$ A.U.
4. $r \approx 4.35$ light-years

Hold your thumb close to your face, and look at it with your left eye closed. Then look at it with your right eye closed.

Did your thumb seem to move, while objects beyond it stayed in the same place? When you change your perspective, objects near you seem to move more than distant ones.

EXPLORE: HOW FAR TO THE NEAREST STAR?

When the earth is at position X in its orbit, the star nearest the sun, Alpha Centauri (A), lines up with a distant star, D. Three months later, the earth is at position Y. At this time, the measure of $\angle Y$, determined by the lines of sight to star A and star D, is about $\frac{1}{4800}$ of a degree.

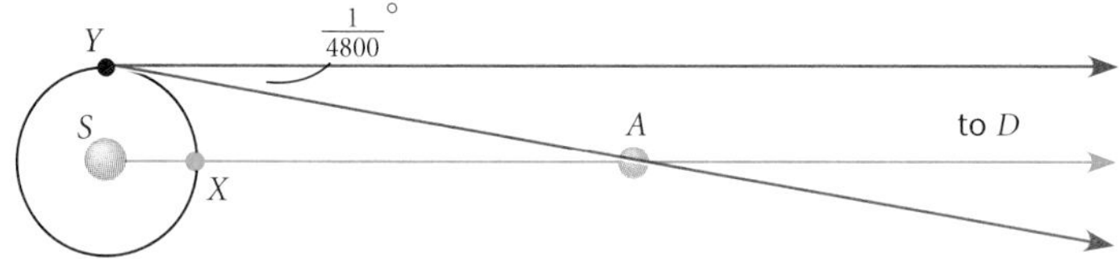

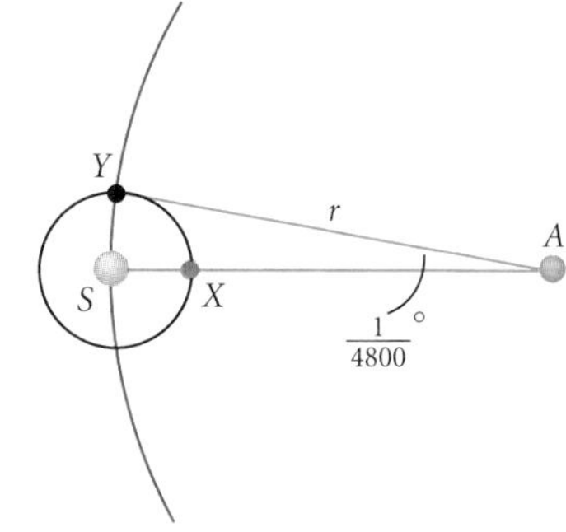

1. Because D is so far away, the rays labeled "to D" are very nearly parallel. Explain why $m\angle Y \approx m\angle XAY$.
2. To find r, the distance to Alpha Centauri, use an imaginary circle whose center is A and whose radius is r. The ratio of $m\angle XAY$ to 360° is approximately equal to the ratio of SY to the circumference of $\odot A$. Set up a proportion involving the measure of the parallax angle ($m\angle XAY$), the distance from the earth to the sun (SY), the distance to the star (r), and 360°. Explain how you set up your proportion.
3. Solve your proportion to find r in astronomical units (A.U.). Remember that the distance from the earth to the sun, SY, is 1 A.U.
4. There are about 63,200 A.U. in a light-year. Find the distance to Alpha Centauri in light-years.

Research Note

The findings [of this study] indicate that less formal strategies [for solving proportions], which previous research had indicated may be more natural for many secondary students and which may be essential to an understanding of generalizations such as the proportion formula, are in fact not often used by [their] teachers. (Linda C. Fisher, "Strategies Used by Secondary Mathematics Teachers to Solve Proportion Problems," *Journal for Research in Mathematics Education,* Sept. 1988, Vol. 19, No. 2, p. 166. © 1988 NCTM.)

REFLECT

1. Give some examples of how you've used proportional thinking to measure distances or lengths earlier in this course.
2. In using parallax to calculate the distance from the earth to a star, we assumed that the length of $\overset{\frown}{SY}$ is the same as the length of $\overline{SY}$ (see, for example, the figure on page 764). Is this true? If not, do you think this assumption will lead to a large error in our calculations? Why or why not?

Exercises

CORE

1. **Getting Started** It takes a radar signal 1000 sec to make a round trip from the earth to the sun. If radar travels at the speed of light (300,000 km/sec), how far away is the sun? Round your answer to the nearest ten million kilometers. 150,000,000 km

The speed of light is approximately 300,000 km/sec. Find the amount of time it takes light to travel between the following bodies. Give your answers in appropriate units.

2. the earth and the moon (average distance: 384,000 km) 1.28 sec
3. the earth and Mars (distance at their closest approach: 56,000,000 km) 3 min, $6\frac{2}{3}$ sec
4. the sun and Saturn (average distance: 1,427,000,000 km) 79 min, $16\frac{2}{3}$ sec
5. There are approximately 63,200 A.U. in a light-year. If the earth did not move, how many times could a beam of light travel back and forth between the earth and the sun in one year? 31,600
6. Recall that the average distance from the earth to the sun is 1 A.U.
   a. Guess the average distance from the sun to Pluto, the most distant known planet, in astronomical units. (This is the average radius of the solar system.)
   b. The average distance from the sun to Pluto is about 5,900,000,000 km. Calculate the average distance from the sun to Pluto in astronomical units. Compare this to your guess in **6a.** a–b. About 39 A.U.
7. From the following group of terms, choose the one that does not belong, and explain why it does not belong.

   light-year, astronomical unit, parallax, mile Parallax; It is not a measure of distance.
8. The speed of light is approximately 186,000 mi/sec (in a vacuum). Using this value, calculate the length, in miles, of a light-year. Briefly explain the method you used to solve this problem.

Journal

Consider 2 and **Reflect** 1 and 2 are suitable for journal entries.

REFLECT

Possible Answers

1. Proportional thinking was used when using similarity to find unknown distances and to calculate distances on scale maps.
2. No. The length of the segment is not the same as the length of the arc. However, since the measure of the central angle is so small, the arc is very close to the line segment and the length difference is not significant.

Part C Exercises

Exercise Notes

Core

9. Students see that the disks of the sun and moon, as seen from the earth, are almost exactly the same size.

   Science Note: This close match explains why total solar eclipses seen from the earth are so spectacular. When the moon's disk just covers the sun, the sun's *corona* (outer atmosphere) becomes visible. If the disk of the moon were smaller, we would just see its silhouette pass across the face of the sun; if it were much larger, it would block out the sun entirely.

Look Ahead

These exercises review the components of our system of geometry and the Parallel Postulate. In 12-2, students see how a change in the Parallel Postulate creates a new geometric system.

More Math Reasoning

19. Students investigate Bode's Law, an inductive pattern that matches the orbits of the planets inside Neptune's orbit extremely well.
20. Introduces students to Kepler's third law. This law illustrates a relationship between a planet's orbital distance and the length of its year.

Ongoing Assessment

Vocabulary
Practice/Skills
Review
Math Reasoning
Problem Solving
Challenge

Self-Assessment Exercises 1, 3, 5, 7, 11

Embedded Assessment Try It b; Exercises 6, 9, 10

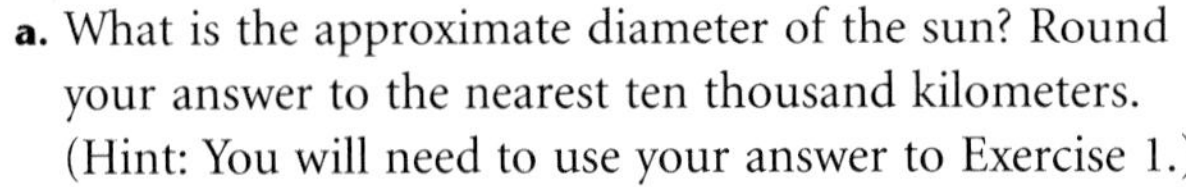

Using Geometry to Model the Earth

Exercise Answers

Core

8. (186,000 mi/sec)(1 year) × $\left(\frac{365 \text{ days}}{1 \text{ year}}\right)\left(\frac{24 \text{ hours}}{1 \text{ day}}\right)\left(\frac{3600 \text{ sec}}{1 \text{ hour}}\right) \approx$ 5.9×10^{12} miles

9. a. 1,390,000 km

b. They are only 0.01° different.

Look Ahead

12. A postulate is an assertion accepted without proof. A theorem must be proved and depends on postulates and definitions.

13. Possible answers: One and only one straight line can be drawn through two given points.
If two planes intersect, then their intersection is a line.
If two lines intersect, then their intersection is a point.
Three noncollinear points are contained in one and only one plane.

14. Through a point not on a line, only one line parallel to the line can be drawn.

PS Science **9. Sizing the Sun** The diameter of the sun covers an arc of about 0.53° in the sky.

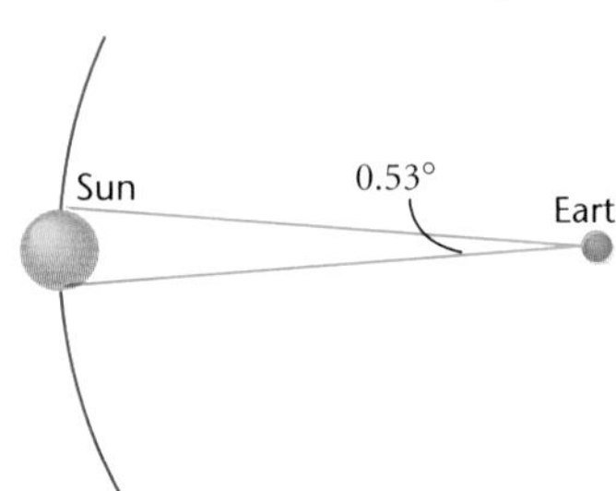

a. What is the approximate diameter of the sun? Round your answer to the nearest ten thousand kilometers. (Hint: You will need to use your answer to Exercise 1.)

b. Compare the measure of the arc covered by the sun to that of the arc covered by the moon, as given in Example 2 on page 762. What do you notice?

PS Science **10. Are You Sirius?** When the earth is at position X in its orbit, the brightest star, Sirius (I), lines up with a distant star, D. When the earth is at position Y, the measure of the parallax angle, $\angle YIX$, is about $\frac{1}{9720}$ of a degree.

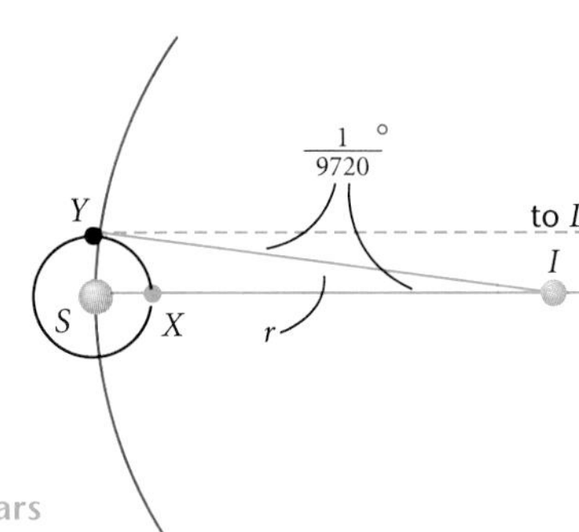

a. Set up and solve a proportion to find r, the approximate distance to Sirius, in astronomical units. (Remember that the distance from the earth to the sun, SY, is 1 A.U.) About 556,900 A.U.

b. Find the distance to Sirius in light-years. 8.8 light-years

PS Science **11. a.** The parallax angle to the star Altair is about $\frac{1}{18,360}$ of a degree. Find the distance to Altair in light-years. 16.6 light-years

b. Which is older, the light that has just reached the earth from Altair, or you? Explain your reasoning. The light is older than any student less than 16.6 years old.

LOOK AHEAD

R **12.** What is a postulate? How is it different from a theorem? Write a brief paragraph that answers these questions.

R **13.** Describe four postulates about points, lines, and planes.

R **14.** State the Parallel Postulate in your own words.

MORE PRACTICE

P **The speed of light is approximately 300,000 km/sec. Find the amount of time it takes light to travel between the following bodies.**

15. the earth and the sun (average distance: 150,000,000 km) 8 min, 20 sec

16. the sun and Mercury (average distance: 57,900,000 km) 3 min, 13 sec

17. the sun and Neptune (average distance: 4,497,000,000 km) 4 hr, 9 min, 50 sec

Key

V Vocabulary
P Practice/Skills
R Review
MR Math Reasoning
PS Problem Solving
C Challenge

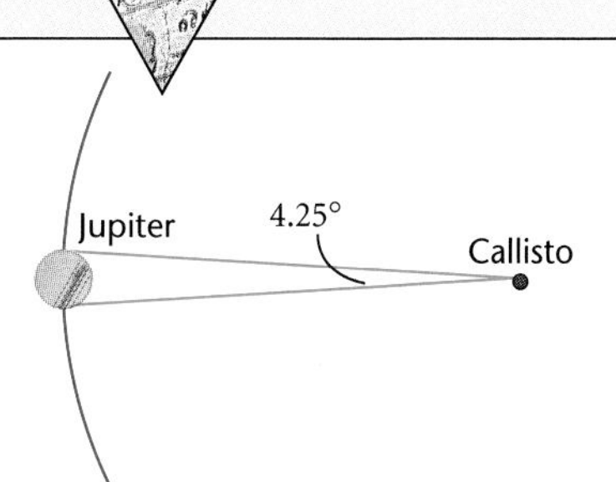

18. From its moon Callisto, Jupiter covers an arc of about 4.25° in the sky. Callisto is about 1,880,000 km from Jupiter. What is Jupiter's approximate diameter? Round your answer to the nearest ten thousand kilometers.
140,000 km

MORE MATH REASONING

19. Planetary Patterns In 1766, Johann Titius identified a relationship among the orbits of the then-known planets, now called Bode's Law.

a. Describe the number pattern in the first row of the table. Then explain how the numbers in the second and third rows are calculated.

First row	0	3	6	12	24	48	96
Second row	4	7	10	16	28	52	100
Bode numbers	0.4	0.7	1.0	1.6	2.8	5.2	10.0

b. The following table gives the average orbital distances (in A.U.) for the planets known in 1766. How well do these numbers agree with the Bode numbers?

Planet	Mercury	Venus	Earth	Mars	Jupiter	Saturn
Distance	0.39	0.72	1.0	1.5	5.2	9.5

c. Use Bode's Law to predict the distances of the next three planets from the sun.

d. In 1781, the seventh planet from the sun, Uranus, was discovered. Its average distance from the sun is 19.2 A.U. Did this discovery follow Bode's Law?

e. In the late 1700s, astronomers began to search for a planet orbiting the sun between Mars and Jupiter. Why do you think they began this search?

f. In 1801, Ceres, the largest of the asteroids, was discovered orbiting the sun at 2.77 A.U. What should its distance from the sun be according to Bode's Law?

g. Neptune, the eighth planet, was discovered in 1846, and Pluto, the ninth, was found in 1930. Their average orbital distances are 30.1 A.U. and 39.4 A.U., respectively. Do the orbits of these planets seem to follow Bode's Law?

20. Kepler's third law states that the cube of a planet's distance to the sun in astronomical units, d, is equal to the square of the time it takes to go around the sun (its *period*, p) in years. Check whether this law is approximately true for these planets.

Planet	Mercury	Venus	Earth	Mars	Jupiter	Saturn
d	0.387	0.723	1.00	1.52	5.20	9.54
p	0.241	0.615	1.00	1.88	11.9	29.5

More Math Reasoning

19. a. Each term is double the term before it except the second term which is 3 more than the previous one. The second row is calculated by adding 4 to the number directly above it. The third row is calculated by dividing the number directly above it by 10.

b. There is close agreement, but there is no planet at 2.8 A.U.

c. 19.6 A.U., 38.8 A.U., 77.2 A.U.

d. Yes

e. Since, according to Bode's Law, there should be a planet at about 2.8 A.U. from the sun.

f. 2.8 A.U.

g. No

20. Kepler's third law, $d^3 = p^2$, is approximately true for the given planets.

12-1

Using Geometry to Model the Earth

PART D At a Glance

Objective

To use latitudes and longitudes to find moonrise times in different cities.

Development

In the **Explore,** students use latitudes and longitudes to calculate moonrise times for January 1, 1994, in three U.S. cities.

Suggested Materials

Teacher Globe, world map transparency, United States map

First Five Minutes

Transparency FFM 12-1D

Briefly describe how the latitude-longitude system works. Include a sketch with your explanation.

EXPLORE

Moonrise Over Columbus

Recommended group size: 4

The Point

To find moonrise times for three cities on January 1, 1994.

Look and Listen...

- For students who are not using the Indianapolis calculations to guide them.

Ask...

- How was the longitude time correction for Indianapolis found? The local time correction? Can you do similar calculations for the other cities?

For Groups That Finish Early

Let x represent a city's longitude. Write formulas for the longitude time correction and local time correction. Assume the city's longitude is between 90° and 105° W.

Longitude correction = $\frac{x}{360} \times 78$
Local correction = $(x - 90) \times 4$

Algebra | Functions | Discrete Math | Probability | Data/Statistics

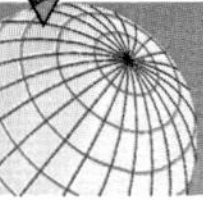

12-1 PART D Making Connections

← CONNECT → ***Geometry has helped people understand the earth for thousands of years. With familiar tools like proportions and new ones like fractals, you've investigated some ways to measure and model the earth, our solar system, and our galaxy.***

The photograph at the left shows a computer-generated fractal. Fractals can be used to model trees, coastlines, and mountains.

The earth itself can be modeled by a sphere, and you have used your knowledge of the angles and arcs of a circle to calculate the distances to stars. In the following Explore, you will use some of these concepts to see how to calculate moonrise times.

EXPLORE: MOONRISE OVER COLUMBUS

What time does the moon rise in your city? This depends on your city's location, the day of the year, and your time zone. For example, moonrise was at 8:56 P.M. near Valencia, Spain (at 0° longitude and 40° N latitude) on January 1, 1994. To calculate the time of moonrise on that day for U.S. cities close to 40° N latitude, you need to make two corrections.

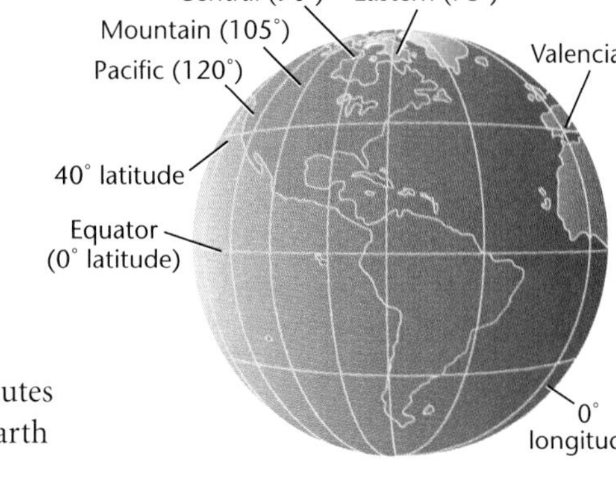

First, because the moon moves, it rises 78 minutes later for every complete 360° rotation of the earth at 40° N. So you need to add a fraction of 78 minutes to the moonrise time in Valencia.

$$\text{Correction for longitude} = \frac{\text{longitude}}{360} \times 78 \text{ min}$$

Second, because the earth turns, you need to correct for how "far along" a city is in a time zone. For every 1° west of the beginning of a time zone, add 4 minutes. Theoretically, time zones begin at 75° W, 90° W, 105° W, and 120° W for the continental United States. (Because of practical considerations, the actual time zone boundaries vary.)

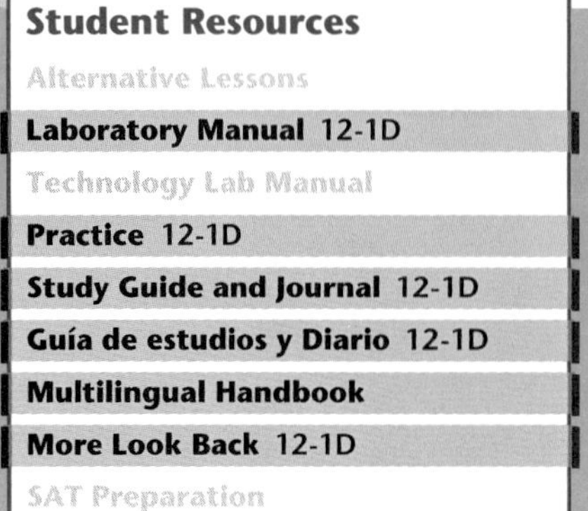

Student Resources

Alternative Lessons
Laboratory Manual 12-1D
Technology Lab Manual
Practice 12-1D
Study Guide and Journal 12-1D
Guía de estudios y Diario 12-1D
Multilingual Handbook
More Look Back 12-1D
SAT Preparation

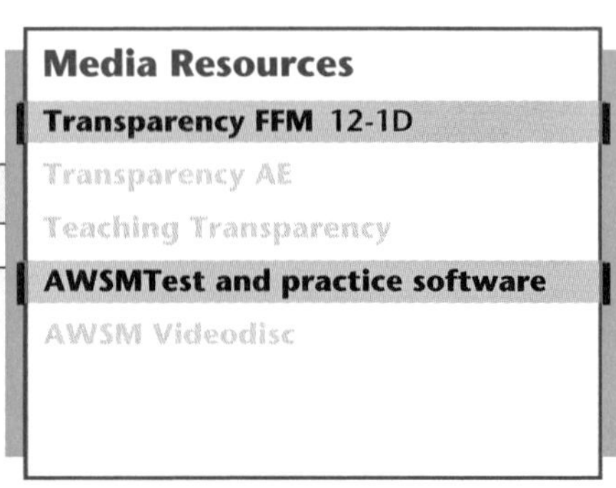

Media Resources

Transparency FFM 12-1D
Transparency AE
Teaching Transparency
AWSMTest and practice software
AWSM Videodisc

ogic/Reasoning | Industry/Careers | Science/Health | Social Science/History | Fine Arts/Literature

1. Complete the following table.

City	Longitude	$\frac{\text{Longitude}}{360}$	Longitude Time Correction	Local Time Correction	Moonrise 1/1/94
Philadelphia	75.17° W				
Columbus	83.02° W				
Indianapolis	86.17° W	0.239	19 min	45 min	10:00 P.M.

2. What information would you need to be able to calculate the time of moonrise on January 1, 1994, in your city? Do you think you might need to make any modifications to this method for your city? (Hint: What is true about all of the cities in the table?)

REFLECT

1. Describe several examples of how geometry can be used to model the earth and the solar system.
2. A friend who hasn't studied fractal geometry likes fractal designs on T-shirts. She asks you to explain what a fractal is. Write an explanation of fractals for your friend.

Self-Assessment

In the following, use 3960 mi for the radius of the earth and 24,900 mi for the circumference of the earth.

1. Sketch the first three stages for the pattern described below.

   Start with an equilateral triangle. Use the following rule.

   a. Find the midpoint of each side of each triangle.
   b. Connect the midpoints, as shown at the right.

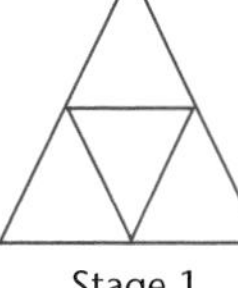

Stage 1

2. Dr. Breen is a scientist who is designing equipment for a future trip to Mars. She determines that each box for soil samples needs to have a 36-in.^{3} volume and that its height should be twice its length. Find the approximate dimensions of the box with the least surface area that satisfies these conditions. [11-2]

3. Light from the sun takes about 760 sec to reach Mars. Find the distance, in kilometers, from the sun to Mars.

ey

Vocabulary
Practice/Skills
Review
MR Math Reasoning
PS Problem Solving
Challenge

Follow Up

Ask students to give their moonrise times for Philadelphia and Columbus.

Possible Answers

1. (Answers rounded to nearest minute.) For Philadelphia:
   $\frac{\text{Long.}}{360} \approx 0.209$
   Long. corr. ≈ 16 min
   Local corr. ≈ 1 min
   Moonrise ≈ 9:13 P.M.
   For Columbus: $\frac{\text{Long.}}{360} \approx 0.231$
   Long. corr. ≈ 18 min
   Local corr. ≈ 32 min
   Moonrise ≈ 9:46 P.M.
2. The latitude and longitude of your city. If the latitude is close to 40° N, this method will give a good approximation; if not, modifications will be needed.

Portfolio

Have students select items from their work that demonstrate their understanding of the material in 12-1.

You may want students to include their best sketch of a fractal, an **Exercise** where they found a continent's width, and an **Exercise** where they found the distance to a planet or star.

REFLECT

Possible Answers

1. The earth can be modeled by a sphere, the orbit of a moon by a circle (or, more exactly, by an ellipse), etc.
2. A fractal is a pattern that is self-similar. Small parts of the figure, when magnified, cannot be distinguished from corresponding parts of the whole figure.

Algebra | Discrete Math | Logic/Reasoning | Science/Health

Using Geometry to Model the Earth

Self-Assessment

Exercise Notes

6. Similar to multiple-choice problems on standardized tests.

7. Points out an important difference between latitude and longitude lines.

8. Students calculate the approximate diameter of Olympus Mons, a huge Martian volcano.

Science Note: The longitude lines for Mars set up by astronomers have no east/west designations; they go from 0° to 360°.

Self-Assessment Answers

1.

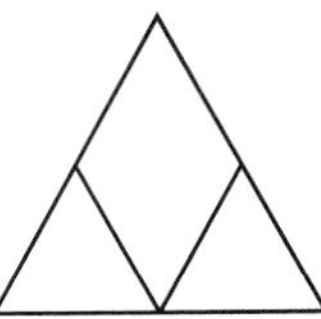

Stage 1

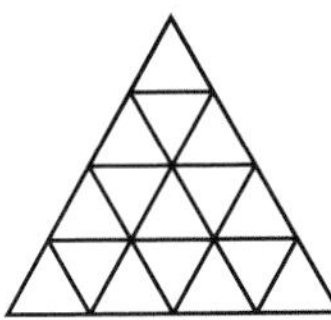

Stage 2

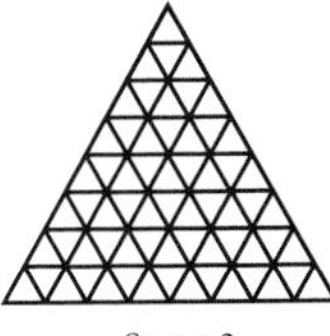

Stage 3

2. 2.4 in. × 3.2 in. × 4.8 in.

3. 228,000,000 km

4. See Additional Answers p. T770.

7. a. Yes; any point other than the four poles can be uniquely described with this system.

b. At opposite points on the equator; West Pole and East Pole

MR, C **4. The Fractal Tree** The following pattern creates a "fractal tree." The trunk is Stage 0. The next stages are made by adding two new branches to each old one, so that all branches make a 120° angle with each other. The new branches are half the length of the old branch.

Stage 0 (trunk) | Stage 1 (120°, 120°, 120°)

a. Sketch the first four stages of the fractal tree.

b. Write an equation for the number of new branches at Stage *n*.

c. The trunk of the fractal tree is 1 unit long. What is the total length of all branches for Stages 0–4? Explain how you found your answer.

d. What is the total length of all branches of the tree at Stage *n*? As the tree grows through an infinite number of stages, will the total length of its branches grow infinitely, or will there be a limit on the length? Explain your reasoning.

PS Science **5. A Vega Answer** When the earth is at position *X* in its orbit, the measure of the parallax angle to the star Vega, $\angle YVX$, is about $\frac{1}{28,800}$ of a degree.

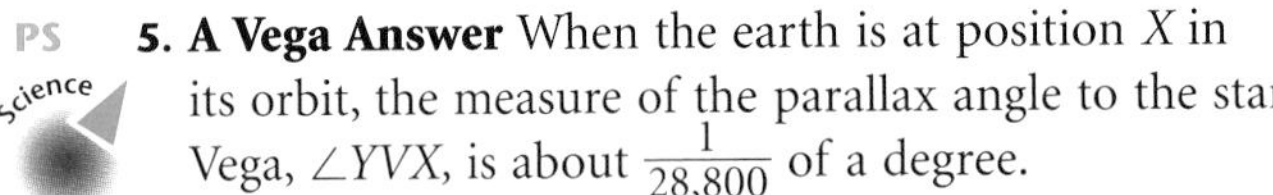

a. Set up and solve a proportion to find *r*, the distance to Vega, in astronomical units. (Remember that the distance from the earth to the sun, *SY*, is 1 A.U.) ≈ 1,650,000 A.U.

b. Find the distance to Vega in light-years. 26.1 light-years

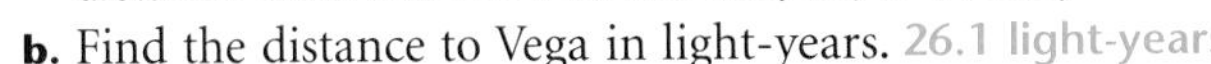

V **6.** Latitude lines (c)

(a) meet at the poles. (b) are perpendicular to the equator.
(c) have different lengths. (d) both (a) and (b)
(e) all of the above

MR **7.** Suppose latitude lines were drawn in the same way as longitude lines, as shown at the right.

a. Would this method work? Could you use it to describe the location of any point on the earth's surface? Why or why not?

b. In this method, there are two new landmarks on the earth's surface. Where are they? What would you call them?

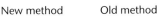

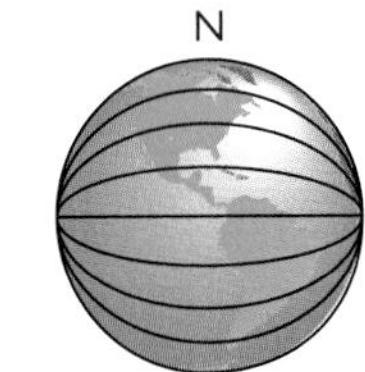

New method

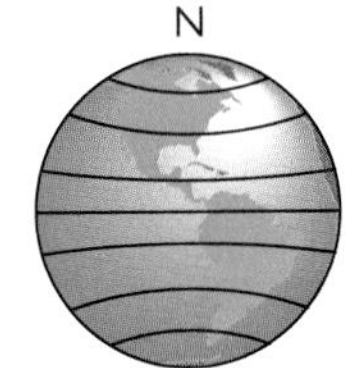

Old method

PS Science **8.** Astronomers have latitude and longitude systems for other planets. Olympus Mons, the huge Martian volcano, stretches approximately from 128° to 138° longitude at 18° N latitude. The radius of Mars is about 2100 mi. Use the figure at the right, trigonometry, and proportions to find the diameter of the base of Olympus Mons. About 349 miles

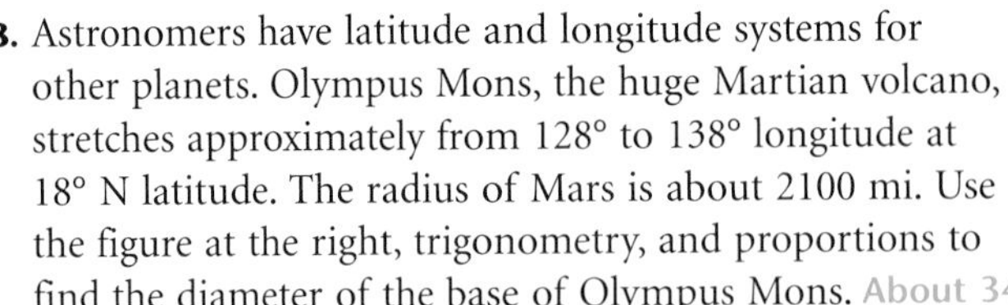

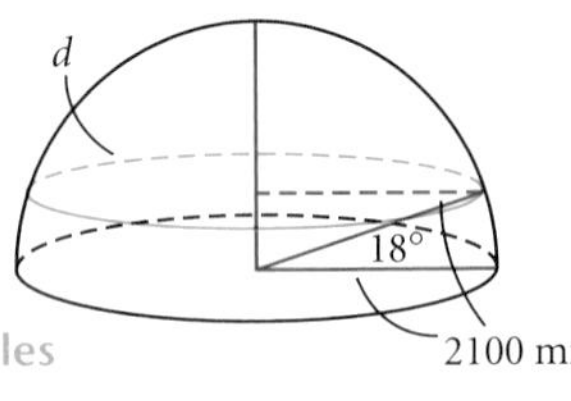

Assessment Resources

Quiz 12-1
Chapter Assessment Form A
Chapter Assessment Form B
Chapter Alternative Assessment
Mid-Year Assessment
End-of-Year Assessment
AWSMTest and practice software

Ongoing Assessment

Self-Assessment Self-Assessment Exercises

Embedded Assessment Explore Step 1; Reflect 1,

12-1 Part A Exercises

21. 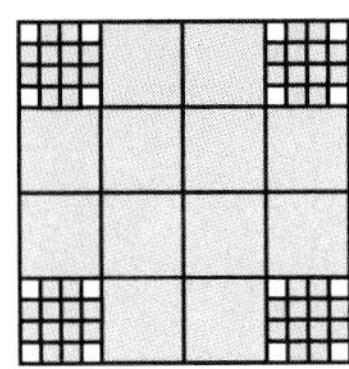

Stage 2

Divide each unshaded square into sixteen congruent smaller squares and shade all but the corner squares.

22. 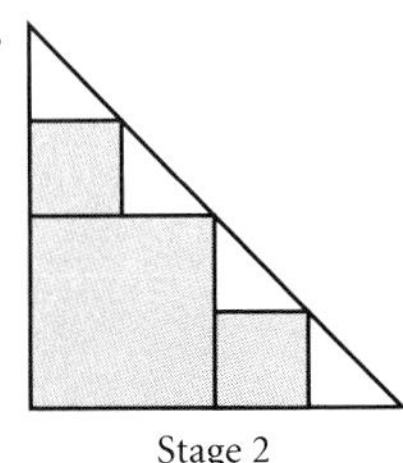

Stage 2

23. 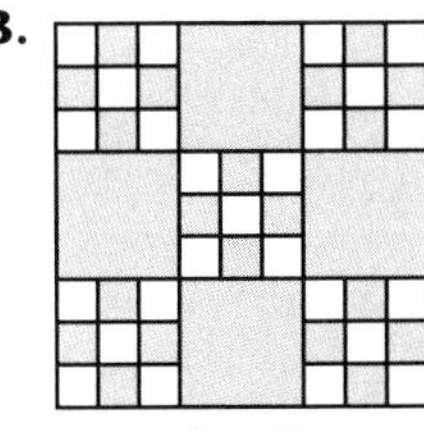

Stage 2

More Math Reasoning

24. a. For stage 0, Segments = 3, Length of each = 1, Perimeter = 3. For stage 1, Segments = 12, Length of each = $\frac{1}{3}$, Perimeter = 4. For stage 2, Segments = 48, Length of each = $\frac{1}{9}$, Perimeter = $\frac{16}{3}$. For stage 3, Segments = 192, Length of each = $\frac{1}{27}$, Perimeter = $\frac{64}{9}$.

25. a. For stage 0, Segments = 3, Triangles added = 0, Additional area = 0, Total area = 1. For stage 1, Segments = 12, Triangles added = 3, Additional area = $\frac{1}{3}$, Total area = $1\frac{1}{3}$. For stage 2, Segments = 48, Triangles added = 12, Additional area = $\frac{4}{27}$, Total area = $1\frac{13}{27}$. For stage 3, Segments = 192, Triangles added = 48, Additional area = $\frac{16}{243}$, Total area = $1\frac{133}{243}$.

12-1 Part D Self-Assessment

4. a. 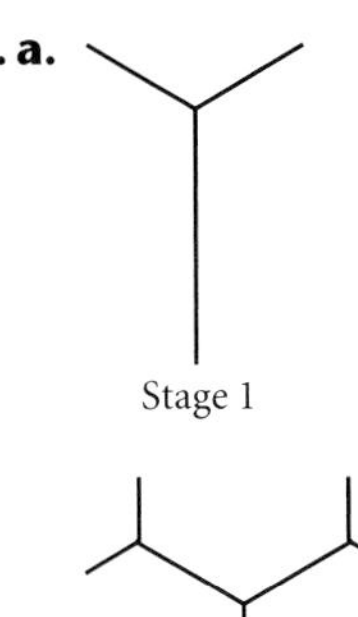

Stage 1

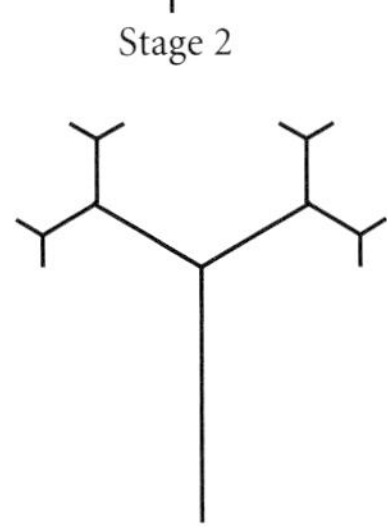

Stage 2

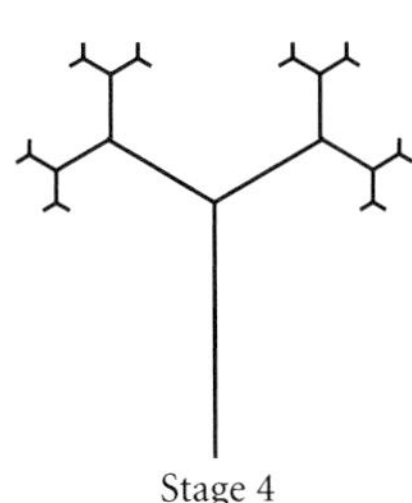

Stage 3

Stage 4

12-1 Part D Self-Assessment

4. b. $B = 2^n$

c. 1 unit; 2 units; 3 units; 4 units; 5 units; At stage n, there are 2^n new branches each with length $\left(\frac{1}{2}\right)^n$. So at each stage n, a total of $(2^n)\left(\frac{1}{2}\right)^n = 1$ unit is added.

d. $n + 1$ units. Total length of branches will grow infinitely since each stage adds 1 unit to the total length.

12-2 Part C Reflect

2.

Geometry	Parallel Postulate	Description of Planes and Lines	Sum of Angle Measures for a Triangle	Circumference and Area of Circle with Radius r
Euclidean	There is exactly one line parallel to a given line through a point not on it.	A plane is flat; a line is straight.	180°	$C = 2\pi r$; $A = \pi r^2$
Riemannian	There is no line parallel to a given line through a point not on it.	A plane is a sphere; a line is a great circle of the sphere.	Greater than 180°	$C < 2\pi r$; $A < \pi r^2$

12-2

Euclidean and Non-Euclidean Geometries

SUPERLESSON AT A GLANCE

Superlesson Goal

Students will see that a change in the Parallel Postulate leads to a new geometry, and will compare Euclidean geometry to a non-Euclidean geometry, Riemannian geometry.

Management Guide

	Topic	Objectives	Key Terms	New Ideas	Materials
Part A	Euclidean Geometry	To review Euclidean postulates and see how a proof of the Triangle Angle-Sum theorem depends on the Parallel Postulate.		The "fact" that the sum of the angle measures of a triangle is 180° depends on our belief in the Euclidean Parallel Postulate.	
Part B	Non-Euclidean Geometry	To explore Riemannian geometry by using a spherical model.	Non-Euclidean	A change in the Parallel Postulate leads to a new geometry with some different theorems.	**Student** Balloons, marking pen, ruler, protractor **Teacher** Globe, world map transparency
Part C	Making Connections	To compare properties of geometric figures on Euclidean and Riemannian planes.	In Making Connections, students apply and synthesize key terms and new ideas.		**Student** Graph paper, scissors, ball, tape

Pacing Chart (45-Minute Periods)

	Comprehensive Course	Core Course	Informal Course
Part A	1	1	0
Part B	1	1	0
Part C	1	1	0
TOTAL periods for Superlesson	3	3	0

NCTM Standards

Mathematics as Problem Solving

Mathematics as Communication

Mathematics as Reasoning

Mathematical Connections

Geometry from a Synthetic Perspective

Mathematical Structure

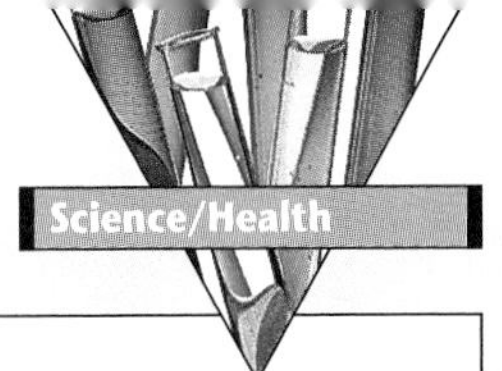

12-2 Euclidean and Non-Euclidean Geometries

THE NATURE OF THE UNIVERSE

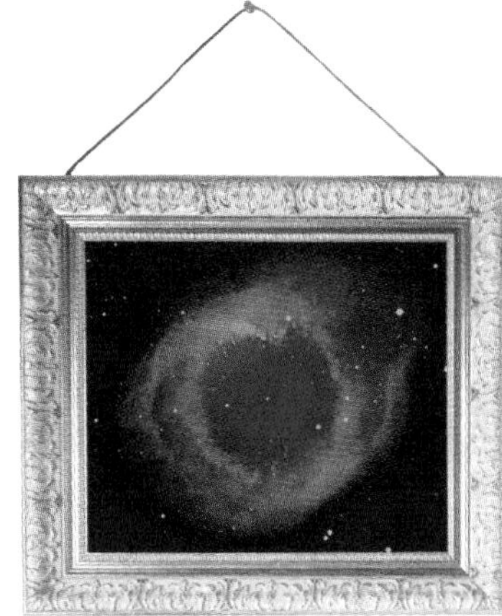

A *nebula* is a luminous, fuzzy celestial body. Before the invention of the telescope, only a few nebulae (including the enormous Milky Way and some smaller, fainter objects) were known. Early telescopes showed that the Milky Way was actually made up of individual stars. But what were the other nebulae? Some astronomers and philosophers believed that they were gas clouds within our Milky Way galaxy; others felt that they were other star systems, completely separate from our own.

In 1864, William Huggins found that some nebulae were indeed gas clouds. But in 1922, Edwin Hubble identified individual stars in the Andromeda nebula, and his estimate of the distance to Andromeda showed that it lay far outside the Milky Way. The debate had been resolved in favor of both sides: some of the nebulae were gas clouds within the Milky Way, and some were actually other Galaxies far beyond our own. Ever since, our model of the universe has featured distinct galaxies separated by light-years of empty space.

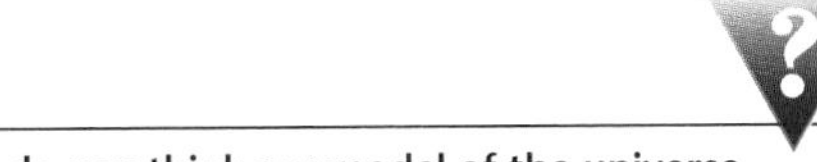

1. How do you think our model of the universe would be different if all nebulae were gas clouds inside the Milky Way?

2. The Milky Way can be seen as a white band stretching across the night sky. In ancient times, it was visible to all observers around the earth; however, there are many people now living who have never seen it. Why? Where do people live who cannot see the Milky Way?

More About Nebulae

Some nebulae, under magnification, show colors. A reddish glow is characteristic of the red light of hydrogen gas. A bluish color indicates that dust in the nebula is reflecting light from stars behind the nebula. Some nebulae, called *dark nebulae,* are dust clouds that are dense enough to be opaque. One of the most famous dark nebulae is the Horsehead Nebula in Orion. The Horsehead Nebula blocks light from a red nebula beyond it, and looks something like a black knight chess piece silhouetted against a red curtain.

Where Are We Now?

Students have seen how a deductive system based on undefined terms, definitions, postulates, and theorems works. They have also seen how the geometry based on this system can model the real world.

Where Are We Going?

In 12-2, students see that a change in the Parallel Postulate can create an entirely new system of geometry, whose new theorems are useful for modeling curved spaces.

Possible Answers

1. We would conclude that the Milky Way was the only galaxy, and, in effect, all stars in the universe would be contained in this relatively "tiny" space.
2. People who have never seen the Milky Way probably live in or near large cities, where bright lights and pollution obscure it.

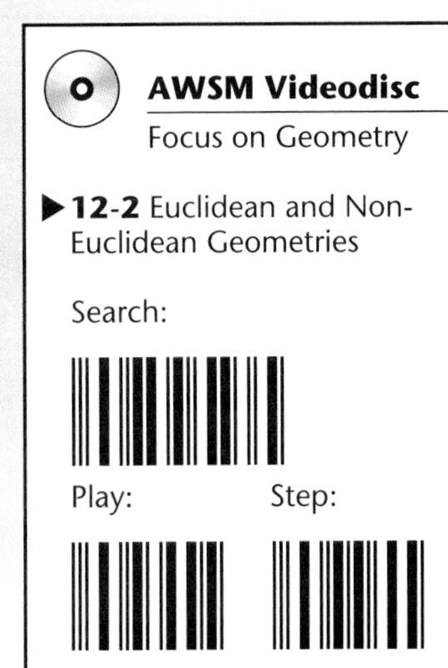

AWSM Videodisc
Focus on Geometry
▶ 12-2 Euclidean and Non-Euclidean Geometries
Search:
Play:
Step:

12-2

Euclidean and Non-Euclidean Geometries

PART A At a Glance

Objective

To review Euclidean postulates and see how a proof of the Triangle Angle-Sum theorem depends on the Parallel Postulate.

Development

First, students review some of the basic postulates of the Euclidean geometric system.

In the **Explore,** students see that the proof of the Triangle Angle-Sum Theorem depends on the Parallel Postulate.

First Five Minutes

Transparency FFM 12-2A

Review the postulates listed on pages 772 and 773. Then do **Try It a–c** on page 773.

Motivate

Ask...

- What is the difference between a postulate and a theorem? Are you more likely to begin a geometric system with a postulate or a theorem?

EXPLORE

Depending on Parallel

Recommended group size: 4

The Point

To write a proof of the Triangle Angle-Sum Theorem and see that it depends on the Parallel Postulate.

Look and Listen...

- For students who do not see that they must justify drawing the line through a vertex parallel to the opposite side.

Ask...

- Are you sure that a line like this exists? Can you state a postulate or theorem that guarantees this?
- Should you include adding the auxiliary line as a step in your proof?

12-2 PART A Euclidean Geometry

← CONNECT → ***We've used some basic postulates to develop our system of geometry. Now you will review these postulates and discover how theorems depend on our belief that the postulates are true.***

The field of flowers shown at the left is planted in parallel rows for efficient harvesting. As you will see, the decision to plant the flowers in this way can be traced to the system of geometry you've been studying.

Euclid developed this system of geometry around 300 B.C. As a model, it works well when measurements are relatively small, like those used in farms and cities. Some of the postulates you've assumed to be true in Euclid's system follow.

POINTS-EXISTENCE POSTULATE

Space contains at least four non-coplanar points. Every plane contains at least three non-collinear points. Every line contains at least two points.

STRAIGHT-LINE POSTULATE

Two points are contained in one and only one line. (Two points determine a line.)

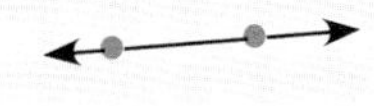

PLANE POSTULATE

Three non-collinear points are contained in one and only one plane. (Three non-collinear points determine a plane.)

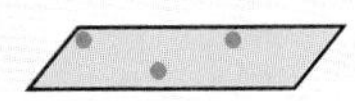

FLAT-PLANE POSTULATE

If two points are in a plane, then the line containing the points is in the same plane.

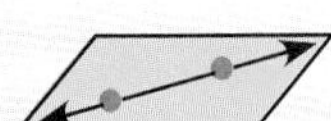

PLANE-INTERSECTION POSTULATE

If two planes intersect, then their intersection is a line.

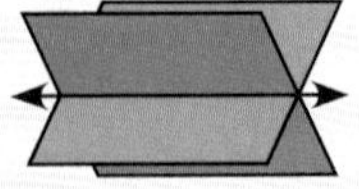

Alert

It is important for students to realize that in Riemannian geometry the terms *plane, line,* and *distance* have new and different meanings.

History Connection

Caroline Herschel (1750–1848) was the first woman known to detect a comet. She found eight in all, and discovered over a dozen nebulae. Caroline spent decades helping her brother, William, catalog heavenly bodies. After his death, Caroline published a catalog of 1500 nebulae. She was awarded a gold medal by the Royal Astronomical Society of England for her work.

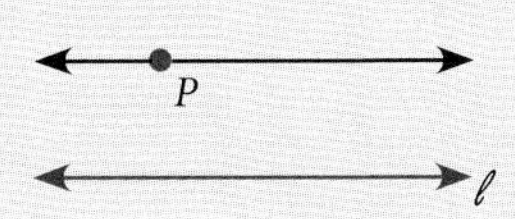

PARALLEL POSTULATE

Through a given point P not on a line ℓ, exactly one line may be drawn parallel to line ℓ.

TRY IT

Name the Euclidean postulate illustrated by each statement. (When we refer to a star or planet, assume that we are referring to its center. Therefore, you can think of it as a point.)

a. The earth, the sun, and Jupiter are contained in exactly one plane. Plane Postulate

b. There is exactly one straight line that passes through the stars Sirius and Altair. Straight-Line Postulate

c. There is only one line through the star Canopus that is parallel to the line that contains Sirius and Altair. Parallel Postulate

We began our deductive system of geometry with undefined terms, definitions, and postulates. Although you've developed many theorems since then—and used these theorems in proofs—every theorem can be traced back to our undefined terms, definitions, and postulates.

You may be surprised to learn that the proofs of the following theorems depend on the Parallel Postulate.

- The sum of the measures of the angles of a triangle is 180°.
- If a circle has radius r, its circumference is equal to $2\pi r$, and its area is equal to πr^2.
- Parallel lines are everywhere equidistant.

In the following Explore, you will investigate the connection between the first of these theorems and the Parallel Postulate.

EXPLORE: DEPENDING ON PARALLEL

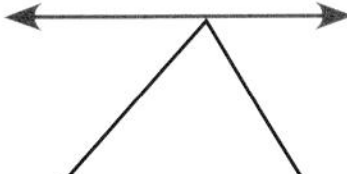

1. Prove that the sum of the measures of the angles of a triangle is 180°. (Hint: Through one of the vertices, draw a line parallel to the opposite side of the triangle.)
2. How does your proof depend on the Parallel Postulate? Discuss your findings with your classmates.

Student Resources

- Alternative Lessons 12-2A
- Laboratory Manual 12-2A
- Technology Lab Manual
- Practice 12-2A
- Study Guide and Journal 12-2A
- Guía de estudios y Diario 12-2A
- Multilingual Handbook
- More Look Ahead 12-2A
- SAT Preparation

Media Resources

- Transparency FFM 12-2A
- Transparency AE
- Teaching Transparency
- AWSMTest and practice software
- AWSM Videodisc

For Groups That Finish Early

What other geometric postulates, theorems, and definitions does your proof of the Triangle Angle-Sum Theorem depend on? **Definition of Linear Pair, Linear-Pair Postulate, Angle-Addition Postulate, parallel lines have congruent alternate interior angles (a postulate).**

Follow Up

Ask a student or group to share a proof with the class. Ask the class how this proof depends on the Parallel Postulate.

Possible Answers

1. *Given:* $\triangle ABC$

Prove: $m\angle B + m\angle BAC + m\angle C = 180°$

Draw auxiliary line $\overleftrightarrow{DE}$ through A parallel to $\overline{BC}$. We know that such a line exists because of the Parallel Postulate. Then $m\angle DAC + m\angle CAE = 180°$ from the Linear-Pair Postulate. Applying the Angle-Addition Postulate and substituting, we find that $m\angle DAB + m\angle BAC + m\angle CAE = 180°$.

Because parallel lines have congruent alternate interior angles, and congruent angles have equal measures, $m\angle B = m\angle DAB$, and $m\angle C = m\angle CAE$. Substituting into the equation above, we find that $m\angle B + m\angle BAC + m\angle C = 180°$.

2. Adding the auxiliary line through A parallel to $\overline{BC}$ depends on the Parallel Postulate.

Euclidean and Non-Euclidean Geometries

Journal

Reflect 1 and 2 and **Exercise** 12 are suitable for journal entries.

REFLECT

Possible Answers

1. Euclid's Parallel Postulate seems obvious—as long as we are working on a flat surface.
2. A mathematical system based on a large number of unproved assumptions seems less certain than one based on fewer assumptions. (This is also true in everyday arguments—the more unsupported assumptions a person makes, the weaker their argument tends to be.) The greater the number of postulates, the easier it is to find postulates that lead to contradictions.

   Mathematical Note: In 1931, Kurt Gödel proved that, for *any* mathematical system, there are statements that can neither be proved nor disproved.

Part A Exercises

Exercise Notes

Core

12. Students are reminded that Columbus was not the first to propose the idea that the earth's surface is curved.

Look Ahead

14. Reminds students that longitude lines are "parallel" lines that intersect. This prepares them for Riemann's Parallel Postulate in 12-2 Part B.

More Math Reasoning

21. Students explore a deductive system about paper clips and string. In Exercise 21d, they see the effect of eliminating a postulate from this system.

For about 2000 years, mathematicians tried to show that the Parallel Postulate didn't need to be a postulate. However, they found that it was impossible to prove the Parallel Postulate and make it a theorem by using the other Euclidean postulates. As you will soon see, some interesting possibilities arise if we make a different assumption about parallel lines.

REFLECT

1. Euclid believed that his postulates were self-evident truths. Do you think Euclid's Parallel Postulate is *obviously* true? Explain.
2. Mathematicians wanted to prove the Parallel Postulate, so that Euclid's system could be based on fewer unproved assumptions. Why do you think this was important to them?

Exercises

CORE

P **Getting Started Name the Euclidean postulate illustrated by each statement. (When we refer to a star or planet, assume that we are referring to its center. Therefore, you can think of it as a point.)**

1. Only one straight line contains Alpha Centauri and the sun. Straight-Line Postulate
2. Pluto, Mercury, and the moon are contained in exactly one plane. Plane Postulate
3. There is a line through the star Deneb that is parallel to the line through the stars Castor and Pollux. Parallel Postulate

R **You first saw the Parallel Postulate in Chapter 2. You've investigated many postulates, theorems, and definitions since then. Give four examples for each of the following from Chapters 3–12.**

4. postulates **5.** definitions **6.** theorems

MR **Use Euclid's system of geometry to answer each of the following questions.**

7. Does a triangle exist that has two right angles? Why or why not?
8. If two coplanar lines are both perpendicular to a third line, are they parallel to each other? Explain.
9. Sketch an angle, and construct its bisector. Explain why this construction works. Which postulates and definitions does this method depend on?

Key

- V Vocabulary
- P Practice/Skills
- R Review
- MR Math Reasoning
- PS Problem Solving
- C Challenge

R **Every theorem in geometry can be traced back to postulates, definitions, and undefined terms. Identify a postulate that is the basis for each theorem.**

10. the LL theorem
SAS Postulate

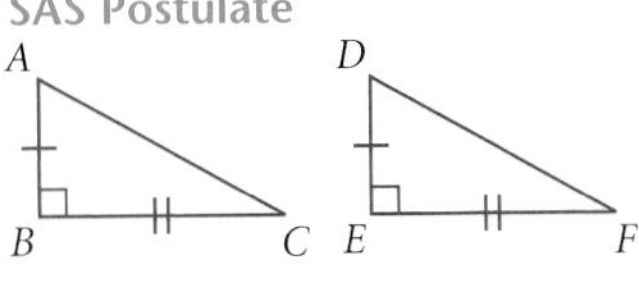

$\triangle ABC \cong \triangle DEF$

11. the formula for the area of a square ($A = s^2$)
Area formula for a rectangle

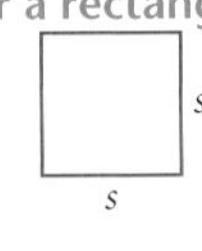

$A = s^2$

C History **12. But It Looks Flat!** The idea that the earth's surface is curved became accepted in Greece in about 400 B.C. One observation that supported this idea was that certain stars visible in Egypt could not be seen in Greece. Explain how this observation suggests that the earth's surface is curved.

PS Science **13.** Apollo astronauts traveled to the moon at the rate of 40,000 km/hr. Suppose astronauts travel to the Andromeda Galaxy (shown at the right), which is 2,000,000 light-years away.

a. If the astronauts travel at 40,000 km/hr, how long will it take them to reach the Andromeda Galaxy?

b. At how many times the speed of light would they have to travel to be able to reach Andromeda in your lifetime? Write a brief description of the method you used to solve this problem.

LOOK AHEAD

R **14.** Describe a model you have studied in which you use "parallel lines" that violate the Parallel Postulate. (Hint: You worked with this model earlier in Chapter 12.)
Longitude and latitude lines on a globe.

MORE PRACTICE

P **Name the Euclidean postulate illustrated by each statement. (When we refer to a star or planet, assume that we are referring to its center. Therefore, you can think of it as a point.)**

15. The straight line through the sun and the earth is in any plane that contains the sun and the earth. Flat-Plane Postulate

16. Venus and Mars are contained in exactly one line. Straight-Line Postulate

17. There are at least four non-coplanar locations in space. Points-Existence Postulate

Ongoing Assessment

Self-Assessment Exercises 1, 3, 5, 7, 11, 13

Embedded Assessment Try It b; Exercises 6, 8, 10, 12

Exercise Answers

Core

4. Possible answers:
SSS Postulate
SAS Postulate
Ruler Postulate
Protractor Postulate

5. Possible answers:
Acute angle—an angle that measures less than 90°.
Circle—the locus of points in a plane equidistant from a given point.
Right Triangle—a triangle which contains a 90° angle.
Rhombus—a quadrilateral with four congruent sides.

6. Possible answers:
If two lines are cut by a transversal and the alternate interior angles are congruent, then the lines are parallel.
If two lines intersect, the vertical angles are congruent.
Isosceles Triangle Theorem.
An equiangular triangle is also equilateral.

7. No; The two right angles would each measure 90°, and the measure of the third angle would be greater than zero, so the sum of the angle measures would exceed 180°.

8. Yes; The third line is a transversal with corresponding angles congruent.

9.

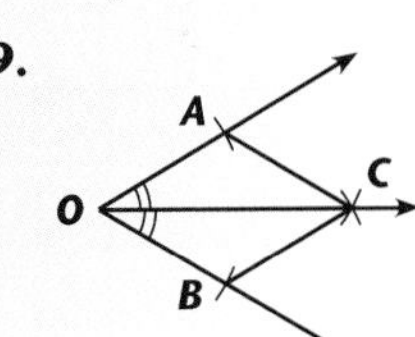

The compass is used to construct $\overline{OA} \cong \overline{OB}$ and $\overline{AC} \cong \overline{BC}$, so that $\triangle OAC \cong \triangle OBC$ and $\angle AOC \cong \angle BOC$; Possible answers: SSS Postulate, Definition of *congruent triangles*, Reflexive Property.

12. The curvature of the earth blocks the straight line view of the star.

Algebra	Functions	Discrete Math	Probability	Data/Statistics

Euclidean and Non-Euclidean Geometries

13. a. 5.4×10^{10} years

b. To reach Andromeda in 70 years, the astronauts would need to travel at $\frac{2{,}000{,}000}{70} \approx 28{,}600$ times the speed of light.

More Math Reasoning

21. a.

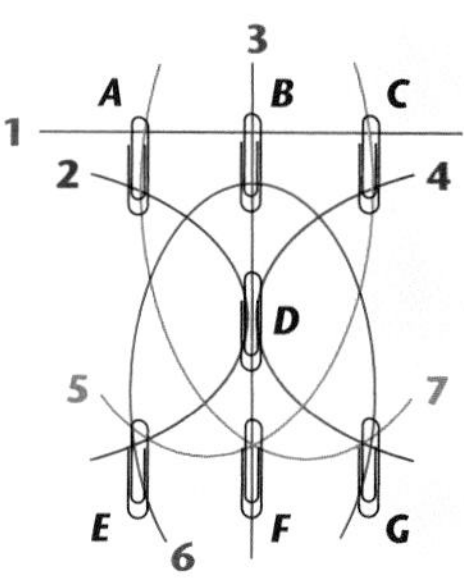

b. There is at least one piece of string (**1**) by Postulate A. By Postulate B, there are at least three paper clips (***A***, ***B***, ***C***). Postulate C implies there is at least one paper clip (***D***) that is not on the first string (**1**). By Postulate D, there is a second string (**2**) passing through one of the paper clips on the first string (***A***) and the fourth paper clip (***D***). By Postulate B, the second string (**2**) must have 3 paper clips on it (***A***, ***D***, ***E***). Therefore, there are at least five paper clips (***A***, ***B***, ***C***, ***D***, ***E***).

c. Seven strings and seven paper clips

d. Four paper clips, one string; Without Postulate D, there is no requirement for a paper clip to have a string through it.

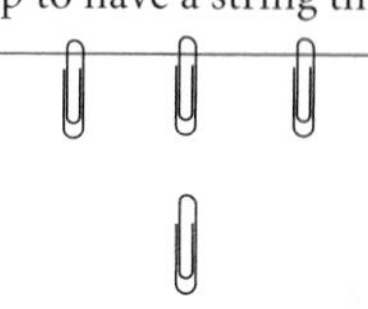

P, MR **In Exercises 18 and 19, use Euclid's system of geometry to answer each question.**

18. Can two parallel lines intersect? Explain. No; By definition they do not intersect.

19. Is the sum of the measures of the angles in a convex quadrilateral always the same? Why or why not? Yes, the measure is always 360°.

R **20.** State the Euclidean postulate illustrated by the figure at the right. Plane-Intersection Postulate

MORE MATH REASONING

MR, C **21. Paper Clip Geometry** Suppose there are five postulates about strings and paper clips.

Postulate A: There is at least one piece of string.

Postulate B: There are exactly three paper clips on every piece of string.

Postulate C: Not all paper clips are on the same string.

Postulate D: There is exactly one string through any two paper clips.

Postulate E: Any two strings have at least one paper clip in common.

a. Make a single sketch that illustrates all of these postulates.

> **Problem-Solving Tip**
>
> You may want to make a model with real objects.

b. Using the above postulates, prove that there are at least five paper clips.

c. What are the minimum numbers of strings and paper clips needed to fulfill all of the conditions of the postulates?

d. How does eliminating Postulate D affect your answer to **21c**? Explain your thinking.

MR **22.** Decide which one of the following theorems depends on the Parallel Postulate and which one does not. Justify your choices.

(a) If two parallel lines are cut by a transversal, then the corresponding angles are congruent. The conclusion depends on parallel lines.

(b) If two angles are congruent and supplementary, then both of the angles are right angles.

Key

V Vocabulary
P Practice/Skills
R Review
MR Math Reasoning
PS Problem Solving
C Challenge

12-2 PART B Non-Euclidean Geometry

← CONNECT → ***In indirect proofs, you assumed that a statement was not true and showed that your assumption led to a contradiction. However, assuming that the Parallel Postulate is not true can lead to the creation of a new geometric system in which there are no parallel lines.***

Since the beginning of time, humans have tried to understand planets (such as Jupiter, shown at the left), the solar system, galaxies, and the universe. When we investigate such vast objects, however, we find that Euclid's geometric model has some shortcomings. A **non-Euclidean** system of geometry comes from the work of Bernhard Riemann (1826–1866). Riemann's version of the Parallel Postulate contradicts Euclid's.

RIEMANN'S PARALLEL POSTULATE

Through a given point P not on a line ℓ, there is *no* line parallel to line ℓ.

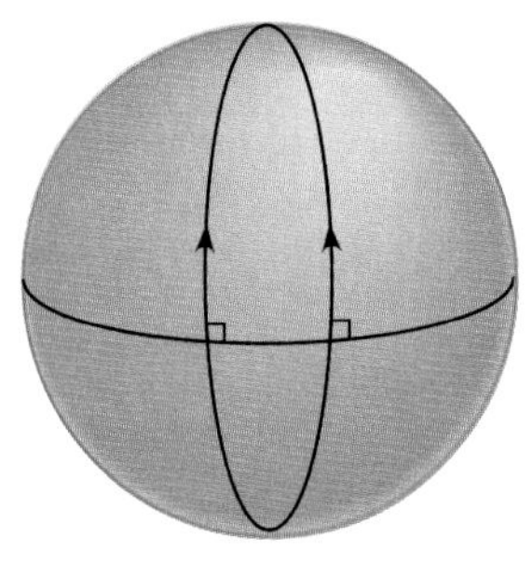

This statement may seem strange or impossible, but there is a familiar model in which Riemann's postulate makes sense.

The most familiar examples of Riemannian lines are the longitude lines on a globe. Although they're perpendicular to the equator (and would therefore be parallel in Euclidean geometry), they get closer and closer until they meet at the poles. A sphere illustrates a simple model of Riemannian geometry.

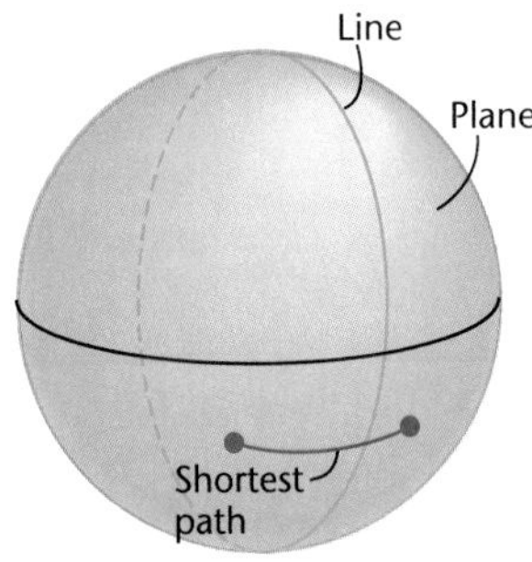

In the model of Riemannian geometry that you will work with, a *plane* is a sphere. In this Riemannian geometry, *lines* are great circles on the plane (sphere). The distance between any two points is the length of the shortest path between them. This path is an arc of a great circle on the sphere, not a straight line segment!

Student Resources

- **Alternative Lessons 12-2B**
- **Laboratory Manual 12-2B**
- Technology Lab Manual
- **Practice 12-2B**
- **Study Guide and Journal 12-2B**
- **Guía de estudios y Diario 12-2B**
- **Multilingual Handbook**
- **More Look Back 12-2B**
- SAT Preparation

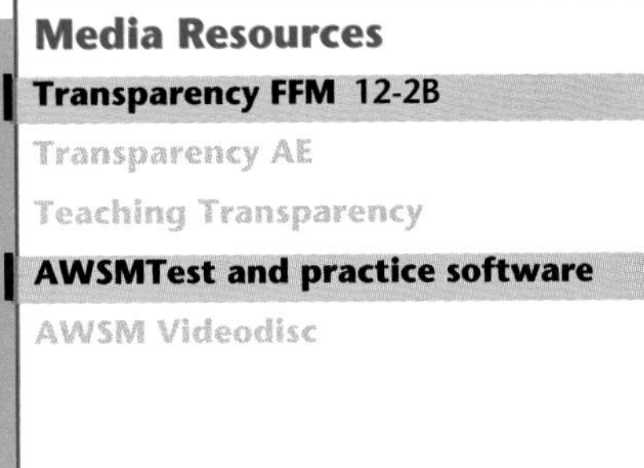

Media Resources

- **Transparency FFM 12-2B**
- Transparency AE
- Teaching Transparency
- **AWSMTest and practice software**
- AWSM Videodisc

PART B At a Glance

Objective

To explore Riemannian geometry by using a spherical model.

Development

Students see Riemann's Parallel Postulate. They are then shown a spherical model of Riemannian geometry.

In the **Explore,** students draw geometric figures on an uninflated balloon and discover how changing the curvature of the surface (inflating the balloon) affects the figures.

Suggested Materials

Student Balloons, marking pen, ruler, protractor

Teacher Globe, world map transparency

Key Terms

Non-Euclidean

First Five Minutes

Transparency FFM 12-2B

In your own words, define *sphere* and *great circle.* Sketch a sphere, and draw and identify a radius and a great circle of the sphere.

Motivate

Ask...

- Suppose we assume that the Parallel Postulate we have used so far is *not* true. What other possibilities are there for the number of lines parallel to a given line through a point not on the line? **No parallel lines through the point; two or more parallel lines through the point.**

12-2

Algebra	Functions	Discrete Math	Probability	Data/Statistics

Euclidean and Non-Euclidean Geometries

EXPLORE

Inflating Euclid's Ideas

Recommended group size: 4

The Point

To investigate the properties of figures, especially lines, triangles, and circles, in Riemannian geometry by projecting them onto a curved surface.

Look and Listen...

- For students who do not see how to measure angles on a curved surface. You may want to explain to them that the measure of the angle is determined by its size at the vertex.
- For students who cannot think of other figures to explore.

Ask...

- Have you seen what happens to a rectangle? a square? perpendicular lines?

For Groups That Finish Early

Inflating the balloon can be thought of as a transformation of the objects you drew on its surface. Is this transformation an isometry? What characteristics of the figure does it preserve? **It is not an isometry; it preserves neither size nor shape. It does preserve orientation.**

Follow Up

Ask students to describe what happens to parallel lines in this model of Riemannian geometry. Then have them state a Triangle Angle-Sum Theorem that seems true for Riemannian geometry.

Possible Answers

2. The parallel lines curve toward one another and, if extended, would intersect. In Euclidean geometry, parallel lines are everywhere equidistant—they never intersect.
3. The sum of the measures of the angles of the triangle on the inflated balloon is greater than 180°.

Many of the definitions and properties of Euclidean geometry still apply in the Riemannian system. For example, right angles still measure 90°, and perpendicular lines still form right angles. But some Euclidean properties are not true in Riemannian geometry. In the following Explore, you will investigate how triangles and lines behave in our model of Riemannian geometry.

EXPLORE: INFLATING EUCLID'S IDEAS

MATERIALS

Balloons
Marking pen
Ruler
Protractor

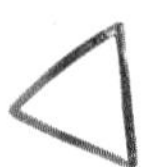

1. Spread a balloon flat on the surface of a table. Carefully draw the largest acute triangle you can on one side of the balloon. Then turn the balloon over, and draw two parallel lines from the top of the balloon to the bottom.
2. Inflate the balloon. What happens to the parallel lines? How is this different from the way parallel lines behave in Euclidean geometry?
3. Measure the angles of the triangle after the balloon has been inflated. How does the sum of the measures of the angles compare to the sum when the balloon was flat? Make a conjecture about the sum of the measures of the angles of a triangle in Riemannian geometry.
4. On a second balloon, draw some geometric figures you'd like to investigate: for example, intersecting lines and other figures. Inflate the balloon, and make any conjectures you can about the properties of these figures in Riemannian geometry. Share your conjectures with your classmates.

In Riemannian geometry, all lines are curved. Albert Einstein (1879–1955) used this idea in the development of his theory of relativity. Einstein said that mass, like that in planets, stars, and galaxies, causes space to curve. (Think of a heavy ball on a sheet of plastic wrap.) Moving objects that are near the ball follow a path in the curved space. This helps explain why planets stay in orbit around stars, and stars stay in orbit around the centers of galaxies.

Tips from Teachers

The larger and sturdier the balloons used in this *Explore,* the better. For sanitary reasons, you may want to suggest that each group designate one person to inflate their balloon.

Mathematics Connection

A third version of the Parallel Postulate, where *more than one* line parallel to a given line can be drawn through a point not on it, also results in an alternate geometry. Lobachevsky (1793–1856) and Bolyai (1802–1860) first developed this idea in the 1820s. In this geometry, the sum of the measures of the angles in a triangle is *less than* 180°.

The following theorems can be proved using Riemann's Parallel Postulate.

- In Riemannian geometry, the sum of the measures of the angles in a triangle is greater than 180°.
- In Riemannian geometry, if a circle has radius r, its circumference is less than $2\pi r$, and its area is less than πr^2.
- In Riemannian geometry, any two coplanar lines intersect.

TRY IT

Answer each question using the properties of Riemannian geometry.

a. If a and b are two coplanar lines, what must be true about them? They must intersect.

b. In $\triangle GHJ$, $m\angle J = 45°$, and $m\angle H = 100°$. What do you know about $m\angle G$? $m\angle G > 35°$

c. Circle M has radius 2 cm. What do you know about its circumference? its area? Circumference $< 4\pi$ cm; Area $< 4\pi$ cm^2

REFLECT

1. Lines drawn on the earth's surface are curved. Explain why they might appear straight for most measurements.
2. Is the shortest distance between two points on the earth's surface really a straight line segment? What does this mean for a pilot trying to determine the shortest flight path from New York to Tokyo?

Exercises

CORE

P **Getting Started Using our model of Riemannian geometry, name the figure that is equivalent to each of the following Euclidean figures.**

1. a line A great circle on the plane (sphere) **2.** a plane A sphere **3.** a line segment An arc of a great circle

P **Answer each question using the properties of Riemannian geometry.**

4. In $\triangle XYZ$, $m\angle X = 23°$ and $m\angle Y = 55°$. What do you know about $m\angle Z$? $m\angle Z > 102°$

5. Circle C has an eight-inch radius. What do you know about its circumference? its area? Circumference $< 16\pi$ in.; Area $< 64\pi$ in.^{2}

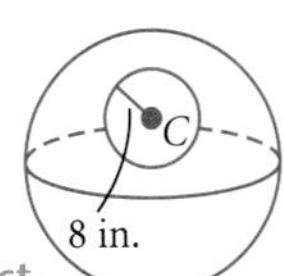

6. If s and t are two coplanar lines, what must be true about them? They intersect.

Journal

Reflect 1 and 2 and **Exercise** 10 are suitable for journal entries.

REFLECT

Possible Answers

1. Over short distances, the curvature of the earth is so slight that it is not noticeable.

2. No. The shortest distance is an arc of a great circle. The shortest route from New York to Tokyo is along a great circle that passes through the two cities.

Part B Exercises

Exercise Notes

Core

9. Shows that betweenness is not an intuitive concept in our Riemannian model.

10. Students explore Saccheri quadrilaterals.

More Math Reasoning

20. Students see that the sum of the angle measures in a triangle in our Riemannian model must be between 180° and 360°.

Key

V Vocabulary
P Practice/Skills
R Review
MR Math Reasoning
PS Problem Solving
C Challenge

Ongoing Assessment

Self-Assessment Exercises 1, 3, 5, 6, 7, 11

Embedded Assessment Try It a; Reflect 1; Exercises 4, 8, 10

Euclidean and Non-Euclidean Geometries

Exercise Answers

Core

9. No. If the points are evenly spaced around a great circle, it becomes unclear which point is between the other two.

10. Greater than 360°. It is made up of two triangles which, in Riemannian geometry, contain more than 180° each.

P, MR **Each of the following statements is true in Euclidean geometry. Determine whether each is true for Riemannian geometry. Explain your thinking.**

7. A triangle cannot have two right angles. F; Triangles have more than 180°.

8. The circumference of a circle with diameter d is πd.
F; Circumference is less than πd.

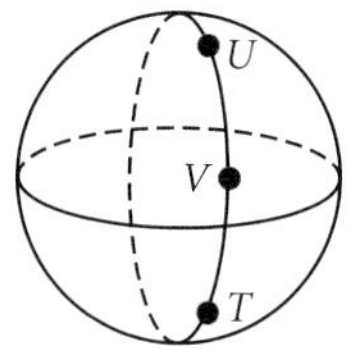

9. In Euclidean geometry, it's easy to tell which of three collinear points is between the other two. Is this true in the Riemannian system? For example, is V between T and U? Why or why not? (Hint: See what happens if the three points aren't all in the same hemisphere.)

MR **10. The Saccheri Quadrilateral** Girolamo Saccheri, an Italian priest, tried (and failed) to prove Euclid's Parallel Postulate, using some special quadrilaterals. In fact, he actually developed part of a non-Euclidean geometry.

A *Saccheri quadrilateral* has two congruent sides that are both perpendicular to its base. In Euclidean geometry, a Saccheri quadrilateral must be a rectangle.

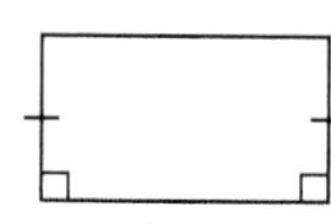

Make a conjecture about the sum of the measures of the angles of a Saccheri quadrilateral in our model of Riemannian geometry. Support your conjecture with an explanation and an illustration.

PS, MR **11.** The Orion Nebula is a gas nebula seen in the constellation Orion. It is within the Milky Way and is about 1500 light-years from the earth. The Andromeda Galaxy, the nearest spiral galaxy to the Milky Way, is about 2×10^6 light-years from the earth.

Science

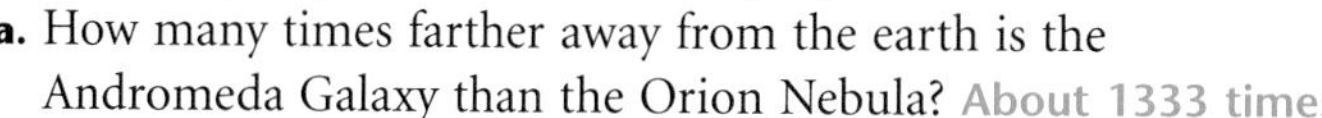

a. How many times farther away from the earth is the Andromeda Galaxy than the Orion Nebula? About 1333 times

b. As seen from the earth, the Orion Nebula and the Andromeda Galaxy are similar in brightness. How is this possible, given the difference in their distances from us? Andromeda has a far greater actual (absolute) brightness

LOOK BACK

PS, R **12.** On the 1992 flight of the space shuttle *Endeavour,* Dr. Kathryn C. Thornton became the second American woman to walk in space. Suppose that at the time of the space walk the space shuttle was at an altitude of 200 mi.

Science

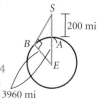

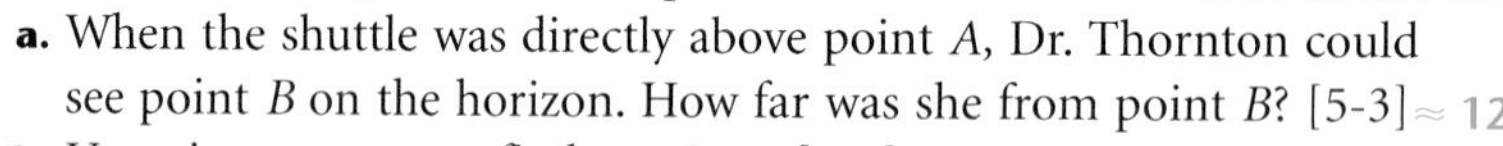

a. When the shuttle was directly above point A, Dr. Thornton could see point B on the horizon. How far was she from point B? [5-3] ≈ 1274.4 miles

b. Use trigonometry to find $m\angle BEA$. [7-3] ≈ 18°

c. Suppose a lake is 1100 mi from point A. Could Dr. Thornton see this lake when she was directly over point A? (Hint: Calculate the length of $\widehat{AB}$.) [8-2] Yes; she could see points up to about 1230 mi from A.

Key

- V Vocabulary
- P Practice/Skills
- R Review
- MR Math Reasoning
- PS Problem Solving
- C Challenge

R 13. Gweru, Zimbabwe (19° S latitude) and Istanbul, Turkey (41° N latitude) have approximately the same longitude. Assuming the earth's radius is 3960 mi, find the distance between Gweru and Istanbul. [12-1] ≈ 4147 mi

MORE PRACTICE

P **Answer each question, using the properties of Riemannian geometry.**

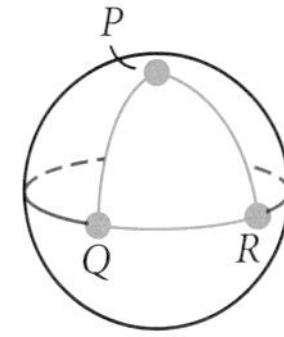

14. If m and n are two coplanar lines, what must be true about them? m and n intersect.

15. In $\triangle PQR$, $m\angle P = 80°$, and $m\angle Q = 90°$. What do you know about $m\angle R$? $m\angle R > 10°$

16. Circle T has radius 4 ft. What do you know about its circumference? its area? Circumference $< 8\pi$ ft; Area $< 16\pi$ ft^2

MR **Each of the following statements is true in Euclidean geometry. Determine whether each is true for Riemannian geometry. Support your answers with an explanation or an illustration.**

17. The measure of an angle in an equilateral triangle is 60°. F; Triangles have more than 180°.

18. If a transversal intersects two coplanar lines so that their alternate interior angles are congruent, then the lines are parallel.

MORE MATH REASONING

MR **19. a.** The average radius of the earth is 3960 mi. If you always travel the shortest possible path along the earth's surface, what is the greatest possible distance between two points on the earth? What is true about those points? Justify your answer.

b. Suppose A and B are points on a sphere of radius r. Find the maximum possible shortest-path distance between these points.

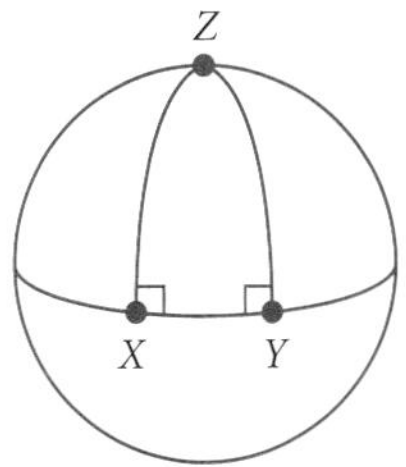

C **20. Triangle Angles** We know that the sum of the angle measures of a triangle in our Riemannian model is always greater than 180°. Is there a maximum value this sum can have? If so, find this number. If not, explain why there is no such value. (Hint: Consider a triangle $\triangle XYZ$ whose base $\overline{XY}$ is on the equator of a globe, whose vertex Z is at the North Pole, and whose base angles are right angles. What happens to the vertex angle, $\angle Z$, if you move X and Y farther apart?) Yes; 360°

More Practice

18. F; There are no parallel lines in Riemannian geometry.

More Math Reasoning

19. a. $3960\pi \approx 12{,}440$ miles. The two points would be endpoints of a diameter of the earth since the largest distance between two points on the earth is $\frac{1}{2}$ its circumference.

b. πr

Algebra | Functions | Discrete Math | Probability | Data/Statistics

Euclidean and Non-Euclidean Geometries

PART C At a Glance

Objective

To compare properties of geometric figures on Euclidean and Riemannian planes.

Development

In the **Explore,** students explore the Pythagorean Theorem and another theorem on a curved surface.

Suggested Materials

Student Graph paper, scissors, ball, tape

First Five Minutes

Transparency FFM 12-2C

List all the differences you can think of between properties of figures in Euclidean geometry and their corresponding properties in our model of Riemannian geometry.

EXPLORE

Is Euclid on the Ball?

Recommended group size: 4

The Point

To compare the Pythagorean Theorem and another theorem on flat and spherical planes.

Look and Listen...

- For students who are taping down all three sides of the triangle in Step 5 and all four sides of the rectangle in Step 6.
- For students who are having difficulty measuring with the graph paper.

Ask...

- Are you curving the strip of graph paper to measure the segments on the ball?

12-2 PART C Making Connections

← CONNECT → ***When we developed our geometric system, we started with postulates similar to those proposed by Euclid. You've seen how changing just one postulate—the Parallel Postulate—has allowed mathematicians to develop a completely different system of geometry.***

The study of the universe has close ties to the assumptions of Euclidean and non-Euclidean geometry. Euclid's geometry assumes that planes are flat surfaces. Riemann developed a non-Euclidean geometry in which a plane has curvature.

The following theorems depend on Euclid's Parallel Postulate.

Pythagorean Theorem: In a right triangle, the square of the length of the hypotenuse is equal to the sum of the squares of the lengths of the legs.

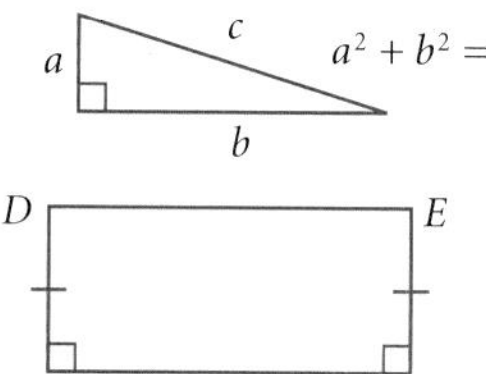

If $\angle G$ and $\angle F$ are right angles, and $\overline{DG} \cong \overline{EF}$, then $DEFG$ is a rectangle.

In the following Explore, you will see whether or not these theorems work in curved space.

EXPLORE: IS EUCLID ON THE BALL?

MATERIALS

Graph paper, Scissors
Ball, Tape

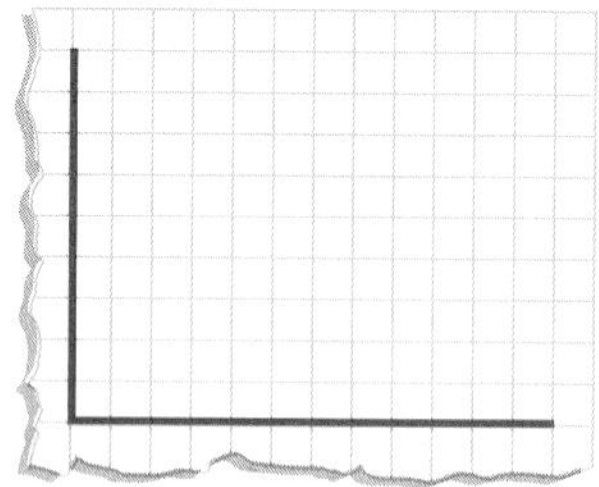

1. Near the bottom of a sheet of graph paper, cut out a long, thin, horizontal strip. You will use this as a ruler later.
2. On the graph paper, draw a right triangle with legs of 9 units and 12 units as shown. According to the Pythagorean Theorem, what should be the length of the hypotenuse? Check by measuring the hypotenuse with your strip of graph paper.

782 12-2 • EUCLIDEAN AND NON-EUCLIDEAN GEOMETRIES

Diversity Issues

The use of manipulatives in this **Explore** and the one in 12-2 Part B should appeal to kinesthetic and visual learners as they investigate Riemannian geometry. Auditory learners may need extra time working with these manipulatives. They may also benefit from a more extended discussion of Riemann's Parallel Postulate and one or more of the "new" theorems.

3. On another sheet of graph paper, draw three sides of quadrilateral $DEFG$ so that $\angle G$ and $\angle F$ are right angles, and $\overline{DG} \cong \overline{EF}$. Using a straightedge, draw a dotted line to connect D and E. What type of figure is $DEFG$? What can you say about $\overline{DE}$ and $\overline{GF}$?
4. Now cut out the legs of the right triangle from Step 2 and the three solid sides of the quadrilateral from Step 3.

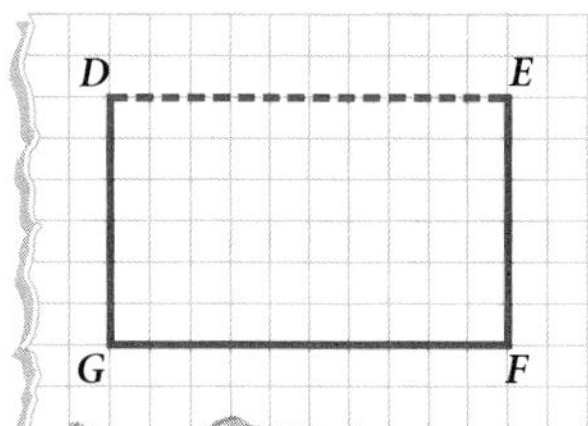

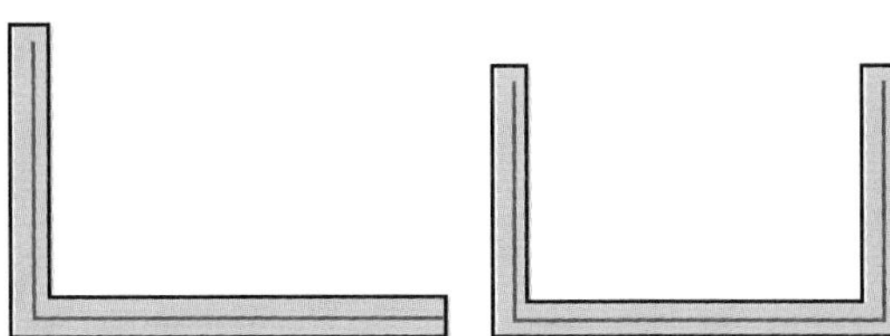

5. Carefully tape the right-angle cutout onto the surface of a beachball or other type of ball. With the strip of graph paper, measure the new hypotenuse. Is it the same length it was on a flat surface, or is it longer or shorter?
6. Tape the three sides of the quadrilateral onto the beachball. With the strip of graph paper, measure the distance across the open side of the quadrilateral. Is it equal to the length of the opposite side? On the ball, is the quadrilateral a rectangle?
7. In general, when is Riemannian geometry a better model than Euclidean geometry?

What is the geometry of the universe? No one knows for sure. Maybe the universe can be described by one of the models that you've examined.

1. Which of the systems of geometry that you've studied do you feel is the best model of the universe? Do you think there may be a different system of geometry that is even better? Why?

As science and technology advance, we need models that explain the universe in greater and greater detail. The geometry that helps us find the height of a tree may not help us measure the size of the universe.

REFLECT

1. Why do you think people from Euclid's time (300 B.C.) to the nineteenth century considered his Parallel Postulate a self-evident truth?

For Groups That Finish Early

Consider the triangle bounded by the equator, the prime meridian, and the 90° E longitude line. (If you do not have a globe, model the triangle on your ball.) Classify the triangle by angles and sides. **Right, equiangular, equilateral.**

Follow Up

Ask students to summarize their results for Steps 5 and 6. Have a class discussion of students' responses to Step 7.

Possible Answers

2. 15 units

3. $DEFG$ is a rectangle. $\overline{DE} \cong \overline{GF}$, and $\overline{DE} \parallel \overline{GF}$.

5. The hypotenuse is shorter.

6. The open side of the quadrilateral is not the same length; the quadrilateral is not a rectangle.

7. Riemannian geometry is a better model on the exterior of a curved figure. Euclidean geometry is a better model on flat surfaces.

Asks students to make a conjecture about whether Riemannian or Euclidean geometry more accurately models the universe.

Possible Answer

1. This issue has not been resolved. It is possible that yet another system of geometry will provide a more accurate model of the universe.

Student Resources

- Alternative Lessons
- **Laboratory Manual 12-2C**
- Technology Lab Manual
- **Practice 12-2C**
- **Study Guide and Journal 12-2C**
- **Guía de estudios y Diario 12-2C**
- **Multilingual Handbook**
- **More Look Back 12-2C**
- SAT Preparation

Media Resources

- **Transparency FFM 12-2C**
- Transparency AE
- Teaching Transparency
- **AWSMTest and practice software**
- AWSM Videodisc

Euclidean and Non-Euclidean Geometries

Portfolio

Have students select items from their work that demonstrate their understanding of the material in 12-2.

You may want them to include an **Exercise** or a step from an **Explore** where they showed how a theorem depends on the Parallel Postulate, an **Exercise** where they explored Riemannian geometry on a sphere, and a **Reflect** question that they found interesting.

REFLECT

Possible Answers

1. In general, people in these times worked with relatively short distances on the earth's surface. Only when distances are very large does Euclidean geometry break down.

2. See Additional Answers p. T770.

Self-Assessment

Exercise Notes

14. Students explore the implications of the two geometric models they have studied as accurate models of the universe. (A Euclidean universe is infinite; a Riemannian universe is bounded.)

2. Complete the following table to contrast the two systems of geometry you've studied.

Geometry	Parallel Postulate	Description of Planes and Lines	Sum of Angle Measures for a Triangle	Circumference and Area of Circle with Radius r
Euclidean				
Riemannian				

Self-Assessment

P **Name the Euclidean postulate illustrated by each statement. (When we refer to a star or planet, assume that we are referring to its center. Therefore, you can think of it as a point.)**

1. Only one straight line contains Pluto and Mercury. Straight-Line Postulate

2. There is a line through the star Rigel that is parallel to the line through the stars Vega and Fomalhaut. Parallel Postulate

3. The intersection of the plane containing Jupiter, Neptune, and Mars with the plane containing the stars Rigel, Aldebaran, and Antares is a straight line. Plane-Intersection Postulate

P **Answer each of the following questions, using Euclid's model of the universe. Then answer the same question, using our Riemannian model.**

4. Can there be a triangle with two right angles? No; Yes

5. If two coplanar lines are cut by a transversal so that the corresponding angles are congruent, are the lines parallel? Yes; No

6. In $\triangle JKL$, $m\angle J = 60°$, and $m\angle K = 60°$. What do you know about $m\angle L$? $m\angle L = 60°$; $m\angle L > 60°$

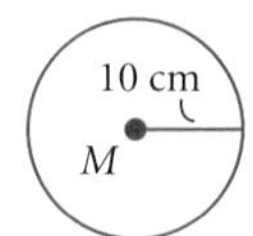

P **7.** In our model of Riemannian geometry, which of the following statements is false? (c)
(a) A sphere is a plane.
(b) A right angle measures 90°.
(c) The sum of the measures of the angles in a triangle is 180°.
(d) There are no parallel lines.
(e) The shortest path between two points is an arc.

P **8.** Circle M has radius 10 cm. Using a Riemannian model, what do you know about its circumference? its area? Circumference $< 20\pi$ cm; Area $< 100\pi$ cm^2

10 cm
M

Key

V Vocabulary
P Practice/Skills
R Review
MR Math Reasoning
PS Problem Solving
C Challenge

R 9. The oldest stone monument in the world, the Step Pyramid at Saqqara, Egypt, has a rectangular base 410 ft long and 358 ft wide.

a. Find the length of a diagonal of the base of this pyramid, using Euclidean geometry. Express your answer in exact form and as a decimal rounded to the nearest tenth. [5-3] $2\sqrt{74,066}$ ft; 544.3 ft.

b. Because the pyramid is on the curved surface of the earth, is the actual length of the diagonal of its base smaller or larger than your exact answer in **9a**? Explain. Smaller; For a right triangle in Riemannian space, $a^2 + b^2 > c^2$

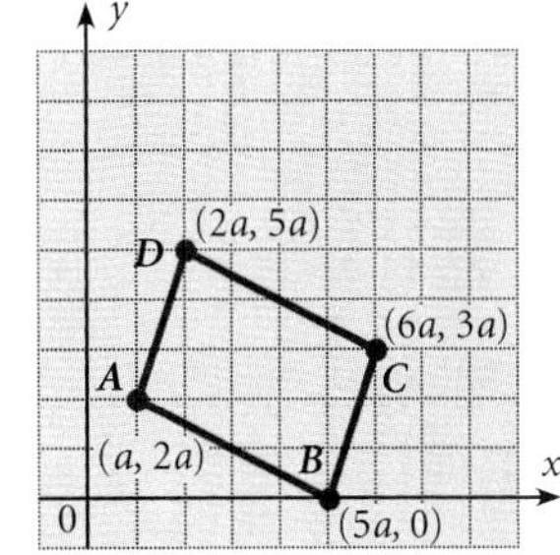

R 10. Prove that quadrilateral $ABCD$ is a parallelogram. [6-2]

R 11. **The Great Wall of Galaxies** The so-called Great Wall of galaxies is about 500 million light-years long, 200 million light-years high, and 15 million light-years thick. Assuming that the Great Wall is a rectangular solid (and using a Euclidean model of the universe!), find its volume. [9-2] 1.5×10^{24} cubic light-years

S 12. a. It takes a radar signal 2.2 sec to make a round trip from Neptune to Triton, one of its moons. If radar travels at the speed of light (300,000 km/sec), how far is Triton from Neptune? Round your answer to the nearest ten thousand kilometers. [12-1] 330,000 km

b. The diameter of Triton covers an arc of about 0.47° in the sky of Neptune. What is Triton's approximate diameter? Round your answer to the nearest hundred kilometers. 2700 km

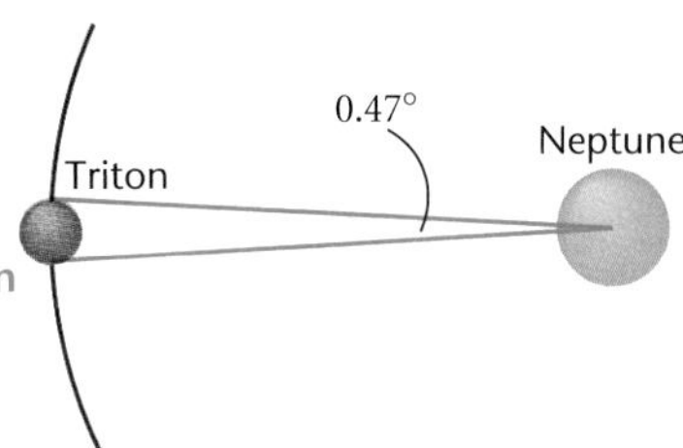

R 13. The three photographs below "zoom in" on parts of a broccoli plant. Write a brief explanation of how these photographs are related to the idea of a fractal. [12-1]

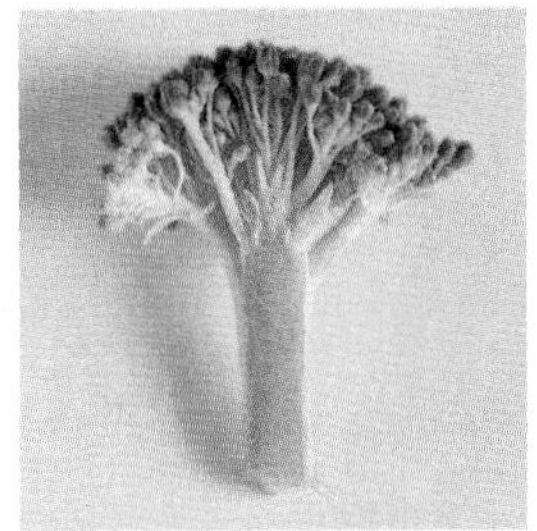

C 14. **How Big Is Forever?** Astronomers have argued about whether the universe goes on forever or whether it has a finite size. Does the Euclidean model support either of these conjectures? If Riemannian geometry is a more accurate model of the universe, what does that suggest about the size of the universe? Give a brief written explanation of your answer. (Hint: Consider the difference between a line in Euclidean geometry and a line in Riemannian geometry.)

Self-Assessment Answers

10. Statement 1: $ABCD$ is a quadrilateral.
Reason 1: Given
Statement 2: $DA = a\sqrt{10}$, $BC = a\sqrt{10}$
Reason 2: Distance Formula
Statement 3: $DC = 2a\sqrt{5}$, $AB = 2a\sqrt{5}$
Reason 3: Distance Formula
Statement 4: $ABCD$ is a parallelogram.
Reason 4: If both pairs of opposite sides of a quadrilateral are congruent then the figure is a parallelogram.

13. Each part of a broccoli plant is similar to the whole.

14. The Euclidean model supports an infinite universe. The Riemannian model suggests a finite universe since all lines are circles.

Assessment Resources

Quiz 12-2
Chapter Assessment Form A
Chapter Assessment Form B
Chapter Alternative Assessment
Mid-Year Assessment
End-of-Year Assessment
AWSMTest and practice software

Ongoing Assessment

Self-Assessment Self-Assessment Exercises

Embedded Assessment Explore Steps 5, 6, 7; Reflect 1, 2

Algebra | Functions | Discrete Math | Probability | Data/Statistics

Chapter 12 Review

Journal

Students can identify **Key Terms** that they do not understand, and look up the definitions in the indicated section or in the glossary. Non-English-speaking students may want to use the *Multilingual Handbook.*

Vocabulary exercises and the **Self-Evaluation** are useful journal entries.

Review Answers

4. a.

Stage 3

Stage 4

b. 122

5. The reference line known as the equator and lines parallel to it are called lines of latitude. The equator is at 0°. The North Pole is at 90° North latitude (90° N) and the South Pole at 90° S. Lines connecting the poles are called lines of longitude. The reference line known as the prime meridian runs north-south through England, Continental Europe, and West Africa. The prime meridian marks 0° longitude. Other longitude lines range from 0° to 180° east or west.

7. Determine the length of the arc of the great circle on which the two points lie.

15.

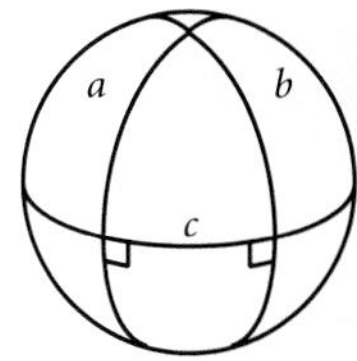

$a \perp c$, $b \perp c$. However, a is not parallel to b.

Chapter 12 Review

In Chapter 12, you learned some indirect techniques that humans have developed to measure the earth and the universe. You were also introduced to fractals, a concept that gives order to what seems to be chaos (and presents us with some fascinating mathematical art on the way).

KEY TERMS

astronomical unit [12-1]	light-year [12-1]	parallax [12-1]
equator [12-1]	longitude [12-1]	prime meridian [12-1]
fractal geometry [12-1]	non-Euclidean [12-2]	self-similar [12-1]
latitude [12-1]		

V **From each group of terms, choose the term that does not belong, and explain why it does not belong.**

1. coastline, broccoli, tomato, Sierpinski Gasket Tomato; Not example of a fractal

2. speed of light, astronomical unit, light-year, kilometer Speed of light; Does not represent a distance

CONCEPTS AND APPLICATIONS

P **3.** The speed of light is about 300,000 km/sec. The mean distance from the sun to Pluto is about 6 billion (6×10^9) km. How long does light take to travel from the sun to Pluto? [12-1] 5 hours, 33 minutes, 20 seconds

Science

P, PS **4.** The rule for the fractal shown is to draw and shade an isosceles right triangle with vertices at the midpoints of the sides of each unshaded triangle. [12-1]

a. Sketch Stages 3 and 4.

b. Look for a pattern to predict the total number of shaded triangles at Stage 6.

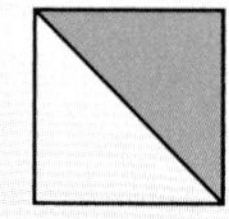
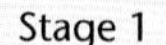

Stage 1

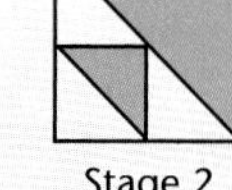

Stage 2

MR **5.** Write a summary of how latitude and longitude are measured.

PS **6.** Manila, Philippines, has latitude 15° N and longitude 120° E. Khartoum, Sudan, also has latitude 15° N and is at longitude 33° E. What is the distance between the two cities? Use 3960 mi for the radius of the earth. [12-1] About 5808 miles

Social Science

MR **7.** Describe how to determine the shortest path on the surface of a sphere between two points on the sphere. [12-2]

Key

V Vocabulary
P Practice/Skills
R Review
MR Math Reasoning
PS Problem Solving
C Challenge

Logic/Reasoning | Industry/Careers | Science/Health | Social Science/History | Fine Arts/Literature

The lengths of two sides of a triangle are given. Write an inequality that represents the range of values for the possible lengths of the third side. [11-1]

8. 11, 14 $3 < s < 25$ **9.** 2, 2 $0 < s < 4$ **10.** m, $2m$ $m < s < 3m$

11. The parallax angle to the star Procyon is about 0.00008°. [12-1]

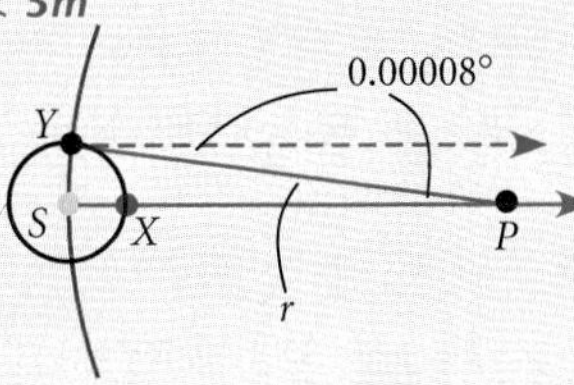

a. Find the distance to Procyon in astronomical units. about 716,000 A.U.

b. A light-year is about 63,200 A.U. How many light-years away is Procyon? 11.3 light-years

Which of the following properties are true in Riemannian geometry? [12-2]

12. Through a point not on a given line, there is no line parallel to the given line. T

13. The measure of a right angle is greater than 90°. F

14. A triangle may have more than one right angle. T

15. Using Riemannian geometry, sketch a situation in which two lines are perpendicular to the same line, but are not parallel to each other. [12-2]

CONCEPTS AND CONNECTIONS

16. History of Astronomy Aristarchus of Samos (ca. 260 B.C.) calculated the ratio of the distance from the earth to the moon, m, to the distance from the earth to the sun, s. He observed that when the moon was half-full, the angle between the lines of sight to the sun and the moon was 87°.

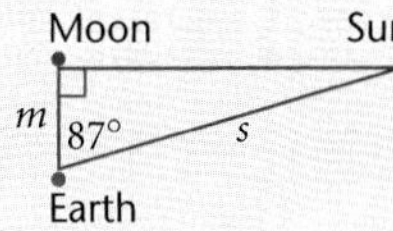

a. Why did Aristarchus conclude that the angle at the moon was a right angle?

b. Use a trigonometric ratio to find Aristarchus's value for $\frac{m}{s}$.

c. Calculate the ratio $\frac{m}{s}$, using the actual values $m = 240{,}000$ mi, and $s = 93{,}000{,}000$ mi. Was Aristarchus's result accurate?

d. The correct angle in the figure is actually 89.83°. How would this have affected Aristarchus's result? Describe how small differences in the measure of an angle close to 90° affect trigonometric ratios, and explain why very accurate measurements are needed in astronomy.

SELF-EVALUATION

Write a summary of the most important facts about fractals, longitude and latitude, astronomical measurement, and non-Euclidean geometries that have been introduced in Chapter 12. For each of these topics, describe how they are connected to ideas from earlier chapters.

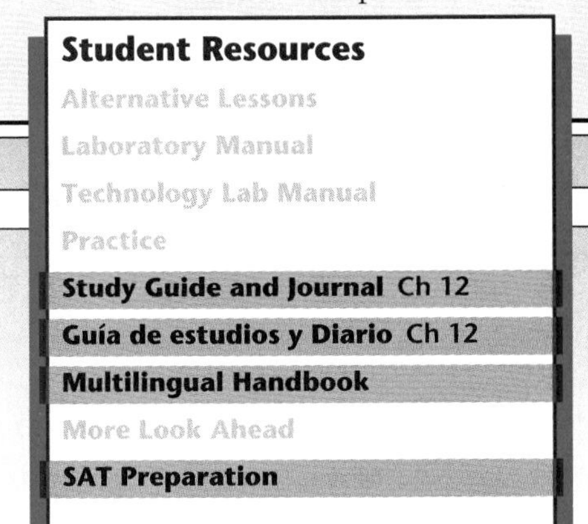

Student Resources
- Alternative Lessons
- Laboratory Manual
- Technology Lab Manual
- Practice
- **Study Guide and Journal** Ch 12
- **Guía de estudios y Diario** Ch 12
- **Multilingual Handbook**
- More Look Ahead
- **SAT Preparation**

Media Resources
- Transparency FFM
- Transparency AE
- Teaching Transparency
- **AWSMTest and practice software**
- AWSM Videodisc

16. a. The moon was exactly half full, so the sunlight was coming exactly "from the side."

b. 0.052 **c.** 0.0026; No

d. This would make his calculation more accurate. Using 89.93°, he would have found $\frac{m}{s} \approx 0.0030$. For angles near 90°, a very small difference in the angle measure results in a large percentage difference in the cosine.

Chapter 12 Assessment

Portfolio

Students may select items that represent their mathematical understanding of the ideas in Chapter 12 and that illustrate the effort that they put into this chapter. One item should include a calculation of the size of or distance to a moon, planet, or star.

A rubric for assessing portfolios is included in the introduction to the Teacher's Edition.

Assessment Answers

1. a.

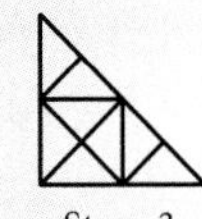

Stage 3 Stage 4

b. 2^{n-1}

4. No. The sum of the lengths of any two sides must be greater than the length of the third side.

5. Yes. The sum of the lengths of any two sides is greater than the length of the third side.

6. No. The sum of the lengths of any two sides must be greater than the length of the third side.

7. About 636 miles; about $\frac{1}{5}$ as wide. On a Mercator map, the longitude lines are drawn as parallel lines and are spaced farther apart near the top than they would be on a globe.

Performance Task

Answer

Possible answer:

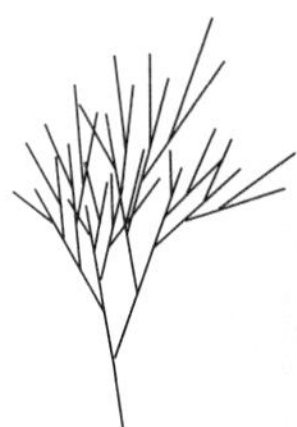

Branches, roots

Suggested Scoring Rubric

Level 4 Full Accomplishment

- Shows full understanding of the idea of generating a fractal through repeated application of a rule.
- Drawing follows rules accurately and has at least four stages.
- Students see that the fractal models the branches or roots of a tree.

Level 3 Substantial Accomplishment

- Shows essential grasp of the idea of generating a fractal through repeated application of a rule.
- Drawing generally follows rules, although some branches may have been omitted. Drawing has at least three stages.
- Students see that the fractal models the branches or roots of a tree.

Level 2 Partial Accomplishment

- Shows partial grasp of the idea of generating a fractal through repeated application of a rule.
- Drawing shows evidence of consistent confusion about one or more of the rules (90% length, 50-50 chance of left-right, $\frac{1}{3}$ of the way up, branch drawn for *each* end segment), but still shows basic characteristics of the fractal.
- Description of relation to nature is consistent with drawing.

Level 1 Little Accomplishment

- Shows little or no grasp of the idea of generating a fractal through repeated application of a rule.
- Drawing shows little evidence of application of the rules.

Chapter 12 Assessment

TEST

Stage 1 Stage 2

P, PS **1.** Start with an isosceles right triangle. For each stage , draw the altitude to the hypotenuse of all isosceles right triangles.

a. Sketch Stages 3 and 4.

b. How many new segments are drawn in Stage *n*?

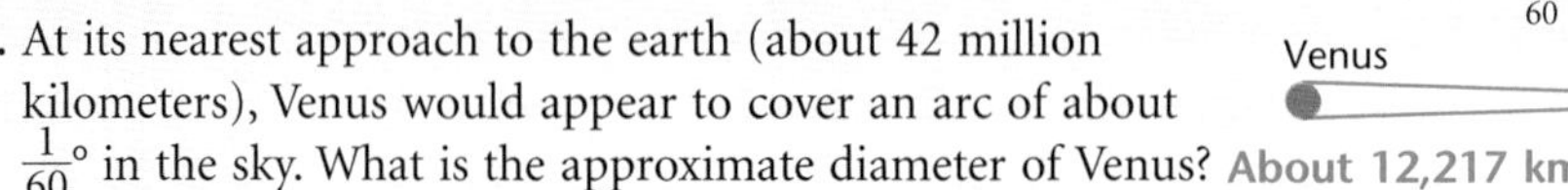

PS Science **2.** At its nearest approach to the earth (about 42 million kilometers), Venus would appear to cover an arc of about $\frac{1}{60}°$ in the sky. What is the approximate diameter of Venus? About 12,217 km

P Science **3.** How long would a transmission traveling at the speed of light (300,000 km/sec) take to reach the earth from Saturn (about 1.5×10^9 km away)?
83 minutes, 20 seconds

R **Determine whether each set of numbers could represent the lengths of the sides of a triangle. Explain your answers.**

4. 4, 7, 3 **5.** 16, 8, 9 **6.** 4.1, 13.8, 9.5

PS, MR Social Science **7.** On many world maps, Greenland appears to be as wide as the United States. At about 80° N latitude, Greenland extends from 20° W to 73° W longitude. Find its width at this latitude. (Use 3960 mi for the earth's radius.) Then compare Greenland's width to the approximate 3000-mi width of the United States. Explain why this distortion of Greenland occurs on some maps.

MR **8.** Describe the main difference between Euclidean and non-Euclidean geometries.
The Parallel Postulate is different; there are no parallel lines in Riemannian geometry.

P **Which of the following properties are true in Riemannian geometry?**

9. No two lines intersect. F

10. The sum of the measures of the angles of a triangle is greater than 180°. T

PERFORMANCE TASK

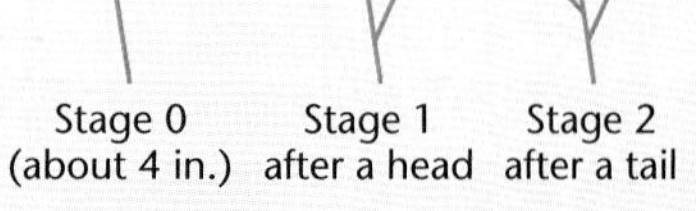

Draw Stage 0 of a fractal, as shown. For Stage 1, draw a segment about 90% as long as the existing segment, about one-third of the way up from the bottom and at a small angle. Flip a coin to determine on which side of the existing segment the new one should be drawn. For a head, draw the segment on the right; for a tail, draw the segment on the left. Flip the coin for each stage, and add a segment to each *end segment,* as shown. Complete and describe Stage 5.

Stage 1 after a tail Stage 2 after a tail

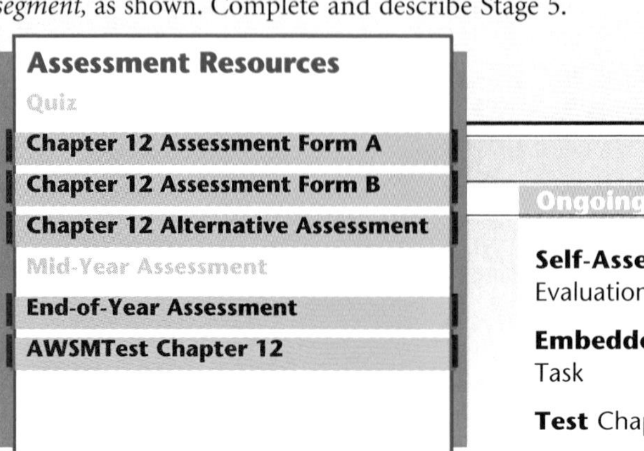
Assessment Resources

Quiz
Chapter 12 Assessment Form A
Chapter 12 Assessment Form B
Chapter 12 Alternative Assessment
Mid-Year Assessment
End-of-Year Assessment
AWSMTest Chapter 12

Ongoing Assessment

Self-Assessment Chapter 12 Review and Self-Evaluation

Embedded Assessment Chapter 12 Performance Task

Test Chapter 12 Test

SYMBOLS

$\overleftrightarrow{AB}$	line containing points A and B
$\overline{AB}$	line segment with endpoints A and B
$\overrightarrow{AB}$	ray with endpoint A that contains B
$\overrightarrow{AB}$	vector with origin A and endpoint B
AB	length of $\overline{AB}$; distance between A and B
$\triangle ABC$	triangle with vertices A, B, and C
$\angle ABC$	angle with sides $\overrightarrow{AB}$ and $\overrightarrow{AC}$
$\angle B$	angle with vertex B
$m\angle ABC$	measure of $\angle ABC$
$^\circ$	degree(s)
$\cong$	is congruent to
$\ncong$	is not congruent to
$\perp$	is perpendicular to
$\not\perp$	is not perpendicular to
$\parallel$	is parallel to
$\nparallel$	is not parallel to
$\sim$	is similar to
$\approx$	is approximately equal to
$\leftrightarrow$	corresponds to
$p \rightarrow q$	p implies q
A'	A prime
$<$	is less than
$>$	is greater than
$\leq$	is less than or equal to
$\geq$	is greater than or equal to
$\lvert x \rvert$	absolute value of x
$\sqrt{x}$	square root of x
$\odot$	circle
$\overset{\frown}{AB}$	arc with endpoints A and B
$\overset{\frown}{ACB}$	arc with endpoints A and B and containing C
π	pi (approximately 3.14)
(a, b)	ordered pair with x-coordinate a and y-coordinate b
$<a, b>$	translation of a units horizontally and b units vertically
$\sin A$	sine of $\angle A$
$\cos A$	cosine of $\angle A$
$\tan A$	tangent of $\angle A$

FORMULAS

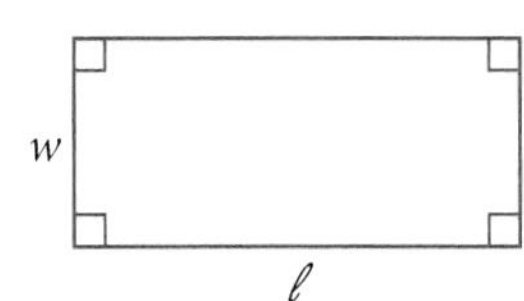 **Rectangle** Area: $A = \ell w$ Perimeter: $p = 2\ell + 2w$	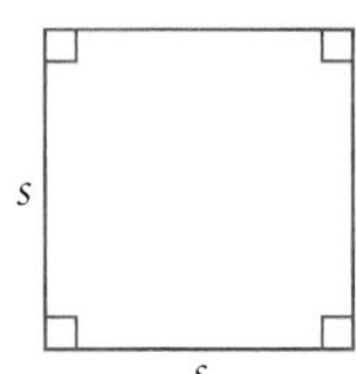 **Square** Area: $A = s^2$ Perimeter: $p = 4s$	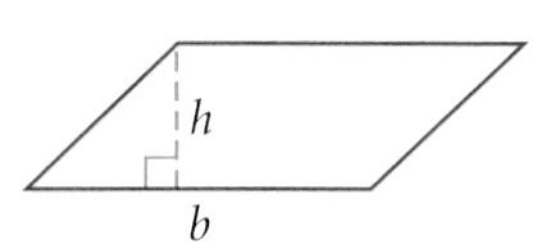 **Parallelogram** Area: $A = bh$
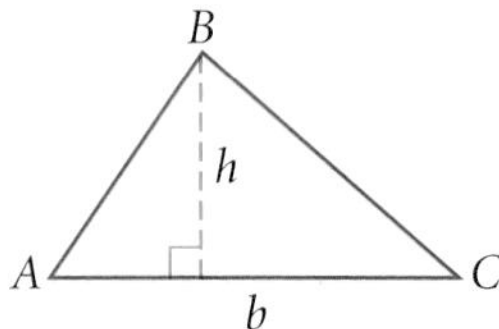 **Triangle** Area: $A = \frac{1}{2}bh$ $m\angle A + m\angle B + m\angle C = 180°$	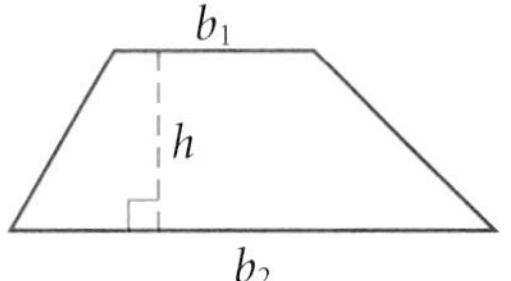 **Trapezoid** Area: $A = \frac{1}{2}h(b_1 + b_2)$	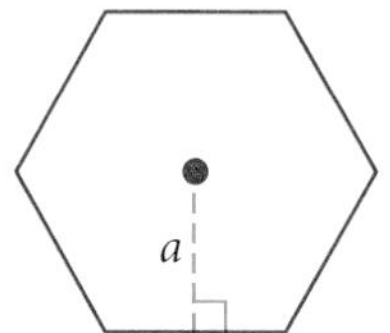 **Regular Polygon** Area: $A = \frac{1}{2}ap$
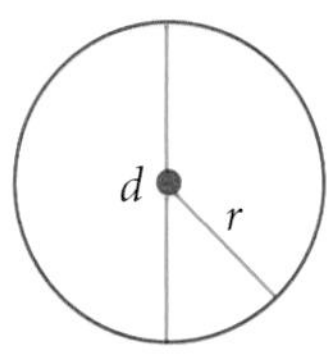 **Circle** Area: $A = \pi r^2$ Circumference: $C = \pi d = 2\pi r$	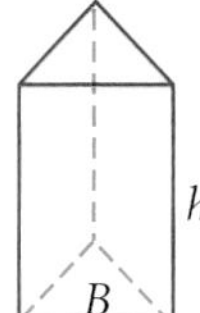 **Right Prism** Volume: $V = Bh$ Lateral Area: $LA = ph$ Surface Area: $SA = ph + 2B$	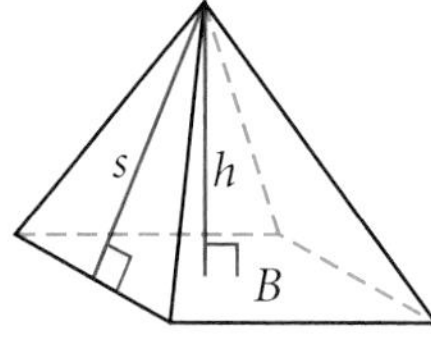 **Regular Pyramid** Volume: $V = \frac{1}{3}Bh$ Lateral Area: $LA = \frac{1}{2}ps$ Surface Area: $SA = \frac{1}{2}ps + B$
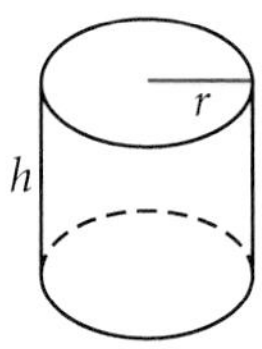 **Right Cylinder** Volume: $V = \pi r^2 h$ Lateral Area: $LA = 2\pi rh$ Surface Area: $SA = 2\pi rh + 2\pi r^2$	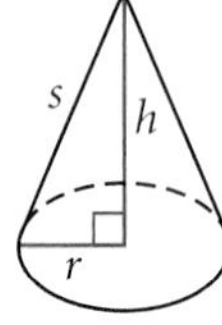 **Right Cone** Volume: $V = \frac{1}{3}\pi r^2 h$ Lateral Area: $LA = \pi rs$ Surface Area: $SA = \pi rs + \pi r^2$	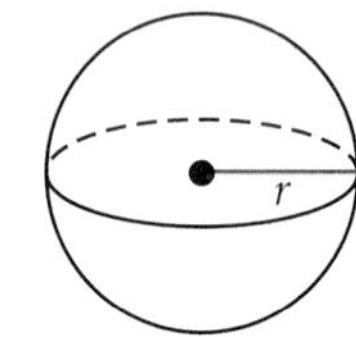 **Sphere** Volume: $V = \frac{4}{3}\pi r^3$ Surface Area: $SA = 4\pi r^2$

POSTULATES AND THEOREMS

POSTULATES

CHAPTER 2

Points-Existence Postulate
Space contains at least four noncoplanar points. Every plane contains at least three noncollinear points. Every line contains at least two points. [p. 116]

Straight-Line Postulate
Two points are contained in one and only one line. (Two points determine a line.) [p. 116]

Plane Postulate
Three noncollinear points are contained in one and only one plane. (Three noncollinear points determine a plane.) [p. 116]

Flat-Plane Postulate
If two points are in a plane, then the line containing the points is in the same plane. [p. 116]

Plane-Intersection Postulate
If two planes intersect, then their intersection is a line. [p. 116]

Ruler Postulate
The points on a line can be paired with the real numbers so that: one of the points has coordinate 0 and another has coordinate 1; for any choice for coordinates 0 and 1 and for each real number x, there is exactly one point on the line with coordinate x; the distance between any two points with coordinates x and y is the absolute value of the difference of their coordinates, $|x - y|$. [p. 120]

Segment-Addition Postulate
Point B is between points A and C if and only if A, B, and C are collinear and $AB + BC = AC$. [p. 121]

Parallel Postulate
Through a given point P not on a line ℓ, exactly one line may be drawn parallel to line ℓ. [p. 143]

CHAPTER 3

Protractor Postulate
Given any line $\overleftrightarrow{AB}$ in a plane with point O between A and B; $\overrightarrow{OA}$, $\overrightarrow{OB}$, and all the rays from point O on one side of line $\overleftrightarrow{AB}$ can be matched one-to-one with the real numbers from 0 through 180 so that: ray $\overrightarrow{OA}$ is matched with 0; ray $\overrightarrow{OB}$ is matched with 180; if ray $\overrightarrow{OR}$ is matched with r and $\overrightarrow{OS}$ is matched with s, then $m\angle ROS = |r - s| = |s - r|$. [p. 192]

Angle-Addition Postulate
If F is in the interior of $\angle EHG$, then $m\angle EHF + m\angle FHG = m\angle EHG$. [p. 194]

Linear-Pair Postulate
The angles in a linear pair are supplementary. [p. 203]

If parallel lines are cut by a transversal, then the alternate interior angles are congruent. [p. 222]

If two lines are cut by a transversal so that a pair of alternate interior angles are congruent, then the lines are parallel. [p. 228]

CHAPTER 4

Side-Side-Side Congruence Postulate (SSS)
If each of the three sides of one triangle are congruent to the sides of another triangle, then the two triangles are congruent. [p. 262]

Side-Angle-Side Congruence Postulate (SAS)
If two sides and the included angle of one triangle are congruent to two sides and the included angle of another triangle, then the two triangles are congruent. [p. 262]

Angle-Side-Angle Congruence Postulate (ASA)

If two angles and the included side of one triangle are congruent to two angles and the included side of another triangle, then the two triangles are congruent. [p. 262]

Side-Angle-Angle Congruence Postulate (SAA)

If two angles and a side opposite one of them in one triangle are congruent to the corresponding parts of another triangle, then the two triangles are congruent. [p. 262]

CHAPTER 5

Area Postulates

For every polygonal region, there is a positive number called the area of the region.

If two polygonal regions are congruent, then they have equal areas. [p. 323]

Area-Addition Postulate

The area of a polygonal region is the sum of the areas of all of its nonoverlapping parts. [p. 323]

The area of a rectangle is the product of its length ℓ and width w. $A = \ell w$ [p. 348]

CHAPTER 7

AA Similarity Postulate

If two angles of one triangle are congruent to two angles of another triangle, then the triangles are similar. [p. 487]

CHAPTER 9

Cavalieri's Principle

Suppose M and N are two solids. If every plane that intersects both M and N at the same height cuts off equal cross-sectional areas on each, then the solids have the same volume. [p. 626]

CHAPTER 12

Riemann's Parallel Postulate

Through a given point P not on a line ℓ, there is *no* line parallel to line ℓ. [p. 777]

THEOREMS AND IMPORTANT RESULTS

CHAPTER 1

The distance between two points on a number line with coordinates *a* and *b* is the absolute value of the difference of their coordinates. [p. 41]

The Distance Formula
The distance between two points on a coordinate plane, whose coordinates are (x_1, y_1) and (x_2, y_2), is $D = \sqrt{(x_1 - x_2)^2 + (y_1 - y_2)^2}$. [p. 41]

The shortest segment from a point not on a line to the line is the perpendicular segment. [p. 48]

Reflections preserve any property of a figure having to do with size. This includes lengths of sides, measures of angles, area, and perimeter. Reflections reverse the orientation of a figure. [p. 74]

CHAPTER 2

If M is the midpoint of $\overline{AB}$, then $AM = \frac{1}{2}AB$. [p. 122]

CHAPTER 3

For vector sums, the following is true: $\overrightarrow{XY} + \overrightarrow{YZ} = \overrightarrow{XZ}$. [p. 167]

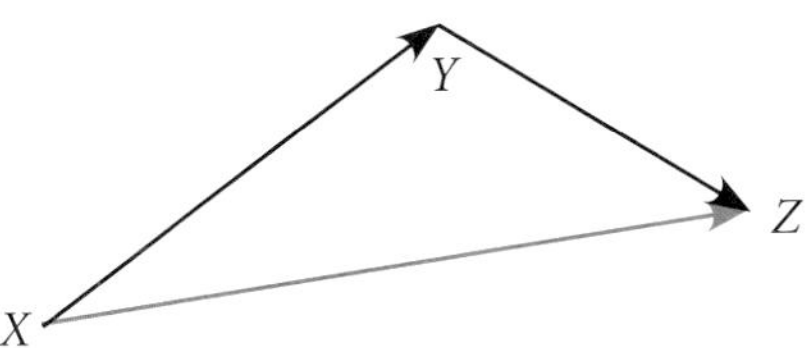

Translations change only the location of a figure. Translations preserve any property that has to do with the size of a figure, including: the lengths of its sides, the measures of its angles, and the area and perimeter of the figure. Translations also preserve the orientation of the figure. [p. 173]

Rotations preserve any property that has to do with the size of a figure, including: the lengths of its sides, the measures of its angles, and the area and perimeter of the figure. Rotations also preserve the orientation of the figure. [p. 186]

Supplements of congruent angles (or of the same angle) are congruent. [p. 204]

Complements of congruent angles (or of the same angle) are congruent. [p. 204]

All right angles are congruent. [p. 205]

Vertical angles are congruent. [p. 209]

Two perpendicular lines form four right angles. [p. 209]

If parallel lines are cut by a transversal, then the corresponding angles are congruent. [p. 222]

If parallel lines are cut by a transversal, then the alternate exterior angles are congruent. [p. 222]

If parallel lines are cut by a transversal, then the same-side interior angles are supplementary. [p. 222]

If two lines are cut by a transversal so that a pair of corresponding angles are congruent, then the lines are parallel. [p. 228]

If two lines are cut by a transversal so that a pair of alternate exterior angles are congruent, then the lines are parallel. [p. 228]

If two lines are cut by a transversal so that a pair of same-side interior angles are supplementary, then the lines are parallel. [p. 228]

CHAPTER 4

Triangle Angle-Sum Theorem
The sum of the measures of the angles of a triangle is 180°. [p. 245]

Exterior Angle Theorem
The measure of an exterior angle of a triangle is equal to the sum of the measures of its remote interior angles. [p. 249]

Exterior Angle Inequality Theorem
The measure of an exterior angle of a triangle is greater than the measure of either of its remote interior angles. [p. 249]

Each angle of an equilateral triangle measures 60°. [p. 249]

The acute angles of a right triangle are complementary. [p. 249]

Properties of Congruence

- Reflexive Property $\overline{AB} \cong \overline{AB}$
- Symmetric Property If $\angle 1 \cong \angle 2$, then $\angle 2 \cong \angle 1$.
- Transitive Property If $\overline{WX} \cong \overline{XY}$ and $\overline{XY} \cong \overline{YZ}$, then $\overline{WX} \cong \overline{YZ}$. [p. 276]

Isosceles Triangle Theorem

If two sides of a triangle are congruent, then the angles opposite those sides are congruent. [p. 287]

Converse of the Isosceles Triangle Theorem

If two angles of a triangle are congruent, then the sides opposite those angles are congruent. [p. 287]

Unique Bisector Theorems

Every segment has a unique midpoint.

Every angle has a unique ray that bisects it. [p. 287]

Leg-Leg Congruence Theorem (LL)

If the legs of a right triangle are congruent to the legs of another right triangle, then the two triangles are congruent. [p. 292]

Hypotenuse-Acute Angle Congruence Theorem (HA)

If the hypotenuse and an acute angle of one right triangle are congruent to the hypotenuse and an acute angle of another right triangle, then the two triangles are congruent. [p. 293]

Leg-Acute Angle Congruence Theorem (LA)

If one leg and one acute angle of a right triangle are congruent to the corresponding leg and acute angle of another right triangle, then the two triangles are congruent. [p. 293]

Hypotenuse-Leg Congruence Theorem (HL)

If the hypotenuse and a leg of one right triangle are congruent to the hypotenuse and a leg of another right triangle, then the two triangles are congruent. [p. 294]

A point is on the perpendicular bisector of a segment if and only if it is equidistant from the endpoints of the segment. [p. 301]

A point is on the angle bisector of an angle if and only if it is equidistant from the sides of the angle. [p. 301]

The centroid of a triangle is two-thirds the distance from each vertex to the midpoint of the opposite side. [p. 307]

CHAPTER 5

The Quadratic Formula

The solutions to the equation $ax^2 + bx + c = 0$ (where $a \neq 0$) are given by $x = \frac{-b \pm \sqrt{b^2 - 4ac}}{2a}$. [p. 333]

The area of a square is the square of its side length s. $A = s^2$ [p. 348]

The area of a triangle is half the product of its base length b and corresponding height h. $A = \frac{1}{2}bh$ [p. 348]

The area of a parallelogram is the product of its base length b and height h. $A = bh$ [p. 348]

The area of a trapezoid is the product of half the sum of the bases, b_1 and b_2, and the height, h. $A = \frac{b_1 + b_2}{2}h$ [p. 354]

Heron's Formula

The area of any triangle with side lengths a, b, and c, is $A = \sqrt{s(s-a)(s-b)(s-c)}$ where s is the semiperimeter (half the perimeter) of the triangle. [p. 355]

Pythagorean Theorem

In a right triangle, the square of the length of the hypotenuse is equal to the sum of the squares of the lengths of the legs. [p. 366]

45°-45°-90° Triangle Theorem

In a 45°-45°-90° triangle, the hypotenuse is $\sqrt{2}$ times as long as either leg. The ratios of the side lengths can be written ℓ-ℓ-$\ell\sqrt{2}$. [p. 372]

30°-60°-90° Triangle Theorem

In a 30°-60°-90° triangle, the hypotenuse is twice as long as the shorter leg (the leg opposite the 30° angle), and the longer leg (opposite the 60° angle) is

$\sqrt{3}$ times as long as the shorter leg. The ratios of the side lengths can be written ℓ-$\ell\sqrt{3}$-2ℓ. [p. 373]

Equation of a Circle

The circle with radius r and center (0, 0) has the equation $x^2 + y^2 = r^2$. [p. 377]

Converse of the Pythagorean Theorem

If the sum of the squares of the lengths of two sides of a triangle equals the square of the length of the third side, then the triangle is a right triangle and the longest side is the hypotenuse. [p. 381]

Pythagorean Inequality Theorems

If the sum of the squares of the lengths of two sides of a triangle is greater than the square of the length of the third side, then the triangle is acute.

If the sum of the squares of the lengths of two sides of a triangle is less than the square of the length of the third side, then the triangle is obtuse. [p. 382]

CHAPTER 6

Angle-Sum Theorem for Quadrilaterals

The sum of the measures of the interior angles of a convex quadrilateral is 360°. [p. 399]

Angle-Sum Theorem for Polygons

The sum of the measures of the interior angles of a convex polygon with n sides is given by $S = (n - 2)180°$. [p. 405]

Exterior Angle Theorem for Polygons

The sum of the measures of the exterior angles of a convex polygon (one at each vertex) is 360°. [p. 405]

Euler's Formula

For any polyhedron, the relationship between the number of faces (F), vertices (V), and edges (E) is $F + V - E = 2$. [p. 411]

The opposite angles of a parallelogram are congruent. [p. 420]

The opposite sides of a parallelogram are congruent. [p. 420]

The consecutive angles of a parallelogram are supplementary. [p. 420]

The diagonals of a parallelogram bisect each other. [p. 420]

If both pairs of opposite angles of a quadrilateral are congruent, then the quadrilateral is a parallelogram. [p. 425]

If both pairs of opposite sides of a quadrilateral are congruent, then the quadrilateral is a parallelogram. [p. 425]

If the consecutive angles of a quadrilateral are supplementary, then the quadrilateral is a parallelogram. [p. 425]

If the diagonals of a quadrilateral bisect each other, then the quadrilateral is a parallelogram. [p. 425]

Theorems About Diagonals of Special Parallelograms

A parallelogram is a rhombus if and only if its diagonals are perpendicular.

A parallelogram is a rectangle if and only if its diagonals are congruent.

A parallelogram is a square if and only if its diagonals are both perpendicular and congruent. [p. 429]

Theorems About Regular Polygons

The area of a regular polygon is one-half the product of its perimeter and its apothem. $A = \frac{1}{2}ap$

Each angle of a regular n-gon measures $\frac{(n - 2)180°}{n}$.

Each exterior angle of a regular n-gon measures $\frac{360°}{n}$. [p. 444]

CHAPTER 7

The ratio of the perimeters of two similar polygons is equal to their similarity ratio. [p. 475]

The ratio of the areas of two similar polygons is equal to the square of their similarity ratio. [p. 475]

The Golden Ratio

In a golden rectangle, the ratio of the length ℓ to the width w is the golden ratio $\frac{1 + \sqrt{5}}{2}$ ($\approx$1.618). [p. 480]

SAS Similarity Theorem
If an angle of one triangle is congruent to an angle of another triangle and the lengths of the sides that include the angles are proportional, then the triangles are similar. [p. 492]

SSS Similarity Theorem
If the lengths of three sides of one triangle are proportional to the lengths of three sides of another triangle, then the triangles are similar. [p. 494]

Dilations change the size of a figure (unless $k = 1$). Dilations preserve: the measures of the angles in a figure, the orientation of a figure, the shape of a figure. [p. 498]

Midsegment Theorem for Triangles
A segment whose endpoints are the midpoints of two sides of a triangle is parallel to the third side and half its length. [p. 502]

Side-Splitting Theorem
If a line parallel to a side of a triangle intersects the other two sides, then it divides those sides proportionally. [p. 506]

CHAPTER 8

Theorems About Tangents to a Circle
If a line is tangent to a circle, then it is perpendicular to a radius at the point of tangency.

If a line coplanar to a circle is perpendicular to a radius of a circle at a point on the circle, then the line is tangent to the circle.

Two tangent segments to a circle from the same exterior point are congruent. [p. 546]

The circumference of a circle is the product of π and its diameter, d. $C = \pi d$ [p. 552]

The circumference of a circle is twice the product of π and its radius, r. $C = 2\pi r$ [p. 552]

The area of a circle is the product of π and the square of its radius, r. $A = \pi r^2$ [p. 557]

Circle Proportions
In $\odot Y$, with central angle $\angle XYZ$, all of the following ratios are equal. $\frac{m\angle XYZ}{360°} = \frac{m\widehat{XZ}}{360°} = \frac{\text{length of } \widehat{XZ}}{\text{circumference of } \odot Y} = \frac{\text{area of sector } XYZ}{\text{area of } \odot Y}$ [p. 572]

The perpendicular bisector of a chord contains the center of the circle. [p. 576]

If a radius of a circle bisects a chord of the circle that is not a diameter, then it is perpendicular to the chord. [p. 576]

If a radius of a circle is perpendicular to a chord of the circle, then it bisects the chord. [p. 576]

In a circle (or in congruent circles), minor arcs are congruent if and only if they have congruent chords. [p. 577]

Two chords of a circle are congruent if and only if they are equidistant from the center. [p. 582]

Inscribed Angle Theorem
The measure of an inscribed angle is half the measure of its intercepted arc. [p. 585]

If two inscribed angles intercept the same arc, then they are congruent. [p. 585]

An inscribed angle that intercepts a semicircle is a right angle. [p. 585]

Tangent-Secant Angle Theorem
The measure of a tangent-secant angle is one-half the difference of the measures of its two intercepted arcs. [p. 590]

Tangent-Tangent Angle Theorem
The measure of a tangent-tangent angle is one-half the difference of the measures of its two intercepted arcs. [p. 590]

Secant-Secant Angle Theorem
The measure of a secant-secant angle is one-half the difference of the measures of its two intercepted arcs. [p. 592]

CHAPTER 9

The lateral area of a right prism is the product of the perimeter of its base and the height of the prism. $LA = ph$ [p. 606]

The surface area of a right prism is the sum of its lateral area and the areas of its bases. $SA = LA + 2B = ph + 2B$ [p. 606]

The lateral area of a regular pyramid is one-half the product of the perimeter of its base and the slant height of the pyramid. $LA = \frac{1}{2}ps$ [p. 611]

The surface area of a regular pyramid is the sum of its lateral area and the area of its base. $SA = LA + B = \frac{1}{2}ps + B$ [p. 611]

Theorems About Cylinders

The lateral area of a right cylinder is the product of the circumference of its base and the height of the cylinder. $LA = 2\pi rh$

The surface area of a right cylinder is the sum of its lateral area and the areas of its bases. $SA = LA + 2B = 2\pi rh + 2\pi r^2$ [p. 616]

Theorems About Cones

The lateral area of a right cone is one-half the product of the circumference of its base and the slant height of the cone. $LA = \frac{1}{2}2\pi rs = \pi rs$

The surface area of a right cone is the sum of its lateral area and the area of its base. $SA = LA + B = \pi rs + \pi r^2$ [p. 616]

The volume of a right rectangular prism is the product of its length, width, and height. $V = \ell wh$ [p. 627]

The volume of any prism is the product of the area of its base and its height. $V = Bh$ [p. 627]

The volume of a pyramid is one-third the product of its base area and its height. $V = \frac{1}{3}Bh$ [p. 632]

The volume of a cylinder is the product of its base area and its height. $V = Bh = \pi r^2 h$ [p. 636]

The volume of a cone is one-third the product of its base area and its height. $V = \frac{1}{3}Bh = \frac{1}{3}\pi r^2 h$ [p. 636]

The surface area of a sphere is 4π times the square of its radius. $SA = 4\pi r^2$ [p. 640]

The volume of a sphere is four-thirds the product of π and the cube of its radius. $V = \frac{4}{3}\pi r^3$ [p. 640]

The ratio of the surface areas of two similar solids is the square of their similarity ratio. [p. 650]

The ratio of the volumes of two similar solids is the cube of their similarity ratio. [p. 654]

CHAPTER 10

Translations, reflections, and rotations are isometries. [p. 669]

CHAPTER 11

If two sides of a triangle have unequal lengths, then the measure of the angle opposite the longer side is greater than the measure of the angle opposite the shorter side. [p. 716]

If two angles of a triangle have unequal measures, then the side opposite the larger angle is longer than the side opposite the smaller angle. [p. 716]

Triangle Inequality Theorem

The sum of the lengths of any two sides of a triangle is greater than the length of the third side. [p. 721]

CHAPTER 12

In Riemannian geometry, the sum of the measures of the angles in a triangle is greater than 180°. [p. 779]

In Riemannian geometry, if a circle has radius *r*, its circumference is less than $2\pi r$ and its area is less than πr^2. [p. 779]

In Riemannian geometry, any two coplanar lines intersect. [p. 779]

GLOSSARY

acute angle

An angle whose measure is less than 90°. [p. 156]

acute triangle

A triangle with three acute angles. [p. 244]

adjacent interior angle

∠1 is the adjacent interior angle to exterior ∠4. [p. 248]

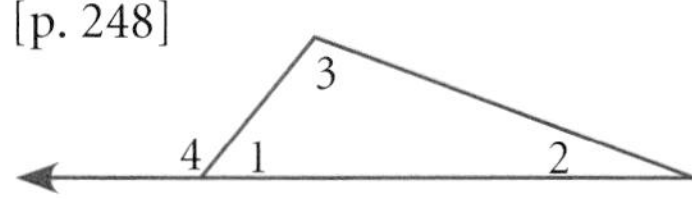

alternate exterior angles

When a transversal t cuts lines p and q as shown, the pairs of alternate exterior angles are: ∠1 and ∠7, ∠2 and ∠8. [p. 216]

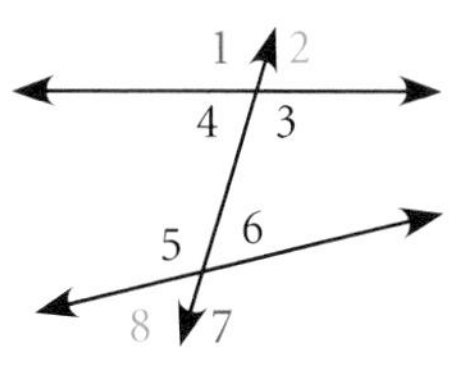

alternate interior angles

When a transversal t cuts lines p and q as shown, the pairs of alternate interior angles are: ∠4 and ∠6, ∠3 and ∠5. [p. 216]

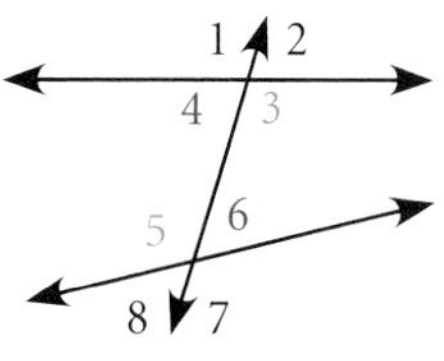

altitude

In a triangle: the perpendicular segment from a vertex to the line containing the opposite side; in a prism or cylinder: a segment (joining the planes of the bases) that is perpendicular to them; in a pyramid or cone: the perpendicular segment from the vertex to the base. [p. 305, 604, 610, 614, 615]

angle

Two rays (that are not collinear) with a common endpoint. [p. 45]

angle bisector

$\overrightarrow{LM}$ is the angle bisector of $\angle NLP$ if and only if M is in the interior of $\angle NLP$ and $\angle NLM \cong \angle MLP$. [p. 208]

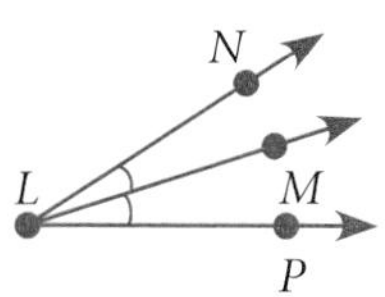

angle of depression

The angle formed by a horizontal line and a line of sight downward from horizontal. The vertex is the eye of the viewer. [p. 518]

angle of elevation

The angle formed by a horizontal line and a line of sight upward from horizontal. The vertex is the eye of the viewer. [p. 518]

angle of rotation

The measure, in degrees, of how far a point, other than the center of rotation, is turned by a rotation. [p. 180]

apothem of a regular polygon

The perpendicular segment (or length of the segment) from the center of the polygon to a side. [p. 442]

arc

Two points and a continuous part of a circle between the points. [p. 565]

area

The number of square units contained in a plane region. [p. 322]

auxiliary line

A line (or part of a line) added to a figure. [p. 288]

axis of a cone

The segment from the vertex to the center of the base. [p. 615]

axis of a cylinder

The segment that joins the centers of the bases. [p. 614]

base angle
In an isosceles triangle, an angle formed by the base and another side. [p. 244]

base of an isosceles triangle
The side opposite the vertex angle. [p. 244]

bases of a prism
Two congruent polygonal faces that lie in parallel planes, whose corresponding vertices are connected by the lateral edges of the prism. [p. 604]

bases of a trapezoid
The parallel sides of the trapezoid. [p. 352]

bearing
Direction given as a three-digit number, representing the number of degrees in a clockwise rotation from due north. [p. 161]

biconditional
A statement that combines a conditional and its converse, when both are true, by using the connector phrase "if and only if." [p. 110]

binomial
A polynomial with two terms. [p. 326]

bisect
Cut into two congruent halves. [p. 68]

center of a circle
The point equidistant from all points of the circle. [p. 540]

center of a regular polygon
The point of intersection of the perpendicular bisectors of the sides. [p. 442]

center of dilation
The unique point which is mapped to itself by a dilation with a nonzero scale factor. [p. 497]

center of rotation
The point about which a rotation turns a set of points. [p. 180]

central angle
An angle whose vertex is the center of a circle is a central angle of the circle. [p. 565]

centroid
Center of balance (or center of gravity). In a triangle, the point of concurrency of the medians. [p. 306]

chord
A line segment that joins two points on a circle. [p. 575]

circle
The locus of points in a plane that are equidistant from a given point. [p. 540]

circumference
The distance around a circle. [p. 189]

circumscribed circle
A circle on which every vertex of a polygon lies. [p. 541]

circumscribed polygon
A polygon whose sides are each tangent to another figure. [p. 541]

collinear
On the same line. [p. 21]

complementary angles
A pair of angles whose measures add up to 90°. [p. 201]

composition of transformations
Two or more transformations performed on a figure, one after another. [p. 673]

concave polygon
A polygon in which a diagonal (excluding the endpoints) lies in the exterior of the polygon. [p. 398]

concentric circles
Two coplanar circles with the same center. [p. 540]

conclusion
The *then* part of a conditional statement. [p. 88]

concurrent lines
Three or more coplanar lines that intersect in the same point. [p. 306]

conditional statement
A statement that can be written in if-then form. [p. 88]

cone
A space figure with a vertex and a circular base. [p. 615]

congruence correspondence
A way of pairing the vertices of two geometric figures so that all pairs of corresponding parts are congruent. [p. 257]

congruent
Having the same shape and size. [p. 52]

congruent angles
Angles with the same measure. [p. 52]

congruent arcs
Arcs in the same circle (or in congruent circles) that have the same measure. [p. 566]

contrapositive
The resulting statement when the hypothesis and conclusion of a conditional are both negated, then interchanged. [p. 94]

converse
The resulting statement when the hypothesis and conclusion of a conditional are interchanged. [p. 94]

convex polygon
A polygon in which each diagonal (except its endpoints) is in the interior of the polygon. [p. 402]

coordinate plane
The plane determined by two axes, typically the x-axis and the y-axis. [p. 11]

coplanar points
Points that lie in the same plane. [p. 109]

correspondence
A way of pairing the vertices of two geometric figures. [p. 257]

corresponding angles
When a transversal t cuts lines p and q as shown, the pairs of corresponding angles are: $\angle 1$ and $\angle 5$, $\angle 2$ and $\angle 6$, $\angle 3$ and $\angle 7$, $\angle 4$ and $\angle 8$. [p. 216]

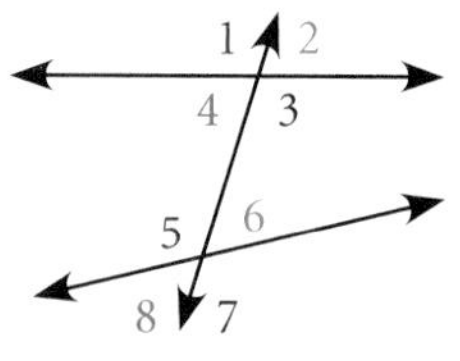

cosine of $\angle A$
For acute $\angle A$ in a right triangle, the ratio of the length of the adjacent leg to the length of the hypotenuse. [p. 512]

counterexample
An example that shows a statement to be false. [p. 25]

cross section
The figure formed by the intersection of a solid and a plane. [p. 400]

cube
A hexahedron with square faces. [p. 8]

cylinder
A space figure having congruent circular bases in a pair of parallel planes. [p. 614]

deductive reasoning
A process where conclusions are drawn from given information by using rules of logic. [p. 31]

degree
A unit used to measure the size of an angle. [p. 46]

diagonal of a polygon
A line segment whose endpoints are any two nonconsecutive vertices of the polygon. [p. 402]

diameter of a circle
A segment, or the length of a segment, that contains the center of the circle and has endpoints on the circle. [p. 540]

dilation

A transformation of a plane that, for a scale factor $k > 0$, maps one point C, the center of dilation, to itself and maps every other point P to a point P' on $\overrightarrow{CP}$ so that $CP' = k(CP)$. [p. 497]

direction of a vector

The degrees of counterclockwise rotation from horizontal of the vector about its origin. [p. 166]

distance from a point to a line

The length of the perpendicular segment from the point to the line. [p. 68]

edge of a polyhedron

A segment that is the intersection of two faces of the polyhedron. [p. 410]

endpoint of a vector

Point B is the endpoint of $\overrightarrow{AB}$. [p. 165]

equal vectors

Vectors with the same direction and length. [p. 166]

equiangular triangle

A triangle whose angles all have the same measure. [p. 244]

equidistant

Having the same distance from a common object. [p. 68]

equilateral triangle

A triangle with three congruent sides. [p. 243]

exterior angle

An angle that forms a linear pair with an interior angle of a polygon. $\angle 4$ is an exterior angle. [p. 247]

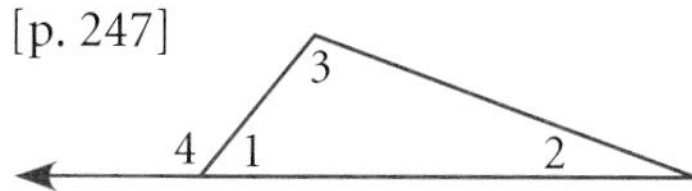

face of a polyhedron

One of the polygons that forms the polyhedron. [p. 410]

fractal

A pattern that is self-similar. [p. 750]

frieze pattern

Repeated translations of a pattern along a line. [p. 688]

function

A relationship between two quantities where the value of one quantity is uniquely determined by the value of the other quantity. [p. 679]

geometric mean

x is the geometric mean between a and b if $\frac{a}{x} = \frac{x}{b}$ and a, b, and x are positive. [p. 489]

geometric probability

The probability of an event as determined by comparing the areas (or perimeters, angle measures, etc.) of the successful regions to the total area of the figure. [p. 338]

glide reflection

A pattern defined by repeating a translation followed by a reflection. [p. 174]

glide-reflection symmetry

The property that a figure coincides with itself after undergoing a translation and a reflection. [p. 688]

golden ratio

The ratio, $\frac{1 + \sqrt{5}}{2}$ ($\approx$1.618), of the length to the width of a golden rectangle. [p. 480]

golden rectangle

Rectangle $ACDF$ is a golden rectangle if and only if, when $ABEF$ is a square, rectangle $CDEB$ is similar to rectangle $ACDF$. [p. 478]

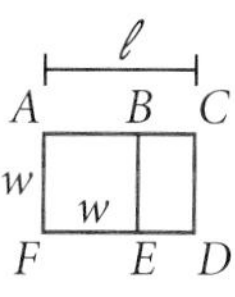

great circle

A circle on a sphere whose center is the center of the sphere. [p. 546]

height

The length of an altitude. [p. 604]

hexagon

A polygon with six sides. [p. 403]

hexahedron
A polyhedron with six faces. [p. 410]

hypotenuse
The side of a right triangle that is opposite the right angle. [p. 244]

hypothesis
The *if* part of a conditional statement. [p. 88]

image
The figure resulting from a transformation. [p. 67]

indirect reasoning
Proving that a statement is true by proving that it cannot be false. [p. 710]

inductive reasoning
Making a conjecture by looking at examples and recognizing a pattern. [p. 22]

inscribed angle
An angle with its vertex on a circle and sides that contain chords of the circle. [p. 584]

inscribed circle
A circle that is tangent to every side of a polygon is inscribed in the polygon. [p. 541]

inscribed polygon
A polygon whose vertices all lie on another figure, the figure in which the polygon is inscribed. [p. 541]

intersection
The set of points that two geometric figures have in common. [p. 20]

inverse
The resulting statement when the hypothesis and conclusion of a conditional are both negated. [p. 94]

isometry
A transformation that preserves distance. [p. 668]

isosceles trapezoid
A trapezoid with congruent legs. [p. 421]

isosceles triangle
A triangle with at least two congruent sides. [p. 243]

kite
A quadrilateral with two distinct pairs of adjacent, congruent sides. [p. 355]

lateral area
The sum of the areas of the lateral faces. [p. 605]

lateral edge of a pyramid
A segment joining the vertex of the pyramid and any vertex of its base. [p. 610]

lateral face
For a prism: one of the parallelogram-shaped faces that connect the bases; for a pyramid: a triangular face whose vertices are the vertex of the pyramid and any two consecutive vertices of its base. [p. 604, 610]

legs of a right triangle
The sides which include the right angle. [p. 244]

legs of a trapezoid
The nonparallel sides of the trapezoid. [p. 352]

legs of an isosceles triangle
A pair of congruent sides. [p. 244]

length of a segment
The distance between the coordinates of its endpoints on a number line. [p. 40]

length of a vector
Distance between the origin and endpoint of the vector. [p. 166]

line of reflection
The line over which a pre-image is reflected to produce its image. [p. 67]

line of symmetry
A line that divides a figure into two mirror-image halves. [p. 62]

line segment

A part of a line consisting of two endpoints and all the points between these points. [p. 20]

line symmetry

The property that a line separates a figure into two mirror-image halves. [p. 62]

linear pair

Two angles, $\angle ABD$ and $\angle DBC$, form a linear pair if and only if A, B, and C are collinear and D is not on $\overleftrightarrow{AC}$. [p. 202]

locus

The set of all the points that satisfy a given condition. [p. 299]

major arc

An arc whose measure is greater than 180°. [p. 565]

mathematical model

A representation of something in the real world, using geometry, algebra, or other mathematical tools. [p. 7]

median of a triangle

A segment whose endpoints are a vertex and the midpoint of the opposite side. [p. 305]

midpoint

Point M is the midpoint of $\overline{AB}$ if and only if it divides $\overline{AB}$ into two congruent segments, $\overline{AM}$ and $\overline{MB}$. [p. 110]

midsegment of a trapezoid

The segment that joins the midpoints of the legs. [p. 438]

midsegment of a triangle

A segment whose endpoints are the midpoints of two of its sides. [p. 501]

minor arc

An arc whose measure is less than 180°. [p. 565]

monomial

A polynomial with one term. [p. 326]

net

A pattern that can be cut out and folded up into a three-dimensional figure. [p. 7]

non-Euclidean geometry

A geometry in which the Parallel Postulate is not true. [p. 777]

oblique

A prism, pyramid, cylinder, or cone that is not a right prism, pyramid, cylinder, or cone. [p. 604, 610, 614, 615]

obtuse angle

An angle whose measure is greater than 90° and less than 180°. [p. 156]

obtuse triangle

A triangle with one obtuse angle. [p. 244]

octagon

A polygon with eight sides. [p. 403]

opposite rays

If point M is between X and Y on line $\overleftrightarrow{XY}$, the rays $\overrightarrow{MX}$ and $\overrightarrow{MY}$ are opposite rays. [p. 157]

opposite vectors

Vectors with the same length and opposite directions. [p. 169]

ordered pair

A pair of numbers denoting the location of a point on the coordinate plane. [p. 11]

origin

The point of intersection of the axes of the coordinate plane, having coordinates (0, 0). [p. 11]

origin of a vector

Point A is the origin of $\overrightarrow{AB}$. [p. 165]

orthogonal or orthographic view
A view of the top, front, back, left side, or right side of an object. [p. 135]

parallel lines
Coplanar lines that do not intersect. [p. 141]

parallelogram
A quadrilateral with two pairs of parallel sides. [p. 346]

pentagon
A polygon with five sides. [p. 403]

perimeter
The distance around a figure. [p. 323]

perpendicular bisector
A line, segment, or ray that is perpendicular to a segment and divides that segment into two congruent segments. [p. 68]

perpendicular lines
Two lines that intersect at right angles. [p. 47]

pi (π)
The ratio of the circumference of a circle to its diameter. [p. 551]

Platonic solid
Any one of the five known convex regular polyhedrons. [p. 448]

point of concurrency
The point of intersection of concurrent lines. [p. 306]

point symmetry
The property that a figure will coincide with itself after some rotation of 180°. [p. 181]

polygon
A plane figure whose sides are three or more coplanar segments that intersect only at their endpoints (the vertices). Consecutive sides cannot be collinear, and no more than two sides can meet at any one vertex. [p. 402]

polygonal region
A polygon and its interior. [p. 322]

polyhedron
A solid whose faces are polygons. [p. 410]

polynomial
An algebraic expression with more than one term. [p. 326]

postulate
A statement that is assumed to be true without proof. [p. 33]

pre-image
The figure to which a transformation is applied, producing its image. [p. 67]

prism
A polyhedron with two congruent faces that lie in parallel planes, whose other faces are parallelograms formed by joining corresponding vertices of the bases. [p. 604]

proportion
An equation stating that two ratios are equal. [p. 468]

pyramid
A polyhedron formed by lateral edges connecting each vertex of a polygonal base with a point, the vertex, not in the plane of the base. [p. 610]

Pythagorean triple
Any set of three integers a, b, and c that satisfy $a^2 + b^2 = c^2$. [p. 367]

quadratic equation
An equation that can be put into the form $ax^2 + bx + c = 0$, where a, b, and c are real numbers and $a \neq 0$. [p. 332]

quadrilateral
A polygon with four sides. [p. 346]

radius of a circle
A segment, or the length of a segment, from the center to any point on the circle. [p. 540]

radius of a regular polygon
The segment, or length of the segment, from a vertex to the center of the polygon. [p. 442]

radius of a sphere
A segment, or the length of a segment, from the center to any point on the sphere. [p. 546]

ray
A part of a line consisting of one point, and all the points on one side of the line from that point. [p. 45]

rectangle
A quadrilateral with four right angles. [p. 346]

rectangular prism
A prism with rectangular bases. [p. 604]

reflection
A transformation of a figure by flipping the figure over a line. [p. 67]

regular polygon
A polygon that is equilateral and equiangular. [p. 442]

regular polyhedron
A polyhedron with congruent edges and faces, faces that are regular polygons, and an equal number of edges meeting at each vertex. [p. 448]

regular pyramid
A pyramid whose base is a regular polygon and whose lateral edges are congruent. [p. 610]

remote interior angle
$\angle 2$ and $\angle 3$ are remote interior angles to exterior $\angle 4$. [p. 247]

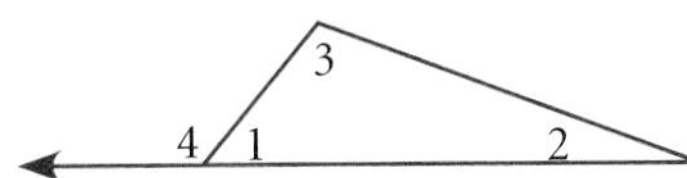

rhombus
A quadrilateral with four congruent sides. [p. 352]

right angle
An angle that measures 90°. [p. 47]

right prism, cylinder, or cone
A prism whose lateral edges are perpendicular to its bases. A cylinder or cone whose axis is perpendicular to its base(s). [p. 604, 614]

right triangle
A triangle with one right angle. [p. 244]

rotation
A transformation that turns a set of points about one point, the center of rotation. [p. 180]

rotational symmetry
The property that a figure can be rotated onto itself with an angle of rotation between 0° and 360°. [p. 181]

same-side interior angles
When a transversal t cuts lines p and q as shown, the pairs of same-side interior angles are: $\angle 3$ and $\angle 6$, $\angle 4$ and $\angle 5$. [p. 216]

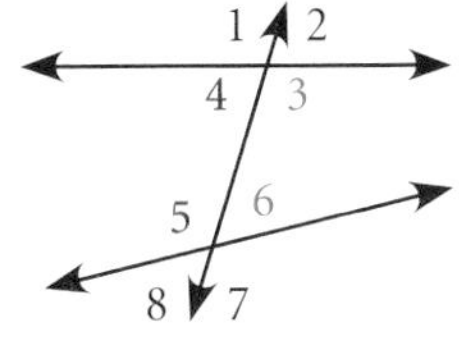

scale factor
A factor by which a figure is enlarged or reduced. [p. 462]

scalene triangle
A triangle with no two congruent sides. [p. 243]

scatter plot
A graph showing a set of points based on paired data. [p. 12]

secant line
A line that intersects a circle or sphere in two points. [p. 544]

secant-secant angle
If each side of an angle is a secant ray to a circle, then the angle is a secant-secant angle of the circle. [p. 592]

sector
A region bounded by two radii and their intercepted arc on a circle. [p. 570]

segment of a circle
The region bounded by an arc of the circle and the segment joining its endpoints. [p. 573]

self-similar
The property that a figure looks the same when viewed at any level of magnification. [p. 750]

sides of an angle
The two rays that form the angle. [p. 45]

similar
The property that figures have the same shape but not necessarily the same size. [p. 462]

similarity correspondence
A way of pairing the vertices of two geometric figures so that all pairs of corresponding angles are congruent and all pairs of corresponding lengths are proportional. [p. 468]

similarity ratio
The ratio of the lengths of two corresponding sides of similar figures. [p. 463]

sine of $\angle A$
For acute $\angle A$ in a right triangle, the ratio of the length of the opposite leg to the length of the hypotenuse. [p. 512]

skew lines
Noncoplanar lines. [p. 142]

slant height of a cone
The length of any segment from the vertex to the circle bounding the base. [p. 616]

slant height of a regular pyramid
The height of any lateral face. [p. 610]

slope
The ratio of the change in value of the vertical coordinates to the corresponding change in the horizontal coordinates, as measured from one point of a line to another. [p. 57]

space
The set of all points. [p. 116]

sphere
The locus of points in space a given distance from a point, the center of the sphere. [p. 546]

square
A quadrilateral with four right angles and four congruent sides. [p. 346]

supplementary angles
A pair of angles whose measures add up to 180°. [p. 201]

surface area of a prism
The total area of all of its faces, including the bases. [p. 605]

symmetry
The property that a figure coincides with itself after some transformation. [p. 62]

tangent line
A line that intersects a circle or sphere at exactly one point is tangent to the circle or sphere. [p. 544, 546]

tangent of $\angle A$
For acute $\angle A$ in a right triangle, the ratio of the length of the opposite leg to the length of the adjacent leg. [p. 512]

tangent plane
A plane that contains exactly one point of a sphere is tangent to the sphere. [p. 546]

tangent-secant angle
If one side of an angle is tangent to a circle and its other side is a secant ray of the circle, then the angle is a tangent-secant angle of the circle. [p. 589]

tangent-tangent angle
If each side of an angle is tangent to a circle, then the angle is a tangent-tangent angle of the circle. [p. 589]

tessellation
A repeating pattern of figures that completely covers a plane region without gaps or overlaps. [p. 242]

tetrahedron
A polyhedron with four faces. [p. 410]

translation
A transformation that moves all the points in a plane a fixed distance in a given direction. [p. 171]

translation symmetry
The property that a figure coincides with itself after a translation. [p. 689]

translation vector
A vector whose direction is that of a given translation and whose length is the distance of the translation. [p. 171]

transversal
A line that intersects two coplanar lines in two different points. [p. 216]

trapezoid
A quadrilateral with exactly one pair of parallel sides. [p. 352]

triangle
A figure formed by three line segments that connect three noncollinear points. [p. 242]

trinomial
A polynomial with three terms. [p. 326]

vector
Vector $\overrightarrow{AB}$ is a model of the straight-line path from point A to point B. [p. 165]

vector sum
If a set of vectors is shown as a sequence where the origin of each vector (except the initial one) coincides with the endpoint of the previous vector, then their sum is the vector with origin at the origin of the initial vector and endpoint at the endpoint of the last vector. [p. 167]

vertex of a polygon
A point at which two sides intersect. [p. 402]

vertex of a polyhedron
A point which is the intersection of three or more faces of the polyhedron. [p. 410]

vertex of a pyramid
The point, not in the plane of the base, which is a vertex of each of the lateral faces. [p. 610]

vertex of an angle
The common endpoint of the rays forming the angle. [p. 45]

vertex of an isosceles triangle
The angle included by two congruent sides. [p. 244]

vertical angles
Two angles whose sides form two pairs of opposite rays. [p. 207]

volume
The number of cubic units contained in a solid. [p. 624]

wallpaper pattern
A plane pattern with translation symmetry along more than one line. [p. 694]

***x*-axis**
Typically the horizontal axis on a coordinate plane. [p. 11]

***x*-coordinate**
The first number of an ordered pair denoting a point on the coordinate plane, denoting the distance left or right from the vertical axis. [p. 11]

***y*-axis**
Typically the vertical axis on a coordinate plane. [p. 11]

***y*-coordinate**
The second number of an ordered pair denoting a point on the coordinate plane, denoting the distance up or down from the horizontal axis. [p. 11]

SELECTED ANSWERS

CHAPTER 1

1-1 Part A Exercises

1. a. 4 triangles, 1 square
b. Square
c. Triangles

3. 8 vertices, 12 edges, 6 faces
5. a. 6, 5, 4 **b.** 7
c. Possible answer:

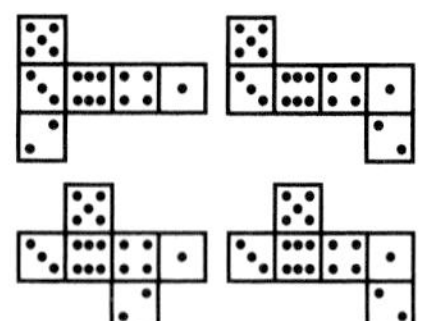

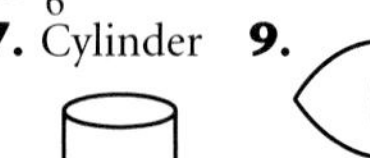

d. $\frac{1}{6}$
7. Cylinder **9.**

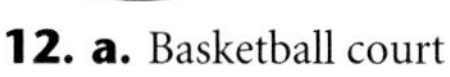

12. a. Basketball court
b. Tomato
15.

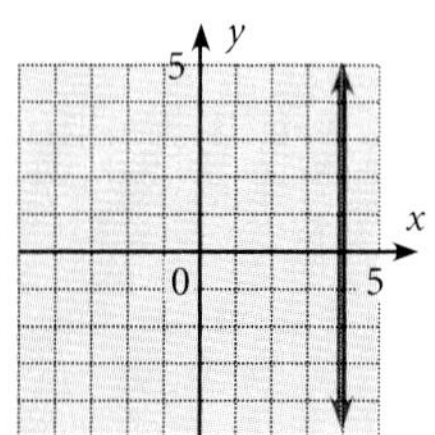

The line is parallel to the y-axis and each point on the line has x-coordinate equal to 4.

17.

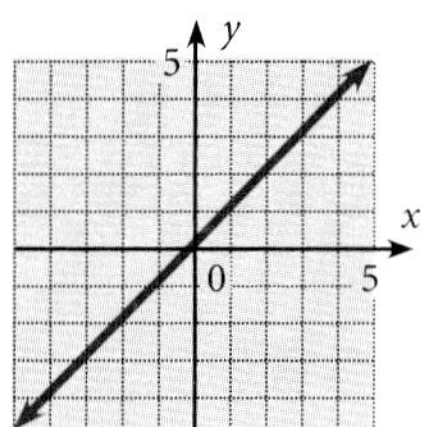

The line splits the angle between the x-axis and y-axis.

19. Possible answer:

21.

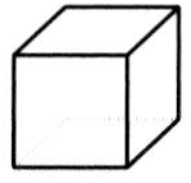

23.

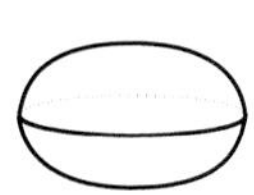

25. 1; 6; 12; 8; 0; 0; 0

1-1 Part B Try It

a–d.

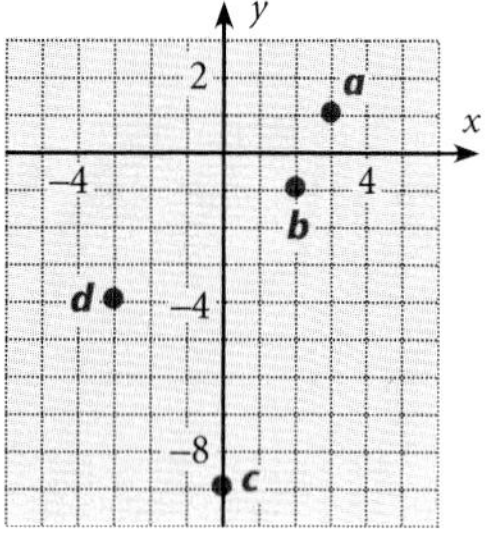

e. Topeka **f.** I: Boston, MA; II: Seattle, WA; III: Phoenix, AZ; IV: Little Rock, AK **g.** x-axis: San Jose; y-axis: Omaha **h.** (1) $(-9, 6)$, (2) $(8, 1)$, (3) $\left(\frac{5}{2}, -2\right)$

1-1 Part B Exercises

1–7.

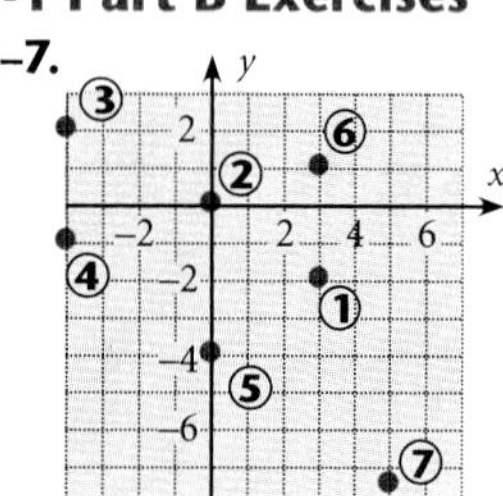

9. $(2, 3)$ **11.** $(-4, -2)$
13.

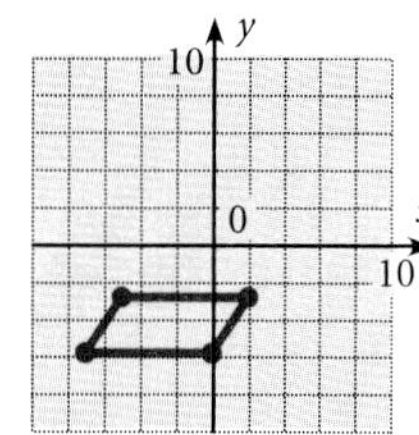

15. Scatter plot **19.** $3y$
21. $3r^2 - 14r$ **23.** 26
25. -216

26–33.

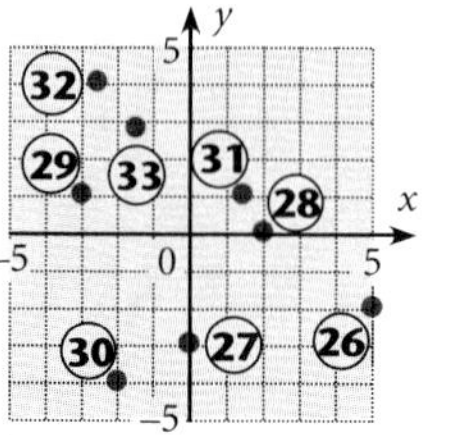

35. $(-2, -1)$ **37.** $(2, 0)$
39. $(0, -3)$
40–41.

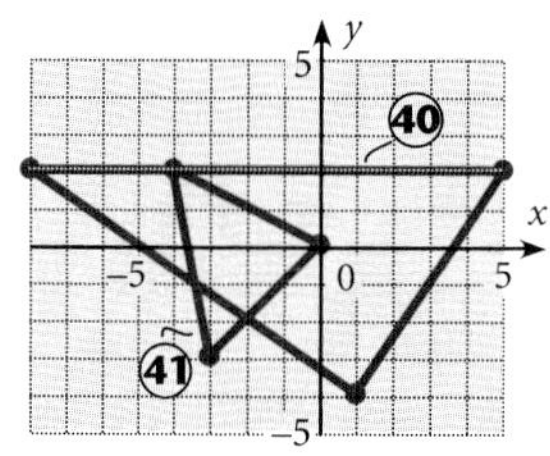

43. a. C **b.** P

1-1 Part C Self-Assessment

2. a, b, e, f
3.

4. a. An object similar to a tuning fork **b.** The left side shows 3 prongs, the right side 2. **5.** $11x$ **6.** $20 - 21z$ **7.** -23 **8.** 49 **9.** (c) **10.** approximately 1.6. **11.** Possible answer: Models can be tested under controlled conditions, modeling does not place astronauts at risk, and it is easier to change a model than to modify a spacecraft. **12. a.** Approximately 45 inches and 64 inches, respectively. **b.** About 82 inches (nearly 7 feet tall). **13.** It appears that length and wins are negatively related (longer named cities have fewer wins). This result is probably just an interesting coincidence.

1-2 Part A Try It

a–b. Possible answer:

X M Y
N

c. $\overline{XM}$, $\overline{MY}$, $\overline{XY}$

1-2 Part A Exercises

1. a-d.

Triangles	1	2	3	4
Perimeter	3	4	5	6

e. $p = n + 2$ **f.** 102 **3.** $\frac{31}{32}$
5. Lines: $\overleftrightarrow{AB}$, (or $\overleftrightarrow{AC}$, $\overleftrightarrow{AD}$, $\overleftrightarrow{BC}$, $\overleftrightarrow{BD}$, or $\overleftrightarrow{CD}$), and $\overleftrightarrow{EC}$ (or $\overleftrightarrow{EF}$ or $\overleftrightarrow{CF}$); points: A, B, C, D, E, F; segments: $\overline{AB}$, $\overline{AC}$, $\overline{AD}$, $\overline{BC}$, $\overline{BD}$, $\overline{CD}$, $\overline{EC}$, $\overline{EF}$, and $\overline{CF}$ **6.** ABC; A, B, D; A, C, D; B, C, D; E, C, F **9.** Segment
11.

Tiers high	Triangles
2	4
3	9
4	16
5	25
10	100
n	n^2

15. F; Not books which have had their pages cut out **17.** F; A robin is a bird, and this bird is a robin. **19.** F; A robin is not a bluejay. **21.** 243; 3^n where n = term number **23.** 25; Sequence is a, a^2, $(a + 1)$, $(a + 1)^2$, etc. **25.** G, I, J **27.** Yes; two points determine a line.
29.

Month	Total pairs
1	1
2	1
3	2
4	3
5	5
6	8
7	13
8	21
9	34
10	55
11	89
12	144

The total number of pairs for each month past the second is the sum of the numbers of pairs for the previous two months.

1-2 Part B Try It

a. Ostrich
b. Parallelogram

1-2 Part B Exercises

1. Possible answer: Roosters are birds but, being male, they don't lay eggs.
3. Possible answer: Let $a = b = 1$
5. True if he buys a newspaper and eats lunch; False if he doesn't buy a newspaper, or doesn't eat lunch, or both
7. **9.**

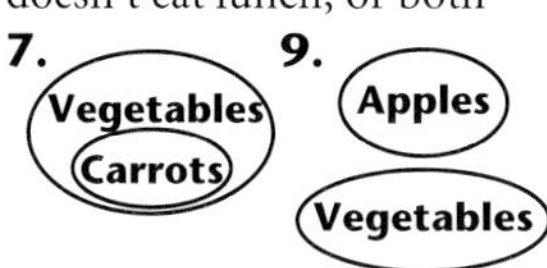

11. F; Line segment
15. $x = 4$
17–19.

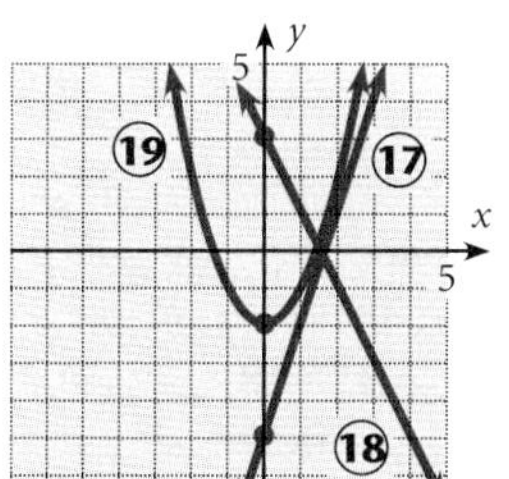

21. Equilateral triangle
23. Possible answer: Kay Bailey Hutchison (R–TX)
25. True if homework done and bedroom cleaned; False if homework not done, or bedroom not cleaned, or both.
27. Some joggers swim (or some swimmers jog). **29.** All squares are quadrilaterals.
31. a.

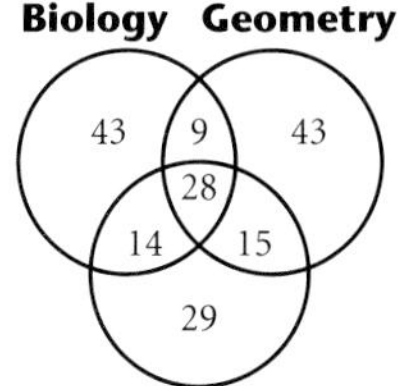

43 will take geometry only
b. $\frac{28}{181}$

1-2 Part C Try It

a. Iguanas have scales.
b. I am not a fish.

1-2 Part C Exercises

1. Fluffy has fur.
2. Chao-Yee does not live in Wyoming. **3.** Kai drew a four-sided figure. **6.** Fill in row 2, column 3, then cell (3, 3), then (1, 1), then the rest in any order to get

5	0	1
7	3	9
8	6	4

8. The statement is true; some snakes are reptiles. However, it is also true that *all* snakes are reptiles.
9. $3x - 2(25 - 3x) = 40$ $3x - 50 + 6x = 40$, Distributive Property; $9x = 90$, added 50 to both sides and combined like terms; $x = 10$, divided both sides by 9. Deductive
13. -1 **15.** -5
17.

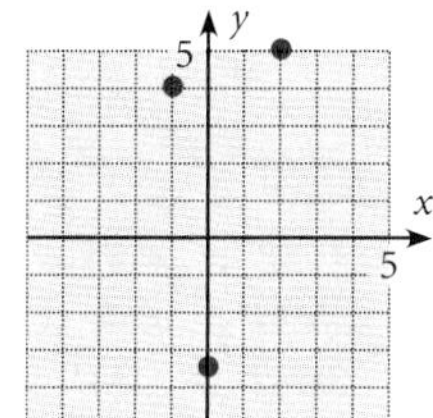

19. Tamika does not live in San Diego. **21.** Every square is a parallelogram.
23. a. Valid **b.** Valid

1-2 Part D Self Assessment

1. Deductive **2.** Inductive
3. Inductive **4.** Deductive
5. 26; $5n + 1$ **6.** 35
7. 125; n^3 **8.** $x = 3$
9. $y = \frac{5}{3}$

10–11.

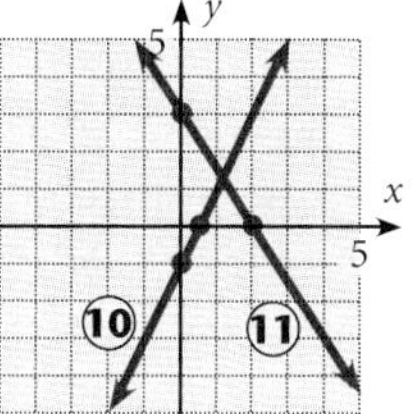

12. Possible answer:
13. (d)
14. a. 2^{n-1}
b. Conjecture: $2^{6-1} = 2^5 = 32$; not valid; works for $n \leq 5$ but not $n = 6$ because for $n = 6$, number of regions $= 30$ or 31

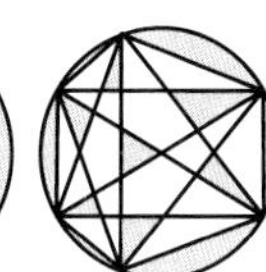

15. $\frac{n(n+1)}{2}$ Inductive, by observing that the *n*th step added *n* small squares. Other reasoning is possible.
16. The *n*th arrival shakes hands with *n* people - Alice and the $(n - 1)$ who arrived earlier. Therefore, the answer is: $\frac{n(n+1)}{2} = \frac{10(11)}{2} = 55$

1-3 Part A Try It

a. $XY = 2.7$; $XZ = 4$; $YZ = 6.7$ **b.** $RS = 5.1$; $ST = 7.1$; $TR = 6$

1-3 Part A Exercises

1. a. $(x_1, y_1) = (-3, 4)$; $(x_2, y_2) = (6, -4)$ **b.** $x_1 - x_2 = -3 - 6 = -9$, $(-9)^2 = 81$ **c.** $y_1 - y_2 = 4 - (-4) = 8$, $8^2 = 64$ **d.** $81 + 64 = 145$ **e.** $\sqrt{145} \approx 12.0$
3. 9 **5.** 6 **7.** 7 **9.** 4.1
11. $LM = 6.3$; $MN = 6.3$; $NL = 5.7$; Perimeter $= 18.3$
14. 10 in. **15. a.** 72 points **b.** 1.5 picas **17.** Points: *R*, *S*, *T*, *U*, *V* **18.** *T*, *S*, *R* and *S*, *U*, *V* **19.** $\overleftrightarrow{TS}$, $\overleftrightarrow{TR}$, $\overleftrightarrow{SR}$, ℓ

21. $\frac{1}{16}$; $\left(-\frac{1}{2}\right)^n$, $n \geq 0$
23. 15 **25.** 4.92 **27.** 5
29. 2.1 **31.** 0.76

1-3 Part B Try It

a. $\overrightarrow{MN}$, $\overrightarrow{MO}$, $\overrightarrow{MP}$ **b.** 90°
c. 45° **d.** 137°

1-3 Part B Exercises

1. $\angle BCD$, $\angle DCB$, $\angle C$, $\angle 1$
3. $\angle DBA$, $\angle DBC$, $\angle ABC$, 3 unique angles **5.** 148°
7. Possible answer:

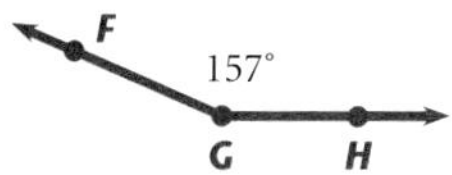

9. Possible answer:

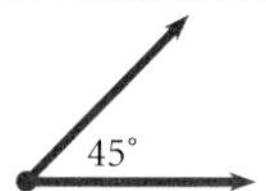

11. Possible answer:

15. 30° **17.** 130° **19.** 90°
21. Possible Answer: 63°
25. 11 **27.** $\overrightarrow{UR}$, $\overrightarrow{US}$, $\overrightarrow{UT}$, $\overrightarrow{UV}$, $\overrightarrow{VU}$ (or $\overrightarrow{VS}$), and $\overrightarrow{SU}$ (or $\overrightarrow{SV}$) **29.** 139°
31. Possible answer:

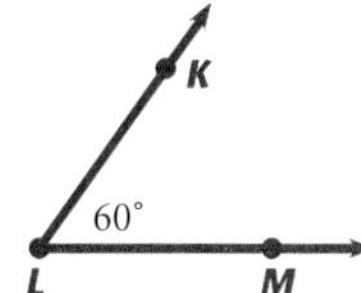

33. Possible answer:

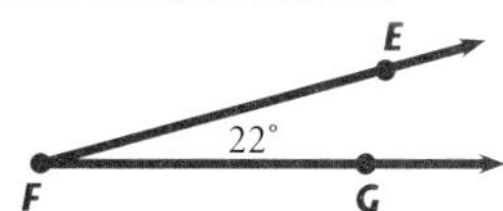

35. $RT < RS$ because the shortest segment from *R* to $\overleftrightarrow{TS}$ is the perpendicular segment. Similarly, $ST < RS$ because the shortest segment from *S* to $\overleftrightarrow{TR}$ is the perpendicular segment.

1-3 Part C Try It

a. Possible answer:

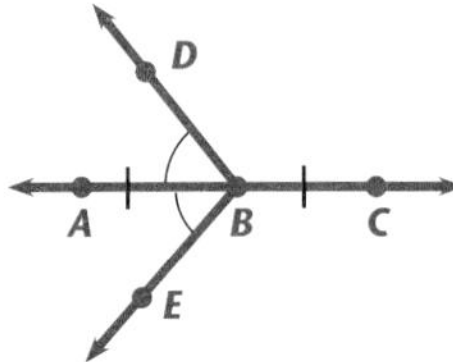

1-3 Part C Exercises

1. *B* and *E*, *A* and *C*, *D* and *F* **2.** Yes, since both have length 2. **9.** 4 **10.** $m\angle ABC = \frac{1}{2} m\angle CBD$ **11.** $x = 8$; $RS = 41$; $MN = 41$ **13.** (c) **19.** Slope = −3, intercept = 1 **21.** 2 **23.** Undefined (vertical line)

25.

27.

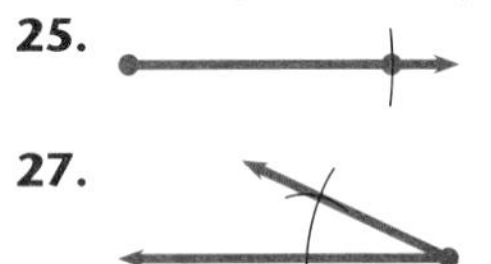

29. $x = 23$; $m\angle DEF = 133°$; $m\angle RST = 133°$

31. Possible answer: Compass may have opened wider while constructing $\angle PQR$, your measurements of $\angle MNO$ and $\angle PQR$ may not be precise, etc.

1-3 Part D Self Assessment

1. No **2.** No **3.** Yes **4.** No, the segment is the same whether it is called $\overline{AB}$ or $\overline{BA}$; Yes, the first letter is the endpoint of the ray; No, the points are any two locations on the line; Yes, the center letter denotes the vertex. **5.** Segments are congruent, lengths are equal. **6.** The notation $\angle PQR$ names the angle, not its size. **7.** 0° < angle size < 180°. **8.** "Congruent angles" requires the angle measures, not the lengths of their sides, to be the same. **9. a.** 72 **b.** 60° **c.** 51.4° **d.** 45° **e.** 40° **f.** 36° **g.** 2 slices of the 5-slice 144° vs. 120°

10.

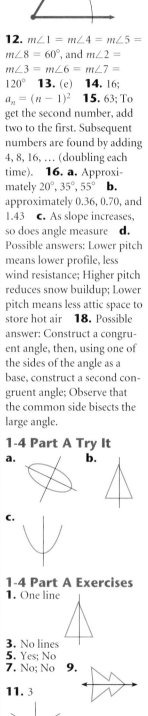

11.

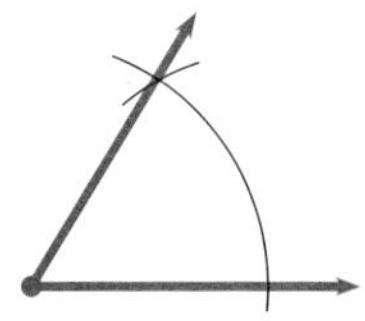

12. $m\angle 1 = m\angle 4 = m\angle 5 = m\angle 8 = 60°$, and $m\angle 2 = m\angle 3 = m\angle 6 = m\angle 7 = 120°$ **13.** (e) **14.** 16; $a_n = (n-1)^2$ **15.** 63; To get the second number, add two to the first. Subsequent numbers are found by adding 4, 8, 16, … (doubling each time). **16. a.** Approximately 20°, 35°, 55° **b.** approximately 0.36, 0.70, and 1.43 **c.** As slope increases, so does angle measure **d.** Possible answers: Lower pitch means lower profile, less wind resistance; Higher pitch reduces snow buildup; Lower pitch means less attic space to store hot air **18.** Possible answer: Construct a congruent angle, then, using one of the sides of the angle as a base, construct a second congruent angle; Observe that the common side bisects the large angle.

1-4 Part A Try It

a. **b.**

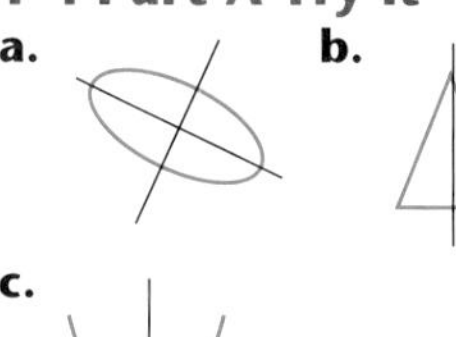

c.

1-4 Part A Exercises

1. One line

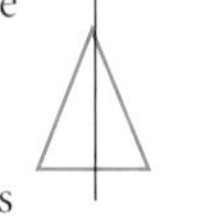

3. No lines
5. Yes; No
7. No; No **9.**

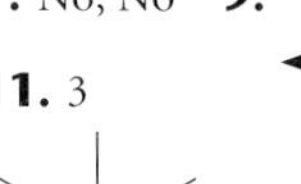

11. 3

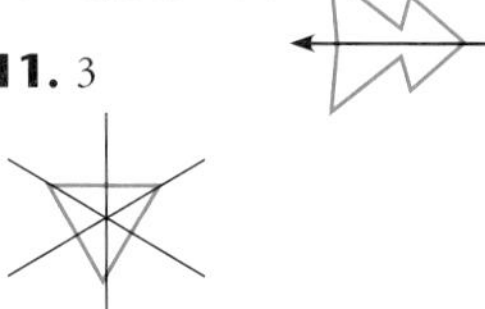

13. 4

15. Line of symmetry (or an axis of symmetry) **17.** Square **20.** Possible answers: WOW, TUT, AVA (name); AHIMOTUVWXY **21.** Possible answers: BOX, BED, HEX; BCDEHIKOX **23.** $\frac{4}{6} = \frac{2}{3}$ **25.** Possible answer: The object and its reflected image form a symmetric pair.

27. **29.**

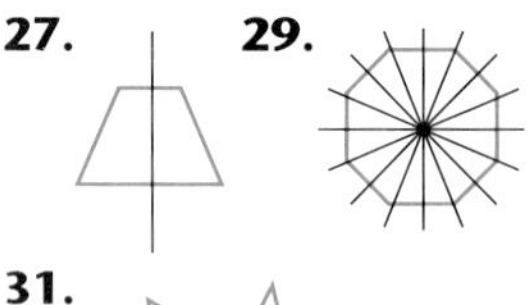

31.

33. a. 6 **37.** If a polygon is divided by a symmetry axis, each side consists of line segments that have congruent segments on the other side.

1-4 Part B Exercises

1.

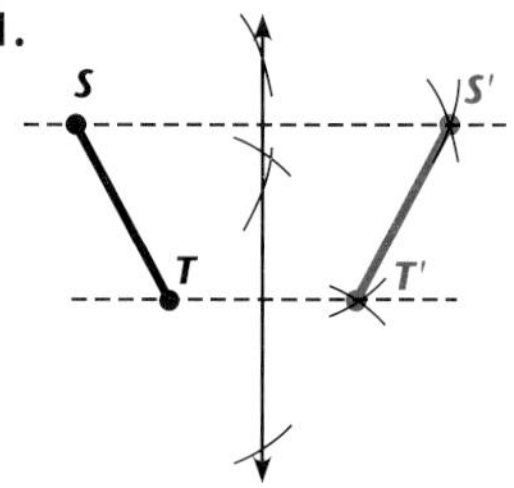

3. *P* **4.** *Q* **5.** $\overline{LK}$ **7.** 90°; In order for *m* to be the line of reflection, it must be a perpendicular bisector of $\overline{XX'}$. **9.** F; Reflection **11. a.** (2, −3) **b.** (−2, 3) **c.** $(a, -b)$ **d.** $(-a, b)$ **12.** One is vertical, one horizontal; The top and bottom halves are reflections of each other, as are the left and right halves.

15. **17.**

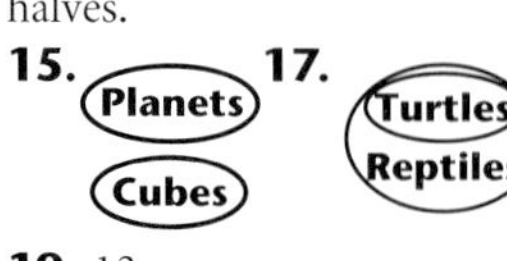

19. 13

21. Possible answer:

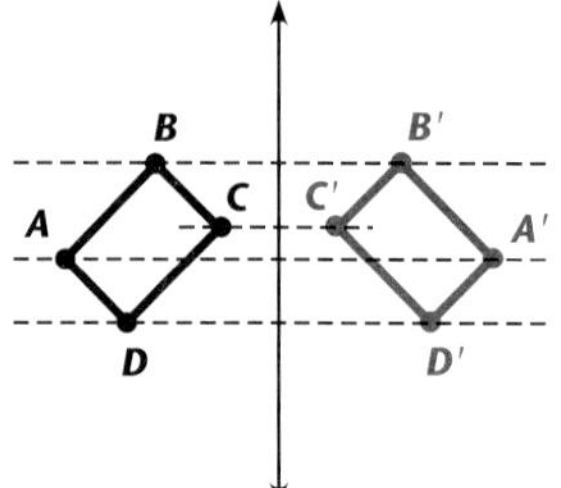

23. *Z* **25.** Triangle *RTS*

27. a.

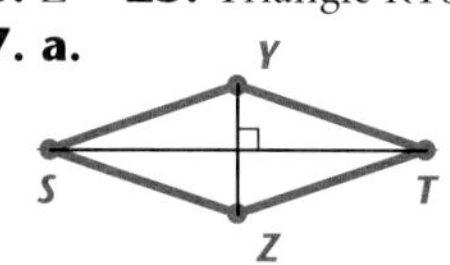

The four segments are congruent.

b.

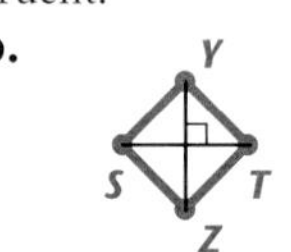

The four segments are congruent **c.** Possible answer: Connecting the endpoints of the bisectors forms an equilateral parallelogram (rhombus). If the bisectors are congruent, the parallelogram is a square.

1-4 Part C Try It

a. $M'P' = 8$ also
b. $m\angle PMN = 75°$ also
c. As you move from M' to P', you are going counterclockwise **d.** Perimeter of triangle *MNP* is 20 **e.** Area of triangle $M'N'P'$ is 24

1-4 Part C Exercises

1. Possible answer:

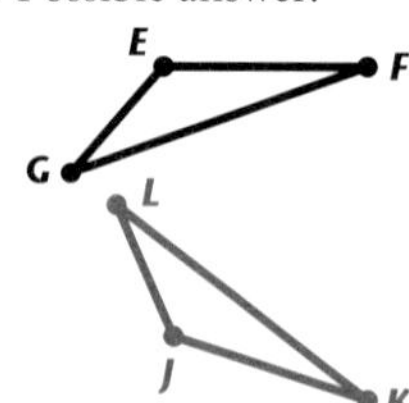

3. 90° **4.** 6 **7.** Possible answer: A segment from a point to its reflection image is perpendicular to the line of reflection. **9.** Possible answer: Reflection preserves the size of a figure.

12.

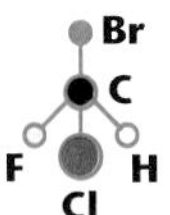

13. If a person lives in San Francisco, then he or she lives in California. **15.** If Kendrick is 16, then he can get a driver's license. **17.** 7.6 **19.** 6
21. Always; Possible answer: Reflection preserves size.
23. Never; Reflection always reverses the orientation.

1-4 Part D Self Assessment

1. P **2.** $\overleftrightarrow{BC}$ **3.** $\overline{PQ}$
4. B **5.** 12 **6.** Yes, the line bisecting the angle

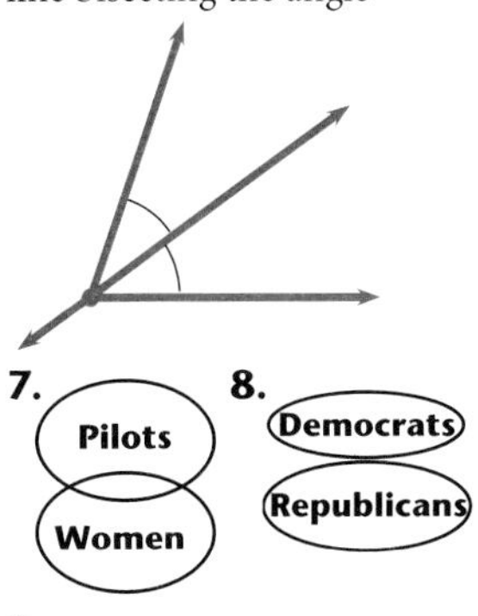

7.

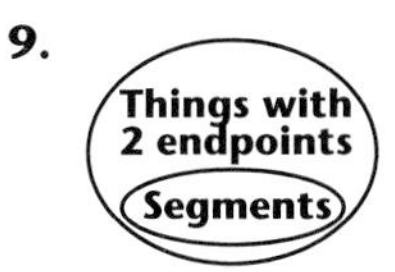

8. Democrats; Republicans

9. Things with 2 endpoints; Segments

10. 10 **11.** 4.7 **12.** Reflection preserves congruence but reverses orientation. Possible answer:

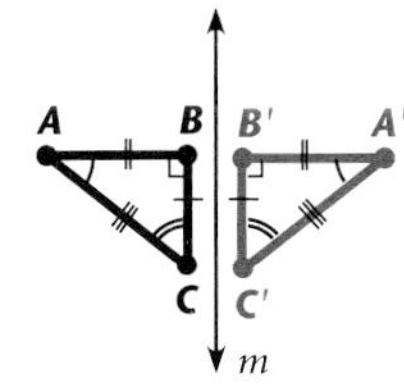

The sides, angles, perimeter and area of both triangles have the same measures as their counterparts; the orientations are reversed.
13. a. Yes **b.** Yes
14. (e)
15. Crossbar of F; Loop of Q; Crossbar of N **16. a.** Possible answer: "is not equal to," "is in the same class as" **b.** Possible answer: is "greater than," "is less than" **17.** (2, 1), (2, 5)
18. (4, 5), (9, 5)

Chapter 1 Review

1. Inductive **2.** Vertex
3. Image **4.** Right angles (90°)
5.

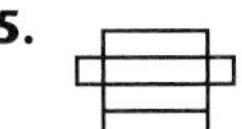

6. $A(1, 40)$, $B(1, 70)$, $C(2, 60)$, $D(2, 90)$, $E(4, 80)$, $F(4, 97)$, $G(5, 100)$, $H(6, 80)$ **7.** H; No
8. About 76 points **9.** $x = -4$ **10. a.** 25 **b.** $4n - 3$
11. Possible answer: Deductive reasoning proceeds from the premises to the conclusion by logical steps; Solving an algebra problem, reasoning from "all triangles have 3 sides" and "John drew a triangle" to "John's figure has 3 sides."
12. Luis is not a freshman.
13. Marie did not draw a triangle. **14.** 9.4 **15.** 8.1
16. $\angle RTS$, $\angle STR$, $\angle T$, $\angle 2$
17.

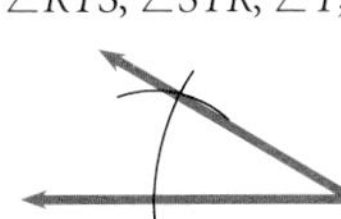

18. Possible answer:

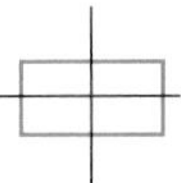

19. K **20.** $\overline{MN}$
21. Triangle ABC

CHAPTER 2

2-1 Part A Try It

a. If you talk on the telephone more than one hour per night, then your grade will drop one letter. **b.** If you use recycled paper, then you will help save our forests.
c. If a whole number has three or more factors, then it is not a prime number.

2-1 Part A Exercises

1. Hypothesis: you want to stay healthy; Conclusion: you should eat fruits, grains, and vegetables **3.** If it rains, then I won't go swimming.
5. If medicine is cherry-flavored, then children will love to take it. **7.** If an integer is divisible by 4, then it is also divisible by 2. **9.** If a student is a geometry student, then he or she is a math student. **11.** T **13.** T
17. 1.875×10^3 **19.** 6.023×10^{23} **21.** 0.0000014
23.

A B

A B

25. Hypothesis: A student enrolls in Algebra II; Conclusion: He will learn about logarithms **27.** If a mosquito bites you, then you will get a bump on your arm. **29.** If the power is off, then the computer won't run. **31.** T
33. F **35. a.** Your wish is my command. **b.** I am the greatest. **c.** I am the greatest.
d. Only when the "if" part is true

2-1 Part B Try It

a. Inverse: If you are not fifteen, then you are not a teenager; Converse: If you are a teenager, then you are fifteen; Contrapositive: If you are not a teenager, then you are not fifteen.

2-1 Part B Exercises

1. Inverse: If you don't live in Kyoto, then you don't live in Japan; Converse: If you live in Japan, then you live in Kyoto; Contrapositive: If you don't live in Japan then you don't live in Kyoto. **2.** Original: F. Inverse: If $x^2 \neq 4$, then $x \neq 2$. T. Converse: If $x = 2$, then $x^2 = 4$. T. Contrapositive: If $x \neq 2$, then $x^2 \neq 4$. F **3.** Original: T. Inverse: If two angles are not right angles, then they are not congruent. F. Converse: If two angles are congruent, then they are right angles. F. Contrapositive: If two angles are not congruent, then they are not (both) right angles. T
5. Original: T. Inverse: If you are not an elephant, then you know how to fly. F. Converse: If you don't know how to fly, then you are an elephant. F. Contrapositive: If you know how to fly, then you are not an elephant. T **7.** T **11.** If $x > 3$, then $x > 7$. **13.** If x is negative, then $-x$ is positive.
17. Original: T. Converse: If two angles have the same measure, then they are congruent; T. Two angles are congruent if and only if they have the same measure. **19.** 135°
21. $m\angle A = 180° - m\angle B$
23. Original: F; Inverse: If $t^2 \leq 0$, then $t \leq 0$. T; Converse: If $t > 0$, then $t^2 > 0$. T; Contrapositive: If $t \leq 0$, then $t^2 \leq 0$. F **25.** Original: (presumed) T. Inverse: If you are over four feet tall, then you are riding the RocketCoaster. F. Converse: If you are not riding the RocketCoaster, then you are not over four feet tall. F. Contrapositive: If you are riding the RocketCoaster, then you are over four feet tall. T.

2-1 Part C Try It

a. If I clean my room, then I'll be able to go to the store.
b. Fran will make the honor roll.

2-1 Part C Exercises

1. $\overline{EG} \cong \overline{HF}$ **3.** Washington state had 11 electoral votes in 1992. **5.** Not possible: The chain rule requires the conclusion of one statement to be the hypothesis of the other.
7. If someone is a baseball player, then he or she wears spikes on natural-grass fields. Ken Griffey Jr. wears spikes on natural-grass fields. **9.** If a number can be written as a fraction, then it is a rational number. If a number is pi, then it can be written as the fraction $\frac{\pi}{1}$. Pi is a rational number. **11.** Law of Detachment **13.** If X, then R. If R, then M. If M, then Y. If Y then A. If A then B.
15. $(x - 3)^2$ **17.** $(c - 3)(3c + 5)$ **19.** Harvey

21. A rectangle is a quadrilateral. **23.** If you reflect a segment across a line, then the segment and its reflected image are congruent. **25. a.** Carlos and Diane

2-1 Part D Self-Assessment

1. If a figure is a square, then it is a quadrilateral. Hypothesis: The figure is a square; Conclusion: The figure is a quadrilateral. **2.** If you want to be happy, then you should buy Frumworts. Hypothesis: You want to be happy; Conclusion: You should buy Frumworts. **3.** If you drive too fast, then you waste gasoline. Hypothesis: You drive too fast; Conclusion: You waste gasoline. **4. a.** Converse: If my book bag is not heavy, then I don't have a lot of homework. Inverse: If I have a lot of homework, then my book bag will be heavy. Contrapositive: If my book bag is heavy, then I have a lot of homework. **b.** Converse and inverse: F; The student might be carrying only a math book but have 500 problems to do. Contrapositive and original: F; The student might be carrying something besides homework materials in the bag.
5.

6. A true conditional (the promise) does not necessarily mean a true inverse, and so Detachment using the inverse won't work. **7.** 3.27×10^2
8. 3.042×10^{-3}
9. 1.86282×10^5 **10.** Fumiko found the real, sausage pizza under the sink.
11. (b), (d), (e) **12. a.** Yes
b. *Given:* A conditional statement and the negation of its conclusion. *Infer:* The negation of the hypothesis.

2-2 Part A Exercises

1. a. If a set of points is collinear, then the points lie on the same line. **b.** If a set of points lie on the same line, then the points are collinear. **c.** A set of points is collinear if and only if the points lie on the same line. **3.** The converse of a conditional statement is formed if and only if the hypothesis and the conclusion of the conditional statement are interchanged. **4.** If an angle is a right angle, then it measures 90°; If an angle measures 90°, then it is a right angle. **5.** If M is the midpoint of $\overline{AB}$, then it divides $\overline{AB}$ into two congruent segments, $\overline{AM}$ and $\overline{MB}$; If a point M divides $\overline{AB}$ into two congruent segments $\overline{AM}$ and $\overline{MB}$, then it is the midpoint of $\overline{AB}$. **7.** If a segment, ray or line, intersects the other segment perpendicularly, and bisects the other segment; A segment, ray or line is a perpendicular bisector if and only if it intersects a segment at right angles and bisects the segment.
9. 6; 12 **11.** 2.5; 2.5
15. F **17.** Two endpoints, part of line, ray, or segment; Part of a line (ray or another segment) is a line segment if and only if it consists of two endpoints and all the points between them. **19.** 15; 30
21. $\frac{9}{10}$; $\frac{9}{10}$ **23.** T **25.** N can be either (0.5, −1.5) or (0.5, −8.5)

2-2 Part B Try It

a. Commutative Property of Addition **b.** Addition Property of Equality
c. Straight-Line Postulate
d. Flat-Plane Postulate
e. Points-Existence Postulate, Flat-Plane Postulate

2-2 Part B Exercises

1. Flat-Plane Postulate
3. F **5.** T; Straight-Line Postulate **7.** F
9. Symmetric Property of Equality **11.** Distributive Property **13.** Addition Property of Equality
15. Plane Postulate
19. Original: F. Converse: If a number is evenly divisible by nine, it is evenly divisible by three. T. Inverse: If a number is not evenly divisible by three, then it is not evenly divisible by nine. T. Contrapositive: If a number is not evenly divisible by nine, then it is not evenly divisible by three. F **21.** Plane Postulate **23.** F; Let F and G be in the line of intersection of 2 planes. **24.** F; Three points may be collinear
25. F **27.** 20; No

2-2 Part C Try It

a. 4.5

2-2 Part C Exercises

1. 4 **3.** $1\frac{1}{8}$ **5.** 19.9 **7.** (a)
9. a. (3) **b.** (4) **c.** (5)
d. (6) **11.** 11 **13.** 11
15. 9 **17.** 1.65 **19.** Yes
21. (2, 3) **23.** $\left(\frac{1}{2}, -\frac{3}{2}\right)$

2-2 Part D Self-Assessment

1. F; Three *noncollinear* points determine three lines;

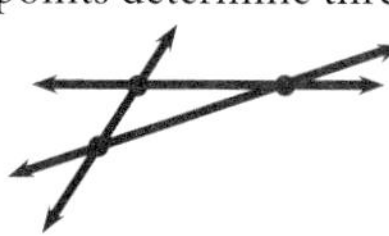

2. F; Two lines ℓ and m intersect at point E. **3.** F; The lines must be coplanar. **4.** T; Plane-Intersection Postulate **5.** Flat-Plane Postulate
6. Flat-Plane and Plane-Intersection Postulates together
7. $LK + KM = LM$; Segment- Addition Postulate
8. P and Q intersect in a line; Plane-Intersection Postulate
9. S is the midpoint of $\overline{RT}$; Definition of Midpoint **10.** (d) **11.** Possible answer: If you are fifteen, then you are a teenager. **12.** Possible answer: If $a > b$, then $b > a$.

13. The result is an inscribed square with half the area **14.** Midpoint between jobs is $\left(\frac{-3+2}{2}, \frac{2-5}{2}\right) = \left(-\frac{1}{2}, -\frac{3}{2}\right)$.
15. No; Postulates cannot be proven.

2-3 Part A Try It

a.

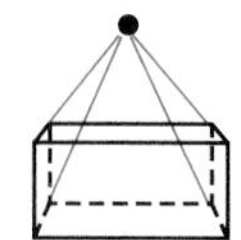

2-3 Part A Exercises

1. One; Directly in line with the reflecting pool **3.** Horizon line
5.

7.

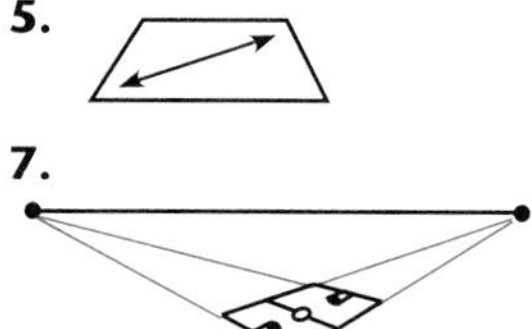

11. $\overline{XY}$ **13.** 56° **15.** T; Flat-Plane Postulate **17.** T; Plane Postulate

2-3 Part B Try It

a. Front and Back Left and Right

2-3 Part B Exercises

1. Orthographic; Shows only one side of the shuttle.
5. Orthographic **7.** (a) **9.** (c)
11. Possible answers:
a. $\overleftrightarrow{GL}$ and $\overleftrightarrow{LK}$ **b.** $\overleftrightarrow{GL}$ and $\overleftrightarrow{NK}$,
c. $\overleftrightarrow{JN}$ and $\overleftrightarrow{LM}$ **d.** (b) **15.** (c)

2-3 Part C Try It

a. $\overleftrightarrow{FG}, \overleftrightarrow{HC}, \overleftrightarrow{ED}$ **b.** $\overleftrightarrow{AB}, \overleftrightarrow{HC}, \overleftrightarrow{BG}, \overleftrightarrow{CD}$

2-3 Part C Exercises

1. $\overleftrightarrow{BF}, \overleftrightarrow{DH}, \overleftrightarrow{AG}$ **3.** Plane with E, F, G, H **5.** Intersecting
7. Parallel **9.** (d) **15.** Possible answer: $y = -3x$ **17.** Possible answer: $y = -\frac{4}{3}x$
19. a. 40% **b.** 20%
23. If two lines are noncoplanar, then they are skew. If two lines are skew, then they are noncoplanar.

25. If point B is between points A and C, then $AB + BC = AC$. If $AB + BC = AC$, then point B is between A and C. **27.** Plane with W, X, Y, Z **29.** Not possible; If $p \parallel n$ and $n \parallel m$, then p must be parallel to m **31.** Possible answer: $y = \frac{3}{7}x$ **33. a.** B: (2, 5, 0), C: (2, 5, 3), D: (2, 0, 3), F: (0, 5, 3), H: (0, 0, 0) **b.** Possible answer: $\overline{AH} \parallel \overline{BE}$, $\overline{HE} \parallel \overline{AB}$, $\overline{AD} \parallel \overline{BC}$

2-3 Part D Self-Assessment

1. F **2.** T **3.** F **4.** T **5.** Orthographic **6.** Possible answers: $y = \frac{3}{2}x$, $y = \frac{3}{2}x + 1$, $y = \frac{3}{2}x + 2$ **7.** $y = -\frac{2}{3}x + 5$ **8.** (a) **a.** 120° **b.** 120° (reflection preserves angle measure) **10.** T **11.** F **12.** T **14.** T **15.** F **16.** T **17.** F; Horizontal and vertical lines

Chapter 2 Review

1. Conditional **2.** Postulate **3.** Parallel **4.** Possible answer: If you are a teenager, then you are fifteen. **5.** Original: F. Inverse: If a number is not divisible by 4, then it is not divisible by 16. T. Converse: If a number is divisible by 16, then it is divisible by 4. T. Contrapositive: If a number is not divisible by 16, then it is not divisible by 4. F **6.** F **7.** T **8.** $(x + 6)(x - 2)$ **9.** (1, −1) **10.** $y = 5x + 6$

CHAPTER 3

3-1 Part A Try It

a. $\overrightarrow{EA}$ and $\overrightarrow{ED}$ **b.** Acute: $\angle AEB$, $\angle BEC$; Right: $\angle AEC$, $\angle CED$; Obtuse: $\angle BED$

3-1 Part A Exercises

1. $\overrightarrow{KJ}, \overrightarrow{KL}$ **3.** $\overrightarrow{KM}, \overrightarrow{KN}$ **5.** J, L **7.** Obtuse; 120° **9.** Acute; 50° **11.** Acute **13.** Possible answer:

A B C D

15. a. 2; $\angle BJD$ and $\angle DJL$ **b.** Number of possible angles: 10 Probability: $\frac{2}{10} = 0.2$ **17.** $m\angle DBC = 35°$ **19.** Possible answer: Whales **21.** F **23.** Possible answer: $\overrightarrow{YT}, \overrightarrow{YW}$ **25.** Possible answer: $\overrightarrow{YT}, \overrightarrow{YV}$ **27.** U **29.** Acute: $\angle TYU$, $\angle UYV$, $\angle WYX$; Right: $\angle VYW$, $\angle TYV$; Obtuse: $\angle XYT$, $\angle UYW$, $\angle VYX$

31.

rays	angles
1	3 = 1 + 2
2	6 = 1 + 2 + 3
3	10 = 1 + 2 + 3 + 4
4	15 = 1 + 2 + 3 + 4 + 5
10	66 = 1 + 2 + 3 + ... + 10 + 11

3-1 Part B Try It

a. i. 000 **ii.** 055 **iii.** 120 **b.** ≈ 235

3-1 Part B Exercises

1. b. 125° **c.** 235 **3.** ≈ 055 **5.** ≈ 025 **7.** South **9.** Southwest **11.** A, B, E, F, I, J, M, N **13.** East **15.** South **17.** Fly 500 miles at bearing 053. **19.** ≈ 315 **21.** ≈ 115 **23.** ≈ 165 **25.** No.

3-1 Part C Try It

a. Length: 2.7 cm, Direction: 138°

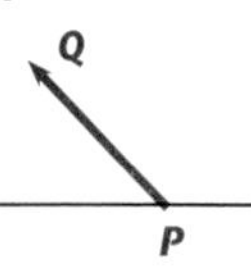

3-1 Part C Exercises

1. $\overrightarrow{CD}$, 33 mm at 126° **2.** $\overrightarrow{QR}$, 28 mm at 72° **3.** $\overrightarrow{XY}$, 52 mm at 354° **5.** 2.7 cm at 247° **7.** $\overrightarrow{JK} + \overrightarrow{KL} = \overrightarrow{JL}$ **9.** (b) **10.** Lengths: $\overrightarrow{OH} = 2\sqrt{5}$, $\overrightarrow{OG} = 4$, $\overrightarrow{OF} = 5$, $\overrightarrow{OI} = \sqrt{29}$; Directions: $\overrightarrow{OH} \approx 153°$, $\overrightarrow{OG} = 90°$, $\overrightarrow{OF} \approx 53°$, $\overrightarrow{OI} \approx 292°$ **12.** $\overrightarrow{AC}$ **17.** $\overrightarrow{RS}$: 2.3 cm at 82° **19.** $\overrightarrow{WV}$: 4.2 cm at 198° **21.** 3 cm at 57° **23. a.** $\overrightarrow{LN}$ **b.** No **25. a.** Same length **b.** $\overrightarrow{XY}$ at 58°, $\overrightarrow{X'Y'}$ at 122° **c.** The lengths of the pre-image and image vectors are the same. If the pre-image makes an angle of measurement a with the horizontal (x-axis) in the counterclockwise direction; then the image makes an angle of measurement a with the x-axis in the opposite direction.

3-1 Part D Try It

a. <1, 4>; $C' = (0, 8)$

3-1 Part D Exercises

1. (c) **3.** (d) **5.** Reflection **7.** F **9.** G **11.** <−1, −7>; P': (3, −2) **13.** $F' = (4, 0)$ **15.** $H' = (-2, 6)$ **17.** (6, 1) **19.** The segment with endpoints (0, 6) and (4, 2) **25.** 180°, 360°, 90° **27.** $\overline{PQ}$ **29.** <2, 5>; H': (−1, 5) **31.** U': (1, −3) **33.** W': (−4, 2) **35.** $(x - 3, y - 2)$ **37.** R': $(c + (t - a), d + (u - b))$

3-1 Part E Self-Assessment

1. Always **2.** Always **3.** Never **4.** Sometimes **5.** Never **6.** Always **7. a.** 0° < measure < 180° **b.** 000 ≤ bearing < 360 **8.** (d) **9.** T **10.** T **11.** F **12.** It is an angle, it measures less than 90°. Angle A is an acute angle if and only if $m\angle A < 90°$. **13.** Reflections and translations both preserve shape, but reflections change orientation. The figure shown is a reflection because orientation is reversed. **14.** <10, 5>

3-2 Part A Try It

a. 180° **b.** No rotational symmetry **c.** 90°, 180°, 270° **d.** 180° **e.** 90°, 180°, 270°

3-2 Part A Exercises

1. F **3.** $\overline{GH}$ **5. a.** 180° **b.** 180° **7.** V **9.** F; Rotational **13.** Yes **15. a.** Six of diamonds does, others do not **b.** $\frac{1}{4}$ **19.** $\overline{IJ}$ **21.** Triangle HIJ **23.** C **27.** Yes; Any number of degrees (either way) **31. a.** 90°, 180°, 270°

3-2 Part B Try It

a. $\overline{CB}$ **b.** S **c.** UT **d.** $\angle CBA$ **e.** SV

3-2 Part B Exercises

1.

A B B' C A'

3. O **5.** $\angle PMN$ **7.** $C'(4, 0)$, $D'(4, -3)$ **8.** $C''(0, -4)$, $D''(-3, -4)$ **9.** $C'''(-4, 0)$, $D'''(-4, 3)$ **11. a.** Clockwise from middle of clock face. **b. i.** 1 hour = 60 min **ii.** 15 min **iii.** 30 min **iv.** 6 min **c. i.** 180° **ii.** 270° **iii.** 6° **17.** Q **19.** (1, 3) **21.** (−1, −3) **23.** A parallelogram with a crossbar; Yes

3-2 Part C Self-Assessment

2. (b) **3.** Any non-equilateral triangle lacks rotational symmetry. **4.** T **5.** R **6.** $\overline{ST}$ **7.** $\angle QRS$ **10.** (−2, 0) **11.** (−1, −4) **12.** (4, −3) **13.** (1, −3) **14.** Twice

3-3 Part A Try It

a. i. 45° **ii.** 10° **iii.** 80° **iv.** 95°; Protractor Postulate **b.** $m\angle PRN = 87°$ **c.** $m\angle BAD = 77°$; $m\angle DAC = 60°$

3-3 Part A Exercises

1. 15° **3.** 110° **5.** 30° **7.** $m\angle BCE - m\angle BCD = m\angle DCE$; 43° **9.** $m\angle BCD + m\angle DCE = m\angle BCE$; $m\angle BCD = 39°$ and $m\angle DCE = 37°$ **11.** 70° **13.** 70° **15.** 160° **17.** 39° **19.** 55°; Angle-Addition Postulate **27.** If a figure is a quadrilateral, then it has four sides. **29.** Yes; 90°, 180°, 270° **31.** Yes; 180° **33.** 80° **35.** 160° **37.** 80° **39.** $m\angle BCD + m\angle DCE = m\angle BCE$; $m\angle BCD = 60°$ and $m\angle DCE = 2°$ **41.** They are all possible except the last.

3-3 Part B Try It

a. Possible answer:

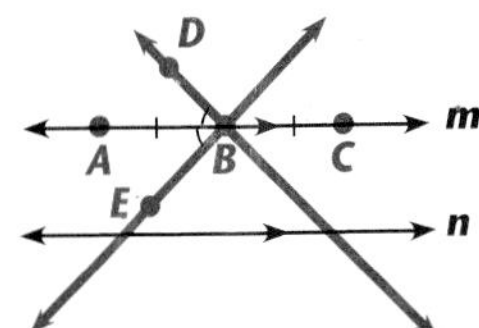

3-3 Part B Exercises

1. Yes **2.** No **3.** Yes **7.** Yes **9.** Yes **11.** No **13.**

15. $m\angle FGH = 55°$; $m\angle PQR = 145°$ **17.** No **19.** No **21.** Possible answer: Assume $\overline{WZ} \cong \overline{ZY}$; Z is midpoint of $\overline{WY}$; W, Z, Y are collinear; Cannot assume: $\overline{WX} \cong \overline{XY}$; $\overline{ZX} \perp \overline{WY}$; $m\angle W = m\angle Y$ **23.** 25 possible angle combinations, 5 of which make the angle congruent: $\frac{5}{25} = \frac{1}{5}$

3-3 Part C Try It

a. $\angle MTR$ and $\angle MTN$, $\angle RTS$ and $\angle NTP$, $\angle MTS$ and $\angle MTP$ **b.** 69° **c.** 159° **d.** 90°

3-3 Part C Exercises

1. $\angle BEC$ and $\angle CED$ **3.** $\angle AEB$ and $\angle BED$ or $\angle AEC$ and $\angle CED$ **5.** Complement: 78.3°; Supplement: 168.3° **7.** $m\angle NRP = 49°$; $m\angle NRO = 139°$ **9.** $m\angle MRN = 12°$; $m\angle NRP = 78°$ **11.** 30° **13.** F; Right **15.** 142° **17.** 35° **21.** If an artist used geometric forms to represent real objects, then he/she was a cubist. If an artist was a cubist, he/she was not a realist. If an artist used geometric forms to represent real objects, then he/she was not a realist. **23.** U **25.** Complement: 70°; Supplement: 160° **27.** Complement: 34.5°; Supplement: 124.5° **29.** $m\angle 1 = 15°$, $m\angle 2 = 30°$, $m\angle 3 = 45°$ **30. a.** Given information. **b.** Definition of right angle. **c.** Angle-Addition Postulate **d.** Substitution **e.** Definition of complementary.

3-3 Part D Try It

a. $m\angle 1 = 46°$; $m\angle 2 = 134°$; $m\angle 3 = 46°$

3-3 Part D Exercises

1. $m\angle 2 = 148°$; $m\angle 3 = 32°$; $m\angle 4 = 148°$ **3.** $m\angle 2 = 55°$; $m\angle 3 = 125°$; $m\angle 4 = 55°$ **5.** $m\angle 5 = 141° = m\angle 11$; $m\angle 6 = 39° = m\angle 12$; $m\angle 7 = 51° = m\angle 9$; $m\angle 8 = m\angle 10 = 129°$ **7.** 29° **9.** 151° **11.** 82° **13.** $m\angle JKL = m\angle MKN = 156°$ **15.** Definition of complementary **17.** Vertex **18.** If two angles are vertical angles, then they are congruent. **20.** 25° **25.** 48° **27.** 90° **29.** $m\angle JKL = m\angle MKN = 72°$ **31.** Bisect a right angle in a linear pair

3-3 Part E Self-Assessment

1. Complement: 25°; Supplement: 115° **2.** Complement: $(90 - x)°$; Supplement: $(180 - x)°$ **3.** Complement: $(70 + x)°$; Supplement: $(160 + x)°$ **4.** 58° **5.** 32° **6.** 148° **7.** 122° **8.** Possible answer: $\angle LBM$ and $\angle MBC$ **9.** $\angle JMB$ and $\angle BMD$ **10.** $\angle BMD$ and $\angle IME$ **11.** $\angle KBL$ and $\angle LBM$ **12. b.** $m\angle TBU = 140°$; $m\angle RBS = 140°$; $m\angle SBT = 40°$ **13.** Can assume: Things that look straight are; Points of intersection are shown accurately; Points shown on a line are collinear; Unless otherwise indicated, all points are coplanar; Relative positions of points are accurate. Cannot assume: Exact measurement and relative sizes of figures; That lines are parallel or perpendicular; That angles (or segments) are congruent. Check students' answers for examples. **14.** (e) **15. a.** Yes; 120°, 240° **b.** No **c.** Yes; 90°, 180°, 270° **16.** The supplement is 90° larger than the complement; x + complement = 90° so complement = $(90 - x)°$; x + supplement = 180° so supplement = $(180 - x)°$; supplement − complement = $(180 - x)° - (90 - x)° = 90°$ **17.** 120°

3-4 Part A Try It

a. r **b.** $\angle 2$ and $\angle 3$; $\angle 6$ and $\angle 7$ **c.** $\angle 4$ and $\angle 8$; $\angle 5$ and $\angle 1$ **d.** $\angle 4$ and $\angle 2$; $\angle 5$ and $\angle 7$; $\angle 3$ and $\angle 1$; $\angle 6$ and $\angle 8$ **e.** $\angle 3$ and $\angle 7$; $\angle 2$ and $\angle 6$

3-4 Part A Exercises

1. $\angle 3$ and $\angle 7$; $\angle 2$ and $\angle 6$ **3.** $\angle 2$ and $\angle 3$; $\angle 7$ and $\angle 6$ **5.** $\angle 4$ and $\angle 6$; $\angle 3$ and $\angle 5$; $\angle 2$ and $\angle 8$; $\angle 1$ and $\angle 7$ **9.** Transversal; A line not an angle **11.** *Rewrite:* Leave as is; *Draw:* A M B

State: Given: M is the midpoint of $\overline{AB}$; *Prove:* $AM = \frac{1}{2}AB$ **13.** $\angle 2$ and $\angle 3$ **15.** Possible answer: If you are an elephant, then you know how to fly. **17.** Complement: 2°; Supplement: 92° **19.** $\angle 5$ and $\angle 3$; $\angle 4$ and $\angle 6$ **21.** $\angle 3$ and $\angle 6$; $\angle 4$ and $\angle 5$ **23.** $\angle 1$ and $\angle 3$; $\angle 2$ and $\angle 4$; $\angle 6$ and $\angle 8$; $\angle 5$ and $\angle 7$ **27.** $\overleftrightarrow{AB}$ and $\overleftrightarrow{HG}$; $\overleftrightarrow{BC}$ and $\overleftrightarrow{EH}$; $\overleftrightarrow{BF}$ and $\overleftrightarrow{DH}$; $\overleftrightarrow{BE}$ and $\overleftrightarrow{CH}$; $\overleftrightarrow{BD}$ and $\overleftrightarrow{FH}$; $\overleftrightarrow{BG}$ and $\overleftrightarrow{AH}$

3-4 Part B Try It

a. $m\angle 1 = m\angle 3 = m\angle 5 = m\angle 7 = 72°$; $m\angle 2 = m\angle 4 = m\angle 6 = m\angle 8 = 108°$

3-4 Part B Exercises

1. $m\angle 1 = m\angle 3 = m\angle 5 = m\angle 7 = 41°$; $m\angle 2 = m\angle 4 = m\angle 6 = m\angle 8 = 139°$ **2.** $m\angle 1 = m\angle 3 = m\angle 5 = m\angle 7 = 105°$; $m\angle 2 = m\angle 4 = m\angle 6 = m\angle 8 = 75°$ **7.** 76° **11.** If the trenches are parallel and the pipeline crossing the street is a transversal, then the two angles are same-side interior angles, and Damaso's angle should measure $180° - 120° = 60°$. **12. a.** iv **b.** iii **c.** i **13.** Inverse: If two angles are not supplementary to the same angle, then they are not congruent. Converse: If two angles are congruent, then they are supplementary to the same angle. Contrapositive: If two angles are not congruent, then they are not supplementary to the same angle. **15.** $m\angle 1, 3, 5, 7 = 160°$; $m\angle 2, 4, 6, 8 = 20°$ **17.** $m\angle 1, 3, 5, 7 = 82.5°$; $m\angle 2, 4, 6, 8 = 97.5°$ **21. a.** No; Definition says parallel lines are coplanar lines that do not intersect. **b.** Yes; Coplanarity and non-intersection are both symmetric. **c.** Yes; If m and n have no common point(s) and if n and p have no common point(s), then m and p have no common points.

3-4 Part C Try It

a. $a \parallel b$ by Congruent Alternate Interior Angles; $b \parallel c$ by Congruent Corresponding Angles; $a \parallel c$ by Congruent Alternate Interior Angles. **b.** Possible answer: Make $\angle 1 \cong \angle 2$, $\angle 1 \cong \angle 4$, or $m\angle 1 + m\angle 3 = 180°$

3-4 Part C Exercises

1. Corresponding angles are congruent **3.** Same-side interior angles are supplementary **5.** $a \parallel b$; Alternate Interior Angles Postulate **7.** $a \parallel c$; Alternate Interior Angles Postulate **9.** $a \parallel b$; Alternate Exterior Angles Theorem **11.** $x = 68°$ **15.** *State: Given:* Transversal cuts ℓ and m such that the corresponding angles 1 and 2 are congruent; *Prove:* $\ell \parallel m$

17. If an angle is acute, then it measures less than 90°. If an angle measures less than 90°, then it is acute. **21.** $c \parallel d$ by Alternate Exterior Angles
23. $y = 0$; $x = 118$
25. $x = 3$; $y = -20$
27. a. Definition of linear pair **b.** Linear-Pair Postulate **c.** Supplementary angles **d.** Congruent **e.** Congruent

3-4 Part D Self-Assessment

1. T **2.** F; $\angle 2 \cong \angle 5$ **3.** T
4. F; $m\angle 3 = 156°$
5. $\overleftrightarrow{AB} \parallel \overleftrightarrow{CD}$ **6.** Possibly none **7.** Possibly none **8.** $\overleftrightarrow{AC} \parallel \overleftrightarrow{BD}$ **9.** $\overleftrightarrow{AC} \parallel \overleftrightarrow{BD}$ **10.** $x = 9$ **11.** $\angle VXW \cong \angle YXZ$ and $\angle VXY \cong \angle WXZ$ because they are vertical angles. **12.** $\angle YXV$ and $\angle VXW$, $\angle YXZ$ and $\angle ZXW$, $\angle VXW$ and $\angle WXZ$, $\angle VXY$ and $\angle YXZ$ because they are linear pairs **13.** (a) **14.** $\angle 1 \cong \angle 3$, each of measure 45° (Corresponding angles of parallel air lines); $m\angle 2 = m\angle 4 = 110°$ (Corresponding angles of parallel water lines); $m\angle 5 = m\angle 6$ (Corresponding angles of parallel water lines); $m\angle 7 = m\angle 8$ (Corresponding angles of parallel air lines);
If water surface $\parallel$ dotted line, then $m\angle 7 = m\angle 8 = 180° - m\angle 1 = 135°$. If water surface and bottom are parallel, then $m\angle 5 = m\angle 6 = 180° - m\angle 2$, or 70°.

Chapter 3 Review

1. T **2.** F; Obtuse **3.** T
4. F; Supplementary **5.** T
6. $\overrightarrow{AD}, \overrightarrow{AB}$ **7.** Possible answer: $\angle DAE$, $\angle EAB$, $\angle CAB$ **8.** E **9.** No; The distance from P to the lake and to the mountain.
10. $\overrightarrow{AB}$: Length $= \sqrt{6^2 + 2^2} = \sqrt{40}$; Direction $\approx 18°$; $\overrightarrow{CD}$: Length $= \sqrt{(-6)^2 + (-4)^2} = \sqrt{52}$; Direction $\approx 214°$; $\overrightarrow{EF}$: Length $= \sqrt{2^2 + (-4)^2} = \sqrt{20}$; Direction $\approx 297°$ **11.** Yes; 90°, 180°, 270° **12.** Yes; 180° **13.** No **14.** $m\angle AOD - m\angle BOC = m\angle AOB + m\angle COD$; $130° - 40° = 90°$; Since $\angle AOB \cong \angle COD$, each has measure 45° **15.** $m\angle AOD = m\angle AOB + m\angle BOC + m\angle COD$; $5x° = (x + 10)° + 40° + 2x° = (3x + 50)°$, so $x = 25$; $m\angle AOB = (x + 10)° = 35°$; $m\angle COD = 2x° = 50°$.
16. $m\angle 1 = 60°$; $m\angle 2 = 30°$; $m\angle 3 = 30°$; $m\angle 4 = 85°$
17.

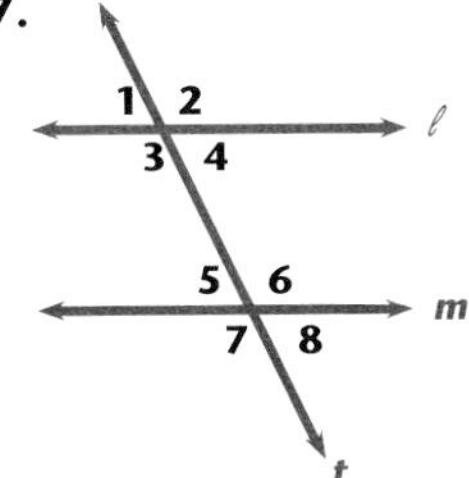

Show for example that $\angle 3 \cong \angle 6$, $\angle 1 \cong \angle 8$ or $\angle 1 \cong \angle 5$, or that $m\angle 3 + m\angle 5 = 180°$.
18. F **19.** T **20.** $a \parallel b$
21. $a \parallel b$ **22.** No parallel lines

CHAPTER 4

4-1 Part A Try It

a. 82°
b. S Vertex, Leg, Leg, P, R

Vertex $\angle S$, legs $\overline{SP}$ and $\overline{SR}$.
c.

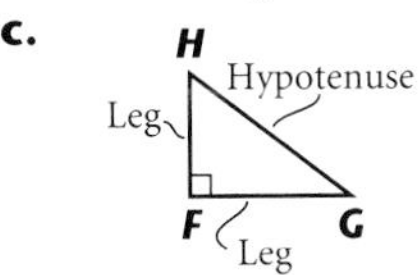

Hypotenuse $\overline{HG}$, Legs $\overline{FH}$ and $\overline{FG}$.

4-1 Part A Exercises

1. Isosceles, right **3.** Equilateral, equiangular **5.** $\triangle MNL$, $\triangle MLN$, $\triangle NML$, $\triangle NLM$, $\triangle LMN$, $\triangle LNM$ **7.** No
9. a. B, C, D, E, V, W, X, Y
b. $G, H, I, J, L, Q, R, S, T$
c. H, L, M, N, O, R **d.** $\frac{3}{4}$
11. 68° **13.** 58°
15. $m\angle A = 53°$, $m\angle B = 24°$, $m\angle C = 103°$ **17.** $m\angle 1 = 90° - m\angle 2$ **19.** 35° **21.** 60° **23.** Yes
25. Scalene **27.** 108° **29.** 65° **31. a.** Right, isosceles
b. 12

4-1 Part B Try It

a. $\angle 1, \angle 2, \angle 3$ **b.** $\angle 4, \angle 5$
c.

$m\angle 1$	$m\angle 2$	$m\angle 3$	$m\angle 4$
83°	40°	57°	97°
32°	84°	64°	148°
55°	71°	54°	125°

4-1 Part B Exercises

1. $\angle 3, \angle 4$ **3.** $\angle 2, \angle 3$
4–7.

$m\angle 5$	$m\angle 6$	$m\angle 7$	$m\angle 8$
104°	76°	33°	71°
108°	72°	8°	100°
137°	43°	68°	69°
156°	$x°$	$(2x+31)°$	$(4x-19)°$

9. F **11.** 30° **13.** 72°
15. 110° **17.** *Rewrite*: If an angle is an exterior angle of a triangle, then its measure is equal to the sum of the measures of its remote interior angles.
Draw:

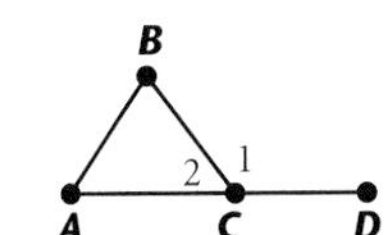

State: *Given*: $\angle 1$ is an exterior angle. *Prove*: $m\angle 1 = m\angle A + m\angle B$ **19.** 45° **25.** By properties of parallel lines, $m\angle 1 = m\angle 5$ and $m\angle 2 = m\angle 4$. Therefore, since $m\angle 3 + m\angle 4 + m\angle 5 = 180°$ (by the Angle-Addition and Linear-Pair Postulates), $m\angle 3 + m\angle 2 + m\angle 1 = 180°$ by substitution.

4-1 Part C Self-Assessment

1. Yes **2.** No **3.** Yes
4. Always **5.** Sometimes
6. Never **7.** Sometimes
8. (c) **9.** *Rewrite*: If a triangle is a right triangle, then its acute angles are complementary. *State*: *Given*: $\triangle ABC$ is a right triangle, $\angle A$ is a right angle. *Prove*: $m\angle B + m\angle C = 90°$

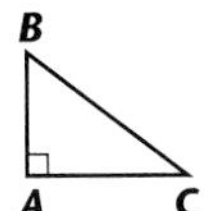

10. The mean is 65.8; The median is 71; The mode is 71.
11. A triangle cannot have those angle measures. Solving gives $x = 30$, but this would give the $(2x - 70)°$ angle a negative measure.
12. $m\angle 1 + m\angle 3 = 120°$ by the Exterior Angle Theorem
13. Possible answer: $m\angle 2 = 60°$ by the Linear-Pair Postulate **14.** Not possible
15. No **16.** In the picture, $\angle 1$, $\angle 2$, and $\angle 3$ form a straight line at the tessellation vertex. Therefore $m\angle 1 + m\angle 2 + m\angle 3 = 180°$. Also in the picture at the tessellation vertex, $\angle 1$ and $\angle 2$ form the exterior angle of $\angle 3$, $\angle 3$ and $\angle 1$ form the exterior angle of $\angle 2$, and $\angle 2$ and $\angle 3$ form the exterior angle of $\angle 1$.

4-2 Part A Try It

a. $\triangle MNO \cong \triangle TUS$

4-2 Part A Exercises

1. $\triangle DEF \cong \triangle XZY$ **5.** $m\angle L$
7. $\overline{RS}$ **9.** 80° **11.** 65°
13. 6 **15.** 3 **17.** Two
18. $R(-2, 3)$, $S(-6, 3)$, $T(-8, 7)$ **21.** 112° **23.** 90°
25. $\overline{RT}$ **27.** $m\angle CBA$
29. 9.1 **31.** 8.1 **33.** $\frac{1}{6}$

4-2 Part B Try It

a. $\triangle ABC$ may be congruent to $\triangle OMN$. More information is needed. **b.** $\triangle DEF \cong \triangle RQP$; SAA Postulate

4-2 Part B Exercises

1. $\overline{MN}$ **3.** $\overline{MP}$ **5.** $\triangle ABC \cong \triangle FDE$; SSS Postulate
7. $\triangle PQR \cong \triangle KJH$; SAS Postulate **9.** $\triangle URS \cong \triangle STU$; SSS Postulate
11. Yes; SAA Postulate
13. Yes; SAA Postulate

15.

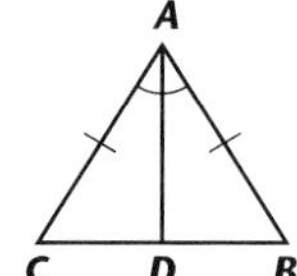

Given: $\overline{CA} \cong \overline{AB}$, D is on $\overline{BC}$, $\angle CAD \cong \angle DAB$ *Prove:* D is the midpoint of $\overline{BC}$
19. Vertical angles are congruent **21.** $\triangle ABC \cong \triangle DEF$; SAS Postulate
23. $\triangle ABC \cong \triangle DEC$; SAA Postulate **25.** $\triangle ABC$ may not be congruent to $\triangle DEC$.

4-2 Part C Try It

a. 1. (b), 2. (d), 3. (e), 4. (b), 5. (c)

4-2 Part C Exercises

1. Possible answer: $\overline{GH} \parallel \overline{JI}$, $\angle GHJ \cong \angle IJH$, $\angle HIJ$ is a right angle, $m\angle HGJ + m\angle GJI = 180°$, $\angle GHI$ is a right angle. **4. a.** 1. (c), 2. (b), 3. (b), 4. (a), 5. (d)
5. Reason 1: Given.
Reason 3: Given.
Statement 4: $\angle PQS \cong \angle RSQ$.
Statement 5: $\triangle PQS \cong \triangle RSQ$.
9. $A, B, C, E, F, G, I, J, K, M, N, O$ **11.** 109° **13.** 123°
15. Reason 1: Given.
Reason 2: Given.
Reason 3: Given.
Reason 4. SSS Postulate.
19. a. Possible answer: X bisects $\overline{VY}$ and $\overline{WZ}$. **b.** Possible answer: Show that $\overline{WX} \cong \overline{ZX}$, $\overline{YX} \cong \overline{VX}$ and $\angle WXV \cong \angle ZXY$ to show that $\triangle WXV \cong \triangle ZXY$ by SAS Postulate.

4-2 Part D Try It

a. *Given:* $\overline{ST} \cong \overline{UT}$, and $\angle VTS \cong \angle VTU$ because they are right angles. $\overline{VT} \cong \overline{VT}$ by the Reflexive Property. Now use the SAS Postulate.
b. $\overline{SV}$ and $\overline{UV}$, $\angle VST$ and $\angle VUT$, $\angle SVT$ and $\angle UVT$

4-2 Part D Exercises

1. a. $\triangle ABC \cong \triangle RST$
b. SSS Postulate **c.** Use CPCTC **3.** F; Symmetric

5. Possible Answer:

Statements	Reasons
1. e	1. Given
2. b	2. Given
3. c	3. Reflexive property
4. a	4. SSS
5. d	5. CPCTC

7.

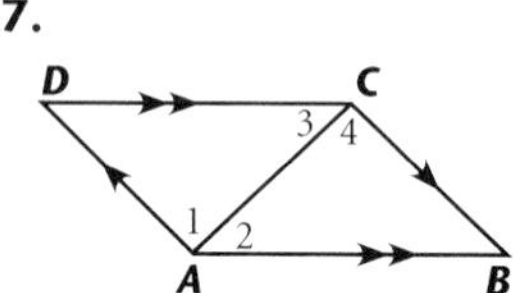

a. $\angle 2$ **b.** $\angle 1$ **c.** If two parallel lines are cut by a transversal, the alternate interior angles are congruent. **d.** Reflexive Property **e.** $\triangle CBA$
f. The ASA Postulate
g. CPCTC **8.** The triangles are congruent by the SAS Postulate. The fences are congruent by CPCTC, so they are the same length. **11.** $\angle N = 96°$; $\overline{OP} \cong \overline{OM}$ and $\overline{OQ} \cong \overline{ON}$ by the definition of *bisect.* $\angle MON \cong \angle POQ$ because vertical angles are congruent. $\triangle MON \cong \triangle POQ$ by the SAS Postulate. $\angle N \cong \angle Q$ by CPCTC. Therefore $x + 48 = 2x$. Solving the equation gives $x = 48$. Then $m\angle N = (x + 48)° = 96°$ **13.** $\angle ADC$
15. $\overline{AD}$, $\overline{DB}$ **17.** 62 cm
19. 21.1 in. **21. a.** The Reflexive Property **b.** Given information **c.** Given information **d.** ABC **e.** CDA
f. The SAA Postulate
g. CPCTC

4-2 Part E Self-Assessment

1. Always **2.** Never **3.** Never **4.** Always **5.** (c)
6. ASA Postulate **7.** SAA Postulate **8.** SAS Postulate
9. $NS = 2.8$ mi, $NT = 2$ mi; $\triangle NST \cong \triangle MTS$ by ASA
10. Possible answer: Prove triangles congruent, then any corresponding sides or angles are also congruent. **11.** 110
12. 210 **13.** 240; they differ by 180°. **14.** 48°

15. 6° **16.** 3° **17. a.** Definition of midpoint **b.** Vertical angles are congruent.
c. Given information **d.** SAA
18. 9 **19.** 26 **20. a.** Reason 1: Given. Reason 2: If two parallel lines are cut by a transversal, the alternate interior angles are congruent.
Statement 3: $\angle S \cong \angle U$.
Statement 4: $\overline{RT} \cong \overline{RT}$.
Statement 5: $\triangle URT \cong \triangle STR$.
Reason 5: SAA Postulate.
Statement 6: $\overline{RS} \cong \overline{TU}$.
Reason 6: CPCTC. **b.** Possible answer: Since it is given that $\overline{RU} \parallel \overline{ST}$, $\angle URT \cong \angle STR$ because if two parallel lines are cut by a transversal, the alternate interior angles are congruent. We are given $\angle S \cong \angle U$. $\overline{RT} \cong \overline{RT}$ by the Reflexive Property. So $\triangle URT \cong \triangle STR$ by the SAA Postulate. Therefore, $\overline{RS} \cong \overline{TU}$ by CPCTC.
22. Reason 1: Given.
Reason 2: Definition of *bisect.*
Reason 3: Vertical angles are congruent. Reason 4: SAS Postulate. Reason 5: CPCTC.
Reason 6: If alternate interior angles are congruent, the lines are parallel.

4-3 Part A Try It

a. $\angle A \cong \angle C$ **b.** 62

4-3 Part A Exercises

1. $\overline{FG}$ and $\overline{GH}$ have the same length. **3.** Definition of an *isosceles triangle* **5.** 25°
7. 19 **9. a.** $\overline{CD}$, $\overline{CE}$
b. Converse of the Isosceles Triangle Theorem **11.** $RS = 17$, $RT = ST = 16$

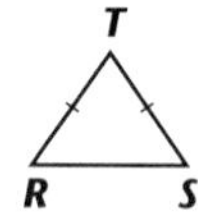

13. *Given:* $\angle 2 \cong \angle 4$ *Prove:* $\triangle XYZ$ is isosceles. *Proof:* 1. (b), Given; 2. (e), Vertical angles are congruent; 3. (a), Transitive Property; 4. (d), Isosceles Triangle Theorem Converse; 5. (c), Definition of *isosceles.* **15.** $\triangle DEF$ is equilateral **17.** SAS Postulate

19. ASA Postulate **21.** 80°
23. 45° **27.** Yes

4-3 Part B Exercises

1. HL Theorem **3.** HA Theorem **5.** $\overline{WX} \cong \overline{ZY}$ or $\overline{ZX} \cong \overline{WY}$ **7.** $\overline{WX} \cong \overline{ZY}$ and $\angle ZWX \cong \angle WZY$, or $\overline{ZX} \cong \overline{WY}$ and $\angle WZX \cong \angle ZWY$ (both). $\overline{WX} \cong \overline{ZY}$ and $\angle WZX \cong \angle ZWY$ or $\overline{ZX} \cong \overline{WY}$ and $\angle ZWX \cong \angle WZY$ (LA only).
9. Reason 1: Given.
Reason 2: Definition of a right triangle.
Statement 3: $\overline{AB} \cong \overline{CD}$.
Statement 4: $\overline{AC} \cong \overline{AC}$.
Reason 4: Reflexive Property.
Reason 5: HL Theorem.
11. a. Possible answer: $\triangle ABH \cong \triangle CBH$, $\triangle ADE \cong \triangle HDE$, $\triangle HFG \cong \triangle CFG$
b. HL Theorem, LL Theorem, LL Theorem, respectively.
15. Reason 1: Given.
Statement 2: $\angle YXZ \cong \angle WXV$.
Reason 3: Given.
Reason 4: If two parallel lines are cut by a transversal, the alternate interior angles are congruent.
Statement 5: $\triangle XVW \cong \triangle XZY$.
Reason 5: SAA Postulate
17. HL Theorem
19. Statement 1: $\angle EDF$ and $\angle CFD$ are right angles.
Reason 1: Given.
Reason 2: Definition of a right triangle.
Reason 3: Given.
Statement 4: $\overline{FD} \cong \overline{FD}$.
Reason 5: HL Theorem.
Statement 6: $\overline{DE} \cong \overline{FC}$.
Reason 6: CPCTC
21. Possible answer: So that we do not conclude that the triangles below are congruent.

4-3 Part C Try It

a. The sphere with radius 2 in. and center at point C.

4-3 Part C Exercises

1. a–c. Possible answer:

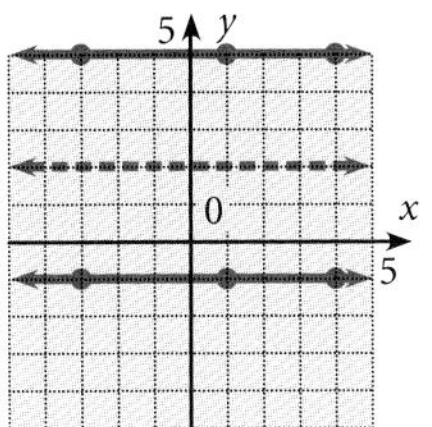

d. $y = 5, y = -1$ **3.** Two lines parallel to *m*, each 8 cm away. **5.** 2 **7.** The angle bisector **9.** It is the line with slope 1 passing through the origin.

11.

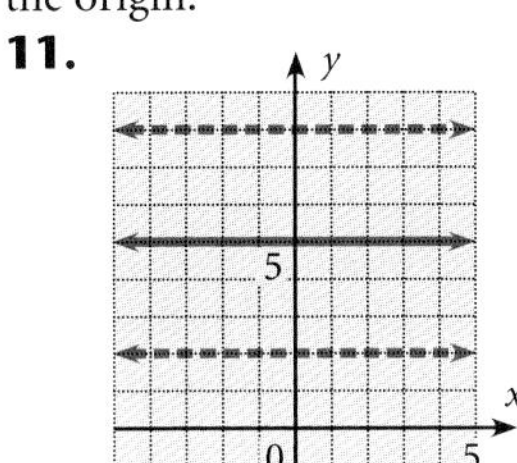

13.

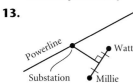

Powerline
Watt
Substation
Millie

Draw the line segment from Millie to Watt. Draw the perpendicular bisector of that line segment until it intersects with the power line. This is where the substation should be: It lies on the perpendicular bisector, so it is equidistant from the two cities. **15.** $\overleftrightarrow{TU}$ **17.** $\overleftrightarrow{VZ} \perp \overleftrightarrow{WY}$ **21.** Sphere with radius 3 in. and center at point *K*. **23.** 10 **25.** 20

4-3 Part D Try It

a.

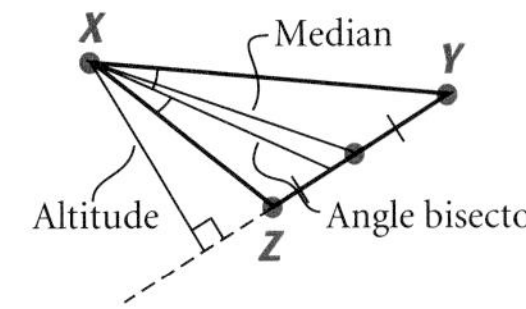

b.

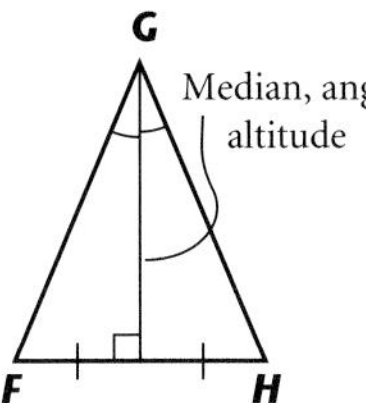

4-3 Part D Exercises

1. $\overline{CG}$ **3.** $\overline{AB}$ **7.** 24 **9. a.** 3 **b.** 6 **c.** 12 **d.** 18 **11.** Since it lies on all three perpendicular bisectors, the point of concurrency is equidistant from any pair of vertices and is therefore equidistant from all vertices. **12. a.** Given **b.** Definition of median **c.** $\overline{AD} \cong \overline{DC}$ **d.** Given **e.** Reflexive Property **f.** $\triangle ABD \cong \triangle CBD$ **g.** CPCTC **15.** $m\angle 1, m\angle 3, m\angle 5, m\angle 7, m\angle 9, m\angle 11, m\angle 13, m\angle 15 = 58°$; $m\angle 2, m\angle 4, m\angle 6, m\angle 8, m\angle 10, m\angle 12, m\angle 14 = 122°$ **17.** $\overline{HJ}$ **19.** $\overline{LK}$ **21.** 16 **23.** An equilateral triangle; Then the earlier results for isosceles triangles apply three times, with each of the angles in turn taken as the vertex.

4-3 Part E Self-Assessment

1. HL Theorem **2.** HL Theorem **3.** HA Theorem **4.** LA Theorem **5.** 128° **6.** (a) **7.** Line parallel to ℓ and *m*, halfway between ℓ and *m*. **8.** The perpendicular bisector of the line segment $\overline{PQ}$. **9.** The angle bisector of $\angle RPQ$. **10.** *C* **11.** $\overline{JK}$ **12.** $\triangle ONJ$ **13.** Reason 1: Given. Statement 2: $\angle 1 \cong \angle 2$. Statement 3: $\overline{BD} \cong \overline{BD}$. Reason 4: SAS Postulate. Reason 5: CPCTC. Statement 6: $\angle DAC \cong \angle DCA$. Reason 6: Isosceles Triangle Theorem. **14. a.** Given information **b.** Definition of right triangles **c.** Reflexive Property **d.** $\overline{XW} \cong \overline{ZW}$ **e.** $\triangle WYX \cong \triangle WYZ$ **f.** CPCTC **g.** *Y* is the midpoint of $\overline{XZ}$ **15. a.** LL **b.** LA **c.** None **d.** HA or LA **16.** Draw the line segment from the post office to the park. Draw the perpendicular bisector of the line segment until it intersects the bike path. This is where the rest shelter should be built.

Chapter 4 Review

1. Hypotenuse **2.** Medians **3.** Isosceles **4.** Locus **5.** 89° **6.** 8° **7.** 102°, 26°, 52° **8.** 242 **9.** $\triangle MNP \cong \triangle RQP$; ASA Postulate **10.** $\triangle UVX \cong \triangle WVX$; SAS Postulate **12.** Reason 1: Given. Reason 2: Linear-Pair Postulate. Reason 3: Supplements of congruent angles are congruent. Statement 4: $\overline{DB} \cong \overline{DB}$. Reason 5: Definition of *perpendicular.* Reason 6: Right angles are congruent. Statement 7: $\triangle ABD \cong \triangle CBD$. Reason 7: SAA Postulate. **13.** Draw the line segment from Carterville to Ely. Draw the perpendicular bisector. Any point on the bisector is equidistant from Carterville and Ely. Draw the angle bisector of the angle formed at the intersection of Highway 381 and Interstate 50. Any point on this bisector is equidistant from the two highways. Therefore the point of intersection of the two bisectors is where the water tower is to be built. **14.** $BN = 6.5$, $BQ = 8$ **15.** It is not possible to create a tesselation with any two triangles.

CHAPTER 5

5-1 Part A Try It

a. Perimeter = 80; Area = 400 **b.** Perimeter = 154; Area = 1176 **c.** Perimeter = 92; Area = 288

5-1 Part A Exercises

1. 24 **3.** Perimeter = 34; Area = 60 **5.** Perimeter = 52; Area = 120 **7.** 47 square units **9.** 53 square units **11.** The units are different; A perimeter could be represented by 100 cm, whereas an area could be represented by 100 cm². **13.** Rectangle = $2l + 2w$; Square = $4s$ **15.** Area = 49 **19.** Binomial **21.** Trinomial **23.** 50.41 m² **24.** 864 in.² or 6 ft² **25.** 20.35 cm² **27.** 24 **29. a.** Blue triangles: 1, 3, 6, 10, 15, ... add 2, add 3, add 4, add 5, ... white triangles: 0, 1, 3, 6, 10, ... add 1, add 2, add 3, add 4, ... **b.** 21:15, 28:21, 36:28 **c.** $\frac{n+1}{n-1}$ **d.** The limit is 1.

5-1 Part B Try It

a. $x^2 + 6x + 8$

b. $(x + 5)(x + 2)$

5-1 Part B Exercises

1. a–c.

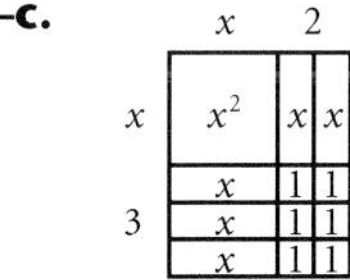

3.

5.

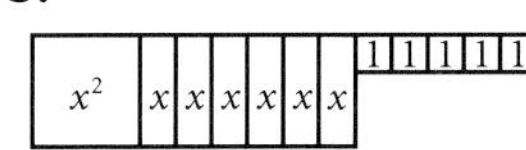

7. $x^2 + 4x + 3$ **9.** $6x^2 + 10x$ **11.** $(x + 3)(x + 5)$ **14.** $x + 2$ **17.** This pair of angles does not help to determine if *a* and *c* are parallel.

19. $a \parallel c$ because same-side interior angles are supplementary. **21.** $a \parallel b$ because alternate exterior angles are congruent. **23.** $\triangle IEF \cong \triangle HGF$; SAA Postulate **29.** $3x^2 + 5x + 2$ **31.** $(x + 3)(x + 1)$ **33.** $(x + 5)(2x + 1)$ **35.** 3, 6, 10: Add 3, add 4; The sum is a perfect square. $\frac{(n)(n+1)}{2} + \frac{(n-1)(n)}{2} = n^2$.

5-1 Part C Try It

a. $x \approx -4.32, x \approx 2.32$

5-1 Part C Exercises

1. a. $x^2 + 4x - 7 = 0$ **b.** $a = 1, b = 4, c = -7$ $x = \frac{-4 \pm \sqrt{(4)^2 - 4(1)(-7)}}{2(1)}$ **c.** $x = \frac{-4 \pm 2\sqrt{11}}{2}$ **d.** $x = -2 \pm \sqrt{11}$ **e.** $x \approx -5.32, x \approx 1.32$ **3.** $x = 4, x = -1$ **5.** $x \approx 1.85, x \approx -0.18$ **7.** $x = -1 \pm \sqrt{6}$ **9.** Length = 97 feet; width = 79 feet **11. a.** Length $= 2w - 6$ **b.** Area $= (2w - 6)w$ **c.** Width = 50; length = 94 **13. a.** $\frac{3}{8}$ **b.** $\frac{1}{4}$ **c.** $\frac{3}{8}$ **d.** $\frac{5}{8}$ **15.** $\frac{2}{3}$; 0.67, 67% **17.** $\frac{2}{5}$; 0.4, 40% **19.** $x \approx 0.21, x \approx 3.12$ **21.** $x \approx -1.95, x \approx 1.95$ **23. a.** The maximum price is \$30 and the minimum price is \$6.25.

5-1 Part D Try It

a. $\frac{1}{3}$ **b.** ≈ 0.37 **c.** 0.3125 **d.** $\frac{1}{12} \approx 0.83$

5-1 Part D Exercises

1. $\frac{3}{8}$ **3.** $\frac{1}{4}$ **5.** 0.25 **7.** 0.17 **11.** Michigan $\approx$ 0.59; Indiana $\approx$ 0.04; Illinois $\approx$ 0.05; Wisconsin $\approx$ 0.32 **13.** Complement = 6°; Supplement = 96° **15.** Complement $= 41\frac{1}{3}°$; Supplement $= 131\frac{1}{3}°$ **17.** 0.28 **19. a.** $\frac{1}{8}$ **b.** $\frac{1}{8}$ **c.** $\frac{1}{2}$

5-1 Part E Self-Assessment

1. 64 **2.** 6.75 **3.** 8.4 **4.** 120 **5.** 76 **6.** 19.8 **7.** 15.42 **8.** 50.8 **9.** $x^2 + 5x + 6$ **10.** $(x + 2)(x + 4)$ **11.** $x \approx -3.56, x \approx 0.56$ **12.** Reason 1: Given. Reason 2: Given. Reason 3: $\overline{RT} \cong \overline{RT}$. Reason 4: $\triangle RUT \cong \triangle TSR$; SSS. Postulate 5: CPCTC. Reason 6. $\overline{RS} \parallel \overline{TU}$; Alternate Interior Angles. **13.** $m\angle 2, 4, 6, 8 = 85°$; 95° **14.** $m\angle 2, 4, 6, 8 = 131°$; $m\angle 3, 5, 7 = 49°$ **15.** $m\angle 2, 4, 6, 8 = 80.8°$; $m\angle 3, 5, 7 = 99.2°$ **16.** (d) **17. a.** The 1990 bar is wider, as well as taller, than the 1980 bar. **b.** The bars should be the same width so that their areas are proportional. **18. a.** 0.16 **b.** 0.06 **19.** $\frac{9x}{x^2 + 9x + 20}$ The total area is $x^2 + 9x + 20$, and the winning area is $9x$.

5-2 Part A Try It

a. 49 **b.** 35.26 **c.** 24.6 in.^{2}

5-1 Part A Exercises

1. 11.04 in.^{2} **3.** 5.4 ft^2 **5.** 166.25 **7.** 2.88 m^2 **9.** 1.7 cm **11.** Possible answer: Quadrilateral does not belong because it is a type of figure, whereas the others are types of quadrilaterals. **13.** 3 (2.7 rounded up) **15.** 0.6 **17.** 0.5 **19. a.** L, M, Q, R, V, W **b.** F, K, P, U, I, N, S, X **c.** P, S **d.** $\frac{3}{10}$ **21.** $(x + 5)(x + 2)$ **23.** 34.04 cm^2 **25.** 3000 ft^2 **27.** 5.54 cm **29.** 11.5 in.

5-2 Part B Try It

a. Trapezoid **b.** Rhombus, parallelogram **c.** Rectangle, parallelogram **d.** Trapezoid **e.** Square, rectangle, rhombus, parallelogram **f.** 47.5 cm^2 **g.** 37.125 **h.** 30

5-2 Part B Exercises

1. 28 **3.** 319.2 **5.** 55 in.^{2} **7.** 7 units **9.** Rhombus **11.** Possible answer: $\triangle DEC$ and $\triangle BEA$ have equal areas, as do $\triangle ADE$ and $\triangle CBE$. For each pair, construct the altitudes and use SAS to show congruence of triangles. Use CPCTC to show congruence of the altitudes and of the corresponding bases. **13. a.** 0.91 mi^2 **15. a.** Each side length is equal to two radii. **b.** 9.0×10^{-14} mm^2 **17.** 420 **19.** 9.94 **21.** 67.5 m^2 **23.** 9.5 m **25.** Short base = 4; Long base = 8; Height = 11

5-2 Part C Exercises

1. a–d.

$x = 0$	$y = 0$
$x = 1$	$y = \frac{1}{2}$
$x = 2$	$y = 2$
$x = 3$	$y = 4.5$
$x = 4$	$y = 8$

b–c.

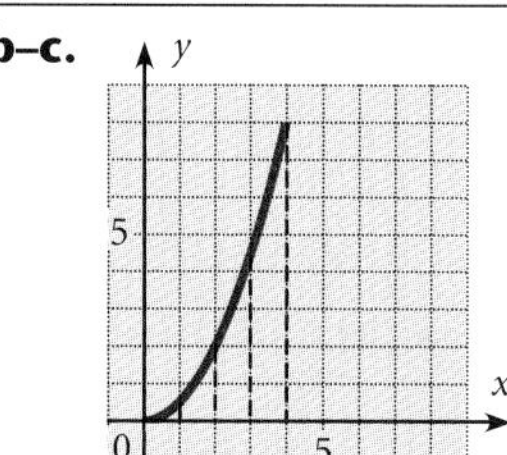

e. First area = 0.25; Second area = 1.25; Third area = 3.25; Fourth area = 6.25 **f.** 11 **3. a.** Approximate area = 36.5 **b.** 0.34 **5.** 19 **7. a.** 8 **b.** 32 **c.** 16 **d.** 48 **9.** $x \approx -0.65, x \approx 4.65$ **11.** 5.625 **13.** Area = 90.

5-2 Part D Self-Assessment

1. 38.08 cm^2 **2.** 2440 ft^2 **3.** 22.04 in.^{2} **4.** 13.1 **5.** $RC = 2$ cm; $\overline{MR}$ is a median. C is two-thirds the length of $\overline{MR}$ away from M on $\overline{MR}$. Therefore $RC = \frac{1}{2}MC$. **6.** $NS = 9$ cm; $\overline{NS}$ is a median. C is two-thirds the length of $\overline{NS}$ away from N on $\overline{NS}$. Therefore $NS = \frac{3}{2}$NC. **7.**

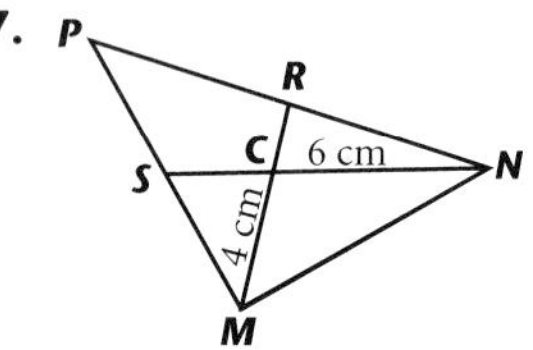

8. 9409 m^2 **9.** Width: 276 miles; Length: 376 miles; Solve the equation $(w)(w + 100) = 103{,}730$. **10.** (d) **11.** Possible answer: Use LL for two right triangles where the diagonals are the hypotenuses. Use CPCTC to show that diagonals are congruent. **12.** Bags of fertilizer = 30; Bags of seed = 5 **13.** 50 **14.** Area = 20 **15.** Area = 50 **16.** The perimeter will get smaller until C is directly above the midpoint of A and B, after which it will increase again. The area will remain constant, since neither the base nor the height will be changing. **17.** 0.16

5-3 Part A Try It

a. 10; Pythagorean triple = 6, 8, 10 **b.** 24; Pythagorean triple = 7, 24, 25 **c.** 5; Pythagorean triple = 5, 12, 13

5-3 Part A Exercises

1. a. 2, 4 **b.** 20 **c.** $2\sqrt{5}$ **d.** 4.47 **3.** 12 **5.** $2\sqrt{14}$, 7.48 **7.** 20 **9.** $\sqrt{5}$ **13.** 37 miles **14.** 13.90″ **15.** 14.8 ft **16.** Pythagorean triple **19.** $2\sqrt{5}$, 4.47 **21.** 4.24 **23.** $2\sqrt{10} \approx 6.32$ **25.** $2\sqrt{34}$, 11.66 **27.** 10 **29.** $\sqrt{5}$

5-3 Part B Try It

a. $y = 4\sqrt{3} \approx 6.93, z = 8$ **b.** $x = 10, y = 10\sqrt{3} \approx 17.32$ **c.** $x = 5, z = 10$ **d.** $x = 2.77, z = 5.54$

5-3 Part B Exercises

1. $PM = 6, PN = 6\sqrt{2}$ **3.** $b = 3, c = 3\sqrt{2} = 4.24$ **5.** $a = 4.6, c = 6.51$ **7.** $g = 7\sqrt{3} = 12.12, h = 14$ **9.** $f = 4, h = 8$ **11.** By the 45°- 45°-90° Theorem, $90\sqrt{2} \approx 127.28$ ft **13.** 389.71 **15.** $10\sqrt{2}$ **17.** $44\sqrt{3}$

18. 12.1 cm **23.** 10.05 **25.** 7.00 **27.** $f = 11$, $g = 11$ **29.** $b = 7\sqrt{3} = 12.12$, $c = 14$ **31.** $a = \frac{7}{3}\sqrt{3} = 4.04$, $c = \frac{14}{3}\sqrt{3} = 8.08$ **33.** $\left(\frac{\sqrt{3}}{2}, \frac{1}{2}\right)$ **35.** $\left(-\frac{\sqrt{2}}{2}, \frac{\sqrt{2}}{2}\right)$

5-3 Part C Try It

a. $\sqrt{409}$ **b.** $5\sqrt{17}$ **c.** 3 **d.** 11 **e.** $\sqrt{21}$

5-3 Part C Exercises

1. 21 **3.** 5.66 **5.** $(d - c)\sqrt{2}$ **9.** $x^2 + y^2 = 100$ **13.** $x^2 + y^2 = (9.3 \times 10^7)^2 \approx 8.65 \times 10^{15}$ **15. a.** Given information **b.** Reflexive Property **c.** Given information **d.** Definition of median **e.** Definition of midpoint **f.** SSS Postulate **g.** CPCTC **h.** Definition of angle bisector **17.** 0.44 **19.** 14.45 **21.** $x^2 + y^2 = 49$ **23.** $x^2 + y^2 = 4$ **25.** $y \approx \pm 7.84 \times 10^7$ mi

5-3 Part D Try It

a. Right **b.** Obtuse **c.** Acute

5-3 Part D Exercises

1. a. 41 **b.** 49 **c.** Obtuse **3.** Acute **5.** Right **7.** Right **9.** $3\sqrt{3} < x < 3\sqrt{5}$ **11.** The pole will be vertical when 25 feet of cable is extended. **21.** Right **23.** Obtuse **25.** Obtuse **27.** Yes, since one can always multiply the numbers of the triple by a constant to obtain a new triple. **29.** 4, 9, 16; $2^2, 3^2, 4^2$

5-3 Part E Self-Assessment

1. $c = 10$ cm **2.** $c < 10$ cm **3.** $c > 10$ **4.** (b) **5.** 0.205 **6.** 0.261 **7.** $\sqrt{300^2 + 225^2} = 375$ cm **8.** $x^2 + y^2 = 100$ **9.** 34.6 ft **10. a.** Two points determine a line **b.** Reflexive Property **c.** Given **d.** Given **e.** $\triangle ABC \cong \triangle CDA$ **f.** CPCTC **11.** 1, $\sqrt{2}$, 2, $\sqrt{5}$, $2\sqrt{2}$, 3, $\sqrt{10}$, $\sqrt{13}$, $3\sqrt{2}$ **12. a.** $\sqrt{7}$ **b.** 0.23

Chapter 5 Review

1. F; Non-overlapping **2.** F; Quadratic equation **3.** T **4.** F; Rectangle **5.** 23 **6.** 48 **7.** 10 m^2 **8.** $8\frac{1}{2}$ in. **9.** 17.07 cm **10.** 288 m **11.** $x^2 + 8x + 15$ **12.** $(x + 10)(x + 2)$ **13. a.** 6.25 ft^2 **b.** 0.16 **14. a.** $4x^2 + 18x + 20$ in. **b.** 0.9 **15.** $AQ = 14$, $BN = 30$ **16.** Possible answer: Show that $\triangle JNK \cong \triangle LNM$ and $\triangle JNM \cong \triangle LNK$, using the SAS Postulate. Use CPCTC to show alternate interior angles congruent, so the sides are parallel. **17.** 17.04 **18.** $4\sqrt{2}$ **19.** 32.0 in. **20.** Applying the Pythagorean Theorem to points on a coordinate plane gives the distance formula. Using the distance formula to find all points in a plane a given distance from the center point gives the equation for a circle. **21.** Possible answer: The farmer will prefer a plan that maximizes the area.

CHAPTER 6

6-1 Part A Try It

a. Possible answers: *DCBA*, *BADC*, *CDAB* **b.** $\overline{DB}$, $\overline{AC}$ **c.** Rectangle **d.** Possible answer: All rectangles are parallelograms. All rectangles are quadrilaterals. Some rectangles are squares.

6-1 Part A Exercises

1. Possible answer: *ZYXW*, *XYZW*, *WZYX* **7.** T **9.** $m\angle 1 = 90°$; $m\angle 2 = 90°$; $m\angle 3 = 105°$; $m\angle 4 = 75°$. The sum of the measures should be 360°. **11.** $\frac{4}{5}$ **13.** $x = 45$; $m\angle E = 100°$; $m\angle F = 135°$; $m\angle G = 45°$; $m\angle H = 80°$ **15.** $m\angle L = 52\frac{5}{7}°$; $m\angle K = 88\frac{3}{7}°$; $m\angle J = 113\frac{3}{7}°$; $m\angle M = 105\frac{3}{7}°$
Possible answers:
19. **21.**

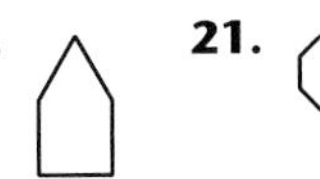

23.

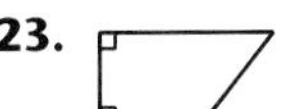

25. Rectangle **27.** Parallelogram **29.** $m\angle C = m\angle A = 60°$; $m\angle ADC = m\angle CBA = 120°$ **31.** $m\angle TXR = 85°$; $m\angle R = 75°$; $m\angle STX = 65°$; $m\angle S = 135°$ **33. a.** 0 **b.** $\frac{4}{25}$ **c.** $\frac{16}{25}$

6-1 Part B Try It

a. Possible answer: *ABCDEF* **b.** Hexagon **c.** 3 **d.** Convex

6-1 Part B Exercises

1. (a) Octagon; (b) Pentagon; (c) Not a polygon; (d) Quadrilateral **3.** Possible answer: *ABCDEF*, *DCBAFE*, *FEDCBA*; Hexagon **5.** Possible answer: Octopus–sea animal with 8 arms; Quadriceps–4 muscles in the upper leg; Quadraphonic–four way sound in stereo. **7.** 8 **11.** 2160° interior, 360° exterior 540° (a pentagon) **13.** 540° (a pentagon) **15.** 12 **17.** Triangles, rectangles **19. a.** 720°; Use the Angle-Sum Theorem for $n = 6$. **b.** 120° **21.** 40 **23.** 55; $\frac{n(n+1)}{2}$ **25.** All; (a) Quadrilateral; (b) Hexagon; (c) Hexagon **27.** Possible answer:

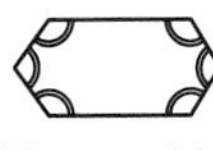

29. Possible answer:

31. Sum of interior angles = 1260°; Sum of exterior angles = 180° **33.** Sum of the interior angles = $(2x - 4)$ 180°; Sum of exterior angles = 360° **35.** 9 **37.** Octagon

6-1 Part C Try It

a. *RST* **b.** *LMTRQ* **c.** 7 faces; 10 vertices; 15 edges

6-1 Part C Exercises

1. *FABE*, *FED*, *EBCD*, *ACDF*, *ABC* **3.** $F = 5$, $V = 6$, $E = 9$ **5.** Face 1 is a triangle; Face 2 is an octagon **7.** $\overline{PN}$, $\overline{NM}$, $\overline{MU}$, $\overline{UT}$, $\overline{TS}$, $\overline{SR}$, $\overline{RQ}$, $\overline{QP}$ **9.** 4; Possible answer: You cannot enclose space with three polygons. **11.** T **17.** Quadrilateral **19.** $F = 12$, $V = 10$, $E = 20$; $12 + 10 - 20 = 2$ **21.** $m\angle C = 64°$; $m\angle B = m\angle D = 116°$ **23.** *HGFE*, *ABCD*, *AHGB*, *GFCB*, *FEDC*, *HEDA* **25.** $F = 6$, $V = 8$, $E = 12$; $6 + 8 - 12 = 2$ **27.** Rectangle **29.** Possible answer:

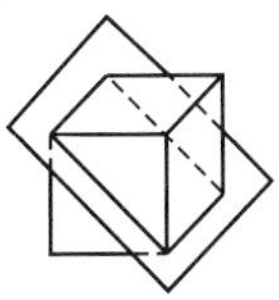

6-1 Part D Self-Assessment

1. $x = 38°$; $m\angle W = 66°$; $m\angle Z = 119°$; $m\angle Y = 38°$; $m\angle X = 137°$ **2.** Sum of interior angles = 1080°; Sum of exterior angles = 360° **3.** Sum of interior angles = 2340°; Sum of exterior angles = 360° **4.** 12 pentagons; 12 triangles; 24 quadrilaterals; one 12-gon
5.

Type	Sum of Interior Angles
Pentagon	540°
Triangle	180°
Quadrilateral	360°
12-gon	1800°

6. (c) **7.** 33.64 **8.** 360 **9.** 600 **10.** Yes; Consider the triangles formed by the poles, their shadows and the rays of the sun. The triangles are congruent by ASA or LA. The poles are the same height by CPCTC. **11.** 3 new faces, 1 new vertex, 4 new edges **12.** $F = 9$, $V = 9$, $E = 16$; $9 + 9 - 16 = 2$
13. Nonahedron
14. Possible answer:

15. Possible answer:

16. Not possible

6-2 Part A Try It

a. 135° **b.** 135° **c.** 45° **d.** 7 **e.** 15 **f.** 5.5 **g.** 10.5

6-2 Part A Exercise

1. a. $\overline{AB} \parallel \overline{DC}, \overline{AD} \parallel \overline{BC}$ **b.** $\overline{AB} \cong \overline{DC}, \overline{AD} \cong \overline{BC}$ **c.** $\angle D \cong \angle B, \angle A \cong \angle C$ **d.** $\angle A$ and $\angle D$; $\angle A$ and $\angle B$; $\angle B$ and $\angle C$; $\angle C$ and $\angle D$ **3.** The opposite angles of a parallelogram are congruent. **5.** The diagonals of a parallelogram bisect each other. **7.** 10 **9.** 78° **11.** $m\angle WXY = 44°$ **13.** (9, 2), (−1, 2), (1, −2) **17.** Possible answer:

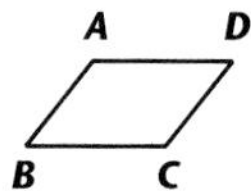

Given: $ABCD$ a parallelogram *Prove:* Angle pairs $\angle A$ and $\angle B$, $\angle B$ and $\angle C$, $\angle C$ and $\angle D$, and $\angle D$ and $\angle A$ are supplementary.
Statement 1: $ABCD$ is a parallelogram.
Reason 1: Given.
Statement 2: $\overline{AD} \parallel \overline{BC}$.
Reason 2: Definition of a *parallelogram.*
Statement 3: $\angle A$ and $\angle B$ are supplementary.
Reason 3: Same-side interior angles of parallel lines are supplementary.
Use similar proof to show that other consecutive angles are supplementary.
21. $\triangle EFG \cong \triangle IHG$; SAS Postulate **23.** $4\sqrt{3}$ in. **25.** 152° **27.** 42° **29.** The computer is listing triangles where $\overline{BD}$ and $\overline{EC}$ are corresponding parts. It will check to see whether these triangles can be proved congruent.

6-2 Part B Try It

a. Parallelogram; Opposite sides are congruent. **b.** Parallelogram; Diagonals bisect each other. **c.** Parallelogram; Consecutive angles are supplementary. **d.** May not be a parallelogram; The congruent sides may not be parallel.

6-2 Part B Exercises

1. Parallelogram; Both pairs of opposite angles are congruent. **3.** May not be a parallelogram; The conditions for a parallelogram may not be satisfied. **5.** May not be a parallelogram; The conditions for a parallelogram may not be satisfied. **7.** Parallelogram; Both pairs of opposite sides are parallel. **9.** Consecutive angles are supplementary. **11.** $x = 7$ and $y = 8$. **13.** $\frac{3}{22}$ **17.** Possible answer:

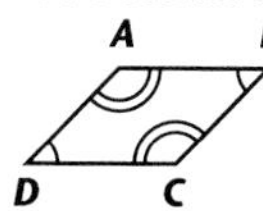

Given: $\angle A \cong \angle C$ and $\angle D \cong \angle B$ *Prove:* $ABCD$ is a parallelogram. *Proof:* $\angle A \cong \angle C$ and $\angle D \cong \angle B$ is given. $m\angle A = m\angle C$ and $m\angle D = m\angle B$ by definition of *congruent.* $m\angle A + m\angle B + m\angle C + m\angle D = 360°$ by the Angle-Sum Theorem for Quadrilaterals. $2(m\angle A) + 2(m\angle B) = 2(m\angle B) + 2(m\angle C) = 360°$ by substituting $m\angle A = m\angle C$ and $m\angle D = m\angle B$. Dividing by two, $m\angle A + m\angle B = m\angle B + m\angle C = 180°$. Therefore the pairs $\angle A$ and $\angle B$, and $\angle B$ and $\angle C$ are supplementary by definition. $\overline{AB} \parallel \overline{CD}$ and $\overline{AD} \parallel \overline{BC}$ since same side interior angles are supplementary. $ABCD$ is a parallelogram by definition. **19.** $3\sqrt{33} \approx 17.23$ **21.** 23.55 **23.** Sum of interior angles = 2520°; Sum of exterior angles = 360° **25.** Parallelogram; Both pairs of opposite sides are congruent. **27.** Parallelogram; The diagonals bisect each other. **29.** Possible answer:

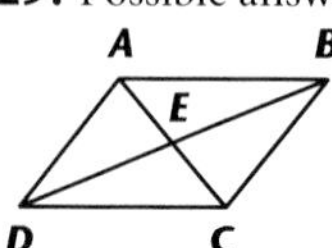

Given: $\overline{AC}$ and $\overline{BD}$ bisect each other. *Prove:* $ABCD$ is a parallelogram. *Proof:* $\overline{AC}$ and $\overline{DB}$ bisect each other by the given information. Let E be the point of intersection. $\overline{AE} \cong \overline{EC}$ and $\overline{DE} \cong \overline{EB}$ by definition of *bisect.* $\angle AEB \cong \angle CED$ and $\angle AED \cong \angle CEB$ because vertical angles are congruent. $\triangle AEB \cong \triangle CED$ and $\triangle AED \cong \triangle CEB$ by the SAS Postulate. Then $\angle BAE \cong \angle DCE$ and $\angle DAE \cong \angle BCE$ by CPCTC. $\overline{AB} \parallel \overline{DC}$ and $\overline{AD} \parallel \overline{BC}$ because alternate interior angles are congruent. Therefore, $ABCD$ is a parallelogram by definition.

6-2 Part C Try It

a. Parallelogram **b.** Rhombus **c.** Rectangle **d.** Square

6-2 Part C Exercises

1. Parallelogram **3.** Rhombus **5.** Parallelogram, rectangle, rhombus, square **7.** Parallelogram, rectangle, rhombus, square **9.** Rectangle, square **11.** Rectangle, square **13.** $3x = 15$ because diagonals bisect each other. So $x = 5$. $y - 5 = 15$ because diagonals are congruent and bisect each other. So $y = 20$. **15.** $(2x - 6)° + (2x - 6)° = 90°$ because diagonals of squares bisect angles and angles of squares are right angles. Solve for x to get $(4x - 12)° = 90°$ or $x = 25.5$. **17.**

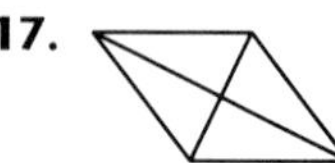

19. a. Rectangle; Diagonals are congruent. **b.** Rhombus; Diagonals are perpendicular but not congruent. **c.** Square; Diagonals are perpendicular and congruent. **23.**

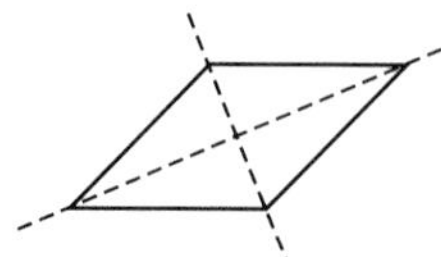

25. Reflect the triangle in one leg. Then reflect the result in the other leg. Reflect once more in the first leg. The four hypotenuses form a rhombus.

27. Possible answer:

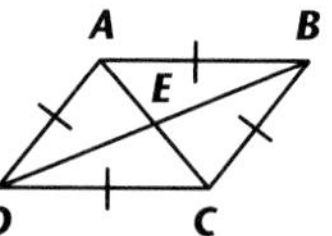

Given: $ABCD$ is a rhombus. *Prove:* $\overline{AC} \perp \overline{DB}$. *Proof:* $ABCD$ is a rhombus by the given information. $\overline{AD} \cong \overline{AB}$ by definition of a *rhombus.* $\overline{AC}$ bisects $\overline{DB}$ because diagonals of a parallelogram bisect each other. $\overline{DE} \cong \overline{EB}$ by definition of *bisect.* $\overline{AE} \cong \overline{AE}$ by the Reflexive Property. $\triangle AEB \cong \triangle AED$ by the SSS Postulate. $\angle AEB \cong \angle AED$ by CPCTC. $m\angle AEB + m\angle AED = 180°$ by the Linear-Pair Postulate. $m\angle AEB = m\angle AED$ by definition of *congruent.* $2(m\angle AEB) = 180°$ by substituting. Divide by 2 to get $m\angle AEB = 90°$. $\angle AEB$ is a right angle by definition of *right angle.* $\overline{AC} \perp \overline{DB}$ by definition of *perpendicular.* **29.** 1, 1, −1 **31.** Yes; The slopes are negative reciprocals of each other. **33.** The diagonals are congruent and bisect each other. **35.** The diagonals are congruent, perpendicular, and bisect each other. **37.** $x = 20$; $y = 70$ **42.** Possible answer: Place two congruent ropes across each other so that they bisect. When the measurements between the adjacent rope ends are equal, mark corners for a square foundation.

6-2 Part D Try It

a. $C(a, a)$, $B(-a, a)$, $A(-a, -a)$, $AB = 2a$ **b.** $C(a, a)$, $B(0, a)$, $A(0, 0)$, $AB = a$ **c.** $D(0, -a)$, $B(0, a)$, $A(-a, 0)$, $AB = a\sqrt{2}$

6-2 Part D Exercises

1. (c, b); $(c + a, 0)$ **3.** $(a + c, b)$ **5.** Slope of $\overline{HJ} = \frac{b}{a}$, slope of $\overline{GF} = \frac{b}{a}$, slope of $\overline{JF} = 0$, slope of $\overline{HG} = 0$. So $\overline{HJ} \parallel \overline{GF}$ and $\overline{JF} \parallel \overline{HG}$. **7. a.** Rectangle; Possible answer: The diagonals are congruent and the opposite sides are congruent. **b.** Possible answer: The distance from (0, 0) to (200, 120) is $\sqrt{(200)^2 + (-120)^2} = 40\sqrt{34}$. The distance from (0, 120) to (200, 0) is $\sqrt{(200)^2 + (120)^2} = 40\sqrt{34}$. The distance from (0, 0) to (0, 120) is 120. The distance from (200, 0) to (200, 120) is 120. The distance from (0, 0) to (200, 0) is 200. The distance from (0, 120) to (200, 120) is 200.
9. Possible answer:

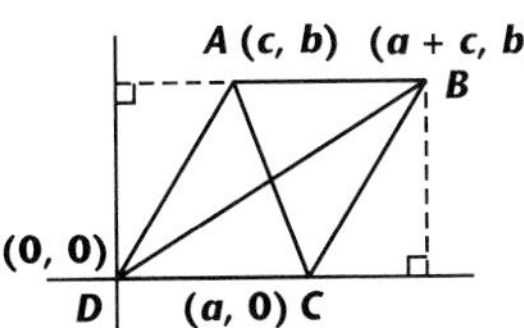

The midpoint of $\overline{DB}$ is $\frac{0 + (a + c)}{2}, \frac{0 + b}{2} = \left(\frac{a + c}{2}, \frac{b}{2}\right)$. The midpoint of $\overline{AC}$ is $\frac{(a + c)}{2}, \frac{0 + b}{2} = \left(\frac{a + c}{2}, \frac{b}{2}\right)$. The midpoints are identical, so $\overline{AC}$ bisects $\overline{DB}$ and $\overline{DB}$ bisects $\overline{AC}$ by definition of *bisect.* **11.** Acute **13.** Obtuse **17.** $F = 5$, $V = 6$, $E = 9$; $5 + 6 - 9 = 2$. **19.** $F(2a, 2b)$ **21.** Possible answer: S is the midpoint of $\overline{LM}$ so its coordinates are $\left(\frac{a}{2}, \frac{b}{2}\right)$. T is the midpoint of $\overline{PN}$ so its coordinates are $\left(\frac{c + d}{2}, \frac{b}{2}\right)$. The slope of $\overline{ST}$ is $\frac{\frac{b}{2} - \frac{b}{2}}{\frac{c + d}{2} - \frac{a}{2}} = 0$. The slope of $\overline{LP}$ is $\frac{0 - 0}{d - 0} = 0$ and the slope of $\overline{MN}$ is $\frac{b - b}{c - a} = 0$. Therefore, $\overline{ST} \parallel \overline{LP}$ and $\overline{ST} \parallel \overline{MN}$. $ST = \frac{c + d - a}{2}$. $MN = c - a$ and $LP = d$. The average of MN and LP is $\frac{MN + LP}{2} = \frac{c + d - a}{2}$. Therefore $ST = \frac{MN + LP}{2}$. **23. a.** A is the computer. It asks questions or makes restatements only. **b.** Possible answer: It asks questions using key words from the previous response.

6-2 Part E Self-Assessment

1. Sometimes; When the rectangle is a square. **2.** Always; The diagonals of a parallelogram bisect each other and a rhombus is a parallelogram. **3.** Never; When the diagonals bisect each other the figure is a parallelogram, and a trapezoid is never a parallelogram. **4.** Rhombus **5.** Rectangle, square **6.** Square **7.** (c) **8.** 115° **9.** 3 **10.** 28° **11.** 10 **12.** 30.0 ft **13.** 90° **14.** 120° **15.** 144° **16.** $\overline{AB}$ is always parallel to the ground and $\overline{DC}$ is always parallel to $\overline{AB}$. $ABCD$ is a parallelogram since $AB = CD$ and $AD = BC$. **17.**

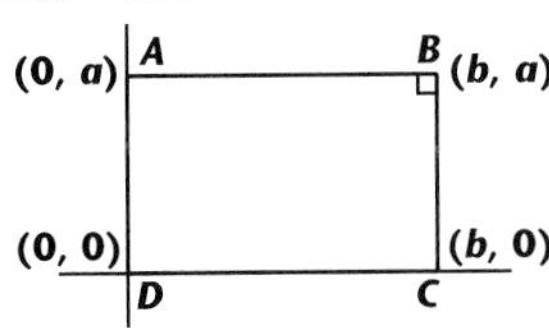

$DB = \sqrt{a^2 + b^2}$. $AC = \sqrt{(0 - b)^2 + a^2} = \sqrt{a^2 + b^2}$. Therefore, $\overline{AC} \cong \overline{DB}$ by definition of *congruent.* **18.** Possible answer: The advantage of a coordinate proof is that you are able to do calculations using the coordinates. A disadvantage is that the coordinate method may involve calculations using the coordinates.

Segments can be shown to be parallel, perpendicular, or congruent using coordinate methods.

6-3 Part A Try It

a. Equilateral **b.** Regular **c.** Equiangular **d.** 1086 cm²

6-3 Part A Exercises

1. Regular **3.** Equiangular **5.** Interior angle = 135°; Exterior angle = 45° **7.** Interior angle = 120°; Exterior angle = 60° **11.** Center **13.** Radius **15.** 1545 cm² **17.** 64 m² **19.** 696 in.² **21.** $a = 6\sqrt{3}$; $r = 12$; Area $= 216\sqrt{3} \approx 374.1$ **23.** $\frac{21\sqrt{3}}{2} \approx 18.2$ ft² **27.** The diagonals are perpendicular, congruent, and bisect each other. **29.** $x = \frac{-7 \pm \sqrt{37}}{2} \approx -0.46$ or -6.54 **31.** $x = \frac{2 \pm \sqrt{34}}{3} \approx -1.28$ or 2.61 **33.** Interior angle = 150°; Exterior angle = 30° **35.** 17.6 ft² **37.** $a = 8$; $r = 8\sqrt{2}$; Area = 256 **39.** $a = \frac{8}{3}\sqrt{3}$; $r = \frac{16}{3}\sqrt{3}$; Area $= 64\sqrt{3} \approx 110.9$ **41. a.** 186 in.² **b.** 714 in.² **c.** 4 times greater

6-3 Part B Try It

a. Regular icosahedron
b. Regular hexahedron (cube)
c. Regular tetrahedron

6-3 Part B Exercises

1. Tetrahedron **3.** Hexahedron **5.** Isosahedron **7.** Regular dodecahedron **11.** Regular hexahedron **13. a.** Cube **b.** $F = 6$, $V = 8$, $E = 12$; $6 + 8 - 12 = 2$ **15.** 324° **16.** Possible answers: $\overrightarrow{BC} = \overrightarrow{AD}$; $\overrightarrow{BH} = \overrightarrow{AE}$; $\overrightarrow{AC} = \overrightarrow{FH}$ **19.** $x = \frac{40}{3}$ **21.** $\frac{7}{2}$ **23.** Regular tetrahedron **25.** 180° **27.** Use a regular tetrahedron and put each number on a side.

6-3 Part C Self-Assessment

1. The faces of regular polyhedrons are regular polygons. **2. a.** 120° **b.** 60° **c.** $a = \frac{5}{2}$ mm; $r = \frac{5}{3}\sqrt{3}$ mm; $A = \frac{25}{2}\sqrt{3} \approx 21.65$ mm² **d.** ≈ 4.62 cells **3.** (b)
4.

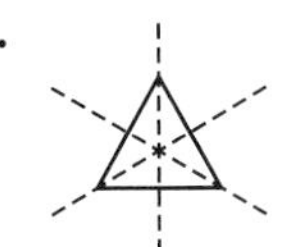

5.

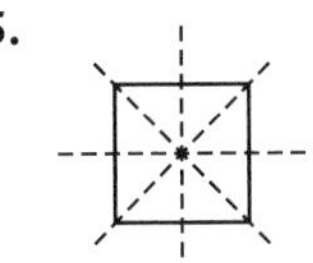

6.

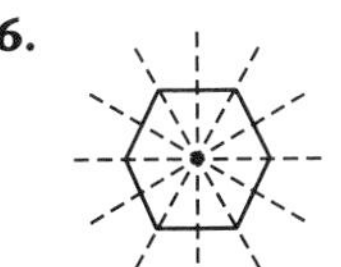

7. n **8.** Possible answer:

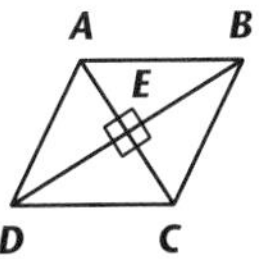

Given: $ABCD$ is a parallelogram, $\overline{AC} \perp \overline{DB}$. *Prove:* $ABCD$ is a rhombus. *Proof:* $ABCD$ is a parallelogram by the given information. $\overline{BD}$ bisects $\overline{AC}$ because diagonals of a parallelogram bisect each other. $\overline{AE} \cong \overline{EC}$ by the definition of *bisect.* $\overline{EB} \cong \overline{EB}$ by the Reflexive Property. $\overline{AC} \perp \overline{DB}$ is given. $\angle AEB$ and $\angle CEB$ are right angles by definition of *perpendicular.* $\triangle AEB \cong \triangle CEB$ by LL. $\overline{AB} \cong \overline{BC}$ by CPCTC. $\overline{AB} \cong \overline{DC}$ and $\overline{AD} \cong \overline{BC}$ because opposite sides of a parallelogram are congruent. $\overline{AB} \cong \overline{DC} \cong \overline{BC} \cong \overline{AD}$ by the Transitive Property. $ABCD$ is a rhombus by definition. **9.** Rectangle; $\overline{AH} \cong \overline{BG}$ and $\overline{AB} \cong \overline{HG}$ so it is a parallelogram. $AG = BH$ so it is a rectangle. It is not a square because $AB \neq AH$. **10.** Let x be the width, then $x(x + 48) = 41{,}040$. So $x^2 + 48x - 41{,}040 = 0$. Solve for x to get $x = 180$ (or $x = -228$). 180 ft wide and 228 ft long **11. a.** 36° **b.** 60°

12. Regular tetrahedron; Regular octahedron; Regular icosahedron **13.** From left to right: cut off vertices of a regular tetrahedron, octahedron, icosahedron, and dodecahedron. **14.** Regular octahedron

Chapter 6 Review

1. Apothem; The other terms are all classifications of polygons and polyhedrons.
2. Center; The other terms all refer to distances/segments. **3.** Interior, 540°; Exterior, 360°
4. Possible answer:

5. Octagon **6.** 8; Octahedron **7.** Parallelogram; The diagonals bisect each other. **8.** May not be a parallelogram; The congruent sides may not be parallel.
9. Parallelogram; Both pairs of opposite sides are parallel.
10. M is at $\left(\frac{b+d}{2}, \frac{c+e}{2}\right)$. N is at $\left(\frac{a+d}{2}, \frac{e}{2}\right)$. O is at $\left(\frac{a}{2}, 0\right)$. P is at $\left(\frac{b}{2}, \frac{c}{2}\right)$. Slope of $\overline{MN}$ is $\frac{\frac{e}{2} - \frac{(c+e)}{2}}{\frac{(a+d)}{2} - \frac{(b+d)}{2}} = \frac{-\frac{c}{2}}{\frac{(a-b)}{2}} = \frac{c}{b-a}$. Slope of $\overline{NO}$ is $\frac{0 - \frac{e}{2}}{\frac{a}{2} - \frac{(a+d)}{2}} = \frac{-\frac{e}{2}}{-\frac{d}{2}} = \frac{e}{d}$.

Slope of $\overline{OP}$ is $\frac{\frac{c}{2} - 0}{\frac{b}{2} - \frac{a}{2}} =$

$\frac{\frac{c}{2}}{\frac{(b-a)}{2}} = \frac{c}{b-a}$. Slope of

$\overline{PM}$ is $\frac{c}{b-a}$. $\frac{\frac{(c+e)}{2} - \frac{c}{2}}{\frac{(b+d)}{2} - \frac{b}{2}} = \frac{\frac{e}{2}}{\frac{d}{2}}$ $= \frac{e}{d}$. So $\overline{MN} \parallel \overline{OP}$ and $\overline{NO} \parallel \overline{PM}$. Therefore, $MNOP$ is a parallelogram by definition.
11. 144° **12.** Put 1, 2, 3, and 4 on two faces each and 5 on the four remaining faces.
13. $a = \sqrt{3}$ in.; $r = 2\sqrt{3}$ in.; Area $= 9\sqrt{3} \approx 15.6$ in.^{2}
14. $h = 2\sqrt{21}$ cm, area $= 34\sqrt{21} \approx 155.8$ cm^2
15. Possible answer: The sum of the interior angles of a convex polygon is given by the formula $(n-2)180°$ where n is the number of sides. The sum of the exterior angles is always 360°.

CHAPTER 7

7-1 Part A Try It

a. Similar; $\frac{1}{2}$ **b.** Similar; 3
c. Not similar **d.** Similar; $\frac{1}{3}$

7-1 Part A Exercises

1. 2 **5.** 22.5 in. × 30 in.
7. F; The length and width of the sides can be changed independently and the second figure can still be a rectangle.
9. T; All angles are 60° (therefore congruent) and all the sides, being equal in length, must be the same multiple of the original triangle's sides.
10. Smallest: 2.6 cm × 3.9 cm Largest: 5.6 cm × 8.4 cm
13. A to $B = \frac{3}{2}$; B to $A = \frac{2}{3}$
15. Similar; $\frac{2}{3}$ **19.** 9 **21.** $2\frac{2}{5}$ **25.** Similar; Similarity ratio $= \frac{2}{1}$ **27.** 8 cm × 12 cm **29.** 11 in. × about 14.67 in.

7-1 Part B Try It

a. $\triangle EFG \sim \triangle JIH$; $\angle E \cong \angle J$, $\angle F \cong \angle I$, $\angle G \cong \angle H$; $\frac{EF}{JI} = \frac{FG}{IH} = \frac{GE}{HJ} = \frac{1}{2}$ **b.** $QRST \sim YXWV$; $\angle T \cong \angle V$, $\angle Q \cong \angle Y$, $\angle R \cong \angle X$, $S \cong \angle W$; $\frac{QR}{YX} = \frac{RS}{XW} = \frac{ST}{WV} = \frac{TQ}{VY} = 3$
c. $m\angle E = 67°$, $m\angle G = 107°$, $m\angle N = 43°$ **d.** $x = 14$, $y = 15$, $z = 25$ **e.** 2.5

7-1 Part B Exercises

1. $\angle A \cong \angle E$, $\angle B \cong \angle F$, $\angle C \cong \angle G$, $\angle D \cong \angle H$ $\frac{AB}{EF} = \frac{BC}{FG} = \frac{CD}{GH} = \frac{DA}{HE}$ **3.** 49°
5. 15 **7.** $\frac{2}{3}$ **11.** 11.57
13. $\frac{DF}{AC} = \frac{3}{7}$ **14.** T: (18, 7); U: (18, 19); V: (2, 19) **15.** T: (6, 7); U: (6, 10); V: (2, 10)
17. 1599 miles **19.** Building will be 31 m × 52.8 m **21.** $a = 155.56$; $c = 155.56$
23. $d = 3023.58$; $e = 6047.17$
25. Interior angle = 140°; Exterior angle = 40°
27. $\angle M \cong \angle P$, $\angle N \cong \angle Q$, $\angle O \cong \angle R$; $\frac{OM}{RP} = \frac{MN}{PQ} = \frac{NO}{QR}$
29. 100° **31.** 12 **33.** $\frac{4}{3}$
34. Yes; Compare a right isosceles triangle and an equilateral triangle.

7-1 Part C Try It

a. 6 cm^2 **b.** 20 cm

7-1 Part C Exercises

1. a. $\frac{5}{4}; \frac{5}{4}$ **b.** $\left(\frac{5}{4}\right)^2 = \frac{25}{16}$
3. Area ratio $= \frac{64}{169}$; Perimeter ratio $= \frac{8}{13}$ **4.** $\frac{3}{2}$
5. $\frac{3}{2}$ **7.** $\frac{5}{4}$ **8.** Multiply by $\sqrt{2}$ **10.** Yes; $\frac{\text{Area}_1}{\text{Area}_2} = \text{ratio}^2$; ratio = 1 here, so that the sides are not only proportional, but congruent. Since the figures are similar, the corresponding angles are also congruent, so the figures are congruent. **15.** Yes; Corresponding angles are congruent (here, 90° each); We are given $\frac{l_1}{w_1} = \frac{l_2}{w_2}$, but this can be rewritten as $\frac{l_1}{l_2} = \frac{w_1}{w_2}$; i.e., corresponding sides are in the same proportion.
17. Area ratio $= \frac{9}{25}$; Perimeter ratio $= \frac{3}{5}$ **19.** $\frac{4}{3}$
21. a. 0.20 **b.** 0.79; 4 times part (a).

7-1 Part D Try It

a. 40.5 **b.** 6.2

7-1 Part D Exercises

1. (b) **3.** 0.618 **5.** 161.80
6. 0.618; 1.618 − 0.618 = 1
8. Golden rectangle; Golden ratio **11.** 19.425
12. 3564.5 **13.** 7.5
15. $x = 30$; $y = 6$; Opposite sides are congruent. **17.** 1.618 **19.** 18.54 **21.** Cut a strip 8.5 − 6.798 = 1.702 in. wide (and 11 in. long) off along the 11 in. side.

7-1 Part E Self-Assessment

1. Always true **2.** Sometimes true **3.** Always true
4. Interior angle = 120°; Exterior angle 60° **5.** Interior angle = 150°; Exterior angle 30° **6.** Interior angle= 157.5°; Exterior angle 22.5° **7.** 5 m by 4 m **8.** 2.9 cm by 1.1 cm **9.** 100 cm; 75 cm **10.** 78.125 ft **11.** 90°
12. 56° **13.** 60 **14.** $\frac{3}{5}$
15. $\frac{5}{3}$ **16.** $x = 5$; $y = 4$; $z = 6$; $w = 65$ **17.** $x = 5.83$; $y = 5.14$; $z = 4.17$; $w = 55$ **18.** (d) **19. a.** 11.12 feet **b.** $\frac{\text{Area of Tremendo}}{\text{Area of Comfy}} = 4 = 2^2$. Screen is 2(18) by 2(11.12), or 36 × 22.24 feet

7-2 Part A Try It

a. $\angle ABE \cong \angle CBD$ since they are vertical angles. $\angle A \cong \angle C$ because they are alternate interior angles ($\overline{AE}$ and $\overline{DC}$ are parallel). By the two congruent angle conjecture $\triangle ABE \sim \triangle CBD$. **b.** $\angle ZVY \cong \angle W$ since both are right angles; $\angle Z$ is used in both $\triangle VZY$ and $\triangle WZX$; By the two congruent angles conjecture $\triangle ZVY \sim \triangle ZWX$.

7-2 Part A Exercises

1. 30° **3.** 60° **5.** Not similar; $\angle N = 70°$, so there is no second pair of congruent angles. **7.** Given $\angle WXZ \cong \angle ZXY$ and $\angle WZX \cong \angle XYZ$, $\triangle XWZ \sim \triangle XZY$ by AA; $x = 7.5$; $y = 4.5$ **9.** 37.5 feet
11. $\angle VXW \cong \angle YXZ$ because they are vertical angles; $\angle W \cong \angle Y$ because they are alternate interior angles of two parallel lines; Thus, by AA, $\triangle VXW \sim \triangle ZXY$. Since the triangles are similar, the corresponding sides are proportional, so $\frac{VW}{YZ} = \frac{WX}{XY}$. **13. a.** $\frac{9}{12} = \frac{12}{16}$, so 12 is the geometric mean of 9 and 16.

b. $\frac{16}{20} = \frac{20}{25}$, so 20 is the geometric mean of 16 and 25. $\frac{9}{15} = \frac{15}{25}$, so 15 is the geometric mean of 9 and 25. **15.** 16 **17.** 128° **19.** $\frac{2}{3}$ **21.** $\frac{4}{9}$ **23.** From the given information, $\angle T \cong \angle Q$. $\angle U \cong \angle R$ because right angles are congruent. By AA, $\triangle TUV \sim \triangle QRS$. **25.** Based on given information, $\triangle FHG \sim \triangle JHI$ by AA; $x = 4$; $y = 1$ **27. a.** Assume $\overline{XY} \parallel \overline{AB}$, so $\angle X \cong \angle B$ and $\angle Y \cong \angle A$ (alternate interior angles); By AA, the triangles are similar. **b.** 3.5 m **c.** 2.5 m

7-2 Part B Try It

a. $\frac{7.8}{5.2} = \frac{8.1}{5.4} = 1.5$; Two pairs of corresponding sides are proportional, and the angles between them are given as congruent, so by SAS; $\triangle JHI \sim \triangle EDF$; $x = 4.8$. **b.** $\frac{TR}{RQ} = \frac{SR}{PR} = \frac{3.2}{9.6} = \frac{1}{3}$. The interior (to the triangles) angles formed by TQ intersecting PS are congruent because they are vertical angles. Thus, by SAS, $\triangle PRQ \sim \triangle SRT$; $x = 8.4$.

7-2 Part B Exercise

1. $\triangle ABC \sim \triangle DEF$ by SAS **2.** $\triangle GHK \sim \triangle GIJ$ by AA **3.** $\triangle KML \sim \triangle PMN$ by SAS **5.** $\triangle FGH \sim \triangle JKH$ by SAS; $x = 124$; $y = 33$ **9.** $x = 60$; SSS **11.** $x = 6$; SAS **13.** If two triangles are equilateral, all angles measure 60° and are congruent. The triangles are similar by AA. **17.** Extend two line segments along $\overline{RS}$ and $\overline{RT}$. Place the compass point at S and mark segment $\overline{SV}$ such that $\overline{RS} \cong \overline{SV}$; Similarly use the compass to create $\overline{TW} \cong \overline{RT}$. $\frac{RV}{RS} = \frac{RW}{RT} = 2$. Both triangles share $\angle R$, so SAS assures similarity of $\triangle RST$ and $\triangle RVW$. **19.** $\triangle GHI \sim \triangle LKJ$; Similarity by SAS; $x = 3.6$; $y = 75.5$ **21.** Possible answer: $x = 15$; SAS

23.

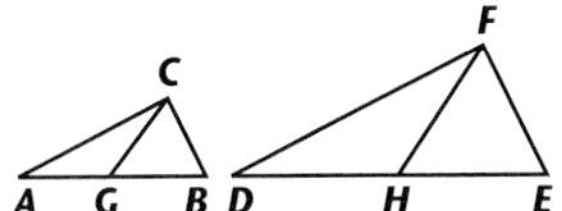

Possible answer: $\triangle ABC \sim \triangle DEF$ and $\overline{CG}$ and $\overline{FH}$ are medians. Show that $\triangle AGC \sim \triangle DHF$ by SAS. Therefore $\frac{AC}{DF} = \frac{GC}{HF}$.

7-2 Part C Try It

a. $IJKL$; C **b.** $\frac{3}{2}$ **c.** $\frac{1}{2}$

7-2 Part C Exercises

1. a. 7 cm **b.** 135° **3.** $k = \frac{1}{3}$ **5.** Scale factor **6.** Similar **9.** Enlargement; $k = 2$; Center of triangles is found by drawing lines through corresponding vertices and observing where lines intersect. **11.** $A' = \left(\frac{3}{2}, 0\right)$, $B' = \left(\frac{7}{2}, 2\right)$, $C' = \left(-\frac{3}{2}, 1\right)$ **13. a.** $\frac{1}{2}$ in. = 60 ft = 60(12) in. = 720 in., so $k = \frac{1}{2(720)} = \frac{1}{1440}$. **c.** Figures and their dilated images are similar, and the ratio of the areas of two similar polygons is (similarity ratio)^2, so $\frac{\text{Area actual}}{\text{Area plan}} = (1440)^2$ **15.** They bisect each other. **17.** They bisect each other and are congruent. **19.** 10 ft × 7 ft **21.** Enlargement; $k = 4$; Center of dilation is one square to the left of the left leg (at the base) of the smaller "A". **23.** $A' = (6, 6)$, $B' = (18, 12)$, $C' = (-3, -9)$ **27.** Dilations preserve the measures of angles in a figure. Hence, a triangle will be similar to its image by AA.

7-2 Part D Try It

a. 8.5 **b.** 57 **c.** 12.4

7-2 Part D Exercises

1. $SW = 50$, $WU = 30$, $US = 40$ **3.** $AC = 20$, $BC = 10$, $BE = 9$ **5.** $m\angle A = 54.5°$; $BE = 8.5$ **9. a.** 16 mm **b.** 8 mm; 20 mm from the horizon measured along the tracks

11. Possible answer: $\overline{EF} \parallel \overline{CB}$ since a midsegment is parallel to the third side. Let G be the point where $\overline{AD}$ intersects $\overline{EF}$. $\angle AFE \cong \angle ABD$ because corresponding angles are congruent. $\angle DAB \cong \angle DAB$ by the Reflexive Property. $\triangle GAF \sim \triangle DAB$ by AA. $\frac{AF}{AB} = \frac{1}{2}$ because $\overline{EF}$ is the midsegment. $\frac{AG}{AD} = \frac{1}{2}$ by the definition of *similar*. $AG = \frac{1}{2}AD$, so $\overline{EF}$ bisects $\overline{AD}$. **13.** Yes; By AA **15.** $GH = 6$, $HJ = 6$, $JK = 18$ **17.** $JK = 14$, $m\angle J = 138°$

19. Reason 1: Given.
Reason 2: Corresponding angles of two parallel lines are congruent.
Reason 3: AA
Reason 4: Corresponding sides of similar triangles are proportional.
Reason 5: Segment Addition Postulate.
Reason 6: Substitution (into Step 4). **21.** 21 **23.** $31\frac{1}{5}$

7-2 Part E Self-Assessment

1. Possible answer: $x = 2\frac{10}{11}$ or 5.5; SAS **2.** $x = 6.66$; SSS **3.** $x = 39$; AA **4.** $\triangle AEB \sim \triangle ADC$; Similar by AA; $x = 3.75$; $y = 9$ **5.** $\triangle HFG \sim \triangle HJI$ by SAS; $x = 53°$; $y = 3.33$ **6.** $\triangle LMK \sim \triangle QPN$ by SSS; $x = 53$; $y = 37$ **7.** 4,629.9 ft **8.** $ST = \frac{1}{2}SV$ and $SU = \frac{1}{2}SW$ since $\overline{TU}$ is the midsegment; So $\frac{ST}{SV} = \frac{SU}{SW} = \frac{1}{2}$. $\angle S \cong \angle S$ by the Reflexive Property. $\triangle STU \sim \triangle SVW$ by SAS. **9.** Area $\triangle ABC = \frac{1}{16}$ area $\triangle XYZ$ **10.** Diagonals bisect each other and are of the same length; $x = 9$, $y = -4$. **11.** Diagonals bisect at right angles; $x = 132$, $y = 14$ **12.** Opposite sides of a rectangle are congruent; $x = 5$, $y = 3$. **13. a.** $\frac{b}{2}$ (half as much); Twice the acreage means twice the crop.

b. If cost per foot of fence is constant, it should cost $\sqrt{2}f$. **15.**

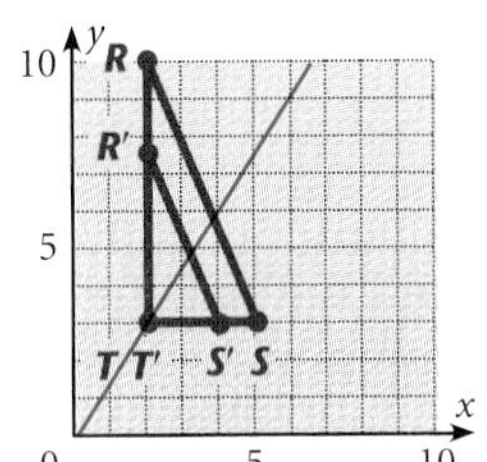

Perimeter ratio = $\frac{3}{2}$; Area ratio = $\frac{9}{4}$ **16.** (a) **17.** Possible answer: Images under dilation are similar to the pre-image **18.** $(k(x - a) + a, k(y - b) + b)$ **19.** Possible answer: Create a scissors-like or pliers-like device where the astronauts can close the handles to pick up/measure the object on the ground by using the distance between the handles to measure the size of the object via similar triangles.

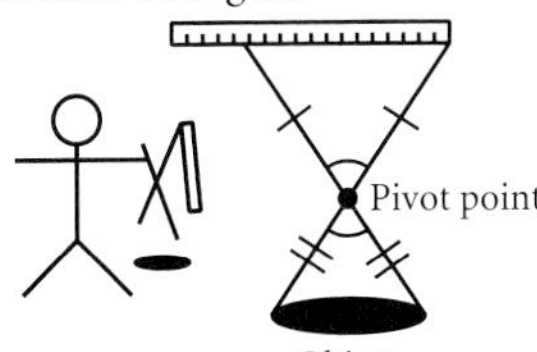

7-3 Part A Try It

a. $\frac{5}{13}$ **b.** $\frac{12}{13}$ **c.** $\frac{12}{13}$ **d.** $\frac{12}{5}$

7-3 Part A Exercises

1. a. $m\angle A = 34°$ **b.** $\tan A = \frac{a}{6}$ **c.** $\tan 34° = \frac{a}{6}$; $6 \tan 34° = a$ **d.** $a \approx 4.05$ **3.** $\frac{15}{17} = 0.88$ **5.** $\frac{15}{17} = 0.88$ **7.** $\frac{15}{8} = 1.88$ **9.** Sine **11.** $\sin 72° = 0.95$, $\cos 72° = 0.31$, $\tan 72° = 3.08$ **13.** $x = 3.18$, $y = 6.24$ **15.** $x = 25.26$, $y = 28.88$ **17.** 250.47 m; 52.08 m **20.** 15.66 feet **23.** The tangent can be greater than 1. **25. a.** $\angle A \cong \angle A$ and $\angle D \cong \angle ABC$ (corresponding angles of parallel lines). $\triangle ABC \sim \triangle ADE$ by AA. **b.** 45.26 m **27.** $\frac{24}{7} \approx 3.43$ **29.** $\sin 18° = 0.31$, $\cos 18° = 0.95$, $\tan 18° = 0.32$

31. $\sin 89° = 1.00$, $\cos 89° = 0.02$, $\tan 89° = 57.29$
33. $x = 27.64$, $y = 26.14$
35. 61.57 m **37. a.** $x = 1$
b. $x = 1$ **c.** $x = 1$
d. For any angle A, $(\sin A)^2 + (\cos A)^2 = 1$

7-3 Part B Try It

a. 34° **b.** 49° **c.** $m\angle 1 = 49°$, $m\angle 2 = 41°$

7-3 Part B Exercises

1. a. 18° **b.** $\tan A = \frac{h}{d}$
3. 42° **5.** 52° **7.** 28°
9. 61° **13.** about 40 ft
15. $\overrightarrow{ST}$: 4 cm, 44°; $\overrightarrow{UV}$: 4.5 cm, 17°, $\overrightarrow{WX}$: 4.7 cm, 199°
17. 2° **19.** 62° **21.** 63°
23. a. 18° **b.** about 800 ft
c. No

7-3 Part C Exercises

1. Due north at 205 mph
3. a–b.

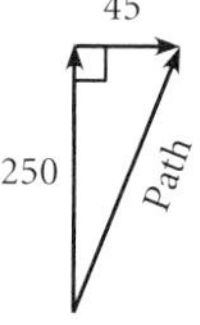

c. 254.02 mph
5. Length = 7.28; $m\angle\mathbf{1} = 16°$

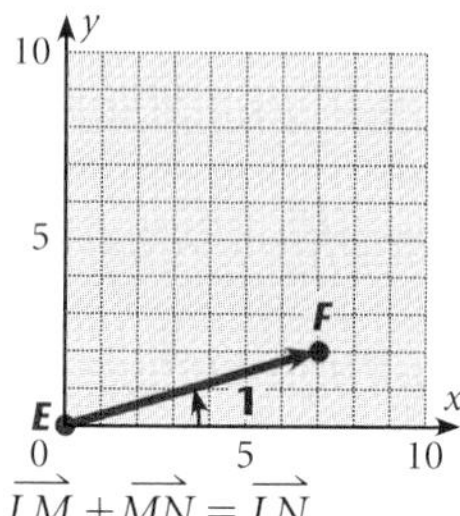

7. $\overrightarrow{LM} + \overrightarrow{MN} = \overrightarrow{LN}$

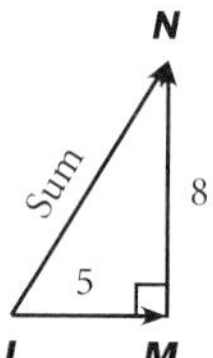

10. $s = 22.83$ mph, $m\angle A = 29°$ **11. a.** Faster
b. Slower **c.** Faster
d. Faster **13.** 166.28 in.^{2}
15. $m\angle VXY = 38°$, $XY = 68.8$

17. Length = 6.32, $m\angle\mathbf{1} = 72°$

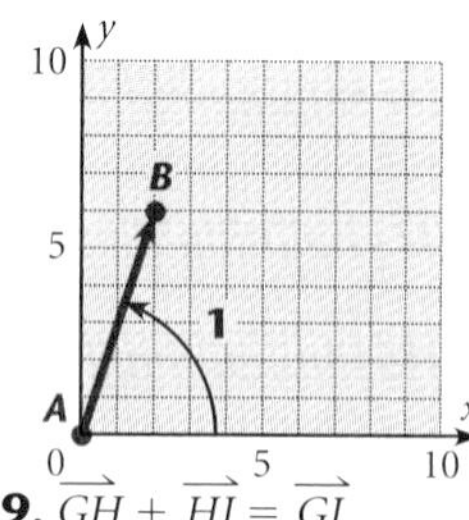

19. $\overrightarrow{GH} + \overrightarrow{HI} = \overrightarrow{GI}$

21. $s = 354.40$ mph, $m\angle\mathbf{1} = 74°$

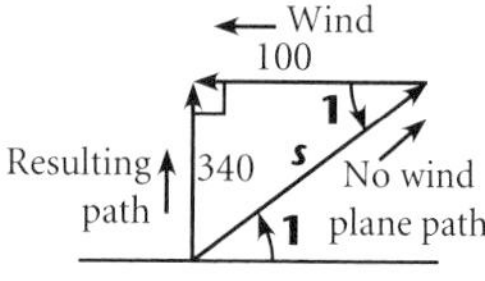

7-3 Part D Self-Assessment

1. $\frac{24}{25} = 0.96$ **2.** $\frac{7}{25} = 0.28$
3. $\frac{24}{7} \approx 3.43$ **4.** $\frac{7}{25} = 0.28$
5. $\frac{24}{25} = 0.96$ **6.** $\frac{7}{24} \approx 0.29$
7. $x = 7.14$ **8.** $x = 39$
9. $x = 28.79$ **10.** 1,117 ft
11. 20.78 cm^2 **12.** 32 cm^2
13. 41.57 cm^2 **14.** $x = 53$; AA **15.** $x = 3.6$; SAS
16. $x = 29$; AA **17.** (a)
18. $\tan 1 = \frac{622}{260} = 2.39$; $m\angle 1 = 67°$

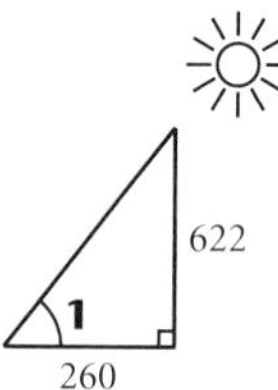

19. 17 m
20. 156.6 mph; $m\angle\mathbf{1} = 17°$

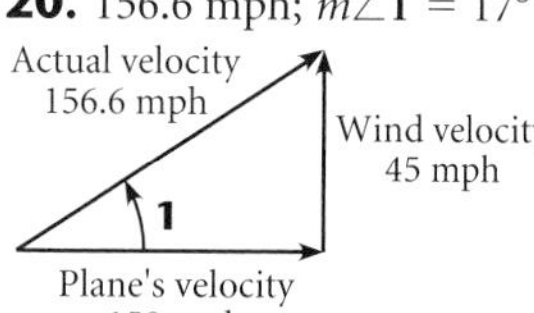

21. Sometimes; $\tan A = \frac{\text{opposite}}{\text{adjacent}}$; If opposite side is shorter than adjacent side, $\tan A < 1$; If opposite side is longer than adjacent side, then $\tan A > 1$.
22. Never; The closer you are, the greater the angle you must look up; As you near the flagpole, you must look nearly straight up; i.e., the angle approaches 90°. **23.** Always; If the acute angle has the known side adjacent, use $\cos A = \frac{\text{known side}}{\text{hypotenuse}}$; If the known side is opposite, $\sin A = \frac{\text{known side}}{\text{hypotenuse}}$; Solve for hypotenuse.

Chapter 7 Review

1. Dilation **2.** The midpoints of two sides **3.** Depression **4.** Greater than
5. T; An equilateral triangle has all angles = 60° and so it is equiangular too; By AA, two such triangles are similar.
6. F; Similarity also requires that the third sides be in proportion, or that the angles between the equal sides be congruent. **7.** $\frac{6}{8} = \frac{3}{4}$
8. 34° **9.** 10 cm **10.** 12.6 cm^2 **11.** $x = 16$, or $x = 9$; SAS **12. a.** $\frac{5}{8}$ in. **b.** 24 ft × 30 ft **13.** Possible answer:

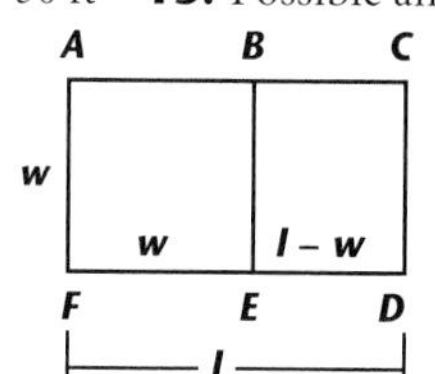

Rectangle $ACDF$ is a golden rectangle if square $ABEF$ with sides of length w makes rectangle $CDEB$ similar to rectangle $ACDF$. That is, if you divide a golden rectangle into a square and a smaller rectangle, the smaller rectangle is also a golden rectangle. All golden rectangles are similar. The ratio of length to width, $\frac{l}{w}$, is a constant called the golden ratio, and $\frac{l}{w} = \frac{1 + \sqrt{5}}{2} \approx 1.618$.

14. $\frac{\text{area } \triangle RUV}{\text{area } \triangle RST} = \left(\frac{UV}{ST}\right)^2 = \left(\frac{1}{2}\right)^2 = \frac{1}{4}$ since triangles are similar by AA. area $\triangle RUV = \left(\frac{1}{4}\right)$ area $\triangle RST = \frac{1}{4}$(area $\triangle RUV$ + area $UVTS$) $= \frac{1}{4}$ area $\triangle RUV + \frac{1}{4}$ area $UVTS$; $\frac{3}{4}$ area $\triangle RUV = \frac{1}{4}$ area $UVTS$;
$\frac{\text{area } \triangle RUV}{\text{area } UVTS} = \frac{\frac{1}{4}}{\frac{3}{4}} = \frac{1}{3}$

15. a. 4.5 **b.** $C' = (4, 6)$
16. $\frac{24}{25} = 0.96$ **17.** $\frac{7}{25} = 0.28$ **18.** $\frac{24}{7} \approx 3.43$
19. $x = 23.66$ **20.** $x = 56$
21. $x = 5.54$ **22.** $P = 89.57$, $A = 249.42$
23. a. 180.26 feet **b.** 18

CHAPTER 8

8-1 Part A Try It

a. Possible answer: $\overline{TS}$
b. $\overline{NM}$ **c.** X, interior; Z, exterior **d.** 2 cm

8-1 Part A Exercises

1. ⊙S **3.** $\overline{RT}$ **5.** 8.2 in.
9.

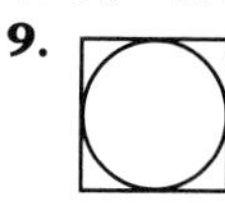

11. Inscribed in **12.** Diameter **13.** 0.2 in. **16.** 4
17. 4 **19.** $x^2 + y^2 = 16$
21. a. 9° **b.** ≈ 3.13
23.

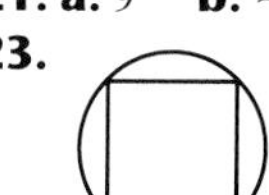

25. $\frac{360}{6} = 60°$; It takes six rotations to go around 360°.
27. a. $\sqrt{(x-1)^2 + (y-2)^2} = 3$ **b.** $(x-1)^2 + (y-2)^2 = 9$; 9 is the square of the radius; 1 and 2 are the center's x- and y-coordinates.
c. $(x-h)^2 + (y-k)^2 = r^2$

8-1 Part B Try It

a. 90° **b.** $AC \approx 40.80$

8-1 Part B Exercises

1. $\overline{AB}$ **3.** $\overleftrightarrow{FG}$; E
5.

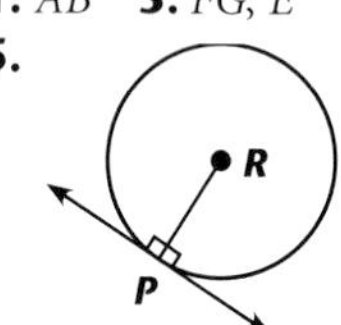

7. Secant **9.** 20 **11.** 6.27 **13.** 2.8 **15.** 3.7 **17.** $\overline{RS} \cong \overline{RT}$; Definition of a *circle.* $\angle S$ and $\angle T$ are right angles; Radii are perpendicular to tangents at points of tangency. $\overline{RQ} \cong \overline{RQ}$; Reflexive Property. $\triangle SRQ \cong \triangle TRQ$; HL theorem. $\overline{QS} \cong \overline{QT}$; CPCTC. **20.** E **21.** $\overleftrightarrow{AB}$ **23.** $\overleftrightarrow{DC}$ **25.** Interior: 135°; Exterior: 45° **27.** $H'(2, 3)$, $L'(2, 9)$, $J'(8, 3)$, $K'(8, 9)$ **29.** 23.32 **31.** $a = 18$ **33.** $c = 13$ **35.** Possible answer: Draw segments $\overline{RB}$, $\overline{RC}$, and $\overline{BC}$. Since $RB = RC$, $\triangle RBC$ is isosceles and $\angle RBC \cong \angle RCB$. Since $\angle RBA$ and $\angle RCA$ are right angles, $\angle ABC$ is complementary to $\angle RBC$ and $\angle ACB$ is complementary to $\angle RCB$. Complements of congruent angles are congruent, so $\angle ABC \cong \angle ACB$. **37.** $LM \approx 1100$ mi; $\triangle ERS \sim \triangle ELM$ by AA so $\frac{LM}{RS} = \frac{EM}{ES}$. Solve for LM.

8-1 Part C Try It

a. 25.1 in. **b.** 22.0 in.

8-1 Part C Exercises

1. 6 in.; 6π in. **3.** 11.4π mm; 35.81 mm **5.** 0.17 in. **7.** 54.85 **9.** 27.99 **11.** 131.95 cm **13. a.** 0.021 **b.** Yes; It differs from π by only about 0.00000027. **15.** 48 **17.** 4.09 **19.** $\frac{1}{2}ap$; 64.95 cm^2 **21.** 27.6π in.; 86.71 in. **23.** $r = 12.27$ yd **25.** $9\pi \approx 28.27$ **28. a.** All sides are straight lines; For an n-gon with a large number of sides, the shape approximates a circle. **b.** $r \approx 0.48$ ft; $\frac{\text{Perimeter}}{2\pi}$ gives the radius.

8-1 Part D Try It

a. $A = 36\pi \approx 113.10$ ft^2; $C = 12\pi \approx 37.70$ ft

8-1 Part D Exercises

1. $d = 10$ cm; $C = 10\pi$ cm; $A = 25\pi$ cm^2 **3.** 10 cm **5.** 9π ft^2; 28.27 ft^2 **7.** 38.48 ft^2; 94.03 ft^2 **9.** $C = 10\pi\sqrt{2} \approx 44.43$ in.; $A = 50\pi \approx 157.08$ in.^{2} **13. a.** Triangle: 2,771.28 yd^2; Square: 3,600 yd^2; Hexagon: 4,156.92 yd^2 **b.** 4583.66 yd^2 **c.** The circle. This is the best possible figure. **14.** 2.55 in.^{2} **15.**

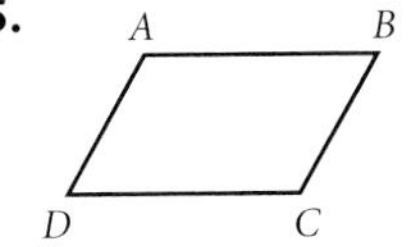

Draw $\overline{AC}$, two points determine a line. $\overline{AB} \cong \overline{DC}$: Opposite sides are congruent. $\overline{AD} \cong \overline{BC}$: Opposite sides are congruent. $\overline{AC} \cong \overline{AC}$: Reflexive Property. $\triangle CAB \cong \triangle ACD$: SSS **17.** 25π ft^2; 78.54 ft^2 **19.** $2\sqrt{563\pi}$ cm; 84.11 cm **21. d.** About 290 cm^2 **e.** 314.16 cm^2 **f.** Make narrower rectangles

8-1 Part E Self-Assessment

1. $\odot P$ **2.** $\overline{BP}$, $\overline{PD}$, $\overline{PC}$ **3.** $\overline{BD}$ **4.** $\overleftrightarrow{AE}$ **5.** m; C **6.** 90° **7.** 3 **8.** 6.71 **9.** 17.50 **10.** $3249\pi \approx 10207.03$ in.^{2} **11.** $r = 2.67$ cm **12.** 38.99 m **13. b.** Square: 63.66%; Hexagon: 82.70% **14.** (a) **15. a.** 880.28 ft; 58.69 ft/sec **b.** 71° **16.** $\angle ABD \cong \angle BDC$: Given. $\overline{AB} \cong \overline{CD}$: Given. $\overline{DB} \cong \overline{DB}$: Reflexive Property. $\triangle ABD \cong \triangle CDB$: SAS. $\angle ADB \cong \angle CBD$: CPCTC: $\overline{AD} \parallel \overline{BC}$: Lines parallel if alternate interior angles are congruent. $\overline{AB} \parallel \overline{CD}$: Lines parallel if alternate interior angles are congruent. $ABCD$ is a parallelogram: Definition of a *parallelogram.* **17.** 9.82 in. **18. a.** $18\pi \approx 56.55$cm **b.** 44.91 cm

8-2 Part A Try It

a. 54° **b.** 306° **c.** 180°

8-2 Part A Exercises

1. Possible answer: $\angle ADB$, $\angle BDC$ **3.** $\widehat{BAC}$, $\widehat{ACB}$ **5.** 45° **7.** 217° **9.** 195° **11.** 90° **13.** 180° **15.** $\frac{1}{4}$ **17.** $\frac{1}{3}$ **19.** 210° **22.** $\triangle PQR$ is isosceles, so $\angle PQR \cong \angle PRQ$; $m\angle QPR = 100°$; Sum of $\angle$'s in $\triangle PQR = 180° = 100° + 2x$; $m\angle PQR = m\angle PRQ = 40°$ **24.** $x = 44$ **27. a.** 63.63 in.^{2} **b.** 15.90 in.^{2} **c.** 10.60 in.^{2} **d.** $\frac{1}{4}$ or $\frac{1}{6}$ of the pie means $\frac{1}{4}$ or $\frac{1}{6}$ of the area. **29.** 65° **31.** 250° **33.** 176° **35.** 78° **37.** 60° **40.** 6°/sec **41.** 270°/sec

8-2 Part B Try It

a. 359.5 in.^{2} **b.** 36.0 in. **c.** $\frac{21}{12}\pi = \frac{7}{4}\pi$

8-2 Part B Exercises

1. a. $A = 25\pi \approx 78.54$ in.^{2}; $C = 10\pi \approx 31.42$ in. **b.**

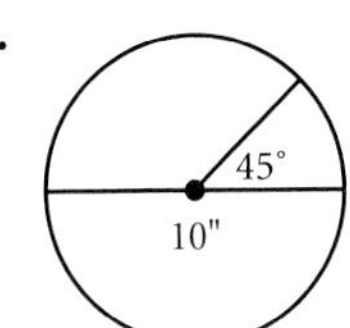

c. 9.8 in.^{2} **d.** 3.9 in. **3.** $L = 6\pi$ in.; $A = 45\pi$ in.^{2} **5.** $L = 4.8$ ft; $A = 12.00$ ft^2 **7.** $3.36\pi \approx 10.561$ **10.** $A = 1.5\pi \approx 4.71$ ft^2; $L = 0.5\pi \approx 1.57$ ft **11. a.** $4.5\pi \approx 14.14$ ft^2 **b.** 12.5% **13.** $\angle ACB \cong \angle ECD$: Vertical angles are congruent. $\angle B \cong \angle E$: Right angles are congruent. $\triangle ACB \sim \triangle DCE$: AA. $\frac{AC}{DC} = \frac{BC}{EC}$: Definition of *similar.* **15.** $A = 64\pi$ in.^{2}; 201.06 in.^{2}; $C = 16\pi$ in.; 50.27 in. **17.** $L = 1.6\pi \approx 5.03$ in.; $A = 6.4\pi \approx 20.11$ in.^{2} **19.** $L = 5.46\pi \approx 17.15$ ft; $A = 24.843\,\pi \approx 78.05$ ft^2 **21. b.** 5707.96 m^2 **c.** No; One cannot tile a square region with circular sectors without either gaps or overlap.

8-2 Part C Try It

a. $\overline{AD} \cong \overline{DC}$ **b.** $\overline{YF} \perp \overline{EG}$ **c.** m contains Z

8-2 Part C Exercises

1. 7 **3.** $\overline{TR}$ is a perpendicular bisector of $\overline{QS}$. **5.** 8 **7.** Secant; It alone extends beyond the boundary of a circle. **10.** 15.35 **11.**

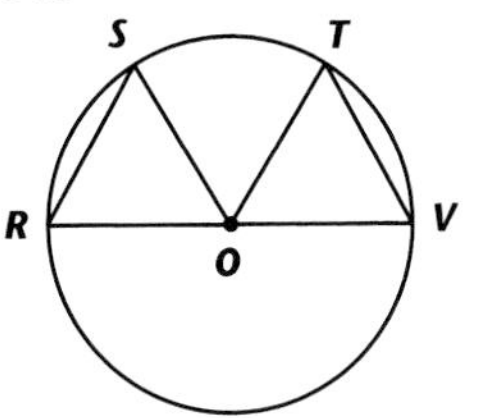

$\widehat{RS} \cong \widehat{TV}$: Given. $m\widehat{RS} = m\widehat{TV}$: Definition of *congruent arcs.* $m\widehat{RS} = m\angle ROS$; $m\widehat{TV} = m\angle TOV$: Definition of *measure of a minor arc.* $m\angle ROS = m\angle TOV$: Substitution. $m\angle ROS \cong m\angle TOV$: Definition of *congruent angles.* $\overline{OS} \cong \overline{OR} \cong \overline{OT} \cong \overline{OV}$: Definition of *circle.* $\triangle OSR \cong \triangle OTV$: SAS. $\overline{RS} \cong \overline{TV}$: CPCTC. **12.** 14 **13.** 14 **15.** 24 **19.** $\angle AOC$ **21.** 18.03 **23.** 13 **25.** 4.69 **27.** Draw $\overline{XV}$, $\overline{VY}$, $\overline{ZV}$, and $\overline{VW}$. $\triangle XVY \cong \triangle ZVW$ by SSS, and $\angle XVY \cong \angle WVZ$ by CPCTC. Since their central angles are congruent, $\widehat{XY} \cong \widehat{WZ}$. **29.** $YZ = 9.75$

8-2 Part D Self-Assessment

1. 67° **2.** 23° **3.** 70° **4.** 290° **5.**

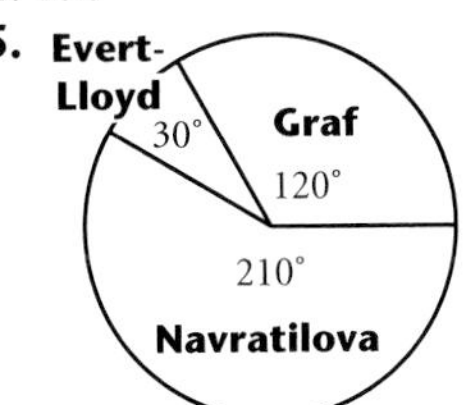

6. (d) **7. a.** 15° **b.** 1041.67 mi **8.** 1298.54^2 cm^2 **9.** $\frac{1}{3}$; 126.71 mm^2 **10.** $\triangle ACB \sim \triangle ECD$. Since $\frac{6.0}{4.0} = \frac{7.5}{5.0} = 1.5$, the triangles are similar by SAS. $x = \frac{5.6}{1.5} \approx 3.73$. **11. a.** $C = 1.766 \times 10^{15}$ km **b.** $r = 2.81 \times 10^{14}$ **c.** $A = 2.48 \times 10^{29}$ km^2

12. 69.81 cm^2; The total area of the circle is 100π cm^2. Since $m\angle FKJ = 80°$, the sector FKJ fills $\frac{80}{360}$ of the total area. **13.** Show that $\triangle ZWY \cong \triangle ZTV$ by HL. Then $\overline{WY} \cong \overline{VT}$ by CPCTC. Use $WY = \frac{1}{2}$ WX and $VT = \frac{1}{2}$ ST, to show that $\overline{WX} = \overline{ST}$. **14.** 767.94 m^2

8-3 Part A Try It

a. 48° **b.** 80° **c.** 90°

8-3 Part A Exercises

1. 136° **3.** 90° **5.** $d = 80$; $e = 140$ **7.** 90° at center; 45° at wall **9.** 98° **11.** 64° **13.** 95° **15.** 47.5° **19.** Angle remains same since intercepted arc doesn't change. **20.** $m\angle A = 135°$; $m\angle B = m\angle D = 90°$; $m\angle C = 45°$ **21.** The measure of an inscribed angle is half the measure of its intercepted arc. For a semicircle the arc measures 180°, so the angle measures 90°.

23.

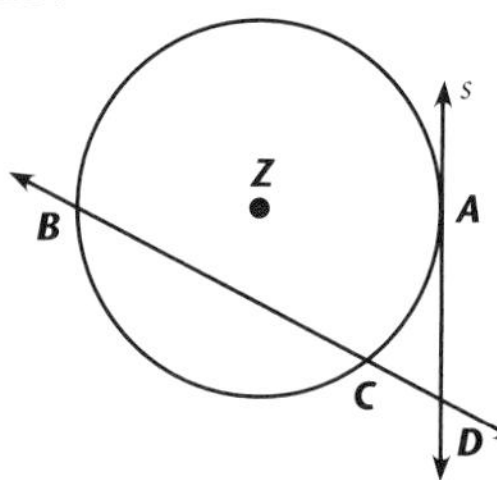

25. 94° **27.** 180° **29.** 118° **31.** 59° **33.** 40° **35.** 110° **38.** 12.99

8-3 Part B Try It

a. $a = 86$ **b.** $b = 60$ **c.** $c = 40$

8-3 Part B Exercises

1. a. 240° **b.** 120° **c.** 60° **3.** 47.5° **5.** 148° **7.** Two **9.** 28° **11.** $m\widehat{ADC} = 224°$; $m\widehat{AC} = 136°$ **13.** 89° **15.** Reason 1: Exterior Angle Theorem.
Reason 2: Algebra; Addition Property of Equality.
Reason 3: Inscribed-Angle Theorem.
Reason 4. Substitution.
17. 69° **19.** $(x - 3)°$ **21.** 51.3 **23.** 90° **25.** 111° **27.** 42° **29.** 2.5° **31.** 18° **33. a.** 25° **b.** 16°

8-3 Part C Self-Assessment

1. 92° **2.** 136° **3.** 64° **4.** 64° **5.** (c) **6.** \$4.95 × 10^{10} **7.** 93° **8.** 104° **9.** 87° **10.** 76° **11.** The danger angle is always $180° - \frac{m\widehat{XY}}{2}$. **12. a.** 7.51 cm **b.** Using trigonometry, $m\angle UVW = 84°$; $m\widehat{UW} = 180° - 84° = 96°$; $m\widehat{USW} = 360° - 96° = 264°$. **c.** 10 cm

Chapter 8 Review

1. T **2.** F; A central angle **3.** F; Inscribed in **4.** 7; $49\pi \approx 153.94$ **5.** $\angle YWZ$ **6.** Possible answer: $\overleftrightarrow{XY}$ **7.** Possible answer: $\widehat{XY}$ **8.** 41° **9.** 82° **10.** 208° **11.** 90° **12.** 63° **13.** $20\pi\sqrt{2}$ cm ≈ 88.86 cm; $200\pi \approx 628.32$ cm^2 **14.** Since the perpendicular from the center to a chord bisects it, $WY = \frac{1}{2}WX = \frac{1}{2}TS = TV$, and $\overline{WY} \cong \overline{TV}$. $\overline{WZ} \cong \overline{TZ}$ because radii are congruent. Then $\triangle WZY \cong \triangle TZV$ by HL for right triangles, and $\overline{ZY} \cong \overline{ZV}$ by CPCTC. Therefore, $ZY = ZV$ by definition of congruent segments. **15.** Probability = 0.21 **16.** Center: (0, 0); Radius: $\sqrt{13}$ **17. a.**

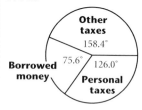

Other taxes
158.4°
Borrowed money
75.6°
126.0°
Personal taxes

b. 0.16 in.^{2} **c.** 75.6°; 0.7 in. **18. b.** $\pi(R - r) = D - d$

CHAPTER 9

9-1 Part A Try It

a. Oblique rectangular
b. Right pentagonal
c. Right triangular

9-1 Part A Exercises

1. Right rectangular **3.** Right hexagonal
5.

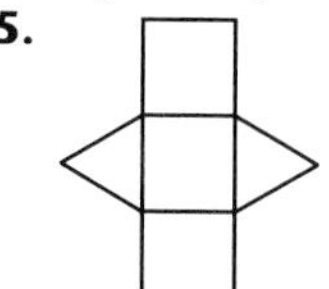

7.

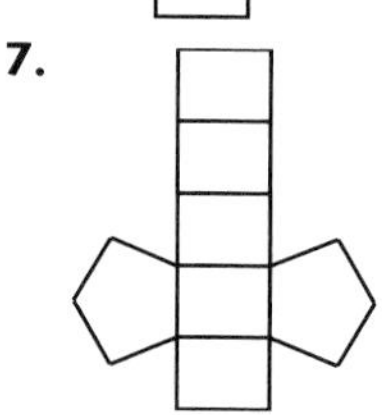

9. $LA = 55.44$; $SA = 74.88$ **11.** $LA = 97.2$; $SA = 109.2$ **13.** Lateral edge **15.** Right prism **17.** In the right prism the faces are rectangles. In the oblique prism the faces are parallelograms. **19.** 188 ft^2 **21. a.** $SA = 10x^2 - 12x$ **b.** $x = 4$ ft **23.** Possible answer: Move one of the top blocks on the left away from the block it is touching to expose two new faces. **25.** $x = 26$ **27.** $x = 6\sqrt{3} \approx 10.4$
29.

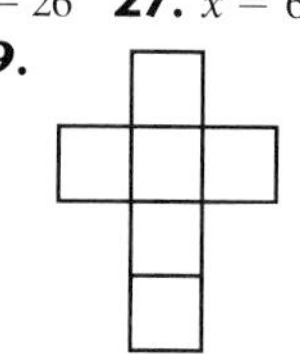

31.

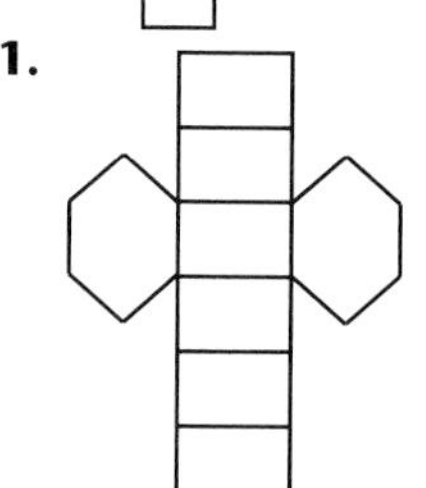

33. 163.88; 179.88 **35.** 36 in.^{2} **37.** 32 in.^{2} **39.** Greater; The lateral area is larger.
41.

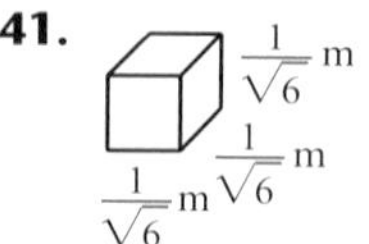

9-1 Part B Exercises

1. a. 4; Triangle **b.** 1000 cm^2 **c.** Square; 400 cm^2 **d.** 1400 cm^2
3.

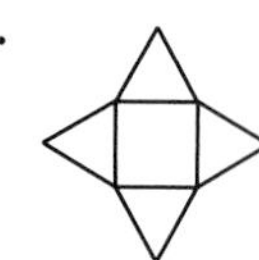

5.

7. 240 cm^2; 340 cm^2
9. 144.18 cm^2; 219.94 cm^2
11. $s = \sqrt{\frac{l^2}{4} + h^2}$;
Lateral edge $= L = \sqrt{\frac{l^2}{2} + h^2}$
13. Vertex **15.** 924,473.1 ft^2 **17.** $x = 5.25$ in.; Use similar triangles
19.

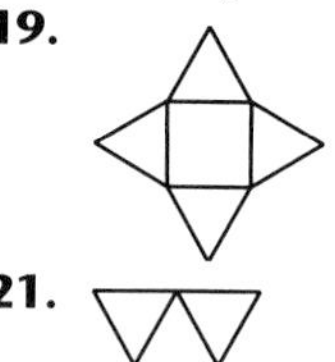

21.

23. 192 ft^2, 336 ft^2
25. 51.78 cm^2; 0.54

9-1 Part C Try It

a. $LA = 201.1$ in.^{2}; $SA = 603.2$ in.^{2} **b.** $LA = 791.7$ cm^2; $SA = 1300.6$ cm^2

9-1 Part C Exercises

1. a. Rectangle/parallelogram **b.** $60\pi \approx 188.5$ cm^2 **c.** 25π cm^2; $50\pi \approx 157.1$ cm^2 **d.** $110\pi \approx 345.6$ cm^2 **3.** $72\pi \approx 226.2$ in.^{2}; $104\pi \approx 326.7$ in.^{2} **5.** $24\pi \approx 75.4$ in.^{2}; $33\pi \approx 103.7$ in.^{2} **7.** 50.8 ft^2; 68.9 ft^2 **9.** T **11.** 304.52 cm^2 **13.** $52\pi \approx 163.4$ in.^{2} more **15.** ≈ 877.8 ft^2 **17.** Possible answer: If you divide the rectangle into squares, it has l rows of w squares each. **19.** $150\pi \approx 471.2$ ft^2; $200\pi \approx 628.3$ ft^2 **21.** $60\pi \approx 188.5$ in.^{2}; $96\pi \approx 301.6$ in.^{2} **23.** 258.9 ft^2; 421.8 ft^2 **25.** $39\pi \approx 122.5$ in.^{2}

9-1 Part D Self-Assessment

1. 118.56; 178.42 **2.** 265; 377.36 **3.** $54\pi \approx 169.6$ cm^2; $72\pi \approx 226.2$ cm^2 **4.** $960\pi \approx 3015.9$ in.^{2}; $1216\pi \approx 3820.2$ in.^{2}

5.

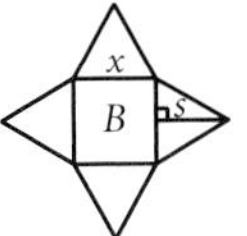

The surface area is the area of the base (B) plus the areas of the triangles. For a base with n sides, the total area of the triangles would be $n\left(\frac{1}{2}xs\right)$. The perimeter is nx, so the total area of the pyramid is $\frac{1}{2}ps + B$. **6.** $(6 \times 10^{-4})\pi \approx 1.9 \times 10^{-3}$ mm^2 **7.** $6\pi x^2 + 24\pi x$ **8.** 12,404.6 cm^2; 6,643.0 cm^2 **9.** (c) **10. a.** 4 **b.** Possible answer: $\triangle AGK$, $\sqrt{3}$; $\triangle ACL$, 2; $\triangle AHP$, $\sqrt{7}$; $\triangle ADQ$, 3. **c.** They all are equilateral, like $\triangle FBA$. **11. a.** $440\pi \approx 1382.3$ cm^2 **b.** $33\frac{1}{3}\pi \approx 104.7$ cm^2 **c.** 120° **12.** About 126.9 cm^2 **13.** $SA = 3\ell^2$ **14.** Cylinder: 296.9 cm^2; Square prism: 324.9 cm^2; Square pyramid: 353.7 cm^2; Cone: 324.3 cm^2. Possible answer: The cylinder, because it uses the least aluminum. **15.** A segment perpendicular to a plane is perpendicular to every line in the plane that contains the point of intersection of the segment and the plane.

9-2 Part A Try It

a. 129.6 in.^{3} **b.** 42,398 mm^3

9-2 Part A Exercises

1. 10^{-4} m^2 **3.** 2500 mm^2 **5.** cm^3 **7.** 27 ft^3

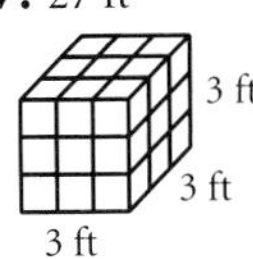

9. 2.24×10^{-2} m^3 **11.** 72,000 cm^3 **13.** $1075.2\sqrt{3}$ m$^3 \approx 1862.3$ **15.** \$0.59 **17.** $3\sqrt{3} \approx 5.2$ cm **21.** 944 cm^2 **23.** $210\pi \approx 659.7$ cm^2 **25.** 0.7 cm^3 **27.** 84,000 cm^3 **29.** $1{,}138.626\sqrt{3} \approx 1972.2$ in.^{3} **31.** 1888.41 in.^{3}

9-2 Part B Try It

a. 480 cm^3 **b.** 80 in.^{3} **c.** $180\sqrt{3}$ mm^3

9-2 Part B Exercises

1. a. 3 in. **b.** 16 in.^{2} **c.** 16 in.^{3} **2.** $53\frac{1}{3}$ cm^3 **3.** 34.692 in.^{3} **5.** 384 ft^3 **7.** 105.35 cm^3 **9.** 3 units **13.** Possible answer:

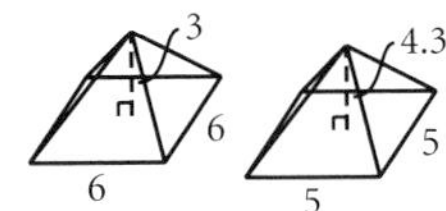

15. 10 in. **17.** Each cross-section is a circle. The cylinder has the larger cross-sectional areas since its side does not taper. **19.** 39.975 mm^3 **21.** $96\sqrt{91} \approx 915.8$ cm^3 **23.** $\frac{1000\sqrt{2}}{3} \approx 471.4$ cm^3

9-2 Part C Exercises

1. a. 4 cm **b.** 78.5 cm^2 **c.** 314.2 cm^3 **3.** $11.913\pi \approx 37.4$ in.^{3} **5.** $17.2\pi \approx 54.0$ cm^3 **7.** $710.803\pi \approx 2233.1$ **9.** $12\pi \approx 37.7$ cm^3 **11. a.** $1{,}089{,}000\pi \approx 3{,}420{,}000$ ft^3 **b.** $433{,}500\pi \approx 1{,}360{,}000$ ft^3 **c.** $2{,}823{,}000\pi \approx 8{,}870{,}000$ ft^3 **13.** $7.5\pi \approx 23.6$ ft^3 **17.** $64\pi \approx 201.1$ cm^2; $16\pi \approx 50.3$ cm **19.** 7 m; $14\pi \approx 44.0$ m **21.** $2042.5\pi \approx 6416.7$ cm^2 **23.** $55.2\pi \approx 173.4$ in.^{2} **25.** About 167,000 ft^2 **27.** $813.12\pi \approx 2554.5$ cm^3 **29.** $392\pi \approx 1231.5$ cm^3 **31. a.** About 884 in.^{3}; About 389 in.^{3} **b.** 117 ft/min

9-2 Part D Try It

a. $V = 166\frac{2}{3}\pi \approx 523.6$ cm^3; $SA = 100\pi \approx 314.2$ cm^2 **b.** $V = 10\frac{2}{3}\pi \approx 33.5$ in.^{3}; $SA = 16\pi \approx 50.3$ in.^{2}

9-2 Part D Exercises

1. $V = 10\frac{2}{3}\pi \approx 33.5$ in.^{3}; $SA = 16\pi \approx 50.3$ in.^{2} **3.** $70.56\pi \approx 221.7$ in.^{2}; $98.784\pi \approx 310.3$ in.^{3} **5.** $\sqrt{2} \approx 1.4$ m; $\frac{8\sqrt{2}}{3}\pi \approx 11.8$ m^3 **7.** 99.82 **9. a.** $V_{cube} = 1000$ cm^3 $V_{sphere} = 166\frac{2}{3}\pi \approx 523.6$ cm^3 **b.** 52.36% **11.** About 0.32 cm^2; About 0.017 cm^3 **13.** 29.65% **15.** $\frac{8}{27}$ **17.** 4 **19.** $100\pi \approx 314.2$ in.^{2}; $166\frac{2}{3}\pi \approx 523.6$ in.^{3} **21.** 4 ft, $85\frac{1}{3}\pi \approx 268.1$ ft^3 **23.** $x^2 + y^2 + z^2 = r^2$. This is the square of the distance formula for a point that is r units away from the origin.

9-2 Part E Self-Assessment

1. 1536 mm^3 **2.** 129.73 cm^3 **3.** $3343.509\pi \approx 10503.9$ ft^3 **4.** $112.5\sqrt{3} \approx 194.9$ **5. a.** 1.08×10^{12} km^3 **b.** 2.21×10^{10} km^3 **c.** $\approx 2.04\%$ **6.** 367,200 ft^3 **7.** 1.09 mi **8.** 33,390.4 cm^2 **9.** 16.8 in.^{2} **10.** $2898\pi \approx 9104.4$ cm^2 **11.** 84 cm^2 **12.** (a) **13. a.** $V_{prism} = 277.83$ m^3; $V_{cone} \approx 72.74$ m^3 **b.** 26.18% **14.** 5.0 in. **15. a.** 8.18 in.^{3} **b.** 2.216 in. $\times$ 2.216 in. **c.** 2.45 in.^{2} **16.** 78.8 cm^3; 8.6 cm^3 is lost; Possible answer: They have indentations to save money on product. **17.** 150 min.

9-3 Part A Try It

a. $\frac{2}{5}$; $\frac{4}{25}$ **b.** 18 in. $\times$ 18 in.

9-3 Part A Exercises

1. Not similar **3.** Not similar **5.** $\frac{3}{2}$ **7.** $\frac{7}{8}$ **10.** 10,000 times as strong **13.** 260° **15.** 80° **17.** $58\frac{1}{3}$ cm^3 **19.** 28 mm^3 **21.** $\frac{4}{5}$ **23.** $\frac{5}{6}$ **25.** $13.5\sqrt{2} \approx 19.1$ in.

9-3 Part B Try It

a. $\frac{1}{8}$ **b.** $\frac{5}{3}$ **c.** 337.5 lb

9-3 Part B Exercises

1. a. $\frac{4}{3}$ **b.** $\frac{16}{9}$ **c.** $\frac{64}{27}$ **3.** $\frac{3}{5}$ **5.** $\frac{27}{125}$ **7.** $\frac{1}{27}$ **9.** Area **11.** 10^6 times as heavy **13.** 3.30 in.; 137.05 in.^{2}; 150.87 in.^{3} **15.** $A'(4, -2)$; $B'(2, -6)$

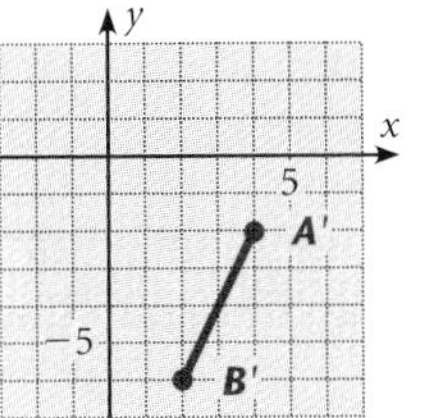

17. $A'(4, 8)$; $B'(12, 4)$

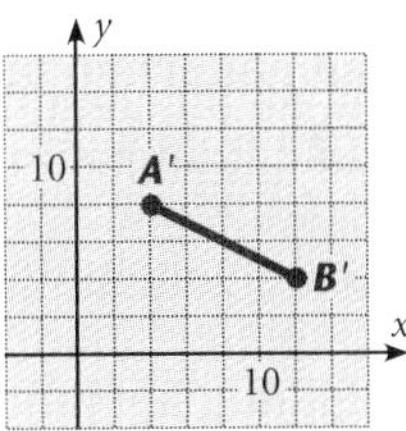

19. $\frac{25}{16}$ **21.** $\frac{15625}{4096}$ **23.** $\approx$ 754 beats/min.

9-3 Part C Self-Assessment

1. $\frac{3}{2}$ **2.** $\frac{3}{2}$ **3.** $\frac{9}{4}$ **4.** $\frac{27}{8}$ **5.** $\frac{3}{4}$, $\frac{9}{16}$ **6.** (d) **7.** The larger box **8.** 106° **9.** 112° **10.** 36° **11.** $545\frac{5}{6}\pi \approx 1714.8$ ft^3 **12. a–b.**

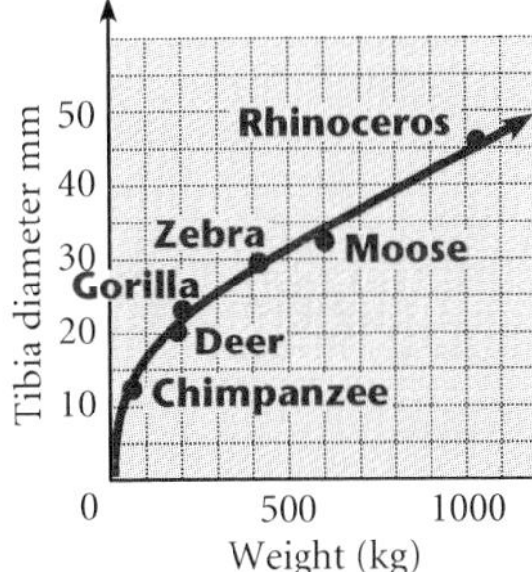

c. $\approx$ 3 mm for a dog; $\approx$ 13.5 mm for a human **d.** Possible answer: Differences between dogs and humans and other animals, including number of legs. **13.** Possible answer: Because of the relation between the mass and the strength of building components, light, cheap materials which would not be suitable for the actual buildings can be used in models. **14. a.** 5 **b.** 50,000 lb **c.** Each leg would be 25 times as strong.

d. Possible answer: No; It is unlikely that its legs would be able to carry the increased weight. **15.** Height ≈ 9.6 cm; Radius ≈ 2.5 cm; The new volume is $\frac{1}{4}$ the old, so multiply old dimensions by $\frac{1}{\sqrt[3]{4}}$. **16.** $\frac{1}{64}$; The answer is the ratio of the volumes of the two cubes, which is the cube of their similarity ratio.

Chapter 9 Review

1. (b) **2.** (d) **3.** 82.8 cm^2; 46.8 cm^3 **4.** SA = 678.6; V = 1017.9 **5.** 360 cm^2; 400 cm^3 **6.** 57.3 mm^2; 28.6 mm^3 **7.** $20.25\pi \approx 63.6$ $in.^2$; $15.1875\pi \approx 47.7$ $in.^3$
8. Yes; They also have the same base area. **9.** Regular triangular prism: surface area $= 3sh + \frac{s^2}{2}\sqrt{3}$, volume $= \frac{s^2h}{4}\sqrt{3}$; Square prism: surface area $= 4sh + 2s^2$, volume $= s^2h$; Regular hexagonal prism: surface area $= 6sh + 3s^2\sqrt{3}$, volume $= \frac{3s^2h}{2}\sqrt{3}$ **10.** $\frac{4}{3}\pi r^3$; This is the volume of a sphere of radius r. **11. a.** 2.75 **b.** 6.5 **c.** The strips of fish will cook more quickly; The single slab of fish will hold its heat better. The ratio of surface area to volume makes the difference. **12.** It will hold 27 times as much petroleum.
13. c. Each time the height is doubled the intensity is multiplied by $\frac{1}{4}$.

CHAPTER 10

10-1 Part A Try It

a. Translation, vector <3, −4> **b.** Rotation, center (0, 0), 90° clockwise
c. Dilation, center (0, 0), scale factor 2

10-1 Part A Exercises

1. Reflection; Isometry
3. Dilation; Not an isometry
5. Translation **7.** Rotation or reflection **9.** Reflection, y-axis **11.** Dilation, center (0, 0), scale factor $\frac{1}{2}$ **14.** 1
17.

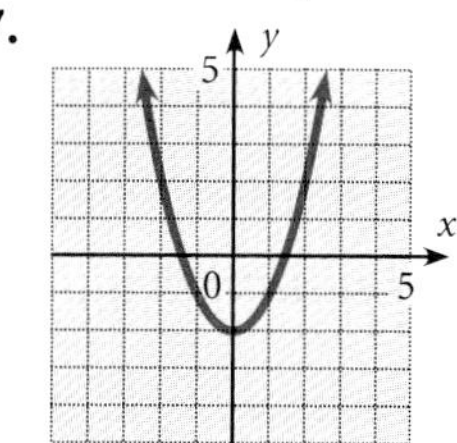

19. A parabola **21.** Reflection; Isometry **23.** Dilation; Not an isometry
25. Dilation, center (−4, −1), scale factor $1\frac{1}{2}$ **27. a.** The equator is its own image.
b. They are the same size.
c. Yes; The North and South poles

10-1 Part B Try It

a. 113° counterclockwise rotation with center (2, 1)
b. Translation with vector <7, 10>

10-1 Part B Exercises

1. Translation **3.** Rotation
5. 117° clockwise rotation with center at (4, −2)
7. Translation with vector <8, 0> **9.** Always; The distance is preserved by each isometry, hence the composition is an isometry.
11. Isometry; The composition of two isometries is always an isometry. **13.** isometry; The composition of two isometries is always an isometry. **15.** $\frac{1}{2}$ **17.** translation <3, −4> **19.** A dilation with scale factor $\frac{2}{3}$ and center at the origin **21.** $5\sqrt{3} \approx 8.7$ **23.** Translation <3,−1> **25.** Isometry; The composition of two isometries is always an isometry.
27. Not an isometry; The dilation does not preserve distance. **29.** No. **30.** 13

10-1 Part C Try It

a–c.

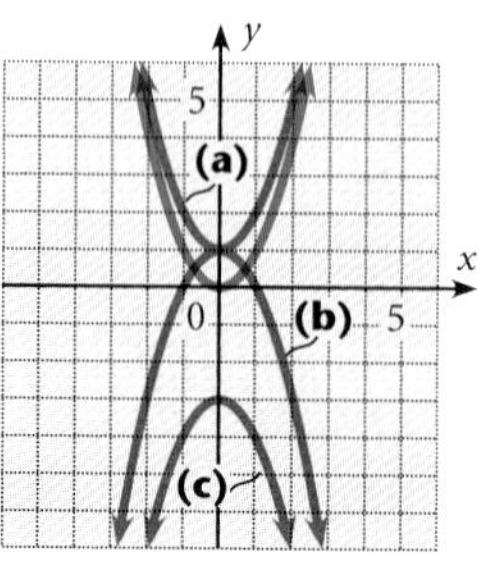

10-1 Part C Exercises

1. a–c.

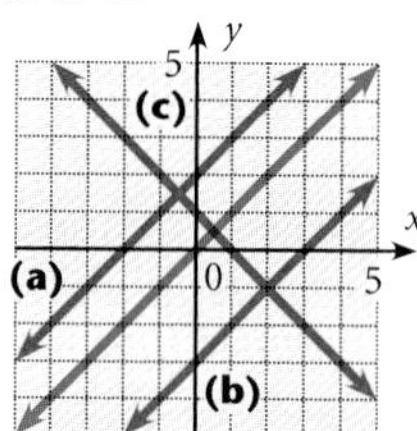

3. a–c.

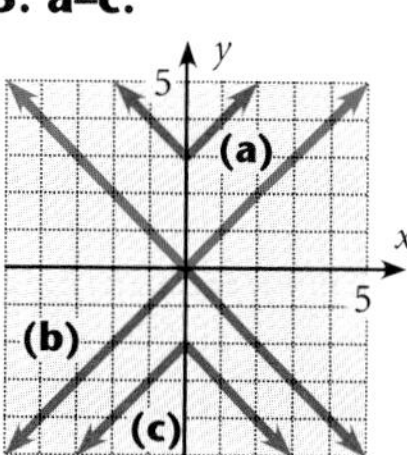

d. Possible answer: The graph of (a) is the graph of $y = |x|$ translated by <0, 3>. The graph of (b) is a reflection of the graph of $y = |x|$ across the x-axis. The graph of (c) is a reflection of the graph of $y = |x|$ across the x-axis followed by the translation <0, −2>. **4.** Translation **5.** Reflection
6. a–c.

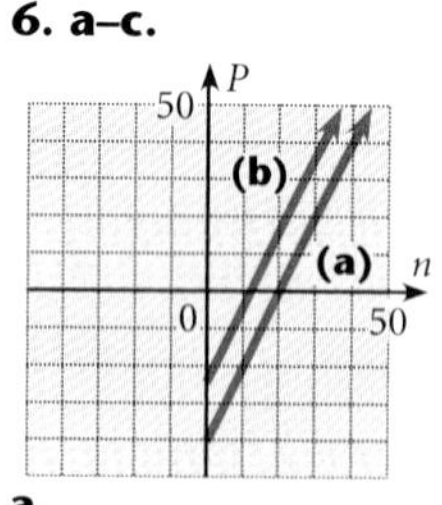

a. $P = 2n - 40$
b. $P = 2n - 24$ **11.** b;
13. c

15. a–c.

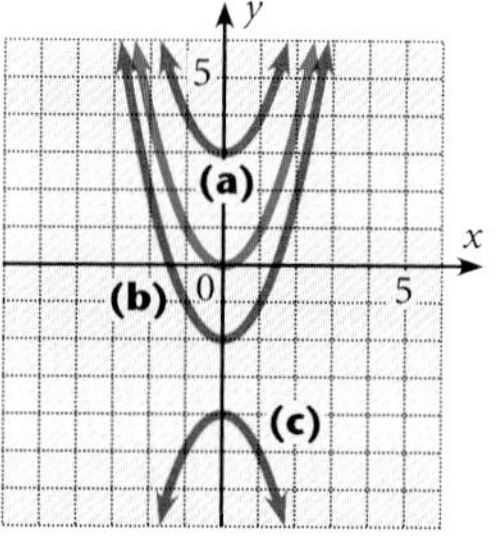

18. $n = 600$, $P = 250{,}000$.

10-1 Part D Self-Assessment

1. Clockwise rotation of $(x + y)°$ around the same center.
2. Translation $<a + c, b + d>$ **3.** A 180° rotation around the intersection point of the two lines **4.** Isometry; The composition of two isometries is always an isometry. **5.** Not an isometry; Dilation does not preserve distance. **6.** Isometry; The composition of two isometries is always an isometry.
7.

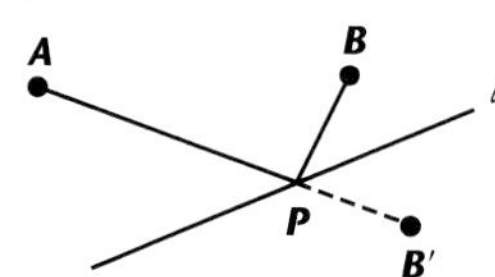

Find B' by reflecting B over ℓ. Locate transformer at P, point of intersection of $\overline{AB'}$ and ℓ.

8–10.

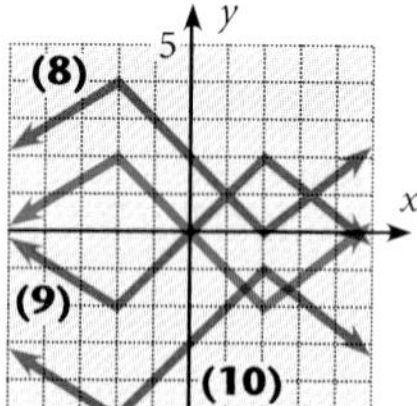

11. The graph of (8) was a translation <0, 2>. The graph of (9) was a reflection across the x-axis. The graph of (10) was a reflection across the x-axis followed by a translation <0, −3>. **12.** ≈ 47.1 m
13. 52 $in.^2$; 24 $in.^3$
14. 282.7 cm^2; 314.2 cm^3
15. 58.8 ft^2; 34.6 ft^3
16. 113.1 cm^2; 113.1 cm^3

18. a. Points with negative co ordinates; Square roots of negative numbers are not defined for real numbers. **b.** $(81, 16) \rightarrow (9, 4) \rightarrow (3, 2) \rightarrow (1.7, 1.4)$; The point seems to be going to (1, 1). No. As you continue to rootate, the coordinates will approach closer to 1, but never reach it. **c.** No, distance is not preserved.

10-2 Part A Try It

a. Translation, glide reflection, horizontal line, vertical line **b.** Translation, vertical line **c.** Translation

10-2 Part A Exercises

1. a. No **b.** No **c.** No **d.** No **3.** Possible answer:

5. F; Translation and a reflection **7.** No
9. Possible answer:

$$\begin{array}{c} \quad CH_3 \\ \quad | \\ CH_2 - C = CH - CH_2 \end{array}$$

11. Translation, point
13. Translation, vertical line, horizontal line, glide reflection, point
15. Possible answer:

18. $\frac{3}{7}$ **21.** $\frac{125}{27}$ **23.** 303° clockwise rotation with center $(-2, -4)$
25. Possible answer:

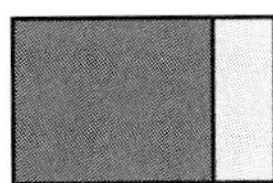

27. Translation, vertical line
29. Translation, vertical line, horizontal line, point, glide reflection **31.** Translation, vertical line **33.** Possible answer: The tool could be a "wheel" with a raised TM frieze pattern for its tread.

10-2 Part B Exercises

1. a. Yes **b.** Yes; Horizontal, vertical, and 45° and 135° to the horizontal **c.** Yes; 90°, 180°, 270° **3.** Translation; Horizontal line, vertical line, lines at 45° and 135° to the horizontal; Rotation: 90°, 180°, 270°; glide reflection **5.** (c) **6.** F; Translation **7.** T **8.** 459 ft^2 **13.** $x \geq 16$ **15.** $z \geq \frac{29}{5}$ **17. a.** 1 km × 3 km and 2 km × 2 km **b.** 2 km × 2 km gives 4 km^2, which is the greatest possible area. The fenced region is a square. **19.** Translation; Rotational: 90°, 180°, 270°; Line: vertical, horizontal, lines at 45° and 135° to the horizontal; Glide reflection **20.** Translation, Rotational: 90°, 180°, 270°, Line: vertical, horizontal, lines at 45° and 135° to the horizontal; Glide reflection
21. Possible answer:

△▽△▽△
▽△▽△▽

24. A reflection and a rotation.

10-2 Part C Self-Assessment

1. Translation; horizontal line; glide reflection **2.** Translation; vertical and horizontal line; point; glide reflection
3. Translation **4.** Translation; Rotational: 180°; Line: vertical, horizontal; Glide reflection **5.** Translation; Rotational: 180°
6. Translation; Rotational, 90°, 180°, 270°; Line: horizontal and vertical; glide reflection **7. a.** 4 **b.** 8
8. The graph of $y = -x^2 + 4$ is the graph of $y = x^2$ reflected across the x-axis and translated by <0, 4>. **9.** (c)
10. Possible answer:

IIII

11. Possible answer:

12. Possible answer:

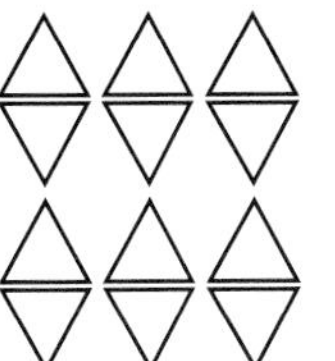

13. Possible answer:

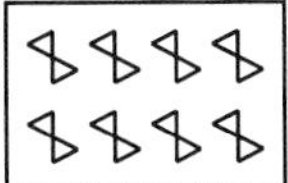

15. (c)

Chapter 10 Review

1. Translation **2.** Translation, reflection (or reflection, rotation) **3.** Reflection **4.** Composition
5. Translation <12, −12>
6. Translation **7.** (d) **8.** $\frac{\pi}{6}$
9–10.

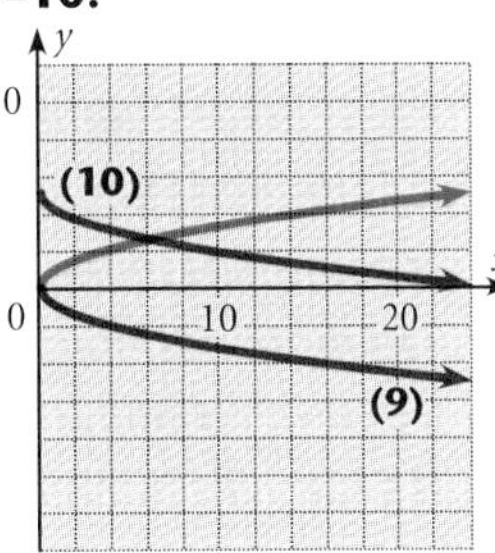

12. Translation; translation, horizontal line; translation, vertical line; translation, horizontal and vertical line; translation, point; translation, vertical line, and glide reflection; translation, glide reflection
13. Translation, vertical line
14. Translation, vertical line, horizontal line, glide reflection, point **15.** 90°, 180°, 270°

CHAPTER 11

11-1 Part A Try It

a. It rains and I do not wash my car. **b.** $m\angle R = 20°$, and $\overline{ST} \not\cong \overline{XY}$.

11-1 Part A Exercises

1. (a), (b) **3.** Tomorrow is not Tuesday. **5.** I will throw it back. **6.** $a + c \neq b + c$ **7.** $\triangle ABC \not\cong \triangle DEF$ **8.** $\angle A \cong \angle B$ **9.** The good of the people is not the most important law.

11. The report of my death wasn't an exaggeration. **12.** $1 - p$ **15.** Possible answer: Suppose there are two right angles. Then the sum of the measures of the angles in the triangle is greater than 180°, which contradicts the Triangle Angle-Sum Theorem.
19. Interior: 135°; Sum: 1080° Exterior: 45°; Sum: 360°
21. Interior: 162°; Sum = 3240°; Exterior: 18°; Sum = 360° **23.** 54 **25.** 40°
27. 32 **29.** $\angle 1$ is a right angle. **31.** $\angle 1 \cong \angle 2$.
33. a. Suppose he went at most 65 mph. Then his trip took at least $\frac{55}{65}$ hours or $50\frac{10}{13}$ minutes, which contradicts the given information.
b. Iona may be telling the truth, since David could have driven at 65 or less while Iona was with him, and driven faster for the rest of the trip.

11-1 Part B Try It

a. Largest: $\angle C$; Smallest: $\angle B$
b. Largest: $\angle E$; Smallest: $\angle D$
c. Largest: $\angle R$; Smallest: $\angle RSP$ **d.** Longest: $\overline{AC}$; Shortest: $\overline{AB}$ **e.** Longest: $\overline{QT}$ or $\overline{QR}$; Shortest: $\overline{TS}$
f. Longest: $\overline{VX}$; Shortest: $\overline{WV}$

11-1 Part B Exercises

1. Largest: $\angle B$; Smallest: $\angle C$
3. Largest: $\angle H$; Smallest: $\angle G$
5. $\overline{QR}$; $\overline{QR}$ is opposite the largest angle in $\triangle QRS$. **7.** $\overline{QS}$; $\overline{QS}$ is opposite the smallest angle in $\triangle QRS$. **9.** $\overline{QS}$
11. Longest: $\overline{RT}$; Shortest: $\overline{RS}$ **13.** Longest: $\overline{EF}$; Shortest: $\overline{DE}$ **17.** $\frac{2}{5}$ **19.** $\frac{2}{5}$
21. Possible answer: Suppose $\overline{JK}$ is the shortest side of $\triangle JKL$, and $\angle L$ is obtuse. Then $m\angle L > 90°$, and since the angle measures must sum to 180°, $m\angle L > m\angle K$ and $m\angle L > m\angle J$. Thus $JK > JL$ and $JK > KL$; $\overline{JK}$ is the longest side, which contradicts the given fact that $\overline{JK}$ is the shortest side. **23.** $x < y < z$ **25.** $5 < c < 25$

27. $\overline{ZX}$; $\overline{ZX}$ is opposite the largest angle in $\triangle WXZ$. **29.** $\overline{WX}$; $\overline{WX}$ is opposite the smallest angle in $\triangle WXZ$. **31.** $\overline{XY}$ **33.** Largest: $\angle Y$; Smallest: $\angle X$ **35.** Largest: $\angle DAC$ and $\angle ACB$; Smallest: $\angle CAB$ and $\angle ACD$ **37.** Longest: $\overline{UR}$; Shortest: $\overline{ST}$ **39.** $\angle F, \angle D, \angle E$ **40.** $70 < 2x - 10 < 3x - 40 < 180$, so $40 < x < 73\frac{1}{3}$

11-1 Part C Try It

a. Yes **b.** No **c.** Yes

11-1 Part C Exercises

1. Yes **3.** No **5.** $11\frac{3}{10} < x < 38\frac{3}{10}$ **7.** The shortest route is M to N to Q to X and the length of the shortest route is between 10 and 18. **9.** Between 701 and 1411 **11.** Between 566 and 2602 **15.** $h = \frac{2A}{b}$ **17.** $r = \pm\frac{1}{2}\sqrt{\frac{A}{\pi}}$ **19.** $y = 2x^2 + 48$ **21.** Yes **23.** Yes **25.** Yes **27.** $5 < y < 25$ **29.** $n < y < 3n$ **31. a.**

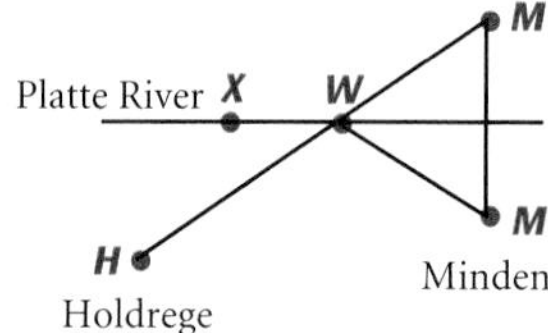

11-1 Part D Self-Assessment

1. The animal does have toes. **2.** $\angle B \not\cong \angle A$ **3.** I cannot make the team. **4.** $\overline{XY}, \overline{YZ}, \overline{XZ}, \overline{WZ}, \overline{XW}$ **5.** $\angle 5, \angle 4, \angle 3, \angle 2, \angle 1$ **6.** Possible answer:

7. $\angle 2, \angle 1, \angle 3$ **8.** Interior: 120°; Sum: 720° Exterior: 60°; Sum: 360° **9.** Interior: 144°; Sum: 1440° Exterior: 36°; Sum: 360° **10.** Interior: 156°; Sum: 2340° Exterior: 24°; Sum: 360° **11.** $x \approx 104.5$ m. **12.** (c) **13.** (a) **14.** Possible answer: Assume $\triangle ABD$ is scalene, $\overline{AC}$ is a median, and suppose $\overline{AC} \perp \overline{BD}$. $\overline{BC} \cong \overline{DC}$ by definition of *median*. $\angle ACB$ and $\angle ACD$ are right angles by definition of perpendicular. $\triangle ACB$ and $\triangle ACD$ are right triangles by definition. $\overline{AC} \cong \overline{AC}$ by the Reflexive Property. $\triangle ACB \cong \triangle ACD$ by the LL Theorem. $\overline{AB} \cong \overline{AD}$ by CPCTC, which contradicts the assumption that $\triangle ABD$ is scalene. Therefore, AC is not perpendicular to BD. **15. a.** Possible answer: Marvin should travel by way of point X, since that route has to be less than twice as long as the other (X to 9 is less than 750 m). **b.** By the Triangle Inequality Theorem, $d + 250 \text{ m} > 500$ m, so $d > 250$ m. Therefore $\angle 3$ is the smallest, because it is opposite the shortest side. It cannot be determined which is the largest, since d may be greater or less than 500 m.; **16.** $\frac{7}{10}$

11-2 Part A Exercises

1. 3.50×3.43 **3.** (4, 3) **5.** (1, 2) **9.** \$1074; 11 items. **10.** A square of side 6 in. **13.** $SA = 2x^2 + 4xh$; $V = x^2h$ **15.** (5, 7) **17.** (1.5, 7) **19.** $m\angle Z = 90°$; The height of the parallelogram is $3 \sin(m\angle Z)$, so the area is $12 \sin(m\angle Z)$. Since the maximum of the sine is when the angle is 90°, $m\angle Z = 90°$.

11-2 Part B Exercises

1. $4.50 \times 3.16 \times 2.25$ **3.** Minimize surface area of carton **5.** Minimize surface area of tube **8.** 6 in. × 3 in. × 2 in. **9.** 0.91 **11.** Maximize volume of cage **13.** Minimize surface area of carton **15.** The box is a $2 \times 2 \times 2$ cube. **17.** $r \approx 4.66$ cm, $h \approx 6.60$ cm; No, the radius is too big for its height so the cone is hard to hold.

11-2 Part C Self-Assessment

1. Maximize the area of the yard. **2.** Minimize the surface area of the tank. **3.** (6, 2) **4.** $\left(\frac{2}{3}, 1\right)$ **5.** (1.4, 1) **6.** (e) **7.** $x = 136.25$ ft; $y = 136.25$ ft **8.** Approximate dimensions are $3 \times 6 \times 4.22$; Yes; Possible answer: Check decimal width values between 2 and 4. **9.** 0.50 **10.** No; Possible answer: Suppose $\overline{AB} \parallel \overline{CD}$ then $\angle BAC \cong \angle DCA$ because they are alternate interior angles of parallel lines. $\overline{AC} \cong \overline{AC}$ and $\overline{AB} \cong \overline{CD}$, so $\triangle BAC \cong \triangle DCA$ by the SAS Postulate. Therefore, $\overline{AD} \cong \overline{BC}$ by CPCTC, which contradicts $AD = 4$ and $BC = 10$. Therefore, $\overline{AB}$ is not parallel to $\overline{CD}$. **11.** No **12.** Yes **13.** Yes **14.** 1.88 in. × 5.65 in. × 2.82 in. **15.** 8.38 in. × 6.38 in. × 1.81 in. **16.** A cube

Chapter 11 Review

1. T **2.** F; Sides **3.** F; Contrapositive **4.** Humans do not have wings. **5.** $\angle A \not\cong \angle B$ **6. a.** The defendant was not found guilty. **b.** The negation implies that the verdict was not "guilty." Possible answer: There was a hung jury, so the case had to be retried. **7.** $\frac{1}{2}$ **8.** Use the angle measures of the triangles and the theorem of opposite sides. In $\triangle RUV$, $RU < RV < VU$. In $\triangle RSU$, $SU < RS < RU$. In $\triangle STU$, $ST < TU < SU$. Therefore the shortest side is $\overline{ST}$. **9.** The longest side is $\overline{VU}$. See exercise **8.** **10.** Between 6.2 cm and 16.2 cm. **11.** \$170 **12.** 250 **13.** $r = h \approx 3.2$ in. **14.** The portrait must be in the silver casket.

CHAPTER 12

12-1 Part A Exercises

2.

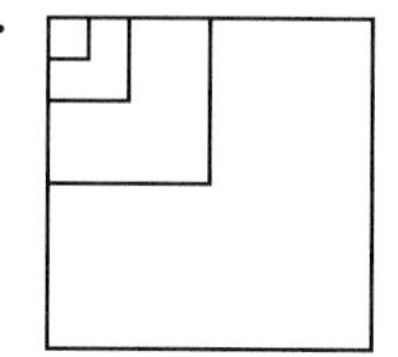

Stage 3

Draw a square in the upper left corner whose side length is half that of the previous square.

3.

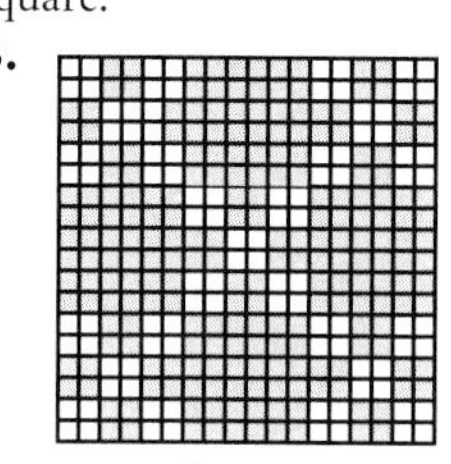

Stage 2

Divide each unshaded square into nine congruent smaller squares and shade the middle squares along the sides of each square just divided.

5.

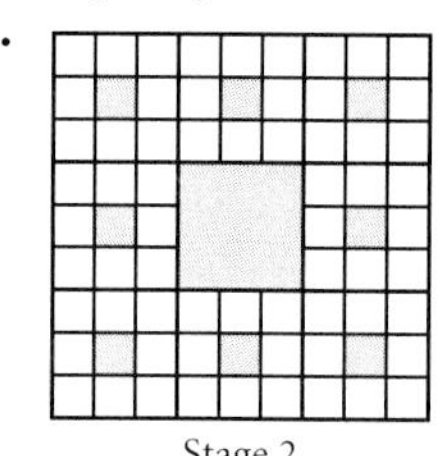

Stage 2

7. a–b.

b. Similar **c.** Similar **9.** Possible answer: A fern. Each branch is similar in shape and structure to the original plant. **11.** 77.9 in. **13.** 24881.4 mi **15.** 20.9 **17.** 3441.5 km **19.** 5673.1 km **21.**

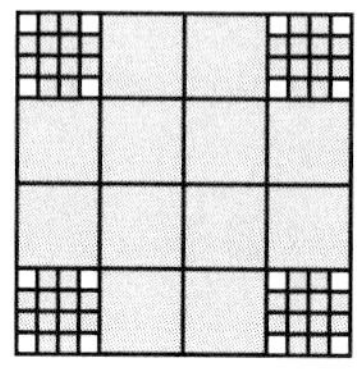

Stage 2

23. 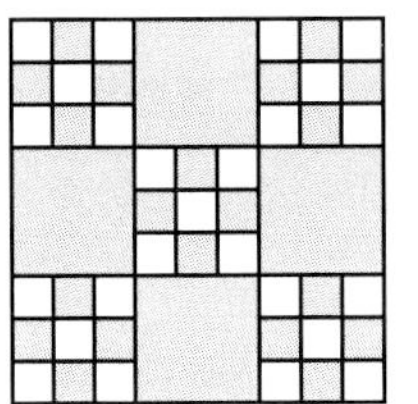

Stage 2

25. b. 192; 4:1 **c.** $N = 3 \cdot 4^{n-1}$ **d.** $\frac{64}{2187}$; $\frac{4}{9}$ **e.** $A = \frac{1}{3}\left(\frac{4}{9}\right)^{n-1}$ **f.** $1\frac{1261}{2187}$; Increasing **g.** There seems to be a limit; The additional area at each stage is $\frac{4}{9}$ smaller than the area added at the preceding stage.

12-1 Part B Try It

a. 18° N, 73° E **b.** 35° N, 140° E **c.** 22° S, 45° W

12-1 Part B Exercises

1. 30° N, 31° E **3.** 7° N, 40° E **5.** About 679 mi **7.** About 3546 mi **9.** About 484 mi **11.** About 12,441 mi; Half the earth's radius **13. a.** 15°; The earth makes a full rotation every 24 hours, so there should be 24 time zones. Therefore, $\frac{360°}{24} = 15°$ per time zone. **b.** 5-6 time zones **15.** Statement 1: $\overline{AB} \parallel \overline{FE}$, $\overline{AB} \cong \overline{FE}$ $\overline{AC} \cong \overline{ED}$.
Reason 1: Given.
Statement 2: $\angle A \cong \angle E$.
Reason 2: Alternate interior angles of parallel lines cut by a transversal are congruent.
Statement 3: $\triangle ABC \cong \triangle EFD$.
Reason 3: SAS Postulate.
17. (1, 6) **19.** 10° N, 67° W **21.** 1° S, 78° W **23.** About 345 mi **25.** About 4882 mi **26.** 17,594 mi; It is $\frac{\sqrt{2}}{2}$ times the radius of the earth **27.** Use the following proportion: $\frac{\text{difference in longitudes}}{360°} = \frac{\text{distance}}{24{,}900}$ **29. a.** $t = \sqrt{h^2 + 12{,}740h}$ **b.** $t \approx 335.9$ km **c.** $s \approx 335.6$ km; Yes

12-1 Part C Try It

a. $139\frac{1}{3}$ sec **b.** 43 min, $14\frac{1}{3}$ sec

12-1 Part C Exercises

1. 150,000,000 km **3.** 3 min, $6\frac{2}{3}$ sec **5.** 31,600 **7.** Parallax; It is not a measure of distance. **11. a.** 16.6 light-years **b.** The light is older than any student less than 16.6 years old. **13.** Possible answers: One and only one straight line can be drawn through two given points. Three noncollinear points are contained in one and only one plane. If two lines intersect, then their intersection is a point. If two planes intersect, then their intersection is a line **15.** 8 min, 20 sec **17.** 4 hr, 9 min, 50 sec **20.** Kepler's third law, $d^3 = p^2$, is approximately true for the given planets.

12-1 Part D Self-Assessment

1.

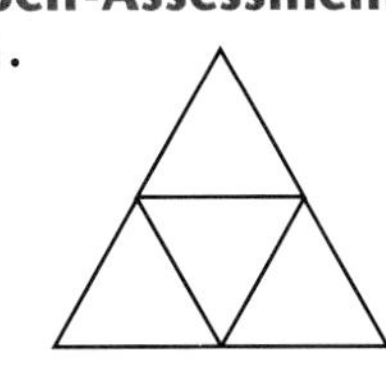

Stage 1

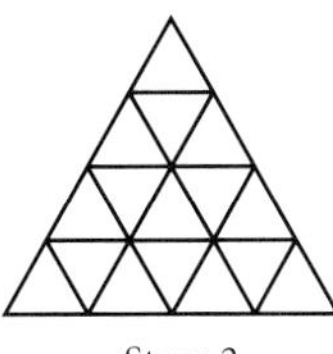

Stage 2

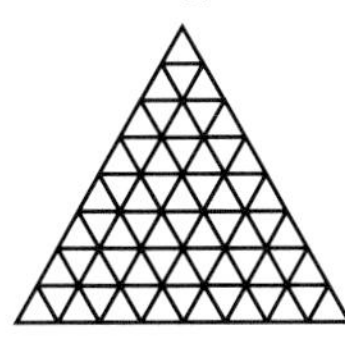

Stage 3

2. 2.4 in. × 3.2 in. × 4.8 in. **3.** 228,000,000 km **b.** $B = 2^n$ **c.** 1 unit; 2 units; 3 units; 4 units; 5 units **d.** $n + 1$ units. Total length of branches will grow infinitely since each stage adds 1 unit to the total length.
5. a. About 1,650,000 AU **b.** 26.1 light years **6.** (c) **7. a.** Yes **b.** At opposite points on the equator; West Pole and East Pole **8.** About 349 miles

12-2 Part A Try It

a. Plane Postulate
b. Straight-Line Postulate
c. Parallel Postulate

12-2 Part A Exercises

1. Straight-Line Postulate
3. Parallel Postulate
5. Possible answers: Acute angles—angles that measure less than 90°. Circle—the locus of points in a plane equidistant from a given point. Right Triangle—a triangle that contains a 90° angle. Rhombus—a quadrilateral with four congruent sides. **7.** No; The two right angles would each measure 90°, and the measure of the third angle would be greater than zero, so the sum of the angle measures would exceed 180°. **11.** Area formula for a rectangle **13. a.** 5.4×10^{10} years **b.** To reach Andromeda in 70 years, the astronauts would need to travel at $\frac{2{,}000{,}000}{70} \approx 28{,}600$ times the speed of light.
15. Flat-Plane Postulate
17. Points-Existence Postulate **19.** Yes, the measure is always 360°. **22.** (a). The conclusion depends on parallel lines.

12-2 Part B Try It

a. They must intersect
b. $m\angle G > 35°$ **c.** Circumference < 4π cm; Area < 4π cm^2

12-2 Part B Exercise

1. A great circle on the plane (sphere) **3.** An arc of a great circle **5.** Circumference < 16π in.; Area < 64π in. **6.** They intersect **7.** F; Triangles have more than 180°. **11. a.** About 1333 times **b.** Andromeda has a far greater actual (absolute) brightness **13.** ≈ 4147 mi **15.** $m\angle R > 10°$ **17.** F; Triangles have more than 180°. **19. a.** $3960\pi \approx 12{,}440$ miles. The two points would be endpoints of a diameter of the earth, since the largest distance between two points on the earth is $\frac{1}{2}$ its circumference. **b.** πr

12-2 Part C Self-Assessment

1. Straight-Line Postulate
2. Parallel Postulate **3.** Plane- Intersection Postulate
4. No; Yes **5.** Yes; No **6.** $m\angle L = 60°$; $m\angle L > 60°$ **7.** (c) **8.** Circumference < 20π cm; Area < 100π cm^2
9. a. $2\sqrt{74{,}066}$ ft; 544.3 ft. **b.** Smaller; For a right triangle in Riemannian space, $a^2 + b^2 > c^2$
10. Statement 1: $ABCD$ is a quadrilateral.
Reason 1: Given.
Statement 2: $DA = a\sqrt{10}$, $BC = a\sqrt{10}$.
Reason 2: Distance Formula.
Statement 3: $DC = 2a\sqrt{5}$, $AB = 2a\sqrt{5}$.
Reason 3: Distance Formula.
Statement 4: $ABCD$ is a parallelogram.
Reason 4: If both pairs of opposite sides of a quadrilateral are congruent then the figure is a parallelogram.
11. 1.5×10^{24} cubic light years **12. a.** 330,000 km **b.** About 2700 km **13.** Each part of a broccoli plant is similar to the whole. **14.** The Euclidean model supports an infinite universe. The Riemannian model suggests a finite universe since all lines are circles.

Chapter 12 Review

1. Tomato; Not example of a fractal **2.** Speed of light; Does not represent a distance

3. 5 hours, 33 minutes, 20 seconds

4. a.

Stage 3

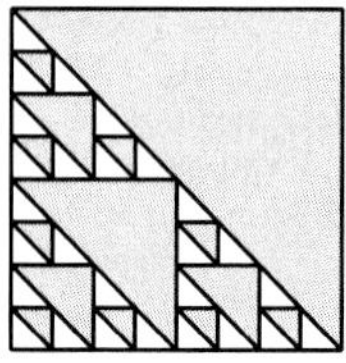

Stage 4

b. 122 **5.** The reference line known as the equator and lines parallel to it are called lines of latitude. The equator is at 0°. The North Pole is at 90° North latitude (90° N) and the South Pole at 90° S. Lines connecting the poles are called lines of longitude. The reference line known as the prime meridian runs north-south through England, Continental Europe, and West Africa. The prime meridian marks 0° longitude. Other longitude lines range from 0° to 180° east or west.

6. About 5808 miles **7.** Determine the length of the arc of the great circle on which the two points lie. **8.** $3 < s < 25$ **9.** $0 < s < 4$ **10.** $m < s < 3m$ **11. a.** About 716,000 AU **b.** 11.3 light years **12.** T **13.** F **14.** T **15.**

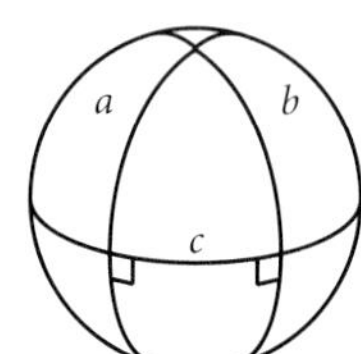

$a \perp c$, $b \perp c$. However, a is not parallel to b. **16. a.** The moon was exactly half full, so the sunlight was coming exactly "from the side."

b. 0.052 **c.** 0.0026; No **d.** This would make his calculation more accurate. Using 89.93°, he would have found $\frac{m}{s} \approx 0.0030$. For angles near 90°, a very small difference in the angle results in a large difference in the cosine.

CREDITS

PHOTOGRAPHS

Front Cover **Top** Art Resource **Bottom** Jerry Jacka Photography/Courtesy: Museum of Northern Arizona, Flagstaff

Spine **Top** Art Resource **Bottom** Jerry Jacka Photography/ Courtesy: Museum of Northern Arizona, Flagstaff

Back Cover **BL** Jerry Jacka Photography/Courtesy: Museum of Northern Arizona, Flagstaff **BCL** Art Resource **TCR** Jerry Jacka Photography **TR** Jon Feingersh/Tom Stack & Assoc. **BCR** Cheryl Fenton* **BR** Antonio M. Rosario/The Image Bank **TCL** Giraudon/Art Resource **TL** Thomas Kitchin/Tom Stack & Assoc.

Front Matter **FM 4–5** Jerry Jacka Photography **FM 5B** Brownie Harris/The Stock Market **FM 5T** Jerry Jacka Photography **FM 6B** Robert Frerck/Odyssey/Chicago **FM 6T** Greg Vaughn/Tom Stack & Assoc. **FM 7B** Kunio Owaki/The Stock Market **FM 7T** Gary Gay/ The Image Bank **FM 8B** Pat O'Hara/DRK Photo **FM 8TL** Baron Wolman **FM 9T** John Ibbotson/AllStock **FM 10BL** Norman Owen Tomalin/Bruce Coleman Inc. **FM 10T** Stan Osolinski/Tony Stone Images **FM 12B** NASA **FM 12C** Greg Vaughn/Tom Stack & Assoc.

Getting Started **i** Ken Karp* **ii** Ken Karp * **iii** Ken Karp*

Chapter 1 **2BC** Frans Lanting/Photo Researchers **2BR** Kjell B. Sandved/Bruce Coleman Inc. **2TR** Roland Birke/OKAPIA/Photo Researchers **6B** ©1960 M. C. Escher Foundation–Baarn–Holland. All Rights Reserved **8BL** Will and Deni McIntyre/AllStock **8TR** NASA **17** Brownie Harris/The Stock Market **22** Flip Nicklin/Minden Pictures **33** Don Mason/The Stock Market **49** Joseph Sohm/ Chromosohm/AllStock **51** NASA **56** Ken Kay/Fundamental Photographs **58** Jim Zuckerman/Westlight **60C** Peter Timmermans/ AllStock **60L** Kathleen Campbell/AllStock **60R** Bud Freund/ Westlight **61** Jerry Jacka Photography **62** Barry Herem/AllStock **65** Dow-Hedren/Westlight **66C** Scott Camazine/Photo Researchers **66L** Science Source/Photo Researchers **66R** Science Source/Photo Researchers **67** Jerry Jacka Photography **71** Jerry Jacka Photography **73T** Larry Lee/Woodfin Camp & Assoc. **77** Jerry Jacka Photography

Chapter 2 **84BR** Laura Riley/Bruce Coleman Inc. **84L** Gordon Langsbury/Bruce Coleman Inc. **84TL** Drawing by Richter, ©1965, 1993 The New Yorker Magazine, Inc. **87** National Museum of American History/Smithsonian Institution **88** National Museum of American History/Smithsonian Institution **89T** National Museum of American History/Smithsonian Institution **96** Dave Bartruff/Stock, Boston **99** Frida Kahlo, *Self Portrait with Monkey,* 1945. Fundacion Dolores Olmedo, Mexico City, Mexico. Schalkwijk/Art Resource, NY **102** Dept. of Clinical Radiology, Salisbury District Hospital/Science Photo Library/Photo Researchers **108** Lisa Quinones/Black Star **114** The Bettmann Archive **118** Greg Vaughn/Tom Stack & Assoc. **129L** Metropolitan Museum of Art, Purchase, Mrs. Charles Wrightsman Gift, 1988 (1988.162) **129R** The Art Institute of Chicago, All Rights Reserved **130** Harald Sund **133L** David Ball/ AllStock **133R** Gustave Caillebotte, French, 1848–1894, *Paris Street; Rainy Day,* oil on canvas, 1877, Charles H. and Mary F. S. Worcester Collection, 1964.336. Photograph ©1994, The Art Institute of Chicago. All Rights Reserved. **138** NASA **144** CityFlash Map ©1994 by Rand McNally **146** Don & Pat Valenti/DRK Photo **147** J. McGuire/ Washington Stock Photo **148** Drawing by Julia Morgan/Courtesy of The College of Environmental Design, UC Berkeley

Chapter 3 **152L** Metropolitan Museum of Art **156** Michael Holford **160** G. Robert Bishop/AllStock **165** Bruce Berman/The Stock Market **169** Chip Carroon/AllStock **171** Robert Frerck/ Odyssey/Chicago **177** Richard Hurley/Courtesy of the John Carter Brown Library at Brown University **180** Mitchell Layton/duomo **182L** Manfred Kage/Peter Arnold, Inc. **182R** Manfred Kage/Peter Arnold, Inc. **191** Bill Ross/Westlight **200** Richard Megna/ Fundamental Photographs **203** Momatiuk/Eastcott/Woodfin Camp & Assoc. **210B** P. Rondeau/Allsport USA **216** Gary Gay/ The Image Bank **232** Richard Megna/Fundamental Photographs

Chapter 4 **241B** Jean Claude Lejeune/Stock, Boston **241T** M. P. L. Fogden/Bruce Coleman Inc. **242** Peter Aaron **247** Harald Sund **249** Kunio Owaki/The Stock Market **260** Michael Townsend/AllStock **274** James Randklev/AllStock **286** Tim Davis/ David Madison Photography **308** Egyptian Museum, Cairo, Egypt

Chapter 5 **318B** Tate Gallery/Art Resource **318BCR** Tate Gallery/Art Resource **319**(background) Baron Wolman **322** Baron Wolman **342** Charles Krebs/AllStock **345B** Lee Boltin Photography **345C** Greg Vaughn/Tom Stack & Assoc. **345T** Werner Forman Archive/Art Resource **346** Cary Wolinsky/Stock, Boston **350T** Jerry Jacka Photography **351** Ford Kristo/DRK Photo **352** Deni McIntyre/AllStock **362** David Hiser/Photographers/Aspen **363** Will & Deni McIntyre/Photo Researchers **365** Columbia University **366** Yale Babylonian Collection **378** Bob Daemmrich/Stock, Boston **380** Michael Holford **385** George A. Plimpton Collection, Columbia University, Rare Book and Manuscript Library

Chapter 6 **395L** Ezra Stoller/Esto Photographic **395R** Armen Kachaturian/The Gamma Liaison Network **396** Pat O'Hara/DRK Photo **398** Greg Vaughn/Tom Stack & Assoc. **400** Greg Probst/ AllStock **402** Larry Ulrich/DRK Photo **406** Phil A. Harrington/Peter Arnold, Inc. **407** Jim Harrison/Stock, Boston **409** Catherine Karnow/Woodfin Camp & Assoc. **415** David R. Frazier Photolibrary/ Photo Researchers **438** UPI/Bettmann Newsphotos **441** Jeff Foott/ Bruce Coleman Inc. **441**(background) M. Antman/The Image Works **442** John Ibbotson/AllStock **449** Paul Silverman/Fundamental Photographs **450** Omikron/Science Source/Photo Researchers **452** John Cancalosi/DRK Photo **454** David L. Brown/Tom Stack & Assoc.

Chapter 7 **458B** America Hurrah Antiques, NYC **458TL** Drawing by Julia Morgan/Courtesy of The College of Environmental Design, University of California, Berkeley **461** © 1994 Turner Entertainment Co. **465** Charles Falco/Science Source/Photo Researchers **469** Kevin Morris/AllStock **473** The Kobal Collection **479C** The Metropolitan Museum of Art, Bequest of Stephen C. Clark, 1960 (61.101.17) **479L** Thomas R. Taylor/Photo Researchers **479R** G. Anderson/The Stock Market **481** Dallas Museum of Art, Foundation for the Arts Collection, gift of the James H. and Lillian Clark Foundation **483** The Kobal Collection; ©Turner Entertainment Co. **485** Shimizu Corp. **511R** Library of Congress **512** Woodcut from *Ryff's Practical Mathematics*/The Bettmann Archive **519** NASA **521** Luis Villota/The Stock Market **522** Vanessa Vick/Photo Researchers

Chapter 8 **542** Runk-Schoenberger/Grant Heilman Photography **548** Alain Evrard/Robert Harding Picture Library **555** Eric Neurath/ Stock, Boston **557** Robert Frerck/Tony Stone Images **558** Courtesy of Sara Bates **559** Stan Osolinski/Tony Stone Images **562** Bernd Kegler/Ulmer Museum **563** NASA **574** Chris Sorensen/The Stock Market **586** Brian Parker/Tom Stack & Assoc. **588** Grant Heilman/ Grant Heilman Photography **594** Frank Rossotto/The Stock Market

Chapter 9 **600B** AP/Wide World Photos **603** Courtesy Chesapeake Display & Packaging Co. **605** David Parker/SPL/Photo Researchers **610** Will & Deni McIntyre/AllStock **614** *Campbell's Soup, 1962* ©1994 The Andy Warhol Foundation for the Visual Arts, Inc. **618** Rob Cousins/Robert Harding Picture Library **623**(background) Wide World Photos **623**(inset) Jeffrey Hutcherson/DRK Photo **624T** Jeff Gnass/The Stock Market **629** Eric Carle/Bruce Coleman Inc. **632** F. Jackson/Bruce Coleman Inc. **639** Norman Owen Tomalin/Bruce Coleman Inc. **644B** David Weintraub/Photo Researchers **644T** Steve Marts/AllStock **647L** Leonard Lee Rue III/Stock, Boston **647R** Stephen P. Parker/Photo Researchers **648** Renee Lynn/AllStock **649** Michael George/Bruce Coleman Inc. **653B** Bob Daemmrich/Stock, Boston **657B** M. P. Kahl/DRK Photo **657T** J. P. Varin/Jacana/Photo Researchers

Chapter 10 **673** Lucasfilm Ltd. **674** Richard Megna/ Fundamental Photographs **687C** Thomas Ives/The Stock Market **687L** Tom Bean/DRK Photo **687R** Cooper-Hewitt Museum **688** Michael Holford **689** Michael Holford from the Verulamium Museum **690** D. Cavagnaro/DRK Photo **694** Jerry Jacka Photography/Courtesy Gallery 10, Scottsdale, Arizona. **700** Jerry Jacka Photography **701** Norman Owen Tomalin/Bruce Coleman Inc. **702** Naval Research Laboratory, Stennis Space Center **704** John T. Biggers' *Third Ward Housing*. Photo by Earlie Hudnall.

Chapter 11 **707**(background) Joe Towers/The Stock Market **709**(inset) Renee Lynn/Photo Researchers **720** C. Yarbrough **727B** Greg Vaughn/Tom Stack & Assoc.

Chapter 12 **746** Giraudon/Art Resource **749** From *Powers of Ten* by Eames and Morrison, ©1982 by Scientific American Library. Used with permission of W. H. Freeman and Co. **752** Antonio M. Rosario/The Image Bank **756** NASA **768** Larry Keenan/The Image Bank **771** Anglo-Australian Observatory **772** Greg Vaughn/Tom Stack & Assoc. **775** Hale Observatories **777** NASA **778B** Tony Craddock/SPL/Photo Researchers

Cheryl Fenton:* viiiTR, xi, xiiT, 2TL, 3(background), 5, 8BC, 8BR, 8TC, 8TL, 9, 10L, 10R, 46, 84TR, 85(background), 95, 153(background), 179, 184, 187, 192, 193, 194, 196, 210T, 238, 239(background), 259, 270, 304, 318T, 319(frame), 341, 370, 392BL, 392R, 393(background), 393(frame), 423, 428, 446, 448, 458TR, 459(background), 468, 528, 536, 537(background), 539B, 550, 570, 579, 600C, 600T, 604, 609, 615, 625B, 641, 653T, 656, 664B, 665(background), 667, 692L, 692R, 696, 706, 709(background), 710, 727T, 734, 740, 747(background), 771, 778T, 785. **Elliott Smith:*** 27 **Geoffrey Nilsen Photography:*** 19BL, 19BR, 19T, 39, 107, 392TL, 413 **GHP Studio:*** ixBR, ixBL, xC, 59, 128, 337, 355, 404, 474, 476B, 476T, 513, 539T, 560, 561L, 561R, 626L, 626R, 635L, 635R **Janice Sheldon:*** 226 **Ken Karp:*** 32, 222, 223, 268, 434, 470, 503, 511L, 583, 620, 624B, 625T, 664T, 669, 715, 728, 729, Look Ahead/Look Back icons **Renee Lynn:*** 6T, 212, 264, 292, 310, 350C, 357 **Tim Davis:*** 21, 43, 73B, 78, 89B, 89C, 92, 104, 115, 131, 135, 137, 152T, 167, 205, 207, 227, 248, 306, 318BCL, 318TC, 324, 364, 418, 514, 564, 568, 601(background)

*Photographed expressly for Addison-Wesley Publishing Co., Inc.

ILLUSTRATIONS

Sherry Bringham: 215b–215r, 218a, 219b, 221b, 224b, 224c, 231a, 232f **Susan Detrich:** 706b **Steve Donatelli/Vivid Entity:** 321b, 461c **Terry Guyer:** 238a, 318a, 458b **Joe Heiner Studio:** 5a, 19a, 39a, 61a, 87a, 107a, 129a, 155a, 179a, 191a, 215a, 241a, 255a, 285a, 321a, 345a, 365a, 395a, 417a, 441a, 461a, 485a, 511a, 539a, 563a, 583a, 603a, 623a, 647a, 667a, 687a, 709a, 727a, 749a, 771a. All icons within section part heads by Joe Heiner Studio. **Kent Leech:** 152a **Maryland Cartographics:** 5d1, 5d2 **Helene Moore:** 16a, 81a, 83a **Chris Peterson:** 2f, 39c, 191d, 238c, 417b **Precision Graphics:** All blackline/full-color technical artwork throughout *AWSM Geometry*; all artwork produced electronically. **Mike Reagan:** 29c, 94a, 96a, 155b, 155c, 155d, 177b, 255b, 360b, 365b, 564a, 746b **George Retseck:** 285b, 285c, 285d **Mary Rich:** 677a, 688b, 689c, 691a,b,c,d, 692a,b,c, 697a,b,c,d, 702a,b,c,d,e **Bill Rieser:** 156a, 161a, 161b, 164c, 214a, 224d, 224e, 281a, 281b, 282b, 283a, 304a, 313c, 315d, 336c, 355c, 368g, 369a, 374g, 375c, 413a, 440d, 451a, 451b, 491a, 494f, 596e, 607a,bc,d, 608g,h,i, 612b,c,d,e, 613e,f,g, 617b, 617c, 619a, 619b, 650b,c,d, 652f, 655c, 658a, 659b, 671a, 671b, 685b, 717h, 722b, 724b, 725a, 741c. All Construction and If/Then icons and suitcases by Bill Rieser. **Rob Schuster:** 486a, 518a, 518b, 519a, 524d, 525a, 529e, 530a, 618a, 618b, 619d, 633a, 642d, 645e, 645k, 651d, 655d, 659c **Joe VanDerBos Illustration:** 2d, 5c, 129b, 191c, 563c, 603b **Tom Ward:** 9d, 25a, 79b, 119b, 126a, 126c, 127a, 134a, 157a, 162a, 163a, 163b, 166c, 189a, 189b, 201b, 292a, 303a, 303b, 311a, 316d, 462c, 540a, 554a, 555a, 764a. Base illustration for all calculator and computer screens by Tom Ward. **Jody Wenger:** 446e, 474c, 484a, 573e **Nick Wilton/Jennie Oppenheimer:** 22a, 26a, 28a, 29a, 35a, 40a, 58b, 91a, 93a, 97a, 183c, 190c, 195f, 212b, 237d, 256a, 290a, 300a, 334a, 335a, 426f, 431d, 445d, 446d

TEXT AND ART

CHAPTER 1 1-2 Part D: p. 36, Explore table data from *The 1993 Information Please Almanac.* Opener 1-3: p. 39, UPS Next Day Air label used with permission of United Parcel Service. Opener 1-4: p. 61, from Anthony Berlant, *Walk in Beauty: The Navajo and Their Blankets* (Boston, MA: Little, Brown and Co., 1977); ©1977 by Anthony Berlant and Mary Hunt Kahlenberg; reprinted by permission of Little, Brown and Company. 1-4 Part D: p. 79, alphabet ©1989 by Scott Kim.

CHAPTER 2 Opener 2-1: p. 87, "Truth in Advertising" from Charles Goodrum and Helen W. Dalrymple, *Advertising in America: The First 200 Years* (NY: Harry N. Abrams, 1990).

CHAPTER 3 Opener 3-1: p. 155, from Alan Villiers, "Magellan: First Voyage Around the World," *National Geographic,* June 1976, National Geographic Society; ©1976 National Geographic Society. Opener 3-2: p. 179, text and art from David Macaulay, *The Way Things Work* (NY: Houghton Mifflin, 1988); compilation ©1988 by Dorling Kindersley Ltd.; text: ©1988 by David Macaulay and Neil Ardley; art: ©1988 by David Macaulay; reprinted by permission of Houghton Mifflin Co.; all rights reserved. Opener 3-3: p. 191, excerpted from Paul Doherty, "Hot Times in the City," *Exploratorium Quarterly,* Vol. 16, No. 1, Spring 1992, with permission of The Exploratorium, 3601 Lyon St., San Francisco, CA 94123. Opener 3-4: p. 215, adapted from Ken Brown, *Calligraphy,* Ken Brown Studio of Calligraphic Art, 1977.

CHAPTER 4 Opener 4-3: p. 285, art from *The 1994 Bridgestone Bicycle Catalogue,* illustrated by George Retseck.

CHAPTER 6 Opener 6-2: p. 417, text and art from Daniel Crevier, *AI: The Tumultuous History of the Search for Artificial Intelligence* (NY: Basic Books, div. of HarperCollins, 1993); ©1993 by Daniel Crevier; reprinted by permission of the publisher. 6-2 Part D: p. 438, Exercise 23: text from Joseph Weizenbaum, *Computer Power and Human Reason* (NY: W. H. Freeman, 1976); ©1976 by W. H. Freeman and Co.; reprinted with permission. 6-3 Part C: p. 454, Exercise 14: art from Grace Chisholm Young, *First Book of Geometry,* 1905.

CHAPTER 7 Opener 7-1: p. 461, excerpts from Marcel Delgado, "King Kong and Me," and Fay Wray, "How Fay Met Kong, or The Scream That Shook The World," ©1969 The New York Times Co., from *The Girl in the Hairy Paw,* Ronald Gottesman and Harold Geduld, eds. (NY: Avon Books, a div. of The Hearst Corp., 1976); ©Ronald Gottesman and Harry M. Geduld. Opener 7-2: p. 485, *San Francisco Chronicle* masthead and text from Bill Workman, "Plans for World's Tallest Building Unveiled at Stanford," *San Francisco Chronicle,* April 14, 1993; ©1993 *San Francisco Chronicle;* reprinted by permission.

CHAPTER 9 Opener 9-2: p. 623, from Patricia Lauber, *The Eruption and Healing of Mount St. Helens* (NY: Bradbury Press, 1986); ©1986 by Patricia Lauber.

CHAPTER 11 11-1 Part A: p. 710, from Ellery Queen, *The Greek Coffin Mystery* (Philadelphia: J. B. Lippincott, 1932); ©1932 by Ellery Queen. Opener 11-2: p. 727, text from Worldwatch Institute as cited in *50 Simple Things You Can Do To Save The Earth* (Berkeley, CA: Earthworks Press, 1989). Photos 73a, 207b, 248c, 324a, 364c, 418a, 669a: from *The Geometer's Sketchpad®;* ©1991 by Key Curriculum Press.

INDEX

A

B

C

Q

R

S

T